INDEX

This Edition Covers Mechanical Specifications and Service Procedures on 1963-69 Models

GENERAL SERVICE INFORMATION SECTION–1

Alternator Service 1-63
Automatic Level Controls .. 1-41
Auto. Trans Quick Service .. 1-321
Brake, Hydraulic System ... 1-422
Brake Boosters, Power 1-440
Brakes, Disc Type 1-430
Carburetor Service 1-124
Crankcase Ventilation (PCV) 1-29
Dash Gauges 1-117
Disc Brakes 1-430
Distributors, Standard 1-53
Distributors, Transistor ... 1-47
Electronic Ignition 1-47
Exhaust Emission Controls .. 1-30
Fans, Variable Speed 1-39
Fuel Pumps 1-120
Generator Service 1-91
Headlamps, Concealed 1-40
Hydraulic Brake System ... 1-422
Ignition Coils and Resistors . 1-24
Instruments, Dash 1-117
Overdrive Service 1-259
Power Brakes 1-440
Starting Switches 1-114
Starting Motors 1-101
Steering Gears, Manual 1-451
Transmissions, Manual Shift:
Three Speed 1-261
Four Speed 1-298
Transmissions, Automatic:
Quick Service 1-321
Trouble Shooting 1-1
Tune Up Service 1-21
Universal Joints 1-418

CAR CHAPTER SECTION–2

BUICK 2-1
Electra • Gran Sport
Invicta • Le Sabre
Riviera • Skylark
Special • Sport Wagon
Wildcat

CADILLAC 2-41

CHEVROLET ... 2-74
Bel Air • Biscayne
Camaro • Caprice
Chevelle • Chevy II
Impala • Nova
Wagons

CHRYSLER 2-136

CORVAIR 2-210

CORVETTE 2-74

DODGE 2-136
Charger • Coronet
Custom 880 • Dart
Monaco • Polara

FORD (Full Size) 2-246
Custom • Galaxie
7 Litre • LTD
XL • Wagons

FORD (Compact & Inter.) 2-294
Fairlane • Falcon
Mustang • Torino

FORD BRONCO . 2-363

IHC SCOUT 2-381

IMPERIAL 2-136

JEEP 2-390

LINCOLN 2-418
Continental • Mark III

MERCURY (Full Size) 2-246
Brougham • Marauder
Marquis • Montclair
Monterey • Park Lane
Wagons

MERCURY (Compact & Inter.) 2-294
Caliente • Capri
Comet • Cougar
Cyclone • GT
Montego • Wagons

OLDSMOBILE .. 2-443
Cutlass • Delmont 88
Delta 88 • Dynamic 88
F-85 • 4-4-2
Jetstar 1 • Jetstar 88
98 • Royale
Starfire • Super 88
Toronado • Vista Cruiser

PLYMOUTH ... 2-136
Barracuda • Belvedere
Fury • GTX
Roadrunner • Satellite
Savoy • Signet
Valiant • VIP

PONTIAC 2-495
Bonneville • Catalina
Executive • Firebird
Grand Prix • GTO
Le Mans • Safari
Sprint • Star Chief
Tempest

RAMBLER 2-542
Ambassador • American
AMX • Classic
DPL • Javelin
Marlin • Rambler
Rebel • Rogue

SCOUT 2-381

THUNDERBIRD . 2-341

VOLKSWAGEN . 2-577

Tune Up Data and Wheel Alignment For 1946-62 Models;—Page 2-629

Foreign Car Tune Up Data:—Page 2-642

Spark Plug Condition Chart:—Page 2-647 Tire Wear Chart:—Page 2-648

Flasher Location Chart:—Inside Back Cover

How to Push and Tow Automatic Drive Cars:—Inside Back Cover

Decimal and Millimeter Equivalents and Top Drill Sizes:—Inside Back Cover

---

MOTOR'S AUTO REPAIR MANUAL

32nd Edition

First Printing

Editor
Louis C. Forier, S.A.E.

Associate Editors
John F. Moran • David W. Opdyke
Galen Royer • Frank E. Bagnati

Editorial Assistant
Connie DiMartino

Published by

MOTOR

250 West 55th St., New York, N. Y. 10019

The Automotive Business Magazine

TROUBLE SHOOTING

Index of Symptoms

ENGINE

Starting a stalled engine 1-1
Closed crankcase ventilation 1-2
Engine won't start 1-2
Hard starting 1-3
Engine stalls 1-3
Engine starts but won't drive car 1-4
Engine misfires 1-4
Lack of power 1-4
Poor high speed performance 1-4
Rough engine idle 1-4
Spark knock 1-5
Pre-ignition 1-5
Engine kickback 1-5
Backfire 1-5
Muffler explosion 1-5
After-burning 1-5
Flat Spot 1-5
Fails to reach operating temperature 1-5
Engine continues to run after ignition is turned off 1-5
Engine overheats 1-6
Engine oil leakage 1-6
High oil consumption 1-7
Oil pressure relief valve leaks 1-7
Engine oil dilution 1-7
No oil pressure 1-7
Low oil pressure 1-7
High oil pressure 1-7
Engine noises 1-7
Fuel pump noise 1-8

ELECTRICAL

Battery requires frequent recharging 1-8
Starter won't rotate or rotates slowly 1-9
Starter spins but won't engage flywheel. 1-9
Starter pinion jammed into flywheel gear 1-9
Starter pinion disengages slowly 1-9
Starter pinion won't release 1-9
Starter noise 1-9
Generator does not charge 1-10
Generator noise 1-10
Generator brush noise 1-10
Alternator troubles 1-10
Locating shorts with test lamp 1-10
Fusible links 1-10
Lights flicker 1-10
Lamps fail to burn 1-11
Lights flare up when engine is speeded up 1-11
Stop light troubles 1-11
Turn signal troubles 1-11
Clock troubles 1-11
Hazard warning flashers 1-11

AUTOMATIC TRANSMISSIONS ①
CLUTCH 1-12
RAMBLER "E-STICK" 1-13
MANUAL TRANSMISSIONS
THREE SPEED 1-13
FOUR SPEED 1-14
OVERDRIVES 1-15
REAR AXLES 1-17
DISC BRAKES .... ①
DRUM BRAKES 1-17
POWER BRAKES .... ①
FRONT SUSPENSION 1-18
STEERING GEARS 1-18
POWER TOPS 1-18
POWER WINDOWS 1-18
POWER SEATS 1-19
WINDSHIELD WIPERS 1-20

①—See Service Chapter.

Engine Troubles

STARTING A STALLED ENGINE

When an engine fails to start the chances are that 90 per cent of the cases will involve the ignition system and seldom the fuel system or other miscellaneous reasons. If a systematic procedure is followed the trouble can almost always be found without the use of special equipment.

To begin with, turn on the ignition switch and if the ammeter shows a slight discharge (or if the telltale lamp lights) it indicates that current is flowing. A glance at the gas gauge will indicate whether or not there is fuel in the tank.

Operate the starter and if the engine turns over freely, both the battery and starter are functioning properly. On the other hand, if the starter action is sluggish it may be due to a discharged or defective battery, loose, corroded or dirty battery terminals, mechanical failure in the starter, starter switch or starter drive. If the starter circuit is okay, skip this phase of the discussion and proceed to ignition.

Starter Circuit Checkout

To determine which part of the starter circuit is at fault, turn on the light switch and again operate the starter. Should the lights go out or become dim, the trouble is either in the battery, its connections or cables. A hydrometer test of the battery should indicate better than 1.250 specific gravity, while a voltmeter, placed across the positive and negative posts, should indicate about 6 volts for a 6-volt battery and 12 volts for a 12-volt system. If either of these tests prove okay, clean and tighten the battery connections and cable terminals or replace any cable which seems doubtful.

If the lights remain bright when the starter is operated, the trouble is between the battery and the starter, or the starter switch is at fault, since it is evident that there is no electrical connection between these points. If these connections are clean and tight, it is safe to assume that the starter or starter switch is defective.

Primary Ignition Checkout

Let's assume that the battery and starter are doing their job, and that fuel is reaching the carburetor, but the car does not start, then the trouble must be somewhere in the ignition circuit. But first, before starting your diagnosis, it is advisable to give the whole system a visual inspection which might uncover obvious things such as broken or disconnected wires etc.

The best way to start tracking down ignition troubles is to begin with the primary circuit since this is where troubles show up most frequently. First remove the distributor cap and block the points open with a piece of cardboard, then turn on the ignition and with a test bulb or voltmeter check to see if there is current at the terminal on the distributor. If you do not get a reading at this point, the current is cut off somewhere in the connections leading back to the ignition switch or it may be that the condenser has an internal short to the ground. The latter possibility can be eliminated if you can restore current at the distributor terminal by disconnecting the condenser from the distributor plate so that its outside shell is not grounded. With the possibility of a bad condenser out of the way, work toward the ignition switch and test for current at each connection until you get to one where you get a reading. Between this connection and the distributor lies the trouble.

On cars with 12-volt systems, that have an external ignition coil ballast resistor, the foregoing steps in checking the primary circuit should include checking the ignition coil resistor for defects or loose connections. As this is done, bear in mind that while the starter cranks the engine, the resistor is by-passed by the starter switch on Ford and Delco-Remy systems (see Ignition Systems Chapter for details). This means that while the circuit through the resistor may be satisfactory, a broken connection or high resistance between the starter switch by-pass terminal and the coil would prevent starting. On the other hand, a satisfactory by-pass circuit might start the engine while the engine would stall immediately upon releasing the starter switch if there was a defect in the coil resistance circuit.

If, to begin with, the test equipment shows a current reading at the distributor terminal, it is safe to assume that the trouble is in the unit itself, most likely burned or dirty breaker points. A final positive test for defective breaker points can be made very simply by removing the cardboard from between the points, and positioning the distributor cam by turning the engine to where the points are closed. With the points closed there should be no current at the distributor terminal. If there is current, replace the points.

In an emergency, the points can be cleaned by using the sanded side of a match box, a knife blade, or the sharp edge of a screwdriver to scrape the scale from the contact faces. After cleaning the points, and a gauge is not available to set the gap, a quick adjustment can be made by using four layers of a piece of newspaper. The thickness of the paper is equivalent to about .020", which is the approximate gap setting for most distributors. Of course, at the earliest opportunity, a precise point adjustment should be made.

If the procedure outlined under "Primary Ignition Checkout" does not uncover the trouble then it will be necessary to continue the tests into the secondary ignition circuit.

Secondary Ignition Checkout

First of all, remove the wire from one of the spark plugs, turn on the ignition and operate the starter. While the engine is cranking, hold the terminal of the spark plug wire about ¼" away from the engine or spark plug base. If the spark is strong and jumps the gap, the trouble is confined to either the spark plugs or lack of fuel. Before going any further, wipe the outside of the plugs to remove any dirt or dampness which would create an easy path for the current to flow, then try to start the engine again. If it still fails to start, remove one of the spark plugs and if it is wet around the base, it indicates that the fuel system is okay, so it naturally follows that the spark plugs are at fault. Remove all the plugs, clean them and set the gaps. An emergency adjustment of spark plug gaps can be made by folding a piece of newspaper into 6 or 7 layers. When changing the gap, always bend the side (ground) electrode and never the center one as there is danger of breaking the insulation.

Fuel System Checkout

If the spark plug that was removed showed no indication of dampness on its base, check the fuel system. A quick check can be made by simply removing the carburetor air cleaner and looking down into the carburetor. Open and close the throttle manually and if fuel is present in the carburetor, the throttle will operate the accelerating pump, causing it to push gasoline through the pump jet. If it does, check the choke valve. If the engine is cold, the choke valve should be closed. If the choke won't close, the engine can be started by covering the carburetor throat while the engine is cranking, provided, of course, that fuel is reaching the carburetor.

Check the operation of the fuel pump by disconnecting the fuel lines from the pump to the carburetor. Crank the engine and if the pump is working, fuel will pulsate out of the line. If not, either the pump isn't working or the line from the tank to the pump is clogged. Before blaming the pump, however, disconnect the line at the inlet side of the pump which leads to the tank and, while a companion listens at the tank, blow through the line. If a gurgling sound is heard back in the tank, the line is open and the trouble is in the pump. Remove the sediment bowl and clean the screen, then replace the bowl and screen, being sure that you have an air-tight fit. If the pump still refuses to function, it should be removed and repaired.

The foregoing discussion will, in most cases, uncover the cause of why an engine won't start. However, if further diagnosis is necessary, the following list will undoubtedly provide the answer.

CLOSED CRANKCASE VENTILATION

If the control valve becomes clogged with carbon or other foreign matter, the ventilation system will not operate and a slight pressure will build up in the crankcase which may cause oil leakage at the rear main bearing or by the piston rings. And should the valve fail to seat it will be impossible to make the engine idle satisfactorily.

SERVICE NOTE: If idle speed is slow, unstable, rolling, frequent stalling, breather backflow and oily engine compartment the ventilator valve may be completely plugged, or the valve may be stuck in the open position. A valve stuck in the closed position is indicated by breather backflow at heavy throttle and oily engine compartment. If the valve is stuck in the intermediate position it will be indicated by rough, fast idle and stalling.

The ventilation valve assembly should be cleaned every six months or 6000 miles (whichever comes first) and more frequently in service such as extensive engine idling during cold weather.

When the valve assembly is removed for cleaning, place a finger over the open end of the ventilator hose or tube and have the engine started. If the ventilator hose or tube and carburetor passages are open and operating normally, a strong suction will be felt and there will be a large change in engine idle quality when the end of the hose is uncovered. If these conditions are not observed, the carburetor passages and/or ventilator hose are plugged and must be cleaned. The carburetor should be removed from the engine and the ventilation passages cleaned by dipping the lower part of the carburetor in the cleaner. A pipe cleaner can be used to aid in cleaning passages.

EXHAUST EMISSION CONTROLS

Details on the operation, trouble shooting and service procedures on these devices are covered elsewhere in this manual. See the main index.

ENGINE WON'T START

IMPORTANT—Alternator equipped cars cannot be push-started when the battery is completely dead because, unlike a generator, there is no residual magnetism in the rotor.

If the engine fires when the ignition switch is turned on but quits when the switch is released to its running position, it indicates that the ignition coil resistor has lost its continuity or there is a bad connection at the resistor terminals.

Due to Open Primary Ignition Circuit

1. Burned or oxidized ignition points.
2. Ignition coil resistance unit burned out or open (12 Volt systems).
3. Starting switch ignition coil resistance by-pass circuit open (12 Volt systems).
4. Ignition points not closing.
5. Breaker arm binding on pivot post, preventing closing of points.
6. Breaker arm spring weak or broken.
7. Breaker arm distorted or bent.
8. Dirty ignition points.
9. Primary lead connection loose at distributor or coil.
10. Primary windings in coil broken.
11. Open ignition switch circuit.

Due to Grounded Primary Ignition Circuit

A grounded coil primary winding, a grounded ignition switch, or a grounded switch-to-coil primary lead will cause excessive current flow and will usually cause wires to burn.

1. Ignition points not opening or closing due to improper adjustment.
2. Ignition points not opening due to worn rubbing block on breaker arm.
3. Faulty bushing in breaker arm.
4. Cracked or faulty insulator at distributor primary terminal.
5. Grounded condenser.
6. Distributor-to-coil lead grounded.
7. Primary coil winding grounded.

Due to Faulty Secondary Ignition Circuit

1. Corroded spark plug cable terminals.
2. Chafed or cracked cable insulation.
3. Ignition coil weak or inoperative.
4. Moisture on ignition coil, terminals, distributor cover, spark plug porcelains, or in distributor
5. Improper type of spark plugs.
6. Cracked distributor cap or a burned carbon track from distributor cap center terminal to housing.
7. Improper installation of spark plug cables (not correct for firing order).
8. Spark plugs damaged, dirty or wet, porcelains cracked, or gaps improperly spaced.
9. Rotor contact spring bent or broken.
10. Distributor rotor grounded.
11. Distributor cap center terminal (inner) broken or missing.
12. Broken or burned out radio suppressor in distributor cap.

Due to Battery

1. Battery run down.
2. Terminals loose or badly corroded.
3. Improper ground.
4. Battery cables frayed or undersize.

Due to Starter Motor

1. Not operating properly.
2. Congealed engine oil due to use of too heavy a grade of oil or to the formation of sludge.
3. Starter gear binding in flywheel gear.
4. Defective starter switch.
5. Faulty neutral safety switch on cars with automatic transmission.

Due to Excessive Fuel Supply (Flooding)

The engine is said to be flooded with fuel when a quantity of liquid fuel collects in the intake manifold, and perhaps also in the cylinders. This condition gives a mixture that is much too rich to ignite.

If the carburetor has a provision for opening the choke valve when the throttle is fully open, crank the engine with the throttle open until engine starts. It will start as soon as the extra fuel is pumped out.

If the choke valve is not designed to open when the throttle is fully opened, tie or block the choke valve open and crank the engine until it starts.

Flooding may also occur on the road. If the carburetor supplies too rich a mixture at full throttle, the intake manifold may be flooded with liquid fuel, with the result that when the engine is stopped, heat evaporates the fuel and thus provides an over-rich incombustible mixture. The engine won't start until the rich mixture is pumped out by cranking.

1. Choke not operating properly.
2. Automatic choke not properly set.
3. Carburetor unloader linkage (if equipped) not properly set.
4. Float level set too high.
5. Dirty, worn or faulty needle valve and seat.
6. Float sticking or rubbing against side of fuel bowl.
7. Leak in float, allowing fuel to get inside.
8. Fuel pump pressure too great.

Due to Insufficient Fuel Supply

1. Carburetor inlet needle stuck in its seat, due to gum in fuel.
2. Float level too low.
3. Clogged inlet screen at carburetor.
4. Faulty fuel pump or one of insufficient capacity.
5. Fuel pump strainer clogged.
6. Faulty fuel pump bowl gasket.
7. Flexible line (if used) twisted, deteriorated or restricted.
8. Fuel line to tank clogged, kinked, restricted or leaking.
9. Vent in fuel tank filler cap clogged or restricted.
10. Worn fuel pump camshaft lobe.

HARD STARTING

When Engine is Hot

This condition is usually caused by an over-supply of fuel due to any of the items listed under *Engine Won't Start Due to Excessive Fuel Supply*. In rare cases, an ignition coil may lose its efficiency when it is hot and cause ignition failure.

When Engine is Cold

Many of the conditions enumerated under *Engine Won't Start* also may cause hard starting in cold weather. Of particular importance, however, are the following:

1. Choke setting too lean.
2. Fuel may have kerosene in it or water, or ice in bottom of tank.
3. Ice in fuel filter bowl.
4. Ice in fuel lines.
5. Engine is cranked too slowly or won't turn over because: (a) engine oil is too thick in sub-zero weather; (b) battery weak due to extremely low temperature.
6. Another possibility, although remote, is that the water pump is jammed with ice, which will interfere with cranking engine if fan belt is tight.

Due to Vapor Lock

The term vapor lock means the flow of fuel to the mixing chamber in the carburetor has been stopped (locked) by the formation of vaporized fuel pockets or bubbles caused by overheating the fuel by hot fuel pump, hot fuel lines or hot carburetor.

The more volatile the fuel the greater the tendency for it to vapor lock. Vapor lock is encouraged by high atmospheric temperature, hard driving, defective engine cooling and high altitude.

A mild case of vapor lock will cause missing and hard starting when engine is warm. Somewhat more severe vapor lock will stop the engine which cannot be started again until it has cooled off enough so that any vaporized fuel has condensed to a liquid.

SERVICE NOTE: Some cars equipped with air conditioning have a vapor bypass system. These cars have a special fuel filter which has a metering outlet in the top. Any vapor which forms is bled off and returned to the fuel tank through a separate line alongside the fuel supply line. This system greatly reduces the possibility of vapor lock. However, if vapor lock is suspected examine the bypass valve to see if it is functioning.

Due to Percolation

Percolation means simply that gasoline in the carburetor bowl is boiling over into the intake manifold. This condition is most apt to occur immediately after a hot engine is shut off. Most carburetors have a provision for relieving the vapor pressure of overheated fuel in the carburetor bowl by means of ports. If, however, percolation should take place, the engine may be started by allowing it to cool slightly and then holding the throttle wide open while cranking to clear the intake manifold of excess fuel.

After Long Storage

1. The more volatile components in the fuel have evaporated and those remaining are not sufficiently volatile to provide a combustible mixture.
2. Low or run-down battery.
3. Corrosion of engine parts may result in so much friction that starter cannot crank engine at proper speed, if at all.
4. Pistons, etc. may be stuck fast by gummy oil.
5. Engine valves may stick open due to gummy deposits.
6. There is the possibility that any small part essential to the running of the engine may be stuck due to gummy film or to corrosion.
7. Some of these troubles are most likely to occur in hot, humid climate and near salt water.

ENGINE STALLS

Many troubles which prevent smooth running at idle may cause stalling. The list includes almost everything that may cause hard starting or missing. Some of the more common causes are:

1. Engine idle speed set too low.
2. Large air leaks in intake manifold such as a disconnected windshield wiper vacuum line.
3. Ignition points need attention.
4. Engine valves leaking.
5. Vapor lock.
6. Over-supply of fuel (flooding).
7. Valves set too tight.

If carburetor is equipped with a fast idle cam, which increases engine speed when the choke is in operation during the warm-up period, the engine may stall if the fast idle device fails to open the throttle due to sticking or need for adjustment.

On some cars equipped with a fluid coupling or torque converter, if the throttle is closed quickly the engine stalls. To avoid this trouble, most cars have a device which retards the speed of the throttle closing; this is called a throttle return check or dashpot and is usually mounted on the carburetor. It consists of a piston or diaphragm and a spring-closed check valve. If the linkage is out of adjustment or the check valve leaks, the engine will stall.

If the engine quits smoothly when car is in operation, the trouble is often caused by sudden lack of fuel due to:

1. Fuel tank empty.
2. Vapor lock.
3. Flooding.
4. Water in fuel.
5. Frozen fuel line.

Carburetor Icing

The carburetor discharges liquid fuel into the air stream in the form of an atomized spray which evaporates readily. The heat required to evaporate the gasoline is drawn from the entering air, thereby lowering its temperature. The cooler air chills the interior of the carburetor and may cause the moisture in the air to condense into droplets.

Under certain conditions of atmospheric temperature and humidity, the liberated moisture actually collects and freezes on the chilled carburetor surfaces, especially on the throttle plate and surrounding throttle body. When the throttle is almost completely closed for idling, this ice tends to bridge the gap between the throttle plate and throttle body, thereby cutting off the air supply and causing the engine to stall. Opening the throttle for restarting breaks the ice bridge but does not eliminate the possibility of further stalling until the engine and carburetor has warmed up.

For carburetor icing to occur, the outside air must be cool enough so that the refrigerating effect of fuel evaporation in the carburetor will lower the temperatures of the throttle plate and body below both the dew point of moist air and the freezing point of water. The air must also contain sufficient moisture for appreciable condensation of water to occur when it is chilled in the carburetor.

Generally speaking, carburetor icing occurs when winter grade gasoline (more volatile than summer grade) is used and when the atmospheric temperature ranges from 30° to 50° F. at relative humidities in excess of 65%.

Carburetor icing problems can be reduced by the use of anti-icing additives, such as alcohols, in the fuel. Some fuel refiners use anti-stalling additives in their gasolines which have proved effective in combating carburetor icing.

Another form of carburetor icing has been observed in some engines during high-speed driving on cool, moist days. When certain cars are driven steadily at 60 to 80 mph, the large quantities of cool air passing through the carburetor may result in gradual ice formation within the carburetor's venturi. Since this ice restricts the venturi passage, the resultant increased vacuum in the venturi tends to increase the rate of fuel flow. The fuel-air mixture thus becomes excessively rich, causing loss of power and high fuel consumption.

ENGINE STARTS BUT WON'T DRIVE CAR

1. Broken part in the drive line anywhere from clutch to rear axle shaft.
2. No oil or not enough oil in fluid coupling or torque converter.
3. Some defect in automatic transmission causes binding or dragging of clutches or slipping bands.
4. Engine develops only enough power to run itself due to: (a) extremely lean or rich mixture; (b) excessive engine friction; (c) throttle does not open; (d) very dirty air cleaner; (e) clogged exhaust system.
5. Oil in fluid coupling or torque converter is semi-solid due to zero temperature. This trouble is unlikely if the recommended oil is used.

ENGINE MISFIRES

At All Speeds

1. Fouled spark plug or broken porcelain.
2. Faulty spark plug cables.
3. Low battery voltage.
4. Low generator voltage.
5. Burned or pitted ignition points.
6. Incorrect ignition point gap.
7. Faulty condenser or coil.
8. Weak spark or no spark in one or more cylinders.
9. Faulty distributor cap or rotor.
10. Primary circuit restricted or open intermittently.
11. Primary circuit detoured by short intermittently.
12. Secondary circuit restricted or open intermittently.
13. Secondary circuit detoured by short intermittently.
14. Blown cylinder head gasket between cylinders. This can be noted when missing occurs in two adjacent cylinders.
15. Sticking valves.
16. Hydraulic tappet holds valve open slightly.
17. Broken valve spring.
18. Leak at intake manifold gaskets.
19. Mixture too rich or too lean.
20. High tension wire shorted in metal manifold.

At High Speed

1. Hot spark plugs. Change to colder type but note that a hot plug may be due to loose installation or lack of a plug gasket (if gasket is called for).
2. Ignition point gap much too wide.
3. Breaker arm binding or sticking.
4. Breaker arm spring weak.
5. Sticking engine valves.
6. Valve springs too weak to close valves promptly.
7. Valve springs broken.
8. Valve springs shimmy.
9. Intermittent delivery of fuel to carburetor so that momentarily the mixture is too weak for combustion.
10. Mild vapor lock.
11. Weak spark.
12. Exhaust manifold clogged with carbon.
13. Exhaust manifold, muffler or tail pipe restricted.
14. Improper ignition timing.
15. Centrifugal advance not functioning properly.
16. Manifold heater valve held closed.
17. Dirty carburetor air cleaner.
18. Choke valve not completely open.
19. Carburetor throttle lever loose on shaft.
20. Improper fuel pump operation.
21. Preignition.
22. Incorrect valve timing.

At Low or Idle Speeds

1. Faulty spark plugs.
2. Spark plugs gaps too narrow.
3. Dirty or corroded secondary circuit connections or faulty ignition cables.
4. Cracked or faulty distributor cap. Radial contacts in cap burned or worn.
5. Dirty air cleaner.
6. Leaky valves.
7. Ignition point gap too narrow.
8. Faulty carburetion due to: (a) float level too high or too low; (b) float valve leaking; (c) incorrect or loose jets; (d) restricted or partially clogged idle air passage or jet; (e) air leak occurring between upper and lower carburetor body; (f) air leak occurring around carburetor throttle shaft.
9. Air leaks in intake manifold or carburetor resulting from: (a) loose manifold connections or leaks occurring in vacuum lines; (b) loose manifold nuts or capscrews; (c) broken or damaged intake manifold or carburetor gaskets; (d) cracked manifold; (e) warped or damaged manifold contacting surface.
10. Slight leaks occurring at fuel pump check valves.
11. Air leak occurring around intake valve stem because of excessive valve stem-to-guide clearance.

When Car is Accelerated

If the engine misses when car is accelerated but does not miss when idling the reason is that the spark plugs stop firing because of increased compression pressure caused by:

1. Weak spark.
2. Plug gaps too wide.
3. Plug fouled or damp.
4. Plug porcelain below par.

LACK OF POWER OR HIGH SPEED PERFORMANCE

It should be noted that the altitude at which the car is operated has a decided effect on performance. A car adjusted for normal altitudes will lack performance at high altitudes, whereas a car which operates normally at high altitudes may have a lean carburetor adjustment and show signs of preignition when operated at sea level.

1. Ignition timing incorrect.
2. Centrifugal governor advance not operating properly.
3. Vacuum advance not operating properly.
4. Ignition points burned, pitted, sticking or bouncing (due to weak breaker arm spring).
5. Faulty spark plugs.
6. Faulty ignition cables.
7. Faulty ignition coil.
8. Faulty carburetion.
9. Lack of engine compression.
10. Preignition.
11. Inoperative manifold heater valve (stuck closed).
12. Restricted carburetor inlet resulting from dirty air cleaner or choke valve not fully open.
13. Carburetor throttle lever loose on shaft.
14. Throttle linkage not properly adjusted.
15. Carburetor throttle valve not completely open.
16. Carburetor accelerating pump not functioning properly.
17. Improper fuel pump operation.
18. Partially restricted exhaust pipe, muffler or tail pipe.
19. Clutch slippage.
20. Excessive rolling resistance resulting from (a) dragging brakes, (b) tight wheel bearings, (c) misalignment of power transmitting units, (d) misalignment of rear axle, (e) underinflated tires.
21. Incorrect rear axle gear ratio.
22. Oversize tires.
23. Incorrect valve timing.
24. Inaccurate speedometer (gives impression of lack of performance).

ROUGH IDLE

The term "rough idle" means that the engine does not run smoothly when idling. The most likely cause is an over-rich mixture but any defect which produces uneven explosions or missing will cause a rough idle. The most common causes are:

1. Dirty idle jets and passages.

2. Rich idle adjustment.
3. Dirty air cleaner.
4. Float level too high.
5. Choke set too rich.
6. Fuel volatility too high or too low.
7. Substantial air leak into intake manifold.
8. Fuel pump pressure too high or too low.
9. Clogged carburetor jets.
10. Ignition point gap too narrow or much too wide.
11. Spark plug gaps too narrow or too wide.
12. Sticking breaker arm.
13. Weak spark which permits some missing.
14. Leaky engine valve.
15. Sticking valve or rocker.
16. Broken valve spring.
17. Insufficient tappet clearance.
18. Hydraulic tappet holds valve open.

SPARK KNOCK, PING, DETONATION

All three expressions mean the same thing. It is a sharp metallic knock caused by vibration of the cylinder head and block. The vibration is due to split-second high-pressure waves resulting from almost instantaneous abnormal combustion instead of the slower normal combustion.

The ping may be mild or loud. A mild ping does no harm but a severe ping will reduce power. A very severe ping may shatter spark plugs, break valves or crack pistons.

Pinging is most likely to occur on open throttle at low or moderate engine speed. Pinging is encouraged by:

1. Overheated engine.
2. Low octane fuel.
3. Too high compression.
4. Spark advanced too far.
5. Hot mixture due to hot engine or hot weather.
6. Heavy carbon deposit which increases the compression pressure.

Tendency to ping increases with mixture temperature including high atmospheric temperature; intake manifold heater valve "on" when engine is warm; hot cooling water; hot interior engine surfaces due to sluggish water circulation or water jackets clogged with rust or dirt especially around exhaust valves. Some of these troubles may be confined to one or two cylinders.

If an engine pings objectionably because of too low octane fuel, retard the spark setting but first be sure that the cooling system is in good condition, the mixture not too lean and the combustion chambers free of carbon deposit.

PRE-IGNITION

Pre-ignition means that the mixture is set on fire before the spark occurs, being ignited by a red hot spot in the combustion chamber such as an incandescent particle of carbon; a thin piece of protruding metal; an overheated spark plug, or a bright red hot exhaust valve. The result is reduction of power and overheating accompanied by pinging. The bright red hot exhaust valve may be due to a leak, to lack of tappet clearance, to valve sticking, or a weak or broken spring.

Pre-ignition may not be noticed if not severe. Severe pre-ignition results in severe pinging. The most common cause of pre-ignition is a badly overheated engine.

When the engine won't stop when the ignition is shut off, the cause is often due to red hot carbon particles resting on heavy carbon deposit in a very hot engine.

ENGINE KICKBACK

If ignition is set too far advanced, spark may occur before top dead center when engine is cranked. The first (and only) explosion runs the engine backward. A kickback may jam the starter or break the starter drive housing.

BACKFIRE

Backfiring is a subdued explosion in the intake manifold. Causes are:

1. Lean mixture (often due to dirt or water in fuel).
2. Engine cold and choke too lean.
3. Leaky or sticking intake valve or weak or broken intake valve spring.
4. Leakage of current across distributor cap may cause backfire by enabling spark to occur in a cylinder which is on its intake stroke. Two mixed-up spark plug wires may also cause this trouble.
5. Popping back is synonymous with backfire.

MUFFLER EXPLOSION

This is a sharp, gun-like report caused by temporary cessation of ignition. If this trouble occurs frequently, once it starts, the most likely causes are:

1. Intermittent open circuit in primary (ammeter needle swings further away from zero when generator is charging).
2. Intermittent short circuit in primary (ammeter needle swings toward zero when generator is charging).
3. Short circuit in coil or in secondary wire from coil to distributor.
4. If just a couple of explosions are heard and then no more for a time (even for days) the trouble may be due to a gradually failing condenser.

AFTER-BURNING

A subdued put-putting at the exhaust tail pipe may be due to leaky exhaust valves which permit the mixture to finish combustion in the muffler. If exhaust pipe or muffler is red hot, better let it cool, as there is some danger of setting the car on fire. Most likely to occur when mixture is lean.

FLAT SPOT

If an engine does not respond promptly when the throttle is opened quickly it (or the carburetor) is said to have a flat spot. This is usually caused by any of the following:

1. Accelerator pump piston (or diaphragm) leaks.
2. Accelerator pump valves leak.
3. Accelerator pump stroke too short.
4. Accelerator pump passages restricted.
5. Fuel volatility too low or too high.
6. Float level too low.
7. Fuel pump pressure too low.
8. The anti-percolating valve (on some carburetors) may open too soon when throttle is closed. If so, carburetor may have flat spot next time throttle is opened when engine is hot.
9. Fuel too hot due to hot engine and hot weather (see Vapor Lock).
10. If carburetor has a metering pin operated by throttle linkage and also a vacuum piston linked to the throttle to give a rich mixture at part throttle and moderate engine speed, a flat spot will be noted if the device fails to function properly because of stuck piston, vacuum leakage or restricted vacuum passages.
11. If carburetor has vacuum piston which provides richer mixture at part throttle and moderate engine speed by opening an additional passage or jet within carburetor, a flat spot will occur if fuel valves fail to work, or fuel passages are restricted, or if piston does not function because it is sticking, vacuum leakage or restricted vacuum passages.
12. Late ignition timing.

ENGINE FAILS TO REACH OPERATING TEMPERATURE

1. Defective thermostat.
2. Thermostat stuck open.
3. Thermostat removed from vehicle (during flushing cooling system and not replaced).
4. Defective temperature sending unit or dash unit.

ENGINE CONTINUES TO RUN AFTER IGNITION IS TURNED OFF

This condition, referred to as "post ignition dieseling", "run on" or "after running", is a condition in gasoline engines whereby the engine continues to run for a short time after the ignition switch is turned off. The contributing factors that cause this condition and how they can be eliminated are as follows:

Contributing Factors

1. The tendency to "run on" increases with increased idle speed setting; lowering engine idle speed reduces this tendency.
2. Enriching the idle fuel mixture decreases the tendency to "run on".
3. Retarded ignition timing increases the tendency to "run on". This is particularly true with a lean idle mixture.
4. An incorrect octane fuel increases the tendency to "run on". High octane fuels tend to reduce "run on".
5. Increased fuel content of lead alkyl increases the tendency to "run on". Phosphates and nickel fuel additives help prevent "run on".

Ways to Reduce "Run On"

1. Check carburetor throttle plates for proper alignment. If the throttle plates are not properly aligned in the carburetor intake bore, a resulting leanness in fuel mixture occurs, thus producing one of the factors of

"run on". This is the most common cause of "run on" and is the first thing that should be checked.

2. If "run on" continues after the throttle plates are properly aligned, check the idle speed and adjust to the specified minimum for the engine in question.
3. If "run on" persists after Steps 1 and 2, enrich the idle fuel mixture.
4. Use the proper heat range spark plug for the type of operation generally used—high speed, low speed or normal. Too high heat range plugs for the type of vehicle operation can provide the necessary ignition for "run on".
5. Be sure to use a high quality grade of fuel recommended for the engine in question.
6. Check electrical system. "Run on" cannot exist without the necessary elements of fuel, air and ignition. Fuel and air are readily available through the carburetor idle system. Normally, during "run on", ignition is self-supplied by a "hot spot", self-igniting fuel, etc. However, there is a possibility of the vehicle's electrical system supplying the necessary ignition. When the ignition switch is turned off, small current can flow from the generator into the primary of the ignition coil through the generator tell-tale light. This is particularly true when the warning light bulb is replaced for one of higher wattage.

NOTE: "Run on" is more prevalent in an engine when the ignition is turned off before the engine is allowed to return to idle. Therefore, it can be reduced by letting the engine return to idle before shutting off the ignition. "Run on" incidence can be reduced on automatic transmission units by turning off the engine when in gear.

A certain amount of "run on" can be expected from any gasoline engine regardless of make, size or configuration. (Diesel engines operate on this principle.) However, if the above suggestions are correctly employed, "run on" will be reduced to an unnoticeable level.

ENGINE OVERHEATS

Water is used to cool the engine and air is used to cool the water. Anything which prevents this water-air system from working properly will cause overheating. Oil or grease in the water will reduce the ability of the water to absorb heat from the block and to transfer heat in the water to the radiator. There are seven basic causes of overheating:

1. Water does not cool engine.
2. Air does not cool water.
3. Slow combustion.
4. Pre-ignition.
5. Pinging.
6. Excessive friction in engine or elsewhere in power transmitting units.
7. Excessive back pressure in exhaust system.

Water Too Hot

1. Slipping fan belt.
2. Not enough water in system.
3. Carburetor mixture too lean.
4. Clogged exhaust system.
5. Late ignition timing.
6. Centrifugal advance fails to advance spark as engine speed increases because weights stick or because of sticking elsewhere in mechanism.
7. Pre-ignition.
8. Pinging.
9. Water circulation impeded by installation of wrong head gasket.
10. Cylinder head gasket installed incorrectly, blocking off water holes.
11. Leaky cylinder head gasket permits exhaust gas to enter water. The gas bubbles interfere with the ability of the water to cool the engine.
12. Water circulation slowed down by rust, scale or dirt in water jackets.
13. Water distributing tube (when used) within cylinder block rusted out, dented or improperly installed so that not enough water reaches some cylinders, thus causing local overheating.
14. Local overheating at one cylinder (or more) due to heavy deposit of rust, scale or dirt in water jacket around cylinder or exhaust valve port.
15. Water circulation impeded by thermostat which fails to open fully or sticks closed.
16. Water temperature increased by thermostat which fails to open at correct temperature. Or the installation of a thermostat which opens at too high a temperature.
17. Any water hose which has rotted on inside, allowing loosened strips of rubber to impede water circulation.
18. The baffle in top tank may be bent in such a way as to interfere with free discharge of water from the hose.
19. Water passages in radiator are partially clogged with dirt, rust, corrosion or scale (mineral salts).
20. Exterior of radiator clogged with dirt, leaves or insects.
21. Rotting of water hose may weaken it so that pump suction causes it to collapse when engine is running fast, thus throttling the water flow.
22. If water pump seal leaks, air may be drawn into the water. Air bubbles in cooling water reduce the cooling ability of the water.
23. Water pump impeller loose on its shaft or impeller blades corroded.
24. Overheats due to alcohol type anti-freeze during mild weather.

Water Leakage

Cylinder Head

1. Loose attaching bolts.
2. Dirty, corroded or burred surface prevents tight fit.
3. Warped surface does not fit tight against gasket.
4. Cracked due to freezing or excessive heat.
5. On overhead valve head, exhaust valve seats may be cracked, allowing water to leak into cylinders and crankcase.

Cylinder Block

1. Dirty, corroded or burred surface prevents tight fit.
2. Warped surface does not fit tight against gasket.
3. Cracked due to freezing or excessive heat.
4. If L-head design, excessive heat may crack exhaust valve seats, allowing water to leak into crankcase.
5. Block cracked due to use of cylinder head bolt which is too long.
6. Leaky expansion plugs or pipe plugs in water jacket.

Cylinder Head Gasket

1. Dirty, corroded or broken.
2. Loose because cylinder head bolts are loose.
3. Leaks because it cannot make tight contact between head and block.

Water Pump

1. Loose pump.
2. Faulty gasket.
3. Improper installation.
4. Warped pump body or dirty metal surfaces.
5. Hole or crack in pump body.
6. Worn seal.
7. Seal improperly installed.
8. Bent pump shaft.
9. Loose bearings or bushings or worn pump shaft.

Radiator

1. Leaks due to freezing or corrosion.
2. Strain due to improper attachment to car.
3. Fan striking radiator.
4. Drain plug or petcock leaks.
5. Radiator baffle bent so that water is directed into overflow pipe.
6. Clogged radiator causing water to pile up in upper tank which causes coolant to flow out overflow pipe.

Hose

1. Hose clamps loose.
2. Hose improperly installed.
3. Hose rotted through.

Heater: See that all heater connections are tight and that its radiator does not leak.

ENGINE OIL LEAKAGE

1. Oil pan drain plug loose or gasket missing.
2. Crack or hole in oil pan.
3. Oil pan gasket leaks due to: (a) loose screws; (b) damaged gasket; (c) improperly installed gasket; (d) bent oil pan flange.
4. Timing case cover gasket leaks due to: (a) loose screws; (b) damaged gasket; (c) improperly installed gasket; (d) bent cover flange; (e) leakage at engine support plate.
5. Front crankshaft oil seal leaks due to: (a) worn oil seal; (b) seal not properly installed; (c) rough surface on crankshaft, or fan pulley or damper; (d) damper or pulley loose; (e) seal or cover not centered on crankshaft; (f) oil return passage to crankcase clogged up.
6. Rear main bearing oil seal leaks due to: (a) worn oil seal; (b) improper oil seal installation; (c) worn rear main bearing; (d) rough crankshaft.
7. Oil return passage to crankcase clogged.
8. Expansion plug in block at rear of camshaft leaks due to poor fit, careless installation, or corrosion.
9. Leakage at any external piping.
10. Plugs at ends of oil passages in cylinder block leak.
11. Oil filter leaks.
12. Leakage at distributor housing.
13. Valve cover leaks due to loose screws, defective gasket, improperly installed gasket or bent cover flange.

14. Rocker arm cover or push rod cover leaks because of loose screws, defective gasket, improper gasket installation or bent cover flange.
15. Pipe connections loose on oil gauge or oil filter lines.
16. Loose oil pump or faulty gasket (if pump is on outside of block).
17. Clogged breather and/or crankcase ventilating discharge pipe, permits increase in pressure within engine, thus causing oil to be forced out past any oil seals or gaskets.
18. If oil pressure relief valve is mounted on outside of block, leakage may occur if unit is loose or its gasket defective.

HIGH OIL CONSUMPTION

1. External oil leaks.
2. Leaky piston rings due to wear.
3. Leaky piston rings due to sticking caused by gummy deposit. Try to free up with suitable solvent poured in fuel tank. Blue smoke at tail pipe indicates badly leaking rings.
4. Worn pistons and cylinders.
5. Cylinder block distorted by tightening cylinder head bolts unevenly.
6. Excessive clearance between intake valve stems and guides allows oil mist to be sucked into cylinders.
7. Punctured vacuum pump diaphragm permits oil from crankcase to be sucked into intake manifold.
8. Worn main or rod bearings allow excessive leakage from bearings. Result is cylinder walls are flooded with oil.
9. Oil pressure too high due to faulty action of oil pressure relief valve, or clogged relief passage.
10. If pressure lubricated, loose piston pins may permit excessive leakage to cylinder walls.
11. Grade of oil used is too light. A poor quality oil may become far too thin when engine is hot. Hard driving on hot days will also consume more oil.
12. Clogged crankcase ventilator screen.

OIL PRESSURE RELIEF VALVE LEAKS

1. Relief valve needs tighter adjustment.
2. Relief valve spring weak or broken.
3. Valve seat worn or distorted.
4. Plunger type valve face worn.
5. Plunger type valve stuck open.
6. Ball type valve damaged.
7. Pump discharge pipe or passages leak.

ENGINE OIL DILUTION

1. Oil contains foam caused by presence of water in oil. Water may be due to condensation within crankcase or to a leaky cylinder head gasket.
2. Extreme dilution of oil by fuel may add enough liquid to oil to mislead. In extreme cases, oil level may increase. Dilution is greatest when frequent stops are made in cold weather.

NO OIL PRESSURE

1. Oil pressure gauge defective.
2. Pipe to oil pressure gauge stopped up.
3. Not enough oil in crankcase.
4. Oil pump inoperative.
5. Oil pressure relief valve stuck open.
6. Oil passages on discharge side of pump stopped up.
7. Oil screen or passages on intake side of pump stopped up.

LOW OIL PRESSURE

1. Oil pressure gauge inaccurate.
2. Pipe to pressure gauge restricted.
3. Oil too thin due to dilution, poor quality, or too light a grade used.
4. Oil pressure relief valve adjustment too light.
5. Relief valve spring weak.
6. Oil pump gears worn.
7. Oil pump cover worn.
8. Oil pump body or cover loose.
9. Oil pump gasket damaged, improperly installed or too thick.
10. Air leak in oil intake pipe (if oil level is low).
11. Air leak in top of floating screen (if used).
12. Oil intake pipe or screen clogged with water, sludge, gummy oil, dirt or ice.
13. Oil leak in discharge pipe.
14. Loose connections in oil lines.
15. Worn main, rod or camshaft bearings.

HIGH OIL PRESSURE

1. Oil pressure gauge defective.
2. Oil too heavy.
3. Oil pressure relief valve adjustment too heavy.
4. Relief valve spring too stiff.
5. Oil pressure relief passage clogged.
6. Plunger type relief valve stuck by gummy oil or plunger is too tight a fit.
7. Main oil passages on pressure side of pump clogged.

ENGINE NOISES

Loose Main Bearing

A loose main bearing is indicated by a powerful but dull thud or knock when the engine is pulling. If all main bearings are loose a noticeable clatter will be audible.

The thud occurs regularly every other revolution. The knock can be confirmed by shorting spark plugs on cylinders adjacent to the bearing. Knock will disappear or be less when plugs are shorted. This test should be made at a fast idle equivalent to 15 mph in high gear. If bearing is not quite loose enough to produce a knock by itself, the bearing may knock if oil is too thin or if there is no oil at the bearing.

Loose Flywheel

A thud or click which is usually irregular. To test, idle the engine at about 20 mph and shut off the ignition. If thud is heard, the flywheel may be loose.

Loose Rod Bearing

A metallic knock which is usually loudest at about 30 mph with throttle closed. Knock can be reduced or even eliminated by shorting spark plug. If bearing is not loose enough to produce a knock by itself, the bearing may knock if oil is too thin or if there is no oil at the bearing.

Piston Pin

Piston pin, piston and connecting rod noises are difficult to tell apart.

A loose piston pin causes a sharp double knock which is usually heard when engine is idling. Severity of knock should increase when spark plug to this cylinder is short-circuited. However, on some engines the knock becomes more noticeable at 25 to 35 mph on the road.

Piston pin rubs against cylinder wall, caused by lock screw being loose or snap ring broken.

Piston & Rings

1. Excessive clearance between pistons and cylinders (piston slap).
2. Out-of-round or tapered bores.
3. Top piston ring strikes ridge at top of cylinder bore.
4. Carbon deposit on top of piston strikes cylinder head.
5. Piston rubs against cylinder head gasket.
6. Broken piston ring.
7. Excessive side clearance of ring in groove.
8. Worn or broken piston ring lands.
9. Broken piston.

Valves

1. Valve click due to too much tappet clearance, hydraulic tappet not working properly, warped valve, sticking valve, binding rocker arm.
2. Insufficient oil to valve mechanism, especially overhead valves.
3. Worn or scored parts anywhere in valve mechanism.
4. Broken valve springs.
5. Weak valve springs.
6. Cocked valve springs.
7. Excessive tappet guide clearance.
8. Lower end of tappet scored, chipped, rough, worn or broken.
9. Very rough surface on cams.
10. Excessive valve stem-to-guide clearance.
11. Valve face not concentric with valve stem.
12. Valve seat face not concentric with valve stem.
13. Valve covers on overhead valve engines tightened excessively will amplify normal valve noise.

Hydraulic Lifters

The malfunctioning of a hydraulic valve lifter is almost always accompanied by a clicking or tapping noise. More or less hydraulic lifter noise may be expected when the engine is cold but if lifters are functioning properly the noise should disappear when the engine warms up.

If all or nearly all lifters are noisy, they may be stuck because of dirty or gummy oil.

If all lifters are noisy, oil pressure to

them may be inadequate. Foaming oil may also cause this trouble. If oil foams there will be bubbles on the oil level dipstick. Foaming may be caused by water in the oil or by too high an oil level or by a very low oil level.

If the hydraulic plungers require an initial adjustment, they will be noisy if this adjustment is incorrect.

If one lifter is noisy the cause may be:

1. Plunger too tight in lifter body.
2. Weak or broken plunger spring.
3. Ball valve leaks.
4. Plunger worn.
5. Lock ring (if any) improperly installed or missing.
6. Lack of oil pressure to this plunger.

If ball valve leaks, clean plunger in special solvent such as acetone and reinstall. Too often, plungers are condemned as faulty when all they need is a thorough cleaning.

Gum and dirty oil are the most common causes of hydraulic valve lifter trouble. Engine oil must be free of dirt. Select a standard brand of engine oil and use no other. Mixing up one standard brand with another may cause gummy oil and sticking plungers. Do not use any special oils unless recommended by the car manufacturer and change oil filter or element at recommended intervals.

Timing Gears

1. Gears loose on hubs or shafts.
2. Gears misaligned.
3. Excessive gear backlash.
4. Eccentric gear, usually due to high key.
5. Teeth meshed too tight (new oversize gear).
6. Too much end play in camshaft or crankshaft.
7. Front crankshaft bearing clearance excessive.
8. Chipped tooth usually on camshaft gear.

Timing Chain

1. Chain loose due to wear.
2. Sprocket teeth worn.
3. Sprockets loose on hubs or shafts.
4. Sprockets misaligned.
5. Front camshaft bearing clearance excessive.
6. Front main bearing clearance excessive.
7. Loose vibration damper or drive pulley.

Loose Engine Mountings

Occasional thud with car in operation. Most likely to be noticed at the moment the throttle is opened or closed.

Excessive Crankshaft End Play

A rather sharp rap which occurs at idling speed but may be heard at higher speeds also. The noise should disappear when clutch is disengaged.

Water Pump

1. Water pump shaft pulley loose.
2. Impeller loose on shaft.
3. Too much end play in pump shaft.
4. Too much clearance between shaft and bearings.
5. Impeller blades rubbing against pump housing.
6. Impeller pin sheared off or impeller broken.
7. Rough bearing.
8. Pump seal too hard.

Fan Belt

1. Belt worn or burned.
2. Wrong belt. Does not fit pulley grooves properly.
3. Belt too tight. Squeaks.
4. Belt or pulley dirty or sticky with gummy oil.
5. Pulley bent, cracked or broken.
6. Belt pulleys misaligned.
7. Belt loose; squeaks when engine is accelerated.

Fan

1. Fan blades bent.
2. Fan blades loose on hub.
3. Fan out of balance when made.
4. Fan blades strike radiator.
5. Fan shaft end play excessive.
6. Fan shaft loose on its bearings.
7. Defective fan bearings.
8. Bearings need lubrication.

Engine Vibration

1. Unequal compression in cylinders.
2. Missing at high speed.
3. Unbalanced fan or loose fan blade.
4. Incorrect adjustment of engine mounts, or damaged mounts.
5. Loose engine mounts.
6. Engine support loose on frame or cylinder block.
7. Unbalanced or sprung crankshaft.
8. Excessive engine friction due to tight pistons, etc.
9. Defective vibration damper.

Fuel Pump Noise

Diagnosis of fuel pumps suspected as noisy requires that some form of sounding device be used. Judgment by ear alone is not sufficient, otherwise a fuel pump may be needlessly replaced in attempting to correct noise contributed by some other component. Use of a stethoscope, a long screwdriver, or a sounding rod is recommended to locate the area or component causing the noise. The sounding rod can easily be made from a length of copper tubing ¼ to ⅜ inch in diameter.

If the noise has been isolated to the fuel pump, remove the pump and run the engine with the fuel remaining in the carburetor bowl. If the noise level does not change, the source of the noise is elsewhere and the original fuel pump should be reinstalled. On models using a fuel pump push rod, check for excessive wear and/or galling of the push rod.

Electrical Troubles

NOTE—Ignition troubles are included in the *Engine Troubles* section under the various operating difficulties these troubles could cause.

BATTERY REQUIRES FREQUENT RECHARGING

Insufficient Current Flow to Battery

1. Glazed or burned generator commutator.
2. Incorrect voltage regulator setting.
3. Regulator contacts oxidized or burned.
4. Sulphated battery.
5. Corroded battery terminals.
6. Regulator not grounded.
7. Loose connections or grounds in lighting or ignition circuits.
8. Slipping fan belt.
9. Blown regulator fuse.
10. Wrong size generator drive pulley.
11. Shorted or open alternator rectifiers.
12. Grounded stator windings in alternator.

Excessive Starting Load Causing Abnormal Current Flow From Battery

1. Frequent use of starting motor.
2. Excessive use of starting motor due to difficulty in starting.
3. Faulty starting motor.
4. Excessive engine friction due to tight pistons, etc., or heavy engine oil.

Excessive Lighting Load

1. Car operation confined largely to night driving.
2. Tail and stop light wires reversed.
3. Stop light switch inoperative (closed at all times).
4. Unnecessary use of head lamps while parking.
5. Ground or short in lighting circuit.

Abnormal Accessory Load

1. Radio.
2. Heater.
3. Windshield defroster.
4. Cigar lighter.
5. Spotlights.

Internal Discharge of Battery

1. Plates badly sulphated.
2. Cell leak due to cracked jar or sealing compound.
3. Water level not maintained at proper height.
4. Plate separators ineffective.
5. Exterior of battery covered with corrosion and acid-soaked dirt which forms a path to ground for current.

Miscellaneous

Radio suppressor connected to generator or regulator field terminal.

STARTER WON'T ROTATE OR ROTATES SLOWLY

If lights become dim or go out when the starter switch is closed, the battery may be too weak to operate the starter. In this case, the engine may be started by pushing the car.

NOTE—Some cannot be started by pushing because these transmissions have no rear oil pump to drive the engine through the transmission. In such cases, a fully charged battery should be installed or a "jumper" circuit should be used from another charged battery.

Due to Starter Circuit

1. Low battery. Lights grow very dim or go out when starter switch is closed.
2. Connections loose, dirty, corroded or broken at battery terminals, starter switch terminal, battery ground strap.
3. Short circuit across starter terminal.

Due to Starter Switch

1. Starter pedal (if any) stuck.
2. Starter switch stuck.
3. Pedal linkage fails to close starter switch (older cars).
4. Defective solenoid.
5. Neutral safety switch on cars with automatic transmissions out of adjustment or defective.
6. Starter switch makes poor contact due to dirt, corrosion, bent parts, weak contact spring.
7. Starter switch fails to close circuit because of sticking or broken contact parts.

Due to Armature & Field Circuits

1. Armature windings burned out, shorted, grounded or open-circuited.
2. Short circuit in armature winding or brush pigtail lead.
3. Broken wire in armature winding or brush pigtail lead.
4. Loose, dirty or corroded connections in armature circuit, including ground.
5. Field coils burned out, shorted or grounded.
6. Broken wire in field winding or broken lead.
7. Loose, dirty or corroded connections in field circuit.

Due to Commutator & Brushes

1. Brush pigtail leads loose or broken.
2. Starter brushes cracked crosswise (prevents flow of current).
3. Arm type brush holder sticks.
4. Brush sticks in sliding brush holder.
5. Bent brush holder misaligns brush and causes poor contact.
6. Starter brushes badly worn.
7. Brush leads shorted or have loose, dirty, corroded or broken connections.
8. Poor brush contact due to weak or broken springs.
9. Brushes coated with oil.
10. High mica between commutator segments prevents brush contact.
11. Commutator bars loose and/or solder melted.
12. Commutator dirty, corroded or burned.

Due to Engine Resistance

1. Piston sticking to cylinders in overheated engine.
2. Pistons stuck to cylinders because of gummy oil.
3. Pistons binding in cylinders because of corrosion after long lay-up.
4. Jammed generator armature.
5. Combustion chamber full of water.
6. Solid ice in water pump.
7. Broken part in engine causes jamming.
8. Excessive engine friction, due to cold weather and too heavy oil.

Due to Improper Engine Repairs

1. New rings too tight.
2. New pistons too tight.
3. Main or rod bearings too tight.
4. New camshaft bearings too tight.

Due to Armature Binding

1. Loose field poles.
2. Armature shaft frozen in bearings.
3. Loose end plates.
4. Windings thrown out of armature slots.
5. Armature locked magnetically to field poles because of loose bearings or worn or bent armature shaft.
6. Bendix spring retaining screws loose (jammed against housing).
7. Cracked or distorted drive housing.
8. Starter misaligned.
9. Starter jams because of burred teeth on drive pinion or flywheel gear.
10. Starter pinion (sliding gear type) jams because of incorrect endwise clearance.

STARTER SPINS BUT WON'T ENGAGE FLYWHEEL GEAR

Bendix Type

1. Bendix pinion stuck on shaft due to dirty or gummy shaft or bent shaft.
2. Bendix spring broken.
3. Bendix spring bolt broken.
4. Pinion housing cracked.
5. Drive key sheared.
6. Pinion teeth broken off.
7. Starter ring gear has several teeth missing.
8. Armature shaft broken.

Sliding Gear Type

1. Weak or broken meshing spring.
2. Fault in sliding gear linkage.
3. Fault in solenoid.
4. Over-running clutch worn out or lubricant caked or gummy.
5. Drive key sheared.
6. Pinion teeth broken off.
7. Flywheel ring gear has several teeth missing.
8. Armature shaft broken, dirty or dry.
9. Wrong starter pinion clearance.

STARTER PINION JAMMED INTO FLYWHEEL GEAR

1. Burred teeth on pinion or ring gear.
2. Misalignment of starter or armature shaft.
3. If engine kicks back when being started, Bendix pinion may jam. Loosen starter to free pinion.

STARTER PINION DISENGAGES SLOWLY

Bendix Type

The most probable cause is a dirty Bendix drive shaft. Or the pinion may bind on its shaft due to a bent shaft or too tight a fit between pinion and splines.

When a Bendix Folo-Thru starter drive stays in mesh too long it is probably due to a sticking release pin which is designed to be released by centrifugal force at a certain engine rpm. In such an instance the drive should be replaced.

Sliding Gear Type

1. Pinion binds on its shaft due to too tight a fit or due to bent or burred shaft.
2. Pinion shaft sticky or dirty.
3. Sliding gear operating linkage sticking or binding.
4. Solenoid does not operate properly.

STARTER PINION WON'T RELEASE

Bendix Folo-Thru Drive

Failure to disengage would most probably be caused by a stuck release pin which is designed to be released by centrifugal force at a given engine rpm. If such is the case, replace the drive unit.

Sliding Gear Type

If solenoid operated, the solenoid may be defective. If pedal operated, the shift linkage may be binding or sticking. May also be caused by a defective starting switch on cars with key-starter switch or by improper starter pinion clearance.

STARTER NOISE

1. Loose pole pieces rubbing against armature.
2. Gear noise due to defective teeth.
3. Flywheel ring gear untrue.
4. Starter drive housing loose on flywheel housing.
5. Starter loose on drive housing.
6. Commutator end plate loose.
7. Armature shaft bent.
8. Worn armature shaft, bearings or bushings.
9. Drive pinion shaft bent.
10. Worn drive pinion shaft, bearings or bushings.
11. Misalignment caused by dirt or burrs on mating surfaces.

GENERATOR DOES NOT CHARGE

1. Fan belt broken or slips badly.
2. Belt pulley slips on armature shaft.
3. Cutout relay fails to close.
4. Armature won't rotate because of seized bearing, etc.
5. External wiring from generator to starter switch terminal short-circuited or circuit is open because of detached wire or very dirty or corroded connection.
6. Voltage regulator inoperative.
7. Open circuit or short circuit in armature or field windings.
8. Brushes stuck.
9. Brushes coated with oil.
10. Brush lead connections dirty or disconnected.
11. Improperly seated brushes.
12. Weak brush springs.
13. Very dirty commutator.
14. Burned or corroded commutator.
15. Commutator bars short-circuited.
16. High mica on commutator.
17. Solder melted at commutator bar connections.

GENERATOR NOISE

1. Generator loose on engine.
2. Generator end plates loose.
3. Armature shaft bent.
4. Armature shaft worn.
5. Bushing or bearing worn or needs lubrication.
6. Armature shaft end play excessive.
7. Generator pulley loose on its shaft.
8. Generator or pulley misaligned.
9. Bent, cracked or broken pulley.
10. Generator fan rubs on generator.

GENERATOR BRUSH NOISE

1. High mica between commutator bars.
2. Sprung armature shaft.
3. Rough, dirty or glazed commutator.
4. Worn or loose brushes.
5. Commutator out of round.
6. Brushes not seating properly.
7. Too little or too much brush spring tension.

ALTERNATORS

Alternator Fails To Charge

1. Drive belt loose.
2. Brushes sticking.
3. Open charging circuit.
4. Open in stator winding circuit.
5. Faulty soldered connections at output terminal stud.
6. Rectifiers open circuited.

Low Unsteady Charging Rate

1. Drive belt loose.
2. High resistance at battery terminal posts.
3. Loose connections.
4. Poor ground between engine and body ground wire.
5. Resistance in charging circuit.
6. Open stator windings.

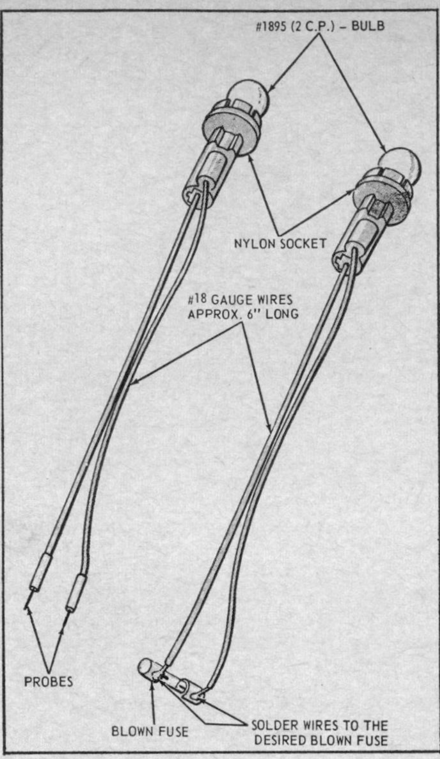

Test lamp for locating shorts

Low Output

1. Grounded stator.
2. Shorted rectifier.
3. Voltage regulator faulty.

Excessive Charging Rate

1. Voltage regulator faulty.
2. Open circuited rectifier.

Noisy Alternator

1. Misaligned belt or pulley, or loose pulley.
2. Shorted rectifier.
3. Worn bearings.
4. Rotor shaft sprung.

Regulator Points Oxidized

1. Poor ground connections.
2. Improper voltage regulator air gap setting.
3. Shorted field in alternator.
4. Voltage regulator setting too high.

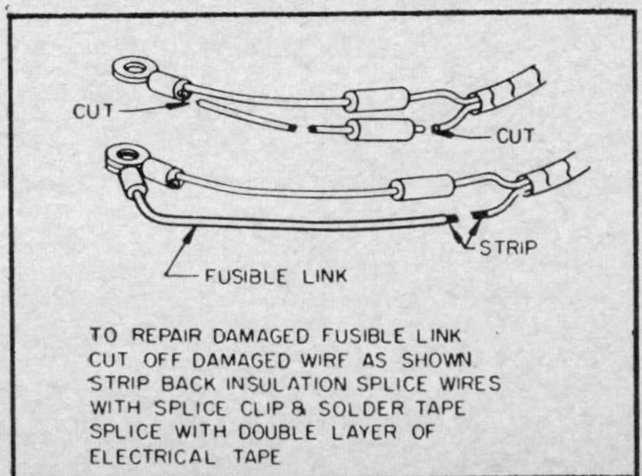

Repairing fusible links

Burned Points or Coil Windings In Regulator

1. Voltage regulator setting too high.

Voltage Regulator Points Stuck

1. Poor ground connections between alternator and regulator.

LOCATING ELECTRICAL SHORTS WITH TEST LAMP

Due to the complexity of locating electrical short circuits where several circuits are protected by the same fuse, fabricate a test lamp from the material shown in the accompanying illustration. By substituting the test lamp for the blown fuse the short circuit can be isolated.

When the test lamp is inserted into the fuse panel, the bulb will light and continue to glow until the short circuit is removed. Determining which circuit is at fault can be accomplished by disconnecting the affected circuits one at a time until the test lamp goes out. Then trace the circuit to find the cause of the short (wire contacting sharp sheet metal edges, wire pinched between two metal objects, etc.).

For circuits that are not connected to the fuse panel but are protected by an in-line fuse cartridge, use a test lamp having two needle point probes in place of the blown fuse. Insert one probe through the insulation and into the wire on each side of the blown in-line fuse and follow the same testing procedure outlined above.

FUSIBLE LINKS

Some cars starting with 1965 models have fusible links located between the battery and the lower ends of the main supply wires. These links are the weakest point in the electrical supply system for the entire car and, as such, will act as a fuse for every wiring harness in the car. Every electrical accessory is still protected by a fuse or circuit breaker, of course, but fusible links have been added to protect the wiring harnesses *before* the fuses.

In the past, if a wire became grounded in the portion between the battery and the fuse block, a long section of the wire would burn out, making replacement of a complete wiring harness necessary. Now, with the fusible links, a short or ground in any unfused wire will cause only a short link to burn out. Because of its location, possibility of a fire, such as was sometimes caused by a burned-out wiring harness, is very remote.

A fusible link is simply a short section of wire that is several sizes smaller in gauge than the wire in the circuit which it protects. If a short or ground occurs the fusible link will melt before the insulation is damaged elsewhere in the circuit. Replace burned-out fusible link as directed in the illustration.

LIGHTS FLICKER

Circuit Breaker Vibrates

When the circuit breaker vibrates and

causes lights to flicker it indicates a short in one of the lighting circuits, which may be traced as follows:

1. Pull switch successively to each lighting position. If circuit breaker vibrates in all positions except "off" the trouble should be found in the tail lamp and license lamp circuit, or instrument, map light, or clock light circuits.
2. If circuit breaker vibrates in parking lamp position only, look for a short in the parking lamp circuit.
3. If circuit breaker vibrates in headlamp position only, inspect headlamp wiring circuit and lamp assemblies. If both filaments in headlamps burn at the same time, check dimmer switch.

LAMPS FAIL TO BURN

1. Burned out bulb.
2. An open circuit in wiring.
3. A defective switch.
4. Burned out fuse.

LIGHTS FLARE UP WHEN ENGINE IS SPEEDED UP

This condition is caused by high voltage in the electrical system due to one or more of the following:

1. Electrolyte in battery low or weak.
2. High resistance in circuit between generator and battery due to loose or dirty connections.
3. Poor ground between generator and engine.
4. Voltage regulator adjusted too high.
5. Voltage regulator inoperative.
6. Ground or short in generator field circuit.

STOP LIGHT TROUBLES

1. If only one stop light fails to burn, check lamp bulb, socket and wiring.
2. If both stop lights fail to burn also check stop light switch and fuse.
3. If stop light burns when brake pedal is released, check stop light switch, brake pedal clearance and for dragging brakes.
4. If compensating port in brake master cylinder is plugged by foreign material, or is covered by the piston primary cup when brake pedal is released, high pressure will be maintained in hydraulic system and stop light switch will remain closed.

TURN SIGNAL TROUBLES

1. If signals are inoperative on both turns, look for a blown fuse or a defective flasher.
2. If stop lights burn, the fuse and rear signal lamp bulbs are okay.
3. An inoperative right signal light may be caused by a burned out bulb at the right indicator or a right signal lamp. The opposite applies for an inoperative left signal light.
4. If bulbs are okay, look for an open circuit or defective switch.
5. If indicator light on dash burns steady when lever is placed in a turn position, check for burned out bulb in park or stop light. If park and stop light bulbs are okay, check for faulty flasher.
6. If indicator light on dash does not burn when lever is in a turn position, check for burned out bulb or a faulty flasher.
7. If switch fails to cancel after completion of turn, remove steering wheel and check for worn or broken mechanism.

ELECTRIC CLOCKS

If clock does not run, check for blown "clock" fuse. If fuse is blown check for short in wiring. If fuse is not blown check for open circuit.

With an electric clock, the most frequent cause of clock fuse blowing is low voltage at the clock which will prevent a complete wind and allow clock contacts to remain closed. This may be caused by any of the following: discharged battery, corrosion on contact surface of battery terminals, loose connections at battery terminals, at junction block, at fuse clips, or at terminal connection of clock. Therefore, if in reconnecting battery or clock it is noted that the clock is not ticking, always check for blown fuse, or examine the circuits at the points indicated above to determine and correct the cause. See *Dash Gauge* chapter for Electric Clock data.

HAZARD WARNING FLASHER TROUBLES

To make a quick check of the system pull Hazard Warning switch to ON position. The rear turn signal bulbs should flash as well as the front turn signal bulbs, turn signal indicator bulbs and pilot bulb. All lights will burn continuously when the brake pedal is depressed; this is normal.

Pilot Bulb Fails To Flash

Check for burned out bulb and loose or defective ground wire. Replace bulb, repair ground wire or tighten ground wire screw. If this does not correct the condition, replace flasher switch and harness assembly. Then repeat quick check procedure.

All Bulbs Fail to Flash

1. Check for loose harness connections at Hazard Warning connectors and secure connectors if necessary.
2. Check for a burned out tail and stop light fuse and replace if necessary.
3. Check for a defective Hazard Warning flasher or switch. This may be done by removing the flasher and installing a known good flasher.
4. Pull switch to ON position. If flasher does not operate properly, replace flasher switch and harness assembly, installing old flasher. If system still does not operate properly, install new flasher along with new switch.

Some Bulbs Fail to Flash While Others are Operative

1. Turn ON ignition switch and turn OFF Hazard Warning switch.
2. Place turn signal lever first to right and then to left turn position. If turn signal circuits operate properly, the Hazard Warning switch and harness assembly should be replaced.
3. If the same bulbs fail to flash, the cause is most likely a burned-out bulb. In the case of turn signal indicator bulbs, a loose or defective ground wire can also cause this condition. Repair as necessary.

NOTE: If any turn signal bulb fails to flash when the turn signal circuit is actuated, the reduced current in the circuit will cause the remaining signals on that side of the car to burn steadily. If the Hazard Warning flasher is energized, however, all turn signal bulbs and indicator bulbs will flash except those that have a circuit defect. They will flash at a constant rate unless the battery is completely run down. This is because the Hazard Warning Flasher overrides the turn signal circuit flasher.

4. If the condition is still not resolved, disconnect the Hazard Warning connectors and again check the operation of the turn signal circuits. If the affected bulbs now flash, replace flasher switch and harness assembly.
5. If the condition is still not resolved, look for defects in the connectors to the affected bulb.
6. Repeat quick check test.

Continued

Clutch Troubles

CLUTCH DRAGS

Clutch drag means that when the clutch pedal is depressed fully the clutch disc is not completely released. In consequence it does not come to rest but continues to rotate, being dragged around by the rotation of the engine. Clutch dragging causes clashing of gears, especially when shifting from neutral to low or reverse.

1. Pedal cannot disengage clutch because of excessive free pedal travel. Pedal linkage should be adjusted so that the pedal shank is about 1" from the under side of the toe-board.
2. Worn clutch linkage.
3. Release levers need adjustment.
4. Clutch disc warped out of true.
5. High spots on clutch facing.
6. Broken or loose facings.
7. Loose rivet in facing.
8. Clutch disc hub binds on splined clutch shaft due to bent shaft, tight fit, burred splines or splines covered with gummy oil or dirt.
9. Clutch disc wobbles because of broken springs in hub.
10. Clutch disc hub out of true.
11. Clutch shaft bent.
12. Clutch shaft out of true because of worn bearings.
13. Transmission is not in alignment with flywheel housing.
14. Clutch pressure plate warped, thus throwing release levers out of adjustment.
15. Flange of clutch cover not in alignment with flywheel because of loose attaching screws, bent flange, dirt between flange and flywheel.
16. Grease on clutch facings.
17. Engine misaligned due to deteriorated or broken engine mounts.
18. Loose flywheel housing-to-engine attaching bolts.
19. Release fork pivot worn.

CLUTCH SLIPS

The clutch disc slips whenever the clutch pressure plate fails to hold it tight against the face of the flywheel. If clutch slippage is severe, the engine speed will rise above normal on full throttle in high gear. Slight but continuous slippage may go unnoticed until the clutch facings are ruined by excessive temperature caused by friction.

In a very high percentage of cases, clutch slippage is due to less than zero clearance between the shank of the pedal and the toe-board because of failure to have the pedal adjusted in time. The consequence is worn and burned clutch facings. Before the clutch starts slipping, the normal wear of the facings causes a gradual reduction in clutch pedal free play. When there is no free play of the pedal the clutch starts slipping.

Other causes of clutch slippage are:

1. Driving with foot resting on pedal.
2. Binding or sticking of pedal or its linkage.
3. Binding or sticking of clutch disc hub on clutch shaft.
4. Binding of release levers.
5. Release bearing sleeve sticks.
6. Weak or broken clutch pressure springs.
7. Worn clutch facings.
8. Facings covered with grease or oil.
9. Facings burned.
10. Release levers improperly adjusted.
11. Pressure plate sticks.

CLUTCH GRABS

A clutch is said to grab when it engages too abruptly. The usual causes are:

1. Loss of tension in cushioning plates in the rim of the steel clutch disc. These plates cause the clutch facings to bulge outward slightly. The resulting springy action of the facings aids in producing a smooth, gentle clutch engagement.
2. Use of wrong type of clutch facing.
3. Grease or oil on facings.
4. Clutch springs too stiff.
5. Momentary binding in clutch linkage while clutch is being engaged.
6. Exposed rivet heads due to excessively worn facings or loose rivets.

CLUTCH CHATTERS

If a clutch chatters while it is being engaged, the trouble is caused by rapid gripping and slipping. The usual causes are:

1. Somewhat sticky clutch friction surfaces due to gummy lubricant.
2. Clutch friction surfaces damp or wet.
3. Weak clutch springs.
4. Slight binding in clutch linkage during engagement.
5. Slight binding of pressure plate during engagement.
6. Loose engine mounts.

CLUTCH PEDAL PULSATES

Clutch pedal pulsation has often been termed a nervous pedal. When a slight pressure is applied on the pedal, with the engine running, the pedal will vibrate or bounce with every revolution of the engine. As the pressure on the pedal is increased, the pulsation will cease.

1. Loose or improperly adjusted engine mounts.
2. Collar on clutch release sleeve does not run true due to a bent clutch shaft, or the clutch shaft misaligned because of misalignment between crankshaft and transmission.
3. Clutch release levers not adjusted to uniform height.

CLUTCH RATTLES

This condition will occur when the engine is idling with transmission in neutral.

1. Excessive clearance at pressure plate driving lugs.
2. Anti-rattle springs or retractor springs on release levers (or release bearing) weak, broken or disconnected.
3. Looseness in clutch pedal operating linkage.

NOISE WHEN PEDAL IS DEPRESSED

1. Clutch release bearing worn, dirty, damaged, broken or inadequately lubricated.
2. Clutch shaft bearing or bushing in crankshaft worn, damaged, broken or inadequately lubricated.
3. Clutch shaft rear bearing at front end of transmission, worn, dirty or lacks lubricant.

NOISE WHEN PEDAL IS RELEASED

1. Misalignment of transmission with engine causing slight wobble of clutch disc hub—noticeable with engine idling or at low road speed.
2. Disc hub loose fit on splined clutch shaft.
3. Disc damper springs weak or broken.
4. No pedal play.
5. Weak or broken pedal return spring.
6. Weak or broken release sleeve spring.
7. Clutch linkage sticks.
8. Clutch pedal sticks.
9. Clutch release sleeve sticks.
10. Clutch release fork binds.

BEARING NOISE

Clutch Release Bearing:—With engine idling, there is a high-pitched rubbing noise when foot rests on clutch pedal.

Clutch Pilot Bearing:—Fairly high-pitched noise when clutch pedal is fully depressed with engine idling.

Rambler "E-Stick" Troubles

NOTE—In addition to the troubles listed below, the clutch is subject to the same troubles, such as Chatter, Grabbing, etc., as the conventional type clutch.

Excessive Slip

1. Low servo oil pressure.
2. Release lever improperly adjusted or release fork not installed on release bearing guide pins.
3. Low engine oil level.
4. Air valve solenoid inoperative or leaking excessively.
5. Check valve orifice blocked in servo.
6. Diaphragm push rod stuck in valve and diaphragm assembly.
7. Diaphragm vent plugged.

Excessive Creep

1. Retractor spring too light or broken.
2. Servo oil pressure too high.
3. Broken retractor straps.

No Clutch Release

1. Bent or damaged diaphragm cover.
2. Vacuum lines leaking.
3. Control valve stuck in valve body.
4. Actuating switch not operating properly.
5. Actuating switch cam out of adjustment.
6. Faulty wiring circuit to air valve solenoid.
7. Air valve solenoid not functioning.
8. Servo piston binding in its bore.
9. Diaphragm push rod sticking.
10. Air vent in servo body plugged.
11. Vacuum diaphragm leaking.

Engine Overspeeds on Clutch Engagement

1. Clutch release lever out of adjustment.
2. Servo piston binding in its bore.
3. Servo body vent hole plugged.
4. Oil regulator valve not seating.
5. Servo check valve sticking on shaft.
6. Check valve orifice in servo restricted.

No Clutch Engagement

1. Actuating switch not operating properly.
2. Actuating switch cam out of adjustment.
3. Faulty wiring circuit to air valve solenoid.
4. Air valve solenoid not functioning.
5. Lube valve stuck closed.
6. Servo piston binding in its bore.
7. Broken spring in dump diaphragm.
8. Oil pressure regulator valve stuck open.
9. Low engine oil level.

Three Speed Transmission Troubles

General Motors Transmission with Second Speed Gear Located at Rear of Mainshaft

Car Application Listed in Three Speed Manual Shift Transmission Chapter

SLIPS OUT OF HIGH GEAR

1. Transmission mounting bolts loose.
2. Control rods interfere with engine mounts or clutch release lever.
3. Control linkage does not work freely.
4. Gear does not fully engage.
5. Damaged mainshaft pilot bearing.
6. Clutch gear bearing retainer broken or loose.
7. Dirt between transmission case and clutch housing (front mounted), or between transmission case and differential carrier (rear mounted).
8. Misalignment of transmission.

SLIPS OUT OF LOW AND/OR REVERSE

1. First and/or reverse gears damaged from operating at part engagement.
2. Improperly mated splines on inside of first and reverse gear and/or external spline on 2nd and 3rd synchronizer sleeve.
3. Improperly adjusted linkage.

NOISY IN ALL GEARS

1. Not enough lubricant.
2. Worn countergear bearings.
3. Worn or damaged clutch gear and countershaft drive gear.
4. Damaged clutch gear or mainshaft ball bearings.
5. Damaged speedometer gears.

NOISY IN HIGH GEAR

1. Damaged clutch gear bearing.
2. Damaged mainshaft bearing.
3. Damaged speedometer gears.

NOISY IN NEUTRAL WITH ENGINE RUNNING

1. Damaged clutch gear bearing.
2. Damaged mainshaft pilot bearing roller.

NOISY IN ALL REDUCTION GEARS

1. Not enough lubricant.
2. Worn or damaged clutch gear or countershaft drive gear.

NOISY IN SECOND ONLY

1. Damaged or worn 2nd speed gears.
2. Worn or damaged countergear rear bearings.

NOISY IN LOW AND REVERSE ONLY

1. Worn or damaged 1st and reverse sliding gear.
2. Damaged or worn low and reverse countergear.

NOISY IN REVERSE ONLY

1. Worn or damaged reverse idler.
2. Worn reverse idler bushings.
3. Damaged or worn reverse countergear.

EXCESSIVE BACKLASH IN SECOND ONLY

1. Second gear thrust washer worn.
2. Mainshaft rear bearing improperly installed in case.
3. Worn countergear rear bearing.

EXCESSIVE BACKLASH IN REDUCTION GEARS

1. Worn countergear bushings.
2. Excessive end play in countergear.

LEAKS LUBRICANT

1. Too much lube in transmission.
2. Loose or broken clutch gear bearing retainer.
3. Clutch gear bearing retainer damaged.
4. Cover loose or gasket damaged.
5. Operating shaft seal leaks.
6. Idler shaft expansion plugs loose.
7. Countershaft loose in case.
8. Lack of sealant on bolts.

Three Speed Transmission Troubles

All Transmissions with Low-Reverse Gear Located at Rear of Mainshaft

Car Application Listed in Three Speed Manual Shift Transmission Chapter

NOISES

When diagnosing transmission noise note the gear position in which the noise occurs. Noise present in all gear positions may be due to worn or damaged constant mesh gears or bearings. Noise present in only one gear can usually be traced to the particular gear involved. Other causes of noise are as follows:

1. Misalignment due to loose mounting bolts.
2. Clutch housing misalignment.
3. Dirt or metal chips in lubricant.
4. Not enough lube in transmission.
5. Improper lubricant.

HARD SHIFTING

1. Clutch linkage out of adjustment.
2. Linkage improperly adjusted.
3. Linkage binding due to bent, worn or broken parts.
4. Gearshift tube binding due to misaligned steering gear housing.
5. Improper lube in transmission.
6. Damaged synchronizer assembly.

JUMPS OUT OF GEAR

1. Improper shift procedure.
2. Linkage parts worn, bent, broken or out of adjustment.
3. Excessive end play caused by wear in shift forks, sliding gear fork grooves, thrust washers, mainshaft and countershaft bearings, or clutch pilot bushing.
4. Misalignment or excessive clearance between sliding gear and mainshaft.
5. Damaged synchronizer.

LEAKAGE

1. Overfilled transmission or using a lube that foams or expands while car is in operation.
2. Loose gearshift housing capscrews.
3. Damaged gaskets.
4. Transmission vent plugged.
5. Extension housing rear seal leaks.

Corvair & 1963 Tempest 4-Speed Trans. Troubles

SLIPS OUT OF HIGH GEAR

1. Transmission loose on differential carrier.
2. Control linkage binds or does not fully engage.
3. Damaged or missing mainshaft pilot bearings.
4. Clutch gear bearing retainer loose or broken.
5. Dirt between transmission case and differential carrier.

NOISY IN ALL GEARS

1. Insufficient lubricant.
2. Worn countergear bearings.
3. Worn or damaged clutch gear and countergear.
4. Damaged clutch gear bearing or mainshaft rear bearing.

NOISY IN HIGH GEAR

1. Damaged clutch gear bearing.
2. Damaged mainshaft bearing.

NOISY IN NEUTRAL

1. Damaged clutch gear bearing.
2. Damaged mainshaft pilot roller bearings.

NOISY IN ALL REDUCTION GEARS

1. Insufficient lubricant.
2. Worn or damaged clutch gear or countergear.

NOISY IN 2nd ONLY

1. Damaged or worn 2nd speed gears.
2. Worn or damaged countergear bearings.

NOISY IN LOW & REVERSE

1. Worn or damaged low and reverse sliding gear.
2. Damaged or worn low and reverse countergear.

NOISY IN REVERSE ONLY

1. Worn or damaged reverse idler gear.
2. Worn reverse idler gear bushings.
3. Worn or damaged countergear reverse teeth.

EXCESSIVE BACKLASH IN ALL REDUCTION GEARS

1. Worn countergear bushings.
2. Excessive end play in countergear.

LEAKS LUBRICANT

1. Excessive amount of lubricant in transmission.
2. Loose or broken clutch gear bearing cover.
3. Clutch gear bearing retainer gasket damaged.
4. Cover loose or gasket damaged.
5. Shifter shaft seal leaks.
6. Countershaft loose in case.

Four Speed Transmission Troubles

All Cars Other Than Corvair & 1963 Tempest

NOISY IN ALL SPEEDS

1. Incorrect lubricant level.
2. Incorrect type lubricant.
3. Countergear bearings worn or damaged.
4. Countergear worn or damaged.
5. Clutch gear bearing worn or damaged.
6. Mainshaft bearing worn or damaged.
7. Clutch gear worn or damaged.
8. Transmission misaligned or loose.

NOISY IN 1st SPEED

1. First gear worn or damaged.
2. Countergear worn or damaged.
3. Countergear bearings worn or damaged.
4. Synchronizers worn or broken.
5. Countershaft worn or damaged.

NOISY IN 2nd SPEED

1. Second gear worn or damaged.
2. Countergear worn or damaged.
3. Countergear bearings worn or damaged.
4. Synchronizers worn or broken.
5. Countershaft worn or damaged.

NOISY IN 3rd SPEED

1. Third gear worn or damaged.
2. Countergear worn or damaged.
3. Countergear bearings worn or damaged.
4. Synchronizers worn or broken.
5. Countershaft worn or damaged.

NOISY IN 4th SPEED

1. Clutch shaft bearing worn or damaged.
2. Mainshaft bearing worn or damaged.
3. Synchronizers worn or broken.

NOISY IN REVERSE

1. Reverse idler gear or shaft worn or damaged.
2. Reverse sliding gear worn or damaged.
3. Shift linkage out of adjustment.
4. Shift linkage bent or damaged.
5. Shift linkage parts loose.
6. Shift levers, shafts or forks worn.

SHIFTS HARD

1. Clutch pedal free travel incorrect.
2. Clutch parts worn or damaged.
3. Shift linkage out of adjustment.
4. Shift linkage bent or damaged.
5. Shift linkage parts loose.
6. Shift levers, shafts or forks worn.
7. Lubricant type incorrect.
8. Lubricant level incorrect.

JUMPS OUT OF GEAR

1. Shift linkage out of adjustment.
2. Shift linkage bent or damaged.
3. Shift linkage parts loose.
4. Shift levers, shafts or forks worn.
5. Shift cover loose or gasket damaged.
6. Transmission misaligned or loose.
7. Synchronizers worn or broken.
8. Clutch gear bearing retainer broken.
9. Clutch gear bearing worn or damaged.
10. Clutch pilot bearing worn or broken.
11. Mainshaft and/or pilot worn or damaged.
12. Mainshaft bearing worn or damaged.

LEAKS LUBRICANT

1. Lubricant level incorrect.
2. Lubricant type incorrect.
3. Vent plugged.
4. Clutch gear bearing retainer or gasket loose.
5. Clutch gear bearing retainer broken.
6. Shift cover loose or gasket damaged.
7. Shifter shaft seals leaking.
8. Shift cover bolts not sealed.
9. Countershaft loose in case bore.

Overdrive Troubles

DIAGNOSIS

Figs. 1 to 4 illustrate the overdrive circuit diagrams in use. Since overdrive troubles may originate not only in the mechanical operation of the unit but also in the electrical circuit which controls that unit, always check the control system before disassembling the overdrive. If the trouble is not found after a thorough inspection of the control system, then the transmission and overdrive should be removed for examination. If the overdrive operation is unsatisfactory, look for:

1. Blown fuse in governor-solenoid circuit.
2. Loose terminals on any of the connecting wires.
3. Incorrect terminal locations of connecting wires.
4. Circuits grounded by water, dirt or deformation.
5. Defective solenoid points.
6. Insufficient travel or unsatisfactory contacts in kickdown switch.
7. Excessive end play in governor shaft.
8. Improper adjustment of governor control springs.
9. Burned governor contact points.
10. Damage to governor cap and contacts.
11. Absence of rubber cover to exclude water and dirt.
12. Insufficient travel of shift rod (adjust control cable).

MECHANICAL TROUBLES

Overdrive Won't Drive Unless Locked Up Manually

1. Occasionally the unit may not drive the car forward in direct drive unless locked up by pulling the dash control. This may be caused by one or more broken rollers in the roller clutch, the remedy for which is to replace the entire set of rollers.
2. This condition may also be caused by sticking of the roller retainer upon the cam. This retainer must move freely to push the rollers into engaging position under the pressure of the two actuating springs.
3. Sometimes this condition is due to slight indentations, worn in the cam faces by the rollers spinning, remedied by replacing the cam.

Overdrive Does Not Engage or Lock-Up Does Not Release

1. Dash control improperly connected.
2. Transmission and overdrive improperly aligned.
3. Kickdown switch improperly adjusted.
4. Improper installation of solenoid.
5. Improper positioning of blocker ring.
6. Broken or slipping governor drive pinion.
7. Too much end play in mainshaft.

Overdrive Engages with Severe Jolt or Noise

Insufficient blocker ring friction may cause the ring to lose its grip on the hub of the sun gear control plate.

Free-Wheels At Speeds Over 30 MPH

If cam roller retainer spring tension is weak the unit will free-wheel at all times.

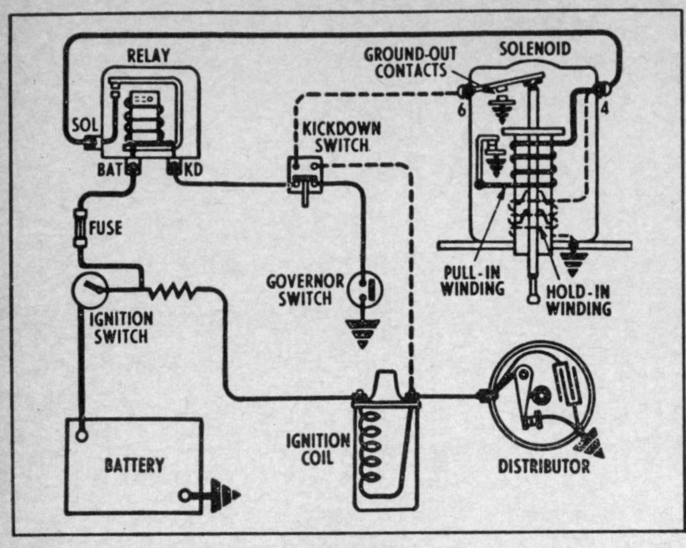

Fig. 1 Overdrive circuit diagram with relay

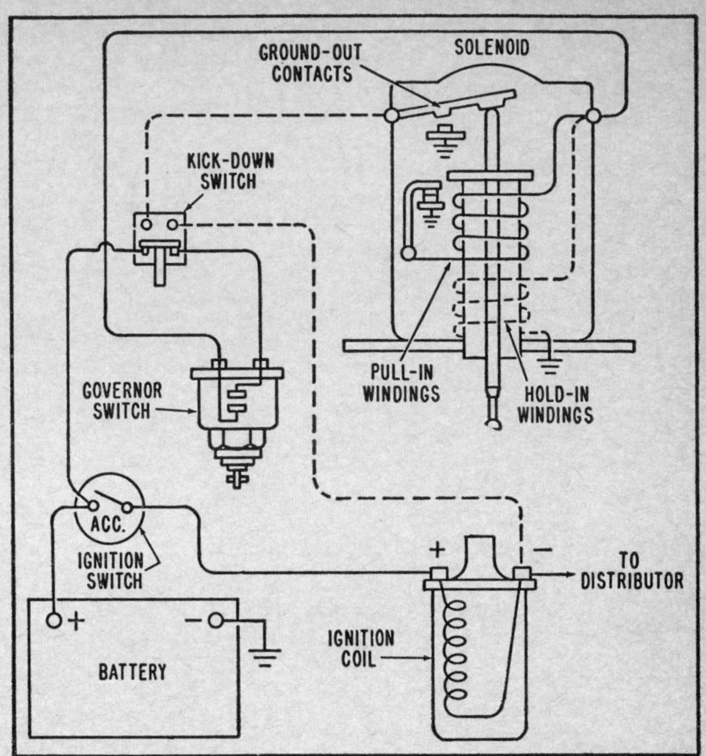

Fig. 2 Overdrive circuit diagram without relay. 1964-69

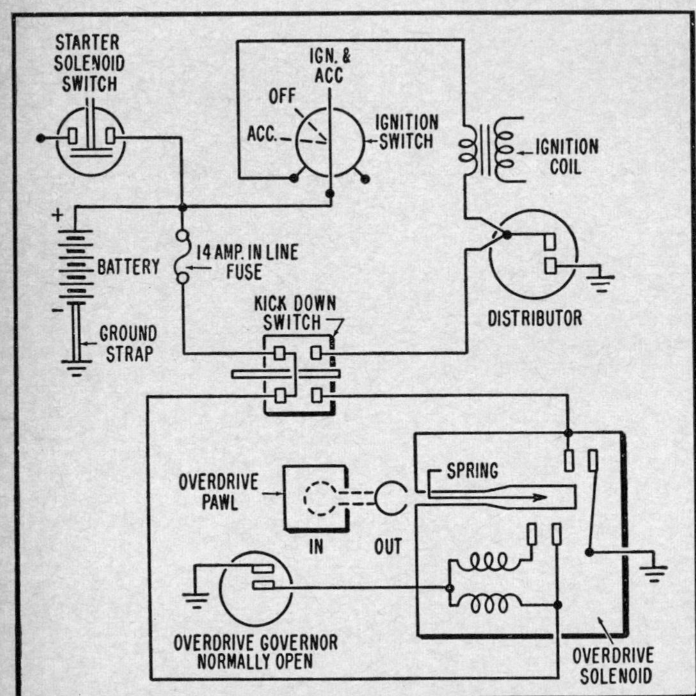

Fig. 3 Overdrive circuit diagram without relay. 1963

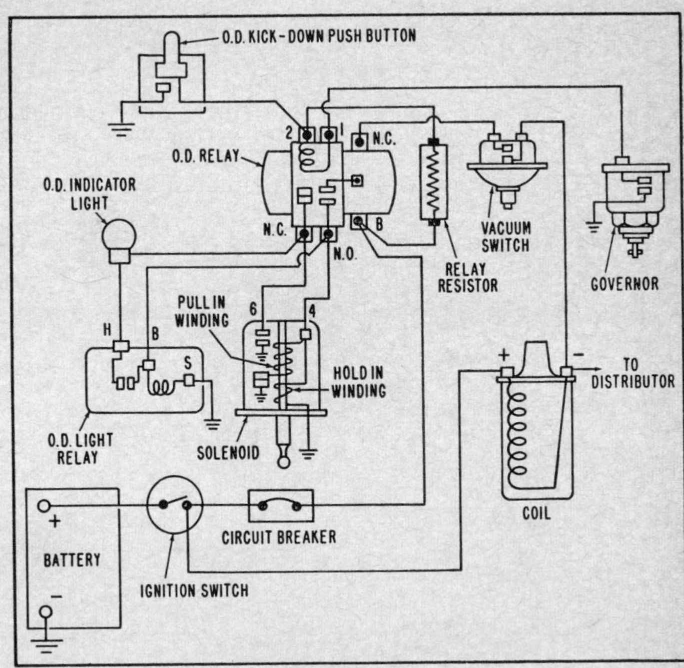

Fig. 4 Rambler twin stick overdrive circuit diagram. 1964-69

Rear Axle Troubles

Noise When Pulling Straight Ahead

1. Not enough oil.
2. Wrong grade of oil.
3. Poor quality oil.
4. Ring gear and pinion have excessive backlash.
5. Ring gear and pinion worn.
6. Pinion shaft bearings worn or loose.
7. Pinion shaft end play excessive.
8. Ring gear and pinion misaligned because of bent axle housing or distorted differential case.
9. Ring gear warped.
10. Differential bearings worn or loose.
11. Ring gear rivets or screws loose.
12. Ring gear and pinion not matched set.

Noise When Coasting In Gear

Any axle noise which is heard when the engine is pulling the car is likely to be heard when coasting although not as loud as when pulling.

If ring gear and pinion are meshed too tight, the noise will be greater when decelerating. The noise will disappear when the engine is pulling unless the gears are very tight.

Excessive end play of pinion shaft due to loose pinion nut or incorrect adjustment.

Intermittent Noise

1. Warped ring gear.
2. Loose ring gear rivets or screws.
3. Ring gear improperly installed on differential case due to dirt or burrs between the two.

Knocks or Clicks

1. Flat spot on ring gear or pinion tooth, or tooth chipped, or particle of metal lodged on tooth.
2. Flat spot on bearing.
3. Loose axle shaft key.
4. Loose splined shafts.
5. Mis-matched differential case halves.

Noise On Turns

1. Differential pinions or side gears chipped, scuffed or teeth broken.
2. Differential pinions binding on pinion shaft.
3. Differential pinions or side gears loose due to worn bushings or shaft.
4. Excessive backlash between pinions and side gears.
5. Excessive axle shaft end play.
6. Contacting surfaces between side gear and differential case burred, scored or otherwise damaged.

Oil Leak At Axle Ends

1. Oil level too high.
2. Oil too light or poor quality.
3. Axle shaft oil seals worn.
4. Axle shaft bearing retainer loose.
5. Cracked rear axle housing.
6. Vent (if any) clogged.

Oil Leak At Pinion Shaft

1. Oil level too high.
2. Oil too light or poor quality.
3. Pinion oil seal worn.
4. Pinion oil seal retainer distorted, loose in housing or improperly installed.
5. Oil return passage in carrier housing restricted.
6. Universal joint companion flange hub rough, scored or out of round.
7. Universal joint companion flange loose on pinion shaft.

Drum Brake Troubles

One Brake Drags

1. Brake line restricted.
2. Improperly adjusted or worn wheel bearing.
3. Distorted or improperly adjusted brake shoe.
4. Faulty retracting spring.
5. Drum out of round.
6. Loose backing plate.
7. Faulty wheel cylinder.
8. Dirty brake fluid.
9. Air in hydraulic system.
10. Insufficient shoe-to-backing plate lubrication.

All Brakes Drag

1. Mechanical resistance at pedal or shoes; damaged linkage.
2. Brake line restricted.
3. Distorted or improperly adjusted brake shoes.
4. Dirty brake fluid.
5. Faulty master cylinder.
6. Sticking booster control valve.

Hard Pedal

1. Mechanical resistance at pedal or shoes; damaged linkage.
2. Brake line restricted.
3. Distorted or improperly adjusted brake shoes.
4. Linings glazed or worn.
5. Oil or grease in lining.

Spongy Pedal

1. Leaks or insufficient fluid.
2. Air in hydraulic system.

Car Pulls to One Side

1. Brake line restricted.
2. Improper tire pressure.
3. Improperly adjusted or worn wheel bearing.
4. Distorted or improperly adjusted brake shoes.
5. Faulty retracting spring.
6. Drum out of round.
7. Linings glazed or worn.
8. Oil or grease in lining.
9. Loose lining.
10. Faulty wheel cylinder.
11. Self-adjusters not operating.

One Wheel Locks

1. Distorted or improperly adjusted brake shoes.
2. Linings glazed or worn.
3. Oil or grease in lining.
4. Loose backing plate.
5. Faulty wheel cylinder.
6. Tire tread worn.

Brakes Chatter

1. Drum out of round.
2. Linings glazed or worn.
3. Oil or grease in lining.
4. Loose backing plate.
5. Loose lining.
6. Poor lining-to-drum contact.
7. Loose front suspension.

Excessive Pedal Travel

1. Leaks or insufficient fluid.
2. Distorted or improperly adjusted brake shoes.
3. Linings glazed or worn.
4. Faulty master cylinder.
5. Air in hydraulic system.
6. Self-adjusters not operating.
7. Cracked drum.

Pedal Gradually Goes to Floor

1. Leaks or insufficient fluid.
2. Faulty master cylinder.

Brakes Uneven

1. Improper tire pressure.
2. Oil or grease in lining.
3. Scored drum.
4. Dirty brake fluid.

Shoe Click Release

1. Self-adjusters not operating.
2. Insufficient shoe-to-backing plate lubrication.
3. "Threads" left by drum turning tool pull shoes sideways.

Noisy or Grabbing Brakes

1. Distorted or improperly adjusted brake shoes.
2. Linings glazed or worn.
3. Oil or grease in lining.
4. Scored drum.
5. Dirt on drum-lining surface.
6. Faulty wheel cylinder.
7. Sticking booster control valve.

Brakes Do Not Apply

1. Leaks or insufficient fluid.
2. Linings glazed or worn.
3. Oil or grease in lining.
4. Dirty brake fluid.
5. Faulty master cylinder.
6. Air in hydraulic system.

Front End & Steering Troubles

Hard Steering

1. Low or uneven tire pressure.
2. Steering gear or connections adjusted too tight.
3. Insufficient or incorrect lubricant used.
4. Excessive caster.
5. Suspension arms bent or twisted.
6. Front spring sagged.
7. Frame bent or broken.
8. Steering knuckle bent.
9. Kingpin galled or frozen in bushing.
10. Excessive steering shaft coupling misalignment.

Excessive Play or Looseness In Steering

1. Steering gear connections adjusted too loose or worn.
2. Steering knuckle bushings worn.
3. Front wheel bearings incorrectly adjusted or worn.
4. Worn ball joints.
5. Worn or loose worm steering shaft bearings.
6. Worn control arm bushings.

Rattle or Chuckle in Steering Gear

1. Insufficient or improper lubricant in steering gear.
2. Excessive backlash in steering gear.
3. Worn or loose worm steering shaft bearings.
4. Pitman arm loose on shaft.

Erratic Steering On Application of Brakes

1. Oil or brake fluid on lining.
2. Brakes improperly adjusted.
3. Front spring weak.
4. Low or uneven tire pressure.
5. Insufficient or uneven caster.
6. Steering knuckle bent.

Car Pulls to One Side

1. Low or uneven tire pressure.
2. Incorrect or uneven caster or camber.
3. Wheel bearings adjusted too tight.
4. Uneven front car height.
5. Toe-in incorrect.
6. Oil or brake fluid on brake lining.
7. Brakes incorrectly or unevenly adjusted.
8. Steering knuckle or knuckle support bent.
9. Frame bent or broken.
10. Shock absorbers inoperative.
11. Rear wheels not tracking with front wheels.
12. Rear axle shifted (spring U bolts loose or center bolt sheared).
13. Broken or weak rear springs.

Scuffed Tires

1. Tire improperly inflated.
2. Toe-in incorrect.
3. Excessive wheel or tire run-out.
4. Steering knuckle bushings worn.
5. Uneven camber.
6. Incorrect toe-out on turns.
7. Suspension arms bent or twisted.
8. Steering knuckle bent.
9. Excessive speed on turns.

Cupped Tires

1. Improper toe-in.
2. Tires improperly inflated.
3. Wheels, tires or brake drums out of balance.
4. Dragging brakes.
5. Worn steering knuckle bushings.
6. Wheel bearings incorrectly adjusted or worn.
7. Uneven camber.
8. Steering knuckle bent.
9. Excessive mileage without rotating tires.

Front Wheel Shimmy

1. Low or uneven tire pressure.
2. Wheels, tires or brake drums out of balance.
3. Excessive wheel or tire run-out.
4. Shock absorbers inoperative.
5. Steering connections incorrectly adjusted or worn.
6. Steering gear incorrectly adjusted.
7. Front wheel bearings incorrectly adjusted or worn.
8. Incorrect or uneven caster.
9. Steering knuckle bushings worn.
10. Toe-in incorrect.
11. Steering knuckle bent.
12. Eccentric or bulged tires.
13. Stabilizer inoperative.
14. Worn ball joints.
15. Worn control arm bushings.

Front Wheel Tramp

1. Wheels, tires or brake drums out of balance.
2. Wheel or tire not concentric.
3. Shock absorbers inoperative.
4. Stabilizer inoperative.

Car Wanders

1. Low or uneven tire pressure.
2. Steering gear or connections adjusted too loose or worn.
3. Steering gear or connections adjusted too tight.
4. Steering knuckle bushings worn.
5. Improper toe-in.
6. Incorrect or uneven caster or camber.
7. Steering knuckle bent.
8. Kingpin bent.
9. Rear axle shifted (spring U bolts loose or center bolt sheared).
10. Stabilizer inoperative.
11. Kingpins or bushings tight.
12. Bind in lower or upper control arm shaft.
13. Bind in rear spring shackles or dry rear springs.
14. Excessive backlash in steering gear.

Road Shocks

1. High air pressure in tires.
2. Steering gear or connections incorrectly adjusted.
3. Excessive caster.
4. Shock absorbers inoperative.
5. Front springs weak or sagged.
6. Wrong type or size of tires used.
7. Steering knuckle bent.

Power Top, Window & Seat Troubles

HYDRO-LECTRIC TYPE

Top Will Not Operate

1. Mechanical interference due to luggage or other objects.
2. Hold down strap not removed.
3. Top not free from windshield header studs.
4. Electrical shorts or loose connections in control switch circuit.
5. Dirty control switch contacts.
6. Inoperative power unit motor.
7. Hydraulic fluid low.
8. Power unit pump inoperative.
9. Stoppage in fluid pipes.
10. Faulty hydraulic control valve.
11. Broken port plate in hydraulic pump.

Top Operates in One Direction Only

1. Mechanical interference due to luggage or other objects.
2. Hold down strap not removed.
3. Top not free from windshield header studs.
4. Electrical shorts or loose connections in control switch circuit.
5. Dirty control switch contact.
6. Improperly adjusted control rod.
7. Hydraulic power cylinder faulty.
8. Stoppage in fluid pipes.
9. Faulty hydraulic control valve.

Window Lift Inoperative

1. Mechanical interference from door arm rest screw.
2. Misaligned glass run channel or window guide.
3. Window lift not connected to lower sash channel.
4. Electrical short or loose connection in battery, motor or cylinder circuit.
5. Cylinder solenoid inoperative.

6. Power unit motor inoperative.
7. Hydraulic fluid low.
8. Hydraulic hoses crimped.
9. Stoppage in fluid pipes.
10. Pump pressure relief valve stuck.
11. Cylinder piston rod disconnected.
12. Broken port plate in pump.

Windows Operate Slowly Upward

1. Mechanical binding due to misalignment.
2. Glass run channels excessively wet.
3. If window does not fully close, stops are improperly adjusted or there is insufficient hydraulic fluid.
4. Electrical failure due to low battery.
5. Hydraulic failure due to stuck pump pressure relief valve.
6. Top control rod improperly adjusted so that control valve is held partially open to allow fluid to enter top lines.

Windows Operate Slowly Downward

1. If a window moves slowly downward when control switch is in neutral position, the solenoid valve in window lift cylinder is leaking.
2. Mechanical binding due to misalignment.
3. Glass run channels excessively wet.
4. Window lift return spring broken.
5. Hydraulic fluid old, congealed or too heavy for prevailing temperatures.
6. Pump pressure relief valve stuck.

Window Raises When Top or Seat Is Operated

1. Electrical control circuit crossed due to switch "CYL" terminal touching "BAT" terminal.
2. Hydraulic pressure too high if more than one window raises.
3. Solenoid valve in window cylinder leaking.

Two Windows Operate From One Switch

1. Electrical control circuit crossed due to switch "CYL" terminals touching.
2. Hydraulic pressure too high.
3. Solenoid valve in window cylinder leaking.

Seat Adjuster Inoperative

1. Mechanical interference from object under seat.
2. Seat adjuster misaligned.
3. Seat adjuster not attached to seat frame or floor.
4. Electrical short or loose connection in battery, motor or cylinder circuit.
5. Cylinder solenoid inoperative.

6. Power unit motor inoperative.
7. Hydraulic fluid low.
8. Hydraulic hoses crimped.
9. Stoppage in fluid pipes.
10. Pump pressure relief valve stuck.
11. Cylinder piston rod disconnected.
12. Broken port plate in pump.

Seat Operates Slowly

Note: Same as windows operating slowly upward or downward.

All Units Operate Slowly

1. Mechanical interference due to misalignment.
2. Electrical fault due to low battery.
3. Hydraulic fluid too heavy.
4. Pump pressure relief valve stuck.
5. Crimped fluid hoses.
6. Stoppage in fluid pipes.

Power Unit Inoperative on Any Control Switch

Note: When running, the power unit has a clearly audible whirring sound.

1. Battery low.
2. Wiring connections between ignition switch and solenoid relay switch loose, dirty or disconnected.
3. Circuit breaker inoperative.
4. Solenoid relay switch inoperative.
5. Power unit motor inoperative.

ELECTRIC TYPE FOR WINDOWS & SEATS

Note: In addition to the electrical troubles listed below, look for the same mechanical troubles given under the *Hydro-Lectric Type.*

Window Won't Operate from Main Switch Only

1. Broken wire between relay and remote switch.
2. Defective switch in master switch group.
3. Break in wire where it enters door opening.

Window Won't Operate from Main or Door Switch

1. Burned out motor or relay.
2. Defective circuit breaker.
3. Break in battery feed wire from starter solenoid to circuit breaker.

Window Operates In One Direction Only from Main or Door Switch

1. Defective relay.
2. Defective switch.
3. Broken ground wires.
4. Burned out motor.
5. Broken control wire.

Circuit Breaker In Door Clicks On and Off Continuously and Window Won't Operate

1. Control wire grounded.
2. Defective switch.
3. Relay points stuck.

Main Or Door Switch Operates Window In Wrong Direction

1. Lead wires are not connected to proper terminals.

Window Operates Sluggishly

1. Binding window regulator.
2. Broken wires or loose connections.
3. Worn motor brushes.

All Windows Do Not Operate

1. Circuit breaker open in control circuit.
2. Circuit breaker open in power circuit.

Seat Regulators Inoperative

1. Circuit breaker open in control circuit.
2. Circuit breaker open in power circuit.

One Seat Regulator Inoperative

1. Defective wiring between relay and circuit breaker.
2. Defective motor.
3. Defective wiring between switch and circuit breaker.
4. Defective relay.

Seat Regulator Operates in One Direction Only

1. Defective wiring between switch and relay that applies to direction of travel desired.
2. Defective toggle switch.

Seat Regulator Operates Sluggishly

1. Binding mechanism.
2. Defective wiring.
3. Loose connectors or poor ground.
4. Worn or dirty brushes in motor.

Continued

Windshield Wiper Troubles

GENERAL INSPECTION

Before deciding that a windshield wiper needs servicing it might be well to consider some of the external factors which affect their operation.

It must be remembered that windshield wipers will operate more slowly when they do their work on dry glass. This is specially true on cars with curved windshields. You will also find that wiper blades may chatter or fail to travel a complete arc on dry glass. It is therefore obvious that any testing of windshield wiper operation should be done after the windshield has been sprayed with water.

Windshield wipers that chatter or do not wipe the glass clean under normal operating conditions (wet windshield) may need only replacement of the wiper arms or blades instead of more extensive service. This can be determined by visual inspection and most replacements can be made simply without the aid of any special tools.

Uneven movement of the wiper arms with respect to one another is usually caused by cables, pivots or cranks that are out of adjustment in the windshield wiper transmission system.

ELECTRIC TYPE

All passenger car electric windshield wiper circuits, regardless of manufacturer, include a control switch, a small shunt wound motor, and the wiring connecting these units to the battery. A circuit breaker or fuse may be mounted as a separate unit or incorporated in the control switch itself. A worm gear on the motor armature shaft drives one or two gears mounted on crankshafts for wiper operation.

A parking switch is mounted on the motor and actuated by a cam on one of the cranks. The parking switch, connected to the battery through a control switch, keeps the motor in operation for a brief period after the control switch has been shut off, allowing the wiper blades to return to the parked position.

Both single and two speed motors are used, the latter incorporating one or several resistors in the field circuit. The resistors may be located either in the parking switch housing or in the control switch.

In the following text you will find a list of the conditions you are likely to encounter when faced with a repair job on electric wipers. By consulting these possibilities you will simplify the job of locating the source of trouble. But before going further a few words of caution are in order: After you have made your diagnosis and are ready to make repairs, disconnect the battery to avoid damage under the dash or possible personal injury from accidental shorts. Also, on models which use off-glass parking windshield wipers, never remove or disassemble the motor while in "park" position.

Wipers Won't Operate

1. Discharged battery.
2. Blown fuse or faulty circuit breaker.
3. No power to control switch.
4. Faulty control switch.
5. Faulty parking switch.
6. Binding pivots, cranks or linkages.
7. Poor connection at switch.
8. No ground at motor.
9. Faulty motor.

Wipers Won't Park

1. Incorrect adjustment of parking switch lever.
2. Open circuit in lead feeding parking switch.
3. Faulty parking switch.
4. Faulty control switch.
5. No ground at control switch (variable speed wipers).
6. Motor crank and parking switch improperly assembled.
7. Cams in linkage reversed or binding (variable speed wipers).

Wipers Operate Slowly

1. Discharged battery.
2. Binding pivots, cranks or linkages.
3. Faulty motor windings.
4. High resistance connections or wiring.
5. High resistance in control switch contacts.
6. No ground at control switch (variable speed wipers).
7. Faulty resistance unit (if only high speed is affected).
8. Dirty commutator or sticking brushes.
9. Worn or damaged motor.

Multiple Speed Wipers Operate Only at Single Speed

1. Short or open in motor wiring harness.
2. Incorrect connections at control switch.
3. Faulty control switch.
4. Faulty resistance unit.
5. No ground at control switch.
6. Open shunt field in motor.

VACUUM TYPE

For satisfactory windshield wiper operation, it is necessary to have an adequate supply of vacuum. On some cars the vacuum is made available by tapping directly into the intake manifold. With this type of arrangement it is considered normal for the wipers to slow down or stop entirely while going up a hill or during acceleration, since under those conditions the manifold vacuum would drop below the 8"-10" needed to operate the wipers. These conditions are almost completely eliminated on cars equipped with a vacuum booster pump. The purpose of this pump is to maintain enough vacuum to work the wipers under any driving condition.

Some of the conditions which prevent satisfactory windshield wiper operation are listed in the following text and may be used as a guide to help you locate the source of trouble. Always disconnect the battery when working under the dash.

Wipers Won't Operate

1. No vacuum supply to motor due to pinch, restriction or leak in the windshield wiper hose. A vacuum leak or a disconnected hose can easily be located because a hissing sound will be heard whenever the engine is running.
2. Faulty vacuum booster pump.
3. Wiper control switch inoperative or disconnected at motor.
4. Faulty wiper motor.
5. Frozen or binding pivots and linkages.
6. Linkages or cables improperly installed.

Wipers Operate Slowly

1. Low vacuum due to pinch or partial restriction in the wiper hose.
2. Loss of vacuum due to leaks at joints, fittings or in the wiper hose itself.
3. Faulty vacuum booster pump.
4. Faulty wiper motor.
5. Wiper control switch does not move operating valve on the motor to full "ON" position due to improper adjustment.
6. Air intake on motor (breather port) clogged.
7. Binding pivots, cranks, linkages or binding or frozen idler pulleys on cable tensioners.
8. Cables adjusted too tight.

Wipers Won't Park

1. Faulty parking valve on motor.
2. Wiper control switch out of adjustment.
3. Wiper arms not positioned properly on pivots.

PRESSURE WIPER

The windshield wiper is hydraulically operated. The hydraulic power for the motor is obtained from the power steering unit. Hydraulic fluid flows from the pump, through the steering gear to the wiper motor, and then to the fluid reservoir. During wiper operation, a part of the fluid is by-passed through the motor by a valve on the motor.

Checks and Adjustments: The only adjustment required is the control cable adjustment. To adjust, remove the seal plate mounting screws and position the plate and seal out of the way. Adjust the cable so that the control knob on instrument panel moves the valve control lever on motor from off to full on.

If the motor operates sluggishly, check the cable adjustment. If this is not the fault, check the hydraulic fluid pressure. If the power steering gear operates satisfactorily, it may be assumed that the fluid pressure is adequate. Check for binding wiper pivot shafts and arms. Repair or replace wiper motor and valves if necessary.

TUNE UP SERVICE

ENGINE TUNE-UP has become increasingly important to the modern automotive engine with its vastly improved power and performance. With the higher compression ratios, improved electrical systems and other advances in design, engines have become more sensitive to usage and operating conditions, all of which have a decided effect on power and performance. It is important, therefore, that this service be performed on the engine every spring and fall or more often if conditions warrant.

Compression Test

Caution: Should it become necessary to turn on the ignition switch to crank the engine under the hood for a compression test or for any other reason, it is highly recommended that the high tension cable be removed from the coil tower or from the distributor cap. This is necessary because on many vehicles the ignition and starter circuits are such that the ignition switch and/or starter solenoid may be damaged if this precaution is not taken. Another reason for removing the cable is to prevent the engine from starting accidentally.

The engine cannot be tuned to develop maximum power and smooth performance unless reasonably high and uniform compression pressure is obtained in each cylinder. The compression in each cylinder should, therefore, be tested before any other tune-up operations are performed.

1. Remove any foreign matter from around spark plugs by blowing out plug area with compressed air. Then loosen all plugs one turn.
2. Start engine and accelerate to a fast idle to blow out loosened carbon. Stop engine and remove spark plugs. *Cleaning out carbon in this manner is important in preventing false compression readings due to particles of carbon lodged under the valves.*
3. Remove air cleaner and block throttle and choke in wide open position.
4. Insert compression gauge firmly in spark plug opening and crank engine through at least four or five compression strokes to obtain highest possible reading.
5. Test and record compression of each cylinder. Compression should read within the limits given in the *Tune Up Charts* in the car chapters. The variation between highest and lowest reading should be less than 20 pounds.
6. If one or more cylinders read low, inject about a tablespoon of engine oil on top of pistons in the low reading cylinders. Crank engine several times and recheck compression.
7. If compression comes up but does not reach normal it indicates worn piston rings. If compression does not improve, valves are sticking or seating poorly. If two adjacent cylinders indicate low compression and injecting oil does not improve the condition, the cause may be a head gasket leak between the cylinders.

Manifold Vacuum Test

Manifold vacuum is affected by carburetor adjustment, valve timing, ignition timing, condition of valves, cylinder compression, condition of positive crankcase ventilation system, and leakage of manifold, carburetor, carburetor spacer or cylinder head gaskets.

Because abnormal gauge readings may indicate that more than one of the above factors are at fault, use care in analyzing an abnormal reading. For example, if the vacuum is low, the correction of one item may increase the vacuum enough so as to indicate that the trouble has been corrected. It is important, therefore, that each cause of an abnormal reading be investigated and further tests conducted, where necessary, in order to arrive at the correct diagnosis of the trouble. To check manifold vacuum, proceed as follows:

1. Operate engine for 30 minutes minimum at a fast idle speed to be sure engine is at normal operating temperature.
2. Connect an accurate vacuum gauge to the intake manifold vacuum fitting.
3. Operate engine at recommended idle speed with transmission selector lever in neutral.
4. Check vacuum reading on gauge.

Test Conclusions

NORMAL READING: 18 inches or more. Allowance should be made for the effect of altitude on the gauge reading. Engine vacuum will decrease with an increase in altitude.

LOW & STEADY: Loss of power in all cylinders possibly caused by late ignition or valve timing, or loss of compression due to leakage around piston rings.

VERY LOW: Intake manifold, carburetor, carburetor spacer or cylinder head gasket leak.

NEEDLE FLUCTUATES STEADILY AS SPEED INCREASES: A partial or complete loss of power in one or more cylinders caused by a leaking valve, cylinder head or intake manifold gasket, a defect in ignition system, or a weak valve spring.

GRADUAL DROP IN READING AT IDLE SPEED: Excessive back pressure in exhaust system.

INTERMITTENT FLUCTUATION: An occasional loss of power possibly caused by a defect in ignition system or a sticking valve.

SLOW FLUCTUATION OR DRIFTING OF NEEDLE: Improper idle mixture adjustment or carburetor, carburetor spacer or intake manifold gasket leak or crankcase ventilation system restricted.

Cylinder Balance Test

It is sometimes difficult to locate a weak cylinder especially in an eight cylinder engine. A compression test, for example, will not locate a leaky intake manifold, a valve not opening properly

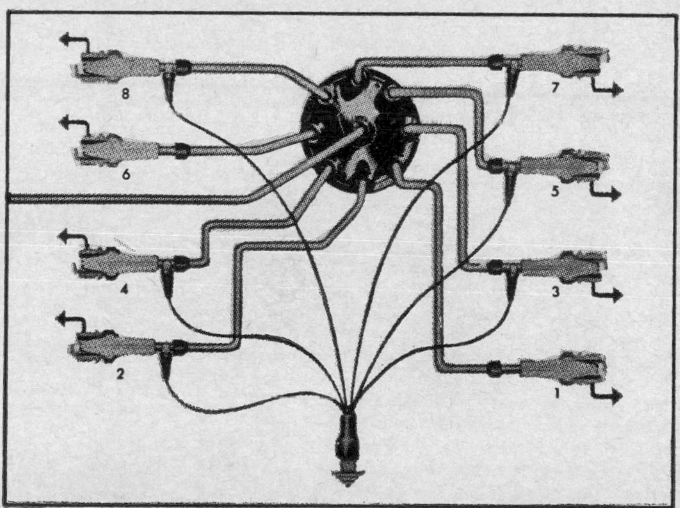

Fig. 1 Cylinder balance test connections. The firing order in this example is 1-8-4-3-6-5-7-2. Therefore, the cylinders to be tested together are 1-6, 8-5, 4-7, 3-2, using the grounding leads as shown

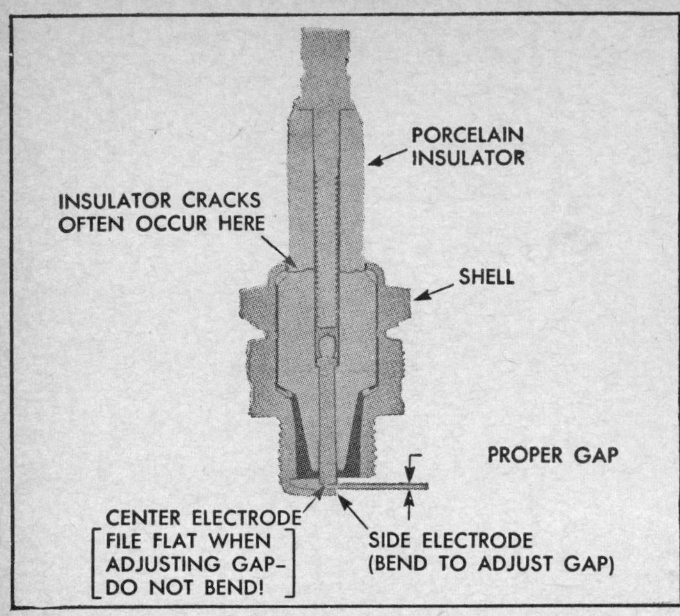

Fig. 2 Spark plug details

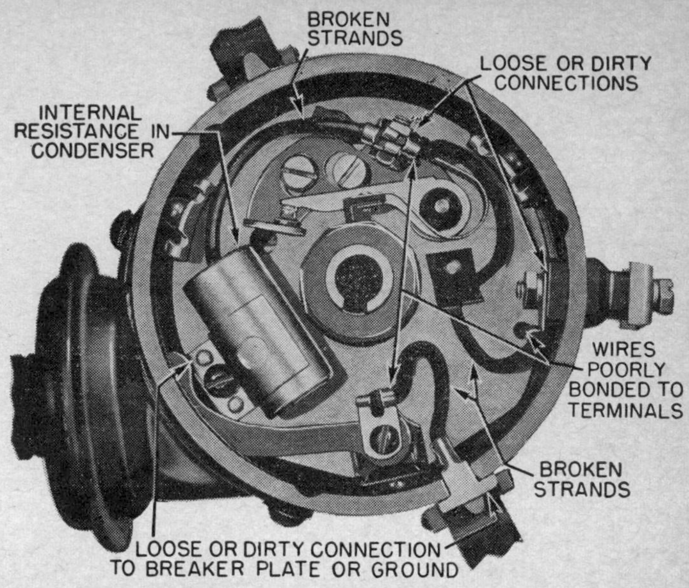

Fig. 4 What to look for when checking for high resistance in the primary circuit of the distributor. In addition to the points indicated, look for external circuit high resistance at ignition switch terminals, ammeter terminals, coil terminals and broken or poorly insulated wires in this circuit

due to a worn camshaft, or a defective spark plug.

With the cylinder balance test, the power output of one cylinder may be checked against another, using a set of grounding leads, Fig. 1. When the power of each cylinder is not equal, the engine will lose power and run roughly. The cylinder balance test is as follows:

1. Connect a tachometer and vacuum gauge.
2. Start engine and run it at a fast idle.
3. Ground large clip of grounding leads and connect individual leads to all spark plugs *except the pair being tested* (see Fig. 1).
4. Divide the firing order in half and write down the first half over the second half. The cylinders to be tested together appear one over the other:

Firing Order	Pairs Tested
1-8-4-3-6-5-7-2	1-6, 8-5, 4-7, 3-2
1-2-7-8-4-5-6-3	1-4, 2-5, 7-6, 8-3
1-5-4-8-6-3-7-2	1-6, 5-3, 4-7, 8-2
1-5-4-2-6-3-7-8	1-6, 5-3, 4-7, 2-8
1-8-7-3-6-5-4-2	1-6, 8-5, 7-4, 3-2
1-6-5-4-3-2	1-4, 6-3, 5-2
1-5-3-6-2-4	1-6, 5-2, 3-4
1-4-5-2-3-6	1-2, 4-3, 5-6
1-3-4-2	1-4, 3-2

5. Operate engine on each pair of cylinders in turn and note engine rpm and manifold vacuum for each pair. A variation of more than one inch of vacuum or 40 rpm between pairs of cylinders being tested indicates that the cylinders are off balance.
6. To isolate one weak cylinder, short out one bank of cylinders at a time. The bank giving the lower readings will include the weak cylinder.

Spark Plugs

1. Examine firing ends of plugs for evidence of oil fouling, gas fouling, burned or overheated condition. *Oil fouling is usually identified by wet, sludgy deposits caused by excessive oil consumption. Gas fouling is identified by dry, black, fluffy deposits caused by incomplete combustion. Burned or overheated spark plugs are identified by white, burned or blistered insulator nose and badly burned electrodes. Improper fuel, insufficient cooling or improper ignition timing normally are the cause. Normal conditions are usually identified by white powdery deposits or rusty-brown to grayish-tan powdery deposits.*
2. Clean plugs with a suitable sand blast cleaner following the manufacturers instructions.
3. Remove carbon and other deposits from threads with a stiff wire brush.
4. Dress electrodes with a small file to secure flat, parallel surfaces on both center and side electrodes, Fig. 2.
5. Use a round wire gauge to check the gap, Fig. 3, and adjust by bending the side (never center) electrode to the proper specifications as shown in the *Tune Up Charts* in the car chapters.
6. If gaskets are used, place new ones on plugs and torque them.

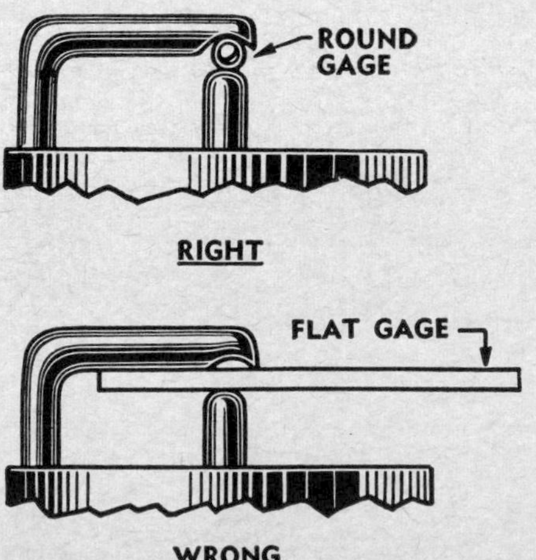

Fig. 3 Correct and incorrect spark plug gauges

IMPORTANT

Improper installation of spark plugs is one of the greatest single causes of unsatisfactory spark plug performance. Improper installation is the result of one or more of the following practices: 1) Installation of plugs with insufficient torque to fully seat the gasket; 2) excessive torque which changes gap settings; 3) installation of plugs on dirty gasket seal; 4) installation of plugs to corroded spark plug hole threads.

Failure to install plugs properly will cause them to operate at excessively high temperatures and result in reduced operating life under mild operation or complete destruction under severe operation where the intense heat cannot be dissipated rapidly enough.

Always remove carbon deposits in hole threads before installing plugs. When corrosion is present in threads, normal torque is not sufficient to compress the plug gasket (if used) and early failure from overheating will result.

Always use a new gasket (if required) and wipe seats in head clean. The gasket must be fully compressed on clean seats to complete heat transfer and provide a gas tight seal in the cylinder. For this reason as well as the necessity of maintaining correct plug gap, the use of correct torque is extremely important during installation.

Ignition System Service

1. Replace brittle or damaged spark plug wires. Install all wires to proper spark plug. The *Tune Up Charts* in the car chapters give firing orders should wires become mixed.
2. Tighten all ignition system connections.
3. Replace or repair any wires that are frayed, loose or damaged, Fig. 4.
4. Remove distributor cap, clean and inspect for cracks, carbon tracks and burned or corroded terminals. Replace cap if necessary.
5. Clean rotor and inspect for damage or deterioration. Replace rotor if necessary.
6. Check distributor centrifugal advance mechanism (if used) by turning distributor rotor in direction of running rotation as far as possible, then release rotor to see if springs return it to its retarded position. If rotor does not return readily, the distributor must be disassembled and cause of trouble corrected.
7. Check to see that the vacuum spark control operates freely by turning the movable breaker plate (if used) or distributor housing in a direction opposite to that of running rotation to see if the spring returns it to the retarded position. Any stiffness in the operation of the spark control will affect ignition timing. Correct any interference or binding condition noted.
8. Examine distributor points and clean or replace if necessary. Points with an overall gray color and only slight roughness or pitting need not be replaced.
9. Dirty points should be cleaned with a clean point file. Use only a few strokes of the file. The file should not be used on other metals and should not be allowed to become dirty or greasy. *Never use emery cloth or sandpaper to clean points since particles will embed and cause arcing and rapid burning of points.* Do not attempt to remove all roughness nor dress the point surfaces down smooth. Merely remove scale or dirt.
10. Replace points that are badly burned or pitted. Where burned or badly pitted points are encountered, the ignition system and engine should be checked to determine the cause of the trouble so it can be eliminated. Unless the condition causing point burning is corrected, new points will provide no better service than the old points. See *Ignition* chapter for an analysis of point burning or pitting, and for proper installation of points.

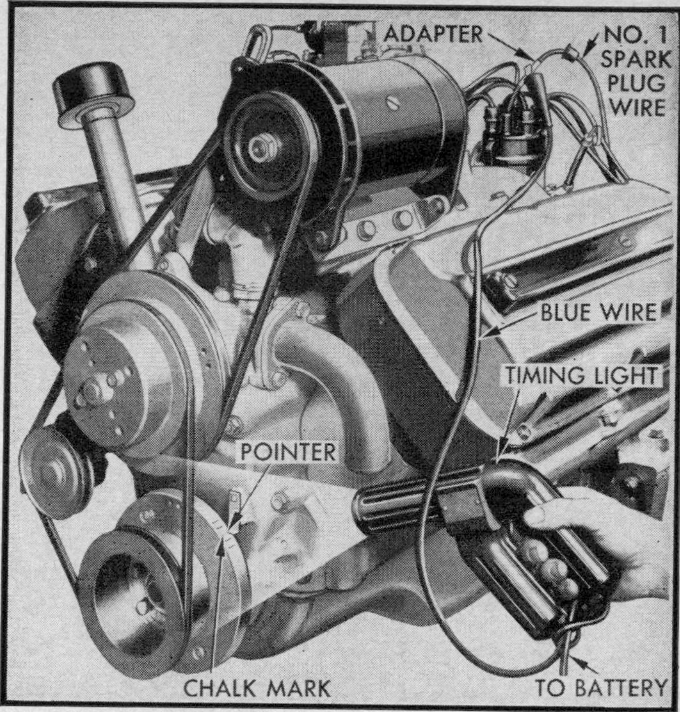

Fig. 5 Checking ignition timing with timing lights

Battery & Cables

Inspect for signs of corrosion on battery, cables and surrounding area, loose or broken carriers, cracked or bulged cases, dirt and acid, electrolyte leakage and low electrolyte level. Fill cells to proper level with distilled water or water passed through a "demineralizer".

The top of the battery should be clean and the battery hold-down bolts properly tightened. Particular care should be taken to see that the tops of 12-volt batteries are kept clean of acid film and dirt because of the high voltage between the battery terminals.

For best results when cleaning batteries, wash first with a dilute ammonia or soda solution to neutralize any acid present and then flush off with clean water. Care must be taken to keep vent plugs tight so that the neutralizing solution does not enter the battery. The hold-down bolts should be kept tight enough to prevent the battery from shaking around in its holder, but not so tight that the battery case will be placed under a severe strain.

To insure good contact, the battery cables should be tight on the battery posts. Oil battery terminal felt washer. If the battery posts or cable terminals are corroded, the cables should be cleaned separately with a soda solution and a wire brush. After cleaning and before installing the clamps, apply a thin coating of vaseline to the posts and cable clamps to help retard corrosion.

If the battery has remained undercharged, check for a loose generator belt, defective generator, high resistance in charging circuit, oxidized voltage regulator contact points, or a low voltage setting.

If the battery has been using too much water, the voltage regulator setting is too high.

Fan Belt & Generator

1. Inspect fan belt condition and check adjustment.
2. Inspect generator commutator and brushes for cleanliness or wear. The commutator should be cleaned if dirty and brushes should be replaced if worn down to less than half their original length. *The commutator may be cleaned by holding a strip of No. 00 sandpaper or a cleaning stone against it while the generator is operating.*
3. Replace or repair frayed or broken generator wires and tighten all wire connections.
4. Lubricate generator by filling hinge cap oilers with light engine oil.

Ignition Timing

The use of a timing light, Fig. 5, is recommended for checking and setting ignition timing. Timing that is set back as much as six degrees from the best setting will definitely decrease acceleration and top speed performance. See the car chapters for ignition timing details.

SERVICE NOTE

Some mechanics pierce the spark plug wire boots at the distributor when connecting a timing light to V8 engines. The pierced hole in the boot will often contribute to spark arcing to the air cleaner, resulting in engine misfire and premature distributor cap failure. The timing light should always be connected to the proper spark plug or an adapter may be used at the distributor to avoid the above mentioned problem.

Carburetion

Since carburetion is dependent in several ways on both compression and ignition, it should always be checked last when tuning an engine. Refer to the *Carburetor Chapter* for pertinent data on this phase of the work.

IGNITION COILS & RESISTORS

IGNITION COILS

If poor ignition performance is obtained and the coil is suspected, it may be tested on the car or it may be removed for the test.

Ignition coils are often condemned when the trouble is actually in the ignition switch. A completely defective ignition switch will produce an open primary circuit, giving the same indications as if the coil were completely dead. A partly defective ignition switch will cause a weak spark. Both of these conditions are often blamed on the coil.

By cutting the ignition switch out of the circuit, it can easily be determined whether or not the coil is defective or whether fault lies with ignition switch.

In the absence of any testing equipment a simple check of an ignition coil can be made as follows: Turn on ignition switch with breaker points closed. Remove the high tension cable from the center socket of the distributor cap and hold it ¼" to ⅜" away from a clean spot on the engine. If the coil and other units connected to it are in good condition a spark should jump from the wire to the engine. If not, use a jumper wire from the distributor terminal to the engine; if the primary is in good condition a spark will occur.

All ignition coils with metal containers can be tested for grounded windings by placing one test clip on a clean part of the metal container and touching the other clip to the primary and high tension terminals. If the lamp lights or tiny sparks appear at the points of contact, the windings are grounded and the coil should be replaced.

Coil Polarity

Most coils are marked positive and negative at the primary terminals. When installing or connecting a coil be sure to make the connections as shown in Figs. 1 and 2. A reversal of this polarity may affect the performance of the engine (or the radio).

If perchance the coil is not marked as to its polarity, it can be checked by holding any high tension wire about ¼" away from its spark plug terminal with the engine running. Insert the point of a wooden lead pencil between the spark plug and the wire, Fig. 3. If the spark flares and has a slight orange tinge on the spark plug side of the pencil, polarity is correct. If the spark flares on the cable side, coil connections should be reversed.

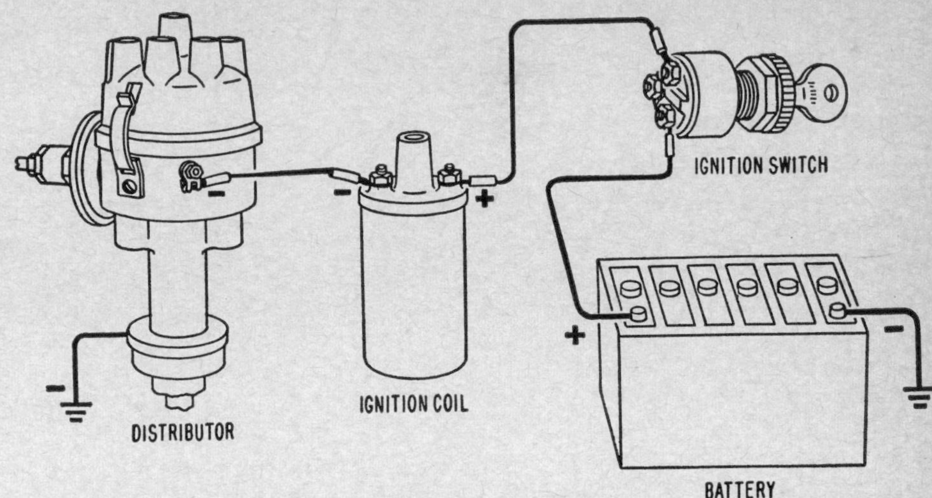

Fig. 1 Wiring connections for coil with negative grounded system

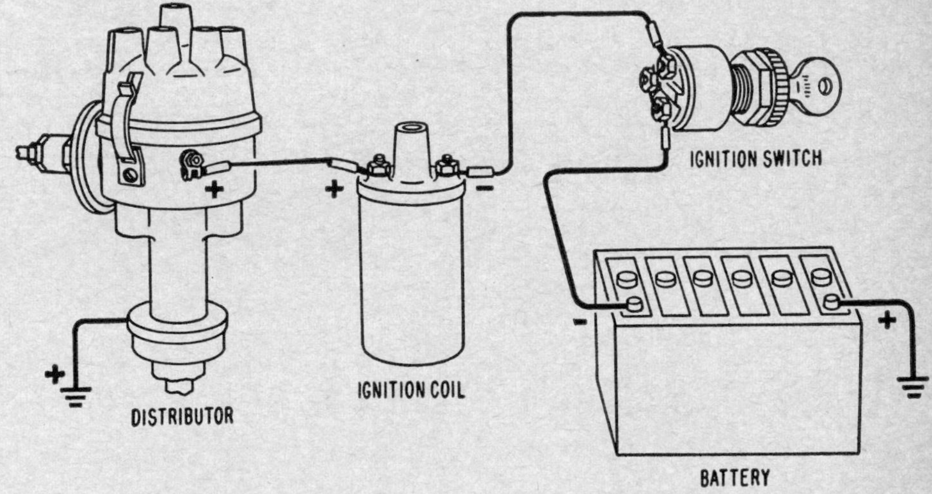

Fig. 2 Wiring connections for coil with positive grounded system

IGNITION RESISTORS

The ignition coils used with 12-volt systems are specially designed *6-volt coils* which operate with a resistor connected in series with the primary ignition circuit. The purpose of the resistor is to prolong the service life of the distributor breaker points.

Block Type Ballast Resistors

This type resistor came into existance with the introduction of the 12-volt battery. Its basic purpose is to allow full battery voltage to the ignition coil during engine starting, and to reduce battery voltage to the coil when the engine is running. The higher voltage during starts means easier starts. But sustained high voltage to the breaker points can cause point failure. The reduced voltage during engine operation increases breaker point life.

These resistors are normally very dependable. But if one fails it can be one of the most difficult of all ignition system malfunctions to check out and diagnose. This type of resistor can fail in several ways. The resistance wire can separate, with a result similar to that caused by an open switch. An open resistor means that no current reaches the coil and the engine cannot operate. It is possible for the resistance wire to warp or bend enough to touch the side of the case and when this happens the engine may continue to run but the overall performance would be poor.

Resistors can change value. Any creeping change in resistance value of a ballast resistor is invariably an increase in resistance. This means that coil output to the spark plugs is reduced proportionately. If a ballast resistor is slowly increasing in value the engine could gradually deliver less and less horsepower, particularly under high load con-

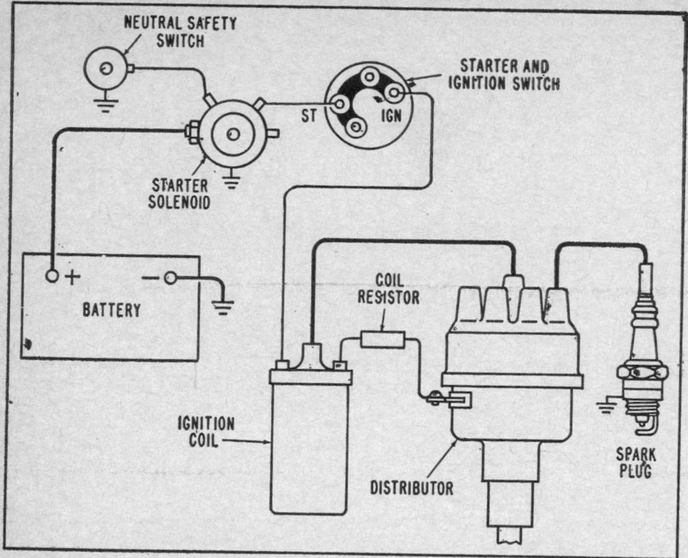

Fig. 4 Auto-Lite and Chrysler ignition circuit diagram with a temperature sensitive block-type resistor

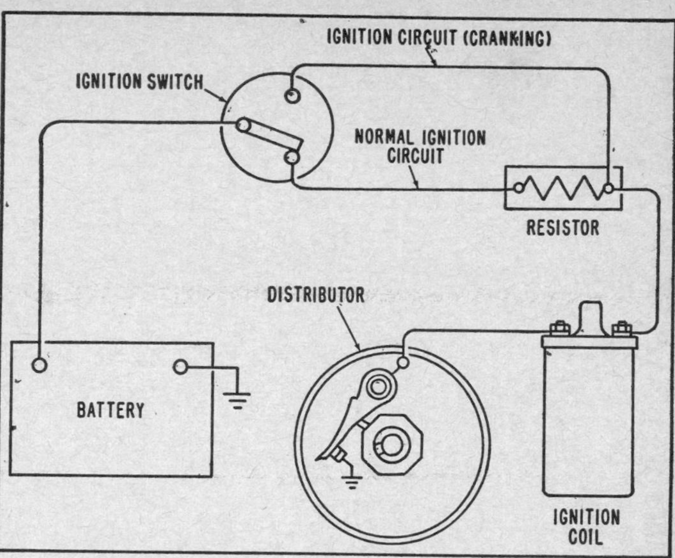

Fig. 5 Delco-Remy ignition circuit diagram with a constant temperature block-type resistor

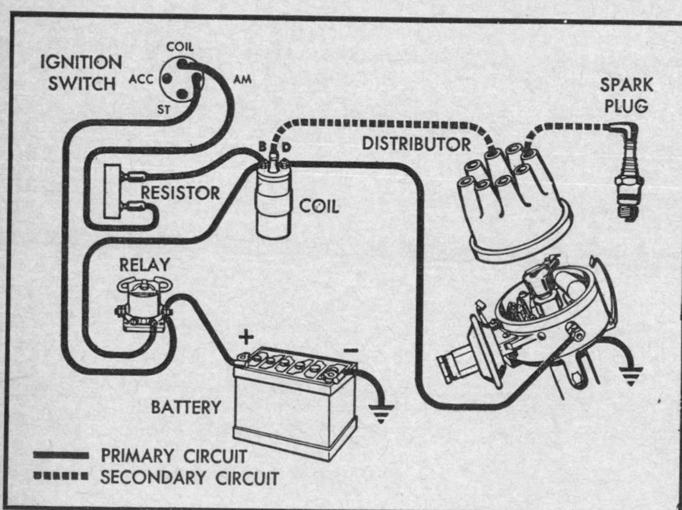

Fig. 6 Ford ignition circuit diagram with a constant temperature block-type resistor

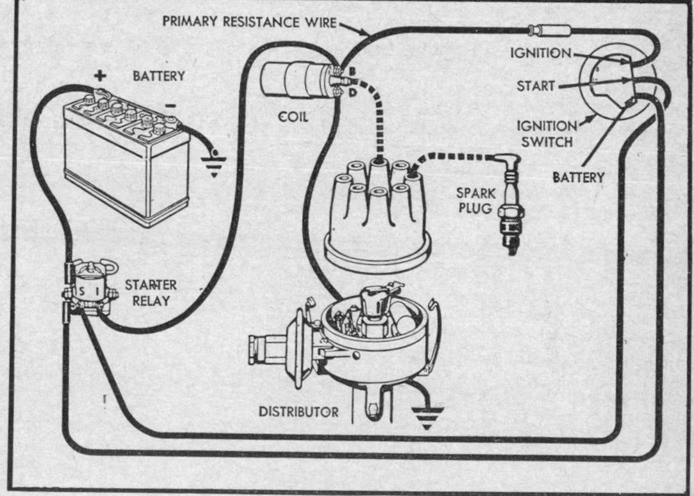

Fig. 9 Ford ignition circuit diagram with a resistance wire connected to a three-terminal ignition switch

ditions. An unsuspecting mechanic could unsuccessfully try to get the engine back to where it will deliver acceptable power output by changing spark plugs, adjusting timing, etc. Replacement of the faulty resistor is the only cure in this case.

To check a ballast resistor, replace it with one of known good quality. Then road-test the vehicle for improved performance.

It is important to remember that new spark plugs can temporarily mask the need for resistor replacement because new plugs require less voltage to fire. This is why a new-plug tune-up may prove satisfactory for a time. But if the ballast resistor is faulty, eventually the engine will misfire under load.

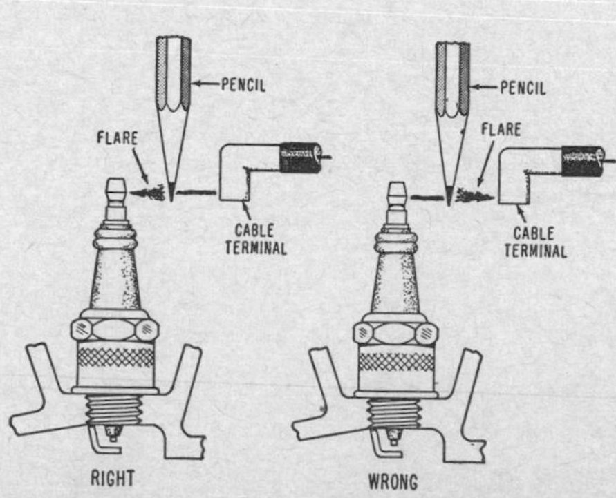

Fig. 3 Checking coil polarity

In Auto-Lite, Prestolite and Chrysler systems the resistor consists of an ordinary resistance wire that is sensitive to temperature, Fig. 4. The wire has a lower resistance value when cold than when hot. When the ignition is first turned on, more current will flow through the primary windings of the coil for a very short time until the resistor heats up.

In Delco-Remy and Ford systems, Figs. 5 and 6, the resistor is of the constant temperature type; that is, it is not affected by temperature and its resistance is approximately the same when cold as when hot. However, a feature is employed which shorts out the resistor while the engine is being cranked by the starter and automatically puts the re-

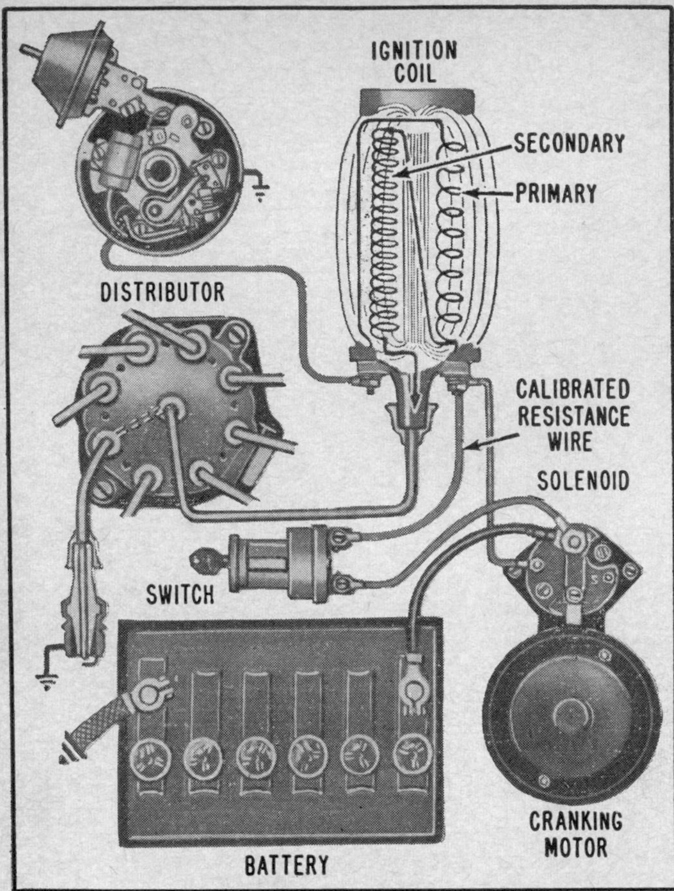

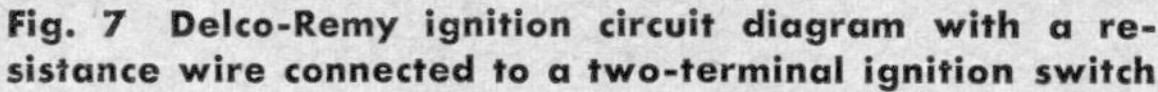
Fig. 7 Delco-Remy ignition circuit diagram with a resistance wire connected to a two-terminal ignition switch

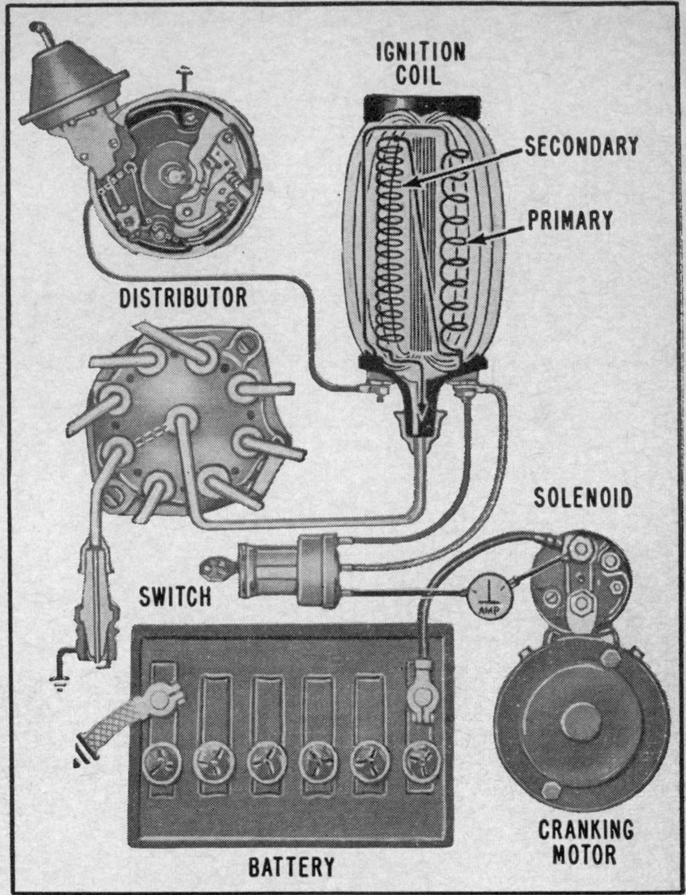

Fig. 8 Delco-Remy igition circuit diagram with a resistance wire connected to a three-terminal ignition switch

sistance back in the coil circuit as soon as the starter switch is released. This is accomplished by by-passing the resistor through the starter solenoid. The solenoid has an additional terminal from which a wire runs directly to the coil.

On Delco-Remy systems, the resistor is by-passed by means of a "finger" inside the solenoid switch housing which is attached to the additional switch terminal.

On Ford systems, Fig. 6, the resistor is by-passed through a terminal on the starter relay which is connected directly to the positive terminal of the coil.

Service Note: If the engine fires when the ignition switch is turned on but quits when the switch is released to its running position, it indicates that the resistor is defective and must be replaced.

Wire Type Resistors

The special resistance wires used with 12-volt systems starting with some 1959 vehicles are five to six feet long and contained in the regular wiring harness. The wire is made of stainless steel or special alloy, plastic-coated and covered with a glass braid. There is a relatively small temperature rise and the resistance wire is switched out of the circuit for starting and back in again for running.

With the Delco-Remy circuit shown in Fig. 7, the resistance wire is by-passed by means of a "finger" inside the starter solenoid housing which is attached to the additional switch terminal.

The Delco-Remy and Ford circuit diagrams shown in Figs. 8 and 9 have the resistance wire connected to a separate terminal on the ignition switch. When the ignition switch is released to its running position after the engine fires, the resistance wire is put back into the circuit.

Service Note: If the engine fires when the ignition switch is turned on but quits when the switch is released to its running position, it indicates that the resistance wire has lost its continuity or there is a bad connection at the resistor terminals. If the wire is defective, it must be replaced. To do this, first identify the terminal to which it is attached to the ignition switch (corresponding to the position of the ignition key when the engine is running). Then note the color code of the wire and disconnect it at both ends. Connect the new wire to the terminals and tape it to the main wiring harness. Finally, cut off the exposed sections of the defective wire.

Important: Do not attempt to operate the engine for an extended length of time with the resistor shorted out by means of a jumper wire as the breaker points will burn up in short order.

Continued

IGNITION COIL & RESISTOR SPECIFICATIONS

BUICK—All Models

Year	Model	Coil Draw, Amps. Engine Stopped	Coil Draw, Amps. Engine Idling	Coil Resistance, Ohms Primary @ 75°F.	Coil Resistance, Ohms Secondary @ 75°F.	Ignition Resistor Ohms @ 75°F.
1963	All	3.7	1.7	1.28–1.42	7200–9500	1.75–1.85
1964–69	All	3.8	2.3	1.28–1.42	7200–9500	1.75–1.85

CADILLAC

Year	Model	Coil Draw, Amps. Engine Stopped	Coil Draw, Amps. Engine Idling	Coil Resistance, Ohms Primary @ 75°F.	Coil Resistance, Ohms Secondary @ 75°F.	Ignition Resistor Ohms @ 75°F.
1963–68	All	2.4	1.25	1.81–1.95	7200–9500	1.30–1.35
1969	All	2.4	1.25	1.77–2.01	3000–20000	1.30–1.35

CHEVROLET, CHEVELLE, CHEVY II, CAMARO

Year	Model	Coil Draw, Amps. Engine Stopped	Coil Draw, Amps. Engine Idling	Coil Resistance, Ohms Primary @ 75°F.	Coil Resistance, Ohms Secondary @ 75°F.	Ignition Resistor Ohms @ 75°F.
1963	4 Cyl.	4.0	1.8	1.45–1.63	5600–6900	1.80
	Chevrolet 6	4.0	1.8	1.45–1.63	5600–6900	1.80
	Chevy II 6	4.0	1.8	1.28–1.42	7200–9500	1.80
	8-283, 327	4.0	1.8	1.28–1.42	7200–9500	1.80
	8-409	4.0	1.8	1.03–1.13	8000–10500	1.80
1964	4 & 6 Cyl.	4.0	1.8	1.45–1.63	5600–6900	1.80
	V8 Std. Ign.	4.0	1.8	1.28–1.32	7200–9500	1.80
	8-409 ①	4.0	1.8	1.03–1.13	8000–10500	1.80
1965	4 Cyl.	4.0	1.8	1.40–1.65	5400–7100	1.80
	6 Cyl.	4.0	1.8	1.45–1.63	5600–6900	1.80
	V8 Std. Ign.	4.0	1.8	1.24–1.46	6500–9500	1.80
	8-409 ①	4.0	1.8	1.03–1.13	6500–9500	1.80
1966–67	4 & 6 Cyl.	4.0	1.8	1.40–1.65	5400–7100	1.80
	V8 Std. Ign.	4.0	1.8	1.24–1.46	6500–9500	1.80
	Trans. Ign.			.38– .51	8200–12400	.43– .68
1968–69	4 & 6 Cyl.	4.0	1.8	1.41–1.63	3000–20000	1.80
	V8 Std. Ign.	4.0	1.8	1.77–2.05	3000–20000	1.35
	Trans. Ign.	4.0	1.8	.41– .51	3000–20000	.43– .68

①—With mechanical valve lifters.

CORVETTE

Year	Model	Coil Draw, Amps. Engine Stopped	Coil Draw, Amps. Engine Idling	Coil Resistance, Ohms Primary @ 75°F.	Coil Resistance, Ohms Secondary @ 75°F.	Ignition Resistor Ohms @ 75°F.
1963–64	All	4.0	1.8	1.02–1.13	8000–10500	1.40–1.62
1965–67	Std. Ign.	4.0	1.8	1.24–1.46	6500–9500	1.80
	Trans. Ign.	...	...	.38– .51	8200–12400	.43– .68
1968	Std. Ign.	4.0	1.8	1.77–2.05	3000–20000	1.35
	Trans. Ign.	...	...	.41– .51	3000–20000	.43– .68

CORVAIR

Year	Model	Coil Draw, Amps. Engine Stopped	Coil Draw, Amps. Engine Idling	Coil Resistance, Ohms Primary @ 75°F.	Coil Resistance, Ohms Secondary @ 75°F.	Ignition Resistor Ohms @ 75°F.
1963–69	All	4.0	1.8	1.28–1.42	7200–9500	1.80

CHRYSLER, DODGE, PLYMOUTH, IMPERIAL—All Models

Year	Model	Coil Draw, Amps. Engine Stopped	Coil Draw, Amps. Engine Idling	Coil Resistance, Ohms Primary @ 75°F.	Coil Resistance, Ohms Secondary @ 75°F.	Ignition Resistor Ohms @ 75°F.
1963–69	①	3.0	1.9	1.65–1.79	9400–11700	.50– .60
	②	3.0	1.9	1.41–1.55	9200–10600	.50– .60

①—Chrysler, Auto-Lite and Prestolite coils. ②—Essex coils.

FORD, MERCURY, LINCOLN, THUNDERBIRD—All Models

Year	Model	Coil Draw, Amps. Engine Stopped	Coil Draw, Amps. Engine Idling	Coil Resistance, Ohms Primary @ 75°F.	Coil Resistance, Ohms Secondary @ 75°F.	Ignition Resistor Ohms @ 75°F.
1963–69	Std. Ign.	4.5	2.5	1.40–1.54	7600–8800	1.30–1.40
1964	Trans. Ign.	4.0 ①	5.0	7.00–9.00	5000–7000	7.00–9.00
1965	Trans. Ign.	4.0 ①	5.0	.23–.25	4900–5680	②
1966–68	Trans. Ign.	4.0 ①	5.0	.226–.251	4900–5680	③

①—Engine cranking. ②—Emitter .30–.36, Collector .39–.47, Base 7.0–9.0 ③—Emitter .31–.35, Collector .41–.45, Base 7.1–7.9

OLDSMOBILE—All Models

Year	Model	Coil Draw, Amps. Engine Stopped	Coil Draw, Amps. Engine Idling	Coil Resistance, Ohms Primary @ 75°F.	Coil Resistance, Ohms Secondary @ 75°F.	Ignition Resistor Ohms @ 75°F.
1963	Model 3147	4.0	2.0	7.5–8.6	7500–10000	1.75–1.85
	All others	4.5	2.0	1.28–1.42	7200–9500	1.75–1.85
1964	F-85	3.8	2.3	1.77–2.05	6500–9500	1.35
	J88	6.0	1.35	1.77–2.05	6500–9500	1.35
	All Others	4.5	2.0	1.77–2.05	6500–9500	1.35
1965	All	6.0	1.35	1.77–2.05	6500–9500	1.35
1966	6 Cyl.	6.0	1.35	1.45–1.63	6500–9500	1.85
	V8s	6.0	1.35	1.77–2.05	6500–9500	1.35
1967-68	Toronado	4.0	2.2	1.77–2.05	6500–9500	1.35
	Delmont	6.0	1.35	1.77–2.05	6500–9500	1.35
	6 Cyl.	4.0	1.8	1.45–1.63	6500–9500	1.85
	All Others	4.0	2.0	1.77–2.05	6500–9500	1.35

IGNITION COIL & RESISTOR SPECIFICATIONS—Continued

Year	Model	Coil Draw, Amps.		Coil Resistance, Ohms		Ignition Resistor Ohms @ 75°F.
		Engine Stopped	Engine Idling	Primary @ 75°F.	Secondary @ 75°F.	
PONTIAC—All Models						
1963–64	Senior Cars	3.4	2.1	1.81–1.95	7200–9500	1.28–1.36
1963	4 Cyl.	3.5	2.8	1.46–1.53	5600–6900	1.80
1964–66	6 Cyl.	3.5	2.8	1.45–1.63	5600–6900	1.80
	All V8s	3.4	2.1	1.81–2.01	7200–9500	1.32
1967	6 Cyl.	2.5	3.8	1.4–1.7	3000–20000	...
	Temp., F-Bird	3.4	2.1	1.7–2.0	3000–20000	...
	Pontiac	3.2–3.6	1.9–2.3	1.7–2.0	3000–20000	...
1968–69	Pontiac	3.2–3.6	1.9–2.3	1.7–2.0	3000–20000	...
	6 Cyl.	3.5	2.8	1.4–1.7	3000–20000	...
	Temp., F-Bird	3.4	2.1	1.7–2.0	3000–20000	...
JEEP						
1963	12 Volt	2.85	2.85	...	...	①
1963–68	J Series	...	...	1.77–2.05	6500–9500	.49– .60

①—Resistor assembled inside of Auto-Lite coils.

Year	Model	Engine Stopped	Engine Idling	Primary @ 75°F.	Secondary @ 75°F.	Ignition Resistor Ohms @ 75°F.
RAMBLER—All Models						
1963	6 Cyl.	3.5	1.6	3.30–4.10	7200–9500	①
	V8s	3.5	1.6	1.28–1.42	7200–9500	1.80
1964–65	L Head 6	3.5	1.6	3.20–4.00	6500–9500	①
	OHV-6	3.5	1.6	3.30–4.10	7200–9500	①
	V8s	3.5	1.6	1.77–2.05	6500–9500	1.35
1966	6 Cyl.	3.5	1.6	3.30–4.10	7200–9500	①
	V8s	3.5	1.6	1.77–2.05	6500–9500	1.30–1.40
1967	6 Cyl. ②	3.5	1.6	3.3–4.1	9400–11700	①
	6 Cyl. ③	3.5	1.6	3.9–4.2	9400–11700	①
	V8–290	3.5	1.6	1.75–2.05	6500–9500	1.30–1.40
	V8–343 ②	3.5	1.6	1.77–2.05	6500–9500	1.30–1.40
	V8–343 ③	3.5	1.6	1.65–1.79	9400–11700	1.30–1.40
1968	6 Cyl.	3.5	1.6	1.40–1.65	3000–20000	...
	V8②	3.5	1.6	1.77–2.05	6500–9500	...
	V8③	3.5	1.6	1.65–1.79	9400–11700	...
1969	6 Cyl.	...	...	1.40–1.65	3000–20000	1.80
	V8②	...	...	1.77–2.05	3000–20000	1.35
	V8④	...	...	1.64–1.80	9300–11800	1.35

①—Resistor assembled inside of coil.
②—Delco-Remy.
③—Prestolite.
④—American Motors

CRANKCASE VENTILATION SYSTEMS

CRANKCASE VENTILATION

Crankcase ventilation has an important function in controlling sludge and keeping the engine lubricating system in good condition. Ineffective or inoperative crankcase ventilators are responsible for lubricating troubles serious enough in some cases to cause engine failure.

Two methods of crankcase ventilation are in use, the road-draft system and manifold vacuum system, both shown schematically in the same drawing in Fig. 1.

In the road draft type, air is driven into the crankcase by fan draft through a copper gauze filter in the oil filler cap. It then circulates around the inside of the engine and is discharged through the ventilator outlet pipe, carrying with it the water vapor which collects in the crankcase, particularly in cold weather. Whenever the oiling system is cleaned, the filler and outlet pipes should be removed and flushed out thoroughly. The gauze filters should also be washed in clean gasoline or kerosene.

In order to control smog, the manifold vacuum system of crankcase ventilation is standard equipment on 1961-62 cars to be used in California and is mandatory on all cars starting with 1963 models. The correct operation of this system depends upon a free flow of air from the carburetor air cleaner through the oil filler tube and engine to the control valve mounted on the intake manifold, Fig. 1. The arrows indicate the direction of the flow of air.

The system sucks crankcase vapors into the intake manifold to be burned in the combustion chamber. The flow of the vapors is controlled by the ventilator valve. The valve is actuated by engine vacuum working against spring tension. The high vacuum at engine idle provides minimum ventilation; low vacuum at road speeds provides maximum ventilation.

Servicing the system consists of checking the valve, the tubing and the air intake. The valve should be removed and checked for proper operation and for harmful deposits. If necessary, disassemble the valve, clean the parts in solvent and dry with compressed air. Inspect each component carefully. If the spring is distorted or the valve is worn the valve should be replaced. When reassembling the valve, make sure the end coil of the spring is snapped into the groove which is usually just under the head of the valve.

Remove the tubing and blow out any deposits with compressed air. When reinstalling the valve and tubing, make sure all connections are tight to prevent air leaks.

On some engines, the system air intake is a hose from the air cleaner to the oil filler tube. Make sure the hose is in good condition, and all connections are air tight. Check the oil filler tube cap to be sure it makes an air tight seal on the tube. Air leaks can easily be checked for by squirting kerosene at the connections.

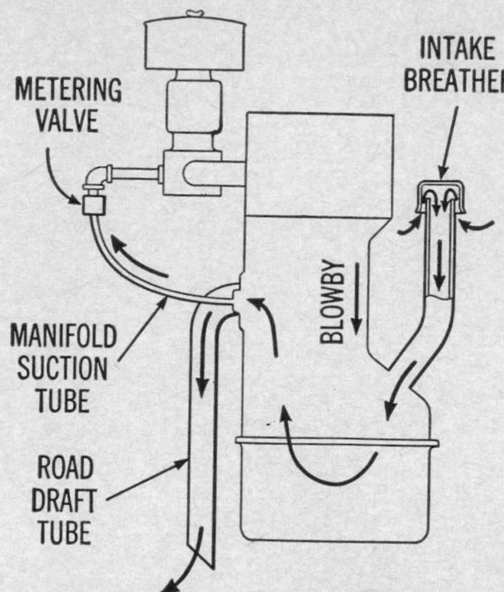

Fig. 1 Schematic drawing showing how either the road draft or manifold suction systems of crankcase ventilation operate

On other engines, the system air intake is a filter type oil filler tube cap. Check the cap filter to be sure it is free of dirt. Clean it in solvent if necessary.

NOTES

If idle speed is slow, unstable, rolling with frequent stalling, breather backflow and oily engine compartment, the ventilator valve may be completely clogged or the valve may be stuck in the open position.

A valve stuck in the closed position is indicated by breather backflow and oily engine compartment.

If the valve is stuck in the intermediate position, it will be indicated by rough fast idle and stalling.

The ventilation valve assembly should be cleaned every six months or 6000 miles (whichever comes first) and more frequently in service such as extensive engine idling during cold weather.

When the valve assembly is removed for cleaning, place a finger over the open end of the hose or tube and have the engine started. If the ventilator hose and carburetor passages are open and operating normally, a strong suction will be felt and there will be a large change in engine idling quality when the end of the hose is uncovered. If these conditions are not observed, the carburetor passages and/or ventilator hose are clogged and must be cleaned. The carburetor should be removed from the engine and the ventilation passages cleaned by dipping the lower part of the carburetor in the cleaner. A pipe cleaner or wire can be used to aid in cleaning the passages.

PCV SYSTEM TESTS

If a condition of rough or loping engine idle speed is evident, do not attempt to compensate for this idle condition by disconnecting the crankcase ventilation system and making carburetor adjustments. The removal of the system from the engine will adversely affect the fuel economy and engine ventilation with resultant shortening of engine life.

To determine whether the loping or rough idle condition is caused by a malfunctioning crankcase ventilation system, perform either of the following tests.

Regulator Valve Test

1. Install a regulator valve known to be good in the crankcase ventilation system.
2. Start engine and compare engine idle condition to the prior idle condition.
3. If the loping or rough idle condition remains when the good regulator valve is installed, the crankcase ventilation system is not at fault. Further engine component diagnosis will have to be made to find the cause of the malfunction.
4. If the idle condition proves satisfactory, replace the regulator valve and clean hoses, fittings, etc.

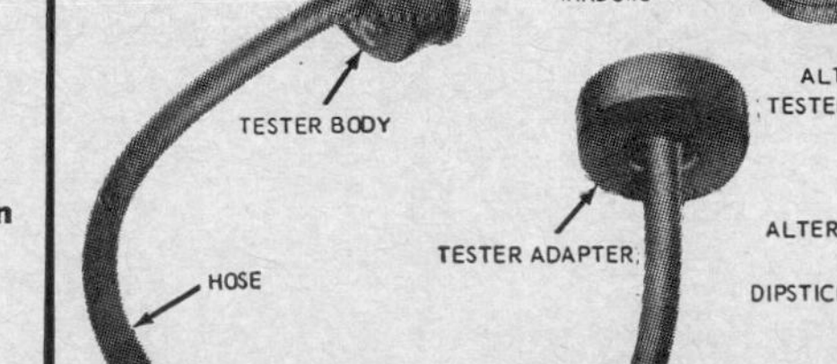

Fig. 2 AC positive crankcase ventilation system tester

Air Intake Test

This test uses the AC positive crankcase ventilation tester, Fig. 2, which is operated by the engine vacuum through the oil filler opening.

1. With engine at normal operating temperature, remove oil filler cap and dipstick.
2. Connect one end of the hose to the tester body and connect the other end of the hose to the tester adapter.
3. Use the dipstick hole plug to plug the opening in the dipstick tube.
4. Insert the tester adapter in the filler cap opening and turn the selector knob to No. 2 (Fig. 2).
5. If the vehicle has a system with the tube from the air cleaner going into the oil filler cap, disconnect the tube at the filler cap and plug the tube.
6. Start engine and let it idle.
7. With plugs secure and tube free of kinks, hold tester body upright and note color in the tester windows. Following lists the various colors and probable cause or related condition of the system.

GREEN: System operating properly.

GREEN & YELLOW

1. Regulator valve or system partially plugged.
2. Slight kink in tester hose.
3. Slight engine blow-by.
4. Plugs from kit or engine vacuum lines are not properly sealed.
5. Tester knob improperly set.

YELLOW

1. Regulator valve or system partially plugged.
2. Tester hose kinked or blocked.
3. Blow-by at maximum capacity of regulator valve.
4. Plugs from kit or engine vacuum lines are not properly sealed.
5. Tester knob improperly set.

YELLOW & RED

1. Regulator valve or system partially or fully plugged.
2. More engine blow-by than regulator valve can handle.
3. Vent hose plugged or collapsed.

RED

1. Regulator valve or system fully plugged or stuck.
2. Vent hose plugged or collapsed.
3. Extreme blow-by.

EXHAUST EMISSION CONTROLS

GENERAL MOTORS C.C.S.

Controlled Combustion System

First used on some 1967 Oldsmobile and Pontiac models in California, the CCS system uses a special calibrated carburetor and distributor, related hoses, plus the component parts of the closed P.C.V. system.

Exhaust emissions are controlled at idle by using a double acting vacuum advance unit to retard the spark. The retard side of the unit is connected to a spark port in the carburetor throttle flange below the throttle plate. When the throttle is opened beyond idle position, vacuum from above the throttle plate is ported to the advance side of the unit which then functions in the normal manner (spark advances).

Exhaust emissions are held below the maximum allowable level under all other operating conditions without the use of the complete A.I.R. system.

The CCS system is designed to keep the air entering the carburetor at approximately 100 deg. F. when the underhood temperature is less than 100 deg. F. By keeping the temperature at 100 deg. F. or above, the carburetor can be calibrated to operate more efficiently without affecting engine performance, provide improved fuel economy, eliminate carburetor icing and improve engine warm-up.

Operation, Figs. 1 to 4

During engine warm-up period, with engine compartment temperatures below 90 to 120 deg. F., the temperature sensor is closed. This allows engine vacuum to be directed to the vacuum motor, closing the valve plate to outside air. With the valve closed, the cool air will flow through the holes in the left side of the shroud where it is heated. The heated air then flows up through the hot air pipe and connector into the air cleaner.

As the temperature inside the air filter element reaches approximately 100 deg. F., the bi-metal temperature sensor bleeds off vacuum to the right vacuum motor, causing the valve to open, allowing underhood air to be mixed with the heated air as needed to keep the air temperature at approximately 100 deg. F.

Under full throttle or below 6 to 8 inches of vacuum, the vacuum motor will

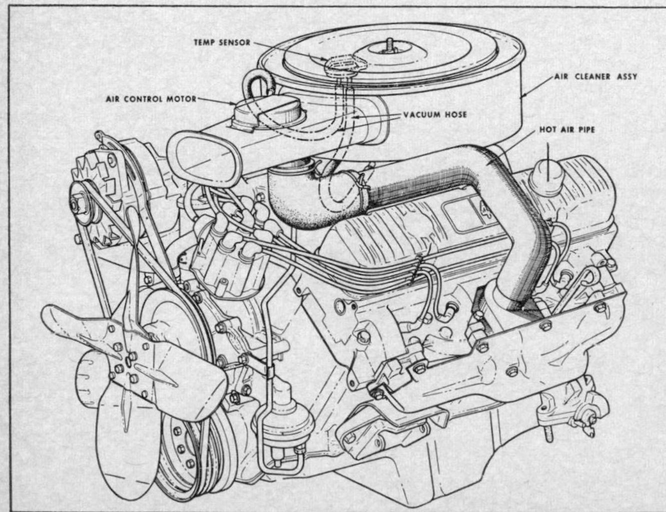

Fig. 1 Controlled Combustion System (CCS) installed on a V8 engine

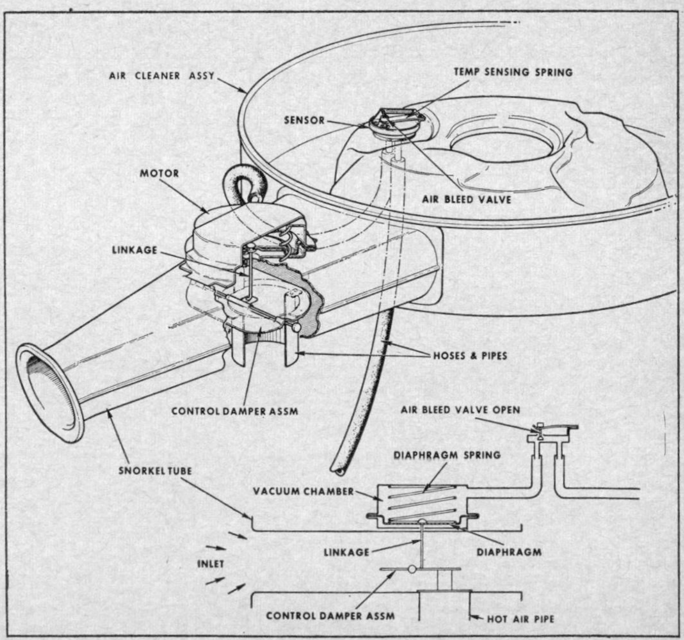

Fig. 2 Cold air door open. CCS

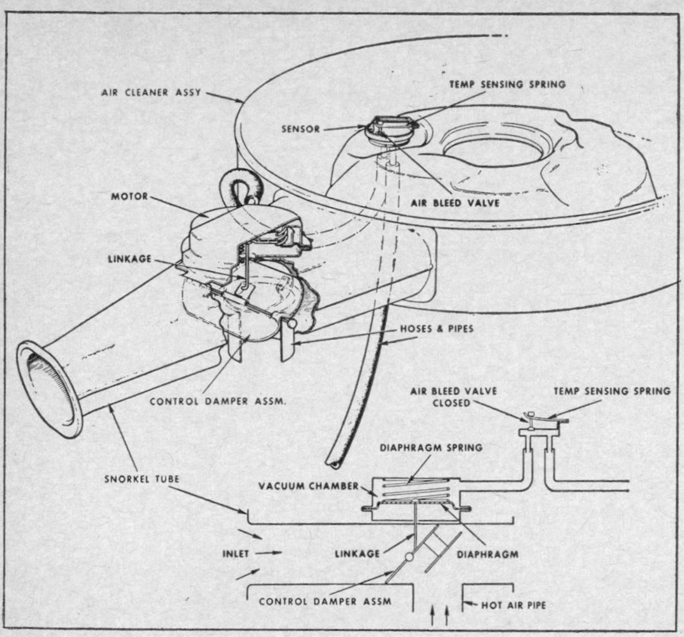

Fig. 3 Hot air door open. CCS

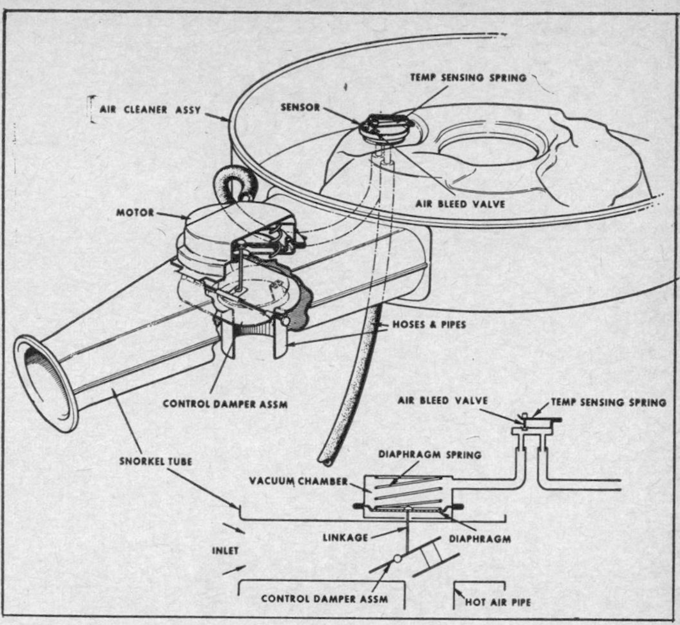

Fig. 4 Cold and hot air doors both partially open. CCS

no longer hold the valve open to hot air. Therefore, the hot air pipe is closed off, allowing only underhood air to enter the air cleaner.

The vacuum motor and valve plate in the left snorkel (when used) is controlled only by intake manifold vacuum. Therefore, this snorkel is always closed until full throttle is desired, allowing maximum air flow into the air cleaner.

Functional Checks

Vacuum Motors and Valve Plates

1. With engine off, the vacuum motors should be holding valve plate or plates open. This can be checked by looking into the right and left snorkel. *On the smaller engines the left snorkel will be blocked closed and does not operate.*
2. Start engine and observe valve plates with engine idling. If equipped, the LEFT valve plate will close immediately, regardless of temperature.
3. If the temperature in the air cleaner

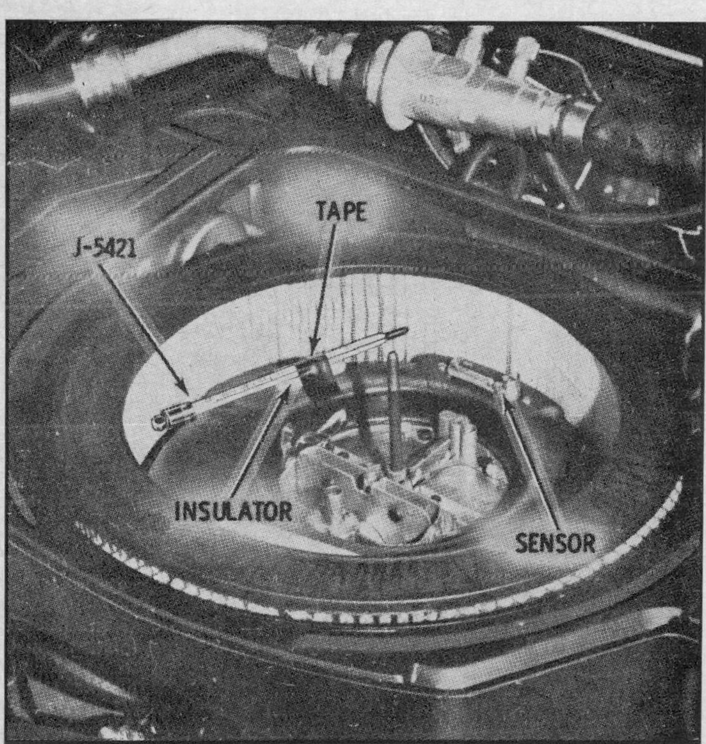

Fig. 5 Checking temperature sensor with thermometer. C.C.S. System

Fig. 6 Idle stop solenoid

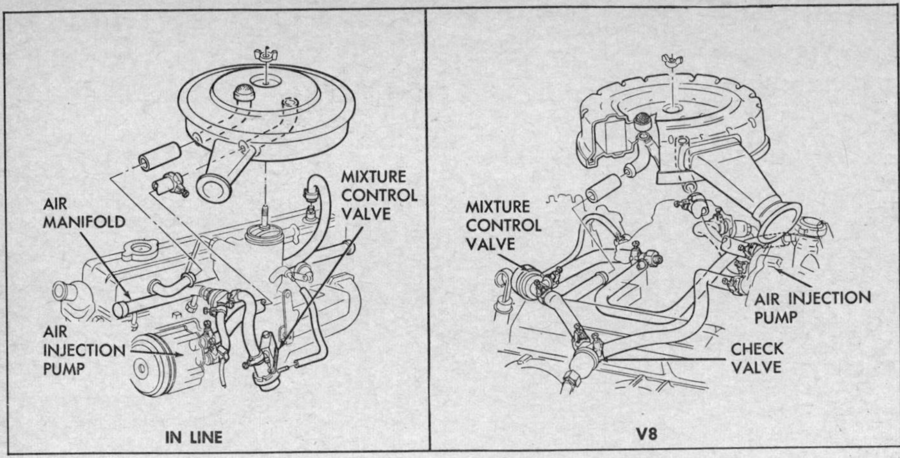

Fig. 7 Typical installation of an air pump system with a mixture control valve, otherwise known as a backfire by-pass valve. 1966-67

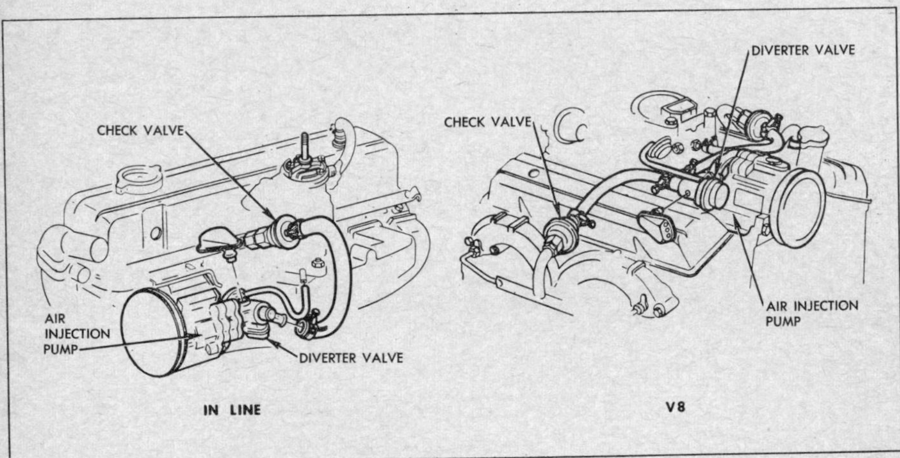

Fig. 8 Typical installation of an air pump system with a diverter valve, otherwise known as an air by-pass valve. 1968

is below 90 deg. F., the RIGHT valve plate will also close to outside air. With temperatures above approximately 100 deg. F., the valve plate will remain open to outside air.

4. If vacuum motors fail to operate with vacuum applied directly to vacuum motor, motor must be replaced.

Temperature Sensor, Fig. 5

1. Remove air cleaner and allow to cool down to 75 deg. F. or below.
2. Install air cleaner on carburetor and attach hot air hose connector and vacuum line.
3. With air filter in position, tape a thermometer in air cleaner as shown.
4. Install cover on air cleaner and start engine.
5. Observe valve plate in right snorkel. When valve plate starts to move toward the open position (to outside air), quickly remove cover on air cleaner and note reading on thermometer. If temperature reading is below approximately 100 deg. F., temperature sensor must be replaced.

NOTE: If the hoses have been removed from connectors for any reason, it is very important that they be correctly repositioned for proper operation.

Idle Stop Solenoid

Starting with 1968 models, most cars equipped with the Controlled Combustion System (CCS), have an idle stop solenoid mounted on the carburetor, Fig. 6. The purpose of this solenoid is to prevent engine operation after the ignition is shut off, a condition known as "dieseling". Dieseling is prevalent with the CCS system, especially when the car has an automatic transmission, for the following reasons:

With the Controlled Combustion System for exhaust emission reduction, the ignition timing is slightly retarded and idle rpm is slightly higher. Also engine operating temperature is higher—195°F.

With automatic transmissions, idle speed is set with the transmission in Drive. When the driver is about to turn off the ignition, the selector lever is shifted to Park or Neutral position. Since the load of the transmission is removed in these ranges, idle rpm rises into the 700 rpm range.

With the engine running at this rpm, plus other factors, such as higher operating temperature, regular fuel and slightly retarded spark, "dieseling" may be encountered. The solenoid eliminates this dieseling possibility by closing the throttle valve(s) when the ignition is turned off.

As shown, the solenoid is mounted on the carburetor and acts upon the throttle valve(s) in the same manner as an idle set screw. When the ignition switch is turned on, the solenoid coil is activated and the plunger is driven to its full extended position. The plunger acts on the throttle valve lever and sets the throttle valve(s) in a position to achieve the specified rpm.

When the ignition switch is turned off, the solenoid is de-energized and the plunger retracts into the solenoid. The throttle valve(s) closes to a position controlled by the low idle adjusting screw. At this point the throttle valve(s) is opened only enough to allow the engine to run at a much lower rpm. This lower setting keeps the throttle valve(s) from completely closing and scuffing the throttle bore(s).

The lower idle speed setting just mentioned is achieved with a set screw when the solenoid is electrically disconnected. The setting for normal idle speed is adjusted, with solenoid energized, through the hex screw in the plunger and/or by repositioning the solenoid in its mounting clamp.

NOTE: To set the solenoid while starting a hot engine, the accelerator pedal must be depressed approximately one-third of its travel. When starting a cold engine, however, the accelerator pedal must be fully depressed to set both the choke and the idle stop solenoid.

CAUTION: As mentioned in previous text and to be further explained, starting with 1968, all vehicles are subject to exhaust emission reduction requirements. Unburned gases emit undesirable amounts of hydro-carbons. These unfavorable emissions are predominant during idle operation. One would naturally think that if the idle mixture is made as lean as possible, exhaust emission would be reduced. This is true up to a point. However, if the idle mixture is made too lean, the hydro-carbon content may increase above acceptable limits. The amount of *carbon monoxide* exceeds acceptable limits when idle mixtures are set too "rich". Conversely, the amount of *hydro-carbon* content exceeds acceptable limits if the idle mixture is set too "lean". Consequently, proper idle adjustment becomes absolutely essential. For this reason, detailed instructions for the proper setting of the carburetor idle speed and mixture is given in the carburetor chapter.

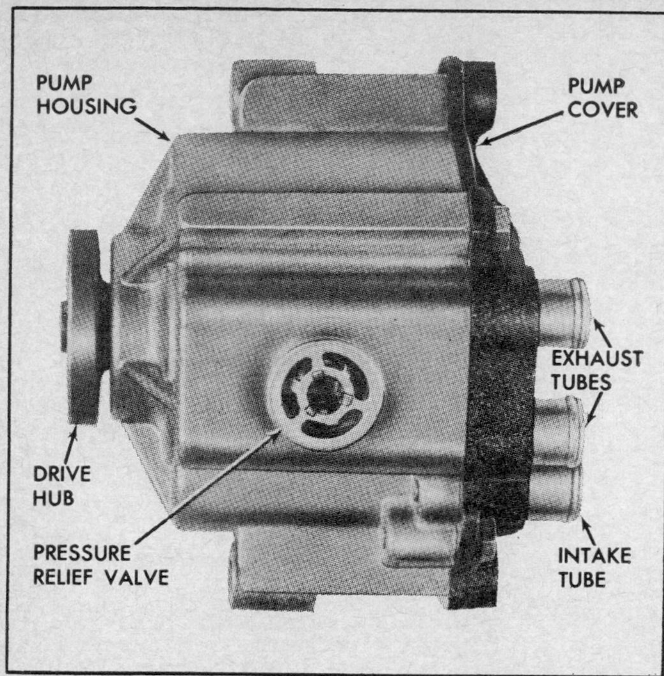

Fig. 9 Air injection pump with separate air filter. 1966-67

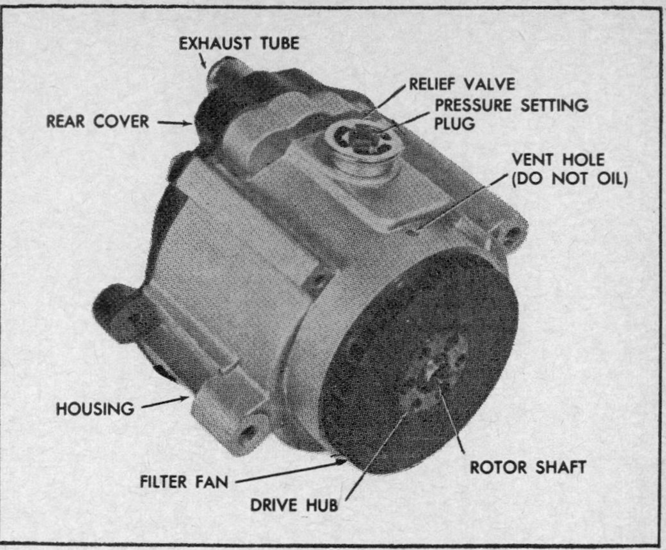

Fig. 10 Air injection pump with integral centrifugal air filter. 1968

AIR PUMP SYSTEMS

GM Air Injection Reactor (A.I.R.), Ford Thermactor, Rambler Air Guard

All air pump systems, Figs. 7 and 8, consist of an air injection pump, air injection tubes (one for each cylinder), a mixture control or backfire by-pass valve (1966-67), a diverter or air by-pass valve (from 1968), check valves (one for In Line engines, two for V8s), air manifolds, tubes and hoses necessary to connect the various components.

Carburetors and distributors for engines with an air pump system are designed particularly for these engines. Therefore, they should not be interchanged with or replaced by a carburetor or distributor designed for an engine without an air pump system.

The air injection pump, Figs. 9 and 10, compresses the air and injects it through the air manifolds, hoses and injection tubes into the exhaust system in the area of the exhaust valves. The fresh air ignites and burns the unburned portion of the exhaust gases in the exhaust system, thus minimizing exhaust contaminations.

The mixture control or backfire bypass valve, Fig. 11, when triggered by a sharp increase in manifold vacuum, supplies the intake manifold with fresh filtered air to lean out the fuel-air mixture and prevent exhaust system backfire.

The diverter or air by-pass valve, Fig. 12, when triggered by a sharp increase in manifold vacuum, shuts off the injected air to the exhaust port areas and prevents backfiring during this richer period. On engine overrun the total air supply is dumped through the muffler on the diverter or air by-pass valve. At high engine speeds the excess air is dumped through the pressure relief valve when the pressure relief valve is part of the air pump, and through the diverter or air by-pass valve when the pressure

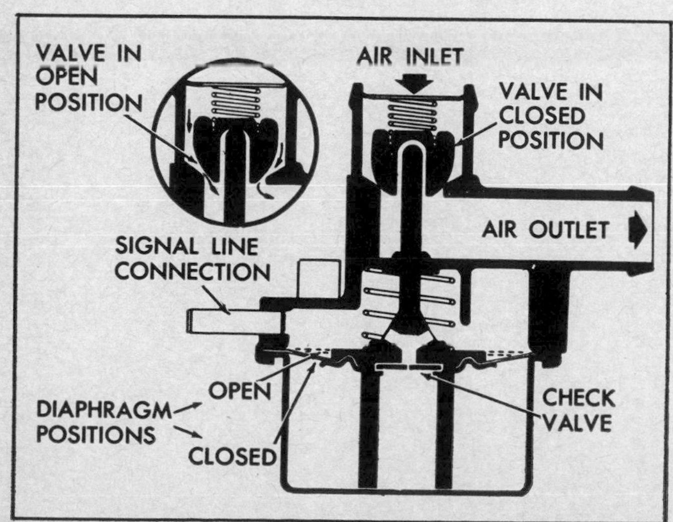

Fig. 11 Typical mixture control or backfire by-pass valve

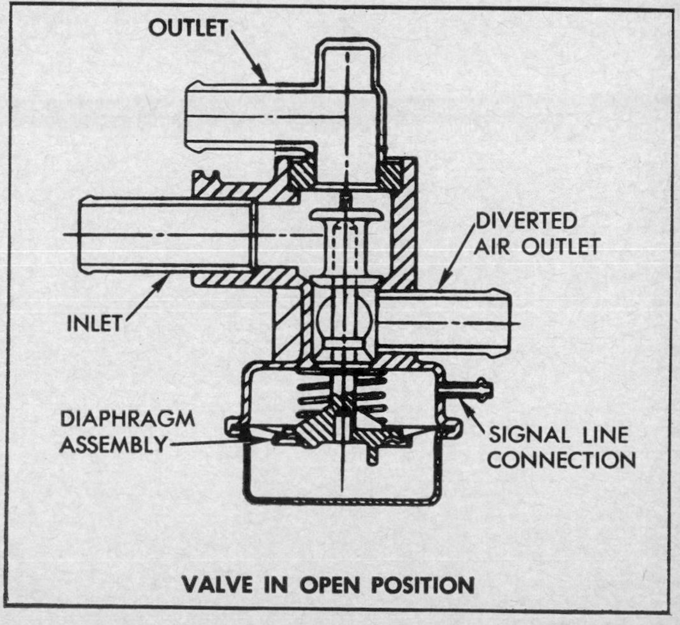

Fig. 12 Typical diverter or air by-pass valve

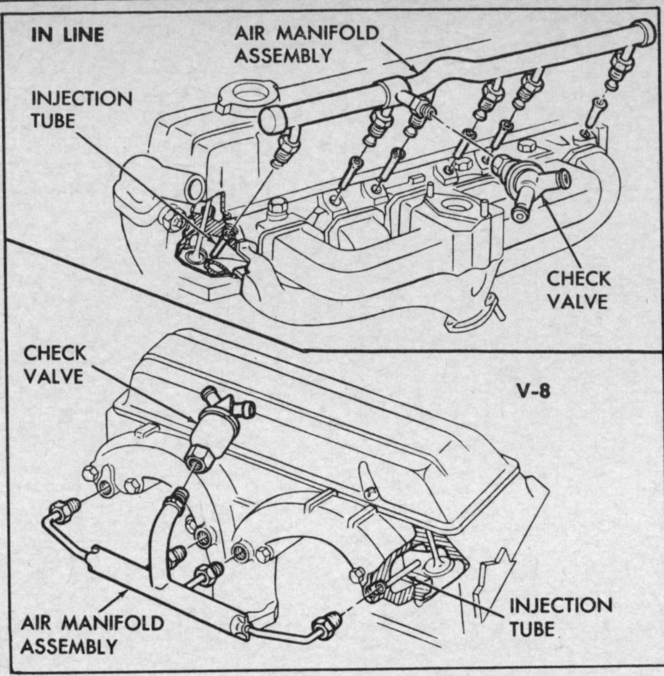

Fig. 13 Typical air manifold installations

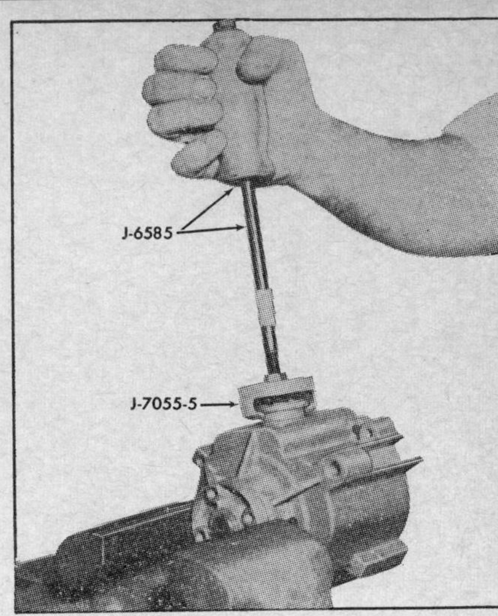

Fig. 14 Removing pressure relief valve with slide hammer tool shown

relief valve is part of the diverter or air by-pass valve.

The check valve or valves prevent exhaust gases from entering and damaging the air injection pump, as back flow can occur even under normal operating conditions.

When properly installed and maintained, the system will effectively reduce exhaust emissions. However, if any system components or any engine component that operates in conjunction with the air pump system should malfunction, the exhaust emissions might be increased.

Maintenance

Because of the relationship between "Engine Tune Up" and "Unburned Exhaust Gases", the condition of the engine tune up should be checked whenever the air pump system seems to be malfunctioning. Particular care should be taken in checking items that affect fuel-air ratio, such as the crankcase ventilation system (PCV), the carburetor and carburetor air cleaner.

Because of the similarity of many parts, typical illustrations and procedures are given in the following text.

Air Manifold, Hose and Tube, Fig. 13

1. Inspect all hoses for deterioration or holes.
2. Inspect all tubes for cracks or holes.
3. Check all tube and hose routing as interference may cause wear.
4. Check all hose and tube connections.
5. If a leak is suspected on the pressure side of the system, or any tubes and/or hoses have been disconnected on the pressure side, the connections should be checked for leaks with a soapy water solution. With the pump running, bubbles will form if a leak exists.
6. To replace any hose or tube, note the routing, then remove the hose(s) or tube(s) as required.

CAUTION: The hoses used with this system are made of special material to withstand high temperature. No other type hose should be substituted.

Check Valves

1. Check valves should be inspected whenever the hose is disconnected from the check valve or whenever check valve failure is suspected.

NOTE: An air pump that has shown any indications of having exhaust gases in the pump would indicate check valve failure.

2. Orally blow through the check valve (toward air manifold) then attempt to suck back through the check valve. Flow should be in one direction only (toward air manifold).
3. To replace a check valve, disconnect pump outlet hose at check valve. Remove check valve from air manifold, being careful not to bend or twist the air manifold.

Diverter or Air By-Pass Valve

1. Check condition and routing of all lines, especially the signal line. All lines must be secure without crimps and not leaking.
2. Disconnect signal line at valve. A vacuum signal must be available with engine running.
3. With engine warmed up to operating temperature and carburetor at curb idle, no air should be escaping through the valve's muffler. Manually open and quickly close the throttle; a momentary blast of air should discharge through the valve's muffler for at least one second. Defective valve should be replaced.

CAUTION: Although sometimes similar in appearance, these valves are designed to meet particular requirements of various engines; therefore, be sure to install the correct valve for the engine being serviced.

4. To replace a valve, disconnect vacuum signal line and valve exhaust hose or hoses.
5. Remove diverter or air by-pass valve from pump; also muffler from valve assembly, noting angle of attachment.
6. Install muffler to new valve at angle previously noted.
7. Install diverter or air by-pass valve to pump or bracket with new gasket.
8. Install outlet and vacuum lines and check system for leaks.

Mixture Control or Backfire By-Pass Valve

1. Check condition of all lines, especially the signal line. A defective signal or outlet line will cause malfunctioning of the mixture control or backfire by-pass valve.
2. Disconnect pump-to-valve inlet hose at pump.
3. A leaking valve will be indicated by an air gushing noise coming from the hose. Place palm of hand over hose; little or no pull with a gradual increase is normal. If an immediate strong pull is felt or air noise is heard, the valve is defective and must be replaced.
4. Open and close throttle rapidly. Air noise should be evident and then gradually decrease. Check valve for proper usage. If a strong pull is not felt immediately or if air noise is not present, the valve is not functioning properly and must be replaced. A noisy valve should also be replaced.
5. To replace the mixture control or backfire by-pass valve, disconnect signal line, air inlet and air outlet hoses, then remove valve.
6. Install new valve and connect air outlet, air inlet and signal line hoses.

CAUTION: Although similar in appearance, mixture control or backfire by-pass valves are designed to meet particular requirements of various engines. Therefore, be sure to install the correct valve for the engine being serviced.

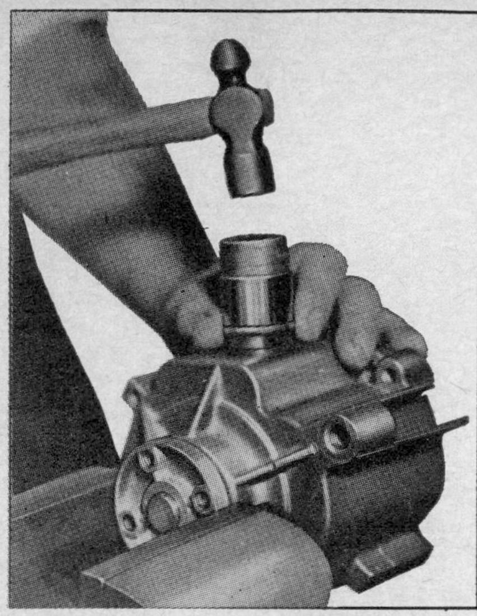

Fig. 15 Installing pressure relief valve

Fig. 16 Removing centrifugal type pump air filter

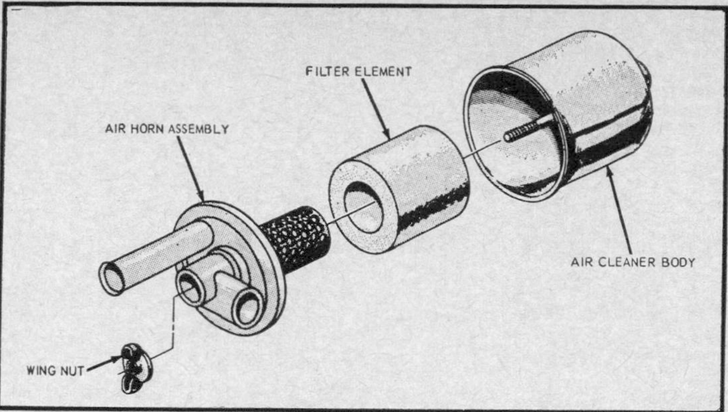

Fig. 17 Conventional type pump air filter

Air Injection Tube

There is no periodic service or inspection for air injection tubes. However, whenever the cylinder head is removed from In Line engines, or whenever exhaust manifolds are removed from V8 engines, inspect the tubes for carbon build-up and warped or burnt tubes. Remove any carbon build-up with a wire brush. Warped or burnt tubes must be replaced.

1. To replace a tube, remove carbon from tubes and, using penetrating oil, work tubes out of cylinder head or exhaust manifold.
2. Install new tubes in cylinder head or manifold.

Air Injection Pump

1. Accelerate engine to about 1500 rpm and observe air flow from hose or hoses. If air flow increases as engine is accelerated, the pump is operating satisfactorily. If air flow does not increase or is not present, proceed as follows:
2. Check for proper drive belt tension.
3. Check for leaky pressure relief valve. Air may be heard leaking with the pump running.

NOTE: The air pump system is not completely noiseless. Under normal conditions noise rises in pitch as engine speed increases. To determine if excessive noise is the fault of the system, operate the engine with the pump drive belt removed. If excessive noise does not exist with the belt removed, proceed as follows:

4. On 1966-67 models, check for proper installation of the relief valve silencer (if equipped).
5. Check for seized air pump.
6. Check hoses, tubes, air manifolds and all connections for leaks and proper routing.
7. Check carburetor air cleaner for proper installation.
8. Check air pump for proper mounting.
9. If none of the above conditions exist and the air pump has excessive noise, remove and replace the pump unit.
10. To replace the pump, disconnect hoses at pump and remove pump pulley.
11. Unfasten and remove pump.
12. Install pump with mounting bolts loose.
13. Install pump pulley and drive belt.
14. Adjust drive belt tension and connect hoses at pump.

Pressure Relief Valve

When the pressure relief valve is incorporated in the diverter or air by-pass valve the complete valve must be replaced. If the relief valve is in the pump, proceed as follows:

1. Pull relief valve from pump, Fig. 14.
2. Using a 15/16″ socket, Fig. 15, tap relief valve into housing until valve shoulders on housing. Use extreme care to avoid distorting housing.

NOTE: Various length pressure setting plugs designed for the particular requirements of the vehicle being serviced determine the pressure required to open the relief valve. Usually, the pressure setting plugs are color-coded. To remove the pressure setting plug, carefully unlock the legs from the inside surface of the relief valve with a small screwdriver. To install the plug, carefully push it into the relief valve until the legs lock. If a pressure setting plug is to be reused be sure the leg angles are sufficient for the plug to lock in place.

Centrifugal Pump Filter

1. To replace the centrifugal type, Fig. 16, remove drive belt and pump pulley. Pry loose outer disc of filter fan, being careful to prevent fragments from entering the air intake hole.
2. Install the new filter by drawing it on with the pulley and pulley bolts. Do not attempt to install a filter by hammering it or pressing it on.
3. Draw the filter down evenly by alternately tightening the bolts. Make certain that the outer edge of the filter slips into the housing. The slight amount of interference with the housing bore is normal.

Conventional Type Filter, Fig. 17

Remove and replace the air filter element as suggested by the illustration. The filter element is not cleanable; it must be replaced. Position the assembled air horn and filter element in the air cleaner body, being sure the tang is fitted into the slot.

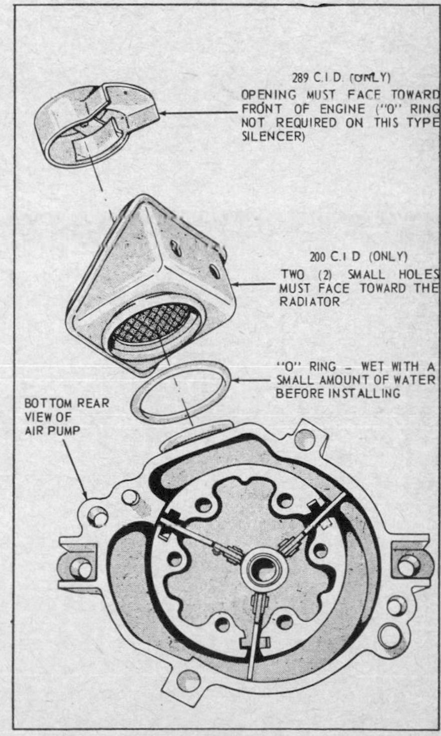

Fig. 19 Air pump pressure relief valve installation on 1966 Fordline cars with 6-200 engine

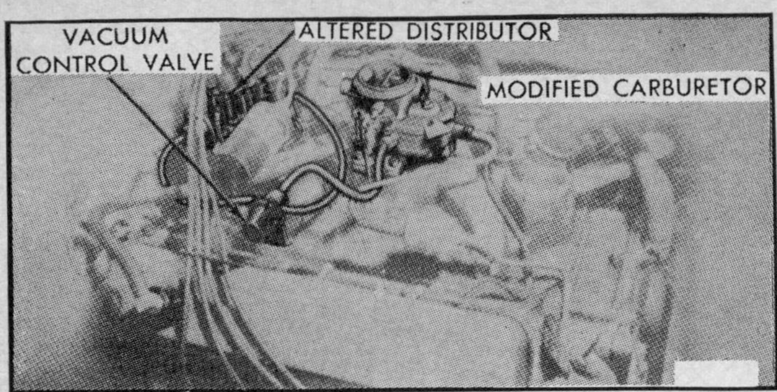

Fig. 20 Chrysler's Cleaner Air Package (CAP). Unlike the others this system uses no air pump

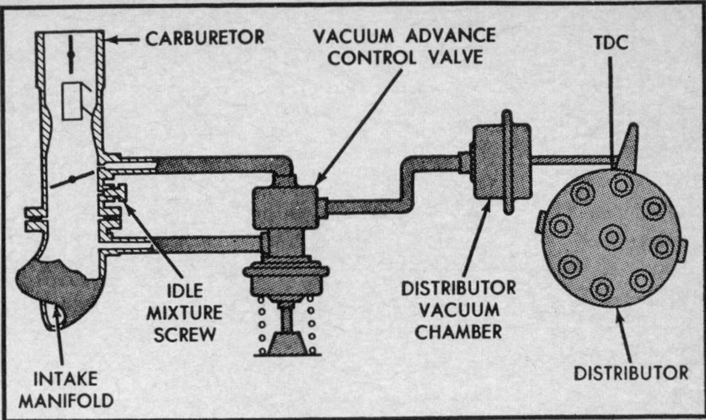

Fig. 21 Relationship of carburetor, vacuum advance control valve and distributor

SERVICE BULLETIN

Air Pump Relief Valve Noise: If this condition occurs in a 1966 Ford-line car with a 6-200 engine, it is caused by insufficient silencing or improper pressure setting plug. The remedy is to replace the silencer with a new design silencer and/or check the set plug. The new silencer is a permanently assembled wedged shaped assembly. It is fitted to the air relief valve housing with a rubber O-ring acting as a snap ring. When installing, note the recommendations given in Fig. 19.

CHRYSLER C.A.P.

Cleaner Air Package

The Cleaner Air Package is in addition to the Positive Crankcase Ventilation (PCV). The PCV device is designed to control the emission of hydrocarbon vapors from the crankcase, whereas the Cleaner Air Package controls the emission of hydrocarbon vapors (unburned gasoline) and carbon monoxide in the vehicle exhaust.

The Cleaner Air Package is engineered to continuously control carburetion and ignition at the best settings for performance and combustion during all driving conditions. These adjustments keep unburned gasoline and carbon monoxide in the exhaust at a minimum concentration.

Only three special components are involved in the CAP installation, Fig. 20. The carburetor and distributor have been re-designed and a new component—the Vacuum Advance Control Valve—has been added. In addition, some cooling system components have been changed to handle the increased heat rejection at idle and low speed.

Special Carburetor and Ignition

The carburetor is specially calibrated to provide leaner mixtures at idle and low speed operation. The distributor is designed to give retarded timing at idle. The vacuum advance control valve, in conjunction with the distributor, provides advanced timing during deceleration.

CAP idle timing for all engines is retarded instead of advanced. Exhaust emission is reduced at idle by using leaner air/fuel mixtures, increased engine speed, and retarded ignition timing. The higher air flow at this idle condition approximates the desirable conditions of cruise. CAP, therefore, is designed to operate with late timing during idle, and with conventional spark advance during acceleration and cruise.

Vacuum Advance Control Valve

Early ignition of the air/fuel mixture is needed during deceleration to provide the most efficient combustion and re-

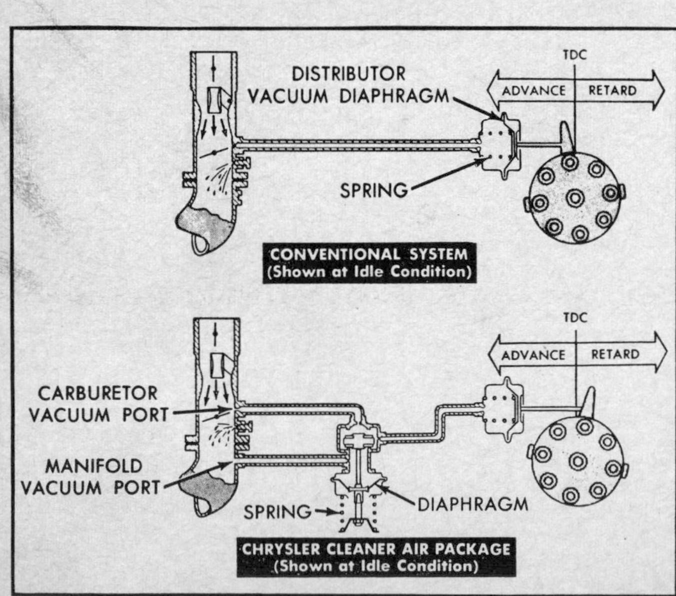

Fig. 22 Engine idle condition

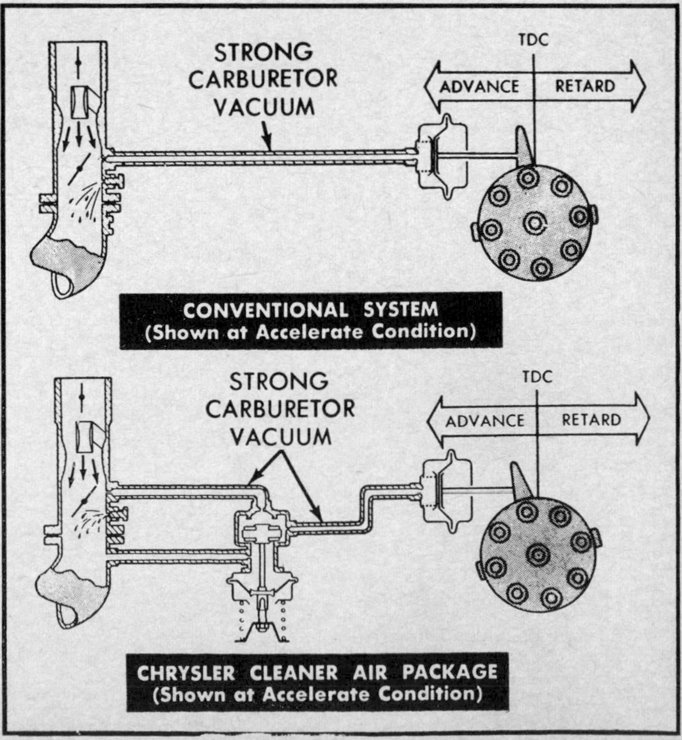

Fig. 23 During acceleration

duced exhaust emissions. The vacuum advance control valve provides the additional spark advance during deceleration. The vacuum advance control valve is connected by vacuum hoses to the carburetor, to the intake manifold, and to the distributor vacuum chamber, Fig. 21.

Carburetor vacuum and manifold vacuum act on the vacuum advance control valve. From these two signals, the vacuum advance control valve senses engine speed and load conditions, and relays a vacuum signal to the distributor to vary spark timing when necessary to reduce emissions to an acceptable level.

Engine Idle, Fig. 22

The initial idle timing is retarded as much as 15 degrees from conventional timing. The vacuum advance control valve does not affect timing at idle because the distributor vacuum chamber receives the same vacuum signal as in the conventional system, namely, carburetor vacuum. At idle it is not strong enough to overcome the distributor vacuum diaphragm spring.

Manifold vacuum acts on the vacuum control valve diaphragm, but is not strong enough to overcome the vacuum control valve spring. So the spring holds the vacuum control valve closed to manifold vacuum and open to the low carburetor vacuum.

Acceleration, Fig. 23

During acceleration and cruise, manifold vacuum is not strong enough to actuate the CAP control valve. Thus the CAP system operates in the same manner as the conventional system. The throttle blade opens enough to permit the distributor vacuum advance to function, and spark timing is advanced according to the amount of vacuum created by the pumping action of the pistons.

Deceleration, Fig. 24

The conventional system provides the highest emissions under deceleration conditions. Carburetor vacuum is too weak to overcome the distributor advance diaphragm spring.

Manifold vacuum is at its strongest under deceleration conditions. Therefore, the CAP system uses manifold vacuum rather than carburetor vacuum to control spark timing.

Manifold vacuum is strong enough to overcome the vacuum advance control valve spring and the distributor vacuum diaphragm spring, moving spark timing to the maximum advance condition.

Service Procedure

Periodic servicing of the system is required to maintain good engine performance and prevent malfunction of the system because of the combustion products deposited in the valve, hose and carburetor passages. Every six months clean and service the system, and replace the valve every year. To service the systems, proceed as follows:

1. In cases of severe service, such as experienced in police, taxicab or other operation involving short trips with prolonged idling, it is recommended that the system be checked for operation with every oil change and serviced as required.

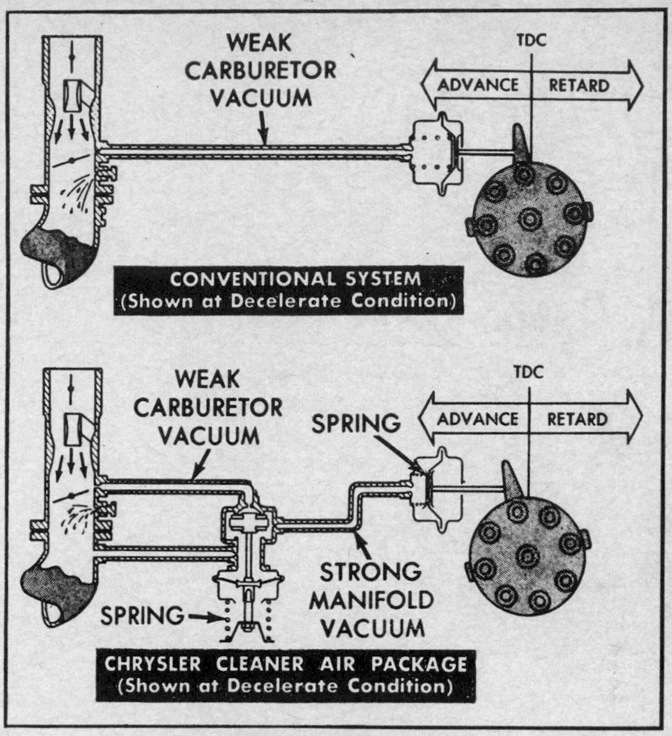

WEAK CARBURETOR VACUUM
TDC
ADVANCE
RETARD
CONVENTIONAL SYSTEM (Shown at Decelerate Condition)
WEAK CARBURETOR VACUUM
SPRING
TDC
ADVANCE
RETARD
STRONG MANIFOLD VACUUM
SPRING
CHRYSLER CLEANER AIR PACKAGE (Shown at Decelerate Condition)

Fig. 24 During deceleration

2. With engine idling, remove ventilator valve assembly from rocker arm cover. If valve is working freely, a hissing noise will be heard as air passes through the valve, and a strong vacuum should be felt when a finger is placed over the valve inlet.
3. If valve is working properly, reinstall ventilator valve assembly and remove oil filler breather cap. With engine idling, loosely hold a piece of stiff paper over the oil filler pipe. After allowing about a minute for crankcase pressure to reduce, the paper should be drawn against the filler pipe with noticeable force. If this occurs a final check should be made to be certain the valve shuttle is free.
4. Shut off engine, remove valve and shake is vigorously. A clicking noise should be heard if valve shuttle is free. If noise is heard, valve is satisfactory and no further service is necessary.
5. If valve does not click when shaken, or the paper is not drawn against the filler pipe with noticeable force, replace valve and recheck the system.

NOTE: Do not attempt to clean the valve. Replace it with a new one that has a black end washer.

6. Remove ventilator valve hose from cap and carburetor. Inspect for deposits and clean if necessary.
7. Remove breather cap and wash it thoroughly in kerosene or other suitable solvent to remove old oil and dirt. Reoil filter element.
8. Service air cleaner element.
9. Remove carburetor. Hand turn a suitable drill through the passages to dislodge foreign particles.

CAUTION: Use a drill that will clean the passages without removing any metal. Blow passages clean. It is not necessary to disassemble the carburetor for this service.

FORD IMCO SYSTEM

Improved Exhaust Emission Control System

Like the Chrysler C.A.P. System, the IMCO system consists of a specially calibrated carburetor and distributor. The carburetor provides leaner fuel mixtures and a controlled rich limit of idle mixture. In general the IMCO system requires a retarded ignition timing of the distributor to the engine. Consequently, the distributor produces some retard from the normal road load spark advance, and allows greater spark retardation when the carburetor throttle plates are in the idle position. Thus, leaner fuel mixtures and retarded (little or no advance) ignition timing effect a more complete combustion of the fuel-air mixture under these conditions.

For service procedure, refer to the Chrysler C.A.P. System section of this chapter.

RAMBLER "ENGINE MOD" SYSTEM

The "Engine Mod" (engine modification) System is used along with the original Air Guard System for exhaust control purposes. The system includes carburetor and distributor modifications and a thick composition cylinder head gasket in place of the usual steel gasket.

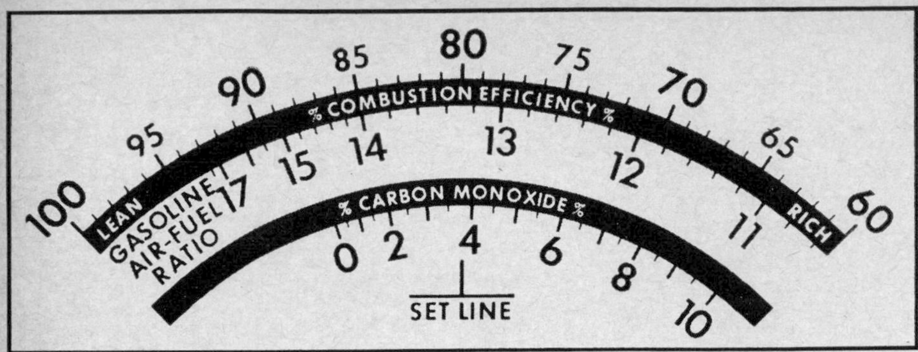

Fig. 25 Lower scale on dial, new on revised exhaust gas analyzer, indicates per cent of carbon monoxide emission from tailpipe

The carburetor incorporates an idle rich limiter which prevents the possibility of inadvertently setting the idle fuel mixture beyond the rich limit. The distributor centrifugal advance is calibrated to provide best performance and economy in the driving range and ignition timing is retarded only at idle (T.D.C.) to reduce exhaust emission level at this slow idle speed.

EXHAUST GAS ANALYZERS

Devices that analyze automobile exhaust gases have been around for quite awhile and up to now have been used mainly for testing engine efficiency and checking out tune-up jobs. Most of the more recent models, however, have added a scale reading to the meter face that indicates the percentage of carbon monoxide in the exhaust gases, Fig. 25. These new devices are almost a "must" for maintaining exhaust-control systems on new cars, starting with the 1968 models nation-wide and on California cars as far back as 1966.

Whatever blows out the exhaust pipes of these cars is going to be watched pretty closely from now on as state laws go on the books covering inspection and maintenance of these exhaust-emission control systems.

Exhaust analyzers, or combustion efficiency testers, provide an accurate method of determining a carburetor's air-fuel ratio as well as the overall relative combustion efficiency of an engine. The federal government, echoing the standards set up by California, has established the maximum hydro-carbon (unburned gasoline) emission from exhaust-controlled cars at 275 parts per million and the maximum carbon monoxide emission at 1.5 per cent by volume. To arrive at these specifications, the carburetor air-fuel ratio must be approximately 14.2 to 1 or leaner at idle speed. The overall relative combustion efficiency of an engine works out to about 86 per cent for an air-fuel ratio of 14.2 to 1.

How They Work

Exhaust analyzers and combustion testers work with exhaust gas samples taken from the vehicle's tail pipe and most of them operate on the heat conductivity principle. One part of the analyzer is exposed to a sample of exhaust gas and another part to a sample of normal air. The difference in density between the two samples varies with the fuel mixture and shows up on the meter, specially calibrated for this purpose.

Operating procedures vary, of course, with the different makes and models commercially available, but here are a few general tips on the use of exhaust analyzers and combustion testers that will help to get more accurate readings and longer service from whatever type is used.

Precautions

Be sure there are no leaks in the exhaust manifold, muffler or tail pipe. Air sucked in at an opening in the exhaust system will dilute the exhaust gases and give an inaccurate reading on the meter.

Always have the engine up to normal operating temperatures and the air cleaner in place before hooking up the analyzer to the exhaust pipe. This assures accurate readings and prevents excess moisture from entering the analyzer unit. On vehicles with dual exhausts, hook up the analyzer to the side opposite the manifold heat control valve.

Never use an exhaust analyzer on an engine while gum solvents or oils are being introduced into the combustion chamber through the carburetor or other means.

It is not advisable to use these devices on an engine that is burning oil badly. Oil leakage must first be eliminated before ideal combustion conditions can be obtained. While oil smoke from a worn engine does not have much effect on the accuracy of most exhaust testing devices, the repeated use of them on engines burning excessive oil will eventually decrease their efficiency from oil vapor fouling.

Always insert the pick-up tube as far as possible into the tail pipe. For dynamometer use or road testing under full load, some manufacturers recommend that a restricting device of some kind be placed inside the tail pipe adapter to avoid inaccurate readings because of the excess pressure.

Set Idle Mixture Accurately

The meter faces on some of the earlier exhaust analyzers include an "idle zone" placed between the 12.1 and 12.5 to 1 range. This is a little on the rich side for today's exhaust controlled engines. So be sure to set the engine idle mixture to specifications, regardless of the dial design.

One vehicle manufacturer advises that some exhaust analyzers may give an improper "rich" reading if the vehicle's air-fuel mixture is extremely lean. To check for this condition, hand-choke the carburetor or rapidly open and close the throttle a few times to enrich the normal mixture. The testing device should register the richer mixture, then move to the lean position as the rich mixture condition disappears. When the carburetor approaches the extreme lean mixture again the meter needle should return to the richer reading. All vehicles equipped with automatic transmissions should be in neutral during this test.

Engines with Air Pump

On engines equipped with the air injection type of exhaust emission control devices, disconnect the air supply hose at the air pump before any exhaust tests or adjustments are made. Some exhaust analyzers are not designed to cope with the large amounts of excess oxygen introduced into the exhaust manifold by air injection systems. They usually show an over-rich mixture because of the increased oxygen content of the exhaust gases. This condition can be interpreted as a malfunction of the vehicle's fuel system.

Do not adjust for any change in engine idle speed which may occur when the air injection system is isolated. However, note the rpm change and allow for it when adjusting the idle mixture screws within the range of the mixture limiter screws. These limiter screws are now installed on most carburetors used with engine modification types of exhaust controls.

Always check air-fuel ratios after the carburetor has been cleaned and the fuel level adjusted to specifications.

Care of Analyzer

After completing the exhaust tests, remove all moisture from the device being used. For testers that are part of a larger console, pull the exhaust hose off the panel and allow the booster pump to run for about five minutes. Drain all water from the hose, pick-up unit and condenser, if used. For individual or portable units, turn unit upside down to drain water and blow water out of pick-up unit and hose. Do not use compressed air on any part of the analyzer.

Exhaust gas analyzers are not designed for use on any two-cycle or diesel engines.

VARIABLE SPEED FANS

The fan drive clutch, Fig. 1, is a fluid coupling containing silicone oil. Fan speed is regulated by the torque-carrying capacity of the silicone oil. The more silicone oil in the coupling the greater the fan speed, and the less silicone oil the slower the fan speed.

Two types of fan drive clutches are in use. On one, Fig. 2, a bi-metallic strip and control piston on the front of the fluid coupling regulates the amount of silicone oil entering the coupling. The bi-metallic strip bows outward with a decrease in surrounding temperature and allows a piston to move outward. The piston opens a valve regulating the flow of silicone oil into the coupling from a reserve chamber. The silicone oil is returned to the reserve chamber through a bleed hole when the valve is closed.

On the other type of fan drive clutch, Fig. 3, a heat-sensitive, bi-metal spring connected to an opening plate brings about a similar result. Both units cause the fan speed to increase with a rise in temperature and to decrease as the temperature goes down.

In some cases a Flex-Fan is used instead of a Fan Drive Clutch. Flexible blades vary the volume of air being drawn through the radiator, automatically increasing the pitch at low engine speeds.

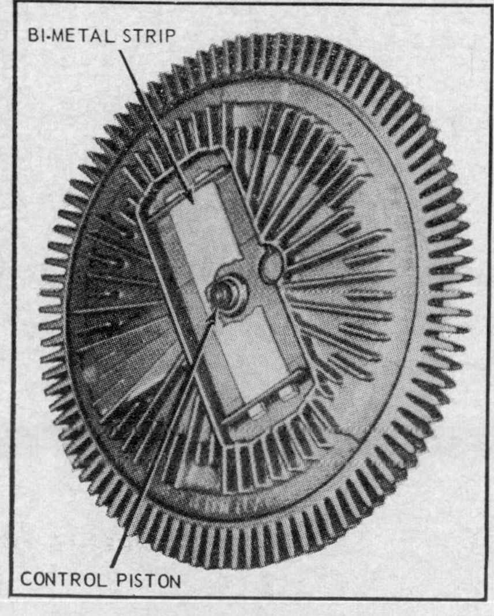

Fig. 2 Variable-speed fan with flat bi-metal thermostatic spring

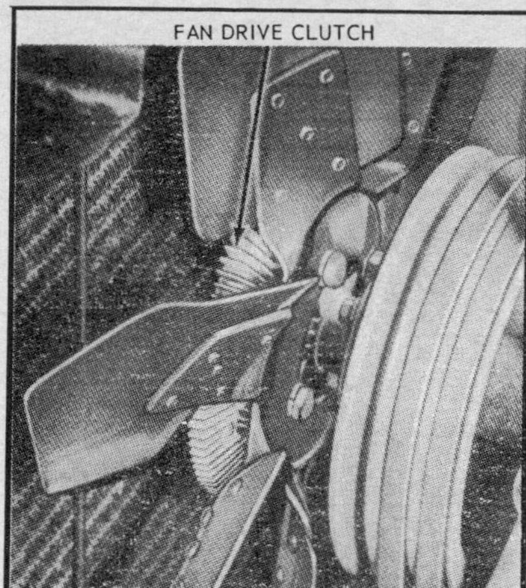

Fig. 1 Typical variable-speed fan installed

Fan Drive Clutch Test

Run the engine at a fast idle speed (1000 rpm) until normal operating temperature is reached. This process can be speeded up by blocking off the front of the radiator with cardboard. Regardless of temperatures, the unit must be operated for at least five minutes immediately before being tested.

Stop the engine and, using a glove or a cloth to protect the hand, immediately check the effort required to turn the fan. If considerable effort is required, it can be assumed that the coupling is operating satisfactorily. If very little effort is required to turn the fan, it is an indication that the coupling is not operating properly and should be replaced.

Service Procedure

CAUTION: When it becomes necessary to remove a fan clutch of the silicone fluid type, Fig. 2, the assembly must be supported in the vertical (on car) position to prevent leaks of silicone fluid from the clutch mechanism. This loss of fluid will render the fan clutch inoperative.

The removal procedure for either type of fan clutch assembly is generally the same for all cars. Merely unfasten the unit from the water pump and remove the assembly from the car.

The type of unit shown in Fig. 2 may be partially disassembled for inspection and cleaning. Take off the capscrews that hold the assembly together and separate the fan from the drive clutch. Next remove the metal strip on the front by pushing one end of it toward the fan clutch body so it clears the retaining bracket. Then push the strip to the side so that its opposite end will spring out of place. Now remove the small control piston underneath it.

Check the piston for free movement of the coupling device. If the piston sticks, clean it with emery cloth. If the bi-metal strip is damaged, replace the entire unit. These strips are not interchangeable.

When reassembling, install the control piston so that the projection on the end of it will contact the metal strip. Then install the metal strip with any identification numerals or letters facing the clutch. After reassembly, clean the clutch drive with a cloth soaked in solvent. Avoid dipping the clutch assembly in any type of liquid. Install the assembly in the reverse order of removal.

The coil spring type of fan clutch cannot be disassembled, serviced or repaired. If it does not function properly it must be replaced with a new unit.

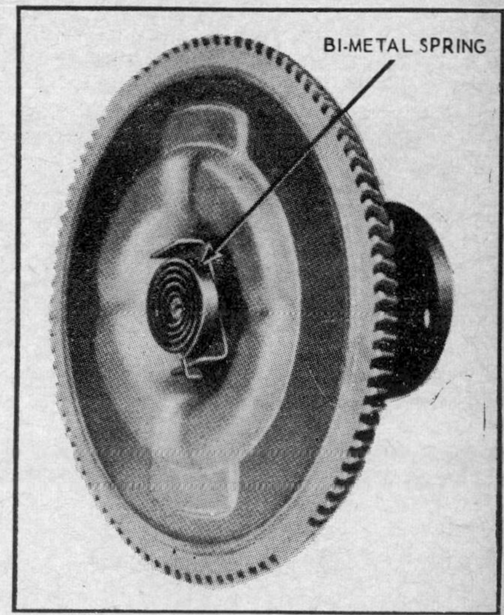

Fig. 3 Variable-speed fan with coiled bi-metal thermostatic spring

CONCEALED HEADLAMPS

VACUUM SYSTEM

Vacuum-operated headlamp covers work much the same from model to model. Engine vacuum is tapped off the engine's intake manifold and is routed by means of a hose through a check valve to a distribution valve. The distribution valve is mechanically controlled by the headlight switch. Its purpose is to distribute vacuum to a motor (or motors) which operate the retractable covers. The distribution valve also routes vacuum to a reservoir. A third function is to receive a vacuum hose from the cover motor which is a relief line.

When the headlight switch is turned to full "ON" position, the distribution valve routes vacuum to the "open" side of vacuum motor diaphragm. The vacuum motor activates the linkage to open the covers. When the headlight switch is turned to "PARK" or "OFF" position, the distribution valve routes vacuum to the "close" side of the vacuum motor, allowing the covers to close.

The vacuum reservoir stores up vacuum during engine operation. This permits opening and closing of the covers for a limited number of cycles when the engine is not running. If reservoir vacuum is depleted, the covers will not function with the engine shut off. Pre-1968 and early 1968 vacuum-operated headlamp covers are equipped with external hinge springs attached to each cover. These are over-center type springs that provide tension to keep covers opened or closed. When headlights are in use, vacuum overcomes this tension to activate the covers so they will open. With this external spring type set-up, if there is a vacuum loss on the road, covers can be opened or closed by hand if the headlight switch is turned on or off.

To open the headlamp doors on the 1968 Chrysler 300, the torsion bar must be removed from the slotted areas in the crank assemblies. Then the headlamp door is rotated to the fully open position and the retainer locks moved down to hold the doors in the open position.

The National Highway Safety Bureau now requires that springs must be placed inside the control motor which will allow covers to open automatically when vacuum fails.

Trouble Shooting

When the cover operation is faulty, first check the vacuum hoses. There are four routings: A hose from manifold to control motor, a return hose from control motor to the distribution valve, a hose from the distribution valve to the headlight switch, and a branch hose to the vacuum reservoir. Hoses are usually color-coded for easy identification.

Examine all hoses for splits which occur most often around connections. Also, look for kinked or pinched hoses, a condition which often occurs when retaining clips are too tight, thus blocking off the vacuum flow.

If inspection reveals that all the hoses are satisfactory, make a section-by-section check of the system with a vacuum gauge. However, first make sure that the engine vacuum is in the normal range of 18 to 21 inches. If engine vacuum is adequate, take another vacuum reading at the control motor. If the car being serviced has two motors, test them both.

Disconnect and hook the vacuum gauge to the hose. With engine running, if the gauge indicates at least 14 inches of vacuum, the problem is in front of the hook-up—probably inside the control motor, which should be replaced, or because of a binding cover or jammed linkage.

If the vacuum gauge indicates less than 14 inches, check vacuum at the vacuum reservoir, distribution valve, check valve and at each hose connection. Other than a defective hose, the most likely cause of the trouble is the check valve.

ELECTRIC SYSTEM

The electric system is activated by turning on the headlight switch, which sends current through wires to an electric motor or motors to open and close the covers by a mechanical linkage.

Trouble Shooting

Failure of the system can be caused by a faulty switch, motor or in the wiring. Sometimes the fault is due to a dirty linkage, causing it to jam. First, clean the linkage thoroughly and then lubricate it. Make sure that the covers themselves are not binding against their housings.

Trouble shoot the electrical part of the system by connecting a jumper wire directly from the battery to the electric motor (or motors). If the covers operate, the trouble most likely is a defective headlight switch. Test the headlight switch with an ammeter. If the switch is eliminated as the cause of the trouble, check the wiring; look for loose connections, broken wires or terminals.

In some cases a motor will seize due to stuck brushes. Try rapping the motor housing to free them up. Should this fail, remove the motor for repairs or install a new or rebuilt one.

AUTOMATIC LEVEL CONTROL

GENERAL MOTORS SYSTEM

The Automatic Level Control System, used in conjunction with Superlift shock absorbers, maintains correct rear trim height of the car under varying load conditions. The Superlift shock absorbers are connected to pressure lines with a "Tee" where a fill valve is located. The shocks are inflated with (or deflated) of compressed air at any gas station to obtain the vehicle level desired with any given load change.

The automatic level system and Superlift shock absorbers supplies its own compressed air. The system, Fig. 1, consists of a vacuum operated air compressor with pressure regulator and integral storage tank, vacuum line to engine, air intake filter and lines, and a height control valve.

The compressor, a two-stage type requiring no lubrication, is designed to operate off engine vacuum to replenish air used from the reservoir. As the compressor cycles, the reservoir air pressure gradually increases (causing a back pressure on the second stage piston) until it equals the engine vacuum pull against the diaphragm. At this point, a balanced condition is reached and the unit stops operating. After reservoir pressure drops due to system air usage the compressor again begins to cycle and replenish the reservoir.

A pressure regulator is attached to the output side of the reservoir. It regulates Superlift supply pressure to approximately 125 psi. The rear standing height is automatically maintained at nearly constant position by a control valve, Fig. 2, attached to the rear suspension crossmember. A link attaches the valve lever to the suspension upper control link. When sufficient load is added to deflect the rear suspension at least ½", the control valve admits air to the Superlifts which raises the car to level. When load is removed and the car rises, the control valve exhausts air from the Superlifts which lowers the car to level. A 4-to 18-second time delay mechanism inside the control valve housing prevents transfer of air when the lever is moved during normal ride motions. In this manner the control valve responds to actual load changes of sufficient duration to overcome the delay action.

The Superlift, Fig. 3, is essentially a conventional shock absorber enclosed in an air chamber. A pliable nylon reinforced boot seals the dust tube (air dome) to the reservoir tube (air piston). The unit will extend when inflated and retract when deflated by the control valve. An 8 to 15 psi air pressure is maintained in the Superlift at all times to minimize boot friction. This is accomplished by a check valve in the exhaust fitting on the control valve.

TROUBLE SHOOTING GUIDE

Car Loaded, Will Not Rise

1. External damage or breakage.
2. Line leak.
3. Linkage to overtravel lever in wrong hole.
4. Control valve setting incorrect.
5. Defective component.

Car Loaded, Raises to Level, Then Leaks Down

1. Line leak.
2. Control valve exhaust leak.
3. Superlift leak.
4. Control valve leak.

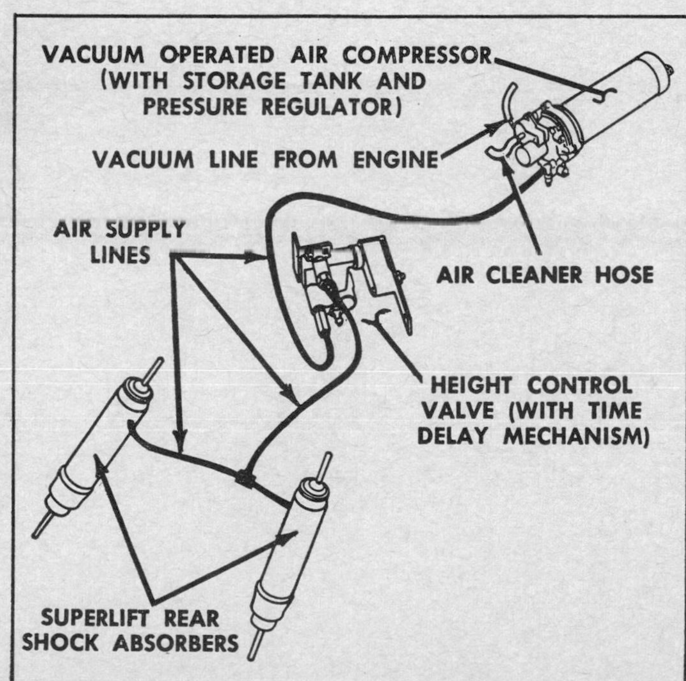

Fig. 1 Schematic diagram of General Motors Automatic Level Control System

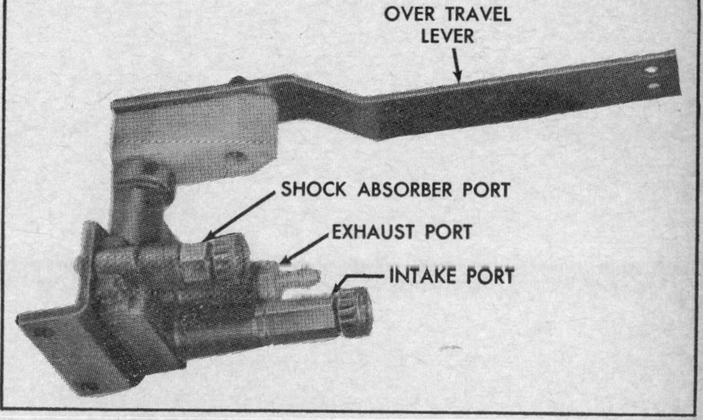

Fig. 2 Height control valve

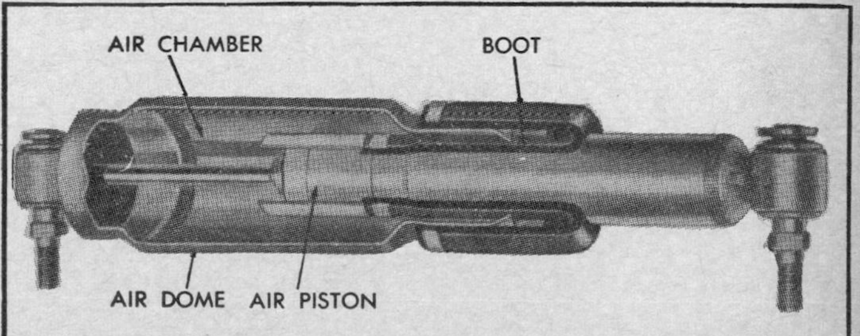

Fig. 3 Superlift shock absorber

Car Loaded, Raises Partially

1. Load excessive (over 500 lbs at axle) on cars with special springs.
2. Control valve setting incorrect.
3. Low supply pressure.

Car Unloaded, Rides too High, Will Not Come Down

1. Control valve setting incorrect.
2. Improper springs.
3. External damage or breakage.
4. Linkage to overtravel in wrong hole.
5. Defective control valve.

Car Rises When Loaded but Leaks Down While Driving

1. Time delay mechanism not functioning properly.

CHECKS & ADJUSTMENTS

Quick Check of System

1. Record rear trim height of empty car (measure from center of rear bumper to ground).
2. Add weight equivalent to two-passenger load to rear of car. Car should begin to level in 4 to 15 seconds, and final position should be (plus or minus) ½″ of measured dimension.
3. Remove weight. After 4 to 18 seconds car should begin to settle. Final unloaded position should be within approximately (plus or minus) ½″ of the original measured dimension.

NOTE: To service the system it will be necessary to secure the gauge set shown in Fig. 4 or make one out of the materials illustrated.

Compressor Output Test

1. With all accessories off, run engine until engine settles to hot idle speed. Then turn off ignition.
2. Deflate system through service valve, then remove high pressure line at regulator adapter and connect test gauge.
3. Inflate reservoir to 70 psi through service valve.
4. Observe test gauge for evidence of compressor air leak.
5. If leaking, proceed to leak-test compressor reservoir and regulator. If not leaking, continue this test.
6. With engine running at hot idle speed, observe reservoir build-up for five minutes. Reservoir pressure should build up to a minimum of 90 psi.
7. If compressor fails to cycle, make sure vacuum and air intake lines are open and unobstructed before removing compressor for repair.
8. If build-up is too slow, repair compressor.
9. Satisfactory build-up indicates system problems to be in the control section. However, again observe the test gauge for evidence of an air leak and proceed accordingly.

Regulator Test & Adjustment

1. Performance test the regulator with a known good compressor on the car.
2. Deflate system through service valve, remove line at regulator and connect test gauge at regulator adapter.
3. Inflate reservoir through service valve to maximum pressure available. If less than 140 psi, start engine to build-up reservoir to this pressure.
4. Regulated pressure on test gauge should build up to 100-130 psi and hold steady within this range.
5. Recheck regulated pressure by momentarily depressing valve core on test gauge and observe gauge reading.
6. If regulated pressure exceeds 130 psi, replace regulator as a unit.

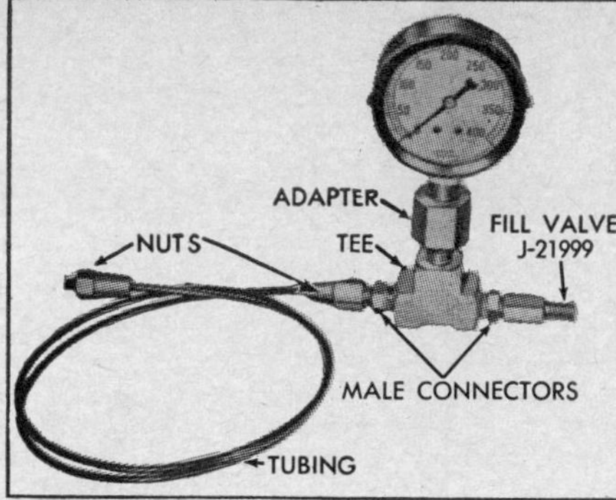

Fig. 4 Test gauge set (Kent-Moore No. J-22124)

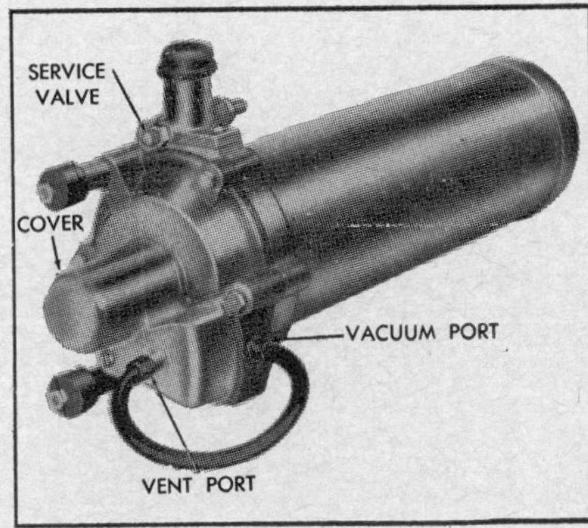

Fig. 5 Assembly leak test preparation

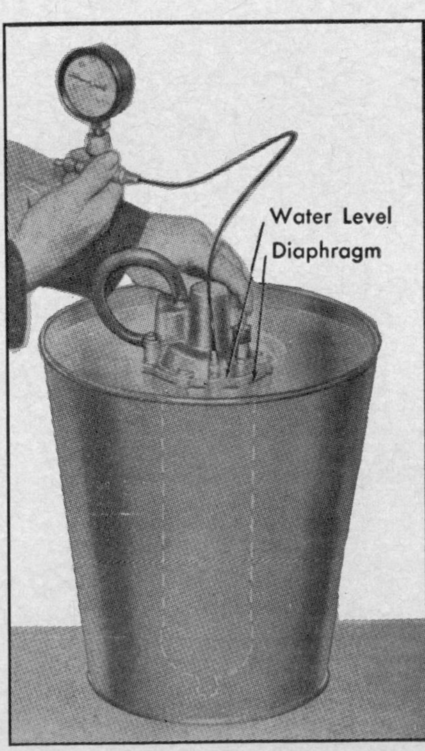

Fig. 6 Checking compressor, reservoir and regulator for leaks

Control Valve Test

Exhaust—Superlifts Inflated

1. Disconnect control valve lever from link.
2. Hold lever down in exhaust position until Superlifts deflate or for a minimum of 15 seconds.
3. If Superlifts deflate, perform Intake Check.
4. If Superlifts do not deflate, remove exhaust adapter from control valve and hold lever down as in Step 2. Replace adapter, O-ring and filter if this deflates Superlifts.
5. Replace control valve if none of the above steps solve problem.

Intake Check—Reservoir Pressure 125 psi Minimum

1. Disconnect overtravel lever from link.
2. Hold lever up in intake position until Superlifts inflate or for a minimum of 15 seconds.
3. If Superlifts inflate and hold, proceed to Time Delay Test.
4. If Superlifts inflate and then leak down, perform leak test on lines and fittings and then on Superlifts and control valve. Repair or replace as required.

Time Delay Test—Reservoir Pressure 125 psi Minimum

1. Record rear trim height of empty car (measure from rear bumper to ground).
2. Add weight equivalent to two-passenger load to rear of car. Car should begin to level in 4 to 18 seconds and final position should be approximately (plus or minus) ½″ of dimension measured above.
3. Remove weight. After 4 to 18 seconds, car should begin to settle. Final unloaded position should be (plus or minus) ½″ of dimension measured above.
4. Replace valve if time delay is not within 4 to 18 seconds.

Trim Adjustment On Car

Trim adjustment should be performed with a full gas tank or the equivalent in load at rate of 6 lbs. per gallon.

Preparation

1. Raise car with rear axle supported.
2. Remove Superlift line at control valve, Fig. 2.
3. Connect a Fill Valve Assembly (see Fig. 4).

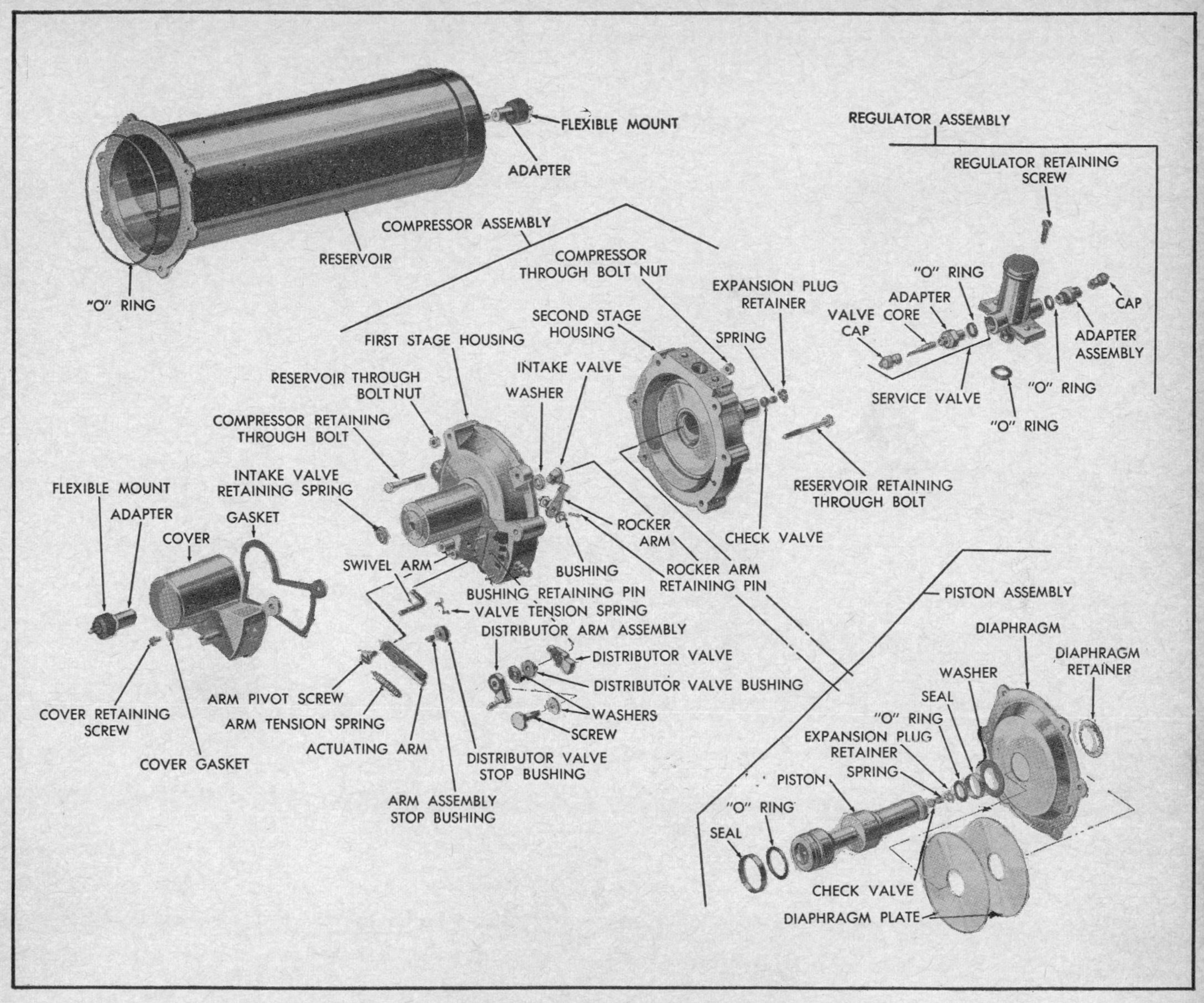

Fig. 7 Exploded view of General Motors compressor, reservoir and regulator

4. Inflate Superlifts to 8 to 18 psi. Jounce car to neutralize suspension.
5. Connect test gauge to Superlift adapter on control valve and attach air pressure source (80 to 110 psi).

Adjustment

1. Loosen overtravel lever adjusting nut.
2. Hold overtravel body down in exhaust position until air escapes from exhaust valve port.
3. Slowly move overtravel body and tighten nut at the point of minimum air bleed. With nut tight, a slight continuous air bleed should be noticeable.

Restore System

1. Remove test gauge and air pressure source from Superlift adapter.
2. Remove Fill Valve Assembly from Superlift line and reconnect line to control valve.
3. Lower car and inflate reservoir through service valve.

Leak Tests

Compressor, Reservoir & Regulator

1. Remove assembly intact.
2. Connect test gauge to regulator. Inflate reservoir through service valve to 80-100 psi.
3. Route an 8" rubber hose between vacuum and vent ports, Fig. 5.
4. Submerge in water, Fig. 6, and observe for air leaks at: a) Reservoir weld seam. b) Reservoir-to-compressor O-ring. c) Regulator-to-compressor O-ring. d) Regulator boot defective. e) Boot internal O-ring defective. f) Diaphragm between 1st and 2nd stage housing. g) Tightening thru bolts may correct leak. h) Cover gasket and retainer screw. A few bubbles here is not a leak. A continuous stream indicates defective compressor check valves. i) Service valve. j) Test gauge connections.
5. Correct any leaks detected by either tightening screws or replacing parts.

Control Valve

1. Remove control valve from car.
2. Clean exterior of valve thoroughly.
3. Connect test gauge and air pressure source to intake adapter and open air pressure (80-110 psi).
4. Submerge unit in water. No air should escape if overtravel lever is in "neutral" position. If bubbles escape from Superlift port, replace control valve.
5. Shut off air pressure and detach test gauge from air intake port. Plug intake port with Fill Valve Assembly.
6. Connect test gauge to Superlift port and open air pressure.

7. With overtravel lever in "neutral" position, no air should escape. If bubbles escape from exhaust port, replace control valve.
8. If air escapes around edge of cover plate, tighten screws or replace gasket.
9. Remove control valve from water. Actuate overtravel lever to expel any water from unit.
10. Shut off air pressure and remove line from Superlift port.

Lines and Fittings

1. Disconnect overtravel lever from link.
2. Hold lever up in intake position for maximum Superlift inflation and release.
3. Leak check all connections with a soap and water solution.

Superlifts

1. Disconnect lines and remove unit from car.
2. Inflate individually to 50-60 psi, utilizing Fill Valve (see Fig. 4). Submerge in water and observe unit for leaks.
3. Install Superlifts.

COMPRESSOR SERVICE

Removal

1. Raise front end of car on hoist or jack stands.
2. For identification purpose, place a piece of tape on the air intake line attached to smooth end fitting on compressor, Fig. 5.
3. Remove air intake and vacuum hoses.
4. Unfasten compressor brackets from mounting points.
5. Remove compressor with brackets attached.
6. Deflate system, using service valve, and remove high pressure fitting at pressure regulator.
7. Remove brackets from compressor.

NOTE: The compressor is a precision-built mechanism, Fig. 7. If an overhaul is contemplated, all parts should be handled carefully. Take care to prevent entrance of dirt or foreign matter. Do not lubricate as unit is designed to run dry.

Installation

1. Attach brackets to compressor.
2. Install compressor to its mounting.
3. Attach air intake and vacuum hoses.
4. Secure air line to compressor pressure regulator.
5. Lower car.
6. Inflate reservoir to 140 psi through compressor service valve.
7. Be sure that vacuum and air intake lines are not rubbing against adjacent parts to prevent chafing.

FORD SYSTEM

This device, Fig. 1, is a supplement to the rear coil spring suspension and will automatically maintain the rear standing height of the vehicle at an approximate constant position compensating for varying loaded conditions. The system consists of a vacuum-operated compressor, control valve, air cylinders and the connecting lines and fittings. In the event of accidental air loss, the conventional coil springs will support the vehicle.

The system air compressor is operated off the engine vacuum and will supply a maximum pressure of 20 psi through the control valve to the air cylinders. The control valve is mounted on the cross-member and senses rear riding height position through a link attached to the rear suspension upper arm, Fig. 2.

The control valve is actuated by adding or removing weight from the vehicle. Adding weight opens the valve and allows air to enter the air cylinder in each rear coil spring to raise the vehicle, commensurate with the additional weight. Likewise as the weight is removed, the control valve will exhaust the air from the cylinders through an exhaust port commensurate with the weight being removed.

A dampening piston incorporated in the height control valve acts as a time delay mechanism within the valve body. This prevents rapid air transfer to and from the air cylinders under normal operation while the vehicle is in motion.

A check valve is also provided in the exhaust port of the height control valve to retain 2 to 4 psi residual pressure in the air cylinders when there is little or no load to prevent the coil springs from scuffing them.

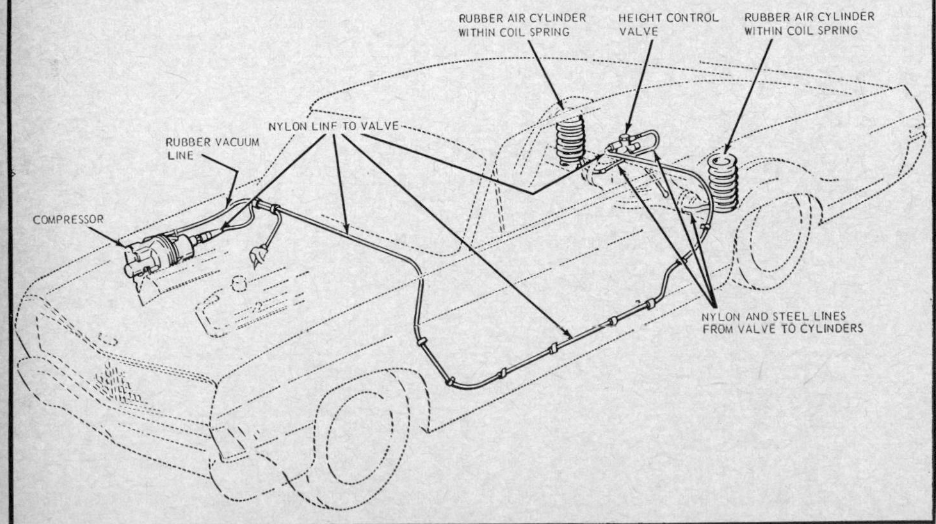

Fig. 1 Ford air leveling system

The air cylinders are made of ¼″ thick butyl rubber and are encased in the rear coil springs.

CHECKING SYSTEM

Quick Check

1. Fill fuel tank or simulate the load at the rate of 6 lbs for each gallon of fuel, otherwise the vehicle should be empty.
2. Add a two-passenger load to the rear bumper or tailgate. Vehicle should lower when weight is added.
3. Start engine and observe rear of vehicle while maintaining load at rear bumper or tailgate.
4. If vehicle does not raise when engine is started or within two minutes, the system is not operating properly.
5. If the vehicle raises, remove the load and observe the rear of the vehicle. Air should then exhaust through the height control valve to lower the vehicle.

Compressor Output Check

1. Disconnect output line from compressor.
2. Connect pressure gauge to compressor.
3. Close one valve and open the other.
4. Start engine and note compressor output on gauge. If it is 12 to 20 psi, with a minimum engine vacuum of 15 inches, it can be considered normal.
5. Remove gauge and connect line.

Compressor-to-Control Valve Line Leak Check

1. Disconnect inlet fitting from height control valve.
2. Disconnect air inlet line from height control valve.
3. Connect pressure gauge to line.

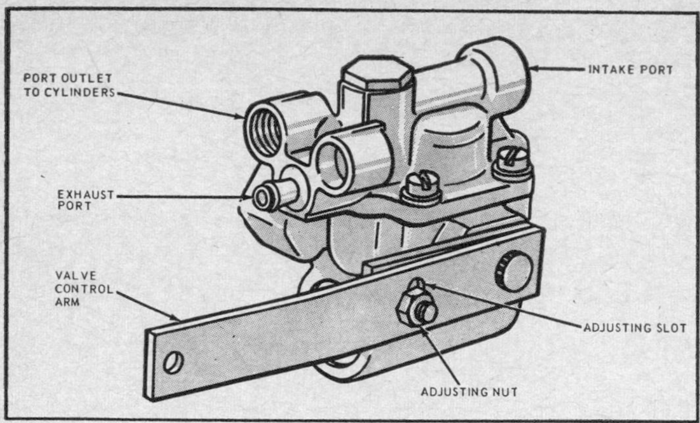

Fig. 2 Height control valve

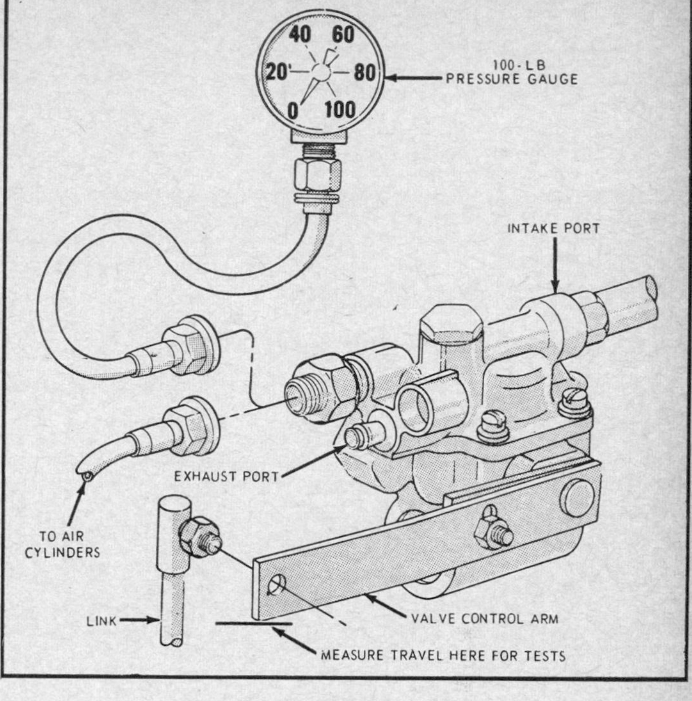

Fig. 4 Test gauge installation

4. Start engine and note pressure reading, which should be 12 to 20 psi.
5. Stop engine and observe reading on gauge. It should hold the maximum reading if line is not leaking.
6. Repair line as required to stop leak.

Trim Adjustment

1. Trim height is the distance between top of rear axle to bottom surface of frame side rail, Fig. 3. Raise vehicle on a hoist or jack that will support rear axle.
2. Load rear of vehicle as required to obtain the specified trim height, Fig. 3.
3. Disconnect link from height control valve lever, Fig. 4.
4. Disconnect air line from inlet port of height control valve.
5. Connect test gauge to inlet port of height control valve.
6. Working from a 20 psi air source, hold height control valve lever in raised position for 60 seconds while inflating the system. Lower lever to the exhaust position. Hold lever in this position until air stops exhausting. This should leave approximately 2 to 4 psi in the air cylinders if the check valve is functioning properly.
7. Jounce vehicle to neutralize system.
8. Connect link to height control valve lever.
9. Readjust vehicle trim height to 4 13/16″ if not at this dimension.
10. Loosen height control valve lever adjusting nut and allow it to neutralize itself. After the lever is neutralized, tighten adjusting nut.
11. Remove gauge and added weight from vehicle.
12. Connect air line to height control valve and check for leaks.

Control Valve Check

Exhaust Check, Air Cylinders Inflated

1. Disconnect link from height control valve lever.
2. Hold lever down (exhaust position) until air cylinders deflate, or for a minimum of 30 seconds. Release arm and allow it to return to neutral position.
3. If cylinders deflate perform a trim adjustment.
4. If cylinders do not deflate, disconnect air cylinder line at height control valve to make sure that there is no restriction in line.
5. Connect air cylinder line to control valve and link to lever.

Intake Check, Compressor at Engine Idle

1. Disconnect link from height control valve lever.
2. Hold lever up (intake position) until cylinders inflate or for a minimum of 60 seconds, then release lever and allow it to return to neutral position.
3. If cylinders inflate and hold perform a trim adjustment.
4. If cylinders inflate then leak down, perform a leak test on lines or fittings then check air cylinders.
5. If cylinders do not inflate, disconnect compressor output line at the height control valve and check it for restrictions.
6. If lines and fittings are satisfactory, check height control valve for leaks.
7. Connect link to control valve lever.

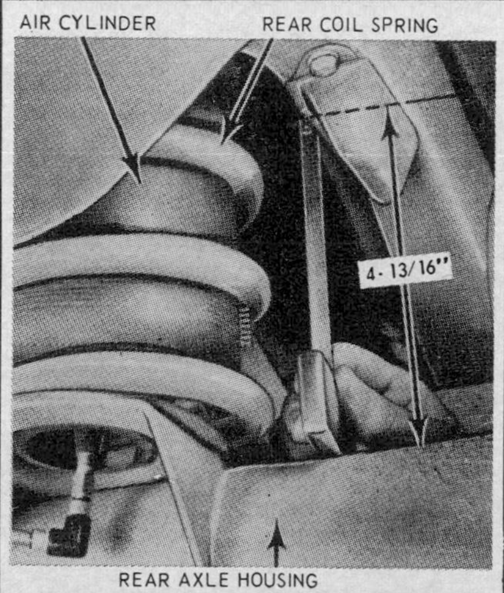

Fig. 3 Measuring trim adjustment. Ford and Mercury 4 13/16", 7 3/8" for Lincoln

Time Delay Check

1. Disconnect link from control valve lever.
2. Disconnect both air lines from height control valve, Fig. 4.
3. Connect test gauge to intake port of control valve. Attach a 20 psi air source to gauge.
4. Move control valve lever downward approximately one inch from the neutral position. One inch distance is measured at end of lever.
5. Move lever upward two inches, at the same time start timing the number of seconds before air is expelled from air cylinder port. The time delay should be from 1 to 6 seconds. Repeat check to obtain an accurate reading. This operation is for air intake time only.
6. Connect air cylinder line to control valve outlet port.
7. Hold control valve lever in raised position and charge air cylinders with 15 to 20 psi air pressure from intake port of control valve.
8. Move lever to neutral position.
9. Move control valve lever upward approximately one inch from neutral position. One inch dimension is measured from end of lever. Quickly move lever downward two inches, at the same time start timing the number of seconds before air is expelled from exhaust port. The time delay should be from 1 to 6 seconds. Repeat check to obtain accurate reading.

10. If either delay is not within specifications, replace height control valve.

System Leak Test

1. Start engine and allow pressure to build up in system.
2. Apply a soap and water solution to all fittings and lines that are suspected to be leaking. If air bubbles appear at any fitting or section of line, make required repairs to eliminate the leak.

TROUBLE DIAGNOSIS

Vehicle Loaded, Will Not Raise

1. External damage or breakage.
2. Line or cylinder leak.
3. Pump inoperative or output inadequate.
4. Control valve setting incorrect.
5. Inadequate time delay.

Vehicle Loaded, Raises Partially

1. Load excessive (over 250 lbs) at axle.
2. Height control valve setting incorrect.
3. Low supply pressure.

Vehicle Unloaded, Rides too High, Won't Come Down

1. Control valve setting incorrect.
2. External damage or breakage.
3. Defective control valve.

Compressor Cycles Continuously

1. Line leak.
2. Air cylinder ruptured.
3. Inadequate time; may take five minutes to balance at idle.

Compressor Does Not Cycle

1. Vacuum hose off or leaking.
2. Pump internal failure.
3. Lines or hoses restricted.
4. Pump filter clogged.

Vehicle Loaded, Raises to Level and Then Leaks Down

1. Line leak.
2. Control valve exhaust leak.
3. Air cylinder leak.
4. Control valve exhaust leak.
5. If leak down while driving, check for control valve time delay less than one second.

ELECTRONIC IGNITION SYSTEMS

DELCO-REMY SYSTEMS

Two types of electronic controlled ignition systems have been developed by the Delco-Remy Division of General Motors Corp. One, introduced in 1967, is the Capacitor Discharge (CD) type, and the Transistor Controlled type used prior to 1967.

Both systems employ an identical Magnetic Pulse Breakerless distributor. This unit, Fig. 1, resembles a conventional distributor. However, in the Magnetic Pulse distributor, an iron timer core replaces the conventional breaker cam, Fig. 2. The timer core has the same number of equally spaced projections as engine cylinders. The timer core rotates inside a magnetic pick-up assembly, which replaces the conventional breaker plate, contact point set and condenser assembly.

The magnetic pick-up assembly consists of a ceramic permanent magnet, a pole piece and pick-up coil. The pole piece is a metal plate having equally spaced internal teeth, one tooth for each cylinder in the engine. The magnetic pick-up assembly is mounted over the main bearing on the distributor housing and is actuated by the vacuum control unit to provide vacuum advance. The timer core is moved by conventional advance weights to provide centrifugal (mechanical) advance.

Ignition Pulse Amplifier

Transistor Controlled Type

This type amplifier, Fig. 3, consists primarily of transistors, resistors, diodes and condensers mounted on a printed circuit panel board. Since there are no moving parts, the control unit is a completely static assembly.

Fig. 4 shows a wiring diagram showing the complete circuit. Note that there are two separate ballast resistors used. The resistor connected directly to the switch is by-passed during cranking, whereas the other resistor is always in the circuit. The use of two resistors permits the required value of resistance to be by-passed during cranking.

In order to fire the spark plug, it is necessary to induce a high voltage in the ignition coil secondary winding by closing and opening the circuit to the coil primary winding. When the switch is closed (engine not running) current flows through part of the circuit. The current comes from the battery, through the switch and ballast resistor to the amplifier unit. Current then flows to two transistors and three resistors, thence to the coil primary winding and ballast resistor to ground, thus completing the circuit back to the battery.

Capacitor Discharge Amplifier

This type amplifier, Fig. 5, consists of transistors, diodes, resistors, a thyristor and a transformer. These components are mounted on a printed circuit panel board. Like the earlier amplifier, it is a solid state unit with no moving parts.

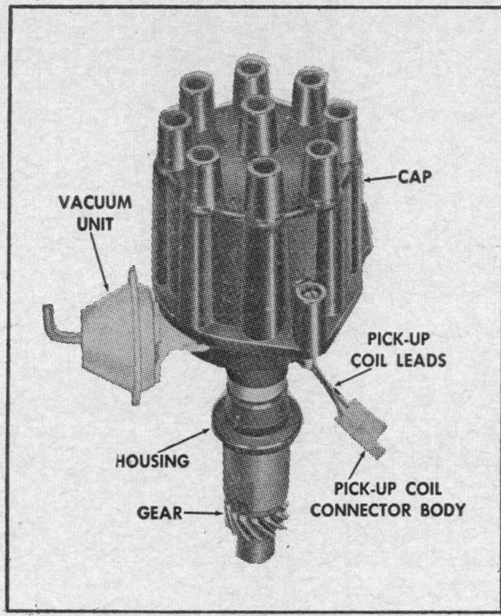

Fig. 1 Delco-Remy Magnetic Pulse distributor

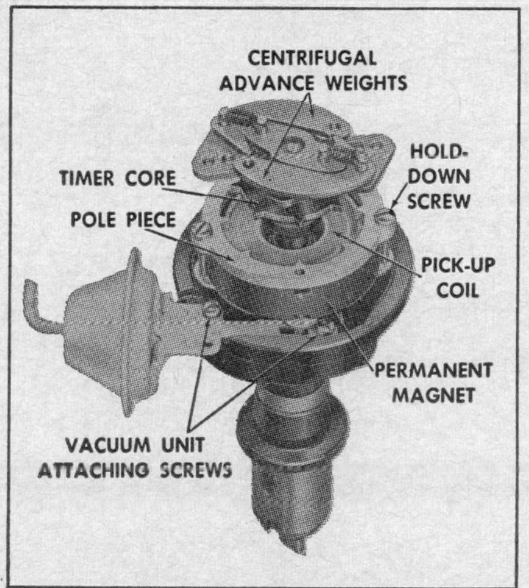

Fig. 2 Magnetic Pulse distributor components

With a capacity of delivering 30,000 volts almost instantaneously, it can fire burned, fouled or even damp spark plugs. As a result, spark plug life is extended several times longer than normal in conventional systems. Because of the extremely high voltage it delivers (about one-third more than the conventional system) the CD system offers faster cold weather starting as well as improved ignition performance throughout the engine speed range.

In the CD system, the ignition coil primary is connected across a high voltage capacitor (condenser). The capacitor is charged to about 300 volts during the time the spark plugs are not firing. On impulse signal voltage from the distributor, the capacitor discharges this high voltage into the ignition coil primary.

Due to the transformer action in the coil, this high voltage primary is increased many times to produce the high voltage secondary to fire the spark plug. Fig. 6 shows a typical circuit diagram.

Voltage is supplied to the transformer which operates through a rectifying bridge circuit of four diodes to keep the capacitor charged. A zener diode limits this charge to 300 volts. This capacitor voltage is maintained at its maximum value during cranking even though battery voltage may be well below its normal 12 volts. This is due to the transformer which acts as a free-running oscillator during cranking. The adverse effect on ignition normally present in conventional ignition systems, especially during cold weather cranking, are therefore eliminated in the CD ignition system.

As the engine turns, the vanes on the rotating timer core in the distributor line up with the internal teeth on the pole piece. This establishes a magnetic path through the center of the pick-up coil. This voltage (after amplification) is applied at the gate of the thyristor, causing it to turn on. The charged capacitor then discharges through the thyristor and primary winding of the special ignition coil, inducing the high voltage in the secondary winding to fire the spark plug. This special ignition coil acts as a step-up transformer to fire the spark plug when the primary current *increases*. This contrasts with the conventional ignition system in which the secondary voltage is induced when the distributor contacts open and the primary current *decreases*.

Periodic Service

Since the amplifier in both systems is completely static, and the distributor shaft and bushings have permanent-type lubrication, no periodic maintenance is required. The distributor lower bushing is lubricated by engine oil through a splash hole in the distributor housing, and a housing cavity next to the upper bushing contains a supply of lubricant which will last between engine overhaul periods. At time of engine overhaul, the upper bushing may be lubricated by removing the plastic seal and then adding SAE 20 oil to the packing in the cavity. A new plastic seal will be required since the old one will be damaged during removal.

Trouble Shooting Procedure

Faulty engine performance usually will be evidenced by one of the following conditions: 1. Engine will not run at all.

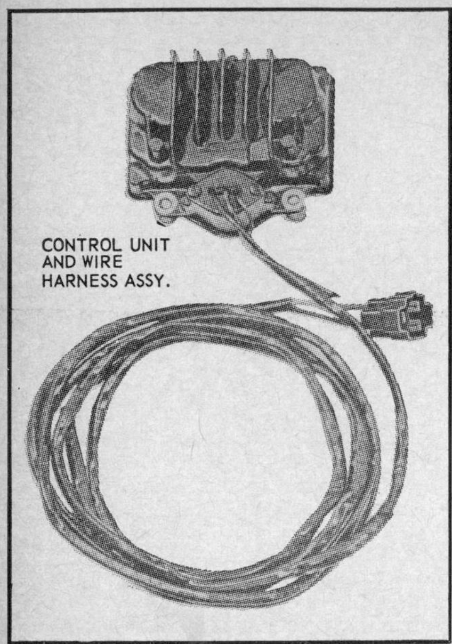

Fig. 3 Transistor controlled amplifier

2. Engine will start but not run. 3. Engine will miss or surge. *The special coil used in both systems cannot be tested on a conventional coil tester.*

Engine will not run at all

To determine if the ignition system is operating, hold one spark plug lead about 1/4 inch from the engine block and crank the engine. If sparking occurs, the trouble most likely is not ignition. If sparking does not occur, and the vehicle fuel system is satisfactory, check the ignition system. The spark plugs, wiring, distributor cap and rotor can be checked in the conventional manner. Only the coil requires a different procedure.

The special coil can be checked for primary and secondary winding continuity with an ohmmeter: With leads disconnected from coil, connect ohmmeter across primary terminals. If reading is infinite, winding is open. To check the secondary, connect ohmmeter to high voltage center tower and coil case. An infinite reading means coil secondary is open. *When checking secondary, use middle or high resistance range on ohmmeter.*

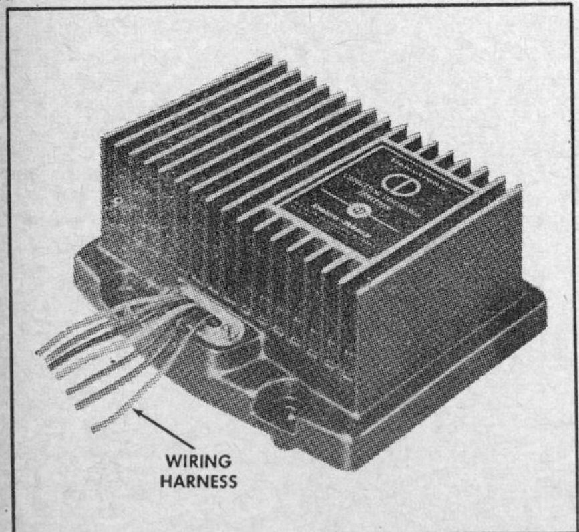

Fig. 5 Capacitor Discharge (CD) amplifier unit

Checking Amplifier:

1. Temporarily connect a jumper lead from amplifier housing to a good ground.
2. If engine now will start and run, the amplifier is not properly grounded.
3. Detach positive and negative leads from coil. *Note carefully the color code so wires can be reconnected in the same manner.*
4. Connect a bulb between the two leads, Fig. 7.
5. Crank engine.
6. If bulb flickers on and off, amplifier is operating properly. In this case, recheck secondary system for the cause of "no run" condition.
7. If bulb does not flicker on and off, check distributor.

Distributor checks:

1. On CD system, be sure that the two distributor leads are connected to distributor connector body, Fig. 8.
2. With distributor connector disconnected from harness connector, connect an ohmmeter (1), Fig. 9, to the two terminals on distributor connector.
3. Connect a test stand vacuum source to the distributor and observe ohmmeter reading throughout vacuum range. (Distributor need not be removed from engine.)
4. Any reading outside the 550-750 ohm range indicates a defective pick-up coil in distributor.
5. Remove one ohmmeter (2) lead, Fig. 9, from connector body and connect to ground.
6. Observe ohmmeter reading throughout vacuum range.
7. Any reading less than infinite indicates a defective pick-up coil.
8. Reconnect harness connector to distributor connector.

Continuity checks-CD system

Carefully inspect all wiring connections to be sure that they are clean and tight. If satisfactory, disconnect amplifier No. 3 and No. 4 leads, Fig. 8, from the two connectors, then proceed as follows:

1. Connect voltmeter from ground to No. 4 connector lead.
2. Turn switch to "Start" position.
3. If reading is zero, circuit is open between connector body and battery.
4. If reading is obtained, connect voltmeter from ground to No. 3 connector lead.
5. Turn switch to the run position.
6. If reading is zero, circuit is open between connector body and switch.
7. If reading is obtained, replace amplifier.

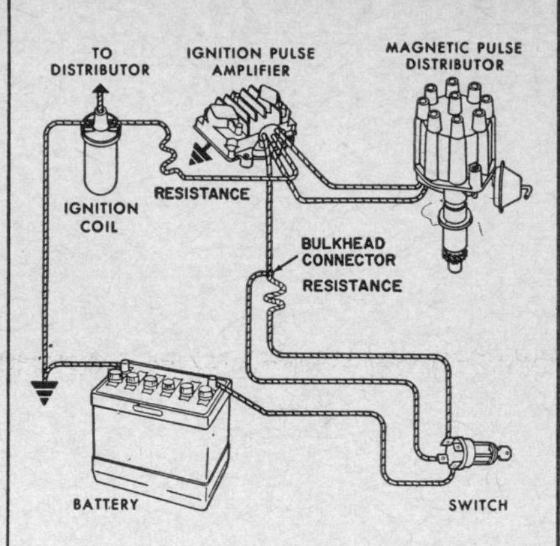

Fig. 4 Circuit diagram of transistor controlled system

Engine will start but not run-CD System

If engine starts but then stops when switch is returned to the run position, proceed as follows:

1. Be sure that leads are properly connected to No. 3 lead connector body.
2. If satisfactory, connect a voltmeter from ground to the terminal con-

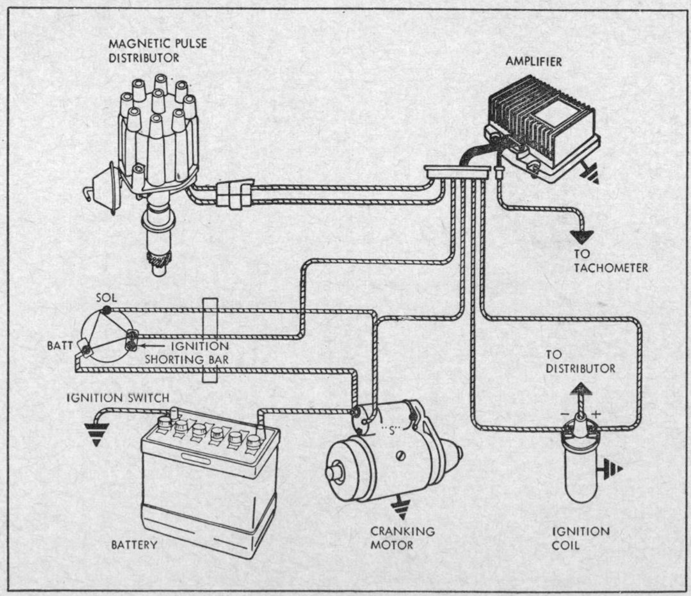

Fig. 6 CD ignition circuit (typical)

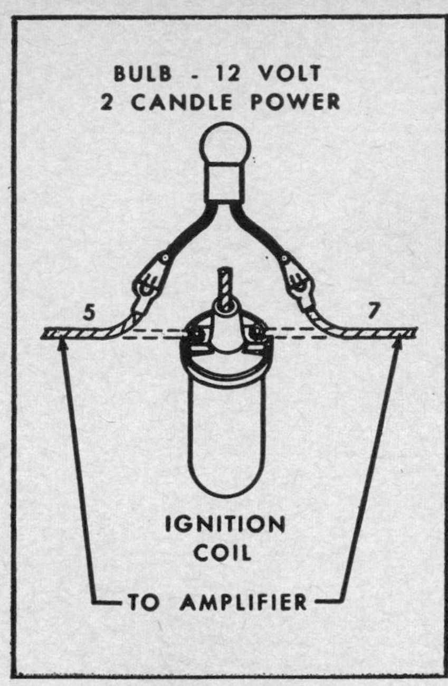

Fig. 7 Amplifier output test

nector inside the connector.
3. Turn switch to run position.
4. If reading is zero, lead between connector and ignition switch is open.
5. If reading is obtained, replace amplifier.

Engine miss or surge:

The vehicle fuel system should be checked in the usual manner. If satisfactory, check the ignition system in the usual manner except the special coil which should be checked with a ohmmeter as described above.

A poorly ground amplifier can cause an engine miss or surge. If it is properly grounded and the plugs, wiring, cap and coil are satisfactory, the most likely cause for the miss or surge is a defective amplifier.

Distributor Service

Remove distributor in the usual manner, being sure to note position of rotor, then pull distributor up until rotor just stops turning and again note position of rotor. To insure correct timing of the distributor, it must be installed with the rotor correctly positioned as noted above.

If necessary to remove secondary wires from cap, mark position on cap tower for lead to No. 1 cylinder. This will aid in reinstallation of leads.

If the engine has been turned after the distributor was removed, it will be necessary to install a jumper wire and crank engine until the timing mark on vibration damper indexes with the proper mark on the engine front cover. If both valves of No. 1 cylinder are closed, the piston will be on top dead center of the firing stroke.

Fig. 10 shows an exploded view of the distributor.

No adjustments can be made on either system and no periodic maintenance is required.

FORD SYSTEMS

NOTE: Due to improvements in transistors, the transistor ignition system for 1966-67 requires fewer components and achieves greater system reliability. Units not required on the 1966-67 system that were used on past models are 1) toroid portion of amplifier, 2) cold start relay, 3) amplifier mounting plate and cover. The tach block, ballast resistor and amplifier are mounted as individual components.

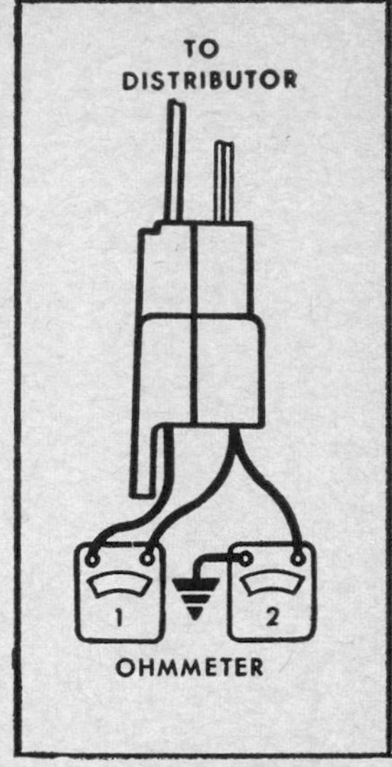

Fig. 9 Distributor test

The ignition coil primary in the transistor system is designed to draw a normal 12-ampere peak current, or approximately 5.5 amperes average current in order to provide high spark plug voltage at the higher engine speeds.

The transistor in the system acts as a switch or relay. It is similar in action to a horn relay except that it has no moving parts and thus acts with very little time lag. The transistor is connected between the battery and the coil and is used to make and break the coil primary circuit.

The distributor controls the transistor. The resistor connected between the distributor and transistor (in wiring harness) limits the transistor control current to 0.5 ampere. The low distributor point current eliminates pitting and gives long distributor point life.

The amplifier assembly, Fig. 11, is mounted under the instrument panel to protect the parts from engine heat.

A ceramic ballast resistor block and a tachometer connector block are mounted in the engine compartment.

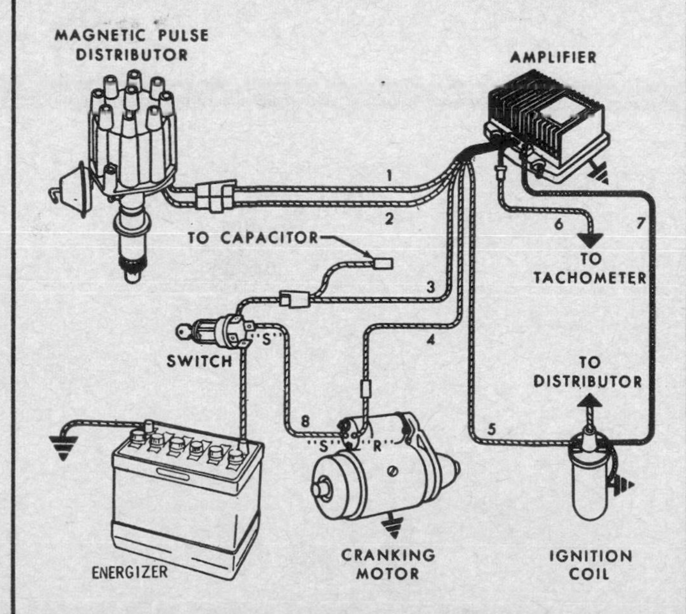

Fig. 8 Pictorial diagram of CD system

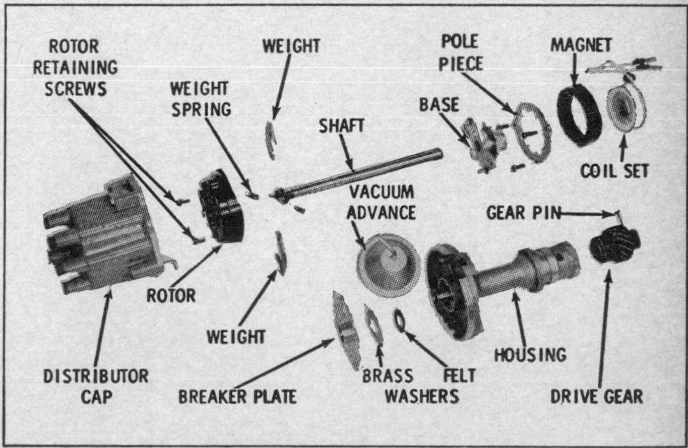

Fig. 10 Exploded view of Magnetic Pulse distributor

A two-ampere fuse between the large terminal of the tachometer block and the coil primary circuit prevents the transistor from being damaged by the application of external devices other than normal testing equipment.

The tachometer block is used to connect a tachometer or other test equipment into the circuit.

CAUTION: Do not connect test equipment into the circuit in any other manner or readings will be inaccurate and damage may occur to the transistor or change its operating characteristics.

Prior to 1966 the system employed a cold start relay (discontinued in 1966). The contacts in this relay are normally closed and they are connected into the circuit only during the starting cycle. When the starter relay is closed, the cold start relay is actuated and opens its contacts. During starting, if the available voltage drops below 10.5 volts, the relay contacts close, by-passing the 0.33-ohm resistor in the ballast resistor block, thus applying full available voltage to the system.

Trouble Shooting

Ignition troubles are caused by a failure in the primary or secondary circuit, or incorrect ignition timing. To isolate the trouble, proceed as follows:

1. Remove high tension coil lead from distributor cap.
2. Disconnect brown wire from starter relay I terminal and red/blue wire from starter relay S terminal.
3. Turn on ignition switch.
4. While holding high tension lead approximately ¼″ away from a good ground, crank engine, using an auxiliary starter switch between starter relay battery and S terminals.
5. If spark is good the trouble lies in the secondary circuit; if there is no spark or a weak spark the trouble is in the primary circuit.
6. Isolate the trouble by checking out the system as outlined in Figs. 12 and 13.

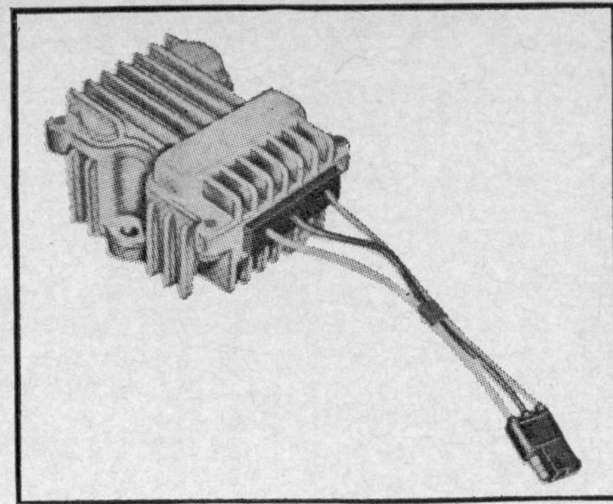

Fig. 11 Ford amplifier assembly

MOTOROLA SYSTEM

Factory installed on fleet models manufactured by Chrysler Corp., this transistor ignition system consists of a special ignition coil, ballast resistor, transistor amplifier and all necessary wiring to complete the installation. These parts are used in conjunction with the conventional ignition system components shown in Fig. 14.

Voltage Check

Fig. 15

1. With ignition on, engine not running, and distributor breaker points open, the voltmeter should read approximately 3 to 5 volts.
2. With ignition on, engine not running, and distributor breaker points closed, voltmeter should read approximately 3 to 5 volts.

NOTE: The above voltmeter readings represent average voltages and may vary from vehicle to vehicle. Some of the causes that contribute to these variations are: condition of battery, breaker points, resistance in ignition switch or wiring.

With engine running, the engine rpm and distributor dwell settings will also affect these voltage readings. However, any marked deviation from the above voltmeter readings indicate a malfunction that should be corrected.

Ballast Resistor By-Pass Check

Fig. 16

1. With ignition on, engine not running, and distributor breaker points open, voltmeter should read 0 volts.
2. With ignition on, engine not running, and distributor breaker points closed, voltmeter should read approximately 6 volts.
3. With engine on, and engine cranking, voltmeter should read approximately 1 volt or less. When the engine starts, voltmeter should read approximately 3 to 5 volts. Any marked deviation from the above voltmeter readings indicates a malfunction which should be corrected.

Trouble Check-out

Fig. 17—With ignition on, engine not running, distributor breaker points closed, and all accessories turned off, the voltmeter should not read more than 1.5 volts. A higher voltage reading indicates that one of the following conditions exist and must be corrected.

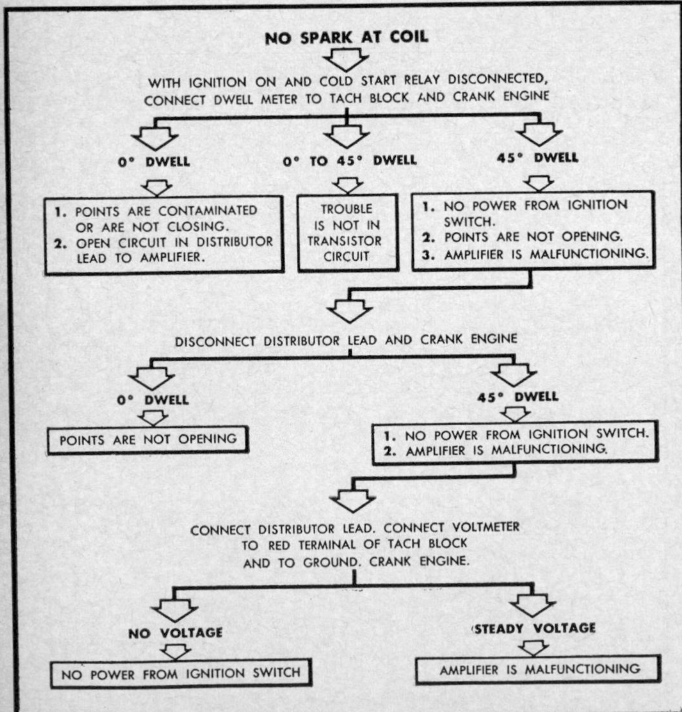

Fig. 12 Ford system test procedures for 1963-65 models

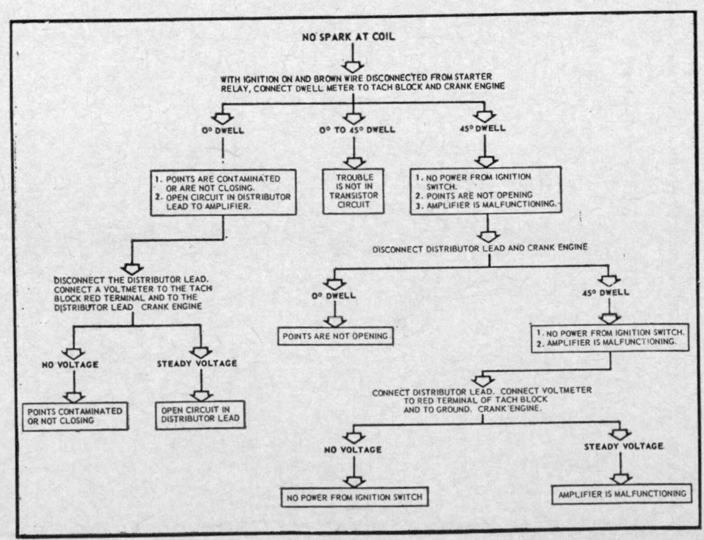

Fig. 13 Ford system test procedures for 1966-67 models

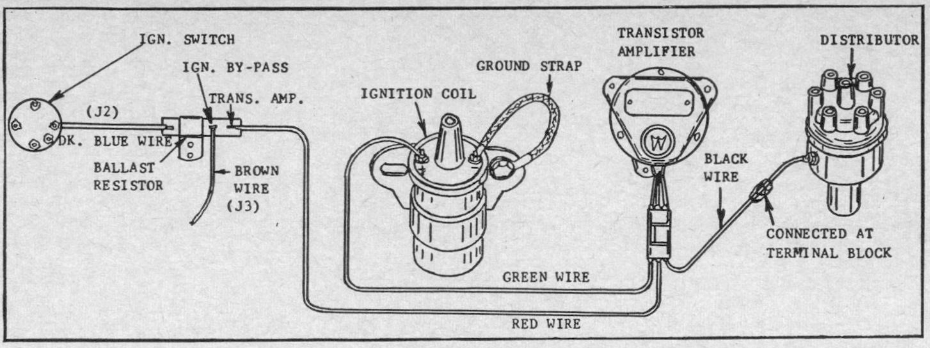

Fig. 14 Motorola transistor ignition system

1. Excessive resistance in the circuit from the battery through the ignition switch to the ballast resistor. Check all wiring for incorrect installation or loose connections.
2. Excessive resistance in the circuit between battery and ballast resistor will cause hard starting, poor acceleration and sluggish engine performance.

Fig. 18—With ignition on, engine not running, distributor breaker points open, and all accessories turned off, the voltmeter should read 9.5 volts or more (battery voltage) on all three ballast resistor terminals. Any marked deviation from this voltmeter reading indicates one

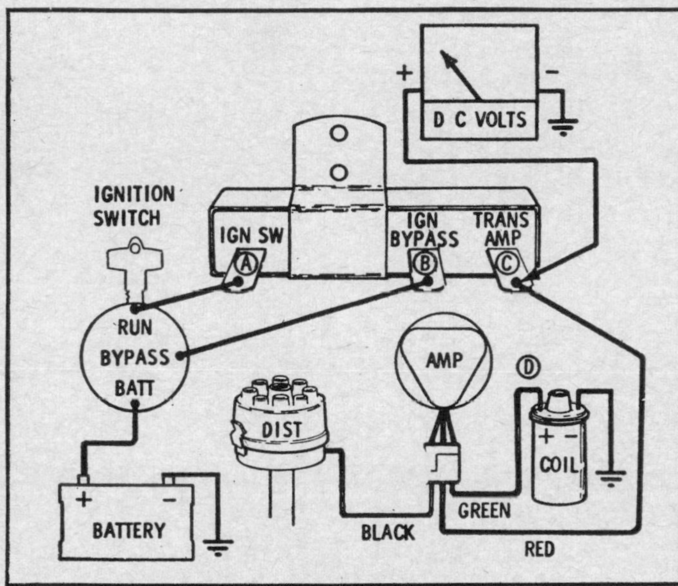

Fig. 15 Motorola voltage check hook-up

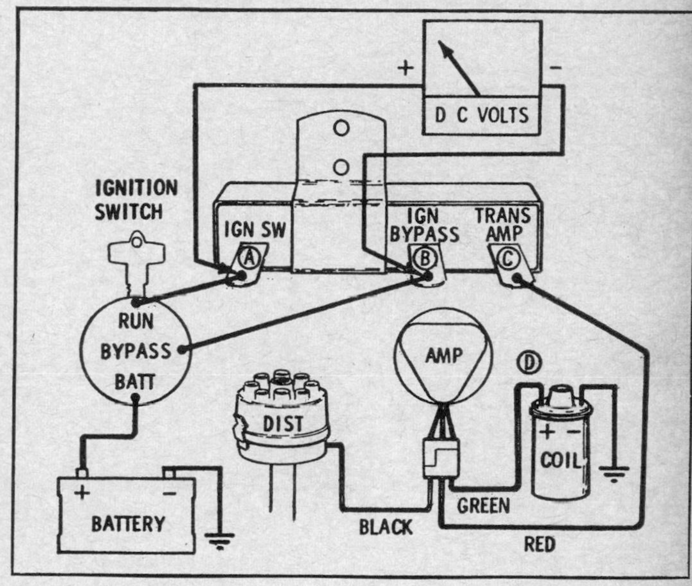

Fig. 16 Motorola ballast resistor by-pass check hook-up

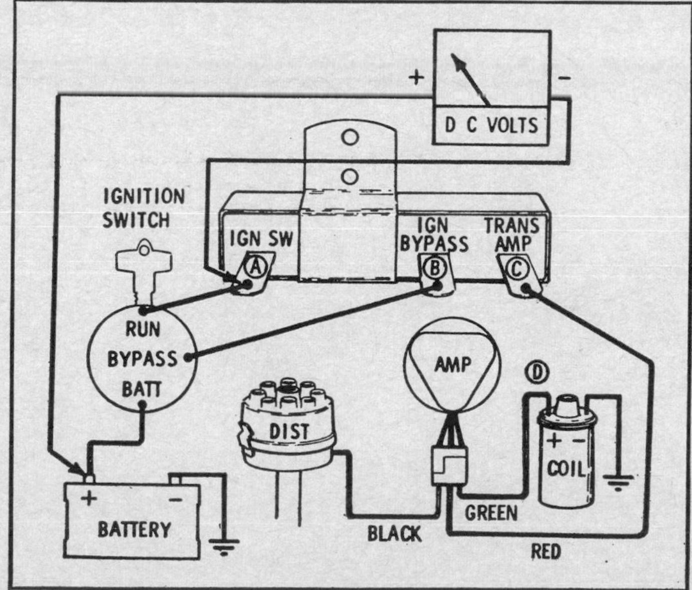

Fig. 17

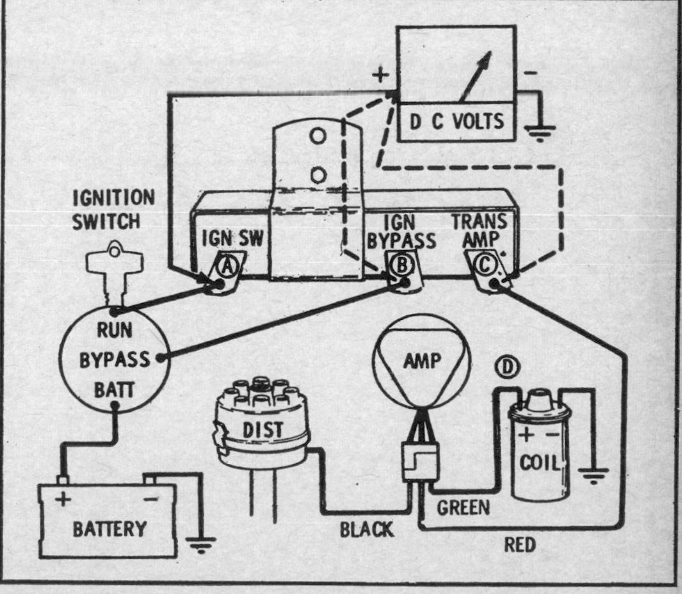

Fig. 18

of the following conditions may exist and must be corrected.

1. If the correct battery voltage (9.5 volts) is present at terminal "A" of the ballast resistor, and there is no voltage at terminals "B" and "C", and the ballast resistor is cool, it indicates that the ballast resistor is defective and must be replaced.
2. If the voltage at terminal "C" is lower than the voltage at terminal "A", the cause may be one of the following:
   a) Defective wiring to distributor breaker points.
   b) Shorted transistor amplifier. Turn off ignition, disconnect the three-prong connector at amplifier. Turn ignition on. If voltage at terminal "C" is now the same as terminal "A", the transistor amplifier is defective and must be replaced.
   c) If voltage at terminal "C" is still not the same as terminal "A", the installation may be incorrect. Check all wiring connections and be sure there are no other connections at the ballast resistor other than what is shown in Fig. 18.
   d) With the amplifier unplugged, disconnect wiring connector from terminal "B" at ballast resistor. If voltage at terminal "C" is now the same as terminal "A", the ignition by-pass wiring is defective. If the voltage at terminal "C" is still lower than at terminal "A", the ballast resistor is defective and must be replaced.

Fig. 15—With ignition on, engine not running and distributor breaker points closed, the voltmeter should read approximately 3 to 5 volts. If the voltmeter reads 9.5 volts or more (battery voltage), the fault may be caused by one of the following conditions:

1. Distributor breaker points not closing or defective wiring to breaker points.
2. Defective transistor amplifier or ignition coil. Measure voltage at positive terminal of ignition coil (D.). If voltmeter reads 9.5 volts or more (battery voltage), the ignition coil is improperly grounded or defective. If zero voltage is indicated at this point (D), the transistor amplifier is defective and must be replaced.
3. If the voltmeter reads zero volts at the transistor amplifier terminal (C) of the ballast resistor, and the ballast resistor is cool, the ballast resistor is defective and must be replaced.

NOTE: If all voltages read as specified in the check-out and trouble procedures, the ignition coil should be checked. This can be done by substituting a known good Motorola coil in the circuit.

CONTENTS

Auto-Lite Distributor Service 1-57
Breaker Contact Service 1-53
Centrifugal Advance Mechanism 1-55
Chrysler Distributor Service 1-57
Condenser 1-55
Delco-Remy Distributor Service 1-58
Holley Distributor Service 1-59
Ignition Timing with Smog Controls 1-61
Vacuum Advance Mechanisms 1-56
Vacuum Advance with Smog Controls ... 1-61

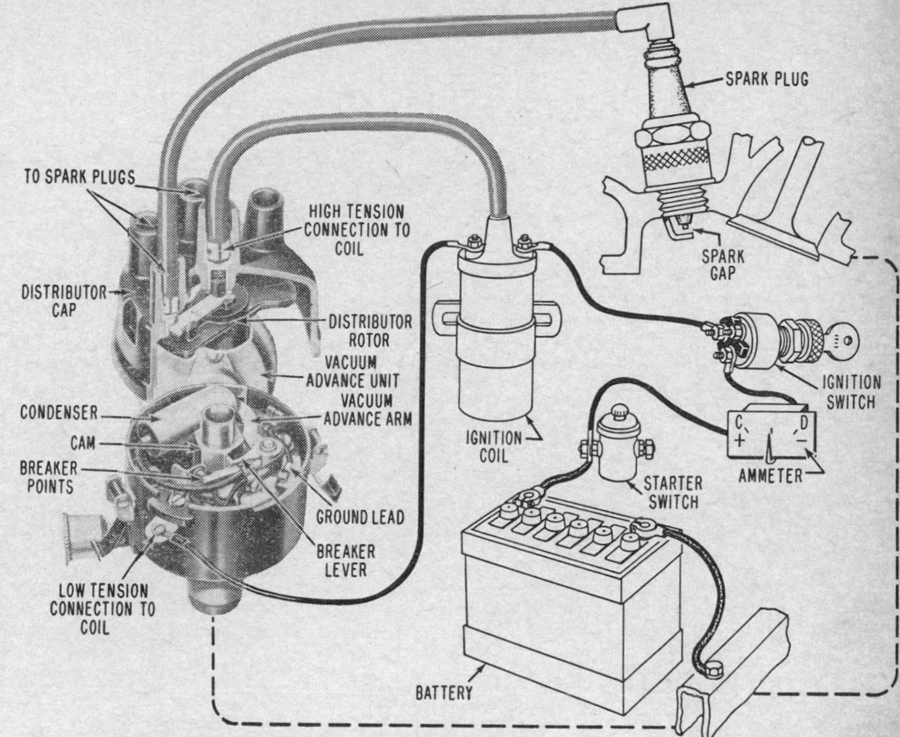

Fig. 1 Typical ignition system

BREAKER CONTACT POINTS

Contact Analysis

The normal color of points should be a light gray. If the contact surfaces are black it is usually caused by oil vapor or grease from the cam. If they are blue, the cause is usually excessive heating due to improper alignment, high resistance or open condenser circuit.

If the contacts develop a crater or depression on one point and a high spot of metal on the other, the cause is an electrolytic action transferring metal from one contact to the other, Fig. 2. This can be the result of some unusual operation of the vehicle. A slow-speed driver in city traffic or door-to-door delivery vehicles will be one extreme, and high-speed, long distance driving would be the other extreme. It may also be due to an unbalanced ignition system, which can sometimes be improved by a slight change in condenser capacity. If the mound is on the positive point, Fig. 3, install a condenser of greater capacity; if on the negative point, Fig. 4, use a condenser of lesser capacity.

One of the most common causes of point failure is the presence of oil or grease on the contact surfaces, usually from over-lubrication of the wick at the top of the cam or too much grease on the rubbing block of the breaker arm.

Breaker Point Gap

Correct contact point opening is important, especially during starting and low speed operation. If points are set too close, arcing and burning will occur, causing hard starting and poor low speed performance. If points are set too wide, the cam angle or dwell will be too small to allow saturation of the coil at high engine speeds, resulting in weak spark.

Contact point opening has a direct bearing on cam angle or dwell which is the number of degrees that the breaker cam rotates from the time the points close until they open again, Fig. 5. The cam angle or dwell increases as point opening is decreased and vice versa. In view of the importance of point opening to low speed engine performance and cam dwell to high speed engine performance, the cam angle or dwell should be checked after adjusting and aligning points. This is done on a distributor testing machine, following the manufacturers instructions.

Breaker Arm Spring Tension

Breaker arm spring tension is important. If the tension is too great the arm will bounce, causing an interruption of the current in the coil and misfiring.

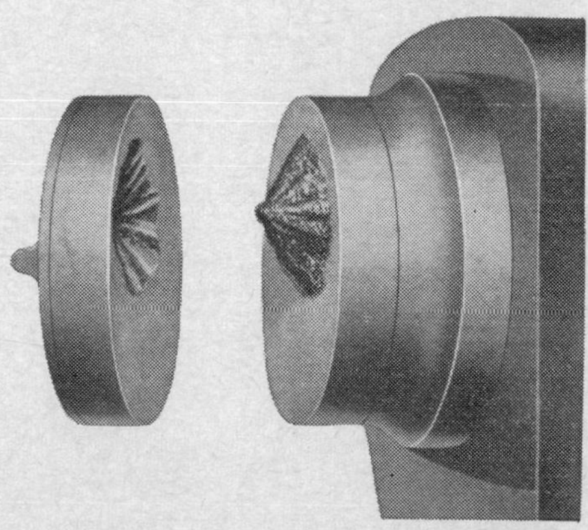

Fig. 2 Showing how metal from one contact transfers to the other

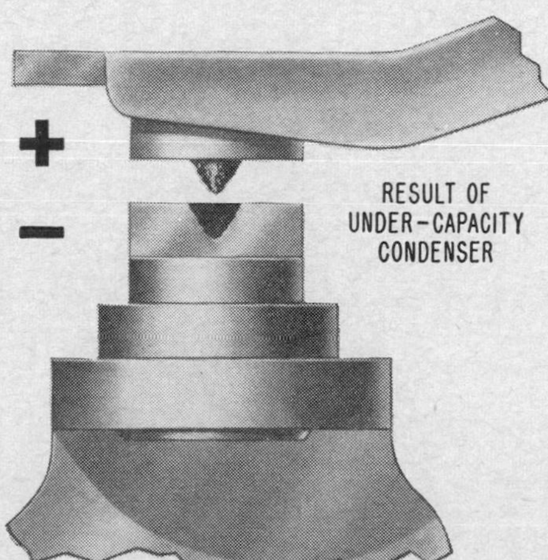

Fig. 3 Mound on positive point

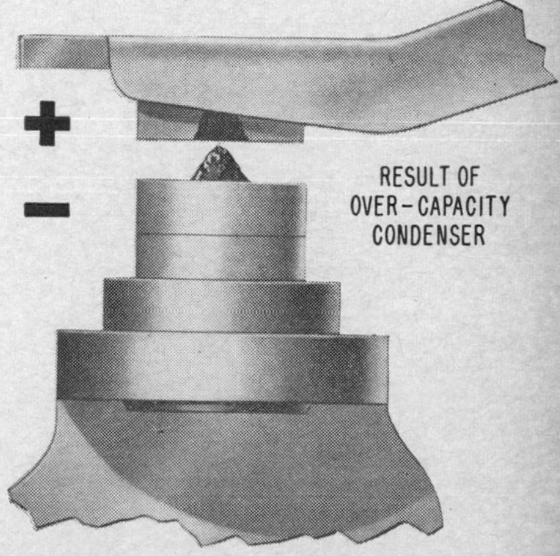

Fig. 4 Mound on negative point

Fig. 5 Cam angle or dwell

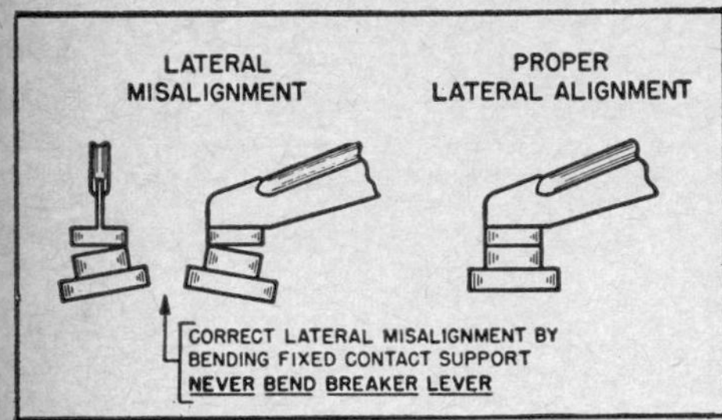

Fig. 7 Breaker point alignment

If the spring tension is too little, the rubbing block will not follow the cam, causing a variation in cam dwell. The spring tension should always be set at the high limit as given in the *Distributor Specifications* chart in the car chapter, as it will be reduced as the rubbing block wears.

Hook a spring scale on the breaker arm and pull in a straight line as shown in Fig. 6. Take a reading as the points start to separate under the slow and steady pull of the scale. If the tension is not within specifications, loosen the screw that holds the end of the point spring and slide the end of the spring in or out as necessary. Tighten the screw and recheck the spring tension.

Breaker Point Alignment

Check alignment of points with points closed, Fig. 7. Align new points where necessary but do not attempt to align used points. Instead, replace used points where serious misalignment is observed. After aligning points, adjust point gap.

Adjusting Breaker Gap

Specifications for breaker gap, *as measured with a wire gauge,* is listed in the *Tune Up Specifications* in the car chapters. However, if at all possible, this opening should be set on a distributor testing machine or with a dial indicator, Fig. 8. This not only eliminates the possibility of an incorrect gap setting but if the points are slightly rough but otherwise in alignment, there is the danger of obtaining an incorrect gap, Fig. 9.

The advantage of a distributor testing machine is that it not only measures cam angle or dwell but it also uncovers irregularities between cam lobes, point bounce, alignment of rubbing block with cam, alignment of contacts and breaker arm spring tension.

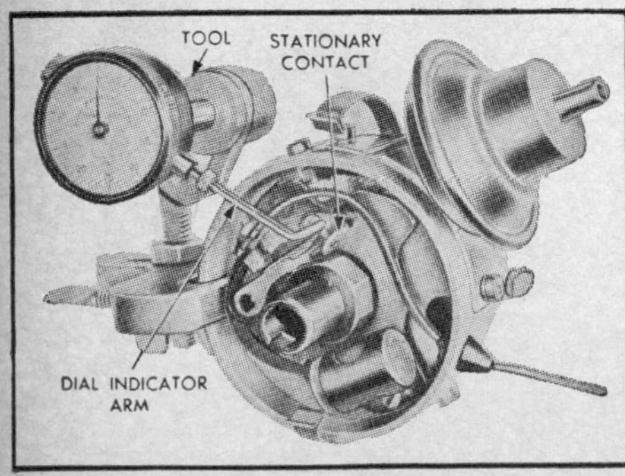

Fig. 8 Dial indicator for measuring breaker gap

Setting Auto-Lite & Chrysler Dual Points

The distributor used on some Chrysler Corp. cars contain two sets of points which permit additional current build-up in the primary winding of the coil, Fig. 10. Thus, maximum voltage is induced in the secondary winding.

The two sets of points are connected in parallel and are positioned in relation to the 8-lobe cam so as to provide a 7-degree overlap of points opening and closing. One set of points (circuit *maker* points) closes the primary circuit in the coil and the second set of points (circuit *breaker* points) opens the circuit, causing a spark at the plug. Immediately after the spark occurs, the circuit *maker* points are closed ahead of the circuit *breaker* points, thus providing a circuit to build-up the primary winding. As the cam rotates further, the secondary points close and just before the secondary points open, the primary points open 7 degrees ahead.

Since the "make" and "break" points are timed to close and open at the exact instant necessary for efficient engine operation, adjustment of the points is an important factor in correct distributor operation.

Feeler Gauge or Dial Indicator Method—Rotate the distributor shaft until the breaker arm rubbing block of one set of points is on the high spot of the cam. Then, with a screwdriver blade in the triangular opening, close or open the points to the proper clearance by turning the screwdriver blade against the stationary point plate. Check the clearance with a clean wire gauge or dial indicator. Then turn the distributor shaft until the rubbing block of the second set of points is on the high spot of the cam and adjust the second set of points in the same manner.

Dwell Meter Method—If this method is used *block one set of points open* with a piece of wrapping paper or calling card. Then adjust the other set of points to the correct dwell angle. Now block open the first set of points and adjust the second set. After both sets of points have been adjusted, allow them to operate together while checking that their total dwell angle measures up to manufacturer's specifications.

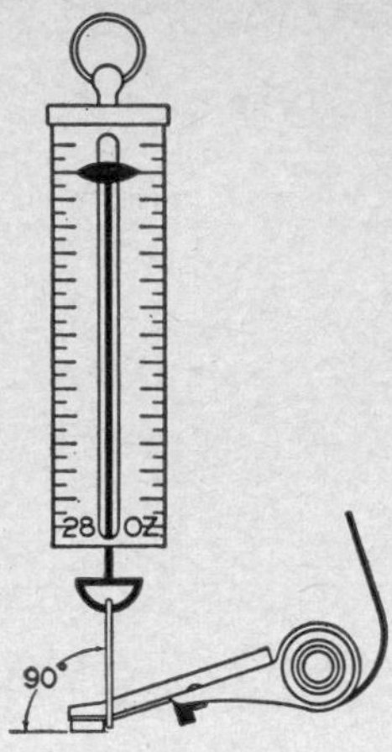

Fig. 6 Measuring breaker spring tension

Auto-Lite & Chrysler Single Point Set Adjustment

Adjustment of breaker gap is accomplished by loosening the lock screw in the stationary point and moving the adjusting screw as required to obtain the correct breaker gap.

Delco-Remy Internal Adjustment Breaker Points

For distributors used starting with 1962 Corvair, Chevy II and Tempest 4, an opening in the point set assembly allows for easy dwell angle or breaker point adjustment, Figs. 11 and 12.

Delco-Remy External Adjustment Breaker Points

With engine running at idle speed, the

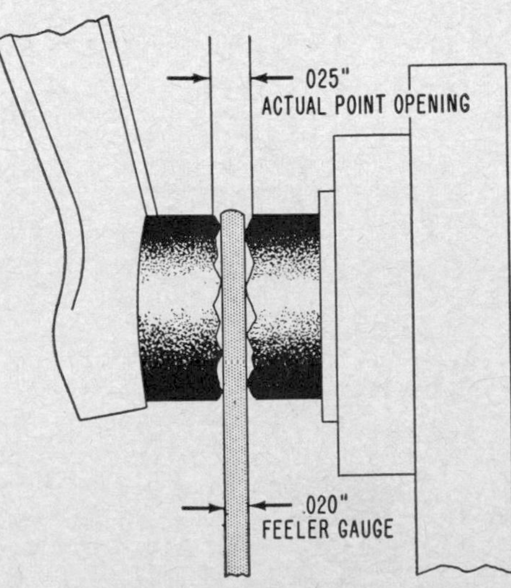

Fig. 9 Why flat feeler gauge will not provide accurate point spacing if points are rough

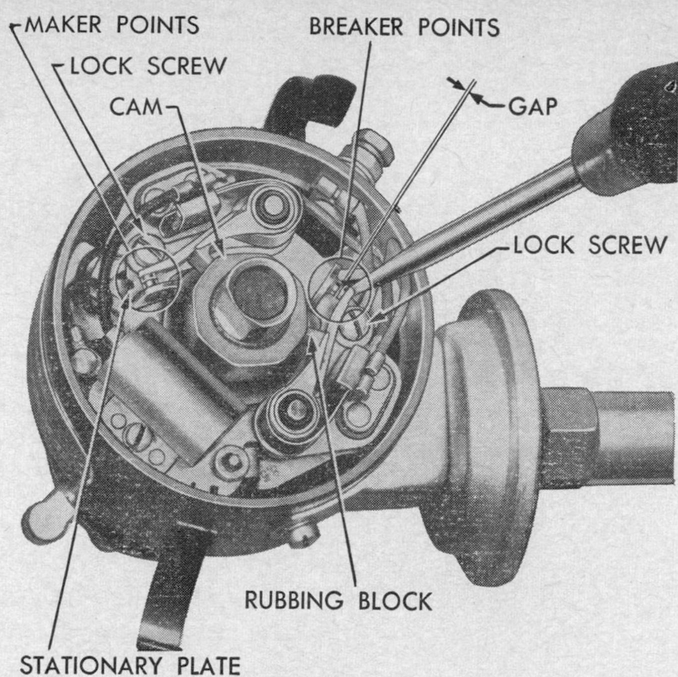

Fig. 10 Auto-Lite dual point distributor

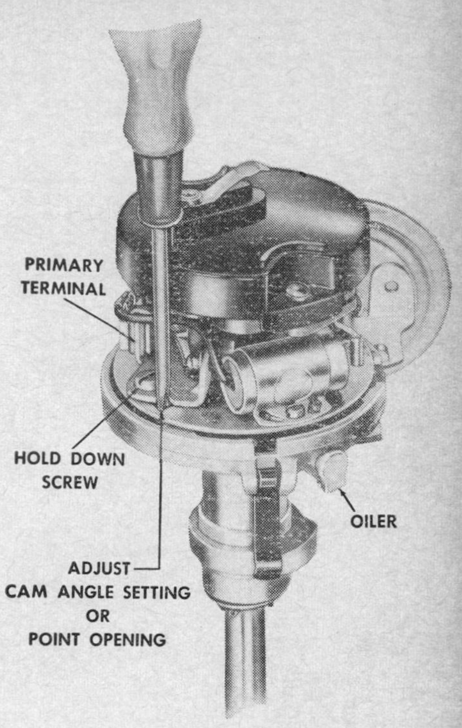

Fig. 11 Adjusting breaker points or cam dwell on Corvair 1960-61

breaker gap is adjusted by first raising the window provided in the cap and inserting a "hex" wrench into the adjusting screw, Fig. 13. Turn the adjusting screw clockwise until the engine begins to misfire. Then give the wrench one-half turn in the opposite direction which will provide the proper breaker gap. If a cam angle meter is to be used, turn the adjusting screw until the correct angle is obtained.

Holley Breaker Points

The breaker point set is attached to the movable breaker plate. A slot in the stationary point bracket allows for easy breaker point adjustment, Fig. 14.

CONDENSER

A condenser should not be condemned because the points are burned or oxidized. Oil vapor, or grease from the cam, or high resistance may be the cause of such a condition.

Condensers should be tested with a good condenser tester for leakage, break-down, capacity, and resistance in series in the condenser circuit. Manufacturers of condenser testers furnish complete instructions as to their use.

CENTRIFUGAL ADVANCE

Except for Holley "full vacuum" type all other distributors utilize an automatic advance mechanism which functions by virtue of centrifugal weights. Some distributors employ both centrifugal and vacuum advance mechanisms while others make use of only the centrifugal mechanism.

When engine speed increases, the spark must be introduced in the cylinder earlier in the cycle in order that the fuel charge can be ignited and will have time to burn and deliver its power to the piston. To provide this spark advance based on engine speed, the centrifugal governor mechanism is used.

This mechanism, Fig. 15, consists of centrifugal advance weights which throw out against spring tension as the engine speed increases. This movement imparts, through a toggle arrangement, rotational motion to the breaker cam, causing it to rotate a number of degrees with respect to the distributor drive shaft. This causes the lobes on the cam to close and open the contacts earlier in the cycle so that the spark is induced and is delivered to the cylinder earlier with respect to the position of the upward moving piston.

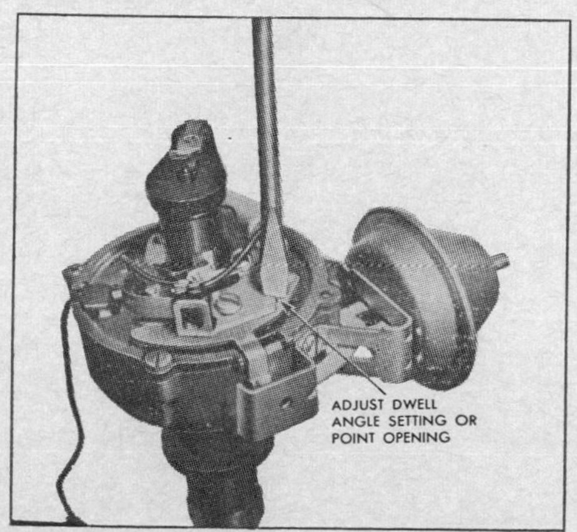

Fig. 12 Breaker point setting. 1963 Corvair, Chevy II, Tempest 4

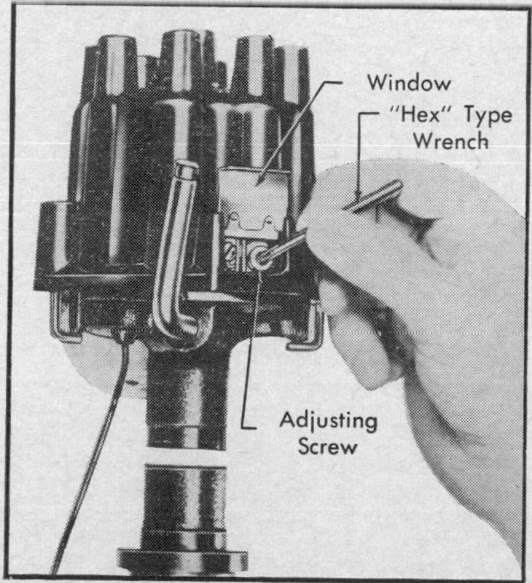

Fig. 13 Adjust breaker point gap through window in distributor cap

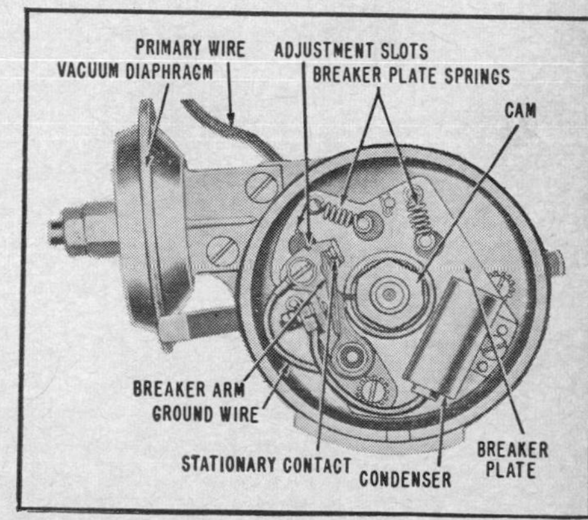

Fig. 14 Breaker plate details. Holley Loadamatic distributor Note slot for adjusting breaker gap

Fig. 15 Top view of Delco-Remy distributor with breaker plate removed to show centrifugal governor mechanism

In servicing the distributor, all weights should be removed from the hinge pins, cleaned and checked for excessive wear, either in the weights or pins, or the plate which is slotted for the movement of the pins on top of the governor weights. Replacement should be made if there is any appreciable wear in the slots, as any wear at this point would change the characteristic of the spark advance.

If these parts are in good condition, the hinge pins should be lubricated before being reassembled, by greasing the hinge pins and filling the pockets in the governor weights with grease. Do not use vaseline for this purpose as its melting point is comparatively low.

When installing new centrifugal governor assemblies, it is important that the spacer washers between the housing and shaft be installed correctly. If incorrectly installed, the governor assembly will be too high, causing it to rub against the bottom of the breaker plate.

On some distributors, both springs are alike, while on others there is one heavy and one light spring, as in Fig. 15. Another combination that may be found is an additional flat spring on the outside of the outer spring posts, Fig. 16. As the governor speed is increased, the flat springs are first pulled against the posts by the eyes of the coil springs to provide a rapid spark advance of a few degrees before the coil springs pull against the spring posts.

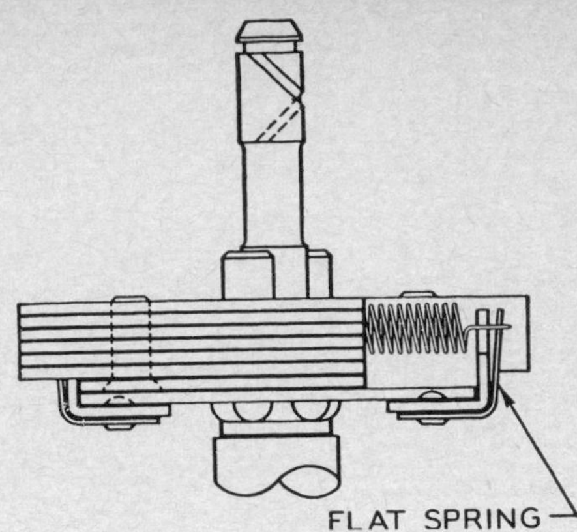

Fig. 16 Flat spring used on some governors to provide a rapid spark advance

VACUUM ADVANCE

The two types of vacuum advance mechanisms used are illustrated in Figs. 17 and 18. Both types make use of a spring-loaded diaphragm which is connected through linkage to the distributor. The spring loaded side of the diaphragm is air tight and is connected through a vacuum line to the carburetor or intake manifold.

When the throttle is open, vacuum from the intake manifold is introduced into the vacuum advance mechanism and the diaphragm is pulled against the spring, causing the distributor to advance.

In Fig. 17 the mechanism is attached to the distributor breaker plate so that the breaker plate rotates. In Fig. 18 the mechanism is connected to the distributor body so that the entire distributor moves. In both cases, the rotational movement carries the contact points around to an advanced position so that the breaker cam closes and opens the points earlier in the cycle.

Auto-Lite IBP Distributors

Used on some late model Chrysler Corp. cars, this distributor uses a very different type vacuum spark advance. Unlike other systems which either rotate the breaker plate or the entire distributor when manifold vacuum is high, the IBP breaker plate is pivoted in such a way that the points swing in an arc about the cam when the vacuum advance unit is in operation. Thus, cam angle and breaker point gap change as high manifold vacuum advances the spark. For this reason cam angle should be checked with the vacuum line disconnected and the point gap checked or adjusted when the vacuum advance unit is in full retard position.

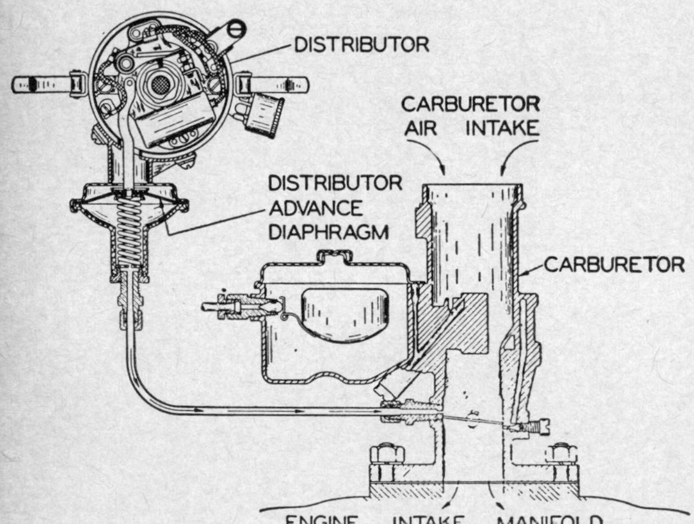

Fig. 17 Auto-Lite vacuum advance mechanism of the type which is mounted on the side of the distributor. Breaker plate is supported on a ball bearing, and the breaker plate alone rotates in the housing as vacuum conditions change

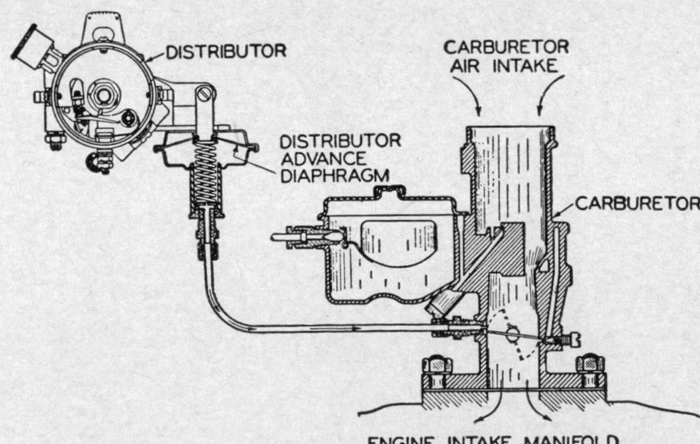

Fig. 18 Auto-Lite vacuum advance mechanism of type which is clamped around the distributor so that the entire distributor is rotated as vacuum conditions change

Distributor Service

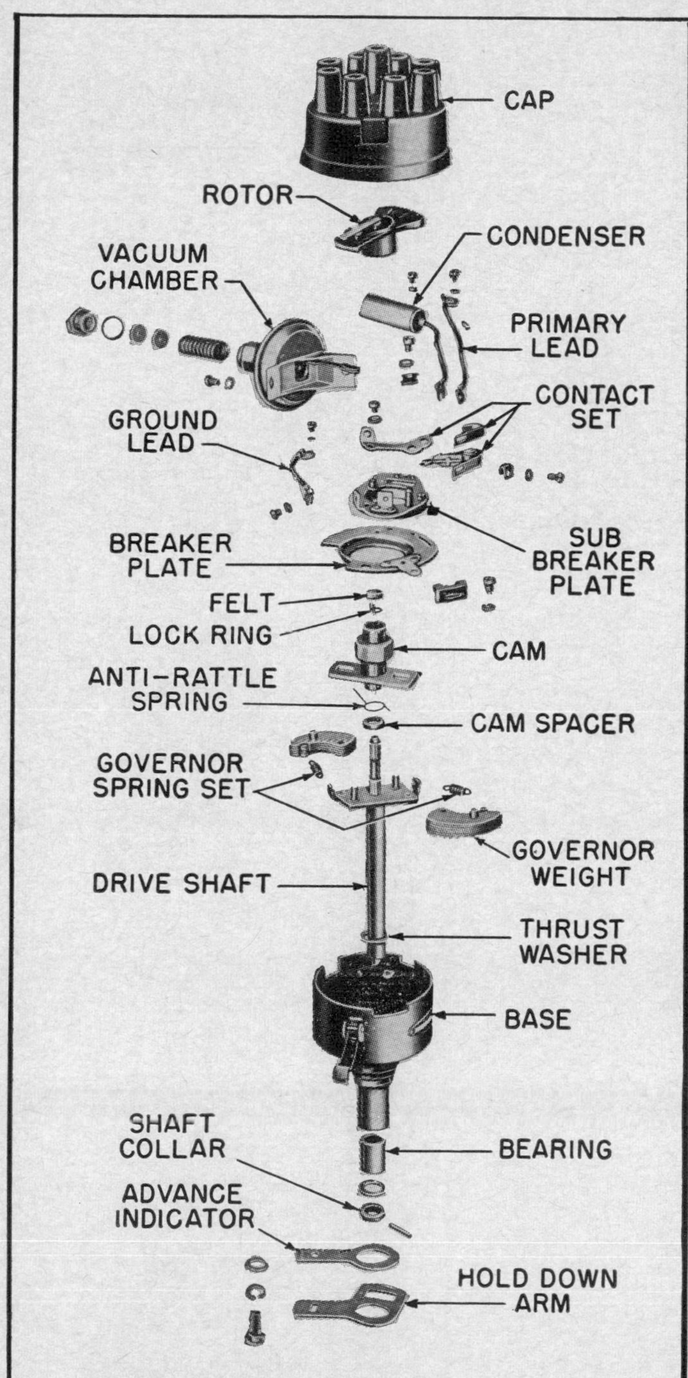

Fig. 19 Exploded view of typical Auto-Lite distributor

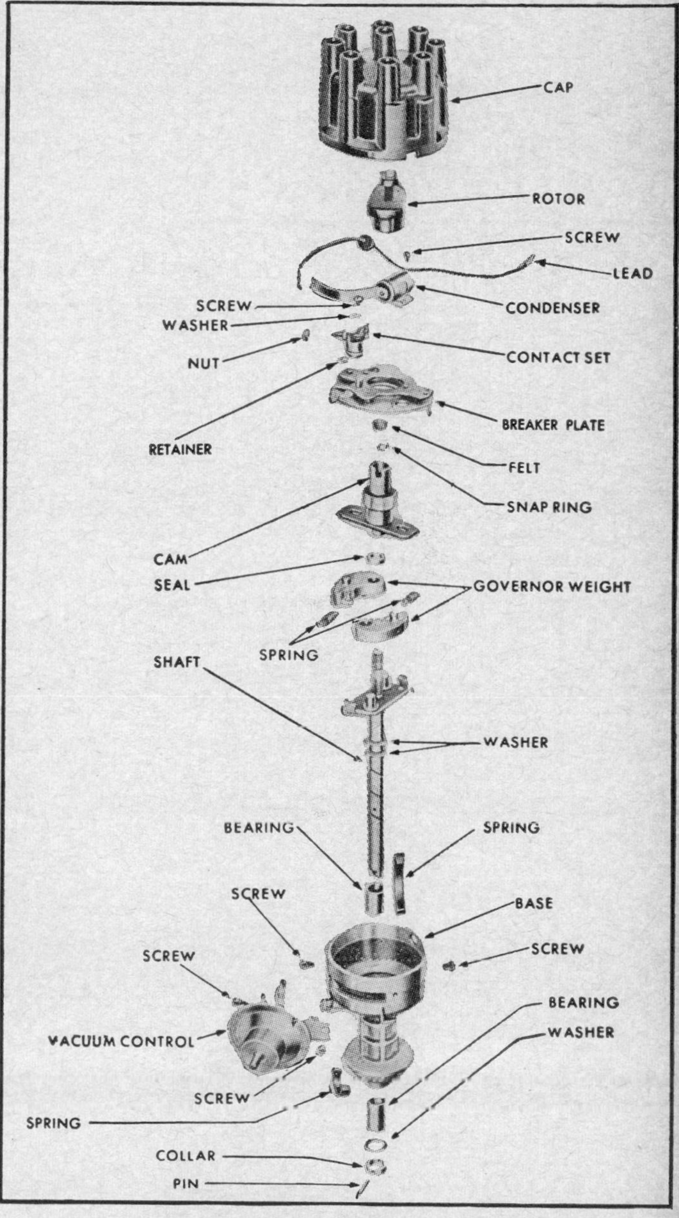

Fig. 20 Exploded view of typical Chrysler distributor

AUTO-LITE & CHRYSLER DISTRIBUTOR SERVICE

If the distributor has been disassembled, reassemble as follows, referring to Figs. 19 and 20 for guidance.

1. Check operation of centrifugal weights and weight springs for distortion. Lubricate governor weights.
2. Inspect all bearing surfaces and pivot pins for roughness, binding, or excessive looseness.
3. Install cam spacer (chamfered end down) on distributor shaft.
4. Slide cam and yoke on distributor shaft. Engage weight lugs with slots in yoke as shown in Fig. 21. Install cam retaining clip, being sure it is properly seated in distributor shaft groove.
5. Lubricate and install two concave washers for Auto-Lite distributors or a single flat thrust washer for Chrysler distributors. Position washers on shaft and slide shaft into distributor body.
6. Position lower thrust washer and drive collar on lower end of shaft and install retainer pin.
7. Install oiler wick and oiler.
8. Install breaker plate assembly, align condenser lead, breaker point spring, primary lead and install attaching screw.

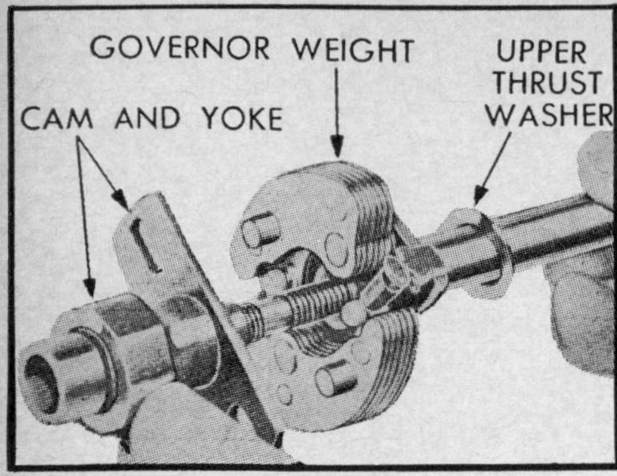

Fig. 21 Distributor shaft details

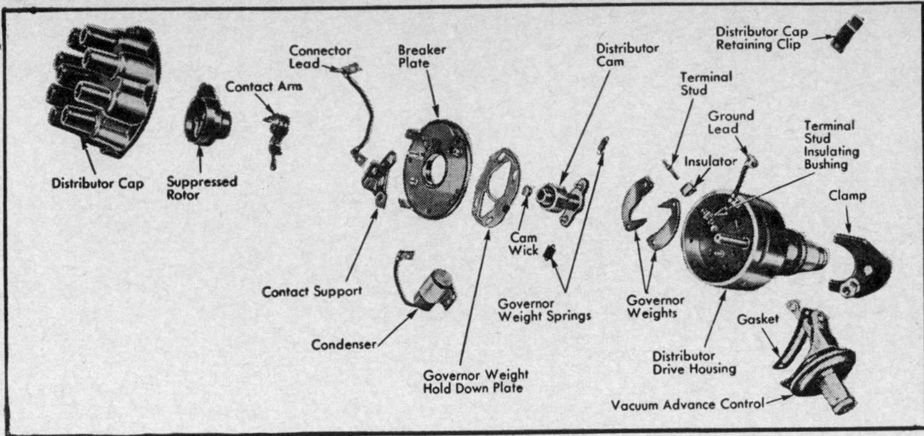

Fig. 22 Exploded view of typical Delco-Remy internal adjustment distributor

9. Install felt wick in top of cam.
10. Attach vacuum advance unit arm to breaker plate and install retainer. Install vacuum unit attaching screws and washers.
11. Test breaker arm spring tension and adjust breaker gap.
12. Lubricate felt pad in top of distributor cam with 3 to 5 drops of light engine oil and install rotor.

DELCO-REMY DISTRIBUTOR SERVICE

Internal Adjustment Type

Fig. 22 shows an exploded view of a typical distributor of this type. Due to its similarity to the Auto-Lite unit, use the Auto-Lite procedure as a guide when assembling this unit.

External Adjustment Type

If the distributor has been disassembled, refer to Fig. 23 for guidance when reassembling.

1. Place gasket on shaft housing.
2. Place felt washer around bushing in housing.
3. Install vacuum advance unit.
4. Install breaker plate in housing and spring retainer on upper bushing.
5. Install condenser.
6. Install breaker point set.
7. Install cam and weight base assembly on shaft. If lubrication in grooves at top of shaft was removed

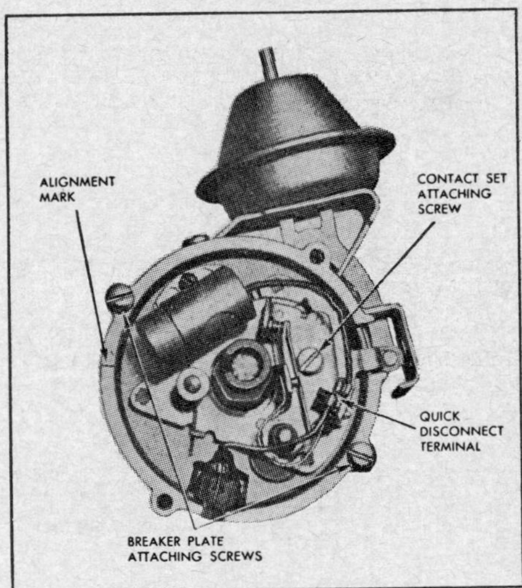

Fig. 24 Breaker plate installation. 1963-67 Corvair, Chevy II, Tempest 4

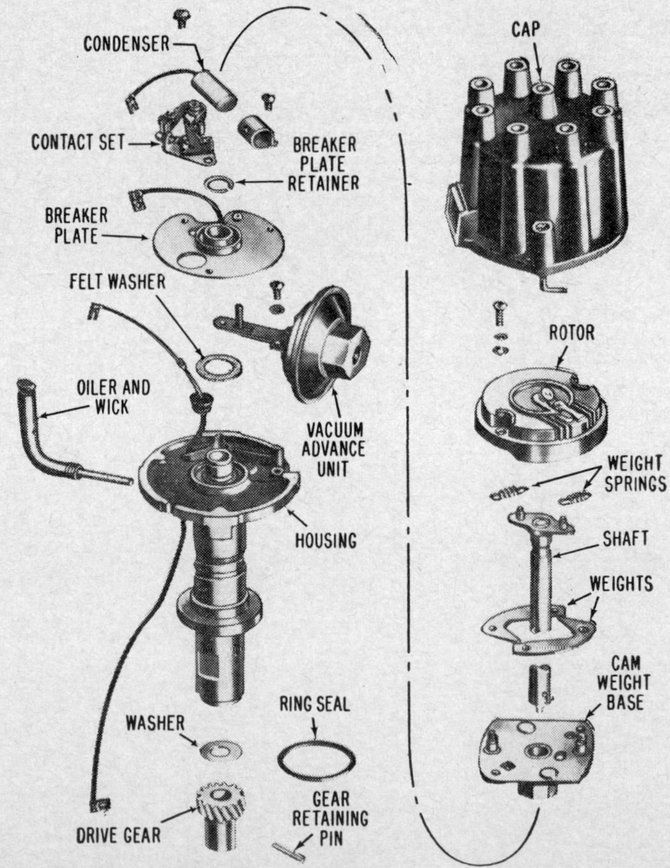

Fig. 23 Delco-Remy external adjustment distributor

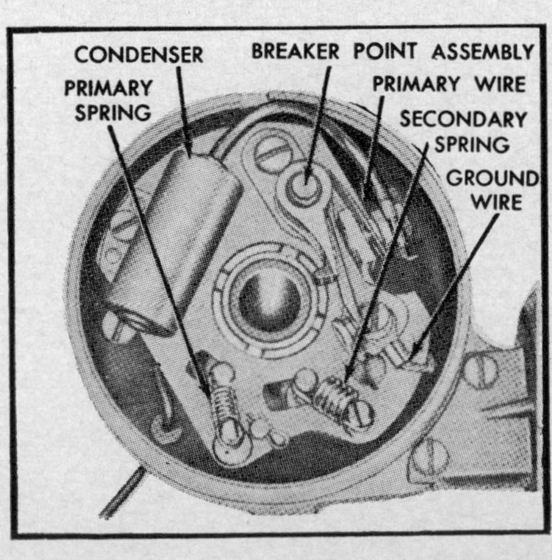

Fig. 25 Breaker plate installation. Holley Loadamatic distributor

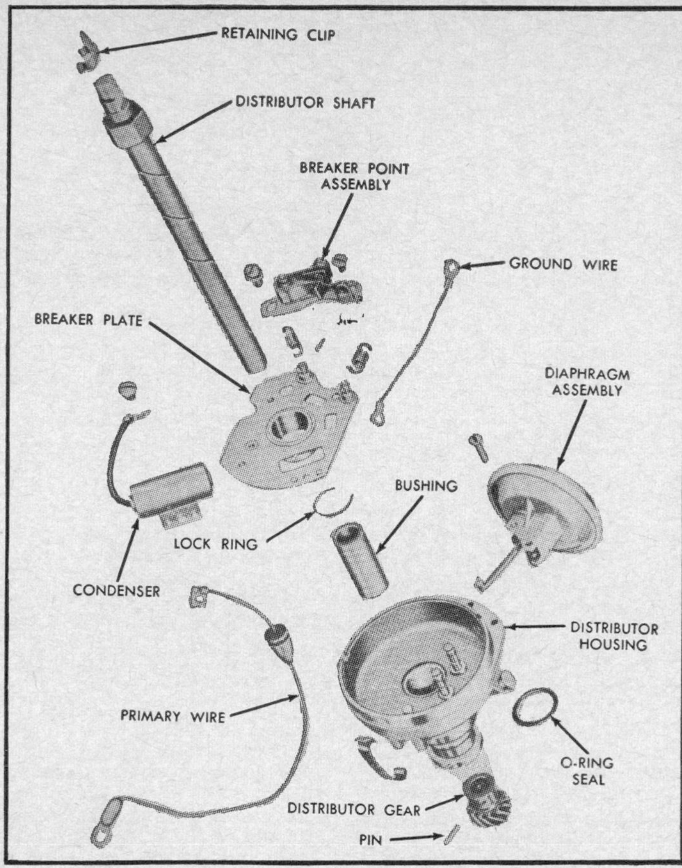

Fig. 26 Exploded view of Holley Loadamatic distributor

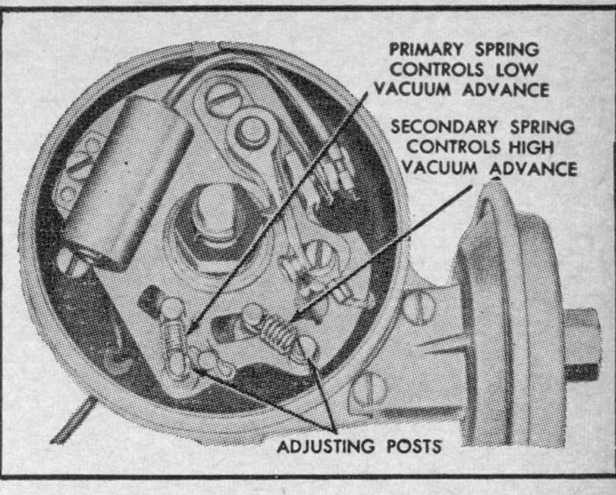

Fig. 27 Spark advance adjustment on Holley Loadamatic distributor

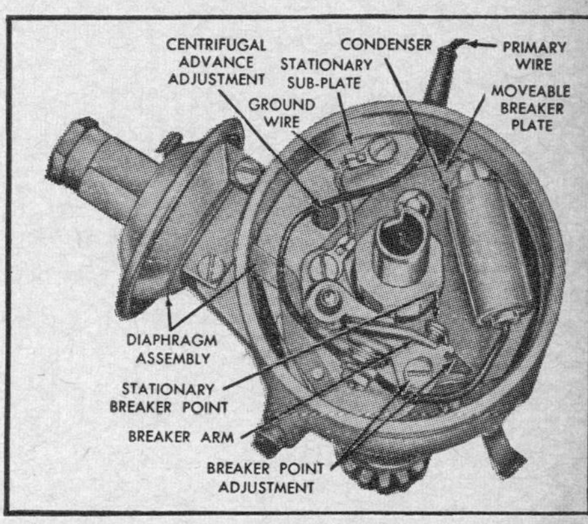

Fig. 28 Breaker plate installation. Holley dual advance distributor

during disassembly, replace with Plastilube #2 or its equivalent.

8. Install shaft and cam weight assembly in housing.
9. Using a pin, install driven gear to shaft.
10. Install advance weights and springs.
11. Install cam lubricator.
12. Install rotor.
13. Check breaker arm spring tension and adjust breaker gap.

Corvair 1962-67 Distributor

If the distributor has been disassembled, reassemble it as follows. Fig. 24 shows the details of the breaker plate and attaching parts.

1. Replace cam assembly to shaft. Lubricate top end of shaft with light engine oil prior to replacing.
2. Install weights on their pivot pins. Install weights, weight cover and stop plate.
3. Lubricate shaft and install in housing.
4. Install thrust washers and driven gear to shaft and secure with roll pins. Check to see that shaft turns freely. Install driven gear with mark on hub in line with rotor segment.
5. Install breaker plate.
6. Attach condenser and breaker point set in proper location with appropriate attaching screws, Fig. 24. Connect primary and condenser leads to breaker point set quick disconnect terminal. *Contact point set pilot must engage matching hole in breaker plate.*
7. Attach vacuum control assembly to distributor housing, using upper mounting holes.
8. Adjust breaker arm spring tension and breaker gap.
9. Install rotor.

HOLLEY DISTRIBUTORS

Ford Loadamatic Type

With these distributors, Figs. 25 and 26, engine speed and load requirements are satisfied by the action of the breaker plate which is controlled by a vacuum-actuated diaphragm working against the tension of two calibrated breaker plate springs. The breaker plate is free to rotate on the shaft bushing.

For distributors used with six-cylinder engines, the diaphragm moves the breaker plate in a counterclockwise direction to advance the spark, and the springs move the breaker plate in a clockwise direction to retard the spark. The degree of spark advance is determined by the strength of the vacuum acting on the diaphragm. For distributors used with eight-cylinder engines, spark is advanced by the diaphragm moving the breaker plate in a clockwise direction, and retarded by the springs moving the plate in a counterclockwise direction. Six-cylinder distributors rotate clockwise, eight-cylinder units counterclockwise.

For all eight-cylinder distributors, a vacuum-actuated spark control valve is attached to the carburetor throttle body to control manifold vacuum to the distributor and regulate spark advance.

Vacuum Advance, Adjust

The two breaker plate springs are precision set at the factory with special stroboscopic equipment. This equipment is available for adjustment purposes commercially. Shops having conventional distributor testers can include a mercury column to take care of the setting of these springs as the conventional vacuum gauge will not provide the required accuracy.

The spring adjusting posts shown in Fig. 27 provide the means of adjusting the spark advance.

Distributor Service

If the distributor has been disassembled, refer to Fig. 26 for guidance on reassembly.

1. Pass primary wire assembly through opening in distributor, working from inside to outside of distributor housing. Pull wire through opening until locating stop is flush with inside of distributor. Install ground wire.
2. Position breaker plate in body and secure with lock ring.
3. Position breaker point set on breaker plate, Fig. 25. Be sure pivot pin enters hole in breaker plate.
4. Connect ground wire to breaker plate at end closest to adjustment

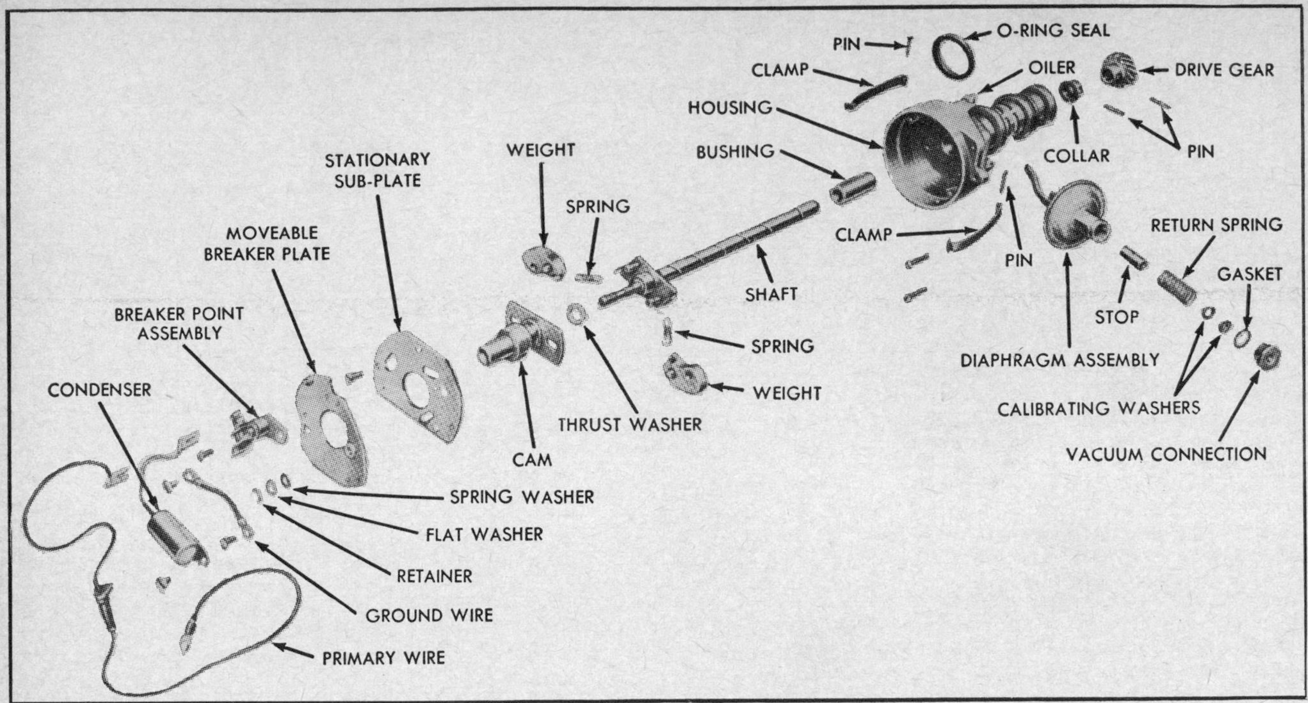

Fig. 29 Exploded view of Holley dual advance distributor

slot. Install other screw and lock washer at opposite end of assembly.
5. Install condenser.
6. Install two return springs on adjustment and breaker plate post, Fig. 27. Make sure secondary spring is adjacent to vacuum chamber.
7. Install vacuum unit.
8. Insert top of vacuum rod through breaker plate. Attach rod with retainer.
9. Slide shaft into body, using care not to damage rubbing block on breaker points.
10. Press gear on shaft. If a new shaft is being installed, place a .028" feeler in position against distributor mounting flange, press gear on shaft until it bottoms against feeler gauge. Remove feeler gauge and secure with ⅛" pin after drilling hole in shaft.
11. Install distributor cap clamps. Lubricate cam with high temperature, non-fiber grease.
12. Adjust breaker arm spring tension, align and adjust breaker points, adjust vacuum advance and cam dwell.

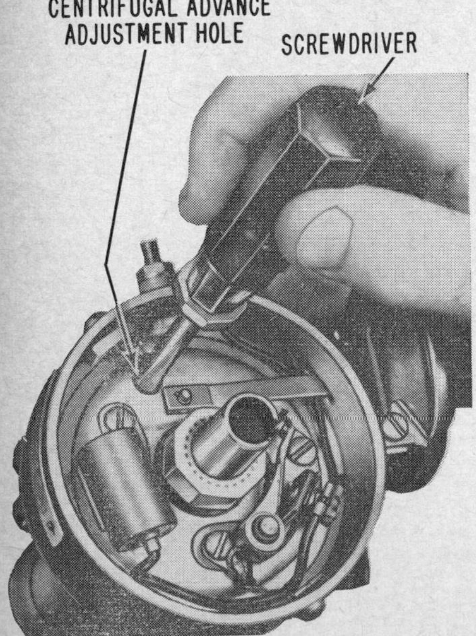

Fig. 30 Centrifugal advance adjustment

Holley Dual Advance Distributor

This distributor, Figs. 28 and 29, is similar to conventional design in that both a centrifugal advance mechanism is provided to regulate ignition timing according to speed and a vacuum advance unit to regulate ignition timing according to load. However, unlike other make distributors, the centrifugal advance mechanism can be adjusted through a slot in the breaker plate. The vacuum advance can also be adjusted by changing the calibration washers between the vacuum chamber spring and nut, Fig. 31.

Adjust centrifugal advance before adjusting vacuum advance. If the correct advance is not indicated when tested on a distributor machine, bend one spring bracket with a screwdriver through the hole in the breaker plate, Fig. 30. Bend bracket away from distributor shaft to decrease advance and toward shaft to increase advance. Identify bracket after adjustment is made. After an adjustment has been made to one spring, check the minimum advance point again. Then operate distributor at the specified rpm to give an advance just below maximum. If this advance is not up to specifications, bend the other spring bracket to give the correct advance.

Vacuum advance can be adjusted by changing the calibrated washers between the vacuum chamber spring and nut, Fig. 31. The addition of one washer will decrease advance and the removal of a washer will increase advance.

Distributor Service

If the distributor has been disassembled, refer to Fig. 29 for guidance upon reassembly.

1. Oil shaft and slide it into distributor body.
2. Place collar in position on shaft and align holes in collar and shaft, then install a new pin.
3. Install distributor cap clamps.
4. Check shaft end play with feeler gauge placed between collar and base of distributor. If shaft end play is not within .024-.035", replace shaft and gear.
5. Fill grooves in weight pivot pin with ball bearing grease.

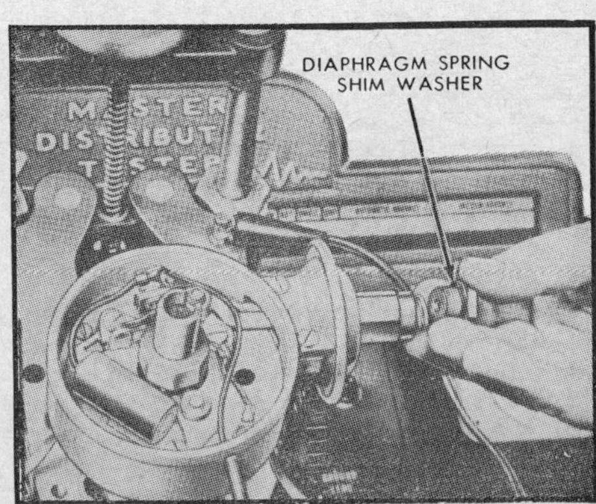

Fig. 31 Vacuum advance adjustment. Holley dual advance distributor

6. Position weights in distributor.
7. Install weight springs, being sure proper weight, spring and adjustment bracket are assembled together.
8. Install upper thrust washer.
9. Fill grooves in upper portion of distributor shaft with ball bearing grease.
10. Install cam assembly, being sure that slots in cam engage pins in weights.
11. Install cam retainer. Apply a light film of cam lubricant to cam lobes. Saturate wick with 10W engine oil. Install wick in cam.
12. Position stationary sub plate in distributor. Install one end of ground wire under plate retaining screw closest to diaphragm mounting flange.
13. Position movable breaker plate in distributor. Install spring washer on pivot pin. Place flat washer on spring washer. Be sure protruding edges of spring washer are facing upward. Install retainer.
14. Install new breaker point assembly. Install ground wire on breaker point attaching screw furthest from point adjustment slot.
15. Install condenser.
16. Working from inside to outside of distributor housing, pass primary wire through opening in distributor. Pull wire through opening until locating stop is flush with inside of distributor.
17. Connect condenser wire and primary wire to breaker points.
18. Position diaphragm and hook its link over pin on breaker plate. Install diaphragm attaching screws. Secure link with retainer. Install oil seal.
19. Adjust breaker arm spring tension, align and adjust breaker points and check and adjust cam dwell, centrifugal and vacuum advance.

IGNITION TIMING WITH SMOG CONTROLS

The new exhaust-emission control systems introduced on 1968 cars brought with them widespread changes in the basic ignition timing specifications and distributor calibration. To get more complete fuel combustion at all speeds, the new idle timing marks hover around top dead center. However, setting the ignition timing according to specifications is not the main problem on the 1968 engines, as there are stickers in the engine compartments of all models that give the idle speed and the basic timing mark.

The real problem in tuning these engines will be in checking and servicing the various new vacuum control devices that are used on some engines to assure more precise timing advance or retard. Each case will have to be sized up according to the equipment installed, as each engine-transmission team has its own distributor-carburetor combination to gain top performance and still meet exhaust control standards.

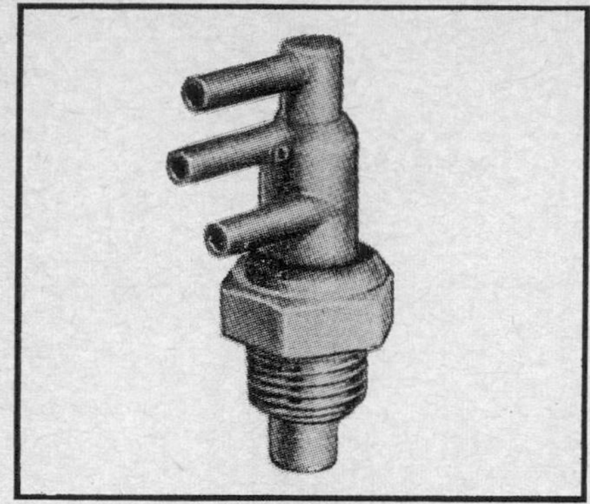

Fig. 32 Distributor vacuum advance control (deceleration) valve used on Ford with IMCO system and Chrysler CAP system of exhaust emission controls

Vacuum Advance Control Valve

To assure proper retarding of ignition timing during idle and deceleration, certain Ford- and Chrysler-built engines are equipped with a vacuum advance control valve as part of the Ford IMCO (Improved Combustion) exhaust control system and Chrysler's Cleaner Air Package (CAP) type of exhaust control, Fig. 32. Ford also uses a dual diaphragm type of vacuum control unit on some distributors, and General Motors cars having the Controlled Combustion System (CCS) type of exhaust control have a "ported" spark advance design to retard ignition timing at idle and during deceleration.

All these fringe mechanisms will have to be considered when a tune-up is performed on any engine that has one or more of them installed. Precise timing cannot be attained or maintained without checking these control devices for proper operation.

The vacuum advance control valve is a deceleration valve that controls the distributor vacuum advance. It is a switching device in the vacuum hose circuit between the engine and distributor vacuum advance unit. The valve has inlet vacuum lines from the carburetor and the intake manifold and an outlet line to the distributor. When the engine is accelerated at part throttle or cruising steadily, vacuum for spark advance is taken from a port in the carburetor throttle housing. But, when the engine is decelerating, the control valve cuts off the lower carburetor vacuum and sends higher manifold vacuum to the distributor to keep the spark advanced during this period.

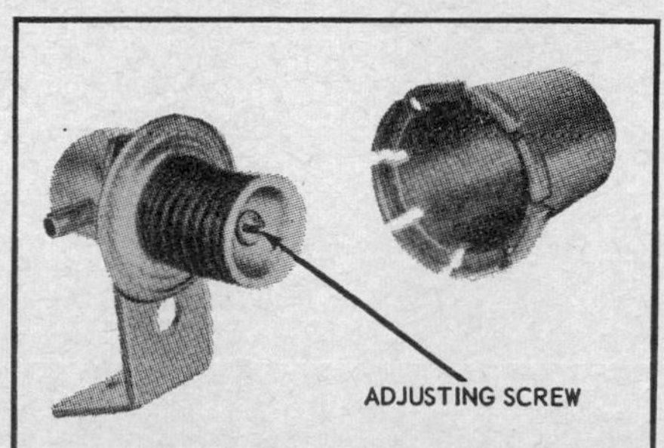

Fig. 33 Distributor vacuum advance control valve with cover removed

Tachometer Checks Operation

To check the operation of this control valve on Ford and Chrysler engines, first bring the engine up to operating temperature. Then connect a tachometer to the engine and a vacuum gauge to the distributor vacuum line. Be sure the T-fitting has the same inside diameter as the vacuum line.

If the carburetor is equipped with a dashpot device, adjust the dashpot plunger so that it does not contact the throttle lever at idle speed. Then disconnect and plug the hose from the intake manifold at the valve and the vacuum line on the distributor.

With the engine operating at specified idle speed and ignition timing, the vacuum reading should be between 0 and 6 in. mercury. If the vacuum is higher than 6 in., recheck idle speed, timing or fuel mixture.

Next, remove plugs from all vacuum hoses and reconnect them to the proper fittings. Take the cover off the vacuum control valve, Fig. 33. Then increase engine speed to 2000 rpm (in neutral) and hold that speed for about five seconds. Release throttle. The distributor vacuum reading should increase to over 16 in. mercury and remain there for at least one second and then fall to below 6 in. mercury within three seconds after the throttle is released.

If the proper vacuum readings are not obtained within the times specified, turn the control valve adjusting screw in the spring end of the valve counterclockwise to increase the time that the vacuum remains above 6 in. mercury and clockwise to decrease this time. One full turn of the adjusting screw will change the valve setting by about ½ in. mercury. If the valve cannot be adjusted to specifications, it should be replaced. After completing this test and adjustment, replace the valve cover and reset the carburetor dashpot.

NOTE: Some engines that are equipped with a distributor vacuum control valve also have a temperature sensing valve located in one of the coolant hoses or elbows, but hooked up to the distributor vacuum line. This valve, which increases engine speed if overheating develops during idling, should not be confused with the vacuum *advance* control valve.

1968 Ford Dual Advance Units

The distributor timing advance and retard devices have been redesigned on these units used on Ford-built engines equipped with the IMCO System. A dual-diaphragm vacuum control unit is used to provide additional timing retard during engine operation. The dual-diaphragm unit can be identified by its flat, circular design and the two vacuum inlet lines. It has two independently operating diaphragms, an outer one that uses carburetor vacuum to advance the spark and an inner one that uses intake manifold vacuum to retard the spark.

On-Car Check

To perform an on-car check of a dual-diaphragm control unit, disconnect the vacuum lines from both the inner and outer diaphragms and plug the line from the inner one. Using a tachometer, increase idle speed by setting the throttle on the first step on the fast idle cam. Then, with a timing light, observe the timing setting. Now connect the carburetor vacuum line to the outer diaphragm fitting. The timing should advance immediately.

To check out the retard operation, readjust engine speed to 550-600 rpm and observe setting. Then remove the plug from the manifold vacuum line and connect it to the inner diaphragm fitting. The timing should retard immediately.

If the advance or retard mechanism is not up to specifications, or if either diaphragm is leaking, the entire vacuum control assembly should be replaced.

To check for a leaking diaphragm, mount the distributor on a standard tester, but do not connect the vacuum lines to the distributor. Adjust the vacuum pressure on the testing unit to its maximum position. Then hold a hand over the end of the tester's vacuum hose and note maximum reading obtained. Do not exceed 25 in. mercury. Now connect the tester's vacuum hose to the vacuum fitting on the diaphragm to be tested without changing any adjustments. The maximum gauge reading should not be less than it was for the preliminary test. If it is, the diaphragm is leaking.

Initial Timing Unchanged

The initial ignition timing procedure is unchanged from previous dual-diaphragm units except that both vacuum lines to the control unit on the distributor should be disconnected and plugged before timing the engine.

General Motors CCS System

The 1968 General Motors engines equipped with the CCS exhaust control system (except Chevrolet V8-307 with two-barrel carburetor) have a "ported" spark advance mechanism. Vacuum for the spark advance is taken from the carburetor throttle housing above the throttle plate while the plate is in closed position. During idle, no vacuum is available at this point; thus the basic ignition timing is kept retarded. Normal advance vacuum will go to work as the throttle is opened and will affect the distributor timing through the usual vacuum advance unit.

Test for Diaphragm Leak

As timing must be more precise than ever on cars with the CCS system, check the distributor vacuum advance unit for excessive wear on the plunger. Then push the rod into the unit as far as possible by hand. Hold a finger over the vacuum line fitting and then release the rod. After about 15 seconds, remove the finger and notice if air is drawn into the unit. If not, the diaphragm is leaking and the entire unit must be replaced.

Centrifugal Advance Unchanged

Centrifugal timing advance mechanisms on the new type distributors are unchanged from previous models and are checked and serviced in the usual manner.

ALTERNATORS

INTRODUCTION

Alternators under discussion here are of the modern type with built-in silicon diode rectifiers. Under normal operating conditions, these alternators have a rating of 30 to 60 amperes, depending upon the requirements of the vehicle, and usually deliver 5 to 10 amperes at curb idle speed.

Alternators are composed of the same functional parts as the conventional D.C. generator but they operate differently: The field is called a rotor and is the turning portion of the unit. A generating part, called a stator, is the stationary member, comparable to the armature in a D.C. generator. The regulator, similar to those used in a D.C. system, regulates the output of the alternator-rectifier system.

The power source of the system is the alternator. Current is transmitted from the field terminal of the regulator through a slip ring to the field coil and back to ground through another slip ring. The strength of the field regulates the output of the alternating current. This alternating current is then transmitted from the alternator to the rectifier where it is converted to direct current.

These alternators employ a three-phase stator winding in which the phase windings are electrically 120 degrees apart. The rotor consists of a field coil encased between interleaved sections producing a magnetic field with alternate north and south poles. By rotating the rotor inside the stator the alternating current is induced in the stator windings. This alternating current is rectified (changed to D.C.) by silicon diodes and brought out to the output terminal of the alternator.

Diode Rectifiers

Six silicon diode rectifiers are used and act as electrical one-way-valves. Three of the diodes have ground polarity and are pressed or screwed into a heat sink which is grounded. The other three diodes (ungrounded) are pressed or screwed into and insulated from the end head; these diodes are connected to the alternator output terminal.

Since the diodes have a high resistance to the flow of current in one direction and a low resistance in the opposite direction, they may be connected in a manner which allows current to flow from the alternator to the battery in the low resistance direction. The high resistance in the opposite direction prevents the flow of current from the battery to the alternator. Because of this feature no circuit breaker is required between the alternator and battery.

CONTENTS

Introduction 1-63
Service Precautions 1-63
Chrysler System 1-63
Delco-Remy System 1-69
Ford Autolite System 1-75
Leece-Neville System 1-80
Motorola System 1-82
Prestolite System 1-86

SERVICE PRECAUTIONS

1. Be certain that the battery polarity of the system is known so that the battery is connected to the proper ground. *Reversed battery polarity will damage rectifiers and regulator.*
2. If booster batteries are used for starting they must be connected to the vehicle battery properly to prevent damage to rectifiers and regulators. Negative cable from booster battery to negative terminal on vehicle battery and positive booster cable to positive terminal.
3. When a fast charger is used to charge a vehicle battery, the vehicle battery cables should be disconnected *unless the fast charger is equipped with a special Alternator Protector,* in which case the vehicle battery cables need not be disconnected. Also the fast charger should never be used to start a vehicle as damage to rectifiers will result.
4. Lead connections to the grounded rectifiers (negative) on Prestolite and Chrysler units should never be soldered as the excessive heat may damage the rectifiers.
5. Unless the system includes a load relay or field relay, grounding the alternator output terminal will damage the alternator and/or circuits. This is true even when the system is not in operation since no circuit breaker is used and the battery is applied to the alternator output terminal at all times. The field or load relay acts as a circuit breaker in that it is controlled by the ignition switch.
6. When adjusting the voltage regulator, do not short the adjusting tool to the regulator base as the regulator may be damaged. The tool should be insulated by taping or by installing a plastic sleeve.
7. Before making any "on vehicle" tests of the alternator or regulator, the battery should be checked and the circuit inspected for faulty wiring or insulation, loose or corroded connections and poor ground circuits.
8. Check alternator belt tension to be sure the belt is tight enough to prevent slipping under load.
9. The ignition switch should be off and the battery ground cable disconnected before making any test connections to prevent damage to the system.
10. The vehicle battery must be fully charged or a fully charged battery may be installed for test purposes.

Chrysler Alternators

The Chrysler Corp. alternator, Figs. C1 and C2, is an A.C. generator with six built-in diodes that convert alternating current into direct current. Direct current is available at the "output" "BAT" terminal. A voltage regulator is used in the field circuit to limit the output voltage. The main components of the alternator are the rotor, the stator, the diode rectifiers, the two end shields and the drive pulley.

The only function of the voltage regulator is to limit the output voltage. The regulator accomplishes this by controlling the flow of current in the rotor field coil, and in effect controls the strength of the rotor magnetic field.

TESTING SYSTEM ON VEHICLE

Field Circuit Resistance Test

1. Referring to Fig. C3, disconnect ignition wire at coil side of ballast resistor and connect a test ammeter and voltmeter in the circuit as shown. All lights and accessories should be turned off.
2. Turn ignition switch on and turn voltmeter selector switch to the low voltage scale and read the meter. The voltage should not exceed .55 volt. A reading in excess of .55 volt indicates high resistance in field circuit between battery and voltage regulator field terminal.
3. If high resistance is indicated, move negative voltmeter lead to each connection along the circuit to the battery. A sudden drop in voltage indicates a loose or corroded connection between that point and the last point tested. To test the terminals for tightness, attempt to move the terminal while observing the voltmeter. Any movement of the meter pointer indicates looseness. *Note: Excessive resistance in the regulator wiring circuit will cause fluctuation in the ammeter.*
4. Turn ignition switch off, disconnect test instrument and reconnect ignition primary wire at the coil side of the ballast resistor.

Charging Circuit Resistance Test

With battery in good condition and fully charged, first disconnect the battery ground cable to avoid accidental shorting of the charging or field circuit when making the test connections shown in Fig. C4.

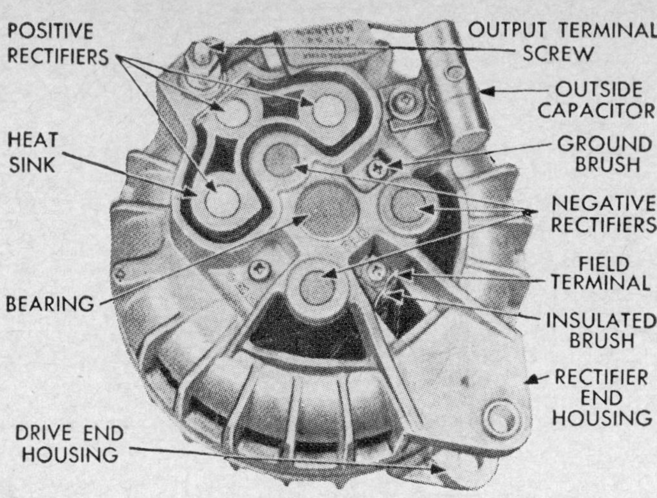

Fig. C1 Chrysler alternator

1. With the test instruments connected as shown and with battery ground cable re-connected, start and operate engine at a speed to obtain 10 amperes flowing in the circuit.
2. The voltmeter should not exceed .3 volt. If a higher voltage drop is indicated, inspect, clean and tighten all connections in the charging circuit. A voltage drop test may be performed at each connection to locate the connection with excessive resistance.
3. Turn ignition switch off. Disconnect ground cable at battery to avoid accidental shorting of the charging or field circuit when disconnecting the test instruments. Connect battery lead to alternator "BAT" terminal and tighten securely. Connect ignition lead to regulator ignition terminal and re-connect ground cable at battery.

Current Output Test

1. With test instruments connected in circuit as shown in Fig. C5, connect an engine tachometer.
2. Start and operate at 1250 rpm.
3. Adjust carbon pile rheostat to obtain a reading of 15 volts on the test voltmeter.
4. Observe reading on test ammeter.
5. If the output is slightly less (5 to 7 amperes) than the rated output of the alternator, it may be an indication of an open-circuited diode or other internal alternator problem.
6. If the output is considerably lower than the rated output of the alternator, it may be an indication of a short-circuited diode or other internal alternator problem. In either case the alternator should be removed and tested. *Note: Turn off the carbon pile rheostat immediately after observing reading on test ammeter.*
7. If the alternator current output tested satisfactorily, turn off the ignition switch and remove the jumper lead from the alternator field terminal and output terminal.

Voltage Regulator Test

UPPER CONTACT TEST

1. With engine at normal operating temperature and test instruments connected as shown in Fig. C6, start and operate the engine at 1250 rpm.

   Adjust carbon pile to obtain a 15 ampere output as indicated on test ammeter. *Note: No current reading on the ammeter would indicate either a low regulator setting or a blown fuse wire inside the voltage regulator between upper stationary contact and "IGN" terminal. Correct the cause and replace the fusible wire.*
2. Operate engine at 1250 rpm and a 15 ampere load for 15 minutes to make sure entire regulator system is stabilized.
3. Measure temperature at regulator by holding a reliable thermometer ¼ inch from regulator cover.
4. Read test ammeter. With fully charged battery and 15 amperes flowing in circuit, voltmeter readings should be within specifications.
5. If regulator operates within specifications, proceed to the lower contact voltage test. If not, remove cover and adjust voltage setting as outlined under "Regulator Adjustments".

LOWER CONTACT VOLTAGE TEST

1. Increase engine speed to 2200 rpm. Vary carbon pile to decrease current load to 7 amperes output as registered on test ammeter. The voltage should *increase* and amperage should *decrease*. *Note: There will be a slightly higher voltage at higher engine speeds above 2200 rpm. However, this increased voltage must not exceed the voltage specified by more than .7 volt at any temperature range.*
2. If the regulator setting is outside the specified limits, the regulator must be removed to remove the cover.
3. To adjust the voltage setting, bend the regulator lower spring hanger *down to increase voltage,* or *up to* decrease voltage setting, Fig. C7. The regulator must be installed, correctly connected, and retested after each adjustment of the lower spring hanger. *Note: If repeated readjustment is required, it is permissible to use a jumper wire to ground the regulator base to the fender splash shield for testing instead of reinstalling the regulator each time. However, it is important that the cover be reinstalled, the regulator connections correctly connected, and the regulator insulated to prevent grounding the regulator terminals or resistances. When testing, the regulator must be at the same at-*

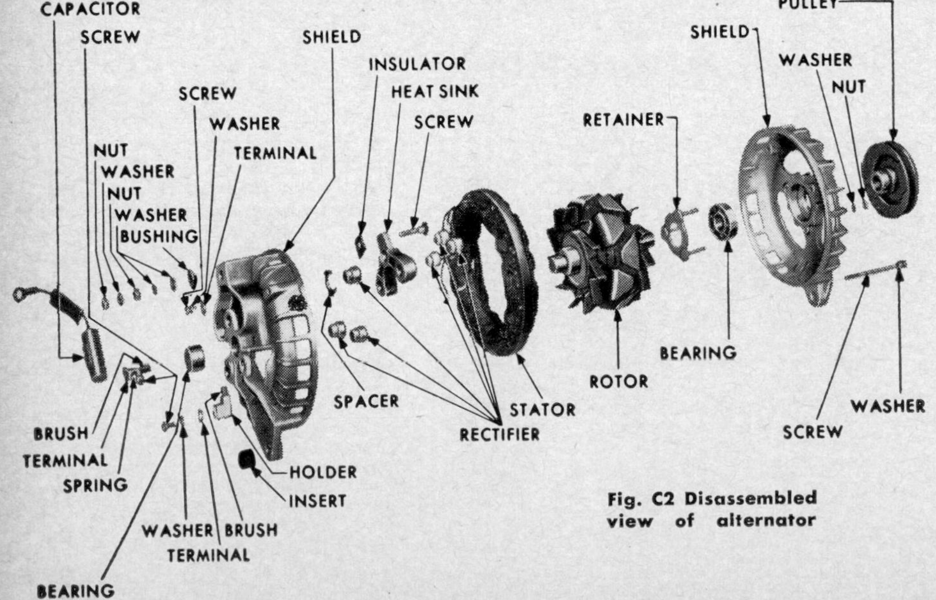

Fig. C2 Disassembled view of alternator

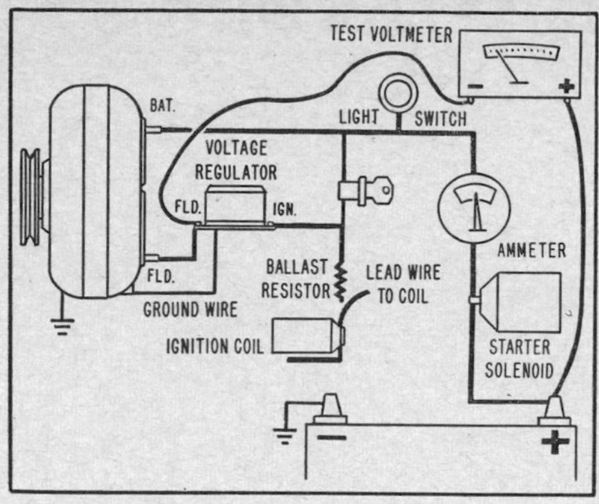

Fig. C3 Field circuit resistance test

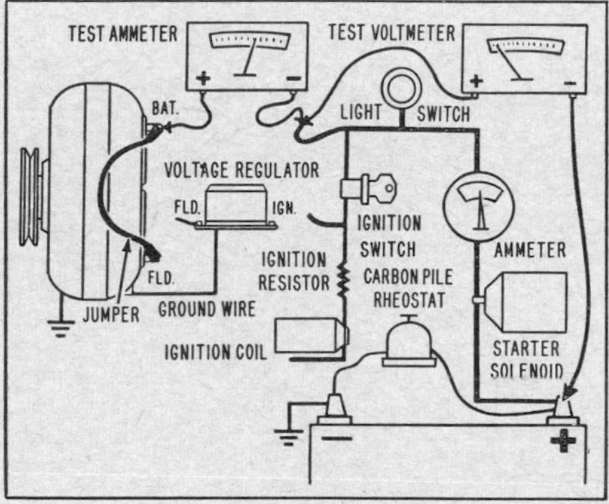

Fig. C4 Charging circuit resistance test

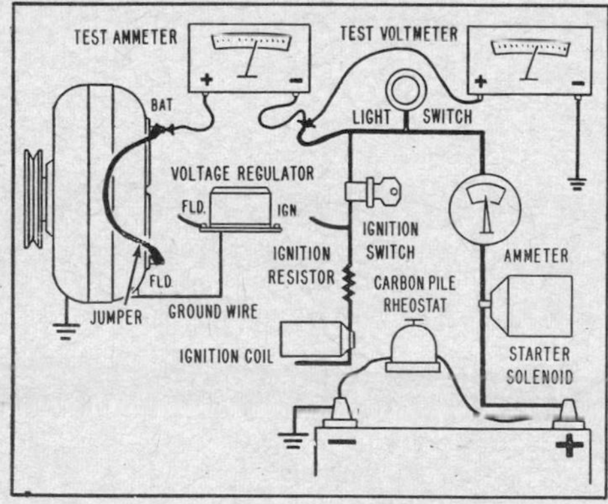

Fig. C5 Current output test

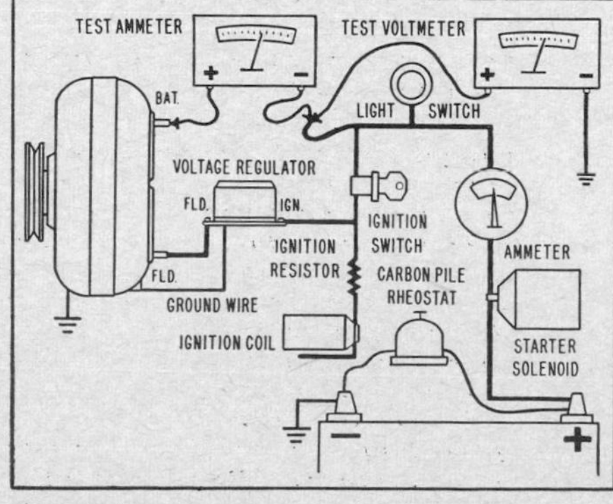

Fig. C6 Voltage regulator test

titude (or angle) as when installed on the vehicle.

4. If the alternator and regulator tested satisfactorily, turn the ignition switch off. Disconnect battery ground cable, then the test instruments. Connect the leads to alternator and regulator. Finally reconnect battery ground cable.

Regulator Adjustments

If the regulator cannot be adjusted for voltage control, or if the regulator performance is erratic or malfunctions, it may be necessary to adjust the air gap and contact point gap.

1. Remove regulator from vehicle and take off cover.
2. Insert a .048" wire gauge between regulator armature and core, next to stop pin on spring hanger side, Fig. C8.
3. Press down on armature (not contact spring) until it contacts wire gauge. Upper contacts should just open. *Note: A battery and test light connected in series to the "IGN" and "FLD" terminals may be used to determine accurately the contact opening. When the contacts open, the test light will go dim.*
4. Insert a .052" wire gauge between armature and core, next to stop pin on spring hanger side.
5. Press down on armature until it contacts wire gauge. The contacts should remain closed and test light should remain bright.
6. If adjustment is required, adjust air gap by loosening the screw and moving the stationary contact bracket. Make sure air gap is measured with attaching screw fully tightened. Re-measure the gap as directed above.
7. Remove wire gauge. Measure lower contact gap with feeler gauge, which should be .012 to .016". Adjust lower contact gap by bending lower stationary contact bracket.
8. Install regulator cover and then the regulator. Finally, make electrical adjustments as outlined above.

BENCH TESTS

If the alternator performance does not meet current output specification limits, it will have to be disassembled for further tests and servicing.

To remove the alternator, disconnect the battery ground cable and the leads at the alternator. Then unfasten and remove the alternator from the vehicle.

Field Coil Draw

1. Connect a test ammeter positive lead to the battery positive terminal of a fully charged battery.
2. Connect ammeter negative lead to the field terminal of the alternator.
3. Connect a jumper wire to negative terminal of battery, and ground it to the alternator end shield.
4. Slowly rotate alternator rotor by hand. Observe ammeter reading. The field coil draw should be 2.3 to 2.7 amperes at 12 volts.

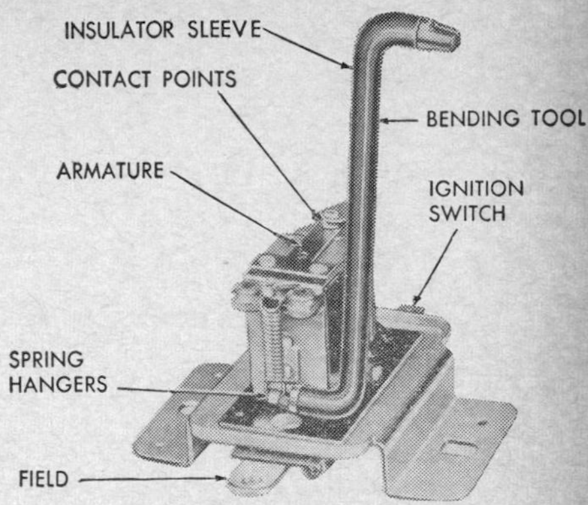

Fig. C7 Adjusting spring tension to obtain correct voltage

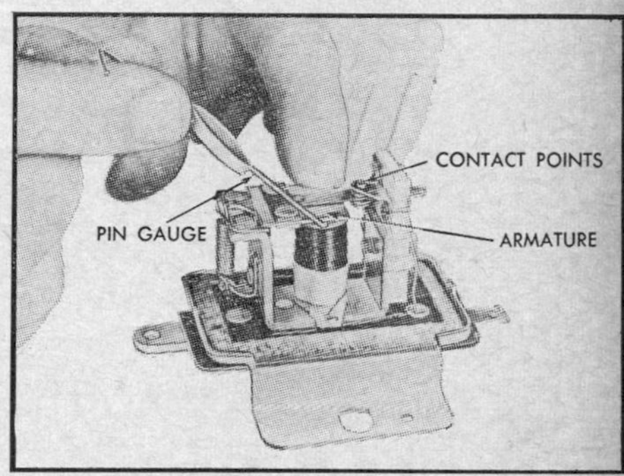

Fig. C8 Measuring armature air gap

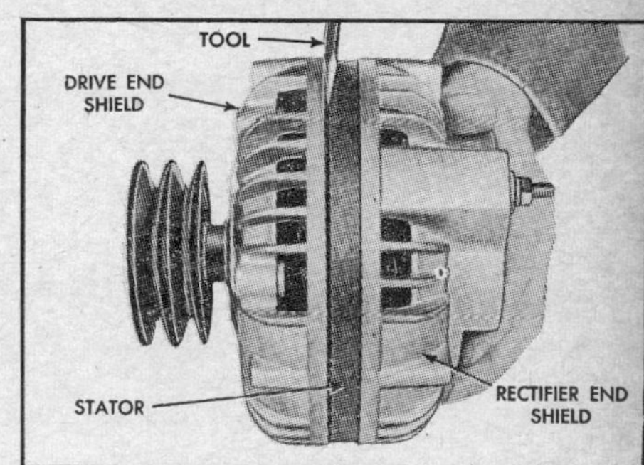

Fig. C9 Separating drive end shield from stator

A low rotor coil draw is an indication of a high resistance in the field coil circuit (brushes, slip rings or rotor coil). A higher rotor coil draw indicates a possible shorted rotor coil or a grounded rotor.

Testing Alternator Internal Field Circuit

1. To test the internal field circuit for a ground, remove the ground brush. Touch one test prod from a 110 volt test lamp to the alternator insulated brush terminal and the remaining test prod to the end shield. If the rotor or insulated brush is not grounded, the lamp will not light.

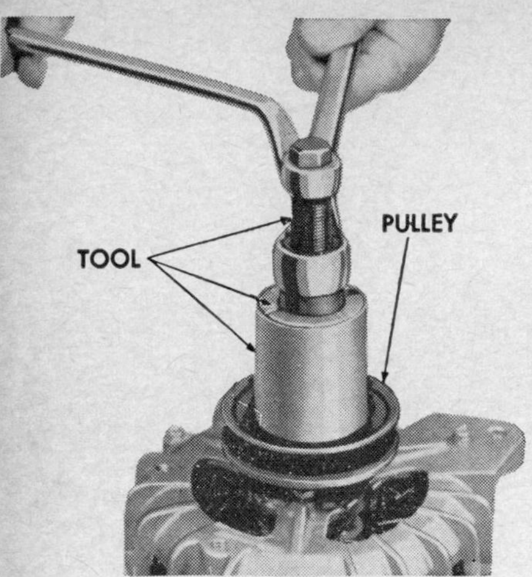

Fig. C10 Removing pulley

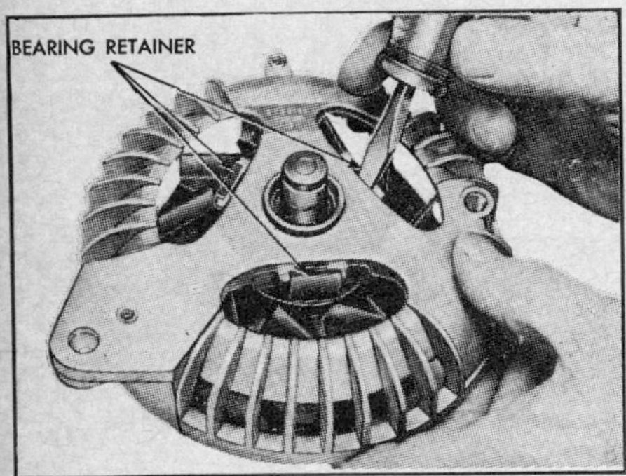

Fig. C11 Disengaging bearing retainer from end shield

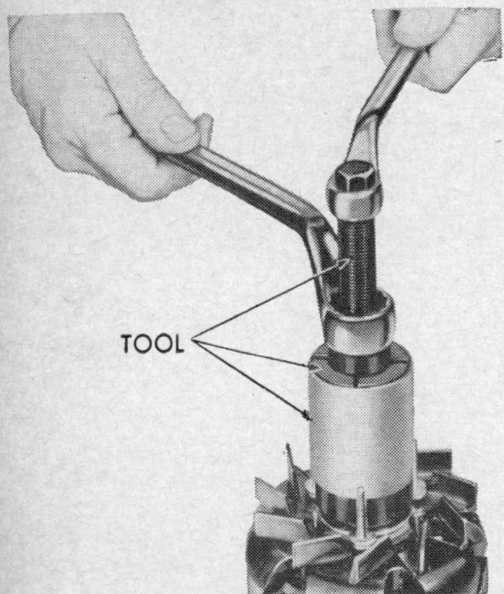

Fig. C12 Removing bearing from rotor shaft

2. If the lamp lights, remove insulated brush (noting how parts are assembled) and separate end shields by removing the three through bolts.
3. Again test by placing one of the test prods to the slip ring and the remaining test prod to the end shield. If the lamp lights, the rotor is grounded and requires replacement. If the lamp does not light after removing the insulated brush and separating the end shields, the insulated brush is grounded.
4. Examine the plastic insulator and screw. *The screw is a special size and must not be substituted by another size.*
5. Install insulated brush holder, terminal, insulated washer, shake proof washer and screw. *If the parts were not assembled in this order or if the wrong screw was used this could be the cause of the ground condition.*

ALTERNATOR REPAIRS

Disassembly

To prevent possible damage to the brush assemblies, they should be removed before proceeding with the disassembly of the alternator. The insulated brush is mounted in a plastic holder that positions the brush vertically against one of the slip rings. A disassembled view of the alternator is shown in Fig. C2.

1. Remove retaining screw lockwasher, insulated washer and field terminal. Carefully lift plastic holder containing the spring and brush from the end housing.
2. The ground brush is positioned horizontally against the remaining slip ring and is retained in a holder that is integral with the end shield. Remove retaining screw and lift the clip, spring and brush from end shield. *Note: The stator is laminated; do not burr it or the end shield.*
3. Remove through bolts and pry between stator and drive end shield with a screwdriver. Carefully separate drive end shield, pulley and rotor from stator and diode rectifier shield, Fig. C9.
4. The pulley is an interference fit on the rotor shaft; therefore, a suitable puller must be used to remove it, Fig. C10.
5. Pry drive end bearing spring retainer from end shield with a screwdriver, Fig. C11.
6. Support end shield and tap rotor shaft with a plastic hammer to separate rotor from end shield.
7. The drive end ball bearing is an interference fit with the rotor shaft; therefore, a suitable puller must be used to remove it, Fig. C12.
8. Remove D.C. output terminal nuts and washers and remove terminal screw and inside capacitor (if equipped). *Note: The heat sink is also held in place by the terminal screw.*
9. Remove the insulator, Fig. C13.
10. The needle roller bearing in the rectifier end shield is a press fit. If it is necessary to remove the rectifier end frame needle bearing, protect the end shield by supporting the shield when pressing out the bearing as shown in Fig. C14.

Testing Diode Rectifiers

A special Rectifier Tester Tool C-3829 provides a quick, simple and accurate method to test the rectifiers without the necessity of disconnecting the soldered rectifier leads. This instrument is commercially available and full instructions for its use is provided. Lacking this tool, the rectifiers may be tested with a 12 volt battery and a test lamp having a No. 67 bulb. The procedure is as follows:

1. Separate the three stator leads at the "Y" connection, Fig. C15. *Cut*

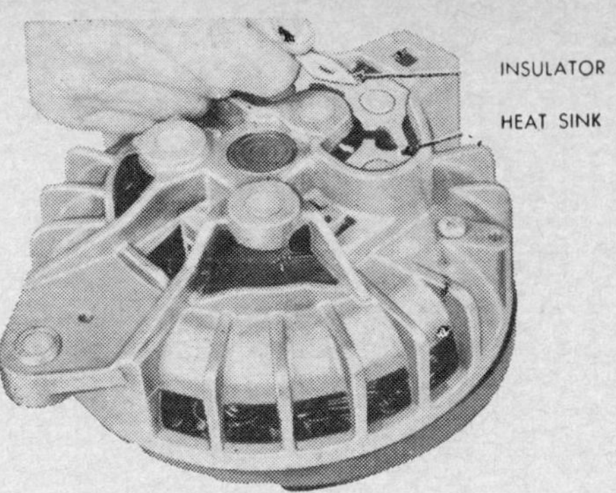

Fig. C13 Removing or installing heat sink insulator

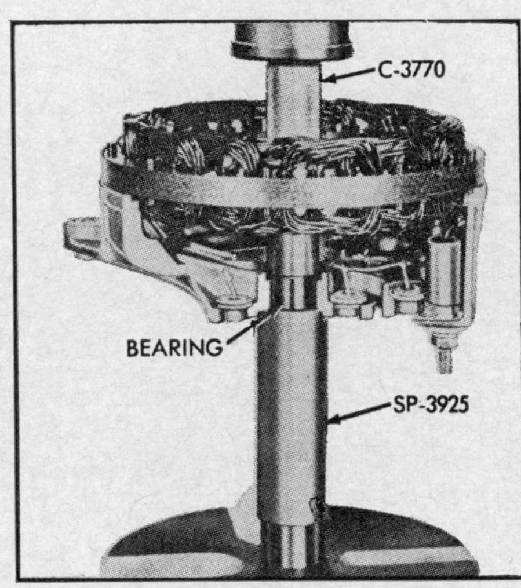

Fig. C14 Removing diode end shield bearing

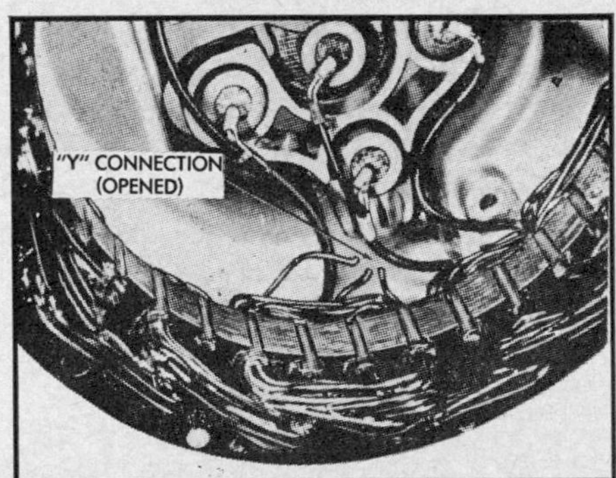

Fig. C15 Separating the three stator leads

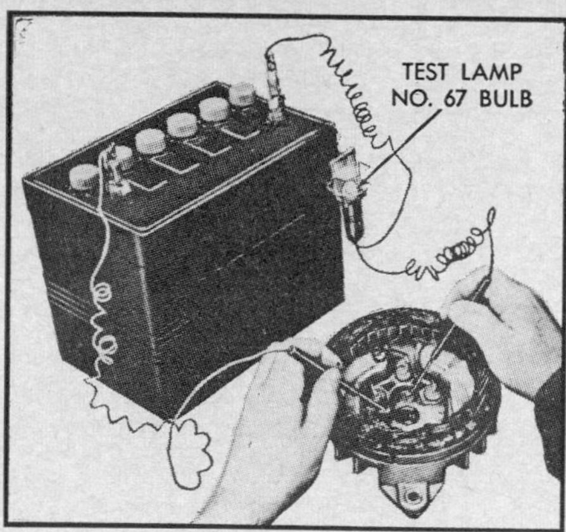

Fig. C16 Testing diodes with a test lamp

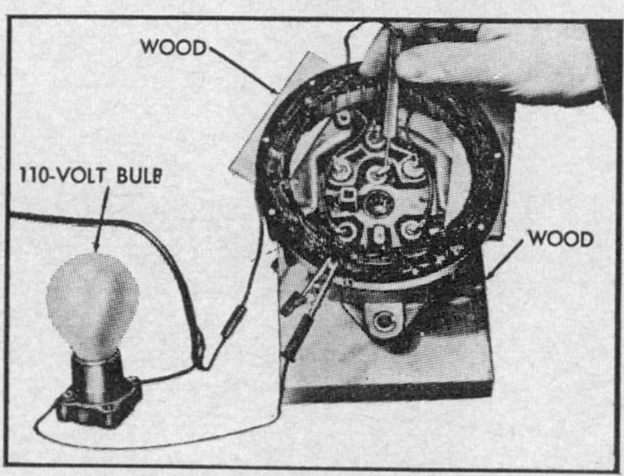

Fig. C17 Testing stator for grounds

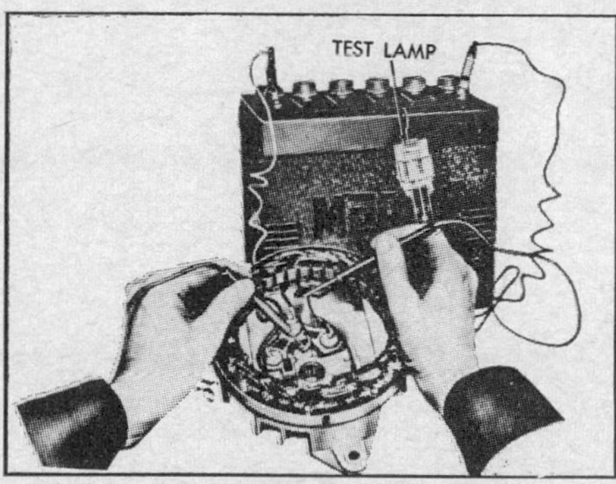

Fig. C18 Testing stator windings for continuity

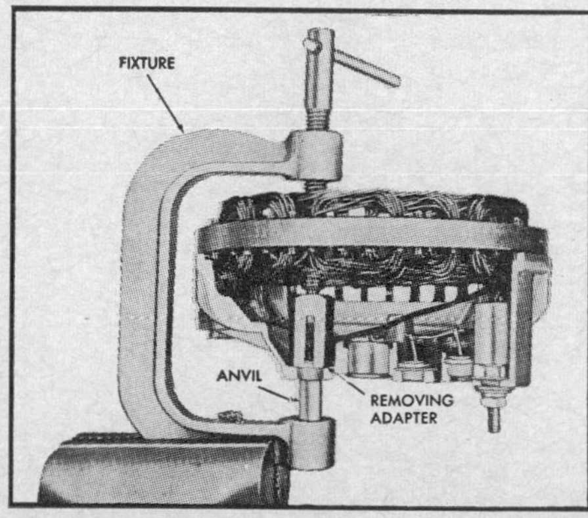

Fig. C19 Removing a diode

the stator connections as close to the connector as possible because they will have to be soldered together again. If they are cut too short it may be difficult to get them together again for soldering.

2. Connect one side of test lamp to positive battery post and the other side of the test lamp to a test probe. Connect another test probe to the negative battery post, Fig. C16.
3. Contact the outer case of the rectifier with one probe and the other probe to the wire in the center of the rectifier.
4. Reverse the probes, moving the probe from the rectifier outer case to the rectifier wire, and the probe from the wire to the case.
5. If the lamp lights in one direction but not in the other, the rectifier is satisfactory. If lamp lights in both directions, the rectifier is shorted. If the lamp does not light in either direction, the rectifier is open. *Note: Possible cause of an open or a blown rectifier is a faulty capacitor or a battery that has been installed on reverse polarity. If the battery is installed properly and the rectifiers are open, test the capacitor capacity, which should be .50 microfarad plus or minus 20%.*

Testing Stator

1. Unsolder rectifiers from stator leads.
2. Test stator for grounds using a 110 volt test lamp, Fig. C17. Use wood slats to insulate the stator from the rectifier shield.
3. Contact one prod of test lamp to the stator pole frame, and contact the other prod to each of the three stator leads. The lamp should not light. If the lamp lights, the stator windings are grounded.
4. To test the stator winding for continuity, connect one prod of the test lamp to all three stator leads at the "Y" connection. Contact each of the three stator leads (disconnected from diodes). The lamp should light when the prod contacts each of the three leads. If the lamp does not light, the stator winding is open, Fig. C18.
5. Install new stator if one tested is defective.

Removing Rectifiers

1. Three diodes are pressed into the heat sink and three in the end shield. When removing the diodes, it is necessary to support the end shield and/or heat sink to prevent damage to these castings.
2. Install the tools shown in Fig. C19, making sure bore of tool completely surrounds diode.
3. Carefully apply pressure to remove diode from end shield.

Replacing Slip Rings

1. Cut through rotor grease retainer with a chisel and remove retainer and insulator.
2. Unsolder field coil leads at solder lugs, Fig. C20.

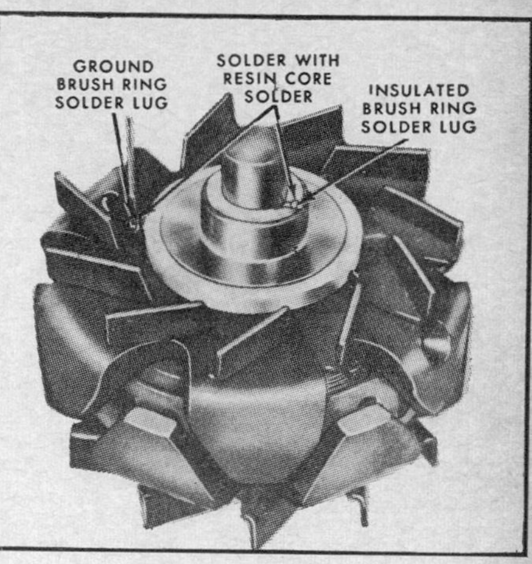

Fig. C20 Soldering points with slip ring installed

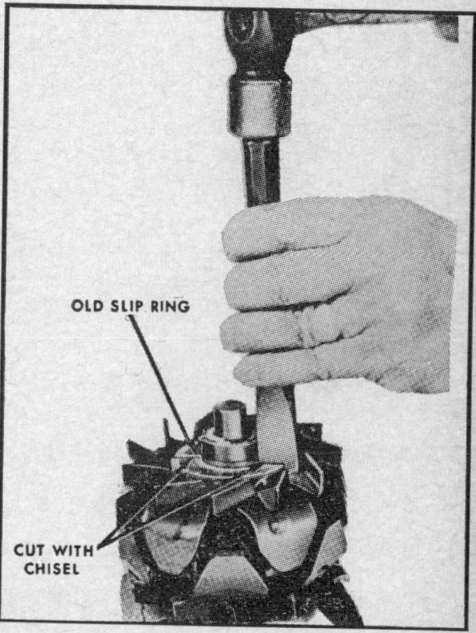

Fig. C21 Cutting old slip rings for removal

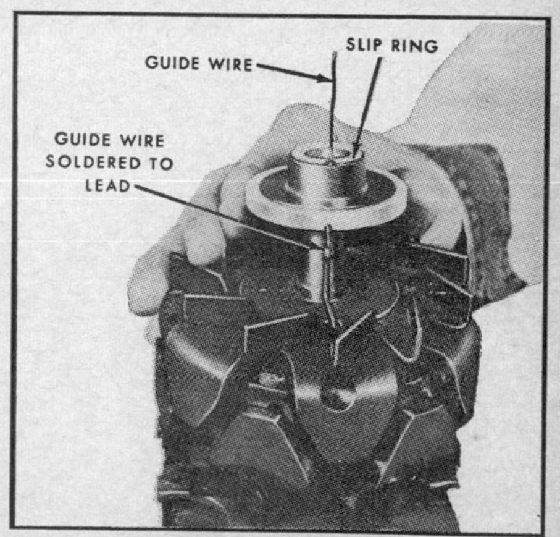

Fig. C22 Aligning slip ring with field wire and guide wire

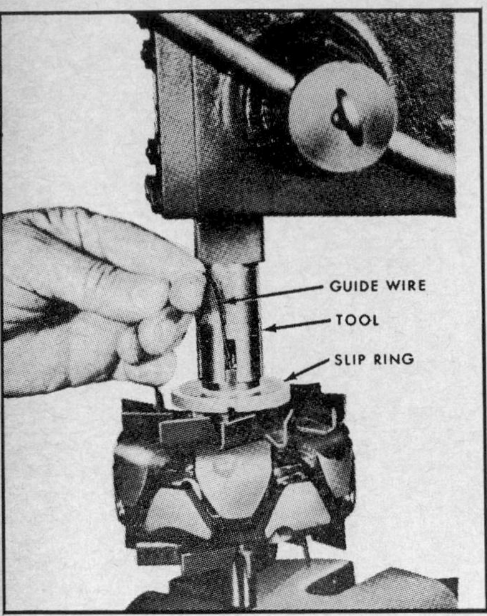

Fig. C23 Installing slip ring

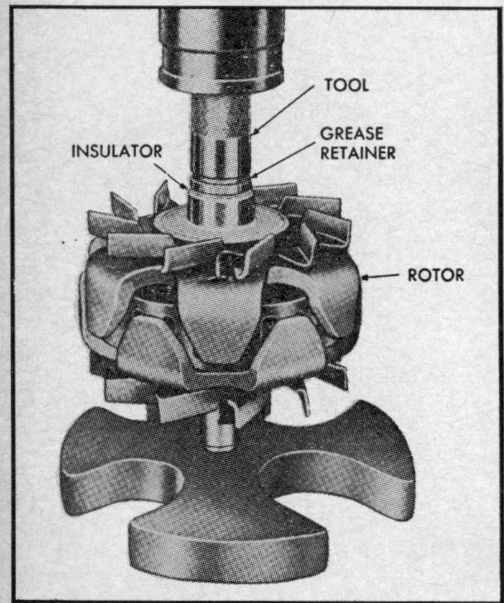

Fig. C24 Installing bearing grease retainer

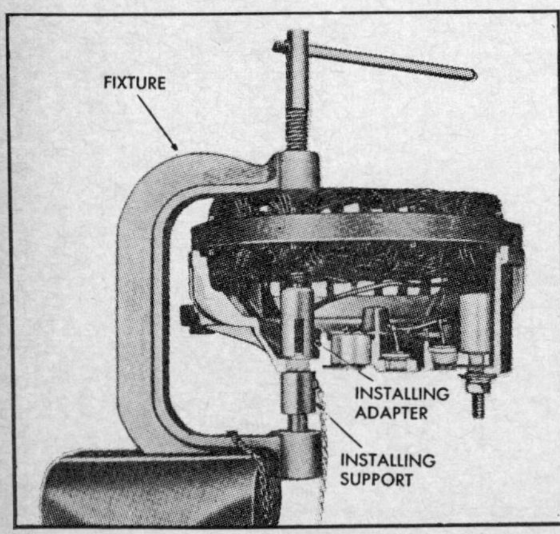

Fig. C25 Installing a diode

3. Cut through copper of both slip rings at opposite points with a chisel, Fig. C21.
4. Break insulator and remove old ring.
5. Clean away dirt and particles of old slip ring from rotor.
6. Scrape ends of field coil lead wires clean for good electrical contact.
7. Scrape one end (about $\frac{3}{16}$") of a piece of bare wire (about 18 gauge) three inches long to be used as a guide wire.
8. Tin the scraped area of the guide wire with resin core solder. Lap the tinned end of the wire over the field coil lead to the insulated ring and solder the two together.
9. Position new slip ring carefully over guide wire and rotor shaft so wire will lay in slip ring groove, Fig. C22. Groove in slip ring must be in line with insulated brush field lead to provide room for lead without damaging it.
10. Place installing tool over rotor shaft with guide wire protruding from slot in tool, Fig. C23.
11. Position rotor, slip ring and tool in arbor press, Fig. C23. Pull on guide wire, being careful to guide insulated field lead into slip ring groove. While guiding insulated field lead through groove, press slip ring on shaft. When slip ring is bottomed on rotor fan, end of field lead should be visible at solder lug, Fig. C20.
12. Unsolder guide wire from insulated brush slip ring lead. Press field lead into solder lug and solder to lug.

Caution: Be sure solder bead does not protrude beyond surface of plastic material. Do not use acid core solder as a short may result and corrosion will definitely occur.

13. Coil ground brush field lead around solder lug and solder with resin core solder.
14. Test slip rings for ground with a 110 volt test lamp by touching one test lead prod to rotor pole shoe and remaining prod to slip rings. The lamp should not light. If lamp lights, slip rings are shorted to ground, possibly due to a grounded insulated field lead when installing slip ring.
15. If rotor is not grounded, lightly clean slip ring surfaces with No. 00 sandpaper and assemble to alternator.
16. Position grease retainer gasket and retainer on rotor shaft and press retainer on shaft, Fig. C24. Retainer is properly positioned when inner bore of installer tool bottoms on rotor shaft.

Alternator Assemble

1. Install diodes as shown in Fig. C25.

Do not use a hammer to start diode in its bore in end shield. Do not hammer or shock diode in any manner as this will fracture the thin silicon wafer in the diode, causing complete diode failure.

2. Clean leads and mate stator lead with diode wire loop and bend loop snugly around stator lead to provide

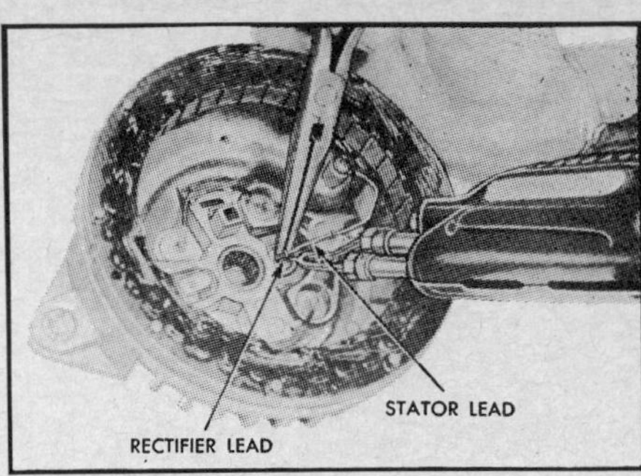

Fig. C26 Soldering diode and stator leads

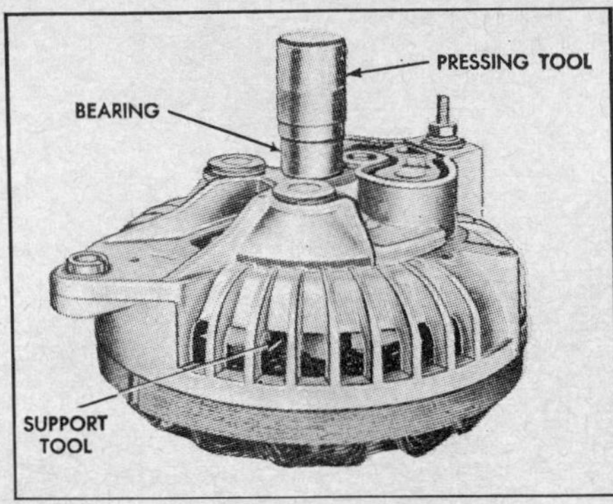

Fig. C27 Installing diode end shield bearing

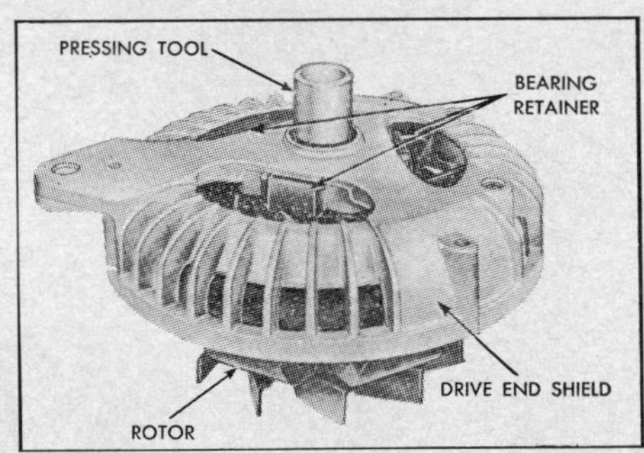

Fig. C28 Installing drive end shield and bearing

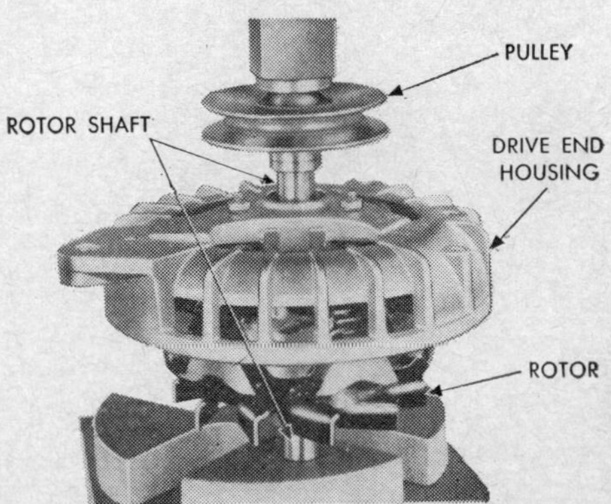

Fig. C29 Installing pulley

a good electrical and mechanical connection. Solder wires with resin core solder. Hold diode lead wire with pliers just below joint while soldering, Fig. C26. Pliers will absorb heat from soldering and protect diode. *Note: After soldering, quickly cool soldered connection by touching a damp cloth against it. This will aid in forming a solid joint.*

3. After soldering, stator leads must be pushed down into slots that are cast into end shield and cemented to protect leads against possible interference with rotor fans. Test each replacement diode to make certain it was not damaged by soldering or pressing operation. (Cement to use is Mopar No. 2299314.)
4. Install diode end shield bearing, Fig. C27.
5. Press bearing on rotor shaft until bearing contacts shoulder on shaft, Fig. C28.
6. Install pulley, Fig. C29. Do not exceed 6800 lbs. pressure. Press pulley on rotor shaft until pulley contacts inner race of drive end bearing.
7. Make sure heat sink insulator is in place. Then install capacitor stud through heat sink and end shield.
8. Install insulating washers, lockwashers and lock nuts.
9. Make sure heat sink and insulator are in position and tighten lock nut.
10. Position stator on diode end shield.
11. Position rotor end shield on stator and diode end shield.
12. Align through bolt holes in stator, diode end shield and drive end shield.
13. Compress stator and both end shields by hand and install through bolts, washers and nuts.
14. Install insulated brush in diode end. Place bronze terminal on plastic holder with tab of terminal in recess in plastic holder.
15. Place nylon washer on bronze terminal and install lockwasher and attaching screws.
16. Install ground brush and attaching screw.
17. Rotate pulley slowly by hand to be sure rotor fans do not touch diodes, capacitor lead and stator connections.
18. Install alternator and adjust drive belt.
19. Connect leads to alternator.
20. Connect battery ground cable.
21. Start and operate engine and observe alternator operation.
22. If necessary, test current output and regulator voltage setting.

DELCOTRON WITH EXTERNAL REGULATOR

DESCRIPTION

Alternator

The "Delcotron", being the trademark of the Delco-Remy alternator, is a continous output, diode rectified alternating current generator, Fig. D1. The rotor is mounted on a ball bearing at the drive end, and a roller bearing at the slip ring end. Each bearing has a grease supply which eliminates the need for periodic lubrication.

Two brushes are used to carry current through the two slip rings to the field coil which is mounted on the rotor. The brushes are extra long and under normal operating conditions will provide long periods of service.

The stator windings are assembled on the inside of a laminated core that forms part of the alternator frame. Fig. D2 illustrates the internal lead connections.

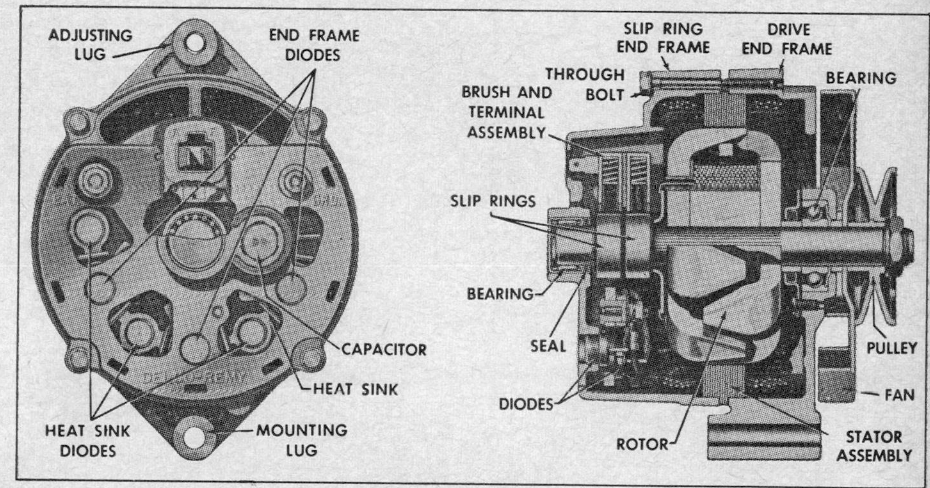

Fig. D1 Sectional end and side views of "Delcotron" alternator

Regulator

The regulator, Fig. D3, similar to those used with D.C. generators, is made up of a double contact voltage regulator. Unlike the regulators used with D.C. generators, however, there is no need for a current regulator. And since the diodes permit current to flow through the circuit in only one direction, the need for a cutout relay is also eliminated.

When the vehicle has a charge indicating light, a field relay is incorporated, as shown in Fig. D3. When the vehicle is equipped with an ammeter, the field relay is not required. Fig. D4 shows a wiring diagram of the system.

On some vehicles, for example the 1963 Pontiac with high performance engine equipped with Delco-Remy Transistorized Ignition, a Transistor regulator is furnished; more about this regulator later on.

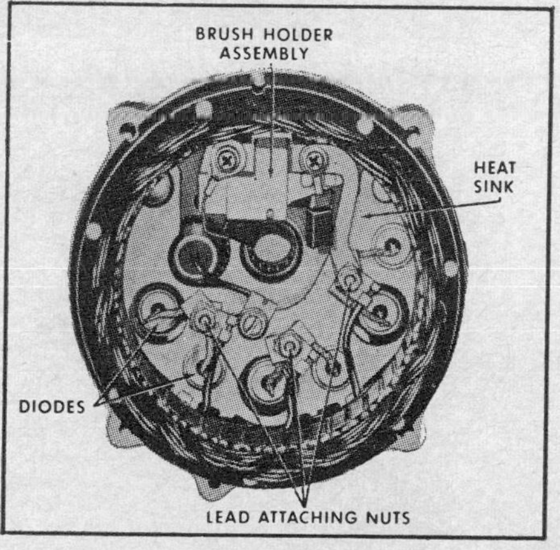

Fig. D2 Alternator internal lead connections

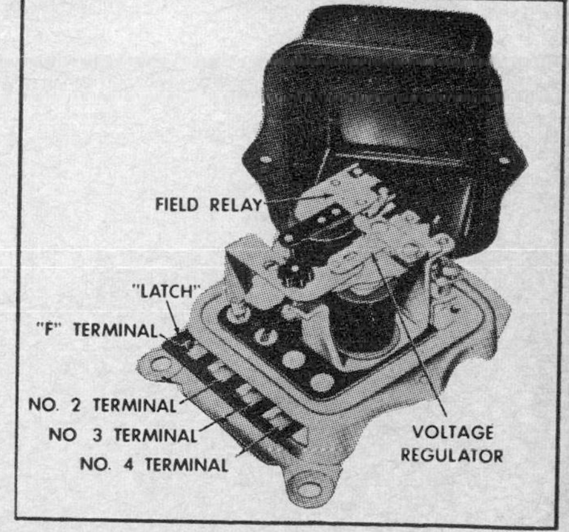

Fig. D3 Voltage regulator. The field relay is used only on vehicles having a charge indicator light instead of an ammeter

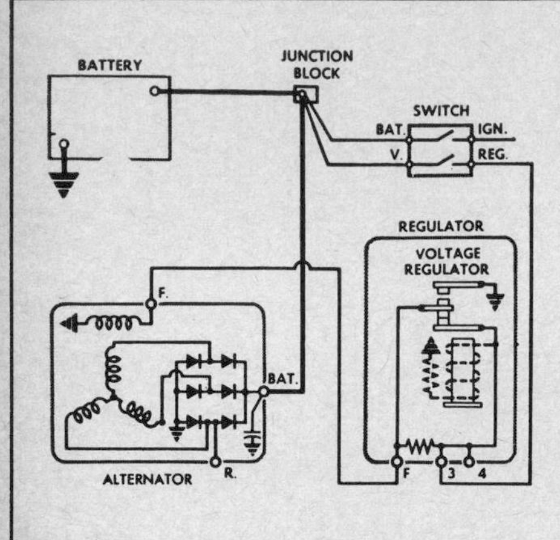

Fig. D4 Wiring diagram of the alternator charging circuit

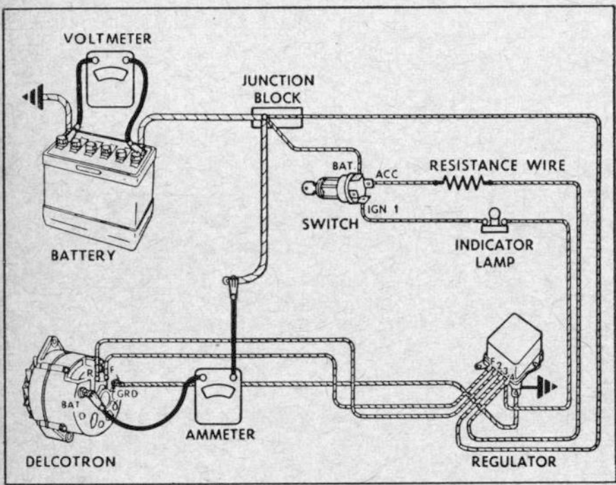

Fig. D5 Alternator test connections

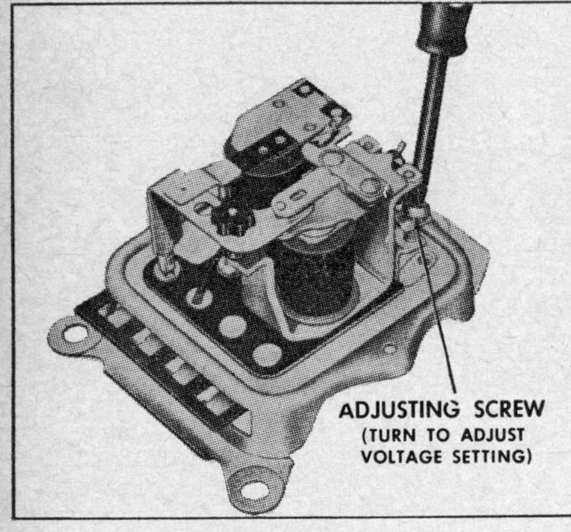

Fig. D7 Adjusting voltage regulator setting

Air Temperature at Regulator	85°	105°	125°	145°	165°
Voltage Setting	13.8-14.6	13.7-14.5	13.5-14.3	13.4-14.2	13.2-14.0

Fig. D6 Voltage regulator settings

TESTING SYSTEM IN VEHICLE

Current Output Test

1. Check and adjust belt tension if necessary.
2. Disconnect ground cable from battery.
3. Connect test ammeter between alternator "BAT" terminal and disconnected lead as shown in Fig. D5.
4. Connect tachometer from distributor terminal of coil to ground.
5. Reconnect battery ground cable and connect a voltmeter across battery.
6. Turn on all possible accessory load.
7. Apply parking brake firmly.
8. Start engine and adjust engine idle speed to the recommended setting (usually 500 rpm in Drive).
9. At this engine speed alternator output should be 5 amperes or more.
10. Shift transmission to Neutral. Then increase engine speed to 1500 rpm. Output should be 25 amperes or more.
11. Shut off engine and turn off all accessories.
12. If output is low in either of the above tests, try supplying the field directly to cause full alternator output. Unplug the connector from the alternator. Then connect a jumper wire from the alternator "F" terminal to the "BAT" terminal. Retest as described above. If the output is still low, the alternator is faulty and must be removed for bench tests and repairs.
13. If the output (using field jumper) is now satisfactory, the trouble is in the voltage regulator or wiring harness. Clean and test regulator, and check all wiring connections.
14. Remove field jumper and reinstall vehicle field connector.

Test & Adjust Regulator

1. Leave all test instruments in place, Fig. D5, but make sure field jumper is removed if one was used (see above).
2. Install a thermometer near the regulator.
3. Run engine at about 1500 rpm for 15 minutes. Make sure all electrical load except ignition is turned off.
4. Check ammeter reading. For an accurate voltage setting check, ammeter must read between 3 and 10 amperes. If ammeter reading is still high after 15 minutes, it may be necessary to substitute a fully charged battery.
5. Momentarily increase engine speed to 2000 rpm and read voltmeter and thermometer. See Fig. D6 to determine if upper voltage regulator setting is within limits for the existing temperature. If setting is within limits and battery condition has been satisfactory, *voltage setting should not be disturbed.*
6. If voltage regulator setting is not within correct limits, make a note of the change required to place voltage in the middle of the specified range. Remove regulator cover, carefully lifting it straight up. *Caution: If cover touches regulator unit, the resulting arc may ruin the regulator assembly.*
7. With cover off, voltage reading will change considerably. Starting with the changed voltage reading, increase or decrease voltage as required as shown in Fig. D7. *Caution: Always make final adjustment by increasing spring tension to assure contact between screw head and spring support.*
8. After making an adjustment, replace cover carefully. Cycle the regulator by unplugging connector from alternator. Reinstall connector in alternator and recheck voltage setting of regulator.

Tailoring Voltage Regulator

It is important to remember that the voltage setting for one type of operating condition may not be satisfactory for a different type of operating condition. Vehicle under-hood temperatures, operating speeds, and night-time service all are factors which help determine the proper voltage setting. The proper setting is attained when the battery remains fully charged with a minimum use of water.

If no circuit defects are found, yet the battery remains undercharged, raise the setting by .3 volt, and then check for an improved battery condition over a service period of reasonable length. If the battery remains overcharged, lower the setting by .3 volt, and then check for an improved battery condition. However, never adjust the voltage setting out of the limits specified in Fig. D6.

ALTERNATOR SERVICE

If the system is not charging properly and the "In Vehicle Tests" indicated that the trouble is in the alternator, it need not be removed from the vehicle unless the drive end frame needs servicing because the slip ring end frame separates from the drive end frame by simply loosening the drive belt and removing the four through bolts. If the drive end frame must be serviced, remove and disassemble the alternator as follows:

Alternator Removal

1. Disconnect battery positive cable to avoid an injury from the hot battery lead at alternator.
2. Remove two leads at alternator.
3. Loosen adjusting bolts and remove drive belt.
4. Remove alternator retaining bolts and take off alternator.

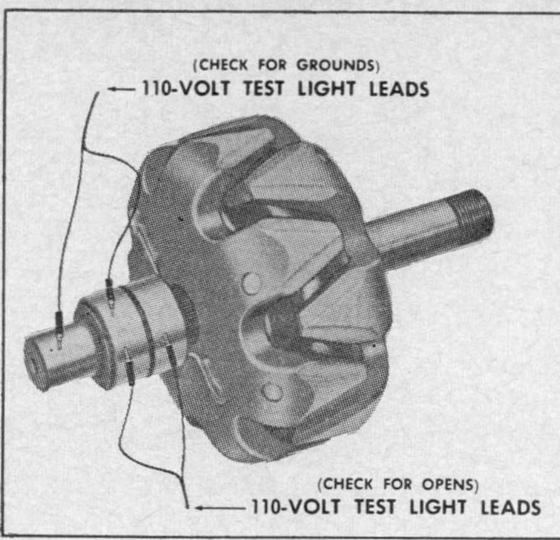

Fig. D8 Checking rotor for opens or grounds

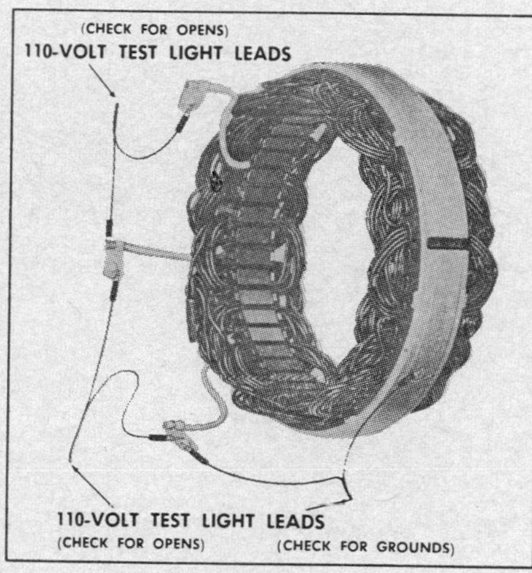

Fig. D9 Checking stator for opens or grounds

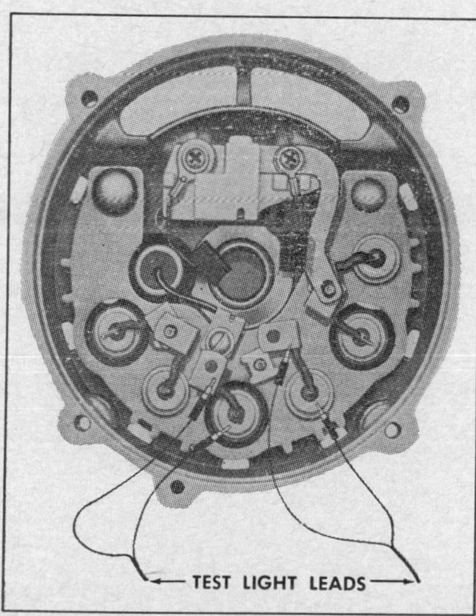

Fig. D10 Checking diodes for opens or shorts

Alternator Disassembly

1. If rotor, drive end frame bearings, or pulley and fan need replacement, remove and replace the shaft nut, using a strap wrench around the fan assembly. *Note: If the nut should happen to be cross-threaded or rusted and unusually difficult to remove, an alternate procedure is to use the strap wrench around the rotor.*
2. Scribe a mark between the two halves of the alternator to help locate the parts in the same position during reassembly.
3. Remove four through bolts.
4. Separate the drive end frame and rotor assembly from the stator assembly by prying apart with a screwdriver at the stator slot. The fit between the two is not tight and the two can be separated easily. The separation is to be made between the stator and drive end frame. *Caution: As the rotor and drive end frame is separated from the slip ring frame, the brushes will fall down onto the shaft and come in contact with the lubricant. Brushes which come in contact with the shaft should be cleaned immediately to avoid contamination by oil, or they will have to be replaced.*

Rotor Checks

1. To check for grounds, connect a 110 volt test lamp from either slip ring to the rotor shaft, Fig. D8. If the lamp lights the field winding is grounded.
2. To check for opens, connect the test lamp to each slip ring. If the lamp fails to light the winding is open.
3. The winding is checked for short circuits by connecting a battery and ammeter in series with the two slip rings. The field current at 12 volts and 80°F. should be between 1.9 and 2.3 amperes. *Note: For vehicles with Delco-Remy transistorized ignition and transistor voltage regulator, the field current should be between 2.8 and 3.2 amperes.*
4. An ammeter reading above the values given indicates shorted windings, and the rotor assembly should be replaced.

Stator Checks

1. To check the stator windings, remove all three stator lead attaching nuts and separate the stator from the end frame.
2. The stator winding may be checked with a 110 volt test lamp. If the lamp lights when connected from any stator lead to the frame, the windings are grounded. If the lamp fails to light when successively connected between each pair of stator leads, the windings are open, Fig. D9.
3. A short circuit in the stator windings is difficult to locate without laboratory test equipment due to the low resistance of the windings. However, if all other electrical checks are normal and the alternator fails to supply rated output, shorted stator windings are indicated.

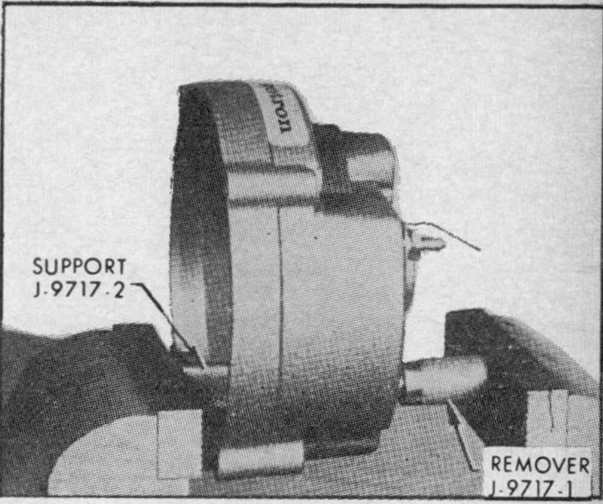

Fig. D11 Removing a diode

Fig. D12 Installing a diode

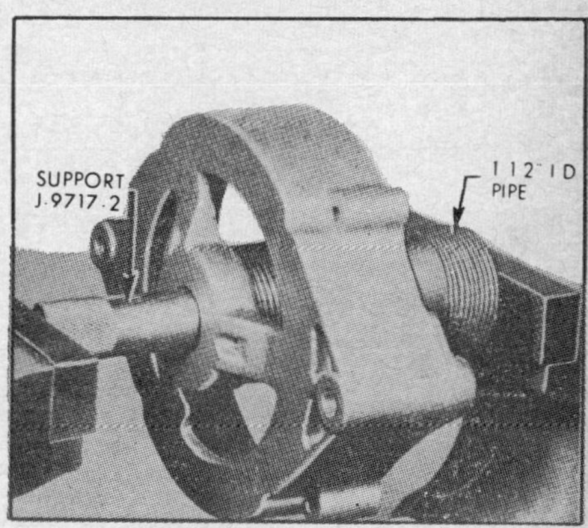

Fig. D13 Removing drive end frame bearing

Fig. D14 Installing drive end frame bearing

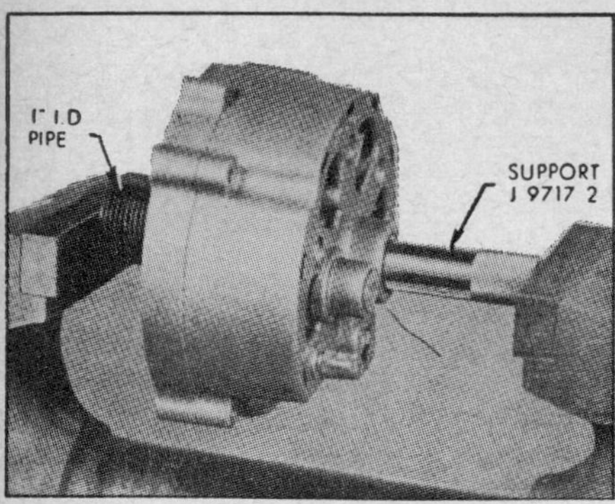

Fig. D15 Removing slip ring end frame bearing

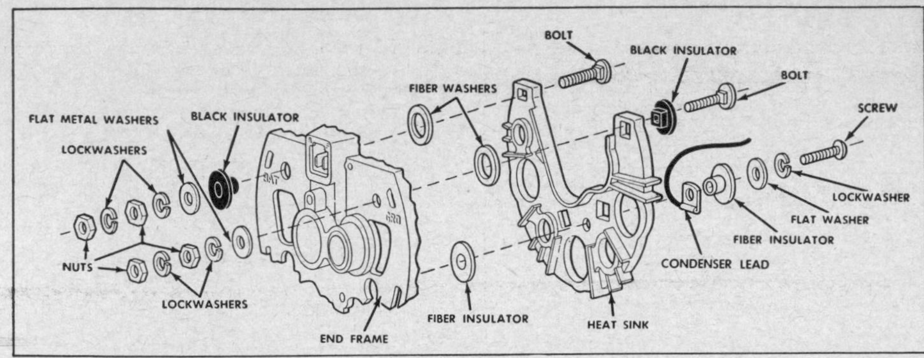

Fig. D18 Disassembled view of heat sink and related parts

Fig. D16 Installing slip ring end frame bearing

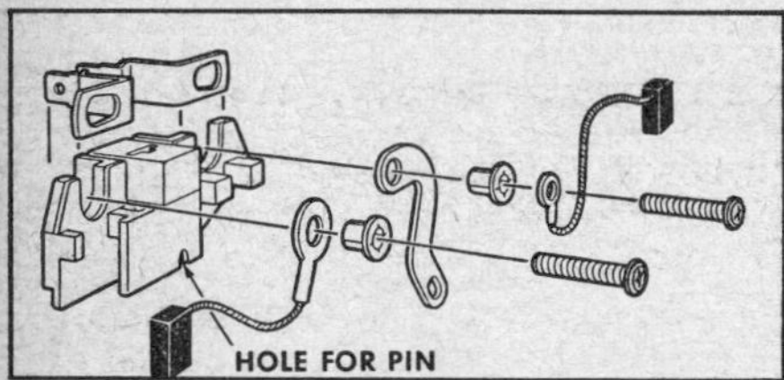

Fig. D17 Assembling brush holder and related parts

Diode Checks

1. Each diode should be checked electrically for a shorted or open condition using a *test lamp of not more than 12 volts*, Fig. D10.
2. With the stator disconnected, connect the test lamp leads across each diode, first in one direction and then in the other.
3. If the lamp lights in both checks, or fails to light in both checks, the diode is defective.
4. When checking a good diode, the lamp will light in only one of the two directions.

Diode Replacement

1. To remove a diode, place slip ring end frame in a vise with the remover equipment mounted as shown in Fig. D11. Tighten the vise to remove the defective diode.
2. To install a diode, place the new diode in the installer, Fig. D12. With the tools installed in the vise as shown, tighten the vise to install the new diode. *Caution: Never attempt to remove or install a diode by striking it as the shock may damage the other diodes.*

Slip Ring Service

If the slip rings are dirty they may be cleaned with No. 400 silicon carbide paper and finish polished with crocus cloth. Spin the rotor in a lathe, or otherwise spin the rotor, and hold the polishing cloth against the slip rings until they are clean.

CAUTION: The rotor must be rotated in order that the slip rings will be cleaned evenly. Cleaning the slip rings by hand without spinning the rotor may result in flat spots on the slip rings, causing brush noise.

Slip rings that are rough or out-of-round should be trued in a lathe to .002" maximum runout as indicated on a dial gauge. Remove only enough material to make the rings smooth and round. Finish polish with crocus cloth and blow away all dust.

Bearing Replacement

1. The bearing in the drive end frame can be removed by detaching the retainer plate screws and then pressing the bearing from the end frame as shown in Fig. D13.
2. To install a new bearing, press in with a tube or collar that just fits over the outer race, Fig. D14. It is recommended that a new retainer plate be installed if the felt seal in the retainer plate is hardened or excessively worn.
3. The bearing in the slip ring end frame can be removed by pressing with a tube or collar that just fits inside the end frame housing. Press from the outside of the housing towards the inside as shown in Fig. D15.
4. To install the new bearing, place a flat plate over the bearing and press in from the outside towards the inside of the frame until the bearing is flush with the outside of the end frame. Support the inside of the frame with the pipe shown to prevent breakage of the end frame, Fig. D16.
5. Saturate the felt seal with S.A.E. 20 oil and reassemble the felt seal and steel retainer.

Brush Replacement

1. When the slip ring end frame assembly is separated from the rotor and drive end frame, the brushes will fall down onto the shaft and come in contact with the lubricant. If the brushes are to be re-used, they must be thoroughly cleaned with a soft dry cloth immediately. Also, the shaft must be thoroughly cleaned before reassembly.
2. The brush springs should be inspected for any evidence of damage or corrosion. If there is any doubt as to the condition of the brush springs, they should be replaced.
3. To install new brushes, remove the brush holder assembly from the end frame by detaching the two screws.
4. Install the springs and brushes into the brush holder, and insert a straight wire or pin into the holes at the bottom of the holder to retain the brushes, Fig. D17.
5. Attach the brush holder assembly to the end frame, noting carefully the proper stack-up of the parts as shown. Allow the straight wire to protrude through the hole in the end frame.

Heat Sink Replacement

1. The heat sink may be replaced by removing the "BAT" and "GRD" terminals from the end frame, and the screw attaching the condenser lead to the heat sink.
2. During reassembly, note carefully the proper stack-up of parts as shown in Fig. D18.

Alternator Reassembly

1. Reassembly is the reverse of disassembly. Refer to Fig. D2 for connection of internal leads.
2. When installing the pulley, secure the rotor in a vise only tight enough to permit tightening the shaft nut to a torque of 50-60 ft. lbs. If excessive pressure is applied to the rotor, the assembly may become distorted.
3. To install the slip ring end frame to the rotor and drive end frame, remove the tape over the bearing and shaft (if used for protection) upon disassembly, and make sure the shaft is perfectly clean.
4. Insert a straight wire as previously mentioned through the holes in the

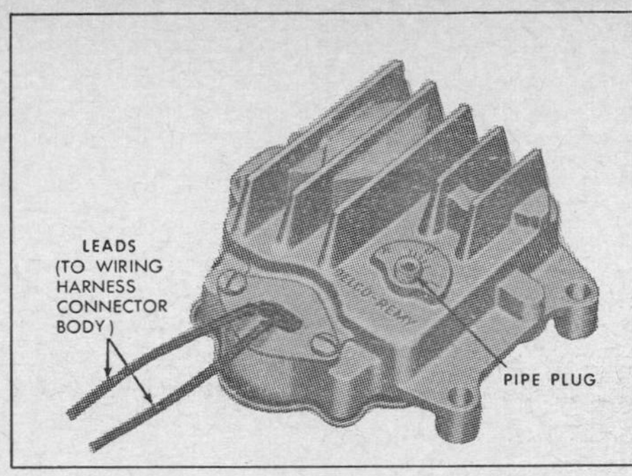

Fig. D19 Transistor regulator

brush holder and end frame to retain the brushes in the holder. Then withdraw the wire after the alternator has been completely assembled. The brushes will then drop onto the slip rings.

TRANSISTOR REGULATOR

The transistor regulator, Fig. D19, is an assembly composed principally of transistors, diodes, resistors, a capacitor, and a thermistor to form a completely static unit containing no moving parts.

The transistor is an electrical devise which limits the alternator voltage to a preset value by controlling the alternator field current. The diodes, capacitor and resistors act together to aid the transistor in controlling the voltage, which is the only function that the regulator performs in the charging circuit. The thermistor provides a temperature-compensated voltage setting.

The voltage at which the alternator operates is determined by the regulator adjustment. The regulator voltage setting can be adjusted externally by removing a pipe plug in the cover, Fig. D19, and turning the adjusting arm inside the regulator. This procedure is explained later on, and permits regulator adjustments without removing the cover.

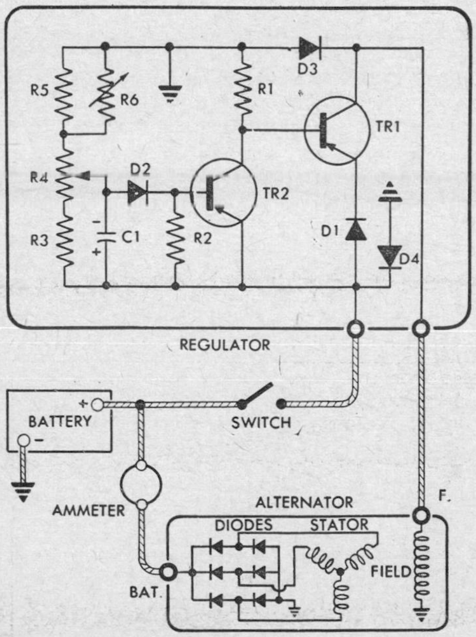

Operating Principles

A typical wiring diagram showing internal circuits is shown in Fig. D20. When the switch is closed, current flows through diode D1 and transistor TR1 in the regulator to the alternator "F" terminal, and then through the alternator field winding to ground.

When alternator voltage reaches a preset value, the other components of the regulator cause transistor TR1 alternately to "turn-off" and "turn-on" the alternator field current. The regulator thus operates automatically to limit the alternator voltage to a preset value.

Fig. D20 Wiring diagram of transistor regulator in charging circuit

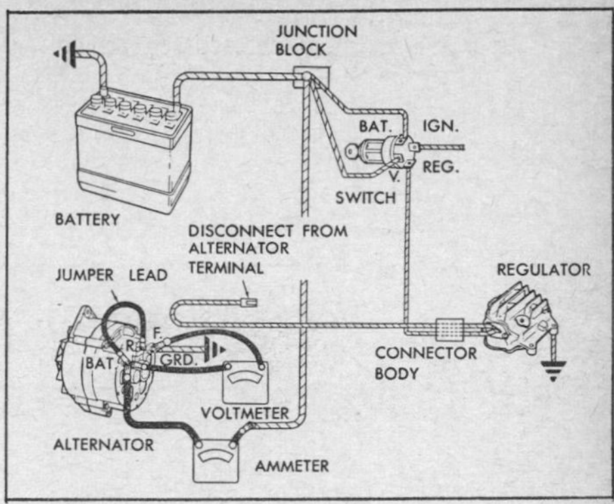

Fig. D21 Checking charging circuit for undercharged battery condition

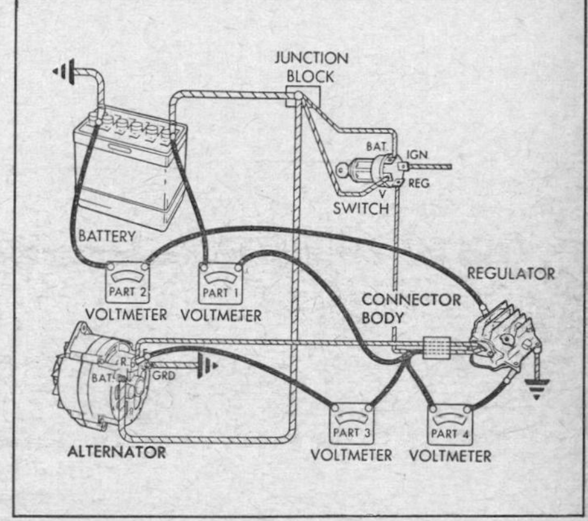

Fig. D22 Checking charging circuit for overcharged battery condition

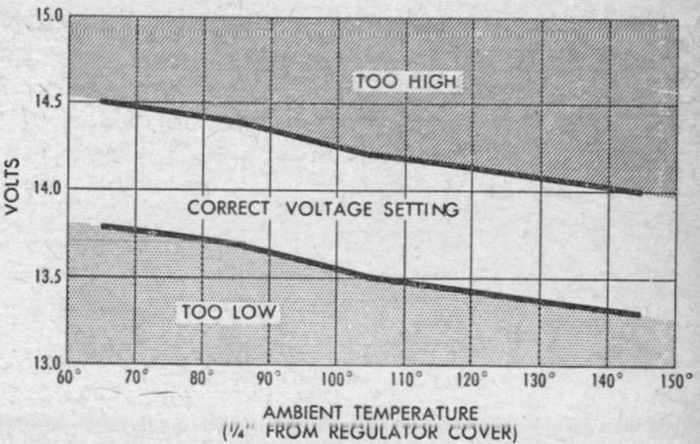

Fig. D23 Temperature correction chart

Checking Circuit

1. Connect test ammeter and voltmeter in circuit as shown in Fig. D21, and connect a jumper wire from alternator "F" terminal to alternator "BAT" terminal.
2. Operate alternator at specified speed, turn on accessories as required to obtain specified voltage and observe output. For example, the alternator used with this regulator on 1963 Pontiac has a rated output of 52 amperes at 14 volts at a speed of 5000 rpm.
3. If current output is low, remove and check the alternator as outlined previously.
4. If the alternator failure was caused by a defective stator or diodes, the repaired alternator may be installed back on the vehicle and no further checks are needed.
5. If the alternator failure was caused by a defective field winding, the repaired alternator may be installed back on the vehicle and the following checks must be made to locate possible damage to regulator.
6. Referring to Fig. D21, remove jumper lead and reconnect wiring harness connector to alternator "F" terminal.
7. Turn on ignition switch but do not start engine.
8. Connect voltmeter positive lead to battery positive terminal and negative lead into regulator black lead connector body to make connection to regulator (Part 1, Fig. D22). Record voltage drop.
9. Connect voltmeter to negative terminal of battery and ground on regulator (Part 2, Fig. D22). Record voltage drop.
10. If addition of voltage readings is greater than .3 volt, check ignition switch for poor contacts and system wiring for high resistance. If voltage difference is less than .3 volt, proceed as follows, referring to Part 3, Fig. D22.
11. Connect voltmeter positive lead to regulator positive terminal and voltmeter negative lead to alternator "F" terminal. Slide voltmeter positive lead into regulator connector body (black lead terminal) to make connection. Record voltage.
12. If the voltage is .9 volt or less, replace regulator, as transistor is shorted. If voltage is 2.0 volts or greater, replace regulator as transistor is open. If voltage is between .9 and 2.0 volts, proceed as follows:
13. Operate engine at approximately 1500 rpm for 10 minutes with low beam headlights on. Referring to Part 4, Fig. D22, with engine running at 1500 rpm, record voltage reading from regulator positive terminal to ground by sliding voltmeter lead into regulator connector body black lead terminal to make connection.
14. Compare with Fig. D23. Ambient temperature is temperature of air measured ¼" from regulator cover.
15. If voltage reading is within specifications, charging system is satisfactory but voltage setting may need

to be changed to a different value to meet the requirements of driving conditions.

16. To do this, remove the pipe plug on regulator and insert a small screwdriver in adjustment slot. Turn counterclockwise for an undercharged battery one or two notches to increase setting.
17. For an overcharged battery, as evidenced by excessive water usage, turn clockwise one or two notches to decrease setting. For each notch moved, voltage setting will change by approximately .3 volt. Then check for an improved battery condition over a service period of reasonable length.
18. If voltage is not within specifications, check to see if the adjustment arm is in the center position. If the voltage reads out of specifications in the center position, replace the regulator.

DELCOTRON INTEGRAL CHARGING SYSTEM

Fig. 1 External view of Delcotron Integral Charging System

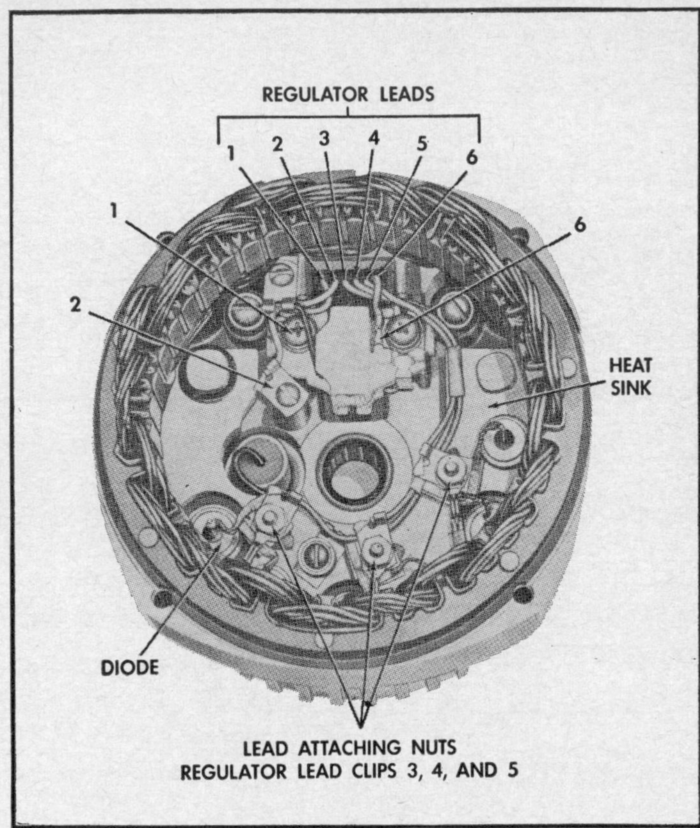

Fig. 2 Slip ring end frame and regulator leads. ICS Delcotron

Description

This unit, Fig. 1, is a self-contained charging system with miniaturized integrated circuitry which eliminates the traditional external regulator. The system voltage is controlled by an integrated regulator within the alternator, Fig. 2. In other words, there is no separate regulator mounting, no external wiring between regulator and alternator, no voltage adjustments for the life of the unit, and no periodic maintenance.

Checking Regulator

The procedures for testing and servicing the alternator proper is similar to the standard Delcotron. However, the integrated regulator may be checked for defects as follows:

1. Separate the stator from the end frame by removing the three stator lead attaching nuts, Fig. 2.
2. Remove numbers 3, 4 and 5 regulator lead clips from the studs.
3. Using the lowest range scale on an ohmmeter having a 1½ volt cell, connect to one of the three discon-

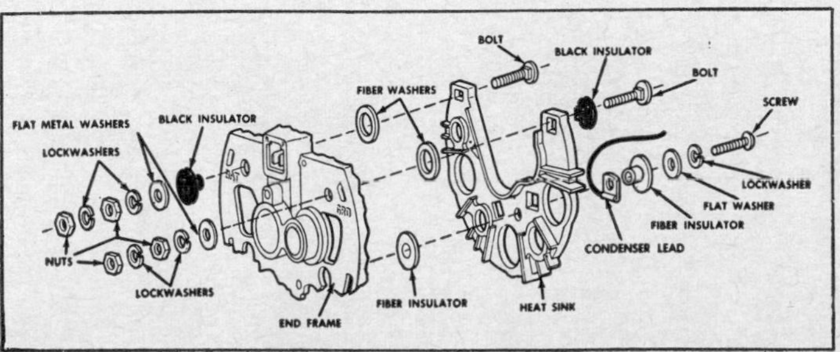

Fig. 4 Exploded view of heat sink. Standard and ICS Delcotrons

nected regulator leads and to the alternator No. 1 terminal as shown in Fig. 3. Note ohmmeter reading.

4. Reverse ohmmeter lead connections and again note ohmmeter readings.
5. If both readings are the same, the regulator is defective and must be replaced. The ohmmeter should give one high and one low reading. Check the other two regulator leads in the same manner.

Regulator, Replace

1. Detach the six regulator lead clips and two regulator heat sink attaching screws, sleeve insulators, and flat washer insulators, Fig. 2.
2. Remove regulator from heat sink by removing the regulator mounting screws. Carefully note stack-up of parts.
3. Attach negative brush connection to regulator heat sink.
4. Assemble regulator, noting carefully the proper stack-up of parts and being sure all electrical connectors at brush holder mounting screws are located under the flat washer insulators. Also check brush lead positions to insure freedom of brush movement and absence of shorts or grounds.

NOTE: Except for attachment of regulator, stack-up of parts in heat sink assembly is the same in both the Integrated unit and the standard alternator, Fig. 4.

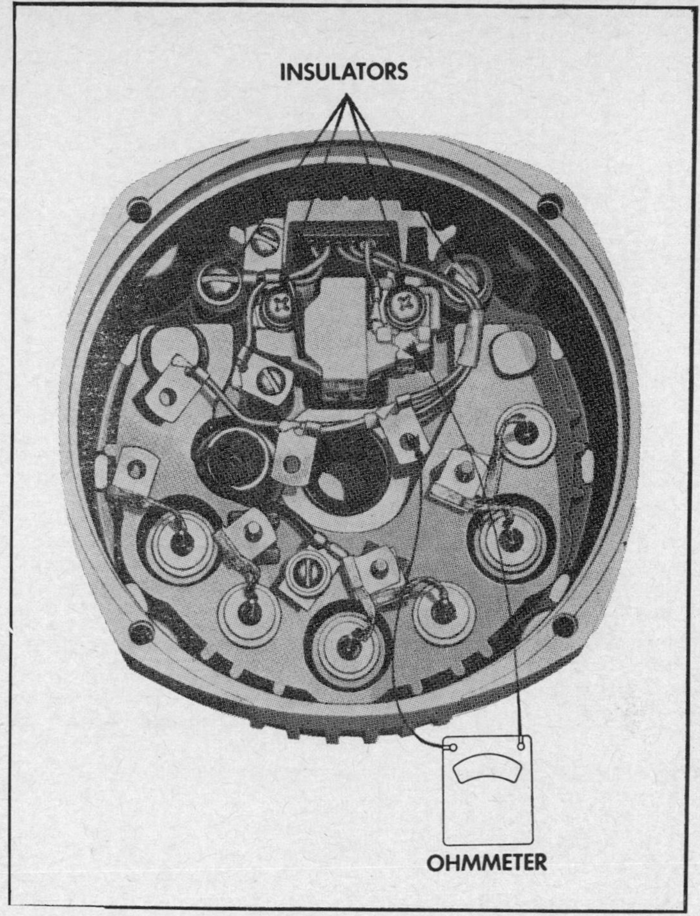

Fig. 3 Checking ICS Delcotron regulator

Ford Autolite Alternator

TESTING SYSTEM IN VEHICLE

Alternator Output Test

1. Make connections as shown in Fig. 2. Be sure that the Generator Field Control is in the "open" position at the start of this test.
2. Close the battery adapter switch. Start the engine, then open the battery adapter switch. *All electrical accessories, including door operated interior lights must be turned off.*
3. Carefully increase engine speed to a tachometer reading of 2900 rpm. *Do not exceed this speed.*
4. Adjust the Generator Field Control until the voltmeter reads exactly 15 volts. Observe the ammeter reading. Add 5 amperes to this reading to obtain total alternator output. The 5-ampere factor represents the field current and the ignition system current, and must be added to the ammeter reading as these currents are not indicated on the ammeter. *Make this test in the shortest possible time and do not exceed 2900 rpm. If the battery was fully charged, it might not be possible to obtain maximum current output. If specified current is not obtained, make the following test before condemning the alternator.*
5. Turn the Generator Field Control to the "open" position. Rotate the tester control knob to the "load" position. Maintain 2900 rpm engine speed.
6. Adjust the Generator Field Control and the "load" control, maintaining a voltmeter reading of 15 volts maximum, until the Generator Field Control is at its maximum clockwise position.
7. Readjust the "load" control until the voltmeter reads exactly 15 volts. Observe the ammeter reading. Add 5 amperes to this reading to obtain total alternator output.
8. Stop the engine, return the Generator Field Control to the "open" position and disconnect the test equipment.

Test Analysis

1. An output of 2 to 5 amperes below specifications indicates an open diode rectifier. An output of approximately 10 amperes below specifications indicates a shorted diode rectifier. *An alternator with a shorted diode will usually whine, which will be noticeable at idling speed.*
2. A shorted *positive* diode may sometimes be accompanied by alternate flashing of the oil pressure and charge indicator lights when the ignition switch is off. The field relay contacts will also be closed and the battery will be discharging through the field to ground.
3. Under this condition, the instrument constant voltage regulator will receive power through the charge indicator light. The operating of the constant voltage through the charge indicator light causes the alternate flashing of the lights. When the regulator contacts close, the oil pressure light becomes dim and the charge indicator light becomes bright. When the contacts open the oil pressure light becomes bright and the charge indicator light becomes dim.

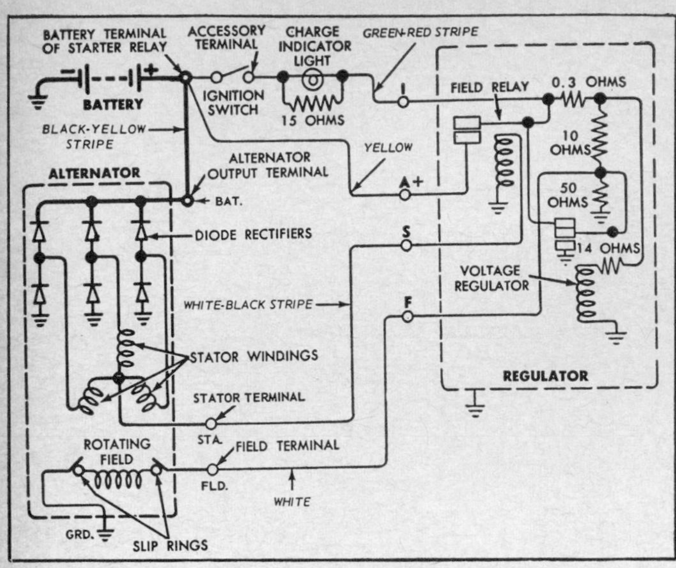

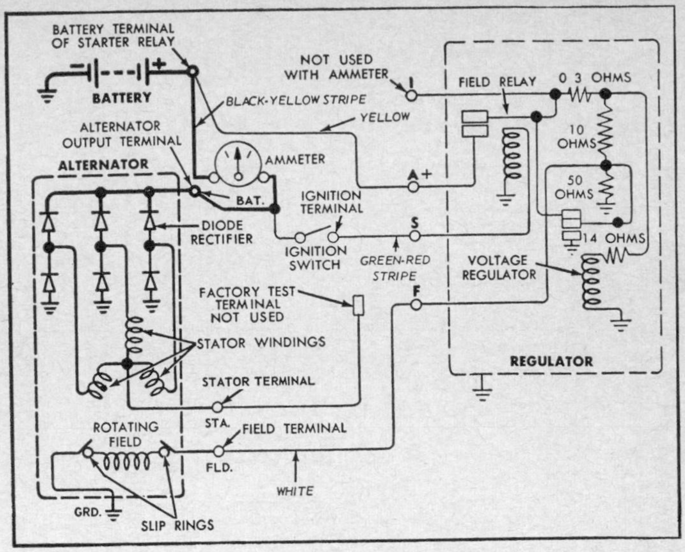

Fig. 1 Ford Autolite alternator wiring diagram with charge indicator light

Fig. 1A Ford Autolite alternator wiring diagram with ammeter

Diode Test

1. To test the positive diodes, make connections shown in Fig. 3. Connect the probe to each diode lead. Make sure that the tip of the probe is sharp and that it penetrates the varnish at the diode terminal.
2. To test the negative diodes, make the connections shown in Fig. 4. Follow the same procedure as for positive diodes.
3. Good diodes will be indicated as on the meter in Figs. 3 and 4, that is, 2 amperes or more and readings alike within 2 scale divisions.

Field Open or Short Circuit Test

1. Make connections as shown in Fig. 5. The normal current draw, as indicated by the ammeter, should be as specified in the *Alternator and Regulator Specifications* chart in the car chapters.
2. If there is little or no current flow, the field has a high resistance or is open, or the brushes are not making proper contact with the slip rings.
3. A current flow considerably higher than that specified (usually 2.9 to 3.1 at 12 volts) indicates shorted or grounded turns.
4. If the test shows that the field is shorted, *and the field brush assembly is not at fault,* the entire rotor must be replaced.

Field Relay Supply Voltage Test

The regulator field relay will close only if the voltage supplied by the neutral terminal of the alternator is sufficient to operate the relay. The wiring from the alternator neutral terminal to the relay "S" terminal also must be intact. The following test will show that both sufficient voltage is available and that the wiring is in good condition.

1. Remove the connector plug from the regulator, remove the regulator, then reinstall the connector plug.
2. Connect the negative voltmeter lead to ground. Start the engine and operate it at 400 to 500 rpm.

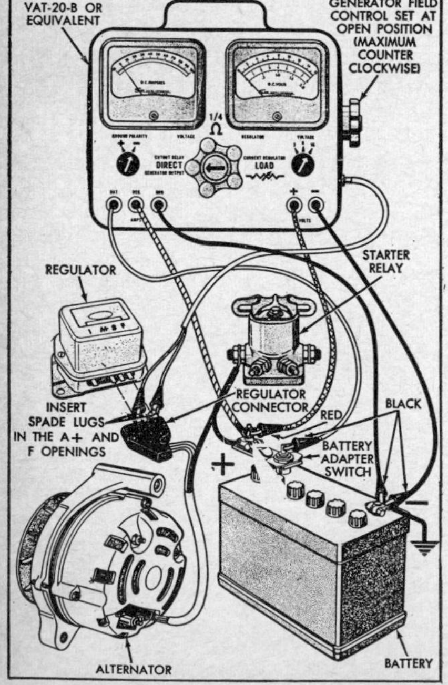

Fig. 2 Alternator output test

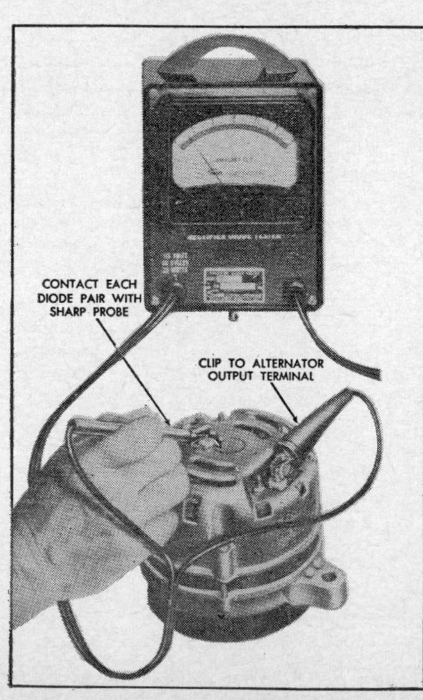

Fig. 3 Positive diode test

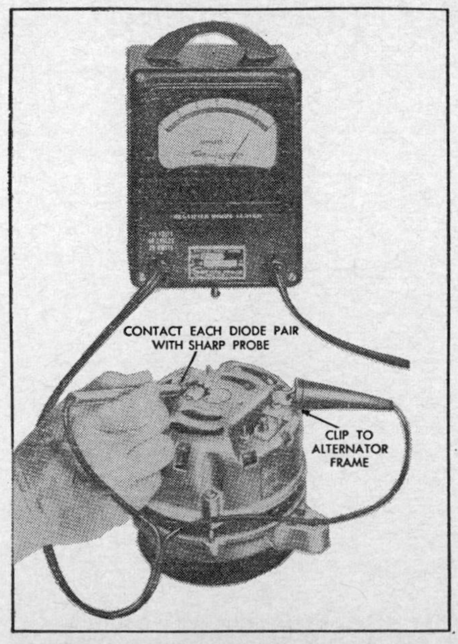

Fig. 4 Negative diode test

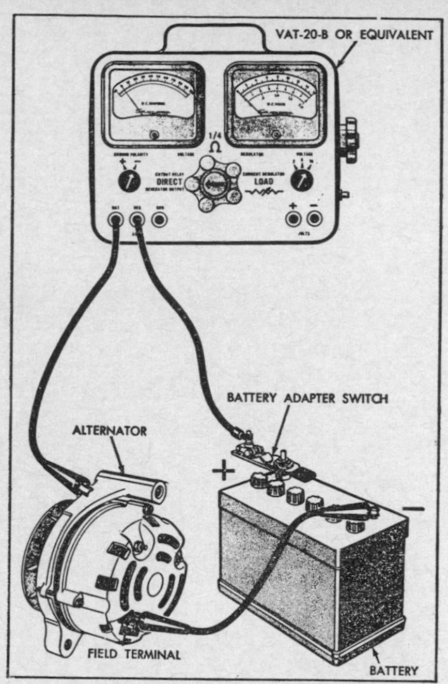

Fig. 5 Field open or short circuit test

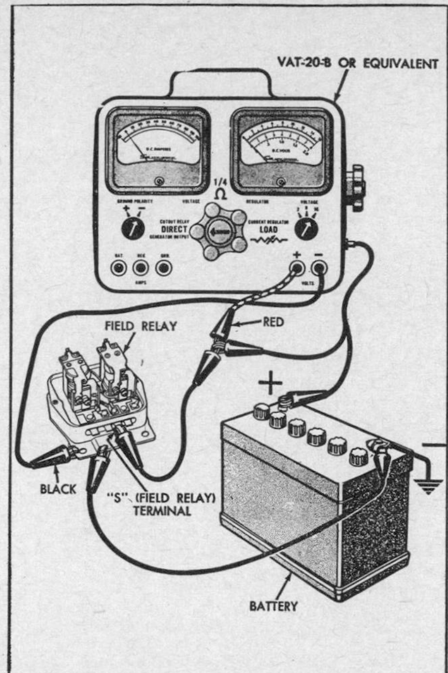

Fig. 6 Field relay test

Fig. 7 Voltage limiter test

3. Connect the positive voltmeter lead to a small screwdriver. Touch the screwdriver to the center rivet at the front of the regulator. *Use care to touch only the rivet or the rivet terminal so as not to short this point to ground or to the other nearby terminals.* The voltmeter should indicate at least 6 volts, and the relay contacts should be closed.
4. Low voltage at this point can be caused by a defective alternator or defective wiring.

REGULATOR TESTS

The following tests are to be made with the regulator in the vehicle. Be sure that the regulator is at "normal" operating temperature. This is equivalent to the temperature after 20 minutes of operation with a 10-ampere load.

Field Relay Test

1. Disconnect regulator terminal plug and remove the regulator cover.
2. Make connections shown in Fig. 6.
3. Slowly rotate field resistance control clockwise from the off position until the field relay contacts close.
4. Observe the voltmeter reading at the moment that the relay closes. This is the relay closing voltage.
5. If the relay closes immediately, even with the field resistance close to the "off" position, use a 6 volt battery for this test.
6. If the closing voltage is not within specifications, adjust the relay.

Voltage Limiter Test

For test purposes, the lower stage regulation is used (armature vibrating of the lower contact). Voltage limiter calibration test must be made with the regulator cover in place and the regulator at "normal" operating temperature (equivalent to temperature after 20 minutes of operation with a 10-ampere load).

1. Make test connections shown in Fig. 7.
2. Turn off all accessories, including door-operated dome lights.
3. Close battery adapter switch, start engine, then open adapter switch.
4. Attach the voltage regulation thermometer to regulator cover.

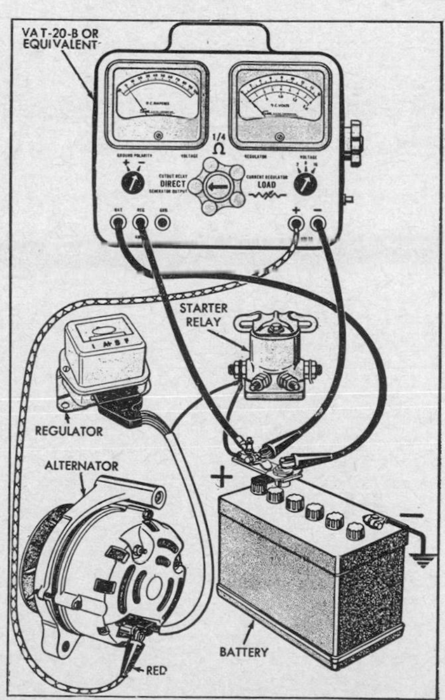

Fig. 9 Voltage drop test from alternator to battery positive terminal

Voltage Regulation Setting (Volts)	Ambient Air Temperature °F
14.3-15.1	50
14.1-14.9	75
13.9-14.7	100
13.8-14.6	125
13.6-14.4	150
13.5-14.3	175

Fig. 8 Voltage regulation versus ambient air temperature

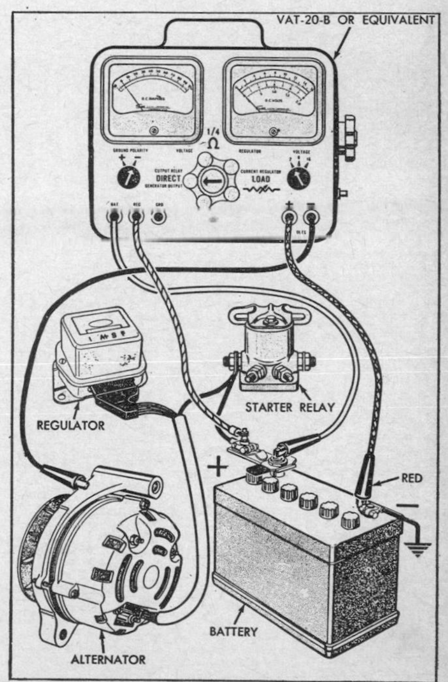

Fig. 10 Voltage drop test from alternator to negative battery terminal

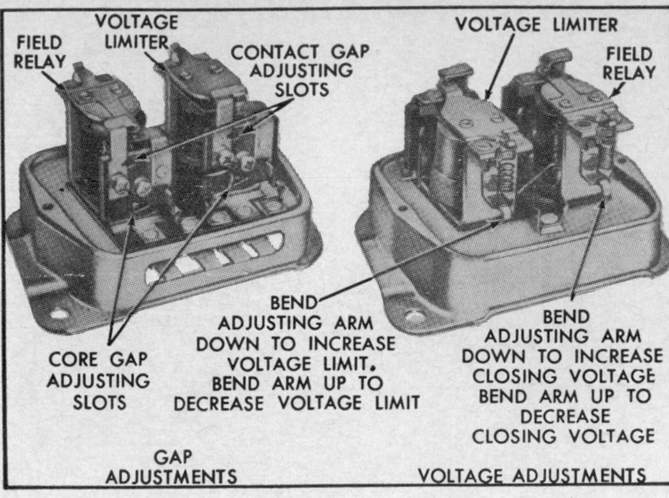

Fig. 11 Regular adjustments

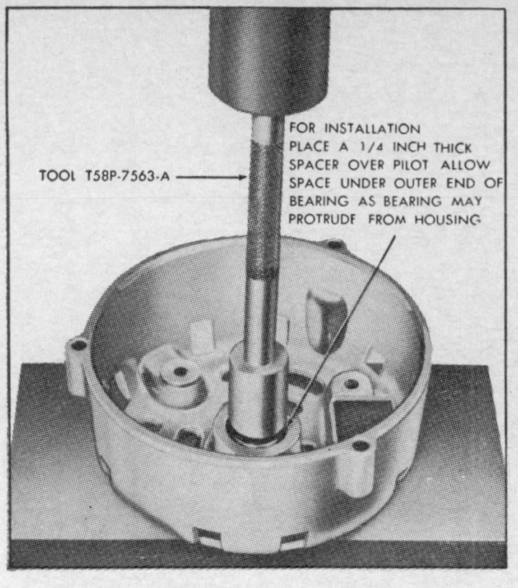

Fig. 13 Rear bearing removal

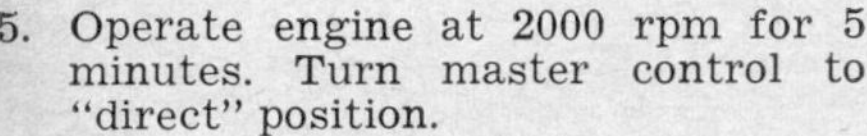

5. Operate engine at 2000 rpm for 5 minutes. Turn master control to "direct" position.
6. If the ammeter indicates more than 10 amperes, remove battery cables and charge the battery.
7. When battery is fully charged, and the voltage regulator has been temperature stabilized, rotate the master control to the "Voltage Reg." position, the ammeter should indicate less than 2 amperes.
8. Cycle the regulator as follows: Stop engine, close adapter switch, start engine, and open adapter switch.
9. Allow battery to normalize for a short time, then read the voltmeter.
10. Read the thermometer, and compare the voltmeter reading with the voltage given in Fig. 8.
11. If the regulated voltage is not within specifications, make a voltage limiter adjustment. *After each adjustment, be sure to cycle the regulator before each reading. Readings must be made with cover in place.*

Circuit Resistance Test

For the purpose of this test, the resistance values of the circuits have been converted to voltage drop readings for a current flow of 20 amperes.

Alternator to Battery Positive Terminal

1. Make connections shown in Fig. 9.
2. Turn off all lights and electrical accessories.
3. Close battery adapter switch, start engine, then open battery adapter switch.
4. Slowly increase engine speed until ammeter reads 20 amperes.
5. Voltage should be no greater than 0.3 volts.

Alternator to Battery Ground Terminal

1. Make connections shown in Fig. 10.
2. Close battery adapter switch, start engine and open battery adapter switch.
3. Slowly increase engine speed until ammeter reads 20 amperes.
4. Voltage indicated should be less than 0.1 volt.

REGULATOR ADJUSTMENTS

Erratic operation of the regulator, indicated by erratic movement of the voltmeter during a voltage limiter test, may be caused by dirty or pitted regulator contacts.

Use a very fine abrasive paper such as silicone carbide, 400 grade, to clean the contacts. Wear off the sharp edges of the abrasive by rubbing against another piece of abrasive paper. Fold the abrasive paper over and pull it through the contacts to clean them. Keep all oil or grease from contacting the points. *Do not use compressed air to clean the regulator. When adjusting the gap spacing, use only hospital clean feeler gauges.*

Regulator Bench Adjustments

The difference between the upper stage and lower stage regulation (0.3

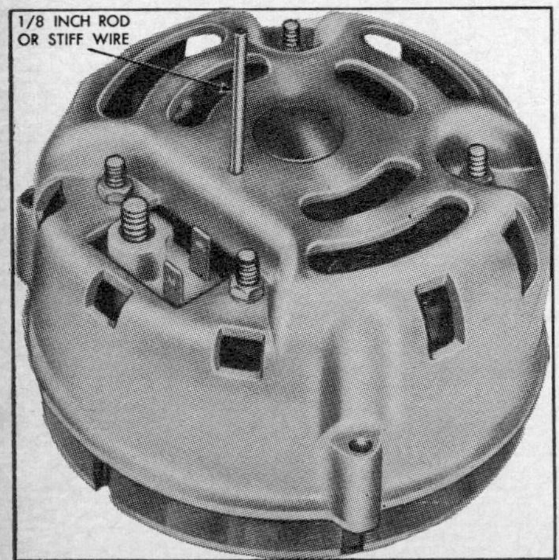

Fig. 12 Retracting alternator brushes

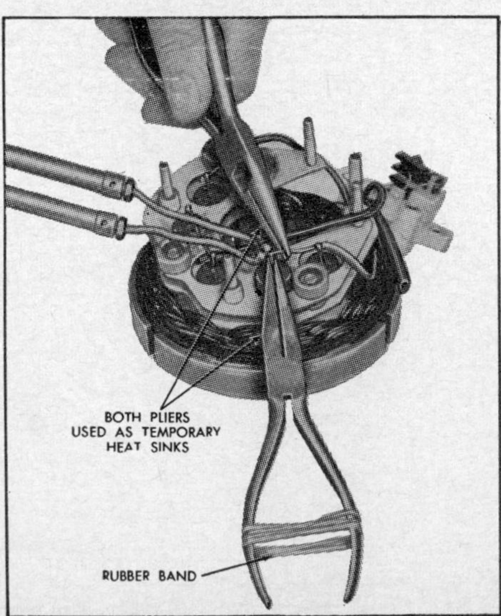

Fig. 14 Soldering diode leads

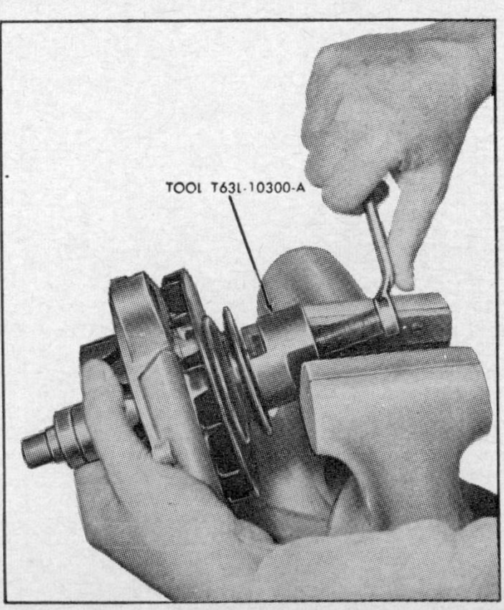

Fig. 15 Removing pulley

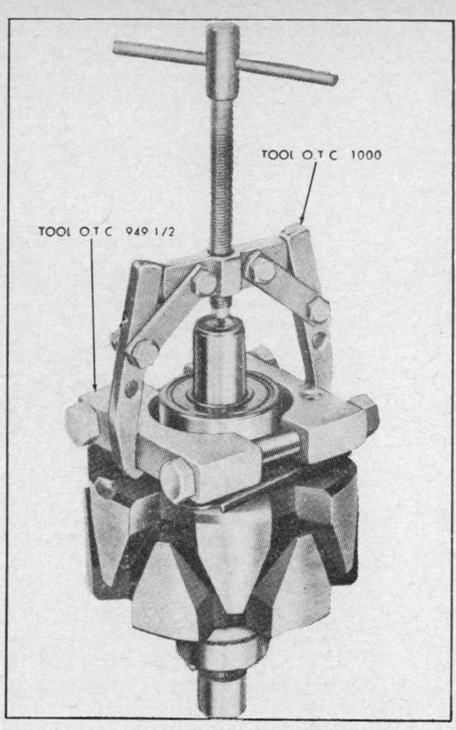

Fig. 16 Removing front bearing

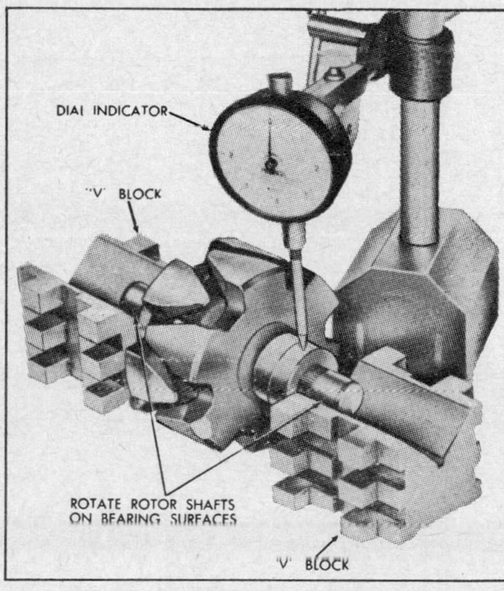

Fig. 17 Checking slip ring runout

volt), is determined by voltage limiter point and core gaps.

Adjust point gap first. Referring to Fig. 11, loosen the left side lock screw ¼ turn. Use a screwdriver blade in the adjustment slot above the lock screw. Adjust the upper contact until there is .010 to .015" gap between lower contacts. Tighten lock screw and recheck the gap.

To adjust the core gap, loosen the center lock screw ¼ turn. Use a screwdriver blade in the slot under the lock screw. Adjust the core gap to .045 to .052" clearance between armature and core at edge of core closest to contact points. Tighten lock screw and recheck core gap.

Regulator Voltage Adjustments

Final adjustment of the regulator must be made with the regulator at operating temperature.

The field relay closing voltage is adjusted by bending the spring arm, Fig. 11. To increase the closing voltage, bend the spring arm down. To decrease the closing voltage, bend the spring arm up.

The voltage limit is adjusted by bending the voltage limiter spring arm, Fig. 11. To increase the voltage bend the adjusting arm downward. To decrease the setting, bend the adjusting arm upward.

Before setting the voltage and before making a final voltage test, the alternator speed must be reduced to zero and the ignition switch opened momentarily to cycle the regulator.

ALTERNATOR REPAIRS

Disassembly

1. Mark both end housings with a scribe mark for reassembly. Reach through a ventilation slot, raise both brushes off slip rings and install a short length of ⅛" rod or stiff wire through hole in rear end housing, Fig. 12, to hold brushes off slip rings.
2. Remove 3 housing through bolts and separate front housing and rotor from rear housing and stator. *Make certain that brushes do not contact the greasy rotor shaft.*
3. Remove nuts from rectifier-to-rear housing studs and remove rear housing. Remove two spacer sleeves from rectifier plate studs.
4. Press bearing from rear end housing, Fig. 13.
5. Remove terminal spacer block from studs and unsolder neutral wire from spacer block neutral terminal.
6. If brushes are being replaced, straighten field brush, terminal blade locking tabs with a pair of pliers and remove terminal blade from terminal spacer block assembly. Remove brushes and holders.
7. If either diode plate is being replaced, carefully unsolder leads from diodes, Fig. 14. Use only a 100 watt soldering iron. Leave the soldering iron in contact with the diode terminals only long enough to remove the wires. Both pliers are used as temporary heat sinks in order to protect diodes. *Excessive heat can damage a good diode.*
8. Remove 3 insulated diode plate screws and insulators, and separate diode plates.
9. Remove drive pulley, Fig. 15.
10. Remove 3 screws that hold front bearing retainer and remove front housing.
11. If the bearing is being replaced, remove it as shown in Fig. 16. Remove bearing retainer and spacer. It will not be necessary to remove the stop ring unless it has been damaged.

Inspection

1. The rotor, stator, diodes and bearings are not to be cleaned with solvent. These parts are to be wiped off with a clean cloth. Cleaning solvent may cause damage to electrical parts or contaminate the bearing internal lubricant. Wash all other parts with solvent and dry them.
2. Rotate front bearing on drive shaft. Check for any scraping noise, looseness or roughness that would indicate that the bearing is excessively worn. As the bearing is being rotated, look for any lubricant leakage. If any of these conditions exist, replace the bearing.
3. Place the rear end bearing on the slip ring end of the shaft and rotate the bearing on the shaft. Make the same check for wear or damage as for the front bearing.

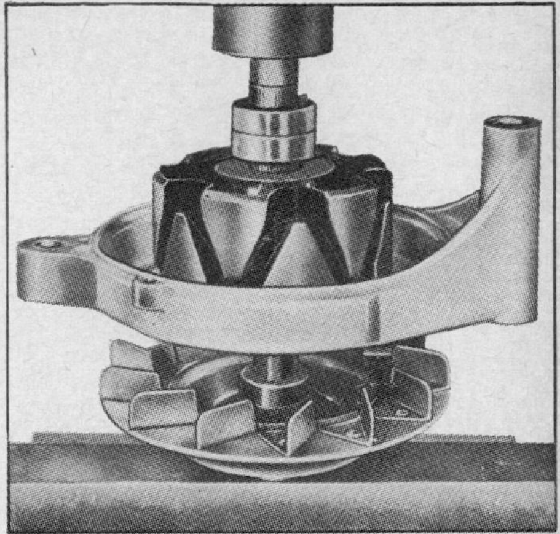

Fig. 18 Installing pulley

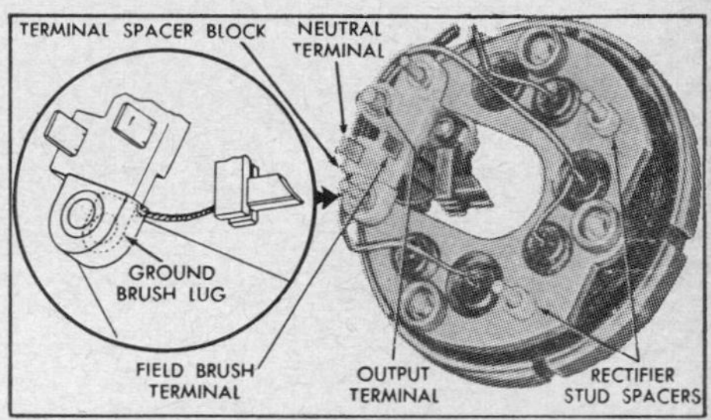

Fig. 19 Stator, heat sink and terminal spacer block assembly

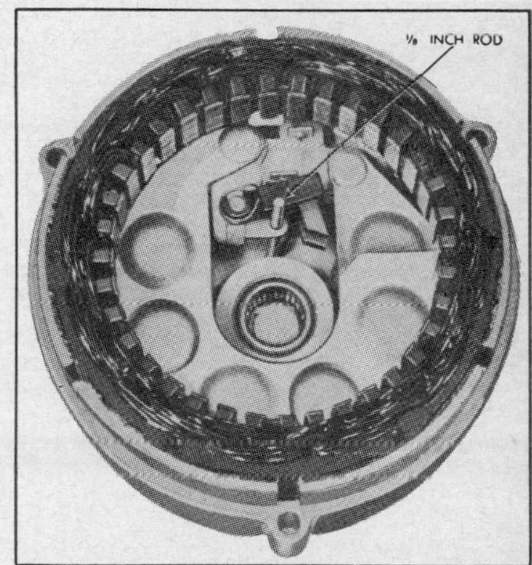

Fig. 20 Brushes retracted for assembly

4. Check the housings for cracks. Check the front housing for stripped threads in the mounting holes. Replace defective housings.
5. Pulleys that have been removed and installed several times may have to be replaced because of the increased bore diameter. A pulley is not suitable for reuse if more than ¼ of the shaft length will enter the pulley bore with light pressure. Replace any pulley that is bent out of shape. After installing the pulley, check for clearance between the fins and the alternator drive end housing.
6. Check all wire leads on both stator and rotor for loose soldered connections and for burned insulation. Resolder poor connections and replace parts that show burned insulation.
7. Check slip rings for damaged insulation. Check the slip rings for runout as shown in Fig. 17. If the slip rings are more than .0005" out of round, take a light cut (minimum diameter limit ½") from the face of the rings to true them up. If the slip rings are badly damaged, the entire rotor will have to be replaced as they are serviced only as a complete assembly.
8. Replace the terminal spacer block assembly if the neutral terminal is loose. Replace any parts that are burned or cracked. Replace brushes that are worn to less than .350" in length. Replace the brush spring if it has less than 7 to 12 ounces tension.

Assembly

1. If the stop ring on the drive shaft was broken, install a new stop ring. Push the new ring on the shaft and into the groove. *Do not open the ring with snap ring pliers.*
2. Position the front bearing spacer on the drive shaft against the stop ring, and position the bearing retainer on the shaft with the flat surface of the retainer outward.
3. Putting pressure on the inner race only, press the new bearing on the shaft until it contacts the spacer.
4. Place the front housing over the shaft with the bearing positioned in the front housing cavity. Install the bearing retainer mounting screws.
5. Press the pulley onto the shaft until the hub just touches the inner race of the front bearing, Fig 18. *A new pulley must be installed if more than ¼ of the shaft length will enter the old pulley bore with light pressure.*
6. If a new diode plate is being installed, mount the two plates together so that they are insulated from each other, Fig. 19. Solder the wire leads to the diodes as shown in Fig. 14, using only a 100 watt iron. *Avoid excessive heat as this can result to damage to the diode.*
7. Insert the new field brush terminal blade into the slot in the terminal spacer block with the brush pigtail extending toward the brush holder pivots, Fig. 19.
8. Install brush holders and brush spring to terminal block, then position brushes in holders.
9. Solder the neutral wire to its terminal. Position terminal spacer block on rectifier plate mounting studs, with the ground brush lug over the mounting stud farthest from the output terminal, Fig. 19.
10. Place spacers on rectifier mounting studs farthest from terminal block.
11. Install rear bearing so that its open end is flush with the inner surface of the housing boss, Fig. 13. Allow for space under the outer end of the bearing during installation.
12. Place rear end housing over rectifier plate and stator assembly and mount rectifier plates to housing.
13. Retract brushes and insert a short piece of ⅛" rod or stiff wire through hole in rear end housing to hold brushes in retracted position, Fig. 20.
14. Wipe clean the rear bearing surface of the rotor shaft.
15. Position rear housing and stator assembly over rotor and, after aligning marks made during disassembly, install housing through bolts. Remove brush retracting rod.

Leece-Neville Alternators

SERIES 6000, 6200

These alternators, Fig. LN1, are the 40 and 50 ampere, three-phase type. The slip rings and brushes, which carry field current to the rotor coil, are enclosed for protection from abrasive dust yet are readily accessible for inspection and servicing. One brush is grounded to simplify the circuit.

The rectifier cells, or diodes, are mounted in the slip ring end housing and are internally connected to the stator windings. One end of each of the three stator windings, or phases, is connected to a positive and a negative diode. The other ends of the stator windings are connected together forming a "Y" type connection. The three negative and the three positive diodes are pressed (in sets) into two plates called "heat sinks". These multiple-purpose heat sinks serve as mountings for the diodes, as radiation plates for heat dissipation, and also as current conductors.

The two-element regulator used with these alternators consists of a voltage regulator and a load relay which is connected to the the auxiliary terminal on the ignition switch, Fig. LN1. The load relay, controlled by the ignition switch, functions as a reverse current relay. When the ignition switch is turned on, the relay contacts close to energize the field coil in the alternator.

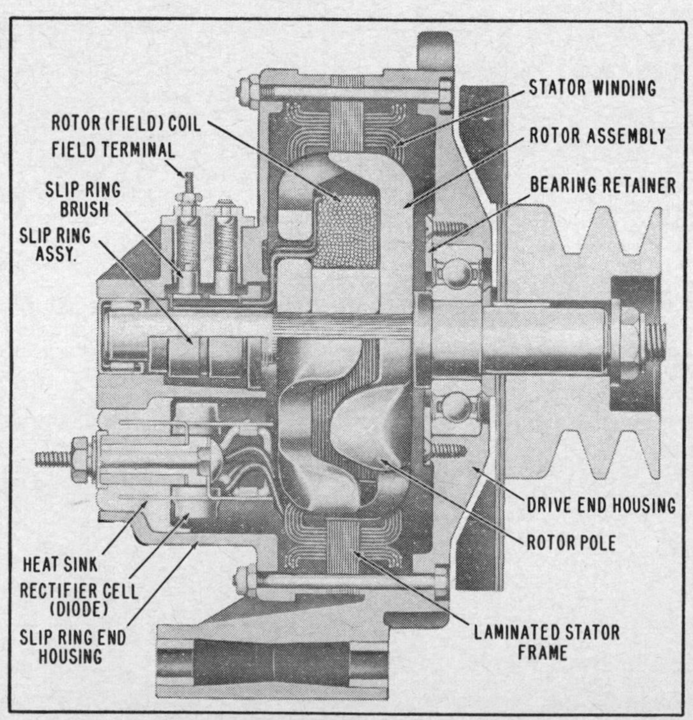

Fig. LN1 Sectional view of a Leece-Neville 6000 Series alternator

TESTING SYSTEM IN VEHICLE

Low or No Output

The field circuit must be closed in order to energize the rotor coil before the alternator can generate current.

A quick check of the field circuit can be made (with engine shut off) by turning on ignition switch and disconnecting the field terminal lead at the voltage regulator and then momentarily striking the FLD terminal with it.

If a medium spark is obtained, field circuit is closed. If spark is very light, a poor brush contact at the slip rings, or a poor connection, is indicated. If no spark is obtained, short or broken brushes, collapsed brush springs, poor or broken solder connections at the slip rings, or an open in the rotor coil, is indicated. A very heavy spark would indicate a short in the rotor coil. (Reconnect FLD terminal lead after making this check.)

If field circuit is found to be closed, alternator can be checked for output as follows:

With the engine at idle speed, remove the "F" lead from the alternator and attach a jumper wire from the "F" terminal to the "B" terminal. This jumper connection will take the regulator out of the circuit and allow the alternator to operate at full field strength.

If the alternator shows a high rate of charge when running with full field strength, the alternator is functioning and the problem lies with the regulator, system wiring or battery.

If the alternator shows a very low or no rate of charge when running with full field strength, the alternator will have to be removed from the engine and checked as outlined below if the system wiring and battery are good.

BENCH TESTS

1. Remove pulley, fan and spacer from shaft. Remove brushes. Remove through bolts holding unit together and remove drive end housing and rotor assembly.
2. To test the rotor without removing it from end housing, measure the resistance of the coil by placing the prods of an ohmmeter on the slip rings. If the meter reads from 3.8 to 4.2 ohms the rotor is good. If very little resistance is read, it would indicate a possible shorted coil circuit. Check for loose or broken wire at the slip rings. If no resistance is read, the coil is open. Should no loose or broken wires be detected at the slip rings, the short or open is within the rotor coils and the rotor is beyond repair.
3. Upon removal of the brushes it is found that the brush springs are collapsed, the rotor has a shorted coil and the rotor should be replaced.
4. Check the slip ring brushes or springs. If the brushes or springs are cracked, broken or burned, they should be replaced. Brushes worn to a length less than 3/16" are too short and must be replaced.

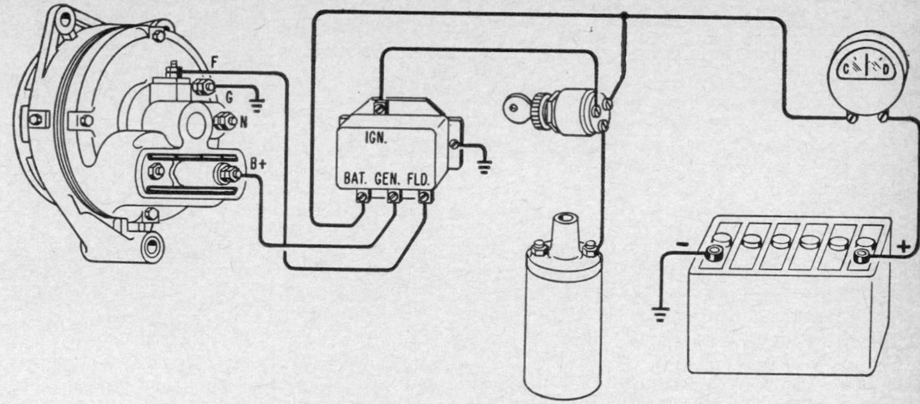

Fig. LN2 Leece-Neville alternator wiring diagram

5. If the rotor checks good, the stator and rectifier sections should be tested. This can be accomplished without removing the stator and rectifier sections from the slip ring end housing.

Rectifier Tests On Units Having An "N" Terminal

Place the positive prod of an ohmmeter on the "N" terminal at the slip ring end housing and the negative prod on the "B" terminal. With the prods in this position, the meter will read approximately 4 to 5 ohms and indicate that this is the positive section rectifiers. With the prods reversed, the meter needle will read infinity (excessive resistance) which will indicate that the rectifiers are good. Color coding on bottom of rectifiers is red.

Place the negative prod of the ohmmeter on the "N" terminal and the positive prod on the "GRD" terminal. The ohmmeter will read approximately 4 to 5 ohms and indicate that this is the negative ground section. Reversing the position of the prods will make the meter read infinity. Color coding on bottom of rectifiers is black.

Rectifier Tests On Units Without "N" Terminal

Since there is no "N" (neutral) terminal, it will be necessary to make the tests at the rectifier sections.

Place the negative prod of an ohmmeter on any one of the three lead connections between the stator and rectifier cells. Place the positive prod on the heat sink of the insulated section of rectifiers. The meter should read 4 to 5 ohms. Reverse the prod position and the meter should read infinity and indicate that this is the positive or grounded section of rectifiers.

Place the positive prod on any of the lead connections between stator and rectifier cells and the negative prod on the opposite heat sink. The meter should read 4 to 5 ohms. Reverse the prod positions and the meter will read infinity indicating that this is the negative rectifier section.

When making the above tests, if the meter readings do not fall in the category mentioned above, one or more of the rectifiers in the section are not operating properly and the section should be replaced. When replacing rectifiers, be certain that the correct section is grounded.

Alternate Rectifier Test

If an ohmmeter is not available a #57 bulb may be used to test the silicon rectifiers. This test is basically the same except that the bulb and battery replaces the ohmmeter.

If the bulb lights in one direction only the rectifiers are good.

If the bulb lights in both directions one or more of the cells in the section are shorted and the section found bad should be replaced.

If the bulb does not light in either direction one or more of the cells in the section are open and the section should be replaced.

Rectifier Section, Replace

To replace one or both rectifier sections, remove the nuts, etc. from the "B" terminal and the bolt holding the rectifier sections opposite the "B" terminal, and in the case of negative ground units, the "N" terminal. Remove stator and rectifier section from slip ring housing and unsolder the stator leads from the rectifier section or sections to be replaced.

When resoldering the rectifier sections to the stator leads, care must be exercised to apply only enough heat to insure a good connection. Overheating may damage the rectifier cells.

Stator Ground Test

To ground test the stator it will be necessary to unsolder the AC stator leads from the rectifiers. Check each stator phase for grounds to the stator core. A 110 volt test lamp is used for this test. No circuit should be present.

Stator Winding Continuity Test

With the test lamp check the continuity of each of the three stator phases. Each phase should show a closed circuit.

ALTERNATOR REPAIRS

After the foregoing tests are completed and the part or parts found inoperative are replaced, the following inspection and cleaning of parts should be done.

Rotor

If the rotor has seen considerable service and the slip rings appear to be worn, they should be replaced. Check shaft threads. Press rotor from housing using an arbor press.

To disassemble rotor, unsolder both field coil leads from the slip rings and, using a small puller, carefully pull off the rings. In some cases it will be impossible to save the old slip rings due to the tight fit on the shaft.

To clean the rotor it may be washed with a brush dipped in a cleaning solvent or paint thinner. Rinse with another brush dipped in unleaded gasoline or kerosene and then wipe with a dry cloth or blow dry with compressed air. *Do not immerse complete rotor in the cleaning fluid.*

Stator

After visual inspection finds the stator free of broken or cracked insulation or other damage which would cause failure, the stator can be cleaned in the same manner described for the rotor.

Brushes, Bearings, Etc.

Replace worn or broken brushes, insulation washers, etc. and inspect all tapped holes for good threads. It is recommended that bearings be replaced at time of overhaul.

Remove bearing retainer screws and bearing retainer from drive end housing. Tap or press out bearing. With bearing removed, housing can be immersed in cleaning solvent or paint thinner for cleaning.

The slip ring end housing bearing needs no special tool for removal or replacement. It may be tapped or pressed out. However, a piece of fiber or similar material should be placed over the new bearing when installing to prevent damage.

Reassembly

The alternator should be assembled in the reverse order of disassembly. Care should be exercised not to damage the housing pilots and stator windings. When completely assembled, spin the rotor by hand for free rotation check.

Reinstall the alternator on the vehicle and run it "full field" as outlined under Alternator System Check.

REGULATOR, ADJUST

Load Relay

To check the load relay, connect leads from a 12 volt battery to the ground and ignition terminals on the regulator, with a variable resistor in series with one lead. Connect a voltmeter across the "IGN" and "GRD" terminals.

Start with all the resistance cut in and then gradually decrease it to allow the voltmeter reading to rise. The load relay should close at 5.8 to 6.2 volts.

To raise the closing voltage, increase the spring tension by bending the lower arm of the spring bracket. To lower the closing voltage decrease the spring tension.

Voltage Regulator

To check the voltage regulator remove the cover. Connect one voltmeter lead to the regulator "BAT" terminal and the other lead to the regulator or alternator ground. Then connect a pair of earphones of not less than 1,000 ohms resistance to the "FLD" and "GEN" regulator terminals to hear the operation of the regulator contacts. *After each of the three steps in the test, open the ignition switch to bring the alternator speed to zero.*

1. Raise alternator speed slowly and listen for the vibration indicating the start of regulation on the upper contacts. This should start within the range of 13.9 and 14.3 volts. To increase the voltage, bend the lower arm of the spring bracket down. To lower the voltage, bend the arm up.
2. Slowly increase alternator speed past the start of regulation until the vibration ceases. Continue until the voltage reaches its maximum value, just before the lower set of contacts starts to vibrate. The maximum should be 14.7 and is adjusted as outlined in Step 1.
3. Increase alternator speed slowly past maximum voltage until the regulator armature vibrates on the lower contacts. The operating voltage should be 13.9 to 14.3 volts. To increase the voltage, increase the armature core gap; reduce the core gap to lower the voltage. The gap is adjusted by loosening the locking screw on the contact block to raise or lower the block.

Motorola Alternator

DESCRIPTION

The electrical circuit of the alternator, Fig. 1, uses 6 silicon diodes in a full wave rectifier circuit. Since the diodes will pass current from the alternator to the battery or load but not in the reverse direction, the alternator does not use a circuit breaker. Fig. 2 shows the charging circuit.

The entire DC output of the system passes through the "Isolation Diode". This diode is mounted in a separate aluminum heat sink and is replaced as an assembly. The isolation diode is not essential for rectification. It is used to:

1. Provide an automatic solid state switch for illuminating the charge-discharge indicator light.
2. Automatically connect the voltage regulator to the alternator and battery when the alternator is operating.
3. Eliminate electrical leakage over the alternator insulators so that maximum leakage is less than one milliampere when the car is not in use.

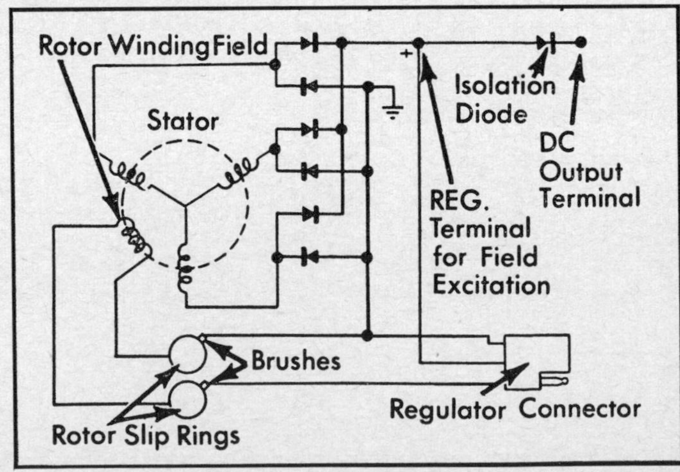

Fig. 1 Alternator circuit diagram

Voltage Regulator

The voltage regulator is an electrical switching device sealed at the factory, requiring no adjustments. It senses the voltage appearing at the regulator terminal of the alternator and supplies the necessary field current for maintaining the system voltage at the output terminal.

TESTING SYSTEM IN VEHICLE

Alternator Output Test, Fig. 3

1. Close by-pass switch on battery post adapter, Fig. 4.
2. Start engine and adjust speed to 2000 rpm.
3. Open by-pass switch.
4. Rotate load control knob to the load position and adjust until voltmeter reads approximately 6 volts.
5. Rotate alternator field control to direct position.
6. Adjust load control to obtain exactly 15 volts.
7. Observe ammeter; it should indicate maximum output of alternator with 25 amperes minimum. If no output is evident, observe voltmeter. *If there is over 12 volts at the regulator terminal and battery voltage is measured at the output terminal, the isolation diode is evidently open and should be replaced.*
8. Rotate alternator field control to open position.
9. Reduce engine speed to idle.
10. Rotate load control to direct position and stop engine.

Isolation Diode Test

If a commercial diode tester is used, follow the Test Equipment Manufacturer's instructions. If a commercial tester is not available, use a DC Test Lamp. *Caution: Do not use a 120 volt test lamp as diodes will be damaged.*

1. Connect test lamp to output terminal and regulator terminal of isolation diode.
2. Reverse test probes.
3. The test lamp should light in one direction but should not light in the other direction.
4. If the test lamp lights in both directions the isolation diode is shorted.
5. If the test lamp does not light in either direction, isolation diode is open.

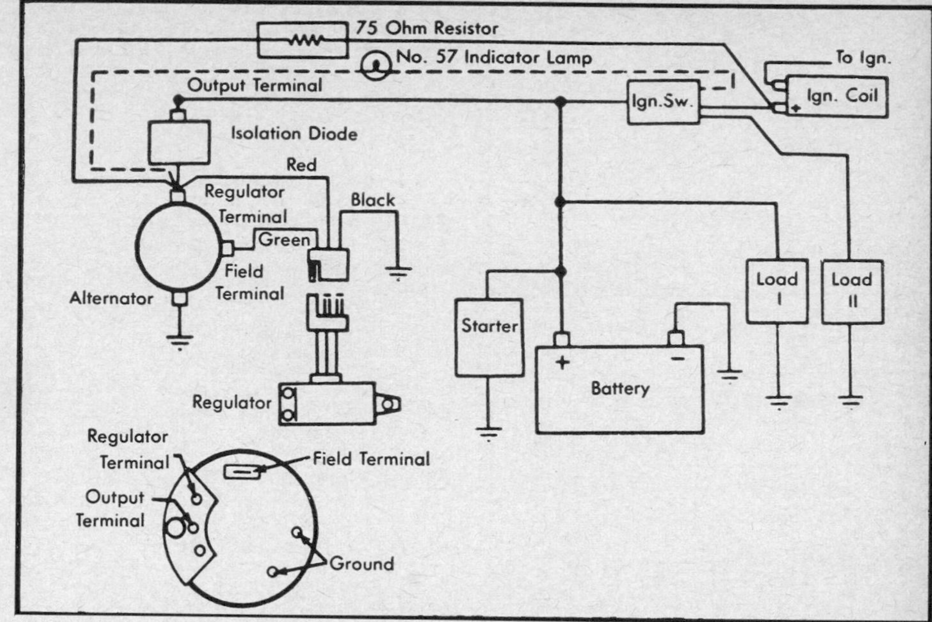

Fig. 2 Charging circuit diagram

Rectifier Diode Tests

Any commercial in-circuit diode tester will suffice to make the test. Follow Test Equipment Manufacturer's instructions.

Check diodes individually after the diodes have been disconnected from the stator. A shorted stator coil or shorted insulating washers or sleeves on positive diodes would make diodes appear to be shorted.

A test lamp will not indicate an open condition unless all three diodes of either assembly are open. However, a shorted diode can be detected. This test is not 100% effective but can be used if so desired when an in-circuit diode tester is not available.

The test lamp should light in one direction but not in the other direction. If the test lamp lights in both directions, one or more of the diodes of the assembly being tested is shorted. If the test lamp does not light in either direction, *all three diodes in the assembly are open.* Check diodes individually after disassembly to ascertain findings.

Note: A shorted stator coil would appear as a shorted negative diode. Also check stator for shorts after disassembly.

Regulator Terminal Voltage Test, Fig. 5

1. Remove alternator field control leads.
2. Remove field jumper leads.
3. Connect voltage regulator plug-in connector.
4. Connect slip-on field connector.
5. Turn on ignition switch.
6. Voltmeter indicates regulator terminal voltage which should be ½ to 2 volts. *Note: If voltmeter indicates battery voltage of less than ½ volt, perform following steps to determine if voltage regulator is defective.*
7. Disconnect regulator plug-in connector.
8. Disconnect slip-on field connector and connect the field jumper lead to the alternator field terminal.
9. Connect field jumper clip to regulator terminal.

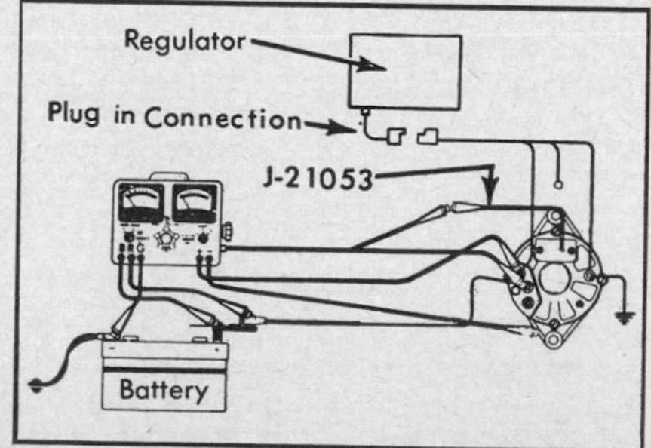

Fig. 3 Alternator output test connections

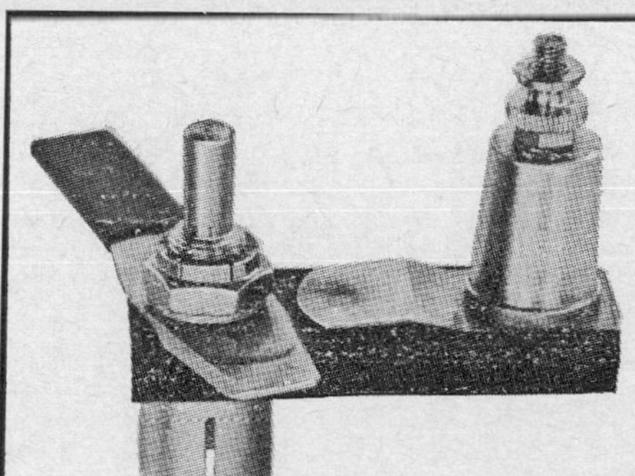

Fig. 4 Battery post adapter tool which provides a convenient method for connecting the ammeter leads of the volt-ammeter tester to the charging system

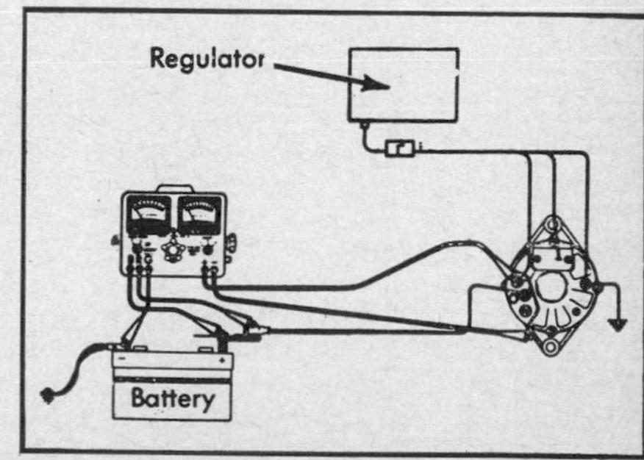

Fig. 5 Regulator terminal test connections

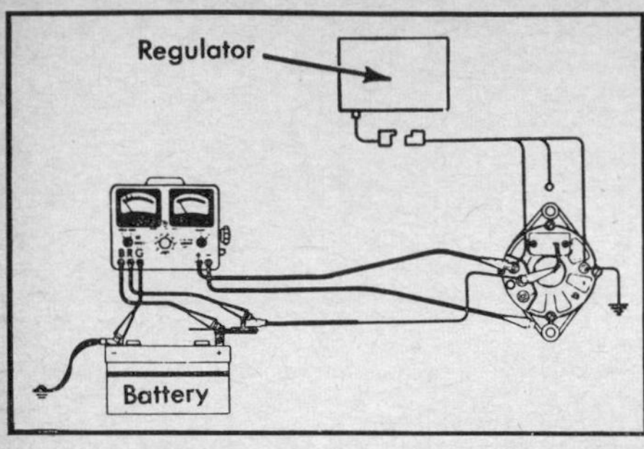

Fig. 6 Field current test connections

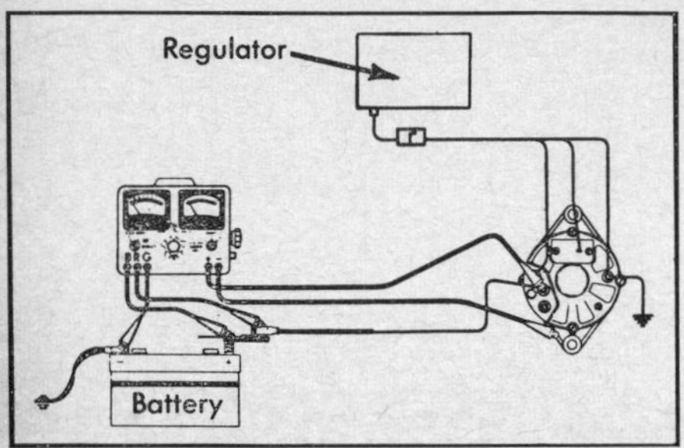

Fig. 7 Voltage regulator test connections

0°-14.6-15.4	80°-14.0-14.8
20°-14.6-15.3	100°-13.8-14.6
40°-14.3-15.0	120°-13.7-14.5
60°-14.1-14.9	140°-13.6-14.4
160°-13.3-14.1	

Fig. 8 Voltages at various ambient temperatures under a 10 ampere load

10. Voltmeter should now read 1 to 2 volts, which indicates voltage regulator is defective. *Note: If results are other than specified, continue with Field Current Test. If field current is within specifications, test voltage regulator circuit.*

Field Current Test, Fig. 6

1. Disconnect voltage regulator plug-in connector.
2. Turn off ignition switch.
3. Disconnect slip-on field connector and connect the field jumper to the alternator field terminal.
4. Connect the clip of the field jumper lead to the alternator output terminal.
5. Ammeter now indicates field current draw which should be 2 to 2½ amperes.
6. Disconnect field jumper lead from output terminal.

Voltage Regulator Test, Fig. 7

1. Remove field jumper lead.
2. Connect voltage regulator plug-in connector.
3. Connect slip-on field connector.
4. Connect positive voltmeter lead to alternator output terminal.
5. Start engine and adjust speed to 1500 rpm.
6. Rotate load control knob to the ¼ ohm position.
7. Voltmeter indicates voltage regulator setting which should be 14 to 14.8 volts at 75 degrees ambient temperature (see Fig. 8).
8. Return load control knob to direct position.
9. Reduce engine speed and shut it off.

Insulated Circuit Resistance Test, Fig. 9

1. Disconnect voltage regulator plug-in connector.
2. Connect field control leads, one to the output terminal and one to the field jumper lead.
3. Connect the negative voltmeter lead to the battery end of the positive battery cable.
4. Close by-pass switch and start engine, then open by-pass switch.
5. Adjust engine speed to approximately 1500 rpm.
6. Rotate alternator field control slowly toward direct until ammeter indicates 10 amperes current flow.
7. Voltmeter now indicates the voltage drop in the alternator insulated circuit which should not exceed .3 volt.

Ground Circuit Resistance Test, Fig. 10

1. Connect negative voltmeter lead to alternator housing.
2. Connect positive voltmeter lead to negative battery post.
3. With ammeter indicating 10 amperes, voltmeter should indicate not more than .05 voltage drop in the alternator ground circuit.
4. Rotate field control to open position. Reduce engine speed to idle and stop engine.

ALTERNATOR REPAIRS

Disassembly, Fig. 11

Brush Assembly

The brush assembly can be removed in most cases with the alternator on the vehicle. The spring clip is bent back so that the field terminal plug can be removed. Remove the two self-tapping screws, field plug retainer spring and cover. Pull brush assembly straight out far enough to clear locating pins, then lift brush assembly out. The complete brush assembly is available for replacement.

Isolation Diode

Remove the 2 lock nuts securing the isolation diode to the rear housing and slide it off the studs. The diode is replaced as an assembly.

Rear Housing

Remove the 4 through bolts and nuts. Carefully separate the rear housing and stator from the front housing by using 2 small screwdrivers and prying the stator from the front housing at 2 opposing slots where the "through bolts" are removed. Do not burr the stator core which would make assembly difficult.

Caution: Do not insert screwdriver blade deeper than 1/16" to avoid damaging stator winding.

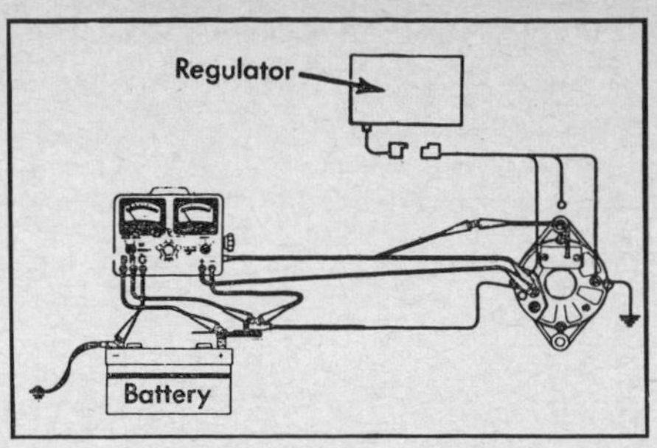

Fig. 9 Insulated circuit resistance test connections

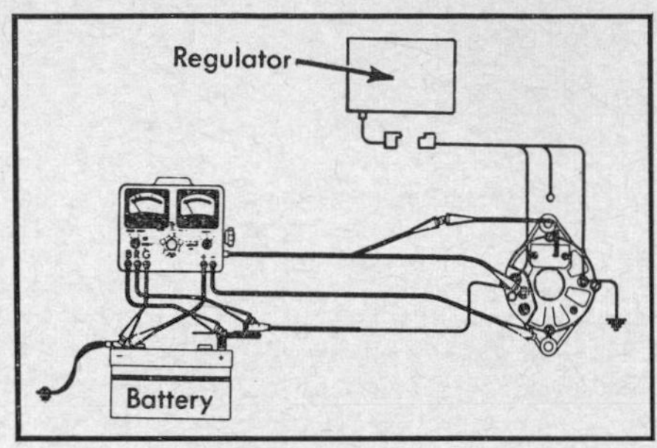

Fig. 10 Ground circuit resistance test connections

Stator and Diode Assembly

Do not unsolder stator-to-diode wire junction. Remove stator and diode as an assembly. Avoid bending stator wire at junction holding positive and negative diode assembly from housing.

Remove 4 lock nuts and insulating washers. The insulating washers and nylon sleeves are used to insulate the positive plate studs from the housing. With the 4 nuts removed, the stator can be separated from rear housing by hand.

Diode Replacement

In soldering and unsoldering leads from diodes, grasp the diode lead with pliers between the diode and stator lead to be removed. This will give better heat dissipation and protect the diode. Do not exert excessive stress on diode lead. *Make note of diode assembly to stator connections, and make sure replacement diode assembly connections are the same. The positive diode assembly has red markings, the negative black markings.*

Rotor

The rotor should only require removal from the front housing if there is a defect in the field coil itself or in the front bearing. Front and rear bearings are permanently sealed, self-lubricating type. If the front housing must be removed from the rotor, use a two-jaw puller to remove the pulley. The split spring washer must be loosened with snap ring pliers through the opening in the front housing. Remove the washer only after the housing is removed. The rotor and front bearing can be removed from the front housing by tapping the rotor shaft slightly. *Note: Make certain that the split spring washer has been removed from its groove before attempting to remove the front housing from the bearing.*

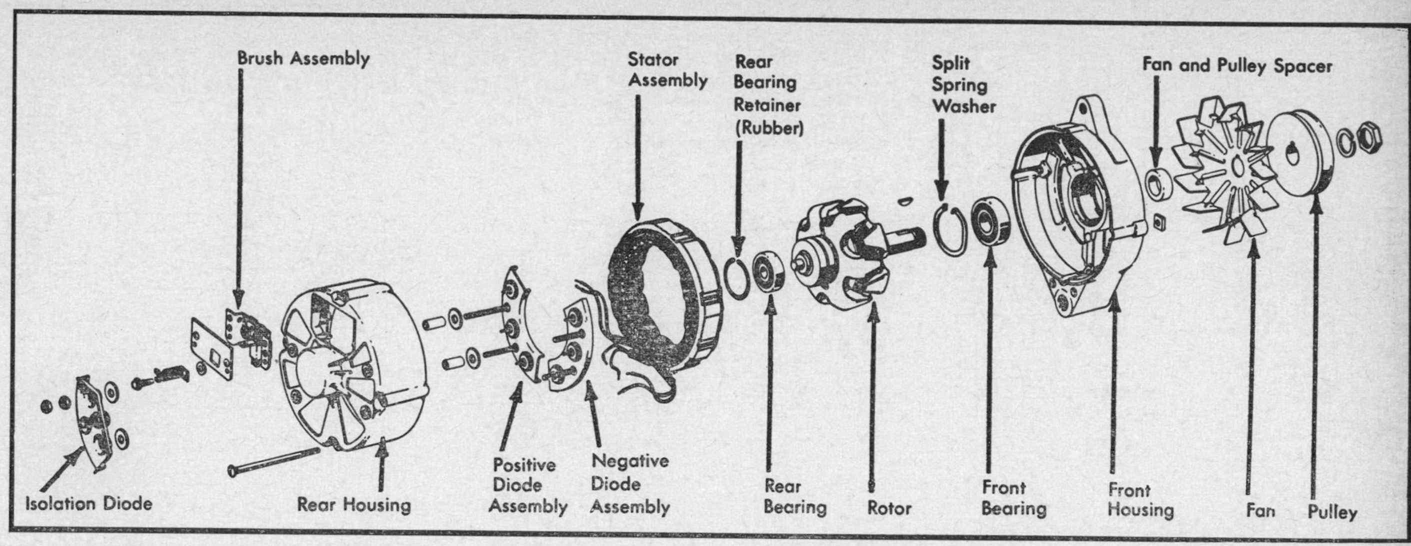

Fig. 11 Alternator disassembled

Alternator Bench Tests

Field Coil Test

The rotor should be tested for grounds and for shorted turns in the winding. The ground test is made with test probes connected in series with a 110 volt test lamp. Place one test probe on the slip ring and the other probe on the rotor core. If the bulb lights the rotor is grounded.

To test for shorted turns, check rotor field current draw as shown in Fig. 12. Slowly reduce resistance of rheostat to zero. With full battery voltage applied to field coil, the field current should be 1.4 to 1.9 amperes. Excessive current draw indicates shorted turn in field winding.

Brush Insulation Test

Connect an ohmmeter or a test lamp to the field terminal and bracket. Resistance should be high (infinite) or test lamp should not light. If resistance is low or if test lamp lights, brush assembly is shorted and must be replaced.

Continuity Test

Connect an ohmmeter to field terminal and brush. Use an alligator clip to assure good contact to brush, test points "A" and "C" in Fig. 13. *Caution: Do not chip brush.*

Resistance reading should be zero. Move brush and brush lead wire to make certain that brush lead wire connections are not intermittent. Resistance reading should not vary when brush and lead wire are being moved around. Connect ohmmeter to bracket and grounded brush, test points "E" and "D", Fig. 13. Resistance reading should be zero.

Stator In-Circuit Test

When making the in-circuit stator leakage test, some consideration must be given to the rectifier diodes that are connected to the stator winding. The negative diode assembly will conduct in one direction when properly polarized. A shorted diode in the negative diode assembly would make the stator appear to be shorted. For this reason, the rectifier diode plate assembly and stator must be checked individually after alternator has been disassembled if the problem is localized to the stator. *Caution: use a special diode continuity light or a DC test lamp. Do not use a 120 volt test lamp as diodes will be damaged.*

1. Connect the test lamp to a diode terminal of the negative assembly and ground terminal.
2. Reverse test probes. The lamp should light in one direction but not in the other.
3. If the test lamp does not light in either direction, this indicates that all three rectifiers in the negative diode assembly are open.
4. If the test lamp lights in both directions, the stator winding is shorted to stator or one of the negative diodes is shorted.
5. Check stator again when it is disassembled from diode assemblies.
6. With alternator disassembled, connect an ohmmeter or test lamp probes to one of the diode terminals and to stator.
7. Resistance reading should be infinite or test lamp should not light.
8. If resistance reading is not infinite or test lamp lights, high leakage or a short exists between stator wind-

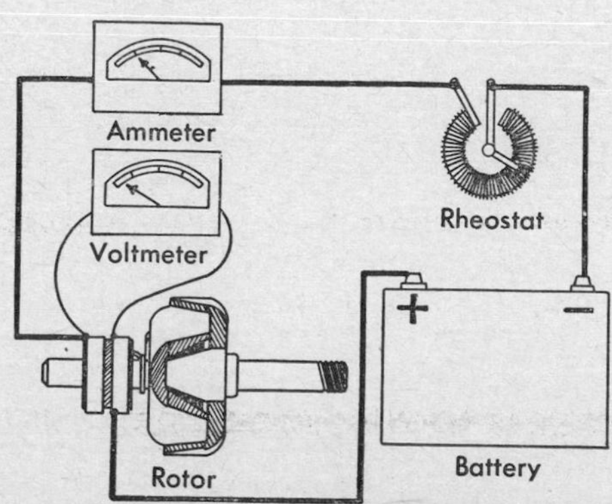

Fig. 12 Field coil test

Bracket
D)
Field Terminal
(A)
(C)
Insulated Brush
(E)
Grounded Brush

Fig. 13 Brush assembly test

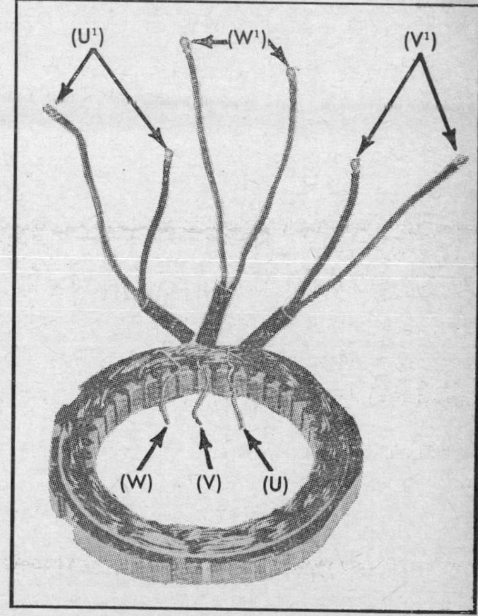

Fig. 14 Stator coil shorts and continuity tests

ing and stator. In either case, stator should be replaced.

Stator Coil Shorts Test

1. This test checks for shorts between stator coil windings. The winding junctions must be separated as shown in Fig. 14. An ohmmeter or test lamp may be used.
2. Connect one of the test probes to test point "U" and the other to test point "V" and then to test point "W". Resistance should be infinite or test lamp should not light.
3. Connect test probes to test V and W. Resistance should be infinite or test lamp should not light. In either test, if resistance reading is not infinite or test lamp lights, high leakage or a short exists between stator windings. Stator should be replaced.

Continuity Test

1. Measure resistance of each winding in stator between test points U and U1, V and V1, W and W1, Fig. 14. Resistance should be a fraction of an ohm (approximately .1 Ohm). An extremely accurate instrument would be necessary to ascertain shorted turns. Only an open condition can be detected with a commercial type ohmmeter.
2. If the alternator has been disassembled because of an electrical malfunction, replace stator only after all other components have been checked and found to be satisfactory.

Assemble Alternator

1. Clean bearing and inside of bearing hub of front housing. Support front housing and, using a suitable driver, apply sufficient pressure to outside race of bearing to seat bearing.
2. Insert split spring washer hub of front housing, seating washer into groove of hub. *Note: Do not use a screwdriver or any small object to compress washer that can slip off and damage bearing seal. Make certain that split spring washer has been installed prior to assembling front housing and rotor.*
3. Use sufficient pressure to seat front bearing against shoulder on rotor shaft. The bearing drive tool must fit the inner race of bearing.
4. Install fan and pulley.
5. Use a $\frac{7}{16}$" socket to fit inside race of rear bearing and apply sufficient pressure to drive bearing against shoulder of rotor shaft.
6. Assemble front and rear housings.
7. Make certain that rear bearing is properly seated in rear housing hub and that diode wires are properly dressed so that rotor will not contact diode wires.
8. Align stator slots with rear housing through bolt holes, then align front housing through bolt holes with respect to rear housing. *Note: The position of the brush and belt adjusting screw boss must be in the same relative position to each other.*
9. Spin rotor to make certain that rotor is not contacting diode wires. Install bolts and tighten evenly.
10. Before mounting isolation diode, make certain that positive rectifier diode plate has been properly insulated from housing.
11. Install brush assembly, cover and field plug retainer spring.

Prestolite Alternators

TESTING SYSTEM IN VEHICLE

Charging Circuit Resistance Test

1. Make connections as shown in Fig. P1.
2. Adjust engine speed and electrical load to obtain 10 amperes in charging circuit. The voltage drop in this circuit should not exceed .2 volt. If more, locate and correct cause of high resistance before proceeding with tests.
3. With the same operating conditions as in Step 2, connect voltmeter leads from ground battery terminal to alternator frame, and from alternator to regulator base. In neither case should the voltage reading exceed .04 volt. If more, locate and correct cause of high resistance ground connections.

Alternator Output Test

1. Make test connections as shown in Fig. P2. *Be sure rheostat is "Off" before connecting leads.*
2. Connect a tachometer and start engine. Adjust engine speed to 1750 rpm. Adjust rheostat to obtain 14.2 volts and observe ammeter reading. It should be as specified for the alternator being serviced.
3. If the alternator fails to reach rated output, it should be removed from the vehicle for repairs. A slightly low ammeter reading may indicate an open rectifier while a considerably lower reading may indicate a shorted rectifier.
4. If the output is only slightly low, a temperature check may be made to determine whether a rectifier is open. With the alternator operating as for the output test place a bulb-type thermometer (250°F scale) on the base of each rectifier heat sink for the bank being checked.
5. The rectifier temperature will normally be several degrees higher than the heat sink temperature. If a rectifier is open its temperature will be the same as that of the heat sink in which it is located.
6. If a rectifier is shorted the temperature of the entire heat sink in which it is located will be abnormally high.

Voltage Regulator Test

The first part of this test checks the

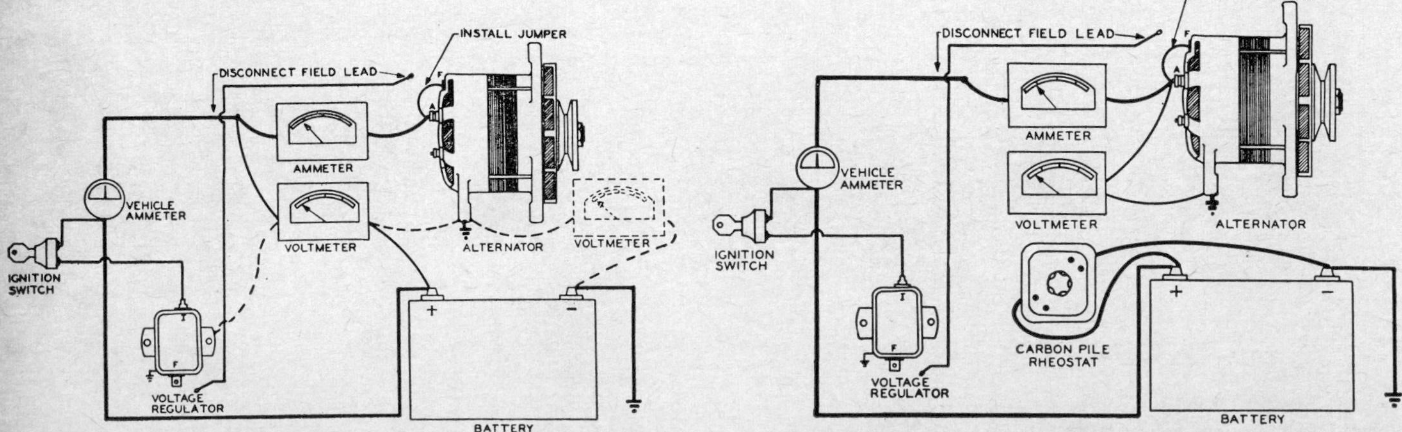

Fig. P1 Meter connections for testing voltage drop in charging circuit

Fig. P2 Meter connections for testing alternator output

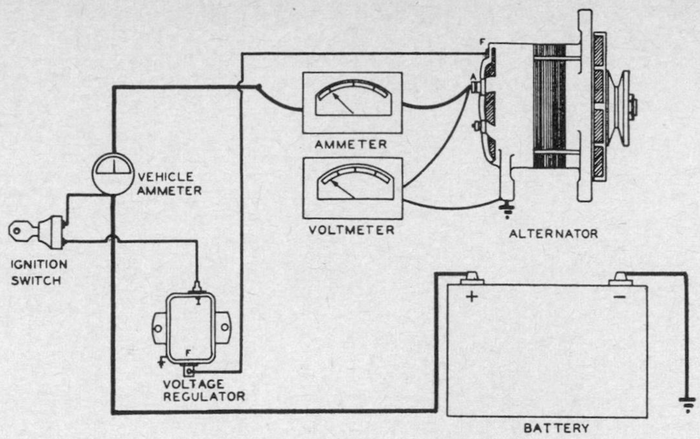

Fig. P3 Meter connections for testing voltage regulator

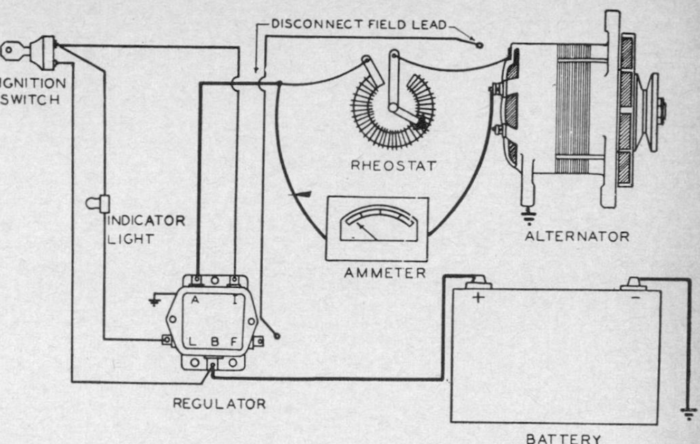

Fig. P4 Meter connections for testing indicator light relay operation

operating voltage of the regulator when operating on the upper contact. Make test connections as shown in Fig. P3.

Be sure the ignition switch is off when connecting the field lead. Grounding of the field circuit while the ignition switch is on will damage the regulator.

---

1. To test voltage regulator setting, start engine and adjust its speed to 750 rpm. Turn on lights and accessories to obtain a 10 ampere charge rate. Operate the system at this speed and load for 15 minutes to normalize the temperature. (This regulator is temperature compensated.)
2. Cycle the system by stopping and restarting the engine; then note the voltmeter reading. If seriously out of adjustment a rough setting may be made. The final setting is not made until the "spread" between operation on the upper contact and operation on the lower contact is established. This value is determined in the next part of the test which checks voltage when the regulator is operating on the lower contact.
3. Test connections remain the same as for the previous part of the test. Increase engine speed to 1500 rpm and turn off all lights and accessories. Voltage should increase and amperage should decrease. The "spread" in voltage between this reading and the reading noted in the first part of the test should be from .1 to .3 volt.
4. If the "spread" is greater or less than specified, remove the regulator cover and adjust by loosening the stationary contact support screw and moving the support up or down. Raising the stationary support will increase voltage "spread".
5. Replace the cover and reduce engine speed to 750 rpm and repeat the first part of the test with the regulator operating on the upper contact. If the voltage setting is not within specifications, remove the cover and adjust by bending the lower spring hanger. Replace the cover and cycle after each trial adjustment to obtain accurate readings.

Indicator Light Relay Test

1. Make meter connections as shown in Fig. P4. *If the vehicle indicator light cannot be seen while making this test, connect a 12-volt test light, using a No. 57 bulb between the "L" and "B" terminals of the regulator.*
2. Turn the rheostat to the "resistance in" position and operate the engine at approximately 800 rpm. Slowly cut out resistance and observe the ammeter reading when the vehicle indicator (or test) light goes out. It should be 4 to 7 amperes.
3. To adjust relay contact opening amperage, remove the cover and bend the lower armature spring hanger up or down. Increasing the spring tension raises the setting. Replace the cover and recheck.

BENCH TESTS

If the regulator voltage is unstable or cannot be adjusted to specifications in the above test, remove the regulator from the vehicle for further tests and adjustments.

Voltage Regulator Contact Gap

Contact gap is checked by placing a .010" gauge between the lower mov-

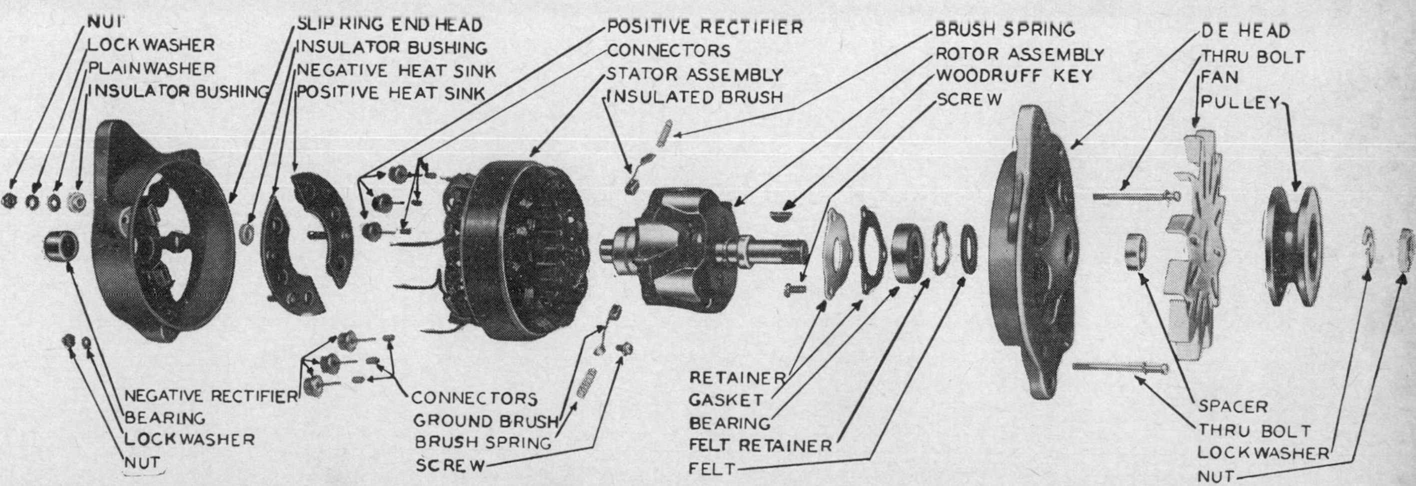

Fig. P5 Exploded view of Prestolite alternator

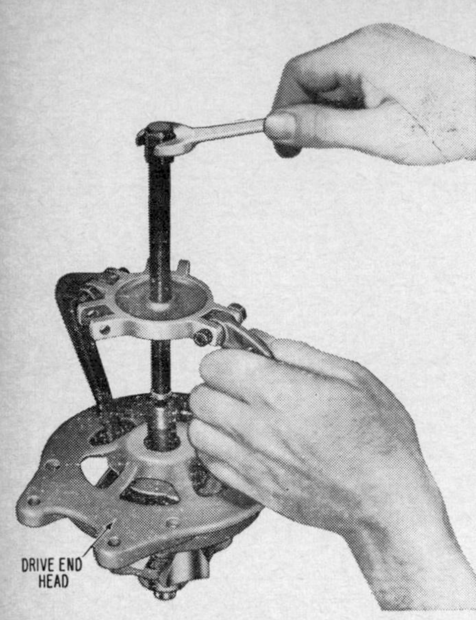

Fig. P6 Removing drive end head and bearing

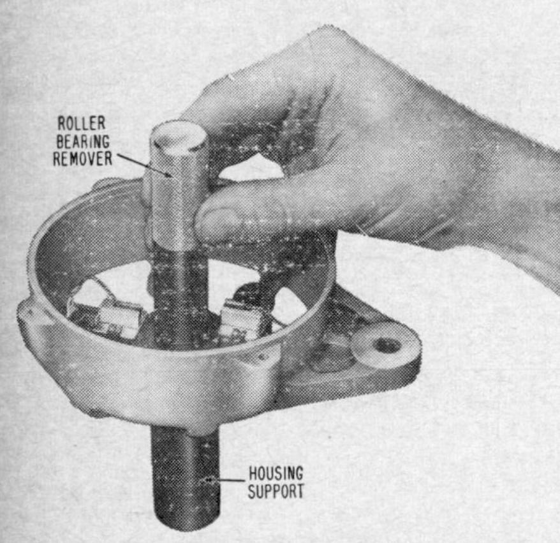

Fig. P7 Removing roller bearing from slip ring end head

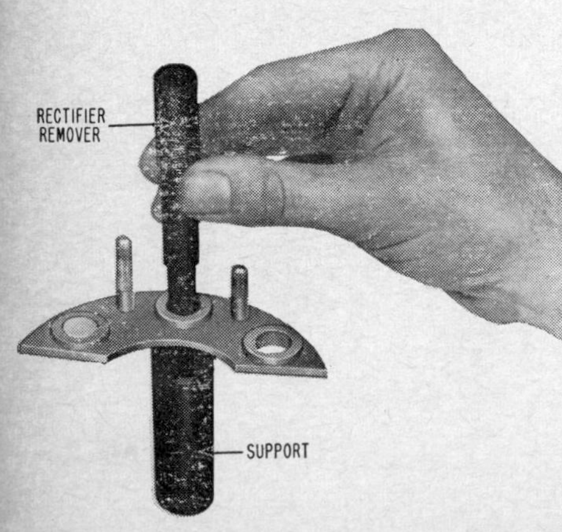

Fig. P8 Removing rectifiers from heat sink

able contact and the lower stationary contact. Adjust by bending the upper stationary contact arm up or down. Be sure that proper contact alignment is maintained.

Voltage Regulator Air Gap

To check the voltage regulator air gap, connect a No. 57 bulb in series with a 12-volt battery between the regulator field terminal and base.

Place a .034″ round wire gauge between the armature and core on the side of the brass stop rivet nearest the center of the core head.

The lower movable contact should barely touch the lower stationary contact when the armature is pressed down against the gauge and the lamp should light. With a .038″ gauge between the armature and core the light should go out.

To adjust to the above specifications, loosen the stationary bracket attaching screw and move the bracket up or down. *This is a preliminary adjustment only as the air gap may be changed when voltage "spread" is established as outlined previously.*

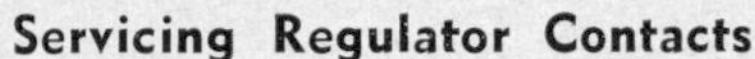

Servicing Regulator Contacts

If the contacts are rough or oxidized, they may be cleaned with an American Swiss No. 6 equalling cut file. After filing, the contacts should be cleaned with a strip of linen tape saturated with a few drops of lighter fluid and drawn between the contacts. Then repeat with a dry strip of tape to remove fluid.

ALTERNATOR REPAIRS

When repairing the alternator, the complete disassembly may not be required. In some cases it will be necessary only to perform those operations which are required to repair or replace the defective part. However, the following material covers the complete overhaul procedure, Fig. P5.

Disassembly

1. Remove through bolts and tap lightly on end heads to separate them from stator.
2. Remove drive end head and rotor.
3. Remove nuts, etc. from rectifier bracket studs. Separate slip ring end from stator.
4. Both brushes are located in slip ring end housing and should be replaced if worn to 5/16″ or less in length. Remove the brushes, being careful that the brush springs are not lost when brushes are removed from holders.
5. Remove pulley with puller or arbor press. Remove fan.
6. Remove drive end head and bearing, Fig. P6.
7. Remove three screws from retainer plate and press bearing out of drive end head, using tool shown in Fig. P13.
8. Remove roller bearing from slip ring end head, Fig. P7.
9. If rectifiers must be removed, cut rectifier wire as near to crimped sleeve as possible. Then remove rectifiers, Fig. P8, using a press.

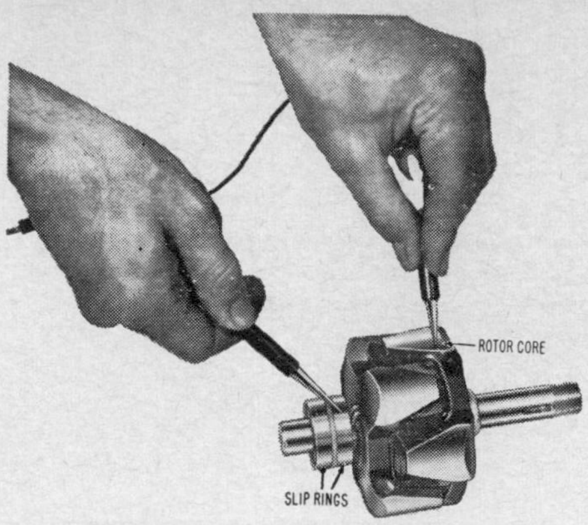

Fig. P9 Testing rotor for grounds

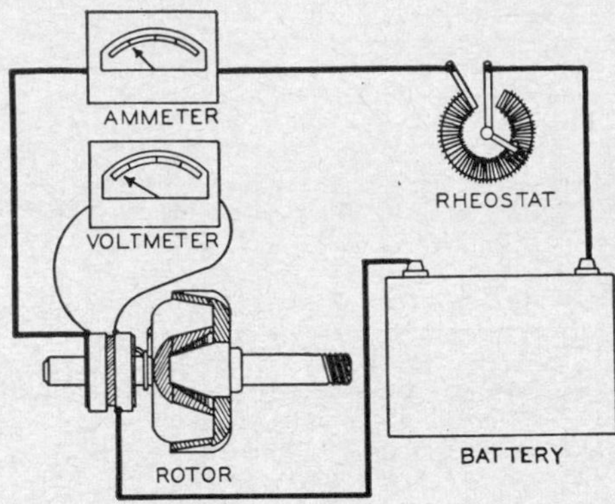

Fig. P10 Meter connections for testing rotor field current draw

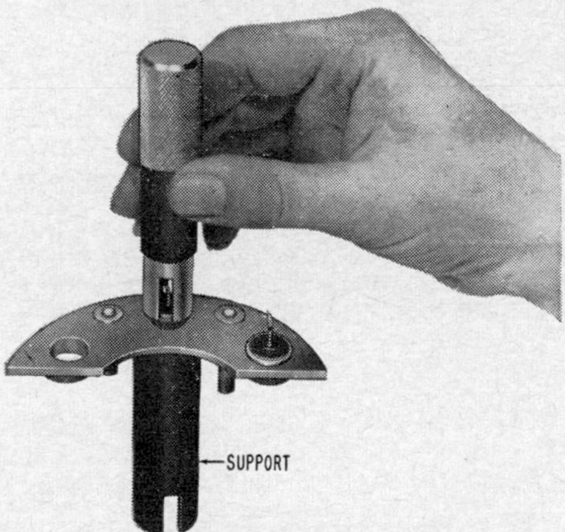

Fig. P11 Installing rectifiers in heat sink

Inspection

1. When disassembled all parts should be wiped clean and visually inspected for wear, distortion or signs of overheating or mechanical interference.
2. Stator windings and leads should be examined for insulation failures or defects. A shorted phase winding or rectifier will normally be evidenced by discoloration.
3. The stator can be checked for shorted windings with an internal-external growler. The test is made with the

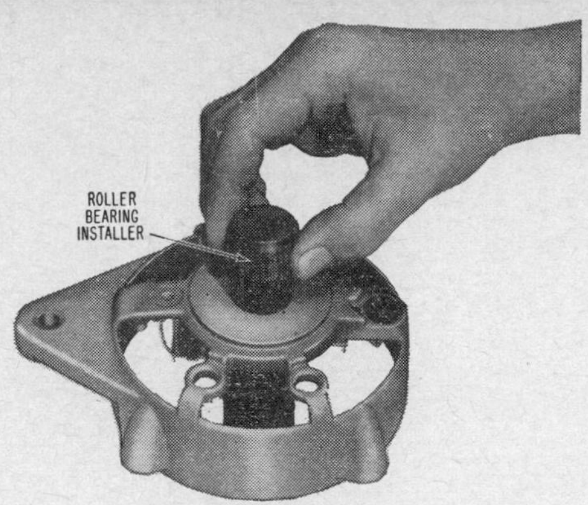

Fig. P12 Installing roller bearing

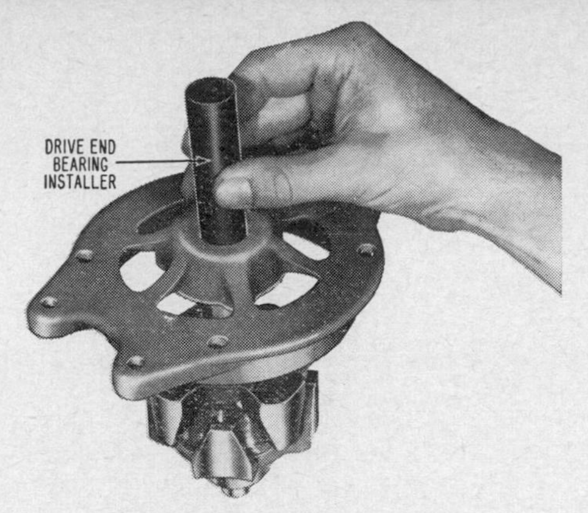

Fig. P13 Installing drive end head and bearing

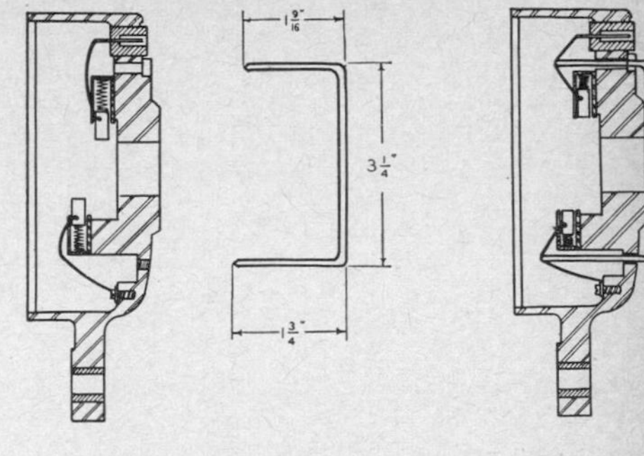

Fig. P14 Brush spreader clip. Right view shows clip installed

stator leads disconnected from the rectifiers.

4. The stator can be checked for grounded windings with a 110 volt test lamp and test probes. *Do not make this test with the rectifiers connected to the stator leads.*
5. Test rectifiers as described below.
6. The rotor should be tested for grounds and for shorted turns in the winding. The ground test is made with the test probes connected in series with a 110 volt bulb as shown in Fig. P9. If bulb lights rotor winding is grounded. To test for shorted turns, check rotor field current draw as shown in Fig. P10. Using the rheostat, adjust voltage to 10 volts and read field current draw on ammeter. Reading should be 2.34 to 2.42 at room temperature (70°F.). Excessive current draw indicates shorted turns in field winding.

Assembly

1. Press the rectifiers in the heat sink, Fig. P11. *Rectifiers are identified by red markings on the positive and black markings on the negative.* Strip the insulation back about ¼″ on stator leads and reconnect them to rectifiers. The connector sleeves should be crimped on rectifier leads. *Do not solder these connections as the excessive heat may damage rectifiers.*
2. Install roller bearing, Fig. P12. Enclosed end of bearing should be flush with outer surface of end frame when installed.
3. Install felt retainer and crinkle washer and press bearing into drive end frame. Use a flat block 2″ square so that pressure is exerted on outer race. Replace retainer plate and gasket on end frame. Make sure snap ring and retainer are in place on rotor shaft and press end frame on, Fig. P13. Press bearing down against snap ring retainer.
4. Replace spacer on shaft and install Woodruff key, fan and pulley.
5. Install brush springs and brushes. Eyelet on ground brush lead is fastened to end frame with a screw and the blade terminal on the insulated brush lead is pushed into slot in field terminal insulator bushing. A tab on blade terminal snaps into insulator bushing. If damaged, this bushing may be replaced.
6. To spread brushes so they will clear slip rings when end head is installed, a wire clip can be made and used as shown in Fig. P14. This clip can be fashioned from a coat hanger or ⅛″ welding rod cut and bent to the dimensions shown. File a "V" groove in ends of wire clip so that it will contact brush leads when inserted through holes in end head.
7. Install negative rectifier heat sink in slip ring end head and replace lockwashers and nuts. Install insulator bushings on positive heat sink studs and install heat sink in end head. Install outer insulator bushings, washers and nuts.
8. Manually press stator in position on slip ring end head and install assembled drive end head and rotor. Make sure that through bolt holes line up on the two end heads. Install and tighten through bolts.
9. Remove brush spreader clip and make sure brush leads do not drag on rotor and that rotor turns freely when rotated by hand. Test alternator when assembled.

TESTING RECTIFIERS

There are two methods of testing diode rectifiers. One method requires the use of Tool C-3829, shown in Figs. P15 and P16. The other is to make the tests with a No. 57 bulb test lamp. The advantage of the former over the latter is that it is not necessary to perform the time consuming job of separating the leads.

If a current output test indicates that the alternator is not operating within specifications, remove the alternator from the car and proceed as follows:

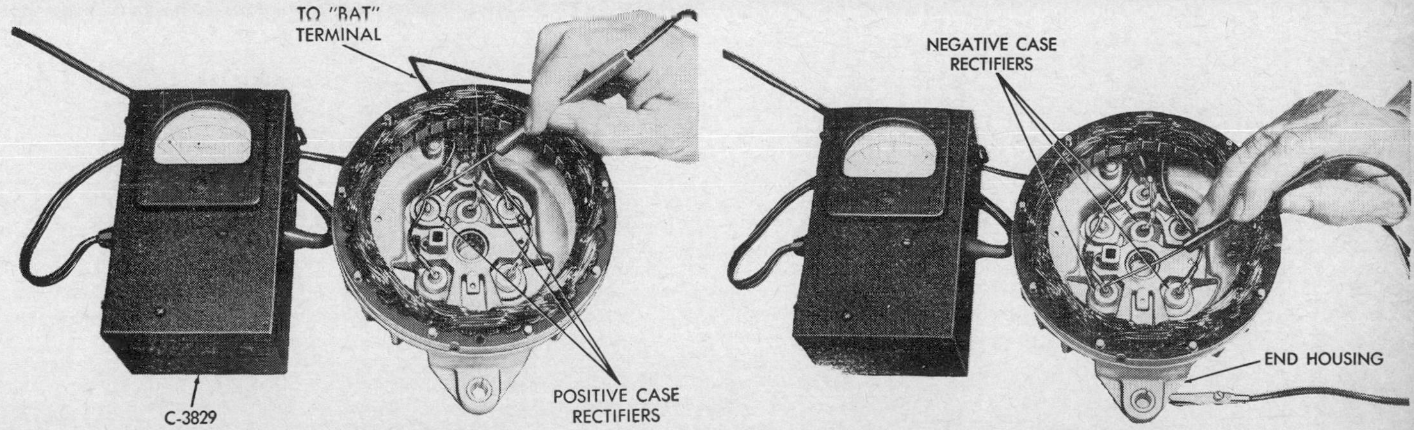

Fig. P15 Testing positive case rectifiers (Chrysler and Prestolite)

Fig. P16 Testing negative case rectifiers (Chrysler and Prestolite)

1. Perform a field coil draw test.
2. Open the alternator by first removing the brushes and then the alternator through bolts. Separate the drive end housing from the rectifier end housing.
3. Inspect the alternator components, paying special attention to the condition of the slip rings for indications of oil, being burnt or worn. Check the brushes for evidences of sticking in the holder or housing.
4. Inspect the bearing surface of the rotor shaft at the rectifier end and the bearing. Make sure the rectifier leads are in good condition, especially at the connections. The insulation should not be worn or broken.

Testing Rectifiers With Tool C-3829

Positive Case Rectifiers In Heat Sink, Fig. P15.—Place the alternator on an insulated pad and plug the instrument (C-3829) into a 110-volt supply. Connect the clip of the instrument to the "Bat" terminal and touch the test prod to the bare metal of each of the positive case rectifier lead wires in the heat sink at the rectifiers.

Always contact the connection nearest the rectifiers. Do not break the sealing on the rectifier lead wire or on top of the rectifier. The sealing material is used for corrosion protection.

The meter reading for each of the rectifiers should be the same. The reading on the meter will indicate two amperes or more for good rectifiers.

Where two of the rectifiers are good and one is shorted, the reading taken at the good rectifiers will be low and the reading at the shorted rectifier will be zero. Cut the lead at the bad rectifier and the reading at the two good rectifiers will come up to normal.

Where one of the rectifiers is open, it will read low (one ampere or less) and the two good rectifiers will show normal.

Negative Case Rectifiers In End Housing, Fig. P16.—Connect the clip of the instrument to the end housing. Touch the test prod to the bare wire of the rectifier leads at the rectifiers.

The test indications are the same for the negative case rectifiers as they are for the positive case rectifiers. However, the meter will read at the opposite end of the scale.

Testing Rectifiers With Test Lamp

1. With alternator disassembled and rectifier leads disconnected, proceed as follows:
2. With a No. 57 test lamp, connect one side of the test lamp to the positive battery post and the other side of the lamp to a test probe. Connect another test probe to the negative battery post.
3. Touch the outer case of the rectifier with one probe and the other probe to the wire in the center of the rectifier.
4. Reverse the probes.
5. If the test lamp lights in one direction the rectifier is good. If the lamp lights in both directions the rectifier is shorted. If the lamp does not light in either direction the rectifier is open.

GENERATORS & REGULATORS

CONTENTS

Generator Service

Generator Not Charging	1-91
Removing Generator	1-92
Replacing Brushes	1-92
Replacing With New Generator	1-94
Polarizing Generator	1-95
Motoring Generator	1-95

Regulator Service

Replacing Regulator	1-95
Electrical Test Service Notes	1-95
Auto-Lite Electrical Tests	1-96
Delco-Remy Electrical Tests	1-97
Ford and Bosch Electrical Tests	1-96
Auto-Lite Mechanical Adjustments	1-99
Delco-Remy Mechanical Adjustments	1-100
Ford and Bosch Mechanical Adjustments	1-101

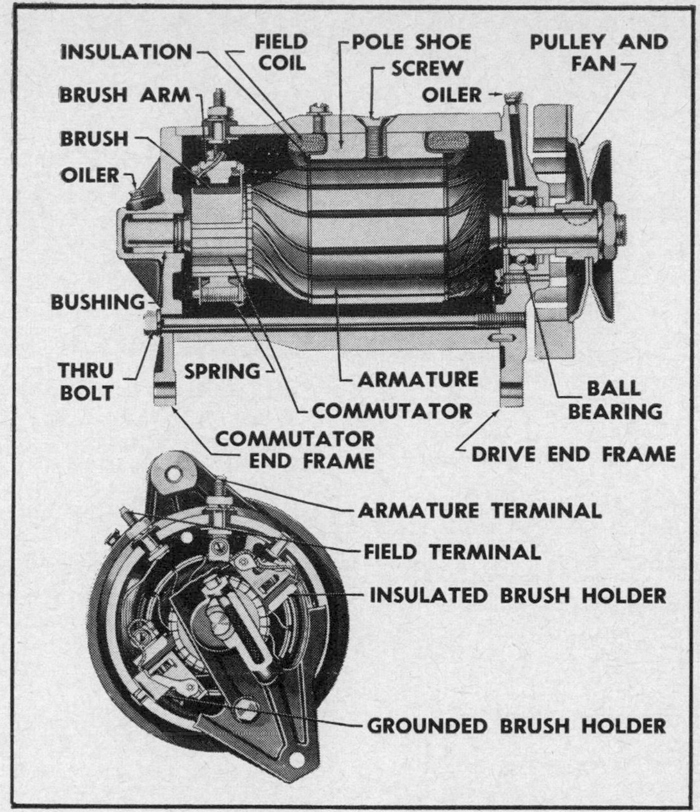

Fig. 1 Details of a typical generator

GENERATOR NOT CHARGING

1. To check out the trouble, first make sure all connections at the generator and the regulator are clean and tight. Then run the engine at a fast idle speed. If the generator still fails to show a charge, proceed with Step 2. But if a charge is indicated on the ammeter or if the indicator light goes out, there was a poor connection in the circuit.
2. If the generator field is internally grounded, connect a jumper wire from the regulator armature terminal to the field terminal. If the generator field is grounded externally through the regulator, ground the field terminal to the regulator base. In both cases, the regulator has been taken out of the circuit. Again run the engine, and if generator now shows a charge regulator is at fault.

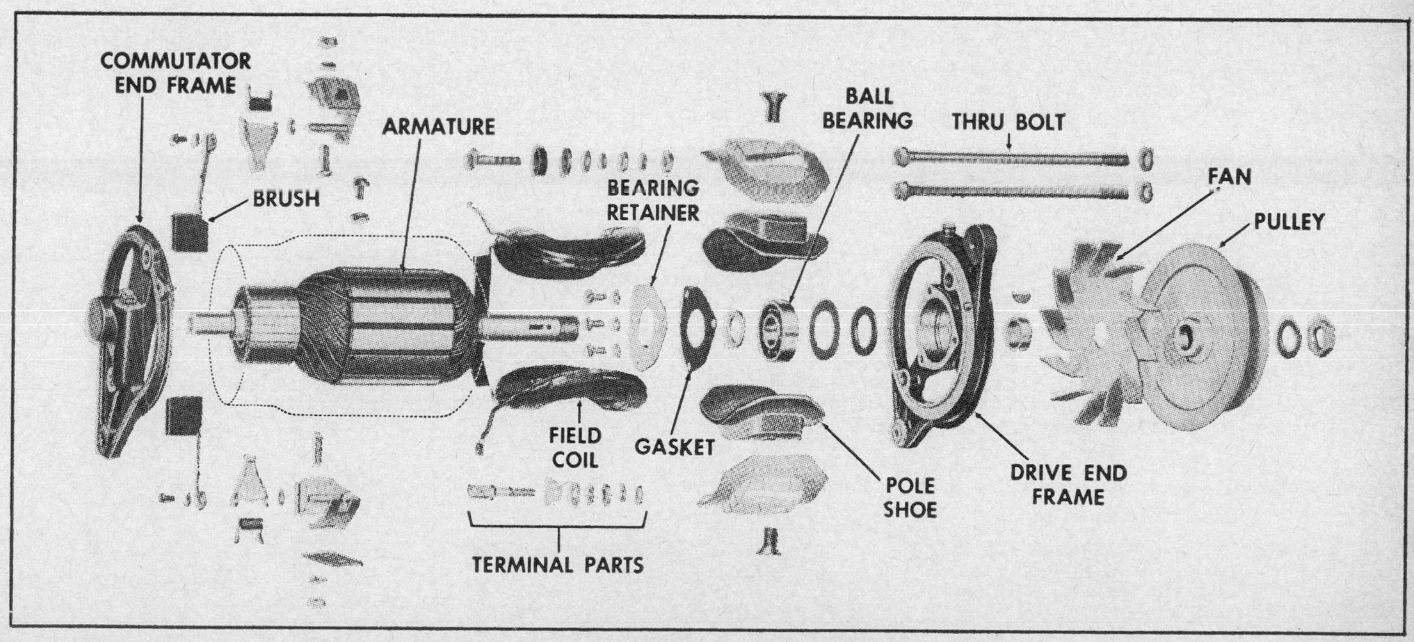

Fig. 2 Exploded view of generator

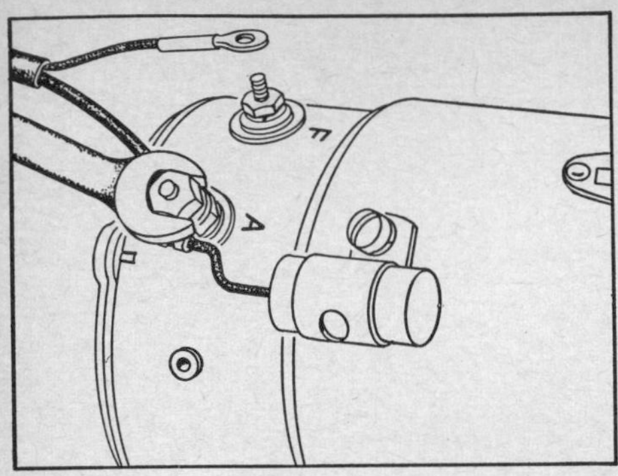

Fig. 3 Note that condenser is always attached to "A" terminal. If connected to "F" terminal it would make the voltage regulator ineffective and the generator would overcharge

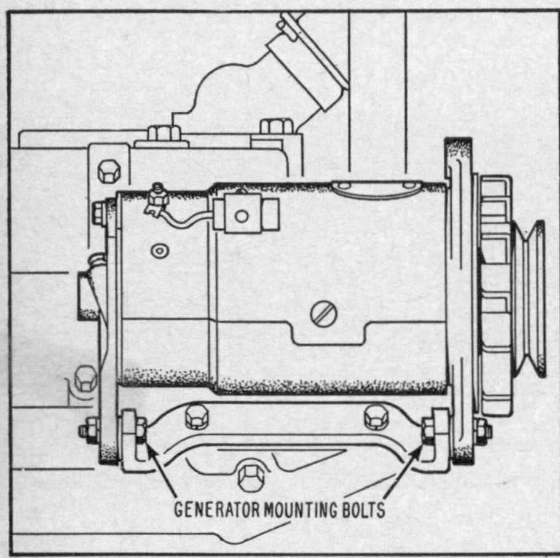

Fig. 4 Typical generator mounting

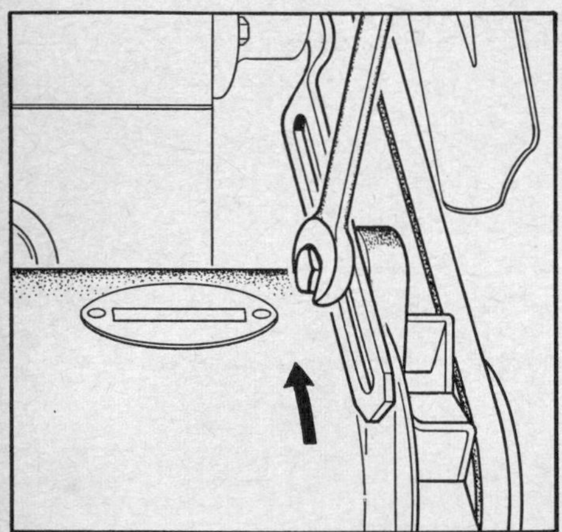

Fig. 5 Removing stud holding adjusting bracket to generator end frame

CAUTION

The foregoing procedure should not be used with double contact voltage regulators. With external ground systems (Delco-Remy), disconnect the field lead and ground it to the regulator base. With internal ground systems, disconnect the field lead and hold it against the armature terminal of the regulator. If this is not done, the lower set of contacts will burn, thereby making the regulator inoperative.

3. If there is still no charge after the foregoing test, short out the circuit breaker and current regulator by connecting a jumper wire from the regulator armature terminal to the battery terminal. Again run the engine, and if the generator now shows a charge, the regulator is at fault. However, if there is still no charge, the trouble is probably in the generator itself, although it may be elsewhere in the charging circuit.

GENERATOR SERVICE

Removing Generator

Figs. 1 and 2 illustrate a typical generator. The following contains tips on servicing and replacing the generator. To replace the brushes, it is assumed that the generator is to be removed from the engine.

1. Remove the leads from the generator terminals, Fig. 3. Identify each lead in order that it can be replaced to the proper terminal. Note that the condenser (for radio suppression) is always attached to the "A" terminal and never to the "F" terminal.
2. The fan belt must be removed from the generator pulley. On some cars it is necessary to remove the nut holding the belt tension idler pulley in place. With tension loosened, the belt can be removed.
3. Remove the generator by removing the bolts holding the generator lugs to the engine mounting bracket, Fig. 4. On some cars, it is necessary to remove the stud holding the adjusting bracket to generator end frame, Fig. 5. Then loosen the nuts holding the generator to the engine mounting bracket. Move generator toward the engine to release the belt from the pulley. Remove mounting bolts and lift generator from bracket.
4. Some applications have a power steering pump driven by an extended generator shaft, Fig. 6. To remove this type generator, the pump must first be removed from the generator by loosening the two mounting screws. The pump can then be pulled off and the generator removed from the engine as previously described.

Replacing Brushes

1. Remove commutator end frame by first removing the through bolts. Some types of through bolts have hex heads whereas others have slotted screw heads. After bolts are removed, it may be necessary to lightly tap the end frame to remove it from the field frame, Fig. 7.
2. Remove drive end frame and armature assembly from field frame, Fig. 8.
3. With a cloth, clean inside of field frame assembly. *Do not dip field coils in any cleaning solvent or puncture field coil insulation during the cleaning process.*
4. Clean commutator end frame, using a cloth dampened in solvent. Place a

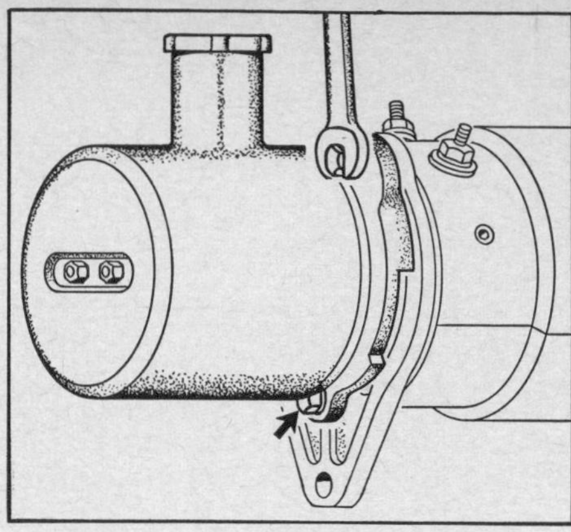

Fig. 6 Removing power steering pump from generator

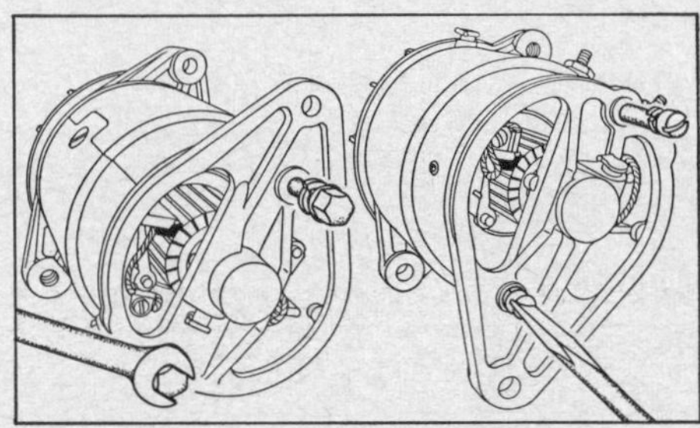

Fig. 7 Removing generator end frame from field frame

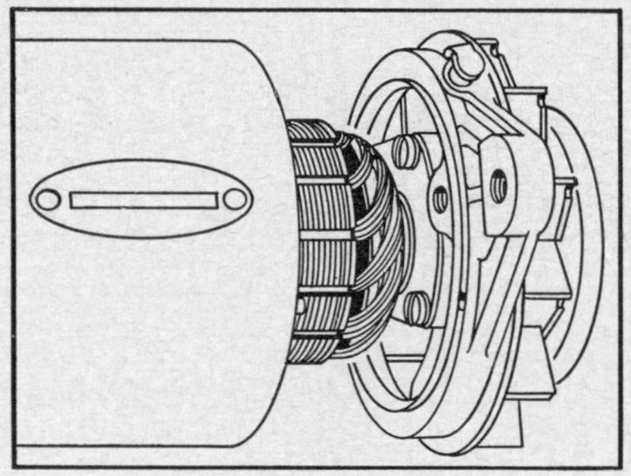

Fig. 8 Removing drive end frame and armature assembly

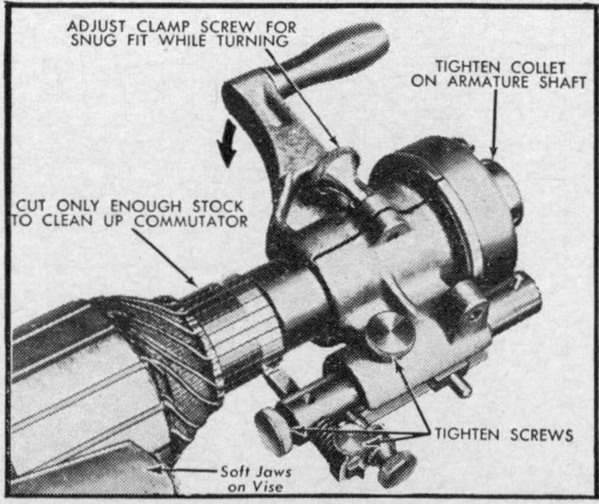

Fig. 9 Turning down commutator with lathe

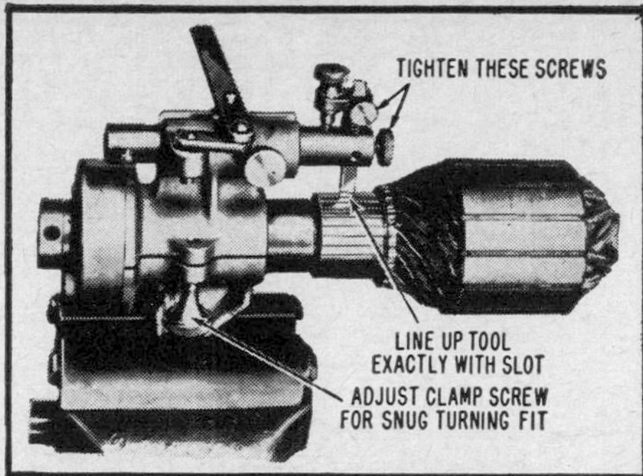

Fig. 10 Undercutting mica insulation. Depth of cut should be 1/32"

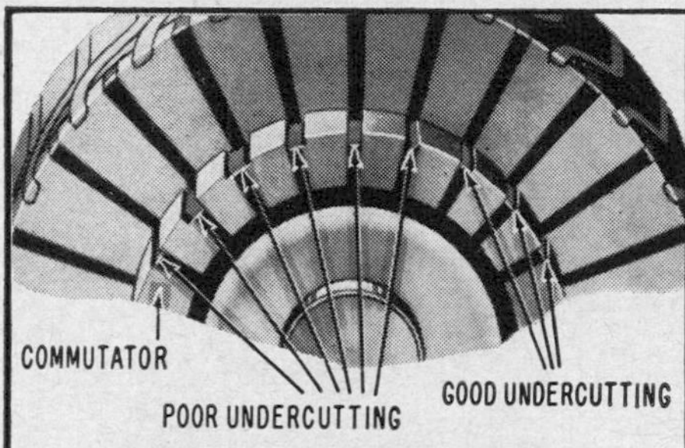

Fig. 11 Examples of proper and improper undercutting

Fig. 12 Testing armature for short circuit. As armature is rotated by hand, steel strip (hacksaw blade) will vibrate is short circuit exists

Fig. 13 Armature test for ground. Using test lamp, place test prod lead on armature core and the other on each commutator bar. If lamp lights armature is grounded and must be replaced

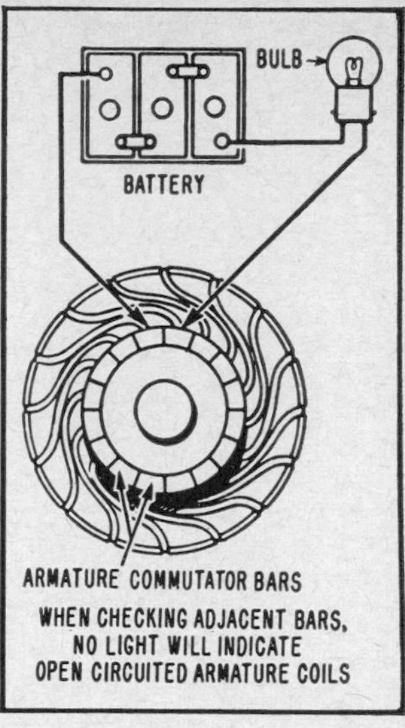

Fig. 14 Armature test for open circuit

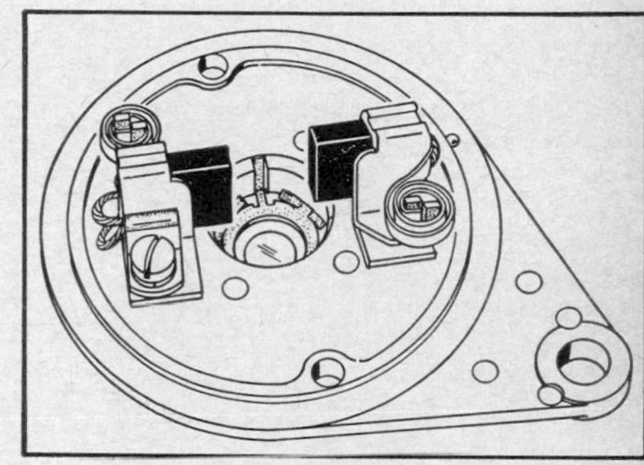

Fig. 15 Brushes mounted to commutator end frame

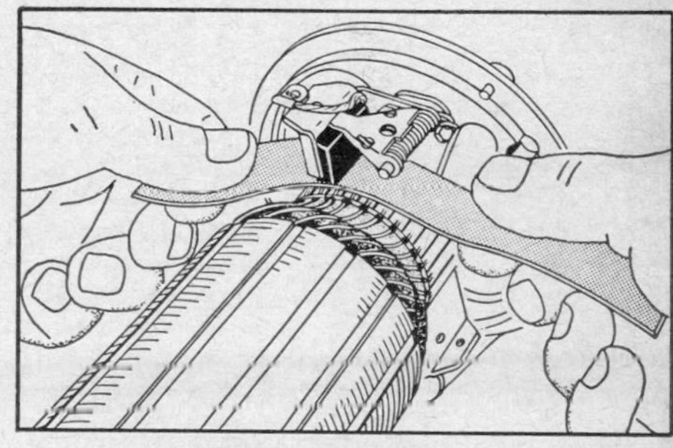

Fig. 16 Seating brushes with sandpaper

drop or two of oil in the bushing type bearing to facilitate reassembly.

5. Clean the armature and drive end assembly with an air hose. A clean dry rag may be used to wipe off dirt if an air hose is not available. *Do not use solvent of any kind on the armature.*
6. Examine commutator for high bars, high mica, pitted bars, or excessive wear. If any of these conditions are found, the commutator should be turned down on a lathe and the mica undercut, Figs. 9, 10, 11. Burned bars may indicate a defective armature which should be tested and replaced if necessary, Figs. 12, 13, 14.
7. If commutator appears to be in good condition except for dirt or minor corrosion, it may be cleaned with a fine grade of sandpaper. After cleaning, blow out abrasive particles left between commutator bars. *Never use emery cloth for this purpose as particles of emery may become embedded in the commutator bars and cause a short.*
8. Remove brushes from field frame. Wipe off brush holders with a rag dampened in solvent. Any corrosion on the brush bearing surface of the brush holders should be removed to permit freedom of brush movement.
9. If brush holders are mounted on the commutator end frame, remove necessary screws allowing complete removal of brushes.
10. Generators with cover bands need not be disassembled, unless so desired, for brush replacement. First remove the cover band and then remove the screws that attach the flexible brush leads to the brush holders. Then lift up on the brush spring arm and pull out the old brush. A new brush is then pushed down into position in the brush holder. The flexible leads of the brush are then re-fastened to the brush holder. If a field coil lead is present, it also must be fastened to the proper brush holder at this same time.
11. To insert new brushes into the brush holders attached to the field frame, push brush into holder from the bottom and shove it up all the way. This will allow the brush arm to lock the brush up into a position for installation over the commutator. Refasten flexible leads to commutator.
12. When brushes are installed, make sure the pre-formed angle on the brush matches the commutator contour.
13. Generators with brush holders mounted to the commutator end frame of the type shown in Fig. 15, should have their brushes inserted and flexible leads securely fastened in place before reassembling the end frame onto the field frame.
14. On some generators the brushes may be seated as shown in Fig. 16, using No. 00 sandpaper cut as wide as the commutator finished surface. Excessive use of sandpaper should be avoided since it will shorten the brush and decrease its life. Blow off

Fig. 17 Field coil test for open circuit. Using test lamp, place one test lead on field terminal and the other on field coil lead to armature terminal. If lamp does not light, field coils are open and must be replaced (unless a loose soldered connection is found at field terminal)

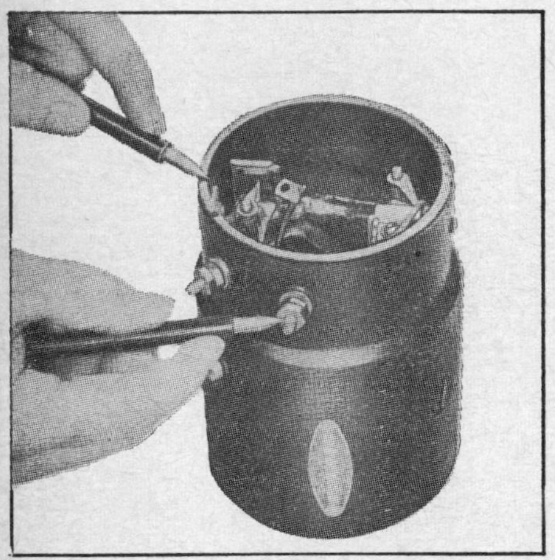

Fig. 18 Field coil test for ground. Using a test lamp, place one test lead on generator frame (ground) and the other on field terminal. Be sure end of field wire is not touching ground and field terminal insulation is not broken. If lamp lights, field coils are grounded. If ground cannot be located or repaired, field coils must be replaced

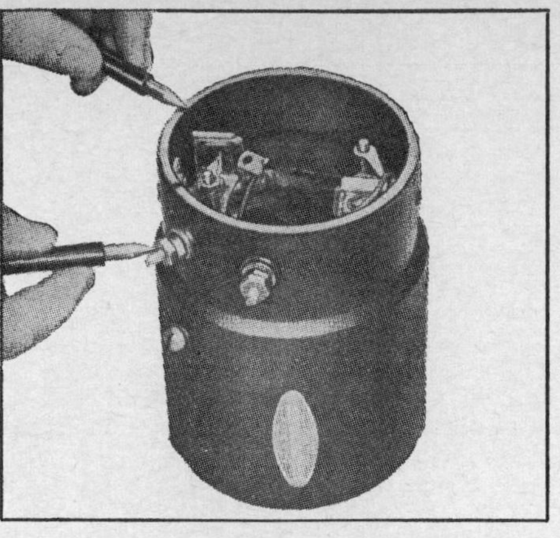

Fig. 19 Armature terminal test for ground. Using a test lamp, place one test lead on armature terminal and the other on generator frame. Be sure loose end of terminal lead is not touching ground. If lamp lights, armature terminal insulation through generator frame is broken down and must be replaced

Fig. 20 Insulated brush holder test for ground. Using a test lamp, place one test lead on insulated brush holder and the other on ground. If lamp lights, brush holder is grounded due to defective insulation at the frame

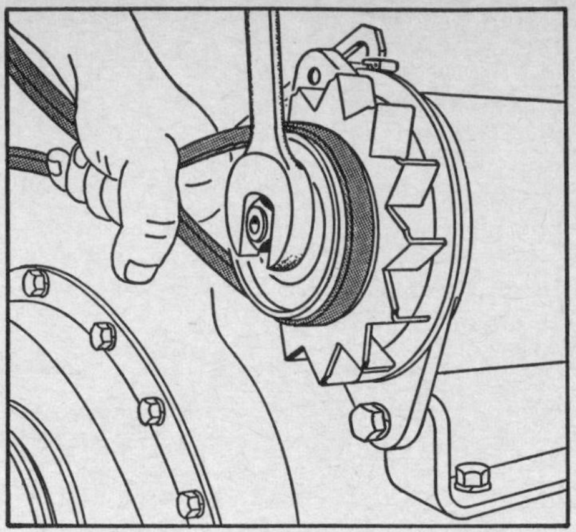

Fig. 21 Holding pulley tight with fan belt while loosening or tightening pulley nut

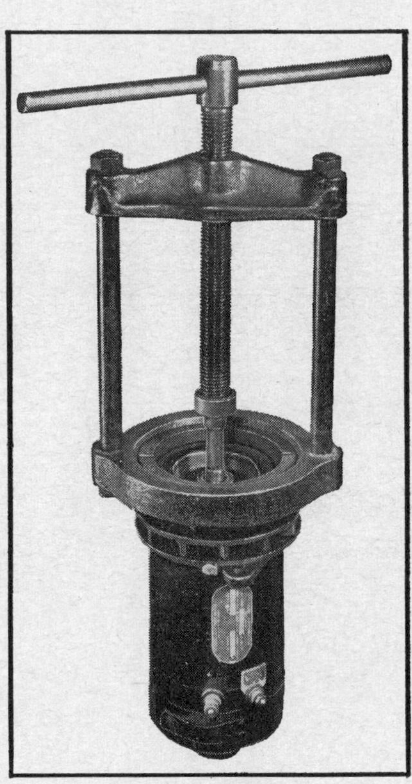

Fig. 22 Using puller to remove pulley

abrasive dust and carbon after completing the seating process.

15. Another method of seating brushes after the generator is reassembled is to spread some brush seating compound on the commutator and then turn the armature by hand for 20 or 30 revolutions. Then blow out the carbon and dust residue left from the brush seating operation.
16. Before reassembling the generator, it may be desirable to check out the field coils and terminals. If so, refer to Figs. 17 to 20.
17. When reassembling generators, make sure brushes are out of the way when brush assembly is slipped over commutator. In the event brushes are held up by the brush arm, make sure they are seated down on commutator before installing generator on engine.

Replacing With New Generator

1. When exchanging the existing generator with a new or replacement generator, it is necessary to remove the pulley and fan assembly from the old generator for use on the new generator. After the generator has been removed from the engine, it may be possible to remove the pulley nut by holding the pulley armature shaft by a belt, Fig. 21.
2. In the event that the pulley nut cannot be loosened by the belt method, it is necessary to disassemble old generator to remove the pulley, armature and drive end frame assembly. This assembly can then be placed in a vise and the pulley nut removed.
3. A pulley puller is then used to remove the pulley from the armature shaft, Fig. 22. Care should be exercised not to bend or distort either the pulley or fan blades during the removal process.
4. The fan and pulley assembly is then placed over the new generator shaft with the keyway in position over the key. Then lightly tap the pulley and fan assembly down on the shaft until the pulley nut can be started on the threaded end of the shaft.
5. After the generator is assembled and brushes properly seated the generator should be run as a motor, the procedure for which is given below. Mount the generator on the engine and tighten the pulley nut to force the pulley into position against the

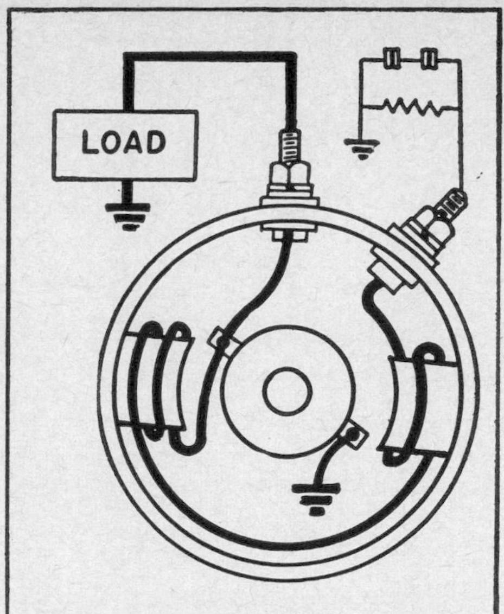

Fig. 23 Wiring diagram of a generator having the field grounded externally through the voltage regulator This can readily be identified by the fact that the grounded brush has only its own lead connected to it

armature shaft shoulder. Use the vehicle belt as a holding device on the pulley.

6. Apply 8 to 10 drops of light engine oil to the oil cups if present on the generator. Sealed bearings do not require lubrication.

Polarizing Generator

After the generator is installed on the engine and all leads are connected, the generator must be polarized before starting the engine. The polarizing procedure depends upon whether the field is grounded externally or internally. This data is included in the *Generator and Regulator Specifications* charts in the vehicle chapters. Having determined which system is used, proceed as follows:

If the generator field is externally grounded, Fig. 23, momentarily connect a jumper wire from the "BAT" to the "GEN" or "ARM" terminals of the voltage regulator. Just a touch of the jumper to both terminals is all that is required.

If the generator field is internally grounded, Fig. 24, disconnect the field wire from the regulator and momentarily touch this wire to the regulator "BAT" terminal.

Motoring Generator

Run the generator as a motor by connecting the ground side of a battery to the generator housing. Connect the ungrounded side of the battery to the generator armature terminal.

On generators with externally grounded fields, connect a jumper wire from the generator field terminal to the generator frame. For internally grounded units connect a jumper wire from the armature terminal to the field terminal.

While motoring, the armature should rotate slowly. If it does not, it may be due to improper bearing fit or alignment, mechanical interference between armature and field coil pole shoes or improper end play. If end play appears excessive, check the tightness of the pulley nut. Make sure that the pole shoe screws are securely tightened. Two or three sharp raps on the generator frame with a rawhide or plastic hammer will often help to free the armature.

VOLTAGE REGULATORS, REPLACE

1. When working on voltage regulators, it is good practice first to remove the battery ground strap or cable from the battery post. This prevents any short circuits or accidental grounds from occuring.
2. To aid in correctly re-wiring to the replacement regulator, identify the wires in some manner that will aid in proper installation.
3. Remove lead or leads connected to the battery terminal of the regulator.
4. Remove lead or leads connected to the armature terminal of the regulator. This terminal is marked "GEN" on Delco-Remy units, and "A" or "ARM" on Autolite, Ford and Bosch units. *If a condenser is present, note that it must be connected to the armature terminal only.*
5. Some regulators have a fuse connected to the regulator battery terminal. This fuse should be removed for use with the replacement regulator. Before installing the fuse, however, it should be tested for continuity with a test lamp. This is to make sure the fuse is not defective or "blown" which would result in an open circuit.
6. After the new regulator has been installed in position, scrape all lead connections or terminals clean to provide a good metal-to-metal contact when re-connected to the regulator terminals.
7. After all leads are connected and before the engine is started, the generator must be polarized as outlined previously.

ELECTRICAL TESTS ON REGULATORS

NOTES

1. Do not attempt to adjust regulators unless its operation is thoroughly understood and accurate meters are available. Even a slight error in the setting of the unit may cause improper functioning, resulting in a run-down or overcharged battery, or damage to the generator or regulator.
2. When electrical tests are made at the regulator terminals, there is great danger of short circuiting the regulator and burning the contact reeds on Autolite units. Whenever possible it is better to connect test apparatus where there is no danger of damaging the regulator. For example:
3. When checking generator output on single contact voltage regulators,

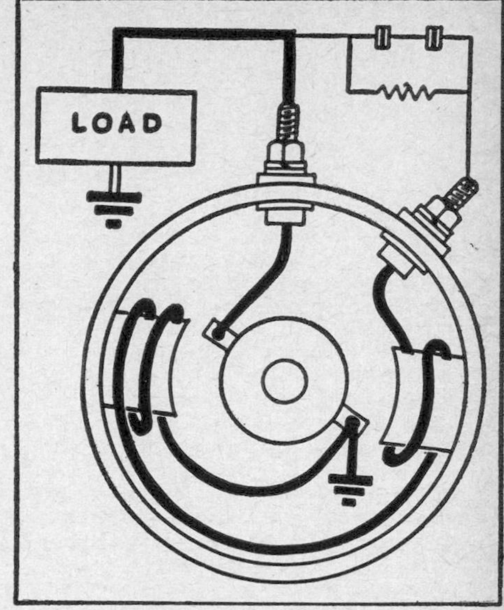

Fig. 24 Wiring diagram of a generator having the field grounded internally through the grounded brush. This can readily be identified by the fact that the grounded brush has both its own lead and the field lead connected to it

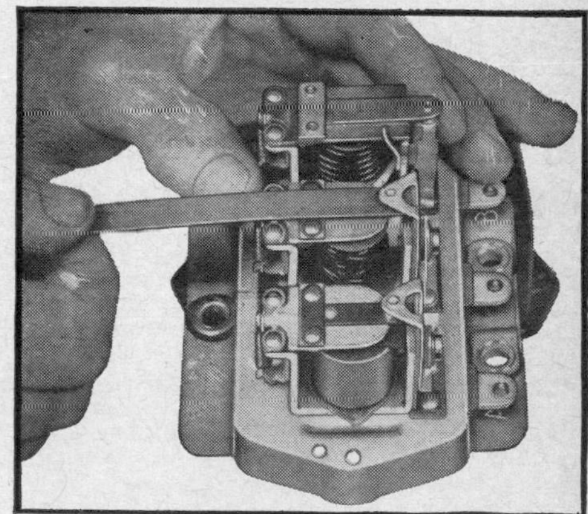

Fig. 25 Auto-Lite, Ford and Bosch regulator contacts should be filed parallel with length of armature

Fig. 26 Cleaning Delco-Remy regulator contact points

ground the field terminal at the generator rather than at the regulator to avoid the possibility of grounding the regulator battery terminal with a screwdriver. *Caution: When making this test on double contact voltage regulators, disconnect the field lead from the generator and ground this lead to the generator frame.*

4. Timing or trouble lights should be connected at the starter solenoid terminal rather than at the regulator battery terminal. This will avoid danger of the clip connector slipping off and simultaneously touching the battery and field terminal of the regulator.
5. Before testing or adjusting the regulator, be sure all connections in the charging circuit are clean and tight, and that the battery is fully charged. Check the generator output and be sure the regulator is the correct unit for use with the particular generator. Be sure regulator is properly grounded.
6. Always make the voltage regulator test before making the current regulator test. When removing or installing the regulator cover, do not allow the cover to touch regulator parts, as this might cause a short circuit and damage the unit.
7. Before starting the tests make sure the contacts are clean and not rough or pitted. If this is not done, subsequent tests will only produce erratic meter indications. When cleaning Autolite, Ford and Bosch contacts, they should be filed parallel to the armature as shown in Fig. 25, using a No. 6 American Swiss cut equaling file. Do not file crosswise as grooves may form which would tend to cause sticking and erratic operation. Delco-Remy recommends the use of a spoon or riffler file, Fig. 26. After filing, use a strip of linen tape dampened with lighter fluid to clean the contacts; then run a strip of dry tape across the points to remove any residue left from filing.

AUTOLITE, FORD & BOSCH ELECTRICAL TESTS

Circuit Breaker

1. With an ammeter connected as shown in Fig. 27, and a voltmeter connected from regulator armature terminal to regulator base, disconnect field lead from regulator field terminal and insert a variable resistance between field lead and its terminal.
2. Run engine at about 800 rpm. Turn variable resistance to the "all in" position. Then slowly reduce the resistance, noting the voltage reading just as the circuit breaker closes. The voltmeter will give a sharp fluctuation at that point and usually a slight click can be heard as the contacts close.
3. On Autolite units, if the closing voltage is not within specifications, remove the regulator cover and change the armature spring tension by bending the lower spring hanger. Bending the spring hanger down in-

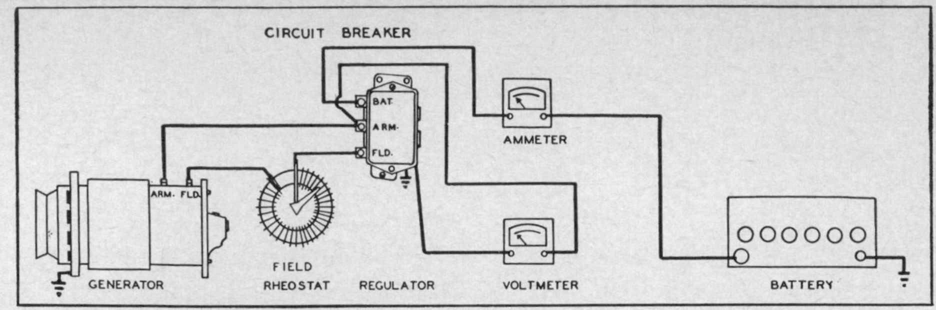

Fig. 27 Circuit breaker test for Auto-Lite, Ford and Bosch regulators

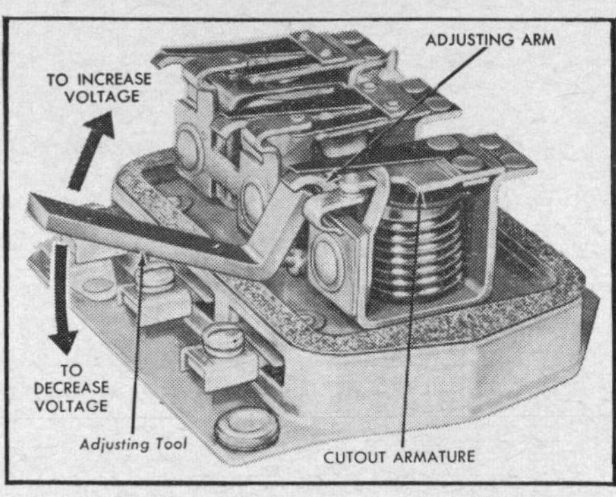

Fig. 28 Adjusting circuit breaker closing voltage on Ford and Bosch regulators

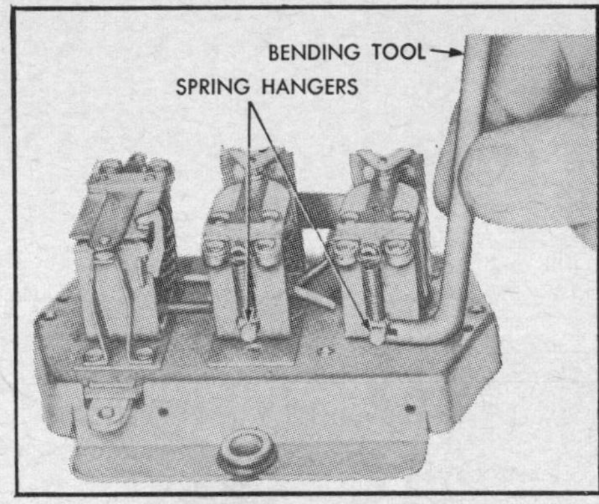

Fig. 29A Adjusting armature spring tension for Auto-Lite voltage and current settings

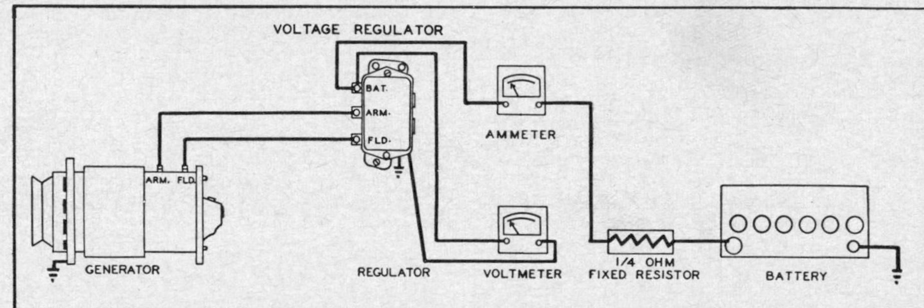

Fig. 29 Voltage regulator test on Auto-Lite Ford and Bosch single contact voltage regulators

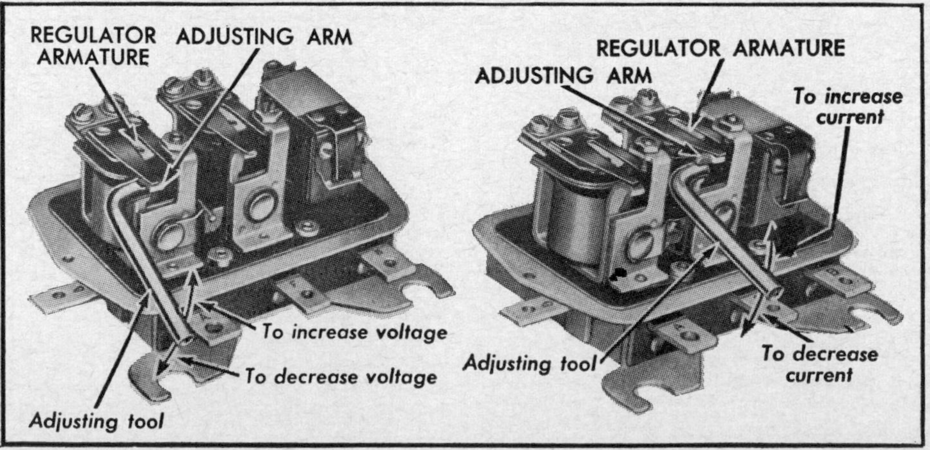

Fig. 30 Adjusting voltage regulator (left) and current regulator (right) on Ford and Bosch regulators

creases spring tension and raises the voltage, and vice versa.

4. If closing voltage is not within specifications on Ford and Bosch units, bend the adjusting arm upward to increase voltage, and vice versa, Fig. 28.

Single Contact Voltage Regulator

1. Leave the ammeter connected as shown and move the voltmeter clip from the regulator armature terminal to the regulator battery terminal, Fig. 29.
2. Disconnect the variable resistance from the regulator field terminal and reconnect the field lead. Then insert a ¼ ohm fixed resistor in series with the ammeter.
3. Increase engine speed to obtain about a 7 ampere charge and operate for about 15 minutes with regulator cover in place.
4. Stop and restart the engine to cycle the generator; then note voltage reading. If not within specifications, adjust as follows:
5. On Autolite units, adjust by bending lower spring hanger, Fig. 29A. Bending the hanger down increases spring tension and raises voltage and vice versa.
6. On Ford and Bosch units, increase spring tension by bending adjusting arm upward to raise voltage and vice versa, Fig. 30.

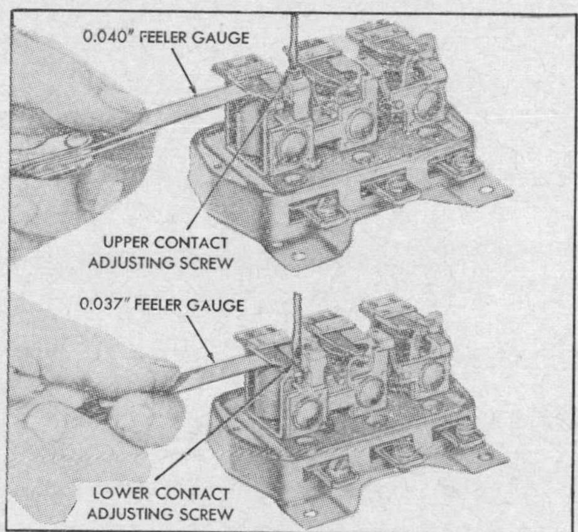

Fig. 31 Adjusting Ford and Bosch double contact voltage regulator

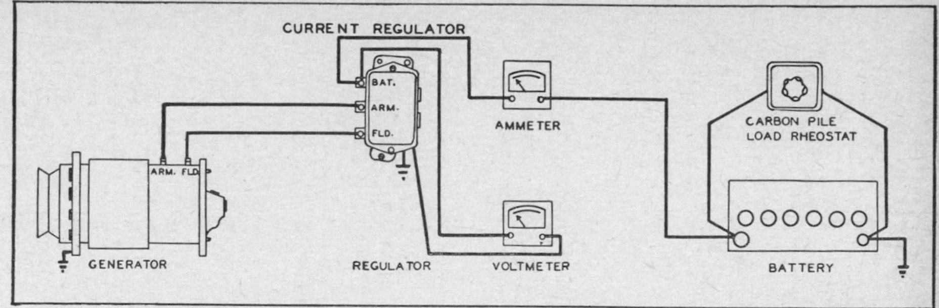

Fig. 32 Current regulator test on Auto-Lite, Ford and Bosch regulators

7. Be sure to stop and restart engine and replace cover after each setting before taking voltage readings.

Ford & Bosch Double Contact Voltage Regulator

If proper voltage cannot be obtained by bending the spring hanger as directed for single contact voltage regulators, further adjustments are required as follows:

1. Disconnect ground terminal from battery.
2. Remove regulator from vehicle and take off cover.
3. Turn upper contact screw in or out to obtain a .040″ gap between armature core and armature, Fig. 31.
4. Turn lower contact screw in or out to obtain a .037″ gap between armature core and armature. While making adjustments, hold contact points together by pressing downward on screwdriver.

Current Regulator

1. Meters are connected as for the voltage regulator test except that the fixed resistor is removed and a carbon pile rheostat is connected across the battery as shown in Fig. 32 to allow full output. An alternate method for allowing the current regulator to operate is to operate the starting motor for 15 or 20 seconds cranking the engine and turning on lights and accessories.
2. Operate engine at about 1800 rpm. Using the carbon pile, increase the load to lower the regulated system voltage approximately one volt and allow the current regulator to operate.
3. When a steady reading is reached which cannot be increased by a slight increase in engine speed, this will be the current regulator setting.
4. After operating at full output for 15 minutes, the current regulator should be within specified limits at operating temperature.
5. Adjustment is made in the same manner as for the voltage regulator.

DELCO-REMY ELECTRICAL TESTS

Figs. 33 and 34 show the generator circuit using single contact voltage regulator and double contact voltage regulator, respectively. In making the following tests, the regulator must be at operating temperature before taking meter readings. Operating temperature may be assumed to exist after not less than 15 minutes continuous operation with a charging rate of about 10 amperes and regulator cover in place.

CAUTION: With charging circuits having the double contact voltage regulator, Fig. 34, it is extremely important never to ground the field terminal of the generator or regulator when these units are connected or operating together. To do so will burn up the upper set of voltage regulator contacts.

For best results, the electrical tests must be made in the order given below.

Single Contact Voltage Regulator

1. Make motor connections as shown in

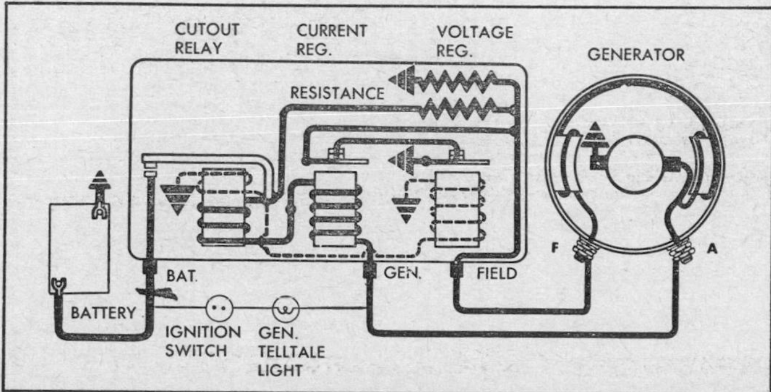

Fig. 33 Delco-Remy charging circuit with single contact voltage regulator

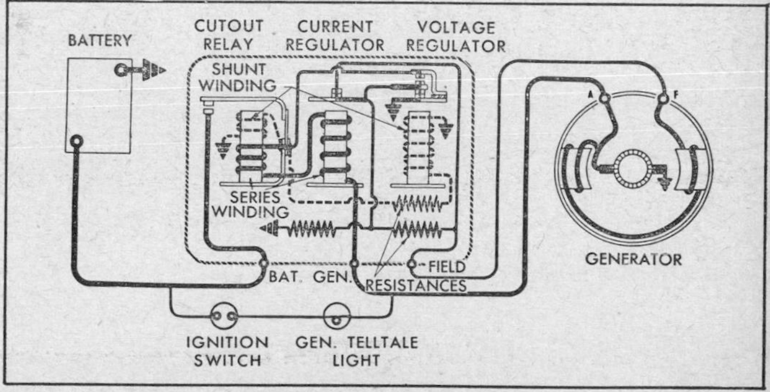

Fig. 34 Delco-Remy charging circuit with double contact voltage regulator

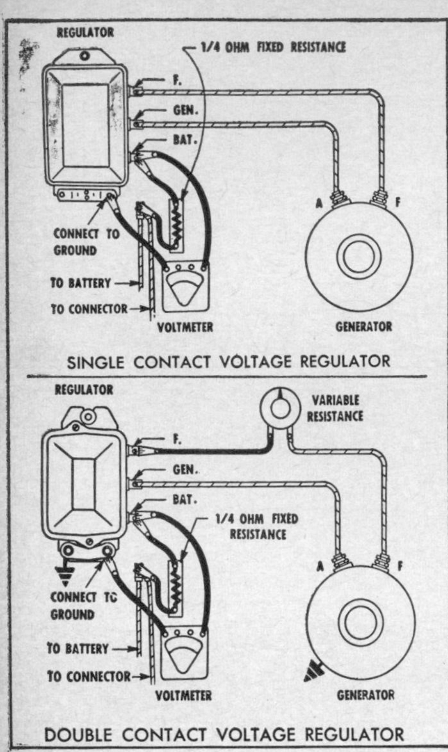

Fig. 35 Checking Delco-Remy voltage regulator setting

REGULATOR AMBIENT TEMPERATURE	VOLTAGE LOW		VOLTAGE HIGH
165° F	13.1	—	13.9
145° F	13.5	—	14.3
125° F	**13.8**		**14.7**
105° F	14.0	—	14.9
85° F	14.2	—	15.2
65° F	14.4	—	15.4
45° F	14.5	—	15.6
	NORMAL SPECIFICATION RANGE		

■ INDICATES PUBLISHED SPECIFICATIONS

Fig. 36 Delco-Remy single contact regulator temperature and voltage factors

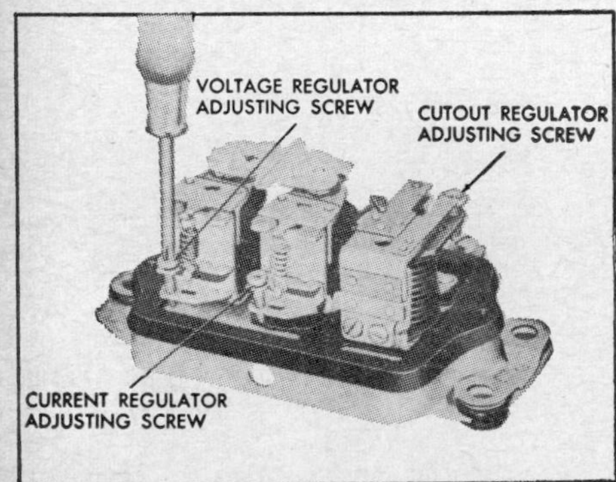

Fig. 37 Delco-Remy regulator adjusting screws

Fig. 35 (upper view), and operate the engine at about 1600 rpm for 15 minutes with the ¼ ohm resistor in the circuit and cover in place to bring the regulator to operating temperature.

2. Cycle the generator by stopping the engine, then restarting and bringing generator speed back to 1600 engine rpm.
3. Note voltmeter reading and ambient temperature (temperature of air surrounding regulator ¼″ from cover). The voltage reading represents setting at ambient temperature. As shown in Fig. 36, setting will be different at other ambient temperatures. *If method of measuring ambient temperature is not available it may be assumed to be 40 degrees above room temperature.*
4. To adjust voltage setting, remove regulator cover and turn voltage regulator adjusting screw, Fig. 37. Turn screw clockwise to increase spring tension and raise voltage, and vice versa. *Final adjustment should always be made by turning screw clockwise to assure contact between screw head and spring support, Fig. 38.*
5. After each adjustment and before taking meter reading, replace cover and recycle generator, as in Step 2.

Double Contact Voltage Regulator

1. Make meter connections as shown in Fig. 35 (lower view).
2. With variable resistance turned out (minimum resistance), operate generator at a speed so that the voltage regulator is operating on the upper set of contacts. Continue to operate for 15 minutes to establish operating temperature. Regulator cover must be in place.
3. Cycle generator by turning variable resistance to the "open" position momentarily, then slowly decrease (turn out all) resistance. Regulator should again be operating on the upper set of contacts.
4. Note voltmeter reading and ambient temperature, and see Fig. 39 for correction factors.
5. Increase (turn in) resistance slowly until voltage regulator begins to operate on the lower set of contacts. The lower set should operate at a lower voltage than the upper set of contacts.
6. To adjust voltage setting on upper set of contacts, do so in the same manner as directed for single contact voltage regulators above.
7. For the lower set of contacts, the difference in voltage between the upper set and lower set is increased by *slightly* increasing the air gap between the armature and center of core and decreased by *slightly* decreasing the air gap, Fig. 40. This adjustment is made while the regulator is operating. If necessary to make this adjustment, recheck the voltage setting of both sets of contacts.

Circuit Breaker Closing Voltage

1. Make connections as shown in Fig. 41.

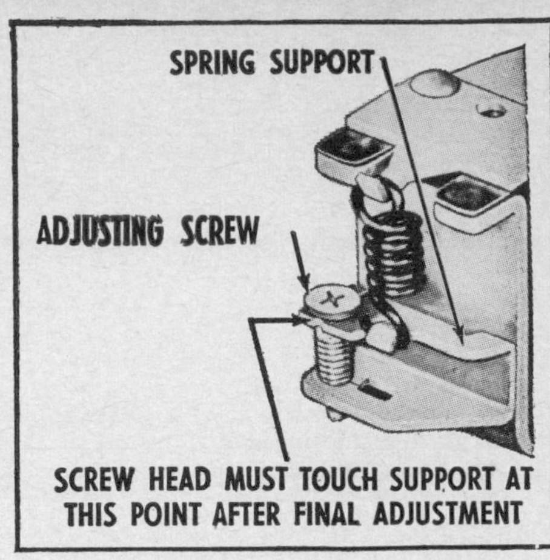

Fig. 38 Proper contact between regulator spring support and adjusting screw on Delco-Remy regulators

REGULATOR AMBIENT TEMPERATURE	VOLTAGE LOW		VOLTAGE HIGH
205° F	13.3	—	14.1
185° F	13.4	—	14.2
165° F	13.5	—	14.4
145° F	13.7	—	14.5
125° F	13.8	—	14.6
105° F	14.0	—	14.8
85° F	14.1	—	14.9
	NORMAL SPECIFICATION RANGE		

Fig. 39 Delco-Remy double contact regulator temperature and voltage factors

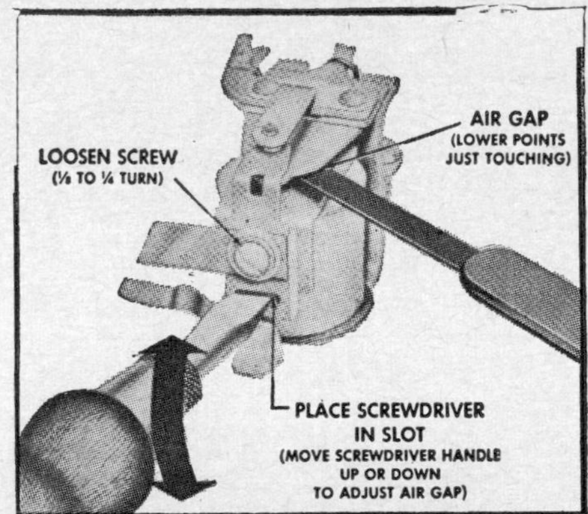

Fig. 40 Adjusting lower set of contacts on Delco-Remy double contact voltage regulator

2. Check closing voltage by slowly increasing generator speed and noting voltage at which points close. Decrease generator speed and make sure points open.
3. If not as specified, adjust voltage by

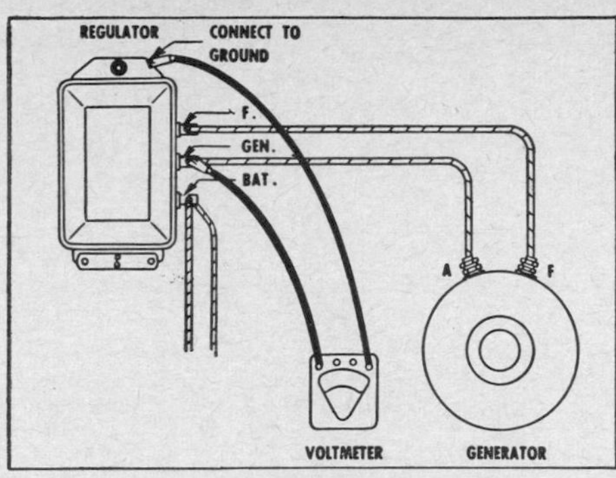

Fig. 41 Delco-Remy circuit breaker test

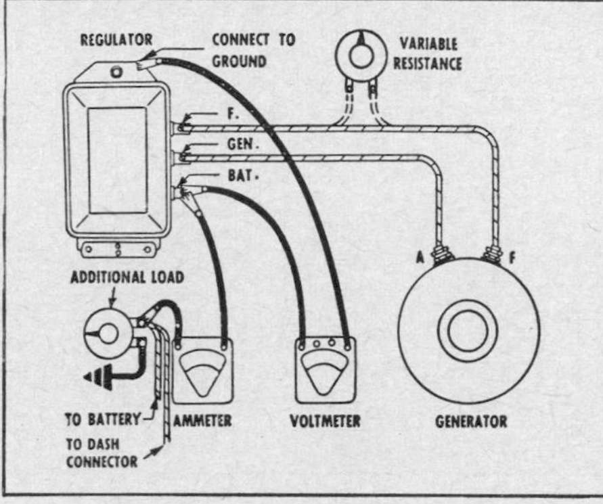

Fig. 42 Delco-Remy current regulator test

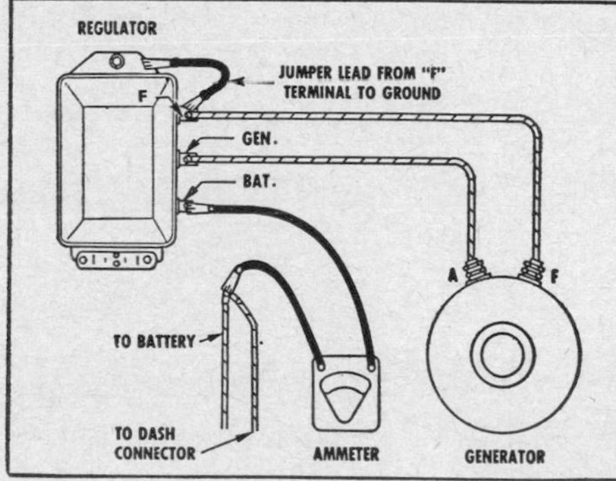

Fig. 43 Checking for oxidized regulator contact points. On double contact regulators do not use jumper wire as shown; Instead remove lead from "F" terminal and ground this lead

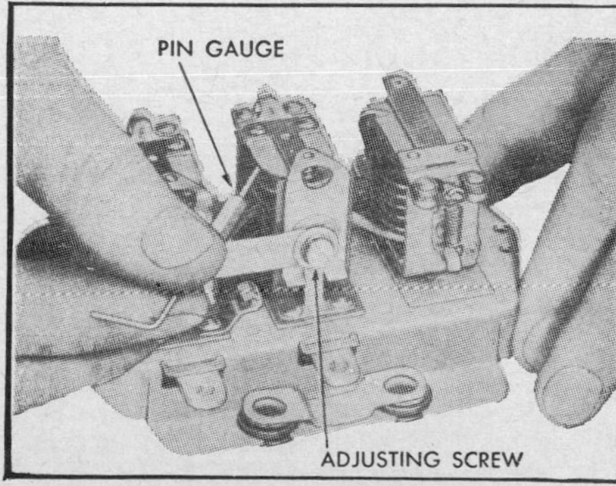

Fig. 44 Checking air gaps on Auto-Lite regulators

turning adjusting screw clockwise to increase voltage and vice versa (see Fig. 37).

Current Regulator

1. Before making connections shown in Fig. 42, disconnect battery ground lead. After completing the hook-up, reconnect battery lead.
2. Turn on all lights and accessories and connect an additional load across the battery, such as a carbon pile or bank of lights, so as to drop the system voltage to 12.5-13.0 volts.
3. Operate generator at 1600 engine rpm for at least 15 minutes with cover in place to establish operating temperature.
4. Cycle the generator as previously directed and note current regulator setting.
5. Adjustment is made in the same manner as outlined for single contact voltage regulators (see Fig. 37).

Check For Oxidized Contacts

1. Oxidized contacts may be the cause of low generator output or a discharged battery. To check for this condition, connect an ammeter into the circuit as shown in Fig, 43, and turn on headlights.
2. Operate generator at a speed that will produce a charge rate of 5 amperes.
3. Ground the "F" terminal of regulator as shown. *Caution: On double contact regulators, remove lead from "F" terminal and ground this lead.*
4. If generator output increases more than 2 amperes, oxidized contact points are indicated. Remove regulator from vehicle and clean points.

AUTOLITE MECHANICAL ADJUSTMENTS

Current & Voltage Regulator Air Gaps

1. Use a pin type gauge which measures .048-.052". Insert gauge on point side of air gap and next to armature stop pin with contact points just seperating, Fig. 44.
2. If an adjustment is necessary, loosen bracket screws and raise or lower contact point brackets until the foregoing clearance is obtained. Tighten screws securely after adjustment.
3. With armature held down so that stop rivet rests on magnet core, the point gap should be .015" when checked with a feeler gauge.

Circuit Breaker Air Gap

1. As shown in Fig. 45, use a flat gauge which measures from .031-.034". Insert gauge between armature and magnet core. Place gauge as near to hinge as possible.
2. To adjust, bend armature stop, Fig. 46, so that space between core and armature is within the foregoing limits. The stop must not interfere with armature movement.
3. Adjust the contact gap to .015" by expanding or contracting the stationary contact bridge, Fig. 46. When making this adjustment, keep the contact points in alignment.

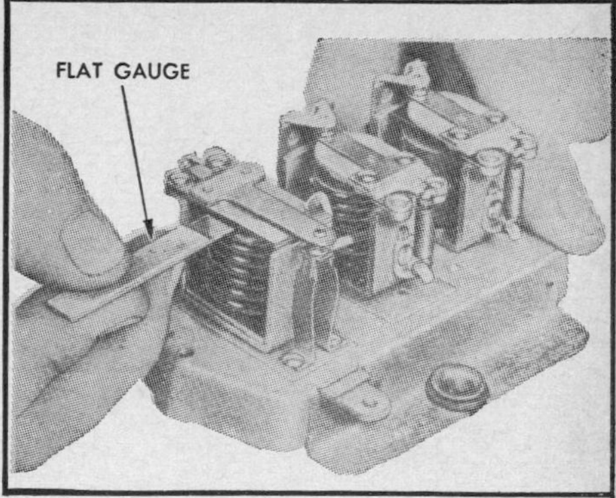

Fig. 45 Checking air gap on Auto-Lite circuit breaker

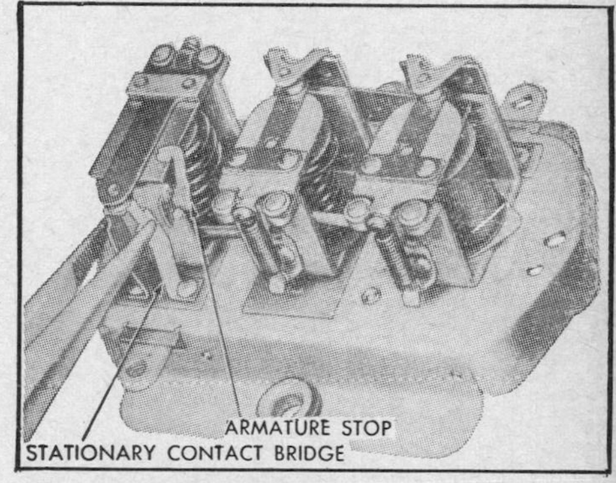

Fig. 46 Adjusting air gap on Auto-Lite circuit breaker

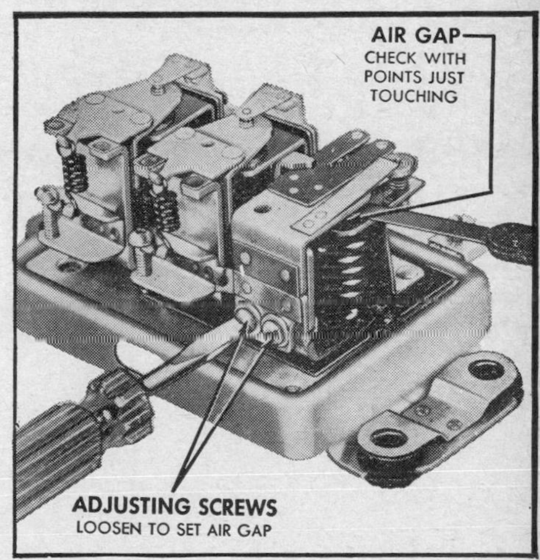

Fig. 47 Adjusting air gap on Delco-Remy circuit breaker

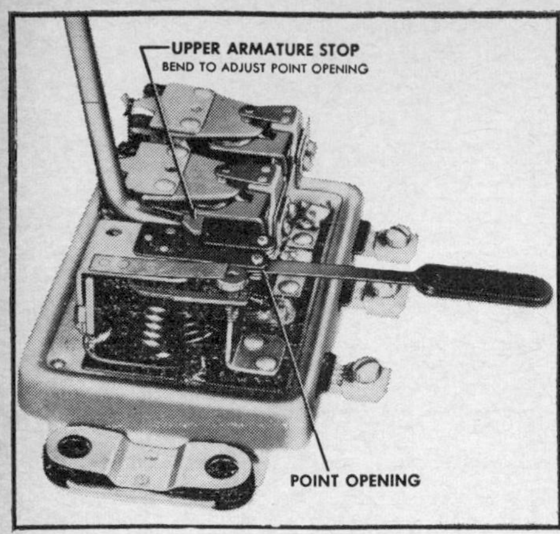

Fig. 48 Adjusting point opening on Delco-Remy circuit breaker

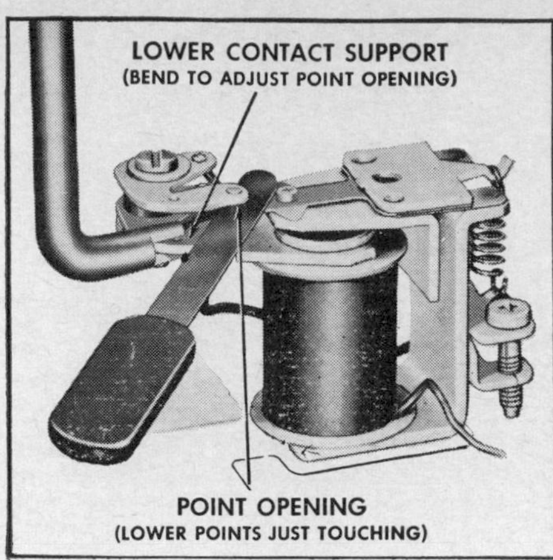

Fig. 51 Adjusting point opening on early type Delco-Remy double contact voltage regulator

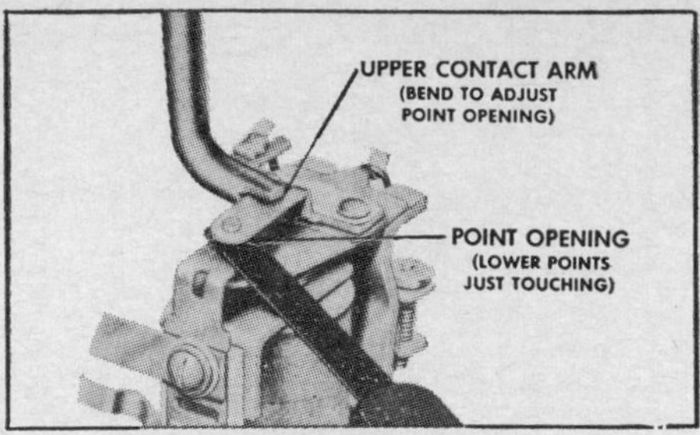

Fig. 52 Adjusting point opening on late type Delco-Remy double contact voltage regulator

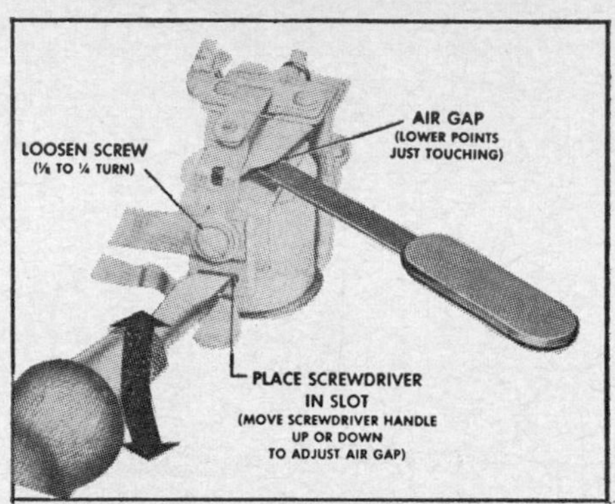

Fig. 53 Adjusting air gap on late type Delco-Remy double contact voltage regulator

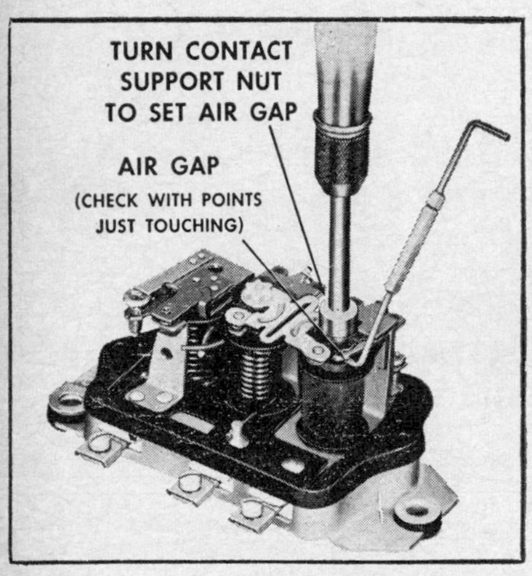

Fig. 49 Adjusting air gap on late type Delco-Remy single contact voltage regulator

DELCO-REMY MECHANICAL ADJUSTMENTS

Circuit Breaker Air Gap & Point Opening

1. Place fingers on armature directly above core and move armature down until points *just* close. Then measure air gap between armature and center core, Fig. 47. Air gap should be .020″.
2. Check to see that both points close simultaneously. If not, bend spring finger so that they do.
3. To adjust air gap, loosen two screws at back of circuit breaker and raise or lower armature as required. Tighten screws securely after adjustment.
4. Check point opening with feeler gauge as shown in Fig. 48 and adjust to .020″ by bending upper armature stop.
5. After both adjustments have been made, recheck closing voltage and make any necessary adjustments.

Voltage Regulator Air Gap On Single Contact Units

1. Referring to Fig. 49, push armature down to core and release it until contact points *just* touch. Then measure air gap with pin gauge between armature and center of core. Air gap should be .075″.
2. On late units, adjust gap by turning nylon nut on top of regulator as shown. On earlier units, adjust as shown in Fig. 50.
3. After making adjustment, recheck voltage setting and make necessary adjustments.

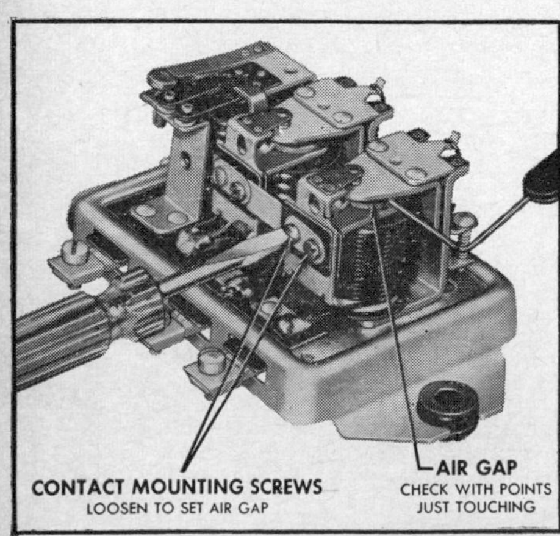

Fig. 50 Adjusting air gap on early type Delco-Remy single contact voltage regulator

Voltage Regulator Air Gap & Point Opening On Double Contact Units

Point Opening

1. With lower contacts touching, measure point opening between upper set of contacts. The opening should be .016″.
2. On early units, adjust as shown in Fig. 51. On late units, adjust as shown in Fig. 52.

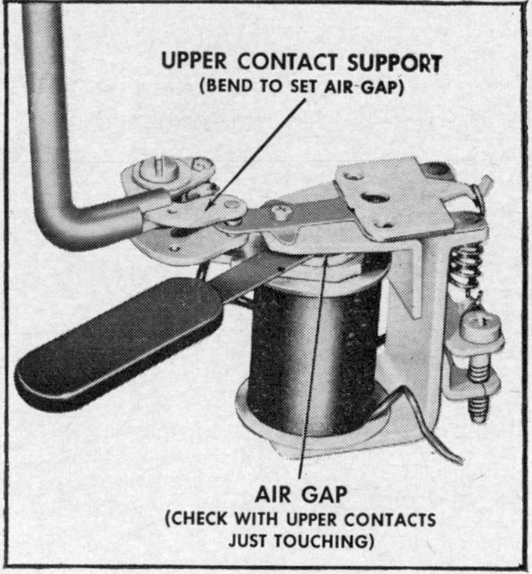

Fig. 54 Adjusting air gap on early type Delco-Remy double contact voltage regulator

Air Gap

1. On late units, Fig. 53, with lower contacts touching, measure air gap and adjust as shown.
2. On early units, first make sure adjusting screw on top of armature is turned all the way in a clockwise direction. Then check and adjust the gap as shown in Fig. 54.

Current Regulator Air Gap

Check and adjust current regulator air gap in exactly the same manner as the single contact voltage regulator. Air gap should be .075". After making the adjustment, recheck current setting and adjust as required.

FORD & BOSCH MECHANICAL ADJUSTMENTS

No mechanical adjustments are provided on these regulators as they are of riveted construction. However, on double contact regulators, the upper and lower voltage regulator contact sets are provided with an adjustment. See text in connection with Fig. 31.

STARTING MOTORS

CONTENTS

Starter Trouble Check-Out 1-101
Starter Service 1-103
Auto-Lite Starters 1-103
Chrysler Direct Drive Starter 1-104
Chrysler Reduction Gear Starter 1-105
Delco-Remy Starters 1-109
Ford Starter With Integral Positive Engagement Drive 1-111
Ford Starter With Folo-Thru Drive 1-113
Starter Drive Troubles 1-113

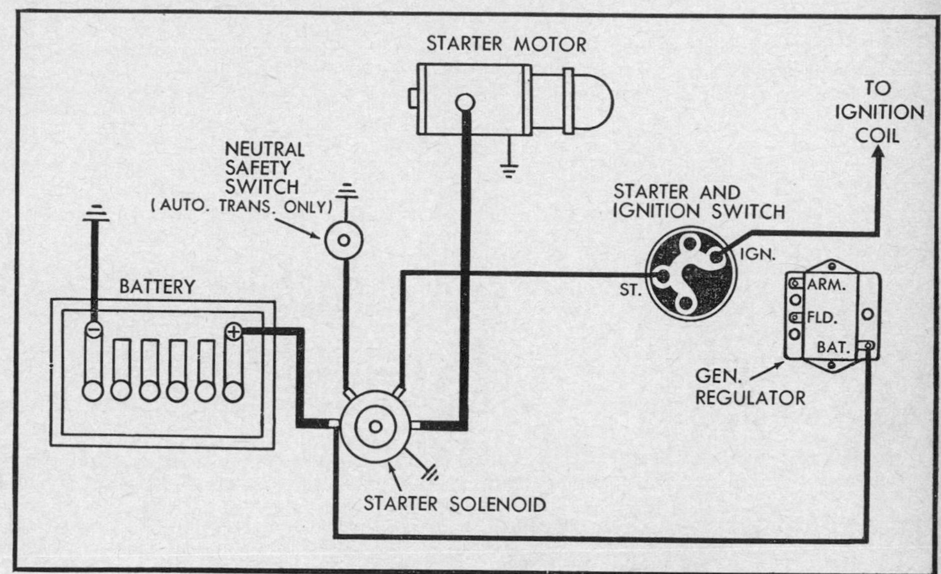

Fig. 1 Wiring diagram of a typical starting circuit

STARTER TROUBLE CHECK-OUT

WHEN TROUBLE develops in the starting motor circuit, and the starter cranks the engine slowly or not at all, several preliminary checks can be made to determine whether the trouble lies in the battery, in the starter, in the wiring between them, or elsewhere. Many conditions besides defects in the starter itself can result in poor cranking performance.

To make a quick check of the starter system, turn on the headlights. They should burn with normal brilliance. If they do not, the battery may be run down and it should be checked with a hydrometer.

If the battery is in a charged condition so that the lights burn brightly, operate the starting motor. Any one of three things will happen to the lights: (1) They will go out, (2) dim considerably or (3) stay bright without any cranking action taking place.

If Lights Go Out

If the lights go out as the starter switch is closed, it indicates that there is a poor connection between the battery and starting motor. This poor connection will most often be found at the battery terminals. Correction is made by removing the cable clamps from the terminals, cleaning the terminals and clamps, replacing the clamps and tightening them securely. A coating of corrosion inhibitor (vaseline will do) may be applied to the clamps and terminals to retard the formation of corrosion.

If Lights Dim

If the lights dim considerably as the starter switch is closed and the starter operates slowly or not at all, the battery may be run down, or there may be some mechanical condition in the engine or starting motor that is throwing a heavy burden on the starting motor. This imposes a high discharge rate on the battery which causes noticeable dimming of the lights.

Check the battery with a hydrometer. If it is charged, the trouble probably lies

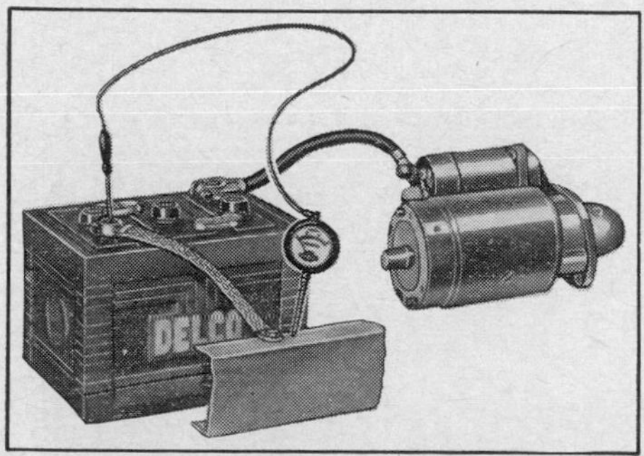

Fig. 2 Checking voltage drop between vehicle frame and grounded battery terminal post

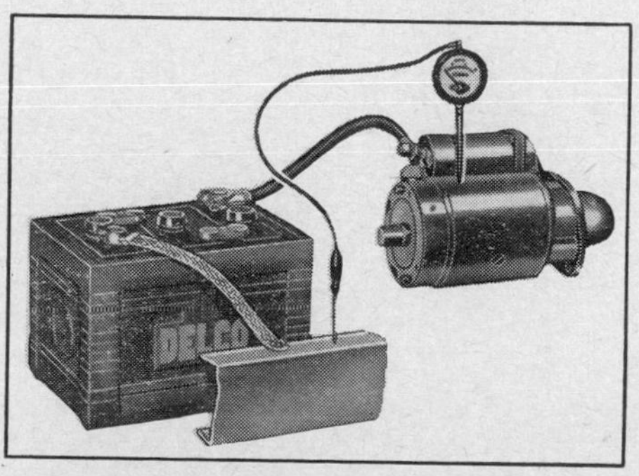

Fig. 3 Checking voltage drop between vehicle frame and starter field frame

Fig. 4 Checking voltage drop between ungrounded battery terminal post and battery terminal on solenoid

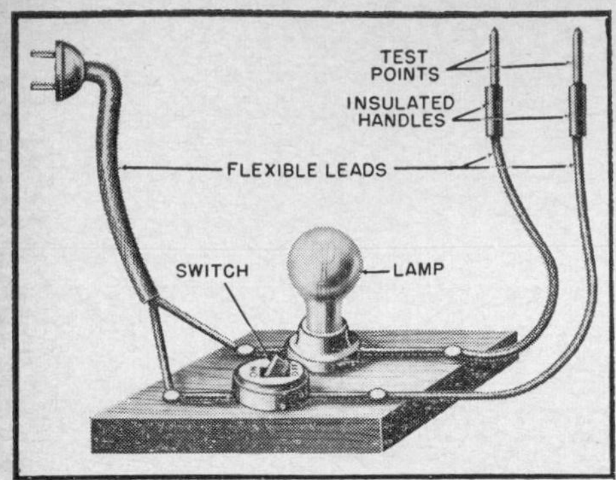

Fig. 5 A simple tester for use in making continuity and ground tests on armature and field windings

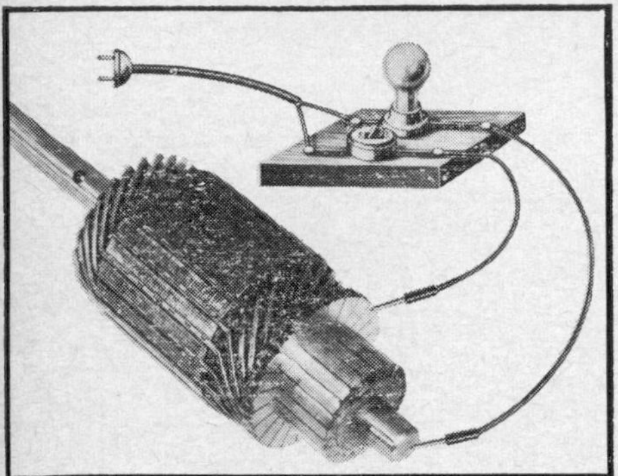

Fig. 6 Checking armature for grounds. If lamp lights armature is grounded and should be replaced

Fig. 7 Measuring commutator runout with dial indicator. Mount shaft in V blocks and rotate commutator. If runout exceeds .003", commutator should be turned in a lathe to make it concentric

in either the engine or starting motor itself. In the engine, tight bearings or pistons or heavy oil place an added burden on the starting motor. Low temperatures also hamper starting motor performance since it thickens engine oil and makes the engine considerably harder to crank and start. Also, a battery is less efficient at low temperatures.

In the starting motor, a bent armature, loose pole shoe screws or worn bearings, any of which may allow the armature to drag, will reduce cranking performance and increase current draw.

In addition, more serious internal damage is sometimes found. Thrown armature windings or commutator bars, which sometimes occur on over-running clutch drive starting motors, are usually caused by excessive over-running after starting. This is the result of such conditions as the driver keeping the starting switch closed too long after the engine has started, the driver opening the throttle too wide in starting, or improper carburetor fast idle adjustment. Any of these subject the over-running clutch to extra strain so it tends to seize, spinning the armature at high speed with resulting armature damage.

Another cause may be engine backfire during cranking which may result, among other things, from ignition timing being too far advanced.

To avoid such failures, the driver should pause a few seconds after a false start to make sure the engine has come completely to rest before another start is attempted. In addition, the ignition timing should be reset if engine backfiring has caused the trouble.

Lights Stay Bright, No Cranking Action

This condition indicates an open circuit at some point, either in the starter itself, the starter switch or control circuit. The solenoid control circuit can be eliminated momentarily by placing a heavy jumper lead across the solenoid main terminals to see if the starter will operate. This connects the starter directly to the battery and, if it operates, it indicates that the control circuit is not functioning normally. The wiring and control units must be checked to locate the trouble, Fig. 1.

If the starter does not operate with the jumper attached, it will probably have to be removed from the engine so it can be examined in detail.

Checking Circuit With Voltmeter

Excessive resistance in the circuit between the battery and starter will reduce cranking performance. The resistance can be checked by using a voltmeter to measure voltage drop in the circuits while the starter is operated. There are three checks to be made:

1. Voltage drop between car frame and grounded battery terminal post (not cable clamp), Fig. 2.
2. Voltage drop between car frame and starting motor field frame, Fig. 3.
3. Voltage drop between insulated battery terminal post and starting motor terminal stud (or the battery terminal stud of the solenoid), Fig. 4.

Each of these should show no more than one-tenth (0.1) volt drop when the starting motor is cranking the engine. Do not use the starter for more than 30 seconds at a time to avoid overheating it.

If excessive voltage drop is found in any of these circuits, make correction by disconnecting the cables, cleaning the connections carefully, and then reconnecting the cables firmly in place. A coating of vaseline on the battery cables and terminal clamps will retard corrosion.

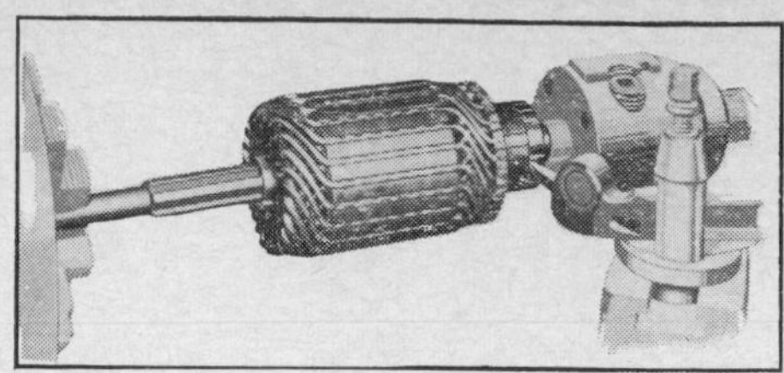

Fig. 8 Turning commutator in a lathe. Take light cuts until worn or bad spots are removed. Then remove burrs with No. 00 sandpaper

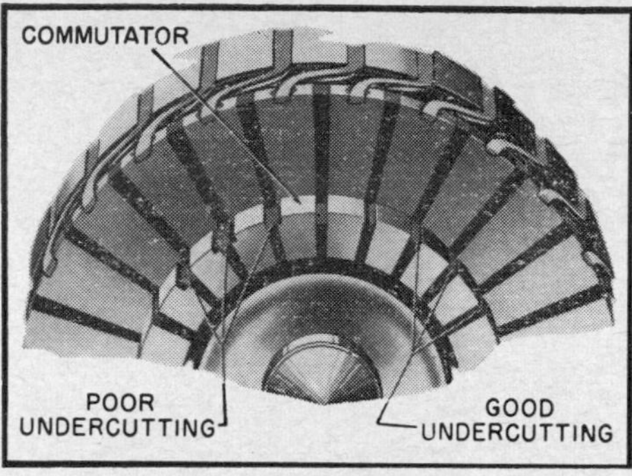

Fig. 9 Good undercutting should be .002" wider than mica insulation, 1/64" deep and exactly centered so that there are no burrs on the mica. Do not undercut molded commutators

Fig. 10 Checking armature for short circuit. As armature is rotated by hand, steel strip (hacksaw blade) will vibrate if short circuit exists

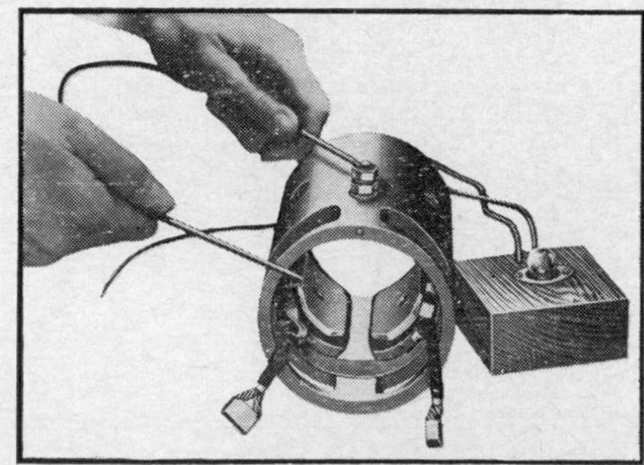

Fig. 11 Testing field coils for grounds. If a ground is present, lamp will light

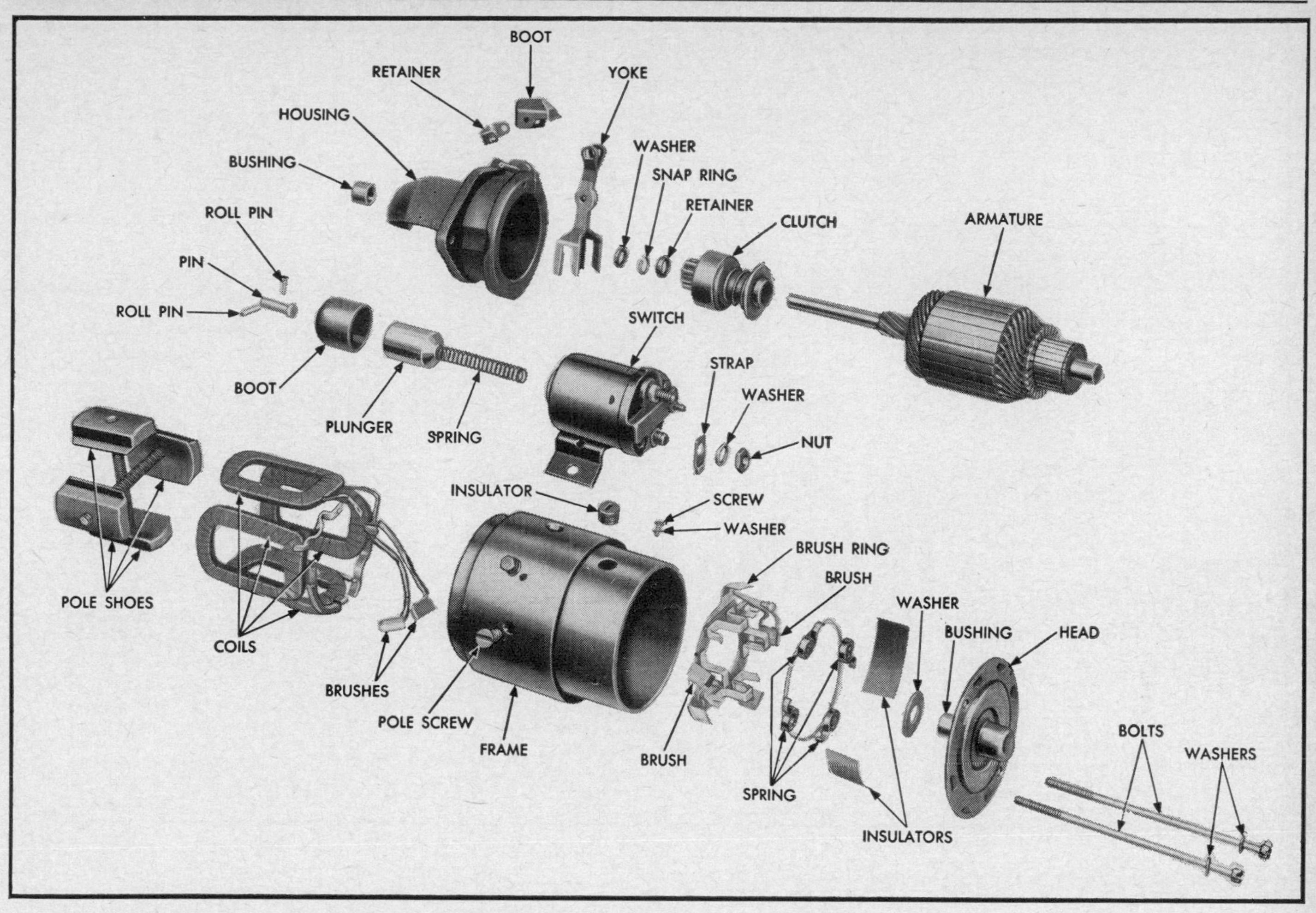

Fig. 12 Auto-Lite starter with over-running clutch drive

NOTE—On some cars, extra long battery cables may be required due to the location of the battery and starter. This may result in somewhat higher voltage drop than the above recommended 0.1 volt. The only means of determining the normal voltage drop in such cases is to check several of these vehicles. Then when the voltage drop is well above the normal figure for all cars checked, abnormal resistance will be indicated and correction can be made as already explained.

STARTING MOTOR SERVICE

To obtain full performance data on a starting motor or to determine the cause of abnormal operation, the starting motor should be submitted to a no-load and torque test. These tests are best performed on a starter bench tester with the starter mounted on it.

From a practical standpoint, however, a simple torque test may be made quickly with the starter in the car. Make sure the battery is fully charged and that the starter circuit wires and terminals are in good condition. Then operate the starter to see if the engine turns over normally. If it does not, the torque developed is below standard and the starter should be removed for further checking.

Remove the starter from the engine as outlined in the vehicle chapters, disassemble it as outlined further on and make the tests as suggested in Figs. 6 through 11.

AUTO-LITE STARTERS

Two types of starters are in general use. Heavy duty engines are equipped with the unit shown in Fig. 12 and light duty engines use the one shown in Fig. 13. In both motors the brush holders are riveted to a separate brush plate and are not serviced separately. Brush replacement is accomplished by removing the bearing end frame and armature.

Disassembling Overrunning Clutch Motor

1. Referring to Fig. 12, remove roll pin from shifting fork and solenoid coupling pin.
2. Remove solenoid.
3. Support solenoid coupling pin and drive out roll pin.
4. Remove solenoid rubber boot, plunger spring and coupling pin.
5. Remove thru bolts and take out commutator and cover, thrust washer and insulators.
6. Remove drive end housing, drive fork and armature from field frame.
7. Remove roll pin attaching shifting fork to pinion housing and remove retainer, dust cover and shifting fork.
8. Remove spacer and slide pinion gear toward commutator end of armature; then drive stop collar toward pinion and remove lock ring.
9. Slide starter drive from armature.
10. Remove brush holder ring from field frame (3 screws).
11. Disconnect field lead wire at brush holder ring, disengage the brushes from the holders and carefully slide brush holder ring from field frame.

Disassembling Folo-Thru Drive Motor

1. Referring to Fig. 13, remove thru bolts and tap commutator end frame from field frame.
2. Remove brush holder ring from field frame (3 screws).
3. Disconnect field lead wire at brush holder ring, disengage brushes from holders and carefully slide brush holder ring from field frame.
4. Remove set screw from drive and armature shaft by prying back drive spring to expose screw under spring.
5. Tap drive assembly from armature shaft and remove woodruff key.
6. Slide center bearing plate from armature shaft.

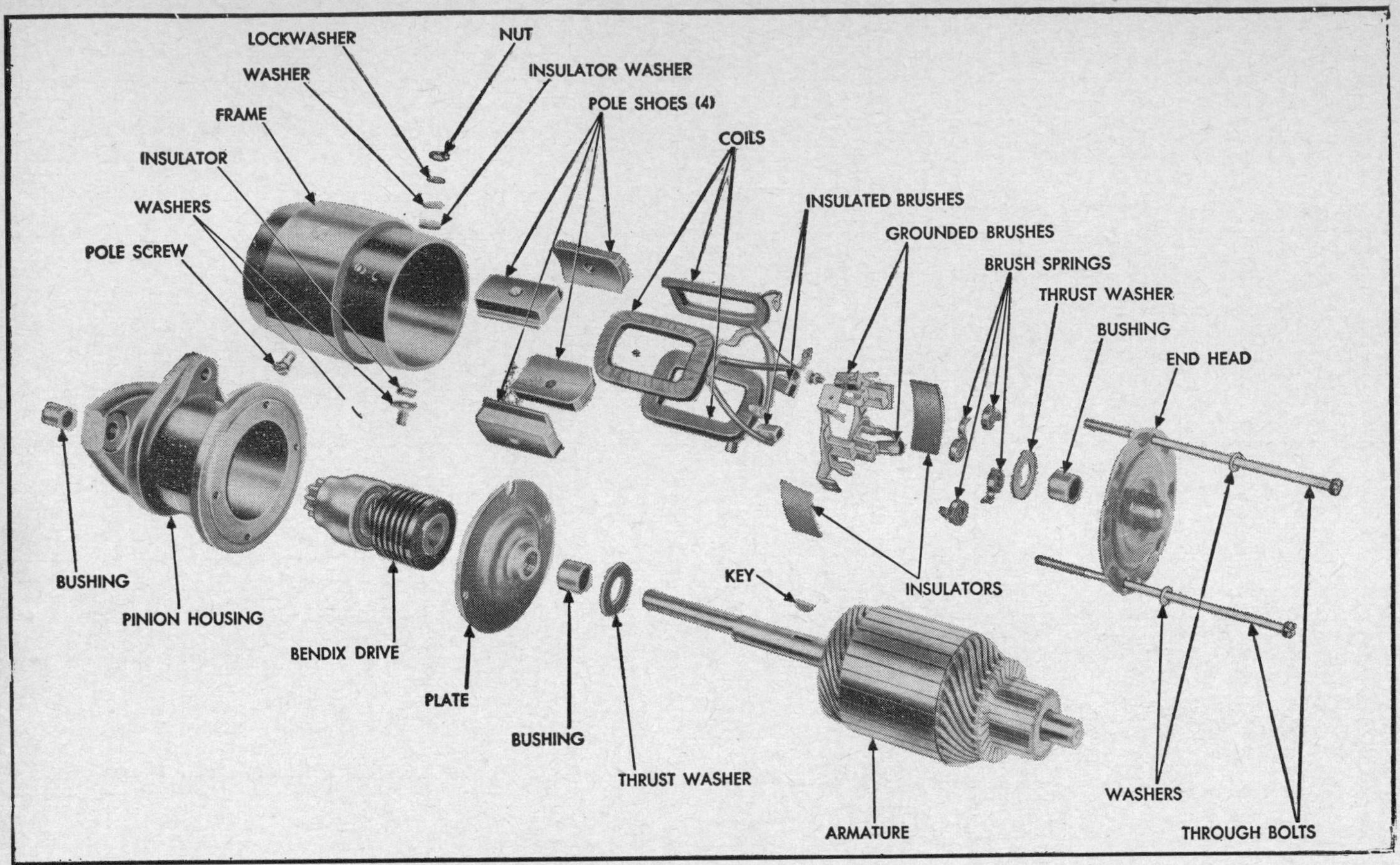

LOCKWASHER
NUT
WASHER
INSULATOR WASHER
FRAME
POLE SHOES (4)
INSULATOR
COILS
WASHERS
INSULATED BRUSHES
POLE SCREW
GROUNDED BRUSHES
BRUSH SPRINGS
THRUST WASHER
BUSHING
END HEAD
BUSHING
PINION HOUSING
KEY
INSULATORS
BENDIX DRIVE
PLATE
BUSHING
THRUST WASHER
WASHERS
ARMATURE
THROUGH BOLTS

Fig. 13 Auto-Lite starter with Folo-Thru drive

Overrunning Clutch

Place drive unit on shaft and, while holding armature, rotate pinion. The drive pinion should rotate smoothly in one direction (not necessarily easily), but should not rotate in the opposite direction. If drive unit does not function properly or pinion is worn or burred, replace drive unit.

Folo-Thru Drive

This type of drive, Fig. 14, is serviced only as an assembly. To clean and oil the drive with armature removed, use a screwdriver to pry back the drive spring to expose the attaching set screw. Back out the set screw far enough to clear armature shaft and slide drive off end of armature shaft. Wipe armature shaft clean and dry and re-oil with SAE 10W oil. Rotate pinion and barrel to the fully engaged position and apply clean kerosene with a brush to the screw shaft threads. Wipe dry and apply a light film of SAE 10W oil to the screw shaft threads and a few drops of oil under the spring on the thrust washer.

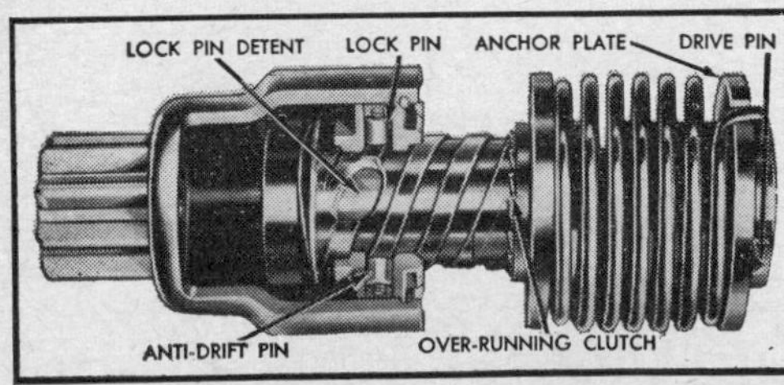

Fig. 14 Folo-Thru starter drive with Bendix spring

Assembling Starter

Reassembly procedure is the reverse of disassembly. However, on Folo-Thru drive motors, be sure the starter drive set screw is seated in the armature shaft; be sure the end frames are positioned on dowel pins; and be sure that the slots in the intermediate bearing and commutator end head line up with the indexing pins in the frame before installing and tightening thru bolts.

CHRYSLER DIRECT DRIVE STARTER

This Chrysler built starting motor, Fig. 15, is a four coil assembly with an overrunning clutch type drive and a solenoid shift-type switch mounted on the motor. The brush holders are riveted to a separate brush plate and are not serviced individually. Brush replacement can be made by removing the commutator bearing end head.

Disassembly

1. Remove through bolts and tap commutator end head from field frame.
2. Remove thrust washers from armature shaft.
3. Lift brush holder springs and remove brushes from holders.
4. Remove brush plate.
5. Disconnect field leads at solenoid connector.
6. Unfasten and remove solenoid and boot assembly.
7. Drive out over-running clutch shift fork pivot pin.
8. Remove drive end pinion housing and spacer washer.
9. Note position of shifter fork on starter and remove fork.
10. Slide over-running clutch pinion gear toward commutator end of armature. Drive stop retainer toward clutch pinion gear to expose snap ring and remove snap ring.
11. Slide clutch drive from armature shaft.
12. If necessary to replace the field coils, remove screw that holds ground brushes and raise brushes with the terminal and shunt wire up and away from field frame. Remove pole shoe screws and take out field coils.

Reassembly

1. Lubricate armature shaft and

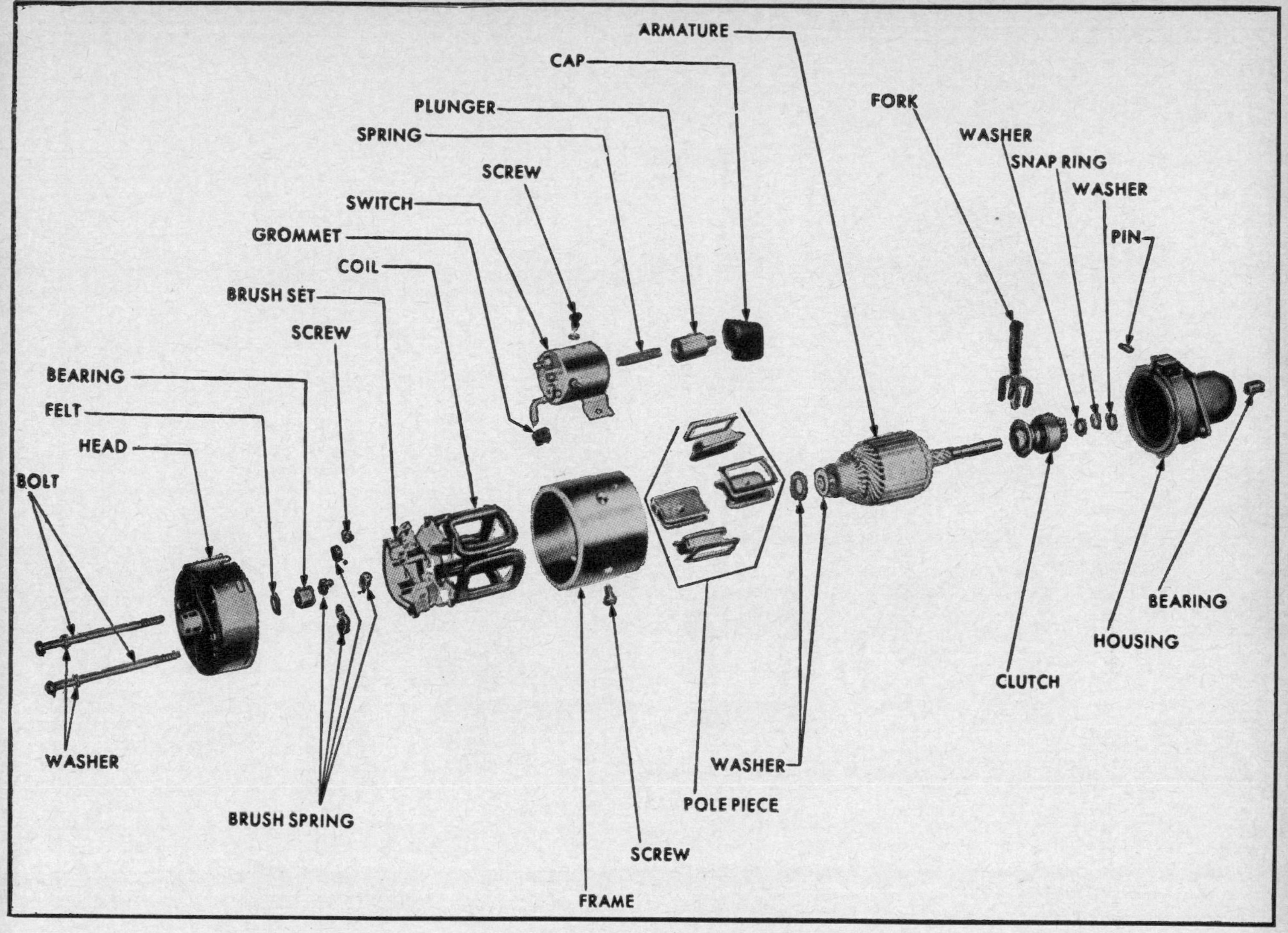

Fig. 15 Chrysler built direct drive starter

splines with SAE 10W or 30W rust preventive oil.

2. Install starter drive, stop collar (retainer), lock ring and spacer washer.
3. Install shifter fork over starter drive spring retainer washer with narrow leg of fork toward commutator. *If fork is not positioned properly, starter gear travel will be restricted, causing a lockup in the clutch mechanism.*
4. Install drive end (pinion) housing on armature shaft, indexing the shift fork with slot in drive end of housing.
5. Install shift fork pivot pin.
6. Install armature with clutch drive, shifter fork and pinion housing. Slide armature into field frame until pinion housing indexes with slot in field frame.
7. Install solenoid and boot assembly and tighten bolts securely.
8. Install ground brushes.
9. Connect field coil leads at solenoid connector.
10. Install brush holder ring, indexing tang of ring in hole of field frame.
11. Position brushes in brush holders. *Be sure field coil lead wires are properly enclosed behind brush holder ring and that they do not interfere with brush operation.*
12. Install thrust washer on commutator end of armature shaft to obtain .010" minimum end play.
13. Install commutator end head.
14. Install through bolts and tighten securely.

Adjusting Pinion Clearance

1. Place starter in vise with soft jaws and tighten vise enough to hold starter. *Place a wedge or screwdriver between bottom of solenoid and starter frame to eliminate all deflection in solenoid when making pinion clearance check.*
2. Push in on solenoid plunger link, Fig. 16 (not fork lever) until plunger bottoms.
3. Measure clearance between end of pinion and pin stop with plunger seated and pinion pushed toward commutator end. Clearance should be ⅛". Adjust by loosening solenoid attaching screws and move solenoid fore and aft as required.
4. Test starter operation for free running and install on engine.

CHRYSLER REDUCTION GEAR STARTER

This reduction gear starting motor, Fig. 17, has an armature-to-engine crankshaft ratio of 45 to 1; a 3½ to 1 reduction gear set is built into the motor assembly. The starter utilizes a solenoid shift. The housing of the solenoid is integral with the starter drive end housing.

Disassembly

1. Place gear housing of starter in a vise with soft jaws. *Use vise as a support fixture only; do not clamp.*
2. Remove through bolts and starter end head assembly.
3. Carefully pull armature up and out of gear housing, and starter frame and field assembly. Remove steel and fiber thrust washer. *The wire of the shunt field coil is soldered to the*

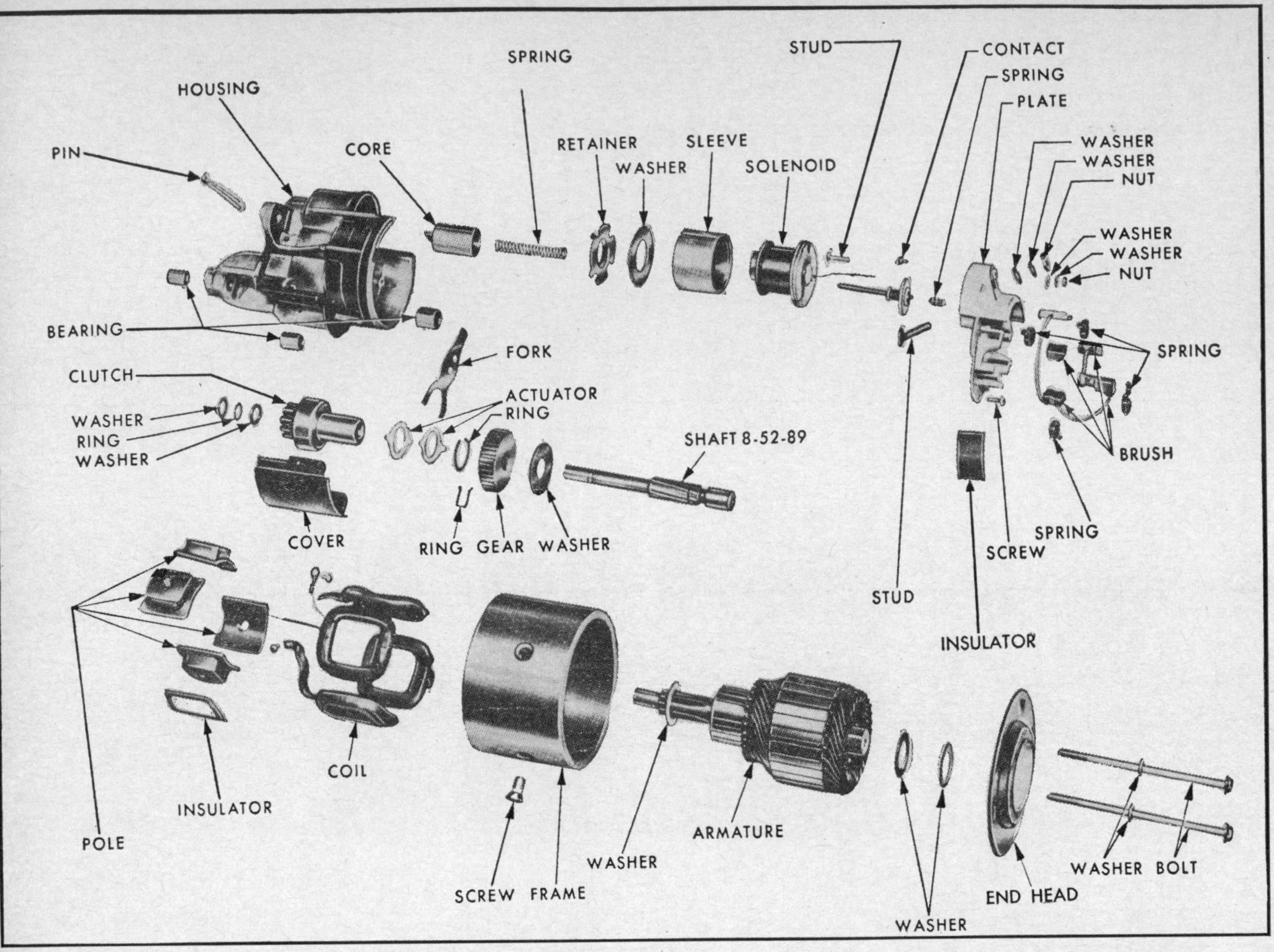

Fig. 17 Chrysler built reduction gear starting motor

brush terminal. One pair of brushes are connected to this terminal. The other pair of brushes is attached to the series field coils by means of a terminal screw. Carefully pull the frame and field assembly up just enough to expose the terminal screw and the solder connection of the shunt field at the brush terminal. Place two wood blocks between starter frame and gear housing, Fig. 18, to facilitate removal of terminal screw and unsoldering of shunt field wire at brush terminal.

4. Support brush terminal by placing a finger behind terminal and remove screw, Fig. 18.
5. Complete the disassembly procedure by referring to Figs. 19 through 33.

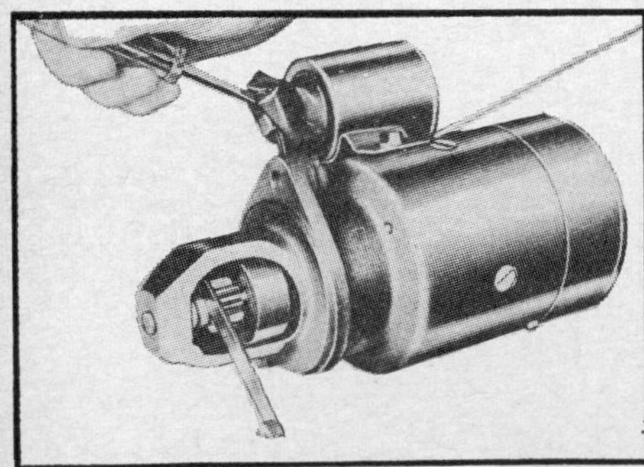

Fig. 16 Clearance between end of pinion and pin stop should be 1/8" with plunger seated and pinion pushed toward commutator end

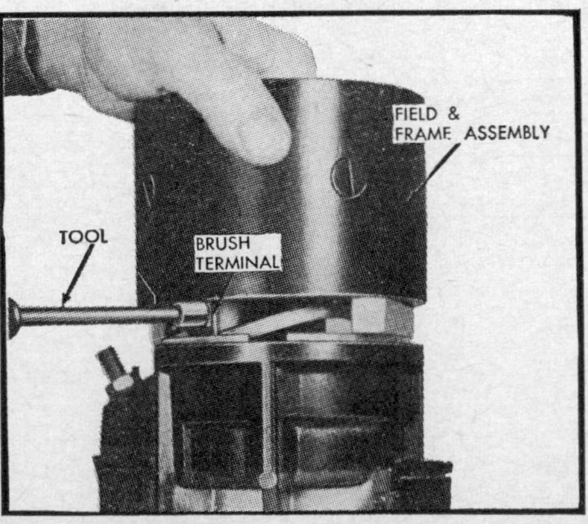

Fig. 18 Removing brush terminal screw

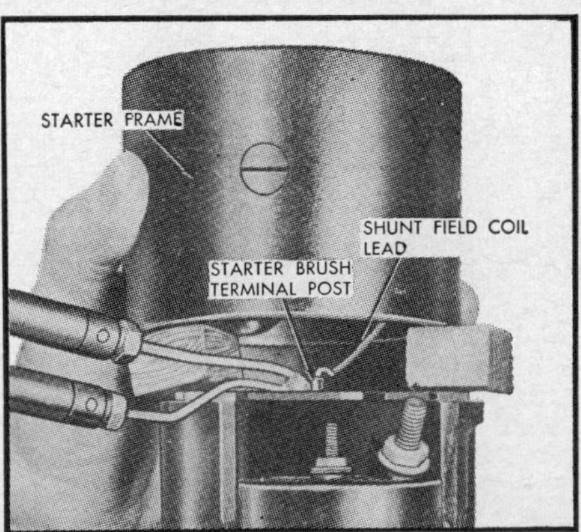

Fig. 19 Unsoldering shunt field coil lead from starter brush terminal

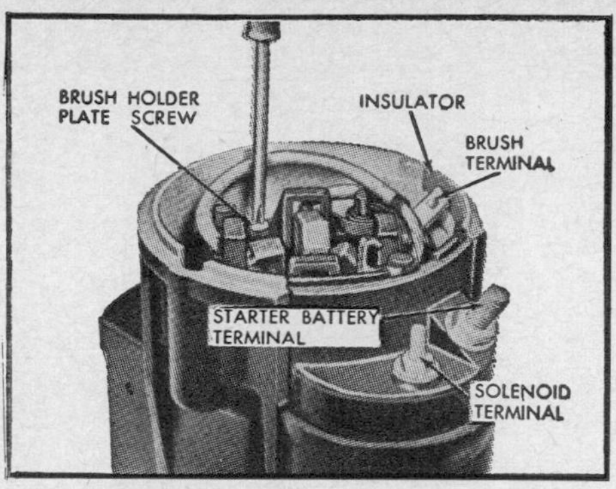

Fig. 20 Remove brush insulator which prevents contact between brush terminal and gear housing. Remove screw attaching brush holder plate to gear housing

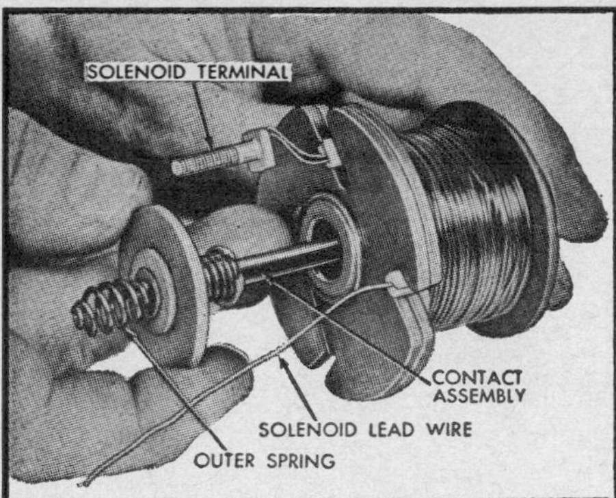

Fig. 24 Remove nut, steel washer and nylon washer from starter battery terminal. Remove terminal from holder plate. Then remove solenoid contact assembly

Fig. 28 Release snap ring that positions driven gear on pinion shaft. This ring is under tension and a cloth should be placed over ring to prevent it from springing away after removal

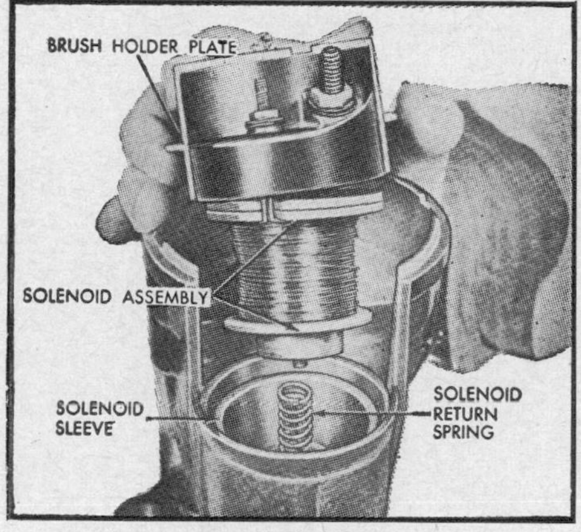

Fig. 21 Remove brush holder plate with brushes and solenoid as a unit

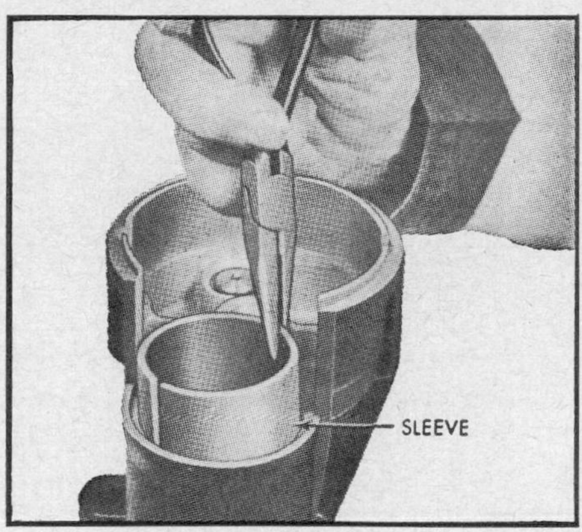

Fig. 25 Remove solenoid coil sleeve

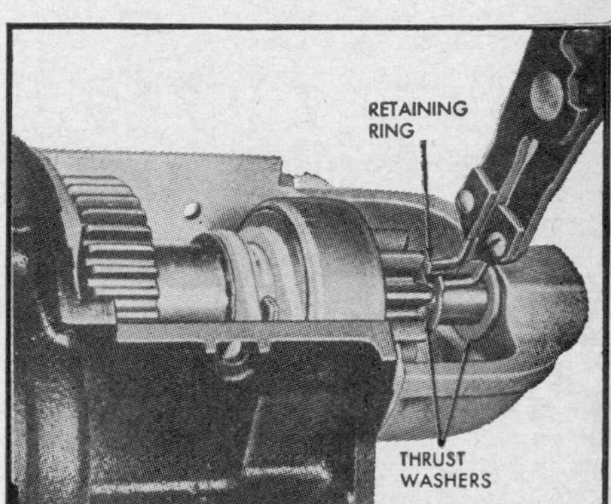

Fig. 29 Release retainer ring at front of pinion shaft. Do not spread ring any greater than the outside diameter of pinion shaft otherwise ring can be damaged

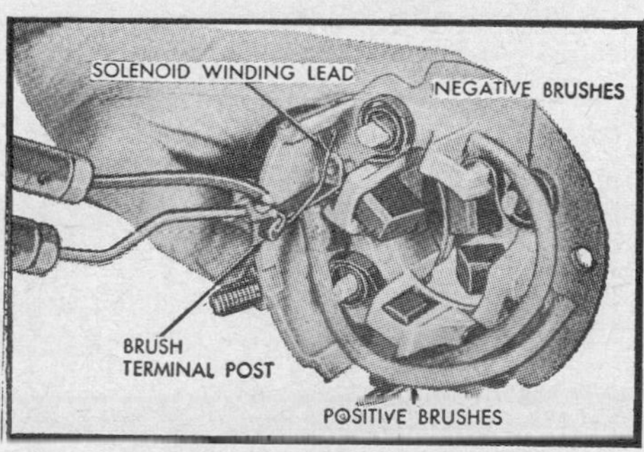

Fig. 22 Unsolder solenoid winding from brush terminal

Fig. 26 Remove solenoid return spring (Fig. 21). Then remove solenoid coil retainer washer and retainer from solenoid housing

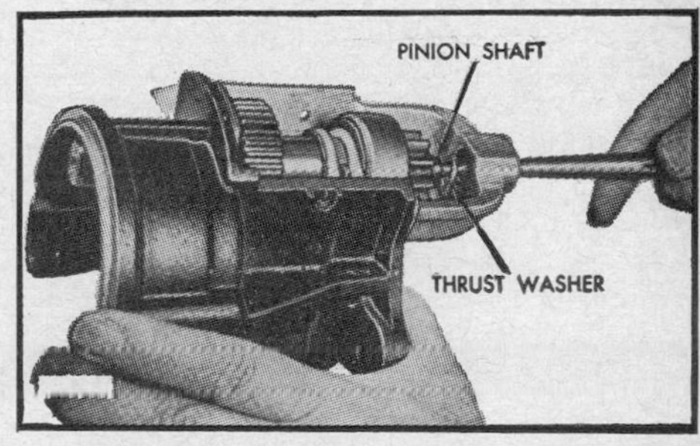

Fig. 30 Push pinion shaft toward rear of housing and remove snap ring and thrust washers

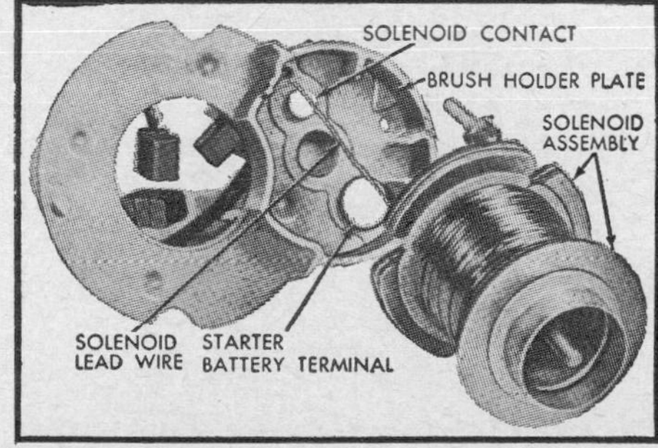

Fig. 23 Remove nut, steel washer and nylon washer from solenoid terminal. Separate brush holder plate from solenoid

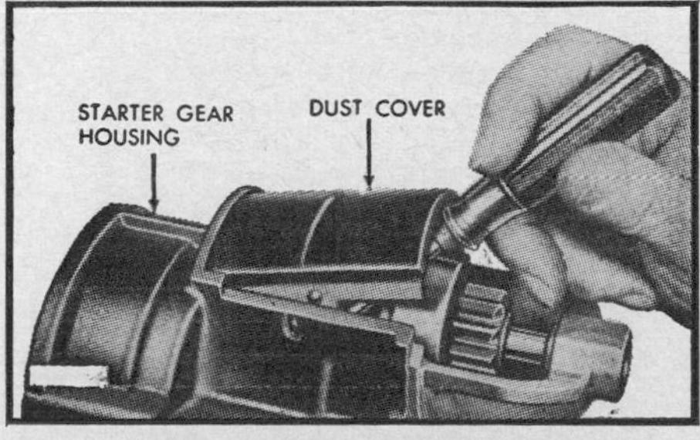

Fig. 27 Remove dust cover from gear housing

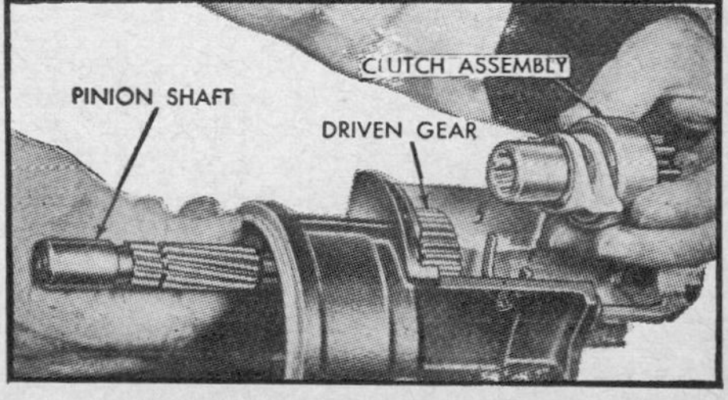

Fig. 31 Lift out clutch and pinion assembly with the two shifter fork nylon actuators

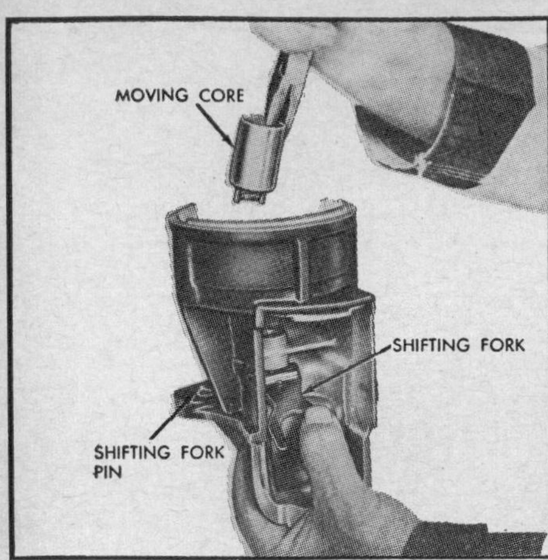

Fig. 32 Remove driven gear and friction washer. Then pull shift fork forward and remove solenoid moving core

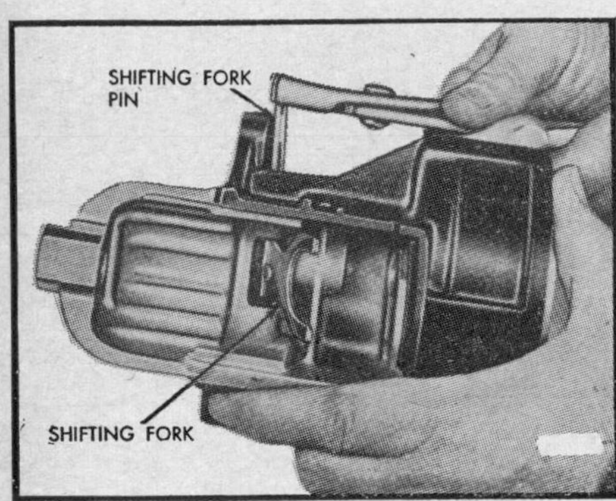

Fig. 33 Remove shift fork retainer pin and take out shift fork

Reassembly

The shifter fork consists of two spring steel plates assembled with two rivets, Fig. 34. There should be about $\frac{1}{16}$" side movement to insure proper pinion gear engagement. Lubricate between plates sparingly with SAE 10 engine oil.

1. Position shift fork in drive housing and install fork retaining pin, Fig. 33. *One tip of pin should be straight, the other tip should be bent at a 15 degree angle away from housing. Fork and pin should operate freely after bending tip of pin.*
2. Install solenoid moving core and engage shifting fork, Fig. 32.
3. Enter pinion shaft in drive housing and install friction washer and driven gear.
4. Install clutch and pinion assembly, Fig. 31, thrust washer, retaining ring, and thrust washer.
5. Complete installation of pinion shaft, engaging fork with clutch actuators, Fig. 35. *Friction washer must be positioned on shoulder of splines of pinion shaft before driven gear is positioned.*
6. Install driven gear snap ring, Fig. 29. Install pinion shaft retaining ring, making sure ring fits tightly in shaft groove.

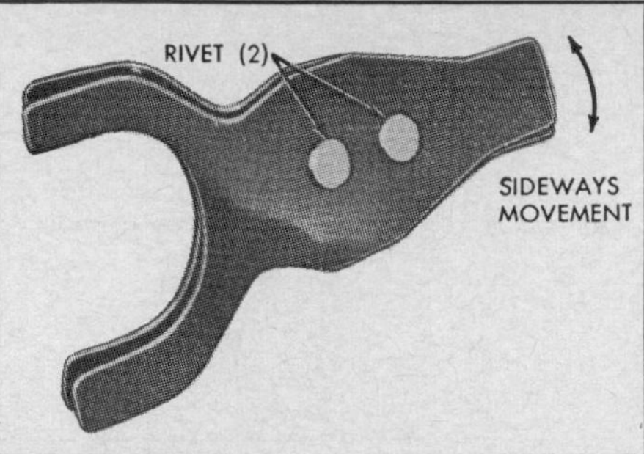

Fig. 34 Shifter fork assembly

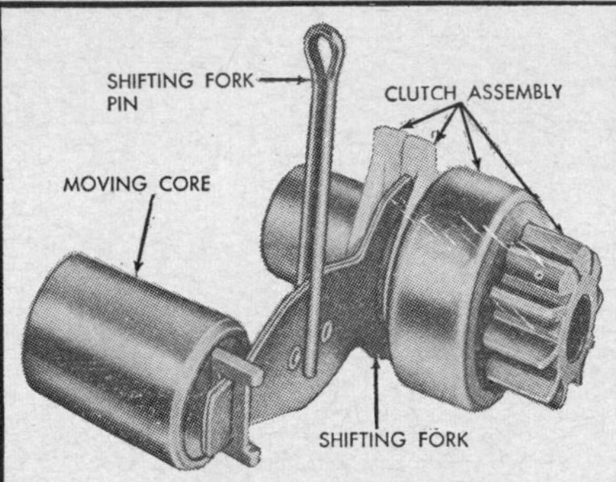

Fig. 35 Shifter fork and clutch arrangement

Fig. 36 Installing solenoid coil and sleeve

7. Install solenoid coil retainer, Fig. 26, with tangs down. *Space retainer in housing bore so that the four tangs rest on ridge in housing bore and not in the recesses.*
8. Install solenoid retainer washer.
9. Install solenoid return spring, Fig. 21. *Inspect condition of solenoid switch contacting washer. If top of washer is burned from arcing, disassemble switch and reverse washer.*
10. Install solenoid contact into solenoid, Fig. 24. Make sure contact spring is positioned in solenoid contact. *Inspect condition of contacts in brush holder plate. If contacts are badly burned, replace brush holder with brushes and contacts as an assembly.*

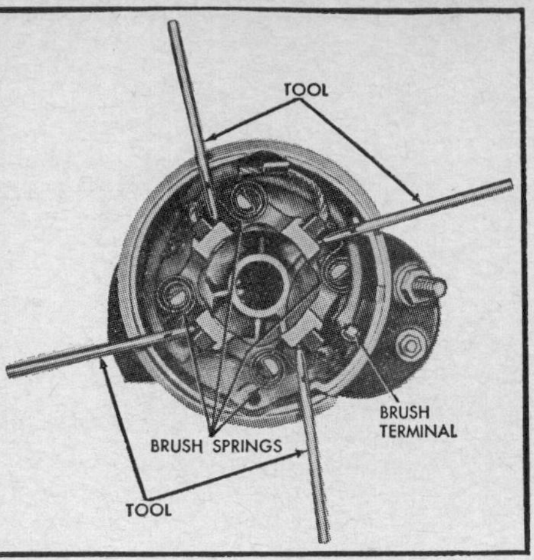

Fig. 37 Positioning of brushes with Tool Set C-3855

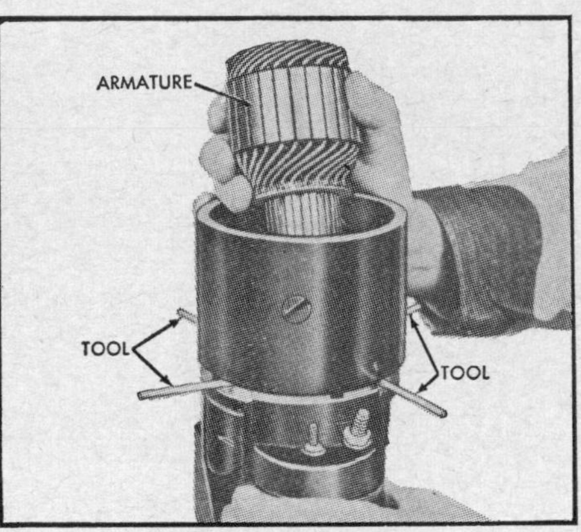

Fig. 38 Installing armature

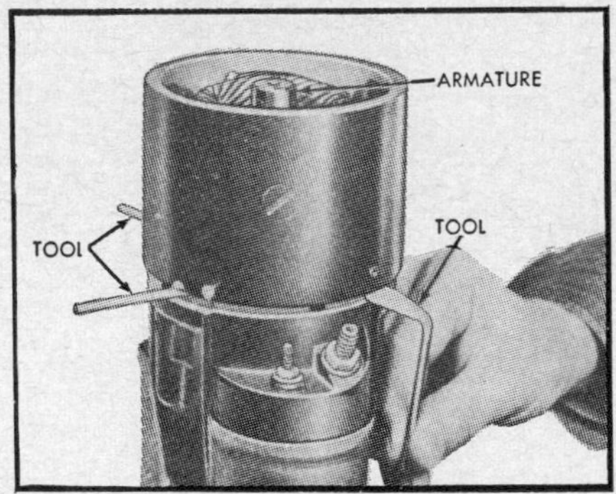

Fig. 39 Removing brush positioning tools

11. Enter solenoid lead wire through hole in brush holder, Fig. 23, and solenoid stud, insulating washer, flat washer and nut.
12. Solder solenoid lead wire to contact terminal, Fig. 22. Wrap wire securely around terminal and solder with a high temperature solder and resin flux.
13. Carefully enter solenoid coil and coil sleeve into bore of gear housing and position brush plate assembly into gear housing, Fig. 36. Align tongue

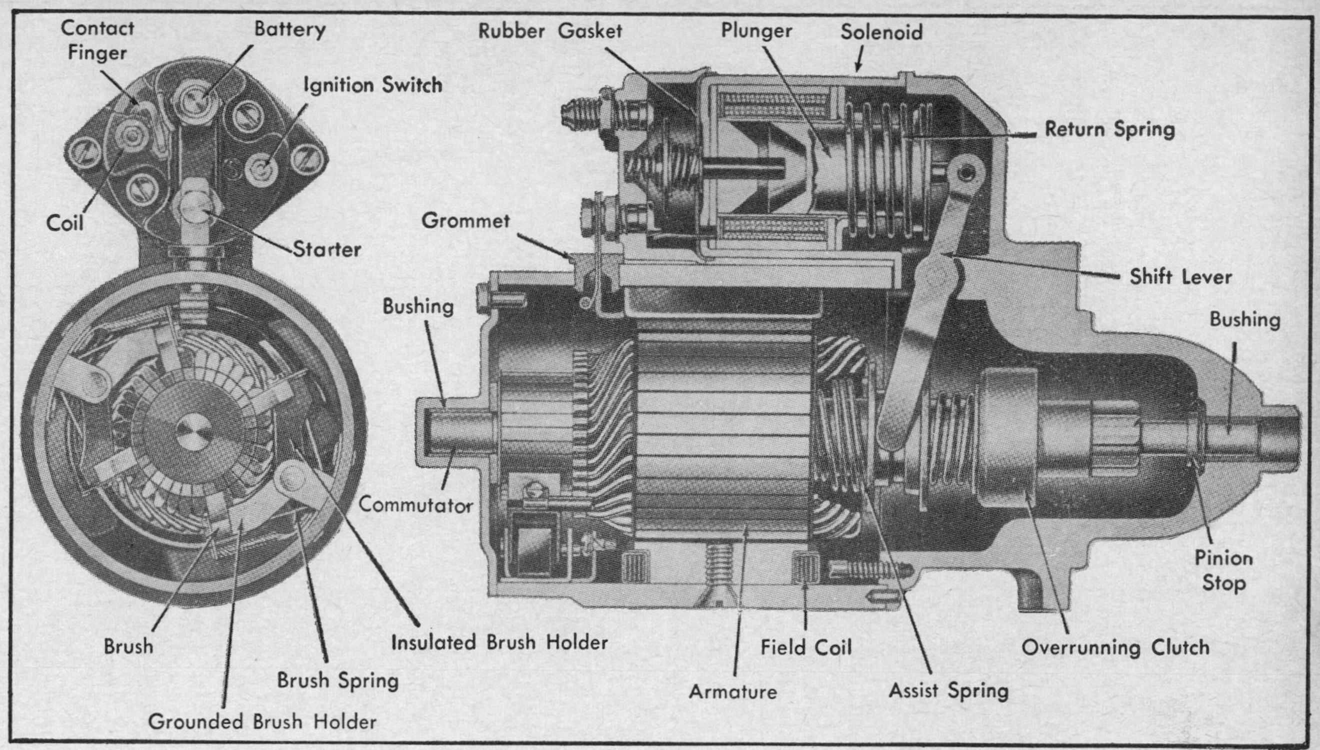

Fig. 40 Delco-Remy starter with enclosed shift lever

of ground terminal with notch in brush holder.

14. After brush holder is bottomed in housing, install attaching screw, Fig. 20. Tighten screw and install flat insulating washer and hold in place with friction tape.
15. Position brushes with tools shown in Fig. 37 or equivalent.
16. Position field frame to exact position and resolder field coil lead, Fig. 19.
17. Install brush terminal screw, Fig. 18.
18. Install armature thrust washer on brush holder plate and enter armature into field frame and gear housing, Fig. 38. Carefully engage splines of shaft with reduction gear.
19. Remove brush positioning tools, Fig. 30. Install fiber and steel thrust washers on armature shaft.
20. Position starter end head, install screws and tighten securely.
21. Install gear housing dust cover. *Make sure dimples on cover are securely engaged in holes provided in gear housing.* Test starter for free running and install on engine.

DELCO-REMY STARTERS

This type starting motor, Fig. 40, has the solenoid shift lever mechanism and the solenoid plunger enclosed in the drive housing, thus protecting them from exposure to road dirt, icing conditions and splash. They have an extruded field frame and an overrunning clutch type of drive. The overrunning clutch is operated by a solenoid switch mounted to a flange on the drive housing.

Solenoid

The solenoid is attached to the drive end housing by two screws. The angle of the nose of the plunger provides a greater bearing area between the plunger and core tube. A molded push rod, Fig. 41, is assembled in the contact assembly. A shoulder molded on the push rod and a cup that can easily be assembled to the rod and locked into position over two molded bosses holds the contact assembly in place.

To disassemble the cup from the push rod, push in on the metal cup and rotate ¼ turn so the molded bosses on the rod are in line with openings in the cup; then slide the metal cup off the rod.

To assemble the metal cup on the rod, locate the parts on the rod as shown and align the large openings in the cup with the molded bosses on the rod; then push in on the cup and rotate it ¼ turn so the small bosses on the rod fall into the keyways of the cup.

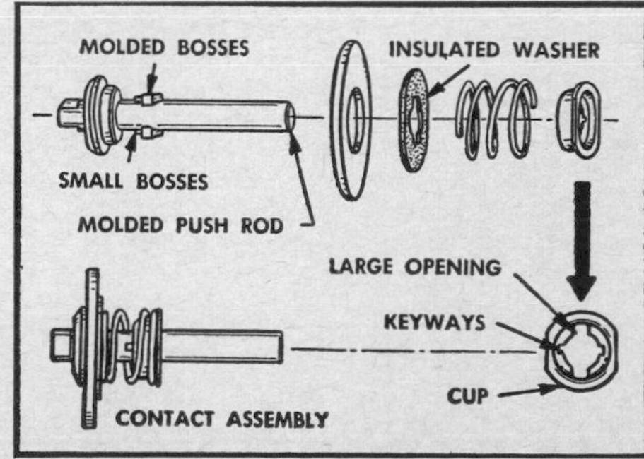

Fig. 41 Solenoid contact assembly

Solenoid Terminals

The terminals of the solenoid are assembled in a molded cover. Some solenoids have an additional small terminal which is identified with the letter "R". To this terminal is attached a small metal finger which makes contact with a disc inside the solenoid when it is energized. On the vehicle, this terminal is connected to the battery side of the ignition coil. The purpose of this is to short out the ignition resistor during cranking and thereby provide high ignition coil output for starting the engine.

Maintenance

Most motors of this type have graphite and oil impregnated bronze bearings which ordinarily require no added lubrication except at times of overhaul when a few drops of light engine oil should be placed on each bearing before reassembly.

Motors provided with hinge cap oilers should have 8-10 drops of light engine oil every 5000 miles, or every 300 hours of operation. Since the motor and brushes cannot be inspected without disassembling the unit, there is no service that can be performed with the unit assembled on the vehicle.

Free Speed Test

With the circuit connected as shown in Fig. 42, use a tachometer to measure armature revolutions per minute. Failure of the motor to perform to specifications may be due to tight or dry bearings, or high resistance connections.

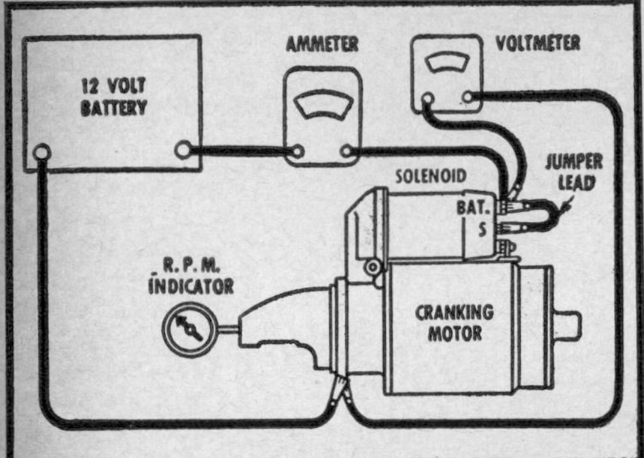

Fig. 42 Connections for checking free speed of motor

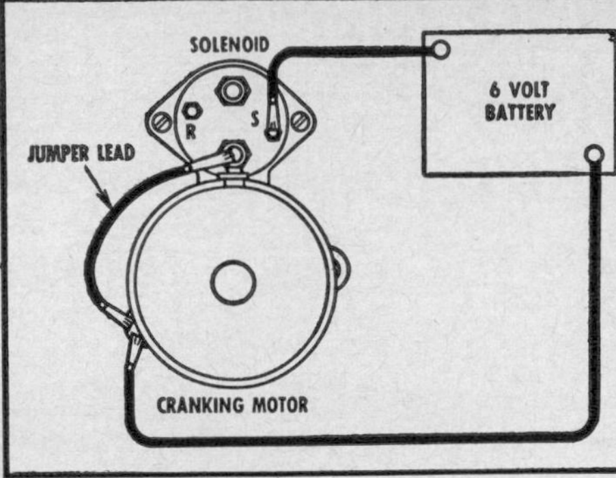

Fig. 43 Connections for checking pinion clearance

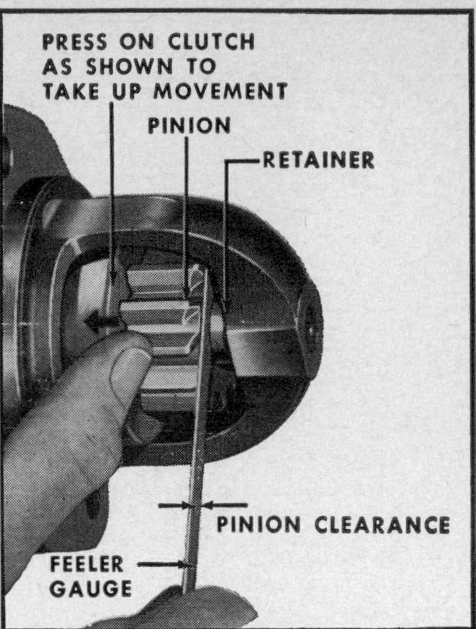

Fig. 44 Checking pinion clearance

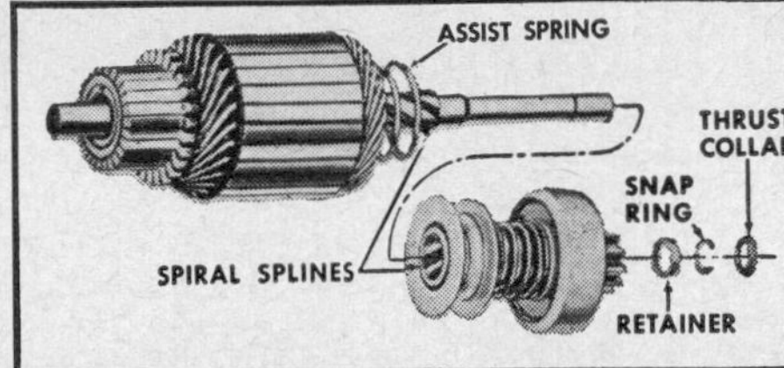

Fig. 46 View of armature and over-running clutch

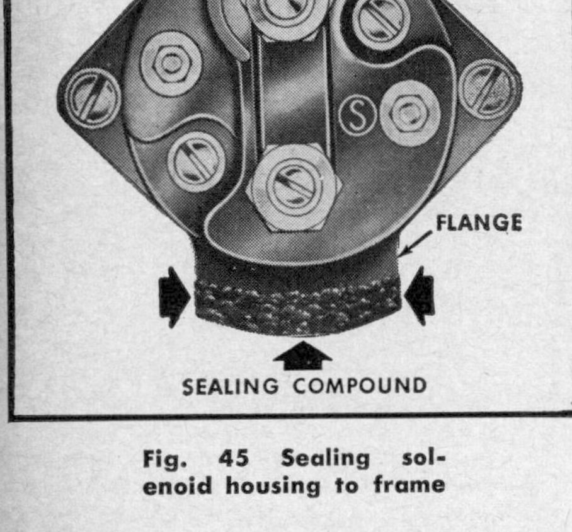

Fig. 45 Sealing solenoid housing to frame

Pinion Clearance

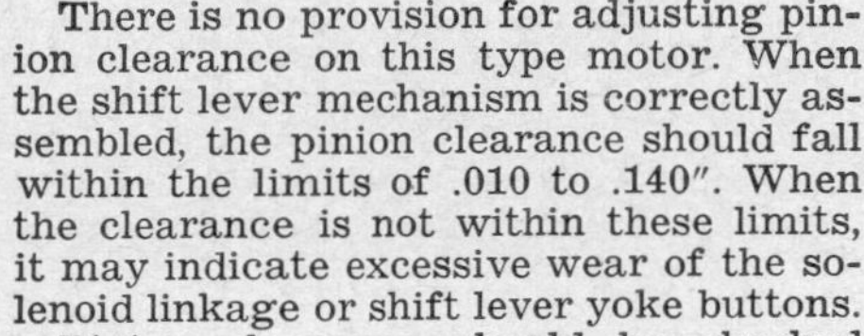

There is no provision for adjusting pinion clearance on this type motor. When the shift lever mechanism is correctly assembled, the pinion clearance should fall within the limits of .010 to .140". When the clearance is not within these limits, it may indicate excessive wear of the solenoid linkage or shift lever yoke buttons.

Pinion clearance should be checked after the motor has been disassembled and reassembled. To check, make connections as shown in Fig. 43. *Caution: Do not connect the voltage source to the ignition coil terminal "R" of the solenoid. Do not use a 12-volt battery instead of the 6 volts specified as this will cause the motor to operate.* As a further precaution to prevent motoring, connect a heavy jumper lead from the solenoid motor terminal to ground.

After energizing the solenoid with the

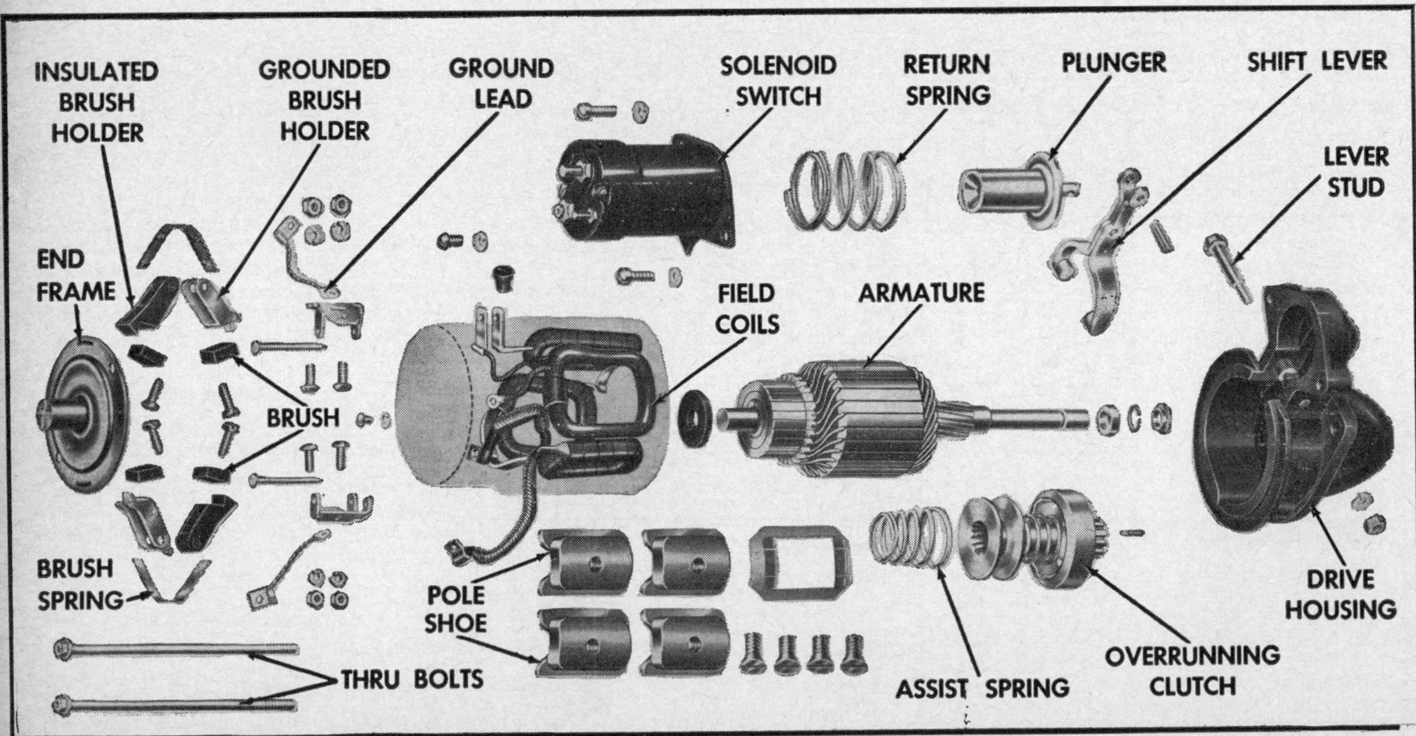

Fig. 47 Disassembled view of Delco-Remy starting motor

clutch shifted toward the pinion stop retainer, push the pinion back toward the commutator end as far as possible to take up any slack movement; then check the clearance with a feeler gauge, Fig. 44.

Disassembling Motor

Normally the motor should be disassembled only so far as necessary to repair or replace defective parts.

1. Disconnect field coil connectors from solenoid "motor" terminal.
2. Remove thru bolts.
3. Remove commutator end frame and field frame assembly.
4. Remove armature assembly from drive housing. On some models it may be necessary to remove solenoid and shift lever assembly from the drive housing before removing the armature assembly. *Important: When solenoid is installed, apply sealing compound between field frame and solenoid flange, Fig. 45.*
5. Remove overrunning clutch from armature shaft as follows:
   a) Slide thrust collar off end of armature shaft, Fig. 46.
   b) Slide a standard ½" pipe coupling or other metal cylinder of suitable size onto shaft so end of coupling or cylinder butts against edge of retainer. Tap end of coupling with hammer, driving retainer toward armature and off snap ring.
   c) Remove snap ring from groove in shaft. If snap ring is too badly distorted during removal, use a new one when reassembling the clutch.
   d) Slide retainer, clutch and assist spring from armature shaft.

Reassembling Motor, Fig. 47

1. Lubricate drive end and splines of armature shaft with SAE 10 oil. *If heavier oil is used it may cause failure to mesh at low temperatures.*
2. Place "assist" spring on drive end of shaft next to armature, with small end against lamination stack.
3. Slide clutch assembly onto armature shaft with pinion outward.
4. Slide retainer onto shaft with cupped surface facing end of shaft.
5. Stand armature on end on wood surface with commutator down. Position snap ring on upper end of shaft and hold in place with a block of wood. Hit wood block with a hammer forcing snap ring over end of shaft. Slide snap ring into groove, squeezing it to ensure a good fit in groove.
6. Assemble thrust collar on shaft with shoulder next to snap ring.
7. Position retainer and thrust collar next to snap ring. With clutch pressed against assist spring, for clearance next to retainer, use two pairs of pliers at the same time (one pair on either side of shaft) to grip retainer and thrust collar. Then squeeze until snap ring is forced into retainer.
8. Place 4 or 5 drops of SAE 10 oil in drive housing bushing. Make sure thrust collar is in place against snap ring and retainer; then slide armature and clutch assembly into place in drive housing.
9. Attach solenoid and shift lever assembly to drive housing. Be sure lever buttons are located between sides of clutch collar.
10. Position field frame over armature, *applying sealing compound between frame and solenoid flange* (Fig. 45). Position frame against drive housing, using care to prevent damage to brushes.
11. Place 4 or 5 drops of SAE 10 oil in bushing in commutator end frame. Make sure leather brake washer is on armature shaft; then slide commutator end frame onto shaft.
12. Install thru bolts and tighten securely.
13. Reconnect field coil connectors to solenoid "motor" terminal.

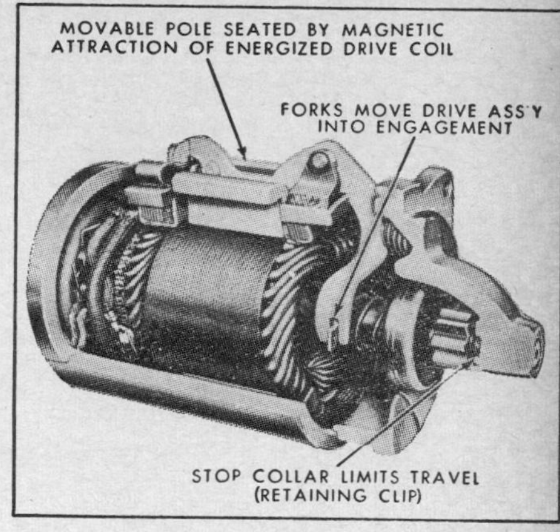

Fig. 49 Starter drive engaged

FORD STARTER WITH INTEGRAL POSITIVE ENGAGEMENT DRIVE

This type starting motor, Fig. 48, is a four pole, series parallel unit with a positive engagement drive built into the starter. The drive mechanism is engaged with the flywheel by lever action before the motor is energized.

When the ignition switch is turned on to the start position, the starter relay is energized and supplies current to the motor. The current flows through one field coil and a set of contact points to ground. The magnetic field given off by the field coil pulls the movable pole, which is part of the lever, downward to its seat. When the pole is pulled down, the lever moves the drive assembly into the engine flywheel, Fig. 49.

When the movable pole is seated, it functions as a normal field pole and opens the contact points. With the points open, current flows through the starter field coils, energizing the starter. At the same time, current also flows through a holding coil to hold the movable pole in its seated position.

When the ignition switch is released from the start position, the starter relay opens the circuit to the starting motor. This allows the return spring to force the lever back, disengaging the drive from the flywheel and returning the movable pole to its normal position, Fig. 50.

Disassembly

It may not be necessary to disassemble the starter completely to accomplish repair or replacement of certain parts. Thus, before disassembling the motor, remove the cover band and starter drive actuating lever cover. Examine brushes to make sure they are free in their holders. Replace brushes if defective or worn beyond their useful limit. Check the tension of each brush spring with a pull scale. Spring tension should not be less than 45 ounces. If disassembly is necessary, proceed as follows:

1. Remove cover band and starter drive actuating lever cover.
2. Remove through bolts, starter drive

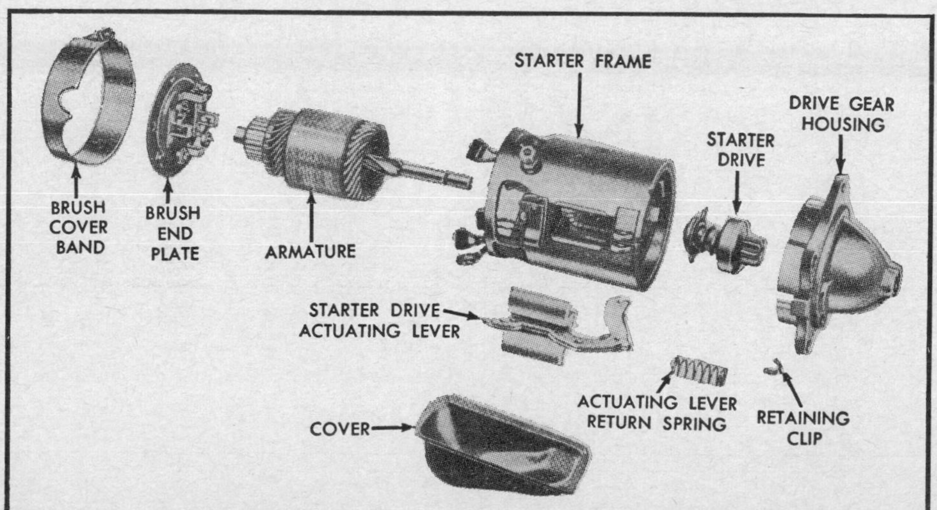

Fig. 48 Ford starter with an integral positive engagement drive

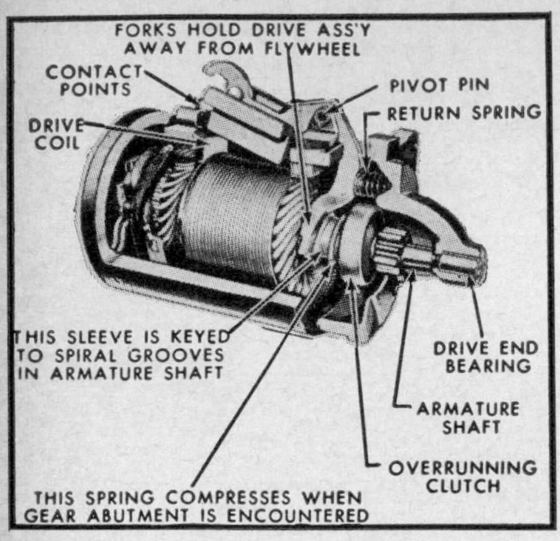

Fig. 50 Starter drive disengaged

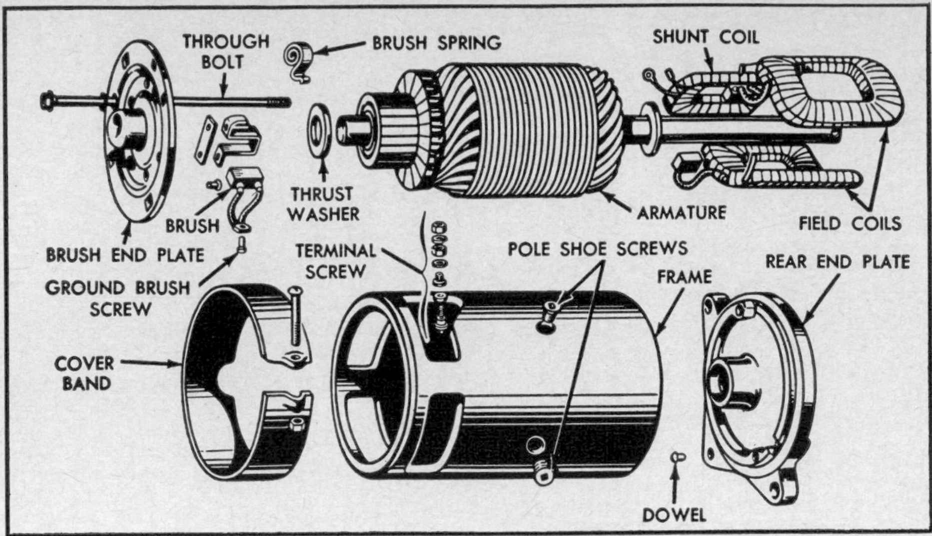

Fig. 53 Ford starter used with Folo-Thru drive

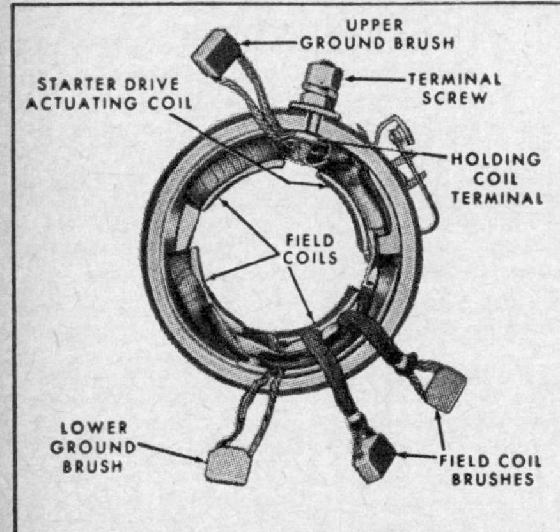

Fig. 51 Field coil assembly

SERVICE BULLETIN

Lincoln 1966 Starter Drive: The starter drive incorporates needle bearings at the drive end of the starter. When servicing this starter, precaution should be taken to avoid loss of needle bearings. If removal of the armature is required, a dummy shaft should be piloted into the drive end housing while removing the armature from the starter motor, Fig. 51A. This dummy shaft should be left within the drive end housing to maintain needle bearing placement until the motor is repaired and the armature is back in position.

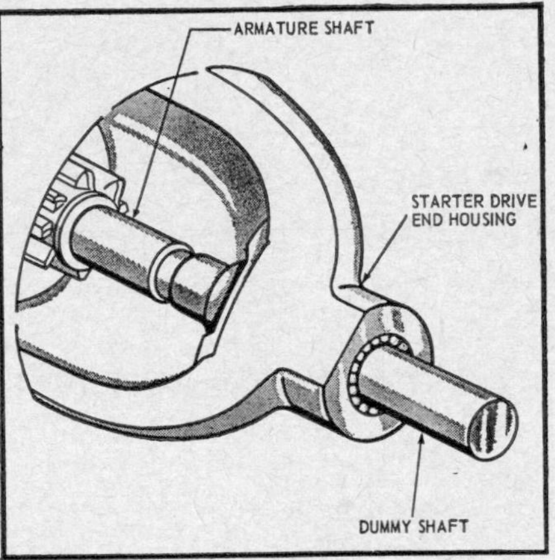

Fig. 51A Using dummy shaft to hold needle bearings in place while servicing 1966 Lincoln starter motor

gear housing, drive gear retaining clip cup and starter drive actuating lever return spring.

3. Remove pivot pin retaining starter gear actuating lever and remove lever and armature.
4. Remove and discard spring clip retaining starter drive gear to end of armature shaft, and remove starter drive gear.
5. Remove commutator brushes from brush holders and remove brush end plate.
6. Remove two screws retaining ground brushes to frame.
7. On the field coil that operates the drive gear actuating lever, bend tab up on field retainer and remove retainer.
8. Remove field coil retainer screws, Fig. 52. Unsolder field coil leads from terminal screw, and remove pole shoes and coils from frame.
9. Remove starter terminal nut and related parts. Remove any excess solder from terminal slot.

Reassembly

1. Install starter terminal, insulator, washers and retaining nut in frame, Fig. 51. Be sure to position slot in screw perpendicular to frame end surface.
2. Install field coils and pole pieces. As pole shoe screws are tightened, strike frame several sharp blows with a soft-faced hammer to seat and align pole shoes, then stake the screws.
3. Install solenoid coil retainer and bend tabs to retain tabs to frame.
4. Solder field coils and solenoid wire to starter terminal, using rosin core solder.
5. Check for continuity and grounds in the assembled coils.
6. Position solenoid coil ground terminal over ground screw hole nearest starter terminal.
7. Position ground brushes to starter frame and install retaining screws, Fig. 51.
8. Position starter brush end plate to frame with end plate boss in frame slot.
9. Install drive gear to armature shaft and install a new retaining spring clip.
10. Position fiber thrust washer on commutator end of armature shaft and install armature in frame.
11. Install starter drive actuating lever to frame and starter drive, and install pivot pin.
12. Position actuating lever return spring and drive gear housing to frame and install through bolts. Do not pinch brush leads between brush plate and frame.
13. Install brushes in holders, being sure to center brush springs on brushes.

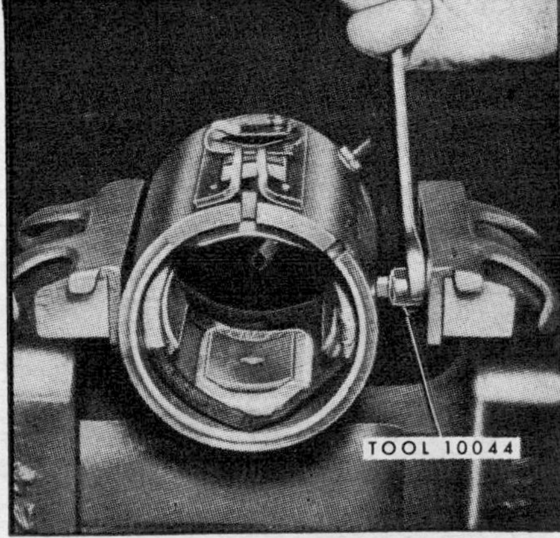

Fig. 52 Removing field coil pole shoe screws

14. Position drive gear actuating lever cover on starter and install brush cover band.

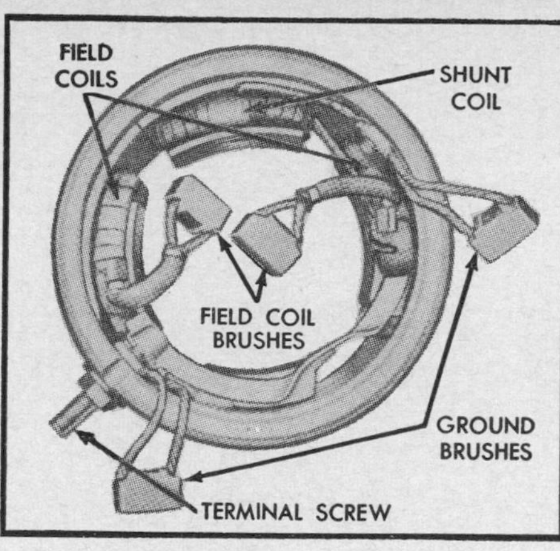

Fig. 54 Field coil assembly

FORD STARTER WITH FOLO-THRU DRIVE

Disassembly

1. Remove starter drive, through bolts and rear end plate, Fig. 53. *Be sure to remove all burrs from shaft to prevent scoring rear end plate bushing.*
2. Remove armature, two thrust washers and cover band.
3. Remove brushes from their holders, and remove brush end plate.
4. Unscrew ground brush screws and remove brushes.
5. Remove pole shoe screws (see Fig. 52). Unsolder field coil leads from terminal screw and remove pole shoes and field coils.
6. Remove starter terminal. Remove any excess solder from terminal slot.

Reassembly

1. Install terminal screw with insulator washers and terminal nut. Be sure to position slot in screw parallel to frame end surface.
2. Install field coils. Use rosin core solder and be sure to position shunt coil ground lead under ground brush terminal farthest from starter terminal, Fig. 54. The other shunt coil lead is soldered to the series field coil lead farthest from starter terminal.
3. Install screws that connect ground brushes to starter frame.
4. Install brush end plate, making sure that brush plate boss is located in slot in starter frame. Do not pinch brush leads between frame and end plate.
5. Place thrust washer on each end of shaft, slide armature in place, and install rear end plate with dowel located in starter frame slot.
6. Install through bolts.
7. Install brushes in their holders, being sure to center brush springs on brushes.
8. Install cover band and starter drive. Check starter for free running.

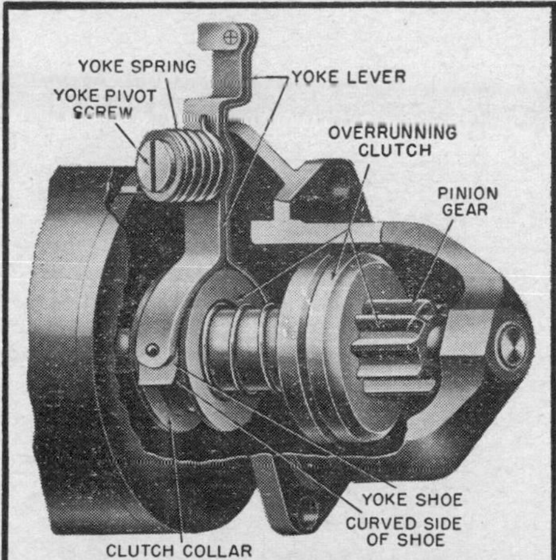

Fig. 55 Overrunning clutch drive. When assembling, make sure curved sides of yoke shoes are toward gear end of clutch. Reversed yoke shoes can cause improper meshing of pinion

STARTER DRIVE TROUBLES

Starter drives fall into one or the other of two basic groups, the type that uses the principle of the over-running clutch, Figs. 55 and 57, and the Bendix, which uses the spinning nut principle, Figs. 56 and 58.

Starter drive troubles are easy to diagnose and they usually cannot be confused with ordinary starter difficulties. If the starter does not turn over at all or if it drags, look for trouble in the starter or electrical supply system. Concentrate on the starter drive or ring gear if the starter is noisy, if it turns but does not engage the engine, or if the starter won't disengage after the engine is started. After the starter is removed, the trouble can usually be located with a quick inspection.

Worn or chipped ring gear or starter pinion are the usual causes of noisy operation. Before replacing either or both of these parts try to find out what caused the damage. With the Bendix type drive, incomplete engagement of the pinion with the ring gear is a common cause of tooth damage. The wrong pinion clearance on starter drives of the over-running clutch type leads to poor meshing of the pinion and ring gear and to rapid tooth wear.

A less common cause of noise with either type of drive is a bent starter armature shaft. When this shaft is bent, the pinion gear alternately binds and then only partly meshes with the ring gear. Most manufacturers specify a maximum of .003" radial run-out on the armature shaft.

When Clutch Drive Fails

The over-running clutch type drive seldom becomes so worn that it fails to engage since it is directly activated by a fork and lever, Fig. 55. The only thing that is likely to happen is that, once engaged, it will not turn the engine because the clutch itself is worn out. A much more frequent difficulty and one

Fig. 56 Folo-Thru starter drive with Bendix spring

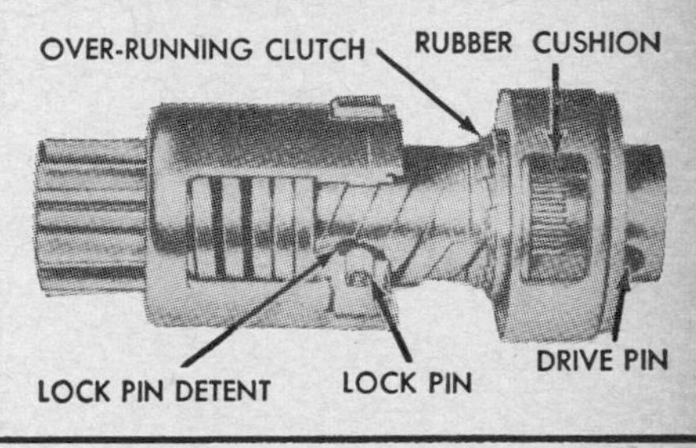

Fig. 57 Folo-Thru starter drive without Bendix spring

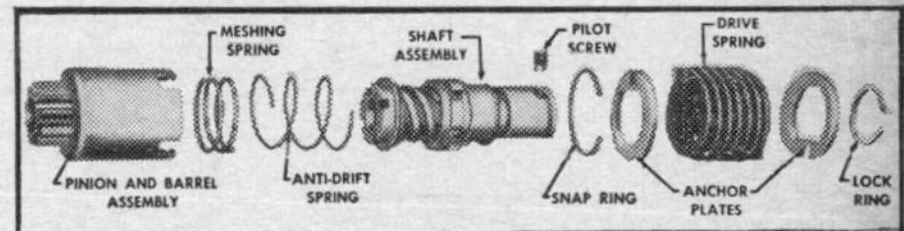

Fig. 58 Barrel type Bendix drive

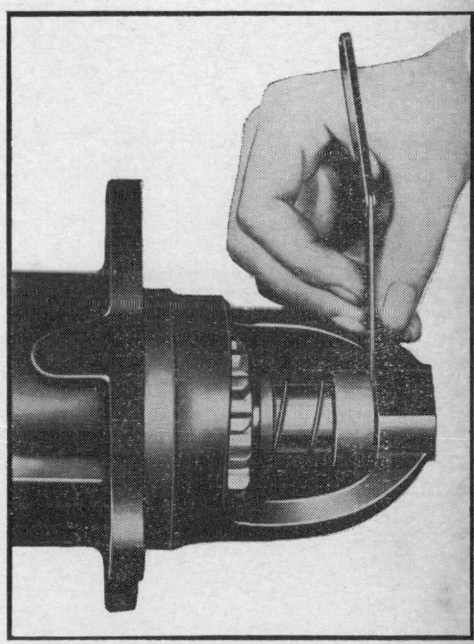

Fig. 59 Measuring overrunning clutch drive stop clearance. Do not compress anti-drift spring as this will give an incorrect clearance. If clearance is not present there is danger of the drive housing being broken as gear or collar slams back against it

that rapidly wears ring gear and teeth is partial engagement. Proper meshing of the pinion is controlled by the end clearance between the pinion gear and the starter housing or the pinion stop, if one is used.

The clearance is set with the starter off the car and with the drive in the engaged position. To check the clearance, supply current to the starter solenoid with the electrical connection between starter and solenoid removed. Supplying current to the solenoid but not the starter will prevent the starter from rotating during the test. Take out all slack by pushing lightly on the starter drive clutch housing while inserting a feeler gauge between pinion and housing or pinion stop, Fig. 59.

On late model cars, the solenoids are completely enclosed in the starter housing and the pinion clearance is not adjustable. If the clearance is not correct, the starter must be disassembled and checked for excessive wear of solenoid linkage, shift lever mechanism, or improper assembly of parts.

Failure of the over-running clutch drive to disengage is usually caused by binding between the armature shaft and the drive. If the drive, particularly the clutch, shows signs of overheating it indicates that it is not disengaging immediately after the engine starts. If the clutch is forced to over-run too long, it overheats and turns a bluish color. For the cause of the binding, look for rust or gum between the armature shaft and the drive, or for burred splines. Excess oil on the drive will lead to gumming, and inadequate air circulation in the flywheel housing will cause rust.

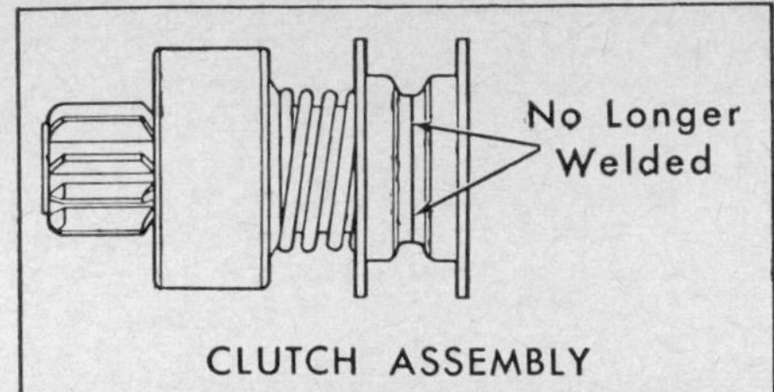

Fig. 60 New design over-running clutch collar

Over-running clutch drives cannot be overhauled in the field so they must be replaced. In cleaning, never soak them in a solvent because the solvent may enter the clutch and dissolve the sealed-in lubricant. Wipe them off lightly with kerosene and lubricate them sparingly with SAE 10 or 10W oil.

NOTE: Beginning in 1968 some Delco Remy starter drives used an overrunning clutch with a split collar. Side by side but not welded together as in previous models, Fig. 60. Do not mistake this split design as a defective collar.

When Bendix Drive Fails

When a Bendix type drive doesn't engage the cause usually is one of three things: either the drive spring is broken, one of the drive spring bolts has sheared off, or the screwshaft threads won't allow the pinion to travel toward the flywheel. In the first two cases, remove the drive by unscrewing the set screw under the last coil of the drive spring and replace the broken parts. Gummed or rusty screwshaft threads are fairly common causes of Bendix drive failure and are easily cleaned with a little kerosene or steel wool, depending on the trouble. Here again, as in the case of overrunning clutch drives, use light oil sparingly, and be sure the flywheel housing has adequate ventilation. There is usually a breather hole in the bottom of the flywheel housing which should be kept open.

The failure of a Bendix drive to disengage or to mesh properly is most often caused by gummed or rusty screwshaft threads. When this is not true, look for mechanical failure within the drive itself.

Bendix Folo-Thru Drive

This type of drive, Figs. 56, 57, is in wide use on late model cars. It incorporates a device that keeps the pinion engaged to the flywheel until the engine reaches a specified rpm. When replacing one of these drives, be sure that you have the correct drive for the car. The drives are rated differently and the correct one must be used for the car being serviced. The Folo-Thru, incidentally, is not supposed to be repaired in the field because of the danger of incorrectly assembling the carefully calibrated springs in the pinion head.

STARTING SWITCHES

MAGNETIC and SOLENOID SWITCHES are designed to perform mechanical jobs electromagnetically such as closing a heavy circuit or shifting the starter drive pinion with the engine flywheel ring gear for cranking. Switches of this type consist basically of contacts and a winding (or windings) around a hollow cylinder containing a movable core or plunger. When the winding (or windings) is energized by the battery through an external control circuit the plunger is pulled inward, producing the necessary mechanical movement.

MAGNETIC SWITCHES

Figs. 1 and 2 illustrate two typical Delco-Remy switches. The switch shown in Fig. 1 is not designed for disassembly and must be replaced if defective.

In the switch shown in Fig. 2 the terminals are assembled into a molded terminal ring which is held in place on the switch case by the cover and screws. Gaskets on both sides of the ring seals the contact compartment as a protection against moisture and dirt. The winding assembly is not removable from the case on this unit although the contact disk, plunger and plunger return spring can be removed after the cover is taken off.

Fig. 3 is a heavy duty magnetic switch. It is completely serviceable and easy to disassemble and assemble. To disassemble, remove the four terminal plate nuts and washers and take off the terminal plate assembly. The contact disk may be removed by taking off the castellated nut. It is necessary to remove the spring and washers on the plunger rod only when the plunger rod needs to be disassembled. To remove the plunger, unscrew the large metal cover, take out the cotter pin in the plunger shaft, remove spring retainer washer and spring, and withdraw the plunger. The winding and switch case is an integral assembly. The only parts that can be removed are the switch terminals. Before removing the switch terminals, the winding leads must be unsoldered from the terminal studs. Whenever the switch is disassembled, upon reassembly, locate the contact disk properly by turning the castellated nut on the disk in or out as required to obtain the dimension shown in Fig. 3 between the contact disk and edge of housing.

NOTE

On vehicles with overrunning clutch starting motors, a magnetic switch is normally used to shift the drive pinion into mesh and to close the starter circuit. There are two variations of three-terminal switches and also one type with four terminals. Any of these switches may be manufactured with either a grounded or insulated base. When installing a switch that is not marked "grounded base" or "insulated base", it must be checked out as follows, using a battery and test lamp in series.

THREE TERMINAL SWITCHES

1. If the switch has a grounded base the test lamp will light when connected between the starter ("S") terminal or ignition ("I") terminal and switch mounting bracket.
2. If the switch has an insulated base the test lamp will light when connected between the "S" and "I" ter-

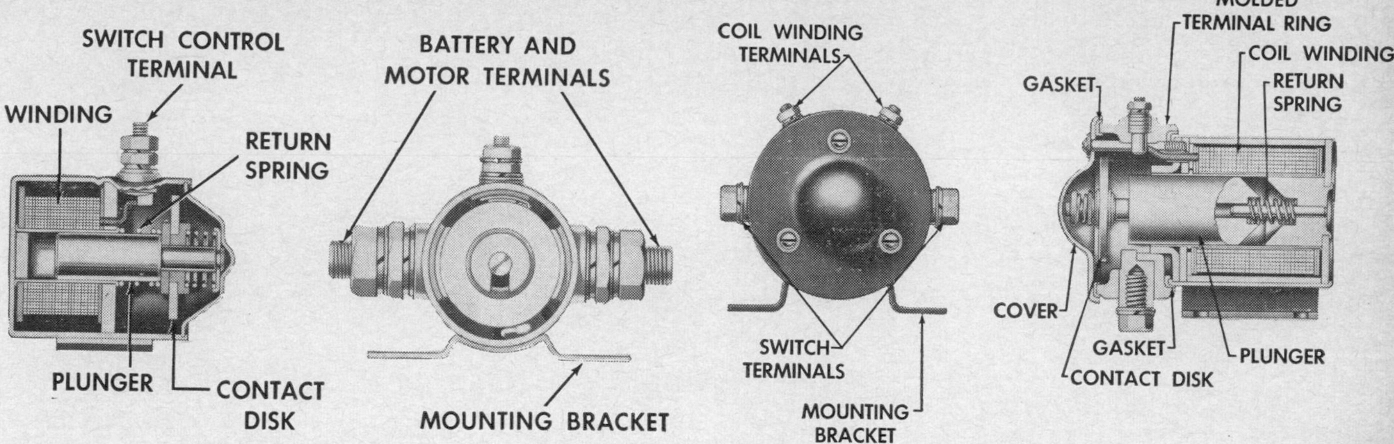

Fig. 1 End and sectional views of a typical magnetic switch

Fig. 2 End and sectional views of a sealed type magnetic switch which uses gaskets to seal the contact compartment

minals and either one of the $\frac{5}{16}''$ threaded studs.

3. If the test lamp fails to light when connected between the "S" and "I" terminals and any external part of the switch, disassemble the switch to determine whether the base is grounded or insulated.

FOUR TERMINAL SWITCHES

1. If the switch has a grounded base the test lamp will light when connected between the "S" terminal and switch mounting bracket.
2. If the switch has an insulated base the test lamp will light when connected between the "S" and "I" terminals.
3. If the test lamp fails to light when connected between the "S" terminal and any other external part of the switch, disassemble the switch to determine whether it has an insulated or grounded base.

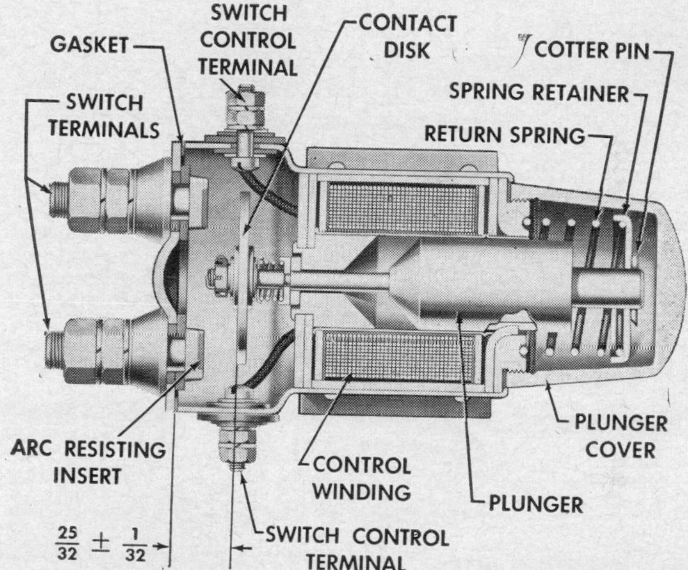

Fig. 3 Sectional view of heavy duty sealed type magnetic switch. To adjust the location of the contact disk turn the nut on the disk in or out as required to obtain the dimension shown

SOLENOID SWITCHES

The solenoid switch on a cranking motor not only closes the circuit between the battery and the cranking motor but also shifts the drive pinion into mesh with the engine flywheel ring gear. This is done by means of a linkage between the solenoid switch plunger and the shift lever on the cranking motor. Some linkages are adjustable while others are not (see *Starting Motors* chapter). The linkage is not adjustable on the type shown in Fig. 4 but adjustment of the entire assembly is made by moving the switch on the motor frame.

Fig. 4 shows two views of a solenoid switch used on vehicles with 12-volt systems. Like other solenoid switches, this type is energized by the battery through a separate starting switch. Note, however, that the switch includes an additional small terminal and contact finger. This terminal has no functional duty in relation to the switch, but is used to complete a special ignition circuit during the cranking cycle only. When the solenoid is in the cranking position, the finger touches the contact disk and provides a direct circuit between the battery and ignition coil.

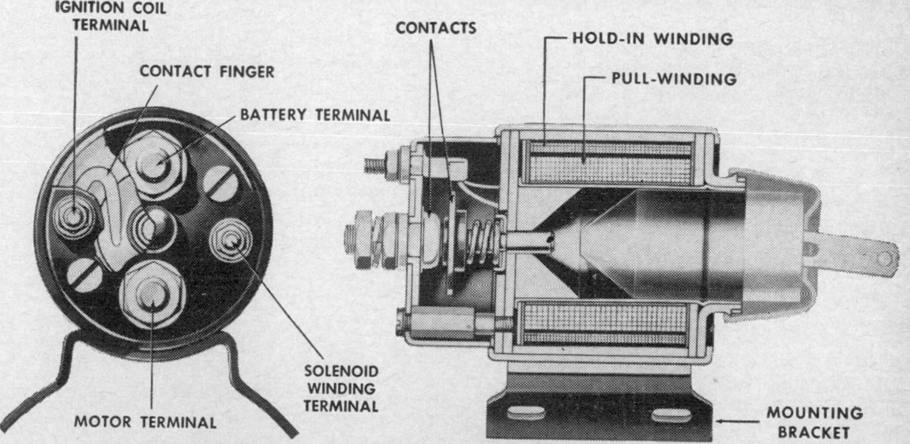

Fig. 4 End and sectional views of a typical solenoid switch. The additional terminal and contact finger are used on 12-volt passenger car applications

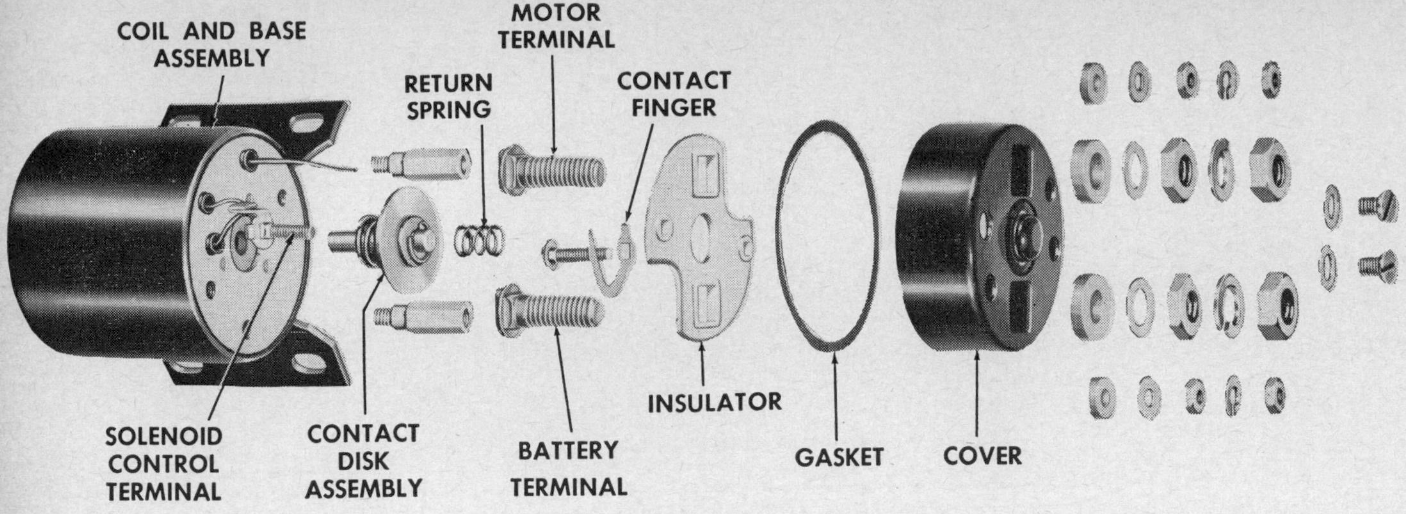

Fig. 5 Exploded view of solenoid switch shown in Fig. 4

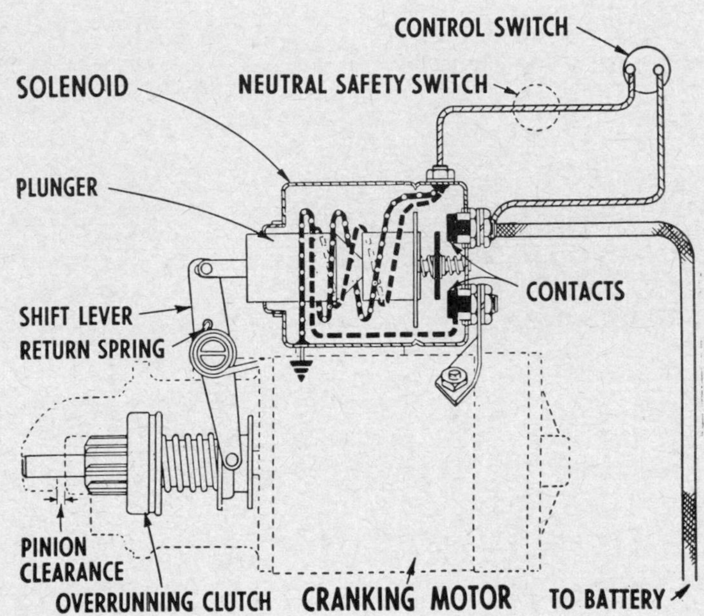

Fig. 6 Wiring circuit of a typical solenoid switch

Fig. 5 is an exploded view of the 12-volt solenoid switch shown in Fig. 4. When reassembling the switch the contact finger should be adjusted to touch the contact disk before the disk makes contact with the main switch terminals. There should be $\frac{1}{16}$″ to $\frac{3}{32}$″ clearance between the contact disk and the main terminals when the finger touches.

Fig. 6 is a wiring circuit of a typical solenoid switch. There are two windings in the solenoid; a pull-in winding (shown as dashes) and a hold-in winding (shown dotted). Both windings are energized when the external control switch is closed. They produce a magnetic field which pulls the plunger in so that the drive pinion is shifted into mesh, and the main contacts in the solenoid switch are closed to connect the battery directly to the cranking motor. Closing the main switch contacts shorts out the pull-in winding since this winding is connected across the main contacts. The magnetism produced by the hold-in winding is sufficient to hold the plunger in, and shorting out the pull-in winding reduces drain on the battery. When the control switch is opened, it disconnects the hold-in winding from the battery. When the hold-in winding is disconnected from the battery, the shift lever spring withdraws the plunger from the solenoid, opening the solenoid switch contacts and at the same time withdrawing the drive pinion from mesh. Proper operation of the switch depends on maintaining a definite balance between the magnetic strength of the pull-in and hold-in windings.

This balance is established in the design by the size of the wire and the number of turns specified. *An open circuit in the hold-in winding or attempts to crank with a discharged battery will cause the switch to chatter.*

To disassemble the solenoid, remove nuts, washers and insulators from the switch terminal and battery terminal. Remove cover and take out the contact disk assembly.

When the solenoid has been removed from the starter motor for repair or replacement, the linkage must be adjusted to provide the correct pinion clearance or pinion travel when the solenoid is remounted on the motor. Some solenoids equipped with relays have an adjustable plunger stud, but others must be moved on the motor frame to adjust pinion travel.

DASH GAUGES

TESTING

Gauge failures are often caused by defective wiring or grounds. Therefore, the first step in locating trouble should be a thorough inspection of all wiring and terminals. If wiring is secured by clamps, check to see whether the insulation has been severed thereby grounding the wire. In the case of a fuel gauge installation, rust may cause failure by corrosion at the ground connection of the tank unit.

CONSTANT VOLTAGE TYPE

Voltage Regulator Test

1. Turn on ignition switch.
2. Check voltage at gauge feed wire at one of the gauges.
3. Voltage should oscillate between zero and about 10 volts.
4. If it does not, voltage regulator is defective, or there is a short or ground between voltage regulator and gauges.

Dash Gauge Test

1. Turn off ignition switch.
2. Connect terminals of two series-connected flashlight batteries to the gauge terminals in question (fuel, oil or temperature).
3. The three volts of the batteries should cause the gauge to read approximately full scale.
4. If the gauge unit is inaccurate or does not indicate, replace it with a new unit.
5. If the gauge unit still is erratic in its operation, the sender unit or wire to the sender unit is defective.

Fuel Tank Gauge Test

1. Test the dash gauge as outlined above.
2. If dash gauge is satisfactory, remove flashlight batteries.
3. Then disconnect wire at tank unit and ground it momentarily to a clean, unpainted portion of the vehicle frame or body *with ignition switch on.*
4. If the dash gauge does not indicate, the wire is defective. Repair or replace the wire.
5. If grounding the new or repaired wire causes the gauge to indicate, the tank unit is faulty and should be replaced.

Oil & Temperature Sending Unit Tests

1. Test dash gauge as outlined above.
2. If dash gauge is satisfactory, remove flashlight batteries.
3. Then start engine and allow it to run to warm up to normal temperature.
4. If no reading is indicated on the gauge, check the sending unit-to-gauge wire by removing the wire from the sending unit and momentarily ground this wire to a clean, unpainted portion of the engine.
5. If the gauge still does not indicate, the wire is defective. Repair or replace the wire.
6. If grounding the new or repaired wire causes the dash gauge to indicate, the sending unit is faulty.

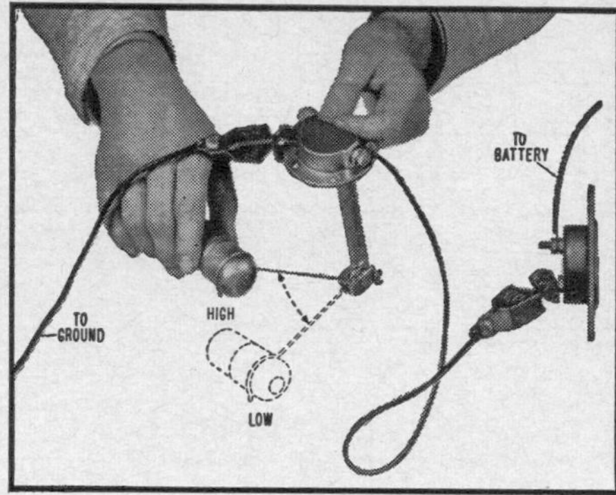

Fig. 1 Hook-up for testing dash gauge with a spare tank unit

VARIABLE VOLTAGE TYPE

The procedure given herewith applies to AC, Auto-Lite and Stewart-Warner systems. The following are two methods of quickly checking the gauge system to determine which component (sender or receiver) of a given system is defective.

Grounded Wire Method

1. Turn on ignition switch.
2. Remove wire connected at sending unit in question (fuel, oil or temperature).
3. Momentarily ground wire by holding it against a clean, unpainted portion of engine, vehicle body or frame.
4. The gauge pointer should indicate a full scale reading within 30 seconds.
5. As soon as the full scale reading is indicated, discontinue grounding the wire.
6. If during the test the gauge does *not* indicate a full scale reading, either the lead wire from the gauge to the sending unit is severed or the gauge is defective.
7. If the gauge *does* indicate a full scale reading, the sending unit is defective and should be replaced.

Fuel Gauge Tank Unit Method

1. Use a spare gauge tank unit known to be correct.
2. To test whether the dash gauge in question (fuel, oil or temperature) is functioning, disconnect the wire at the gauge which leads to the sending unit.
3. Attach a wire lead from the dash gauge terminal to the terminal of the "test" tank gauge, Fig. 1.
4. Ground the test tank unit to an unpainted portion of the dash panel and move the float arm.
5. If the gauge operates correctly, the sending unit is defective and should be replaced.
6. If the gauge does not operate during this test, the dash gauge is defective and should be replaced.

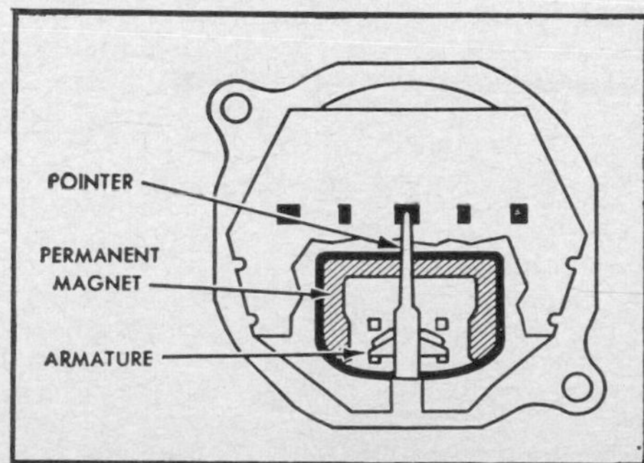

Fig. 2 Drawing of a typical automobile ammeter

AMMETERS

This instrument shows whether the battery is being charged by the generator or alternator or is being discharged by lights, radio, engine, etc. If a constant discharge is indicated on the ammeter, it is a signal that the battery is being run down. It is often a signal that the generator is out of order. Since both a charged battery and a working generator are very necessary—especially with vehicles equipped with many electricity-consuming devices such as heater, defroster, fog lights, radio, etc.—an inoperative ammeter should be given prompt attention.

The typical ammeter, Fig. 2, consists of a frame to which a permanent magnet is attached. The frame also supports an armature and pointer assembly.

When no current flows through the ammeter, the magnet holds the pointer armature so that the pointer stands at the center of the dial. When current passes in either direction through the ammeter, the resulting magnetic field attracts the armature away from the effect of the permanent magnet, thus giving a reading proportional to the strength of the current flowing.

Trouble Shooting

When the ammeter apparently fails to register correctly, there may be trouble in the wiring which connects the ammeter to the generator and battery or in the generator or battery themselves.

To check the connections, first tighten the two terminal posts on the back of the ammeter. Then, following each wire from the ammeter, tighten all connections on the ignition switch, battery and generator. Chafed, burned or broken insulation can be found by following each ammeter wire from end to end.

All wires with chafed, burned or broken insulation should be repaired or replaced. After this is done, and all connections are tightened, connect the battery cable and turn on the ignition switch. The needle should point slightly to the discharge (-) side.

Start the engine and speed it up a little above idling speed. The needle should then move to the charge side (+), and its movement should be smooth.

If the pointer does not behave correctly, the ammeter itself is out of order and a new one should be installed.

GENERATOR INDICATOR LIGHT

A red generator or alternator "no charge" light is used on many cars in lieu of an ammeter. This light flashes on if the battery is discharging and the generator or alternator is not supplying current.

The light should glow when the ignition is turned on and before the engine is started. If the bulb does not light, either the bulb is burned out or the indicator light wiring has an open circuit. After the engine is started, the light should be out at all times with the alternator system. With the D.C. generator system, the light should also be out at all times with the engine running except in cases where the engine idling speed is set too low; however, when the engine is speeded up the light should go out.

If the light fails to go out when the engine is running, the drive belt may be loose or missing or the generator or alternator or voltage regulator may be defective.

Light Circuit With D.C. Generator

The light is usually connected between the armature terminal of the generator regulator and the necessary terminal on the ignition switch, Fig. 3. If the ignition switch is on and the cutout relay contacts are open, the light will glow, indicating that the generator is not electrically connected to the battery. As soon as the generator is speeded up, the cutout relay contacts close. This by-passes the indicator light and thus indicates that the battery is electrically connected to the generator.

Light Circuit With Alternator

A double contact voltage regulator together with a field relay is used on Delco-Remy and Ford alternators when used with the indicator light. The circuit is as follows:

With the ignition switch turned on (engine not running), current flow is through the ignition switch through the indicator light on the dash panel. From there it goes to a terminal of the regulator (marked "4" or "L" on Delco-Remy or "I" on Ford). The circuit continues through the lower contacts of the voltage regulator (held closed by a spring), out the "F" terminal of the regulator, in the "F" terminal of the alternator, through a brush and slip ring, through another brush and slip ring to ground.

After the engine is started, the voltage output of the alternator immediately closes the field relay. This causes battery voltage from the battery terminal of the regulator (marked "3" or

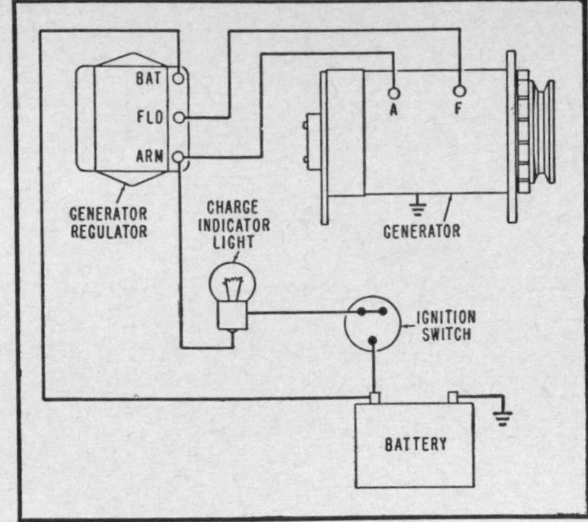

Fig. 3 Wiring diagram of a typical charge indicator light circuit

"V" on Delco-Remy, "B" on Ford) to be present at the "4", "L" or "I" terminal. Since battery voltage is present on both sides of the indicator light, the light goes out.

If the generator light comes on with the engine running, the charging circuit should be tested as soon as possible to determine the cause of the trouble.

OIL PRESSURE INDICATOR LIGHT

Many cars utilize a warning light on the instrument panel in place of the conventional dash indicating gauge to warn the driver when the oil pressure is dangerously low. The warning light is wired in series with the ignition switch and the engine unit—which is an oil pressure switch.

The oil pressure switch contains a diaphragm and a set of contacts. When the ignition switch is turned on, the warning light circuit is energized and the circuit is completed through the closed contacts in the pressure switch. When the engine is started, build-up of oil pressure compresses the diaphragm, opening the contacts, thereby breaking the circuit and putting out the light.

Trouble Shooting

The oil pressure warning light should go on when the ignition is turned on. If it does not light, disconnect the wire from the engine unit and ground the wire to the frame or cylinder block. Then if the warning light still does not go on with the ignition switch on, replace the bulb.

If the warning light goes on when the wire is grounded to the frame or cylinder block, the engine unit should be checked for being loose or poorly grounded. If the unit is found to be tight and properly grounded, it should be removed and a new one installed. (The presence of sealing compound on the threads of the engine unit will cause a poor ground).

If the warning light remains lit when it normally should be out, replace the engine unit before proceeding further to determine the cause for a low pressure indication.

The warning light sometimes will light up or will flicker when the engine is idling, even though the oil pressure is adequate. However, the light should go out when the engine is speeded up. There is no cause for alarm in such cases; it simply means that the pressure switch is not calibrated precisely correct.

TEMPERATURE INDICATOR LIGHTS

A temperature (bimetal) switch, located in cylinder head, controls the operation of a "Cold" temperature indicator light with a green lens and a "Hot" temperature indicator light with a red lens. When the cooling system water temperature is below approximately 110 degrees F., the temperature switch grounds the "Cold" indicator circuit and the green light goes on. When the green light goes out, the water temperature is high enough so that the heater can be turned on and be effective. *Note: The car should never be subjected to full throttle accelerations or high speeds until after the green light has gone out.*

If the engine cooling system is not functioning properly and the water temperature should reach a point where the engine approaches an overheated condition, the red light will be turned on by the temperature switch.

Note: As a test circuit to check whether the red bulb is functioning properly, a wire which is connected to the ground terminal of the ignition switch is tapped into its circuit. When the ignition is in the "Start" (engine cranking) position, the ground terminal is grounded inside the switch and the red bulb will be lit. When the engine is started and the ignition switch is in the "On" position, the test circuit is opened and the bulb is then controlled by the temperature switch.

Trouble Shooting

If the red light is not lit when the engine is being cranked, check for a burned out bulb, an open in the light circuit, or a defective ignition switch.

If the red light is lit when the engine is running, check the wiring between light and switch for a ground, temperature switch defective, or overheated cooling system.

If the green light is not lit when ignition is on and engine cold, check for a burned out bulb, an open in the light circuit, or a defective temperature switch.

If the green light stays on after normal engine warm-up period, check for a ground between light and switch, defective temperature switch, or a defective cooling thermostat.

SPEEDOMETERS

The following material covers only that service on speedometers which is feasible to perform by the average service man. Repairs on the units themselves are not included as they require special tools and extreme care when making repairs and adjustments and only an experienced speedometer mechanic should attempt such servicing.

The speedometer has two main parts —the indicating head and the speedometer drive cable. When the speedometer fails to indicate speed or mileage, the cable or cable housing is probably broken.

Speedometer Cable

Most cables are broken due to lack of lubrication, or a sharp bend or kink in the housing.

A cable might break because the speedometer head mechanism binds. If such is the case, the speedometer head should be repaired or replaced before a new cable or housing is installed.

A "jumpy" pointer condition, together with a sort of scraping noise, is due, in most instances, to a dry or kinked speedometer cable. The kinked cable rubs on the housing and winds up, slowing down the pointer. The cable then unwinds and the pointer "jumps".

To check for kinks, remove the cable, lay it on a flat surface and twist one end with the fingers. If it turns over smoothly the cable is not kinked. But if part of the cable flops over as it is twisted, the cable is kinked and should be replaced.

Lubrication

The speedometer cable should be lubricated with special cable lubricant every 10,000 miles. At the same time, put a few drops of the lubricant on the wick in the speedometer head.

Fill the ferrule on the upper end of the housing with the cable lubricant. Insert the cable in the housing, starting at the upper end. Turn the cable around carefully while feeding it into the housing. Repeat filling the ferrule except for the last six inches of cable. Too much lubricant at this point may cause the lubricant to work into the indicating hand.

Installing Cable

During installation, if the cable sticks when inserted in the housing and will not go through, the housing is damaged inside or kinked. Be sure to check the housing from one end to the other. Straighten any sharp bends by relocating clamps or elbows. Replace housing if it is badly kinked or broken. Position the cable and housing so that they lead into the head as straight as possible.

Check the new cable for kinks before installing it. Use wide, sweeping, gradual curves where the cable comes out of the transmission and connects to the head so the cable will not be damaged during its installation.

Arrange the housing so it does not lean against the cylinder head because heat from the engine may dry out the lubricant.

If inspection indicates that the cable and housing are in good condition, yet pointer action is erratic, check the speedometer head for possible binding.

The speedometer drive pinion should also be checked. If the pinion is dry or its teeth are stripped, the speedometer may not register properly.

The transmission mainshaft nut must be tight or the speedometer drive gear may slip on the mainshaft and cause slow speed readings.

ELECTRIC CLOCKS

Regulation of electric clocks used on automobiles is accomplished automatically by merely resetting the time. If the clock is running fast, the action of turning the hands back to correct the time will automatically cause the clock to run slightly slower. If the clock is running slow, the action of turning the hands forward to correct the time will automatically cause the clock to run slightly faster (10 to 15 seconds a day).

Winding Clock When Connecting Battery or Clock Wiring

The clock requires special attention when reconnecting a battery that has been disconnected for any reason, a clock that has been disconnected, or when replacing a blown clock fuse. *It is very important that the initial wind be fully made.* The procedure is as follows:

1. Make sure that all other instruments and lights are turned off.
2. Connect positive cable to battery.
3. Before connecting the negative cable, press the terminal to its post on the battery. Immediately afterward strike the terminal against the battery post to see if there is a spark. If there is a spark, allow the clock to run down until it stops ticking, and repeat as above until there is no spark. Then immediately make the permanent connection before the clock can again run down. The clock will run down in approximately two minutes.
4. Reset clock after all connections have been made. *The foregoing procedure should also be followed when reconnecting the clock after it has been disconnected, or if it has stopped because of a blown fuse. Be sure to disconnect battery before installing a new fuse.*

Trouble Shooting

If clock does not run, check for blown "clock" fuse. If fuse is blown check for short in wiring. If fuse is not blown check for open circuit.

With an electric clock, the most frequent cause of clock fuse blowing is low voltage at the clock which will prevent a complete wind and allow clock contacts to remain closed. This may be caused by any of the following: discharged battery, corrosion on contact surface of battery terminals, loose connections at battery terminals, at junction block, at fuse clips, or at terminal connection of clock. Therefore, if in reconnecting battery or clock it is noted that the clock is not ticking, always check for blown fuse, or examine the circuits at the points indicated above to determine and correct the cause.

FUEL PUMPS

NOTE: Fuel pump pressures are listed in Tune Up Charts in car chapters.

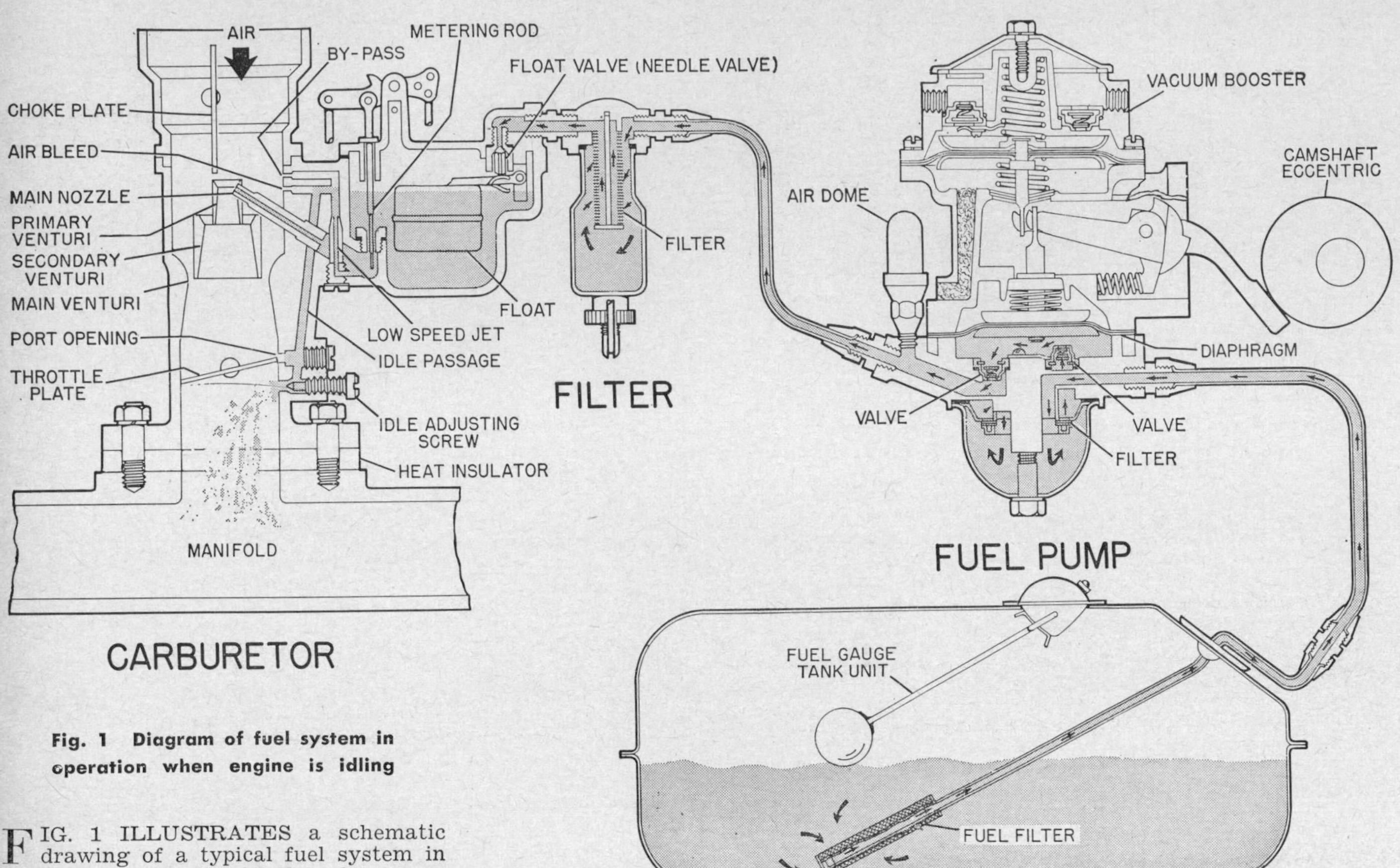

Fig. 1 Diagram of fuel system in operation when engine is idling

FIG. 1 ILLUSTRATES a schematic drawing of a typical fuel system in which a combination fuel and vacuum pump is incorporated. All fuel pumps used on passenger cars are of the diaphragm type, Figs. 2 and 3. Fig. 1 differs in that the pump has a vacuum booster section. The booster section has nothing to do with the fuel system except that it is operated by the pump arm.

Fuel Pump Operation

During the first or suction stroke, the rotation of the eccentric on the camshaft actuates the pump operating arm which pulls the lever and diaphragm downward against the pressure of the diaphragm spring, producing a suction in the pump chamber. The suction holds the outlet valve closed and pulls the inlet valve open, making the fuel flow from the supply tank through the inlet up through the filter screen and down through the inlet valve into the pump chamber. During the return stroke, the diaphragm is forced up by the diaphragm spring, the inlet valve closes and the outlet valve is forced open, allowing the fuel to flow through the outlet to the carburetor.

Vacuum Section Operation

The vacuum section of combination pumps operates the windshield wipers at almost constant speed. The rotation of the camshaft eccentric in this type pump also operates the vacuum booster section by actuating the pump arm which pushes a link and bellows diaphragm downward, expelling the air in the vacuum chamber through its exhaust valve out into the intake manifold of the engine. On the return stroke of the pump arm, the diaphragm is moved upward, producing a suction in the vacuum chamber. This suction operates the vacuum section and draws air through the inlet passage from the windshield wiper.

Fuel Pump Performance

It is essential that the fuel pump deliver sufficient fuel to supply the requirements of the engine under all operating conditions and that it maintain sufficient pressure in the line between the pump and carburetor to keep the fuel from boiling and to prevent vapor lock.

Excessive fuel pump pressure holds the carburetor float needle valve off its seat, causing high gasoline level in the float chamber which in turn increases gasoline consumption.

The pump usually delivers a minimum of ten gallons of gasoline per hour at top engine speeds, under an operating pressure of from 2 to 6 psi (see table). The highest operating pressure will be attained at idling speed and the lowest at top speed.

Fuel Pump Tests

The fuel pump can be tested on the car with a pressure gauge, a hose and a pint measuring can. With this equipment, it is possible to check the fuel pump to see if it is delivering the proper amount of gasoline at the correct pressure.

Pressure Test

To make the pressure test, disconnect the fuel pipe at the carburetor inlet and attach the pressure gauge and hose between the carburetor inlet and the disconnected fuel pipe, Fig. 4. Take the pressure reading with the engine running. The pressure should be within the limits given in the *Tune Up* chart in each car chapter, depending on the pump model and the car on which it is installed. The pressure should remain constant or return very slowly to zero when the engine is stopped.

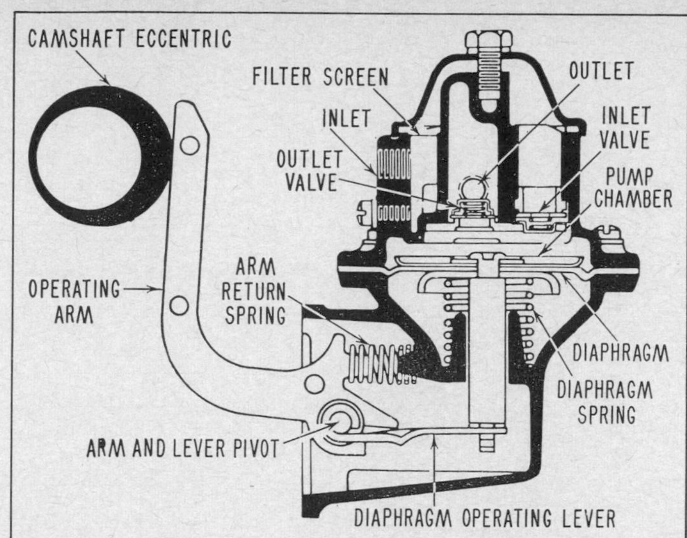

Fig. 2 Fuel pump with built-in fuel filter

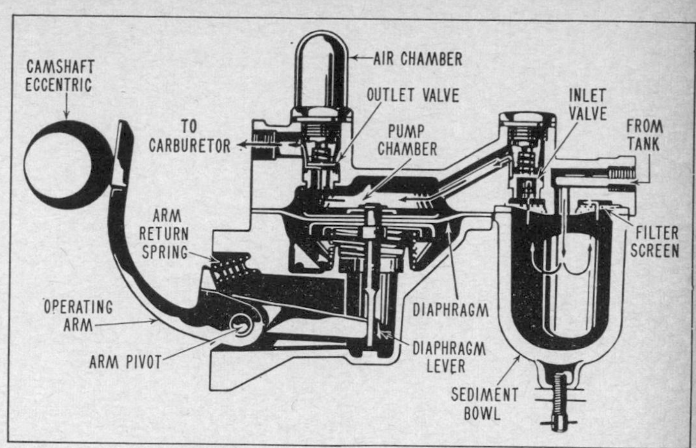

Fig. 3 Fuel pump with separate fuel filter

Capacity Test

To make this test, connect the hose so the pump will deliver gasoline into the pint measure held at carburetor level. Run the engine at idle speed and note the time it takes to fill the measure. On the average it should take from 20 to 30 seconds, depending on the pump tested.

When Pressure Is Low

Low pressure indicates extreme wear on one part, small wear on all parts, ruptured diaphragm, dirty valve or gummy valve seat.

Wear in the pump usually occurs at the rocker arm pivot pin and on the contacting surfaces of the rocker arm and links. Due to the leverage design, wear at these points is multiplied five times in the movement of the diaphragm. It is apparent therefore, that very little wear will materially reduce the stroke of the diaphragm. The worn parts must be replaced for a satisfactory correction.

The diaphragm pull rod has an oil seal around it which prevents the hot oil vapors from the crankcase coming in contact with the diaphragm. If this seal is damaged, the oil vapors have a tendency to shorten the life of the diaphragm.

The first three conditions—extreme wear on one part, small wear on all parts, and ruptured diaphragm—are brought about by usage, while dirty and/or poor fuel is usually the cause of valve trouble.

When Pressure Is High

High pressure is caused by a tight diaphragm, fuel between diaphragm layers, diaphragm spring too strong, pump link frozen to rocker arm.

A tight diaphragm will stretch slightly on the down stroke. As the pump operates, the diaphragm will rebound on the up stroke beyond its normal position, much as a stretched rubber band when it is suddenly released. This rebound will cause a higher than normal pressure in the pump chamber.

A loose diaphragm retainer nut or poor riveting on the diaphragm assembly may allow fuel to seep between the diaphragm layers. This will cause a bulge in the diaphragm and have the same effect as a diaphragm that is too tight.

A diaphragm spring that is too strong also causes a high pressure for the diaphragm will operate longer before pressure of the fuel on the diaphragm will overcome the diaphragm spring.

On a combination pump there are times when the operating parts may become badly corroded and the links freeze to the rocker arm. In this condition the pump operates continually, resulting in a very high pressure and a flooding carburetor.

The remedy for all these conditions is to remove the pump for replacement or repair, using a repair kit.

When Capacity Is Low

A pump is extra efficient and will never starve the engine when it supplies fuel equal to or above the capacity of the pump. The pressure, of course, must be within specifications.

Fig. 4 Testing fuel pump pressure

Low capacity is usually caused by an air leak in the intake pipe at these points: fuel pipe fitting at pump, bowl flange or diaphragm flange, fuel bowl. (It is assumed that the conditions of too little fuel have already been checked and the pump is the cause of the difficulty.)

An air leak at fuel pipe fittings indicates either poor installation of pump or a defective fitting. The fitting should be tightened or replaced.

A leak at the diaphragm flange may be caused by a warped cover casting, loose diaphragm cover screws or foreign material between cover casting and diaphragm.

A leak at the bowl flange of the cover casting can usually be corrected by the installation of an extra gasket. A warped top cover indicates that the pump must be replaced.

A chipped glass or bent metal bowl may cause a leak at the bowl flange as may a defective gasket or foreign material between gasket and bowl or cover casting. A chipped glass bowl must be replaced while a dented metal bowl can be straightened.

Vacuum Pump Troubles

To assist the manifold vacuum to operate the windshield wiper at a uniform rate under any engine load is the only function of the vacuum pump. Of course, "uniform rate" infers a wet windshield and not one covered with snow or ice. Failure to do the above indicates difficulty in either the vacuum system of the pump, windshield wiper motor, or tubes and connections.

Symptoms of trouble in the vacuum section show up in four ways: oil consumption, slow windshield wiper action, poor idle, noise.

In some cases it has been found that an engine which has given very good oil mileage suddenly appears to be using oil. Upon investigation, it will often be found that the vacuum booster has a ruptured diaphragm and is drawing oil fumes from the crankcase into the intake manifold. This can be checked by removing the cover of the vacuum section.

When the windshield wiper slows down

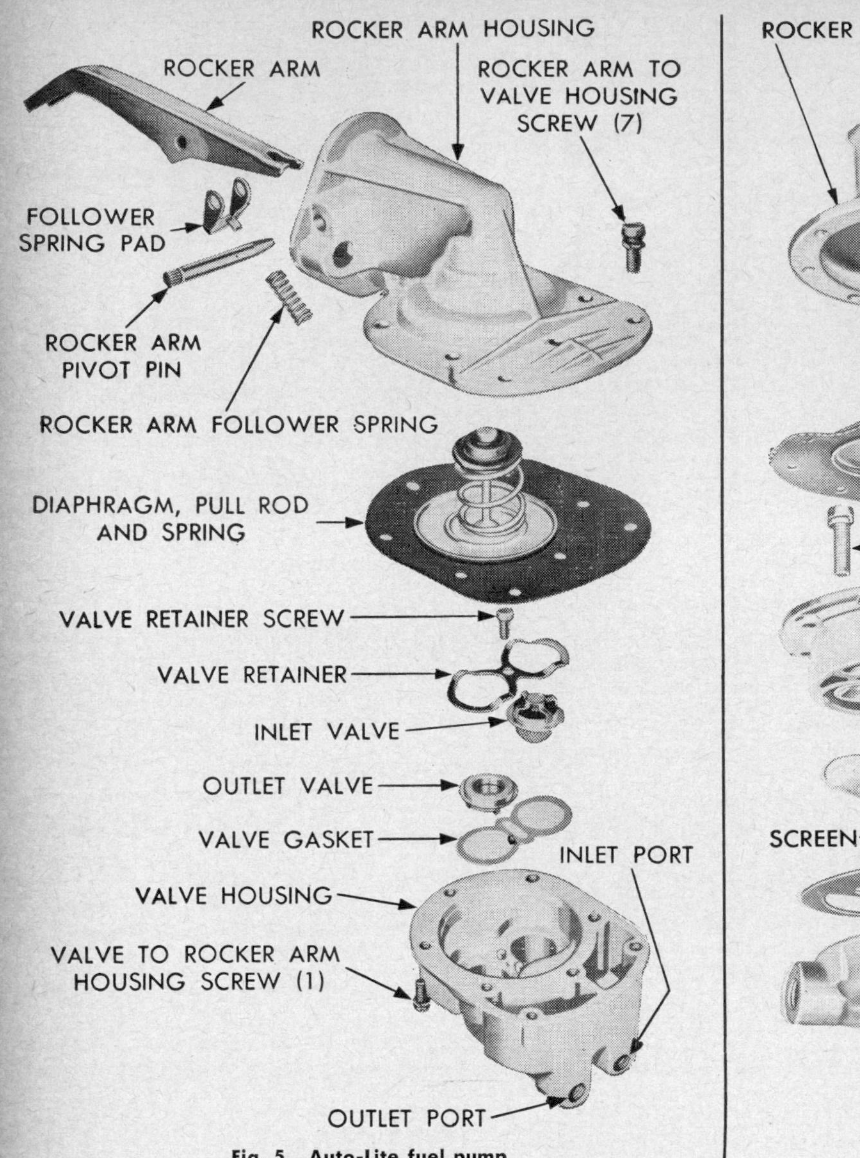

Fig. 5 Auto-Lite fuel pump

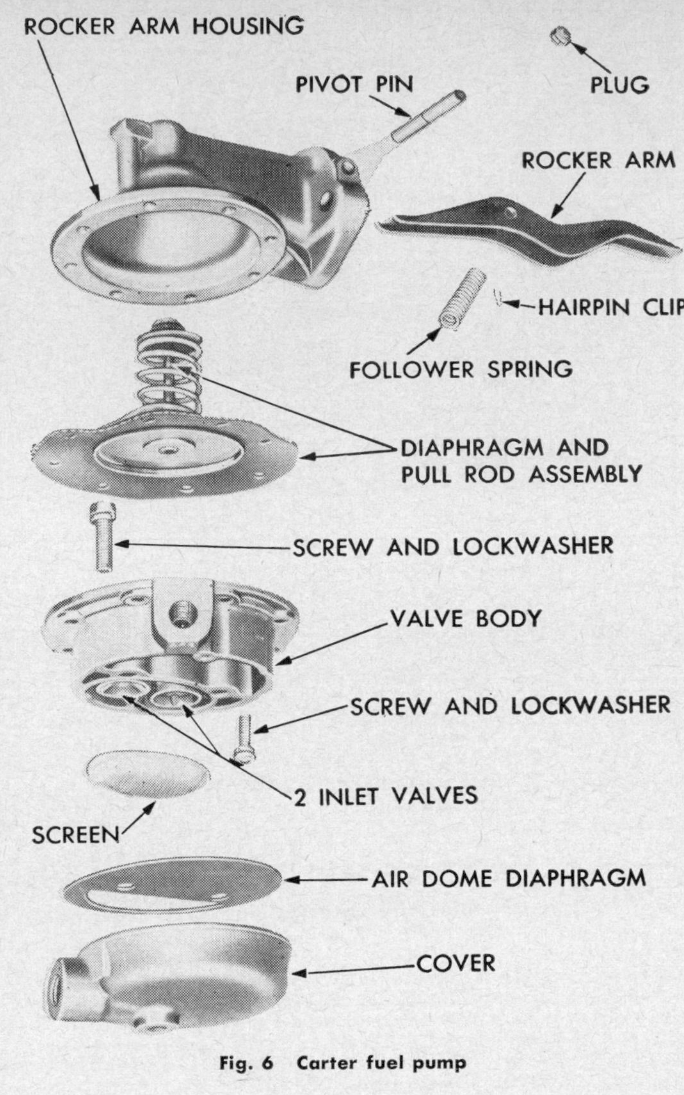

Fig. 6 Carter fuel pump

excessively under engine load, it usually is an indication of a ruptured vacuum diaphragm or defective valve in the vacuum pump. This condition may not be discovered immediately as the windshield wipers may not be used for long intervals.

Oil will be evidenced in the cover casting recesses if the diaphragm is ruptured. The pump should be removed and the diaphragm replaced.

On some cars the engine will idle very poorly when the vacuum diaphragm is ruptured. This is true when the tube from the vacuum pump is connected to one end of the intake manifold. The air leak through the vacuum section will give those cylinders on the end a lean mixture which results in a miss or poor idle. In many cases, this leads one to believe the valves of the engine are sticking; but if they are ground, the miss or poor idle remains.

This condition can be checked by removing the vacuum pump tube at the manifold and plugging the hole. If the miss or rough idle disappears, the trouble is an air leak through the pump or tube connections. The pump should be removed and repaired or the connections tightened to eliminate this trouble.

Sometimes a combination pump will give off a peculiar grunting sound on idle. In some cases this can be remedied by stuffing curled horse hair into the pump breather.

Vacuum Pump Test

With a combination fuel and vacuum pump the windshield wiper should operate at 80 to 100 strokes per minute through all ranges of car speed and load. The windshield should be wet when the test is made, otherwise the action will be slow.

Checking With Vacuum Gauge

To check the vacuum section, disconnect both inlet and outlet tubes and attach a vacuum gauge to the inlet (side that goes to windshield wiper). It is assumed that the engine, windshield wiper motor and blade, and connecting tubing have been checked and are in satisfactory condition.

Read the vacuum gauge when the engine is running at 1000 rpm (about 20 mph). It should read from 7 to 12 inches of vacuum on a normal pump. If the reading is less than 7, the pump should be removed and repaired or replaced. When making this test, the tube to the manifold should be plugged and the pump outlet should always be open or damage may result to the mechanism.

Checking Without Gauge

Disconnect the outlet tube (to manifold) from the pump and plug the end. Then operate the engine from an idle through slow acceleration to about 40 mph. If the wiper starts operating at about 15 mph and reaches full speed at about 40 mph, the vacuum section is okay. If it does not operate, it may be the windshield wiper motor. This can be

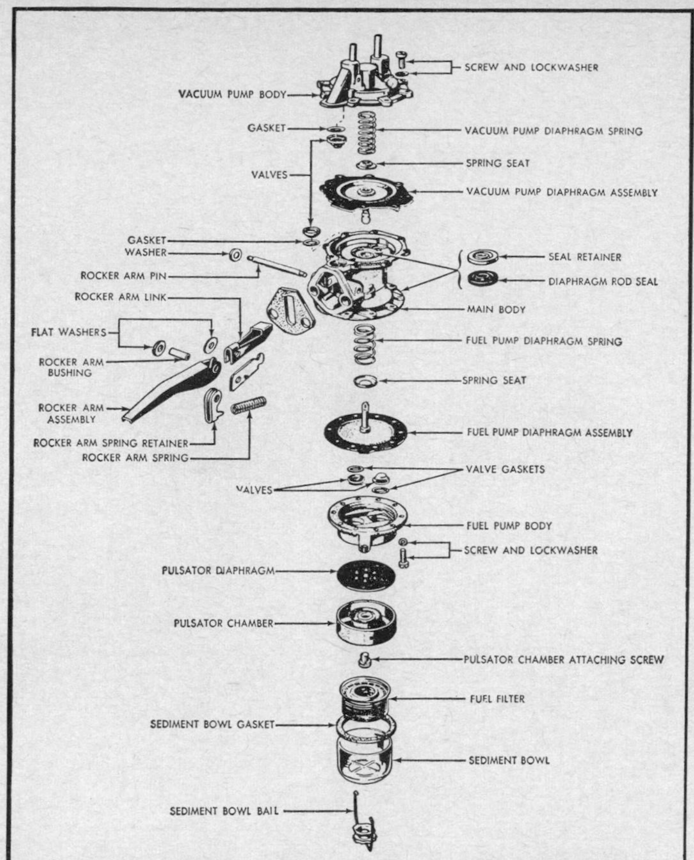

Fig. 7 A.C. combination pump with four vacuum valves and built-in fuel filter

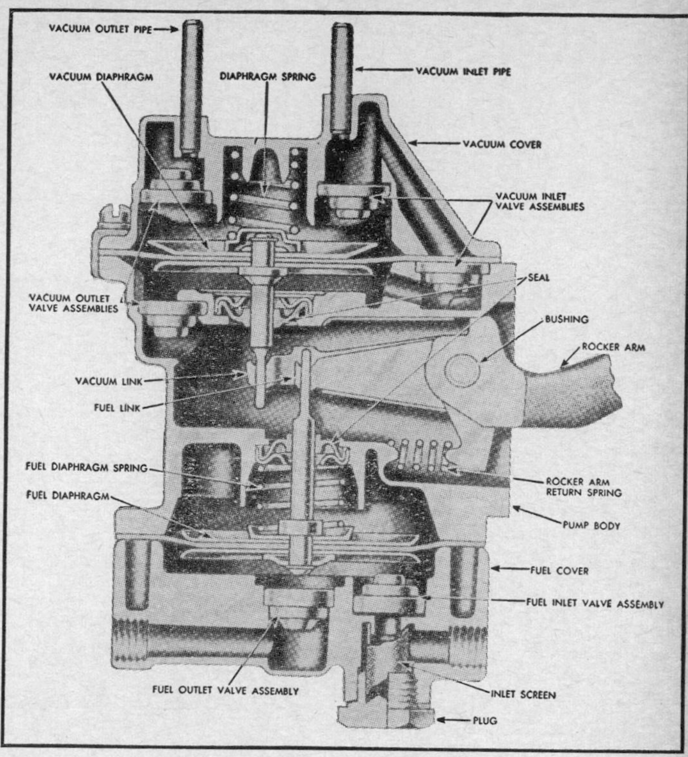

Fig. 8 A.C. combination pump with four vacuum valves

checked by connecting the intake manifold directly to the windshield wiper tube. Then slowly accelerate the engine from idle to about 25 mph. The wiper should operate at full speed. If it does not it can be assumed that the wiper motor or tubing is defective.

Fuel Pump Service

Illustrated are representative fuel pumps among the many models that have been produced. Before disassembling any pump, scribe a mark across the housings in such a manner that they may be reassembled with inlet and outlet fitting holes in correct location.

When disassembled, clean all parts (except diaphragms) in solvent and blow dry with compressed air. Examine the diaphragm for cracks, torn screw holes or ruptures. If deteriorated, install new diaphragm and pull rod assembly. Check the strainer screen and if found to be corroded or clogged, install a new screen. Check the rocker arm for wear or scoring on that portion that contacts the camshaft eccentric. If arm is scored or worn install a new one.

When reassembling a pump, do not use shellac or other adhesive on a diaphragm.

CARBURETORS

INDEX

PAGE NO.

CARTER MODELS

AFB Adjustments 1-161
Specifications 1-157
AS Adjustments 1-126
Specifications 1-126
AVS Adjustments 1-150
Specifications 1-149
BBD Adjustments 1-142
Specifications 1-141
BBS Adjustments 1-136
Specifications 1-136
RBS Adjustments 1-134
Specifications 1-134
WCD Adjustments 1-147
Specifications 1-147
WCFB Adjustments 1-154
Specifications 1-154
YF Adjustments 1-130
Specifications 1-128
YH Adjustments 1-132
Specifications 1-132

FORD MODELS

1100-1V Adjustments 1-167
Specifications 1-165
2100-2V Adjustments 1-176
Specifications 1-172
4100-4V Adjustments 1-176
Specifications 1-174
4300-4V Adjustments 1-184
Specifications 1-182

HOLLEY MODELS

1904 Adjustments 1-189
1908 Adjustments 1-189
1909 Adjustments 1-191
Specifications 1-187
1920 Adjustments 1-191
Specifications 1-186
1931 Adjustments 1-193
Specifications 1-187
2209 Adjustments 1-196
Specifications 1-187
2300 Adjustments 1-200
Specifications 1-186
4150, 4160 Adjustments ... 1-203
Specifications 1-201

ROCHESTER MODELS

B, BC, BV Adjustments ... 1-210
Specifications 1-209
HV Adjustments 1-213
Specifications 1-213
M, MV Adjustments 1-248
Specifications 1-246
2G, 2GC, 2GV Adjustments 1-221
Specifications 1-216
4GC Adjustments 1-229
Specifications 1-226
4MC, 4MV Adjustments .. 1-238
Specifications 1-234

STROMBERG MODELS

WA, WW Adjustments ... 1-252
Specifications 1-251

CARBURETION

Since carburetion is dependent in several ways on both compression and ignition, it should always be checked last when tuning an engine. See the car chapter for adjustments for the unit you are interested in.

Before adjusting the carburetor, consider the factors outlined below and which definitely affect engine performance.

Performance Complaints

Flooding, stumble on acceleration or other performance complaints are in many instances caused by the presence of dirt, water or other foreign matter in the carburetor. To aid in diagnosing the cause of the complaint, the carburetor should be carefully removed from the engine without draining the fuel from the bowl. The contents of the fuel bowl may then be examined for contamination as the carburetor is disassembled.

Check the fuel in the bowl for contamination by dirt, water, gum or other foreign matter. A magnet moved through the fuel in the bowl will pick up and identify any iron oxide dust that may have caused intake needle and seat leakage.

Inspect gasketed surfaces between body and air horn. Small nicks or burrs should be smoothed down to eliminate air or fuel leakage. On carburetors having a vacuum piston, be especially particular when inspecting the top surface of the inner wall of the bowl around the vacuum piston passage. A poor seal at this location may contribute to a "cutting out" on turns complaint.

Fill the carburetor bowl with clean fuel before installing on manifold. This will help prevent dirt trapped in the fuel system from being dislodged by the free flow of fuel as the carburetor is primed. The operation of the floats and intake needle and seats may be checked under pressure if a fuel pump is used at the bench to fill the carburetor bowl. Operate the throttle several times and visually check the discharge from pump jets.

Cases of poor mileage and engine loading may be due in many instances to sluggish choke valve opening during cold driveaway, caused by insufficient vacuum in choke housing, a plugged or restricted heat pipe or inlet in choke cover. To check for this condition, have engine warm and running at slow idle. Remove choke heat pipe and hold a finger over the heat inlet hole (hole is on choke housing on some carburetors). If there is little or no vacuum pull on the finger, check the choke housing for gasket leaks or plugged vacuum passages. If these are OK, check choke vacuum passages in carburetor between choke housing and manifold.

Dirty or Rusty Choke Housing

In cases where it is found that the interior of the choke housing is dirty, gummed or rusty while the carburetor itself is comparatively clean, look for a punctured or eroded manifold heat tube (if one is used).

Manifold Heat Control Valve

An engine equipped with a manifold heat control valve can operate with the valve stuck in either the open or closed position. Because of this, an inoperative valve is frequently overlooked at vehicle lubrication or tune-up.

A valve stuck in the "heat-off" position can result in slow warm up, deposits in combustion chamber, carburetor icing, flat spots during acceleration, low gas mileage and spark plug fouling.

A valve stuck in the "heat-on" position can result in power loss, engine knocking, sticking or burned valves and spark plug burning.

To prevent the possibility of a stuck valve, check and lubricate the valve each time the vehicle is lubricated or tuned-up. Check the operation of the valve manually. To lubricate the valve, place a few drops of penetrating oil on the valve shaft where it passes through the manifold. Then move the valve up and down a few times to work the oil in. *Do not use engine oil to lubricate the valve as it will leave a residue which hampers valve operation.*

Carburetor Flange

Check the flange for looseness on the manifold. If one of the flange nuts is loose as little as one-half turn, a sufficient amount of air will enter the intake manifold below the throttle plate to destroy engine idle and all engine performance.

If a tight fit cannot be obtained by tightening the nuts, install a new gasket but be sure that all the old gasket material has been removed.

Throttle Linkage

If the throttle linkage is adjusted so that the accelerator pedal will strike the floor board before the throttle plate is wide open, it will result in low top speed.

Fuel Lines

A restriction of the fuel line will result in an apparent vapor lock action or a definite cut-off of gasoline. This can generally be corrected by blowing out the line with compressed air. In some cases, it may be necessary to replace the line.

Fuel Pump

The pump should be tested to make sure that it will draw an adequate supply of fuel from the tank and deliver it to the carburetor under all conditions of operation. If the pump functions inefficiently, proper adjustment and operation of the carburetor is impossible because the fuel will not be maintained at the prescribed level in the idle passages and main discharge jet (or jets) of the carburetor under all operating conditions.

Fuel Tank

The fuel tank should not be overlooked as a possible source of trouble with carburetion. A shortage of fuel at the fuel pump or carburetor may be caused by pieces of filling station pump hose or other material obstructing the mouth of the feed pipe in the tank, or by a restriction of the air vents in the filler cap and neck.

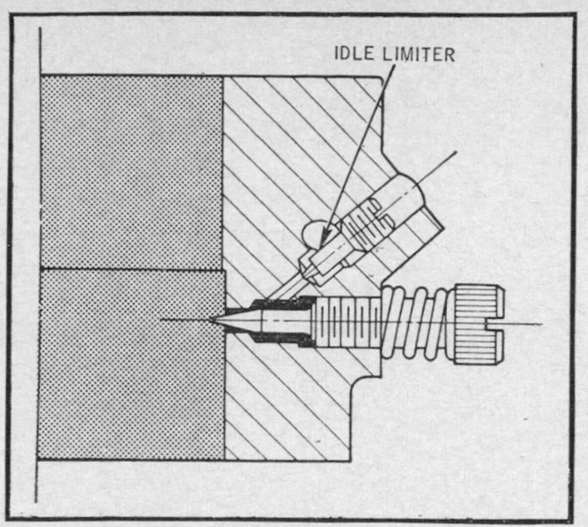

Internal idle mixture limiter

An unusual amount of dirt, water or gum in the fuel filter indicates that the tank is contaminated with these substances, which should be cleaned out to prevent future failure of the pump or carburetor.

Intake Manifold Leaks

Leakage of air into the intake manifold at any point will affect carburetion and general engine performance. Air may leak into the manifold through the joints at the carburetor or cylinder head, cracks in the manifold, cracks or poor connections in the windshield wiper or windshield washer hose lines, or the connections of any accessories which may be connected to the manifold. All such joints should be tested for leaks.

To test the intake manifold for leaks, apply oil from an oil can along the gasket joints with the engine idling. An air leak is indicated when oil is drawn past the gaskets by the suction of the engine. Tighten the nuts or cap screws holding the manifold to the engine and retest for leaks. If tightening fails to stop the leaks, replace the manifold gaskets. If the new gaskets fail to stop the leaks, carefully inspect the manifold for cracks and test any suspicious area with oil.

Air Cleaner

An air cleaner with a dirty element, or with oil that is dirty, too heavy, or too high in the sump, will restrict the air flow through the carburetor and cause a rich mixture at high speeds. In such a condition the air cleaner likewise will not properly remove dirt from the air, and the dirt entering the engine will cause rapid formation of carbon, sticking valves, and wear of piston rings and cylinder bores.

Automatic Choke

The choke mechanism must be inspected and cleaned to make sure it is operating freely. Sluggish action or sticking of the choke will cause excessive fuel consumption, poor performance during warm-up, and possibly hard starting.

The choke thermostat should be set in accordance with the average air temperature as well as the volatility of the fuel being used. It is desirable to have the thermostat set as lean as operating conditions permit in order to avoid an over-rich mixture during engine warm up.

Choke Thermostat

If necessary to adjust the choke more than two marks from the specified setting, either rich or lean, it indicates that the thermostat spring may be bent or has lost its tension.

Carter Float Settings

When replacing a solid float needle and seat with the new type resilient seat, the float setting should be reduced $\frac{1}{32}$" on AFB, WCFB, WGD and WCD carburetors.

Stromberg Carburetor Ball Checks

Whenever it becomes necessary to dismantle a carburetor be sure to account for the ball checks that may be found under pump plungers and compensating or power valves.

CARBURETOR IDLE ADJUST

Cars Without Exhaust Emission Controls

NOTE: The following text outlines the general procedure for idle and mixture settings on vehicles not equipped with Exhaust Emission Control devices. This, together with pertinent data given in the *Tune Up Charts* in the car chapters should suffice for these vehicles.

Turn the screw clockwise by hand until it just contacts its seal. Then turn it out one turn as an initial setting. Start the engine and run it until it reaches normal operating temperature, at which time the choke valve should be wide open with the idle speed screw resting on lowest step of fast idle cam. Slowly turn the idle mixture screw a little at a time until the engine shows a tendency to hesitate and stall. Then turn it to the left until the engine runs smoothly. Continue turning the screw to the left until the fuel mixture is rich and the engine starts to "lope" or "gallop". Finally turn the screw to the right until the engine runs evenly.

On two-barrel carburetors, there is an idle mixture screw for each barrel. On four-barrel carburetors there are also two idle mixture screws on the primary side of the carburetor. When idle ports are provided on the secondary side, they are non-adjustable or they are rendered non-functional by being blocked with gaskets.

When adjusting the idle mixture on two- and four-barrel carburetors, adjust one screw at a time until the engine runs smoothly as directed above. Then adjust the other screw in like manner.

After the idle mixture has been adjusted, it is recommended that a tachometer (engine speed indicator) be used to set the slow idle speed to the rpm indicated in the *Tune Up* table in the car chapter. If a tachometer is not available,

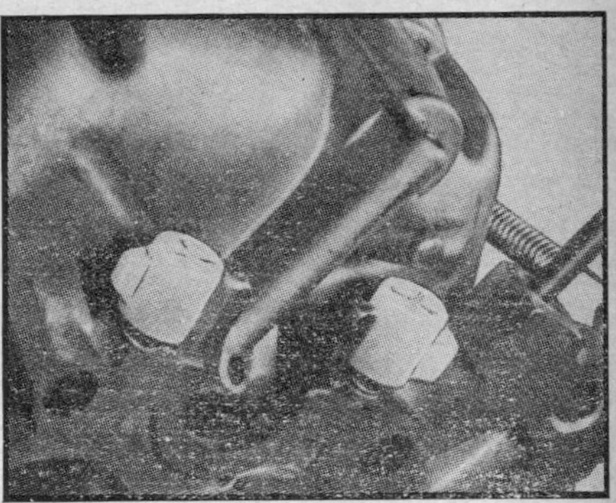

External idle mixture limiter

adjust the idle speed screw until the engine runs smoothly without racing. If the car has an automatic transmission, place the shift lever in Drive range with hand brake off. Then very slowly increase engine speed until the car begins to creep, then back off slightly until creeping is eliminated.

Cars With Exhaust Emission Controls

There are two basic types of exhaust emission control systems—air injection type and engine modification type (see the *Exhaust Emission Systems* chapter). With both types, the slow idle adjustment method, referred to as "Lean Roll" is to be used. This method insures proper idle, ignition timing and mixture settings for greatest possible exhaust emission reduction and proper engine operation. It should be noted here that smooth idle is extremely sensitive to vacuum leaks. If rough idle is noted, check for vacuum leaks at the carburetor, manifold, etc.

Carburetor Idle Limiters

Some carburetors are equipped with idle adjustment limiters which restrict the maximum idle richness of the air/fuel mixture and prevents overly rich adjustments. There are two types of idle limiters: internal and external (see illustrations). The internal needle limiter is located in the idle channel and is not visible externally. This limiter is set and sealed at the factory and, under no circumstances, during normal service or during overhaul, should the seal be removed and adjustments made to this needle.

The other type of idle limiter is an external idle limiter cap installed on the knurled head of the idle mixture adjusting screw. Any adjustment to the idle fuel mixture on carburetors with this type of limiter must be made within the range of the limiter cap.

Under no circumstances may the limiter cap, the stop boss or the power valve cover, which the limiter caps stop against, be mutilated or deformed in any way to render the limiter inoperative. A satisfactory idle is obtainable within the range of the limiter cap.

The addition of idle limiters does not eliminate the need for adjusting idle speed and mixture. All the limiters do is prevent overly rich mixtures, which increase the amount of hydro-carbons emitted into the atmosphere.

1. With engine at operating temperature, set parking brake and block drive wheels.
2. Make sure choke valve is wide open.
3. On C.C.S. equipped vehicles, see that the air cleaner thermostatic valve is open.
4. On carburetors so equipped, hold hot idle compensator hole closed with eraser on pencil.
5. Turn air conditioner off or on according to directions given in *Tune Up Charts* in car chapters.
6. Set idle mixture screw(s) for maximum idle rpm.
7. Adjust speed screw (or idle stop solenoid screw on C.C.S.) to obtain the specified rpm in Drive or Neutral as specified. (See C.C.S. section of Exhaust Emission Controls Chapter for details on idle stop solenoid.)
8. Set ignition timing according to specifications with vacuum advance line disconnected and hole in manifold plugged.
9. Adjust mixture screw IN to obtain a 20 rpm drop (lean roll).
10. Adjust mixture screw OUT ¼ turn.
11. Repeat Steps 9 and 10 for second mixture screw (2 and 4 barrel carbs).
12. Readjust speed screw (or solenoid screw) if necessary to obtain specified rpm.
13. On C.C.S. with idle solenoid stop on carburetor, electrically disconnect solenoid and adjust carburetor idle speed screw to obtain 400 rpm in neutral, then reconnect wire to solenoid.

NOTE: Exact instructions for each C.C.S. equipped engine-transmission combination is given for this Lean Roll (low idle) speed method on a decal permanently affixed to the vicinity of the radiator support as well as in the *Tune Up Charts* in the car chapter of this manual.

Carter Carburetor Section

CARTER AS ADJUSTMENT SPECIFICATIONS

See Tune Up Chart in car chapter for hot idle speed.

Year	Carb. Model	Idle Screw (Mixture) Turns Open	Float Level	Pump Setting	Metering Rod Setting	Fast Idle Setting	Unloader Setting	Choke Setting
RAMBLER								
1963	3536S	¼–1¼	3/32	See Text	See Text	.033–.037	⅛	On Index

MODEL AS ADJUSTMENTS

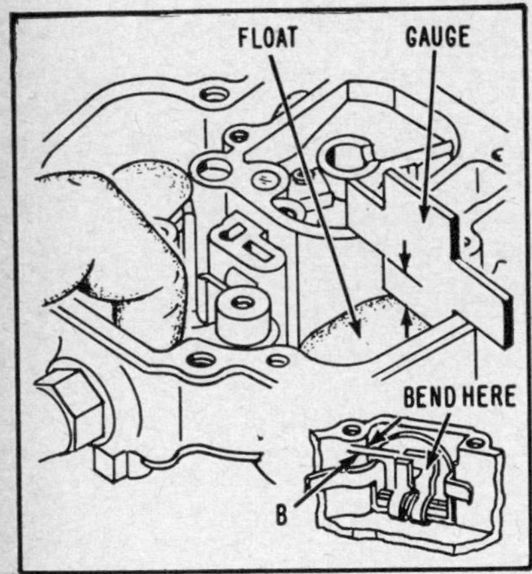

Fig. 2 AS float adjustment

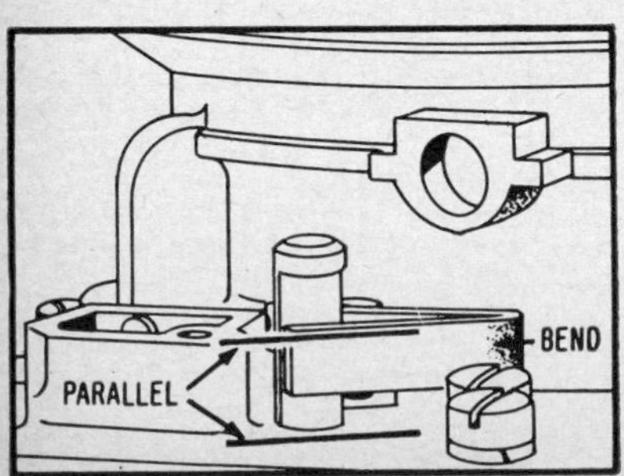

Fig. 3 AS pump adjustment

This carburetor, Fig. 1, is a single-barrel, downdraft unit which incorporates two aluminum castings. Readily accessible adjustments and the combined body flange casting make it easy to service. All fuel and vacuum passages are confined to the two castings. Calibration points are easy to check and clean in service. All major gasket surfaces are above the fuel level to minimize fuel leakage. A two-stage high-speed metering control is used to produce instantaneous response to engine demands. One is mechanically controlled and the other is actuated by manifold vacuum.

Float Adjustment

Fig. 2—With bowl cover and gasket removed, invert carburetor bowl, holding thumb on float pin retainer to keep pin at bottom of its guide slots. Place float gauge on carburetor bowl as shown. The static weight of float assembly resting on the fuel needle should allow the float just to contact the gauge. The distance from top of casting to top of float should be as listed in the *AS Specifications Chart.*

To adjust floats it is recommended that the pin retainer be removed and a holding tool be used to prevent damage to the resilient seat when bending the float arm. Adjust each float individually, remove the holding tool, and recheck both floats after each adjustment.

Check the float travel in the bowl for proper side clearance. Adjust as required by bending the arms, then recheck float level.

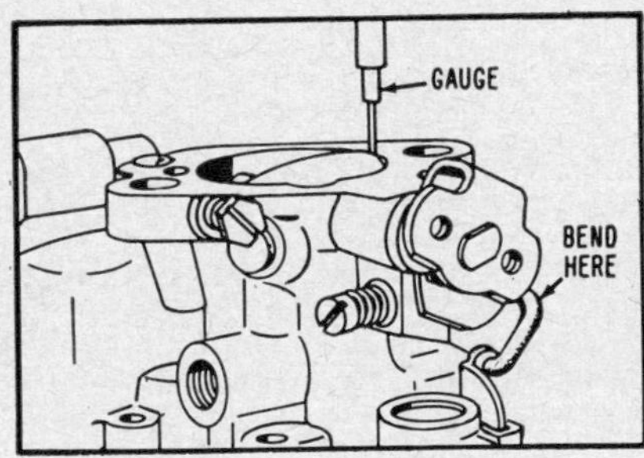

Fig. 4 AS fast idle adjustment

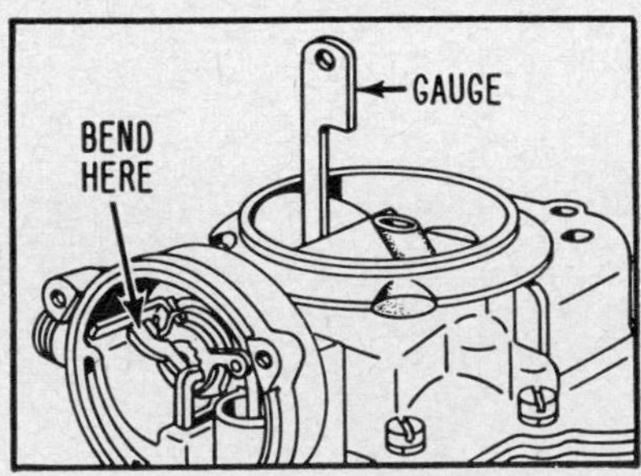

Fig. 5 AS unloader adjustment

Pump Adjustment

Fig. 3—Open throttle to wide open position. Top of pump arm on lifter link should be parallel to top surface of bowl cover. To adjust, bend pump arm as required.

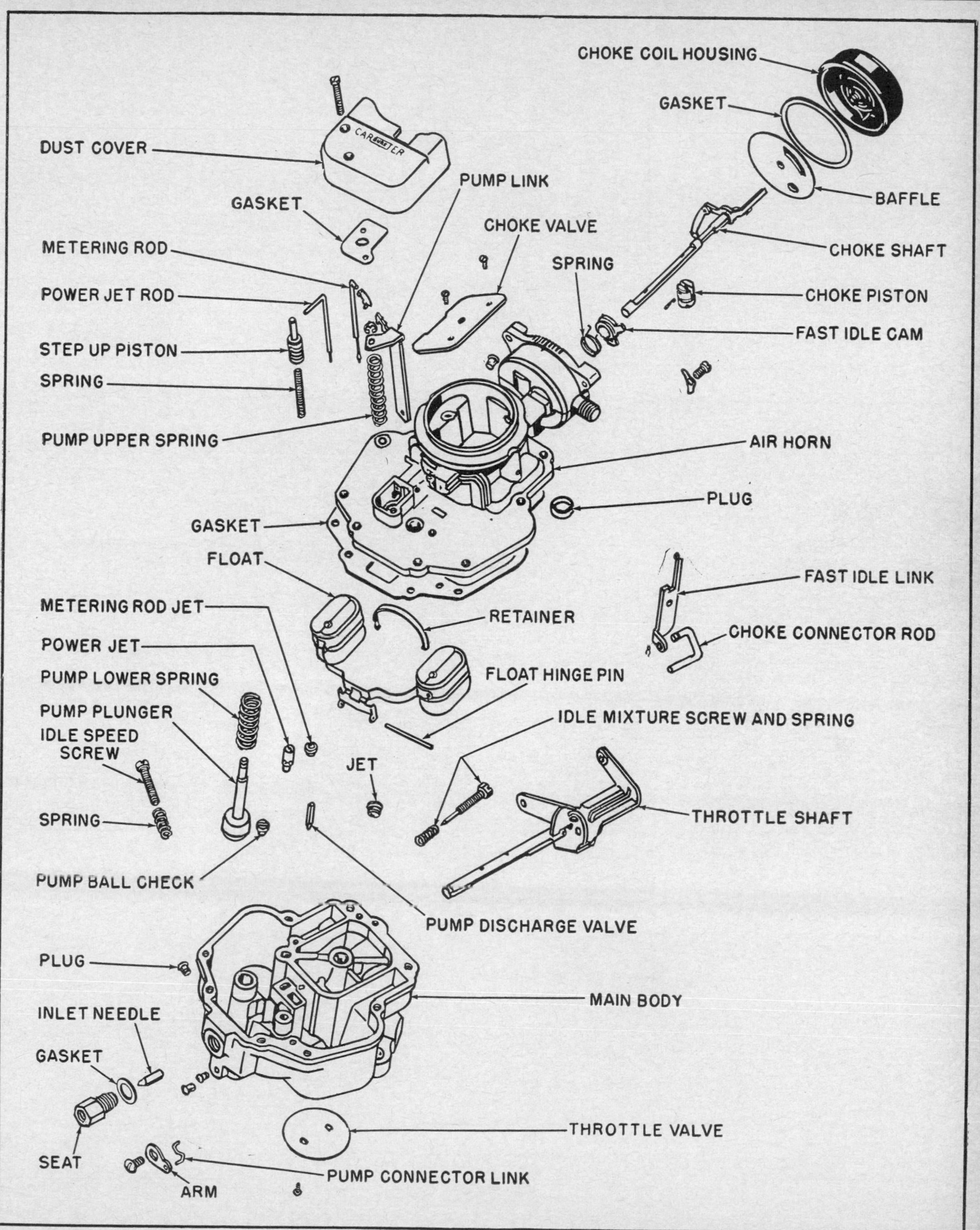

Fig. 1 Carter Model AS single barrel carburetor

Metering Rod Adjustment

This adjustment must be made after the pump adjustment. With throttle valve wide open the metering rod should just bottom in the carburetor casting. If the rod is properly adjusted, some movement can be noted around the rod in the eye of the metering rod retainer clip when throttle is moved slightly from wide open position. If the rod is too low, it will tend to push the metering rod retainer clip up; if the rod is too high it will be possible to push the rod down. To adjust, bend metering rod arm.

Fast Idle Adjustment

Fig. 4—Remove choke coil housing gasket and baffle plate. Crack throttle valve and hold choke valve closed to rotate the fast idle cam to the fast idle position. There should be the clearance shown in the *AS Specifications Chart* between edge of throttle plate and carburetor bore (side opposite idle port). To adjust, bend connector link.

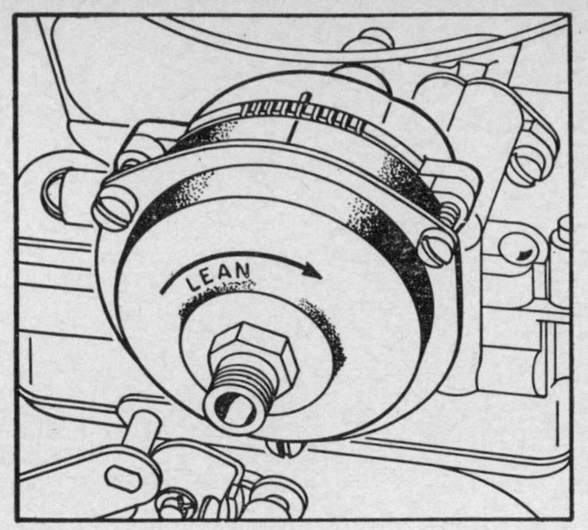

Fig. 6 AS choke adjustment

Unloader Adjustment

Fig. 5—This adjustment must be made after the fast idle adjustment. Hold throttle valve wide open and close choke valve as far as possible without forcing.

The clearance between the upper edge of the choke valve and inner wall of air horn should be as listed in the *AS Specifications Chart*. To adjust, bend lever as shown.

Automatic Choke Setting

Fig. 6—Loosen screws retaining choke cover and turn cover so that the line or "Index" mark on cover lines up with the mark specified in the *AS Specifications Chart* on the choke housing.

CARTER YF ADJUSTMENT SPECIFICATIONS

See Tune Up Chart in car chapter for hot idle speed.

CHEVROLET ENGINES

Year	Carb. Model	Initial Idle Mixture Screw Setting	Float Level	Float Drop	Idle Vent Setting	Fast Idle Setting	Choke Unloader Setting	Vacuum Break Setting	Choke Setting
1963–65	3379S	1½	7/16	1 3/16	.025–.030	See Text	—	—	—
	3402S	1½	7/16	1 3/16	.025–.030	See Text	—	—	—
1966	3379SA	1½	½	1 3/16	.035	See Text	—	—	—
	3402SB	1½	½	1 3/16	.035	See Text	—	—	—
	4079S	1½	½	1 3/16	.035	See Text	.260	.320	See Text
	4080S	1½	½	1 3/16	.035	See Text	.260	.300	See Text
1967	4367S	1½	7/32	1 3/16	.065	See Text	.25	.240	See Text
	4368S	1½	7/32	1 3/16	.065	See Text	.250	.220	See Text
	4373S	1½	7/32	1 3/16	—	See Text	.250	—	—
	4374S	1½	7/32	1 3/16	—	See Text	.250	—	—
	4377S	1½	7/32	1 3/16	.065	See Text	.250	.240	See Text
	4378S	1½	7/32	1 3/16	.065	See Text	.250	.220	See Text
	4387S	1½	7/32	1 3/16	.065	See Text	.250	.240	See Text

COMET, FAIRLANE, FALCON, MUSTANG

Year	Carb. Model	Initial Idle Mixture Screw Setting	Float Level	Float Drop	Idle Vent Setting	Fast Idle Setting	Choke Unloader Setting	Vacuum Break Setting	Choke Setting
1967	C7ZF-A①	1½	7/32	—	—	.065	.250	—	1 Rich
1968	C8DF-A	1½	7/32	—	—	.035	.280	—	Index
	C8DF-B	1½	7/32	—	—	.046	.280	—	1 Lean
1969	C8AF-BF	—	7/32	—	—	—	.280	—	Index
	C8DF-G	—	7/32	—	—	—	.280	—	Index
	C8DF-H	—	7/32	—	—	—	.280	—	1 Lean

①—Identification tag marked "Autolite".

JEEP

Year	Carb. Model	Initial Idle Mixture Screw Setting	Float Level	Float Drop	Idle Vent Setting	Fast Idle Setting	Choke Unloader Setting	Vacuum Break Setting	Choke Setting
1963–65	938 Series	1½	5/16	13/16	—	See Text	—	—	—
	951S, SA	1½	5/16	13/16	—	See Text	—	—	—
	2932S	1½	9/32	13/16	—	See Text	—	—	—
	2467S	1½	9/32	13/16	—	See Text	—	—	—
	4002S	1½	½	13/16	—	See Text	—	—	—
1968	4366S	1½	¼	1¼	—	See Text	—	—	—

OLDSMOBILE

Year	Carb. Model	Initial Idle Mixture Screw Setting	Float Level	Float Drop	Idle Vent Setting	Fast Idle Setting	Choke Unloader Setting	Vacuum Break Setting	Choke Setting
1966–67	4072SA	1½	7/32	2¼	.060	See Text	¼	.215	See Text
	4367S	1½	7/32	2¼	.060	See Text	¼	.230	See Text

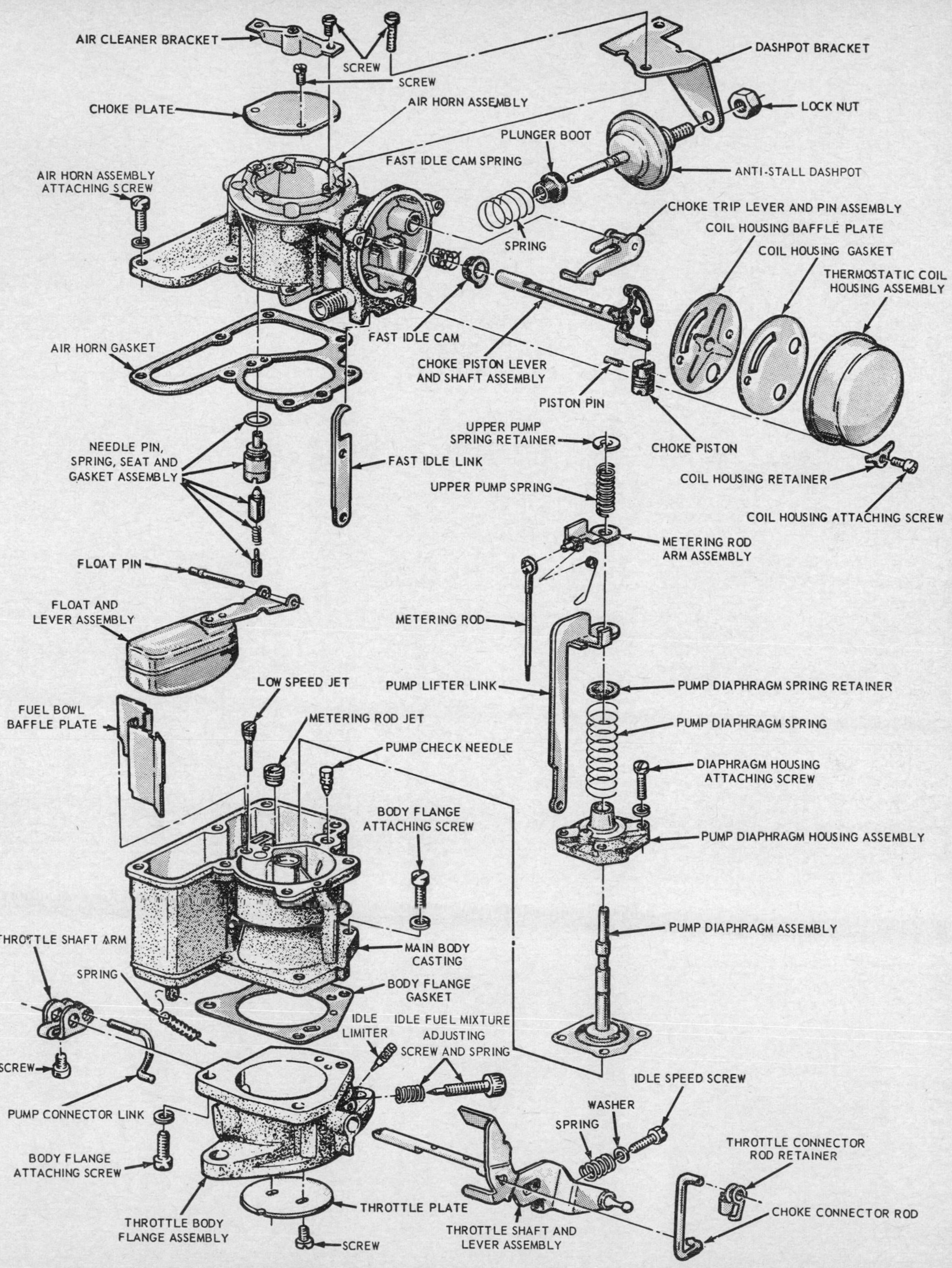

Fig. 1 Carter Model YF carburetor with built-in automatic choke. Note that this unit is provided with an idle limiter screw which is used to prevent an overly rich mixture on cars with exhaust emission control

MODEL YF ADJUSTMENTS

The YF carburetor, Figs. 1 and 2, is a single-barrel, downdraft unit combining the fundamental features of other Carter carburetors. In addition, it features a diaphragm-type accelerating pump. It also has a diaphragm-operated metering rod, both vacuum and mechanically controlled.

The 1966 version of this carburetor, Fig. 2, with an automatic choke used in conjunction with a temperature sensing choke coil (mounted in a cast depression on the exhaust manifold) is used with Chevy II six-cylinder engines when the *Air Injection Reactor System* is used.

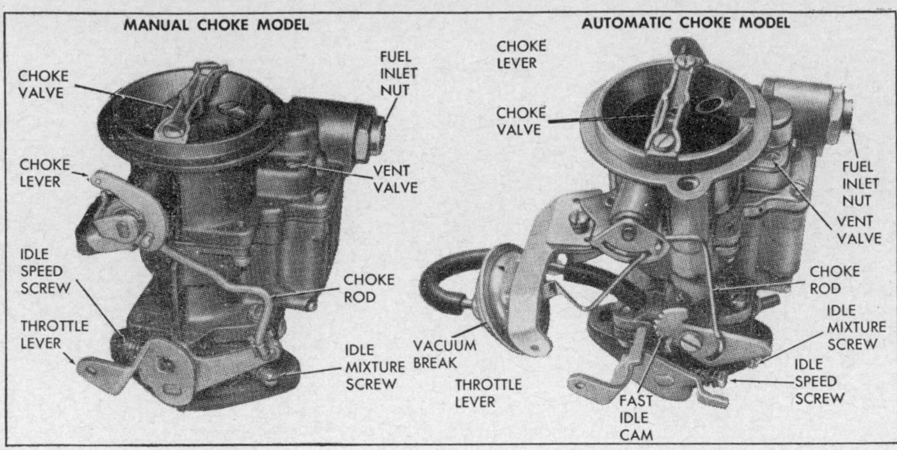

Fig. 2 YF carburetor exteriors. The automatic choke model has the choke coil mounted on the exhaust manifold of the engine

Float Adjustment

Fig. 3—Invert bowl cover and measure float level (distance between float and cover at free end of float). Adjust by bending lip of float (not float arm) that rests on needle.

Hold cover in upright position (allowing float to hang down, Fig. 4), and measure float drop from cover to float at end opposite hinge. If the measurement does not correspond to the dimension listed in the *YF Specifications Chart,* adjust by bending stop tab on float arm.

Pump Adjustment

With throttle valve seated in bore of carburetor, press down on upper end of diaphragm shaft until it reaches its bottom position. The metering rod arm should now contact the pump lifter link at the outer end nearest the springs. Adjust by bending the pump connector link at its lower angle.

Metering Rod Adjustment

Fig. 5—With throttle valve seated in bore of carburetor, press down on upper end of diaphragm shaft until diaphragm bottoms in vacuum chamber. Metering rod should contact bottom of metering rod well, and metering rod arm should contact lifter link at the outer end nearest the springs and at supporting lug. Adjust by bending lip of metering rod arm to which metering rod is attached, up or down as required.

Idle Vent Adjustment

Fig. 6—This adjustment should be made after completing pump and metering rod adjustments. Install bowl cover and air horn assembly with gasket. With throttle valve tightly closed in carburetor bore, there should be the clearance listed in the *YF Specifications Chart* between idle vent valve and inside of bowl cover. Adjust idle vent screw as required.

Fast Idle Adjustment

Unit With Built-In Auto. Choke

Referring to Fig. 7, remove choke coil housing, gasket and baffle plate. Crack throttle valve (barely open) and hold choke valve firmly in closed position, then close throttle valve. This will allow the fast idle cam to revolve to the fast idle position.

With choke valve held tightly closed, and with slight tension on throttle lever, there should be the clearance listed in the *YF Specifications Chart* between the throttle valve and carburetor bore (side opposite idle port). Adjust by bending connector link as required.

With Manual Choke, Fig. 8

With choke valve in wide open position, tang on throttle lever should just contact stop boss on carburetor body. To adjust, bend rod at offset portion as required.

With Automatic Choke, Fig. 9

With choke valve fully closed, bend choke rod at offset to obtain a slight clearance (.015") between fast idle cam and boss on carburetor bowl.

With choke valve fully closed, index mark on fast idle cam must be at the mid-point of the fast idle tang on throttle lever. Bend fast idle tang up or down to adjust.

Choke Unloader Adjustment

With throttle valve held wide open and choke valve held toward closed position with a rubber band, there should be the clearance listed in the *YF Specifications Chart* between lower edge of choke valve and inner air horn wall.

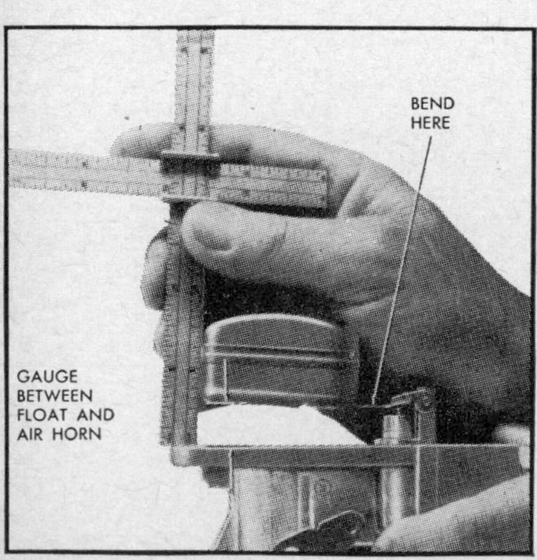

Fig. 3 YF float level adjustment

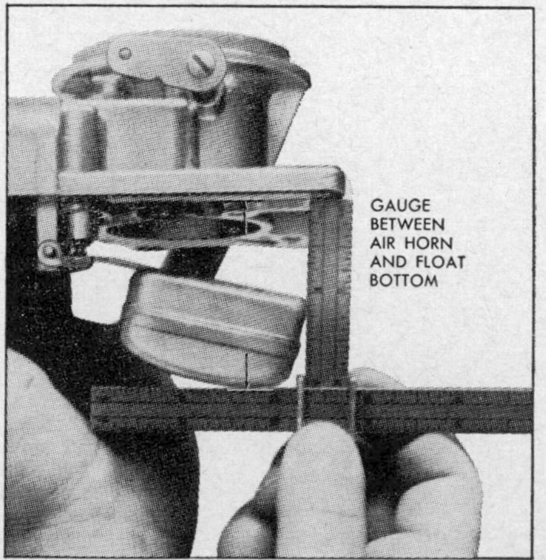

Fig. 4 YF Float drop adjustment

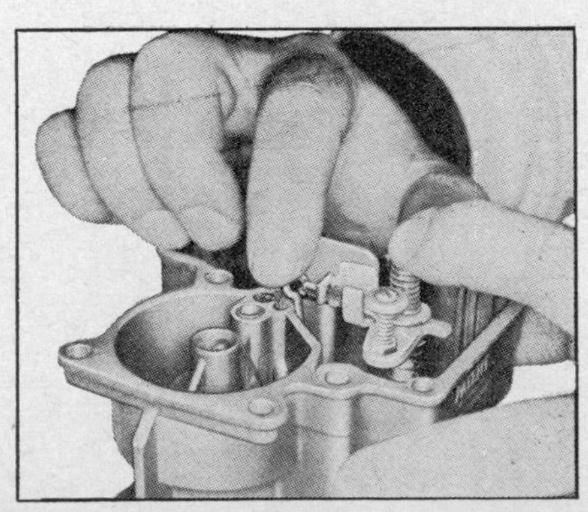

Fig. 5 YF metering rod adjustment

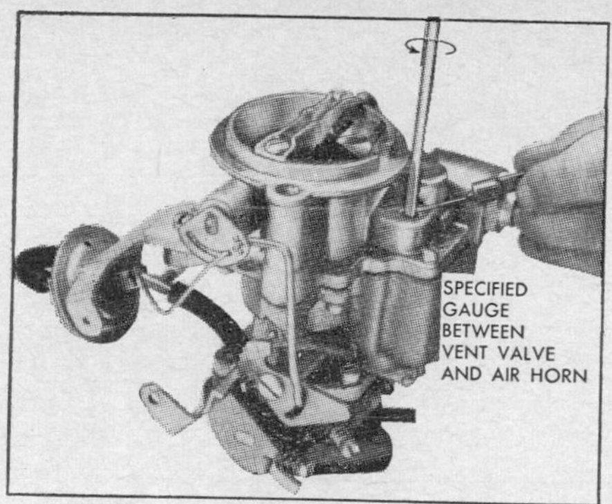

Fig. 6 YF idle vent adjustment

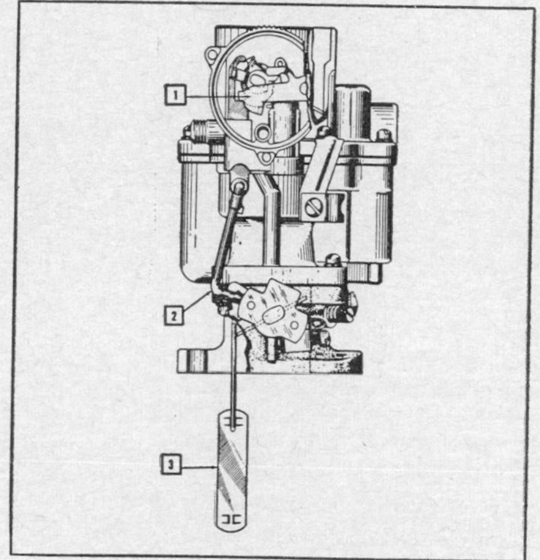

Fig. 7 YF fast idle adjustment for Fig. 1 carburetors. 1) Fast idle cam. 2) Bend at connector link. 3) Gauge

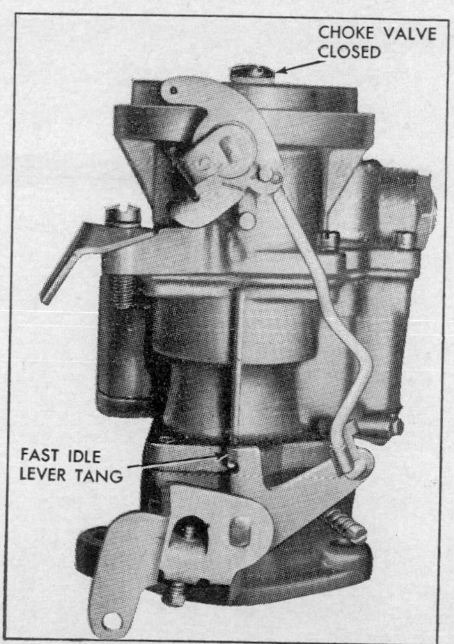

Fig. 8 YF choke rod adjustment (manual choke) for Fig. 2 carburetors

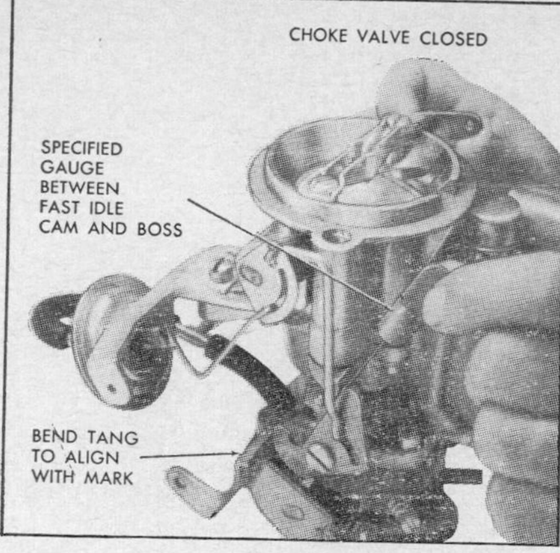

Fig. 9 YF choke rod adjustment (automatic choke) for Fig. 2 carburetors

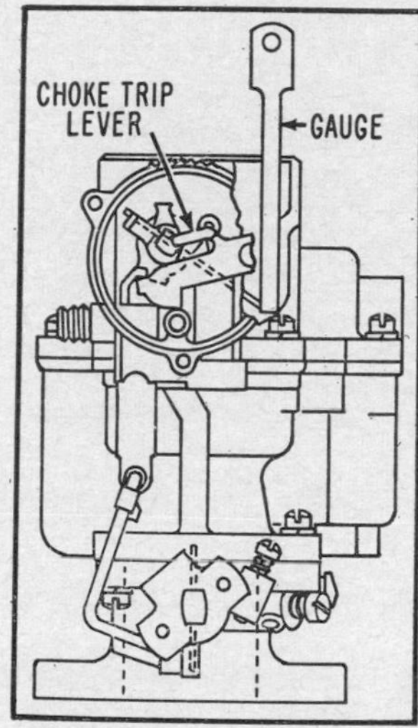

Fig. 10 YF unloader adjustment for Fig. 1 carburetors

On Fig. 1 carburetors, adjust by bending arm on choke trip lever, Fig. 10. On Fig. 2 carburetors adjust by bending unloader tang on throttle lever, Fig. 11.

Vacuum Break Adjustment

Fig. 12—With vacuum break arm held against its stop, and choke valve held toward closed position with a rubber band, bend vacuum break link to obtain the clearance listed in the *YF Specifications Chart* between lower edge of choke valve and air horn wall.

Automatic Choke Adjustment

For Fig. 1 Units
Loosen choke cover retaining screws and turn choke cover so that line or Index mark on cover lines up with the specified mark listed in *YF Specifications Chart* on choke housing.

Choke Diaphragm Linkage

For Fig. 2 Units
With vacuum diaphragm bottomed, close choke valve as far as possible without forcing. Adjust choke diaphragm connector rod to give the clearance listed in the *YF Specifications Chart* between lower edge of choke valve and inner wall of air horn. Remove connector rod to prevent damage to diaphragm.

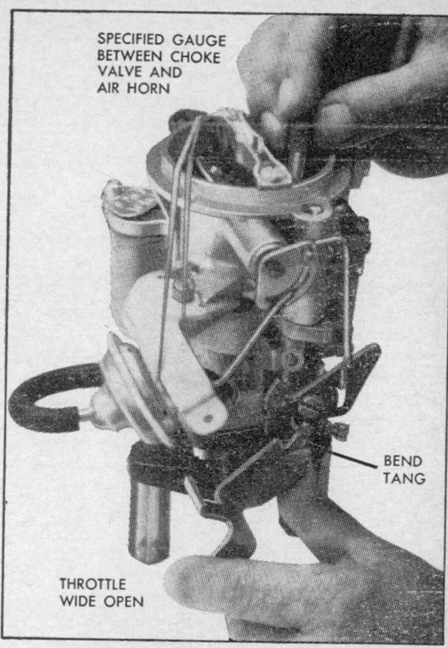

Fig. 11 YF unloader adjustment for Fig. 2 carburetors

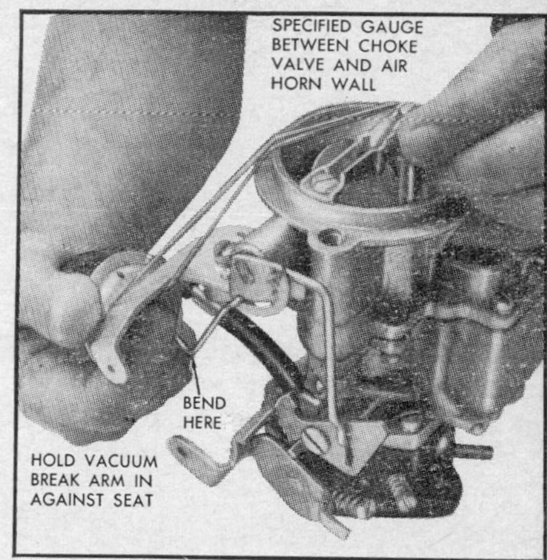

Fig. 12 YF vacuum break adjustment for Fig. 2 carburetors

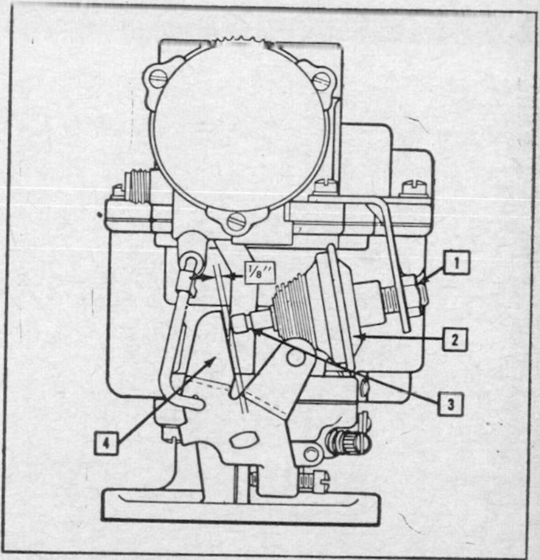

Fig. 13 YF dashpot adjustment (Rambler). 1) Locknut. 2) Dashpot. 3) Dashpot stem. 4) Throttle lever

CARTER YH ADJUSTMENT SPECIFICATIONS

See Tune Up Chart in car chapters for hot idle speed.

Year	Carb. Model	Idle Screw (Mixture) Turns Open	Float Level	Float Drop	Metering Rod	Pump	Fast Idle	Unloader	Automatic Choke	Dashpot
CORVAIR TURBOCHARGED										
1963	3569S	1/4–2	5/8	2 3/8	See Text	See Text	.033	7/16	1 Lean	—
	3586S-SA	1/4–2	5/8	2 3/8	See Text	See Text	.033	7/16	1 Lean	—
1964	3692S-SA	1/4–2	5/8	2 3/8	See Text	See Text	.033	7/16	1 Lean	—
1965	3902S	1/4–2	5/8	2 3/8	See Text	See Text	.033	7/16	1 Lean	—
	4020S	1/4–2	5/8	2 3/8	See Text	See Text	.033	7/16	On Index	—
1965–66	4141S-SA	1/4–2	5/8	2 3/8	See Text	See Text	.033	7/16	1 Lean	—

MODEL YH ADJUSTMENTS

The YH carburetor, Figs, 1 and 2, is comparable to the YF model except that the circuits are rearranged to operate in a horizontal or sidedraft position, and in conjunction with the Turbocharger on Corvair cars.

Float Adjustment

Figs. 3 and 4—With bowl cover inverted, distance between cover gasket surface and float (at center) should be as listed in the *YH Specifications Chart*. Adjust by bending float arm as required.

To adjust float drop, invert cover to upright position as shown, allowing float to hang down. Distance between cover gasket surface and bottom of free end of float should be as listed. Adjust by bending tang on hinge end.

Metering Rod Adjustment

Fig. 5—Insert gauge in place of metering rod. With throttle valve tightly closed, press down on diaphragm shaft until metering rod arm contacts lifter link at diaphragm stem. With diaphragm shaft held in this position, metering rod pin must rest lightly on metering rod gauge (T109-104). To adjust, bend metering rod arm.

Accelerating Pump

There is no adjustment provided. If acceleration is not satisfactory, examine diaphragm for wear or damage. Clean and blow out all passages. Replace all worn or damaged parts.

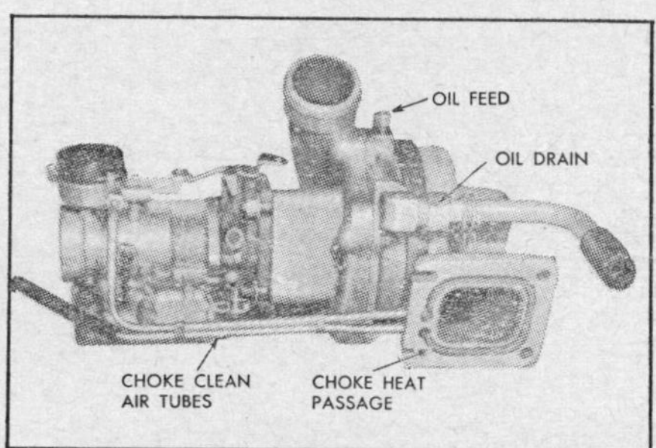

Fig. 2 YH carburetor exterior

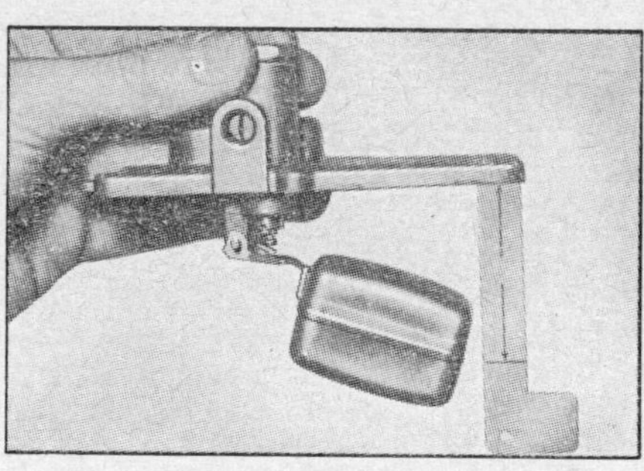

Fig. 4 YH float drop adjustment

Fast Idle Adjustment

Fig. 6—With choke coil housing removed, have choke valve tightly closed and with fast idle link on high step of cam. Adjust choke connector rod to give the clearance listed in the *YH Specifications Chart* between edge of throttle valve and carburetor bore (side opposite idle port). To adjust, bend fast idle connector link at curvature.

Choke Unloader Adjustment

Hold throttle valve wide open and close choke valve. There should be the clearance listed in the *YH Specifications Chart* between lower edge of choke valve and inner wall of air horn. To adjust, bend choke shaft unloader tang, Fig. 6.

Automatic Choke Adjustment

Loosen choke coil housing retaining screws and rotate housing by hand to the setting listed in the *YH Specifications Chart*. Hold in position and tighten screws.

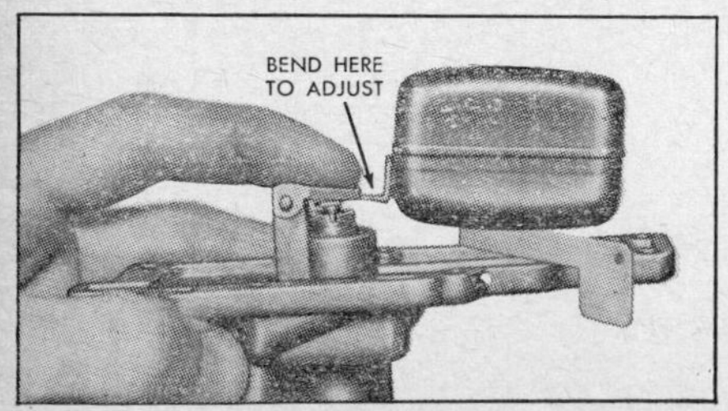

Fig. 3 YH float level adjustment

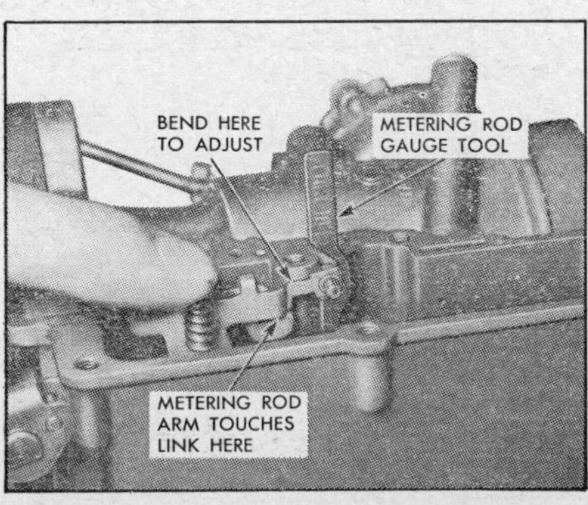

Fig. 5 YH metering rod adjustment

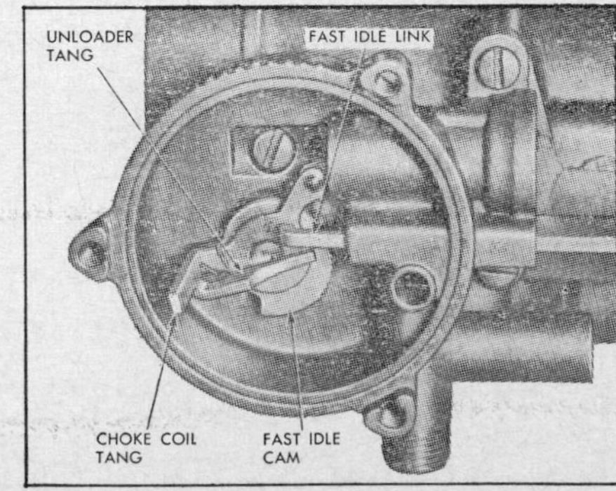

Fig. 6 YH fast idle adjustment

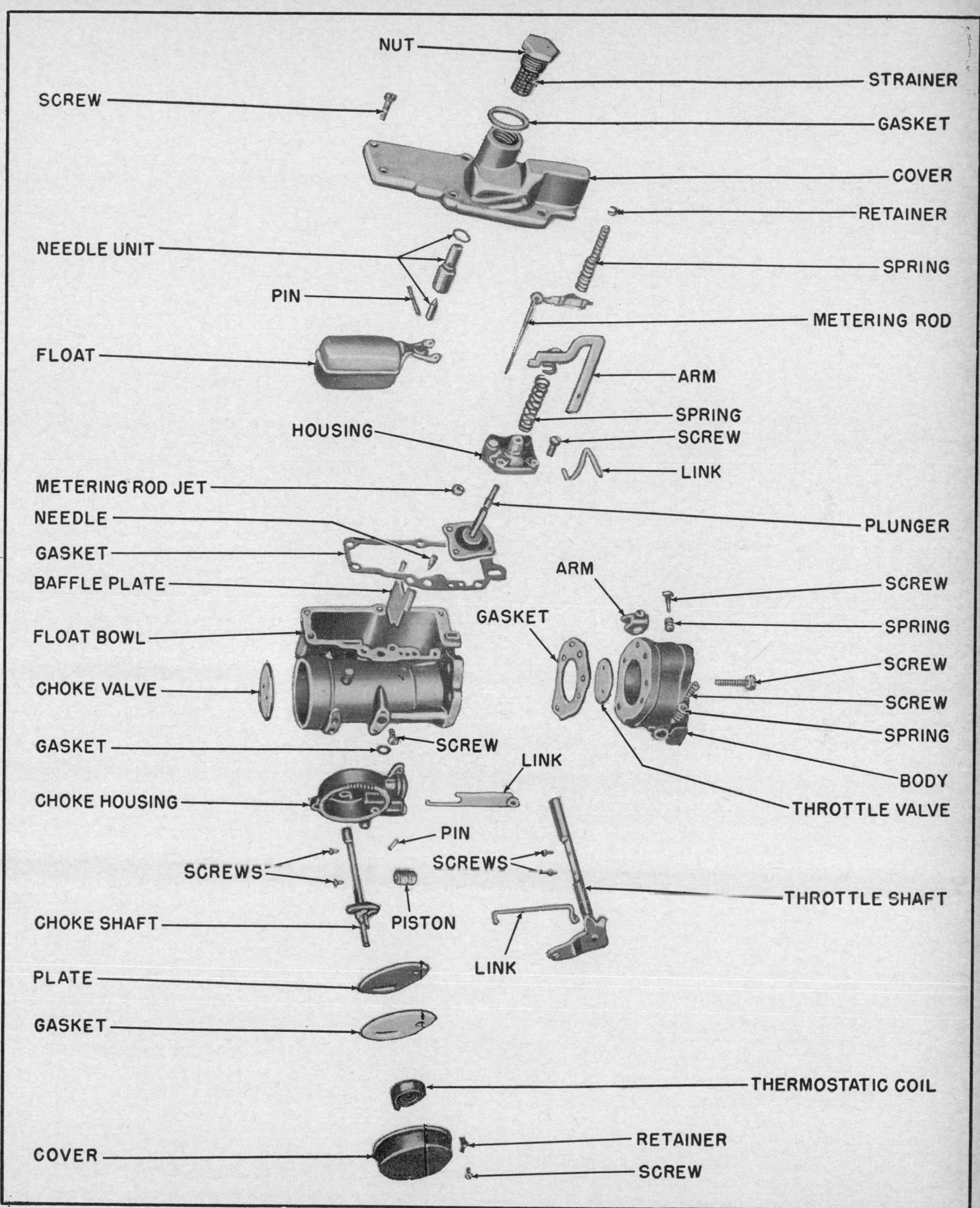

Fig. 1 Carter Model YH used with Corvair Turbocharged engines

CARTER RBS ADJUSTMENT SPECIFICATIONS

See Tune Up Chart in car chapter for hot idle speed.

Year	Carb. Model	Idle Screw (Mixture) Turns Open	Float Level	Step-Up Rod	Pump & Bowl Vent	Fast Idle Linkage	Fast Idle Throttle Valve	Choke Unloader	Dashpot Setting	Choke Setting
JEEP										
1966–68	4016S	¼–1¾	21/32	—	1/16	See Text	.028	⅛	—	1 Rich
	4163S	¼–1¾	21/32	—	1/16	See Text	.052	—	—	—
	4252S	¼–1¾	21/32	—	1/16	See Text	.052	—	3/32–⅛	—
	4253S	¼–1¾	21/32	—	1/16	See Text	.035	⅛	3/32–⅛	1 Rich
RAMBLER										
1963	3487S	¼–1¾	15/32	.040	1/16	See Text	.033	⅛	—	On Index
	3498S	¼–1¾	15/32	—	1/16	See Text	.033	⅛	3/32–⅛	On Index
1964	3488S	¼–1¾	15/32	—	1/16	See Text	.033	⅛	—	1 Lean
	3708S	¼–1¾	15/32	—	1/16	See Text	.033	⅛	—	On Index
	3709S	¼–1¾	15/32	—	1/16	See Text	.033	⅛	3/32–⅛	On Index
	3727S	¼–1¾	15/32	—	1/16	See Text	.033	⅛	—	2 Lean
	3728S	¼–1¾	15/32	—	1/16	See Text	.033	⅛	3/32–⅛	2 Lean
1965–66	3765S	¼–1¾	15/32	—	1/16	See Text	.028	⅛	—	1 Rich
	3766S	¼–1¾	15/32	—	1/16	See Text	.040	⅛	—	1 Rich
1966–67	3882S	¼–1¾	15/32	—	1/16	See Text	.033	⅛	—	1 Rich
1968	4470S	1	9/16	—	5/64	See Text	.035	⅛	—	2 Rich
	4626S	½–1½	9/16	—	5/64	See Text	.035	⅛	—	2 Rich
1969	4631S	1	9/16	—	5/64	See Text	—	⅛	7/32	Index
	4633S	1	9/16	—	5/64	See Text	—	3/16	7/32	Index
	4634S	1	9/16	—	5/64	See Text	—	3/16	—	2 Rich
	4666S	1	9/16	—	5/64	See Text	—	⅛	—	2 Rich

MODEL RBS ADJUSTMENTS

This carburetor, Fig. 1, incorporates a single aluminum casting with a pressed steel bowl. Adjustments are readily accessible and most calibration points are located in the single casting.

Fuel pickups are located near the centerline of the carburetor bore to gain the benefits of a concentric bowl carburetor, yet so located that engine heat being radiated through the bore are conducted through the casting but is not readily conducted to the fuel in the bowl.

Vapor vents allow rapid dissipation of the vapors to assure smooth idle and to minimize hard starting while the engine is hot. A diaphragm controlled step-up provides instantaneous response to engine demands.

The carburetor model number is stamped on the side of the flange near the throttle lever.

Float Level Adjustment

Fig. 2—With carburetor inverted, bowl and bowl gasket removed, and only weight of float pressing needle into its seat, measure vertical distance from casting to the small "bump" at outer ends of float. Gauge both ends of float. If the vertical distance is not as listed in the *RBS Specifications Chart,* adjustment can be made by removing float from casting, or by holding lip end of float bracket securely with needle-nose pliers. However, be sure to hold float lip away from needle when adjusting. To adjust, bend bracket at its narrowest portion.

Step-Up Rod Adjustment

This adjustment can be made only on early 1963 units as indicated in the *RBS Specifications Chart.* Late 1963 and later units cannot be adjusted as the diaphragm and rod are crimped together.

With bowl removed and carburetor inverted, fully depress step-up rod. There should be the clearance listed in the chart between top of step-up rod and step-up jet. To adjust, move rod up or down as required. Rod is fastened in sleeve of diaphragm assembly.

Fig. 2 RBS float level adjustment

Fig. 3 RBS pump adjustment

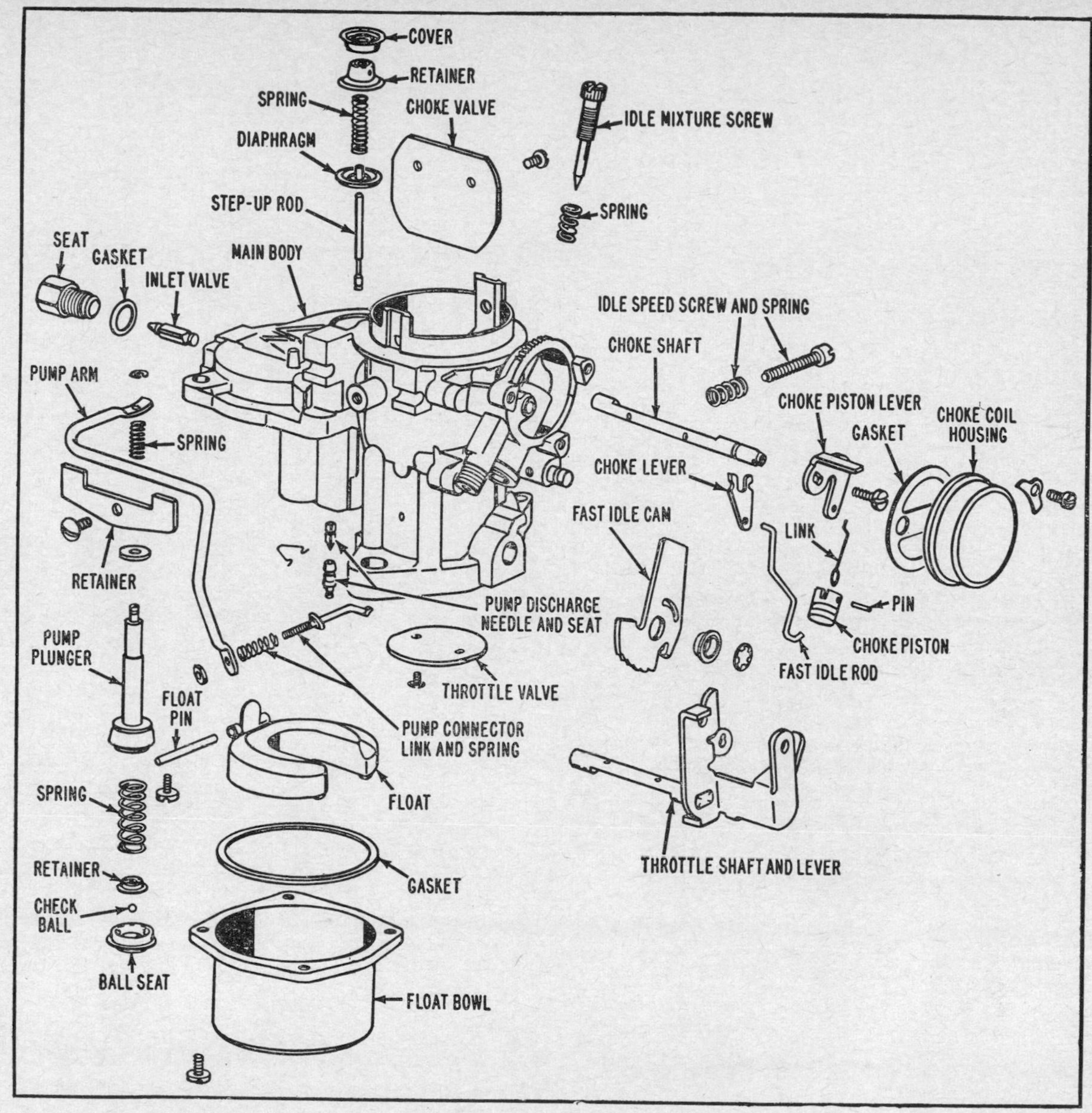

Fig. 1 Carter model RBS single barrel carburetor

Pump & Bowl Vent Adjustment

Fig. 3—Back out throttle lever (idle speed) adjusting screw and hold choke valve wide open so throttle valve seats in carburetor bore. Turn pump adjusting nut to obtain the clearance listed in the *RBS Specifications Chart* between washer on pump plunger and bushing.

Fast Idle Linkage Adjustment

With choke valve tightly closed and choke connector rod in upper end of slot in cam, align cam index with center of fast idle tang.

On model 4163, with choke valve wide open and throttle valve tightly closed, adjust nut on choke connector rod to align index mark on cam with center of throttle lever tang.

On all other models, adjust by bending choke connector rod at lower angle.

Fast Idle Throttle Valve Clearance Adjustment

With choke valve closed there should be the clearance listed in the *RBS Specifications Chart* between edge of throttle valve and carburetor bore (at idle port side) and highest part of cam (this applies to model 4163). For all other models, the clearance is between the edge of throttle valve and carburetor bore with center of fast idle tang on index mark. On all models, adjust by bending fast idle tang.

Choke Unloader Adjustment

With throttle valve wide open, there should be the clearance listed in the *RBS Specifications Chart* between top edge of choke valve and inner wall of air horn. To adjust, bend unloader arm on throttle lever.

Dashpot Adjustment

Rambler—With throttle valve tightly closed and diaphragm stem fully depressed, adjust dashpot to give the clearance listed in the *RBS Specifications Chart* between stem and throttle lever.

Automatic Choke Adjustment

Loosen retainer screws and turn choke cover so that line or index mark on cover lines up with the specified mark on choke housing (see *RBS Specifications Chart*).

CARTER BBS ADJUSTMENT SPECIFICATIONS

See Tune Up Chart in car chapter for hot idle speed.

Year	Carb. Model	Initial Idle Mixture Screw Turns Open	Float Level	Pump Travel Inch	Bowl Vent Drill Size	Choke Unloader Drill Size	Fast Idle Cam Position Drill Size	Choke Vacuum Kick Drill Size	Automatic Choke Setting
DODGE & PLYMOUTH									
1963	3462S	1	7/32	—	.060	3/16	See Text	—	4 Rich
	3463S	1	7/32	—	.060	3/16	See Text	—	4 Rich
	3464S	1	7/32	—	.060	3/16	See Text	—	4 Rich
	3465S	1	7/32	—	.060	3/16	See Text	—	4 Rich
	3466S	1	7/32	—	.060	3/16	See Text	—	4 Rich
	3468S	1	7/32	—	.060	3/16	See Text	—	4 Rich
1964	3675S	1	1/4	—	.060	3/16	15/64	11/64	2 Rich
	3676S	1	1/4	—	.060	3/16	7/32	1/8	2 Rich
	3677S	1	1/4	—	.060	3/16	7/32	11/64	2 Rich
	3678S	1	1/4	—	.060	3/16	3/16	1/8	2 Rich
	3679S	1	1/4	—	.060	3/16	7/32	11/64	2 Rich
	3680S	1	1/4	—	.060	3/16	3/16	1/8	2 Rich
	3681S	1	1/4	—	.060	3/16	15/64	11/64	2 Rich
1965	3833S	1	1/4	—	.060	3/16	5/64	5/32	2 Rich
	3834S	1	1/4	—	.060	3/16	5/64	41 Drill	2 Rich
	3835S	1	1/4	—	.060	3/16	5/64	5/32	2 Rich
	3836S	1	1/4	—	.060	3/16	5/64	41 Drill	2 Rich
	3837S	1	1/4	—	.060	3/16	5/64	1/8	2 Rich
	3838S	1	1/4	—	.060	3/16	5/64	41 Drill	2 Rich
	3839S	1	1/4	—	.060	3/16	5/64	1/8	2 Rich
	3840S	1	1/4	—	.060	3/16	5/64	41 Drill	2 Rich
	3841S	1	1/4	—	.060	3/16	5/64	5/32	2 Rich
1966	4099S	1-2	1/4	—	.060	3/16	48 Drill	22 Drill	2 Rich
	4100S	1-2	1/4	—	.060	3/16	48 Drill	35 Drill	2 Rich
	4101S	1-2	1/4	—	.060	3/16	48 Drill	22 Drill	2 Rich
	4102S	1-2	1/4	—	.060	3/16	48 Drill	28 Drill	2 Rich
	4103S	1-2	1/4	—	.060	3/16	48 Drill	22 Drill	2 Rich
	4104S	1-2	1/4	—	.060	3/16	48 Drill	35 Drill	2 Rich
	4105S	1-2	1/4	—	.060	3/16	48 Drill	22 Drill	2 Rich
	4106S	1-2	1/4	—	.060	3/16	48 Drill	28 Drill	2 Rich
1967	4286S	1-2	1/4	—	.060	3/16	48 Drill	20 Drill	2 Rich
	4287S	1-2	1/4	—	.060	3/16	48 Drill	41 Drill	2 Rich
	4302S	1-2	1/4	—	.060	3/16	48 Drill	20 Drill	2 Rich
	4303S	1-2	1/4	—	.060	3/16	48 Drill	28 Drill	2 Rich
1968	4414S	2	1/4	—	.960	3/16	48 Drill	20 Drill	2 Rich
	4415S	2½	1/4	—	.060	3/16	48 Drill	35 Drill	2 Rich
1969	4601S	1-2	1/4	—	.060	3/16	48 Drill	35 Drill	2 Rich
	4602S	1-2	1/4	—	.060	3/16	48 Drill	35 Drill	2 Rich

MODEL BBS ADJUSTMENTS

Early models of this carburetor incorporated the familiar built-in automatic choke as shown in Fig. 1. Later models, Fig. 2, employ the so-called well type automatic choke. This type choke is thermostatically operated and is mounted in a well in the intake manifold.

Float Level Adjustment

Fig. 4—Hold needle valve against its seat as shown and measure from top of floats (at center) to top of main body. If proper gauge is not available, the float level should be as listed in the *BBS Specifications Chart*. If an adjustment is necessary, bend lip of float arm as required.

Bowl Vent Adjustment

Fig. 5

This adjustment automatically adjusts the accelerator pump as well. The procedure is as follows:

1. Back off idle speed adjusting screw. Open choke valve so that when throttle valve is closed the fast idle adjusting screw will not contact fast idle cam.
2. Be sure pump operating rod is in center hole in throttle lever and that bowl vent clip on pump stem is in center groove.
3. Close throttle valve tightly. It should be possible to insert a drill of

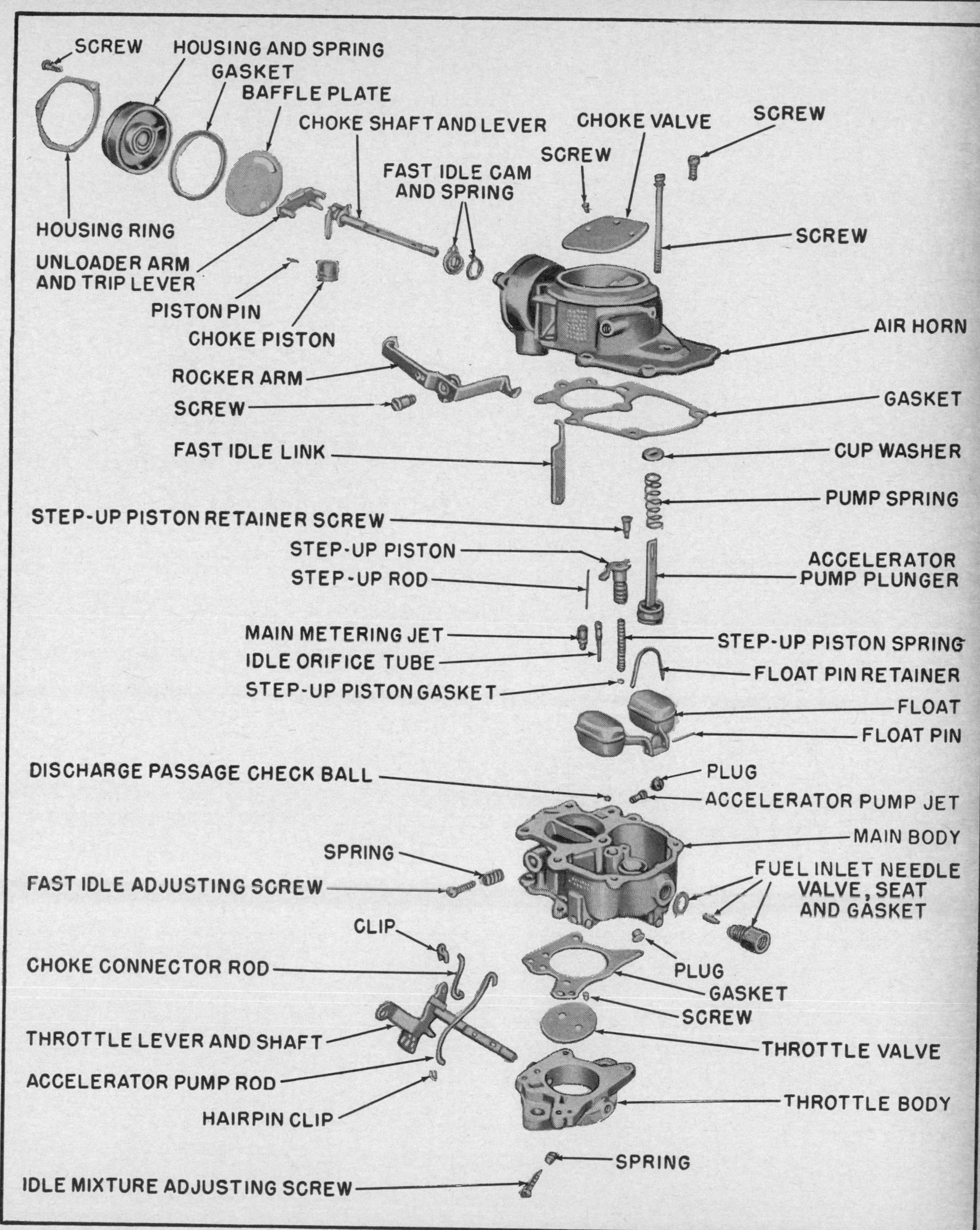

Fig. 1 Carter Model BBS single barrel carburetor with built-in automatic choke

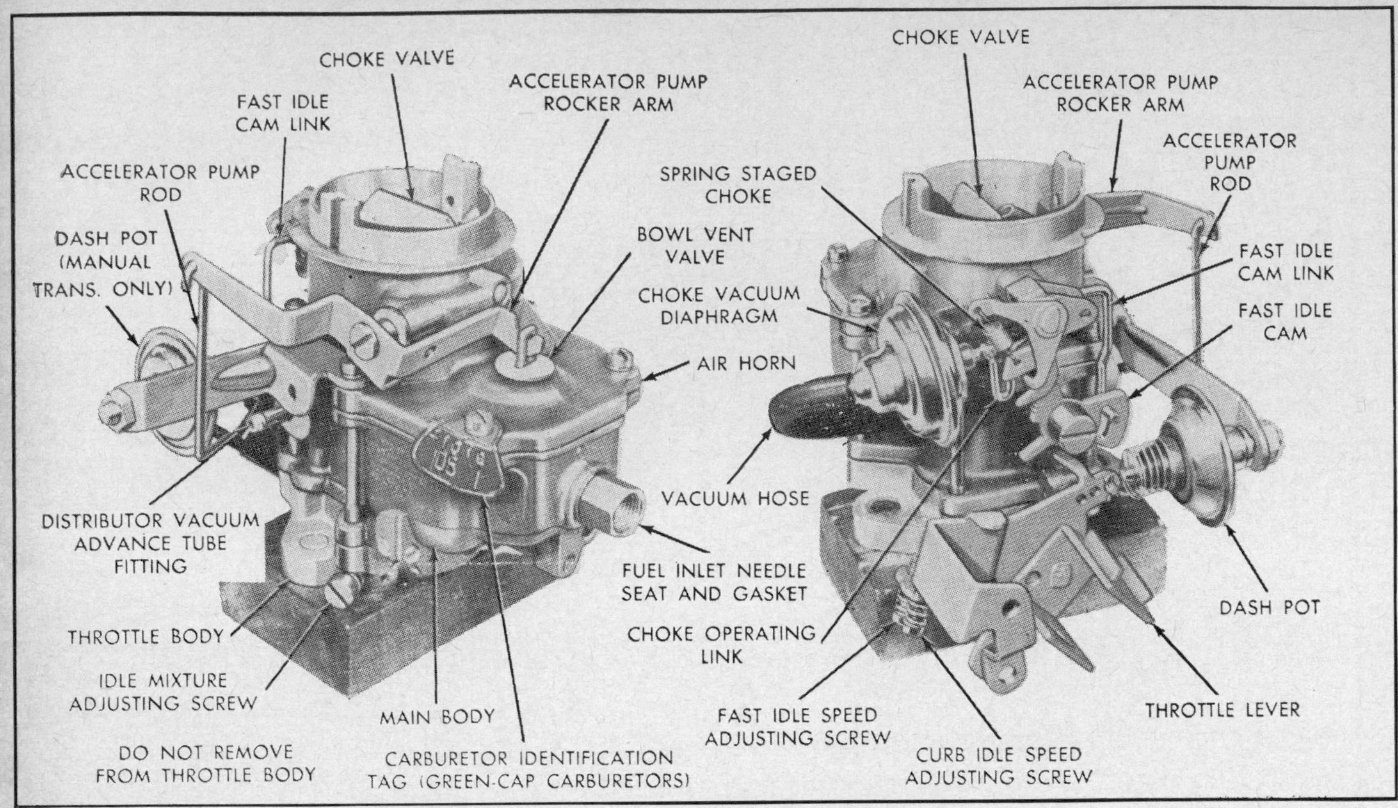

Fig. 2 Exterior of late model BBS carburetor used with C.A.P.

the specified size between bowl vent and air horn.

4. If an adjustment is necessary, bend pump operating rod at the lower angle as required to obtain the correct bowl vent opening.

NOTE: This is an important adjustment since too much lift at the bowl vent will result in considerable loss in low speed fuel economy. If the pump operating rod is moved to either the short or long stroke position, a corresponding change must be made in the location of the bowl vent clip, and the amount of lift of the bowl rechecked and adjusted.

Choke Unloader Adjustment

Fig. 6—Hold throttle valve in wide open position. Insert a drill of the specified size between upper edge of choke valve and inner wall of air horn. With a finger lightly pressing against choke valve, a slight drag should be felt as the drill is being withdrawn. If an adjustment is necessary, bend unloader tang on throttle lever as required.

Fast Idle Cam Position

1963, Fig. 7

1. Open throttle valve and hold choke valve fully closed; then close throttle valve. This will position fast idle cam to fast idle position.
2. Release choke valve slowly. This positions fast idle cam to fast idle. The index mark on cam should split the center of the fast idle adjusting screw as shown.
3. If an adjustment is necessary, bend fast idle connector rod at the angle as required.

1964-68, Fig. 8

1. With fast idle speed adjusting screw contacting the second highest step on the fast idle cam, move choke valve toward closed position with

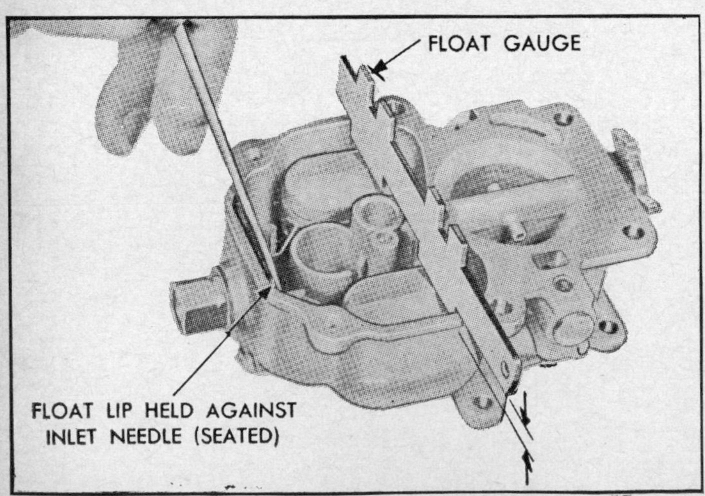

Fig. 4 Checking float level. BBS carburetors

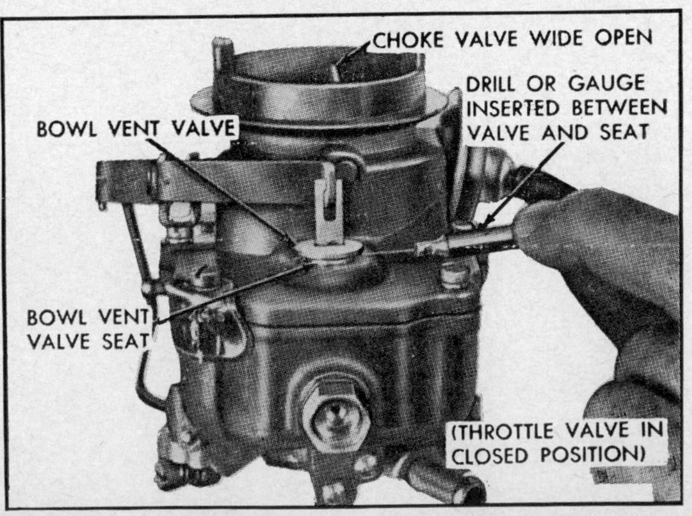

Fig. 5 Bowl vent adjustment. 1963-68 BBS carburetors

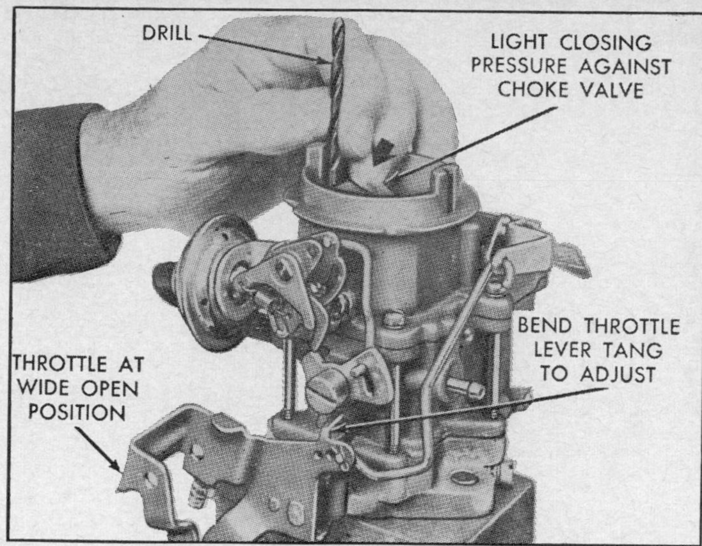

Fig. 6 Checking choke unloader setting (wide open kick). BBS carburetors

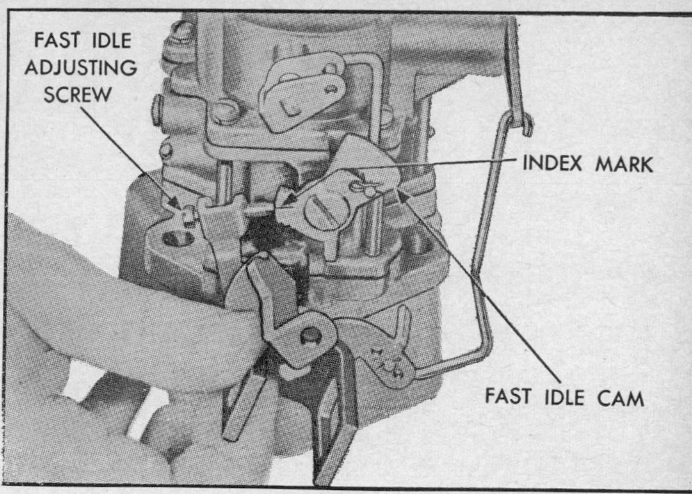

Fig. 7 Fast idle cam position. 1963 BBS carburetors

light pressure on choke shaft lever.

2. Insert specified drill between choke valve and wall of air horn. If an adjustment is necessary, bend fast idle rod at upper angle until correct valve opening has been obtained.

Vacuum Kick Adjustment

1964-68, Fig. 9

The choke diaphragm adjustment controls the fuel delivery while the engine is running. It positions the choke valve within the air horn by action of the linkage between the choke shaft and diaphragm. The diaphragm must be energized to measure the vacuum kick adjustment. Use a vacuum source, or vacuum supplied by another vehicle. Adjust as follows:

1. If adjustment is to be made with the engine running, back off the fast idle speed screw until choke can be closed to the kick position with engine at curb idle. *Note number of screw turns required so that fast idle can be returned to original adjustment.* If an auxiliary vacuum source is to be used, open throttle valve (engine not running) and move choke to closed position. Release throttle first, then release choke.
2. When using an auxiliary vacuum source, disconnect vacuum hose from carburetor and connect it to hose from vacuum supply with a small length of tube to act as a fitting. Removal of hose from diaphragm may require forces which change the system. Apply a vacuum of 10 inches or more of mercury.
3. Insert specified drill between choke valve and wall of air horn. Apply sufficient closing pressure on lever to which choke rod attaches to provide a minimum stroke valve opening without distortion of diaphragm link. Note that cylindrical stem of diaphragm will extend as internal spring is compressed. This spring must be fully compressed for proper measurement of vacuum kick adjustment.
4. An adjustment will be necessary if a slight drag is not obtained as drill is being removed. Shorten or lengthen diaphragm link to obtain correct choke opening. Length changes should be made carefully by bending (open or closing) the bend provided in the diaphragm link. *Do not apply twisting or bending force to diaphragm.*
5. Reinstall vacuum hose on correct carburetor fitting. Return fast idle screw to its original location if disturbed as suggested in Step 1.
6. Check the adjustment as follows: With no vacuum applied to diaphragm, *choke valve should move freely between open and closed positions.* If movement is not free, examine linkage for misalignment or interferences caused by bending operation. Repeat adjustment if necessary to provide proper link operation.

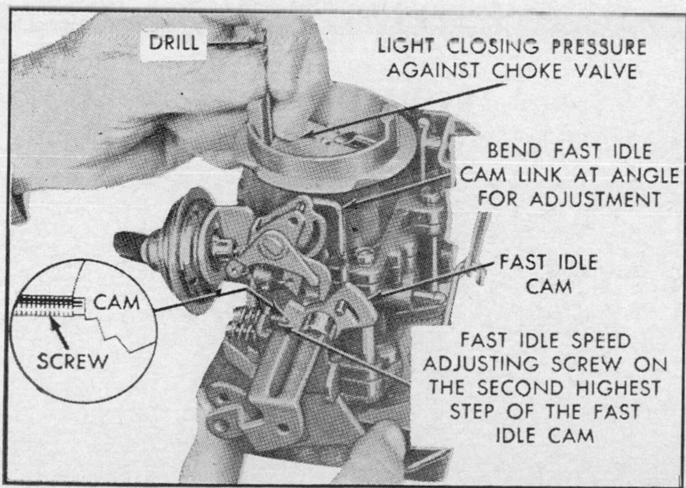

Fig. 8 Fast idle cam position. 1964-68 BBS carburetors

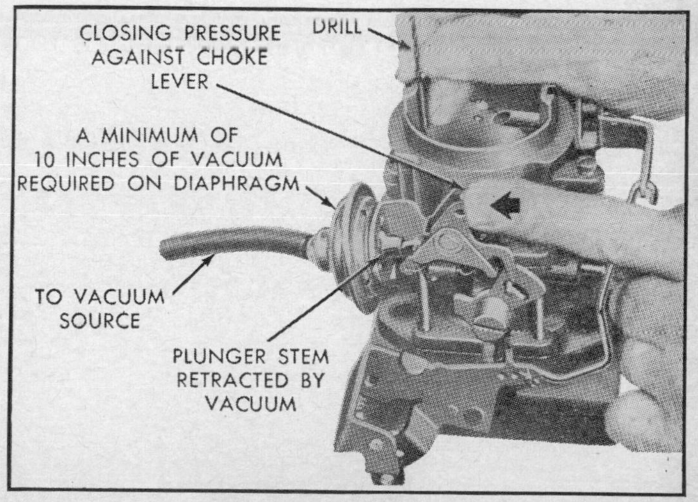

Fig. 9 Vacuum kick adjustment. 1964-68 BBS carburetors

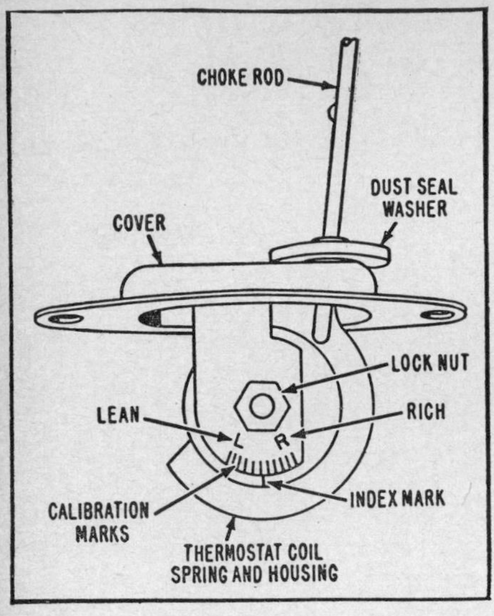

Fig. 11 BBS well-type choke setting

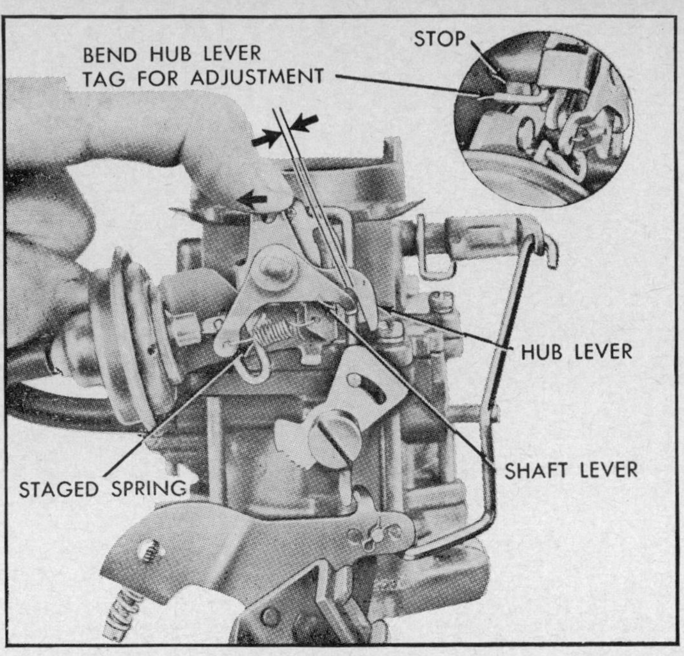

Fig. 10 Spring staged choke adjustment. BBS carburetors

Spring Staged Choke Adjustment

Fig. 10

The spring staged choke is a device incorporated in the choke mechanism that limits the choke blade closing torque when cranking the engine at temperatures below zero. Thus the spring staging of the choke is a better match for the engine's starting mixture requirements at low temperatures.

To check the spring staged choke for correct operating clearance, proceed as follows:

1. Push on hub lever with finger at closed choke position. A small opening should exist between shaft and hub levers as indicated.
2. Using a drill or gauge, measure the opening which should be from .010 to .040".
3. If adjustment is necessary, bend hub lever tang until correct opening is obtained.

Choke Adjustment

Fig. 11—Loosen mounting post lock nut and turn mounting post with screwdriver until index mark on disc is positioned as listed in the *BBS Specifications Chart.* Hold in this position with screwdriver and tighten lock nut.

NOTE: Screwdriver may be held in a vise so that one hand may be used to support housing while tightening nut. After adjustment is completed and coil housing and rod and carburetor are installed on engine, lift cover disc and open and close choke valve manually to see if connector rod clears sides of hole in housing cover without binding. If rod does not clear housing cover without binding, replace with a new unit since connecting rod cannot be bent without affecting calibration.

Dashpot Adjustment

C.A.P. Carburetors

The dashpot is used only on cars equipped with the Cleaner Air Package and manual transmission, Fig. 2.

To adjust the dashpot, have the curb idle speed and mixture properly adjusted, and install a tachometer. Position throttle lever so that actuating tab on lever is contacting stem of dashpot but not depressing it. The tachometer should read 2000 rpm if the setting is correct. If not correct, screw dashpot in or out as required, then tighten lock nut on dashpot against the bracket.

CARTER BBD ADJUSTMENT SPECIFICATIONS

See Tune Up Chart in car chapter for hot idle speed.

Year	Carb. Model	Initial Idle Mix. Screws Turns Open	Float Level	Pump Travel Inch	Bowl Vent Drill Size	Choke Unloader Drill Size	Choke Vacuum Kick Drill Size	Fast Idle Cam Position Drill Size	Automatic Choke Setting
CHRYSLER, DODGE & PLYMOUTH									
1963	3472S	1	1/4	—	1/16	1/4	—	See Text	On Index
	3473S	1	1/4	—	1/16	1/4	—	See Text	On Index
	3475S	3/4	1/4	1	.060	1/4	—	See Text	2 Rich
	3438S	3/4	1/4	1	.060	1/4	—	See Text	2 Rich
1964	3682S	1	1/4	—	1/16	1/4	3/16	1/4	On Index
	3683S	1	1/4	—	1/16	1/4	3/16	1/4	On Index
	3684S	3/4	5/16	1	1/16	1/4	11/64	15/64	2 Rich
	3685S	3/4	1/4	1	1/16	1/4	11/64	15/64	2 Rich
1965	3843S	1	1/4	—	1/16	1/4	16 Drill	7/64	On Index
	3844S	1	1/4	—	1/16	1/4	30 Drill	7/64	On Index
	3847S	1	1/4	—	1/16	1/4	16 Drill	7/64	On Index
	3848S	1	1/4	1	1/16	1/4	25 Drill	7/64	On Index
	3849S	3/4	5/16	1	1/16	1/4	11 Drill	35 Drill	2 Rich
	3850S	3/4	5/16	1	1/16	1/4	22 Drill	35 Drill	2 Rich
1966	4113S	1	1/4	—	.060	1/4	16 Drill	41 Drill	2 Rich
	4114S	1	1/4	—	.060	1/4	30 Drill	41 Drill	2 Rich
	4115S	2	1/4	—	—	1/4	16 Drill	41 Drill	On Index
	4116S	2	1/4	—	—	1/4	30 Drill	41 Drill	On Index
	4125S	1	5/16	1	1/16	1/4	15 Drill	30 Drill	2 Rich
	4126S	1	5/16	1	1/16	1/4	15 Drill	30 Drill	2 Rich
	4127S	1	5/16	1	1/16	1/4	26 Drill	30 Drill	2 Rich
	4128S	1	5/16	1	.050	1/4	26 Drill	30 Drill	2 Rich
1967	4113SA	1	1/4	—	.060	1/4	15 Drill	41 Drill	2 Rich
	4114SA	1	1/4	—	.060	1/4	1/8	41 Drill	2 Rich
	4115SA	2	1/4	—	—	1/4	15 Drill	41 Drill	On Index
	4116SA	2	1/4	—	—	1/4	1/8	41 Drill	On Index
	4296S	1½	5/16	29/32	1/16	1/4	20 Drill	42 Drill	2 Rich
	4297S	1½	5/16	29/32	1/16	1/4	42 Drill	42 Drill	2 Rich
	4306S	1½	5/16	1	.050	1/4	20 Drill	42 Drill	2 Rich
	4307S	1½	5/16	1	.050	1/4	30 Drill	42 Drill	2 Rich
	4463S	2	1/4	—	1/16	1/4	28 Drill	41 Drill	2 Rich
1968	4416S	3	1/4	—	1/16	1/4	4 Drill	50 Drill	2 Rich
	4417S	3	1/4	—	1/16	1/4	41 Drill	50 Drill	2 Rich
	4420S	2½	1/4	—	1/16	1/4	4 Drill	41 Drill	2 Rich
	4421S	2½	1/4	—	1/16	1/4	28 Drill	41 Drill	2 Rich
	4422S	1½	5/16	29/32	.050	1/4	1 Drill	30 Drill	2 Rich
	4423S	1½	5/16	29/32	.050	1/4	16 Drill	30 Drill	2 Rich
	4578S	1½	11/32	1	3/64	1/4	11/64	30 Drill	2 Rich
1969	4605S	2	1/4	—	1/16	1/4	20 Drill	41 Drill	On Index
	4606S	2	1/4	—	1/16	1/4	41 Drill	41 Drill	On Index
	4607S	1	1/4	—	1/16	1/4	20 Drill	41 Drill	On Index
	4608S	1	1/4	—	1/16	1/4	28 Drill	41 Drill	On Index
	4613S	1½	5/16	1	1/16	1/4	20 Drill	30 Drill	2 Rich
	4614S	1½	5/16	1	1/16	1/4	20 Drill	30 Drill	2 Rich

MODEL BBD ADJUSTMENTS

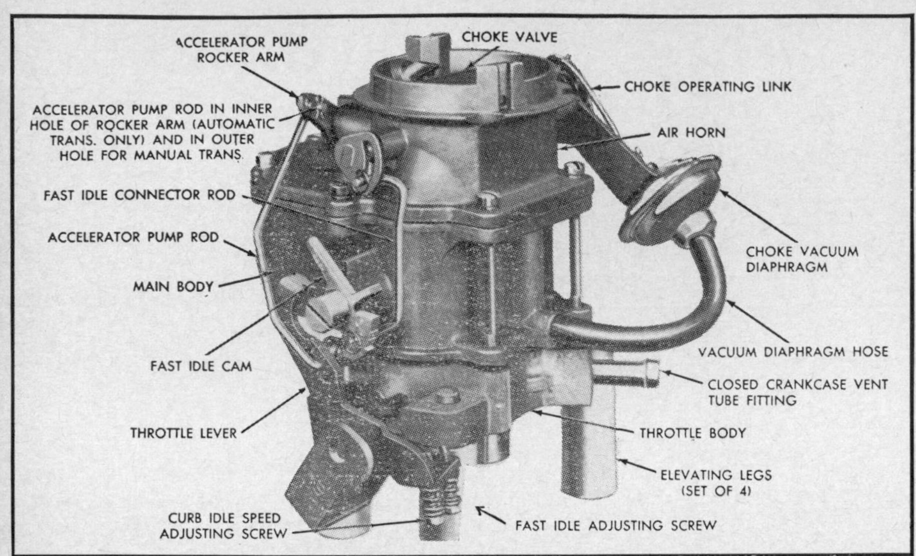

Fig. 3 Late model BBD carburetor used on the smaller V8 engines

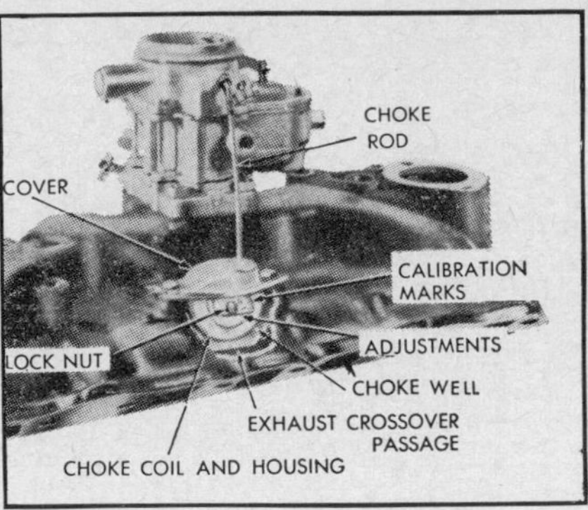

Fig. 2 Well-type automatic choke mounted on intake manifold

Fig. 1 is an exploded view of a BBD two-barrel carburetor with the familiar built-in automatic choke as used on earlier models. Later models employ a Well-type automatic choke mounted on the intake manifold. The choke housing containing the thermostatic coil spring is located in a well at the exhaust crossover passage, Fig. 2.

The carburetor shown in Fig. 3 is a standard model when the vehicle is equipped with either a manual shift or automatic transmission. When used with C.A.P. (Cleaner Air Package) equipment, a dashpot (slow closing throttle device) is provided for vehicles with manual transmission only.

The carburetors illustrated in Fig. 4 are used on the larger V8 engines; the one on the right is a standard model while the one at the left is used with C.A.P. equipment. Note that the C.A.P. model incorporates a dashpot for use with manual shift transmissions only.

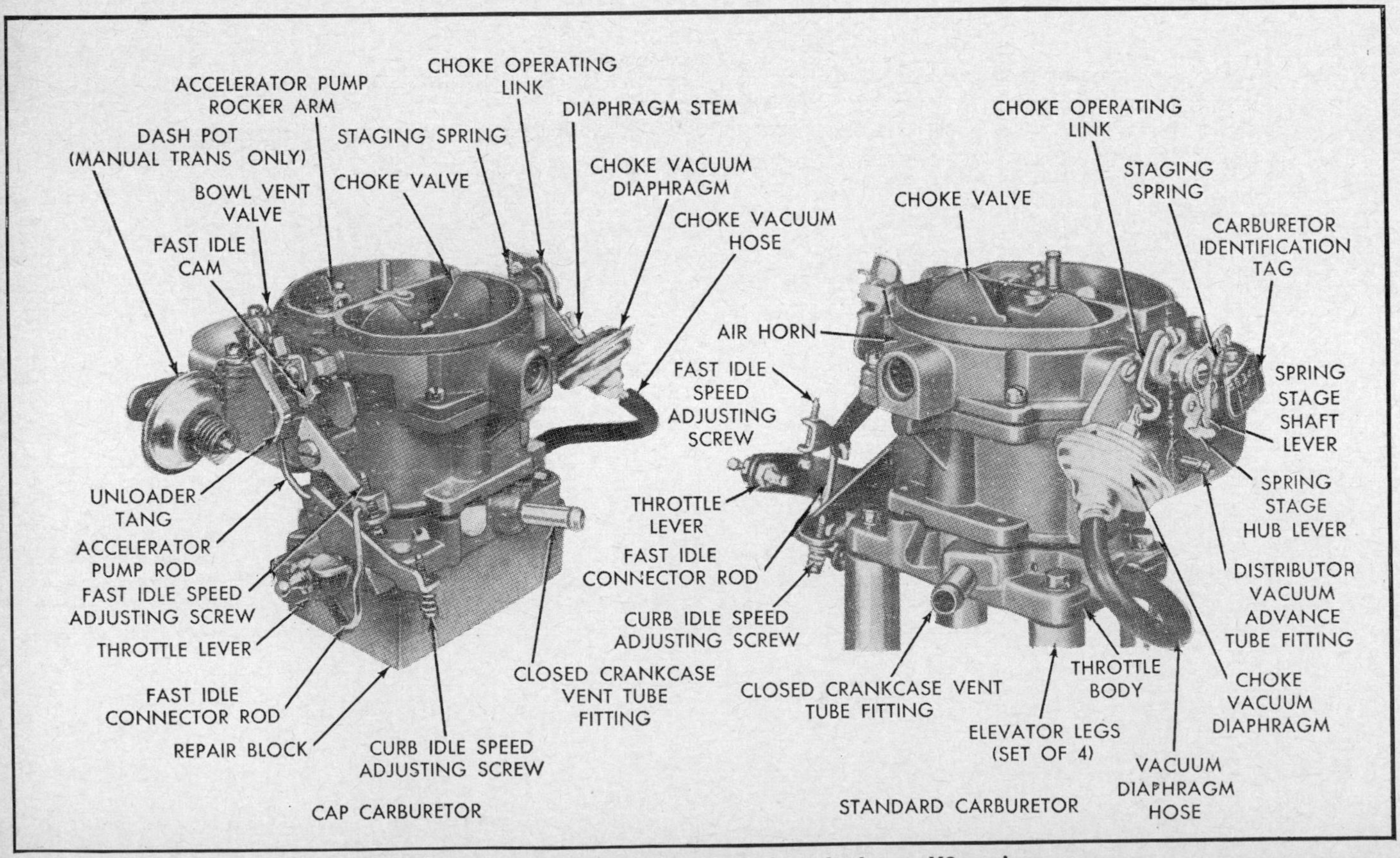

Fig. 4 Late model BBD carburetors used on the larger V8 engines

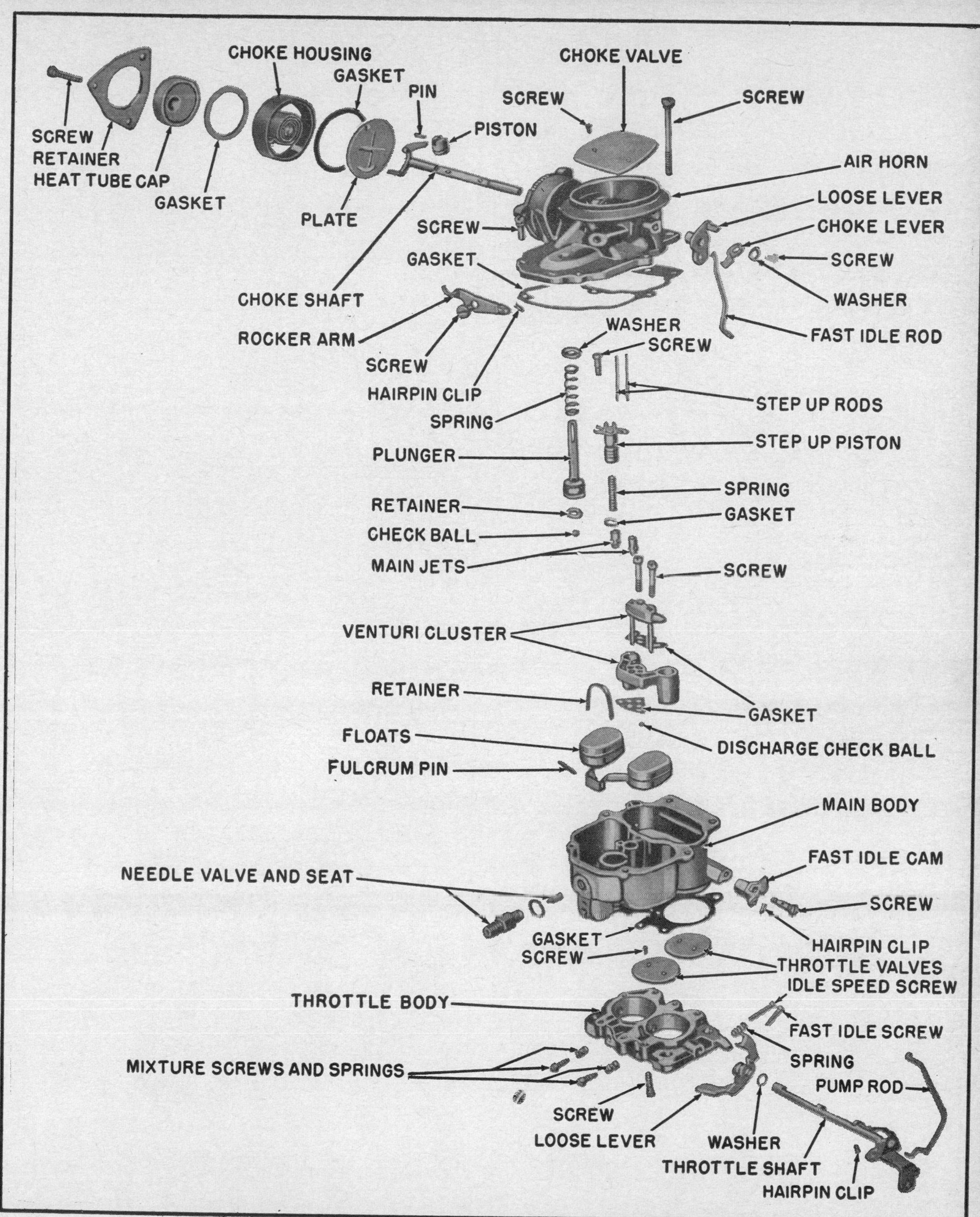

Fig. 1 Carter Model BBD two-barrel carburetor with built-in automatic choke

Fig. 5 Checking float level. BBD carburetors

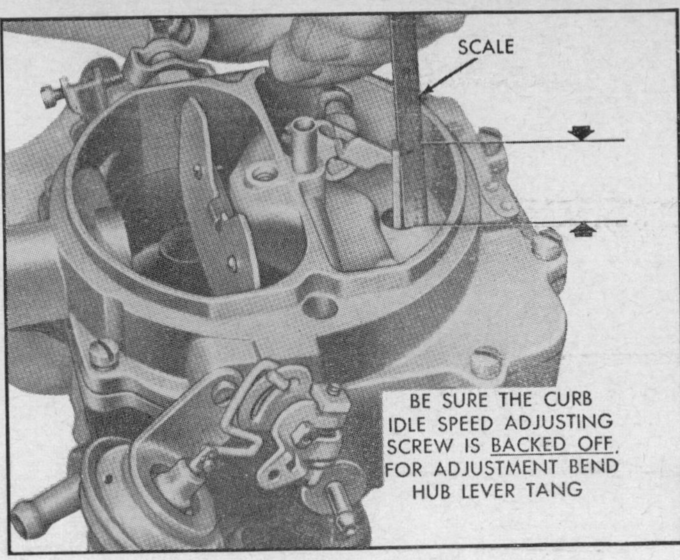

Fig. 6 Checking accelerator pump travel. BBD 1 9/16" bore carburetors

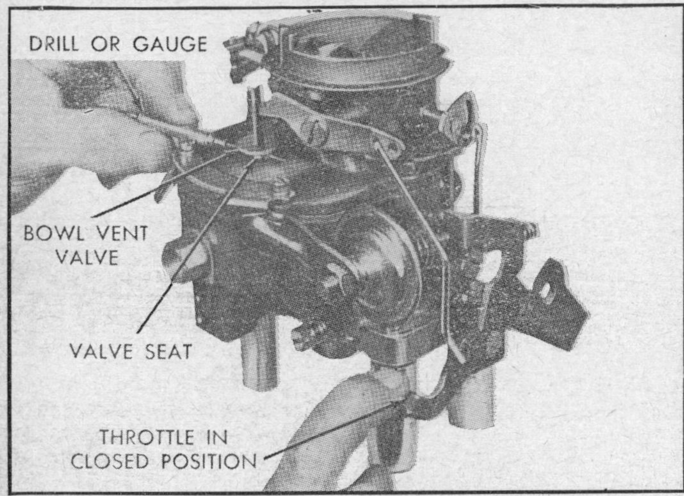

Fig. 7 Checking bowl vent opening. BBD 1 1/4" bore carburetors

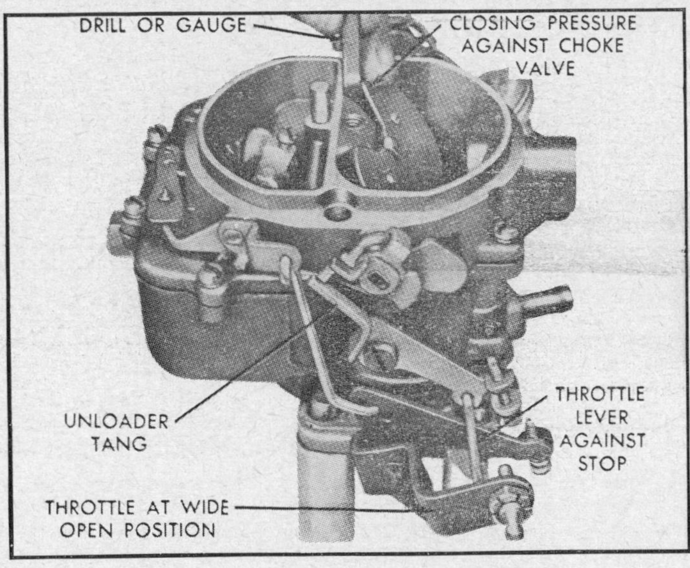

Fig. 8 Choke unloader setting. BBD carburetors

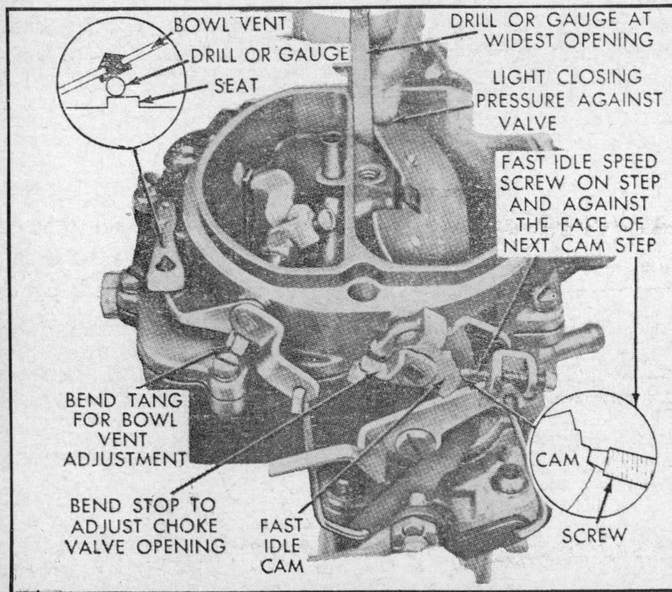

Fig. 10 Fast idle cam position adjustment. BBD 1 9/16" bore carburetors, 1964-68

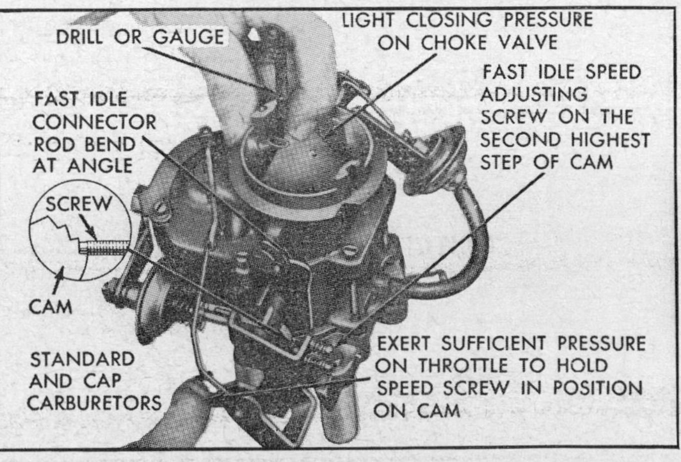

Fig. 9 Fast idle cam position adjustment. BBD 1 1/4" bore carburetors, 1964-68

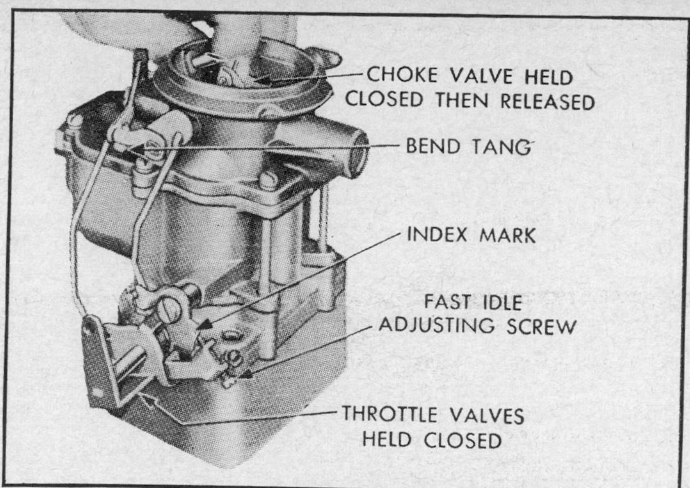

Fig. 11 Fast idle index mark alignment. BBD 1 1/4" bore carburetors, 1963

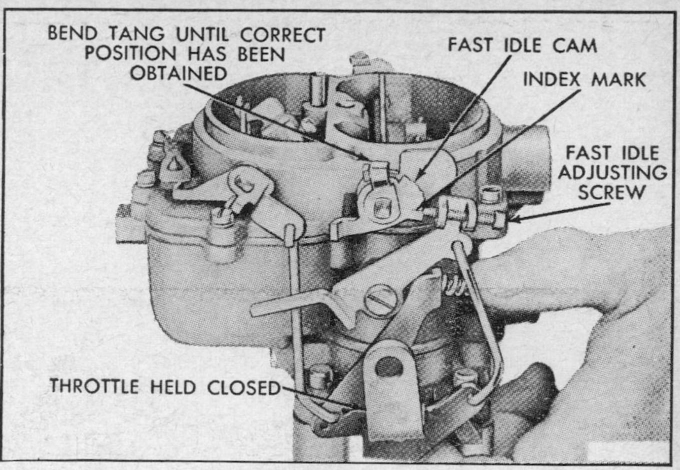

Fig. 12 Fast idle index mark alignment. BBD 1 9/16" bore carburetors, 1963

Float Level Adjustment

Fig. 5—With carburetor body inverted so that weight of floats ONLY is forcing needle against its seat, use a T-scale or the tool shown, and check the float level from surface of fuel bowl to crown of each float at center.

If an adjustment is necessary, hold floats on bottom of bowl and bend float lip as required to give the specified dimension.

CAUTION: When bending the float lip, do not allow the lip to push against the needle as the synthetic rubber tip (if used) can be compressed sufficiently to cause a false setting which will affect correct level of fuel in bowl. After being compressed, the tip is very slow to recover its original shape.

Accelerator Pump

1 9/16" Bore Units, Fig. 6

1. Back off idle adjusting screw. Open choke valve so that fast idle cam allows throttle valves to fully close. Be sure that pump connector rod is installed in center hole of throttle lever.
2. With throttle valves closed tightly, measure distance between top of air horn and end of pump plunger shaft. If the dimension is not as specified, bend pump connector rod at the angle on the rod until correct setting is obtained.

Accelerator Pump and Bowl Vent

1 1/4" Bore Units, Fig. 7

1. Back off idle speed adjusting screw. Open choke valve so that fast idle cam allows throttle valves to close completely.
2. Be sure pump operating rod is in medium stroke hole in throttle lever, and that bowl vent clip on pump stem is on center notch.
3. With throttle valves closed tightly, it should be just possible to insert the specified gauge or drill size between bowl vent and its seat.
4. If an adjustment is necessary, bend pump operating rod at the angle. On CAP carburetors, bend pump operating rod to give the height of pump plunger stem above bowl cover as specified in the table.

NOTE: This is an important adjustment, since too much lift at the bowl vent will result in considerable loss in low speed fuel economy.

Remember that if the pump operating rod is moved to either the short or long stroke position, a corresponding change must be made in the location of the bowl vent clip, and the amount of lift of the bowl vent rechecked.

Bowl Vent Adjustment

Models with Separate Pump Adjustment
With throttle valves closed tightly, it should be possible to insert a gauge or drill of the size listed between the bowl vent valve and air horn. If an adjustment is necessary, bend the short tang on the vent valve operating lever until the specified clearance has been obtained.

Choke Unloader Adjustment

Fig. 8—The choke unloader is a mechanical device to partially open the choke valve at wide open throttle. It is used to eliminate choke enrichment during engine cranking. Engines that have been flooded or stalled by excessive choke enrichment can be cleared by the use of the unloader. Adjust as follows:

1. Hold throttle valve in wide open position. Insert the specified drill size between upper edge of choke valve and inner wall of air horn.
2. With a finger lightly pressing against choke valve, a slight drag should be felt as the drill is being withdrawn.
3. If an adjustment is necessary, bend unloader tang on throttle lever until specified opening has been obtained.

Fast Idle Cam Position

1964-68, Figs. 9 and 10

1. With fast idle adjusting screw contacting second highest step on fast idle cam, move choke valve toward closed position with light pressure on choke shaft lever.
2. Insert the specified size drill between choke valve and air horn wall. An adjustment will be necessary if a slight drag is not obtained as drill is being removed.
3. If an adjustment is required, bend the fast idle connector rod at the angle on 1 1/4" bore units, or, on 1 9/16" carburetors, bend stop on choke shaft.

1963, Figs. 11 and 12

1. Open throttle valves and hold choke valve in fully closed position; then close throttle valves. This will position fast idle cam to the fast idle position.
2. Release choke valve only. The index mark on cam should split the center of the fast idle screw shank.
3. If an adjustment is necessary, bend tang on choke shaft lever until index mark on cam aligns with adjusting screw.

Choke Vacuum Kick Adjustment

1964-68, Figs. 13 and 14

The choke diaphragm adjustment controls the fuel delivery while the engine is running. It positions the choke valve within the air horn by action of the linkage between choke shaft and diaphragm. The diaphragm must be energized to measure the vacuum kick adjustment. Use either a distributor test machine with a vacuum source, or vacuum supplied by another vehicle.

1. If adjustment is to be made with engine running, disconnect fast idle linkage to allow choke to close to kick position with engine at curb idle. If an auxiliary vacuum source is to be used, open throttle valves (engine not running) and move choke to closed position. Release throttle first, then release choke.
2. When using an auxiliary vacuum source, disconnect vacuum hose from carburetor and connect it to hose from vacuum supply with a small length of tube to act as a fitting.

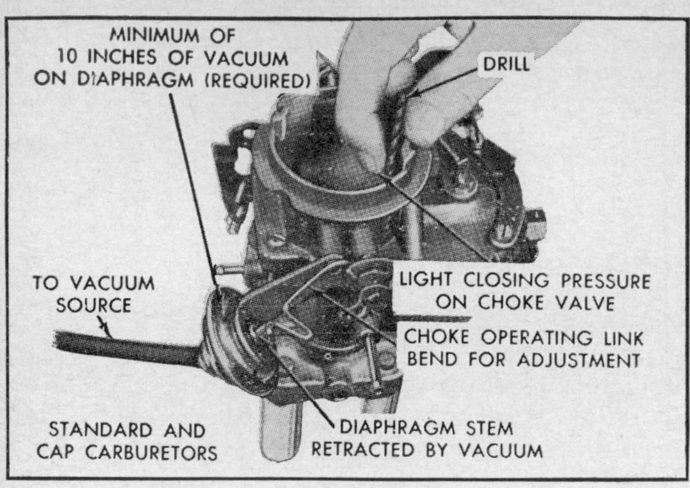

Fig. 13 Choke vacuum kick setting. BBD 1 1/4" bore carburetors, 1964-68

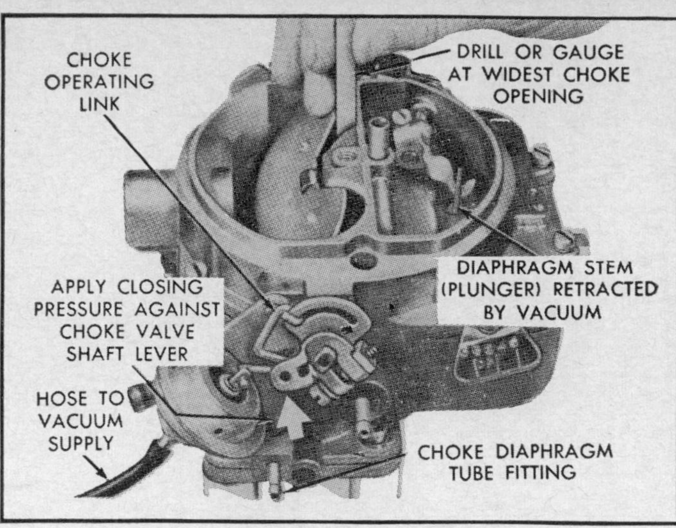

Fig. 14 Choke vacuum kick setting. BBD 1 9/16" bore carburetors, 1964-68

Removal of hose from diaphragm may require forces which damage the system. Apply a vacuum of 10 or more inches of mercury.

3. Insert the specified drill size between choke valve and wall of air horn. Apply sufficient closing pressure on lever to which choke rod attaches to provide a minimum choke valve opening without distortion of diaphragm link. Note that the cylindrical stem of diaphragm will extend as internal spring is compressed. This spring must be fully compressed for proper measurement of vacuum kick adjustment.
4. An adjustment will be necessary if a slight drag is not obtained as drill is being removed. Shorten or lengthen diaphragm link to obtain correct choke opening. Length changes should be made carefully by bending (opening or closing) the bend provided in the diaphragm link. *Do not apply twisting or bending force to diaphragm.*
5. Reinstall vacuum hose on correct carburetor fitting. Return fast idle linkage to its original condition if it has been disturbed as in Step 1.
6. Check as follows: With no vacuum applied to diaphragm, choke valve should move freely between open and closed positions. If movement is not free, examine linkage for misalignment or interferences caused by bending operation. Repeat adjustment if necessary.

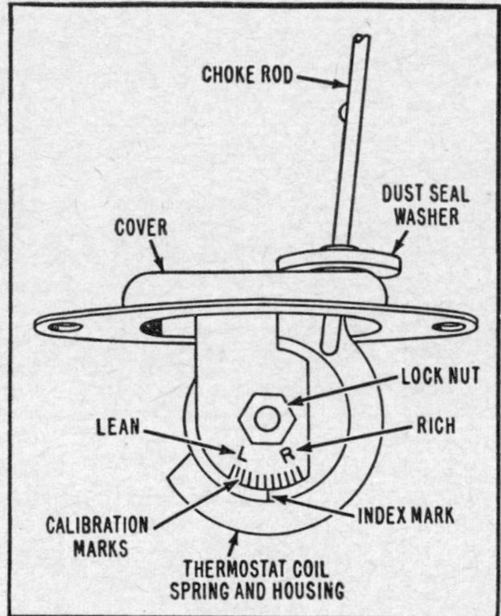

Fig. 15 BBD Well-type choke setting

Well-Type Choke Setting

Fig. 15—Loosen mounting post lock nut and turn mounting post with screwdriver until index mark on disc is positioned as listed in the *BBD Specifications Chart*. Hold in this position with screwdriver and lock nut.

NOTE: Screwdriver may be held in vise so that one hand may be used to support housing while tightening nut. After adjustment is completed and coil housing, rod and carburetor are installed on engine, lift cover disc and open and close choke valve manually to see if connector rod clears sides of hole in housing cover without binding. If rod does not clear housing cover without binding, replace with a new unit since connecting rod cannot be bent without affecting calibration.

Dashpot Adjustment

C.A.P. Carburetors

The dashpot is used only on vehicles with the Cleaner Air Package and manual shift transmission, Fig. 4.

To adjust the dashpot, have the curb idle speed and mixture properly adjusted, and install a tachometer. Position throttle lever so that actuating tab on lever is contacting stem of dashpot but not depressing it. Tachometer should read 2000 rpm if the setting is correct. If not correct, screw dashpot in or out as required, then tighten lock nut on dashpot against the bracket.

CARTER WCD ADJUSTMENT SPECIFICATIONS

See Tune Up Chart in car chapter for hot Idle speed.

Year	Carb. Model	Idle Screw (Mixture) Turns Open	Float Level	Pump Setting	Metering Rod	Fast Idle Setting	Choke Unloader	Dashpot Setting	Automatic Choke
JEEP									
1963–65	2204S	1–2½	3/16	11/32	See Text	.016	1/8	—	On Index
RAMBLER									
1963	3434S	¼–1¾	②	See Text	See Text	.020	3/16	3/32–1/8	On Index
	3535S	¼–1¾	②	See Text	See Text	.020	3/16	—	On Index
1964–65	3706S	¼–1¾	1/8	See Text	See Text	.020	3/16	—	On Index
1964	3707S	¼–1¾	1/8	See Text	See Text	.020	3/16	3/32–1/8	On Index
1965–67	3888S	¼–1¾	①	See Text	See Text	.020	3/16	—	On Index
1966	4191S	¼–1¾	17/64	See Text	See Text	.015	3/16	—	2 Rich
1967	4365S	¼–1¾	7/32	See Text	See Text	—	3/16	—	2 Rich
1968	4410S	1	7/32	See Text	See Text	—	3/16	1/16–3/32	On Index
	4537S	1	7/32	See Text	See Text	—	3/16	1/16–3/32	On Index
1969	4667S	1½	/32	See Text	See Text	—	3/16	7/64	On Index
	4668S	1½	/32	See Text	See Text	—	3/16	7/64	On Index

①—With green inspection tag ¼″, others ⅛″. ②—With solid needle seat 5/32″, with resilient seat ⅛″.

MODEL WCD ADJUSTMENTS

The WCD carburetor, Fig. 1, is a two-barrel unit containing the five basic circuits. The carburetor uses a single needle valve even though two floats are provided. On some WCD units the two floats operate independently of each other so that the highest float always controls the fuel level. This is necessary when the carburetor is mounted with the centerline of the floats parallel to the centerline of the engine.

Float Adjustment

Lateral Adjustment—Referring to Fig. 2 and with bowl cover inverted and gasket removed, place float gauge directly under floats with notched portions of gauge fitted over edges of casting. Sides of float should barely touch vertical uprights of float gauge. Adjustment is made by bending arms of floats.

Vertical Adjustment—With float gauge in same position as shown, floats should just clear horizontal portion of gauge. The vertical distance between top center of float and machined surface of casting must be the dimension given in the *WCD Specifications Chart*. Adjust by bending float arms as required. Remove floats, install bowl cover gasket and reinstall floats.

Pump Adjustment

Fig. 3—Install pump connector link in outer hole (long stroke) of pump arm

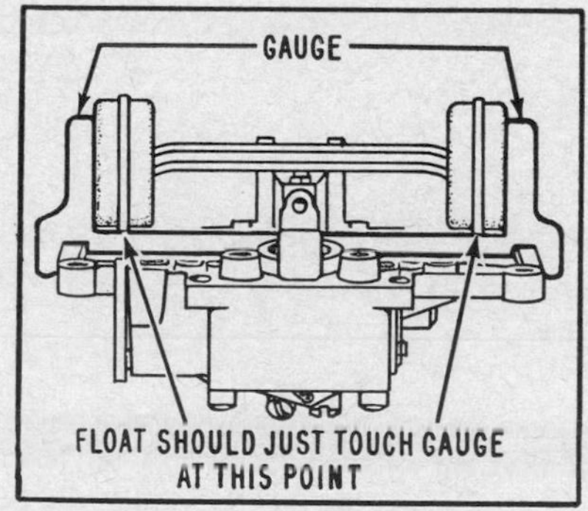

Fig. 2 WCD float level adjustment

with ends extending away from countershaft arm. Back out throttle lever set screw until throttle valves seat in carburetor bores. Be sure fast idle adjusting screw does not hold throttle open.

Hold straightedge across top of dust cover boss at pump arm. The flat on top of pump arm should be parallel to straightedge. Adjust by bending throttle connector rod to the upper angle.

Metering Rod Adjustment

This adjustment must be made after completing the pump adjustment. No metering rod gauges are necessary. Adjust as follows:

1. Back out throttle lever set screw to allow throttle valves to seat in bores of carburetor and loosen metering rod arm clamp screw.
2. With metering rod in place, press down on vacumeter link until metering rods bottom in carburetor body casting.
3. While holding rods in downward position and throttle valves seated, revolve metering rod arm until finger on arm contacts lip of vacuumeter link. Hold in place and carefully tighten clamp screw.

Fast Idle Adjustment

Fig. 4—Loosen choke lever clamp screw on choke shaft. Insert a .010″ feeler gauge between lip of fast idle cam and boss of flange casting. Hold choke valve tightly closed and take slack out of linkage by pressing choke lever towards closed position.

With choke valve tightly closed, tighten fast idle adjusting screw until there is the clearance listed in the *WCD Specifications Chart* between throttle valve and carburetor bore (side opposite idle port). Be sure fast idle adjusting screw is on high step of cam or index mark while making this adjustment.

Choke Unloader Adjustment

Fig. 5—With throttle valves wide open, there should be the clearance listed in the *WCD Specifications Chart* between

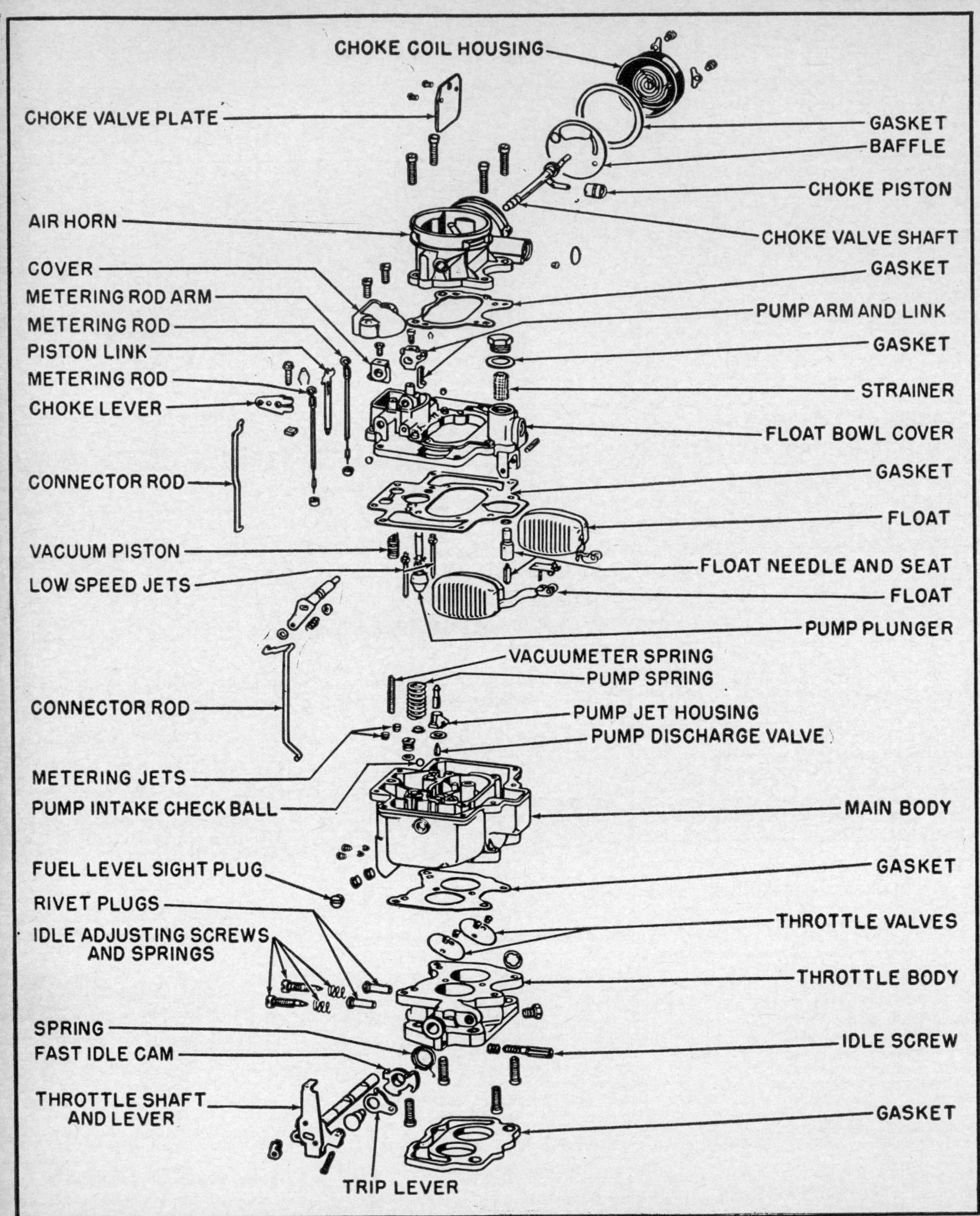
CHOKE COIL HOUSING
CHOKE VALVE PLATE
GASKET
BAFFLE
CHOKE PISTON
AIR HORN
CHOKE VALVE SHAFT
COVER
GASKET
METERING ROD ARM
PUMP ARM AND LINK
METERING ROD
GASKET
PISTON LINK
METERING ROD
STRAINER
CHOKE LEVER
FLOAT BOWL COVER
GASKET
CONNECTOR ROD
FLOAT
VACUUM PISTON
FLOAT NEEDLE AND SEAT
LOW SPEED JETS
FLOAT
PUMP PLUNGER
VACUUMETER SPRING
PUMP SPRING
CONNECTOR ROD
PUMP JET HOUSING
PUMP DISCHARGE VALVE
METERING JETS
PUMP INTAKE CHECK BALL
MAIN BODY
FUEL LEVEL SIGHT PLUG
GASKET
RIVET PLUGS
THROTTLE VALVES
IDLE ADJUSTING SCREWS AND SPRINGS
THROTTLE BODY
SPRING
IDLE SCREW
FAST IDLE CAM
THROTTLE SHAFT AND LEVER
GASKET
TRIP LEVER

Fig. 1 Carter Model WCD two-barrel carburetor

Fig. 3 WCD pump adjustment

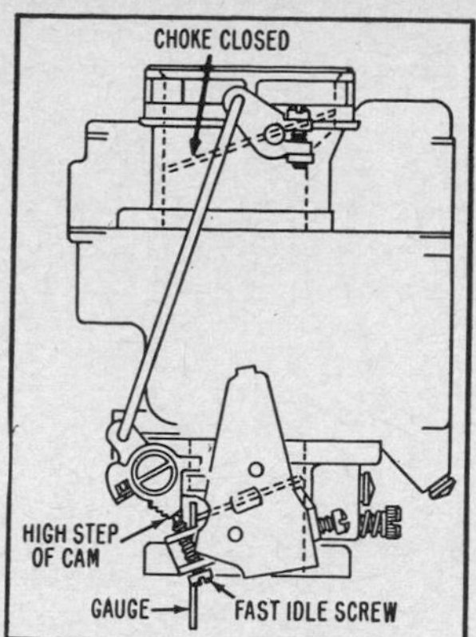

Fig. 4 WCD fast idle adjustment

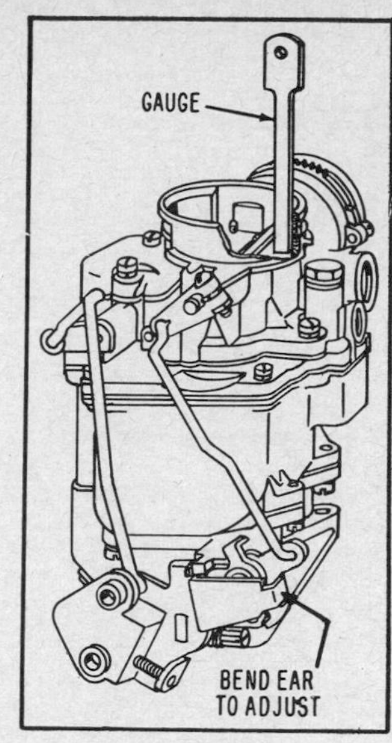

Fig. 5 WCD unloader adjustment

upper edge of choke valve and inner wall of air horn. Adjust by bending unloader lip (ear) on throttle shaft lever.

Dashpot Adjustment

Rambler—With throttle valves tightly closed and diaphragm stem fully depressed, adjust dashpot to give the clearance listed in the *WCD Specifications Chart* between dashpot stem and throttle lever.

Automatic Choke Adjustment

Loosen choke cover retaining screws and turn cover so that line or index mark on cover lines up with the specified mark on choke housing (see *WCD Specifications Chart).*

CARTER AVS ADJUSTMENT SPECIFICATIONS

See Tune Up Chart in car chapter for hot idle speed.

Year	Carb. Model	Idle Screw (Mixture) Turns Open	Float Level	Float Drop	Pump Travel	Bowl Vent	Fast Idle Throttle Valve Clearance	Choke Unloader	Choke Vacuum Break	Secondary Throttle Lockout
CHEVROLET, CHEVELLE, CHEVY II										
1966	4027S–SA	1–2½	15/64	23/32	33/64	.065	.015	11/64	.120	.020
	4028S–SA	1–2½	15/64	23/32	33/64	.065	.015	11/64	.160	.020
CHRYSLER, DODGE, PLYMOUTH, IMPERIAL										
1968	4401S	1–2	5/16	23/32	7/16	1/8	.016	1/4	3/32	.020
	4424S	1–2	7/32	23/32	7/16	1/8	.015	1/4	3/16	.020
	4425S	1–2	7/32	23/32	7/16	1/8	.012	1/4	5/64	.020
	4426S	1–2	5/16	23/32	7/16	1/8	.012	1/4	7/16	.020
	4428S	1–2	7/32	23/32	7/16	1/8	.014	1/4	3/16	.020
	4429S	1–2	7/32	23/32	7/16	1/8	.014	1/4	5/32	—
1969	4611S	1–2	7/32	1/2	7/16	1/8	50 Drill①	1/4	35 Drill	.020
	4612S	1–2	7/32	1/2	7/16	1/8	50 Drill①	1/4	50 Drill	.020
	4615S	1–2	5/16	1/2	7/16	1/8	50 Drill①	1/4	35 Drill	.020
	4616S	1–2	5/16	1/2	7/16	1/8	50 Drill①	1/4	50 Drill	.020
	4617S	1–2	7/32	1/2	7/16	1/8	50 Drill①	1/4	25 Drill	.020
	4618S	1–2	7/32	1/2	7/16	1/8	50 Drill①	1/4	35 Drill	.020
	4638S	1–2	5/16	1/2	7/16	1/8	50 Drill①	1/4	50 Drill	.020
	4639S	1–2	7/32	1/2	7/16	1/8	50 Drill①	1/4	50 Drill	.020
	4640S	1–2	7/32	1/2	7/16	1/8	50 Drill①	1/4	35 Drill	.020
	4682S	—	5/16	1/2	7/16	1/8	50 Drill①	1/4	50 Drill	.020
	4711S	1–2	5/16	1/2	7/16	1/8	50 Drill①	1/4	35 Drill	.020

①—With fast idle adjusting screw contacting second highest speed step on fast idle cam the clearance between choke valve and wall of air horn should be as specified.

MODEL AVS ADJUSTMENTS

The AVS carburetor, Figs. 1, 2, 3, is used in conjunction with a temperature sensing choke coil mounted on the intake manifold over the exhaust crossover passage. The AVS is similar to the more familiar AFB which employs a built-in automatic choke.

AVS means "Air Valve Secondary". The spring loaded air valve, located above the secondary fuel nozzles, gives smooth response whenever the secondary throttle valves are actuated.

The primary side of the carburetor uses venturi clusters for fine fuel control in the idle and economy ranges. The use of fuel nozzles pressed into the secondary side of the fuel bowl virtually eliminates secondary bore restriction, thus giving this carburetor high air capacity in the power ranges.

A hot idle compensator, consisting of a bi-metal strip, a valve and a mounting bracket, is located between the secondary bores to supply additional air to the idle mixture during prolonged hot idle periods.

Float Alignment

Fig. 4—Sides of floats should be parallel to edge of casting with minimum clearance between lever and air horn lugs without binding. To adjust, bend float lever.

Float Level Adjustment

Fig. 5—There should be the dimension listed in the *AVS Specifications Chart* between top of floats (at outer end) and air horn gasket. To adjust, bend float lever.

Float Drop Adjustment

Fig. 6—There should be the dimension listed in the *AVS Specifications Chart* between top of floats (at outer end) and air horn gasket. To adjust, bend stop tabs on float brackets.

Pump Adjustment

Fig. 7—With throttle valves tightly closed there should be the dimension listed in the *AVS Specifications Chart* from top of bowl cover to top of pump plunger shaft with throttle connector rod in inner hole of pump arm. To adjust, bend throttle connector rod.

Fast Idle Linkage Adjustment

Fig. 8—With choke valve closed, index mark on cam should align with adjusting screw. To adjust, bend fast idle connector rod.

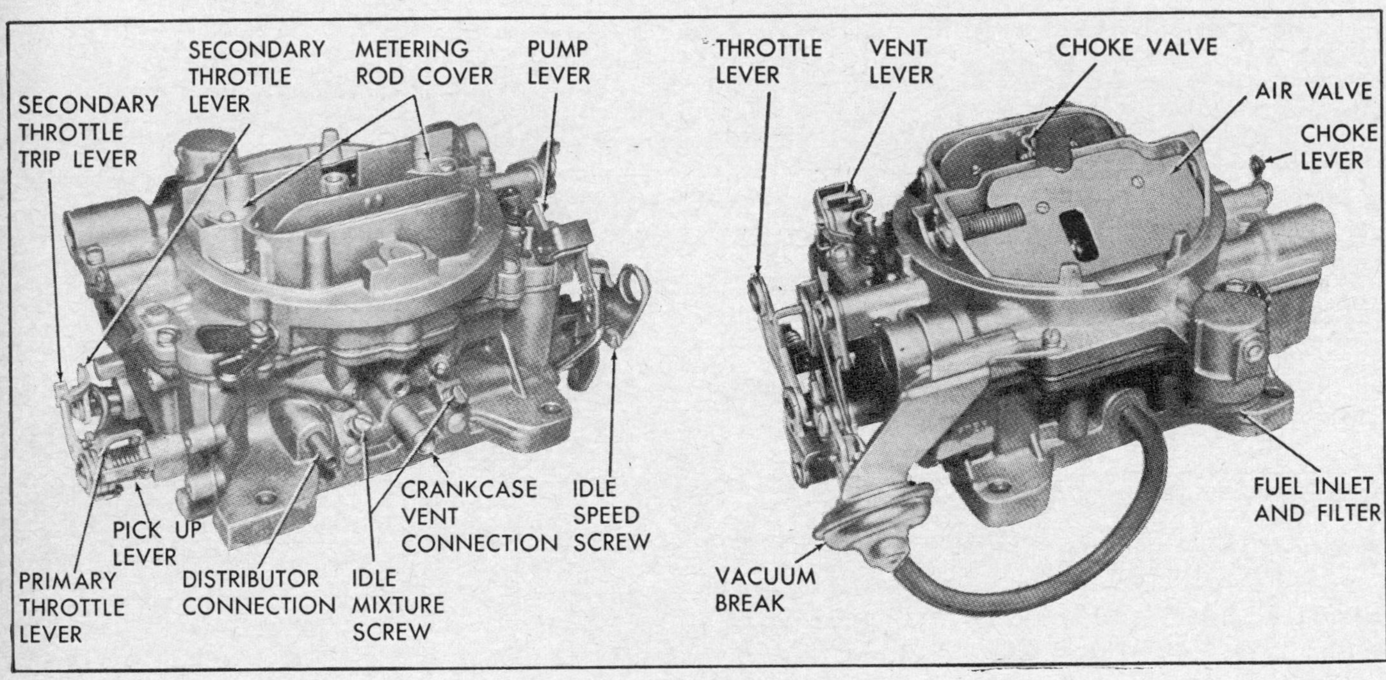

Fig. 1 Carter Model AVS four-barrel carburetor

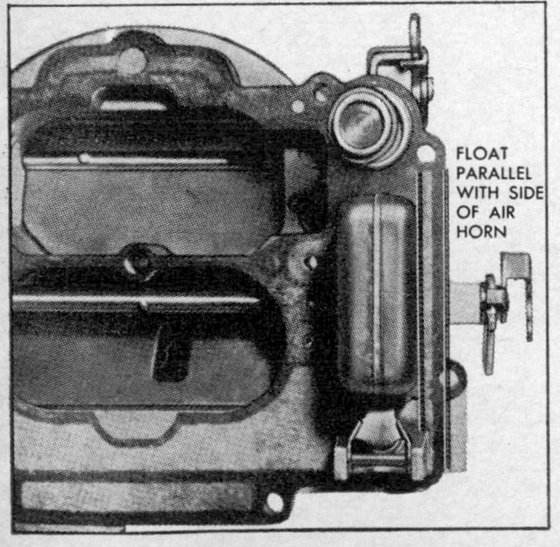

Fig. 4 AVS float alignment

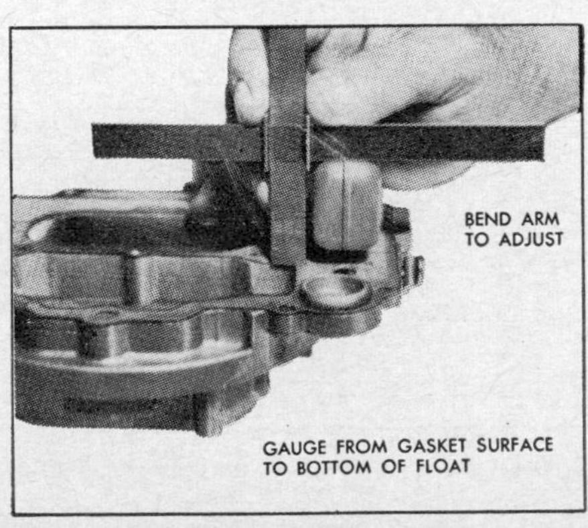

Fig. 5 AVS float level

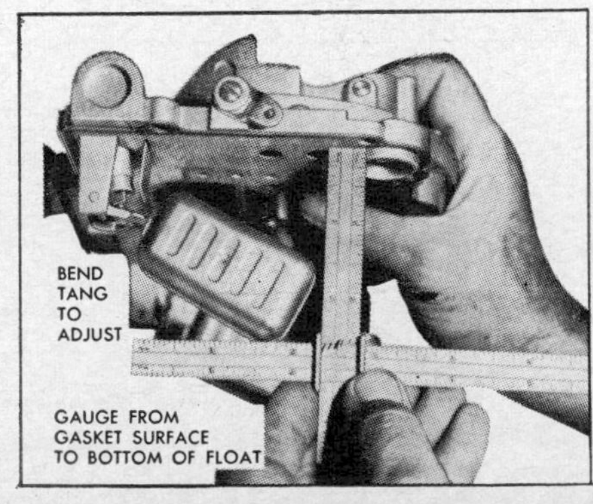

Fig. 6 AVS float drop

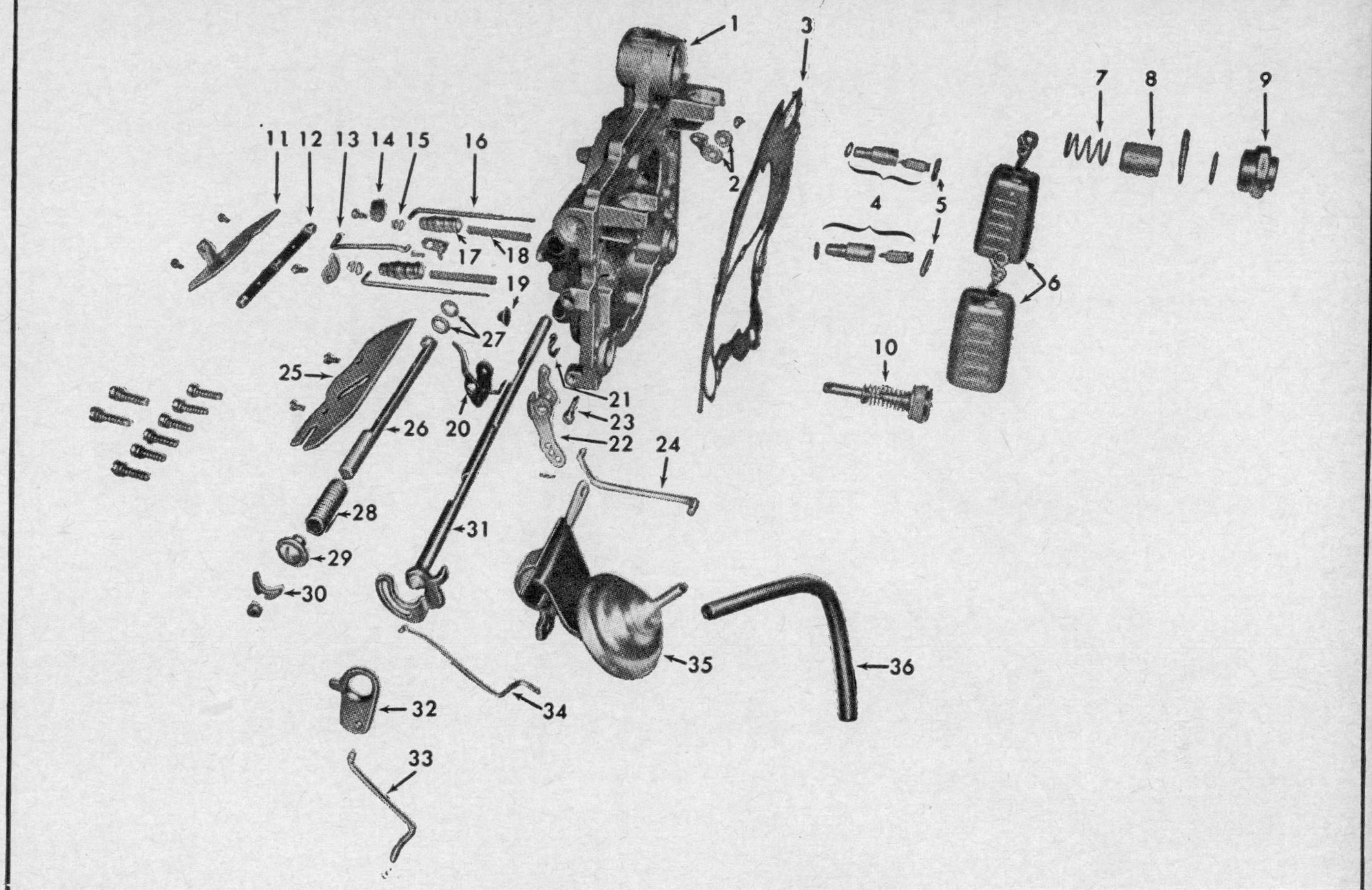

1. Air Horn
2. Choke Lever and Retainer
3. Air Horn Gasket
4. Needle and Seat Assembly
5. Float Hinge Pin
6. Float
7. Fuel Filter Spring
8. Fuel Filter
9. Fuel Inlet Fitting
10. Accelerator Pump Assembly
11. Choke Valve
12. Choke Shaft
13. Choke Actuating Link and Lever
14. Power Piston Cover
15. Metering Rod Spring
16. Metering Rod
17. Power Piston
18. Power Piston Spring
19. Idle Vent Valve
20. Vent Valve Lever
21. Pump "S" Link
22. Pump Lever
23. Pump Pivot Screw
24. Pump Rod
25. Air Valve
26. Air Valve Shaft
27. Shaft Bushing and Washer
28. Air Valve Spring
29. Air Valve Bearing
30. Bearing Retainer
31. Intermediate Choke Shaft and Lever
32. Choke Kick Lever
33. Choke Rod
34. Vacuum Break Link
35. Vacuum Break Assembly
36. Vacuum Break Hose

Fig. 2 AVS air horn parts exploded

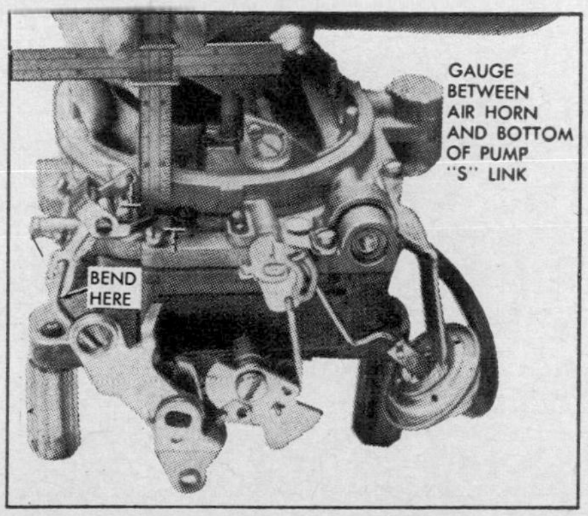

Fig. 7 AVS pump adjustment

Fast Idle Throtte Valve Clearance

There should be the clearance listed in the *AVS Specifications Chart* between lower edge of throttle valve and carburetor bore with adjusting screw on index mark of cam.

Choke Unloader Adjustment

Fig. 9—With throttle valves wide open there should be the clearance listed in the *AVS Specifications Chart* between upper edge of choke valve and inner wall of air horn. To adjust, bend unloader lip on throttle lever.

Bowl Vent Adjustment

Fig. 10—With throttle valves seated there should be the clearance listed in the *AVS Specifications Chart* between heel of rubber grommet and its seat on bowl

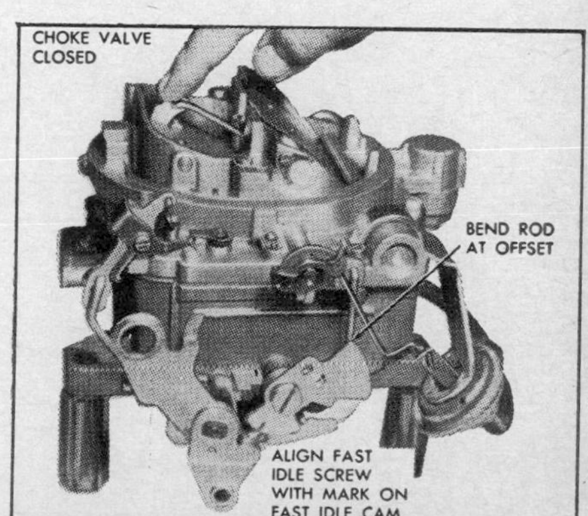

Fig. 8 AVS fast idle linkage adjustment

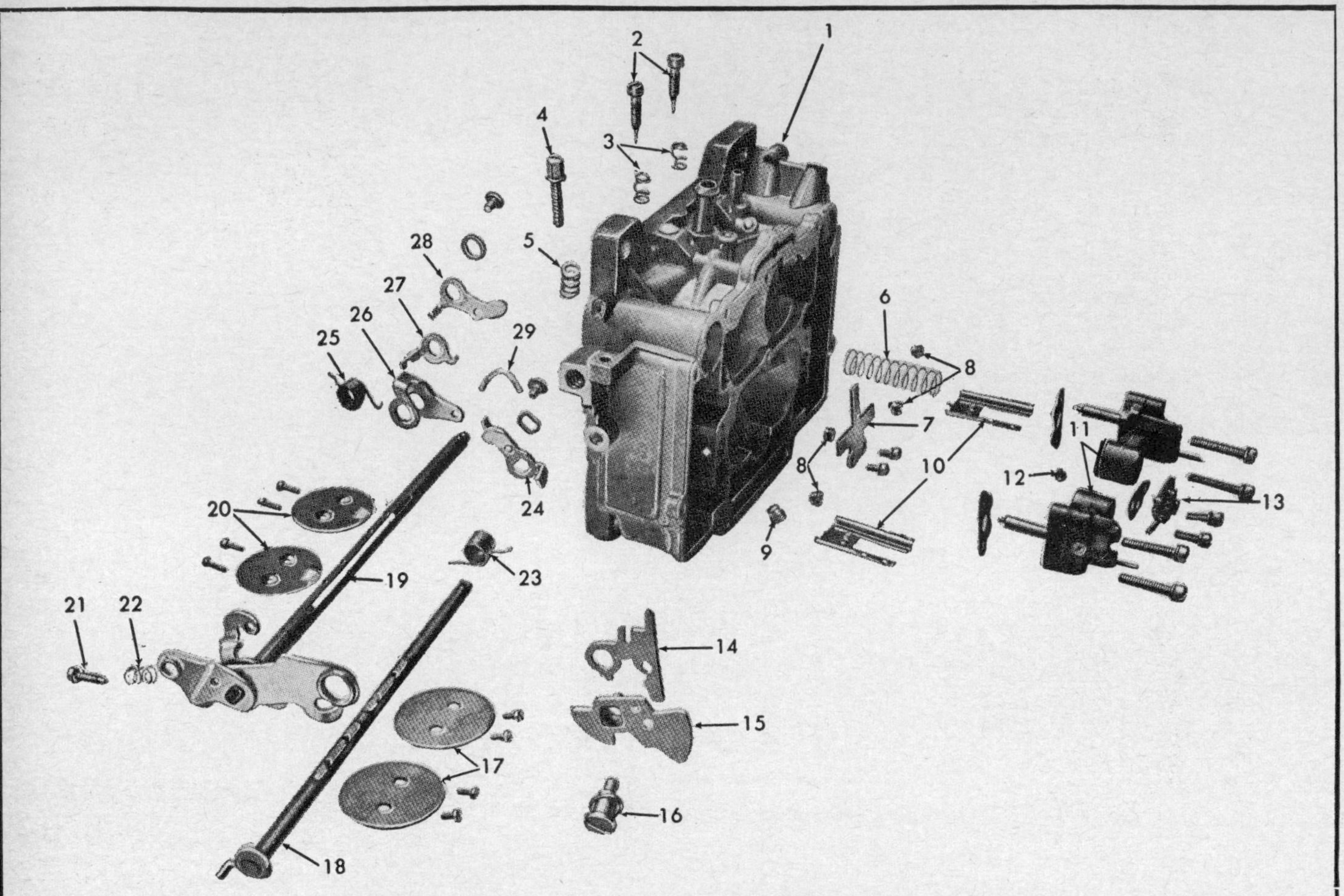

1. Main Body
2. Idle Mixture Needle
3. Idle Mixture Spring
4. Idle Speed Screw
5. Idle Speed Spring
6. Pump Return Spring
7. Hot Idle Compensator
8. Main Metering Jet
9. Pump Inlet Assembly
10. Splash Shield
11. Venturi Cluster
12. Pump Discharge Check Ball
13. Pump Nozzle
14. Lockout Dog
15. Fast Idle Cam
16. Pivot Screw
17. Secondary Throttle Valve
18. Secondary Throttle Shaft
19. Primary Throttle Shaft
20. Primary Throttle Valve
21. Fast Idle Screw
22. Fast Idle Spring
23. Secondary Throttle Shaft Spring
24. Secondary Throttle Shaft Dog Lever and Retainer
25. Primary Throttle Shaft Spring
26. Secondary Throttle Trip Lever
27. Spring Pick Up Lever
28. Primary Throttle Shaft, Arm and Retainer
29. Secondary Actuating Link

Fig. 3 AVS main body parts exploded

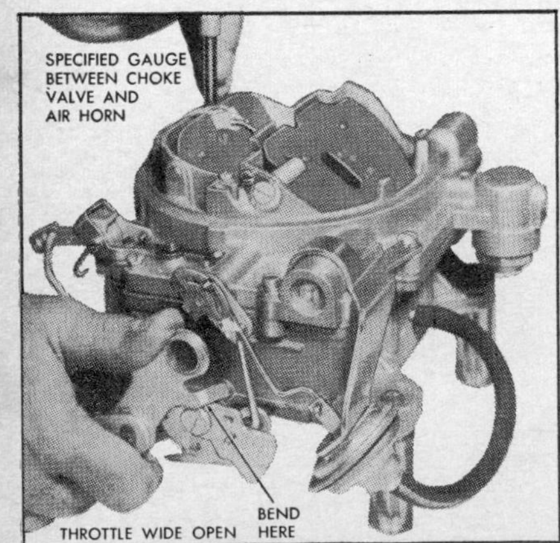

Fig. 9 AVS choke unloader adjustment

cover. To adjust, bend lip on vent arm. *If pump has been changed from standard setting, readjust vent arm.*

Choke Vacuum Break

Fig. 11—Holding vacuum break in against its stop and choke valve toward the closed position with a rubber band, bend vacuum break link at the offset to obtain specified clearance between upper edge of choke valve and air horn wall.

Secondary Air Valve Adjustment

Fig. 12—

1. Release air valve retainer screw that locks air valve shaft nylon bushing. This releases air valve spring and air valve should now be wide open.
2. Check at this point that air valve and shaft are free to operate and not binding in any position.
3. To adjust, use a screwdriver in slot of air valve shaft bushing. Turn shaft bushing slowly in a counter-clockwise direction until air valve spring contacts air valve. Then turn

Fig. 10 AVS bowl vent adjustment

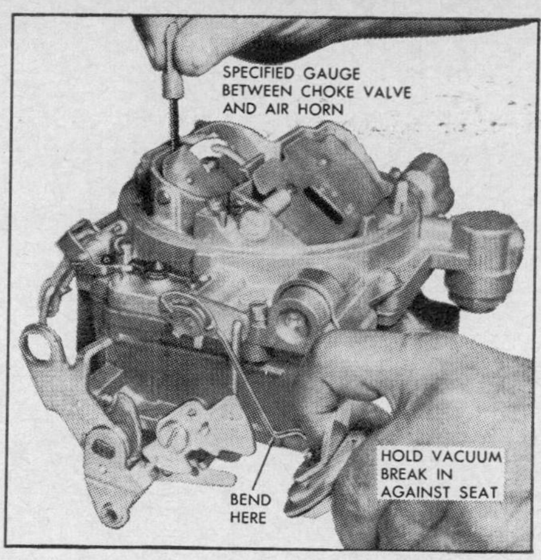

Fig. 11 AVS choke diaphragm linkage adjustment

Fig. 12 AVS secondary air valve adjustment

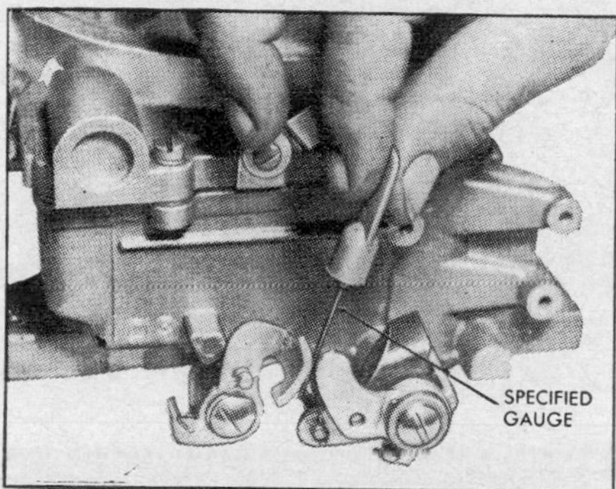

Fig. 13 AVS closing shoe adjustment

shaft bushing 2¼ turns more. This should bring the valve to its proper setting (plus or minus ¼ turn). At this point, hold shaft bushing in place and tighten air valve retainer screw.

Closing Shoe Adjustment

Fig. 13—With primary and secondary throttle valves closed, bend secondary closing shoe to obtain .020" clearance between positive closing shoes on primary and secondary throttle levers. To adjust, bend shoe on secondary lever.

Secondary Throttle Opening

Fig. 14—The pickup lever, located on the primary throttle shaft, has two points of contact with the loose lever on the primary shaft. Care should be taken that the pickup lever contacts the loose lever at both points at the same time. If they do not make this contact, bend pickup lever to obtain proper engagement.

The primary and secondary throttle valves must come to the wide open position at the same time. If the secondary throttle valve opening is not synchronized with that of the primary, bend the connecting link.

Secondary Throttle Lockout

Fig. 15—Crack throttle valves and manually open and close choke valve. Tang on secondary throttle lever should freely engage in notch of lockout dog. To adjust, bend tang on secondary throttle lever.

Automatic Choke Coil

The AVS carburetor must be removed to replace the remote choke actuating coil. After removing carburetor, pry shield off coil after which remove the coil and actuating rod.

When replacing, the locating tab on the choke coil should engage the locating hole in the intake manifold, Fig. 16. Install the choke rod in the coil. Leave the shield off. Carefully lower carburetor into place, but do not bolt it down.

Hold choke valve closed and push rod against stop on thermostat bracket. The bottom of rod should be even with bottom of hole in choke lever. If necessary, bend choke rod at the offset angle to change its length. The rod should enter the hole freely and squarely to prevent binding. Then remove carburetor, being careful not to change the adjustment.

Lower choke shield over the rod and install over coil. Move it along the manifold for best fit. Install carburetor. Check for freedom of action from full open to full-closed. Warm up engine and observe operation.

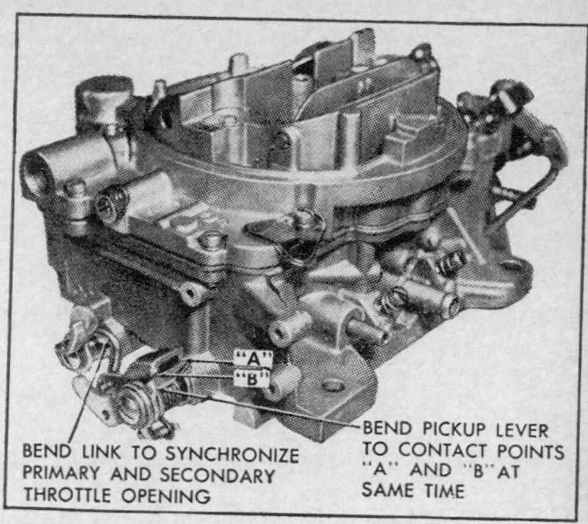

Fig. 14 AVS secondary throttle opening adjustment

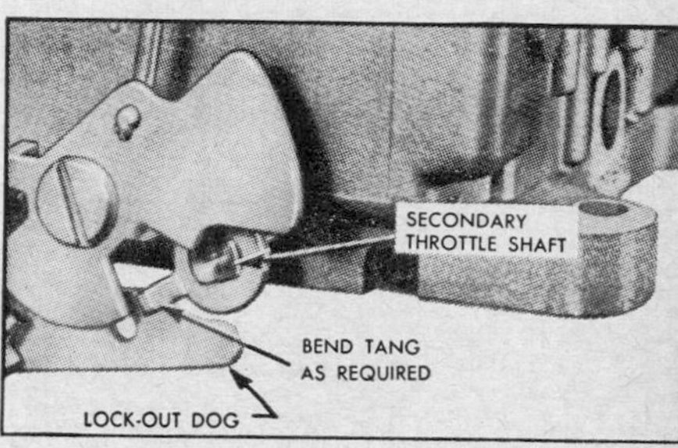

Fig. 15 AVS throttle lockout adjustment

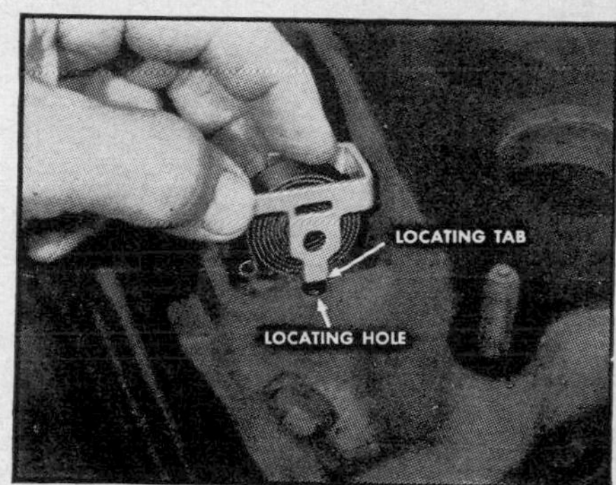

Fig. 16 AVS choke coil location on intake manifold

CARTER WCFB ADJUSTMENT SPECIFICATIONS

See Tune Up Chart in car chapters for hot idle speed.

Year	Carb. Model	Idle Screw (Mixture) Turns Open	Float Level	Float Drop	Pump Travel	Bowl Vent	Inter. Choke Rod	Fast Idle	Choke Unloader	Secondary Throttle Lever	Choke Setting
CHEVROLET, CORVETTE											
1963	3500S	½–2¼	④⑤	2	See Text	3/32	.053	.020	¼	.020	On Index
	3501S	½–2¼	④⑤	2	See Text	3/32	.053	.020	¼	.020	On Index
1964–65	3696S	½–2	⑥⑦	2	See Text	3/32	.053	.020	7/32	.020	On Index
	3697S	½–2	⑥⑦	2	See Text	3/32	.053	.020	7/32	.020	On Index

④—With solid needle seat: primary 5/32″, secondary 9/32″.
⑤—With resilient needle seat: primary 1/8″, secondary 1/4″.
⑥—With solid needle seat: primary 7/32″, secondary 9/32″.
⑦—With resilient needle seat: primary 3/16″, secondary 1/4″.

MODEL WCFB ADJUSTMENTS

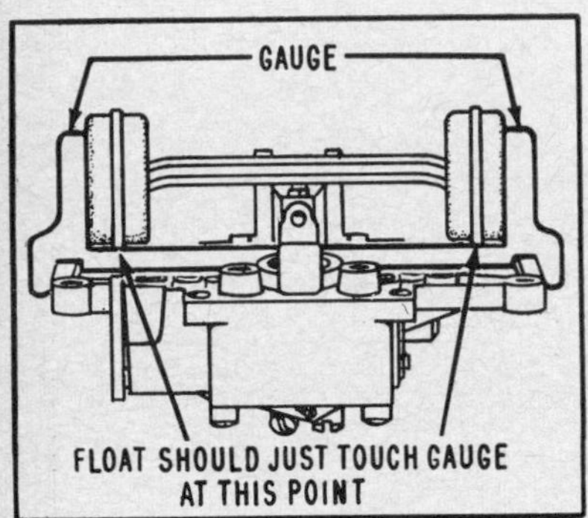

Fig. 2 WCFB float level

The WCFB carburetor, Fig. 1, is basically two WCD two-barrel carburetors contained in one assembly. The section containing the metering rods, accelerating pump and choke is termed the primary side of the carburetor while the other section is called the secondary side.

Float Adjustments

Lateral Adjustment, Fig. 2
With bowl cover assembly inverted, gasket removed and float resting on seated needle, place float gauge directly under center of floats with notched portion of gauge fitted over edge of casting. Side of floats should just clear vertical uprights of float gauge. Adjustment should be made by bending float arms.

Vertical Adjustment, Fig. 2
There should be the dimension listed in the *WCFB Specifications Chart* between top of floats and machined surface of casting. Adjust by bending float arms.

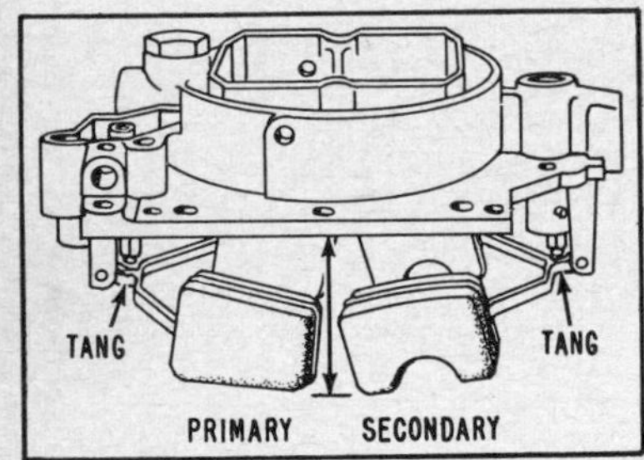

Fig. 3 WCFB float drop (except Fig. 4)

Float Drop Adjustments

Fig. 3—This adjustment refers to all models except those listed in Fig. 4.

With bowl cover held in upright position, gasket removed and measuring from free end of floats, distance between bottom of floats and bowl cover should be as listed in the *WCFB Specifications Chart,* plus or minus 1/16″. Adjust by bending stop tabs on float brackets.

Fig. 4—Models listed in picture caption. With bowl cover held in upright position and measuring from center of floats, the distance between top of floats and bowl cover should be as listed in the *WCFB Specifications Chart.* Adjust by bending stop tabs on float brackets.

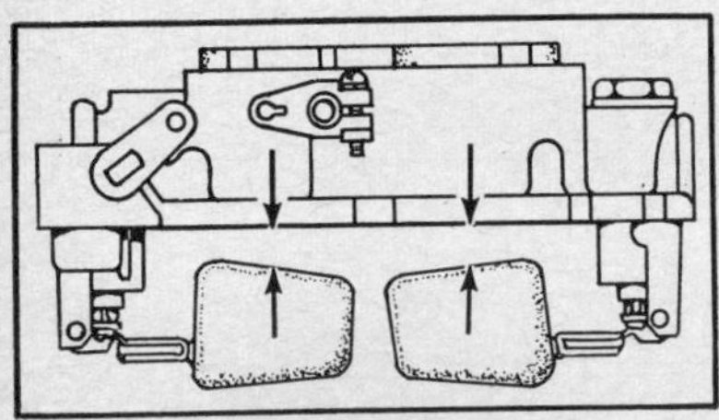

Fig. 4 WCFB float drop for models 2613-14-26-27, 3181-82

Pump Adjustments

Fig. 5—Install pump connector link in outer hole (long stroke) of pump arm with ends extending toward countershaft arm. (On models listed in the Fig. 4 picture caption, install pump connector link in inner hole).

On all models, back out throttle lever stop screw until throttle valves seat in carburetor bores. Hold straightedge across top of dust cover boss at pump arm as shown. Flat on top of pump arm should be parallel to straightedge. Adjust by bending throttle connector rod at the offset angle.

Fig. 5 WCFB pump adjustment

Metering Rod Adjustment

This adjustment is important and must be made after completing the pump ad-

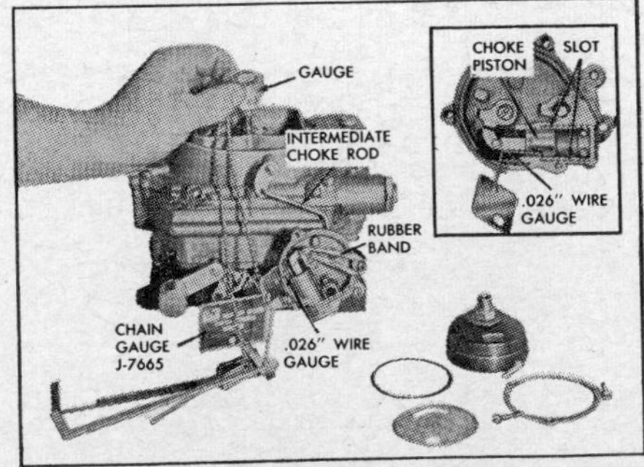

Fig. 6 WCFB intermediate choke rod adjustment

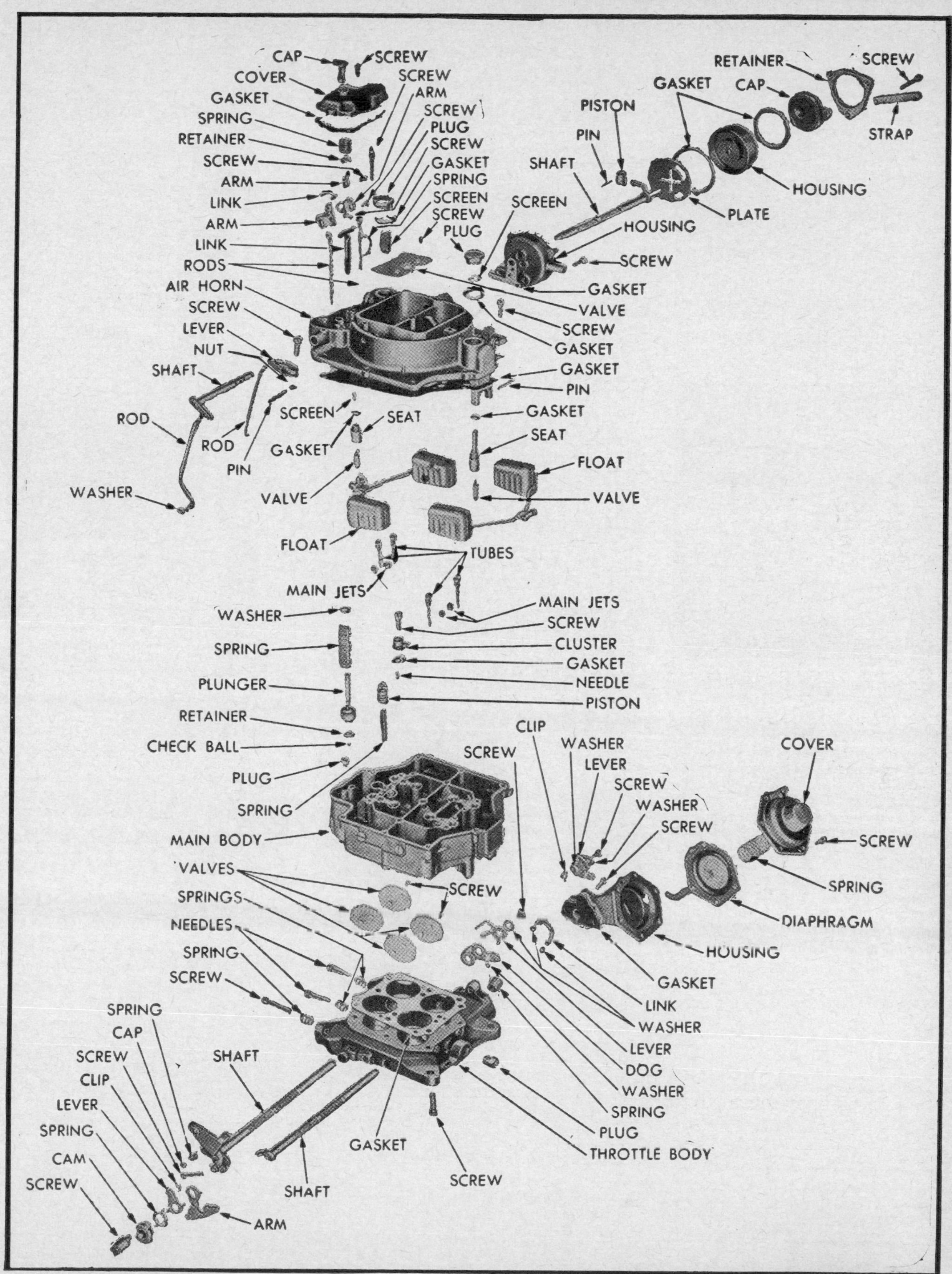

Fig. 1 Carter Model WCFB four-barrel carburetor

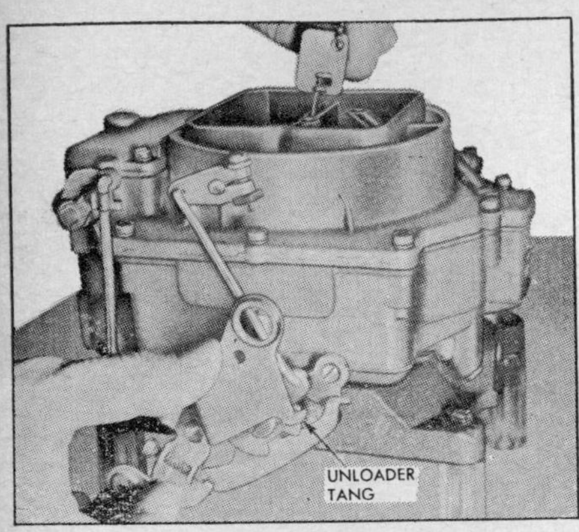

Fig. 7 WCFB choke unloader adjustment

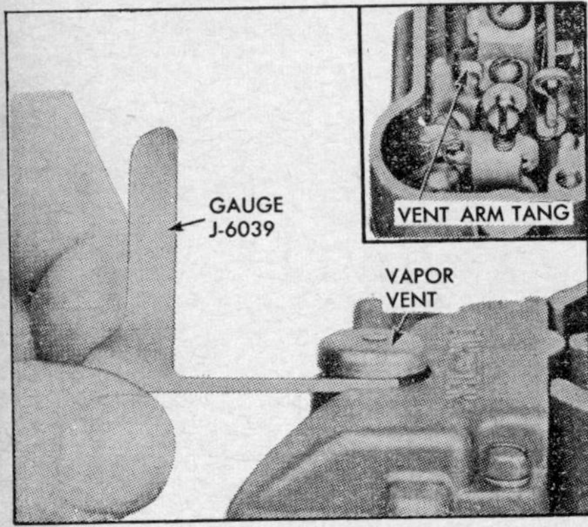

Fig. 8 WCFB bowl vent adjustment

justment. No gauges are necessary.

1. Back out throttle lever stop screw to allow throttle valves to seat in bores of carburetor and loosen metering rod arm clamp screw.
2. With metering rods in place, press down on vacumeter link until metering rods bottom in carburetor body casting.
3. Holding rods in downward position and with throttle valves seated, revolve metering rod arm until finger on arm contacts lip of vacumeter link. Hold in place and carefully tighten clamp screw.

Intermediate Choke Rod

Fig. 6

1. Bend a .026″ wire gauge approximately ⅛″ from its end to a 90-degree angle.
2. Remove choke housing, gasket and baffle plate and block throttle about half open so that fast idle cam does not contact its adjusting screw.
3. Open choke valve and insert wire gauge so that bent portion is between top of slot in choke piston cylinder and bottom of slot in piston.
4. Hold wire gauge in position and close choke valve by pressing on piston lever in choke housing until resistance is felt.
5. There should now be the dimension listed in the *WCFB Specifications Chart* between top of choke valve and inner wall of air horn.
6. To adjust, bend choke connector rod.

Fast Idle Adjustment

Loosen choke lever clamp screw on choke shaft. Insert a gauge of a size listed in the *WCFB Specifications Chart* between lip of fast idle cam and boss of flange casting. Hold choke valve tightly closed and take slack out of linkage by pressing choke lever toward closed position. Hold in place and tighten clamp screw.

No adjustment is necessary for fast idle throttle valve clearance. This is determined by the normal idle position of the speed screw.

Choke Unloader Adjustment

Fig. 7—With throttle valves wide open there should be the clearance listed in the *WCFB Specifications Chart* between upper edge of choke valve and inner wall of air horn. Adjust by bending unloader lip on throttle shaft lever.

Bowl Vent Adjustment

Fig. 8—This adjustment should be made after completing the pump and metering rod adjustment.

Install dust cover gasket and dust cover tightly assembled against tabs on gasket. Back out throttle lever stop screw to allow throttle valves to seat in bores of carburetor. There should be the clearance listed in the *WCFB Specifications Chart* between lower edge of bowl vent valve and dust cover. To adjust, remove dust cover and bend vent arm tang.

Secondary Throttle Lever

Fig. 9

1. Block choke valve wide open.
2. Back out throttle lever stop screw so that primary valves seat in carburetor bores.
3. With primary valves open $\frac{7}{32}$″, the secondary valves should just start to open.
4. To adjust, bend throttle operating rod.

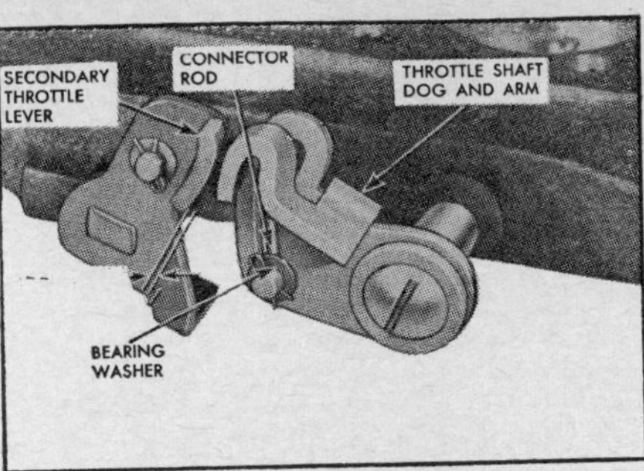

Fig. 9 WCFB secondary throttle lever clearance

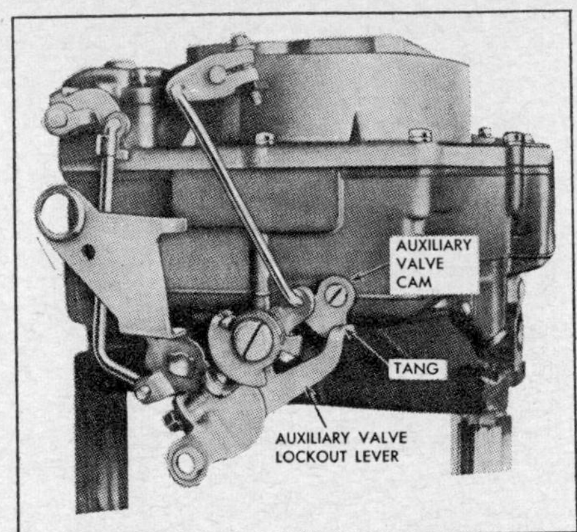

Fig. 10 WCFB auxiliary throttle lockout adjustment

NOTE: Secondary valves will be a few degrees from wide open when primary valves are wide open. With primary and secondary valves tightly closed, there should be the clearance listed in the *WCFB Specifications Chart* between positive closing shoes on primary and secondary throttle levers as shown. To adjust, bend shoe on secondary throttle lever.

Auxiliary Throttle Lockout

Fig. 10—Crack throttle valves and manually open and close choke valve. Tang on lockout arm should freely engage in notch of auxiliary shaft dog. To adjust, bend tang on lockout arm.

Automatic Choke Setting

Loosen retaining screws and turn choke cover to that index mark or line on cover lines up with specified mark on choke housing listed in the *WCFB Specifications Chart.*

CARTER AFB ADJUSTMENT SPECIFICATIONS

See Tune Up Chart in car chapters for hot idle speed.

Year	Carb. Model	Idle Screws (Mixture) Turns Open	Float Level	Float Drop	Pump Travel	Fast Idle Throttle Valve Clearance	Choke Unloader Setting	Secondary Throttle Lever Setting	Vacuum Choke Break Setting	Choke Piston Linkage Setting	Choke Setting
BUICK											
1963	3503S	1/4–1 3/4	①	23/32	7/16	.030	7/32	.020	—	3/32	On Index
	3578S	1/4–1 3/4	①	23/32	7/16	.030	7/32	.020	—	3/32	On Index
1964	3633S	1/4–1 3/4	15/64	23/32	7/16	.020	7/32	.020	—	3/32	On Index
	3634S	1/4–1 3/4	15/64	23/32	1/2 ②	.014	7/32	.020	—	3/32	On Index
	3635S	1/4–1 3/4	15/64	23/32	7/16	.030	7/32	.020	—	3/32	On Index
	3645 All	1/4–1 3/4	15/64	23/32	1/2	.030	7/32	.020	—	—	—
	3646S	1/4–1 3/4	15/64	23/32	1/2 ②	.030	7/32	.020	—	3/32	On Index
	3665S	1/4–1 3/4	15/64	23/32	7/16	.030	7/32	.020	—	3/32	On Index
1965	3826S	1/4–1 3/4	11/64	23/32	7/16	.024	1/8	.020	—	3/32	1 Rich
	3827S	1/4–1 3/4	11/64	23/32	7/16	.024	1/8	.020	—	3/32	On Index
	3921S	1/4–1 3/4	15/64	23/32	7/16	.030	7/32	.020	—	1/8	On Index
	3922S	1/4–1 3/4	15/64	23/32	7/16	.030	7/32	.020	—	1/8	On Index
	3923S	1/4–1 3/4	15/64	23/32	7/16	.030	7/32	.020	—	1/8	On Index
	3924 All	1/4–1 3/4	15/64	23/32	1/2 ②	.014	7/32	.020	—	1/8	On Index
	3925 All	1/4–1 3/4	15/64	23/32	1/2 ②	.030	7/32	.020	—	1/8	On Index
1966	4053S	1/4–1 3/4	15/64	23/32	7/16	.033	7/32	.020	—	.109	On Index
	4054S	1/4–1 3/4	15/64	23/32	7/16	.029	7/32	.020	—	.109	On Index
	4055S	1/4–1 3/4	11/64	23/32	7/16	.033	5/32	.020	—	.095	1 Rich
	4056S	1/4–1 3/4	11/64	23/32	7/16	.026	5/32	.020	—	.082	On Index
	4059S	1/4–1 3/4	15/64	23/32	7/16	.033	7/32	.020	—	.102	On Index
	4060S	1/4–1 3/4	15/64	23/32	1/2 ②	.029	7/32	.020	—	.109	On Index
	4061S	1/4–1 3/4	11/64	23/32	7/16	.033	5/32	.020	—	.088	1 Rich
	4179S	1/4–1 3/4	15/64	23/32	1/2 ②	.029	7/32	.020	—	.135	On Index
	4180S	1/4–1 3/4	15/64	23/32	1/2 ②	.033	7/32	.020	—	.128	On Index
	4181S	1/4–1 3/4	15/64	23/32	1/2 ②	.033	7/32	.020	—	.109	On Index
1967	4331S	1	1 13/32	3/4	7/16 ③	.033	.160	.020	—	.090	1 Rich
	4332S	1	1 13/32	3/4	7/16 ③	.026	.160	.020	—	.090	Index
	4344S	1	1 13/32	3/4	17/32 ④	.033	.160	.020	—	.090	2 Rich

①—With solid seat 7/32″, resilient seat 3/16″. ②—Throttle connector rod in inner hole. ③—Center Hole. ④—Top Hole.

Year	Carb. Model	Idle Screws (Mixture) Turns Open	Float Level	Float Drop	Pump Travel	Fast Idle Throttle Valve Clearance	Choke Unloader Setting	Secondary Throttle Lever Setting	Vacuum Choke Break Setting	Choke Piston Linkage Setting	Choke Setting
CADILLAC											
1963	3480S	3/4–1 3/4	①	15/16	15/32	.032	5/16	.020	—	Flush	1 Rich
	3481S	3/4–1 3/4	①	15/16	15/32	.032	5/16	.020	—	Flush	1 Rich
1964	3655S	3/4–1 3/4	①	15/16	15/32	.023	5/16	.020	—	Flush	On Index
	3656S	3/4–1 3/4	①	15/16	15/32	.023	5/16	.020	—	Flush	On Index
1965	3903S	3/4–1 3/4	①	15/16	15/32	.023	9/32	.020	—	Flush	On Index
1966	4168S	1–2 3/4	②	15/16	31/64	.020	5/16	.020	—	Flush	On Index
	4169S	1–2 3/4	②	15/16	31/64	.020	5/16	.020	—	Flush	On Index
	4170S	2 1/2–4	②	15/16	31/64	.020	5/16	.020	—	Flush	1 Rich
	4171S	2 1/2–4	②	15/16	31/64	.020	5/16	.020	—	Flush	1 Rich

①—Solid seat 3/8″, resilient seat 21/64″. ②—Solid seat 3/8″, resilient seat 11/32″.

Year	Carb. Model	Idle Screws (Mixture) Turns Open	Float Level	Float Drop	Pump Travel	Fast Idle Throttle Valve Clearance	Choke Unloader Setting	Secondary Throttle Lever Setting	Vacuum Choke Break Setting	Choke Piston Linkage Setting	Choke Setting
CHEVROLET											
1963–65	3361S	1/4–1 1/2	①	23/32	33/64	—	—	.020	—	3/32	—
1963–64	3362S	1/4–1 1/2	①	23/32	33/64	.015	1/4	.020	—	3/32	On Index
1963	3460S	1/8–2 1/4	①	23/32	33/64	.015	1/4	.020	—	.080	1 Lean
	3461S	1/8–2 1/4	①	23/32	33/64	.015	1/4	.020	—	.080	1 Lean
1963–64	3499S	1/4–1 1/2	①	23/32	33/64	.025	1/4	.020	—	3/16	2 Lean
1964–65	3720 All	1/8–2 1/4	①	23/32	33/64	.015	1/4	.020	—	.080	1 Lean
	3721 All	1/8–2 1/4	①	23/32	33/64	.015	1/4	.020	—	.080	1 Lean
	3783S	1/4–1 1/2	①	23/32	33/64	.025	1/4	.020	—	3/16	2 Lean
	3804S	1/4–1 1/2	①	23/32	33/64	.015	1/4	.020	—	3/32	On Index

CARTER AFB ADJUSTMENT SPECIFICATIONS—Continued

See Tune Up Chart in car chapters for hot idle speed.

Year	Carb. Model	Idle Screws (Mixture) Turns Open	Float Level	Float Drop	Pump Travel	Fast Idle Throttle Valve Clearance	Choke Unloader Setting	Secondary Throttle Lever Setting	Vacuum Choke Break Setting	Choke Piston Linkage Setting	Choke Setting
CHEVROLET—Continued											
1965	3963S	1/8–2 1/4	①	23/32	33/64	.015	1/4	.020	—	.080	1 Lean

①—Solid seat 15/64", resilient seat 13/64".

Year	Carb. Model	Idle Screws (Mixture) Turns Open	Float Level	Float Drop	Pump Travel	Fast Idle Throttle Valve Clearance	Choke Unloader Setting	Secondary Throttle Lever Setting	Vacuum Choke Break Setting	Choke Piston Linkage Setting	Choke Setting
CHRYSLER, IMPERIAL, DODGE, PLYMOUTH											
1963–64	3447 All	1/4–1 3/4	③	23/32	7/16	—	—	.020	—	—	—
1964	3505 All	1/4–1 3/4	③	23/32	7/16	.020	—	.020	—	—	—
	3611S	1/4–2 1/2	②	23/32	7/16	.020	3/8	.020	—	—	On Index
	3612S,13S	1/4–2 1/2	②	23/32	7/16	.020	3/8	.020	—	—	2 Rich
	3614S	1/4–2 1/2	②	23/32	7/16	.020	3/8	.020	—	—	On Index
	3615S	1/4–2 1/4	②	23/32	7/16	.020	3/8	.020	—	—	2 Rich
	3644S	1/4–2 1/4	②	23/32	7/16	.020	3/8	.020	—	—	2 Rich
	3705S	1/4–1 3/4	④	23/32	⑦	—	—	.020	—	—	—
1965	3853S	1/4–2 1/2	②	23/32	7/16	.020	7/32	.020	1/8	—	2 Rich
	3854S	1/4–2 1/2	②	23/32	7/16	.020	7/32	.020	3/32	—	2 Rich
	3855S	1/4–2 1/2	②	23/32	7/16	.020	3/8	.020	1/8	—	On Index
	3856S	1/4–2 1/2	②	23/32	7/16	.020	3/8	.020	7/64	—	On Index
	3858S	1/4–2 1/2	②	23/32	7/16	.020	3/8	.020	7/64	—	2 Rich
	3859 All	1/4–2 1/2	②	23/32	7/16	.020	3/8	.020	1/8	—	On Index
	3860S	1/4–2 1/2	②	23/32	7/16	.020	3/8	.020	7/64	—	On Index
	3861S	1/4–1 3/4	⑤	23/32	9/16⑥	—	—	.020	—	—	—
	3871S	1/4–2 1/2	②	23/32	7/16	.020	3/8	.020	7/64	—	2 Rich
1966	4119S	1/4–2 3/4	②	23/32	7/16	.013	7/32	.020	1/8	—	2 Rich
	4120S	1/4–2 3/4	②	23/32	7/16	.020	7/32	.020	3/32	—	2 Rich
	4121S	1/4–2 3/4⑧	②	23/32	7/16	.018	7/32	.020	1/8	—	On Index
	4122S	2 1/4–3 1/4⑧	②	23/32	7/16	.018	7/32	.020	1/8	—	On Index
	4130S	1 1/4–2 3/4	②	23/32	7/16	.020	3/8	.020	1/8	—	2 Rich
	4131S	1/4–2 3/4	②	23/32	7/16	.025	3/8	.020	7/64	—	2 Rich
	4132S	1 1/2–2 1/2	②	23/32	7/16	.018	5/16	.020	5/64	—	On Index
	4133S	2 1/2–3 1/2⑧	②	23/32	7/16	.018	5/16	.020	5/64	—	On Index
	4136S	1 1/2–2 1/2⑧	②	23/32	7/16	.018	5/16	.020	5/64	—	On Index
	4137S	2 1/2–3 1/2⑧	②	23/32	7/16	.018	5/16	.020	5/64	—	On Index
1966-67	4139S	1/4–2 3/4	③	23/32	7/16	—	—	.020	—	—	—
1966	4140S	1/4–2 3/4	②	23/32	7/16	.030	1/4	.020	—	—	1 Rich
1967	4294S	1–2	7/32	3/4	7/16	—	7/32	.020	—	—	2 Rich
	4295S	1–2	7/32	3/4	7/16	—	7/32	.020	—	—	2 Rich
	4298S	1–2	7/32	3/4	7/16	—	3/8	.020	—	—	2 Rich
	4299S	1–2	7/32	3/4	7/16	—	3/8	.020	—	—	2 Rich
	4304S	1–2	5/16	3/4	7/16	—	7/32	.020	—	—	On Index
	4305S	1–2	5/16	3/4	7/16	—	7/32	.020	—	—	On Index
	4309S	1–2	5/16	3/4	7/16	—	5/16	.020	—	—	On Index
	4310S	1–2	5/16	3/4	7/16	—	5/16	.020	—	—	On Index
	4311S	1–2	5/16	3/4	7/16	—	5/16	.020	—	—	On Index
	4312S	1–2	5/16	3/4	7/16	—	5/16	.020	—	—	On Index
	4324S	1–2	5/16	3/4	7/16	—	—	.020	—	—	—
	4325S	1–2	7/32	3/4	7/16	—	1/4	.020	—	—	1 Rich
	4326S	1–2	7/32	3/4	7/16	—	3/8	.020	—	—	On Index
	4327S	1–2	7/32	3/4	7/16	—	3/8	.020	—	—	On Index
	4328S	1–2	5/16	3/4	7/16	—	3/8	.020	—	—	On Index
	4329S	1–2	5/16	3/4	7/16	—	3/8	.020	—	—	On Index
	4343S	1–2	7/32	3/4	7/16	—	3/8	.020	—	—	1 Rich

CARTER AFB ADJUSTMENT SPECIFICATIONS—Continued

See Tune Up Charti n car chapters for hot idle speed.

CHRYSLER, IMPERIAL, DODGE, PLYMOUTH—Continued

Year	Carb. Model	Idle Screws (Mixture) Turns Open	Float Level	Float Drop	Pump Travel	Fast Idle Throttle Valve Clearance	Choke Unloader Setting	Secondary Throttle Lever Setting	Vacuum Choke Break Setting	Choke Piston Linkage Setting	Choke Setting
1968	4430S	—	19/64	23/32	7/16	—	—	17/64	—	—	—
	4431S	3	7/32	23/32	7/16	.013	1/4	17/64	—	3/32	2 Rich
	4432S	3 1/2	7/32	23/32	7/16	.013	1/4	17/64	—	7/64	2 Rich
1969	4619S	—	7/32	3/4	7/16	—	—	17/64	—	—	—
	4620S	1–2	7/32	3/4	7/16	50 Drill⑨	1/4	17/64	—	39 Drill	2 Rich
	4621S	1–2	7/32	3/4	7/16	50 Drill⑨	1/4	17/64	—	39 Drill	2 Rich

②—Solid seat 7/32″, resilient seat 3/16″.
③—Solid seat 19/64″, resilient seat 17/64″.
④—Solid seat 15/64″, resilient seat 13/64″.
⑤—Solid seat 5/32″, resilient seat 1/8″.
⑥—Place connector rod in 3rd hole from end of lever.
⑦—With 64-209S plunger (early) 1/2″, with 64-279S plunger 7/16″.
⑧—When adjusting idle mixture screw, do not turn screw more than 1/16 turn at a time. Idle screw is not removable and the screw locks approximately a maximum of 2 3/4 turns open on 4121, 3 1/4 turns on 4122, 2 1/2 turns on 4132 and 4136, 3 1/2 turns on 4133 and 4137.
⑨—With fast idle speed adjusting screw contacting second highest speed step on fast idle cam the clearance between choke valve and wall of air horn should be as specified.

LINCOLN

Year	Carb. Model	Idle Screws (Mixture) Turns Open	Float Level	Float Drop	Pump Travel	Fast Idle Throttle Valve Clearance	Choke Unloader Setting	Secondary Throttle Lever Setting	Vacuum Choke Break Setting	Choke Piston Linkage Setting	Choke Setting
1963–64	3521S	1/4–2	②	23/32	17/32①	.026	1/8	.020	—	3/32	1 Rich
	3522S	1/4–2	②	23/32	17/32①	.026	1/8	.020	—	3/32	1 Rich
	3523S	1/4–2	②	23/32	15/32	.026	1/8	.020	—	3/32	1 Rich
	3524S	1/4–2	②	23/32	15/32	.026	1/8	.020	—	3/32	1 Rich
1965	3928S	1/4–2	②	23/32	17/32①	.026	1/8	.020	—	3/32	1 Rich
	3929S	1/4–2	②	23/32	17/32①	.026	1/8	.020	—	3/32	1 Rich
	3930S	1/4–2	②	23/32	15/32	.026	1/8	.020	—	3/32	1 Rich
	3931S	1/4–2	②	23/32	15/32	.026	1/8	.020	—	3/32	1 Rich
1966	4147S	1/2–1 1/2	②	23/32	15/32	.026	1/8	.020	—	7/64	1 Rich
	4148S	1/2–1 1/2	②	23/32	15/32	.026	1/8	.020	—	7/64	1 Rich
	4204S	1/4–1 3/4	②	23/32	15/32	.026	1/8	.020	—	7/64	1 Rich
	4205S	1/4–1 3/4	②	23/32	15/32	.026	1/8	.020	—	7/64	1 Rich
1967	C7VF-A③	1/2–1 1/2	3/16	23/32	①	.026	1/8	.020	—	7/64	1 Rich
	C7VF-B③	1/2–1 1/2	3/16	23/32	①	.026	1/8	.020	—	7/64	1 Rich
	C7VF-C③	1/2–1 1/2	3/16	23/32	①	.026	1/8	.020	—	7/64	1 Rich
	C7VF-D③	1/2–1 1/2	3/16	23/32	①	.026	1/8	.020	—	7/64	1 Rich
1968	C8VF-E③	1	3/16	23/32	①	.026	1/8	.020	—	7/64	1 Lean

①—Place connector rod in inner hole.
②—Solid seat 3/16″, resilient seat 5/32″.
③—Identification tag on carburetor bowl is marked "Autolite".

PONTIAC

Year	Carb. Model	Idle Screws (Mixture) Turns Open	Float Level	Float Drop	Pump Travel	Fast Idle Throttle Valve Clearance	Choke Unloader Setting	Secondary Throttle Lever Setting	Vacuum Choke Break Setting	Choke Piston Linkage Setting	Choke Setting
1963	3474S	1/4–2 1/4	①	23/32	31/64	.026	5/32	.020	—	Flush	1 Rich
	3477S	1/4–1 3/4	②	23/32	31/64	.026	5/32	.020	—	Flush	1 Rich
	3479S	1/4–2 1/4	①	23/32	31/64	.026	5/32	.020	—	Flush	1 Rich
	3502S	1/4–1 3/4	③	23/32	31/64	.026	5/32	.020	—	Flush	1 Rich
	3545 All	1/4–2 1/4	①	23/32	31/64	.026	5/32	.020	—	Flush	1 Rich
1964	3647S	1/4–2 1/4	11/32	23/32	31/64	.026	5/32	.020	—	Flush	1 Rich
	3648S	1/4–2 1/4	11/32	23/32	31/64	.026	5/32	.020	—	Flush	1 Rich
	3649S	1/4–2 1/4	11/32	23/32	31/64	.026	5/32	.020	—	Flush	1 Rich
	3650S	1/4–2 1/4	11/32	23/32	31/64	.026	5/32	.020	—	Flush	1 Rich
	3651S	1/4–2 1/4	11/32	23/32	31/64	.026	5/32	.020	—	Flush	1 Rich
	3686S	1/4–1 3/4	11/32	23/32	31/64	.026	5/32	.020	—	Flush	1 Rich
	3687 All	1/4–1 3/4	11/32	23/32	31/64	.026	5/32	.020	—	Flush	1 Rich
1965	3895S	1/4–2 1/2	5/16	23/32	31/64②	.027	5/32	.020	—	Flush	1 Rich
	3896S	1/4–2 1/2	5/16	23/32	31/64②	.027	5/32	.020	—	Flush	1 Rich
	3898S	1/4–2 1/2	3/8	23/32	31/64②	.027	5/32	.020	—	Flush	1 Rich
	3899S	1/4–2 1/2	3/8	23/32	31/64	.027	5/32	.020	—	Flush	1 Rich
	3900S	1/4–2 1/2	5/16	23/32	31/64②	.027	5/32	.020	—	Flush	1 Rich

Continued

CARTER AFB ADJUSTMENT SPECIFICATIONS—Continued

See Tune Up Chart in car chapters for hot idle speed.

Year	Carb. Model	Idle Screws (Mixture) Turns Open	Float Level	Float Drop	Pump Travel	Fast Idle Throttle Valve Clearance	Choke Unloader Setting	Secondary Throttle Lever Setting	Vacuum Choke Break Setting	Choke Piston Linkage Setting	Choke Setting
PONTIAC—Continued											
1966	4030S	¾–2½	¼	23/32	35/64	.027	5/32	.020	—	Flush	1 Rich
	4031S	¾–2½	5/16	23/32	35/64	.027	5/32	.020	—	Flush	1 Rich
	4033S	½–2¼	5/16	23/32	35/64	.027	5/32	.020	—	Flush	1 Rich
	4034S	½–2¼	5/16	23/32	35/64	.031	5/32	.020	—	Flush	1 Rich
	4035S	½–2¼	⅜	23/32	35/64	.027	5/32	.020	—	Flush	1 Rich
	4036S	½–2¼	¼	23/32	35/64	.031	5/32	.020	—	Flush	1 Rich
	4037S	½–2¼	5/16	23/32	35/64	.031	5/32	.020	—	Flush	1 Rich
	4041S	¾–2½	5/16	23/32	35/64	.027	5/32	.020	—	Flush	1 Rich
1967	4242S	½–3	5/16	23/32	⅜	.031	5/32	.020	—	Flush	1 Rich
	4243S	½–3	⅜	23/32	⅜	.027	5/32	.020	—	Flush	1 Rich
	4244S	1–2½	¼	23/32	⅜	.031	5/32	.020	—	Flush	1 Rich
	4245S	1–2½	5/16	23/32	⅜	.027	5/32	.020	—	Flush	1 Rich
	4246S	½–3	5/16	23/32	⅜	.031	5/32	.020	—	Flush	1 Rich
	4248S	2–3½	5/16	23/32	⅜	.031	5/32	.020	—	Flush	1 Rich

①—Solid seat 21/64″, resilient seat 5/16″. ③—Solid seat 5/16″, resilient seat 9/32″.
②—With connector rod in inner hole of pump arm.

Year	Carb. Model	Idle Screws (Mixture) Turns Open	Float Level	Float Drop	Pump Travel	Fast Idle Throttle Valve Clearance	Choke Unloader Setting	Secondary Throttle Lever Setting	Vacuum Choke Break Setting	Choke Piston Linkage Setting	Choke Setting
RAMBLER											
1967	4216S	¾–1¾	5/16	2	⅜	.018	9/32	.020	—	9/64	2 Rich
	4258S	¾–1¾	5/16	2	⅜	.018	5/32	.020	—	3/32	1 Rich
	4352S	1–2	5/16	2	⅜	.018	9/64	.020	—	3/32	On Index
	4353S	½–1½	5/16	2	⅜	.018	9/64	.020	—	3/32	2 Rich
	4354S	¾–1¾	5/16	2	⅜	.018	9/32	.020	—	9/64	2 Rich
	4358S	½–1½	5/16	2	⅜	.018	5/32	.020	—	3/32	On Index
1968	4467S	1	11/32	23/32	13/32	.014	5/32	.020	—	.088	2 Rich
	4468S	1	11/32	23/32	7/16	.018	5/32	.020	—	.120	1 Rich
	4469S	1	11/32	23/32	7/16	.018	5/32	.020	—	.110	2 Rich
	4583S	2–3	11/32	23/32	13/32	.020	5/32	.020	—	.110	2 Rich
	4584S	2–3	11/32	23/32	7/16	.020	5/32	.020	—	.096	1 Rich
	4585S	2–3	11/32	23/32	7/16	.024	5/32	.020	—	.096	1 Rich
	4622S	—	11/32	23/32	13/32	.014	5/32	.020	—	.088	2 Rich
	4623S	—	11/32	23/32	7/16	.018	5/32	.020	—	.120	1 Rich
	4624S	—	11/32	23/32	7/16	.018	5/32	.020	—	.110	2 Rich
1969	4660S	2	11/32	2	21/64	—	5/32	.020	—	5/64	2 Rich
	4661S	2	11/32	2	21/64	—	5/32	.020	—	⅛	On Index
	4662S	2	11/32	2	21/64	—	5/32	.020	—	7/64	On Index
	4663S	2	11/32	2	21/64	—	5/32	.020	—	⅛	On Index
	4664S	2	11/32	2	21/64	—	5/32	.020	—	7/64	On Index
	4665S	2	11/32	2	21/64	—	5/32	.020	—	⅛	On Index

MODEL AFB ADJUSTMENTS

The AFB carburetor, Figs. 1 and 2, contains many features, some of which are the locations of the step-up rods and pistons. The step-up rods, pistons and springs are accessible for service without removing the air horn or the carburetor from the engine. The venturi assemblies (primary and secondary) are replaceable and contain many of the calibration points for both the high and low speed systems. One fuel bowl feeds both the primary and secondary nozzles on the right side while the other fuel bowl takes care of the primary and secondary nozzles on the left side. This provides excellent performance in cornering, quick stops and acceleration.

All the major castings of the carburetor are aluminum, with the throttle body integral with the main body. This allows an overall height reduction in the carburetor. The section containing the accelerating pump is termed the primary side of the carburetor; the rear section is the secondary.

Float Alignment

Fig. 3—Sight down side of float to determine if it is parallel to the outer edge of the air horn casting. To adjust, bend float lever by applying just enough pressure to make the adjustment. Apply the pressure on the end of the float with the fingers while supporting the float lever with the thumb.

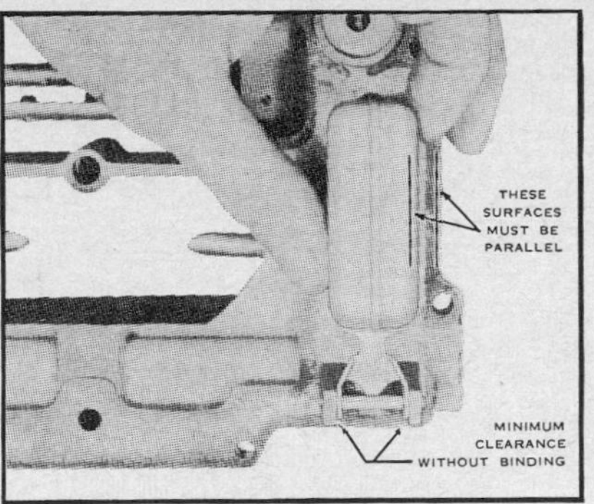

Fig. 3 AFB float alignment

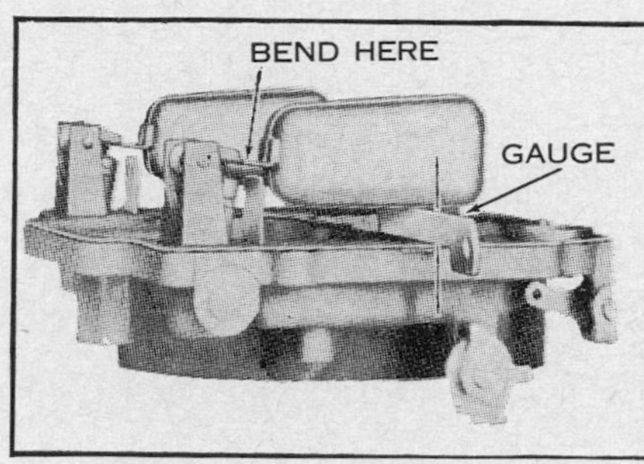

Fig. 4 AFB float level adjustment

After aligning the float, remove as much clearance as possible between arms of float lever and lugs on air horn by bending the float lever. Arms of float lever should be as parallel to the inner surfaces of the lugs on the air horn as possible. Floats must operate freely without excess clearance on its hinge pin.

Float Level Adjustment

Fig. 4—With air horn inverted, bowl cover gasket in place and needle seated, clearance between top of float (at outer end) and air horn gasket should be as listed in the *AFB Specifications Chart*. To adjust, bend float arm. Adjust both floats and recheck float alignment.

Float Drop Adjustment

Fig. 5—With bowl cover held in upright position, measure between outer end of each float, the distance between top of floats and bowl cover gasket should be as listed in the *AFB Specifications Chart*. To adjust, bend tabs on float brackets.

Pump Adjustment

Fig. 6—Back out idle speed screw until throttle valves seat in carburetor bores. With throttle connector rod in center hole (medium stroke) of pump arm, distance from top of bowl cover to top of pump plunger shaft should be as listed

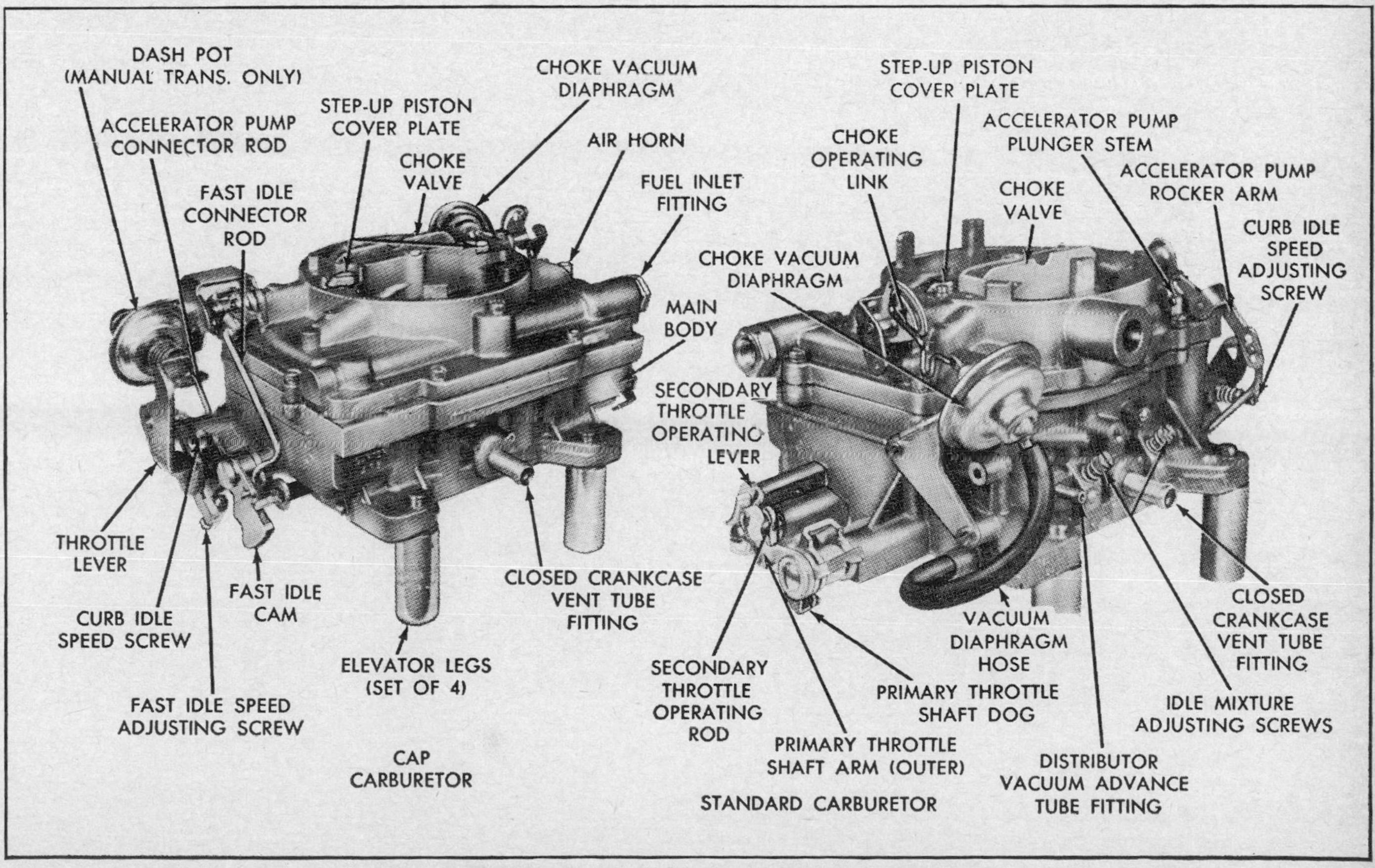

Fig. 2 AFB exterior views (Chrysler). The unit at left is used with C.A.P. equipment, the one at right is a standard unit

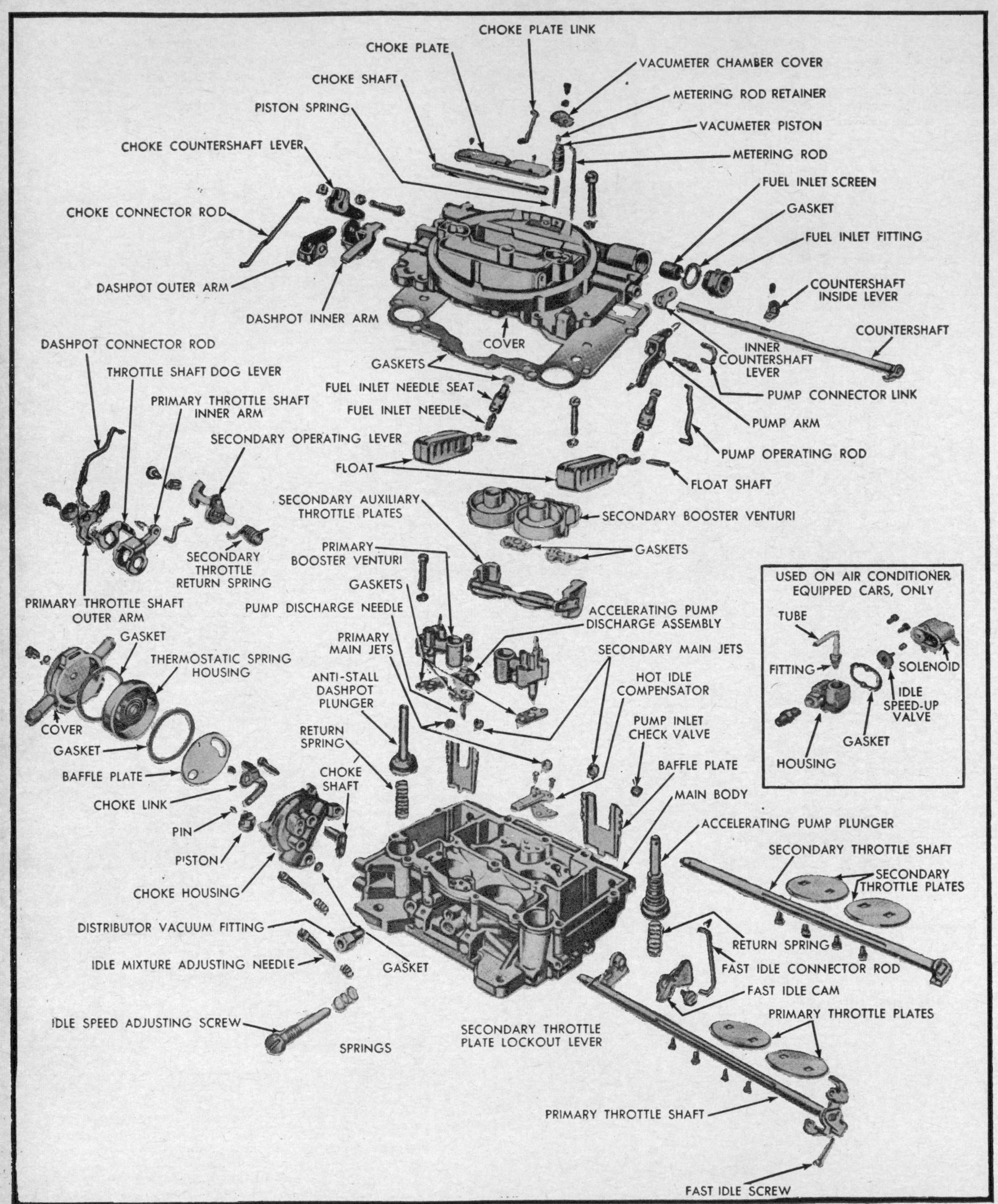

Fig. 1 Carter Model AFB four-barrel carburetor

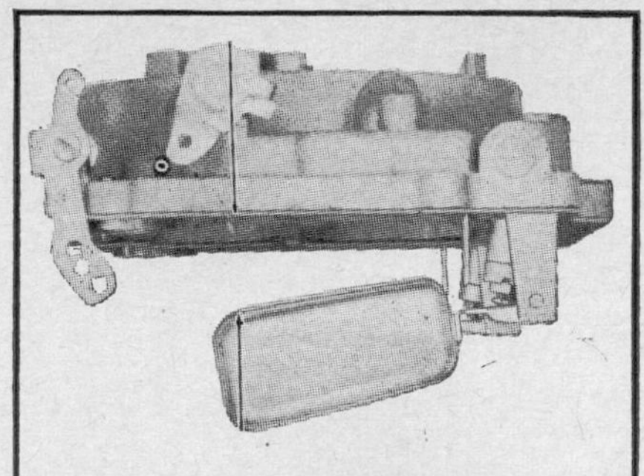

Fig. 5 AFB float drop adjustment

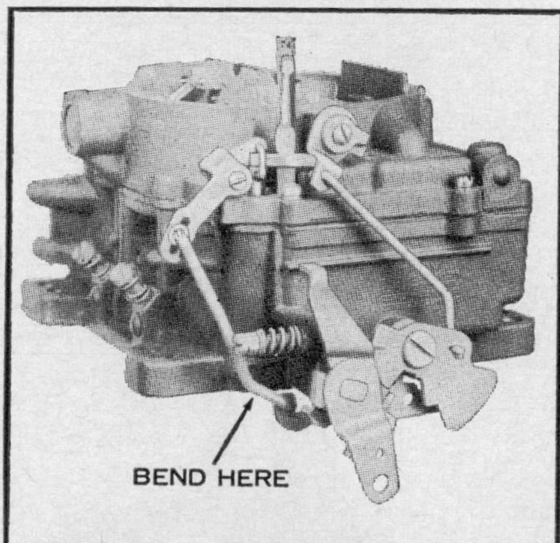

Fig. 6 AFB pump adjustment

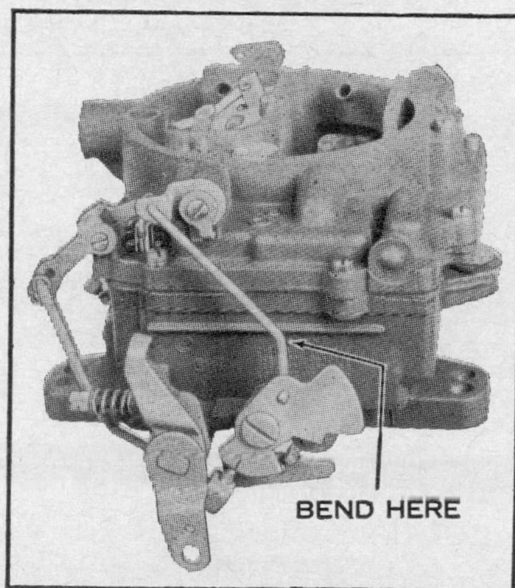

Fig. 7 AFB fast idle linkage adjustment

in the *AFB Specifications Chart.* Adjust by bending throttle connector rod at its offset angle.

NOTE: Some models require the throttle connector rod to be placed in either the inner hole (long stroke) or outer hole (short stroke). In such cases the chart will indicate the proper hole connection.

Fast Idle Linkage Adjustment

Fig. 7—With choke valve tightly closed and lug on outer choke shaft lever contacting stop on inner choke shaft lever, align center of fast idle screw with index mark on cam. To adjust, bend fast idle connector rod. On some models it may be necessary to bend stop lug on fast idle cam.

Fast Idle Throttle Valve Clearance

Fig. 8—With choke valve tightly closed, tighten fast idle adjusting screw on index mark on cam until the clearance between throttle valve and carburetor bore (side opposite idle port) is as listed in the *AFB Specifications Chart.*

Choke Unloader Adjustment

Fig. 9—With throttle wide open, clearance between upper edge of choke valve and inner wall of air horn should be as listed in the *AFB Specifications Chart.* To adjust, bend unloader lip on throttle shaft lever.

Secondary Throttle Lever Adjustment

Figs. 10 and 11. Block choke valve wide open. Secondary throttle valves should just start to open when primary throttle valves are opened to the clearance listed in the *AFB Specifications Chart* between lower edge of throttle valve and carburetor bore (side opposite idle port). To adjust, bend throttle operating rod, Fig. 10.

Primary and secondary throttle valves should reach wide open position at the same time.

With primary and secondary throttle valves tightly closed, there should be the clearance listed in the *AFB Specifications Chart* between the positive closing shoes and primary and secondary throttle levers. To adjust, bend shoe on secondary lever.

Secondary Throttle Lockout

Fig. 12—Crack throttle valves and manually open and close choke valve. Tang on secondary throttle lever should freely engage in notch of lockout dog. To adjust, bend tang on secondary throttle lever.

On Cadillac models, with lockout dog held tight against stop on flange casting and secondary throttle valves partially open, there should be .026″ clearance between tang on secondary throttle lever and lockout arm. To adjust, bend arm at slot of lockout dog. Fast idle cam may be removed to facilitate gauging and adjusting.

On Lincoln 1963 and later units, with choke valve closed, adjust tang on secondary throttle lever to give .070″ opening of secondary valves (high side of valves adjacent to throttle lever) when primary valves are wide open.

Choke Piston Lever Adjustment

All Cadillac and Pontiac

Choke piston should be flush with top of piston housing with choke valve closed. Choke valve should be held closed by applying pressure to piston lever in piston housing. To adjust, bend choke connector rod.

Choke Piston Linkage Adjustment

Fig. 13—Except Cadillac and Pontiac

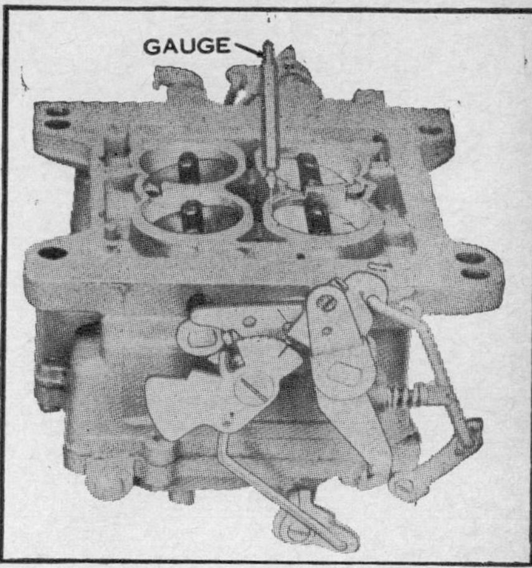

Fig. 8 AFB throttle valve clearance adjustment

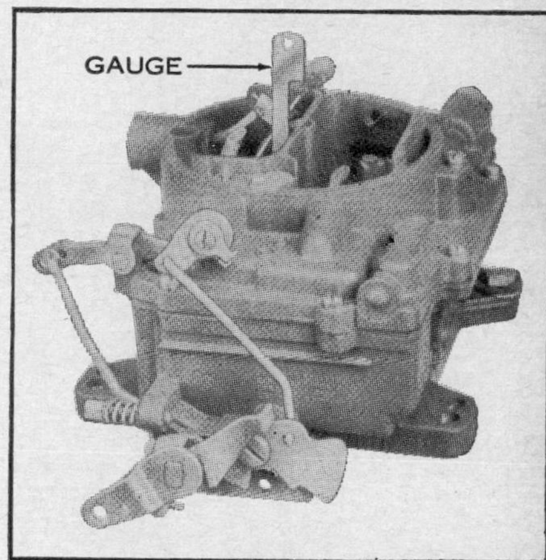

Fig. 9 AFB choke unloader adjustment

Fig. 10 AFB secondary throttle lever adjustment

Bend a .026″ wire gauge at a 90-degree angle approximately 1/8″ from its end. Open choke valve and insert the wire gauge so that bent portion is between top of slot in choke piston cylinder and bottom of slot in piston.

Hold wire gauge in position and close choke valve by pressing on piston lever in choke housing until resistance is felt. There should now be the clearance listed in the *AFB Specifications Chart* between top of choke valve and air horn wall. To adjust, bend choke connector link.

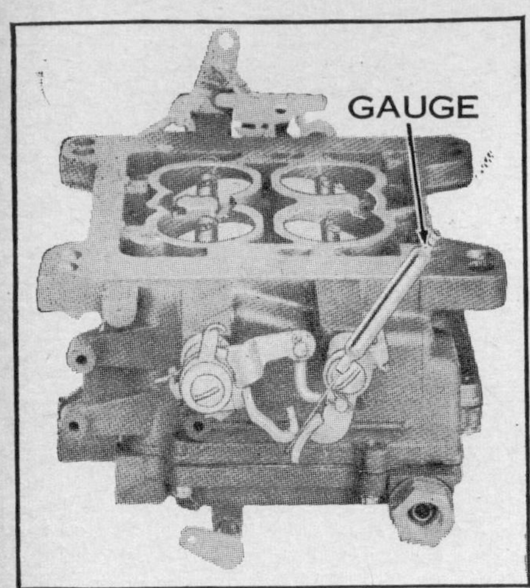

Fig. 11 AFB Gauging clearance between positive closing shoes on primary and secondary throttle valves

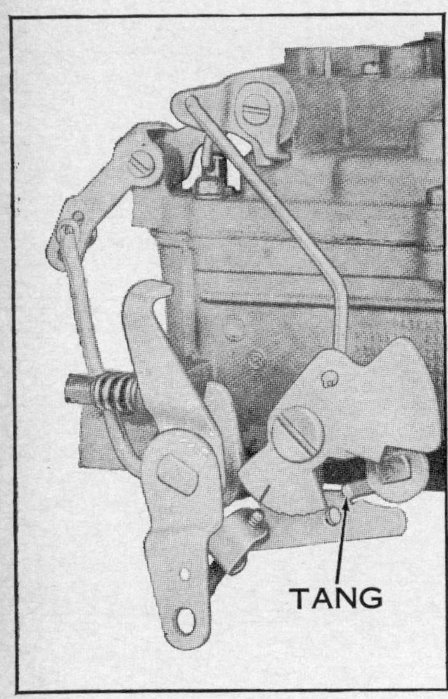

Fig. 12 AFB secondary lockout adjustment

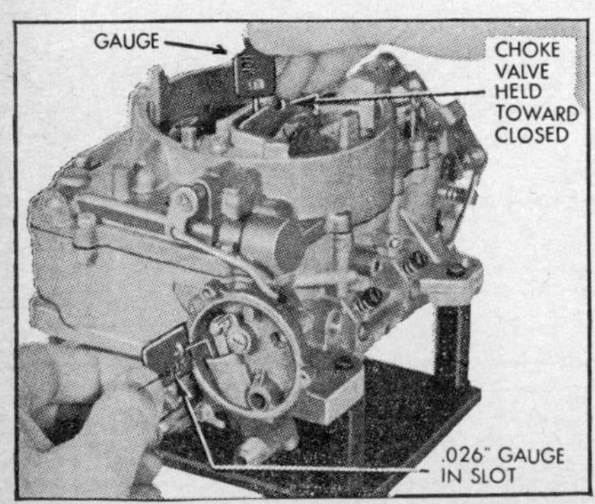

Fig. 13 AFB choke piston clearance

Automatic Choke Setting

Built-In Type, Fig. 14

Loosen retaining screws and turn choke cover so that index mark or line on cover lines up with specified mark on choke housing listed in the *AFB Specifications.*

Well-Type Choke

Loosen mounting post lock nut and turn mounting post with screwdriver until index mark on disc is positioned as listed in the *AFB Specifications Chart.* Hold in this position with a screwdriver and tighten lock nut, Fig. 15.

After adjustment is completed and coil housing and carburetor are installed on engine, lift cover disc and open and close choke valve manually to see if connector rod clears sides of hole in housing cover without binding. If binding exists, replace with a new unit since the connector rod cannot be bent without affecting calibration.

Dashpot Adjustment

Chrysler Line with C.A.P.

Use only on cars with manual transmission, make the dashpot adjustment after the fast idle setting. Then with the fast idle screw on highest step of cam, adjust dashpot for a clearance of .052" between dashpot stem and lever. Tighten lock nut.

Lincoln

There should be 1/8" clearance between top of bowl cover to top of plunger shaft with primary throttle valves tightly closed. To adjust, bend flat portion of dashpot lever. Check to be sure lever does not contact bowl cover screw.

Vacuum "Choke Break" Setting

Chrysler Line Only

With vacuum diaphragm plate (not stem) bottomed, close choke valve as far as possible without forcing. Then adjust connector rod to give the clearance listed in the *AFB Specifications Chart* between top edge of choke valve and inner wall of air horn. Remove connector rod to adjust to prevent damage to diaphragm.

Idle Air Adjustment

Fig. 16—Used on most Cadillac and Pontiac carburetors and on some Chrysler and Lincoln units, the idle air adjustment screw is employed in lieu of the familiar throttle speed screw.

With engine at normal operating temperature, turn the air adjustment screw outward to increase engine speed, which will also lean the mixture supplied to the manifold. This must be compensated for by adjusting the idle mixture screws.

A/C Fast Idle Device

Cadillac with Air Conditioner, Fig. 18

This adjustment must be made with carburetor installed, engine at normal operating temperature and slow idle speed properly adjusted. With shift lever in neutral and A/C turned on, engine should idle at 900-950 rpm. On 1962 models, adjustment is made by loosening lock nut on diaphragm shaft and adjusting knurled nut to obtain the specified rpm, then tighten lock nut. On 1963 and later models, adjust by holding diaphragm shaft with a wrench, then adjust screw to get the desired rpm.

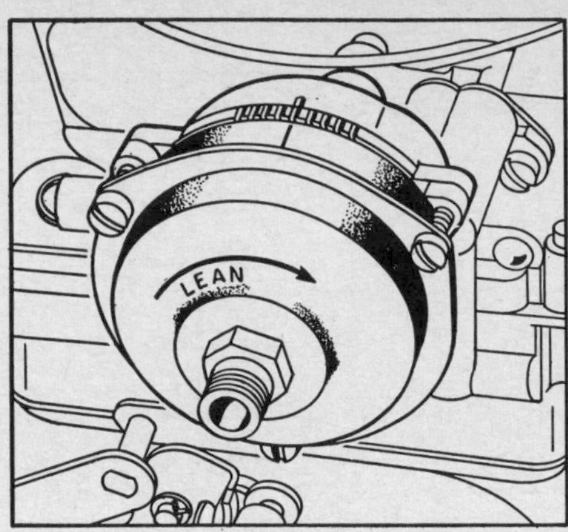

Fig. 14 AFB choke setting (built-in type)

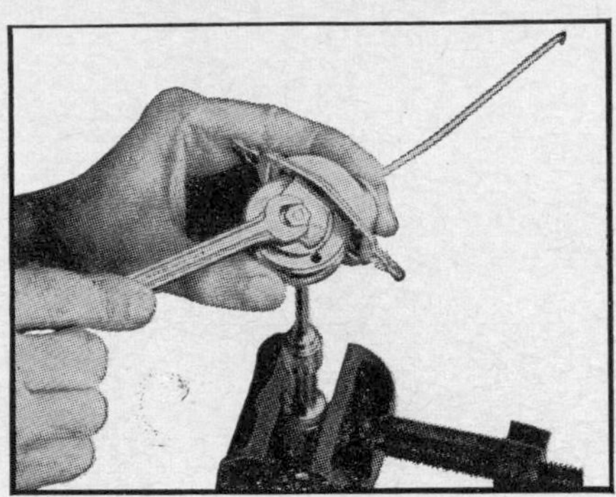

Fig. 15 AFB well-type choke setting (Chrysler line)

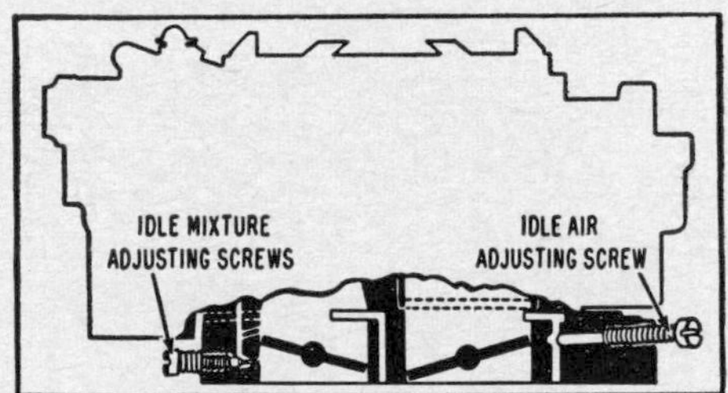

Fig. 16 AFB slow idle air adjusting screw

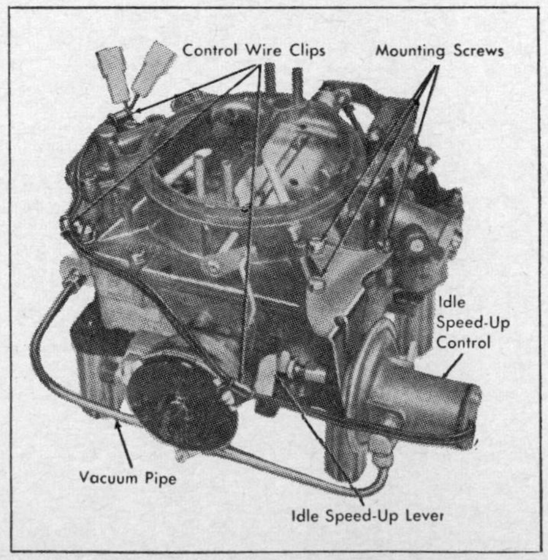

Fig. 18 AFB idle speed-up device used on Cadillac air-conditioned cars

Ford Autolite Carburetor Section

AUTOLITE 1100-1V CARB. ADJUSTMENT SPECIFICATIONS

See Tune Up Chart in car chapters for hot idle speeds.

Year	Carb. Model (Code 9510)	Idle Screw (Mixture) Turns Open	Float Setting (Dry)	Pump Setting	Dashpot Setting	Fast Idle Cam Linkage Clearance	Fast Idle Speed	Manual Choke Plate Clearance	Automatic Choke Plate Clearance	Dechoke Clearance ①	Automatic Choke Setting
1963	C3AF-A	4–5	1	3/16	—	—	—	5/32	—	—	—
	C3AF-B	4–5	1	3/16	3½	—	—	5/32	—	—	—
	C3AF-C	4–5	1	3/16	—	—	—	5/32	—	—	—
	C3AF-D	4–5	1	3/16	3½	—	—	5/32	—	—	—
	C3DF-A	3–4	1	3/16	—	—	—	5/32	—	—	—
	C3DF-B	3–4	1	3/16	3½	—	—	5/32	—	—	—
	C3GA-F	3–4	1	3/16	—	—	—	—	5/32	¼	At Index
	C3GF-B	3–4	1	3/16	3½	—	—	—	5/32	¼	At Index
	C3OF-A	3–4	1	3/16	—	—	—	5/32	—	—	—
	C3OF-B	3–4	1	3/16	3½	—	—	5/32	—	—	—
	C3YF-A	3–4	1	3/16	—	—	—	—	5/32	¼	At Index
	C3YF-B	3–4	1	3/16	3½	—	—	—	5/32	¼	At Index
	C3YF-H	3–4	1	3/16	—	—	—	5/32	—	—	—
1964	C3AF-BL	1–1½	1	3/16	—	—	—	5/16	—	—	—
	C3AF-BM	1–1½	1	3/16	3½	—	—	5/16	—	—	—
	C3AF-BS	1–1½	1	3/16	—	—	—	3/8	—	—	—
	C3AF-BT	1–1½	1	3/16	3½	—	—	3/8	—	—	—
	C3DF-R	1–1½	1	3/16	—	—	—	3/8	—	—	—
	C3DF-S	1–1½	1	3/16	3½	—	—	3/8	—	—	—
	C3GF-E	1–1½	1	3/16	—	—	—	3/8	—	—	—
	C3OF-AK	1–1½	1	3/16	—	—	—	3/8	—	—	—
	C3OF-AL	1–1½	1	3/16	3½	—	—	3/8	—	—	—
	C3OF-AM	1–1½	1	3/16	3½	—	—	5/16	—	—	—
	C3YF-F	1–1½	1	3/16	—	—	1300	—	1/8	¼	At Index
	C3YF-G	1–1½	1	3/16	3½	—	1500	—	1/8	¼	At Index
	C3YF-H	1–1½	1	3/16	3½	—	1500	—	1/8	¼	At Index
	C4AF-DM	1–1½	②	5/16	—	—	—	3/8	—	—	—
	C4AF-DN	1–1½	②	5/16	3½	—	—	3/8	—	—	—
	C4OF-BA	1–1½	②	5/16	—	—	—	3/8	—	—	—
	C4OF-BB	1–1½	②	5/16	3½	—	—	3/8	—	—	—
	C4OF-BE	1–1½	②	5/16	3½	—	—	5/16	—	—	—
1965	C4ZF-A	1–1½	②	3/16	—	—	1300	—	.140	¼	At Index
	C4ZF-B	1–1½	②	3/16	3½	—	1500	—	.140	¼	At Index
	C4ZF-J	1–1½	②	3/16	—	—	1300	—	.140	¼	At Index
	C4ZF-K	1–1½	②	3/16	3½	—	1500	—	.140	¼	At Index
	C5AF-T	1–1½	②	13/64	—	.020	1300	—	.200	¼	At Index
	C5AF-U	1–1½	②	13/64	3½	.020	1500	—	.200	¼	At Index
	C5AF-V	1–1½	②	13/64	—	.020	1300	—	.200	¼	At Index
	C5AF-Y	1–1½	②	13/64	3½	.020	1500	—	.200	¼	At Index
	C5DF-E	1–1½	②	3/16	—	—	1300	—	.110	¼	2 Lean
	C5DF-F	1–1½	②	3/16	3½	—	1500	—	.150	¼	At Index
	C5DF-G	1–1½	②	3/16	—	—	1300	—	.110	¼	2 Lean
	C5DF-H	1–1½	②	3/16	3½	—	1500	—	.150	¼	At Index
	C5OF-E	1–1½	②	3/16	—	—	1300	—	.140	¼	1 Lean
	C5OF-F	1–1½	②	3/16	3½	—	1500	—	.145	¼	At Index
	C5OF-H	1–1½	②	3/16	—	—	1300	—	.140	¼	1 Lean
	C5OF-N	1–1½	②	3/16	—	—	1300	.140	—	—	—
	C5OF-R	1–1½	②	3/16	3½	—	1500	.150	—	—	—
	C5OF-S	1–1½	②	3/16	3½	—	1300	.180	—	—	—

AUTOLITE 1100-1V CARB. ADJUSTMENT SPECIFICATIONS—Continued

See Tune Up Chart in car chapter for hot idle speeds.

Year	Carb. Model	Idle Screw (Mixture) Turns Open	Float Setting (Dry)	Pump Setting	Dashpot Setting	Fast Idle Cam Linkage Clearance	Fast Idle Speed	Manual Choke Plate Clearance	Choke Plate Clearance (Pulldown)	Dechoke Clearance ①	Automatic Choke Setting
1966	C5DF-C	1-1½	1.090	.190	—	—	1300	—	.120	1/16	1 Lean
	C5DF-L	1-1½	1.090	.190	—	—	1400	—	.100	1/16	2 Lean
	C5DF-M	1-1½	1.090	.190	3½	—	1500	—	.150	1/16	At Index
	C5OF-AC	1-1½	1.090	.190	—	—	1400	—	.140	1/16	1 Lean
	C5OF-Y	1-1½	1.090	.190	—	—	1400	—	.140	1/16	1 Lean
	C5OF-Z	1-1½	1.090	.190	3½	—	1500	—	.150	1/16	At Index
	C6AF-M	1-1½	1.093	.210	—	.020	1500	—	.200	1/16	At Index
	C6AF-N	1-1½	1.093	.210	3½	.020	1600	—	.150	1/16	At Index
	C6AF-R	1-1½	1.093	.210	—	.020	1500	—	.200	1/16	At Index
	C6AF-S	1-1½	1.093	.210	3½	.020	1600	—	.200	1/16	At Index
	C6AF-V	1-1½	1.093	.210	—	.020	1500	—	.200	1/16	At Index
	C6AF-Y	1-1½	1.093	.210	3½	.020	1600	—	.200	1/16	At Index
	C6DF-D	1-1½	1.090	.190	3½	—	1500	—	.150	1/16	At Index
	C6DF-G	1-1½	1.090	.190	3½	—	1500	—	.150	1/16	At Index
1967	C6AF-R	1-1½	1.093	.210	—	.020	1500	—	.200	1/16	At Index
	C6DF-R	1-1½	1 3/32	.190	3½	—	1500	—	.150	1/16	Index
	C6DF-S	1-1½	1 3/32	.190	—	—	1300	—	.110	1/16	2 Lean
	C6AF-AK	1-1½	1 3/32	.210	6	—	1500	—	.180	1/16	Index
	C6AF-BL	1-1½	1 3/32	.210	6	—	1600	—	.180	1/16	Index
	C6AF-BM	1-1½	1 3/32	.210	6	—	1600	—	.125	1/16	2 Rich
	C6OF-AB	1-1½	1 3/32	.190	—	—	1300	—	.140	1/16	1 Lean
	C6OF-AC	1-1½	1 3/32	.190	3½	—	1500	—	.150	1/16	Index
	C6OF-AD	1-1½	1 3/32	.190	—	—	1300	—	.140	1/16	1 Lean
	C6TF-F	1-1½	1.020	.190	—	—	—	—	.375	—	—
	C6TF-G	1-1½	1.020	.190	—	—	—	—	.375	—	—
	C6UF-AF	1-1½	1 3/32	.210	—	—	—	—	.375	—	—
	C6UF-V	1-1½	1 3/32	.210	—	—	—	—	.375	—	—
	C7AF-AA	1-1½	1 3/32	.210	2	—	1500	—	.200	1/16	Index
	C7AF-AB	1-1½	1 3/32	.210	2	—	1600	—	.200	1/16	1 Lean
	C7DF-J	1-1½	1 3/32	.190	2	—	1400	—	.110	1/16	2 Lean
	C7DF-K	1-1½	1 3/32	.190	2	—	1500	—	.150	1/16	Index
	C7OF-N	1-1½	1 3/32	.190	2	—	1400	—	.110	1/16	2 Lean
	C7OF-R	1-1½	1 3/32	.190	2	—	1500	—	.150	1/16	Index
	C7TF-K	1-1½	1 1/16	.190	2	—	—	—	.375	—	—
	C7UF-A, B	1-1½	1 3/32	.190	2	—	—	—	.375	—	—
	C7UF-C, D	1-1½	1 1/32	.210	2	—	—	—	.375	—	—
	C5UF-L, M	1-1½	1 3/32	.190	—	—	—	—	.375	—	—
1968–69	C8AF-E④	1-1½	1 3/32	.190	.080	—	1600	—	.280	15/64	3 Lean
	C80F-A③	1-1½	1 2/32	.190	.080	—	1400	—	.234	15/64	2 Lean
	C80F-B④	1-1½	1 3/32	.190	.100	—	1500	—	.234	15/64	1 Lean
1969	C9DF-B	—	1 3/32	.150	3	—	1400	—	.150	1/4	3 Lean
	C9OF-A	—	1 3/32	.190	.080	—	1600	—	.200	.160	3 Lean
	C9OF-B	—	1 3/32	.190	.080	—	1400	—	.200	.160	1 Lean
	C9OF-J	—	1 3/32	.190	—	—	1400	—	.200	.160	1 Lean
	C9OF-K	—	1 3/32	.190	—	—	1600	—	.200	.160	3 Lean

①—Minimum clearance between choke plate and air horn with throttle plates wide open.

②—Rubber float 1″, metal float 1 3/32″.

③—Thermactor system.

④—Imco system.

MODEL 1100-1V ADJUSTMENTS

Figs. 1 and 2 illustrate exterior views of the two types of one-barrel carburetors while Figs. 3 and 4 illustrate the units exploded. Fig. 1 carburetor is available only with an automatic choke whereas Fig. 2 unit may be had with or without an automatic choke.

As shown, both types consist of two main assemblies, the upper body (air horn) and the lower (throttle) body. The upper body contains the metering components which include the main and idle fuel systems with power valve, float chamber vent and fuel inlet system. The lower body contains the fuel bowl, accelerating pump, idle mixture adjusting screw (needle) and spark valve.

On 1100 models a built-in hydraulic dashpot is incorporated in the lower body as shown. However, the 1101 model differs in that it has an externally mounted dashpot fastened to a bracket on the upper body.

Float Level Adjustment

Fig. 5—With air horn inverted and gasket removed, measure distance from gasket surface of air horn to top of float. If the dimension is not as listed in the *Ford Specifications Chart,* bend float arm tab as required to obtain the specified dimension.

Vent Valve Adjustment

Fig. 6—With throttle valve fully closed, groove on vent valve rod should be even with open end of vent. To adjust, bend arm on vent valve rod actuating lever (where it contacts pump lever) to align groove with edge of bore.

Pump Adjustment

Position throttle and choke valve linkage so that throttle valve will be completely closed. Hold throttle valve closed and place a gauge of the thickness listed in the *Ford Specifications Chart* between roll pin and cover surface, Fig. 7. Bend pump actuating rod to obtain specified clearance between cover and roll pin in pump lever.

Acceleration requirements in various climates are satisfied by controlling the amount of fuel discharged from the pump. The pump stroke is controlled by changing the location of the roll pin in the lever stop hole, Fig. 8.

For operation in temperatures of 50 degrees and below, place the roll pin in the hole marked "HI". For best performance and fuel economy at normal temperatures and high altitudes (5000 ft.) place roll pin in hole marked "LO".

Dashpot Adjustment

Fig. 9—With throttle valve fully closed, turn dashpot adjusting screw outward until it clears dashpot plunger. Turn adjusting screw inward until it just contacts dashpot plunger, then continue turning inward the number of turns listed in the *Ford Specifications Chart* against the dashpot plunger.

Manual Choke (Pull-Down) Adjustment

Fig. 10—This adjustment refers to Fig. 2 carburetor only. Place choke linkage in full-choke position. Then insert a gauge or drill of a size listed in the *Ford Specifications Chart* between choke valve and inner wall of air horn. While maintain-

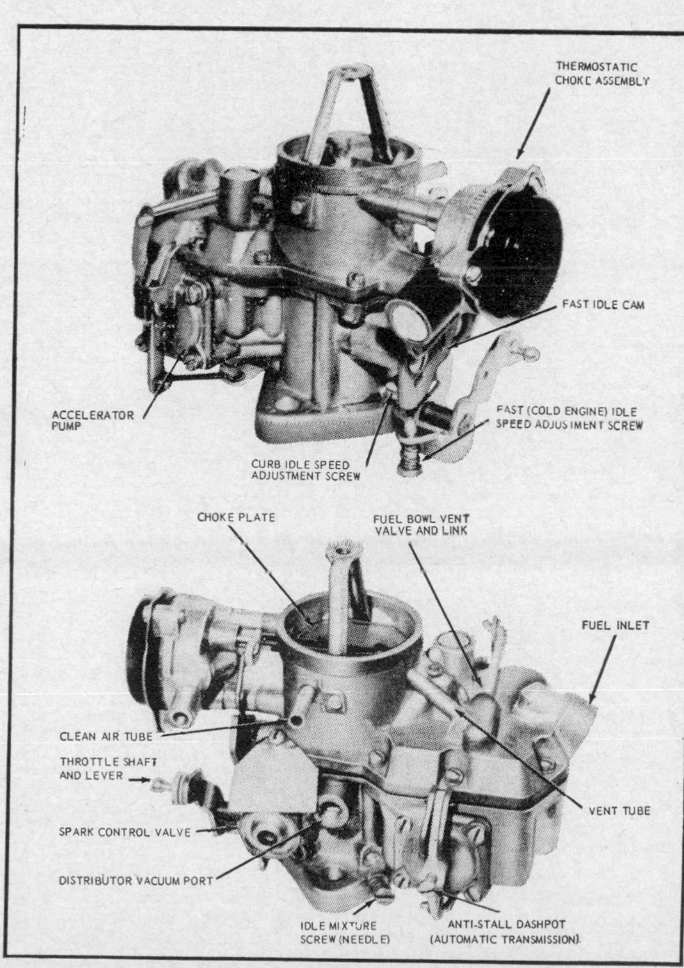

Fig. 1 Autolite 1100 carburetor with automatic choke mounted on air horn

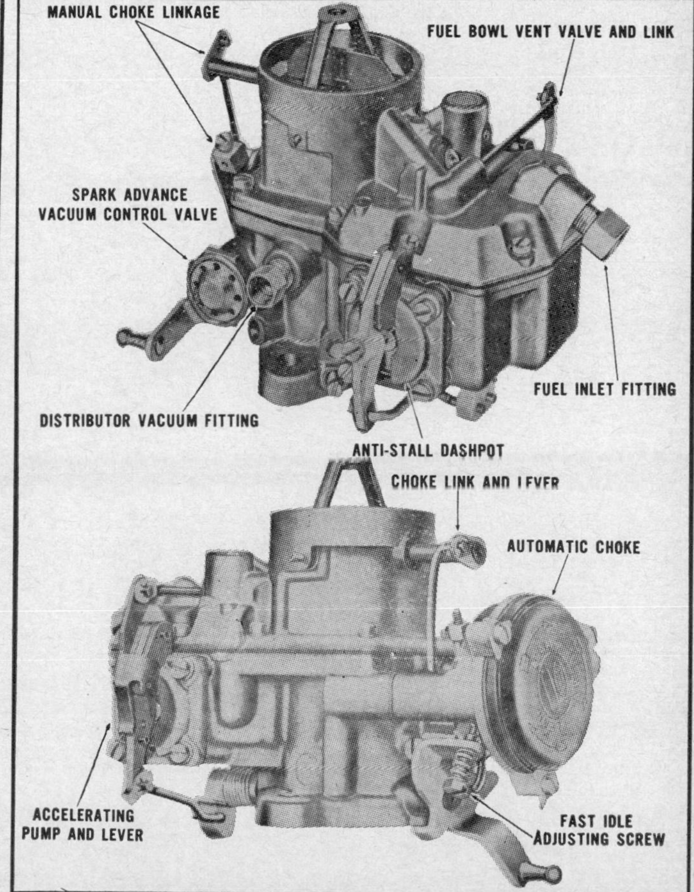

Fig. 2 Autolite 1100 carburetor with automatic choke mounted on throttle body

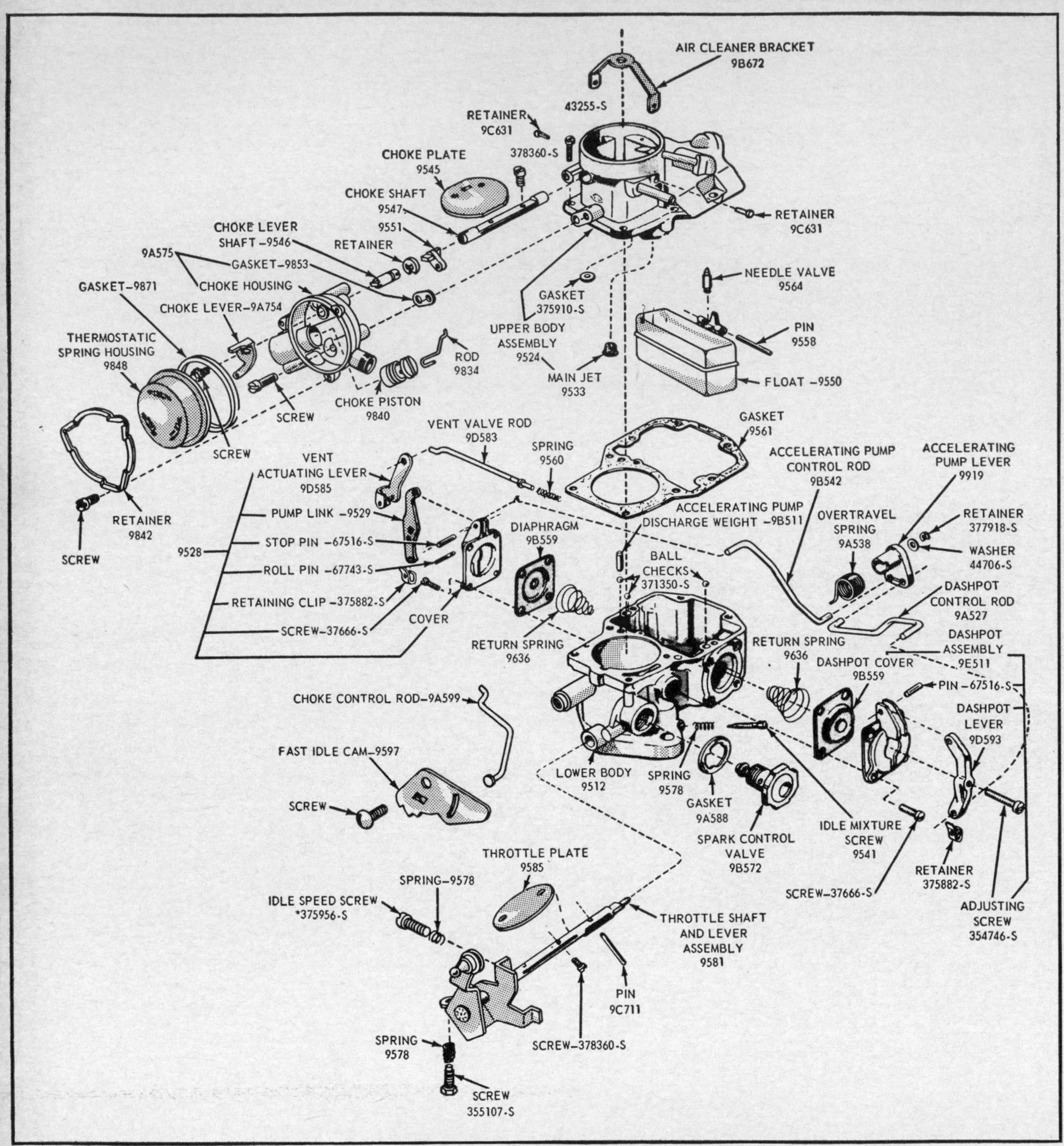

Fig. 3 Exploded view of Autolite 1100 carburetor shown in Fig. 1

ing full-choke position, adjust choke pull-down nut so it just contacts swivel on cam lever.

Automatic Choke Fast Idle Adjustment

Fig. 11—This adjustment refers to Fig. 2 carburetor only. Insert a gauge or drill of the size listed in the *Ford Specifications Chart* between throttle valve and carburetor bore. Close choke valve and turn fast idle adjusting screw inward until it just contacts fast idle cam.

Automatic Choke Linkage (Pull-Down) Adjustment

Fig. 12—This adjustment refers to Fig. 2 carburetor only. The fast idle adjustment must be made before making this adjustment because the position of the pull-down rod is one of the determining factors affecting throttle-to-choke opening relationship.

Place a drill or gauge of a size listed in the *Ford Specifications Chart* between choke valve and inner wall of air horn. Close choke valve on gauge or drill and hold it securely. Close throttle until fast idle screw touches fast idle cam. Adjust plastic nut to just contact swivel on choke lever.

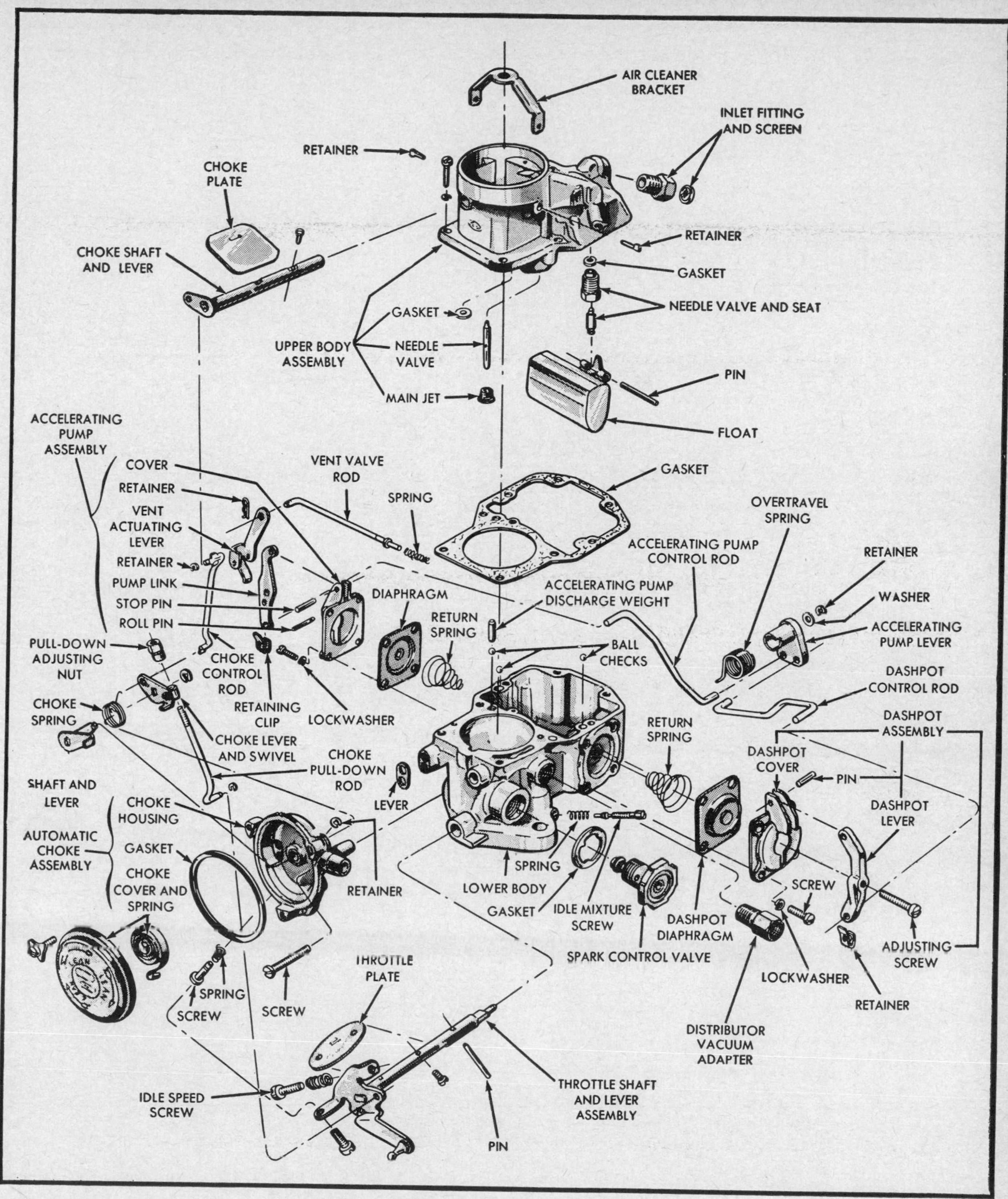

Fig. 4 Exploded view of Autolite 1100 carburetor shown in Fig. 2

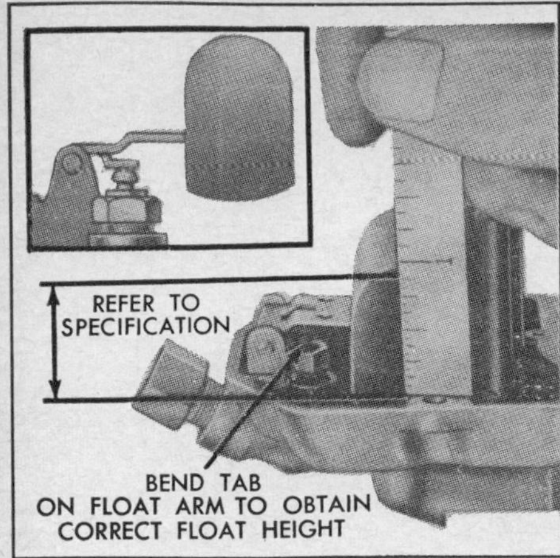
REFER TO SPECIFICATION
BEND TAB ON FLOAT ARM TO OBTAIN CORRECT FLOAT HEIGHT

Fig. 5 Float level adjustment

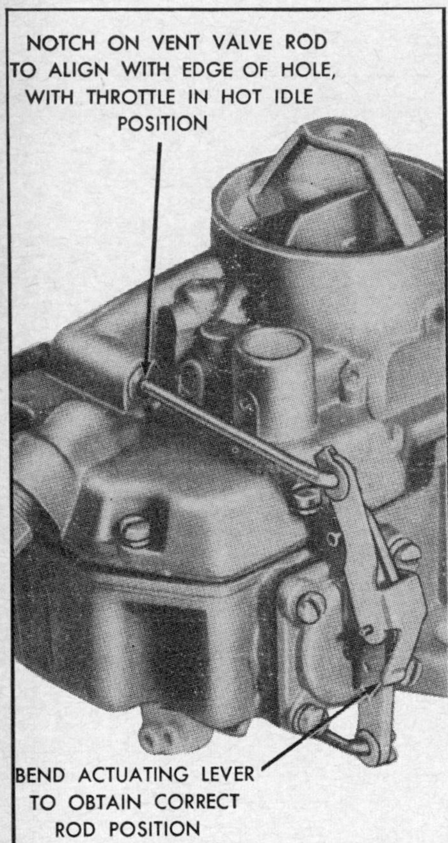
NOTCH ON VENT VALVE ROD TO ALIGN WITH EDGE OF HOLE, WITH THROTTLE IN HOT IDLE POSITION
BEND ACTUATING LEVER TO OBTAIN CORRECT ROD POSITION

Fig. 6 Vent valve adjustment

WITH THROTTLE PLATE FULLY CLOSED INSERT A *Gauge* THAT EQUALS THE SPECIFIED CLEARANCE BETWEEN THE PIN AND COVER
LO
HI
FAST IDLE SCREW NOT TOUCHING IDLE CAM
BEND ROD FOR CLEARANCE ADJUSTMENT

Fig. 7 Accelerator pump adjustment

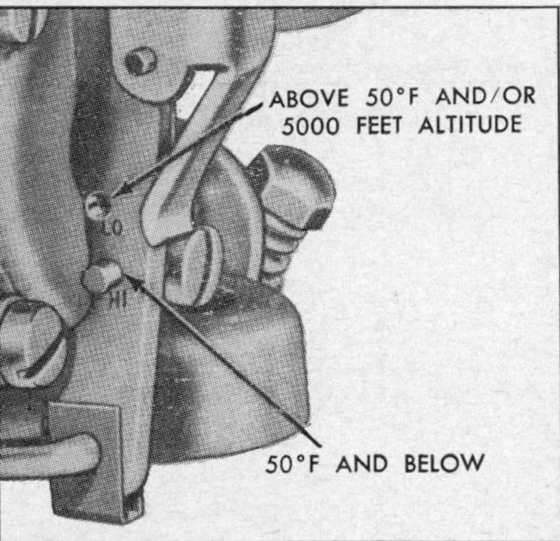
ABOVE 50°F AND/OR 5000 FEET ALTITUDE
LO
HI
50°F AND BELOW

Fig. 8 Accelerator pump lever adjustment

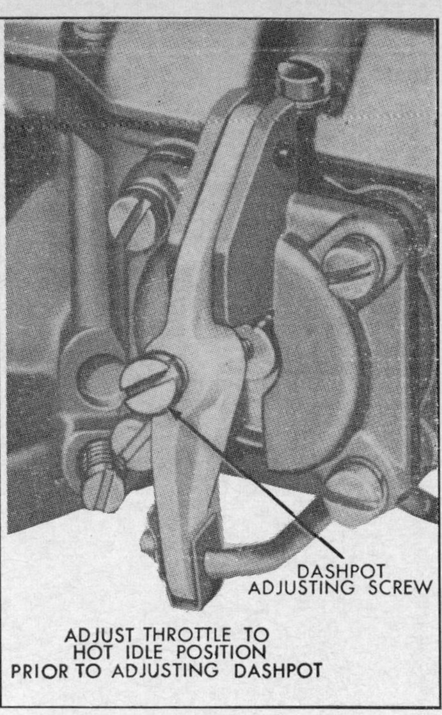
DASHPOT ADJUSTING SCREW
ADJUST THROTTLE TO HOT IDLE POSITION PRIOR TO ADJUSTING DASHPOT

Fig. 9 Anti-stall dashpot adjustment

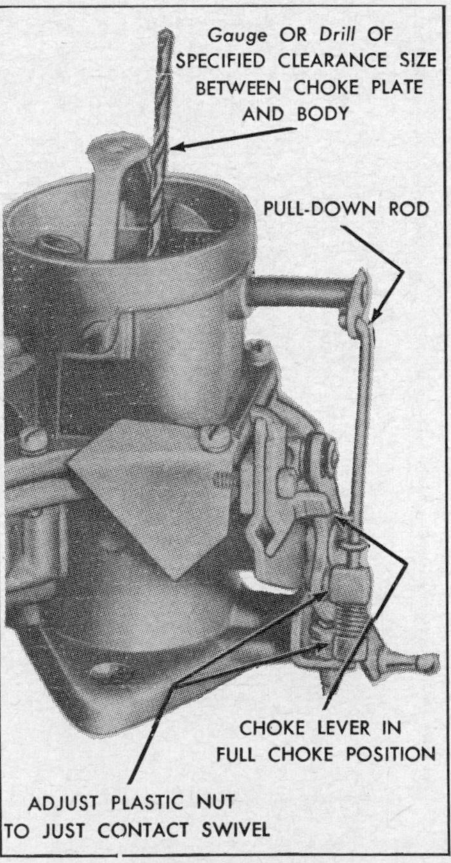
Gauge OR *Drill* OF SPECIFIED CLEARANCE SIZE BETWEEN CHOKE PLATE AND BODY
PULL-DOWN ROD
CHOKE LEVER IN FULL CHOKE POSITION
ADJUST PLASTIC NUT TO JUST CONTACT SWIVEL

Fig. 10 Manual choke adjustment (Fig. 2 unit)

Choke Plate Clearance & Fast Idle Linkage

Figs. 13 and 14—These adjustments refer to Fig. 1 carburetor only.

1. Remove air cleaner and choke thermostatic spring housing from carburetor.
2. Bend a .036" wire gauge as shown in inset, Fig. 13.
3. Block throttle about half open so that fast idle cam does not contact fast idle adjusting screw.
4. Insert bent end of gauge between lower end of piston slot and upper edge of right-hand slot in choke housing, Fig. 13, and pull choke piston lever counterclockwise until gauge is snug in piston slot.
5. Hold gauge in place by exerting light pressure on choke piston lever.
6. Gradually bend rod (link) between choke piston and piston lever until choke plate opens just wide enough to allow gauge or drill of the specified size between front of choke plate and air horn, Fig. 13 (see *Ford Specifications Chart)*.
7. Install thermostatic spring housing and gasket on choke housing and secure with clamp and screws.
8. Rotate spring housing counterclockwise (rich direction) to align center index mark on choke housing with index mark on spring housing; then rotate spring housing 90 degrees counterclockwise.

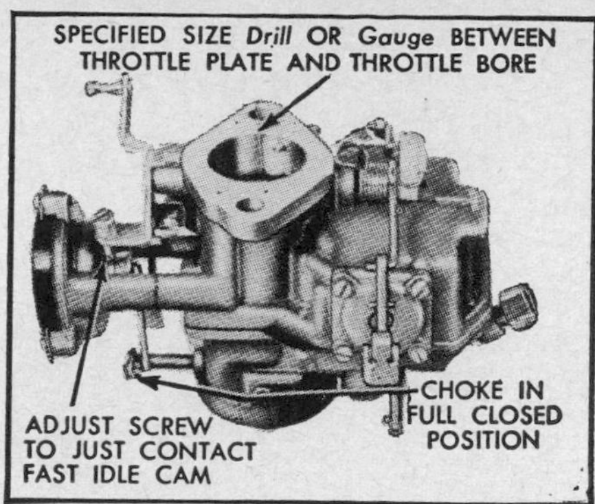

Fig. 11 Automatic choke fast idle adjustment (Fig. 2 unit)

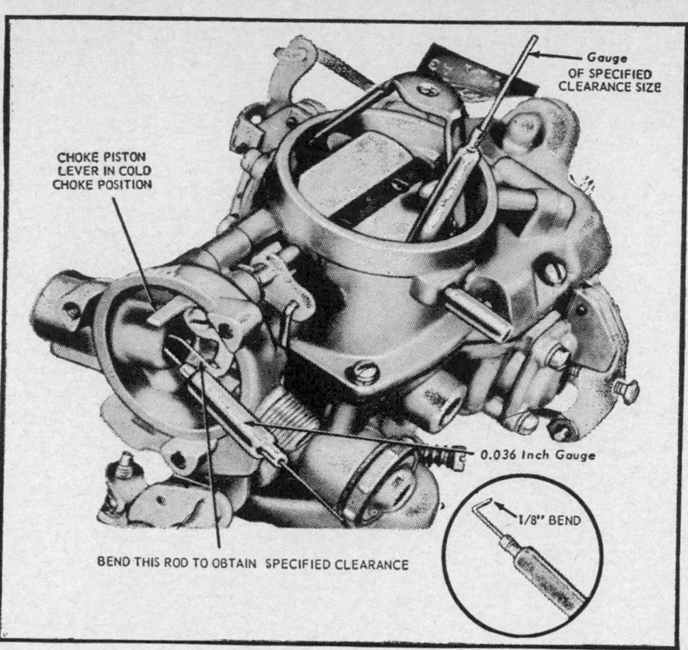

Fig. 13 Choke plate clearance adjustment (Fig. 1 unit)

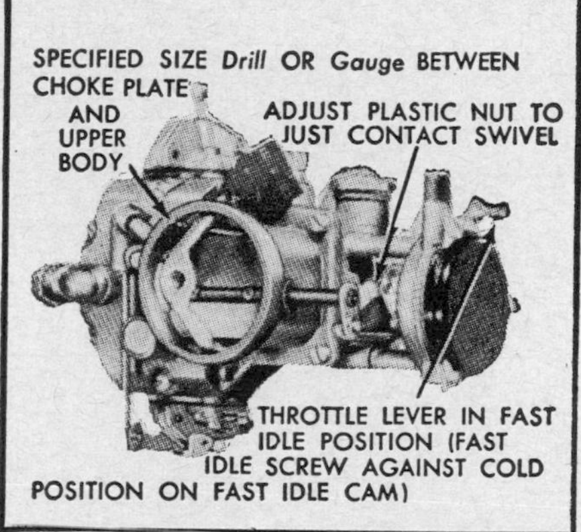

Fig. 12 Automatic choke linkage adjustment (Fig. 2 unit)

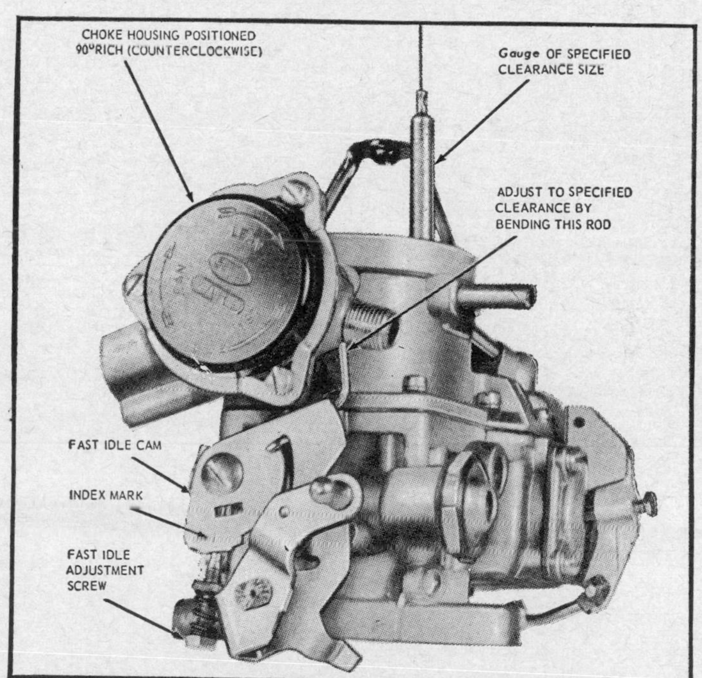

Fig. 14 Fast idle cam linkage adjustment (Fig. 1 unit)

Fig. 15 Automatic choke setting

9. Position fast idle adjusting screw on index mark on fast idle cam, Fig. 14.
10. Adjust fast idle cam linkage to specification by bending choke control rod, Fig. 14, to provide the specified clearance between front of choke plate and air horn. Bend rod inward to decrease (outward to increase) clearance. Make certain fast idle screw remains on index mark of fast idle cam during adjustment procedure.
11. Set thermostatic spring housing to specified mark listed in the *Ford Specifications Chart.*

NOTE: If the foregoing adjustments were made with the carburetor installed on the engine, adjust engine idle speed and mixture, fast idle speed and dashpot as outlined above.

Automatic Choke Setting

Fig. 15—Loosen retaining screws and set thermostatic spring housing to the mark specified in the *Ford Specifications Chart* and tighten retaining screws.

AUTOLITE 2100-2V CARB. ADJUSTMENT SPECIFICATIONS

See Tune Up Chart in car chapters for hot idle speeds.

Year	Carb. Model (Code 9510) ①	Idle Screws (Mixture) Turns Open	Float Level (Dry)	Fuel Level (Wet)	Pump Setting Hole No.	Choke Plate Clearance (Pull-Down)	Fast Idle Cam Linkage Clearance	Fast Idle Speed (Hot Engine)	Dechoke Clearance ⑧	Dashpot Setting	Choke Setting
1963	C3AF-E	1-1½	21/32	29/32	⑥	3/16	.050⑤	1200⑦	1/16	—	At Index
	C3AF-F	1-1½	21/32	29/32	⑥	5/32	.050⑤	1500⑦	1/16	.060-.090	2 Lean
	C3MF-A	1-1½	21/32	29/32	⑥	3/16	.050⑤	1200⑦	1/16	—	2 Lean
	C3MF-B	1-1½	21/32	29/32	⑥	5/32	.050⑤	1500⑦	1/16	.060-.090	2 Lean
	C3OF-E	1-1½	21/32	29/32	⑥	1/8	.050⑤	1200⑦	1/16	—	4 Lean
	C3OF-F	1-1½	21/32	29/32	⑥	7/64	.050⑤	1500⑦	1/16	.060-.090	4 Lean
1964	C4AF-B	1-1½	5/8	7/8	⑥	7/64	3/32	1300⑦	1/16	—	2 Rich
	C4AF-C	1-1½	5/8	7/8	⑥	7/64	3/32	1600⑦	1/16	1/16-3/32	2 Rich
	C4AF-DD	1-1½	15/32	7/8	⑥	9/64	1/8	1400⑦	1/16	—	At Index
	C4AF-DE	1-1½	15/32	7/8	⑥	1/8	7/64	1600⑦	1/16	5/64	2 Rich
	C4AF-J	1-1½	5/8	7/8	⑥	7/64	3/32	1600⑦	1/16	1/16-3/32	2 Rich
	C4DF-E	1-1½	1/2	3/4	⑥	7/64	3/32	1300⑦	1/16	—	2 Rich
	C4DF-F	1-1½	1/2	3/4	⑥	7/64	3/32	1600⑦	1/16	1/16-3/32	2 Rich
	C4DF-J	1-1½	19/64	3/4	⑥	3/32	3/32	1300⑦	1/16	5/64	2 Rich
	C4DF-K	1-1½	19/64	3/4	⑥	3/32	3/32	1600⑦	1/16	5/64	2 Rich
	C4DF-N	1-1½	19/64	3/4	⑥	3/32	3/32	1400⑦	1/16	—	2 Rich
	C4MF-A	1-1½	5/8	7/8	⑥	3/16	9/64	1500⑦	1/16	1/16-3/32	2 Lean
	C4MF-D	1-1½	21/32	29/32	⑥	3/16	1/16	1300⑦	1/16	—	1 Lean
	C4MF-E	1-1½	21/32	29/32	⑥	5/32	1/16	1500⑦	1/16	1/16-3/32	1 Lean
	C4OF-A	1-1½	1/2	3/4	⑥	7/64	3/32	1300⑦	1/16	—	2 Rich
	C4OF-B	1-1½	1/2	3/4	⑥	7/64	3/32	1600⑦	1/16	1/16-3/32	2 Rich
	C4OF-AE	1-1½	19/64	3/4	⑥	5/64	1/16	1600⑦	1/16	5/64	2 Rich
	C4OF-AK	1-1½	19/64	3/4	⑥	1/8	7/64	1400⑦	1/16	—	2 Lean
	C4OF-K	1-1½	19/64	3/4	⑥	3/32	3/32	1300⑦	1/16	5/64	2 Rich
	C4OF-L	1-1½	19/64	3/4	⑥	5/64	1/16	1600⑦	1/16	5/64	2 Rich
1965	C4ZF-E	1-1½	19/64	3/4	⑥	.078	.062	1600⑨	1/16	5/64	2 Rich
	C4ZF-F	1-1½	19/64	3/4	⑥	.125	.093	1400⑨	1/16	—	2 Rich
	C5AF-A	1-1½	15/32	7/8	⑥	.140	.130	1400⑦	1/16	—	At Index
	C5AF-AH	1-1½	15/32	7/8	⑥	.140	.130	1400⑦	1/16	—	At Index
	C5AF-AJ	1-1½	15/32	7/8	⑥	.1[illegible]0	.1[illegible]0	16[illegible]0⑦	1/16	5/64	2 Rich
	C5AF-B	1-1½	15/32	7/8	⑥	.120	.120	1600⑦	1/16	5/64	2 Rich
	C5MF-A	1-1½	15/32	7/8	⑥	.160	.140	1300⑦	1/16	—	2 Rich
	C5MF-B	1-1½	15/32	7/8	⑥	.180	.150	1500⑦	1/16	5/64	2 Rich
	C5MF-C	1-1½	15/32	7/8	⑥	.180	.150	1500⑦	1/16	5/64	2 Rich
	C5MF-D	1-1½	15/32	7/8	⑥	.160	.140	1300⑦	1/16	—	2 Rich
	C5MF-E	1-1½	15/32	7/8	⑥	.180	.150	1500⑦	1/16	5/64	2 Rich
	C5MF-F	1-1½	15/32	7/8	⑥	.180	.150	1500⑦	1/16	5/64	2 Rich
	C5ZF-A	1-1½	15/32	7/8	⑥	.140	.130	1400⑨	1/16	—	At Index
	C5ZF-B	1-1½	15/32	7/8	⑥	.130	.120	1600⑨	1/16	5/64	2 Rich
	C5ZF-G	1-1½	15/32	7/8	⑥	.140	.130	1400⑨	1/16	—	At Index
	C5ZF-H	1-1½	15/32	7/8	⑥	.130	.120	1600⑨	1/16	5/64	2 Rich
1966	C6AF-A	1-1½	.491	.875	⑥	.140	.150	1400	1/16	—	At Index
	C6AF-AA	1-1½	.371	.750	⑥	.120	.110	1600	1/16	—	2 Rich
	C6AF-AH	1-1½	.431	.810	⑥	.200	.160	1500	1/16	—	At Index
	C6AF-B	1-1½	.491	.875	⑥	.120	.110	1600	1/16	.060-.090	2 Rich
	C6AF-C	1-1½	.491	.880	⑥	.200	.160	1400	1/16	—	At Index
	C6AF-Z	1-1½	.371	.750	⑥	.140	.130	1400	1/16	—	At Index
	C6DF-A	1-1½	.491	.875	⑥	.140	.150	1400	1/16	—	At Index
	C6DF-B	1-1½	.491	.875	⑥	.120	.110	1600	1/16	.060-.090	2 Rich
	C6DF-E	1-1½	.371	.750	⑥	.140	.130	1400	1/16	—	At Index
	C6DF-F	1-1½	.371	.750	⑥	.120	.110	1600	1/16	.060-.090	2 Rich
	C6MF-A	1-1½	.491	.880	⑥	.180	.160	1400	1/16	.060-.090	At Index
	C6MF-D	1-1½	.431	.810	⑥	.180	.160	1500	1/16	—	At Index
	C6OF-B	1-1½	.491	.880	⑥	.200	.160	1300	1/16	—	At Index
	C6OF-C	1-1½	.491	.880	⑥	.180	.160	1400	1/16	.060-.090	At Index
	C6OF-K	1-1½	.431	.810	⑥	.200	.160	1300	1/16	—	At Index
	C6OF-L	1-1½	.431	.810	⑥	.180	.160	1500	1/16	.060-.090	At Index

AUTOLITE 2100-2V CARB. ADJUSTMENT SPECIFICATIONS—Continued

See Tune Up Chart in car chapters for hot idle speeds.

Year	Carb. Model (Code 9510) ①	Idle Screws (Mixture) Turns Open	Float Level (Dry)	Fuel Level (Wet)	Pump Setting Hole No.	Choke Plate Clearance (Pull-Down)	Fast Idle Cam Linkage Clearance	Fast Idle Speed (Hot Engine)	Dechoke Clearance ⑧	Dashpot Setting	Choke Setting
1966	C6TF-BG	1-1½	.450	29/32	⑥	.250	—	—	—	—	—
	C6TF-BH	1-1½	.450	29/32	⑥	.250	—	—	—	—	—
1967	C7AF-N	1-1½	.484	.875	⑥	.140	.130	1400	1/16	—	Index
	C7AF-R	1-1½	.484	.875	⑥	.120	.110	1600	1/16	—	2 Rich
	C7AF-S	1-1½	.531	.905	⑥	.120	.110	1400	1/16	.130	Index
	C7AF-T	1-1½	.531	.905	⑥	.120	.110	1600	1/16	.130	2 Rich
	C7AF-U	1-1½	.484	.875	⑥	.200	.160	1300	1/16	—	Index
	C7AF-V	1-1½	.375	.750	⑥	.180	.150	1400	1/16	—	2 Rich
	C7AF-Y	1-1½	.531	.905	⑥	.200	.170	1300	1/16	.095	Index
	C7AF-Z	1-1½	.531	.905	⑥	.180	.150	1500	1/16	.095	Index
	C7DF-AJ	1-1½	17/32	29/32	⑥	.120	.110	1400	.060	—	2 Rich
	C7DF-AL	1-1½	3/8	3/4	⑥	.120	.110	1600	.060	1/8	2 Rich
	C7DF-E	1-1½	.375	.750	⑥	.120	.110	1400	1/16	—	Index
	C7DF-F	1-1½	.531	.905	⑥	.120	.110	1600	1/16	.075	2 Rich
	C7DF-G	1-1½	.531	.905	⑥	.120	.110	1400	1/16	.125	Index
	C7DF-H	1-1½	.531	.905	⑥	.120	.110	1600	1/16	.125	2 Rich
	C7DF-R	1-1½	3/8	3/4	⑥	.120	.110	1600	.060	1/8	2 Rich
	C7DF-S	1-1½	17/32	29/32	⑥	.120	.110	1400	.060	—	2 Rich
	C7OF-J	1-1½	.484	.875	⑥	.200	.160	1300	1/16	—	Index
	C7OF-K	1-1½	.375	.750	⑥	.180	.150	1400	1/16	—	2 Rich
	C7OF-L	1-1½	.531	.905	⑥	.200	.170	1300	1/16	.095	Index
	C7OF-M	1-1½	.531	.905	⑥	.180	.150	1500	1/16	.095	Index
	C7TF-C	1-1½	.531	.905	⑥	.250	—	1400	—	—	—
	C7TF-D	1-1½	.531	.905	⑥	.250	—	1400	—	.125	—
1968	C8AF-AK	1-1½	3/8	3/4	⑥	.120	.110	1200	.060	—	Index
	C8AF-L	1-1½	3/8	3/4	⑥	.140	.120	1400	.060	.125	1 Lean
	C8AF-M	1-1½	31/64	7/8	⑥	.210	.170	1300	.060	—	Index
	C8AF-AN	1-1½	31/64	7/8	⑥	.120	.100	1500	.060	.125	Index
	C8AF-N	1-1½	31/64	7/8	⑥	.120	.100	1500	.060	.125	Index
	C8OF-K	—	31/64	7/8	⑥	.120	.100	1500	.060	1/8	Index
	C8OF-U	—	31/64	7/8	⑥	.120	.100	1500	.060	1/8	Index
	C8ZF-G	—	3/8	3/4	⑥	.140	.120	1400	.060	1/8	1 Lean
1968-69	C8AF-BD	—	3/8	3/4	⑥	.130	.110	1400	.060	1/8	2 Rich
1969	C9AF-A	—	3/8	3/4	⑥	.120	.110	1600	.060	1/8	Index
	C9AF-B	—	31/64	7/8	⑥	.210	.170	1300	.060	1/8	1 Rich
	C9AF-C	—	31/64	7/8	⑥	.130	.100	1500	.060	1/8	2 Rich
	C9OF-C	—	31/64	7/8	⑥	.120	.100	1600	.060	—	2 Rich
	C9ZF-A	—	9/16	15/16	⑥	.150	.130	1300	.060	7/64	1 Rich
	C9ZF-B	—	31/64	7/8	⑥	.120	.100	1600	.060	—	2 Rich
	C9ZF G	—	3/8	3/4	⑥	.120	.110	1600	.060	1/8	Index
	C9MF-A	—	31/64	7/8	⑥	.150	.120	1500	.060	1/8	2 Rich

RAMBLER

Year	Carb. Model	Idle Screws (Mixture) Turns Open	Float Level (Dry)	Fuel Level (Wet)	Pump Setting Hole No.	Choke Plate Clearance (Pull-Down)	Fast Idle Cam Linkage Clearance	Fast Idle Speed (Hot Engine)	Dechoke Clearance	Dashpot Setting	Choke Setting
1968	8HM2	1-1½	3/8	3/4	⑥	.125	.120	1600	—	—	Index
	8HA2	1-1½	3/8	3/4	⑥	.140	.120	1600	—	.095	Index
	8ZA2	1-1½	3/8	3/4	⑥	.140	.120	1600	—	.095	Index
1969	9HM2	2	1/2	13/16	⑥	.125	.120	1600	.080	.140	Index
	9HA2	2	1/2	13/16	⑥	.140	.120	1600	.080	.140	Index
	9ZA2	2	1/2	13/16	⑥	.140	.120	1600	.080	.140	Index

①—Stamped on left side of fuel bowl or on tag attached to bowl cover.

⑤—With throttle plates half open, clearance is measured between top side of fast idle cam and back of choke housing.

⑥—With link in inboard hole in pump lever, place overtravel lever in the longest stroke hole for extremely cold weather, intermediate stroke holes for moderate weather, and short stroke hole for extremely warm weather.

⑦—With fast idle screw on kickdown step of cam.

⑧—Minimum clearance between choke plate and air horn wall with throttle plates wide open.

⑨—With fast idle screw aligned with arrow on cam.

Continued

AUTOLITE 4100-4V ADJUSTMENT SPECIFICATIONS

See Tune Up Chart in car chapters for hot idle speeds.

Year	Carb. Model (Code 9510) (1)	Idle Screws (Mixture) Turns Open	Float Level (Dry)	Fuel Level (Wet)	Pump Setting (Hole No.)	Choke Plate Clearance (Pull-Down)	Fast Idle Cam Linkage Clearance	Fast Idle Speed (Hot Engine)	Secondary Throttle Plate Clearance (2)	Dechoke Clearance (3)	Dashpot Setting	Choke Setting
1963	C3AF-N	1-1½	47/64	63/64	(4)	3/16	.050(8)	1200(10)	.009(7)	1/16	—	At Index
	C3AF-R	1-1½	47/64	63/64	(4)	5/32	.050(8)	1500(10)	.009(7)	1/16	.060–.090	2 Lean
	C3AF-S	1-1½	47/64	63/64	(4)	3/16	.050(8)	1200(10)	.009(7)	1/16	—	2 Lean
	C3AF-T	1-1½	47/64	63/64	(4)	3/16	.050(8)	1200(10)	.009(7)	1/16	—	2 Lean
	C3SF-A	1-1½	47/64	63/64	(4)	5/32	.050(8)	1500(10)	.009(7)	1/16	.060–.090	2 Lean
1964	C3AF-BU	1-1½	21/32	29/32	(4)	3/16	1/16	1300(10)	¾ Turn	1/16	—	1 Rich
	C3AF-BV	1-1½	21/32	29/32	(4)	5/32	1/16	1500(10)	¾ Turn	1/16	1/16–3/32	1 Lean
	C3AF-BY	1-1½	21/32	29/32	(4)	3/16	1/16	1300(10)	¾ Turn	1/16	—	1 Rich
	C3AF-BZ	1-1½	21/32	29/32	(4)	5/32	1/16	1500(10)	¾ Turn	1/16	1/16–3/32	1 Lean
	C3OF-AJ	1-1½	21/32	29/32	(4)	3/16	1/16	1800(10)	¾ Turn	1/16	1/16–3/32	3 Lean
	C4AF-N	1-1½	21/32	29/32	(4)	3/16	1/16	1300(10)	¾ Turn	1/16	—	1 Lean
	C4AF-R	1-1½	21/32	29/32	(4)	5/32	1/16	1500(10)	¾ Turn	1/16	1/16–3/32	3 Lean
	C4GF-D	1-1½	21/32	29/32	(4)	5/32	1/16	1300(10)	¾ Turn	1/16	—	1 Lean
	C4GF-E	1-1½	21/32	29/32	(4)	9/64	1/16	1500(10)	¾ Turn	1/16	1/16–3/32	3 Lean
	C4OF-AL	1-1½	29/64	29/32	(4)	7/32	1/16	1800(10)	¾ Turn	—	—	—
	C4OF-AT	1-1½	29/64	29/32	(4)	7/32	1/16	1800(10)	¾ Turn	—	5/64	—
	C4SF-B	1-1½	21/32	29/32	(4)	3/16	1/16	1500(10)	¾ Turn	1/16	1/16–3/32	1 Lean
1965	C4GF-AE	1-1½	29/64	29/32	(4)	.140	.125	1400(13)	¾ Turn	1/16	—	At Index
	C4GF-AF	1-1½	29/64	29/32	(4)	.125	.109	1600(13)	¾ Turn	1/16	5/64	2 Rich
	C4OF-AL	1-1½	(11)	(12)	(4)	.218	—	1800(13)	¾ Turn	—	—	—
	C4OF-AT	1-1½	(11)	(12)	(4)	.218	—	1800(13)	¾ Turn	—	5/64	—
	C5AF-AA	1-1½	(11)	(12)	(4)	.120	.120	1500(10)	¾ Turn	1/16	5/16	At Index
	C5AF-AC	1-1½	(11)	(12)	(4)	.120	.120	1500(10)	¾ Turn	1/16	5/16	At Index
	C5AF-AD	1-1½	(11)	(12)	(4)	.130	.130	1300(10)	¾ Turn	1/16	—	At Index
	C5AF-AE	1-1½	(11)	(12)	(4)	.120	.120	1500(10)	¾ Turn	1/16	5/16	At Index
	C5AF-AK	1-1½	(11)	(12)	(4)	.130	.130	1500(10)	¾ Turn	1/16	—	At Index
	C5AF-AL	1-1½	(11)	(12)	(4)	.120	.120	1500(10)	¾ Turn	1/16	5/16	At Index
	C5AF-AN	1-1½	(11)	(12)	(4)	.120	.120	1500(10)	¾ Turn	1/16	5/16	At Index
	C5AF-AR	1-1½	(11)	(12)	(4)	.130	.130	1300(10)	¾ Turn	1/16	—	At Index
	C5AF-AS	1-1½	(11)	(12)	(4)	.120	.120	1500(10)	¾ Turn	1/16	5/16	At Index
	C5AF-Z	1-1½	(11)	(12)	(4)	.160	.130	1300(10)	¾ Turn	1/16	—	At Index
	C5OF-J	1-1½	29/64	(12)	(4)	.230	—	1800(13)	¾ Turn	1/16	—	—
	C5OF-K	1-1½	29/64	(12)	(4)	.230	—	1800(13)	¾ Turn	1/16	5/64	—
	C5OF-L	1-1½	(11)	(12)	(4)	.230	—	1400(13)	¾ Turn	—	—	—
	C5OF-M	1-1½	29/64	(12)	(4)	.230	—	1600(13)	¾ Turn	—	5/64	—
	C5SF-A	1-1½	15/32	7/8	(4)	3/16	1/8	1500(10)	¾ Turn	1/16	1/16–3/32	At Index
	C5ZF-C	1-1½	29/64	29/32	(4)	.120	.120	1400(13)	¾ Turn	1/16	—	2 Rich
	C5ZF-D	1-1½	29/64	29/32	(4)	.120	.100	1600(13)	¾ Turn	1/16	5/64	2 Rich
	C5ZF-E	1-1½	29/64	29/32	(4)	.120	.120	1400(13)	¾ Turn	1/16	—	2 Rich
	C5ZF-F	1-1½	29/64	29/32	(4)	.120	.100	1600(13)	¾ Turn	1/16	5/64	2 Rich
	C5ZF-J	1-1½	29/64	29/32	(4)	.120	.120	1400(13)	¾ Turn	1/16	—	2 Rich
	C5ZF-K	1-1½	29/64	29/32	(4)	.120	.100	1600(13)	¾ Turn	1/16	5/64	2 Rich
1966	C6AF-AB	1-1½	(14)	(15)	(4)	.160	.130	1300	—	1/16	—	2 Rich
	C6AF-AC	1-1½	(14)	(15)	(4)	.140	.120	1500	—	1/16	—	1 Rich
	C6AF-AF	1-1½	(16)	(17)	(4)	.160	.130	1300	—	1/16	—	At Index
	C6AF-AG	1-1½	(16)	(17)	(4)	.140	.120	1500	—	1/16	—	1 Rich
	C6AF-AJ	1-1½	(14)	(15)	(4)	.120	.120	1500	—	1/16	—	1 Rich
	C6AF-E	1-1½	(16)	(17)	(4)	.160	.130	1200	1 Turn	1/16	—	2 Rich
	C6AF-F	1-1½	(16)	(17)	(4)	.140	.120	1300	1 Turn	1/16	.060–.090	1 Rich
	C6AF-K	1-1½	(16)	(17)	(4)	.140	.120	1300	1 Turn	1/16	.060–.090	1 Rich
	C6AF-L	1-1½	.531	.910	(4)	.140	.120	1500	1 Turn	1/16	.060–.090	At Index
	C6OF-D	1-1½	(16)	(17)	(4)	.160	.130	1200	1 Turn	1/16	—	2Rich
	C6OF-E	1-1½	(16)	(17)	(4)	.140	.120	1300	1 Turn	1/16	.060–.090	1 Rich
	C6OF-H	1-1½	(14)	(15)	(4)	.160	.130	1300	1 Turn	1/16	—	2 Rich
	C6OF-J	1-1½	(14)	(15)	(4)	.140	.120	1500	1 Turn	1/16	.060–.090	1 Rich
	C6ZF-A	1-1½	.531	.910	(4)	.110	.120	1400	1 Turn	1/16	—	2 Rich
	C6ZF-B	1-1½	(18)	(19)	(4)	.120	.100	1600	1 Turn	1/16	.060–.090	2 Rich

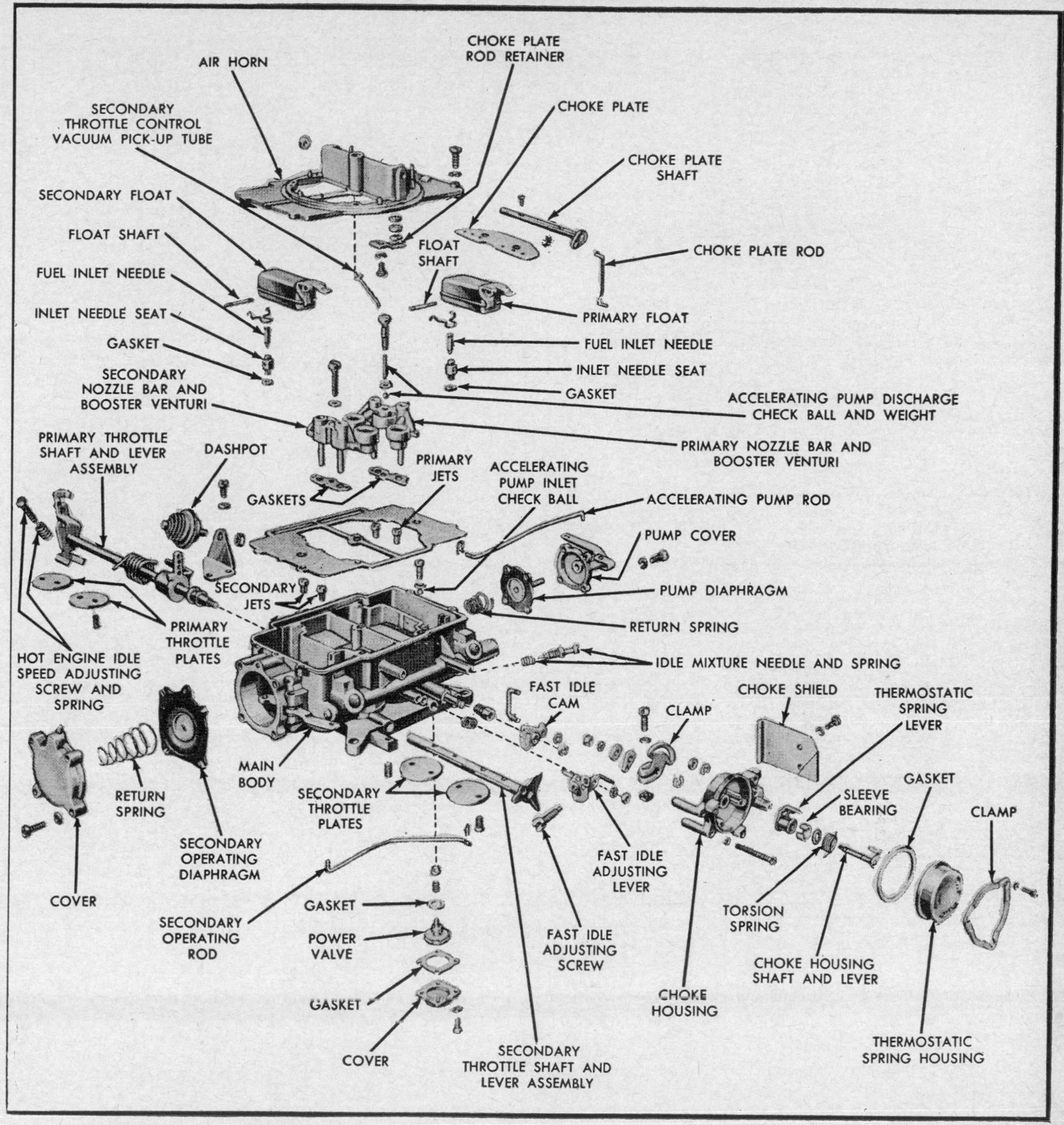

Fig. 22 Exploded view of a typical Autolite 4100 four-barrel carburetor

6. If the fuel level is not as listed in the *Ford Specifications Chart,* stop the engine to avoid any fire hazard due to fuel spray when float setting is disturbed.
7. To adjust fuel level, bend float tab (contacting fuel inlet needle) upward in relation to original position to raise the fuel level, and downward to lower it.
8. Each time an adjustment is made to the float tab to alter the fuel level, the engine must be started and permitted to idle for at least three minutes to stabilize the fuel level. Check fuel level after each adjustment until the specified level is achieved.
9. Assemble carburetor with a new air horn gasket. Then adjust idle speed and mixture, and anti-stall dashpot, if so equipped.

Accelerating Pump Adjustment

Fig. 25—The primary throttle shaft lever (overtravel lever) has 4 holes and the accelerating pump link has 2 holes to control the pump stroke for various atmospheric temperatures and operating condition of the engine.

The pump operating rod should be in the hole specified in the *Ford Specifications Chart* in the overtravel lever and the inboard hole (closest to pump plung-

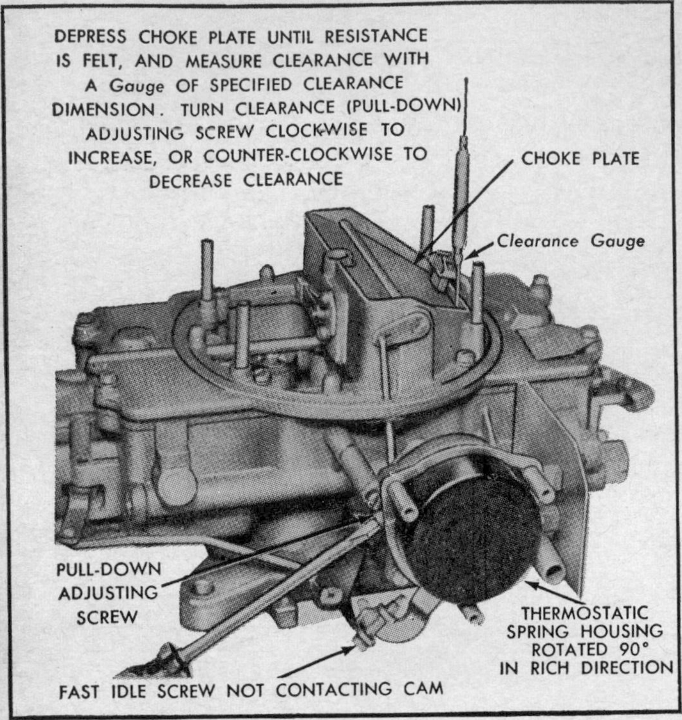
DEPRESS CHOKE PLATE UNTIL RESISTANCE IS FELT, AND MEASURE CLEARANCE WITH A Gauge OF SPECIFIED CLEARANCE DIMENSION. TURN CLEARANCE (PULL-DOWN) ADJUSTING SCREW CLOCKWISE TO INCREASE, OR COUNTER-CLOCKWISE TO DECREASE CLEARANCE
CHOKE PLATE
Clearance Gauge
PULL-DOWN ADJUSTING SCREW
THERMOSTATIC SPRING HOUSING ROTATED 90° IN RICH DIRECTION
FAST IDLE SCREW NOT CONTACTING CAM

Fig. 27 Mechanical linkage choke plate clearance adjustment. 1963-64 2100, 4100

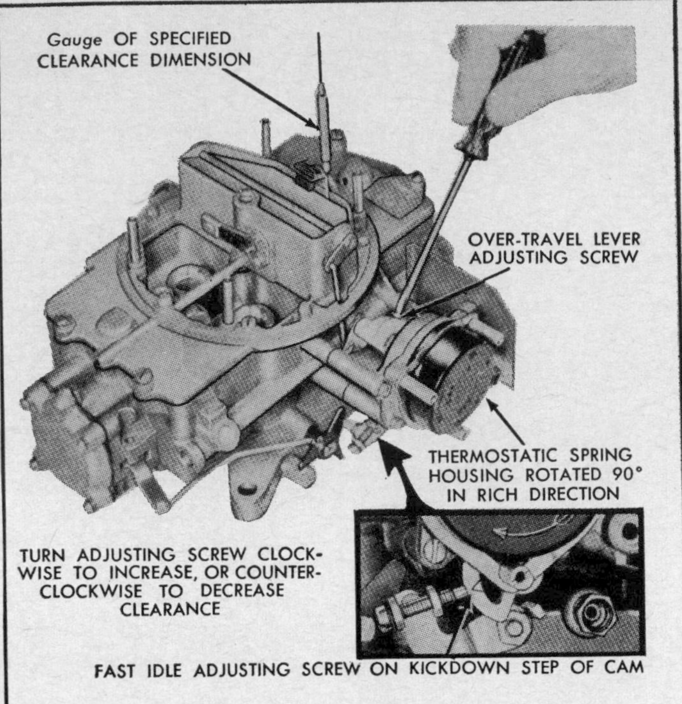
Gauge OF SPECIFIED CLEARANCE DIMENSION
OVER-TRAVEL LEVER ADJUSTING SCREW
THERMOSTATIC SPRING HOUSING ROTATED 90° IN RICH DIRECTION
TURN ADJUSTING SCREW CLOCKWISE TO INCREASE, OR COUNTER-CLOCKWISE TO DECREASE CLEARANCE
FAST IDLE ADJUSTING SCREW ON KICKDOWN STEP OF CAM

Fig. 28 Fast idle cam linkage adjustment. 1964 2100, 4100 with mechanical choke linkage

er) in the pump link.

1. To release rod from retainer clip, press tab end of clip toward rod. Then, at the same time, press rod away from clip until it is disengaged.
2. Position clip over specified hole in overtravel lever. Press ends of clip together and insert operating rod through clip and lever. Release clip to engage rod.

Secondary Throttle Plate

Fig. 26, 4-Barrel Units
Hold secondary throttle plate closed. Turn secondary throttle shaft lever adjusting screw out (counterclockwise) until the secondary throttle plates stick in throttle bores. Turn screw in (clockwise) until it just contacts secondary lever. Then turn it the additional number of turns listed in the *Ford Specifications Chart.*

Choke Plate Clearance & Fast Idle Cam Linkage

1963-64 2B and 4B with Mechanical Choke Linkage—If heater hose and mounting bracket, and carburetor air cleaner have not been previously removed, remove them from the carburetor. Then make adjustments as follows:

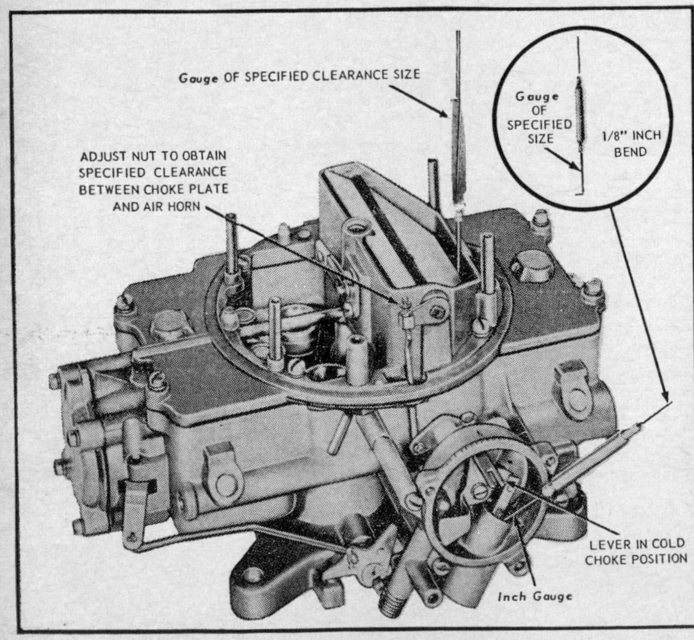
Gauge OF SPECIFIED CLEARANCE SIZE
ADJUST NUT TO OBTAIN SPECIFIED CLEARANCE BETWEEN CHOKE PLATE AND AIR HORN
Gauge OF SPECIFIED SIZE
1/8" INCH BEND
LEVER IN COLD CHOKE POSITION
Inch Gauge

Fig. 29 Vacuum piston type choke plate clearance adjustment. 1964-68 2100, 4100

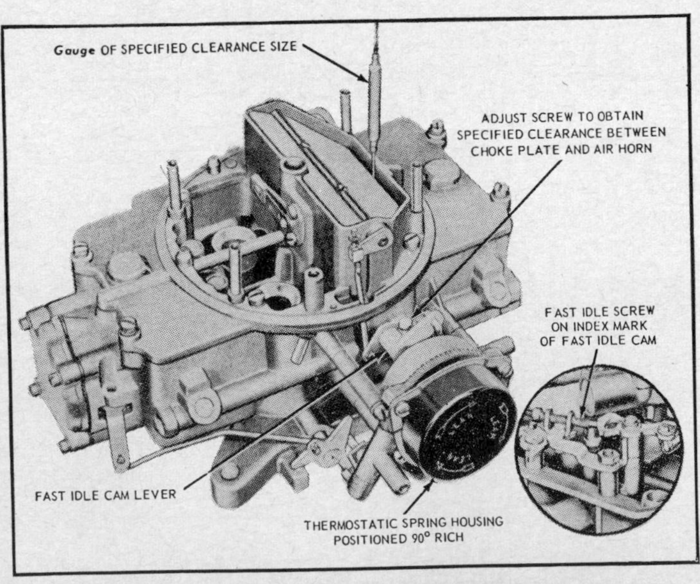
Gauge OF SPECIFIED CLEARANCE SIZE
ADJUST SCREW TO OBTAIN SPECIFIED CLEARANCE BETWEEN CHOKE PLATE AND AIR HORN
FAST IDLE SCREW ON INDEX MARK OF FAST IDLE CAM
FAST IDLE CAM LEVER
THERMOSTATIC SPRING HOUSING POSITIONED 90° RICH

Fig. 30 Vacuum piston type choke fast idle cam linkage adjustment. 1964-68 2100, 4100

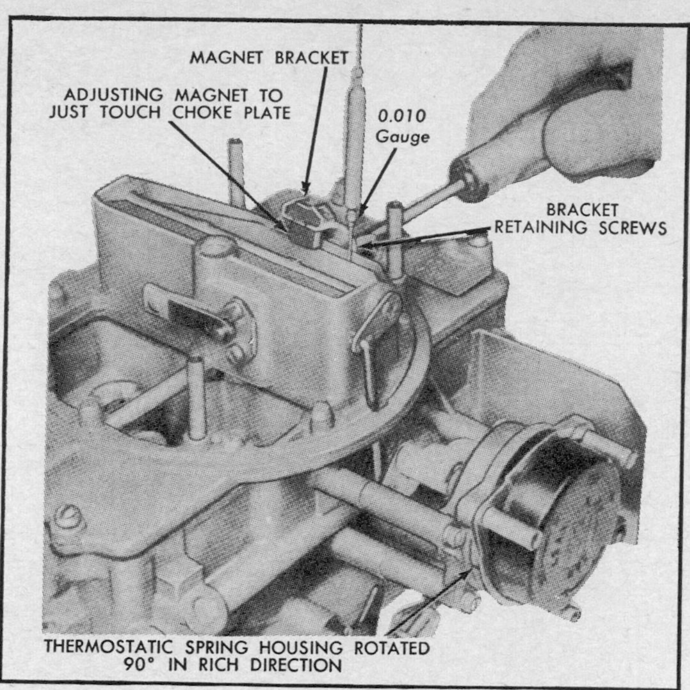

Fig. 32 Choke magnet and bracket adjustment. 1964 4100

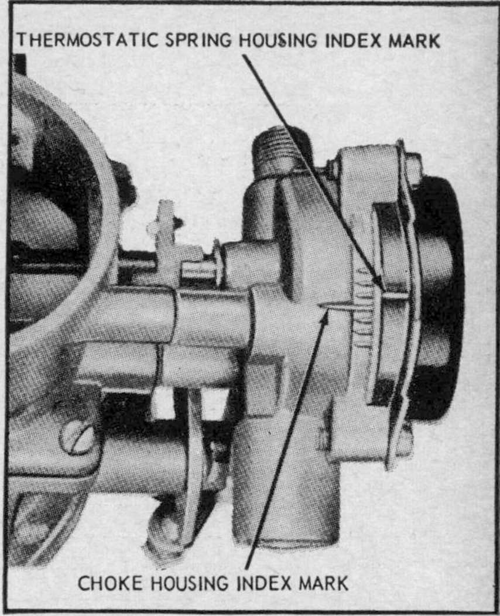

Fig. 31 Automatic choke adjustment. 2100, 4100

Fig. 33 Anti-stall dashpot adjustment. 2100, 4100

1. Rotate choke thermostatic spring housing 90 degrees in the "rich" direction (counterclockwise).
2. Open throttle plates so that fast idle screw does not contact fast idle cam.
3. Depress front side of choke plate downward lightly until resistance is felt. The clearance between downward side of choke plate and air horn is the choke plate pull-down clearance, Fig. 27.
4. Check the clearance by placing a gauge or drill shank of the size specified in the *Ford Specifications Chart* between front edge of choke plate and air horn wall.
5. If choke plate clearance is not within specification, turn pull-down adjusting screw inward to increase (outward to decrease) clearance.
6. Set fast idle adjusting screw on kickdown stop of fast idle cam, Fig. 28.
7. Check clearance between front edge of choke plate and air horn wall. If clearance is not as listed in the *Ford Specifications Chart,* turn overtravel lever adjusting screw inward to increase (outward to decrease) clearance, Fig. 28.
8. Set choke thermostatic coil housing to specified mark and tighten clamp screws.

1965-68 2B and 4B and 1964 2B with Vacuum Piston Choke

1. Bend a .036" pin gauge as shown in inset of Fig. 29.
2. Block throttle about half-way open so that fast idle cam does not contact fast idle adjustment screw.
3. Insert bent edge of gauge between lower edge of piston slot and upper edge of right-hand slot in choke housing as shown.
4. Pull choke countershaft lever counterclockwise until gauge is snug in piston slot.
5. Hold gauge in place by exerting light pressure on countershaft lever, and adjust choke plate clevis adjusting nut to obtain the clearance listed in the *Ford Specifications Chart* between front of choke plate and air horn, Fig. 29.
6. Install choke thermostatic spring housing.
7. Rotate spring housing counterclockwise to align center index mark on choke housing with index mark on spring housing. Then rotate spring housing an additional 90 degrees counterclockwise, Fig. 30, and tighten spring housing retaining screws.
8. Position fast idle adjusting screw on index mark on fast idle cam, Fig. 30.
9. Check clearance between front of choke plate and air horn as shown.
10. If clearance is not as listed in the *Ford Specifications Chart,* turn fast idle cam lever adjusting screw inward to increase (outward to decrease) clearance. Make certain fast idle screw remains on index mark of fast idle cam during adjustment.
11. Set thermostatic choke housing to specified position as listed in the *Ford Specifications Chart* and tighten retaining screws, Fig. 31.

Choke Magnet Adjustment

1964 4B, Fig. 32

1. Rotate thermostatic spring housing 90 degrees counterclockwise.
2. Place a .010" feeler gauge or wire between front side of choke plate and air horn wall.
3. Loosen magnet bracket screws and adjust magnet so it just contacts choke plate. Tighten screws and remove gauge. Then stake screws securely.
4. Set choke according to specifications.

Automatic Choke Valve Tension

Turn thermostatic spring cover against spring tension until index mark on cover is aligned with mark specified in the *Ford Specifications Chart* on choke housing, Fig. 31.

Anti-Stall Dashpot Adjustment

Fig. 33—With engine idle speed and mixture properly adjusted and with engine at normal operating temperature, loosen dashpot lock nut. Hold throttle in closed position and depress plunger with screwdriver as shown. Check clearance between throttle lever and plunger tip. If clearance is not as listed in the *Ford Specifications Chart,* turn dashpot in its bracket as required to obtain the desired clearance. Tighten lock nut.

AUTOLITE 4300-4V ADJUSTMENT SPECIFICATIONS

See Tune Up Chart in car chapters for hot idle speeds.

Year	Carb. Model (Code 9510) ①	Idle Screws (Mixture) Turns Open	Float Level (Dry)	Pump Setting (Hole No.)	Choke Plate Clearance (Pull-Down)	Fast Idle Cam Linkage Setting	Fast Idle Speed (Hot Engine)	Secondary Throttle Plate Clearance	Dechoke Clearance	Dashpot Setting	Choke Setting
1966	C6AF-BU	1-1½	25/32	#2	.120	.090	1200	7/16	1/16	—	Index
1967	C7AF-F	1-1½	25/32	#2	.200	.100	1400	7/16	1/16	—	Index
	C7AF-L	1-1½	25/32	#2	.210	.100	1300	7/16	1/16	1/8	Index
	C7AF-M	1-1½	25/32	#2	.200	.100	1500	7/16	1/16	1/8	Index
	C7AF-AC	1-1½	25/32	#1	.200②	.100②	1200	7/16	1/16	—	Index
	C7AF-AD	1-1½	25/32	#2	.110	.090	1200	7/16	1/16	—	Index
	C7AF-AE	1-1½	25/32	#2	.210②	.100②	1200	7/16	1/16	—	Index
	C7AF-AF	1-1½	25/32	#2	.120	.090	1200	7/16	1/16	—	Index
	C7AF-AG	1-1½	25/32	#1	.200	.100	1300	7/16	1/16	1/8	Index
	C7AF-AH	1½	25/32	#3	.100	.080	1200	7/16	1/16	—	Index
	C7AF-BH	1½	25/32	#3	.100	.080	1200	7/16	1/16	—	Index
	C7AF-AV	1½	25/32	#2	.120	.090	1200	7/16	1/16	—	Index
	C7AF-BJ	1½	25/32	#2	.100	.080	—	7/16	1/16	—	Index
	C7AF-AY	1½	25/32	#2	.120	.090	1500	7/16	1/16	—	Index
1968	C8AF-A	1-1½	25/32	#3	.300	.100	1300	—	—	.093	③④
	C8AF-B	1-1½	25/32	#3	.300	.100	1400	—	—	.093	③④
	C8VF-F	—	25/32	#1	.230	.160	1500	—	.300	3/32	1 Rich
	C8VF-H	—	25/32	#2	.230	.160	1300	—	.300	3/32	1 Rich
	C8ZF-C	—	13/16	#2	.120	.090	1900	—	.300	.100	—
	C8ZF-D	—	13/16	#1	.140	.100	2100	—	.300	.100	—
1969	C8SF-H	—	25/32	#2	.230	.160	1300	—	.300	3/32	1 Rich
	C8VF-J	—	25/32	#2	.230	.160	1300	—	.300	3/32	1 Rich
	C9AF-G	—	25/32	#2	.270	.220	1200	—	.300	3/32	Index
	C9AF-R	—	25/32	#2	.230	.160	1300	—	.300	—	1 Rich
	C9OF-D	—	13/16	#2	.160	.100	1400	—	.300	—	1 Lean
	C9OF-E	—	13/16	#3	.250	.230	1400	—	.300	—	1 Lean
	C9ZF-C	—	13/16	#2	.170	.130	1250	—	.300	3/32	2 Lean
	C9ZF-D	—	13/16	#2	.160	.100	1400	—	.300	—	1 Lean
	C9ZF-E	—	13/16	#3	.230	.210	1300	—	.300	1/8	Index
	C9ZF-F	—	13/16	#3	.250	.230	1400	—	.300	—	1 Lean

①—Tag attached to bowl cover.
②—Front.
③—8-390 with Imco 2 Rich, with Thermactor 1 rich.
④—8-428 with Imco Index, with Thermactor 1 rich.

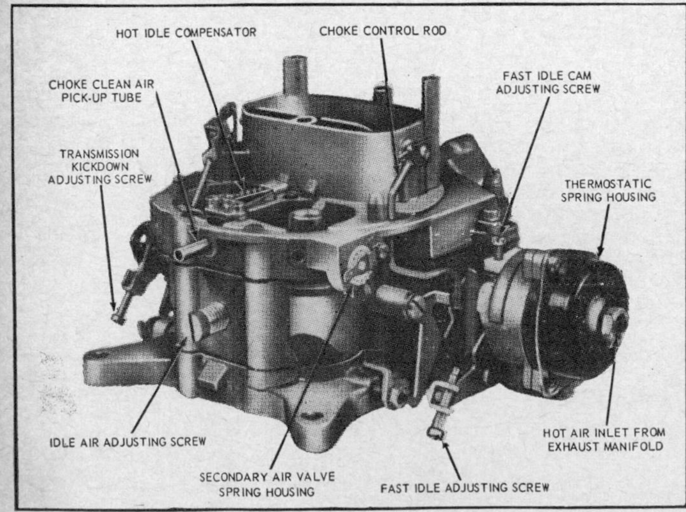

Fig. 34 Right rear view of Autolite 4300-4V carburetor

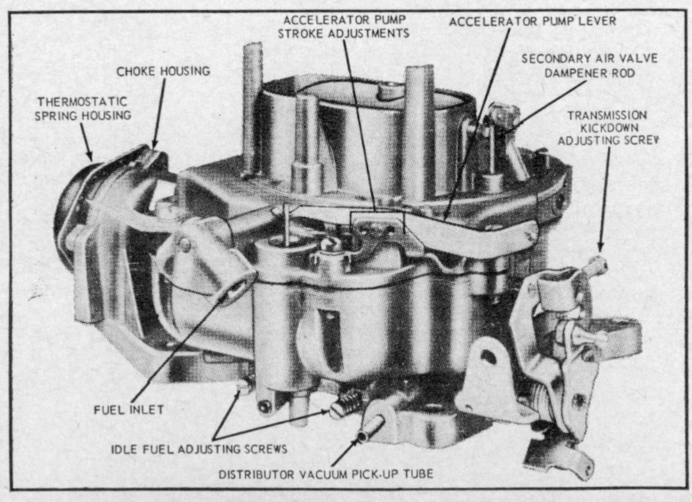

Fig. 35 Left rear view of Autolite Model 4300-4V carburetor

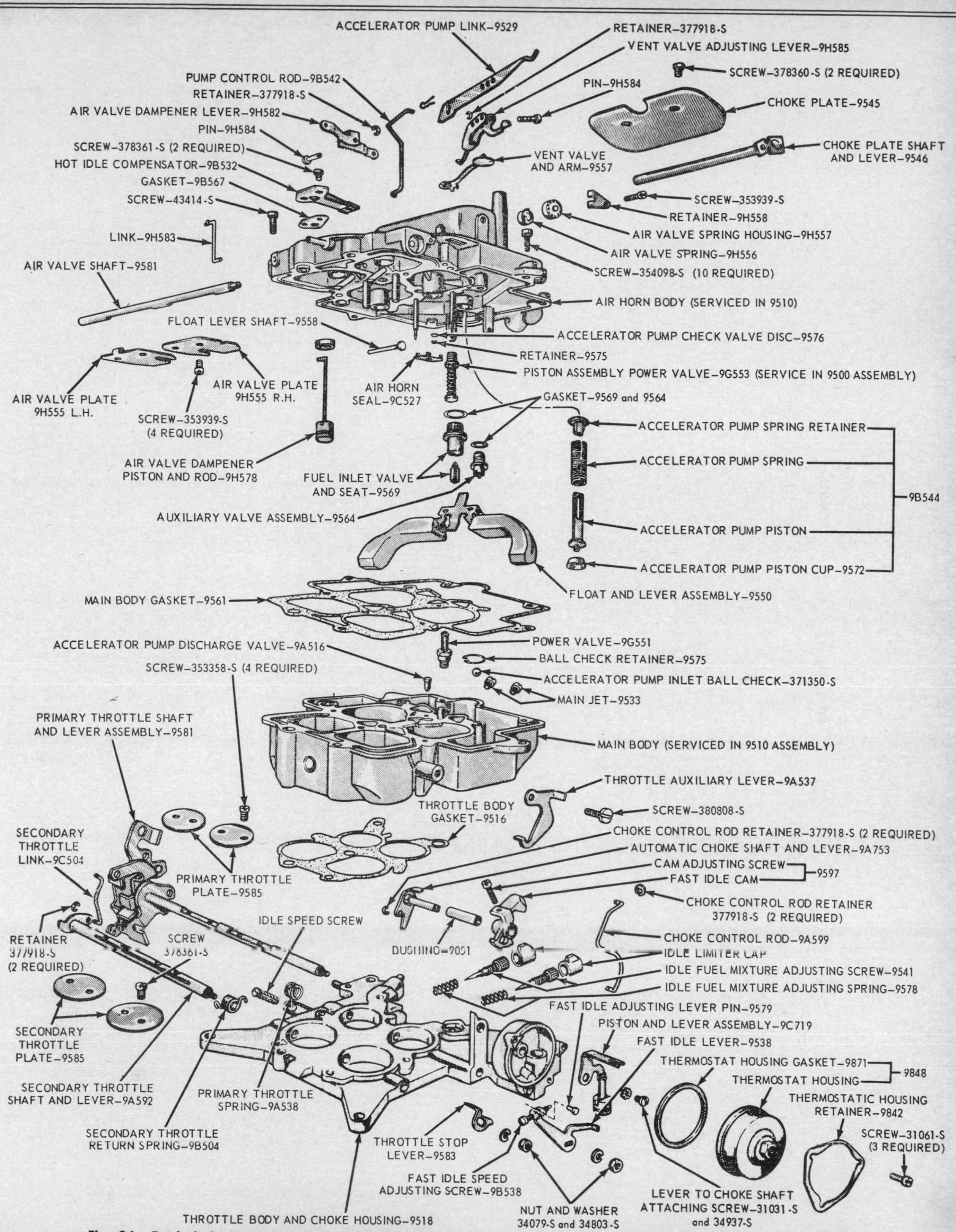
ACCELERATOR PUMP LINK–9529
RETAINER–377918-S
VENT VALVE ADJUSTING LEVER–9H585
SCREW–378360-S (2 REQUIRED)
PUMP CONTROL ROD–9B542
PIN–9H584
RETAINER–377918-S
CHOKE PLATE–9545
AIR VALVE DAMPENER LEVER–9H582
PIN–9H584
CHOKE PLATE SHAFT AND LEVER–9546
SCREW–378361-S (2 REQUIRED)
VENT VALVE AND ARM–9557
HOT IDLE COMPENSATOR–9B532
GASKET–9B567
SCREW–353939-S
SCREW–43414-S
RETAINER–9H558
AIR VALVE SPRING HOUSING–9H557
LINK–9H583
AIR VALVE SPRING–9H556
AIR VALVE SHAFT–9581
SCREW–354098-S (10 REQUIRED)
AIR HORN BODY (SERVICED IN 9510)
FLOAT LEVER SHAFT–9558
ACCELERATOR PUMP CHECK VALVE DISC–9576
RETAINER–9575
PISTON ASSEMBLY POWER VALVE–9G553 (SERVICE IN 9500 ASSEMBLY)
AIR VALVE PLATE 9H555 R.H.
AIR HORN SEAL–9C527
AIR VALVE PLATE 9H555 L.H.
GASKET–9569 and 9564
SCREW–353939-S (4 REQUIRED)
ACCELERATOR PUMP SPRING RETAINER
ACCELERATOR PUMP SPRING
AIR VALVE DAMPENER PISTON AND ROD–9H578
FUEL INLET VALVE AND SEAT–9569
9B544
AUXILIARY VALVE ASSEMBLY–9564
ACCELERATOR PUMP PISTON
ACCELERATOR PUMP PISTON CUP–9572
FLOAT AND LEVER ASSEMBLY–9550
MAIN BODY GASKET–9561
ACCELERATOR PUMP DISCHARGE VALVE–9A516
POWER VALVE–9G551
BALL CHECK RETAINER–9575
SCREW–353358-S (4 REQUIRED)
ACCELERATOR PUMP INLET BALL CHECK–371350-S
MAIN JET–9533
PRIMARY THROTTLE SHAFT AND LEVER ASSEMBLY–9581
MAIN BODY (SERVICED IN 9510 ASSEMBLY)
THROTTLE AUXILIARY LEVER–9A537
THROTTLE BODY GASKET–9516
SCREW–380808-S
SECONDARY THROTTLE LINK–9C504
CHOKE CONTROL ROD RETAINER–377918-S (2 REQUIRED)
AUTOMATIC CHOKE SHAFT AND LEVER–9A753
CAM ADJUSTING SCREW
FAST IDLE CAM
9597
PRIMARY THROTTLE PLATE–9585
CHOKE CONTROL ROD RETAINER 377918-S (2 REQUIRED)
IDLE SPEED SCREW
RETAINER 377918-S (2 REQUIRED)
SCREW 378361-S
CHOKE CONTROL ROD–9A599
IDLE LIMITER CAP
IDLE FUEL MIXTURE ADJUSTING SCREW–9541
IDLE FUEL MIXTURE ADJUSTING SPRING–9578
SECONDARY THROTTLE PLATE–9585
FAST IDLE ADJUSTING LEVER PIN–9579
PISTON AND LEVER ASSEMBLY–9C719
FAST IDLE LEVER–9538
THERMOSTAT HOUSING GASKET–9871
THERMOSTAT HOUSING
9848
SECONDARY THROTTLE SHAFT AND LEVER–9A592
PRIMARY THROTTLE SPRING–9A538
THERMOSTATIC HOUSING RETAINER–9842
SECONDARY THROTTLE RETURN SPRING–9B504
THROTTLE STOP LEVER–9583
SCREW–31061-S (3 REQUIRED)
FAST IDLE SPEED ADJUSTING SCREW–9B538
LEVER TO CHOKE SHAFT ATTACHING SCREW–31031-S and 34937-S
NUT AND WASHER 34079-S and 34803-S
THROTTLE BODY AND CHOKE HOUSING–9518

Fig. 36 Exploded view of a typical Autolite 4300 four-barrel carburetor. Note that this unit is provided with idle limiter caps which are used to prevent an overly rich mixture on cars with exhaust emission control

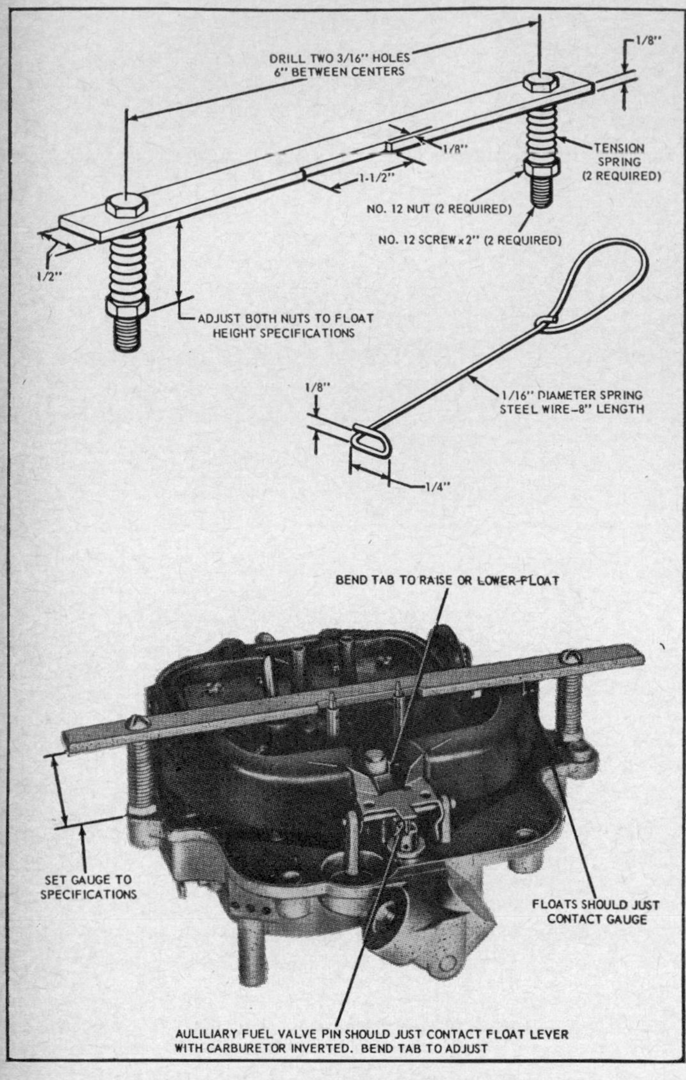

Fig. 37 Float and auxiliary fuel valve setting

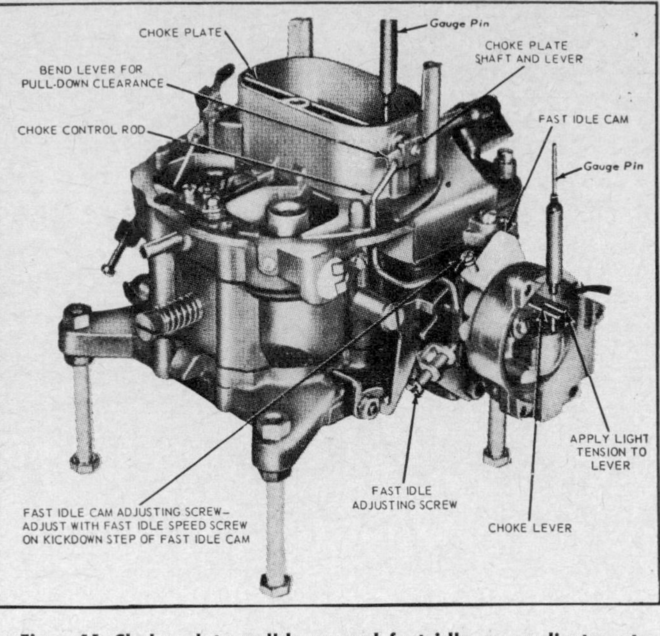

Fig. 41 Choke plate pulldown and fast idle cam adjustment

NO. 1 HOLE–DECREASE FUEL
NO. 2 HOLE–NORMAL
NO. 3 HOLE–INCREASE FUEL

Fig. 38 Accelerator pump stroke adjustment

MODEL 4300-4V ADJUSTMENTS

First used on late 1966 Galaxie with V8-428 engine, this carburetor, Figs. 34, 35 and 36, has several physical differences when compared to the Model 4100 carburetor. The Model 4300 is a four-barrel, three-piece, separately cast design consisting of air horn, main body and mounting flange. A cast-in center fuel inlet has provision for a supplementary fuel inlet system. The fuel bowl is vented by an internal balance vent, and a mechanical atmospheric vent operates during idle. An idle air by-pass system is designed to provide a more consistent idle and a hot idle compensator is used to help idle stability. A dashpot is not required on non-Thermactor engines.

The main (primary) fuel system has booster-type venturii cast integral with the air horn, and the main venturii are cast integral with the main body. The secondary throttle plates are mechanically operated from the primary linkage. Air valve plates are located above the main venturii and an integral hydraulic dashpot dampens sudden movement of the air valve plates to help prevent plate flutter and erratic engine operation.

A single fuel bowl supplies both the primary and secondary fuel systems. Pontoon-type floats are used to help stabilize fuel level during cornering and hill-climbing. The accelerator pump is of the piston type. It is located in the fuel bowl for more positive displacement and a safeguard against external leaks.

Float Setting

Fig. 37

1. Adjust gauge to specified height.
2. Insert gauge into air horn outboard holes as shown.
3. Check clearance and alignment of float pontoons to gauge. Both pontoons should just touch gauge for proper setting. Align pontoons if necessary by slightly twisting pontoons.

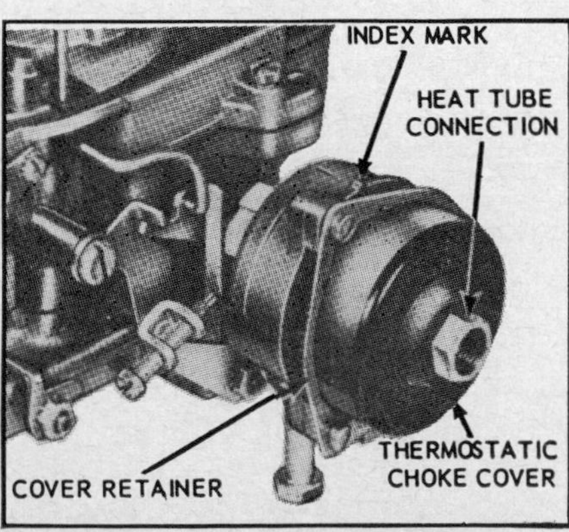

Fig. 39 Automatic choke setting

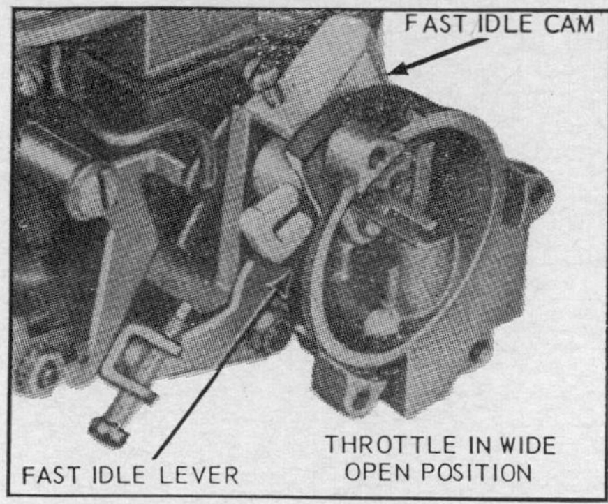

Fig. 40 Dechoke clearance setting

4. If it is necessary to adjust float clearance, bend primary needle tab downward to raise float and upward to lower float.

NOTE: To raise float, insert open end of bending tool to *right* side of float lever tab and between needle and float hinge. Raise float lever off needle and bend tab downward.

To lower float, insert open end of bending tool to *left* side of float lever tab, between needle and float hinge. Support float lever and bend tab upward.

Auxiliary Valve Setting

Fig. 37

1. Adjust float gauge to specified auxiliary valve setting.
2. Insert gauge in outboard holes in air horn.
3. Invert air horn and allow floats to rest on gauge. Valve pin should just contact tab on float lever.
4. If necessary to bend tab for proper contact, use bending tool to bend tab up or down as required.

Idle Speed Adjustment

1. Referring to Fig. 34, turn idle air bypass screw clockwise until it lightly seats, then turn screw counterclockwise 3½ turns.
2. Final adjustments are made on the car with engine running and engine temperature normalized. Install a tachometer and check hot idle speed.
3. Turn idle air adjusting screw clockwise to decrease engine speed and counterclockwise to increase engine speed.
4. Turn one idle fuel adjusting screw, Fig. 35, clockwise until engine rpm begins to drop, then turn screw counterclockwise ¼ turn. Repeat for other idle fuel screw.
5. Slightly rotate idle adjusting screws as required for smoothest idle quality. The screws should be within 1/8 turn of each other.

Accelerator Pump Stroke

Fig. 38

The accelerator pump stroke has been calibrated to inject a pre-determined quantity of fuel into the air stream with the pump pivot pin in the center (No. 2) hole. The amount of fuel injected into the air stream may be altered by inserting the pivot pin into the left (No. 1) hole to decrease the fuel quantity, or to the right

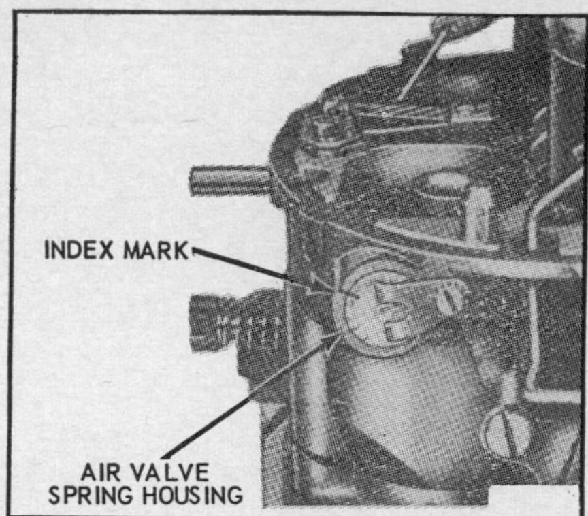

Fig. 42 Secondary air valve spring adjustment

(No. 3) hole to increase the fuel quantity. If necessary to alter the setting, proceed as follows:

1. Remove pump rod from pump arm.
2. Remove pump pivot pin.
3. Insert pivot pin into desired hole. *Holes in fuel bowl vent lever, main body casting and pump lever must be in line.*
4. Install pivot pin retainer. Position pump rod end into pump arm and install retainer.
5. Adjust vent valve clearance as outlined further on.

Automatic Choke Setting

Fig. 39

1. If carburetor is installed on engine, loosen choke heat tube nut.
2. Loosen choke cover retaining screws.
3. Rotate choke cover clockwise to reduce choking action or counterclockwise to increase choking action.
4. Tighten choke cover screws and choke heat tube nut.

Dechoke Clearance

Fig. 40

1. Open and hold throttle plate to wide open position.
2. Rotate choke plate toward closed position until pawl on fast idle speed lever contacts fast idle cam.
3. Check clearance between upper edge of choke plate and air horn wall.
4. Adjust clearance to specifications by bending pawl on fast idle speed lever forward to increase (backward to decrease) clearance.

Choke Plate Pulldown and Fast Idle Cam

Fig. 41

1. Remove choke cover.
2. Bend a .036″ wire gauge at a 90° angle, approximately 1/8″ from the end.
3. Insert bent edge of gauge between piston slot and upper edge of right hand slot in choke housing.
4. Rotate automatic choke lever counterclockwise until gauge is snug in piston slot. Exert light pressure on choke lever to hold gauge in place.
5. Using a gauge pin, check pulldown clearance between lower edge of choke plate and air horn wall.

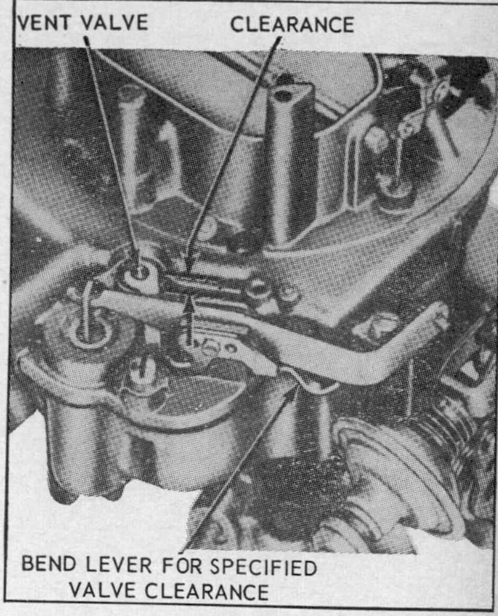

Fig. 43 Fuel bowl vent valve adjustment

6. Adjust pulldown clearance to specifications by bending adjusting arm on choke shaft lever. Bend downward to increase (upward to decrease) clearance.
7. Remove gauge and install choke cover loosely so it can rotate. Be sure thermostatic spring end is engaged in choke lever slot.
8. Rotate choke cover to 90° rich.
9. Position fast idle adjusting screw end to kickdown step on fast idle cam and hold in this position.
10. Using a gauge pin, check fast idle cam clearance between lower edge of choke plate and air horn wall.
11. Adjust fast idle cam clearance to specifications by turning adjusting screw clockwise to increase (counterclockwise to decrease) clearance.
12. Install choke cover and rotate it to specified setting, then tighten cover.

Secondary Air Valve Spring

Fig. 42

The secondary air valve spring and housing are adjusted to apply a pre-determined load on the secondary air valve shaft. If the spring housing has been moved or maladjusted, adjust the spring tension as follows:

1. Loosen housing screw and let housing rotate to no-load position.
2. With air valves closed, scribe an index mark on air horn casting and nylon spring housing.
3. Rotate spring housing counterclockwise 140 degrees (7 knobs on spring housing).
4. Position retainer and tighten screw.

NOTE: If secondary air valve spring requires replacement, make sure open end of spring hook is facing to left of bottom of housing cavity in air horn.

Fuel Bowl External Vent Valve

Fig. 43

1. Set throttle plates in closed position.
2. Check clearance between vent valve and valve seat.
3. If clearance is not as specified, bend end of vent valve lever downward to decrease (upward to increase).

Holley Carburetor Section

HOLLEY ONE & TWO BARREL CARB. ADJUSTMENT SPECIFICATIONS

See Tune Up Chart in car chapter for hot idle speeds.

Year	Carb. Part No.(1)	Carb. Model	Idle Screw (Mixture) Turns Open	Float Level (Dry)	Fuel Level (Wet)	Pump Setting	Bowl Vent Clearance	Fast Idle		Choke Unloader Clearance	Anti-Stall Dashpot Clearance	Choke Setting
								Bench	On Car			
CHEVROLET ENGINES												
1967	R3659-A	2300	1½	.350	(3)	.015	—	.025	2200	—	—	—
	R3660-A	2300	1½	.350	(3)	.015	—	.025	2200	.275	—	—
	R3888-A	2300	1½	.350	(3)	.015	—	.025	2200	.275	—	—
1968-69	R4055-A	2300	1½	.350	(3)	.015	—	.025	2200	.275	—	—
	R4056-A	2300	1½	.350	(3)	.015	—	.025	2200	—	—	—
	R3659-A	2300	1½	.350	(3)	.015	—	.025	2200	—	—	—
CHRYSLER ENGINES												
1963	R-2533A	1920	1	See Text	11/16	(6)	—	—	1500(7)	(8)	—	2 Rich
	R-2534A	1920	1	See Text	11/16	(6)	—	—	1500(7)	(8)	—	2 Rich
	R-2535A	1920	1	See Text	11/16	(6)	—	—	1500(7)	(8)	—	2 Rich
	R-2536A	1920	1	See Text	11/16	(6)	—	—	1500(7)	(8)	—	2 Rich
	R-2537A	1920	1	See Text	11/16	(6)	—	—	1500(7)	(8)	—	2 Rich
	R-2538A	1920	1	See Text	11/16	(6)	—	—	1500(7)	(8)	—	2 Rich
1964	R-2765A	1920	1	See Text	11/16	(6)	—	—	700(9)	(8)	—	2 Rich
	R-2766A	1920	1	See Text	11/16	(6)	—	—	700(9)	(8)	—	2 Rich
	R-2767A	1920	1	See Text	11/16	(6)	—	—	700(9)	(8)	—	2 Rich
	R-2768A	1920	1	See Text	11/16	(6)	—	—	700(9)	(8)	—	2 Rich
	R-2769A	1920	1	See Text	11/16	(6)	—	—	700(9)	(8)	—	2 Rich
	R-2770A	1920	1	See Text	11/16	(6)	—	—	700(9)	(8)	—	2 Rich
1965	R-3055A	1920	1	See Text	27/32	(6)	—	—	700(10)	(8)	—	2 Rich
	R-3056A	1920	1	See Text	27/32	(6)	—	—	700(10)	(8)	—	2 Rich
	R-3057A	1920	1	See Text	27/32	(6)	—	—	700(10)	(8)	—	2 Rich
	R-3058A	1920	1	See Text	27/32	(6)	—	—	700(10)	(8)	—	2 Rich
	R-3059A	1920	1	See Text	27/32	(6)	—	—	700(10)	(8)	—	2 Rich
	R-3060A	1920	1	See Text	27/32	(6)	—	—	700(10)	(8)	—	2 Rich
	R-3149A	1920	1	See Text	27/32	(6)	—	—	700(10)	(8)	—	2 Rich
	R-3150A	1920	1	See Text	27/32	(6)	—	—	700(10)	(8)	—	2 Rich
	R-3151A	1920	1	See Text	27/32	(6)	—	—	700(10)	(8)	—	2 Rich
	R-3152A	1920	1	See Text	27/32	(6)	—	—	700(10)	(8)	—	2 Rich
1966	R-3271A	1920	2	See Text	27/32	(6)	—	—	700(9)	(8)	—	2 Rich
	R-3272A	1920	2	See Text	27/32	(6)	—	—	700(9)	(8)	—	2 Rich
	R-3273A	1920	2	See Text	27/32	(6)	—	—	1550(11)	(8)	—	2 Rich
	R-3274A	1920	2	See Text	27/32	(6)	—	—	1550(11)	(8)	—	2 Rich
	R-3275A	1920	2	See Text	27/32	(6)	—	—	700(9)	(8)	—	2 Rich
	R-3276A	1920	2	See Text	27/32	(6)	—	—	700(9)	(8)	—	2 Rich
	R-3277A	1920	2	See Text	27/32	(6)	—	—	1550(11)	(8)	—	2 Rich
	R-3278A	1920	2	See Text	27/32	(6)	—	—	1550(11)	(8)	—	2 Rich
	R-3279A	1920	2	See Text	27/32	(6)	—	—	700(9)	(8)	—	2 Rich
	R-3280A	1920	2	See Text	27/32	(6)	—	—	700(9)	(8)	—	2 Rich
	R-3281A	1920	2	See Text	27/32	(6)	—	—	1550(11)	(8)	—	2 Rich
	R-3282A	1920	2	See Text	27/32	(6)	—	—	1550(11)	(8)	—	2 Rich
1967	R-3275-1A	1920	2	See Text	27/32	(6)	3/32	—	700(9)	(8)	—	2 Rich
	R-3276-1A	1920	2	See Text	27/32	(6)	3/32	—	700(9)	(8)	—	2 Rich
	R-3279-1A	1920	2	See Text	27/32	(6)	3/32	—	700(9)	(8)	—	2 Rich
	R-3280-1A	1920	2	See Text	27/32	(6)	3/32	—	700(9)	(8)	—	2 Rich
	R-3671-A	1920	2	See Text	27/32	(6)	3/32	—	1550(11)	(8)	—	—
	R-3672-A	1920	2	See Text	27/32	(6)	3/32	—	1550(11)	(8)	—	2 Rich
	R-3673-A	1920	2	See Text	27/32	(6)	3/32	—	1550(11)	(8)	—	2 Rich
	R-3674-A	1920	2	See Text	27/32	(6)	3/32	—	1550(11)	(8)	—	—

HOLLEY ONE & TWO BARREL CARB. ADJUSTMENT SPECIFICATIONS—Continued

See Tune Up Chart in car chapter for hot idle speeds.

Year	Carb. Part No.①	Carb. Model	Idle Screw (Mixture) Turns Open	Float Level (Dry)	Fuel Level (Wet)	Pump Setting	Bowl Vent Clearance	Fast Idle		Choke Unloader Clearance	Anti-Stall Dashpot Clearance	Choke Setting
								Bench	On Car			
CHRYSLER ENGINES—Continued												
1968	R-3919-A	1920	2	See Text	27/32	⑥	3/32	—	1400⑪	⑧	—	2 Rich
	R-3920-A	1920	2	See Text	27/32	⑥	3/32	—	1600⑪	⑧	—	2 Rich
	R-3921-A	1920	2	See Text	27/32	⑥	3/32	—	1400⑪	⑧	—	2 Rich
	R-3922-A	1920	2	See Text	27/32	⑥	3/32	—	1600⑪	⑧	—	—
	R-3924-A	1920	2	See Text	27/32	⑥	3/32	—	1400⑪	⑧	—	—
1969	R-4161-A	1920	2	See Text	27/32	⑥	3/32	—	1600⑪	9/32⑮	—	2 Rich
	R-4162-A	1920	2	See Text	27/32	⑥	3/32	—	1800⑪	9/32⑮	—	2 Rich
	R-4163-A	1920	2	See Text	27/32	⑥	3/32	—	1600⑪	9/32⑮	—	2 Rich
	R-4164-A	1920	2	See Text	27/32	⑥	3/32	—	1800⑪	9/32⑮	—	2 Rich
	R-4165-A	1920	2	See Text	27/32	⑥	3/32	—	1700⑪	9/32⑮	—	—
JEEP												
1963–64	R-2640A	2300	1	See Text	③	.015	1/16	—	—	—	.070	On Index
1964	R-2647A	1920	1	See Text	3/4	⑥	—	—	—	—	1/16	—
	R-2647AS	1920	1	See Text	3/4	⑥	—	—	—	—	1/16	—
1965–68	R-2647-1A	1920	1	See Text	3/4	⑥	—	—	—	—	1/16	—
1964	R-2651A	1920	1	See Text	3/4	⑥	—	—	2100⑫	⑧	1/16	On Index
	R-2651AS	1920	1	See Text	3/4	⑥	—	—	2100⑫	⑧	1/16	On Index
1965–68	R-2651-1A	1920	1	See Text	3/4	⑥	—	—	2100⑫	⑧	1/16	On Index
1964	R-2934A	2300	1	See Text	③	.015	1/16	—	—	—	.070	On Index
1965–68	R-3234A	2209	1	9/16	5/8	②	5/64	.020	1800⑫	3/16	5/32	On Index
	R-3262A	2209	1	9/16	5/8	②	5/64	.020	1800⑫	3/16	—	On Index
RAMBLER												
1963	R-2387A	1909	1–2 3/4	5/16	—	②	5/32	—	750⑨	9/32	—	1 Lean
1963	R-2442A	2300	1–1 1/2	See Text	③	⑬	1/16	.024⑭	1700⑫	.180	3/32	On Index
1964	R-2442-1A	2300	1–1 1/2	See Text	③	⑬	1/16	.024⑭	1700⑫	.180	3/32	On Index
1963	R-2463A	2300	1–1 1/2	See Text	③	⑬	1/16	.024⑭	1700⑫	.180	3/32	On Index
1964	R-2463-1A	2300	1–1 1/2	See Text	③	⑬	1/16	.024⑭	1700⑫	.180	3/32	On Index
1963	R-2555A	1909	1–2 3/4	5/16	—	②	5/32	—	750⑨	9/32	—	On Index
1964	R-2555-2A	1909	1–2 3/4	5/16	—	②	5/32	—	750⑨	9/32	—	On Index
1965	R-2555-3A	1909	1–2 3/4	27/64	—	②	5/32	—	750⑨	9/32	—	On Index
1963	R-2556A	1909	1–2 3/4	5/16	—	②	3/32	—	750⑨	9/32	9/64	On Index
1964	R-2556-2A	1909	1–2 3/4	5/16	—	②	5/32	—	750⑨	9/32	9/64	On Index
1963	R-2557A	1909	1–2 3/4	5/16	—	②	5/32	—	750⑨	9/32	9/64	1 Lean
1964	R-2697A	1931	1/4–2 1/4	5/16	—	②	1/16	—	1400⑪	15/64	—	On Index
1965	R-2697-1A	1931	1/4–2 1/4	5/16	—	②	1/16	—	1400⑪	15/64	—	On Index
	R-2699A	2209	1–1 1/2	11/32	1/2	②	5/64	—	—	3/16	—	On Index
1964–65	R-2880A	1931	3/4–1 1/4	5/16	—	②	1/16	—	1350⑪	15/64	—	On Index
1965	R-2968A	2209	1–1 1/2	11/32	1/2	②	5/64	—	1800⑫	3/16	.150	On Index
1963–64	R-3075A	2300	1–1 1/2	See Text	③	⑬	1/16	.024⑭	1700⑫	.180	3/32	On Index
1965	R-3199A	1931	3/4–1 1/4	5/16	—	②	1/16	—	1400⑪	15/64	—	On Index
	R-3200A	1931	3/4–1 1/4	5/16	—	②	1/16	—	1400⑪	15/64	—	On Index
	R-3217A	2209	1–1 1/2	11/32	1/2	②	5/64	—	1800⑫	3/16	5/32	On Index
	R-3218A	2209	1–1 1/2	11/32	1/2	②	5/64	—	1800⑫	3/16	—	On Index
1966	R-3250-1A	1931	3/4–1 1/4	5/16	—	②	1/16	—	1600⑦	15/64	3/32	On Index
	R-3251A	1931	3/4–1 1/4	5/16	—	②	1/16	—	1500⑦	15/64	—	1 Lean
	R-3292A	1931	3/4–1 1/4	5/16	—	②	1/16	—	1600⑦	15/64	3/32	On Index
	R-3304A	2209	1–1 1/2	11/32	1/2	②	5/64	—	1800⑫	3/16	5/32	On Index
	R-3305A	2209	1–1 1/2	11/32	1/2	②	5/64	—	1800⑫	3/16	—	On Index
	R-3388A	2209	1–1 1/2	11/32	1/2	②	5/64	—	1800⑫	3/16	5/32	On Index
	R-3438A	1931	3/4–1 1/4	5/16	—	②	1/16	—	1600⑦	15/64	—	1 Rich

Continued

HOLLEY ONE & TWO BARREL CARB. ADJUSTMENT SPECIFICATIONS—Continued

See Tune Up Chart in car chapter for hot idle speeds.

Year	Carb. Part No.①	Carb. Model	Idle Screw (Mixture) Turns Open	Float Level (Dry)	Fuel Level (Wet)	Pump Setting	Bowl Vent Clearance	Fast Idle		Choke Unloader Clearance	Anti-Stall Dashpot Clearance	Choke Setting
								Bench	On Car			
RAMBLER—Continued												
1967	R-3253	1931	1½-3½	5/16	—	②	1/16	—	1400⑦	15/64	—	1 Lean
	R-3307-1	2209	1-1½	11/32	½	②	5/64	—	1650⑦	3/16	5/32	1 Lean
	R-3308-1	2209	1-1½	11/32	½	②	5/64	—	1650⑦	3/16	—	1 Lean
	R-3483-1	2209	1-1½	11/32	½	②	5/64	—	1600⑦	3/16	5/32	1 Lean
	R-3484-1	2209	1-1½	11/32	½	②	5/64	—	1400⑦	3/16	3/16	1 Rich
	R-3704	1931	1-1½	5/16	—	②	1/16	—	1400⑦	15/64	3/32	On Index
	R-3705	1931	1-1½	5/16	—	②	1/16	—	1400⑦	15/64	—	On Index
	R-3706	1931	¾-1½	5/16	—	②	1/16	—	1550⑦	15/64	3/32	1 Rich
	R-3707	1931	1½-3½	5/16	—	②	1/16	—	1600⑦	15/64	3/32	On Index
	R-3708	1931	1-1½	5/16	—	②	1/16	—	1400⑦	15/64	—	1 Rich
	R-3709	1931	¾-1½	5/16	—	②	1/16	—	1400⑦	15/64	—	1 Rich
	R-3978	1931	½-1½	5/16	—	②	1/16	—	1550⑪	15/64	3/32	1 Rich
1968	3966A	1931	1	5/16	—	②	1/16	—	1600⑦	15/64	3/32	1 Rich
	3967A	1931	1	5/16	—	②	1/16	—	1600⑦	15/64	—	1 Rich
	3968A	1931	1	5/16	—	②	1/16	—	1600⑦	15/64	3/32	1 Rich
	4102A	1931	1	5/16	—	②	1/16	—	1600⑦	15/64	—	1 Rich
1969	4294A	1931	1	5/16	—	②	1/16	—	1600⑦	15/64	—	1 Rich

①—Located on tag attached to carburetor or on casting.
②—Seasonal setting holes in lever; long stroke for cold weather, short stroke for warm weather.
③—At lower edge of sight plug opening.
⑥—Seasonal setting; use center hole for moderate weather, long stroke hole for cold weather, and short stroke hole for warm weather.
⑦—Engine hot and screw on second step of cam.
⑧—See "Fast idle index adjustment" in text.
⑨—Engine hot and screw on lowest step of cam.
⑩—With headlights on A-C operating (if equipped); engine hot and screw on lowest step of cam.
⑪—Engine hot and screw on second highest step of cam.
⑫—Engine hot and screw on highest step of cam.
⑬—Lever touching screw; then tighten screw ¼ turn.
⑭—Between throttle valve and carburetor bore.
⑮—With fast idle speed adjusting screw contacting second highest step on fast idle cam there should be 1/16″ clearance between choke valve and wall of air horn. When this adjustment is correct the choke unloader clearance should be as specified in the chart.

HOLLEY ONE & TWO BARREL CARBURETOR ADJUSTMENTS

MODELS 1904, 1908

These carburetors, Figs. 1, 2 and 3, are quite similar except that the 1908 is equipped with an automatic choke while the 1904 is not. An economy carburetor is also used, its economy resulting in the lack of the spark control valve.

Float Level Setting

Fig. 4—With carburetor inverted, measure from roof of float chamber to lowest point of float. Adjust by bending horizontal float tab on float arm. Unless a float bumper spring is used, float drop cannot be adjusted. When a float bumper spring is present, and if the float level must be adjusted more than $\frac{1}{32}$", check float drop with carburetor in upright position. There should be $\frac{3}{16}$" clearance between bottom of float at its lowest point and floor of float chamber. Adjust by bending vertical tab on float arm. After installing carburetor, check fuel level as outlined below.

Checking Fuel Level

Fig. 5—With carburetor installed, crank engine until fuel ceases to flow into fuel bowl. Remove economizer valve parts and measure distance from top surface of economizer hole to level of fuel in

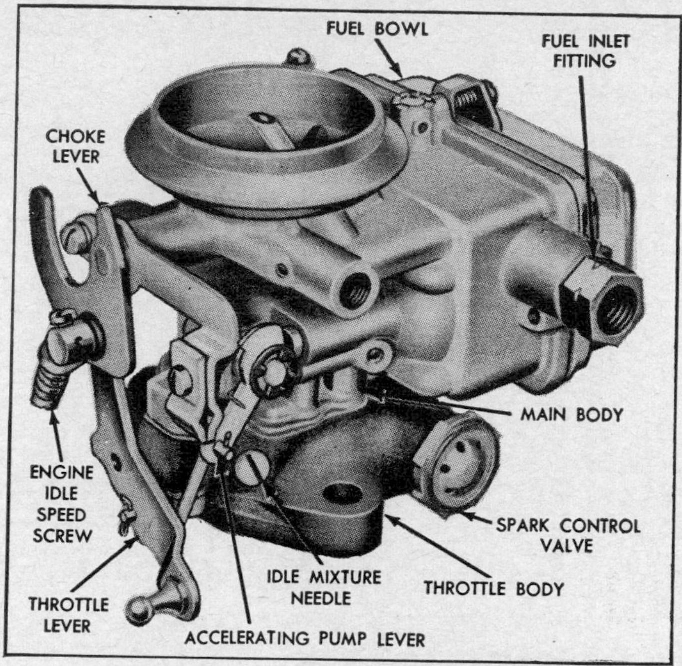

Fig. 1 Holley Model 1904 single-barrel manual choke carburetor. Model 1908 is the automatic choke version of this carburetor

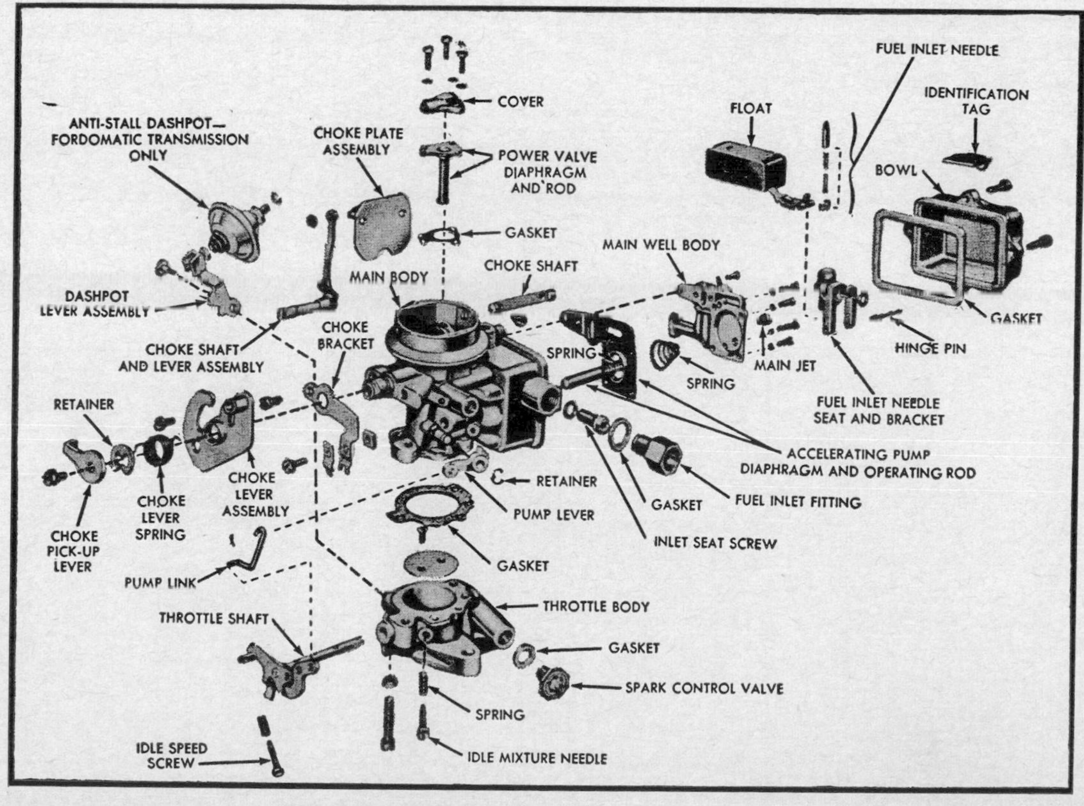

Fig. 2 Exploded view of Holley 1904 carburetor

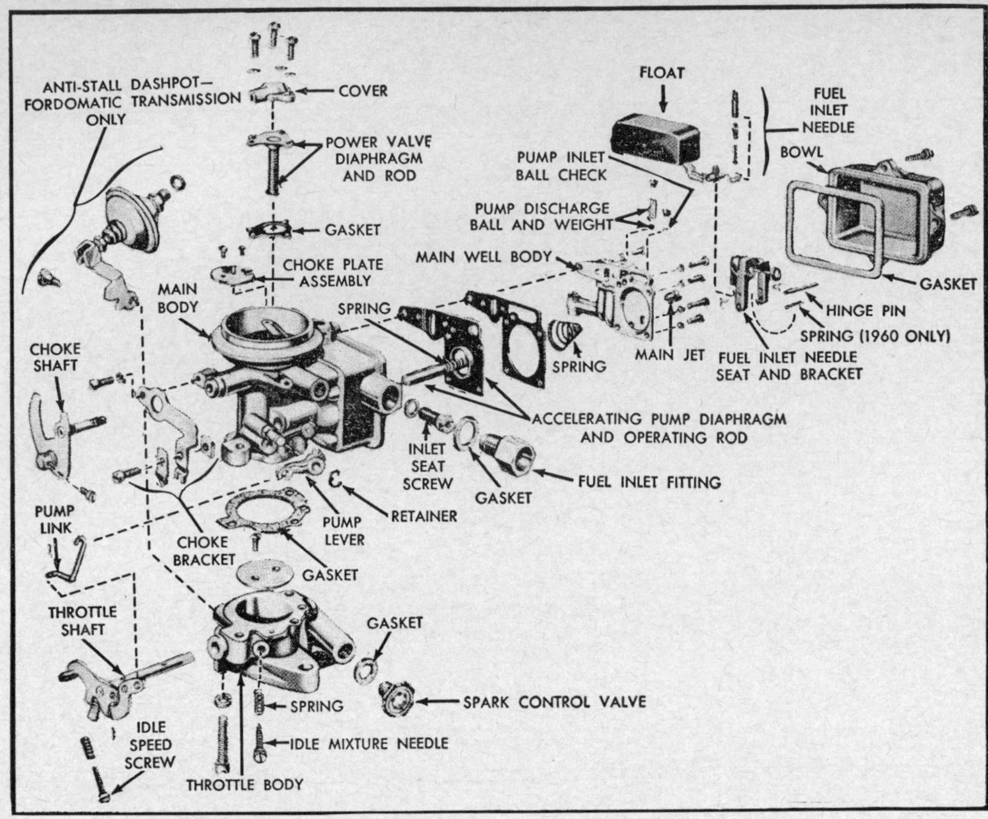

Fig. 3 Exploded view of Holley 1908 carburetor

bowl. The setting will be correct when the distance is within $\frac{1}{32}$" of the dimension listed in the *Holley Specifications Chart*. If adjustment is required, bend tab on float lever.

Accelerating Pump Stroke

Two holes are provided in the throttle lever for seasonal setting of the pump link, Fig. 6. Use the hole marked "B" for cold weather operation and the hole marked "A" for moderate and warm weather operation.

Choke Unloader Setting

Model 1908, Fig. 7—Hold throttle wide open and close choke valve until choke lever rests against choke unloader lever. Measure clearance between upper edge of choke valve and inner wall of air horn. If the dimension is not as listed in the *Holley Specifications Chart,* bend unloader lever as required.

Anti-Stall Dashpot Setting

Fig. 8—On models equipped with automatic transmission, check the dashpot setting after adjusting hot idle speed. Hold throttle closed and depress dashpot plunger with a screwdriver. Then turn adjusting screw in dashpot operating lever as required to establish the clearance listed in the *Holley Specifications Chart* between screw head and dashpot plunger.

Automatic Choke Setting

Model 1908—Loosen retaining screws and turn choke cover against thermostatic spring tension until index mark on cover is aligned with specified mark on choke housing, listed in *Holley Specifications Chart*. Tighten screws and check to see that choke valve is completely closed but is free to open with light finger pressure.

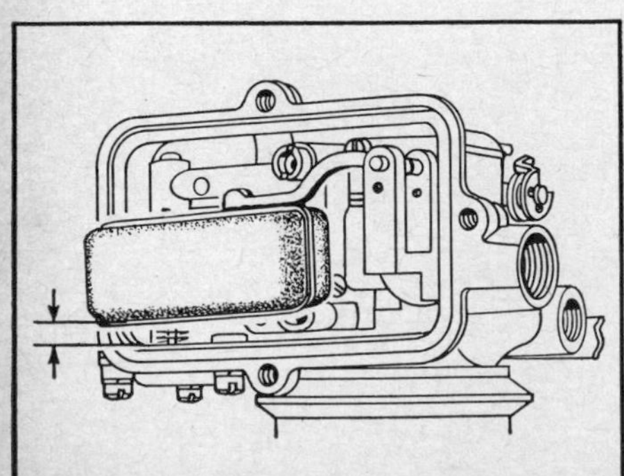

Fig. 4 Float level adjustment on 1904 and 1908 carburetors

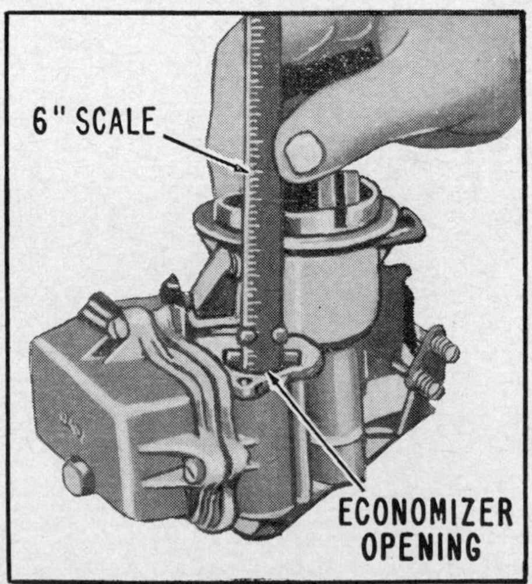

Fig. 5 Fuel level adjustment on 1904 and 1908 carburetors

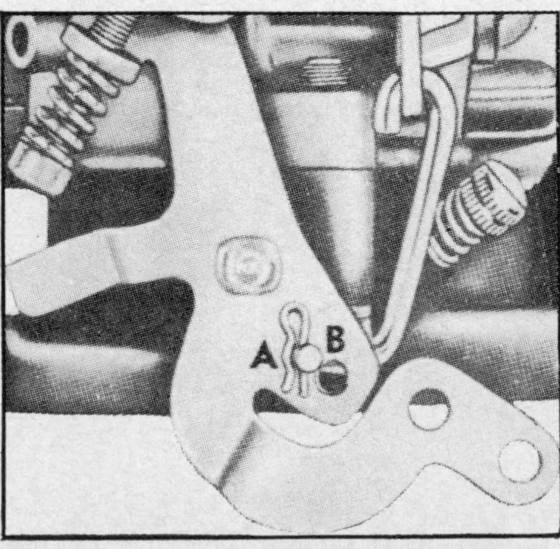

Fig. 6 Accelerating pump setting on 1904 and 1908 carburetors

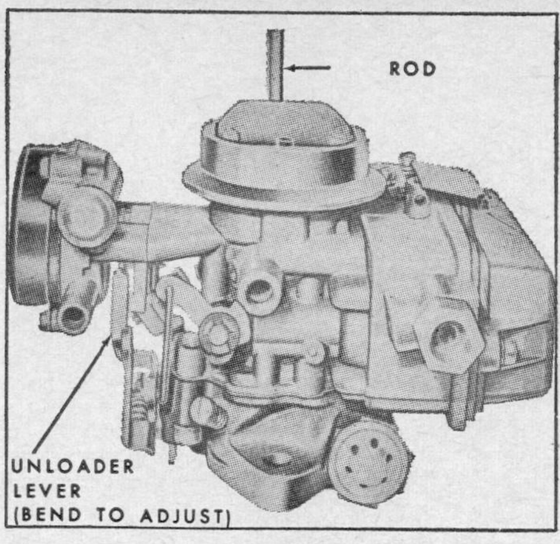

Fig. 7 Choke unloader setting on 1908 carburetor

Fig. 8 Anti-stall dashpot setting on 1904 and 1908 carburetors

Float Level Setting

Fig. 11—Adjust float level at a point ¼" from end of float so gauge shown will just fit between float and air horn when float needle is seated. To decrease float level bend float tab with needle nose pliers. To avoid damage to float and needle tip, never decrease float level by pressing down on float. If checking gauge is not available, measure float level as shown with needle valve seated. If the level is not as listed in the *Holley Specifications Chart,* adjust as required.

Accelerating Pump Stroke

Fig. 12—Two holes are provided in the throttle lever for seasonal setting of the pump link. Use the hole marked "B" for cold weather operation, and the hole marked "A" for moderate and warm weather operation.

Choke Unloader Setting

Fig. 13—With throttle lever held in wide open position, clearance between choke plate and inner air horn wall should be as listed in the *Holley Specifications Chart*. Adjust by bending unloader lever portion of throttle shaft lever as shown.

Anti-Stall Dashpot Setting

Fig. 14—Loosen dashpot lock nut and screw dashpot away from throttle operating lever. Hold throttle closed. Bottom plunger with a screwdriver, then turn dashpot toward throttle lever until the clearance listed in the *Holley Specifications Chart* exists between lever and tip of plunger.

Automatic Choke Setting

Fig. 15—Loosen retaining screws, pull out choke cover and then mesh teeth on cover with teeth on adapter to the specified point on the adapter, as listed in the *Holley Specifications Chart*. When assembling, tab on thermostatic spring must be positioned so that spring pressure closes choke plate.

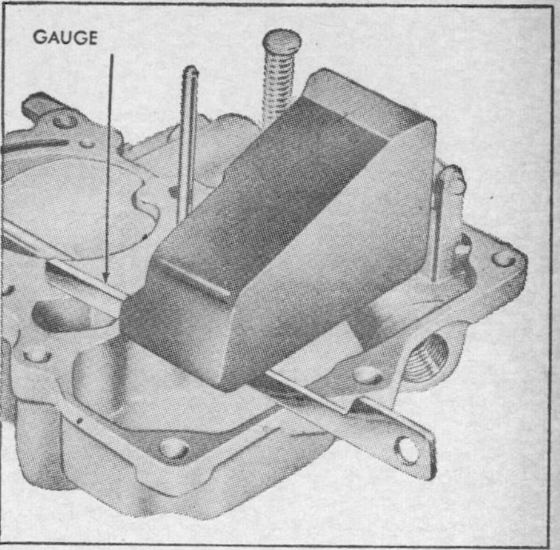

Fig. 11 Checking float level on 1909 carburetor

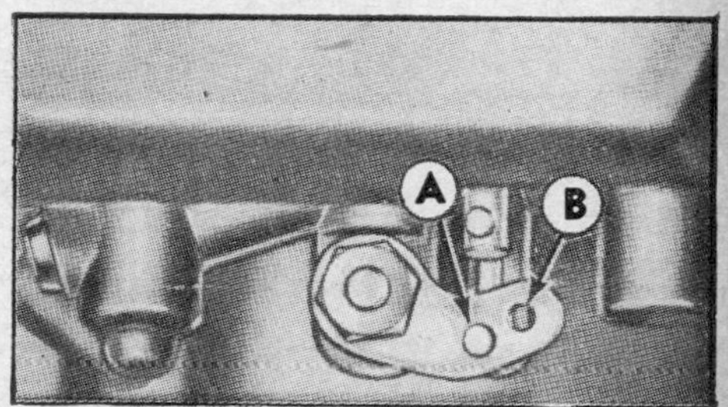

Fig. 12 Accelerating pump setting on 1909 carburetor

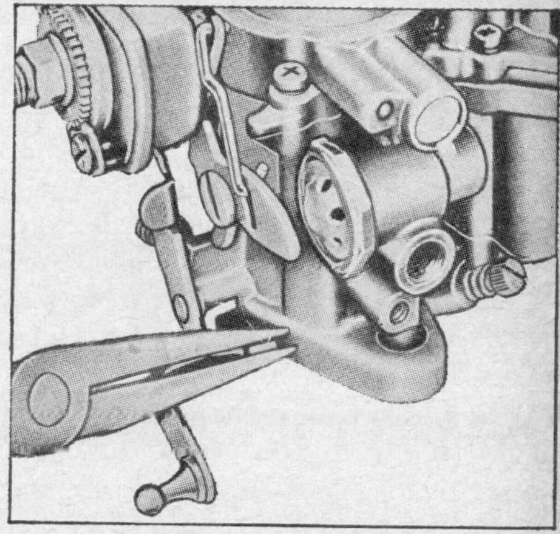

Fig. 13 Choke unloader setting on 1909 carburetor

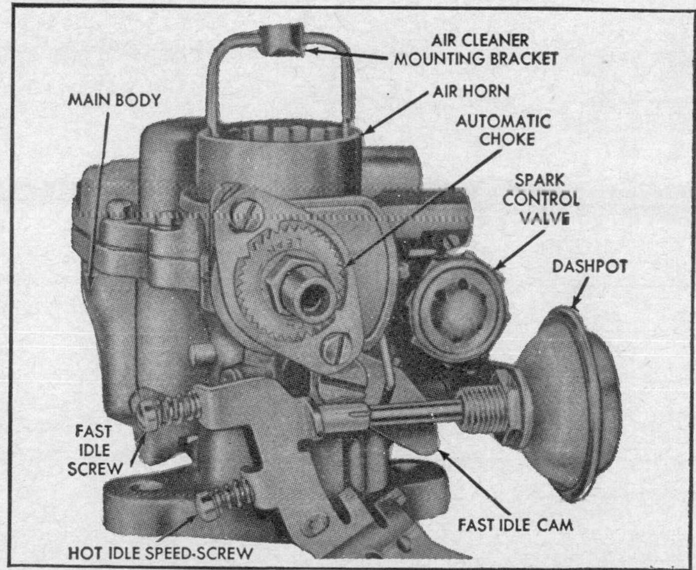

Fig. 9 Holley Model 1909 single-barrel carburetor

MODEL 1909

This carburetor, Figs. 9 and 10, consists of an aluminum die cast carburetor body and a zinc airhorn assembly.

MODEL 1920

These carburetors, Figs. 16 and 17, closely resemble models 1904 and 1908. However, the choke valve located in the carburetor bore is connected to a well-type automatic choke mounted in a well in the exhaust manifold.

Some models are equipped with a spring-staged choke, shown in Fig. 16, which is a device incorporated in the choke mechanism that limits the choke valve closing torque when cranking the engine at temperatures below zero. The spring-staging of the choke is suited for starting mixture requirements at both low and moderate temperatures.

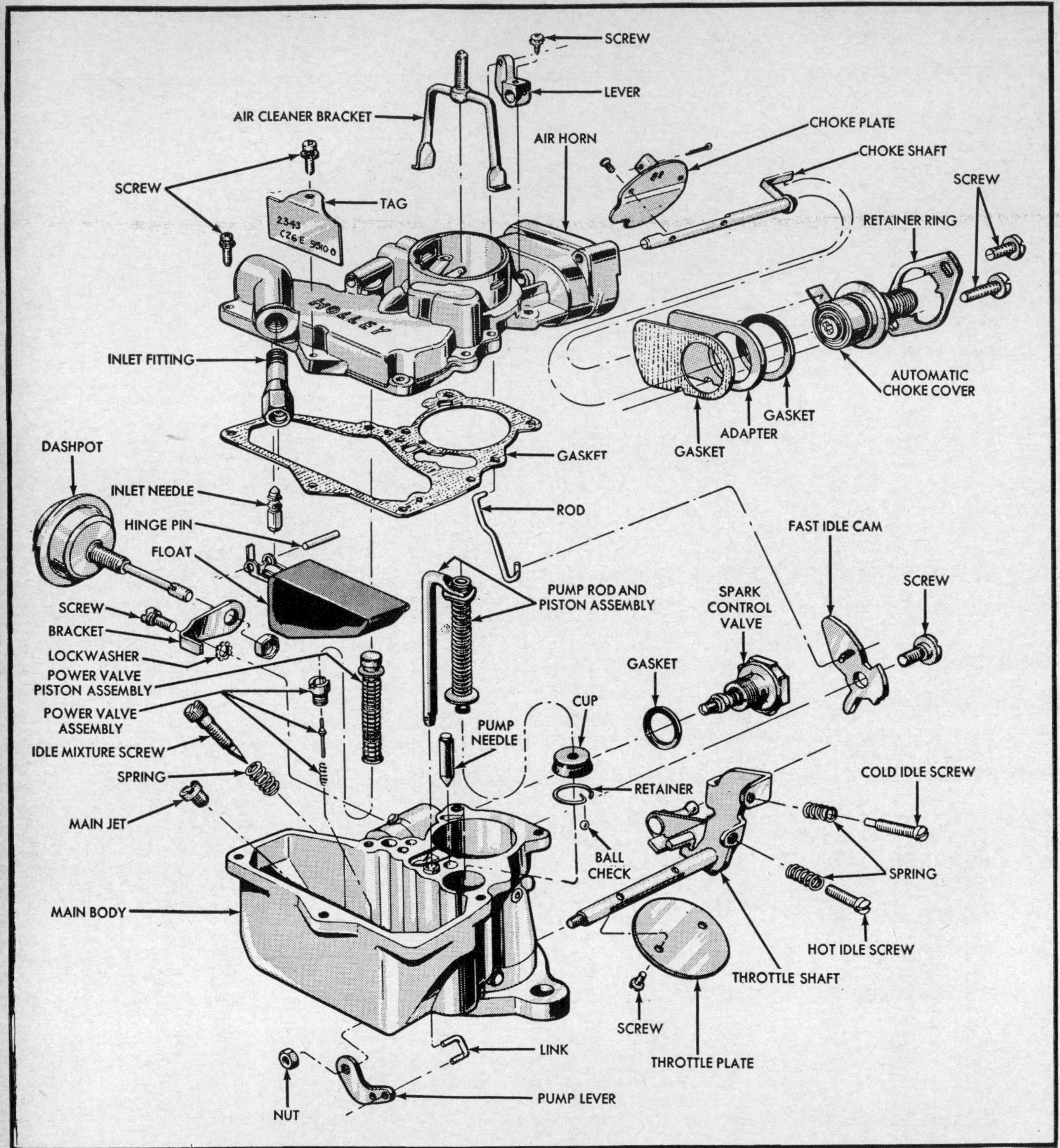

Fig. 10 Exploded view of Holley 1909 carburetor

Float Level Setting

Fig. 18—With carburetor inverted, slide float gauge into position and test setting on "touch" leg of gauge. Float should just touch gauge. Reverse gauge and test "no touch" leg. Float should just clear gauge. To adjust, bend float tab which touches head of fuel inlet needle, using needle nose pliers.

NOTE: Do not allow float tab to contact float needle head during the adjustment procedure as the rubber tip of the needle can be compressed, giving a false reading.

Checking Fuel Level

Fig. 19—With engine running and vehicle on a level floor, measure fuel level through the economizer diaphragm opening. Using a 6" scale with a depth gauge, measure distance from machined surface of the opening to the exact fuel surface. If the level is not as listed in the *Holley Specifications Chart,* adjust the float level as outlined above.

Float Bowl Vent Valve Setting

Fig. 14 Anti-stall dashpot setting on 1909 carburetor

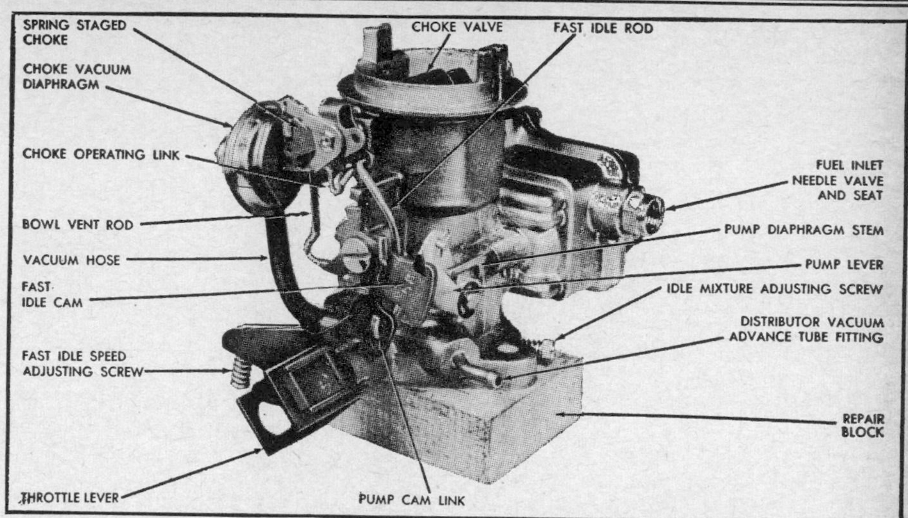

Fig. 16 Holley Model 1920 single-barrel carburetor

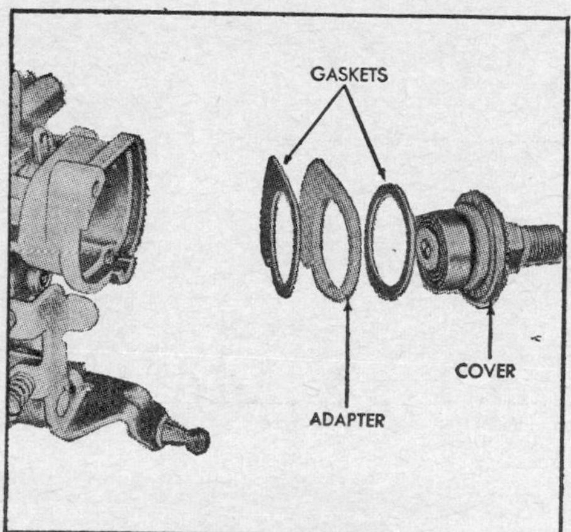

Fig. 15 Automatic choke setting on 1909 carburetor

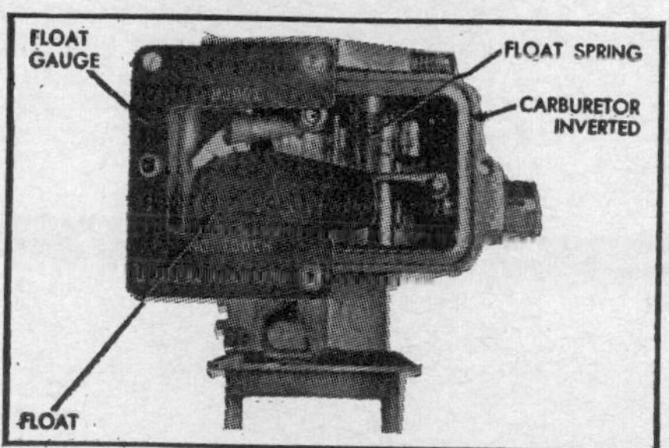

Fig. 18 Measuring float level on 1920 carburetor

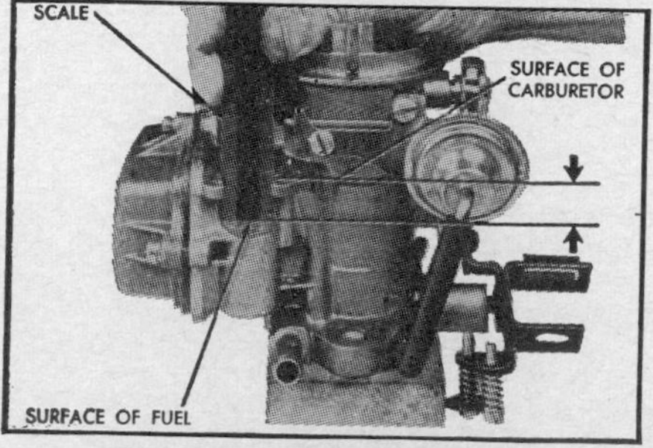

Fig. 19 Measuring fuel level on 1920 carburetor

Fig. 20—With throttle valve closed, bowl vent should be adjusted so that the shank of a drill of the size listed in the *Holley Specifications Chart* can be inserted between valve and surface of carburetor body. Adjust by bending bowl vent operating lever up or down as required. Be sure vent rod does not bind in the guide after adjusting.

Fast Idle Index & Choke Unloader

Fig. 21—Open throttle valve and hold choke valve fully closed. Now close throttle valve. Index mark on fast idle cam should split center of fast idle adjusting screw. Adjust by bending fast idle connector rod. This adjustment also positions the choke unloader mechanism.

Well-Type Automatic Choke

Fig. 22—To function properly, it is important that all parts be clean and move freely. Other than an occasional cleaning, the choke requires no attention. However, it is important that the choke control unit work freely in the well and at the choke shaft. Move the choke rod up and down to check for free movement on the pivot. If the unit binds, a new choke unit should be installed.

This type choke is serviced only as a unit. Do not attempt to repair or change the setting.

When installing the choke unit, be certain that the coil housing does not contact the sides of the well in the exhaust manifold. Any contact at this point will affect choke operation. Do not lubricate any parts of the choke or the control unit. This causes an accumulation of dirt which will result in binding of the mechanism.

Spring Staged Choke Adjustment

To test the adjustment on carburetors equipped with this feature, press against the choke lever firmly, Fig. 23. Measure clearance between hub lever and shaft lever. If the clearance is not within .010" and .025", bend fast idle rod slightly until normal clearance is obtained. The cam position and unloader setting resulting from such bending of the choke link are satisfactory.

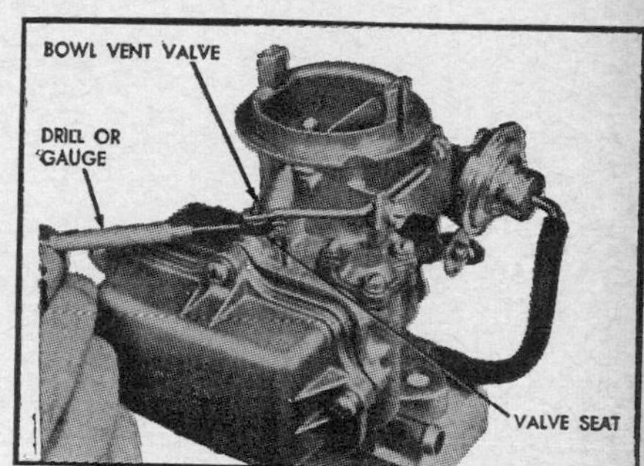

Fig. 20 Measuring bowl vent opening on 1920 carburetor

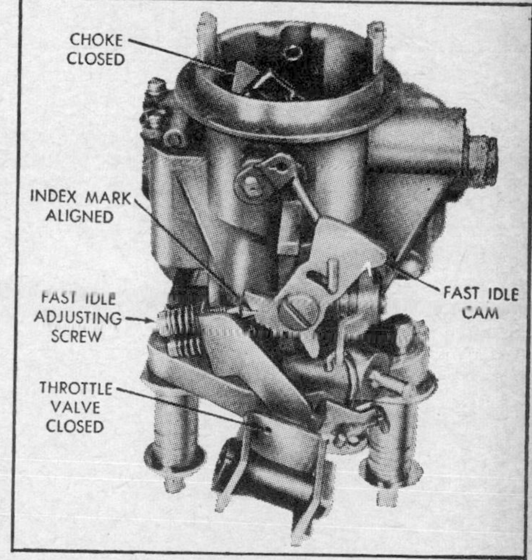

Fig. 21 Fast idle index and choke unloader setting on 1920 carburetor

MODEL 1931

This carburetor, Figs. 24 and 25, features a one-piece main body and throttle body casting together with a large capacity fuel bowl. The fuel inlet and float assembly, located in the center of the fuel bowl cover, maintains a stable fuel level for best performance on turns. The large capacity fuel bowl is designed to handle

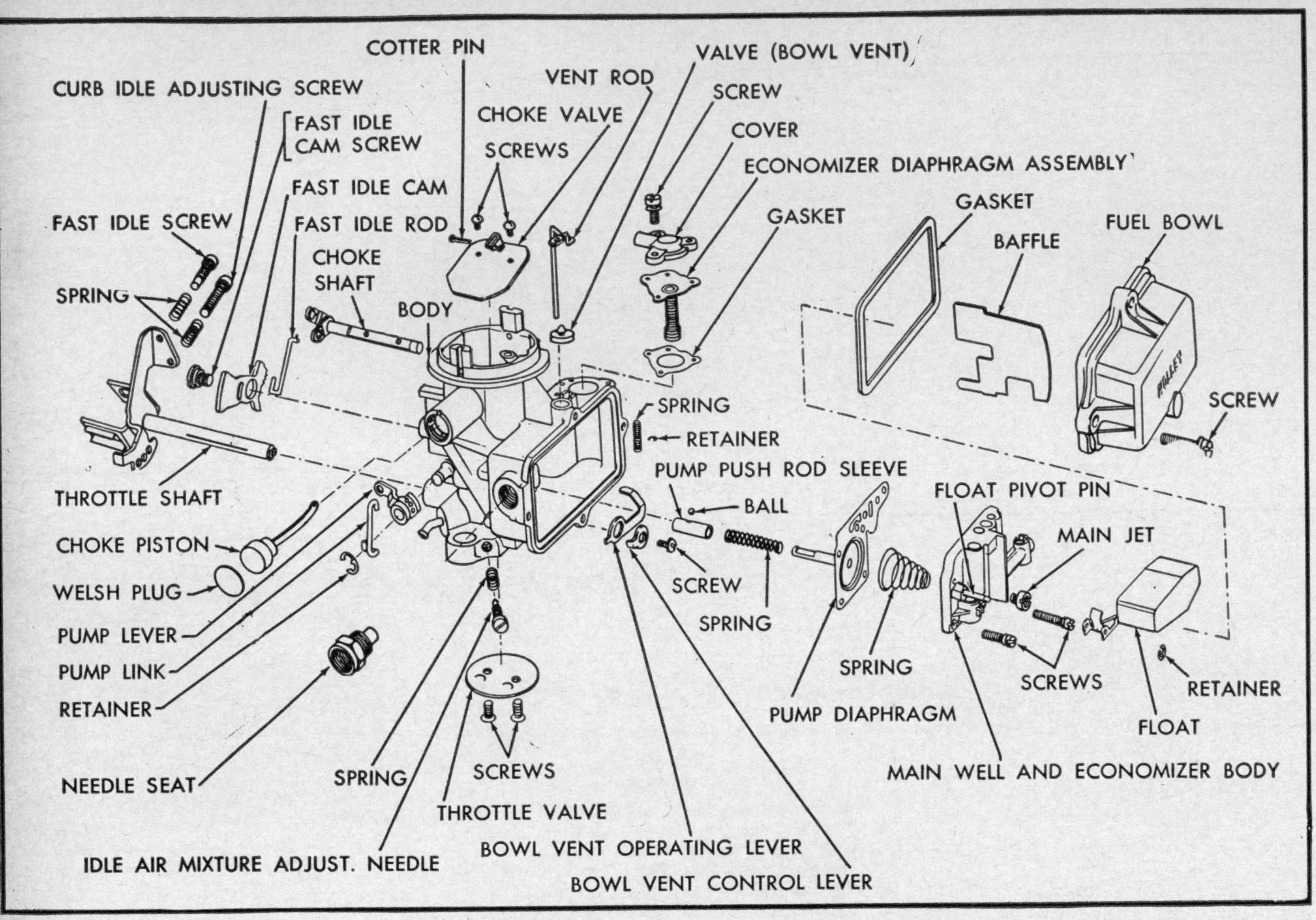

Fig. 17 Exploded view of Holley 1920 carburetor

efficiently vapor loaded fuels and fuel vapors.

The automatic choke is mounted in a heat sink on the exhaust manifold and is connected to the carburetor by a choke rod.

Float Adjustment

Figs. 26, 27, 28—Invert carburetor fuel bowl cover and check float setting at both ends, Fig. 26. If float adjustment is necessary the float may be lowered by pulling on the center of the float, Fig. 27. The float may be raised by pushing on the center of the float, Fig. 28.

CAUTION: During float adjustment do not allow the float tab to contact the fuel inlet needle as the resilient tip of the needle can be damaged or compressed, resulting in an improper float setting and a leaky needle and seat.

If the proper gauge is not available, measure the distance between the roof of the float cover and top of float. If the setting is not as listed in the *Holley Specifications Chart,* adjust as required.

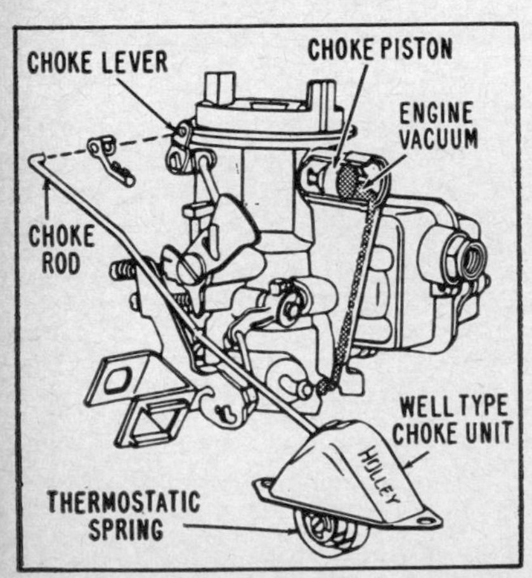

Fig. 22 Well-type automatic choke used with 1920 carburetor

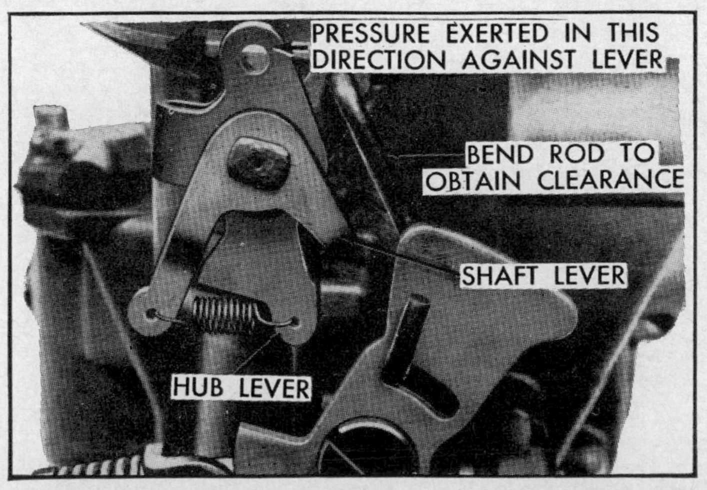

Fig. 23 Spring-staged choke adjustment on 1920 carburetor

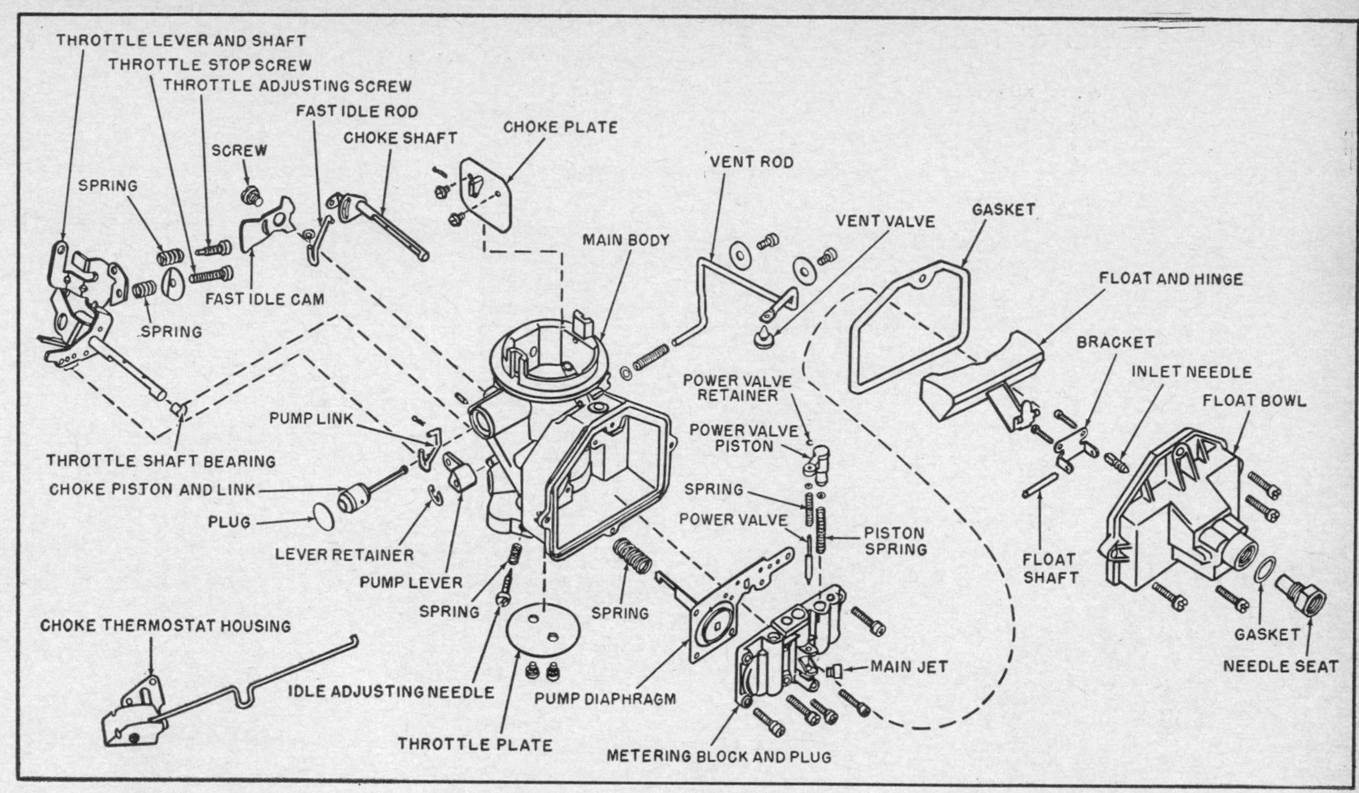

Fig. 25 Exploded view of Holley 1931 carburetor

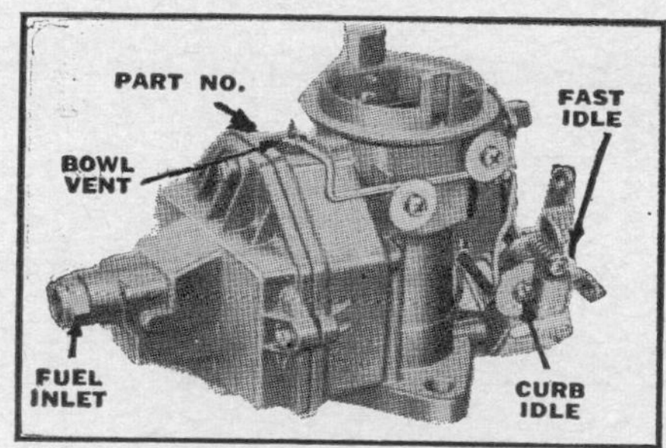

Fig. 24 Holley Model 1931 single-barrel carburetor

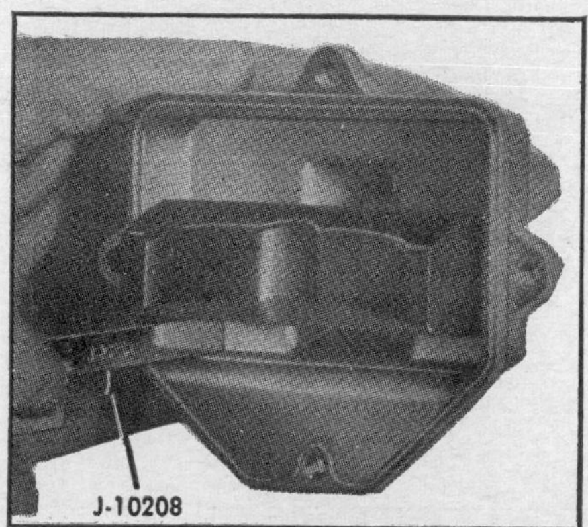

Fig. 26 Checking float level on 1931 carburetor

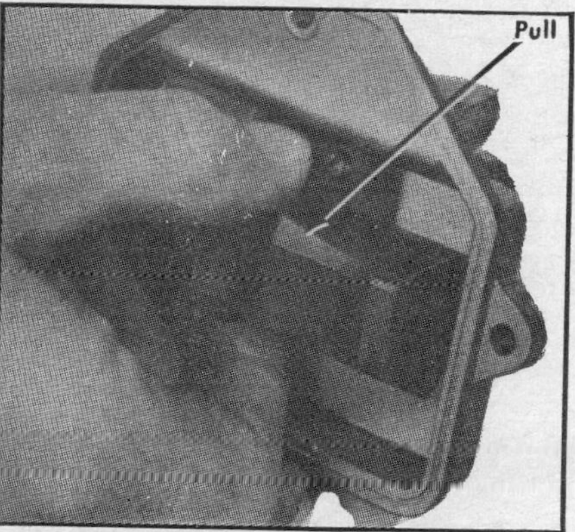

Fig. 27 Lowering float by pulling it out on 1931 carburetor

Bowl Vent Setting

Fig. 29—With throttle set at curb idle, clearance between vent valve and seat should be as listed in the *Holley Specifications Chart.* If an adjustment is necessary, bend vent rod at the horizontal portion above the fuel bowl. Check operation of vent rod for binding.

Accelerator Pump Setting

The accelerator link is set in the middle hole in the throttle lever for normal driving conditions. In the event a richer pump discharge is required, place the pump link in the outer hole of the throttle lever. For a leaner pump discharge, place the pump link in the inner hole of the throttle lever.

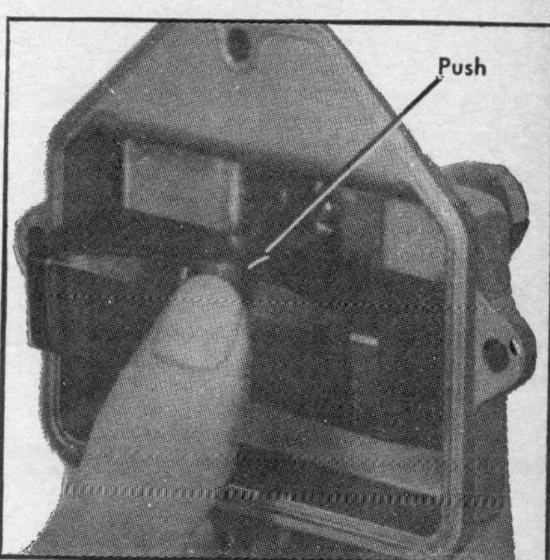

Fig. 28 Raising float by pushing it in on 1931 carburetor

Fast Idle Adjustment

With the fast idle screw resting on second step of fast idle cam, and engine at normal operating temperature, the fast idle rpm should be as listed in the *Holley Specifications Chart.* Turning the fast idle screw in clockwise increases (counterclockwise decreases) speed.

Choke Unloader Setting

Fig. 30—With throttle valve held in wide open position and choke plate rotated toward closed position, the distance between top edge of choke plate and flat portion of air horn should be as listed in the *Holley Specifications Chart.* Adjust by bending tab on throttle lever.

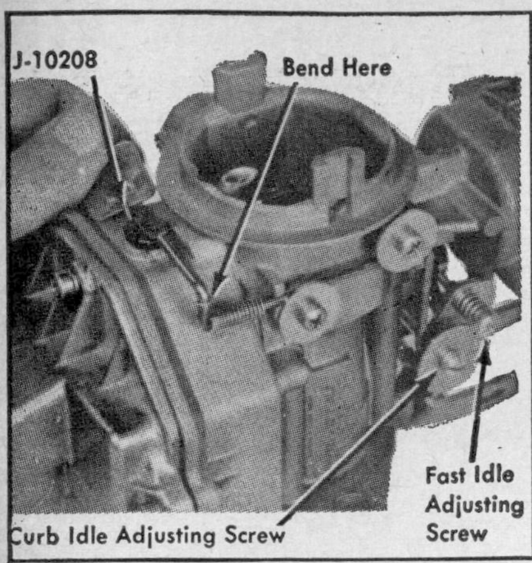

Fig. 29 Bowl vent adjustment on 1931 carburetor

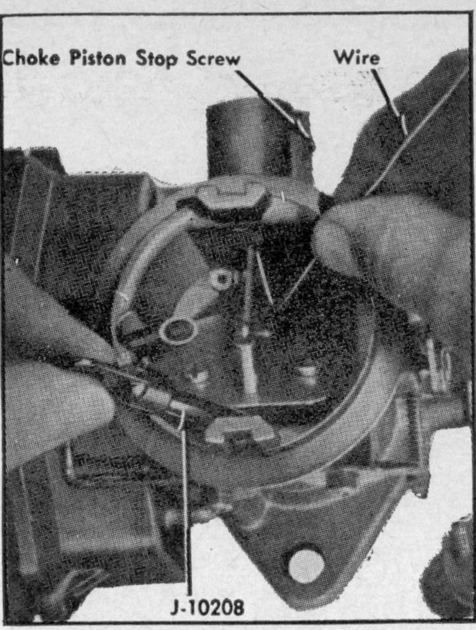

Fig. 31 Choke piston stop adjustment on 1931 carburetor

Fig. 34 Float adjustment on 2209 carburetor

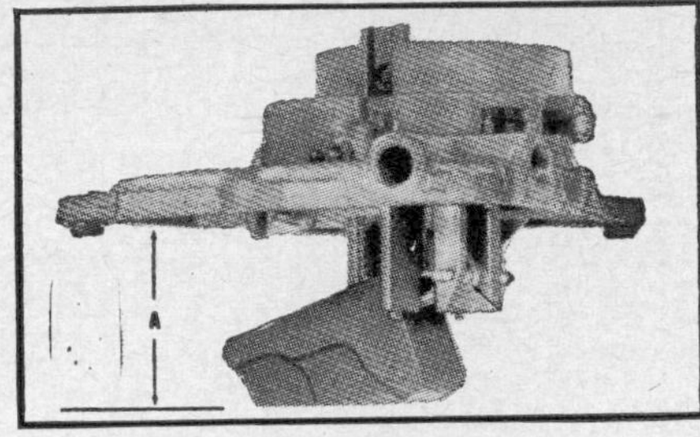

Fig. 35 Float drop adjustment on 2209 carburetor

Fig. 30 Choke unloader adjustment on 1931 carburetor

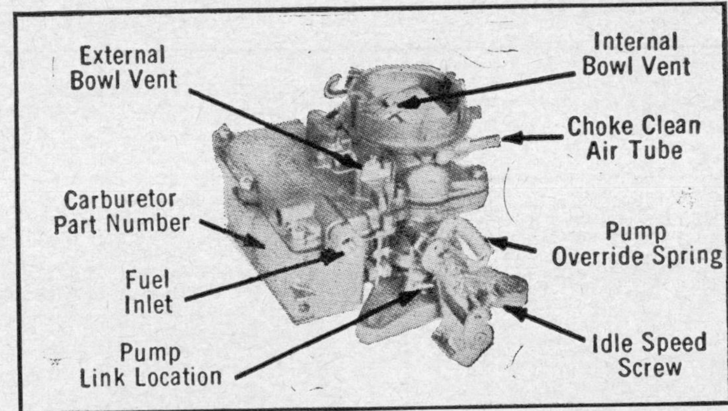

Fig. 32 Holley Model 2209 two-barrel carburetor

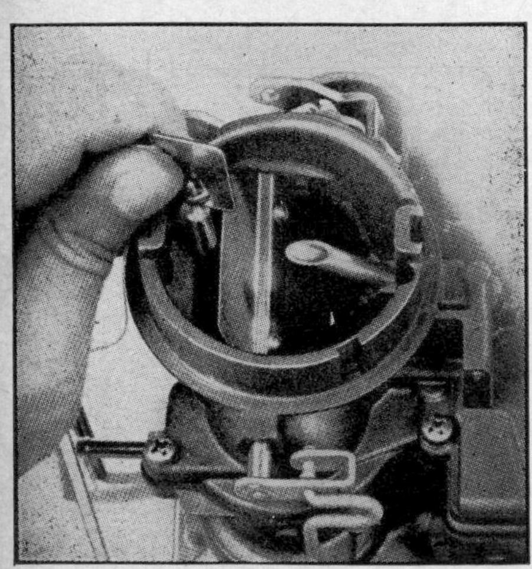

Fig. 36 Choke unloader adjustment on 2209 carburetor

Choke Piston Stop Adjustment

Fig. 31—Hold choke piston against stop screw with a wire inserted in slot above choke piston link. Rotate choke plate toward closed position until link is firm. The distance between top edge of choke plate and flat portion of air horn should by $\frac{3}{16}$". Adjust by turning piston stop screw in or out as required.

Automatic Choke Setting

The adjustment is made by loosening choke cover screws and rotating cover in the desired direction as indicated by an arrow on the cover. The choke should be set to the mark specified in the *Holley Specifications Chart* for all normal driving. Never set the choke more than two graduations in either direction of the specified setting.

Fig. 37 Automatic choke setting on 2209 carburetor

MODEL 2209

This carburetor, Figs. 32 and 33, features a large capacity side inlet fuel bowl with a separate throttle body. The large capacity fuel bowl is designed to handle

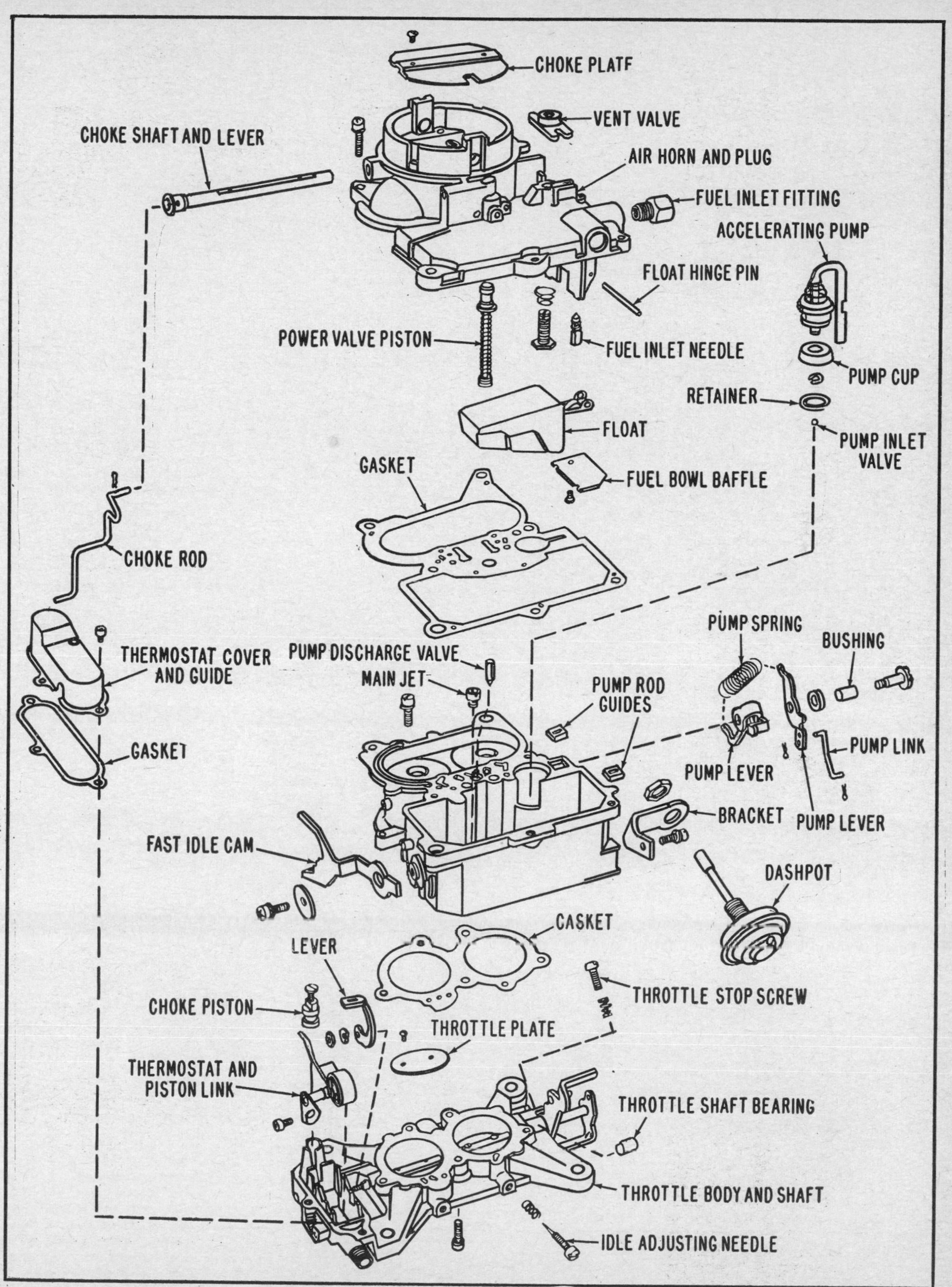
CHOKE PLATE
VENT VALVE
CHOKE SHAFT AND LEVER
AIR HORN AND PLUG
FUEL INLET FITTING
ACCELERATING PUMP
FLOAT HINGE PIN
POWER VALVE PISTON
FUEL INLET NEEDLE
PUMP CUP
RETAINER
FLOAT
PUMP INLET VALVE
GASKET
FUEL BOWL BAFFLE
CHOKE ROD
PUMP SPRING
BUSHING
THERMOSTAT COVER AND GUIDE
PUMP DISCHARGE VALVE
MAIN JET
PUMP ROD GUIDES
GASKET
PUMP LINK
PUMP LEVER
BRACKET
PUMP LEVER
FAST IDLE CAM
DASHPOT
GASKET
LEVER
THROTTLE STOP SCREW
CHOKE PISTON
THROTTLE PLATE
THERMOSTAT AND PISTON LINK
THROTTLE SHAFT BEARING
THROTTLE BODY AND SHAFT
IDLE ADJUSTING NEEDLE

Fig. 33 Exploded view of Holley 2209 carburetor

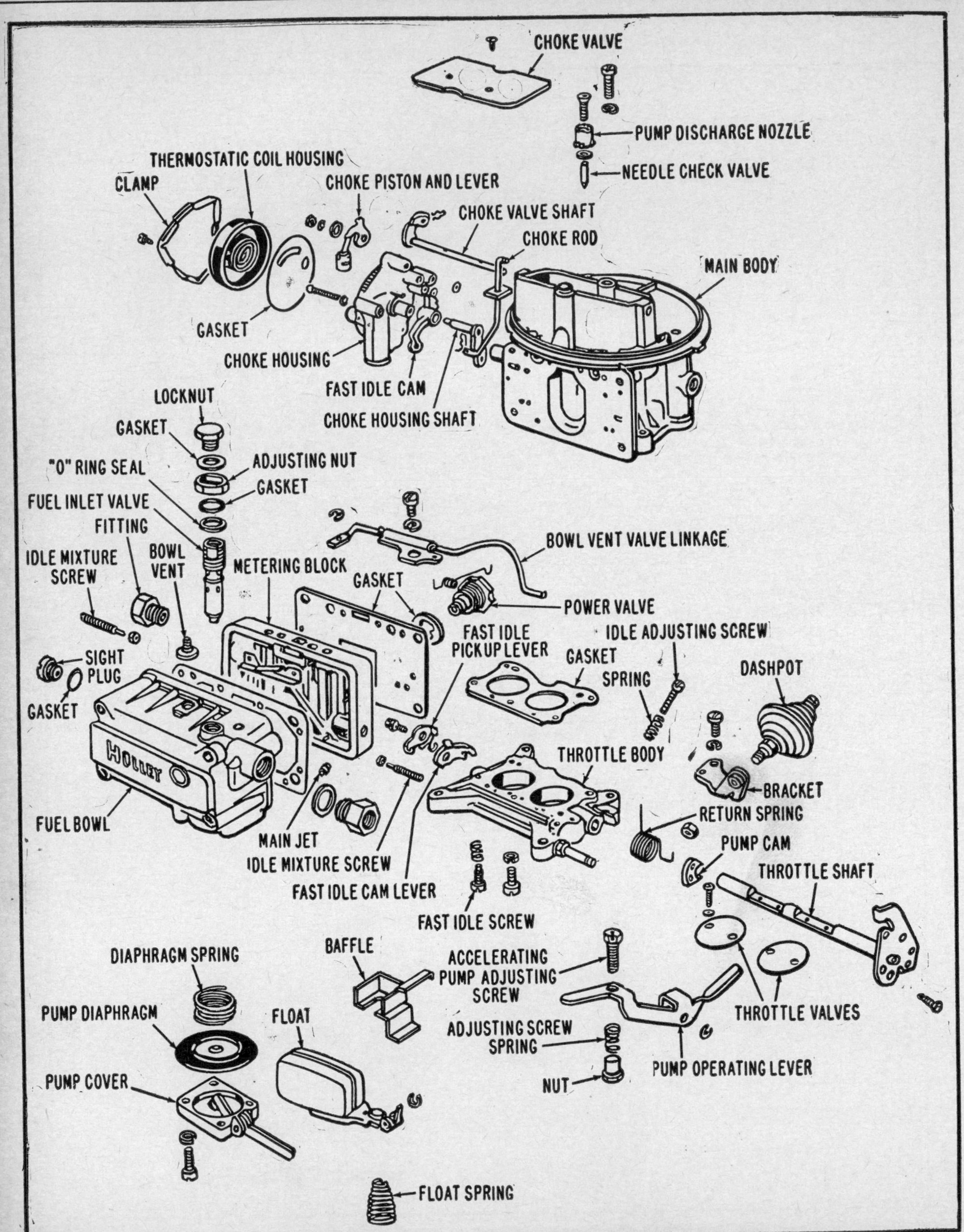

Fig. 40 Exploded view of Holley 2300 carburetor

Fig. 38 Fast idle setting on 2209 carburetor

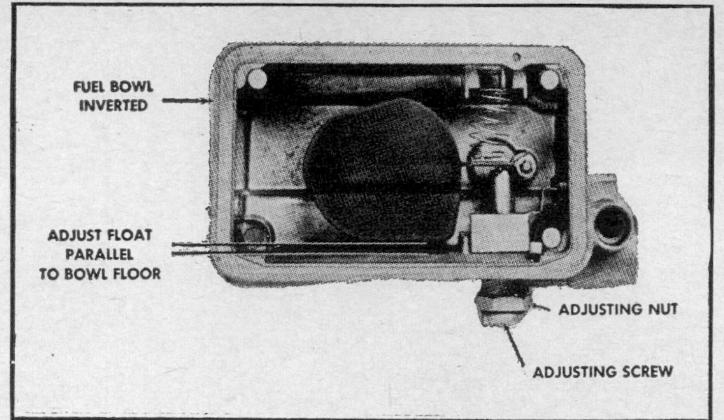

Fig. 41 Float adjustment on 2300 carburetor

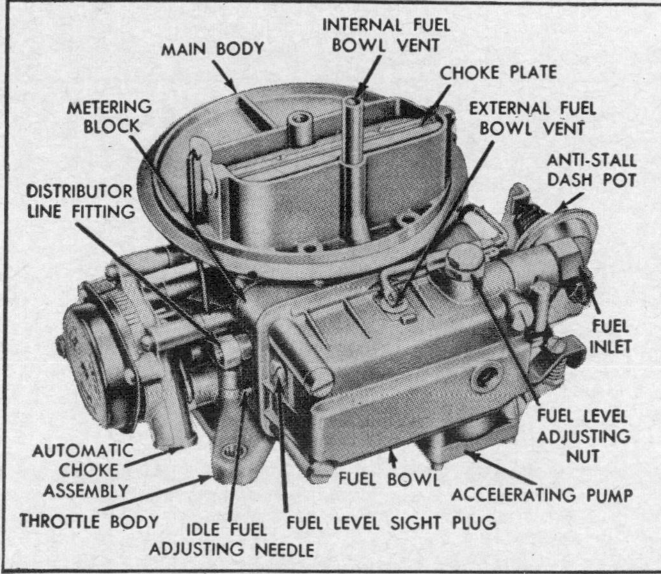

Fig. 39 Holley Model 2300 two-barrel carburetor

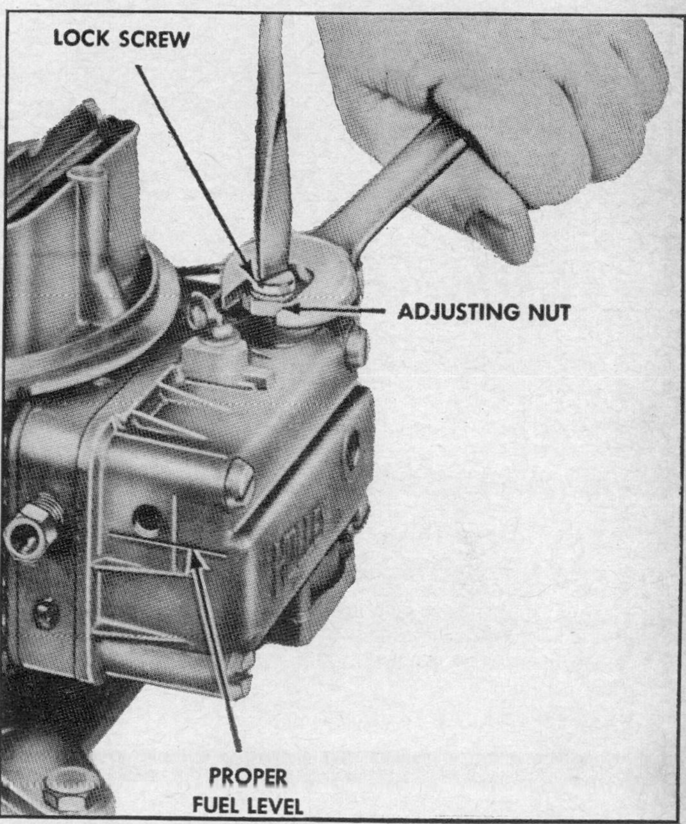

Fig. 42 Fuel level adjustment on 2300 carburetor

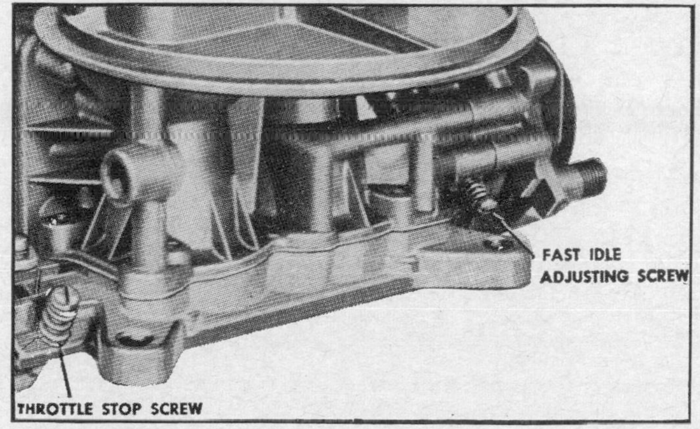

Fig. 43 Fast idle adjustment on 2300 carburetor

efficiently vapor loaded fuels and fuel vapors. The separate throttle body and gasket creates a thermal barrier which reduces heat transfer to the fuel. The automatic choke is part of the throttle body and is connected to the choke plate by a choke rod.

Float Level Setting

Fig. 34—Check float setting with float dry and air horn inverted. Measure distance between float and air horn. If dimension is not as listed in the *Holley Specifications Chart,* adjust by bending float tab as required.

Checking Float Drop

Fig. 35—With air horn held upright, bottom surface of float should be parallel with air horn as shown. Adjust by bending float drop tab.

Choke Unloader Setting

Fig. 36—With throttle held in wide open position, there should be the clearance listed in the *Holley Specifications Chart* between top edge of choke plate and air horn wall as shown. Adjust by bending tab on fast idle cam.

Choke Adjustment

Fig. 37—Set automatic choke on index mark for all normal driving. If for some

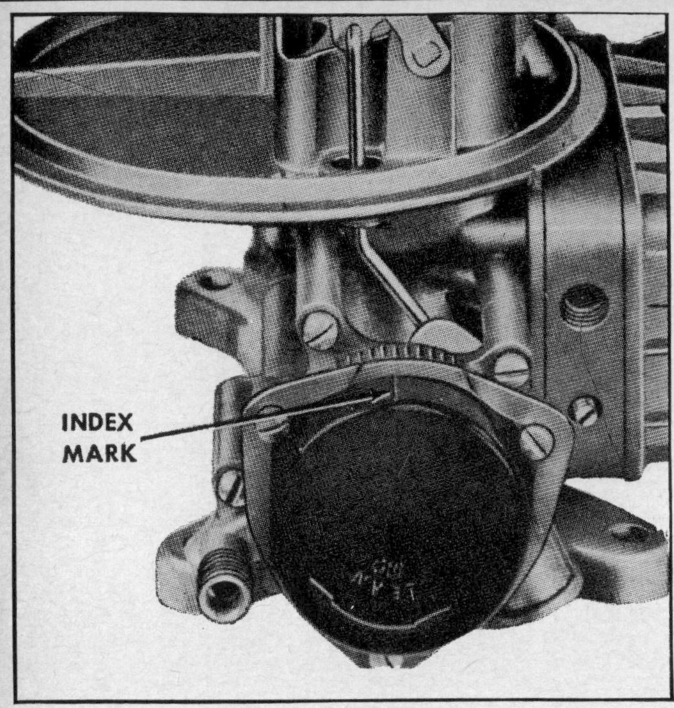

Fig. 44 Automatic choke setting on 2300 carburetor

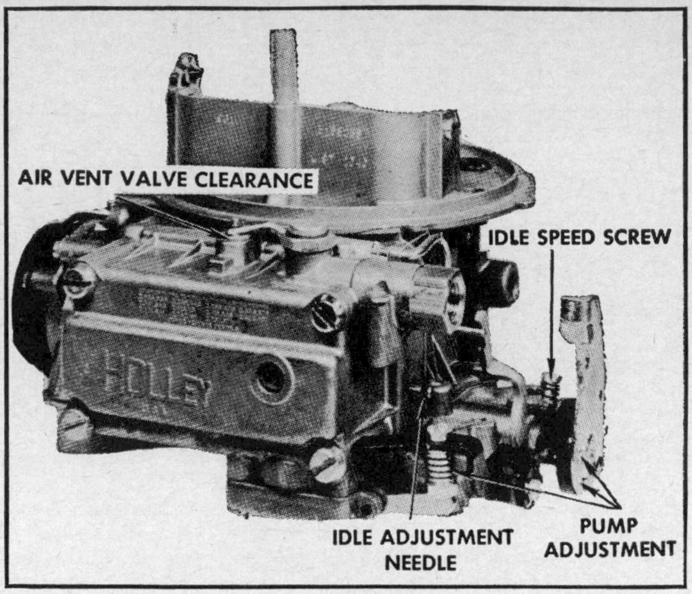

Fig. 45 Carburetor adjustments on 2300 carburetor

reason a richer or leaner mixture is desired during warm-up period, the choke can be reset by rotating choke thermostat shaft clockwise for a richer (counterclockwise for leaner) mixture. Never set the choke more than 2 graduations in either direction from the specified mark listed in the *Holley Specifications Chart*.

Fast Idle Adjustment

Fig. 38—With throttle stopped on high step of fast idle cam, the fast idle speed should be as listed in the *Holley Specifications Chart* with engine at normal temperature. Adjust by bending tab on throttle lever as shown.

Accelerator Pump Adjustment

The accelerating pump operating link is set in the inner hole of the pump lever for all normal driving conditions. If a leaner pump discharge is required, set the link in the outer hole.

Anti-Stall Dashpot Setting

With the throttle set at curb idle, there should be the clearance listed in the *Holley Specifications Chart* between dashpot stem and tab on throttle lever. Loosen lock nut and position dashpot to obtain this clearance. Tighten nut against bracket and recheck clearance.

MODEL 2300

This carburetor, Figs. 39 and 40, is a two-barrel unit but can be considered as two carburetors built side by side into one unit, utilizing the same fuel inlet and air inlet. Each barrel has its own venturi, idle system, main metering system, booster venturi and throttle plate.

Float Adjustment

Fig. 41—With fuel bowl inverted so that float arm rests on fuel inlet needle holding it closed, set the float crease line parallel with the horizontal crease line of the fuel bowl. This adjustment is made by turning the fuel inlet needle and seat assembly adjusting nut as shown. The adjustment must be rechecked with the carburetor on the engine for proper wet fuel level as outlined below.

Wet Fuel Level

Fig. 42—With car on a level floor and engine idling, remove sight plug from fuel bowl. Fuel level should be in line with threads at bottom of sight plug hole. To adjust, loosen lock screw and turn adjusting nut as required to raise or lower fuel level.

Fast Idle Setting

Fig. 43—This adjustment with the carburetor off the car is made by turning the fast idle screw to obtain the clearance listed in the *Holley Specifications Chart* between throttle valve and carburetor bore on side opposite idle port with fast idle screw resting on high step of fast idle cam.

Automatic Choke Setting

Fig. 44—The choke setting listed in the *Holley Specifications Chart* is for all normal driving conditions. If a richer or leaner mixture is desired during warm-up period, it can be obtained by rotating the thermostat cover. Never set the index mark on the cover more than two graduations in either direction of the specified setting.

Choke Unloader Setting

The choke unloader dimension listed in the *Holley Specifications Chart* is measured from the top edge of choke plate to forward top edge of air horn wall with throttle plates wide open. To adjust, bend tab on throttle shaft lever where it contacts fast idle cam.

Accelerator Pump Setting

Fig. 45—The pump screw should be in the No. 1 position on the throttle lever for all normal driving conditions. For extreme cold weather operation the No. 2 position can be used to provide maximum pump discharge.

The pump override spring is adjusted with throttle plates fully open and pump lever in compressed position. With screw just touching pump lever, tighten screw ¼ turn. To insure positive pump action, there must be no lag in the pump linkage. The slightest movement of the throttle lever from curb idle must actuate the pump lever. To remove any lag in this linkage, lengthen the pump override spring screw.

Bowl Vent Adjustment

Fig. 45—The bowl vent opening should be as listed in the *Holley Specifications Chart* and is adjusted by bending the operating lever as required.

HOLLEY 4150 & 4160 CARB. ADJUSTMENT SPECIFICATIONS

See Tune Up Chart in car chapters for hot idle speeds.

Year	Carb. Part No. ①	Float Level (Dry)	Fuel Level (Wet)	Pump Lever Clearance	Choke Setting	Choke Unloader Clearance	Bowl Vent Clearance	Fast Idle		Choke Vacuum Break	Dashpot Setting
								Bench	On Car		
CHEVROLET ENGINES											
1964–65	R2818-A	See Text	See Text	.015	1 Lean	3/16	—	.028	2350	—	—
1965	R3043-A	See Text	See Text	.015	3 Lean	3/16	—	.028	2350	—	—
1966	R3123-A	②	④	.015	See Text	.260	.065	.035	2200	.170	—
	R3139-1A	②	④	.015	See Text	.260	.065	.035	2000	.170	—
	R3140-1A	②	④	.015	See Text	.260	.065	.035	2000	.170	—
	R3230-A	②	④	.015	See Text	.260	.065	.035	2000	.170	—
	R3245-A	②	④	.015	See Text	.260	.065	.025	2200	.180	—
	R3246-A	③	④	.015	See Text	.350	.065	.025	2200	.350	—
	R3247-A	③	④	.015	See Text	.350	.065	.025	2200	.350	—
	R3312-A	②	④	.015	See Text	.260	.065	.025	2200	.180	—
	R3327-A	②	④	.015	See Text	.260	.065	.035	2000	.180	—
	R3328-A	②	④	.015	See Text	.260	.065	.035	2000	.180	—
	R3367-A	②	④	.015	See Text	.260	.065	.035	2200	.170	—
	R3370-A	②	④	.015	See Text	.260	.065	.035	2000	.180	—
	R3416-A	②	④	.015	See Text	.260	.065	.035	2200	.170	—
	R3419-A	②	④	.015	See Text	.260	.065	.035	2000	.170	—
	R3420-A	②	④	.015	See Text	.260	.065	.035	2000	.170	—
	R3433-A	②	④	.015	See Text	.260	.065	.035	2000	.180	—
1967	R3418-A	③	④	.015	See Text	.350	.065	.025	2200	.350	—
	R3806-A	②	④	.015	See Text	.265	.065	.025	2200	.190	—
	R3807-A	②	④	.015	See Text	.265	.065	.025	2200	.190	—
	R3810-A	②	④	. 15	See Text	.265	.065	.035	2200	.190	—
	R3811-A	②	④	.015	See Text	.265	.065	.035	2200	.175	—
	R3814-A	②	④	.015	See Text	.265	.065	.035	2000	.175	—
	R3815-A	②	④	.015	See Text	.265	.065	.035	2200	.175	—
	R3836-A	②	④	.015	See Text	.265	.065	.035	2200	.175	—
	R3837-A	②	④	.015	See Text	.265	.065	.035	2200	.175	—
	R3838-A	②	④	.015	See Text	.265	.065	.035	2200	.175	—
	R3839-A	②	④	.015	See Text	.265	.065	.035	2200	.175	—
1968	R4053-A	⑩	④	.015	See Text	.350	.065	.025	2200	.300	—
	R4054-A	⑩	④	.015	See Text	.350	.065	.025	2200	.300	—
1969	R4053-A	⑩	④	.015	⑬	.350	—	.025	2200	.300	—
	R4296-A	⑩	④	.015	⑬	.350	—	.025	2200	.350	—
	R-4346	⑩	④	.015	⑬	.350	—	.025	2200	.300	—
CHRYSLER ENGINES											
1967	R3575-A	⑦	—	.015	2 Rich	5/32	—	700⑧	—	—	—
	R3667-A	⑦	—	.015	2 Rich	5/32	—	700⑧	—	—	—
1968	R3918-A	⑪	⑨	.015	2 Rich	5/32	50 Drill	46 Drill	700⑧	—	—

Continued

HOLLEY 4150 & 4160 CARB. ADJUSTMENT SPECIFICATIONS—Continued

See Tune Up Chart in car chapters for hot idle speeds.

Year	Carb. Part No. ①	Float Level (Dry)	Fuel Level (Wet)	Pump Lever Clearance	Choke Setting	Choke Unloader Clearance	Bowl Vent Clearance	Fast Idle		Choke Vacuum Break	Dashpot Setting
								Bench	On Car		
FORD ENGINES											
1963	C1AE-AM	See Text	④	.015	Index	—	—	—	1500	—	—
1964	C3AE-B	See Text	④	.015	Index	—	—	—	1800	—	—
1964–65	C3AF-BJ	See Text	④	⑤	Index	—	—	—	—	—	—
	C3AF-BK	See Text	④	⑤	—	—	—	—	—	—	—
1965	C4AF-CU	See Text	④	⑤	Index	—	—	—	—	—	—
	C4AF-CV	See Text	④	⑤	—	—	—	—	—	—	—
1966–67	C5AF-BC	See Text	④	⑤	—	—	—	—	—	—	—
	C5AF-BD	See Text	④	⑤	3 Lean	—	—	—	—	—	—
1966	C6OF-M	See Text	④	.015	Index	—	.080	—	1200	—	—
	C6OF-N	See Text	④	.015	Index	—	.080	—	1300	—	.075
1967	C7OF-A	See Text	—	—	3 Rich	—	—	—	2100	—	—
	C7OF-B	See Text	—	—	3 Rich	—	—	—	2100	—	—
	C7OF-C	See Text	—	—	2 Rich	—	—	—	2100	—	—
	C7OF-D	See Text	—	—	2 Rich	—	—	—	2100	—	—
1968	C8OF-AA	See Text	—	—	Index	—	—	—	1350	—	—
	C8OF-AB	See Text	—	—	Index	—	—	—	1550	—	.100
	C8OF-C	See Text	—	—	3 Rich	.300	—	—	1900	—	.100
	C8OF-D	See Text	—	—	3 Rich	.300	—	—	2100	—	.100
	C8AF-AD	See Text	—	—	—	.300	—	—	2100	—	.100
1969	C9AF-M	See Text	—	—	2 Rich	.300	—	—	1350⑫	—	.100
	C9AF-N	See Text	—	—	1 Rich	.300	—	—	1550⑫	—	.100
	C9OF-H	See Text	—	—	1 Rich	.300	—	—	1550⑫	—	.100
RAMBLER											
1963–64	1957-1	See Text	④	⑥	1 Lean	.180	.060	.025	1700	—	—
	2464	See Text	④	⑥	1 Lean	.180	.060	.025	1700	—	3/32
1965	3044	See Text	④	.015	1 Lean	.180	.060	.025	1700	—	—
	3045	See Text	④	.015	1 Lean	.180	.060	.025	1700	—	3/32
1966–67	3201	See Text	④	.015	1 Lean	3/16	1/16	.025	2000	—	—
	3202	See Text	④	.015	1 Lean	3/16	1/16	.025	2000	—	3/32

①—Located on tag attached to carburetor, on casting or on choke plate flange.
②—Primary .170″, secondary .300″.
③—Primary .350″, secondary .450″.
④—Use sight plug hole in fuel bowl as outlined in text.
⑤—Seasonal setting in pump lever holes; long stroke for cold weather, short stroke for moderate weather.
⑥—With lever touching screw, then tighten 1/4 turn more.
⑦—Primary 7/64″, secondary 15/64″.
⑧—No. 5 Step on cam.
⑨—Primary 9/16″, secondary 13/16″.
⑩—Primary .350″, secondary .500″.
⑪—Primary 15/64″, Secondary 17/64″.
⑫—On top step of cam.
⑬—Top of rod even with bottom of hole.

MODELS 4150, 4160 ADJUSTMENTS

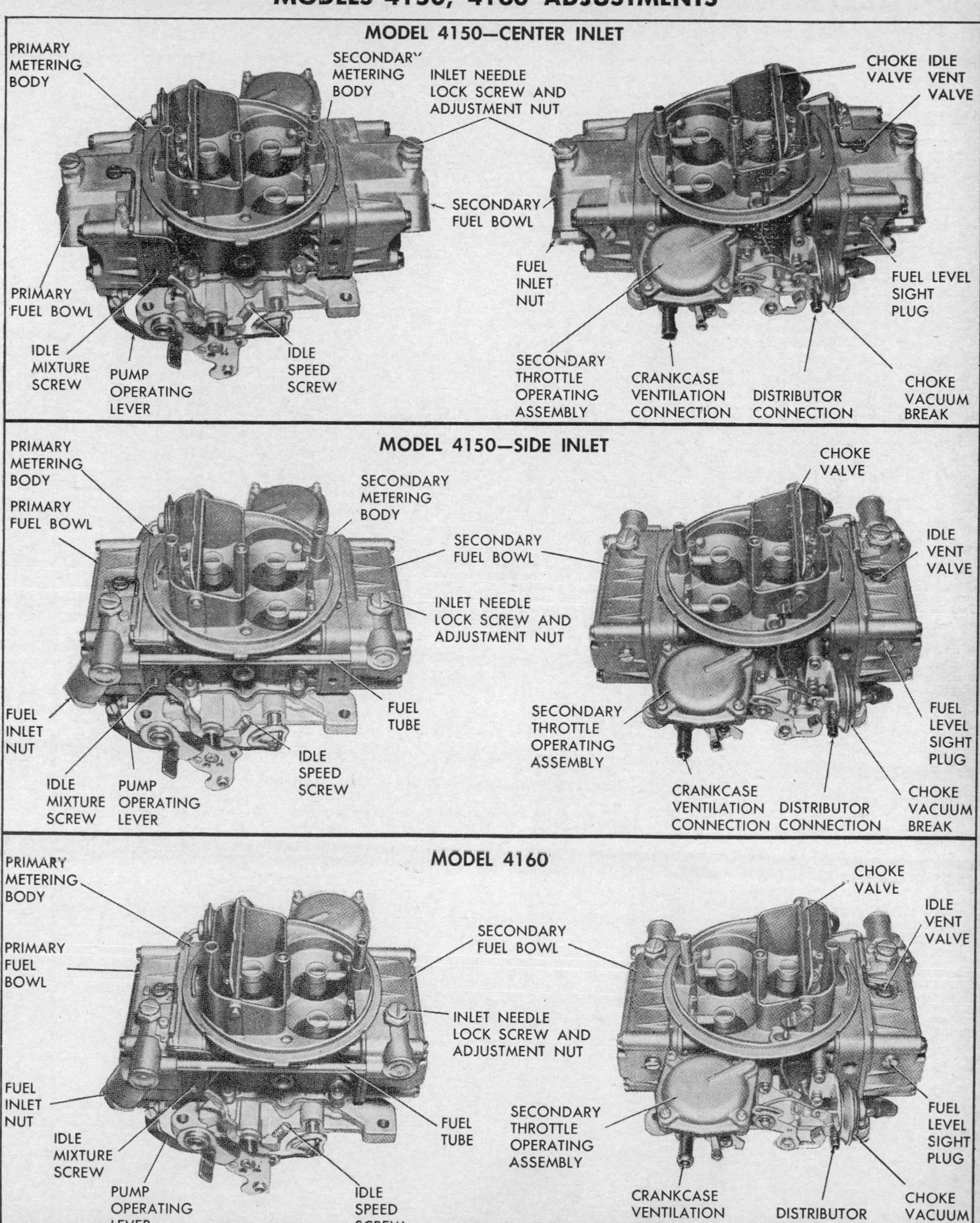

Fig. 46 Holley Models 4150 and 4160 late model four-barrel carburetors

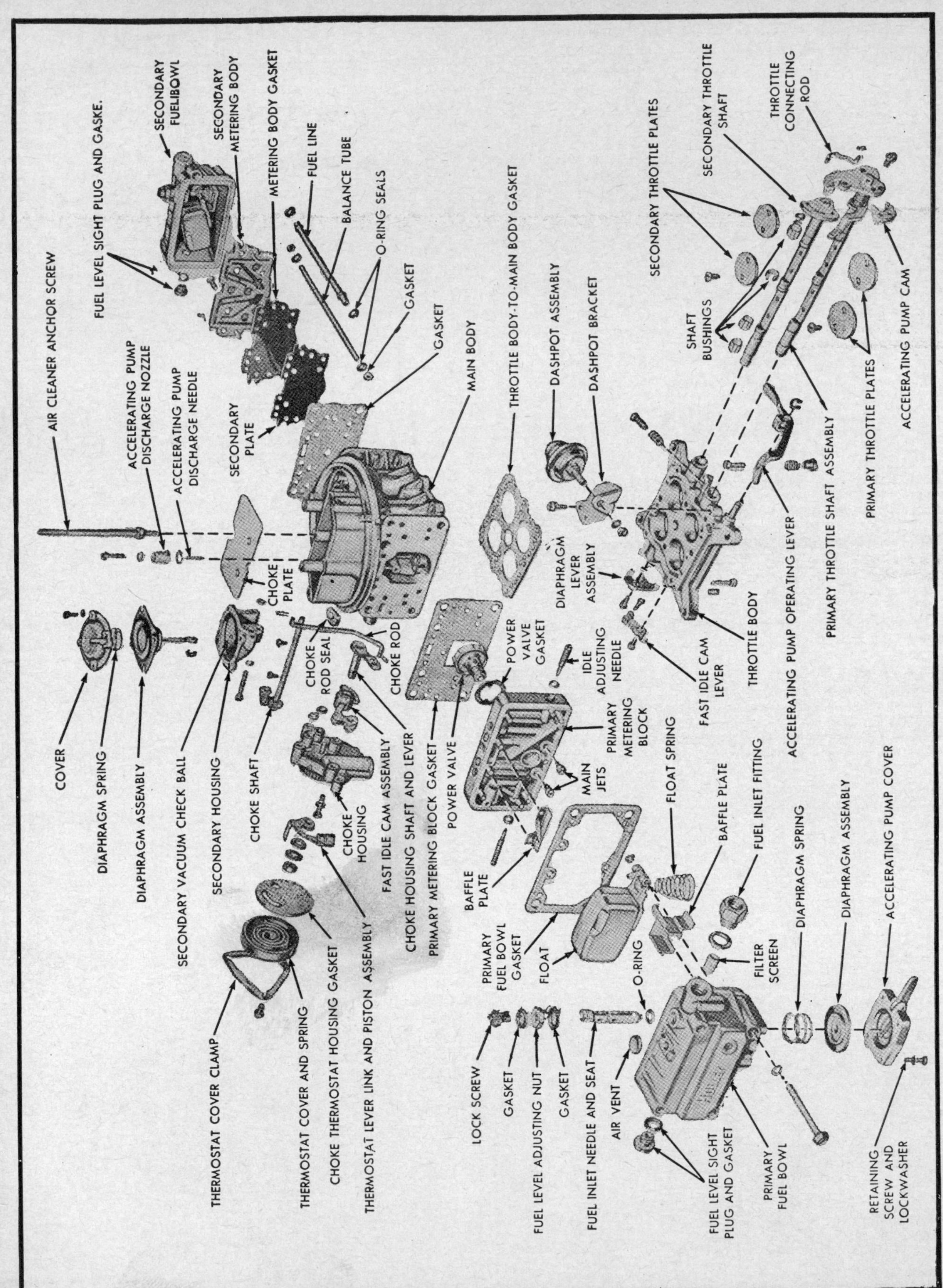

Fig. 47 Exploded view of a typical 4150 and 4160 carburetor

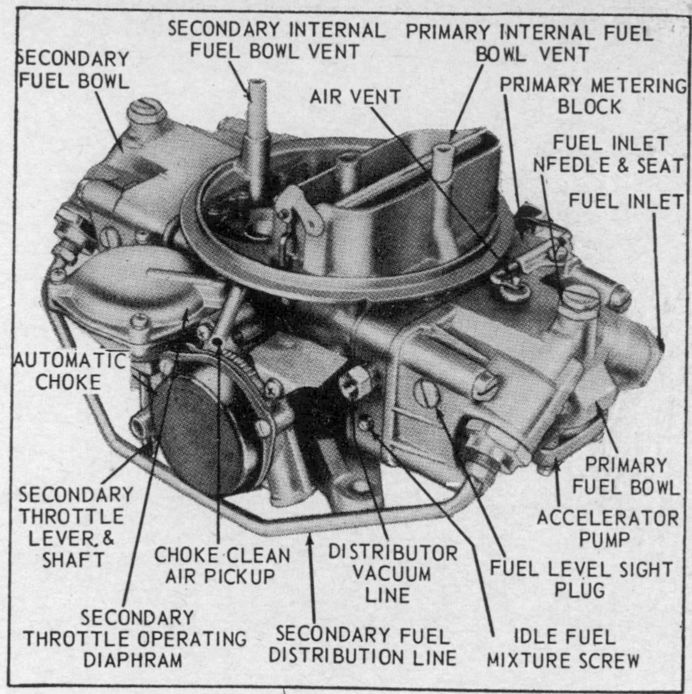

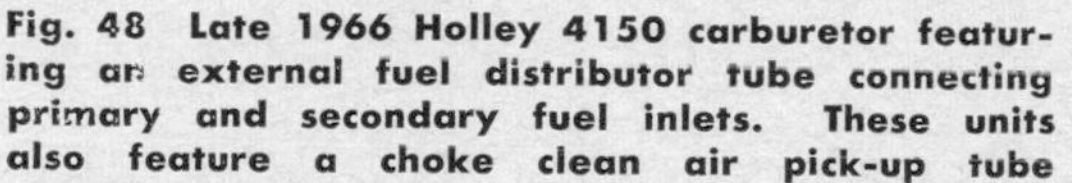
Fig. 48 Late 1966 Holley 4150 carburetor featuring an external fuel distributor tube connecting primary and secondary fuel inlets. These units also feature a choke clean air pick-up tube

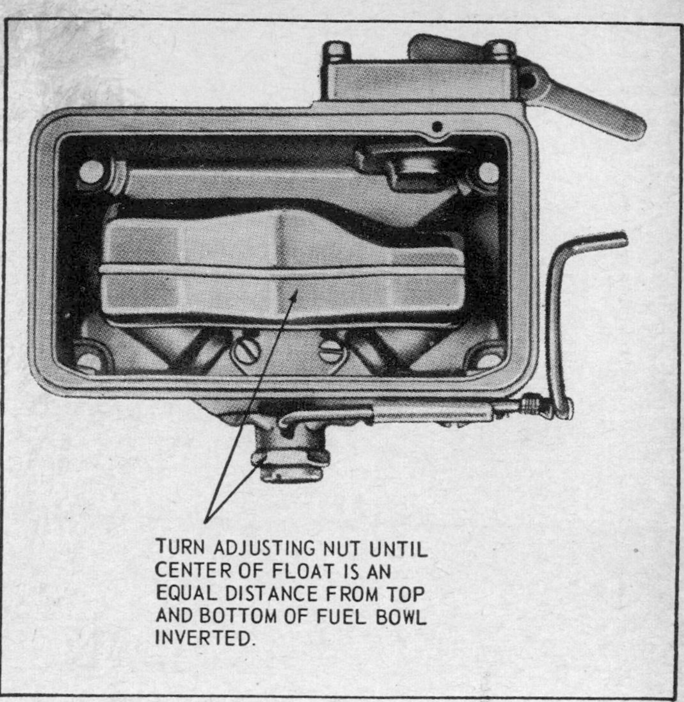

Fig. 50 Float adjustment on Fig. 48 type carburetors

These carburetors, Figs. 46 and 47, are essentially two dual carburetors with two primary bores that supply the fuel-air mixture throughout the entire range of engine operation while the two secondary bores function only when speed or load requires them.

To provide effectively the correct fuel-air mixture during all phases of engine operation the primary side of the carburetor contains all the basic systems that make up a complete carburetor. In addition there is the secondary system that has a fuel transfer system and a by-pass system which operates only when a greater quantity of fuel-air mixture is required.

A fuel inlet system for both primary and secondary barrels provides the various fuel metering systems with a constant supply of fuel.

As shown in Fig. 46, some late models of the 4150 carburetor have a central fuel inlet whereas other 4150 and 4160 units have a side entrance for the fuel inlet. With the center fuel inlet type the float is hinged at the center while with the side fuel inlet the float is hinged at the float end.

Late production 1966 Ford-built cars equipped with the 4150 carburetor have a fuel inlet system that contains an external fuel distribution tube that routes fuel from the primary fuel inlet to the secondary fuel inlet. In addition, a choke clean air pick-up tube is also provided, Fig. 48.

Dry Float Setting

Fig. 46 Units Only—Invert fuel bowl. Loosen lock screw enough to allow adjusting nut to rotate. Turn adjusting nut until base of float is parallel with floor of fuel bowl, Fig. 49. Tighten lock screw and recheck adjustment. This is a temporary adjustment as the fuel level should be checked after the carburetor is installed on the engine.

For Fig. 48 Units Only—Referring to Fig. 50, adjust float so that its center is an equal distance from top and bottom of fuel bowl with fuel bowl inverted. After carburetor is installed on engine, check and adjust fuel level.

Fuel Level Adjustment

Fig. 51—With car on a level floor and engine idling, fuel level should be at the

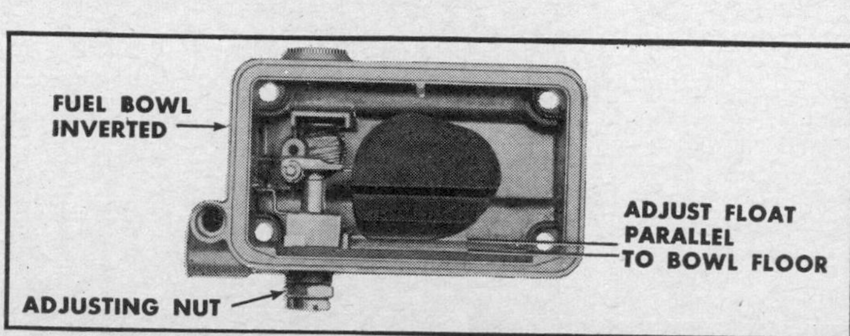

Fig. 49 Float adjustment on Fig. 46 type carburetors

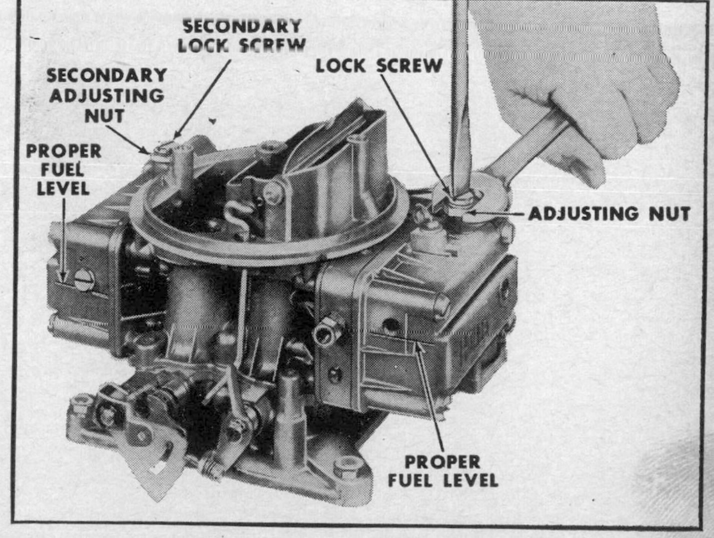

Fig. 51 Fuel level adjustment on all 4150 and 4160 carburetors

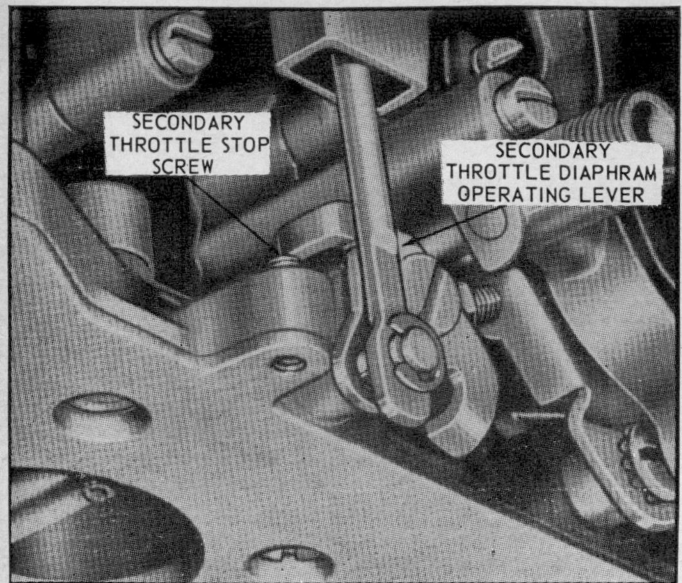

Fig. 52 Secondary throttle plate adjustment on Fig. 48 type carburetors

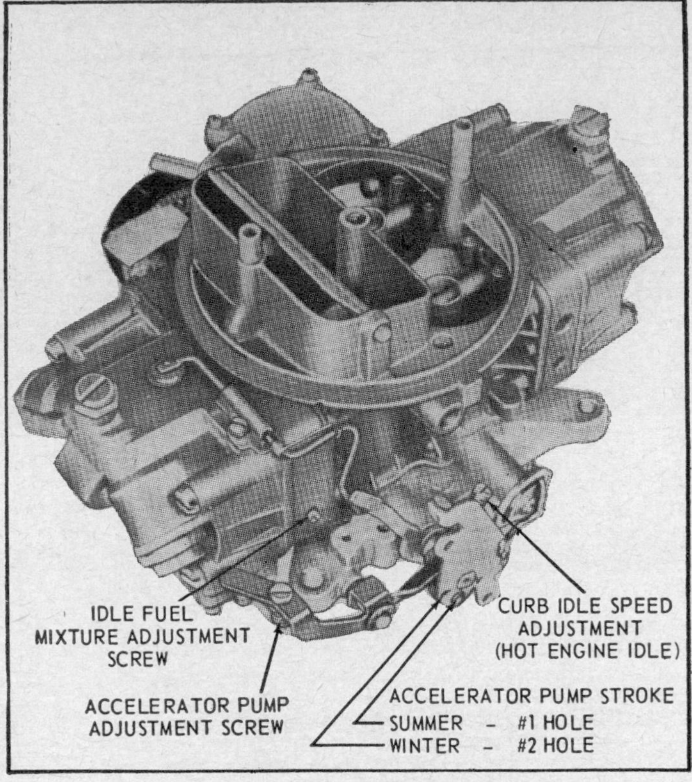

Fig. 53 Carburetor adjustment points on Fig. 48 type carburetors

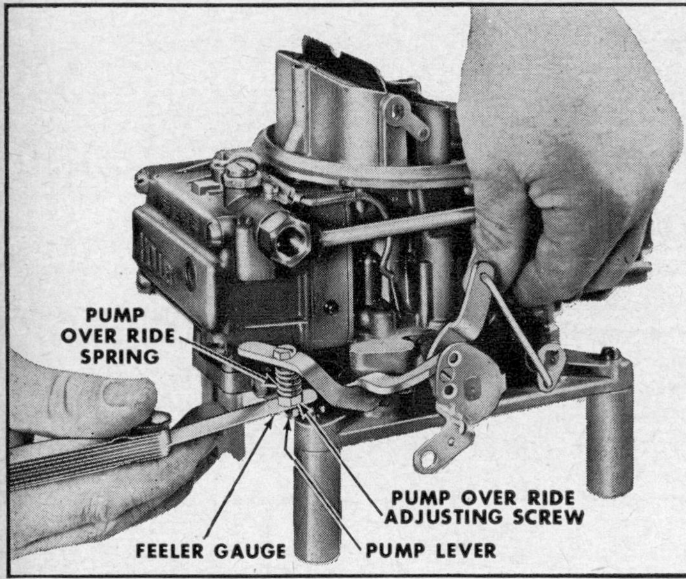

Fig. 54 Pump adjustment on Fig. 46 type carburetors

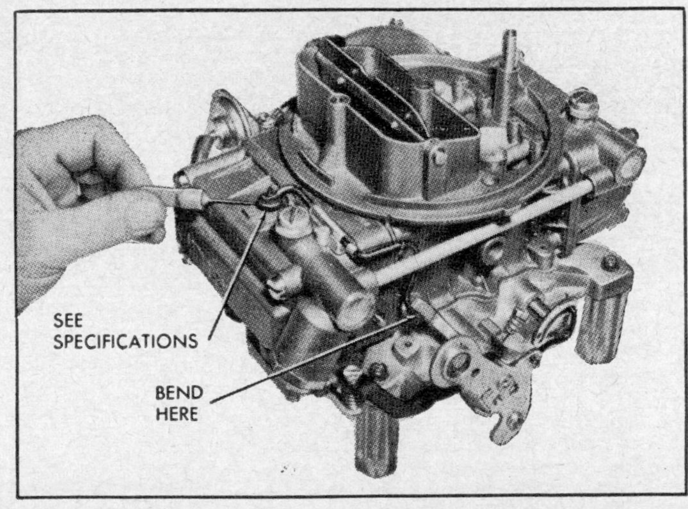

Fig. 55 Bowl vent valve clearance adjustment on 4150 and 4160 carburetors

level with the threads on the bottom of the sight plug hole (plus or minus $\frac{1}{16}$"). To adjust, loosen lock screw and turn adjusting nut as required.

Secondary Throttle Plate Adjustment

For Fig. 48 Units Only—Referring to Fig. 52, back the secondary throttle stop screw out until secondary throttle plates are closed in the bores. Turn screw in (clockwise) until it touches stop on secondary throttle lever; then turn it in an additional ½ turn.

Accelerating Pump Adjustment

For Fig. 48 Units Only—Using a feeler gauge and with primary throttle plates in wide open position, there should be the clearance listed in the *Holley Specifications Chart* between pump operating lever adjusting screw and pump arm when pump arm is fully depressed manually, Fig. 53. Turn adjusting screw in to increase (out to decrease) clearance. One-half turn of adjusting screw is equal to .015".

To satisfy acceleration requirements in various climates, the pump discharge can be adjusted, Fig. 53. The bottom hole (No. 2) in the cam provides a maximum pump discharge for extreme cold weather and the top hole (No. 1) provides the minimum pump discharge for warm weather operation.

For Fig. 46 Units Only—Referring to Fig. 54, the pump cam screw should be in the No. 1 position on the throttle lever for all normal operating conditions. For extreme cold weather the No. 2 position can be used to provide maximum pump discharge.

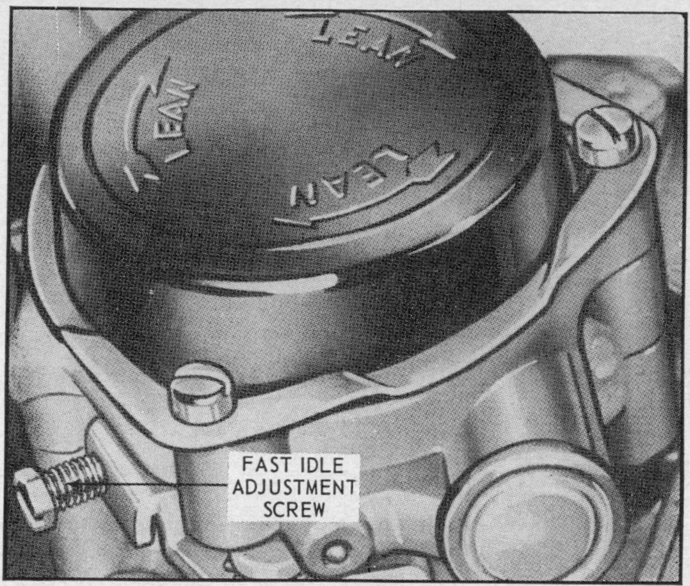

Fig. 56 Fast idle adjustment on Fig. 48 type carburetors

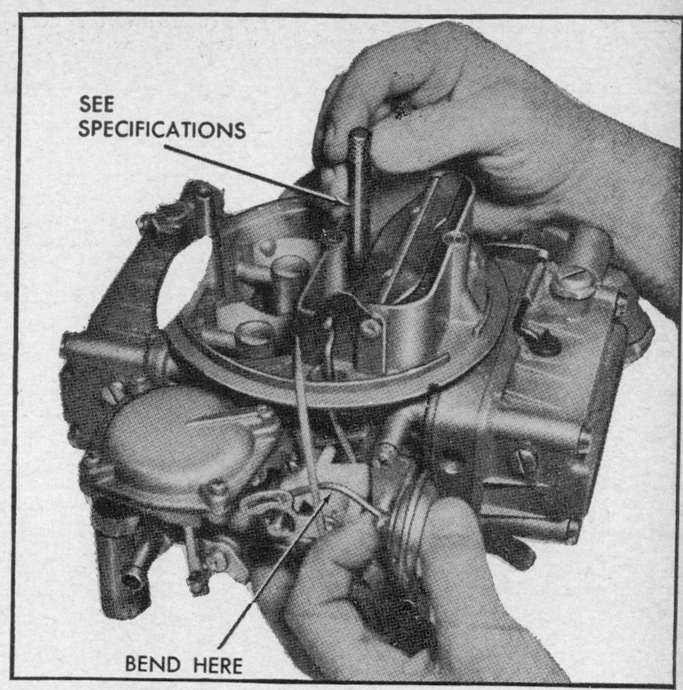

Fig. 57 Vacuum break adjustment on Chevrolet engines with remote type choke

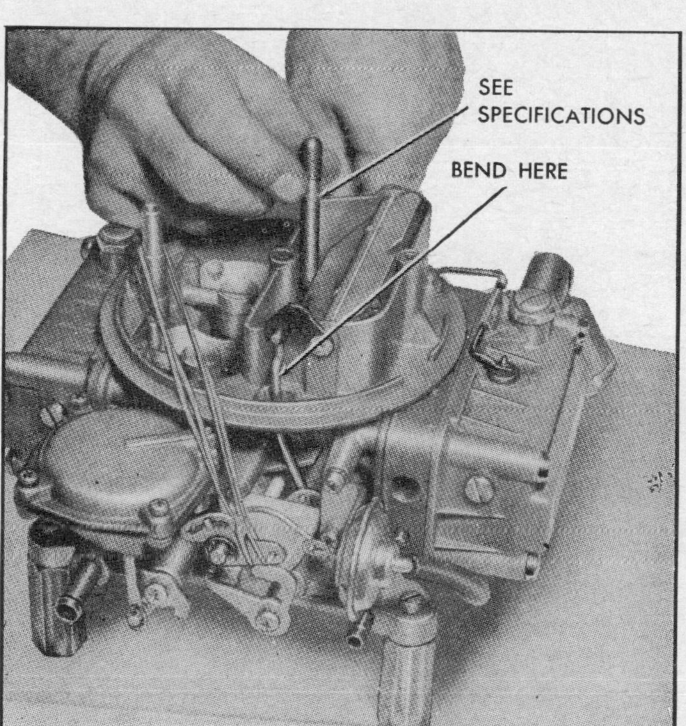

Fig. 58 Choke unloader adjustment on Fig. 46 type carburetors

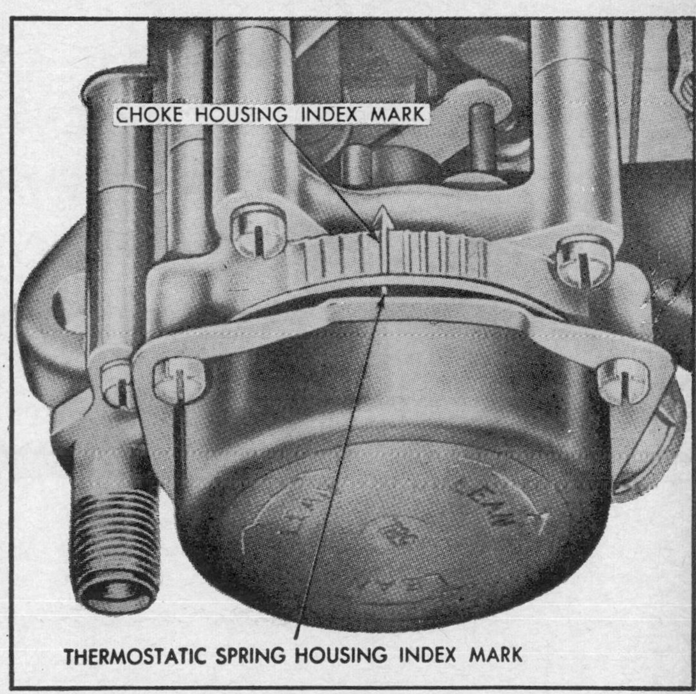

Fig. 59 Built-In Automatic choke adjustment

With throttle plates held in wide open position, there should be the clearance listed in the *Holley Specifications Chart* between the pump diaphragm actuating lever and the lower portion of the pump override spring screw.

This adjustment *must* be rechecked with the throttle plates closed to make certain that there is no lag between throttle linkage and pump lever. The slightest movement of the throttle lever must correspondingly actuate the pump lever. Should there be any lag, a stumble or flat spot will result. To eliminate the lag, lengthen the adjusting screw.

Bowl Vent Valve Adjustment

Fig. 55—The fuel bowl vent valve clearance must be adjusted whenever the accelerator pump lever and/or pump stroke adjustments have been changed. A change in the pump adjustments will affect the fuel bowl vent valve clearance.

With engine temperature stabilized and engine operating at curb idle speed, check clearance between bottom of vent valve and top of fuel bowl at vent opening. If clearance is not as listed in the *Holley Specifications Chart,* bend vent rod as required.

Fast Idle Speed

For Fig. 48 Units Only—With hot idle speed properly adjusted, set fast idle speed with transmission in neutral, engine at normal operating temperature, tachometer attached, headlamps turned on, and air conditioner operating (if so equipped). Referring to Fig. 56, align kickdown step of fast idle cam with the adjusting screw, and turn adjusting screw to obtain the specified rpm listed in the *Holley Specifications Chart.*

For Fig. 46 Units Only—With fast idle lever on high step of cam and choke valve wide open (engine warm) set fast idle to give the rpm listed in *Holley Specifications Chart.* Adjust fast idle screw on 4150 units or bend fast idle lever on 4160 units.

Fast Idle Cam Setting

For Fig. 46 Units Only—The fast idle setting with the carburetor off the car is made by turning the fast idle adjusting screw to obtain the clearance listed in the *Holley Specifications Chart* between throttle valve and carburetor bore (idle port side) with fast idle screw on high step of cam.

Vacuum Break Adjustment

Fig. 57—On models so equipped, hold choke valve closed with a rubber band. Hold vacuum break in against its stop. Measure distance between lower edge of choke valve and wall of air horn. If the clearance is not as listed in the *Holley Specifications Chart,* bend vacuum break link to adjust.

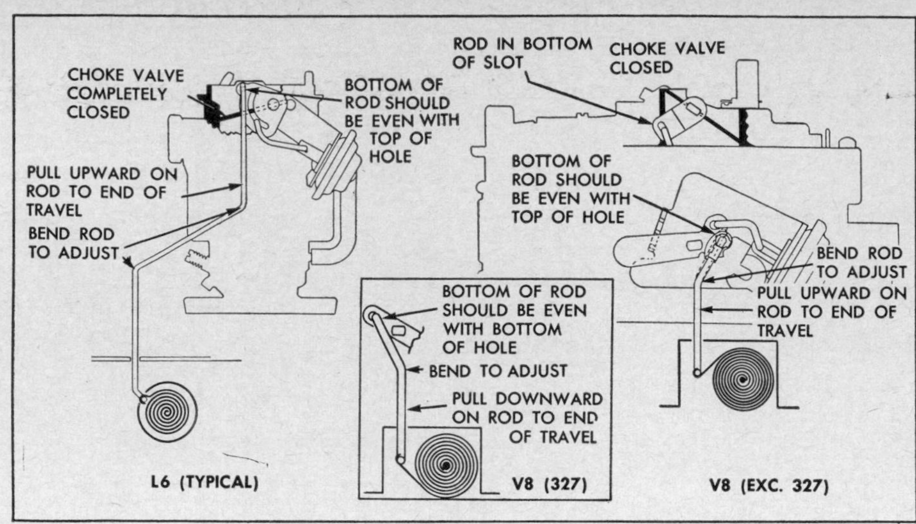

Fig. 60 Remote type choke adjustments

Choke Unloader Adjustment

Fig. 58—Hold throttle lever wide open with a rubber band. Hold choke valve toward closed position toward unloader tang of throttle shaft. Then measure opening between lower edge of choke valve and air horn wall. If the opening is not as listed in the *Holley Specifications Chart,* bend choke rod at offset angle.

Built-In Choke Setting

Fig. 59—Loosen retaining screws and turn choke cover so that index mark or line on choke cover lines up with specified mark on choke housing. See *Holley Specifications Chart.*

Remote Choke Adjustment

Chevrolet 1965-66 Engines—This type choke is adjusted as directed in Fig. 60 for the various engines.

Rochester Carburetor Section

ROCHESTER B, BC, BV CARBURETOR ADJUSTMENT SPECIFICATIONS

See Tune Up Chart in car chapter for hot idle speeds.

Year	Carburetor Part No. ①	Carb. Model	Float Level	Float Drop	Vacuum Break	Automatic Choke	Choke Rod	Choke Unloader	Idle Vent
BUICK INTERMEDIATE MODELS									
1964	7024148	BC	$1\frac{9}{32}$	$1\frac{7}{8}$	—	On Index	.075	.300	—
	7024149	BC	$1\frac{9}{32}$	$1\frac{7}{8}$	—	On Index	.075	.300	—
1965	7025148	BC	$1\frac{9}{32}$	$1\frac{7}{8}$	—	On Index	.075	.300	—
	7025149	BC	$1\frac{9}{32}$	$1\frac{7}{8}$	—	On Index	.075	.300	—
CHEVROLET ENGINES									
1963–64	7023000	BV	$1\frac{9}{32}$	$1\frac{3}{4}$	.160	—	.060	.350	.050
	7023003	BV	$1\frac{9}{32}$	$1\frac{3}{4}$	.160	—	.060	.350	.050
	7023105	BV	$1\frac{9}{32}$	$1\frac{3}{4}$	.160	—	.060	.350	.050
	7023108	BV	$1\frac{9}{32}$	$1\frac{3}{4}$	.140	—	.060	.350	.050
1964	7024000	BV	$1\frac{9}{32}$	$1\frac{3}{4}$	.260	—	.100	.350	.050
	7024001	BV	$1\frac{9}{32}$	$1\frac{3}{4}$	.260	—	.100	.350	.050
1965–67	7025000	BV	$1\frac{9}{32}$	$1\frac{3}{4}$	.140	—	.090	.350	.050
1965–66	7025003	BV	$1\frac{9}{32}$	$1\frac{3}{4}$	.160	—	.100	.350	.050
1965–67	7025105	BV	$1\frac{9}{32}$	$1\frac{3}{4}$	.160	—	.100	.350	.050
	7025108	BV	$1\frac{9}{32}$	$1\frac{3}{4}$	.140	—	.090	.350	.050
1966–67	7026027	BV	$1\frac{9}{32}$	$1\frac{3}{4}$	.160	—	.100	.350	.050
	7026028	BV	$1\frac{9}{32}$	$1\frac{3}{4}$	.140	—	.090	.350	.050
1967	7022503	BV	$1\frac{9}{32}$	$1\frac{3}{4}$	.160	—	.100	.350	.050
	7025000	BV	$1\frac{9}{32}$	$1\frac{3}{4}$	.140	—	.090	.350	.050
	7025105	BV	$1\frac{9}{32}$	$1\frac{3}{4}$	.160	—	.100	.350	.050
	7025108	BV	$1\frac{9}{32}$	$1\frac{3}{4}$	.140	—	.090	.350	.050
	7026027	BV	$1\frac{9}{32}$	$1\frac{3}{4}$	.160	—	.100	.350	.050
	7026028	BV	$1\frac{9}{32}$	$1\frac{3}{4}$	.140	—	.090	.350	.050
JEEP									
1966–68	7025149	BC	$1\frac{9}{32}$	$1\frac{1}{8}$	—	On Index	.075	.300	—
OLDSMOBILE INTERMEDIATE MODELS									
1964	7024148	BC	$1\frac{9}{32}$	$1\frac{7}{8}$	—	On Index	.075	.300	—
	7024149	BC	$1\frac{9}{32}$	$1\frac{7}{8}$	—	On Index	.075	.300	—
1965	7025148	BC	$1\frac{9}{32}$	$1\frac{7}{8}$	—	On Index	.075	.300	—
	7025149	BC	$1\frac{9}{32}$	$1\frac{7}{8}$	—	On Index	.075	.300	—
1966–67	7026027	BV	$1\frac{9}{32}$	$1\frac{7}{8}$	.140	On Index	.075	.300	.050
	7026028	BV	$1\frac{9}{32}$	$1\frac{7}{8}$	.160	On Index	.075	.300	.050
1967	7016627	BV	$1\frac{9}{32}$	$1\frac{3}{4}$	.160	—	.100	.350	.050
	7016628	BV	$1\frac{9}{32}$	$1\frac{3}{4}$	.140	—	.090	.350	.050
PONTIAC INTERMEDIATE MODELS									
1963	7023067	B	$1\frac{9}{32}$	$1\frac{3}{4}$	—	—	—	—	—
	7023068	BC	$1\frac{9}{32}$	$1\frac{3}{4}$	—	On Index	.080	.160	—
1964	7024164	BV	$1\frac{9}{32}$	$1\frac{3}{4}$	.140	—	.060	.230	.040
	7024166	BV	$1\frac{9}{32}$	$1\frac{3}{4}$	.140	—	.060	.230	.040
1965	7025167	BV	$1\frac{9}{32}$	$1\frac{7}{8}$	.160	—	.060	.230	.040
	7025168	BV	$1\frac{9}{32}$	$1\frac{7}{8}$	.140	—	.060	.230	.040
1966–67	7026167	BV	$1\frac{9}{32}$	$1\frac{7}{8}$	.170	—	.060	.230	.040
	7026168	BV	$1\frac{9}{32}$	$1\frac{7}{8}$	.150	—	.060	.230	.040
1966	7026169	BV	$1\frac{9}{32}$	$1\frac{7}{8}$	.150	—	.060	.230	.040
1966–67	7036167	BV	$1\frac{9}{32}$	$1\frac{7}{8}$	.170	—	.060	.230	.040

Continued

ROCHESTER B, BC, BV CARBURETOR ADJUSTMENT SPECIFICATIONS—Continued

See Tune Up Chart in car chapter for hot idle speeds.

Year	Carburetor Part No.①	Carb. Model	Float Level	Float Drop	Vacuum Break	Automatic Choke	Choke Rod	Choke Unloader	Idle Vent
PONTIAC INTERMEDIATE MODELS—Continued									
1966–67	7036168	BV	1 9/32	1 7/8	.150	—	.060	.230	.040
1967	7027167	BV	1 5/16	1 7/8	.170	—	.060	.230	.040
	7027168	BV	1 5/16	1 7/8	.160	—	.060	.230	.040
	7037167	BV	1 5/16	1 7/8	.170	—	.060	.230	.040
	7037168	BV	1 5/16	1 7/8	.160	—	.060	.230	.040
1968	7028168	BV	1 9/32	1 3/4	.160	—	.080	.230	.050

①—Located on tag attached to or stamped on carburetor.

MODELS B, BC, BV ADJUSTMENTS

The basic Model B carburetor is a single-barrel downdraft type equipped with a manually-operated choke. Model BC is the same basic unit except it has a fully automatic choke mounted on the air horn.

The Model BV unit, Fig. 1, uses a fully automatic choke. However, instead of the conventional choke piston and housing, a vacuum operated diaphragm plunger is used. The thermostatic coil is mounted on the exhaust manifold instead of the choke housing and is connected to the carburetor choke shaft by connecting linkage. An exploded view of the BC models is shown in Fig. 2.

Design features included in all three carburetors include the following:

A concentric type float bowl is used which allows fuel in the float bowl to completely surround the main carburetor bore and venturi. The concentric float bowl design plus the centrally located main fuel discharge nozzle prevents fuel spill-over during abnormal car maneuvers such as sharp turns, quick starts and stops.

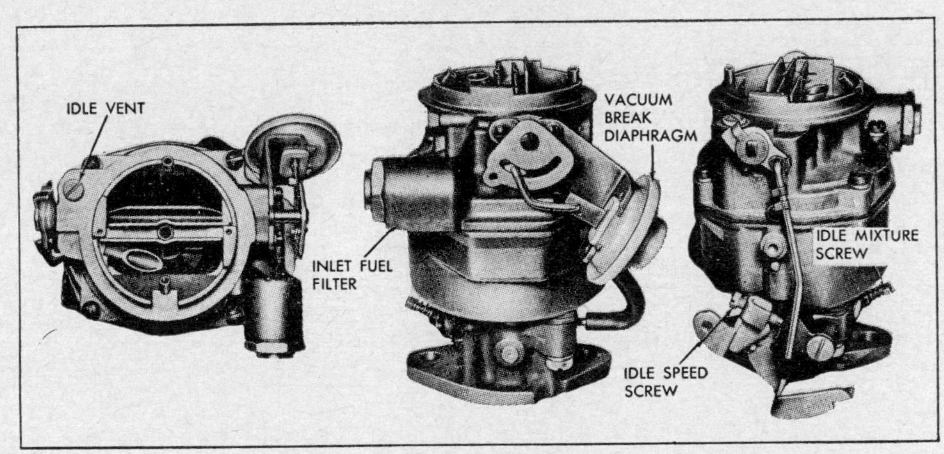

Fig. 1 Rochester Model BV single-barrel carburetor

The main assembly is a detachable unit which contains the metering parts of the carburetor. It is attached to the air horn and is easily removed for inspection and service. It is suspended in the fuel in the float chamber which insulates it from heat which may be transmitted from the engine directly to the bottom of the float bowl. This type design helps maintain more accurate fuel metering because less fuel vapors enter the main metering parts of the assembly during hot engine operation.

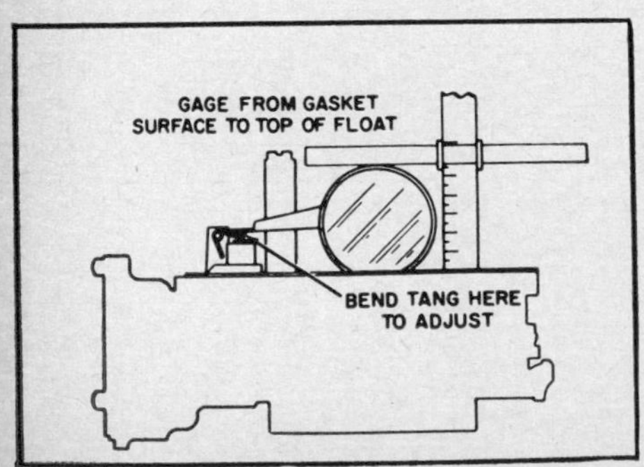

Fig. 3 Float level adjustment for B, BC, BV carburetors

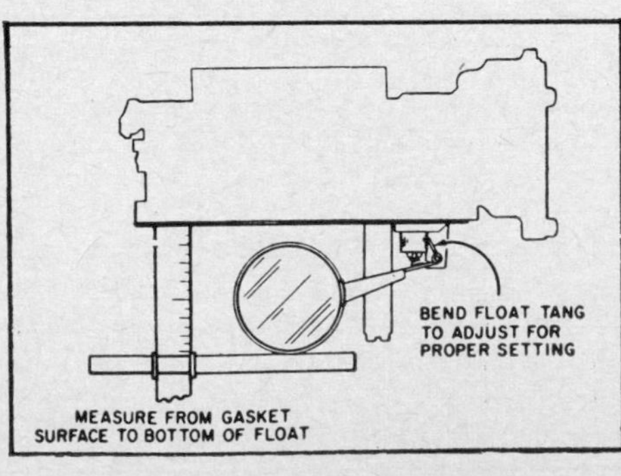

Fig. 4 Float drop adjustment for B, BC, BV carburetors

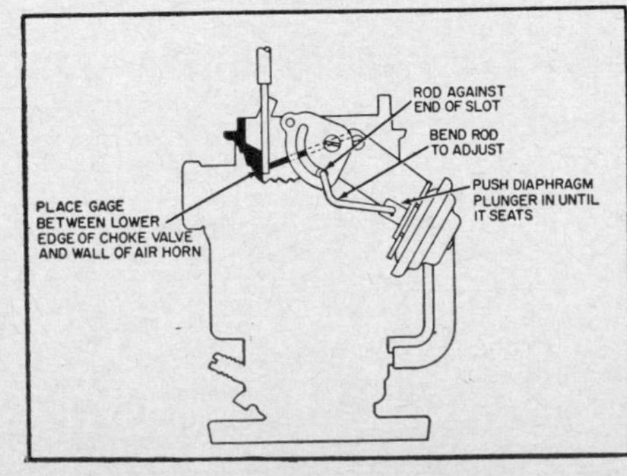

Fig. 5 Vacuum break adjustment for BV carburetors

ROCHESTER H & HV CARB. ADJUSTMENT SPECIFICATIONS

See Tune Up Chart in car chapter for hot idle speeds.

Year	Carburetor Part No. ①	Float Level	Float Drop	Idle Vent	Vacuum Break	Choke Rod	Choke Unloader	Fast Idle	Secondary Lockout Lever Stop
CORVAIR									
1963	7023100	$1\frac{3}{16}$	$1\frac{3}{4}$	—	.160	.170	.245	.065	—
	7023101	$1\frac{3}{16}$	$1\frac{3}{4}$	—	.160	.170	.245	.050	—
	7023102	$1\frac{3}{16}$	$1\frac{3}{4}$	—	.160	.170	.245	.050	—
1964	7024023	$1\frac{1}{16}$	$1\frac{13}{16}$	.015	.190	.190	.325	.075	—
	7024024	$1\frac{1}{16}$	$1\frac{13}{16}$	.015	.190	.190	.325	.075	—
	7024025	$1\frac{1}{16}$	$1\frac{13}{16}$	.015	.190	.190	.325	.075	—
1965	7025023	$1\frac{1}{16}$	$1\frac{13}{16}$	.015	.190	.190	.325	.075	—
	7025024	$1\frac{1}{16}$	$1\frac{13}{16}$	.015	.190	.190	.325	.075	—
	7025025	$1\frac{1}{16}$	$1\frac{13}{16}$	.015	.190	.190	.325	.075	—
1965-66	7025226	$1\frac{1}{16}$	$1\frac{13}{16}$	.015	.190	.190	.325	—	.060
	7025227	$1\frac{1}{16}$	$1\frac{13}{16}$	.015	.190	.190	.325	—	.060
1966	7026023	$1\frac{1}{16}$	$1\frac{13}{16}$	.015	.190	.190	.325	—	—
	7026024	$1\frac{1}{16}$	$1\frac{13}{16}$	.015	.190	.190	.325	—	—
	7026026	$1\frac{1}{16}$	$1\frac{13}{16}$	.015	.190	.190	.325	—	—
1966–67	7036014	$1\frac{1}{16}$	$1\frac{13}{16}$	.015	.190	.190	.325	—	—
	7036015	$1\frac{1}{16}$	$1\frac{13}{16}$	.015	.190	.190	.325	—	—
	7036023	$1\frac{1}{16}$	$1\frac{13}{16}$	.015	.190	.190	.325	—	—
	7036024	$1\frac{1}{16}$	$1\frac{13}{16}$	.015	.190	.190	.325	—	—
1966-69	7027026	$1\frac{1}{16}$	$1\frac{13}{16}$	—	—	—	—	—	.060
1968	7028004	$1\frac{1}{16}$	$1\frac{9}{16}$	.015	.190	.190	.500	—	—
1968-69	7028005	$1\frac{1}{16}$	$1\frac{13}{16}$	.015	.190	.190	.500	—	—

①—Located on tag attached to or stamped on carburetor.

MODEL H & HV ADJUSTMENTS

Starting with 1962, two HV carburetors, each with an automatic choke, is mounted on an intake manifold and separated from the manifold by an insulator block, Fig. 12. The automatic choke mechanism consists of a thermostatic coil mounted to the lower side of the cylinder head and linked directly to the choke valve shaft; a vacuum diaphragm is provided on the air horn.

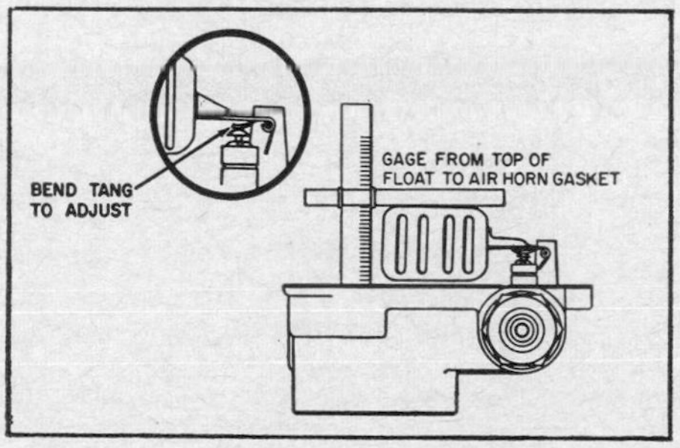

Fig. 14 Float level adjustment for HV carburetors

Float Level Adjustment

Fig. 14—With air horn inverted and gasket in place, check height of each float. Bend tang that contacts needle until each pontoon is set to the specified dimension listed in the *Rochester Specifications Chart*. Float pontoons should be parallel with air horn surface when set correctly. Align floats to prevent interference in bowl.

Float Drop Adjustment

Fig. 15 With air horn assembly held upright and floats suspended freely, measure dimension from air horn gasket to bottom of float pontoon at the toe. Adjust to dimension listed in the *Rochester Specifications Chart* by bending the tang that contacts seat at rear of float arm.

Pump Rod Adjustment

Fig. 16—Back out idle stop screw until throttle valves are completely closed in bore. Bend pump rod as shown until index line on upper pump lever just aligns with sharp edge on air horn casting.

NOTE: On Powerglide applications using a two-hole lower pump lever, setting should be made with pump rod placed in outer hole. After setting is made, pump rod should be moved to inner hole on lever for proper operation.

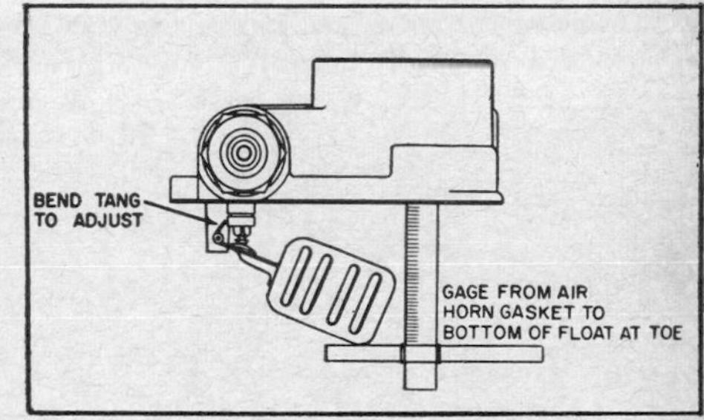

Fig. 15 Float drop adjustment for HV carburetors

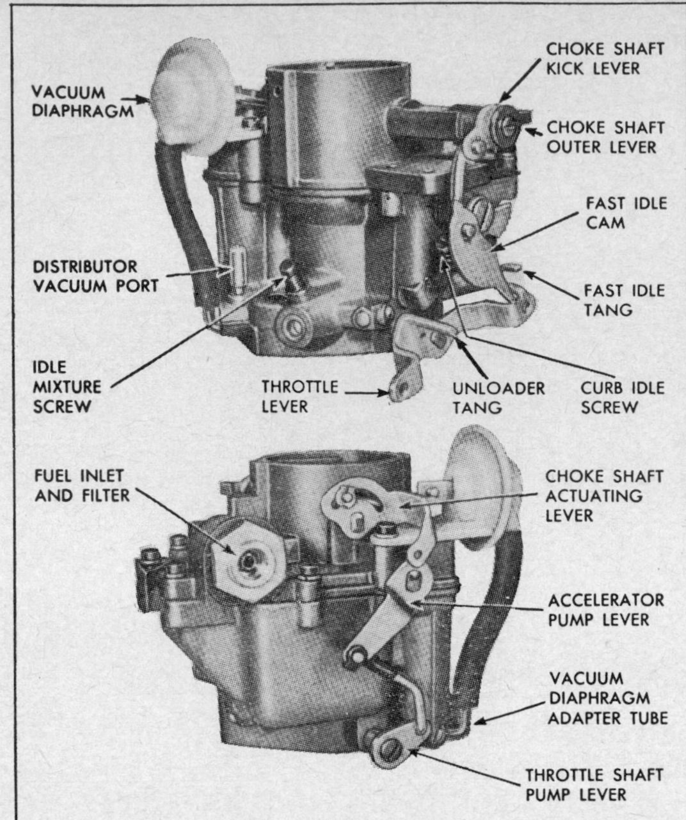

Fig. 12 Rochester Model HV single-barrel carburetor

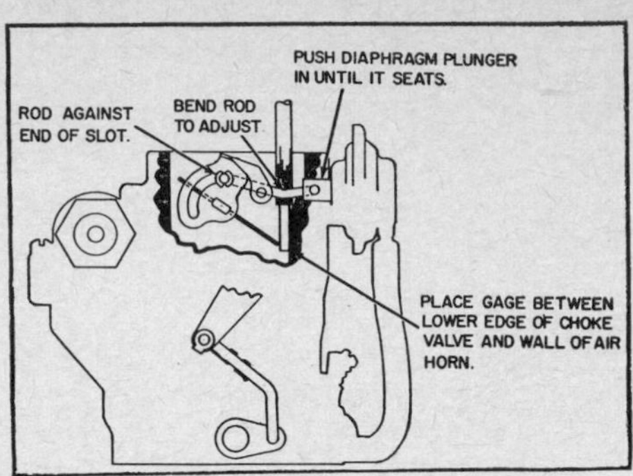

Fig. 18 Vacuum break diaphragm adjustment for HV carburetors

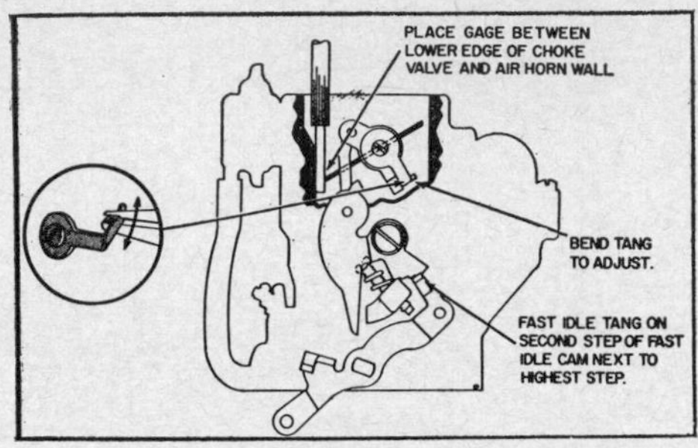

Fig. 19 Choke rod adjustment for HV carburetors

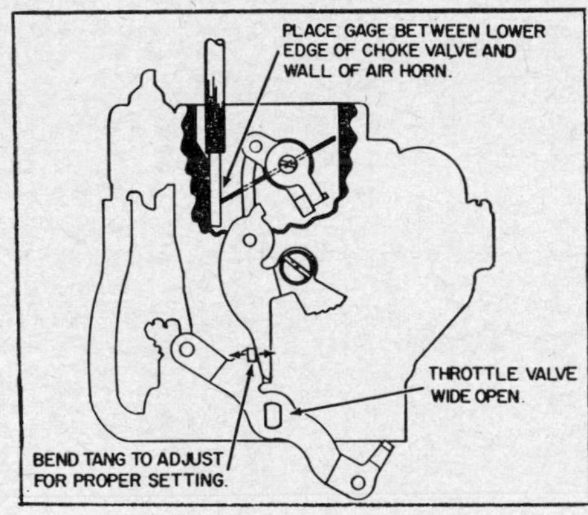

Fig. 20 Choke unloader adjustment for HV carburetors

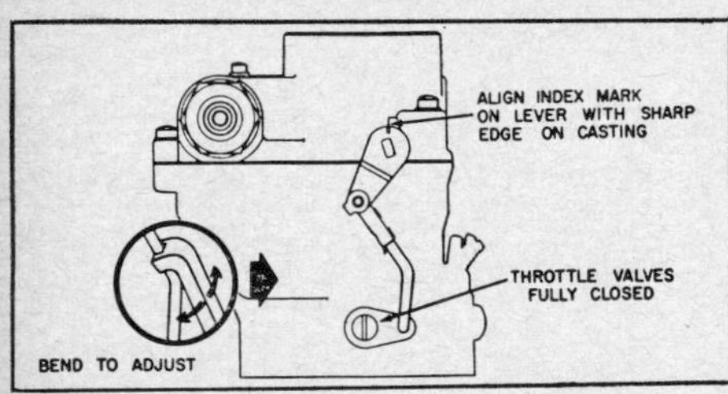

Fig. 16 Pump rod adjustment for HV carburetors

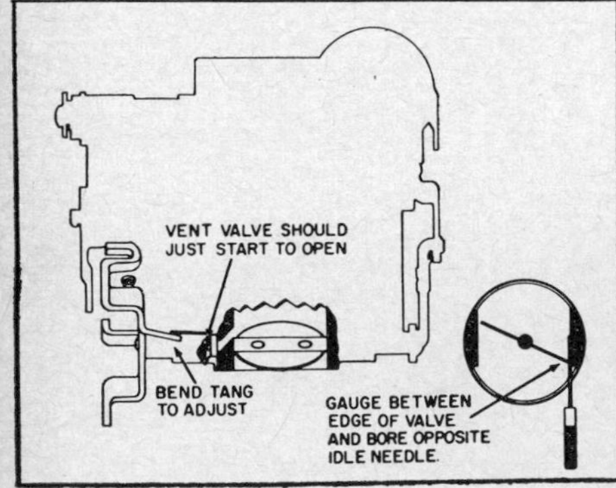

Fig. 17 Idle vent valve adjustment for HV carburetors

Idle Vent Valve Adjustment

Model HV, Fig. 17—To adjust, bend tang on throttle lever so that when vent valve just starts to open, the proper gauge size will just go between throttle valve and bore directly opposite the idle needle (see *Rochester Specifications Chart*). *Do not bend spring arm on vent valve as distortion may result.*

Vacuum Break Diaphragm Adjustment

Model HV, Fig. 18—To adjust, push diaphragm plunger in until seated. Then close choke valve to a point where connecting rod is to end of slot in choke lever. With choke valve in this position, specified gauge size should fit between lower edge of choke valve and inner air horn wall as shown (see *Rochester Specifications Chart*). To adjust, bend connecting rod at point shown.

Choke Rod Adjustment

Model HV, Fig. 19—To adjust, place fast idle tang on second step of fast idle cam next to highest step. Close choke valve so that trip lever on choke shaft just contacts choke tang on lever and collar.

Specified gauge size listed in *Rochester Specifications Chart* should just fit between lower edge of choke valve and inner wall of air horn. To adjust, bend tang on trip lever up or down as required.

Choke Unloader Adjustment

Fig. 20—With throttle valve wide open (accelerator pedal pressed to floor), the specified gauge size listed in the *Rochester Specifications Chart* should just fit between lower edge of choke valve and inner air horn wall. To adjust, bend unloader tang on throttle lever.

Fast Idle Adjustment

Model HV, Fig. 21—To check this adjustment, place fast idle tang on second step of fast idle cam next to highest step. With idle speed screw set to normal idle position (approximately ¾ turn in from closed throttle valve), measure clearance between idle stop screw and edge of throttle lever. To adjust, bend fast idle tang up or down as required (see *Rochester Specifications Chart*).

Synchronizing Carburetors

Models with Four Carburetors

1. Synchronize primary carburetors, leaving choke rods disconnected.
2. With primary choke valve in full

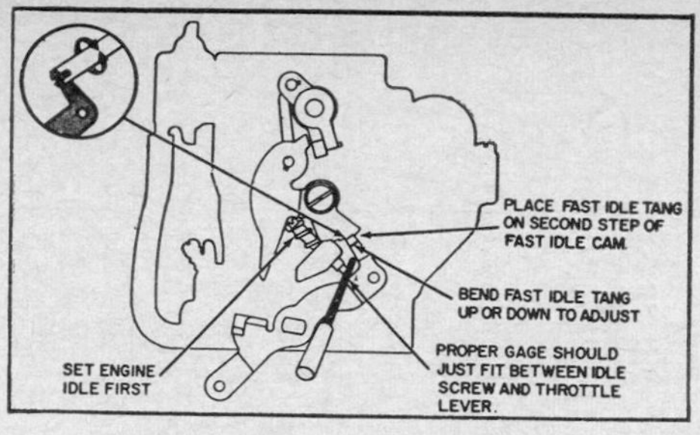

Fig. 21 Fast idle adjustment for HV carburetors

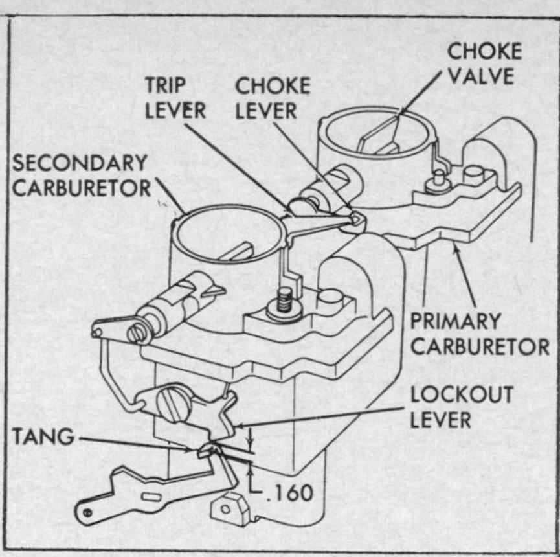

Fig. 22 Secondary linkage adjustment (4 carb. installations)

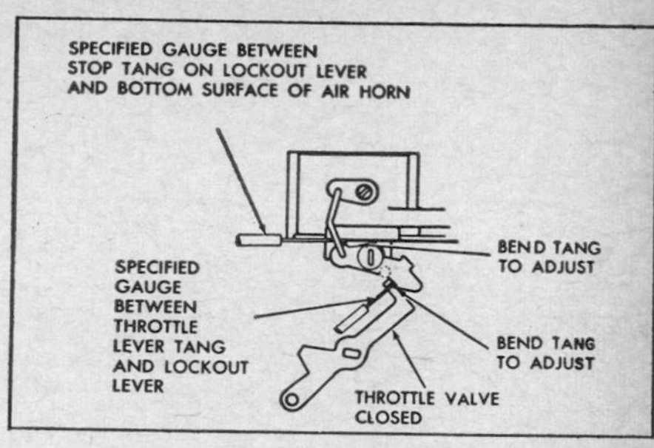

Fig. 23 Secondary lockout adjustment (4 carb. installations)

open position and a .160" gauge between secondary carburetor lockout lever and lockout tang on throttle lever, bend secondary carburetor trip lever so it just contacts carburetor choke lever, Fig. 22. Repeat operation on other secondary carburetor.

3. Hold choke valves closed and actuate accelerator cross shaft (to set fast idle cams). Pull choke rod upward to end of travel and adjust rod until bottom of rod is even with top of hole in choke lever. Connect choke rod and repeat operation on remaining choke.
4. Disconnect left and right secondary carburetor actuating rods. Then hold carburetor cross shaft so primary carburetors are in full open position.
5. With choke valves closed (secondary throttles locked out) adjust secondary carburetor actuating rod so actuating spring is fully compressed and clevis will just enter hole in cross shaft lever. Then back off adjustment a minimum of 2 and a maximum of 3 turns. Repeat operation on other actuating rod.
6. Connect both secondary actuating rods and, with choke valves held wide open, slowly rotate carburetor cross shaft to the full throttle position, checking that all carburetors reach full throttle simultaneously.
7. With choke valves held closed, rotate carburetor cross shaft to full throttle position and check primary carburetors for full throttle position; check that secondary carburetors are locked out and that secondary actuating springs are fully compressed.

Secondary Lockout Adjustment

Fig. 23—With throttle closed and edge of throttle lever lockout tang flush with lockout lever, bend throttle lever tang to obtain specified clearance listed in the *Rochester Specifications Chart* between notch in lockout lever and throttle lever tang.

With throttle lever in locked-out position, bend stop tang on lockout lever to obtain specified clearance between stop tang and bottom surface of air horn.

NOTE: The primary carburetor choke mechanism operates the lockout mechanism on the secondary carburetor. Therefore, final adjustment must be made with the carburetor installed on the engine.

ROCHESTER 2G, 2GC, 2GV CARBURETOR ADJUSTMENT SPECIFICATIONS

See Tune Up Chart in car chapters for hot idle speeds.

★Located on tag attached to or stamped on carburetor.

Year	Carb. Part No. ★	Float Level	Float Drop	Pump Rod	Idle Vent	Intermediate Choke Rod	Vacuum Break	Automatic Choke	Choke Rod	Choke Unloader	Fast Idle Speed
BUICK											
1963	7023041	21/32	1 29/32	1 7/16	—	Flush	—	On Index	.095	.260	—
	7023042	21/32	1 29/32	1 7/16	—	Flush	—	On Index	.095	.260	—
	7023043	21/32	1 29/32	1 7/16	—	Flush	—	On Index	.095	.260	—
	7023046	21/32	1 29/32	1 11/32	—	—	—	On Index	.050	.160	—
	7023047	21/32	1 29/32	1 11/32	—	—	—	On Index	.050	.160	—
	7023048	21/32	1 29/32	1	—	—	—	1 Rich	.055	.160	—
	7023049	21/32	1 29/32	1	—	—	—	On Index	.055	.160	—
	7023142	21/32	1 29/32	1 11/32	—	—	—	On Index	.050	.160	—
	7023145	21/32	1 29/32	1 7/16	—	Flush	—	On Index	.095	.260	—
	7023146	21/32	1 29/32	1 7/16	—	Flush	—	On Index	.095	.260	—
1964	7024046	1/2	1 29/32	1 11/32	—	—	—	2 Rich	.040	.085	—
	7024047	1/2	1 29/32	1 11/32	—	—	—	On Index	.040	.085	—
1965	7025046	19/32	1 29/32	1 5/32	—	—	—	On Index	.055	.140	—
	7025047	19/32	1 29/32	1 5/32	—	—	—	On Index	.055	.140	—
1966	7026046	1/2	1 27/32	1 5/32	—	—	—	On Index	.055	.140	—
	7026047	1/2	1 27/32	1 11/32	—	—	—	On Index	.055	.140	—
	7026144	1/2	1 27/32	1 5/32	—	—	—	On Index	.055	.140	—
	7026145	1/2	1 27/32	1 11/32	—	—	—	On Index	.055	.140	—
	7026146	15/32	1 9/16	1 5/32	1 1/16	—	—	On Index	.055	.140	—
	7026147	15/32	1 9/16	1 11/32	—	—	—	On Index	.055	.140	—
	7036046	1/2	1 27/32	1 5/32	1 1/16	—	—	On Index	.055	.140	—
	7036048	1/2	1 27/32	1 11/32	1 1/16	—	—	On Index	.055	.140	—
	7036144	1/2	1 27/32	1 1/16	31/32	—	—	On Index	.055	.140	—
1967	7027040	1/2	1 9/32	1 1/16	31/32	—	—	On Index	.055	.140	—
	7027041	1/2	1 9/32	1 1/16	31/32	—	—	On Index	.055	.140	—
	7027042	1/2	1 9/32	1 5/32	31/32	—	—	On Index	.055	.140	—
	7027044	15/32	1 9/16	1 5/32	31/32	—	—	On Index	.055	.140	—
	7027045	15/32	1 9/16	1 5/32	31/32	—	—	On Index	.055	.140	—
	7027046	15/32	1 9/16	1 5/32	31/32	—	—	On Index	.055	.140	—
	7027049	15/32	1 9/16	1 5/32	31/32	—	—	On Index	.055	.140	—
1968	7028140	15/32	1 9/32	1 11/32	.025②	—	.120	①	.050	.140	—
	7028141	15/32	1 9/32	1 11/32	.025②	—	.120	①	.050	.140	—
1969	7029140	15/32	1 7/32	1 11/32	.020②	—	.110	③	.055	.140	—
	7029141	15/32	1 7/32	1 11/32	.020②	—	.110	③	.055	.140	—

①—Rod is installed in lower of two lever holes.

②—At slow idle RPM vent valve should be open to specified dimension.

③—Holes in lever are marked "ALT" or "STD". Install in proper hole.

Year	Carb. Part No. ★	Float Level	Float Drop	Pump Rod	Idle Vent	Intermediate Choke Rod	Vacuum Break	Automatic Choke	Choke Rod	Choke Unloader	Fast Idle Speed
CHEVROLET ENGINES											
1963	7023007	3/4①	1 29/32	1 1/8	1	—	—	1 Lean	.090	.350	—
	7023008	3/4①	1 29/32	1 1/8	1	—	—	On Index	.090	.350	—
	7023018	3/4①	1 29/32	1 1/8	1	—	—	On Index	.090	.350	—
1964	7024100	3/4①	1 3/4	1 1/8	1	—	.090	—	.070	.200	—
	7024102	3/4①	1 3/4	1 1/8	1	—	.090	—	.070	.200	—
	7024106	3/4①	1 3/4	1 1/8	1	—	.090	—	.070	.200	—
	7024108	3/4①	1 3/4	1 1/8	1	—	.090	—	.070	.200	—
1964–66	7024101	3/4①	1 3/4	1 1/8	1	—	.120	—	.060	.200	—
	7024110	3/4①	1 3/4	1 1/8	1	—	.090	—	.060	.200	—
	7024112	3/4①	1 3/4	1 1/8	1	—	.090	—	.060	.200	—
1965–66	7025103	3/4①	1 3/4	1 1/8	1	—	.120	—	.060	.200	—
	7036101	3/4①	1 3/4	1 1/8	1	—	.130	—	.060	.200	—
	7036103	3/4①	1 3/4	1 1/8	1	—	.130	—	.060	.200	—
	7036110	3/4①	1 3/4	1 1/8	1	—	.120	—	.060	.200	—
	7036112	3/4①	1 3/4	1 1/8	1	—	.120	—	.060	.200	—

ROCHESTER 2G, 2GC, 2GV CARBURETOR ADJUSTMENT SPECIFICATIONS—Continued

See Tune Up Chart in car chapters for hot idle speeds.
★Located on tag attached to or stamped on carburetor.

Year	Carb. Part No. ★	Float Level	Float Drop	Pump Rod	Idle Vent	Intermediate Choke Rod	Vacuum Break	Automatic Choke	Choke Rod	Choke Unloader	Fast Idle Speed
CHEVROLET ENGINES—Continued											
1966	7036146	15/32②	1 9/16	1 5/32	1 1/16	—	—	On Index	.055	.140	—
	7036248	15/32②	1 9/16	1 5/32	1 1/16	—	—	On Index	.055	.140	—
1967	7027101	3/4②	1 3/4	1 1/8	1	—	.120	—	.060	.215	—
	7027103	3/4②	1 3/4	1 1/8	1	—	.120	—	.060	.215	—
	7027110	3/4②	1 3/4	1 1/8	1	—	.110	—	.060	.215	—
	7027112	3/4②	1 3/4	1 1/8	1	—	.110	—	.060	.215	—
	7037101	3/4②	1 3/4	1 1/8	1	—	.130	—	.060	.215	—
	7037103	3/4②	1 3/4	1 1/8	1	—	.130	—	.060	.215	—
	7037110	3/4②	1 3/4	1 1/8	1	—	.110	—	.060	.215	—
	7037112	3/4②	1 3/4	1 1/8	1	—	.110	—	.060	.215	—
	7027114	3/4②	1 3/4	1 1/8	1	—	.110	—	.060	.200	—
	7027116	3/4②	1 3/4	1 1/8	1	—	.110	—	.060	.200	—
	7037034	15/32②	1 9/16	1 5/32	31/32	—	—	On Index	.055	.140	—
1968	7028110	3/4②	1 3/4	1 1/8	.025③	—	.100	—	.060	.200	—
	7028101	3/4②	1 3/4	1 1/8	.025③	—	.100	—	.060	.200	—
	7028112	3/4②	1 3/4	1 1/8	.025③	—	.100	—	.060	.200	—
	7028103	3/4②	1 3/4	1 1/8	.025③	—	.100	—	.060	.200	—
1969	7029101	27/32②	1 3/4	1 1/8	.020	—	.100	—	.060	.215	—
	7029102	3/4②	1 3/4	1 13/32	.020	—	.215	—	.085	.275	—
	7029103	27/32②	1 3/4	1 1/8	.020	—	.100	—	.060	.215	—
	7029104	3/4②	1 3/4	1 13/32	.020	—	.215	—	.085	.275	—
	7029110	27/32②	1 3/4	1 1/8	.020	—	.100	—	.060	.215	—
	7029112	27/32②	1 3/4	1 1/8	.020	—	.100	—	.060	.215	—
	7029117	3/4②	1 3/4	1 13/32	.020	—	.215	—	.085	.275	—
	7029118	3/4②	1 3/4	1 13/32	.020	—	.215	—	.085	.275	—
	7029119	5/8②	1 3/4	1 13/32	.020	—	.215	—	.085	.275	—
	7029120	5/8②	1 3/4	1 13/32	.020	—	.215	—	.085	.275	—
	7029127	3/4②	1 3/4	1 13/32	.020	—	.215	—	.085	.275	—
	7029129	3/4②	1 3/4	1 13/32	.020	—	.215	—	.085	.275	—

①—Gauge from toe of float to air horn gasket.
②—Gauge from lip at toe of float to air horn gasket.
③—At slow idle RPM vent valve should be open to specified dimension.

JEEP

Year	Carb. Part No. ★	Float Level	Float Drop	Pump Rod	Idle Vent	Intermediate Choke Rod	Vacuum Break	Automatic Choke	Choke Rod	Choke Unloader	Fast Idle Speed
1966–68	7026082	1 5/32①	1 3/4	1 5/32	—	—	—	—	—	—	—
	7026086	2 1/[illegible]	1 27/[illegible]	1 5/[illegible]	—	—	—	—	—	—	—
	7026089	1 5/32①	1 3/4	1 5/32	—	—	—	On Index	.055	.140	—
	7027082	1 5/32①	1 3/4	1 5/32	—	—	—	—	—	—	—
	7027089	1 5/32①	1 3/4	1 5/32	—	—	—	On Index	.055	.140	—
	7028088	1 5/32①	1 3/4	1 1/16	.025②	—	.120	—	.050	.140	—

①—Gauge from top of float at toe to air horn gasket.
②—At slow idle RPM vent valve should be open to specified dimension.

OLDSMOBILE

Year	Carb. Part No. ★	Float Level	Float Drop	Pump Rod	Idle Vent	Intermediate Choke Rod	Vacuum Break	Automatic Choke	Choke Rod	Choke Unloader	Fast Idle Speed
1963	7023052	13/32	1 13/16	1 7/16	1 11/32	1st Groove	—	1 Lean	.150	.160	1900②
	7023053	13/32	1 13/16	1 7/16	1 11/32	1st Groove	—	1 Lean	.150	.160	1900②
	7023056	25/32	1 13/16	1 3/16	—	—	—	On Index	.080	.260	1800②
	7023058	25/32	1 13/16	1 3/16	—	—	—	On Index	.080	.260	1800②
1964	7024052	19/32	1 13/16	1 7/16	1 11/32	1st Groove	—	On Index	.150	.160	1100③
	7024053	7/16	1 13/16	1 7/16	1 11/32	1st Groove	—	On Index	.150	.160	1100③
	7024056	11/16	1 13/16	1 3/32	1	—	—	1 Lean	.080	.260	—
	7024057	17/32	1 13/16	1 3/32	1	—	—	1 Lean	.080	.260	—
	7024058	11/16	1 13/16	1 3/32	1	—	—	1 Lean	.080	.260	—
	7024059	17/32	1 13/16	1 3/32	1	—	—	1 Lean	.080	.260	—
	7024155	11/16	1 13/16	1 3/32	1	—	—	1 Lean	.080	.260	—
	7024156	11/16	1 13/16	1 3/32	1	—	—	1 Lean	.080	.260	—

ROCHESTER 2G, 2GC, 2GV CARBURETOR ADJUSTMENT SPECIFICATIONS—Continued

See Tune Up Chart in car chapters for hot idle speeds.

★Located on tag attached to or stamped on carburetor.

Year	Carb. Part No. ★	Float Level	Float Drop	Pump Rod	Idle Vent	Intermediate Choke Rod	Vacuum Break	Automatic Choke	Choke Rod	Choke Unloader	Fast Idle Speed
OLDSMOBILE—Continued											
1965	7025052	3/4	1 7/8	1 7/16	1 11/32	.030 Out	—	On Index	.150	.160	900③
	7025053	19/32	1 7/8	1 7/16	1 11/32	.030 Out	—	On Index	.150	.160	900③
	7025056	3/4	1 7/8	1 7/16	1 11/32	Flush	—	On Index	.150	.160	900③
	7025057	19/32	1 7/8	1 7/16	1 11/32	Flush	—	On Index	.150	.160	900③
	7025058	3/4	1 7/8	1 7/16	1 11/32	Flush	—	On Index	.150	.160	900③
	7025152	3/4	1 7/8	1 7/16	1 11/32	Flush	—	1 Lean	.150	.160	900③
	7025156	3/4	1 7/8	1 7/16	1 11/32	Flush	—	On Index	.150	.160	900③
	7025159	3/4	1 7/8	1 7/16	1 11/32	Flush	—	On Index	.150	.160	900③
	7025252	3/4	1 7/8	1 7/16	1 11/32	.030 Out	—	On Index	.150	.160	900③
	7025253	19/32	1 7/8	1 7/16	1 11/32	.030 Out	—	On Index	.150	.160	900③
	7025254	3/4	1 7/8	1 7/16	1 11/32	Flush	—	1 Lean	.150	.160	900③
1966	7026052	3/4	1 7/8	1 7/16	1 11/32	Flush	—	On Index	.150	.160	900③
	7026053	19/32	1 7/8	1 7/16	1 11/32	—	Flush	On Index	.150	.160	900③
	7026054	3/4	1 7/8	1 7/16	1 11/32	Flush	—	1 Lean	.150	.160	900③
	7026055	3/4	1 3/4	27/32	—	—	—	—	—	—	—
	7026056	5/8	1 3/4	1 11/32	1 9/32	—	.260	—	.100	.160	—
	7026057	3/4	1 3/4	27/32	—	—	—	—	—	—	—
	7026058	3/4	1 7/8	1 7/16	1 11/32	Flush	—	On Index	.150	.160	900③
	7026059	3/4	1 7/8	1 7/16	1 11/32	Flush	—	On Index	.150	.160	900③
	7036052	3/4	1 7/8	1 7/16	1 11/32	Flush	—	On Index	.150	.160	900③
	7036053	19/32	1 7/8	1 7/16	1 3/8	—	Flush	On Index	.150	.160	900③
	7036058	3/4	1 7/8	1 7/16	1 11/32	Flush	—	On Index	.150	.160	900③
	7036152	3/4	1 7/8	1 7/16	1 11/32	Flush	—	1 Lean	.150	.160	900③
	7036159	3/4	1 7/8	1 7/16	1 11/32	Flush	—	On Index	.150	.160	900③
1967	7027033	19/32	1 3/8	1 7/16	1 5/16	—	Flush	On Index	.150	.160	—
	7027035	19/32	1 3/8	1 7/16	1 5/16	—	1st Groove	On Index	.150	.160	—
	7027133	19/32	1 3/8	1 7/16	1 5/16	—	1st Groove	On Index	.150	.160	—
	7027136	19/32	1 3/8	1 7/16	1 5/16	—	1st Groove	On Index	.150	.160	—
	7027139	9/16	1 3/8	1 7/16	1 5/16	—	Flush	On Index	.150	.160	—
	7037050	19/32	1 3/8	1 7/16	1 5/16	—	1st Groove	On Index	.150	.160	—
	7037051	19/32	1 3/8	1 7/16	1 5/16	—	1st Groove	On Index	.150	.160	—
	7037052	19/32	1 3/8	1 7/16	1 5/16	—	1st Groove	On Index	.150	.160	—
	7037053	19/32	1 3/8	1 7/16	1 5/16	—	1st Groove	On Index	.150	.160	—
	7037054	19/32	1 3/8	1 7/16	1 5/16	—	Flush	On Index	.150	.160	—
	7037055	19/32	1 3/8	1 7/16	1 5/16	—	Flush	On Index	.150	.160	—
	7037056	1/2	1 3/8	1 7/16	1 5/16	—	Flush	On Index	.150	.160	—
	7037057	1/2	1 3/8	1 7/16	1 5/16	—	Flush	On Index	.150	.160	—
	7037058	19/32	1 3/8	1 7/16	1 5/16	—	Flush	1 Lean	.150	.160	—
1968	7028154	9/16	1 3/8	1 7/16	.025②	—	1st Groove	On Index	.150	.160	—
	7028155	9/16	1 3/8	1 7/16	.025②	—	Flush	1 Lean	.150	.160	900③
	7028156	9/16	1 3/8	1 7/16	.025②	—	1st Groove	On Index	.150	.160	900③
	7028157	9/16	1 3/8	1 7/16	.025②	—	1st Groove	On Index	.150	.160	900③
	7028158	9/16	1 3/8	1 7/16	.025②	—	Flush	On Index	.150	.160	900③
	7028159	9/16	1 3/8	1 7/16	.025②	—	Flush	1 Lean	.150	.160	900③
1969	7029155	9/16	1 3/8	1 7/16	.025②	—	.180	1 Lean	.140	.170	900③
	7029156	9/16	1 3/8	1 7/16	.025②	—	.180	On Index	.140	.170	900③
	7029158	9/16	1 3/8	1 7/16	.025②	—	.180	On Index	.140	.170	900③
	7029159	9/16	1 3/8	1 7/16	.025②	—	.180	On Index	.140	.170	900③

①—Tag marked "A" 1/2"; others 13/32". ②—At slow idle RPM vent valve should open to specified dimension. ③—On low step of cam.

ROCHESTER 2G, 2GC, 2GV CARBURETOR ADJUSTMENT SPECIFICATIONS—Continued

See Tune Up Chart in car chapters for hot idle speeds.

★Located on tag attached to or stamped on carburetor.

Year	Carb. Part No. ★	Float Level	Float Drop	Pump Rod	Idle Vent	Intermediate Choke Rod	Vacuum Break	Automatic Choke	Choke Rod	Choke Unloader	Fast Idle Speed
PONTIAC											
1963	7013063	23/32	1 3/4	7/8	—	—	—	—	—	—	—
	7013064	23/32	1 3/4	1 3/16	15/32	—	—	On Index	.055	.160	—
	7013065	23/32	1 3/4	7/8	—	—	—	—	—	—	—
1963–64	7023060	5/8	1 3/4	1 11/32	1 9/32	Flush	—	On Index	.080	.160	—
	7023061	5/8	1 3/4	1 11/32	1 9/32	Flush	—	On Index	.080	.160	—
1963	7023062	5/8	1 3/4	1 11/32	1 9/32	.040 Out	—	On Index	.080	.160	—
1963–64	7023063	11/16	1 3/4	1 1/8	1 3/32	—	—	On Index	.055	.160	—
	7023064	11/16	1 3/4	1 1/8	1 3/32	—	—	On Index	.055	.160	—
	7023066	11/16	1 3/4	1 1/8	1 3/32	—	—	On Index	.055	.160	—
	7023071	5/8	1 3/4	1 11/32	1 9/32	Flush	—	On Index	.080	.160	—
1963	7023073	23/32	1 3/4	1 1/8	1 1/32	—	—	On Index	.055	.160	—
	7023075	23/32	1 3/4	1 1/8	1 1/32	—	—	On Index	.055	.160	—
	7023077	23/32	1 3/4	1 1/8	1 1/32	—	—	On Index	.055	.160	—
	7023078	23/32	1 3/4	7/8	—	—	—	—	—	—	—
	7023079	23/32	1 3/4	7/8	—	—	—	—	—	—	—
	7023161	23/32	1 3/4	1 1/8	1 3/32	—	—	On Index	.055	.160	—
	7023162	27/32	1 3/4	1 1/8	1 3/32	—	—	On Index	.055	.160	—
1964	7024062	5/8	1 3/4	1 11/32	1 9/32	.040 Out	—	On Index	.080	.160	—
	7024074	11/16	1 3/4	1 1/8	1 1/32	—	—	On Index	.055	.160	—
	7024075	11/16	1 3/4	1 1/8	1 1/32	—	—	On Index	.055	.160	—
1964–66	7024078	21/32	1 3/4	27/32	—	—	—	—	—	—	—
	7024079	21/32	1 3/4	27/32	—	—	—	—	—	—	—
1964	7024173	11/16	1 3/4	1 1/8	1 1/32	—	—	On Index	.055	.160	—
	7024175	11/16	1 3/4	1 1/8	1 1/32	—	—	On Index	.055	.160	—
1964–66	7024178	21/32	1 3/4	27/32	—	—	—	—	—	—	—
	7024179	21/32	1 3/4	27/32	—	—	—	—	—	—	—
1965	7025060	19/32	1 3/4	1 11/32	1 9/32	Flush	—	On Index	.085	.160	—
	7025061	19/32	1 3/4	1 11/32	1 9/32	Flush	—	On Index	.085	.160	—
	7025062	19/32	1 3/4	1 11/32	1 9/32	Flush	—	On Index	.085	.160	—
	7025066	19/32	1 3/4	1 11/32	1 9/32	Flush	—	On Index	.085	.160	—
	7025070	11/16	1 3/4	1 1/8	1 1/32	—	—	On Index	.055	.160	—
	7025071	19/32	1 3/4	1 11/32	1 9/32	Flush	—	On Index	.085	.160	—
	7025074	11/16	1 3/4	1 1/8	1 1/32	—	—	On Index	.055	.160	—
	7025075	11/16	1 3/4	1 1/8	1 1/32	—	—	On Index	.055	.160	—
1965–66	7025078	21/32	1 3/4	27/32	—	—	—	—	—	—	—
	7025079	21/32	1 3/4	27/32	—	—	—	—	—	—	—
1965	7025173	11/16	1 3/4	1 1/8	1 1/32	—	—	On Index	.055	.160	—
	7025175	11/16	1 3/4	1 1/8	1 1/32	—	—	On Index	.055	.160	—
	7025177	11/16	1 3/4	1 1/8	1 1/32	—	—	On Index	.055	.160	—
1965–66	7025178	21/32	1 3/4	27/32	—	—	—	—	—	—	—
	7025179	21/32	1 3/4	27/32	—	—	—	—	—	—	—
1965	7026060	19/32	1 3/4	1 11/32	—	Flush	—	On Index	.085	.160	—
	7026061	19/32	1 3/4	1 11/32	—	Flush	—	On Index	.085	.160	—
	7026062	19/32	1 3/4	1 11/32	1 9/32	Flush	—	On Index	.085	.160	—
	7026066	19/32	1 3/4	1 11/32	—	Flush	—	On Index	.085	.160	—
	7026071	19/32	1 3/4	1 11/32	1 9/32	Flush	—	On Index	.085	.160	—
	7036060	19/32	1 3/4	1 11/32	—	Flush	—	On Index	.085	.160	—
	7036061	19/32	1 3/4	1 11/32	—	Flush	—	On Index	.085	.160	—
	7036062	19/32	1 3/4	1 11/32	1 9/32	Flush	—	On Index	.085	.160	—
	7036071	19/32	1 3/4	1 11/32	1 9/32	Flush	—	On Index	.085	.160	—
1966	7026074	19/32	1 3/4	1 11/32	1 9/32	—	.160	—	.095	.160	—
	7026075	19/32	1 3/4	1 11/32	1 9/32	—	.230	—	.095	.160	—
	7036175	19/32	1 3/4	1 11/32	1 9/32	—	.230	—	.095	.160	—

ROCHESTER 2G, 2GC, 2GV CARBURETOR ADJUSTMENT SPECIFICATIONS—Continued

See Tune Up Chart in car chapters for hot idle speeds.

★Located on tag attached to or stamped on carburetor.

Year	Carb. Part No. ★	Float Level	Float Drop	Pump Rod	Idle Vent	Intermediate Choke Rod	Vacuum Break	Automatic Choke	Choke Rod	Choke Unloader	Fast Idle Speed
PONTIAC—Continued											
1967	7027060	9/16	1 9/16	1 11/32	1 9/32	Flush	—	Index	.085	.160	2800
	7027061	9/16	1 9/16	1 11/32	1 9/32	Flush	—	Index	.085	.160	2800
	7027062	9/16	1 9/16	1 11/32	1 9/32	Flush	—	Index	.085	.160	2800
	7027066	9/16	1 9/16	1 11/32	1 9/32	Flush	—	Index	.085	.160	2500
	7027071	9/16	1 9/16	1 11/32	1 9/32	Flush	—	Index	.085	.160	2500
	7037061	9/16	1 9/16	1 11/32	1 9/32	Flush	—	Index	.085	.160	2500
	7037062	9/16	1 9/16	1 11/32	1 9/32	Flush	—	Index	.085	.160	2500
	7037066	9/16	1 9/16	1 11/32	1 9/32	Flush	—	Index	.085	.160	2500
	7037071	9/16	1 9/16	1 11/32	1 9/32	Flush	—	Index	.085	.160	2500
	7037162	9/16	1 9/16	1 11/32	1 9/32	Flush	—	Index	.085	.160	2500
1968	7028060	9/16	1 3/4	1 11/32	—	—	.150	—	.085	.180	—
	7028062	9/16	1 3/4	1 11/32	—	—	.150	—	.085	.180	—
	7028066	9/16	1 3/4	1 11/32	—	—	.170	—	.085	.180	—
	7028071	9/16	1 3/4	1 11/32	—	—	.160	—	.085	.180	—
1969	7028066	9/16	1 3/4	1 11/32	—	—	.170	①	.085	.180	—
	7028071	9/16	1 3/4	1 11/32	—	—	.160	①	.085	.180	—
	7029060	9/16	1 3/4	1 11/32	—	—	.150	①	.085	.180	—
	7029062	9/16	1 3/4	1 11/32	—	—	.150	①	.085	.180	—

①—With choke valve closed, pull upward on choke rod to the limit of its travel. The end of rod should fit the guage notch on the choke lever.

2G, 2GC, 2GV ADJUSTMENTS

The basic model designation of Rochester two-barrel carburetors is "G". The "2" ahead of the "G" means that the carburetor has two bores, two venturi and two separate but identical metering systems, one for each carburetor bore. The two-bore carburetor is normally used on V8 engines where each bore supplies the air/fuel mixture to four cylinders through a divided intake manifold. Fig. 24 illustrates a Model 2GV carburetor while Fig. 25 is an exploded view of a 2GC model.

There are two different throttle body flanges used on these carburetors—1¼" and 1½". The flange size used for a particular application is usually determined by the carburetor bore size. Larger engines normally have more air capacity, hence larger carburetor bores and flanges are needed on these applications.

Model 2G carburetor is equipped with a manually-operated choke valve. Its major applications are on trucks and marine engines where an automatic choke is not an absolute necessity. However, on multiple carburetor applications, such as the "Tri-Power" set-up used on some Pontiacs where three carburetors are used, the two end carburetors are 2G models, the center one being equipped with an automatic choke. Models 2GC and 2GV use an automatic choke.

There are four different designs of automatic choke systems used on Rochester two-barrel carburetors: 1) The carburetor-mounted thermostatic coil; 2) the exhaust manifold-mounted coil; 3) the hot water choke system, and 4) the split linkage system.

The carburetor-mounted choke, Fig. 26, may have the choke housing assembly mounted on the air horn or on the throttle body. On units with the choke housing on the throttle body, an intermediate choke rod adjustment is required.

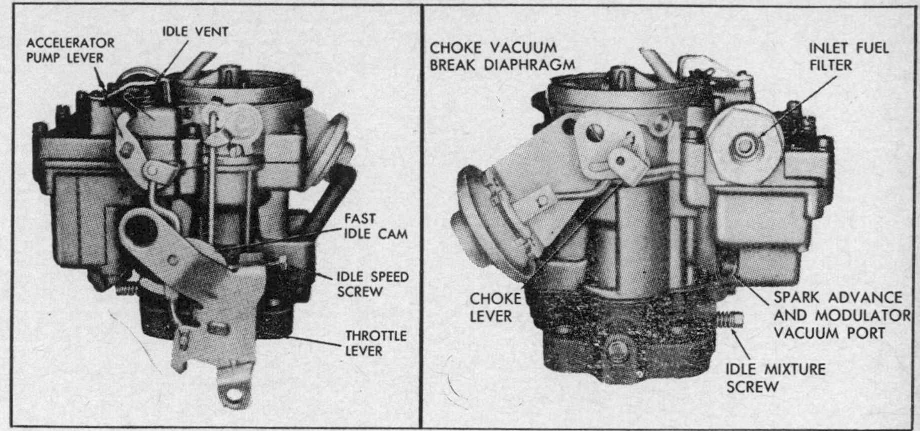

Fig. 24 Rochester Model 2GV two-barrel carburetor

The exhaust manifold-mounted choke system is used on 2GV units and consists of a choke valve located in the carburetor air horn, a vacuum diaphragm unit, fast idle cam, choke linkage and a thermostatic coil located on the engine manifold, Fig. 27. The thermostatic coil is connected to the choke valve by a rod. Choke operation is controlled by a combination of intake manifold vacuum, the offset choke valve, and temperature.

The split linkage choke, Fig. 28, is designed to let the choke valve and fast idle cam work independently. The operation of the choke coil and piston is the same as used on the conventional carburetor-mounted choke.

The hot water choke system, Fig. 29, differs from the conventional in that, instead of using hot air from the exhaust manifold to heat the thermostatic coil, heat from the engine hot water is used. The hot water is circulated directly from the engine to the chamber in the choke cover. The device has an inner and outer cover. The inner cover retains the choke coil while the outer cover provides the chamber through which the hot water is circulated.

Float Level Adjustment

Fig. 30—Adjust float level as directed for the type of float shown in the specification listed in the *Rochester Specifications Chart*.

Float Drop Adjustment

Fig. 31—Adjust float drop as directed for the type of float shown in the specification listed in the *Rochester Specifications Chart*.

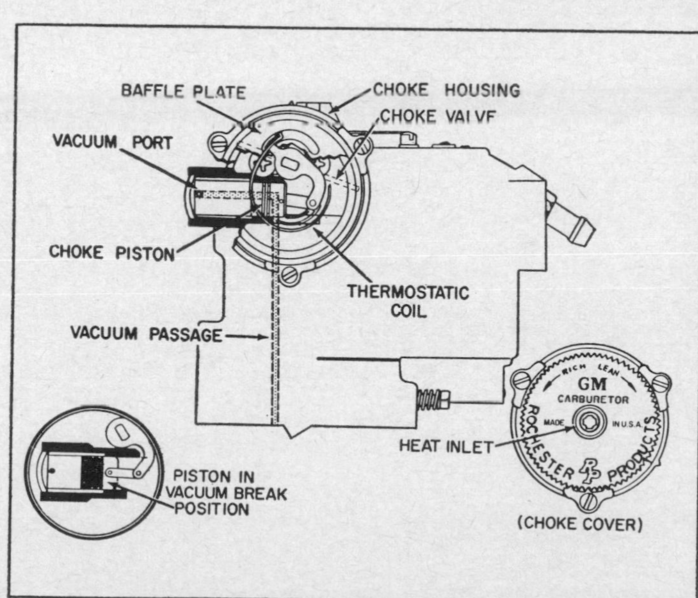

Fig. 26 Carburetor mounted automatic choke

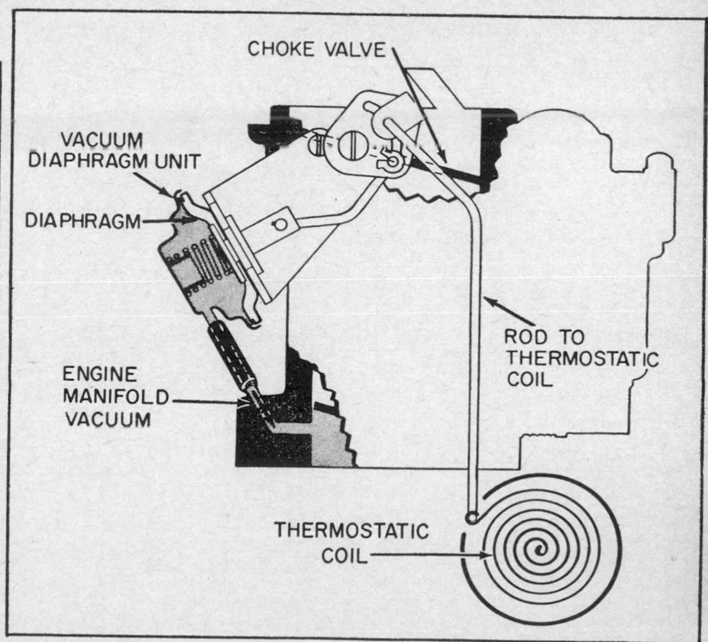

Fig. 27 Exhaust manifold mounted thermostatic coil

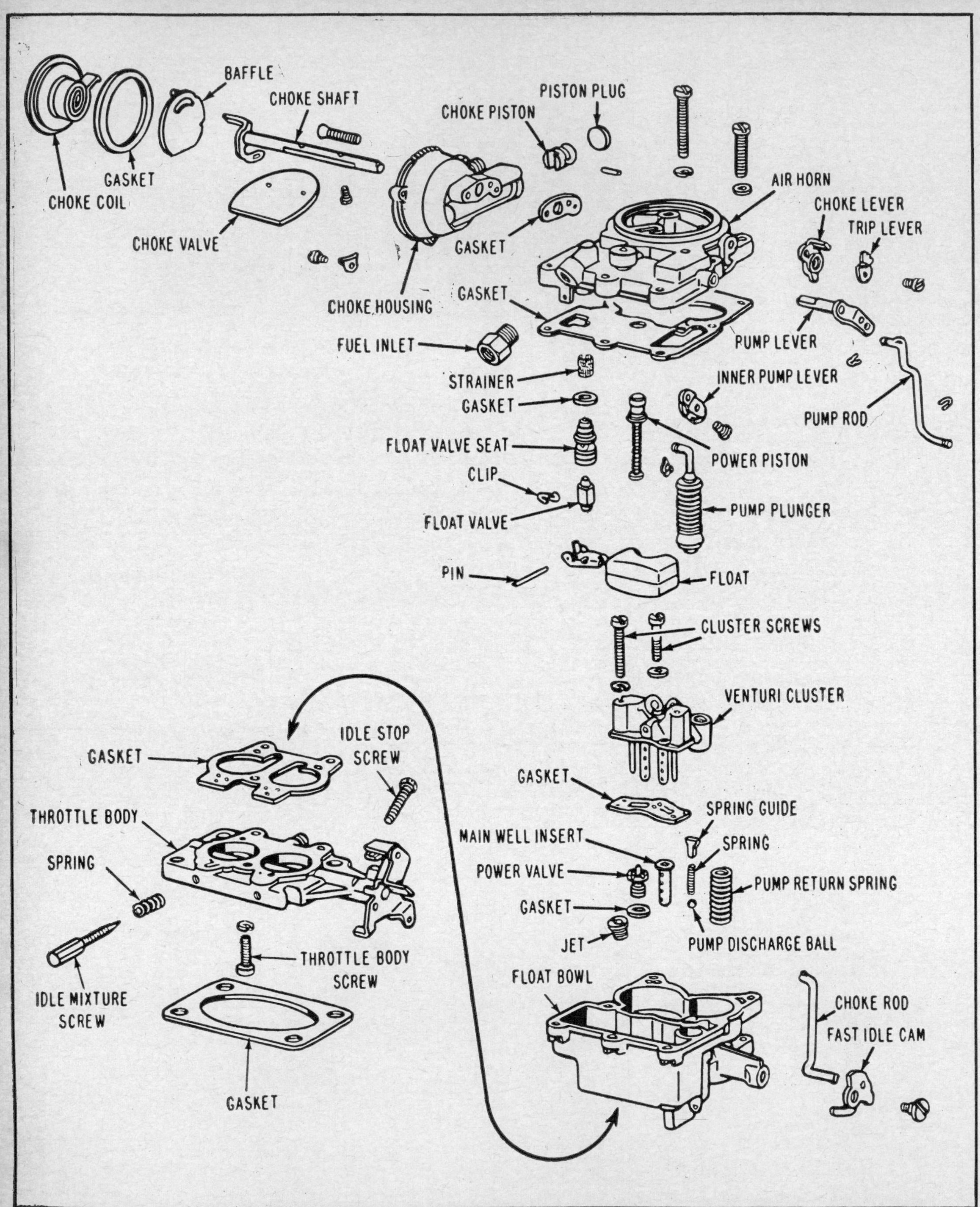

Fig. 25 Exploded view of Rochester two-barrel carburetor

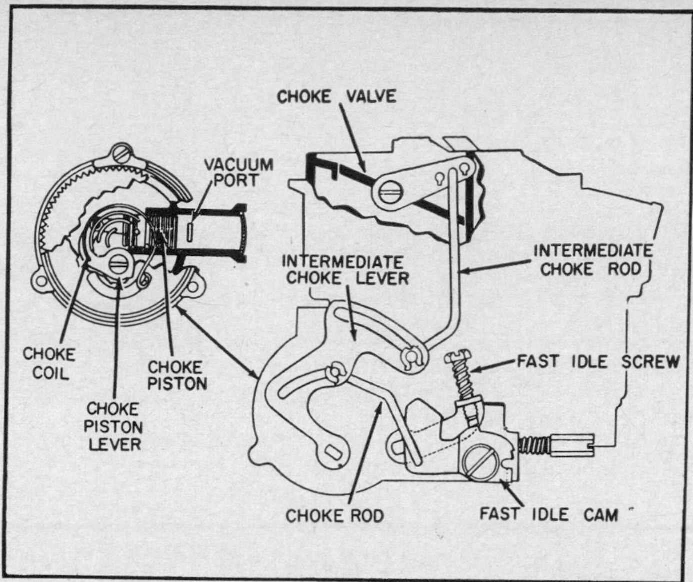

Fig. 28 Split linkage type automatic choke

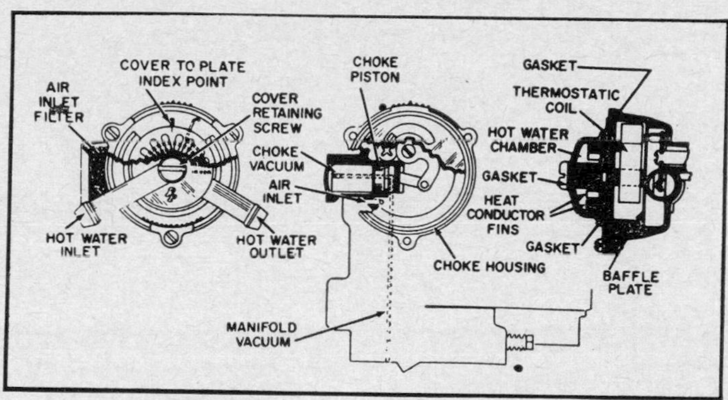

Fig. 29 Hot water choke system

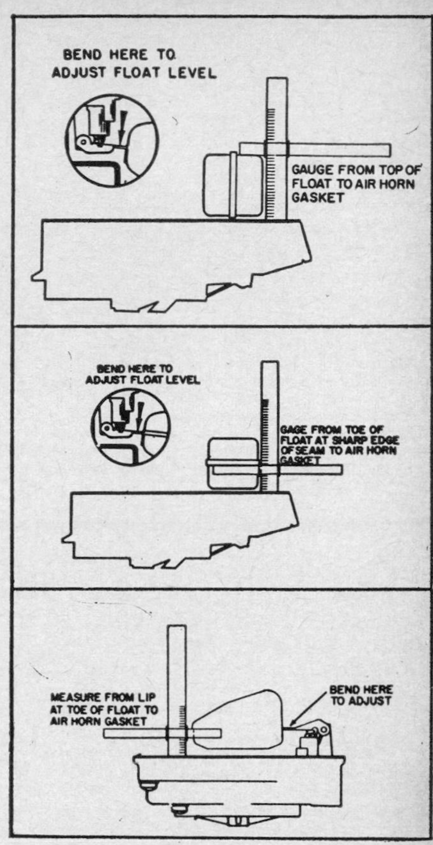

Fig. 30 Float level adjustment. Rochester 2G, 2GC, 2GV

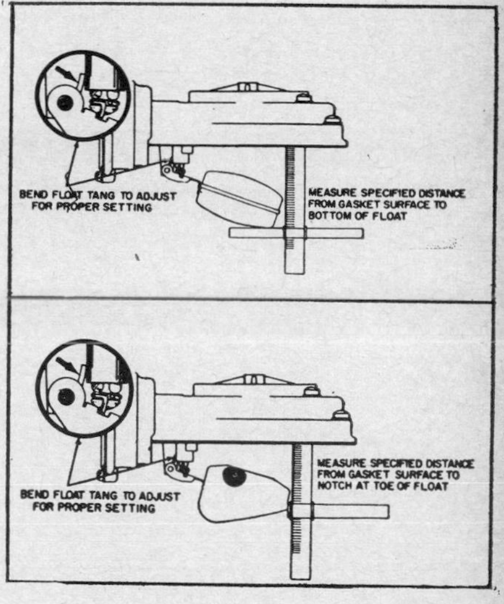

Fig. 31 Float drop adjustment. Rochester 2G, 2GC, 2GV

Pump Rod Adjustment

Fig. 32—Back out idle stop screw and completely close throttle valves in bore. Place proper size gauge listed in the *Rochester Specifications Chart* on top of air horn ring. Bend pump rod at lower angle to obtain specified dimension to top of pump rod.

Idle Vent Adjustment, 1963-67

Fig. 33—Open throttle until vent valve just closes. Place proper size gauge on top of air horn ring. Dimension to top of pump rod should be as specified in the *Rochester Specifications Chart.* Adjust by bending tang on pump lever.

Intermediate Choke Rod Adjustment

Choke Mounted on Throttle Body, Fig. 34—Remove thermostat cover and coil assembly and inside baffle plate. Hold choke valve completely closed and bend intermediate choke rod as necessary so that end of choke piston is as specified in the *Rochester Specifications Chart* with end of choke piston bore.

Split Linkage Choke, Fig. 35—Remove thermostat cover and coil assembly and inside baffle plate. Open throttle valves and hold choke valve completely closed

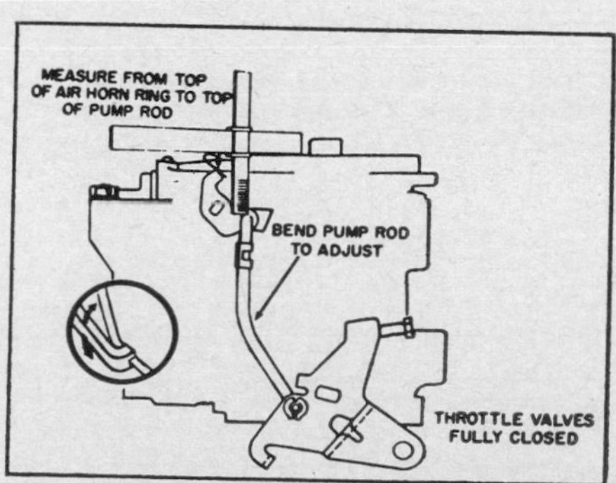

Fig. 32 Pump rod adjustment for 2G, 2GC, 2GV carburetors

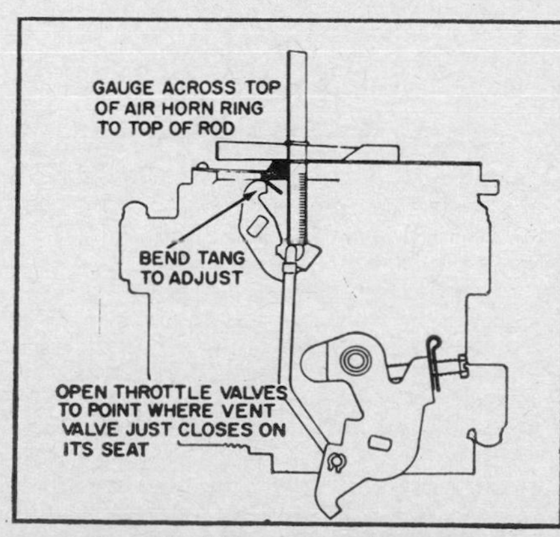

Fig. 33 Idle vent adjustment for 2G, 2GC, 2GV carburetors

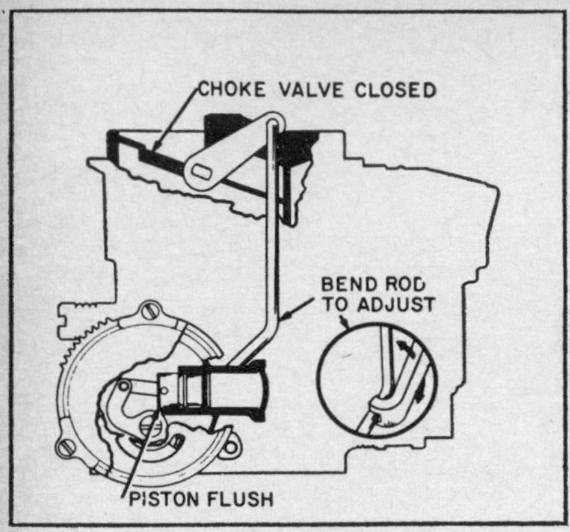

Fig. 34 Intermediate choke rod adjustment for 2GC chokes mounted on throttle body

by pushing upward on intermediate choke lever. Adjust intermediate choke rod as necessary by bending so that choke piston is in the location shown in the illustration.

Vacuum Break Adjustment

Model 2GV, Fig. 36—Push vacuum break diaphragm plunger in until it is seated and make sure choke valve is closed so that connecting rod is at end of slot in choke shaft lever. In this position, adjust rod by bending so that specified gauge will fit between upper edge of choke valve and inner wall of air horn (see *Rochester Specifications Chart*). Adjust by bending connecting rod at point shown.

Automatic Choke Setting

Carburetor Mounted Choke, Fig. 37—Loosen three retaining screws and rotate

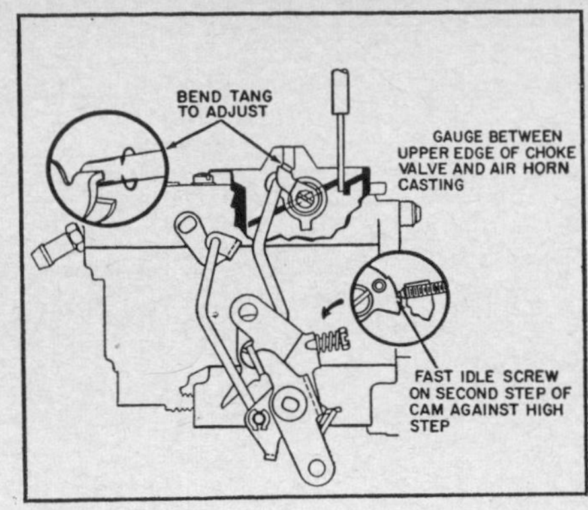

Fig. 39 Choke rod adjustment for 2GC carburetor mounted chokes

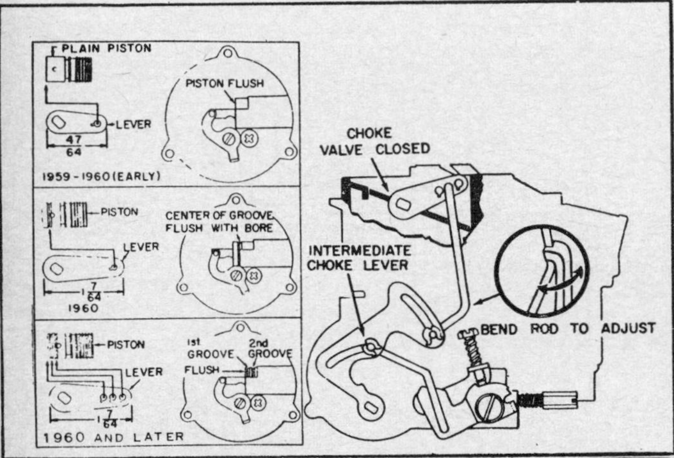

Fig. 35 Intermediate choke rod adjustment for 2GC carburetors having split linkage chokes

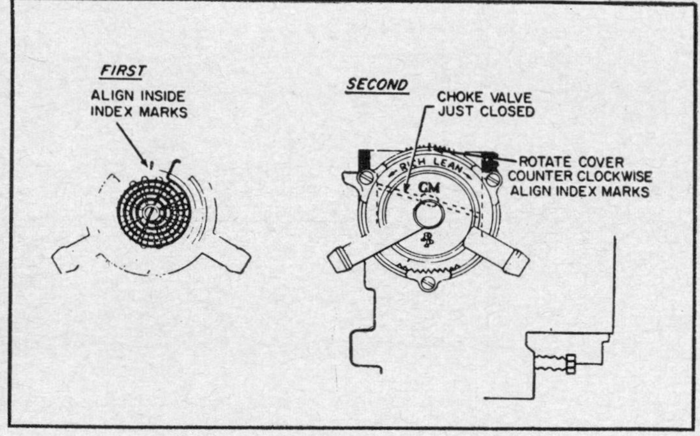

Fig. 38 Hot water choke coil adjustment on some 2GC carburetors

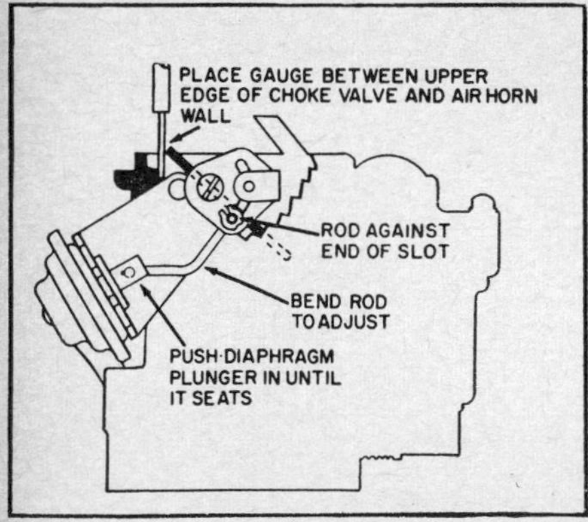

Fig. 36 Vacuum break adjustment for 2GV carburetors

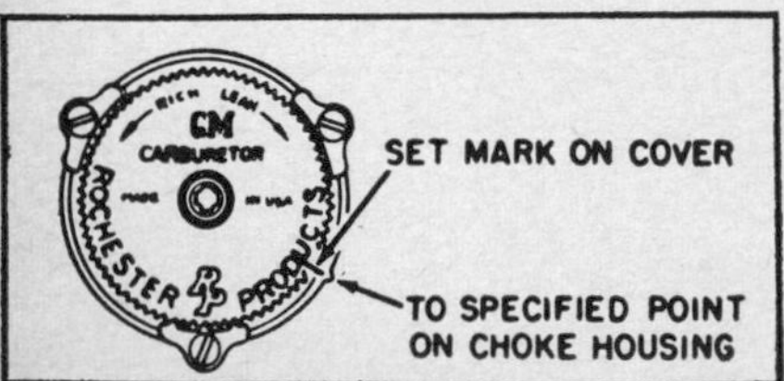

Fig. 37 Automatic choke adjustment for 2GC carburetors

choke cover against coil tension until index mark is in line with specified point on choke housing (see *Rochester Specifications Chart*).

Hot Water Choke Coil, Fig. 38—There are two adjustments necessary to provide proper choke indexing. The inner choke cover containing the thermostatic coil must be indexed with the outer cover. This indexing can be accomplished by aligning the scribe mark on the inner cover with the index point on the outer cover as shown. The complete choke cover assembly has a scribe mark on the outside which must be aligned with the proper index point on the choke housing.

Choke Rod Adjustment

Carburetor Mounted Choke, Fig. 39—It is important to position both slow idle and fast idle screws as follows before making choke rod adjustment.

1. On models using a single idle stop screw, turn stop screw in until it just contacts bottom step of fast idle cam. Then turn screw in one full turn farther.
2. On models using both a slow idle and a fast idle screw, turn slow idle stop screw in until it just contacts stop. Then turn this screw in one full turn from this point. Next turn the fast idle screw in until it touches bottom step of fast idle cam.
3. On all models, place idle screw on second step of fast idle cam against shoulder of high step. While holding screw in this position, check clearance between upper edge of choke valve and air horn wall as shown. Adjust to specified dimension by bending tang on choke lever and collar assembly (see *Rochester Specifications Chart*).

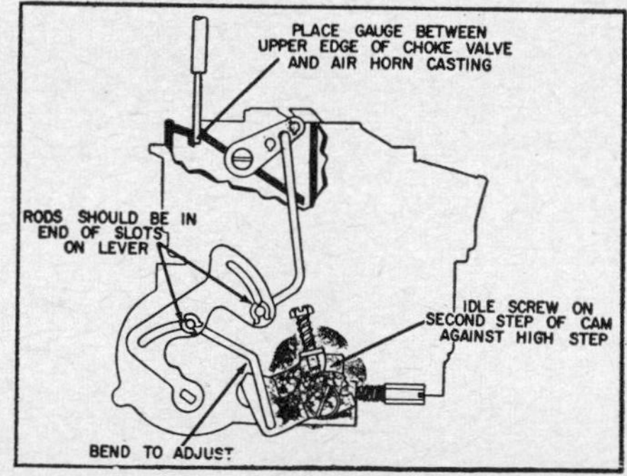

Fig. 40 Choke rod adjustment for 2GC split linkage type chokes

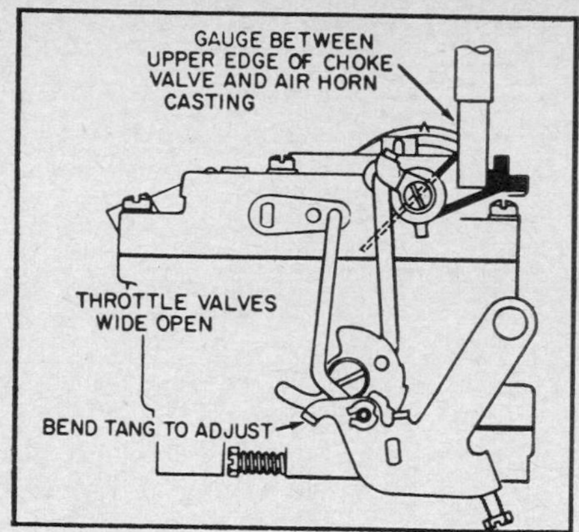

Fig. 41 Choke unloader adjustment for 2GC, 2GV carburetors

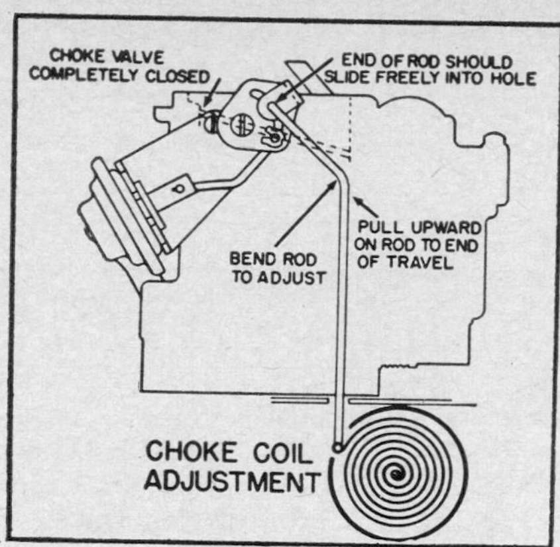

Fig. 42 Thermostatic coil rod adjustment for 2GV carburetors

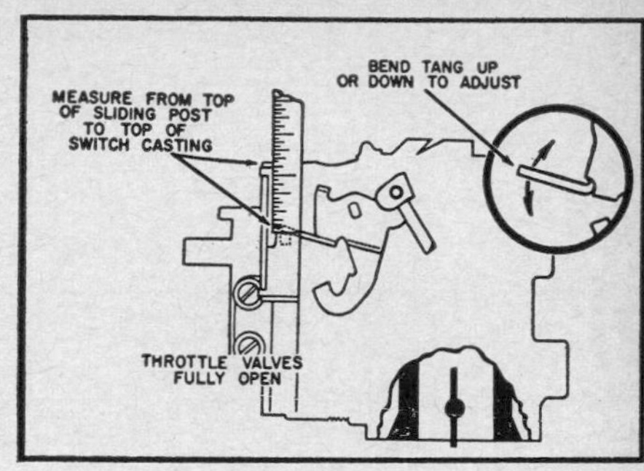

Fig. 43 Vacuum switch adjustment for some 2GC carburetors

Split Linkage Choke, Fig. 40—Position slow idle and fast idle screws as outlined in Steps 1 and 2 above. Then place fast idle screw on second step of fast idle cam next to high step as shown. Make sure intermediate choke rod and choke rod are in ends of slots in intermediate choke lever by pushing upward on lever. Bend choke rod until specified gauge size will just fit between upper edge of choke valve and inner wall of air horn (see *Rochester Specifications Chart*).

Choke Unloader Adjustment

Fig. 41—With throttle valves held wide open, the choke valve should be open just enough to admit the specified gauge between upper edge of choke valve and air horn wall (see *Rochester Specifications Chart*). To adjust, bend tang on throttle lever.

Thermostatic Coil Rod Adjustment

Model 2GV, Fig. 42—Disconnect upper end of thermostatic coil rod from choke lever. Hold choke valve completely closed and pull upward on coil rod to the limit of its travel. Bottom of rod should be even with top of hole in choke shaft lever. Adjust by bending coil rod.

Vacuum Switch Adjustment

Fig. 43—With throttle wide open measure distance from top of post to top of switch. This distance should be $1\frac{3}{32}$". If adjustment is required, loosen switch attaching screws and move switch up or down to correct.

Be careful not to bend or bump lever after adjustment has been made. Open and close throttle to be sure that arm on pump lever does not bind post on switch.

ROCHESTER 4GC FLOAT ADJUSTMENT SPECIFICATIONS

Year	Carburetor Part No. ①	Float Level		Float Toe		Float Drop		Vacuum Assist Spring
		Primary	Secondary	Primary	Secondary	Primary	Secondary	
BUICK								
1963	7023040	1 11/32	1 3/8	9/16	3/8	1 7/16	1 1/4	—
	7023044	1 11/32	1 3/8	9/16	3/8	1 9/16	1 9/32	—
	7023045	1 11/32	1 3/8	9/16	3/8	1 9/16	1 9/32	—
	7023143	1 11/32	1 3/8	9/16	3/8	1 7/16	1 1/4	—
1964	7024040	1 11/32	1 3/8	17/32	13/32	1 7/16	1 3/16	—
	7024044	1 11/32	1 3/8	19/32	3/8	1 19/32	1 3/16	—
	7024045	1 11/32	1 3/8	19/32	3/8	1 19/32	1 3/16	—
1965	7025040	1 13/32	1 13/32	—	—	1 1/16	1 1/4	—
	7025140	1 13/32	1 13/32	—	—	1 1/16	1 1/4	—
1966	7026040	1 7/16	1 7/16	—	—	1 1/16	1 1/16	—
CADILLAC								
1963	7023030	1 7/16	1 3/8	5/8	5/8	1 1/2	1 1/4	1 1/16
	7023031	1 7/16	1 3/8	5/8	5/8	1 1/2	1 1/4	1 1/16
1964	7024030	1 7/16	1 3/8	5/8	5/8	1 1/2	1 1/16	1 1/16
	7024031	1 7/16	1 3/8	5/8	5/8	1 1/2	1 1/16	1 1/16
1965	7025030	1 7/16	1 3/8	5/8	5/8	1 1/2	1 1/16	1 1/16
	7025031	1 7/16	1 3/8	5/8	5/8	1 1/2	1 1/16	1 1/16
1966	7026030	1 7/16	1 3/8	5/8	5/8	1 1/2	1 1/16	1 1/16
	7026031	1 7/16	1 3/8	5/8	5/8	1 1/2	1 1/16	1 1/16
CHEVROLET ENGINES								
1963	7020023	1 1/2	1 5/16	13/16	1/2	1 1/2	1 1/8	1 7/32
	7020024	1 1/2	1 5/16	13/16	1/2	1 1/2	1 1/8	1 7/32
	7023006	1 17/32	1 19/32	—	—	2 1/4	2 1/4	—
	7023012	1 17/32	1 19/32	—	—	2 1/4	2 1/4	—
1964	7024120	1 17/32	1 19/32	—	—	2 1/4	2 1/4	—
	7024121	1 17/32	1 19/32	—	—	2 1/4	2 1/4	—
	7024122	1 17/32	1 19/32	—	—	2 1/4	2 1/4	—
	7024123	1 1/2	1 5/16	13/16	1/2	1 1/2	1 1/8	1 7/32
	7024124	1 1/2	1 5/16	13/16	1/2	1 1/2	1 1/8	1 7/32
	7024125	1 17/32	1 19/32	—	—	2 1/4	2 1/4	—
	7024126	1 17/32	1 19/32	—	—	2 1/4	2 1/4	—
	7024127	1 1/2	1 13/32	25/32	21/32	1 1/2	1 7/16	1 5/32
	7024128	1 1/2	1 13/32	25/32	21/32	1 1/2	1 7/16	1 5/32
	7024220	1 17/32	1 19/32	—	—	2 1/4	2 1/4	—
	7024225	1 17/32	1 19/32	—	—	2 1/4	2 1/4	—
	7024226	1 17/32	1 19/32	—	—	2 1/4	2 1/4	—
1965	7025121	1 17/32	1 19/32	—	—	2 1/4	2 1/4	—
	7025122	1 17/32	1 19/32	—	—	2 1/4	2 1/4	—
	7025123	1 1/2	1 13/32	25/32	21/32	1 1/2	1 7/16	1 5/32
	7025124	1 1/2	1 13/32	25/32	21/32	1 1/2	1 7/16	1 5/32
1965–66	7025126	1 17/32	1 19/32	—	—	2 1/4	2 1/4	—
	7025127	1 17/32	1 19/32	—	—	2 1/4	2 1/4	—
	7025128	1 17/32	1 19/32	—	—	2 1/4	2 1/4	—
	7036118	1 17/32	1 19/32	—	—	2 1/4	2 1/4	—
	7036119	1 17/32	1 19/32	—	—	2 1/4	2 1/4	—
	7036120	1 17/32	1 19/32	—	—	2 1/4	2 1/4	—
	7036121	1 17/32	1 19/32	—	—	2 1/4	2 1/4	—

ROCHESTER 4GC FLOAT ADJUSTMENT SPECIFICATIONS—Continued

Year	Carburetor Part No. ①	Float Level		Float Toe		Float Drop		Vacuum Assist Spring
		Primary	Secondary	Primary	Secondary	Primary	Secondary	
OLDSMOBILE								
1963	7023050	1 25/32	1 3/8	11/16	3/8	1 1/2	1 3/16	1 3/16
	7023051	1 15/32	1 3/8	11/16	3/8	1 1/2	1 3/16	1 1/16
	7023054	1 7/16	1 3/8	17/32	3/8	1 3/8	1 1/8	—
	7023055	1 7/16	1 3/8	17/32	3/8	1 3/8	1 1/8	—
1964	7024050	1 15/32	1 3/8	11/16	3/8	1 1/2	1 3/16	1 1/32
	7024051	1 15/32	1 3/8	11/16	3/8	1 1/2	1 3/16	1 1/32
	7024054	1 15/32	1 3/8	17/32	3/8	1 3/8	1 1/8	—
	7024055	1 15/32	1 3/8	17/32	3/8	1 3/8	1 1/8	—
	7024153	1 15/32	1 3/8	11/16	3/8	1 1/2	1 3/16	1 1/32
	7024154	1 15/32	1 3/8	11/16	3/8	1 1/2	1 3/16	1 1/32
1965	7025050	1 15/32	1 3/8	3/4	3/8	1 1/2	1 3/16	1 3/32
	7025051	1 15/32	1 3/8	5/8	3/8	1 1/2	1 3/16	1 1/8
	7025054	1 7/16	1 7/16	—	—	1 1/4	1 1/4	—
	7025055	1 7/16	1 7/16	—	—	1 1/4	1 1/4	—
	7025150	1 15/32	1 3/8	—	—	1 1/16	1 1/16	13/16
	7025151	1 15/32	1 3/8	—	—	1 1/16	1 1/16	11/16
	7025157	1 7/16	1 7/16	—	—	1 1/4	1 1/4	—
	7025158	1 7/16	1 7/16	—	—	1 1/4	1 1/4	—
	7025255	1 15/32	1 3/8	—	—	1 1/16	1 1/16	11/16
PONTIAC								
1963	7023069	1 11/32	1 11/32	9/16	9/16	1 1/4	1 1/4	—
	7023070	1 11/32	1 11/32	9/16	9/16	1 1/4	1 1/4	—

①—Located on tag attached to or stamped on carburetor.

ROCHESTER 4GC ADJUSTMENT SPECIFICATIONS (Except Float Data)

See Tune Up Chart in Car Chapters for Hot Idle Speeds.

Year	Carb. Part No.①	Pump Rod	Idle Vent	Intermediate Choke Rod	Auto. Choke	Choke Rod	Fast Idle Speed	Choke Unloader	Anti-Stall Dashpot	Secondary	
										Lockout	Contour
BUICK											
1963	7023040	1②	—	Flush	Index	.050	650③	.130	—	.015	.030
	7023044	29/32②	—	Flush	Index	.045	650③	.130	—	.015	.030
	7023045	29/32②	—	Flush	Index	.045	650③	.130	—	.015	.030
	7023143	1②	—	Flush	Index	.050	650③	.130	—	.015	.030
1964	7024040	1 1/32②	—	Flush	Index	.030	650③	.120	—	.015	.030
	7024044	31/32②	—	Flush	2 Rich	.050	650③	.120	—	.015	.030
	7024045	31/32②	—	Flush	Index	.050	650③	.120	—	.015	.030
1965	7025040	1②	—	.030 Out	Index	.060	650③	.120	—	.015	.030
	7025140	1②	—	.030 Out	Index	.060	650③	.120	—	.015	.030
1966	7026040	1②	—	.030 Out	Index	.060	650③	.120	—	.015	.030
CADILLAC											
1963	7023030	27/32	—	Flush	1 Rich	.040	1700⑤	.130	—	.015	.015
	7023031	27/32	—	Flush	1 Rich	.040	1700⑤	.130	—	.015	.015
1964	7024030	13/16②	—	Flush	Index	.040	1700	.130	—	.020	.020
	7024031	13/16②	—	Flush	Index	.040	1700	.130	—	.020	.020

Continued

ROCHESTER 4GC ADJUSTMENT SPECIFICATIONS (Except Float Data)—Continued

See Tune Up Chart in Car Chapters for Hot Idle Speeds.

Year	Carb. Part No.(1)	Pump Rod	Idle Vent	Intermediate Choke Rod	Auto. Choke	Choke Rod	Fast Idle Speed	Choke Unloader	Anti-Stall Dashpot	Secondary	
										Lockout	Contour
CADILLAC—Continued											
1965	7025030	13/16(2)	—	Flush	Index	.040	1700	.130	—	.020	.020
	7025031	13/16(2)	—	Flush	Index	.040	1700	.130	—	.020	.020
1966	7026030	13/16(2)	—	Flush	Index	.040	1700	.130	—	.020	.020
	7026031	13/16(2)	—	Flush	Index	.040	1700	.130	—	.020	.020
CHEVROLET ENGINES											
1963	7020023	1	29/32	Flush	Index	.070	—	.130	—	.015	.015
	7020024	1	29/32	Flush	Index	.070	—	.130	—	.015	.015
	7023006	1 1/16	31/32	Flush	Index	.055	—	.230	—	.015	.015
	7023012	1 1/16	31/32	Flush	Index	.055	—	.230	—	.015	.015
1964	7024120	1 1/16	31/32	Flush	Index	.055	—	.230	—	.015	.015
	7024121	1 1/16	31/32	Flush	Index	.055	—	.230	—	.015	.015
	7024122	1 1/16	31/32	Flush	Index	.055	—	.230	—	.015	.015
	7024123	1 1/32	15/16	Flush	Index	.055	—	.130	—	.015	.015
	7024124	2 /32	13/16	Flush	Index	.055	—	.130	—	.015	.015
	7024125	1 1/16	31/32	Flush	Index	.055	—	.230	—	.015	.015
	7024126	1 1/16	31/32	Flush	Index	.055	—	.230	—	.015	.015
	7024127	1 1/32	15/16	Flush	Index	.090	—	.130	—	.015	.015
	7024128	29/32	13/16	Flush	Index	.090	—	.130	—	.015	.030
	7024220	1 1/16	31/32	Flush	Index	.055	—	.230	—	.015	.015
	7024225	1 1/16	31/32	Flush	Index	.055	—	.230	—	.015	.015
	7024226	1 1/16	31/32	Flush	Index	.055	—	.230	—	.015	.015
1965	7025121	1 1/16(2)	31/32	Flush	Index	.055	—	.250	—	.015	.015
	7025122	1 1/16(2)	31/32	Flush	Index	.055	—	.250	—	.015	.015
	7025123	1 1/32	15/16	Flush	Index	.090	—	.130	—	.015	.015
	7025124	1 1/32	15/16	Flush	Index	.090	—	.130	—	.015	.015
1965–66	7025126	1 1/16(2)	31/32	Flush	Index	.055	—	.250	—	.015	.015
	7025127	1 1/16(4)	31/32	Flush	Index	.055	—	.250	—	.015	.015
	7025128	1 1/16(2)	31/32	Flush	Index	.055	—	.250	—	.015	.015
	7036118	1 1/16(2)	31/32	Flush	Index	.055	—	.250	—	.015	.015
	7036119	1 1/16(2)	31/32	Flush	Index	.055	—	.250	—	.015	.015
	7036120	1 1/16(2)	31/32	Flush	Index	.055	—	.250	—	.015	.015
	7036121	1 1/16(2)	31/32	Flush	Index	.055	—	.250	—	.015	.015
OLDSMOBILE											
1963	7023050	1(4)	29/32	Flush	Index	.050	1600(6)	.120	.020	.015	.030
	7023051	1(4)	29/32	Flush	Index	.050	1600(6)	.120	.020	.015	.030
	7023054	1(7)	29/32	Flush	2 Rich	.050	1600(6)	.190	—	.015	.030
	7023055	1(7)	29/32	Flush	2 Rich	.050	1600(6)	.190	—	.015	.030
1964	7024050	1(4)	29/32	Flush	Index	.050	(8)	.115	—	.015	.030
	7024051	1(4)	29/32	Flush	Index	.050	(8)	.115	—	.015	.030
	7024054	1	29/32	Flush	Index	.050	(8)	.190	—	.015	.030
	7024055	1	29/32	Flush	Index	.050	(8)	.190	—	.015	.030
	7024153	1(4)	29/32	Flush	Index	.050	(8)	.115	—	.015	.030
	7024154	1(4)	29/32	Flush	Index	.050	(8)	.115	—	.015	.030
1965	7025050	1(7)	29/32	Flush	1 Rich	.050	1100(3)	.120	—	.015	.030
	7025051	1(7)	29/32	Flush	1 Rich	.050	1100(3)	.120	—	.015	.030
	7025054	1(7)	29/32	Flush	1 Rich	.050	1100(3)	.120	—	.015	.030
	7025055	1(7)	29/32	Flush	1 Rich	.050	1100(3)	.120	—	.015	.030
	7025150	1(7)	29/32	Flush	1 Rich	.050	1100(3)	.120	—	.015	.030
	7025151	1(7)	29/32	Flush	1 Rich	.050	1100(3)	.120	—	.015	.030

ROCHESTER 4GC ADJUSTMENT SPECIFICATIONS (Except Float Data)—Continued

See Tune Up Chart in Car Chapters for Hot Idle Speeds.

Year	Carb. Part No.①	Pump Rod	Idle Vent	Intermediate Choke Rod	Auto. Choke	Choke Rod	Fast Idle Speed	Choke Unloader	Anti-Stall Dashpot	Secondary	
										Lockout	Contour
OLDSMOBILE—Continued											
1965	7025157	1⑦	29/32	Flush	1 Rich	.050	1100③	.120	—	.015	.030
	7025158	1⑦	29/32	Flush	1 Rich	.050	1100③	.120	—	.015	.030
	7025255	1⑦	29/32	Flush	1 Rich	.050	1100③	.120	—	.015	.030
PONTIAC											
1963	7023069	15/16④	27/32	Flush	Index	.030	2800	.150	—	.030	.015
	7023070	15/16④	27/32	Flush	Index	.030	3000	.150	—	.030	.015

①—Located on tag attached to or stamped on carburetor.
②—In center hole.
③—On low step of cam.
④—In inner hole.
⑤—Second step of cam.
⑥—High step of cam.
⑦—In outer hole.
⑧—Three-step cam 700, four-step cam 1000.

4GC ADJUSTMENTS

These carburetors are four-barrel units that provide the advantages of two 2-barrel carburetors in one housing. The 4G model has a manually-operated choke while the 4GC has a completely automatic choke. Fig. 44 illustrates a "Low Silhouette" 4GC unit with the automatic choke mounted on the throttle body. The standard 4GC has the choke mounted on the carburetor air horn. Fig. 45 is an exploded view of one of these carburetors.

The carburetor is divided into a primary and secondary side. The primary side covers the forward half of the unit and is essentially a complete two-bore carburetor containing a float system, adjustable idle system, main metering system, pump system, power system, and choke system.

The secondary side is a supplementary two-bore carburetor that feeds extra air and fuel to the engine when needed for power requirements. This section contains only a float system, main metering system and, on some applications, a fixed idle system. It also has a set of throttle valves and separate auxiliary valves that are located in the bores above the throttle valves.

Both high and low float bowl designs are used in these carburetors. The type used is dependent upon engine demands and underhood clearance. Both round and "D" shaped float pontoons are used in the high float bowl. A smaller wedge-shaped float is used in the low bowl design.

Float assist springs are used on some high bowl and all low bowl applications. Their purpose is to assist the floats in holding the float needle valve closed, especially where fuel pressures are encountered.

Fig. 46 shows an idle compensator valve used on some standard and air-conditioned models. A thermostatic valve mounted on the secondary side of the float bowl between secondary venturi, allows additional air to enter the primary bores under extreme "hot idle" conditions.

Some 4GC models use an idle air by-pass system, Fig. 47. The purpose of this system is to allow the primary throttle valves to be completely closed during curb idle operation. The design prevents carbon and gum formations which may form around the throttle valves from disrupting engine idle speed.

There are three designs of automatic choke systems used on 4GC carburetors: 1) the conventional system mounted on the carburetor; 2) the split linkage system, and 3) the hot water system. All three of these systems are illustrated and described briefly in the Rochester two-barrel carburetor section of this chapter.

Float Level Adjustment

Fig. 48—With air horn inverted and gasket in place, gauge from gasket surface to top of each float next to seam.

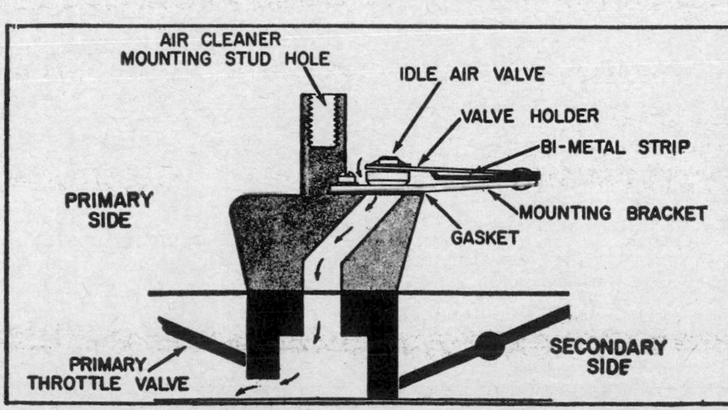

Fig. 46 Hot idle compensator on some 4GC carburetors

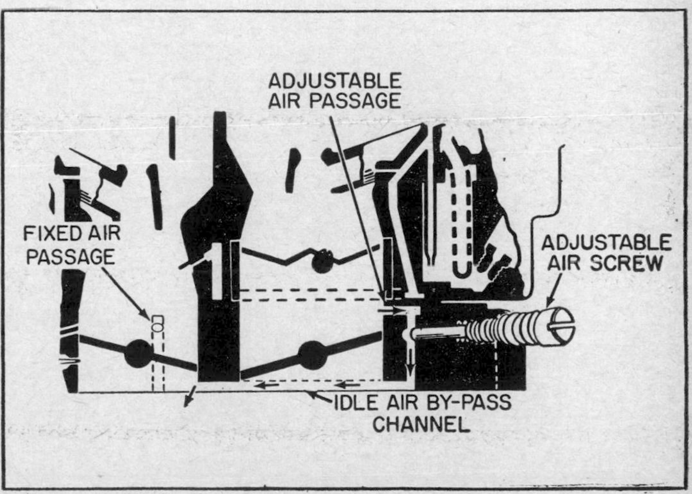

Fig. 47 Idle air by-pass system on some 4GC carburetors

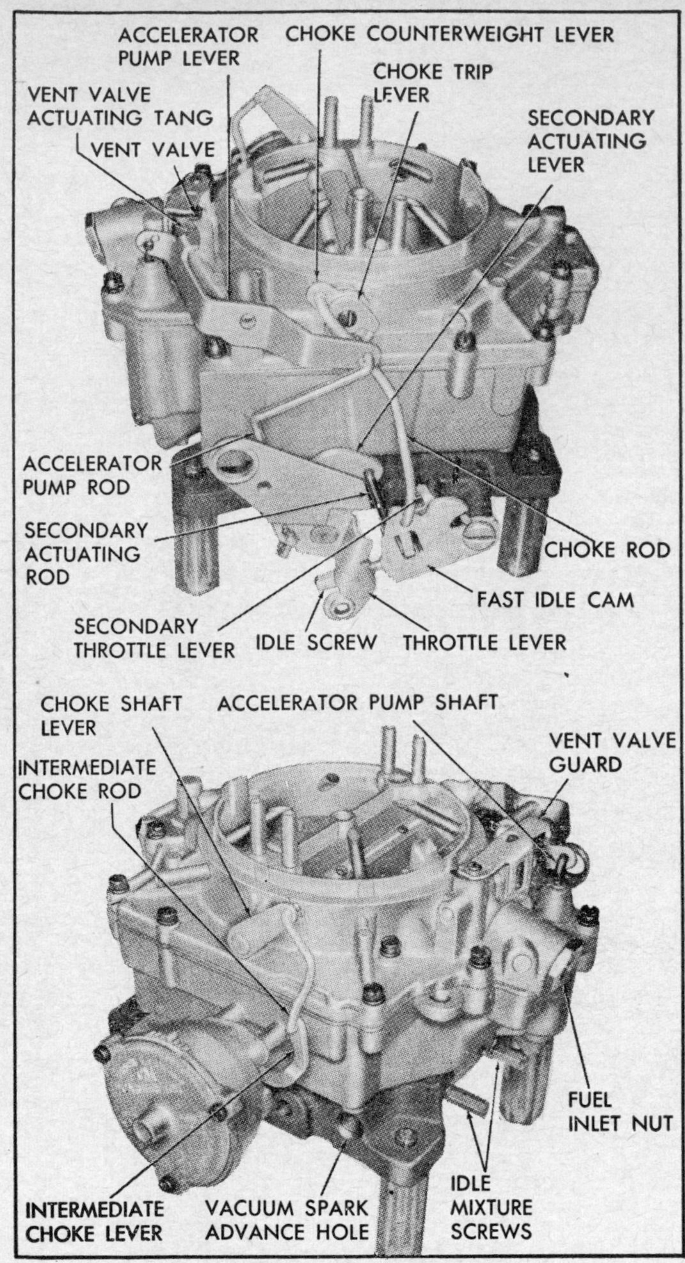

Fig. 44 Rochester 4GC "Low Silhouette" four-barrel carburetor

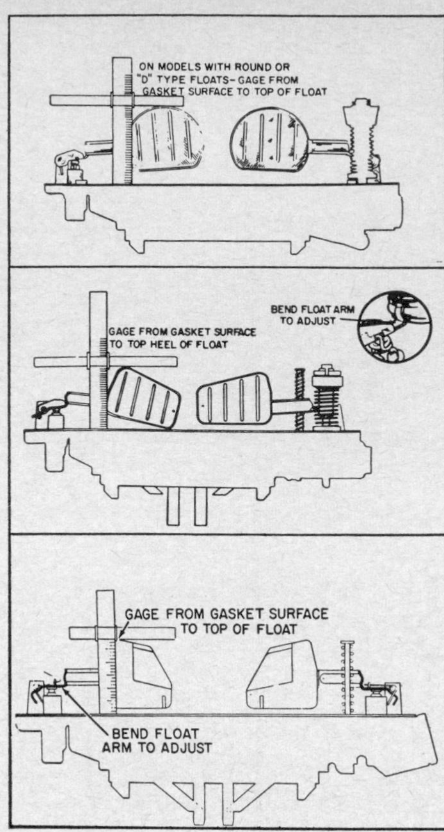

Fig. 48 Float level adjustment on 4GC carburetors

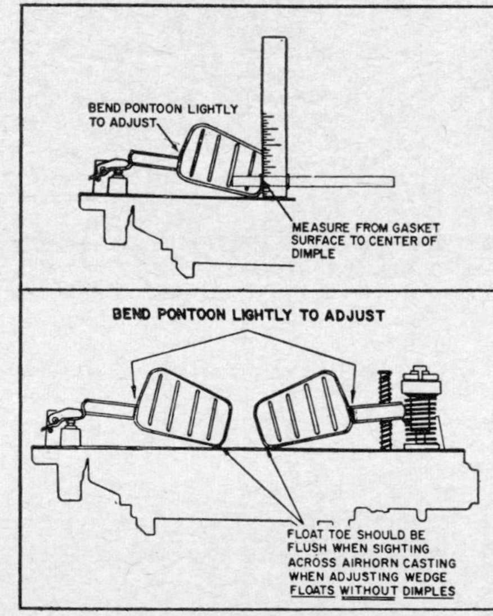

Fig. 49 Float toe adjustment on 4GC carburetors

Adjust to specified dimension by bending float arms at junction point near needle and seat (see *Rochester Specifications Chart*).

Float Toe Adjustment

Fig. 49—With air horn inverted and gasket in place, measure distance from gasket to center of dimple of each float at toe (small end). Adjust to specified dimension by bending toe of each float up or down as required (see *Rochester Specifications Chart*).

NOTE: Wedge type floats that do not have dimples in sides of floats should be adjusted so lower tip of float toe is flush with air horn casting when sighting across air horn casting as shown in lower view, Fig. 49.

Float Alignment

Fig. 50—Align screw holes in air horn gasket with screw holes in air horn. Then make sure floats are centered in the cut-out section of gasket and sides of float pontoons are parallel with adjacent edges of gasket. Bend float arms as necessary to adjust.

Float Drop Adjustment

Fig. 51—With air horn upright and level, gasket in place and floats hanging freely, measure distance on each float from gasket surface to center of dimple, or bottom of scribe line (wedge floats). Measure to lower edge of toe for wedge floats without dimple. Measure to lowest point on "D" or round pontoon floats. Adjust to specified dimension by bending tang that contacts seat or spring (see *Rochester Specifications Chart*).

Vacuum Assist Spring Adjustment

Fig. 52—With air horn held upright and level, hold power piston in full up position (with thumb). Jounce pontoon light-

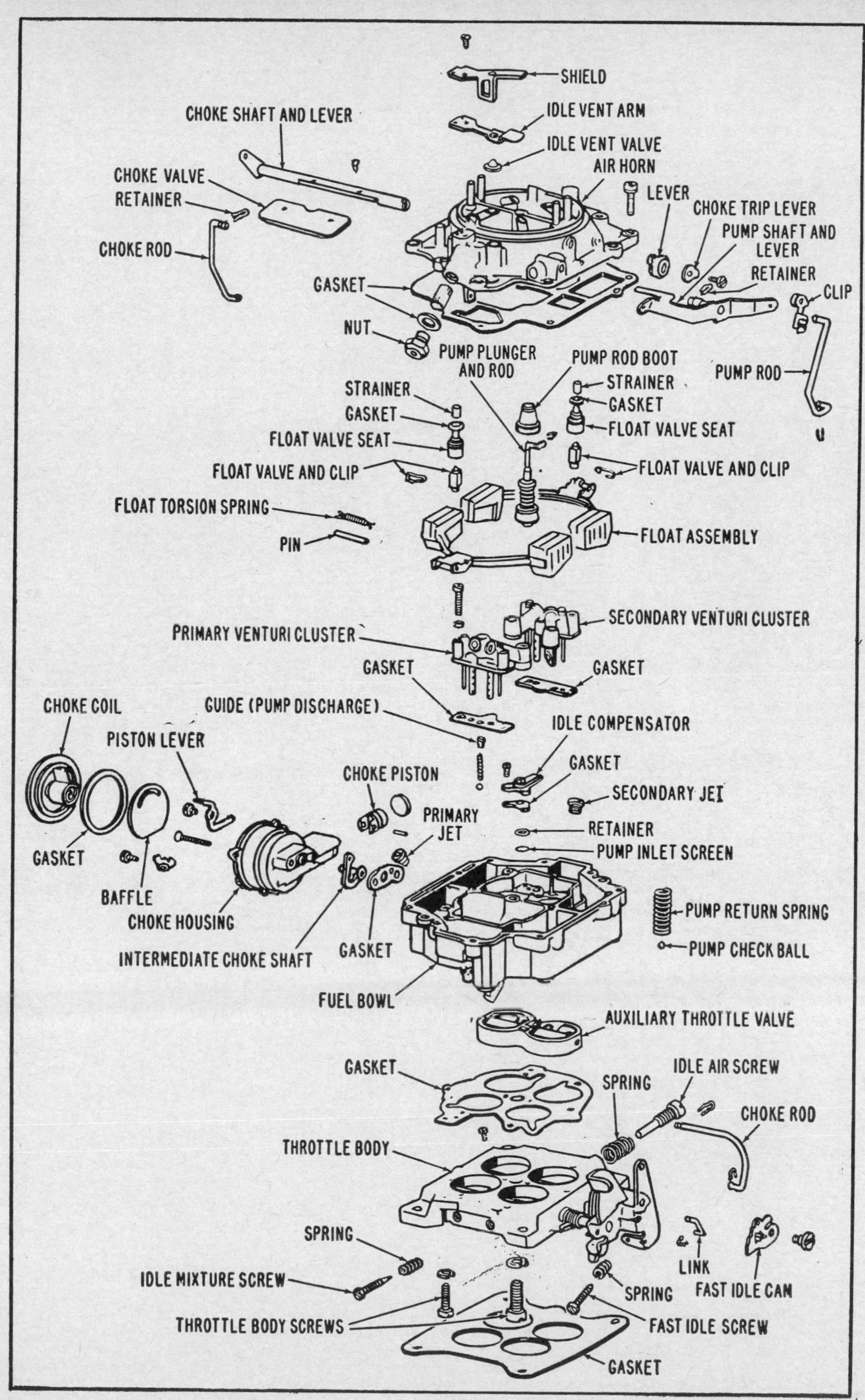

Fig. 45 Exploded view of Rochester 4GC carburetor

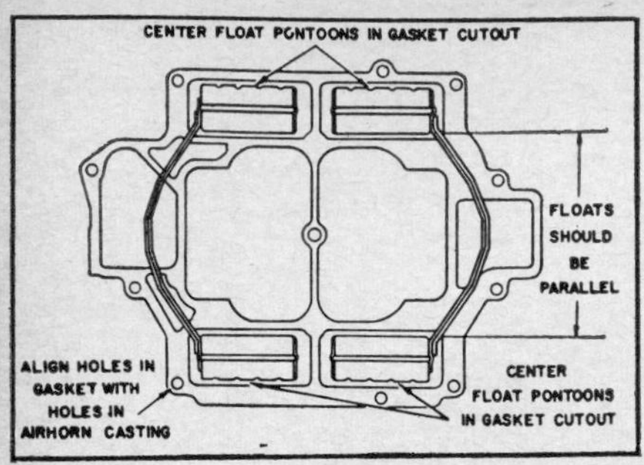

Fig. 50 Float alignment on 4GC carburetors

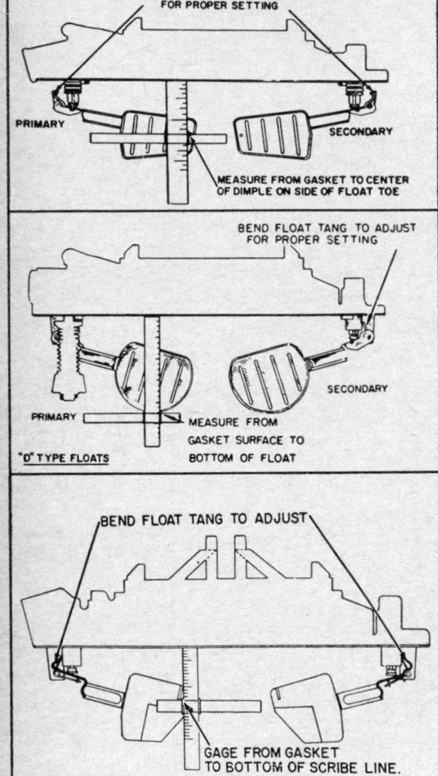

Fig. 51 Float drop adjustment on 4GC carburetors

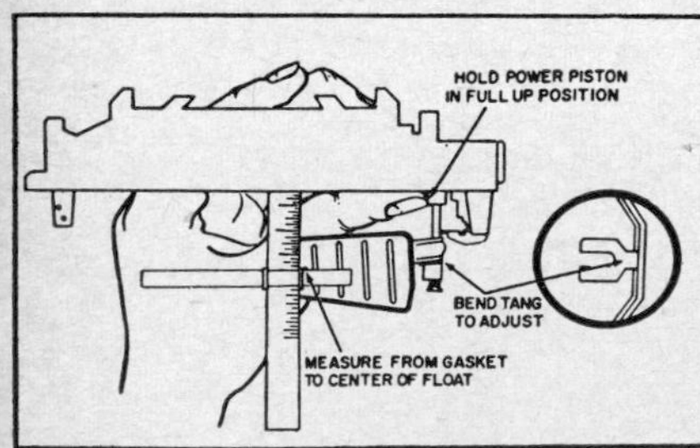

Fig. 52 Vacuum assist spring adjustment on 4GC carburetors

ly to make sure cup retainer on vacuum assist spring is not binding on power piston stem. Measure distance from gasket to center of dimple on float pontoon at toe. To adjust, bend tang at center of float arms (see *Rochester Specifications Chart*). *Always hold power piston in "up" position.*

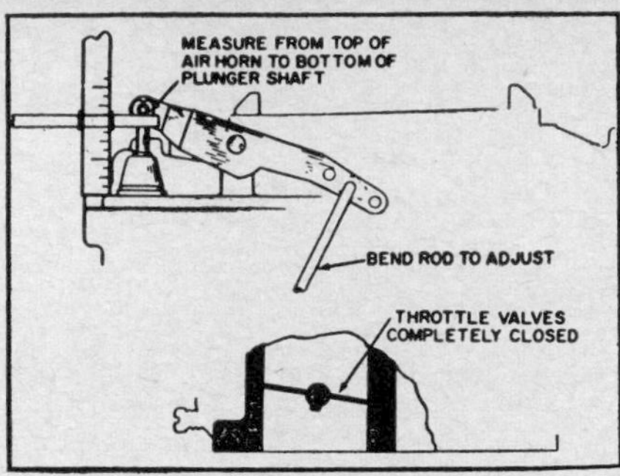

Fig. 53 Pump rod adjustment on 4GC carburetors

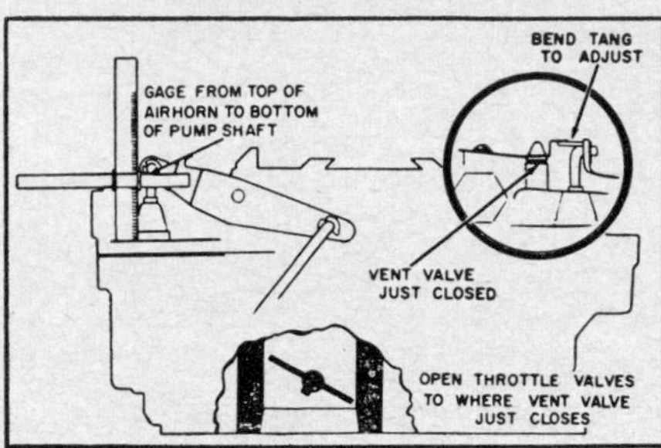

Fig. 54 Idle vent adjustment on 4GC carburetors

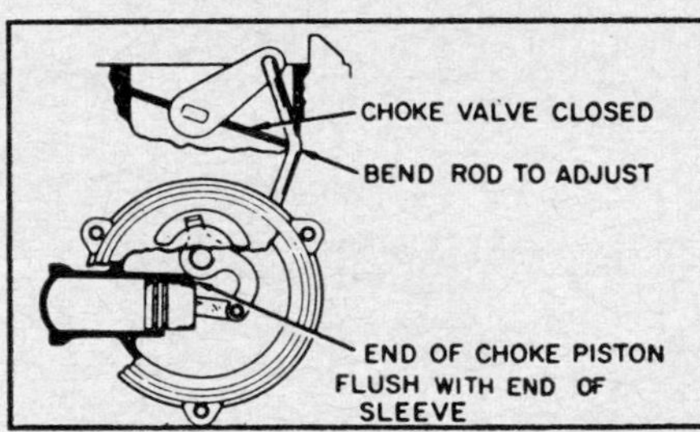

Fig. 55 Intermediate choke rod adjustment on some 4GC carburetors

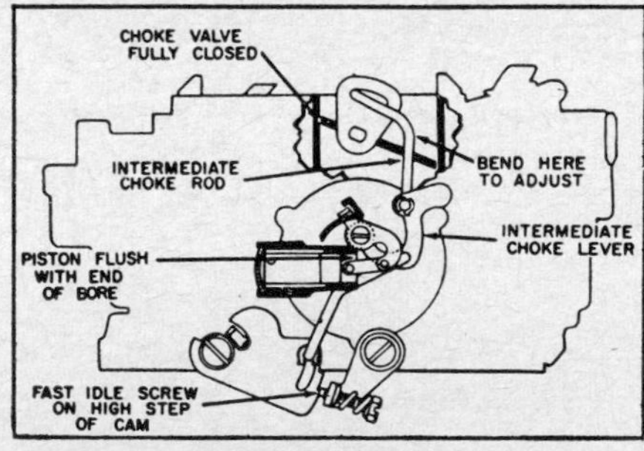

Fig. 56 Intermediate choke adjustment on some 4GC carburetors

Pump Rod Adjustment

Fig. 53—Install pump rod in hole specified for model being serviced. Back out slow idle screw until throttle valves are completely closed. Place proper size gauge on top of air horn next to pump plunger. With throttle valves closed and lower edge of gauge resting on top of air horn, distance from top of air horn to bottom of pump plunger shaft should be as specified in the *Rochester Specifications Chart*. Bend pump rod to adjust.

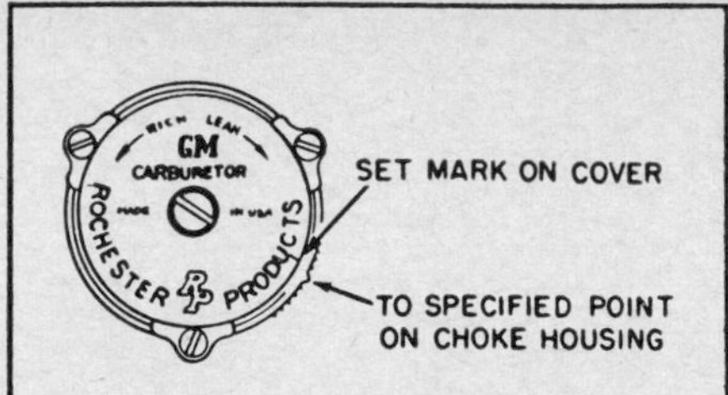

Fig. 57 Automatic choke adjustment on 4GC carburetors

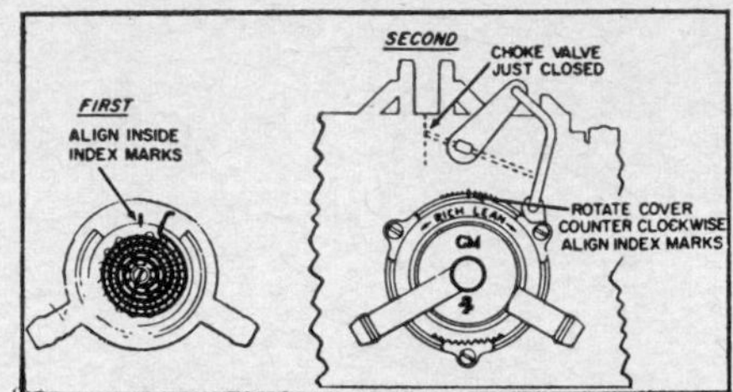

Fig. 58 Hot water choke coil adjustment on some 4GC carburetors

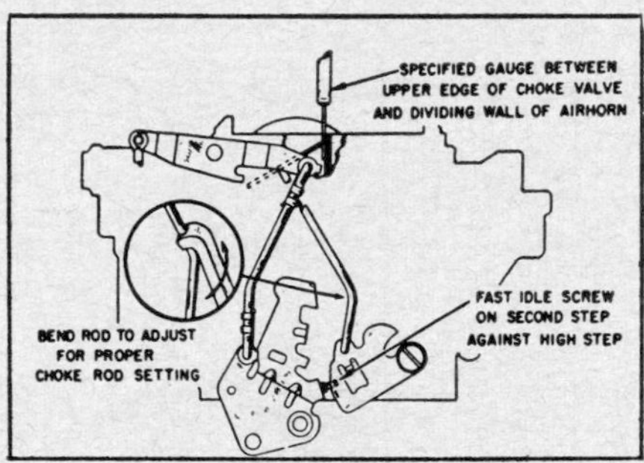

Fig. 59 Choke rod adjustment for chokes mounted on air horn. 4GC carburetors

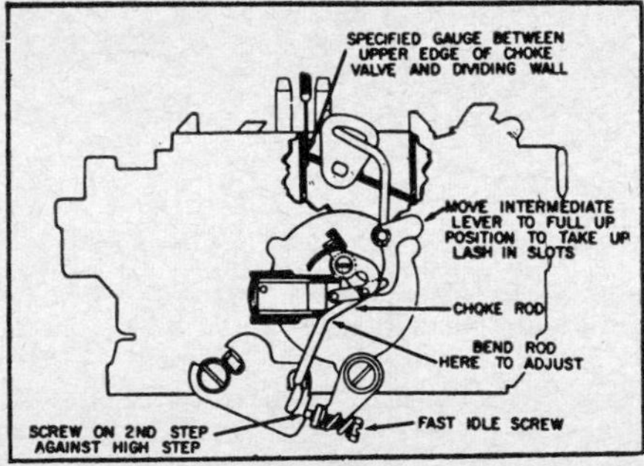

Fig. 60 Choke rod adjustment for chokes mounted on throttle body. 4GC carburetors

NOTE: After adjusting pump rod to the specified dimension, the rod can be moved to the inboard hole (where used) for richer pump discharge or to the outboard hole (where used) for leaner pump discharge.

Idle Vent Adjustment

Fig. 54—After making pump adjustment, open throttle valves enough to obtain the specified measurement from air horn to

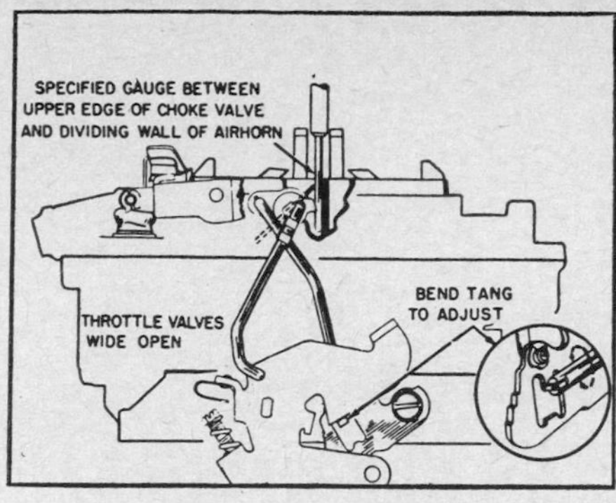

Fig. 61 Choke unloader adjustment on 4GC carburetors

Fig. 62 Secondary lockout adjustment on 4GC carburetors

bottom of pump plunger shaft. At this point the idle vent should just close. To adjust, bend tang on pump lever as shown.

On older models, adjust by bending tang that contacts face of valve under pump lever.

Intermediate Choke Rod Adjustment

Fig. 55—This applies only to models with the choke mounted on throttle body or bowl. Holding choke valve closed, bend intermediate choke rod as necessary so that end of choke piston is flush with end of choke piston sleeve.

Intermediate Choke Adjustment

Fig. 56—Place fast idle screw on high step of fast idle cam and raise intermediate choke lever to its full up position. Be sure all lash is removed from rods in slots. The choke piston should be flush with end of choke piston bore. Bend intermediate choke rod to position the choke piston correctly.

Automatic Choke Adjustment

Fig. 57—Loosen three retaining screws and rotate choke cover against coil tension until index mark on cover is aligned with specified mark on housing (see *Rochester Specifications Chart*).

Hot Water Choke Coil Adjustment

Fig. 58—There are two adjustments necessary to provide proper choke indexing. The inner choke cover containing the thermostatic coil must be indexed with the outer cover. This indexing can be accomplished by aligning the scribe mark on the inner cover with the index point on the outer cover as shown. The complete choke cover assembly has a scribe mark on the outside which must be aligned with the proper indexing point on the choke housing (see *Rochester Specifications Chart*).

Choke Rod Adjustment

Models With Air Horn Mounted Chokes, Fig. 59—It is important to position both slow idle and fast idle before making the choke rod adjustment.

1. On models having a single idle screw, turn stop screw in until it contacts bottom step of fast idle cam. Then turn screw in one full turn.
2. On models using a separate fast idle screw, turn slow idle stop screw in until it touches the stop, then turn screw in one additional turn. Turn fast idle screw in until it touches bottom step of fast idle cam.
3. After positioning slow and fast idle screws, position idle screw on second step of fast idle cam against shoulder of high step. Then check clearance between upper edge of choke valve and air horn wall (see *Rochester Specifications Chart*). To adjust, bend choke rod as required.

Models With Intermediate Choke Rod, Fig. 60 — Position slow and fast idle screws as outlined above. Then position fast idle screw on second step of fast idle cam and raise intermediate choke lever to the full open position. Be sure intermediate rod and choke rod are at the upper limit of travel in the slots. Adjust choke rod by bending to obtain the specified clearance between choke valve and the dividing wall of air horn (see *Rochester Specifications Chart*).

Choke Unloader Adjustment

Fig. 61 Fully open primary throttle valves. While holding lever in this position, check for specified clearance between upper edge of choke valve and air horn wall (see *Rochester Specifications Chart*). To adjust, bend unloader tang on fast idle cam.

On a few models, this adjustment is made by bending unloader tang on pump lever.

Fig. 63 Secondary contour adjustment on 4GC carburetors

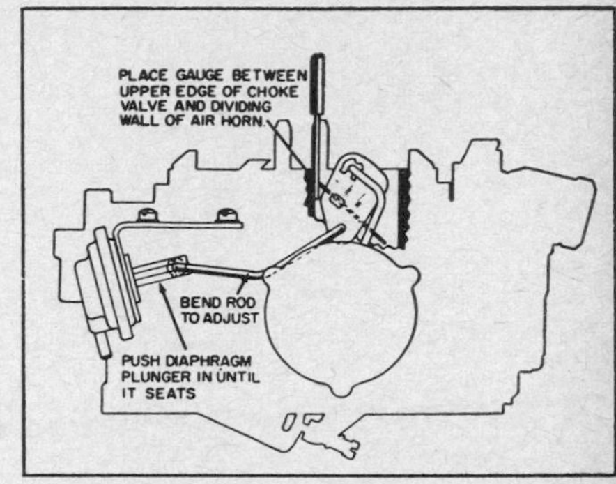

Fig. 64 Vacuum break adjustment on some 4GC carburetors

Secondary Lockout Adjustment

Fig. 62—With choke valve fully closed, bend lockout lever as shown to obtain specified clearance between the cam and widest surface of lockout lever (see *Rochester Specifications Chart*).

Secondary Contour Adjustment

Fig. 63—With choke valve wide open, bend lockout lever to obtain specified clearance between the cam and narrowest surface of lockout lever at point shown *(see Rochester Specifications Chart)*.

Vacuum Break Adjustment

Fig. 64—Push diaphragm plunger in until it seats. While holding plunger sealed, close choke valve to the point where vacuum diaphragm connecting rod is in end of plunger. At this point, a .060" gauge should just fit between upper edge of choke valve and the dividing wall of air horn. To adjust for proper clearance, bend rod.

ROCHESTER QUADRAJET 4MC & 4MV ADJUSTMENT SPECIFICATIONS

See Tune Up Chart in car chapters for hot idle speeds.

Year	Carb. Model	Float Level	Pump Rod		Idle Vent	Air Valve	Fast Idle (Bench)	Choke Rod	Vacuum Break	Air Valve Dash-pot	Choke Unloader	Air Valve Lockout	Secondary Metering Rods	Air Valve Valve Spring Wind-Up
			Hole	Adj.										
BUICK														
1966	7026240	1/4	Inner	9/32	3/8	1 3/16	2 Turns	.140①	.230	1 1/16	.325	.030	53/64	5/8
	7026242	1/4	Inner	9/32	3/8	1 3/16	2 Turns	.140①	.230	1 1/16	.325	.030	53/64	5/8
	7036240	1/4	Inner	9/32	3/8	1 3/16	2 Turns	.140①	.230	1 1/16	.325	.030	53/64	5/8
	7036242	1/4	Inner	9/32	3/8	1 3/16	2 Turns	.140①	.230	1 3/16	.325	.030	53/64	5/8
1967	7027140	9/32	Inner	9/32	7/16	—	2 Turns	.130	.200	.030	.325	.045	53/64	1/2
	7027141	9/32	Outer	13/32	7/16	—	2 Turns	.130	.200	.030	.325	.045	53/64	1/2
	7027146	7/32	Outer	9/32	1/2	—	2 Turns	.130	.200	.030	.325	.045	53/64	1/2
	7027147	7/32	Outer	13/32	1/2	—	2 Turns	.130	.200	.030	.325	.045	53/64	1/2
	7027148	7/32	Inner	9/32	3/8	—	2 Turns	.130	.215	.030	.325	.015	53/64	1/2
	7027149	7/32	Inner	9/32	3/8	—	2 Turns	.130	.215	.030	.325	.015	53/64	1/2
	7027240	9/32	Inner	9/32	7/16	—	2 Turns	.130	.200	.030	.325	.045	53/64	1/2
	7027241	9/32	Outer	13/32	7/16	—	2 Turns	.130	.200	.030	.325	.045	53/64	1/2
	7027244	1/4	Outer	13/32	1/2	—	2 Turns	.130	.200	.030	.325	.045	53/64	1/2
	7027246	1/4	Inner	9/32	3/8	—	2 Turns	.120	.215	.030	.325	—	53/64	1/2
	7027248	5/16	Inner	9/32	7/16	—	2 Turns	.120	.200	.030	.325	.045	53/64	1/2
1968	7028240	②	③	④	1/2	—	2 Turns	.130	.200	.030	.325	.045	53/64	1/2
	7028242	3/8	Inner	9/32	1/2	—	2 Turns	.130	.180	.030	.325	.045	53/64	1/2
	7028243	7/16	Outer	11/32	1/2	—	2 Turns	.140	.215	.030	.325	—	53/64	1/2
	7028244	5/16	Outer	13/32	1/2	—	2 Turns	.130	.200	.030	.325	.045	53/64	1/2
	7028245	5/16	Outer	13/32	1/2	—	2 Turns	.130	.215	.030	.325	—	53/64	1/2
	7028248	9/32	Outer	13/32	1/2	—	2 Turns	.130	.180	.030	.325	.045	53/64	1/2
1969	7029240	3/8	Outer	13/32	1/2	—	—	.130	.180	.030	.325	.045	53/64	1/2
	7029241	5/16	Outer	13/32	1/2	—	—	.130	.180	.030	.325	.045	53/64	1/2
	7029242	3/8	Outer	13/32	1/2	—	—	.130	.180	.030	.325	.045	53/64	1/2
	7029243	3/8	Outer	13/32	1/2	—	—	.140	.215	.030	.325	.015	53/64	1/2
	7029244	5/16	Outer	13/32	1/2	—	—	.130	.190	.030	.325	.045	53/64	1/2
	7029245	5/16	Outer	13/32	1/2	—	—	.130	.215	.030	.325	.015	53/64	1/2

①—4MC carburetor; set choke thermostat cover on index mark. ②—Early 3/8″; late 7/16″. ③—Early, inner; late, outer.
④—Early 9/32″; late 13/32″.

Year	Carb. Model	Float Level	Pump Rod Hole	Pump Rod Adj.	Idle Vent	Air Valve	Fast Idle (Bench)	Choke Rod	Vacuum Break	Air Valve Dash-pot	Choke Unloader	Air Valve Lockout	Secondary Metering Rods	Air Valve Valve Spring Wind-Up
CADILLAC														
1967	7027230	1/4	Outer	11/16	—	—	1 Turn	.090	.180	.030	.300	.015	55/64	1/4
	7027231	1/4	Outer	11/16	—	—	1 Turn	.090	.180	.030	.300	.015	55/64	1/4
	7027233	1/4	Outer	11/16	—	—	1 Turn	.090	.180	.030	.300	.015	55/64	1/4
	7027234	1/4	Outer	11/16	—	—	1 Turn	.090	.180	.030	.300	.015	55/64	1/4
	7027235	1/4	Outer	11/16	—	—	1 Turn	.090	.180	.030	.300	.015	55/64	1/4
	7037230	1/4	Outer	11/32	—	—	1 Turn	.090	.180	.030	.300	.015	55/64	1/4
	7037231	1/4	Outer	11/32	—	—	1 Turn	.090	.180	.030	.300	.015	55/64	1/4
	7037234	1/4	Outer	11/32	—	—	1 Turn	.090	.180	.030	.300	.015	55/64	1/4
	7037235	1/4	Outer	11/32	—	—	1 Turn	.090	.180	.030	.300	.015	55/64	1/4
1968	7028230	1/4	Outer	11/32	—	—	1 1/2 Turns	.090	.180	.030	.300	.030	55/64	1/2
	7028231	1/4	Outer	11/32	—	—	1 1/2 Turns	.090	.180	.030	.300	.030	55/64	1/2
	7028234	11/32	Outer	11/32	—	—	1 1/2 Turns	.090	.180	.030	.300	.030	55/64	7/16
	7028235	11/32	Outer	11/32	—	—	1 1/2 Turns	.090	.180	.030	.300	.030	55/64	7/16
	7028236	1/4	Outer	11/32	—	—	1 1/2 Turns	.090	.215	.030	.300	.030	55/64	1/2
	7028237	1/4	Outer	11/32	—	—	1 1/2 Turns	.090	.215	.030	.300	.030	55/64	1/2
	7028238	11/32	Outer	11/32	—	—	1 1/2 Turns	.090	.215	.030	.300	.030	55/64	7/16
	7028239	11/32	Outer	11/32	—	—	1 1/2 Turns	.090	.215	.030	.300	.030	55/64	7/16
1969	Exc. Below	1/4	Outer	11/32	—	—	—	.090	.230	.030	.300	.015	.840	1/2
	Eldorado	11/32	Outer	11/32	—	—	—	.090	.230	.030	.300	.015	.840	1/2

ROCHESTER QUADRAJET 4MC & 4MV ADJUSTMENT SPECIFICATIONS—Continued

See Tune Up Chart in car chapters for hot idle speeds.

Year	Carb. Model	Float Level	Pump Rod		Idle Vent	Air Valve	Fast Idle (Bench)	Choke Rod	Vacuum Break	Air Valve Dash-pot	Choke Unloader	Air Valve Lockout	Secondary Metering Rods	Air Valve Valve Spring Wind-Up
			Hole	Adj.										
CHEVROLET ENGINES														
1965	7025200	3/16	Inner	9/32	13/32	1 1/16	2 Turns	.150	.160	—	.325	—	27/32	1
	7025201	3/16	Inner	9/32	13/32	1 1/16	2 Turns	.150	.245	—	.325	—	27/32	1
	7025220	3/16	Inner	9/32	13/32	1 1/16	2 Turns	.120	.160	—	.325	—	27/32	1
	7025221	3/16	Inner	9/32	13/32	1 1/16	2 Turns	.120	.245	—	.325	—	27/32	1
1966	7026200	1/4	Inner	9/32	3/8	1 1/4	2 Turns	.100	.160	—	.300	.015	27/32	1
	7026201	1/4	Inner	9/32	3/8	1 1/4	2 Turns	.100	.245	—	.300	—	27/32	1
	7026202	1/4	Inner	9/32	3/8	1 1/8	2 Turns	.110	.150	—	.245	.015	53/64	1
	7026203	1/4	Inner	9/32	3/8	1 1/8	2 Turns	.110	.200	—	.300	—	53/64	1
	7026204	1/4	Inner	9/32	3/8	1 1/4	2 Turns	.100	.160	—	.300	.015	27/32	1
	7026205	1/4	Inner	9/32	3/8	1 1/4	2 Turns	.100	.245	—	.300	—	27/32	1
	7026210	1/4	Inner	9/32	3/8	1 1/8	2 Turns	.110	.150	—	.245	.015	53/64	1
	7036200	1/4	Inner	9/32	3/8	1 1/4	2 Turns	.100	.160	—	.300	.015	27/32	1
	7036201	1/4	Inner	9/32	3/8	1 1/4	2 Turns	.100	.245	—	.300	—	27/32	1
	7036202	1/4	Inner	9/32	3/8	1 1/8	2 Turns	.110	.150	—	.245	.015	53/64	1
	7036203	1/4	Inner	9/32	3/8	1 1/8	2 Turns	.110	.200	—	.300	—	53/64	1
	7036204	1/4	Inner	9/32	3/8	1 1/4	2 Turns	.100	.160	—	.300	.015	27/32	1
	7036205	1/4	Inner	9/32	3/8	1 1/4	2 Turns	.100	.245	—	.300	—	27/32	1
	7036210	1/4	Inner	9/32	3/8	1 1/8	2 Turns	.110	.150	—	.245	.015	53/64	1
1967	7027200	9/32	—	9/32	3/8	—	2 Turns	.100	.160	.015	.180	.015	27/32	7/8
	7027201	9/32	—	9/32	3/8	—	2 Turns	.100	.245	.015	.180	—	27/32	7/8
	7027202	9/32	—	9/32	3/8	—	2 Turns	.110	.160	.015	.180	.015	27/[illegible]	7/8
	7027203	9/32	—	9/32	3/8	—	2 Turns	.100	.200	.015	.180	—	27/32	7/8
	7027210	3/16	Inner	9/32	3/8	—	2 Turns	.100	.160	.015	.180	.015	27/32	7/8
	7027211	3/16	Inner	9/32	3/8	—	2 Turns	.100	.245	.015	.180	—	27/32	7/8
	7027212	9/32	Inner	9/32	3/8	—	2 Turns	.110	.160	.015	.180	.015	27/32	7/8
	7027213	9/32	Inner	9/32	3/8	—	2 Turns	.100	.200	.015	.180	—	27/32	7/8
	7027216	3/16	Inner	9/32	3/8	—	2 Turns	.100	.160	.015	.180	—	27/32	7/8
	7027218	9/32	Inner	9/32	3/8	—	2 Turns	.110	.160	.015	.180	—	27/32	7/8
	7037200	9/32	—	9/32	3/8	—	2 Turns	.100	.160	.015	.180	.015	27/32	7/8
	7037201	9/32	—	9/32	3/8	—	2 Turns	.100	.245	.015	.180	—	27/32	7/8
	7037202	9/32	—	9/32	3/8	—	2 Turns	.110	.160	.015	.180	.015	27/32	7/8
	7037203	9/32	—	9/32	3/8	—	2 Turns	.110	.230	.015	.180	—	27/32	7/8
	7037210	3/16	Inner	9/32	3/8	—	2 Turns	.100	.160	.015	.180	.015	27/32	7/8
	7037211	3/16	Inner	9/32	3/8	—	2 Turns	.100	.245	.015	.180	—	27/32	7/8
	7037212	9/32	Inner	9/32	3/8	—	2 Turns	.110	.160	.015	.180	.015	27/32	7/8
	7037213	9/32	Inner	9/32	3/8	—	2 Turns	.110	.230	.015	.180	—	27/32	7/8
	7037216													
	7037218													
1968	7028212	1/4	Inner	9/32	3/8	—	2 Turns	.100	.180	.015	.260	.010	27/32	3/8
	7028213	1/4	Inner	9/32	3/8	—	2 Turns	.100	.245	.015	.300	.010	27/32	3/8
	7028229	1/4	Inner	9/32	3/8	—	2 Turns	.100	.245	.015	.300	.010	27/32	7/8
	7028208	1/4	Inner	9/32	3/8	—	2 Turns	.100	.180	.015	.260	.010	27/32	3/8
	7028207	1/4	Inner	9/32	3/8	—	2 Turns	.100	.245	.015	.300	.010	27/32	3/8
	7028219	1/4	Inner	9/32	3/8	—	2 Turns	.100	.245	.015	.300	.010	27/32	7/8
	7028218	3/16	Inner	9/32	3/8	—	2 Turns	.100	.160	.015	.300	.010	27/32	7/8
	7028217	3/16	Inner	9/32	3/8	—	2 Turns	.100	.245	.015	.300	.010	27/32	7/8
	7028210	3/16	Inner	9/32	3/8	—	2 Turns	.100	.160	.015	.300	.010	27/32	7/8
	7028211	3/16	Inner	9/32	3/8	—	2 Turns	.100	.245	.015	.300	.010	27/32	7/8
	7028216	3/16	Inner	9/32	3/8	—	2 Turns	.100	.160	.015	.300	.010	27/32	7/8
	7028209	3/16	Inner	9/32	3/8	—	2 Turns	.100	.245	.015	.300	.010	27/32	7/8
1969	7029202	7/32	Inner	5/16	3/8	—	2 Turns	.100	.180	.015	.450	.015	—	7/16
	7029203	7/32	Inner	5/16	3/8	—	2 Turns	.100	.245	.015	.450	.015	—	7/16
	7029204	1/4	Inner	5/16	3/8	—	2 Turns	.100	.180	.015	.450	.015	—	13/16
	7029207	3/16	Inner	5/16	3/8	—	2 Turns	.100	.245	.015	.450	.015	—	13/16
	7029215	1/4	Inner	5/16	3/8	—	2 Turns	.100	.245	.015	.450	.015	—	13/16

ROCHESTER QUADRAJET 4MC & 4MV ADJUSTMENT SPECIFICATIONS—Continued

See Tune Up Chart in car chapters for hot idle speeds.

OLDSMOBILE

Year	Carb. Model	Float Level	Pump Rod Hole	Pump Rod Adj.	Idle Vent	Air Valve	Fast Idle (Bench)	Choke Rod	Vacuum Break	Air Valve Dash-pot	Choke Unloader	Air Valve Lockout	Secondary Metering Rods	Air Valve Valve Spring Wind-Up
1966	7026250	11/32	Inner	9/32	3/8	1 1/8	2 Turns	.120	.190	—	.300	.015	7/8	3/4
	7026254	11/32	Inner	9/32	3/8	1 1/8	2 Turns	.130	.200	—	.300	.015	7/8	1/2
	7026255	11/32	Inner	9/32	3/8	1 1/8	2 Turns	.130	.200	—	.300	.015	7/8	5/8
	7026256	11/32	Inner	9/32	3/8	1 1/8	2 Turns	.120	.190	—	.300	.015	7/8	3/4
	7036250	11/32	Inner	9/32	3/8	1 1/8	2 Turns	.120	.190	—	.300	.015	7/8	3/4
	7036254	11/32	Inner	9/32	3/8	1 1/8	2 Turns	.130	.200	—	.300	.015	7/8	1/2
1967	7027032	1/4	Inner	5/16	3/8	—	2 Turns	.140	.200	.030	.325	.020	7/8	3/4
	7027036	1/4	Inner	5/16	3/8	—	2 Turns	.140	.200	.030	.325	.020	7/8	1/2
	7027130	1/4	Inner	5/16	3/8	—	2 Turns	.140	.200	.030	.325	.020	7/8	3/4
	7027131	1/4	Inner	5/16	3/8	—	2 Turns	.140	.200	.030	.325	.020	7/8	3/4
	7027132	1/4	Inner	5/16	3/8	—	2 Turns	.140	.200	.030	.325	.020	7/8	3/4
	7027135	1/4	Inner	5/16	3/8	—	2 Turns	.140	.200	.030	.325	.020	7/8	1/2
	7027153	1/4	Inner	5/16	3/8	—	2 Turns	.140	.200	.030	.325	.020	7/8	1/2
	7027156	1/4	Inner	5/16	3/8	—	2 Turns	.140	.200	.030	.325	.020	7/8	3/4
	7027157	1/4	Inner	5/16	3/8	—	2 Turns	.140	.200	.030	.325	.020	7/8	3/4
1968	7028250	1/4	—	5/16	—	—	—	.140	.180	.030	.200	.020	—	1/2
	7028251	1/4	—	5/16	—	—	—	.140	.180	.030	.200	.020	—	3/4
	7028252	1/4	—	5/16	—	—	—	.140	.180	.030	.200	.020	—	3/4
1969	7029250	1/4	Inner	5/16	—	—	—	.140	—	.030	.200	.020	—	1/2
	7029251	1/4	Inner	5/16	—	—	—	.140	—	.030	.200	.020	—	3/4
	7029252	1/4	Inner	5/16	—	—	—	.140	—	.030	.200	.020	—	3/4
	7029253	1/4	Outer	3/8	—	—	—	.120	—	.050	.200	.020	—	3/4
	7029254	1/4	Inner	5/16	—	—	—	.140	—	.030	.200	.020	—	3/4
	7029255	1/4	Inner	5/16	—	—	—	.090	—	.050	.200	.020	—	3/4

PONTIAC

Year	Carb. Model	Float Level	Pump Rod Hole	Pump Rod Adj.	Idle Vent	Air Valve	Fast Idle (Bench)	Choke Rod	Vacuum Break	Air Valve Dash-pot	Choke Unloader	Air Valve Lockout	Secondary Metering Rods	Air Valve Valve Spring Wind-Up
1966	7026260	7/32	Inner	9/32	3/8	1 1/8	2 Turns	.090	.140	.030	.300	.015	53/64	1/2
	7026261	7/32	Inner	9/32	3/8	1 1/8	2 Turns	.090	.140	.030	.300	.015	53/64	1/2
1967	7027260	7/32	Inner	9/32	3/8	—	2 Turns	.085	.245	.030	.325	.020	53/64	1/2
	7027261	7/32	Inner	9/32	3/8	—	2 Turns	.085	.245	.030	.325	.020	53/64	1/2
	7027262	3/16	Inner	9/32	3/8	—	2 Turns	.040	.160	.030	.325	.020	53/64	1/2
	7027263	3/16	Inner	9/32	3/8	—	2 Turns	.090	.230	.030	.325	.020	53/64	1/2
	7027268	3/16	Inner	9/32	3/8	—	2 Turns	.085	.245	.030	.325	.020	53/64	1/2
	7027269	3/16	Inner	9/32	3/8	—	2 Turns	.085	.245	.030	.325	.020	53/64	1/2
	7027272	3/16	Inner	9/32	3/8	—	2 Turns	.085	.060	.030	.325	.020	53/64	1/2
	7027273	3/16	Inner	9/32	3/8	—	2 Turns	.090	.230	.030	.325	.020	53/64	1/2
	7037260	7/32	Inner	9/32	3/8	—	2 Turns	.085	.245	.030	.325	.020	53/64	1/2
	7037261	7/32	Inner	9/32	3/8	—	2 Turns	.085	.245	.030	.325	.020	53/64	1/2
	7037262	3/16	Inner	9/32	3/8	—	2 Turns	.040	.160	.030	.325	.020	53/64	1/2
	7037263	3/16	Inner	9/32	3/8	—	2 Turns	.090	.230	.030	.325	.020	53/64	1/2
	7037268	3/16	Inner	9/32	3/8	—	2 Turns	.085	.245	.030	.325	.020	53/64	1/2
	7037269	3/16	Inner	9/32	3/8	—	2 Turns	.085	.245	.030	.325	.020	53/64	1/2
	7037271	3/16	Inner	9/32	3/8	—	2 Turns	.085	.060	.030	.325	.020	53/64	1/2
	7037272	3/16	Inner	9/32	3/8	—	2 Turns	.085	.060	.030	.325	.020	53/64	1/2
	7037273	3/16	Inner	9/32	3/8	—	2 Turns	.090	.230	.030	.325	.020	53/64	1/2
	7037276	3/16	Inner	9/32	3/8	—	2 Turns	.085	.060	.030	.325	.020	53/64	1/2
1968	7028260	5/16	Inner	9/32	3/8	—	2 Turns	.085	.245	.030	.300	.015	53/64	1/2
	7028261	5/16	Inner	9/32	3/8	—	2 Turns	.085	.245	.030	.300	.015	53/64	1/2
	7028262	1/4	Inner	9/32	3/8	—	2 Turns	.100	.230	.030	.300	.015	53/64	1/2
	7028263	1/4	Inner	9/32	3/8	—	2 Turns	.100	.245	.030	.300	.015	53/64	1/2
	7028264	1/4	Inner	9/32	3/8	—	2 Turns	.100	.230	.030	.300	.015	53/64	1/2
	7028265	1/4	Inner	9/32	3/8	—	2 Turns	.100	.245	.030	.300	.015	53/64	1/2

ROCHESTER QUADRAJET 4MC & 4MV ADJUSTMENT SPECIFICATIONS—Continued

See Tune Up Chart in car chapters for hot idle speed.

Year	Carb. Model	Float Level	Pump Rod		Idle Vent	Air Valve	Fast Idle (Bench)	Choke Rod	Vacuum Break	Air Valve Dash-pot	Choke Unloader	Air Valve Lockout	Secondary Metering Rods	Air Valve Valve Spring Wind-Up
			Hole	Adj.										
PONTIAC—Continued														
1968	7028266	1/4	Inner	9/32	3/8	—	2 Turns	.100	.230	.030	.300	.015	53/64	1/2
	7028267	1/4	Inner	9/32	3/8	—	2 Turns	.100	.245	.030	.300	.015	53/64	1/2
	7028268	1/4	Inner	9/32	3/8	—	2 Turns	.100	.230	.030	.300	.015	53/64	1/2
	7028269	1/4	Inner	9/32	3/8	—	2 Turns	.100	.245	.030	.300	.015	53/64	1/2
	7028271	1/4	Inner	9/32	3/8	—	2 Turns	.100	.245	.030	.300	.015	53/64	1/2
	7028274	1/4	Inner	9/32	3/8	—	2 Turns	.100	.230	.030	.300	.015	53/64	1/2
	7028275	1/4	Inner	9/32	3/8	—	2 Turns	.100	.245	.030	.300	.015	53/64	1/2
	7028276	1/4	Inner	9/32	3/8	—	2 Turns	.100	.230	.030	.300	.015	53/64	1/2
	7028277	1/4	Inner	9/32	3/8	—	2 Turns	.100	.245	.030	.300	.015	53/64	1/2
1969	7028270	1/4	Inner	9/32	3/8	—	3 Turns	.100	.245	.030	.300	.015	53/64	1/2
	7028273	1/4	Inner	9/32	3/8	—	3 Turns	.100	.245	.030	.300	.015	53/64	1/2
	7029260	3/16	Inner	9/32	3/8	—	3 Turns	.100	.150	.030	.300	.015	53/64	1/2
	7029261	3/16	Inner	9/32	3/8	—	3 Turns	.100	.180	.030	.300	.015	53/64	1/2
	7029262	9/32	Inner	9/32	3/8	—	3 Turns	.100	.245	.030	.300	.015	53/64	1/2
	7029263	9/32	Inner	9/32	3/8	—	3 Turns	.100	.245	.030	.300	.015	53/64	1/2
	7029268	9/32	Inner	9/32	3/8	—	3 Turns	.100	.245	.030	.300	.015	53/64	1/2
	7029270	9/32	Inner	1/4	3/8	—	3 Turns	.100	.245	.030	.300	.015	53/64	1/2
	7029273	9/32	Inner	1/4	3/8	—	3 Turns	.100	.245	.030	.300	.015	53/64	1/2

QUADRAJET 4MV, 4MC ADJUSTMENTS

The Quadrajet unit, Figs. 65, 65A, has two stages in operation. The primary (fuel inlet) side has small bores with a triple venturi equipped with plain tube nozzles. The triple venturi feature, plus the smaller primary bores, give a more stable and finer fuel control in the idle and economy ranges of operation. Fuel metering in the primary side is accomplished with tapered metering rods positioned by a manifold vacuum responsive piston.

The secondary side has two very large bores which have greatly increased air capacity to meet all engine demands. The air valve principle is used in the secondary side for metering control and supplements fuel flow from the primary bores.

Using the air valve principle, fuel is metered in direct proportion to the air passing through the secondary bores.

The fuel reservoir is centrally located to avoid problems of fuel slosh causing engine turn cut-out and delayed fuel flow to the carburetor bores. The float system uses a single float pontoon for ease of service. The float needle valve is pressure balanced to overcome problems encountered with high fuel pump pressures and to permit use of a small float to control fuel "shut-off" through the large fuel inlet needle seat. It has a synthetic tip which gives added insurance against flooding problems caused by dirt.

The primary side of the carburetor has six systems of operation: float, idle, main metering, power, pump and choke. The secondary side has one metering system which supplements the primary main metering system and receives fuel from a common float chamber.

Model 4MV Choke System

Fig. 66—The choke system consists of a choke valve located in the primary air horn bore, a vacuum diaphragm unit, fast idle cam, connecting linkage, air valve lockout lever and a thermostatic coil. Some applications may use a split choke pick-up spring or a vacuum break modulating spring. The thermostatic coil is located in the engine manifold and is connected to the intermediate choke shaft and lever assembly. Choke operation is controlled by a combination of engine intake manifold vacuum, the offset choke valve, temperature and throttle position.

Model 4MC Choke System

Fig. 67—The choke consists of a choke valve located in the primary air horn bore, a choke housing and vacuum diaphragm assembly, fast idle cam, connecting linkage, air valve lockout lever, and thermostatic coil. Choke operation is controlled by a combination of intake manifold vacuum, the offset choke valve, temperature, and throttle position.

Air Valve Operation

Fig. 68—When the engine reaches a point where the primary bores cannot meet engine air and fuel demands, the primary throttle lever, through connecting linkage to the secondary throttle shaft lever, begins to open the secondary throttle valves. As air flow through the secondary bores creates a low pressure (vacuum) beneath the air valve, atmospheric pressure on top of the air valve forces the air valve open against spring tension. This allows the required air for increased engine speed to flow past the air valve.

Air Valve Dashpot Operation

Fig. 69—The secondary air valve has an attached piston assembly which acts as a damper to prevent oscillation of the valve due to engine pulsations. The damper piston operates in a well that is filled with fuel from the float bowl. The motion of the piston is retarded by fuel which must by-pass the piston when it moves up in the fuel well. The piston is attached loosely to a plunger rod. The rod has a rubber seal which retains the damper piston to the plunger rod and also acts as a valve. The purpose of the valve is to seat on the piston when the air valve opens and the piston rod moves upward. This closes off the area through the center of the piston and slows down the air valve opening to prevent secondary discharge nozzle lag.

ADJUSTMENTS

Float Level Adjustment

Fig. 70—With adjustable T-scale, measure from top of float bowl gasket surface

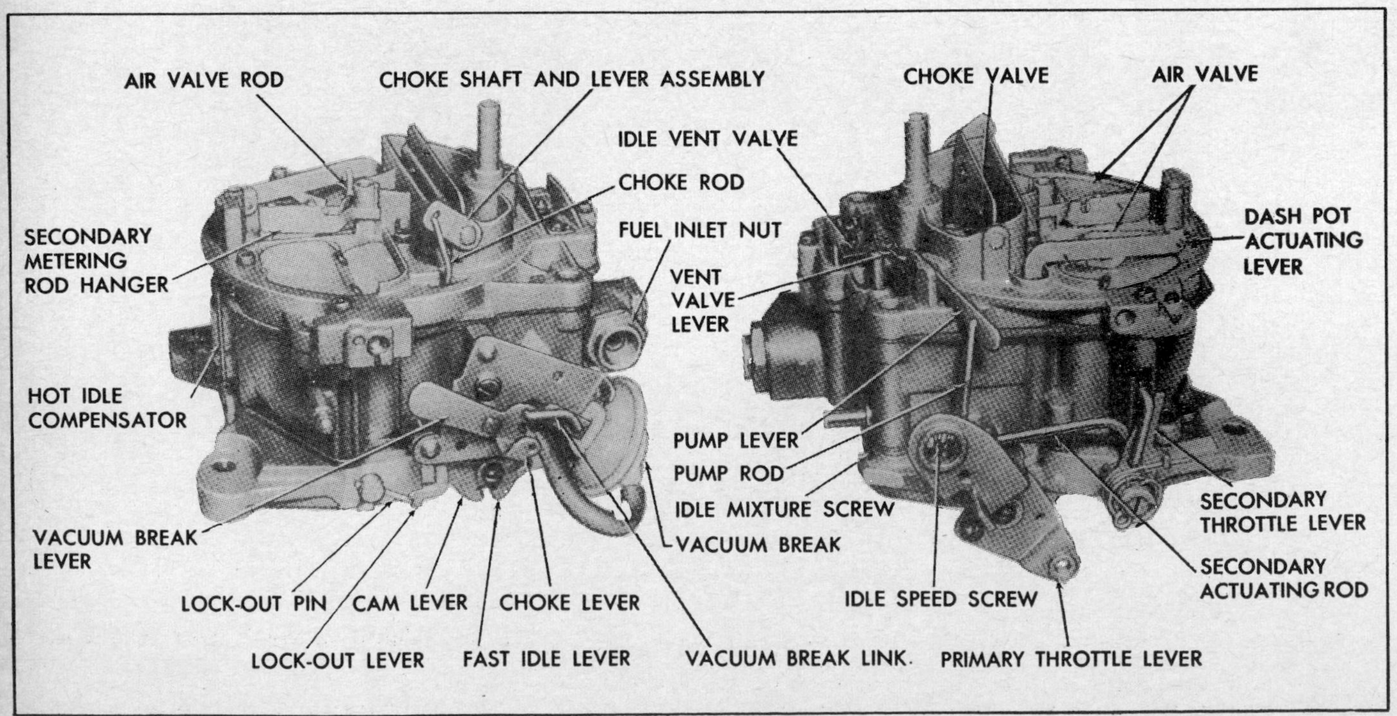

Fig. 65A Rochester Quadrajet Model 4MV carburetor

(gasket removed) to top of float at toe (locate gauging point $\frac{3}{16}$" back from toe). Adjust as directed in the illustration to the dimension listed in the *Rochester Specifications Chart.* Make sure retaining pin is held firmly in place and tang of float is seated on float needle.

Pump Rod Adjustment

Fig. 71—With throttle valves completely closed and pump rod in specified hole in pump lever, measure from top of choke valve wall (next to vent stack) to top of pump stem. Dimension should be as listed in the *Rochester Specifications Chart.* To adjust, bend pump lever as required.

Idle Vent Adjustment

Fig. 72—After pump rod adjustment has been made, open primary throttle valve to a point where the idle vent just closes. With T-scale, measure distance from top of choke valve wall (next to vent stack) to top of pump plunger stem. If dimension is not as specified in the *Rochester Specifications Chart,* bend wire tang on pump lever.

Air Valve Adjustment

Fig. 73—With air valve wide open and valve against stop tang, distance between upper inside edge of air valve and back of choke valve wall (at torsion spring end) should be as specified in the *Rochester Specifications Chart.* To adjust, bend stop tang on dashpot lever.

Fast Idle Adjustment

Fig. 74—With primary throttle valves completely closed, and the cam follower over the high step of the fast idle cam, turn fast idle screw 3 turns (2 on 1967) after screw makes contact on lever.

Choke Rod Adjustment

Fig. 75—With the fast idle adjustment made, and cam follower on second step of fast idle cam and against the high step, rotate choke valve toward closed position by pushing down on vacuum break lever (Model 4MV) or thermostatic coil tang (Model 4MC). Dimension between lower edge of choke valve (at choke lever end) should be as specified in the *Rochester Specifications Chart.* Adjust by bending choke rod.

Fig. 66 Rochester Model 4MV choke system

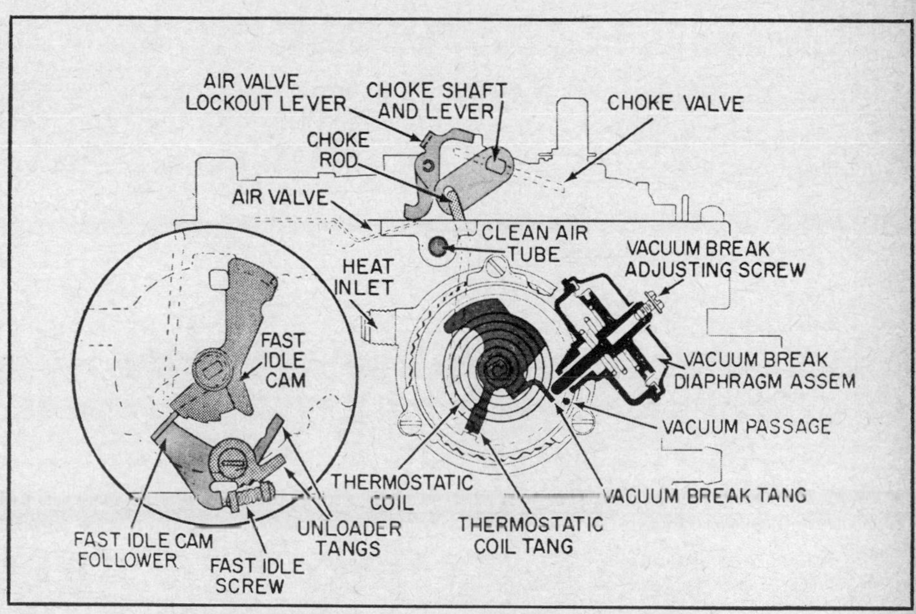

Fig. 67 Rochester Model 4MC choke system

Vacuum Break Adjustment

1967-68 4MV, Fig. 76

With vacuum break diaphragm stem against its seat and choke valve held toward the closed position, the dimension between lower edge of choke valve and air horn, at choke lever end, should be as specified. To adjust, bend vacuum break tang.

1965-66 Except 1966 Buick, Fig. 77

With choke spring pick-up located in specified notch, hold choke valve toward closed position, using a rubber band on vacuum break lever. Hold vacuum break diaphragm stem against its seat so vacuum link is at end of slot. Dimension between lower edge of choke valve and air horn should be as specified. Adjust by bending vacuum link.

1966 4MC Buick, Fig. 78

With choke valve closed, and choke rod in bottom of slot in upper choke lever, align thermostatic pick-up tang directly over index tab on inside of choke housing. After tang is aligned, adjust vacuum break tang to the specified dimension between tang and vacuum break pin.

With vacuum break diaphragm seated and tang against vacuum break pin, the dimension between wall and lower edge of choke valve should be as specified. Make sure choke rod is in bottom of slot in choke lever when gauging. Turn screw on vacuum break cover to adjust. Install baffle and thermostat cover, adjusting cover to specified mark.

Air Valve Dashpot Adjustment

Fig. 79—With vacuum break diaphragm seated, there must be the specified clearance between dashpot rod and end of slot in air valve lever. To adjust, bend rod at air valve end.

Split Choke Spring Adjustment

Fig. 80—With split choke spring in specified notch, (see automatic choke specifications) open choke valve by pushing upward on vacuum break lever to end of travel, making sure choke rod is in upper

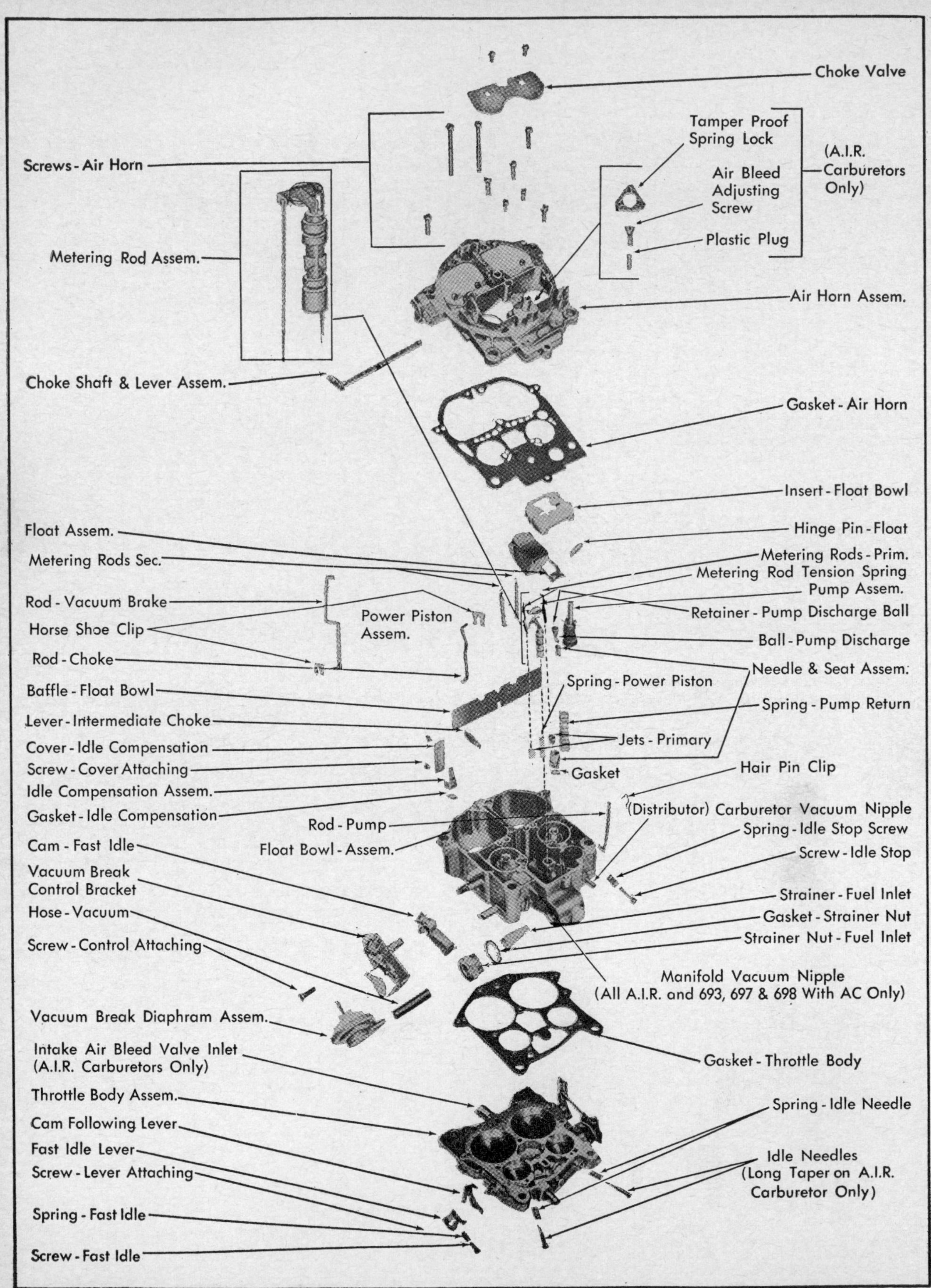

Choke Valve
Tamper Proof Spring Lock
(A.I.R. Carburetors Only)
Screws - Air Horn
Air Bleed Adjusting Screw
Plastic Plug
Metering Rod Assem.
Air Horn Assem.
Choke Shaft & Lever Assem.
Gasket - Air Horn
Insert - Float Bowl
Float Assem.
Hinge Pin - Float
Metering Rods Sec.
Metering Rods - Prim.
Metering Rod Tension Spring
Pump Assem.
Rod - Vacuum Brake
Retainer - Pump Discharge Ball
Power Piston Assem.
Horse Shoe Clip
Ball - Pump Discharge
Rod - Choke
Needle & Seat Assem.
Spring - Power Piston
Baffle - Float Bowl
Spring - Pump Return
Lever - Intermediate Choke
Jets - Primary
Cover - Idle Compensation
Gasket
Screw - Cover Attaching
Hair Pin Clip
Idle Compensation Assem.
Gasket - Idle Compensation
(Distributor) Carburetor Vacuum Nipple
Rod - Pump
Spring - Idle Stop Screw
Cam - Fast Idle
Float Bowl - Assem.
Screw - Idle Stop
Vacuum Break Control Bracket
Strainer - Fuel Inlet
Hose - Vacuum
Gasket - Strainer Nut
Strainer Nut - Fuel Inlet
Screw - Control Attaching
Manifold Vacuum Nipple
(All A.I.R. and 693, 697 & 698 With AC Only)
Vacuum Break Diaphram Assem.
Intake Air Bleed Valve Inlet
(A.I.R. Carburetors Only)
Gasket - Throttle Body
Throttle Body Assem.
Spring - Idle Needle
Cam Following Lever
Fast Idle Lever
Idle Needles
(Long Taper on A.I.R. Carburetor Only)
Screw - Lever Attaching
Spring - Fast Idle
Screw - Fast Idle

Fig. 65 Rochester 4MV Quadrajet carburetor. 1967-68 Cadillac

end of slot in choke lever. Dimension between end of torsion spring and tang should be as specified in the *Rochester Specifications Chart*. Bend tang to adjust.

Choke Unloader Adjustment

1965-68, Figs. 81 and 82

With choke valve held closed by means of a rubber band on vacuum break lever, open throttle valves fully. With valves in this position, dimension between lower edge of choke valve and air horn wall should be as specified. To adjust, bend tang on fast idle lever.

Air Valve Lockout Adjustment

1967-68 Models, Fig. 83

With choke valve wide open, apply sufficient force to thermostat tang to move the choke rod to the *top of the slot* in the choke lever. If necessary, bend the upper end of the valve lockout lever to obtain the specified opening between the lockout tang and front edge of air valve.

1966 Oldsmobile, Fig. 84

A—Opening Clearance: With cam follower positioned against rise to lowest step of fast idle cam, apply a light force to vacuum break lever in the direction of closed choke and rotate choke valve to

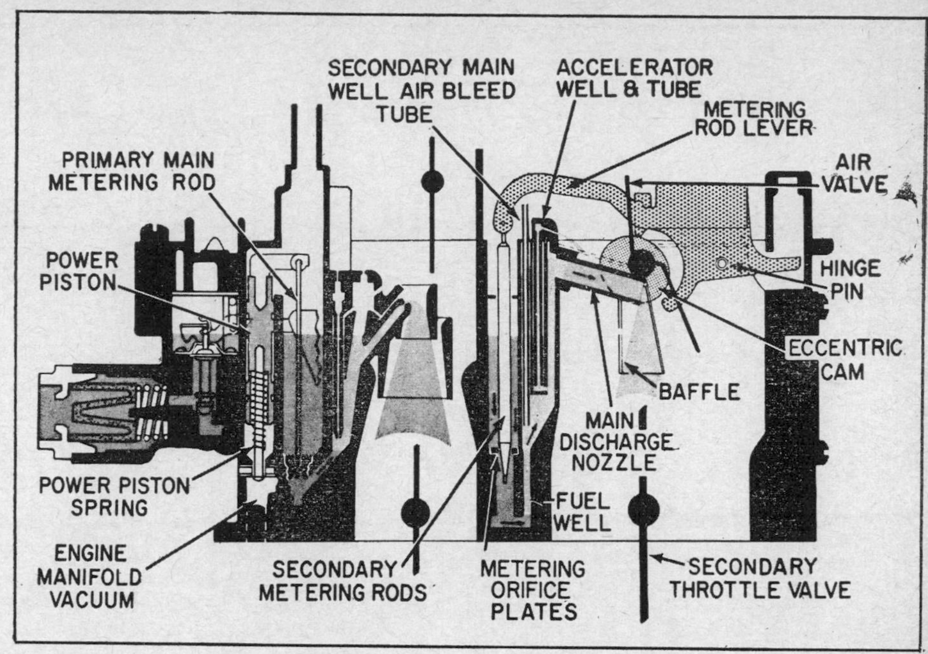

Fig. 68 Diagram of Quadrajet power system

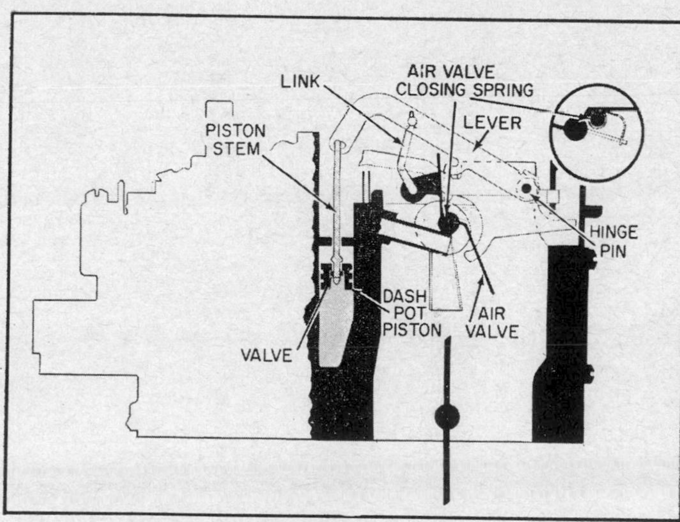

Fig. 69 Quadrajet air valve dashpot

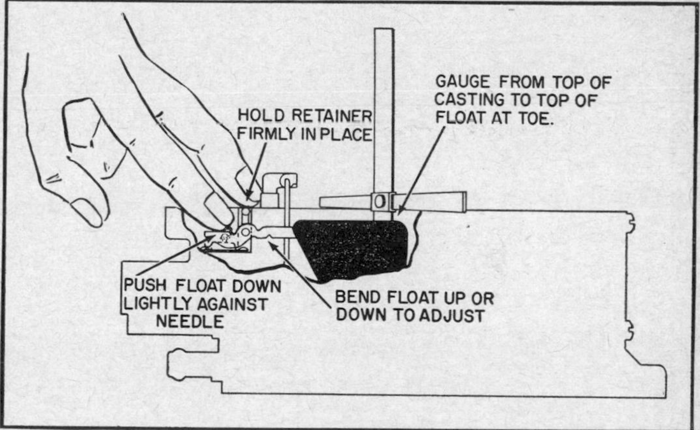

Fig. 70 Quadrajet float level adjustment

its wide open stop by applying force to the UP side of the choke valve. Move air valves to open position. Bend upper end of air valve lockout lever, if necessary, to give the specified opening between lockout tang and front edge of choke valve.

B—Lockout Clearance: With cam follower positioned against the rise to the lowest effective step of the fast idle cam, apply a light force to the vacuum break lever in the direction of closed choke. Rotate choke valve in closed direction by applying a light force to the UP side of the choke valve so that the choke link is at the upper end of the slot in the choke lever. Air valves must be locked closed. If any adjustment is necessary, the opening clearance must be rechecked.

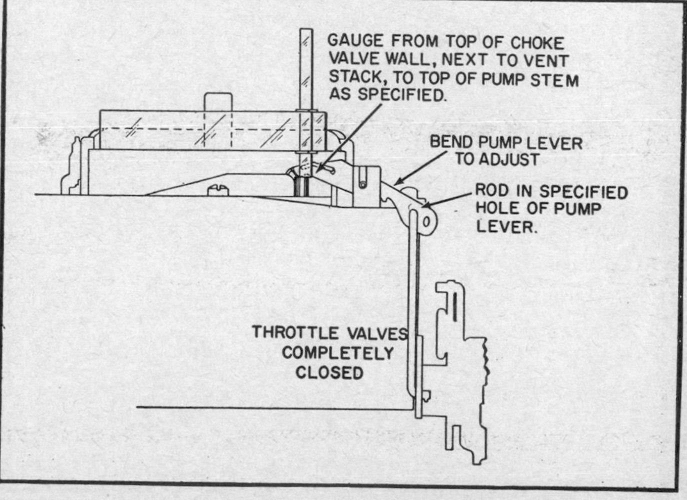

Fig. 71 Quadrajet pump rod adjustment

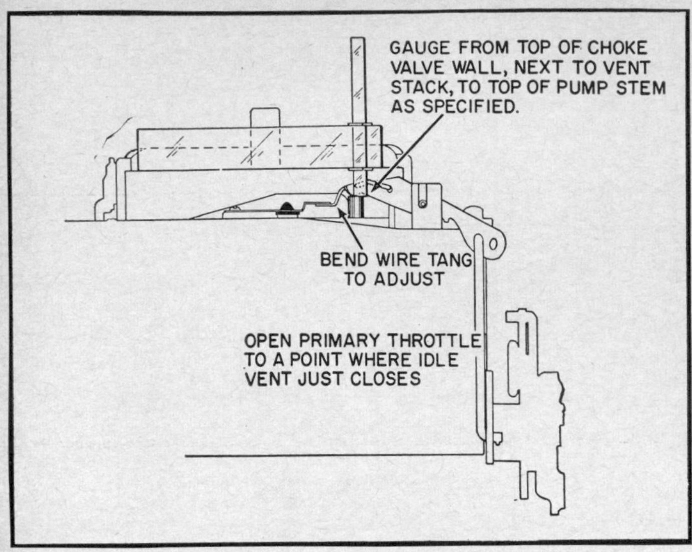

Fig. 72 Quadrajet idle vent adjustment

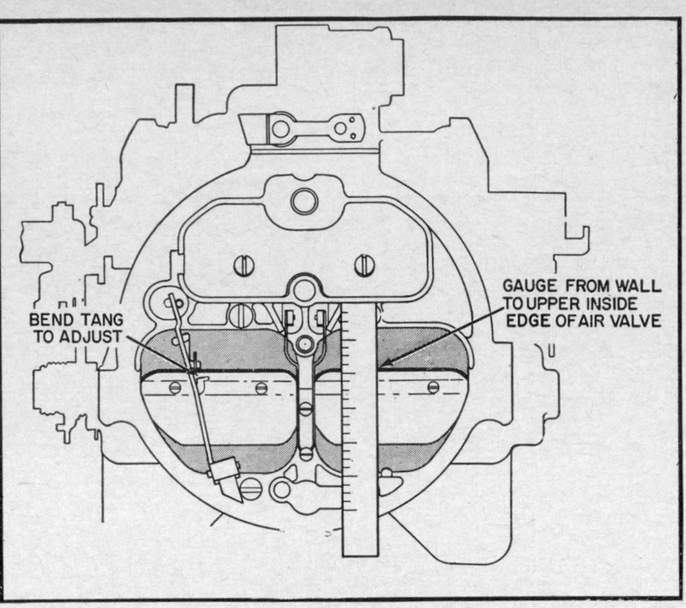

Fig. 73 Quadrajet air valve adjustment

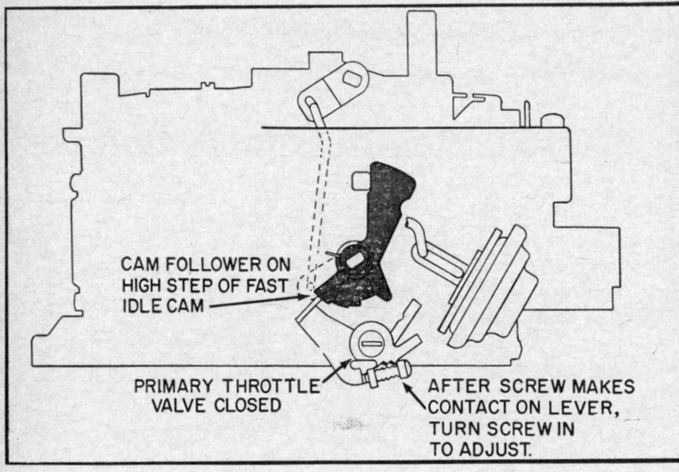

Fig. 74 Quadrajet fast idle adjustment

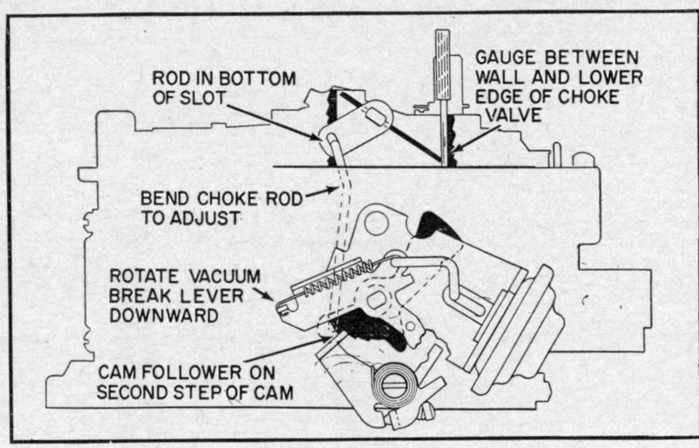

Fig. 75 Quadrajet choke rod adjustment

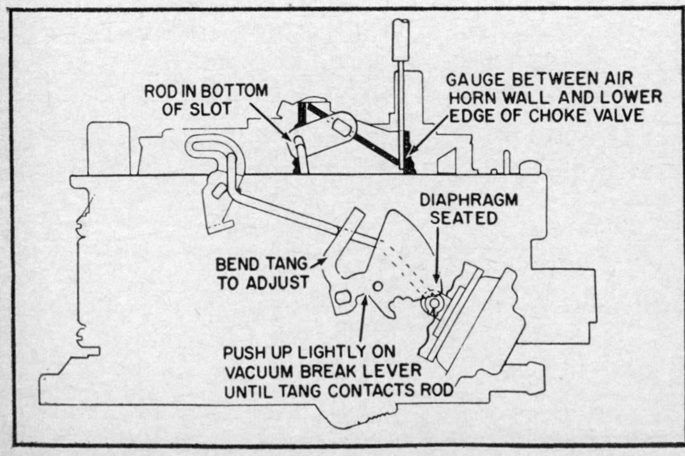

Fig. 76 Quadrajet vacuum break adjustment. 1967-68

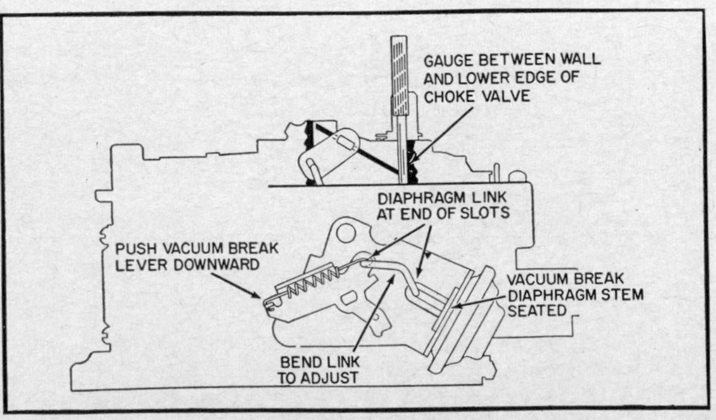

Fig. 77 Quadrajet vacuum break adjustment. 1965-66 Chevrolet, Olds and Pontiac

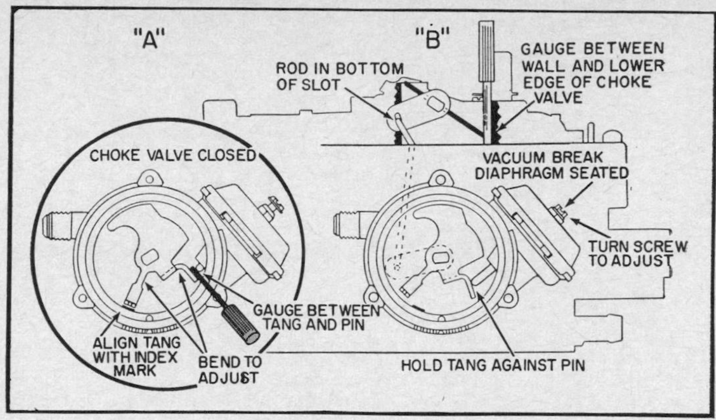

Fig. 78 Quadrajet vacuum break adjustment. 1966 Buick

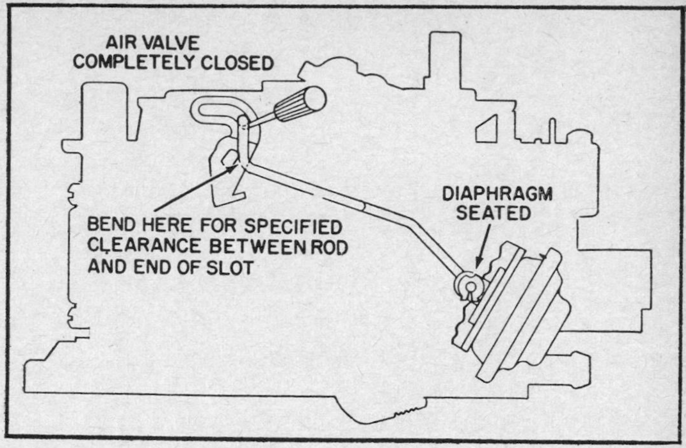

Fig. 79 Quadrajet air valve dashpot adjustment

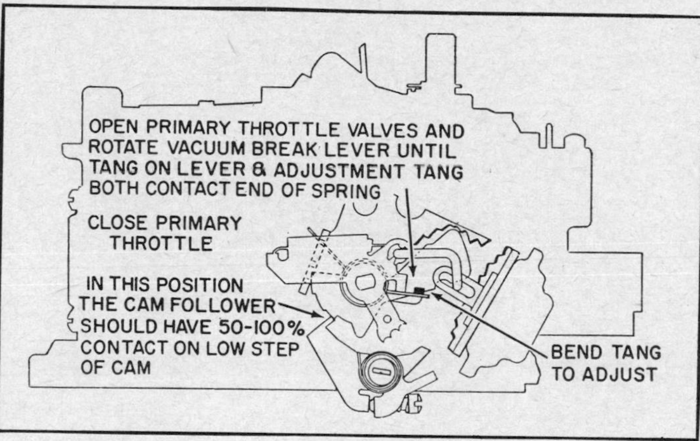

Fig. 80 Quadrajet split choke spring adjustment

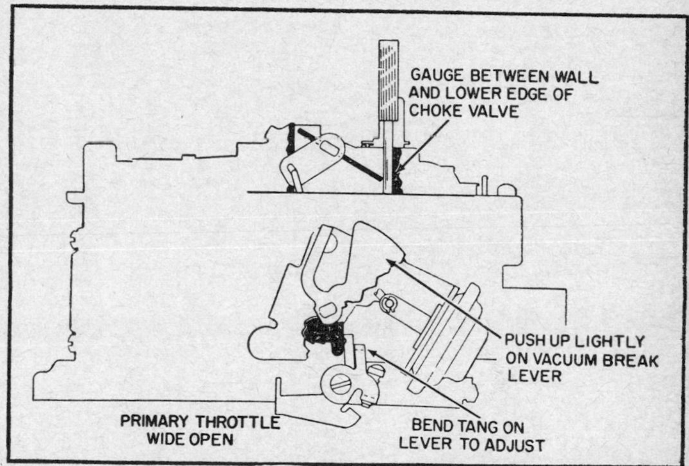

Fig. 81 Quadrajet unloader adjustment. 1967-68

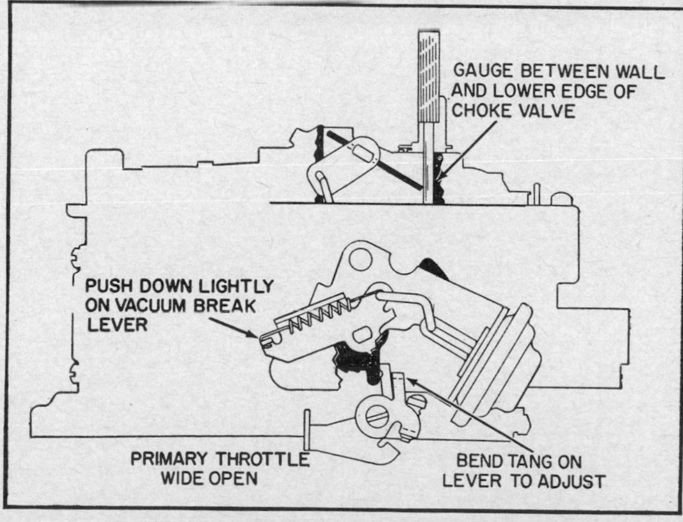

Fig. 82 Quadrajet unloader adjustment. 1965-66

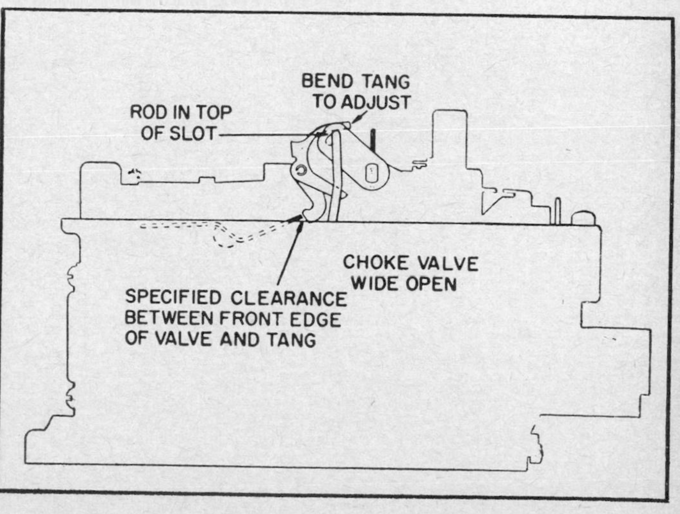

Fig. 83 Quadrajet air valve lockout adjustment. 1967-68

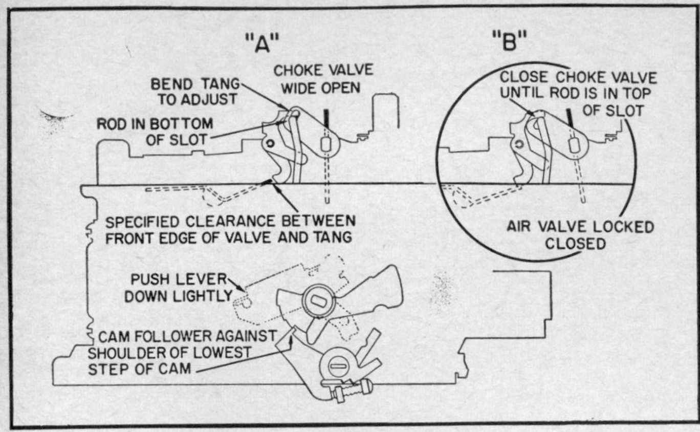

Fig. 84 Quadrajet air valve lockout adjustment. 1966 Olds

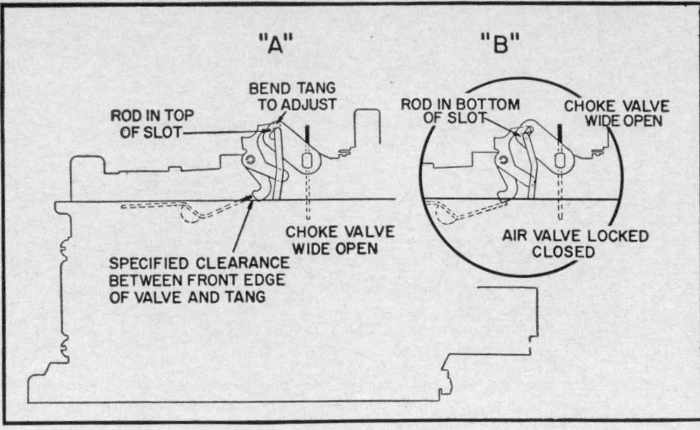

Fig. 85 Quadrajet air valve lockout adjustment. 1965-66 Buick, Chevrolet and Pontiac

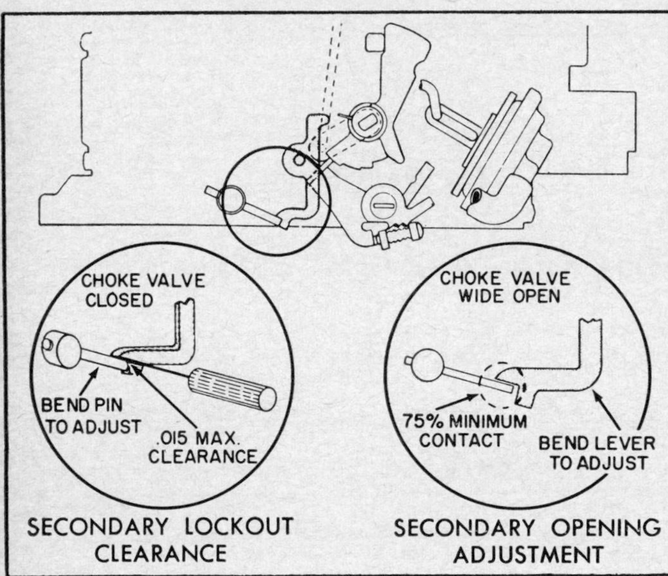

Fig. 86 Quadrajet secondary lockout clearance and secondary opening adjustment

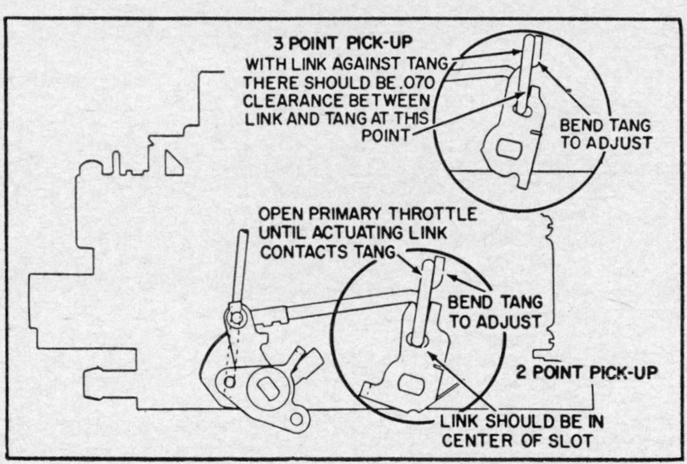

Fig. 87 Quadrajet secondary throttle valves opening adjustment. 1967-68

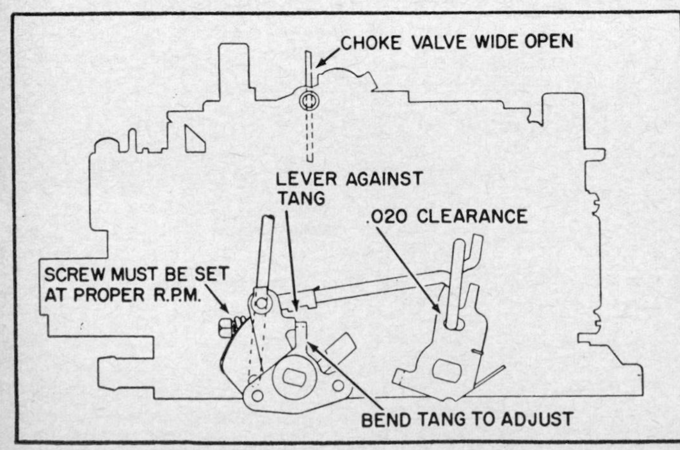

Fig. 88 Quadrajet secondary throttle valves closing adjustment. 1967-68

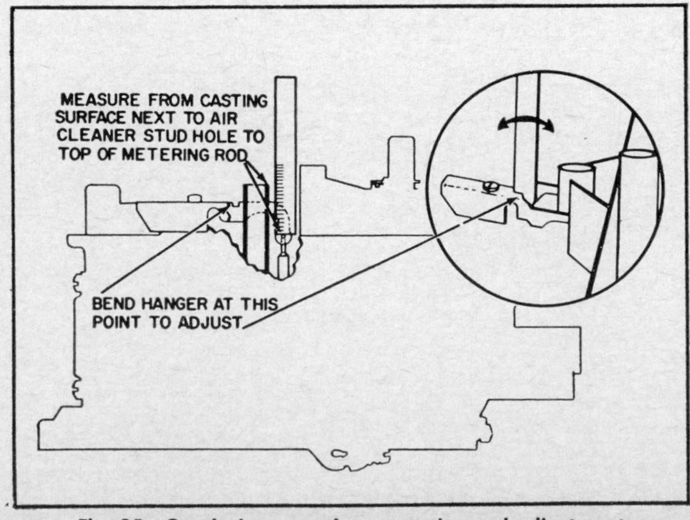

Fig. 89 Quadrajet secondary metering rod adjustment

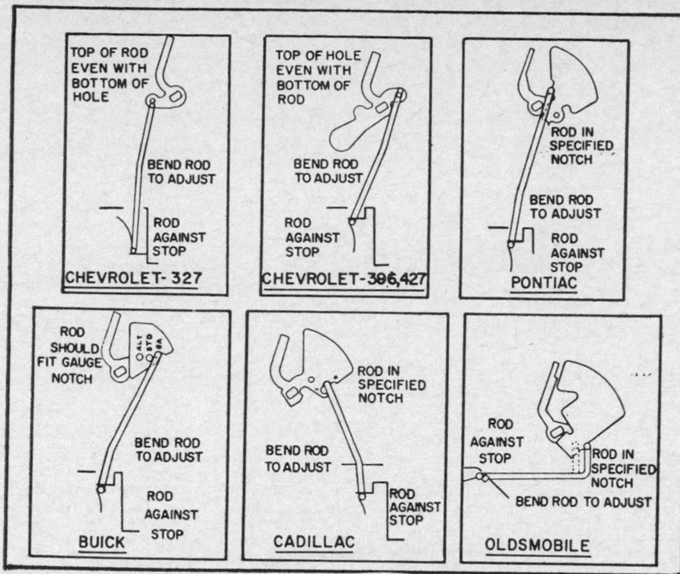

Fig. 91 Quadrajet choke coil rod adjustments. 1967-68

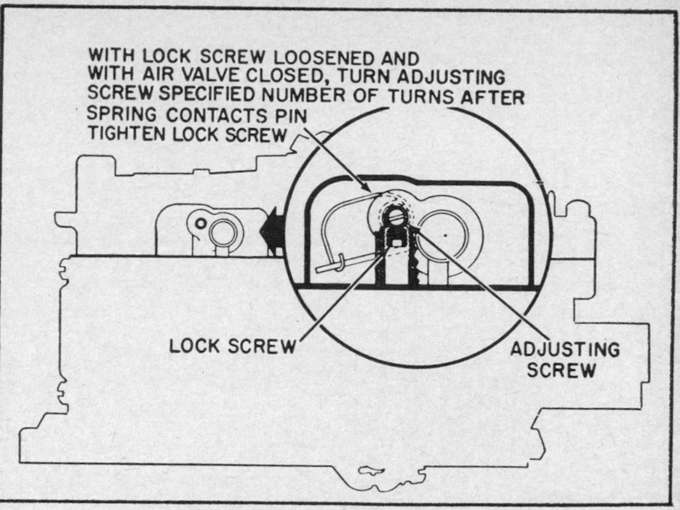

Fig. 90 Quadrajet air valve spring adjustment

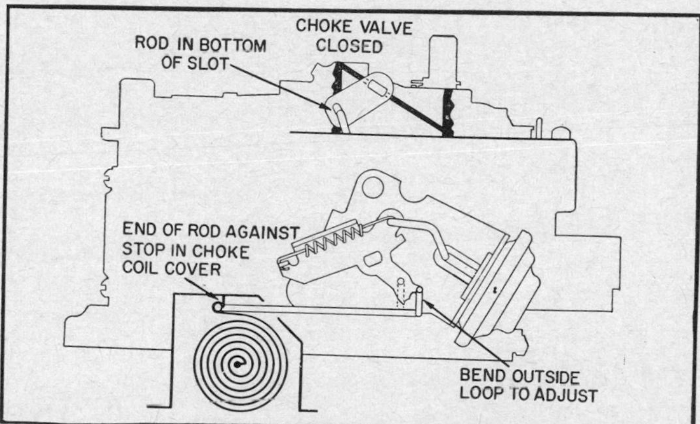

Fig. 92 Quadrajet choke coil rod adjustments. 1966 Olds

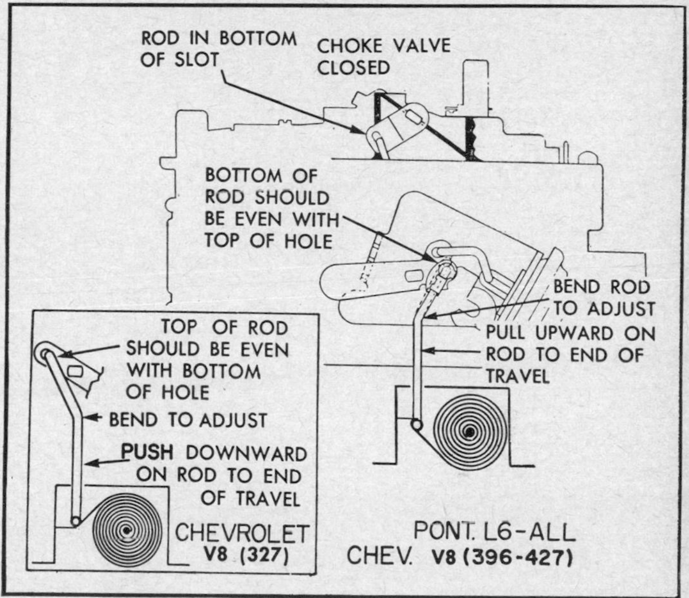

Fig. 93 Quadrajet choke coil rod adjustments. 1965-66 Chevrolet and Pontiac

1965-66 Buick, Chevrolet, Pontiac, Fig. 85

A—Opening Clearance: With choke valve wide open, apply sufficient force to thermostat tang to move choke rod *to top of slot* in choke lever. Move air valve in open direction. Bend upper end of air valve lockout lever, if necessary, to give the specified opening between lockout tang and front edge of air valve.

B—Lockout: With all other adjustments made, open choke valve fully by applying force to the UP side of choke valve. Making sure choke rod is in *bottom of slot* in choke lever, the air valve lockout tang must hold air valve closed.

Secondary Lockout Clearance

Fig. 86—With choke valve and both primary and secondary throttle valves fully closed, the lockout lever should not contact lockout pin. Clearance must not exceed .015". Bend lockout pin to adjust.

Secondary Opening Adjustment

Fig. 86—Holding choke valve and primary throttle valves in wide open position and secondary throttle valves closed, the lockout pin should have a minimum of 75% contact on lockout lever. To adjust, bend lockout lever.

1967-68 Secondary Throttle Valves, Adjust

Throttle Opening, Fig. 87

With a two-point pickup, open primary throttle valves until actuating link contacts tang on secondary lever. With valves in this position, bottom of link should be in center slot of secondary lever.

With a three-point pickup, there should be .070" clearance between link and tang as indicated. If necessary to adjust, bend tang on secondary lever.

Throttle Closing, Fig. 88

Set curb idle screw to recommended rpm (listed in *Tune-Up Specifications* table in car chapters), making sure cam follower is not resting on fast idle cam. There should be .020" clearance between actuating link and front of slot in secondary lever when tang of actuating lever on primary shaft is against pin. If necessary to adjust, bend tang on primary actuating lever.

Secondary Metering Rod Adjustment

Fig. 89

Measure from top of metering rod to top of air horn casting next to air cleaner stud hole. Dimension should be as specified. To adjust, bend metering rod hanger at point shown. *Make sure both rods are adjusted to the same dimension.*

Air Valve Spring Adjustment

Fig. 90

To adjust the air valve spring wind-up, loosen Allen head lockscrew and turn adjusting screw counterclockwise to remove all spring tension. With air valve closed, turn adjusting screw clockwise the specified number of turns after the torsion spring contacts pin on shaft. Hold adjusting screw in this position and tighten lock screw.

Choke Coil Rod Adjustment

1967-68 Models, Fig. 91

With choke valve completely closed and choke rod in bottom of choke lever slot, pull or push choke coil rod to end of travel. Rod should be positioned as shown. Bend choke coil rod to adjust.

Oldsmobile 1966, Fig. 92

With choke valve completely closed and choke rod in bottom of choke lever slot, pull forward on choke coil rod until rod is against stop on choke coil cover. Bend outer loop on rod to specified position. Connect choke coil rod to vacuum break lever and secure with clip.

Chevrolet & Pontiac, 1965-66, Fig. 93

With choke valve completely closed and choke rod in bottom of choke lever slot, pull upward or push downward on choke coil rod to end of travel. Thermostat rod position should be as specified in illustration. To adjust, bend choke coil rod, connect rod to vacuum break lever and secure with clip.

ROCHESTER MONOJET M, MV ADJUSTMENT SPECIFICATIONS

See Tune Up Charts in car chapters for hot idle speeds.

Year	Carb. Part No. ①	Initial Idle Mix Screw Turns Open	Float Level	Metering Rod	Idle Vent	Fast Idle Off Car	Choke Rod	Vacuum Break	Unloader	Fast Idle R.P.M.
BUICK										
1968	7028014	1½–2	5/16	.120	.050	②	.180	.245	.350	②
	7028047	1½–2	5/16	.140	.020	②	.190	.275	.325	②
1969	7029014	2	1/4	.070	.050	—	.170	.245	.350	620④
	7029047	2	9/32	.140	.020	—	.190	.275	.350	720④
CHEVROLET ENGINES										
1968	7028008	1½–2	9/32	.080	.050	1½③	.150	—	—	2400⑤
	7028009	1½–2	9/32	.080	.050	1½③	.150	—	—	2400⑤
	7028014	1½–2	9/32	.120	.050	1½③	.150	.245	.350	2400⑤
	7028015	1½–2	9/32	.130	.050	1½③	.150	.275	.350	2400⑤
	7028017	1½–2	9/32	.130	.050	1½③	.150	.275	.350	2400⑤
1969	7029008	3	1/4	.080	.050	.100	.150	—	—	2400⑤
	7029014	3	1/4	.070	.050	.100	.170	.245	.350	2400⑤
	7029015	3	1/4	.090	.050	.100	.200	.275	.350	2400⑤
	7029017	3	1/4	.090	.050	.100	.200	.275	.350	2400⑤
OLDSMOBILE										
1968	7028014	1½–2	9/32	.120	.050	—	.180	.245	.350	650④
	7028057	1½–2	9/32	.130	.050	—	.190	.275	.350	650④
1969	7029014	—	1/4	.070	.050	—	.170	.245	.350	750④
	7029057	—	5/16	.120	.030	—	.180	.260	.350	750④
PONTIAC										
1968	7028067	1½–2	5/16	.085	.040	—	.200	.300	.245	2400⑤
	7028075	1½–2	5/16	.085	.040	—	.200	.290	.245	2400⑤
	7028065	1½–2	5/16	.075	.040	—	.200	.300	.245	2400⑤
1969	7029165	5	9/32	.085	.040	—	.200	.275	.450	2400⑤
	7029166	5	9/32	.085	.040	—	.180	.260	.450	2800⑤
	7029167	5	9/32	.085	.040	—	.200	.275	.450	2600⑤
	7029168	5	9/32	.085	.040	—	.180	.260	.450	2800⑤

①—On tag attached to carburetor.
②—20 RPM above slow idle speed.
③—Turns in from slow idle position.
④—On low step of cam.
⑤—On high step of cam.

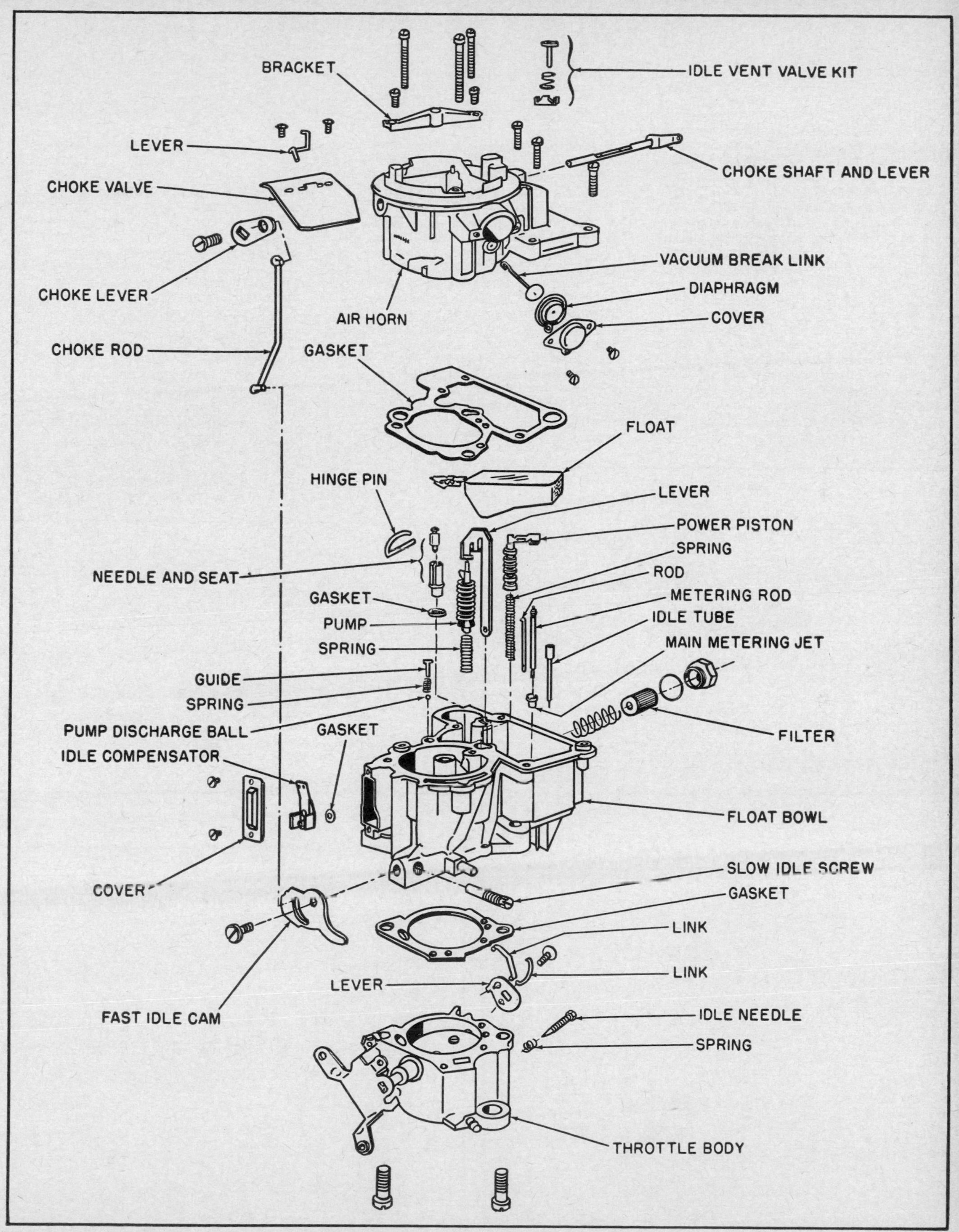

Fig. 1 Monojet Model MV carburetor. Model M has manual choke

MONOJET M & MV ADJUSTMENTS

The Monojet carburetor is a single-bore downdraft unit with a triple venturi coupled with a refined metering system which results in a unit having superior fuel mixture control and performance.

A plain tube nozzle is used in conjunction with the multiple venturi. Fuel flow through the main metering system is controlled by a mechanically and vacuum operated variable orifice jet. This consists of a specially tapered rod which operates in the fixed orifice main metering jet and is connected directly by linkage to the main throttle shaft. A vacuum-operated enrichment system is used in conjunction with the main metering system to provide good performance during moderate to heavy accelerations.

A separate and adjustable idle system is used in conjunction with the main metering system to meet fuel mixture requirements during engine idle and low speed operation. The off-idle discharge port is of a vertical slot design which gives good transition between curb idle and main metering system operation.

The idle system incorporates a hot idle compensator on some models where necessary to maintain smooth engine idle during periods of extreme hot engine operation.

The main metering system has an adjustable flow feature which enables production to control the fuel mixture more accurately than attained heretofore.

The Monojet carburetor is designed so that a manual or automatic choke system can be used. The conventional choke valve is located in the air horn bore. On automatic choke models, the vacuum diaphragm unit is an integral part of the air horn. The automatic choke coil is manifold mounted and connects to the choke valve shaft by connecting linkage.

The choke system has a new feature to give added enrichment during cold start. This feature greatly reduces starting time and yet allows the use of low torque thermostatic coils for increased economy.

The carburetor has internally balanced venting through a vent hole in the air horn. An external idle vent valve is used on some models where necessary for improved hot engine idle and starting.

Float Level Adjustment

Fig. 2

1. Hold float retaining pin firmly in place and float arm against top of float needle by pushing downward on float arm at point between needle seat and hinge pin as shown.
2. With adjustable T-scale, measure distance from top of float at toe to float bowl gasket surface (gasket removed). Measurement should be made at a point 1/16" in from end of flat surface at float toe (not on radius).
3. Bend float pontoon up or down at float arm junction to adjust.

Metering Rod Adjustment

Fig. 3

1. Remove metering rod by holding throttle valve wide open. Push down-

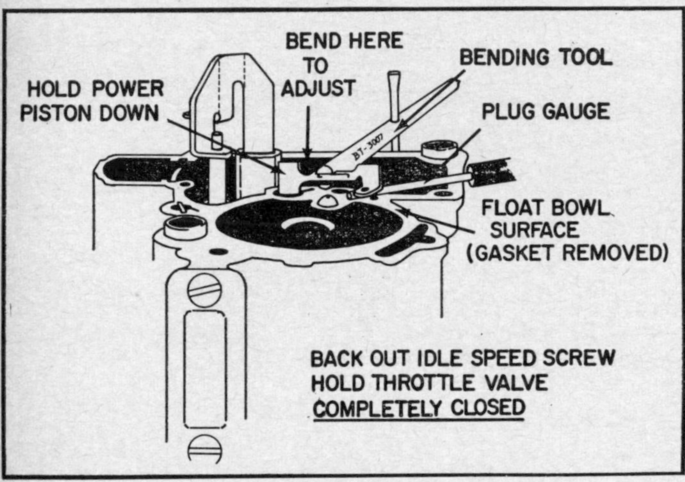

Fig. 3 Monojet metering rod adjustment

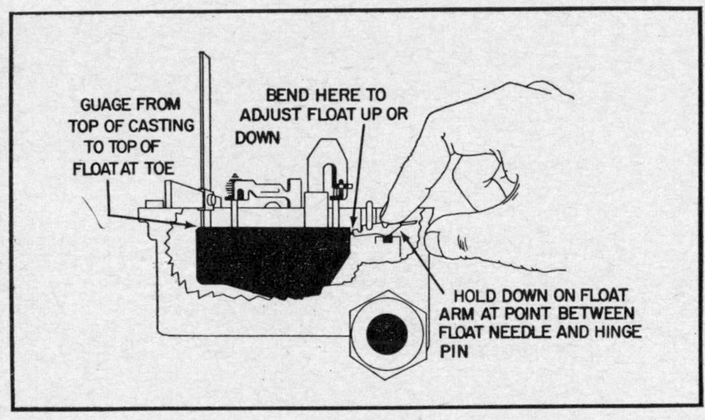

Fig. 2 Monojet float level adjustment

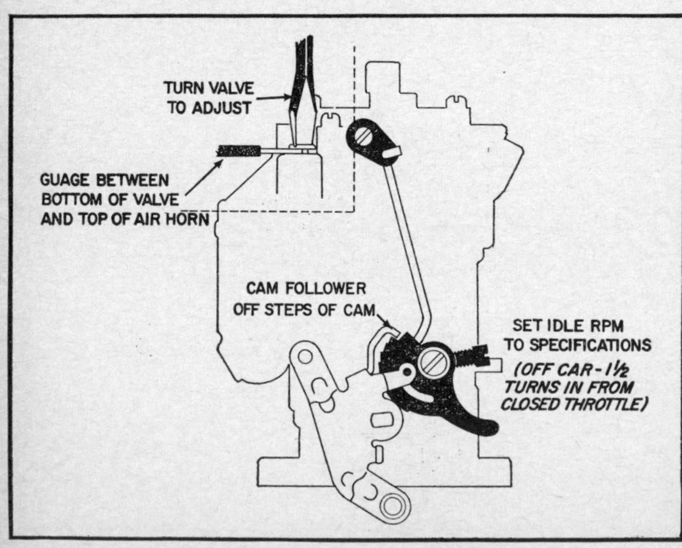

Fig. 4 Monojet idle vent adjustment

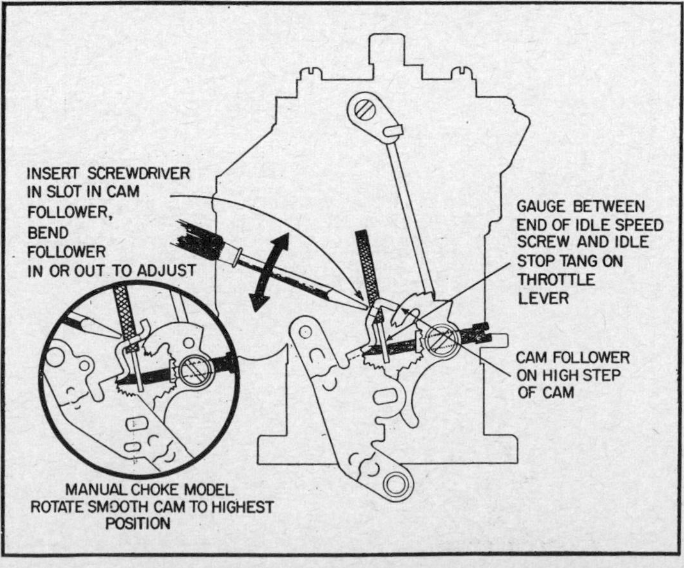

Fig. 5 Monojet fast idle adjustment (off car)

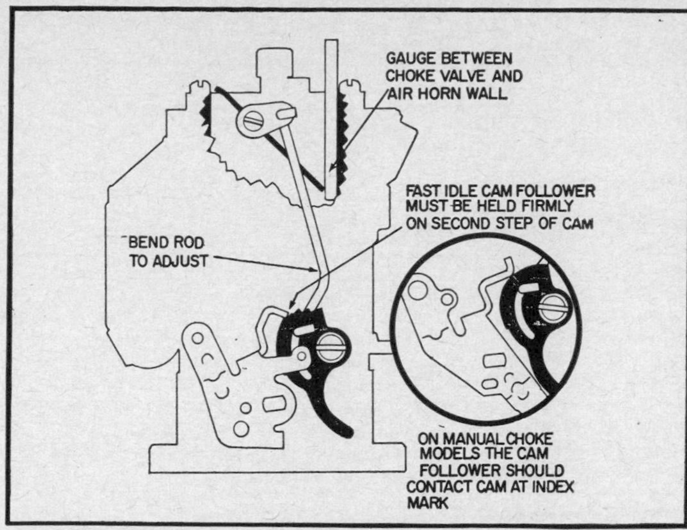

Fig. 6 Monojet choke rod adjustment

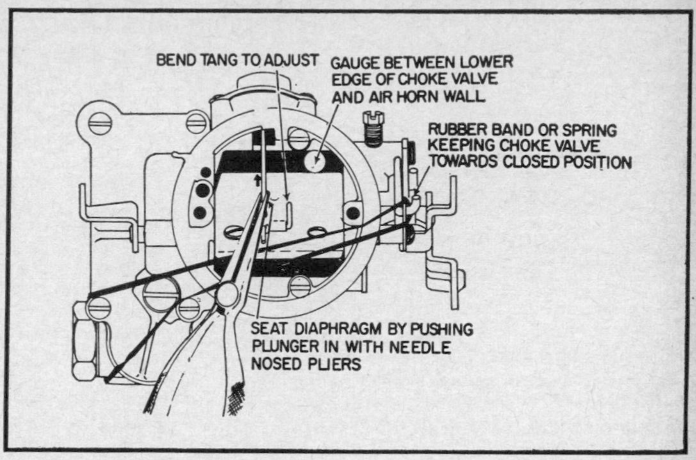

Fig. 7 Monojet vacuum break adjustment

ward on metering rod against spring tension, then slide metering rod out of slot in holder and remove from main metering jet.

2. To check adjustment, back out slow idle screw and rotate fast idle cam so that fast idle cam follower is not contacting steps on cam.
3. With throttle valve completely closed, apply pressure to top of power piston and hold piston down against its stop.
4. While holding downward pressure on power piston, swing metering rod holder over flat surface of bowl casting next to carburetor bore.
5. Use specified size drill and insert between bowl casting sealing bead and lower surface of metering rod holder. Drill should have a slide fit between both surfaces as shown.
6. To adjust, carefully bend metering rod holder up or down at point shown.
7. After adjustment, install metering rod.

Idle Vent Adjustment

Fig. 4

1. Set engine idle rpm to specification and hold choke valve wide open so that fast idle cam follower is not hitting fast idle cam.

NOTE: Initial idle setting can be made with the carburetor off the car by turning idle speed screw in $1\frac{1}{2}$ turns from closed throttle valve position. Recheck setting on the car as follows:

2. With throttle stop screw held against idle stop screw, the idle vent valve should be open as specified.

To measure, insert specified size drill between top of air horn casting and bottom surface of vent valve.

3. To adjust, turn slotted vent valve head with a screwdriver clockwise (inward) to decrease clearance and counterclockwise to increase clearance as required.

NOTE: On models provided with the idle stop solenoid, make sure solenoid is activated when checking and adjusting vent valve. How the idle stop solenoid operates is described in the *Exhaust Emission Controls* chapter.

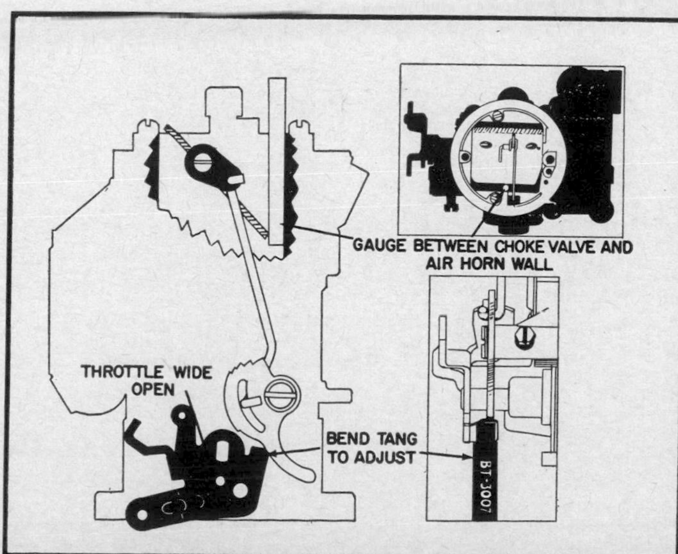

Fig. 8 Monojet unloader adjustment

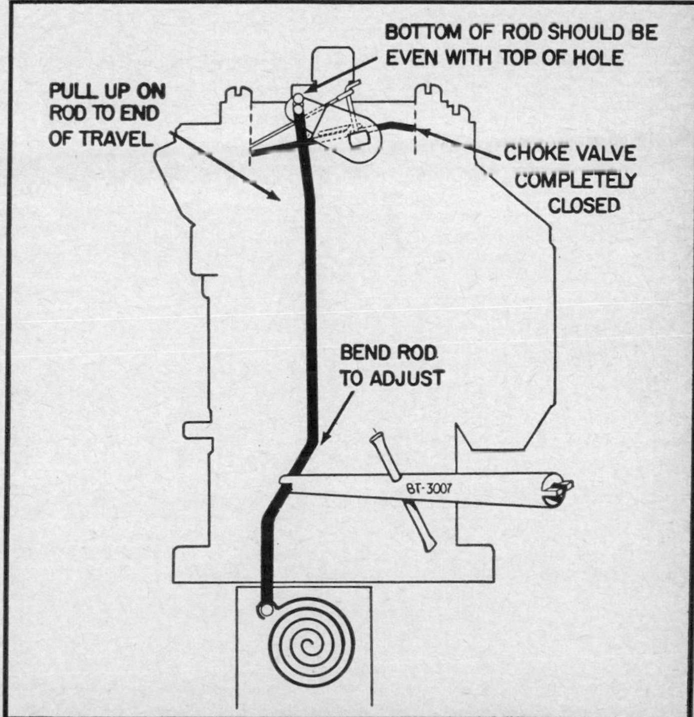

Fig. 9 Monojet choke coil adjustment

Fast Idle Adjustment

Automatic Choke Models, Fig. 5

1. Set normal engine idle speed.
2. Place fast idle cam follower tang on highest step of cam.
3. With tang held against cam, check clearance between end of slow idle speed screw and idle stop tang on throttle lever. It should be as specified.
4. To adjust, insert screwdriver in slot provided in fast idle cam follower tang and bend inwards (towards cam) or outward to obtain specified dimension.

Manual Choke Models

Use same procedure as above except in Step 2 rotate fast idle cam clockwise to its farthest up position.

Choke Rod Adjustment

Automatic Choke Models, Fig. 6

1. With fast idle adjustment made, place fast idle cam follower on second step of fast idle cam and hold firmly against the rise to the high step.
2. Rotate choke towards direction of closed choke by applying force to choke coil lever.
3. Bend choke rod at point shown to give specified opening between lower edge of choke valve (at center of valve) and inside air horn wall.

Manual Choke Models

Use same procedure as above except in Step 1. As there are no steps on the manual choke cam, the index line on side of cam should be lined up with contact point of fast idle cam follower tang.

Vacuum Break Adjustment

Fig. 7

1. Open throttle valve so that cam follower on throttle lever will clear highest step on fast idle cam.
2. Rotate choke valve to closed position. If thermostatic coil is warm, hold choke valve closed with rubber band or spring attached between choke shaft lever and stationary part of carburetor.
3. Grasp vacuum break plunger rod with needle nose pliers and push straight inward until diaphragm seats.
4. With specified drill size, measure clearance between lower edge of choke valve and inside air horn wall at center of valve as shown.
5. Bend end of vacuum break lever at point shown to adjust.

Unloader Adjustment

Fig. 8

1. Hold choke valve in closed position by applying a light force to choke coil lever.
2. Rotate throttle lever to wide open throttle valve position.
3. Bend unloader tang on throttle lever to obtain specified dimension between lower edge of choke valve (at center) and air horn wall.

Choke Coil Adjustment

Fig. 9

1. Hold choke valve closed.
2. Pull upward on coil rod to end of travel.
3. Bottom of rod end which slides into hole in choke lever should be even with top of hole. *On Pontiac applications rod should be adjusted to fit in notch in top of choke lever.*
4. Bend choke coil rod at point shown to adjust.
5. Connect coil rod to choke lever and install retaining clip.

Fast Idle Adjustment

1. With carburetor installed on vehicle, warm up engine.
2. Place fast idle cam follower on specified step of fast idle cam.
3. With cam follower held against specified step, insert screwdriver in adjustment slot and bend tang towards or away from cam to obtain specified rpm.

Stromberg Carburetor Section

STROMBERG CARBURETOR ADJUSTMENT SPECIFICATIONS

See Tune Up Chart in car chapters for hot idle speeds.

Year	Carb. Model	Initial Idle Mixture Screws Turns Open	Float Level Inch	Fast Idle R.P.M.	Fast Idle Cam Position		Vacuum Kick	Choke Unloader	Pump Travel Inch	Bowl Vent	Choke Setting
					Idle Screw Turns In	Clearance					
CHRYSLER, DODGE & PLYMOUTH											
1962	3-198	1 1/4	7/32	1250	7 1/2	13/64	13/32	15/64	—	5/64	On Index
	3-199	1 1/4	7/32	1250	7 1/2	13/64	13/32	15/64	—	5/64	On Index
	3-200	1 1/4	7/32	1250	7 1/2	13/64	13/32 ①	15/64	—	5/64	On Index
	3-201	1 1/4	1/8	1400	3 1/2	15/64	#18 Drill	15/64	9/16	3/32	1 Rich
1963	3-219	3/4-1	11/32	1400	4	19/64	#1 Drill	11/32	—	.060	2 Rich
	3-222	1 1/4	7/32	1400	4	13/64	3/8	15/64	—	5/64	On Index
	3-223	1 1/4	7/32	1400	4	13/64	19/64	15/64	—	5/64	On Index
	3-221	1 1/4	1/8	1400	3 1/2	11/64	1/8	15/64	—	5/64	1 Rich
1964	3-239	1 1/4	7/32	700	—	5/16	15/64	15/64	—	5/64	On Index
	3-240	1 1/4	7/32	700	—	17/64	13/64	15/64	—	5/64	On Index
	3-242	1 1/2	5/32	700	—	1/4	11/64	15/64	—	1/16	1 Rich
	3-244	1 1/2	5/32	600	—	17/64	7/32	15/64	—	1/16	1 Rich
1965	3-248	1 1/4	7/32	700	—	9/64	17/64	5/16	—	5/64	On Index
	3-249	1 1/4	7/32	700	—	9/64	#4 Drill	5/16	—	5/64	On Index
	3-250	1 1/4	7/32	700	—	9/64	17/64	5/16	—	5/64	On Index
	3-251	1 1/4	7/32	700	—	9/64	15/64	5/16	—	5/64	On Index
	3-254	1 1/2	5/32	700	—	#41 Drill	#17 Drill	15/64	11/32	3/64	1 Rich
	3-255	1 1/2	5/32	700	—	#41 Drill	#35 Drill	15/64	7/16	5/64	1 Rich
1966	3-258	1 1/4	7/32	700	—	#28 Drill	G Drill	5/16	—	.060	2 Rich
	3-259	1 1/4	7/32	700	—	#28 Drill	D Drill	5/16	—	.060	2 Rich
	3-260	1/2	7/32	1450	—	#28 Drill	G Drill	5/16	—	.050	On Index
	3-261	1/2	7/32	1600	—	#28 Drill	D Drill	5/16	—	.050	On Index
	3-262	1 1/2	5/32	700	—	#38 Drill	#28 Drill	15/64	7/16	.040	2 Rich
	3-263	1 1/2	5/32	1300	—	#38 Drill	#22 Drill	15/64	7/16	.020	On Index
1967	3-272	1 1/4	7/32	700	—	#20 Drill	A Drill	5/16	—	.060	2 Rich
	3-273	1 1/4	7/32	700	—	#20 Drill	#4 Drill	5/16	—	.060	2 Rich
	3-274	1 1/2	7/32	1400	—	#20 Drill	A Drill	5/16	—	.050	On Index
	3-275	1 1/2	7/32	1400	—	#20 Drill	#4 Drill	5/16	—	.050	On Index
	3-276	1 1/2	5/32	700	—	#42 Drill	#42 Drill	15/64	7/16	.040	2 Rich

①—With automatic transmission 21/64″.

STROMBERG ADJUSTMENTS

MODELS WA & WW

These carburetors, Figs. 1 and 2, are fundamentally the same, the WA model being a one-barrel unit whereas the WW model is a two-barrel carburetor.

Both models consist of two main assemblies, namely the air horn and the main body. The air horn serves as a fuel bowl cover and includes parts of the idle system, choke system, accelerating and power systems. The main body includes the fuel inlet, fuel bowl, fuel metering systems and throttle mechanism. Exploded views of these carburetors are shown in Figs. 3 and 4.

Float Level Adjustment

Figs. 5 and 6

1. Install float with fulcrum pin and retaining spring in main body.
2. Install needle, seat and gasket in body and tighten securely.
3. Invert main body so that weight of float *only* is forcing needle against seat.
4. Using the tool shown or a T-scale, check float level from surface of bowl with gasket removed to top of float at center.
5. If an adjustment is necessary, hold float on bottom of bowl, then bend float lip toward or away from needle. Recheck setting again, then repeat lip bending operation if required.

CAUTION: When bending float lip, do not allow lip to push against the needle as the synthetic rubber tip (if equipped) can be compressed sufficiently to cause a false setting which will affect correct level of fuel in bowl. After lip is compressed the tip is very slow to recover its original shape. It is important that float lip be perpendicular to the needle or slant not more than 10 deg. away from the needle when float is set correctly.

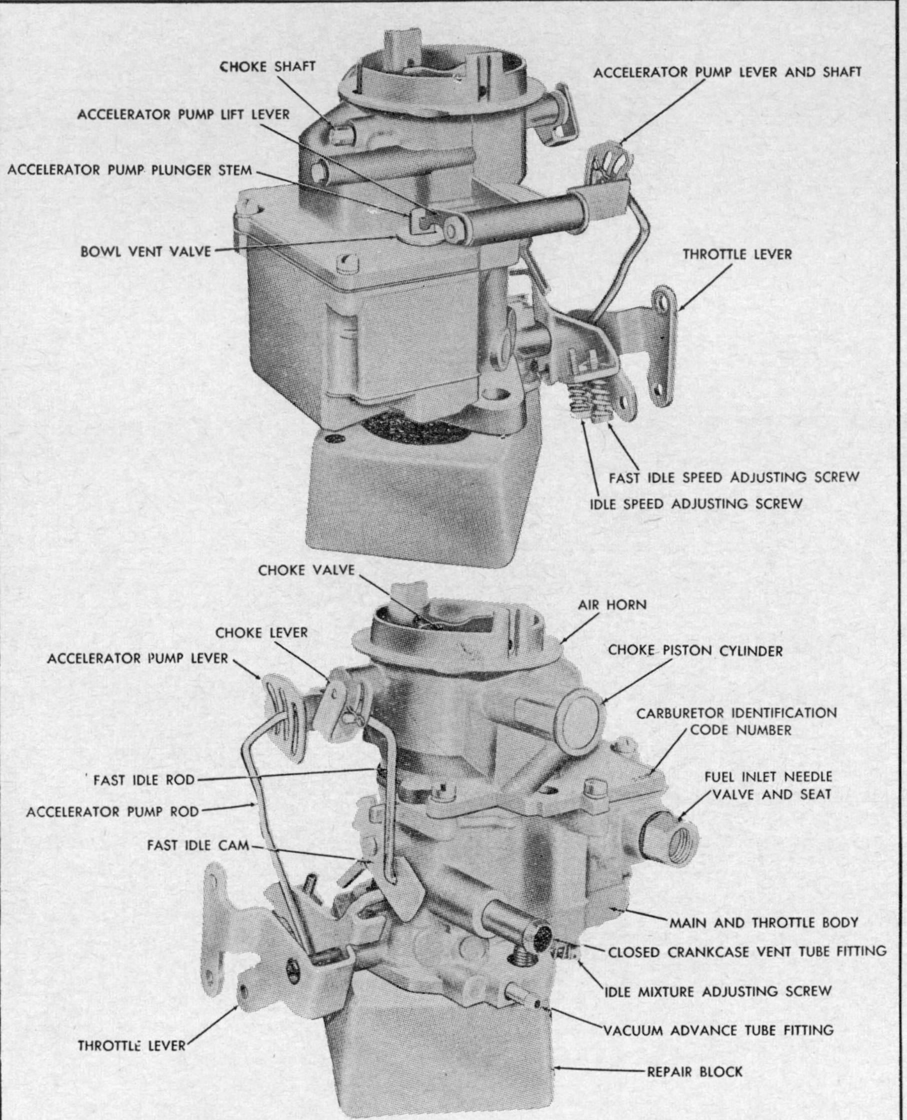

Fig. 1 Stromberg Model WA single-barrel carburetor

Fast Idle Cam Setting

1962-63, Fig. 7

1. Turn idle speed adjusting screw out far enough to clear throttle lever tang when throttle valves are closed.
2. Hold throttle valves in closed position, then turn fast idle adjusting screw out until fast idle screw can be positioned on second highest step of cam.
3. From points of initial contact with step on cam, turn fast idle screw in the number of turns specified in adjustment chart.
4. With screw held in this position, move choke valve with light pressure toward closed position and insert the specified gauge or drill between choke valve and air horn wall.
5. If adjustment is necessary, bend fast idle rod at the bend as required.

1964-68, Figs. 8 and 9

1. With fast idle speed adjusting screw on second highest step of fast idle cam, move choke valve toward closed position with light pressure on choke shaft lever.
2. Insert specified gauge or drill size between choke valve and air horn wall. An adjustment will be necessary if a slight drag is not obtained as drill or gauge is being removed.
3. To adjust, bend stop on choke shaft as required (1½" units); on 1¼" units, bend fast idle rod at the angle.

Vacuum Kick Adjustment

1962-63, Fig. 10

1. Bend a paper clip or a piece of .040" wire into a shape shown. Insert bent end into slot on side of vacuum piston bore.
2. Apply light closing pressure against choke valve.
3. With wire held in place between piston and end of slot, it should be possible to insert the specified gauge or drill between choke valve and air horn wall.
4. If necessary to adjust, bend ear on choke piston lever to obtain correct clearance.
5. Place a new welch plug in piston bore and secure by rapping with a ball peen hammer on center of plug. Test for freeness of choke shaft and piston.

1964-68, Figs. 11 and 12

The choke diaphragm adjustment con-

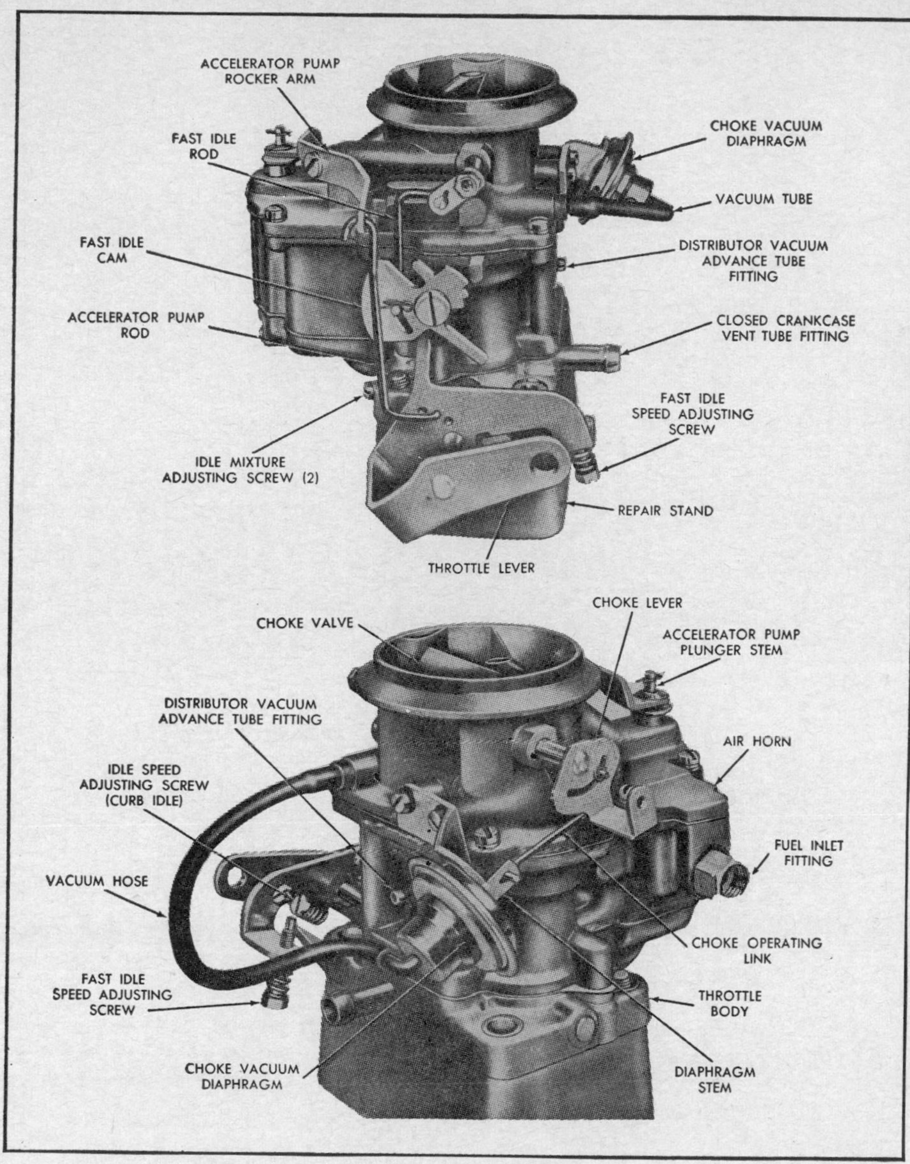

Fig. 2 Stromberg Model WW two-barrel carburetor

The choke diaphragm adjustment controls fuel delivery while the engine is running. It positions the choke valve within the air horn by action of the linkage between the choke shaft and diaphragm. The diaphragm must be energized to measure the vacuum kick adjustment. Use either a distributor test machine with a vacuum source or vacuum supplied by another vehicle. Adjust as follows:

1. If adjustment is to be made with engine running, disconnect fast idle linkage to allow choke to close to kick position with engine at curb idle. If an auxiliary vacuum source is to be used, open throttle valves (engine not running) and move choke to closed position. Release throttle first, then release choke.
2. When using an auxiliary vacuum source, disconnect vacuum hose from carburetor and connect it to a hose from vacuum supply with a small length of tube to act as a fitting. Removal of hose from diaphragm may require forces which damage the system. Apply a vacuum of 10 or more inches of mercury.
3. Insert specified drill between choke valve and air horn wall. Apply sufficient closing pressure on lever to which choke rod attaches to provide a minimum choke valve opening without distortion of diaphragm link. Note that link must deflect a wire spring before it reaches end of travel within lever slot. Link must travel to end of slot for proper measurement of kick adjustment.
4. An adjustment will be necessary if a slight drag is not obtained as drill is being removed. Shorten or lengthen diaphragm link to obtain correct choke opening. Length changes should be made carefully by bending (open or closing) the bend provided in diaphragm link. *Do not apply twisting or bending force to diaphragm.*
5. Reinstall vacuum hose on correct carburetor fitting. Return fast idle linkage to its original condition if it was disturbed as in Step 1.
6. Make following check: With no vacuum applied to diaphragm, choke valve should move freely between open and closed positions. If movement is not free, examine linkage for misalignment or interferences caused by the bending operation. Repeat adjustment if necessary to provide proper link operation.

Choke Unloader Adjustment

Figs. 13 and 14

The choke unloader is a mechanical device to partially open the choke valve at wide open throttle. It is used to eliminate choke enrichment during engine cranking. Engines that have been flooded or stalled by excessive choke enrichment can be cleared by use of the unloader. Adjust as follows:

1. With throttle valve held in wide open position, insert the specified drill size between upper edge of choke valve and air horn wall.
2. With finger lightly pressing against choke valve, a slight drag should be felt as drill is being withdrawn.
3. If an adjustment is necessary, bend unloader tang on throttle lever until correct opening has been obtained.

Accelerator Pump Adjustment

1½" Carburetors, Fig. 15

1. With throttle valves closed, measure pump travel from fully closed to fully open throttle.
2. If the dimension is not as specified, bend pump rod as shown until correct travel is obtained.

Bowl Vent Adjustment

1½" Carburetors, Fig. 16

This setting is made after the pump setting. Adjust as follows:

1. With throttle valves at curb idle, there should be the specified clearance between bowl vent valve and air horn when measured at center of vent valve and seat with a gauge or drill shank.
2. If an adjustment is necessary, bend bowl vent lever as required. *Any adjustment to the accelerator pump means that the bowl vent must be readjusted.*

Bowl Vent & Pump Adjustment

1¼" Carburetors, Fig. 17

When assembling the pump to the air horn, note that the horseshoe clip (which opens the bowl vent) can be placed in any one of three positioning notches. These notches correspond to the long, medium and short pump stroke holes in the throttle lever. Normally the bowl vent clip on the pump stem will be in the middle notch and the pump rod in the medium stroke hole. The proper procedure is to adjust the amount of bowl vent opening instead of measuring and setting the height of the pump plunger. Adjust as follows:

1. Back off idle speed adjusting screw. Open choke valve so that when

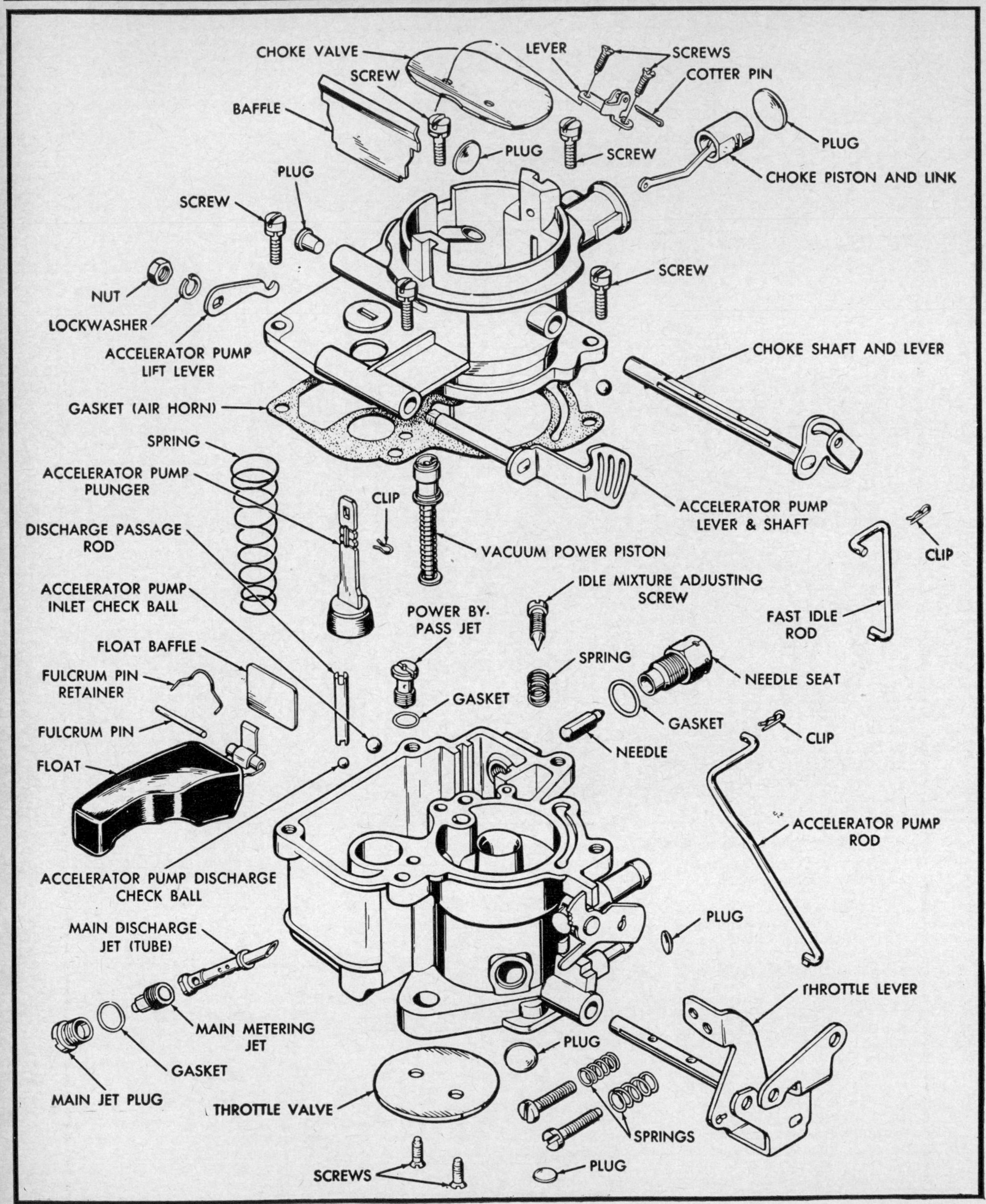

Fig. 3 Exploded view of Stromberg WA single-barrel carburetor

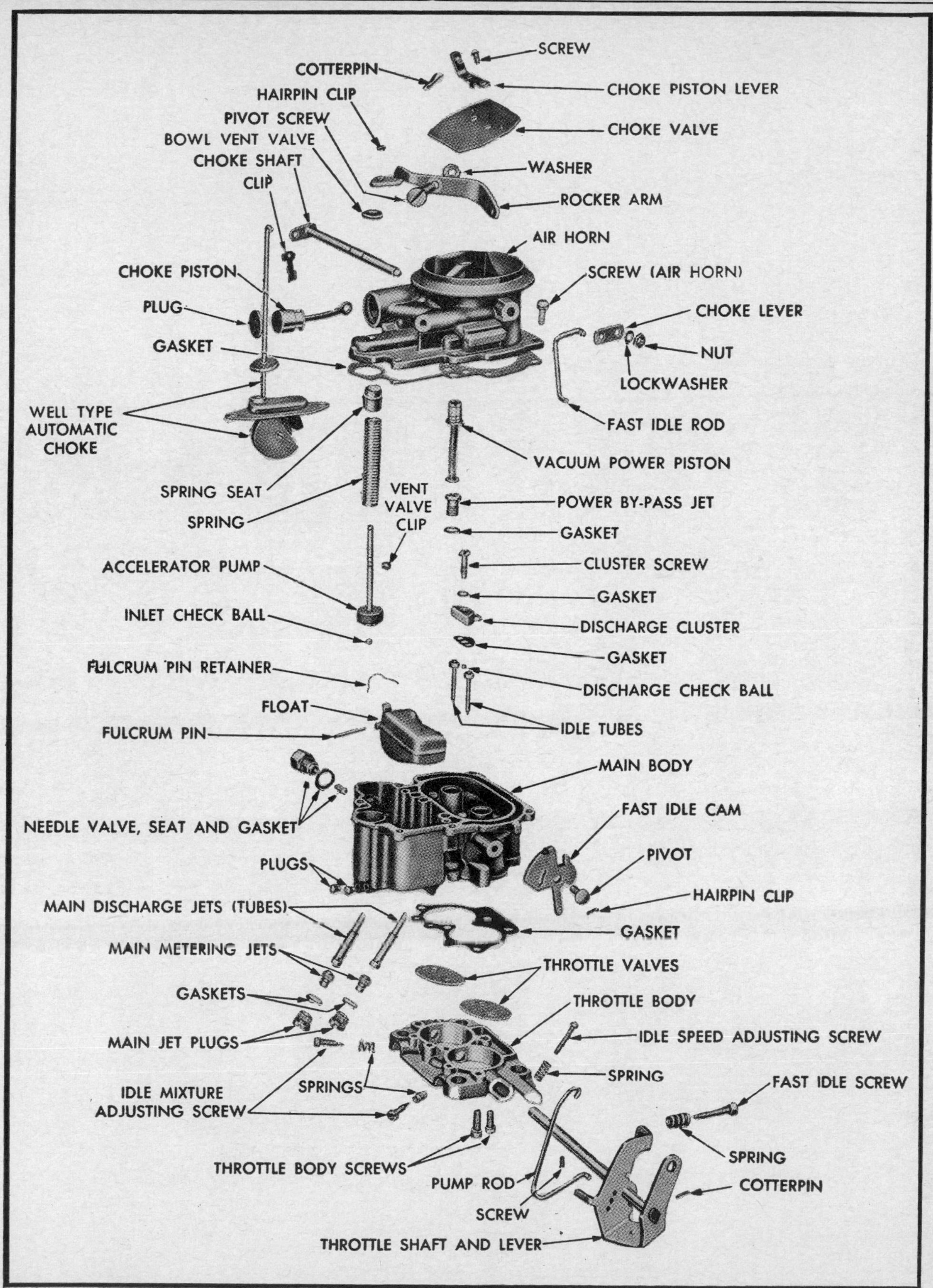

Fig. 4 Exploded view of Stromberg WW two-barrel carburetor

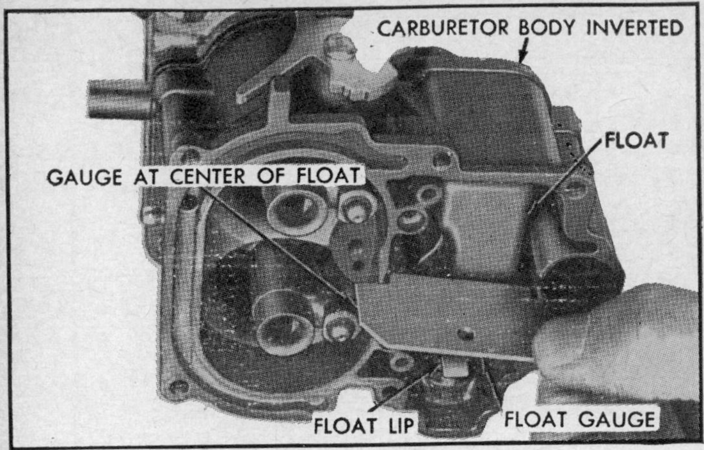

Fig. 5 Checking float level on Stromberg 1 1/4" units

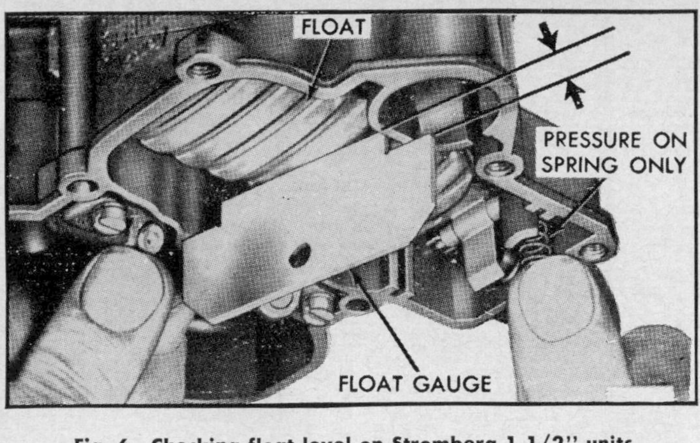

Fig. 6 Checking float level on Stromberg 1 1/2" units

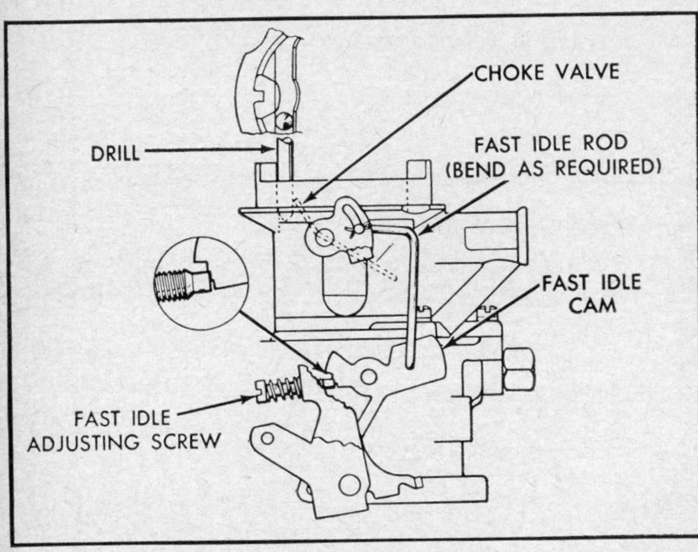

Fig. 7 Fast idle cam setting. Stromber 1963

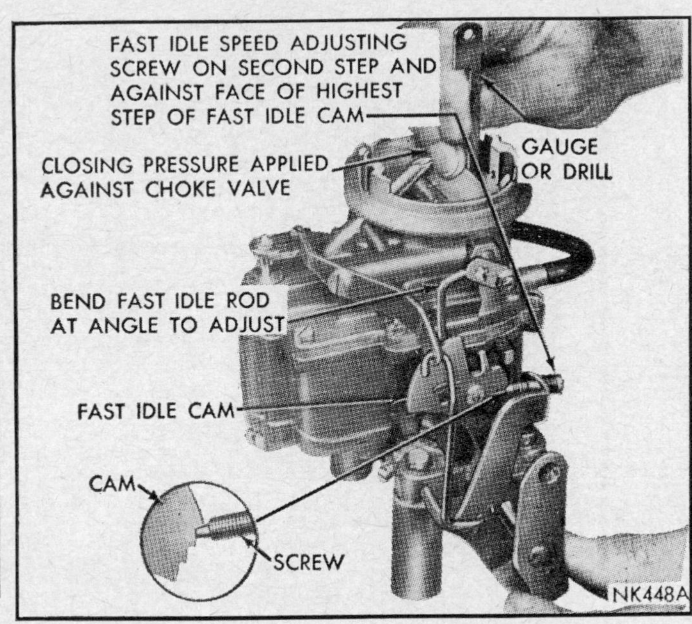

Fig. 8 Fast idle cam position. Stromberg 1964-68 1 1/4" units

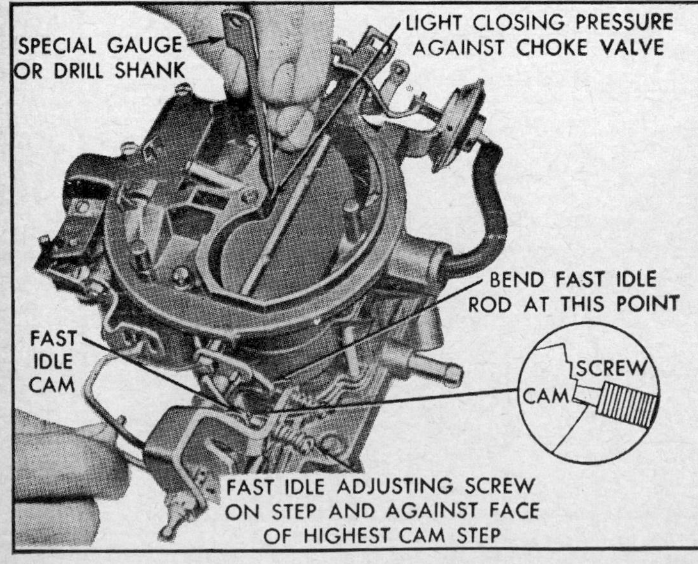

Fig. 9 Fast idle cam position. Stromberg 1964-68 1 1/2" units

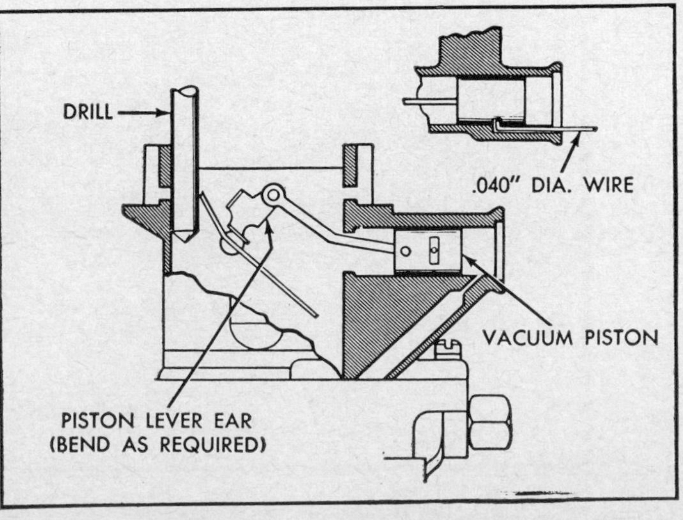

Fig. 10 Vacuum kick adjustment. Stromberg 1963 units

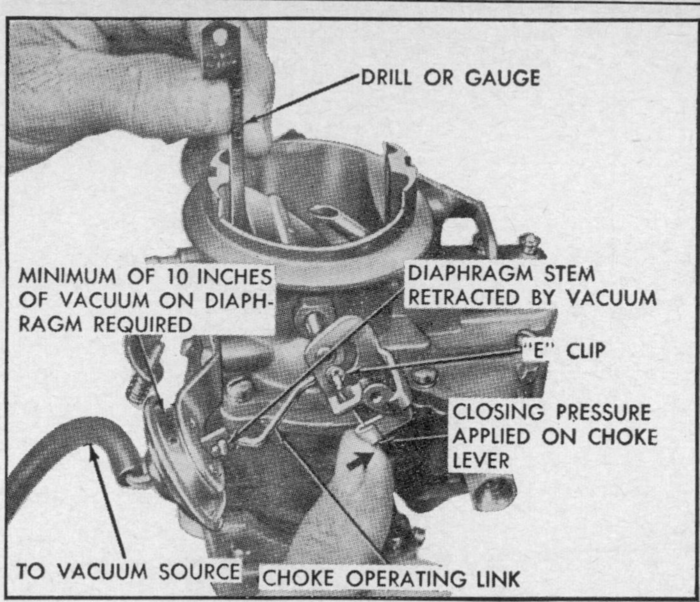

Fig. 11 Vacuum kick adjustment. Stromberg 1964-68 1 1/4" units

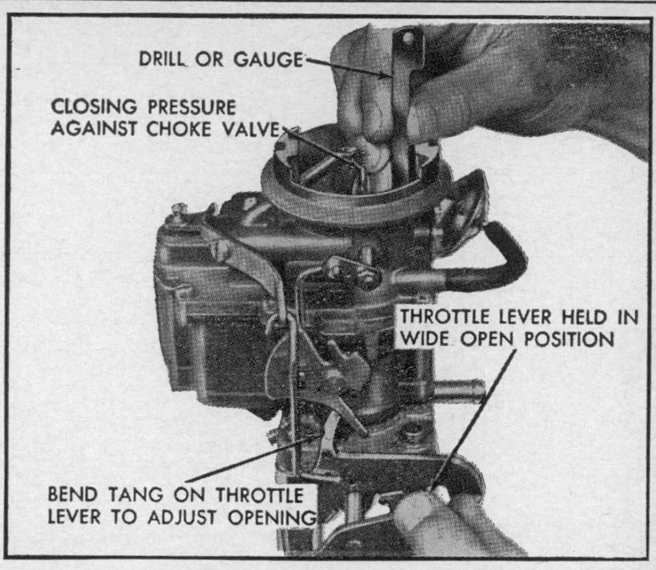

Fig. 13 Choke unloader adjustment. Stromberg 1 1/4" units

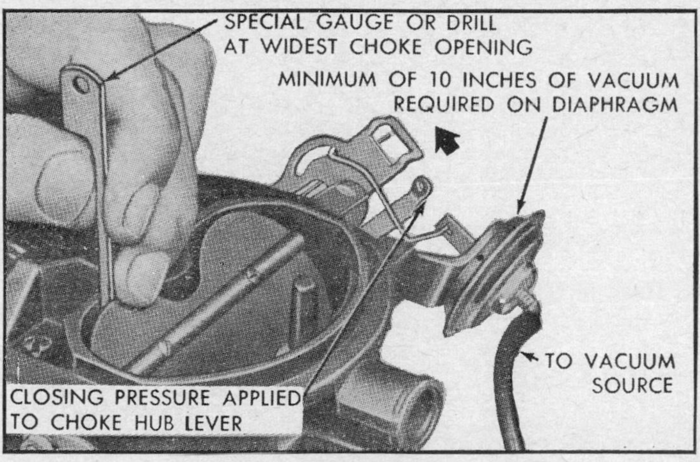

Fig. 12 Vacuum kick adjustment. Stromberg 1964-68 1 1/2" units

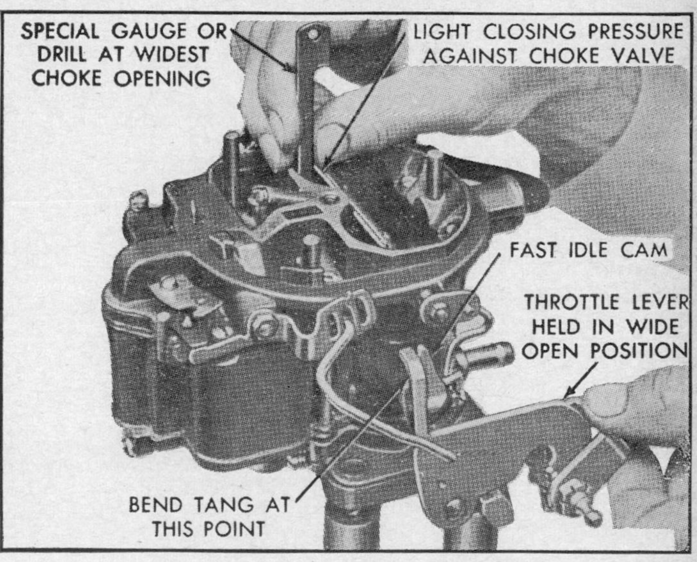

Fig. 14 Choke unloader adjustment. Stromberg 1 1/2" units

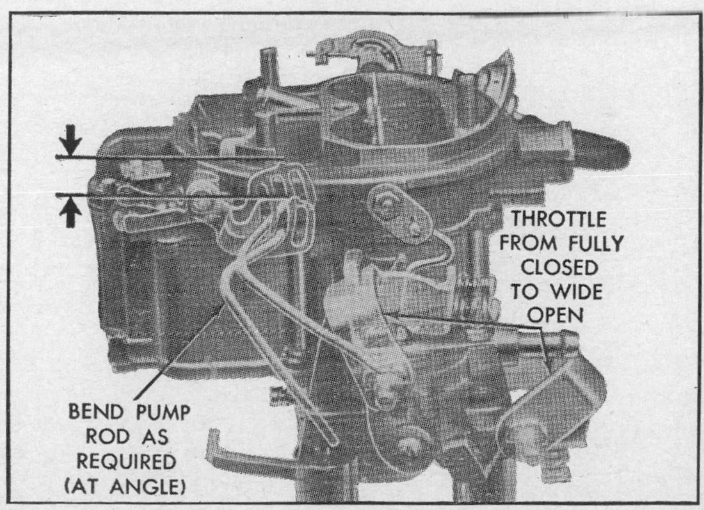

Fig. 15 Accelerator pump adjustment. Stromberg 1 1/2" units

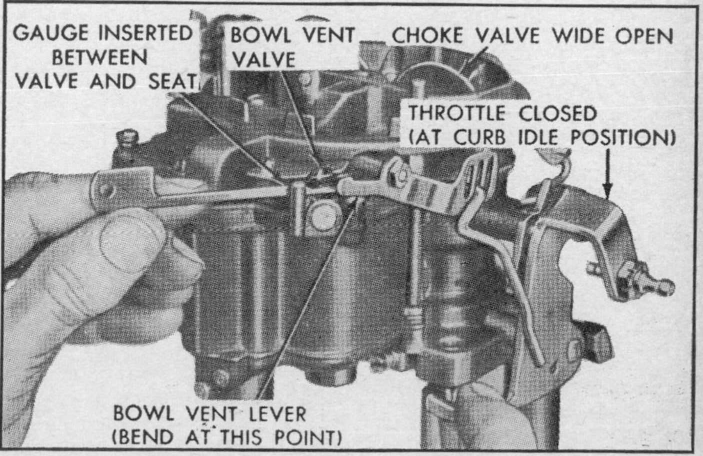

Fig. 16 Bowl vent adjustment. Stromberg 1 1/2" units

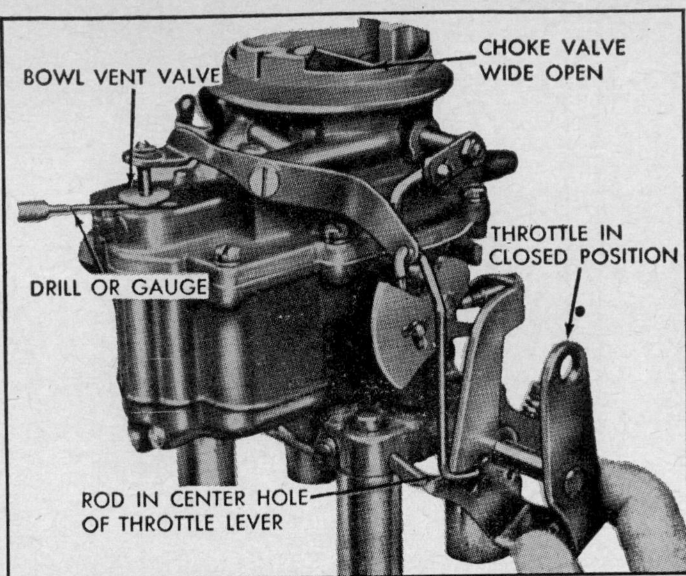

Fig. 17 Bowl vent adjustment. Stromberg 1 1/4" units

throttle valves are closed, the fast idle adjusting screw will not contact fast idle cam.

2. Be sure pump rod is in medium stroke hole in throttle lever and that bowl vent clip on pump stem is in center notch.
3. Close throttle valves tightly. It should be just possible to insert the specified gauge or drill between bowl vent and vent seat.
4. If an adjustment is necessary, bend pump rod at lower angle as required to obtain correct bowl vent opening.

NOTE: This is an important adjustment since too much lift at bowl vent will result in considerable loss in low speed fuel economy. Remember that if the pump rod is moved to either the short or long stroke position a corresponding change must be made in the location of the bowl vent clip, and the amount of lift of the bowl vent rechecked and adjusted. The pump travel is automatically taken care of when the bowl vent is properly adjusted.

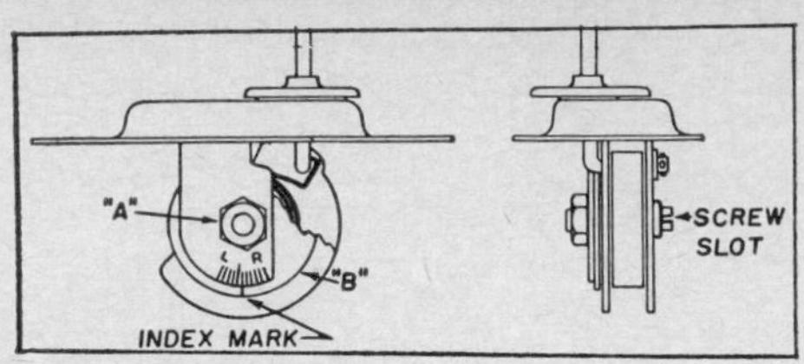

Fig. 18 Well-type automatic choke on Chrysler engines

Automatic Choke Setting

Well-Type Choke, Chrysler Engines, Fig. 18—The choke control, mounted in the intake manifold well, is accurately adjusted when originally assembled. Under normal service operations, it is recommended not to change the setting or to disassemble the components for servicing. However, if the setting has been disturbed, loosen the locknut "A" and turn part with a screwdriver until index mark on disc "B" coincides with mark listed in the *Stromberg Specifications Chart*. Hold in correct position with screwdriver while tightening locknut. When installed, lift cover disc to see that rod has clearance when choke is opened and closed. If there is any binding in the rod, replace the choke assembly.

OVERDRIVE

See Trouble Shooting Chapter For Diagnosis Procedure On These Units

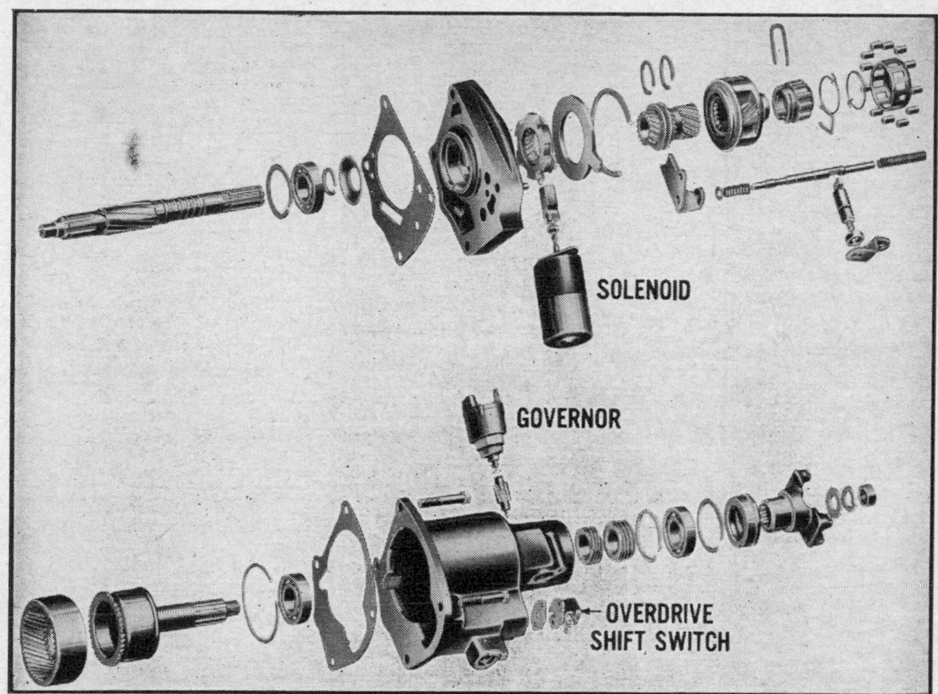

Fig. 2 Second version of full-electric overdrive with centrifugal governor. This unit is similar to the first version except the design of the second version is more compact. Some models do not use the shift (lockout) switch

OVERDRIVE UNITS are essentially automatic two-speed planetary transmissions attached to the rear of conventional three-speed transmissions. As shown in Fig. 1, the heart of the overdrive is the planetary unit consisting of sun gear, planetary pinions and internal (ring) gear. In overdrive, the pinions are connected to the mainshaft, and revolve around the sun gear which holds against rotation. The internal gear, connected to the tailshaft, is thus forced to rotate at a speed greater than the mainshaft. The engagement of the gearset is controlled by coupling the internal gear to the tail shaft, or holding the sun gear stationary, or by a combination of the two methods.

By following the procedure shown pictorially in Figs. 3 through 12, no difficulty should be experienced in servicing these units.

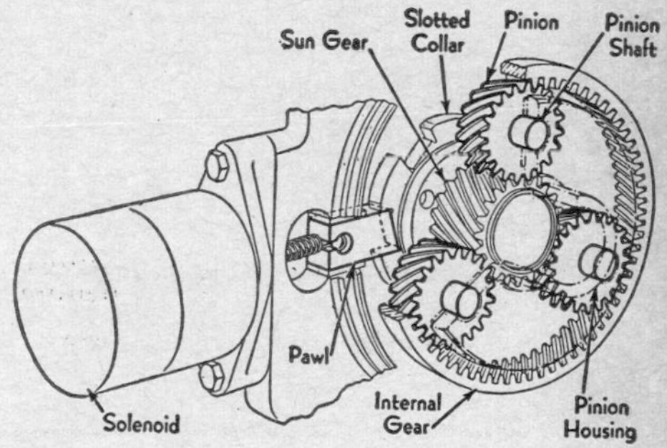

Fig. 1 Through the planetary unit shown, the overdrive provides a higher gear ratio, and when in operation, engine speed is approximately 30 per cent slower than when operating in conventional high gear

Fig. 3 Remove companion flange and governor. Also lockout switch if so equipped

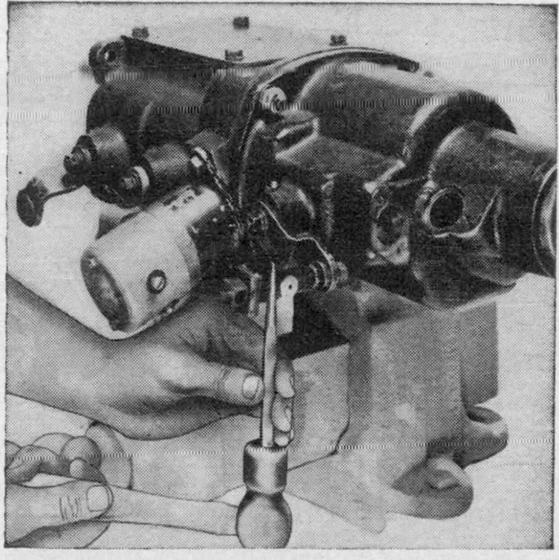

Fig. 4 After driving out locating pin, pull shift shaft as far as possible to disengage operating cam from shift rail. Remove overdrive housing. Tap end of shaft to prevent its coming off with housing and spilling free wheel rollers. Parts inside housing may then be removed

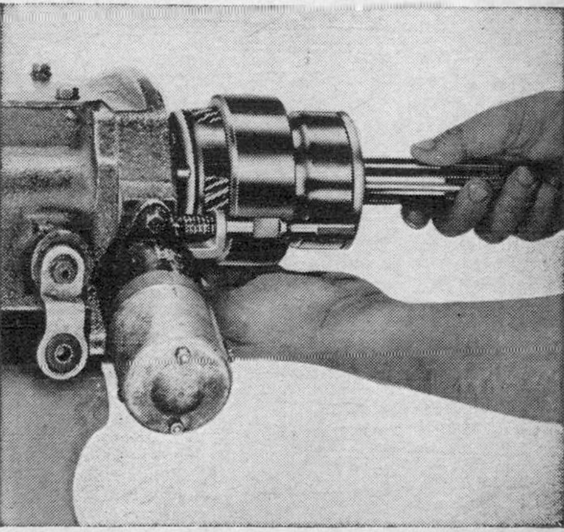

Fig. 5 Hold the adapter plate to the transmission case with one screw and remove the overdrive shaft, catching the free wheel rollers as shown. Removing snap ring permits ring gear to be taken off shaft

Fig. 6 Remove retaining clip and take off free wheel unit and pinion cage

Fig. 7 Separate pinion cage from free wheel unit by removing retaining clip

Fig. 8 Remove overdrive sun gear and shift rail

Fig. 9 Remove attaching screws, rotate solenoid 1/4 turn and take off

Fig. 10 After releasing snap ring from adapter plate, remove sun gear cover plate, blocker and solenoid pawl

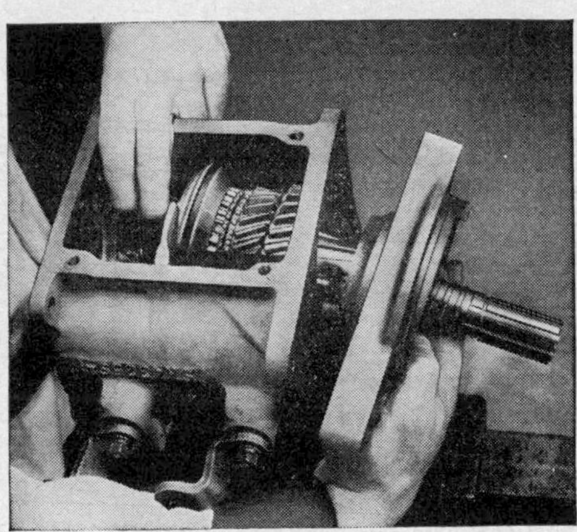

Fig. 11 At this point, if repairs are to be made on the transmission, remove the mainshaft, adapter plate, gears and synchronizer as a unit

Fig. 12 Reverse the order of disassembly to assemble the unit. After inserting the pawl with the notched side up as shown, install blocker assembly and cover plate, being sure blocker ring and pawl are properly positioned. Then install large snap ring in adapter plate

THREE SPEED MANUAL SHIFT TRANSMISSIONS

See Car Chapters for procedures on removing the transmission and adjusting the gearshift linkage

APPLICATION INDEX

	Type No.	Page
BUICK—Seniors		
1963	9	1-282
1964-65 V8-401	9	1-282
1964-65 V8-330	1	1-262
1966-69 Wildcat	7	1-277
1966-69 Exc. Wildcat	13	1-291
BUICK—Intermediates		
1963	3	1-269
1964-65 Except Below	1	1-262
1965-69 Floor Shift	7	1-277
1966-69 Column Shift	13	1-291
CAMARO		
1967-68 (Exc. Heavy Duty)	13	1-291
1967-68 Heavy Duty	12	1-287
CHEVELLE		
1964-65	1	1-262
1966-68 (Exc. Heavy Duty)	13	1-291
1966-68 Heavy Duty	12	1-287
CHEVROLET		
1963-65 Except Below	1	1-262
1965-68 Heavy Duty	12	1-287
1966-68 Exc. Heavy Duty	13	1-291
CHEVY II		
1963-65 Exc. Heavy Duty	1	1-262
1966-68 Exc. Heavy Duty	13	1-291
1965-68 Heavy Duty	12	1-287
CHRYSLER		
1963-68	5	1-274
COMET & MONTEGO		
1963-66 Six	8	1-280
1963-69 V8	7	1-277
1967-69 Six	7	1-277
CORVAIR		
1963-65	4	1-272
1966-69	14	1-294
CORVETTE		
1963-65 Except Below	1	1-262
1965-68 With V8-396	12	1-287
1966-68 Exc. V8-396	13	1-291

	Type No.	Page
COUGAR		
1967-69	7	1-277
DODGE DART		
1963-69	6	1-274
DODGE		
1963-69 (Exc. Below)	6	1-274
1963-69 Heavy Duty	5	1-274
1963-64 V8-426	10	1-283
FAIRLANE		
1963-66 Six	8	1-280
1963-67 W/O.D.	11	1-284
1963-69 V8, 1967-69 Six	7	1-277
FALCON		
1963-67 Six	8	1-280
1963-69 V8, 1968-69 Six	7	1-277
FORD		
1963-69 Exc. Below	7	1-277
1963-65 V8-352, 390 With O.D.	10	1-283
1963-67 Six With O.D.	11	1-284
1963-67 V8-260, 289 With O.D.	11	1-284
FORD BRONCO		
1966-69	7	1-277
JEEP		
1963-69 Two Wheel Drive	8	1-280
1963-69 Four Wheel Drive	①	
①—See Jeep Chapter		
MERCURY		
1963-69 Standard Unit	7	1-277
1965 With Overdive	11	1-284
MUSTANG		
1964-69 V8, 1967-69 Six	7	1-277
1965-66 Six	8	1-280

	Type No.	Page
OLDSMOBILE—Seniors		
1963-64 Except Jetstar 88	2	1-265
1964-65 Jetstar 88	1	1-262
1965 Exc. Jetstar 88	10	1-283
1966-69	7	1-277
OLDS—Intermediates		
1963	3	1-269
1964-65 Column Shift	1	1-262
1965-69 Floor Shift	7	1-277
1966-69 Column Shift	13	1-291
PLYMOUTH		
1963-69 Standard Unit	6	1-274
1963-69 Heavy Duty Unit	5	1-274
1963-64 V8-426	10	1-283
PONTIAC—Seniors		
1963, 1964 Early	1	1-262
1964 Late; 1965-69	7	1-277
PONTIAC—Intermediates		
1963	4	1-272
1964-65	1	1-262
1966-69 Exc. Heavy Duty	13	1-291
1966-69 Heavy Duty	7	1-277
1967-69 Firebird	13	1-291
1968-69 Firebird H-D	7	1-277
RAMBLER		
1963-67 (Exc. V8-327)	8	1-280
1963-66 V8-327	10	1-283
1968-69 6-199	8	1-280
1968-69 Exc. 6-199	15	1-296
SCOUT		
1963-69	①	
①—See Scout Chapter		
VALIANT		
1963-69	6	1-274
VOLKSWAGEN	①	
①—See Car Chapter		

Type One

DISASSEMBLE TRANS.

1. Referring to Fig. 1, remove side cover.
2. Remove extension housing and mainshaft, Fig. 2.
3. Slide low-reverse gear off clutch sleeve and remove through side cover opening.
4. Remove clutch from clutch gear and take it out through side cover opening.
5. Remove pilot rollers from clutch gear.
6. Remove clutch gear bearing retainer.
7. Using tool shown in Fig. 3, or a dummy shaft, remove countershaft and lower cluster gear to bottom of case.
8. Remove bearing snap ring, Fig. 4.
9. Tap clutch gear and bearing back into case, Fig. 5, and remove through rear of case.
10. Lift cluster gear out through rear of case.
11. Using a drift pin, drive idler shaft lock pin into shaft. Then drive idler gear shaft out of case, Fig. 6.

CAUTION: Do not allow idler shaft to rotate, causing lock pin to drop down, as damage to thrust washers could result.

12. Remove idler gear, thrust washer, bearing and bearing washer.

UNIT REPAIRS

Mainshaft Repairs

DISASSEMBLE:

1. Referring to Fig. 7, expand bearing snap ring and tap rear of mainshaft with a soft hammer. Then remove mainshaft assembly through extension housing.
2. Remove speedometer drive gear.
3. Remove snap ring and press bearing off shaft.
4. Remove washer and 2nd speed gear.

ASSEMBLE:

1. Lubricate bore of 2nd speed gear and install on mainshaft.

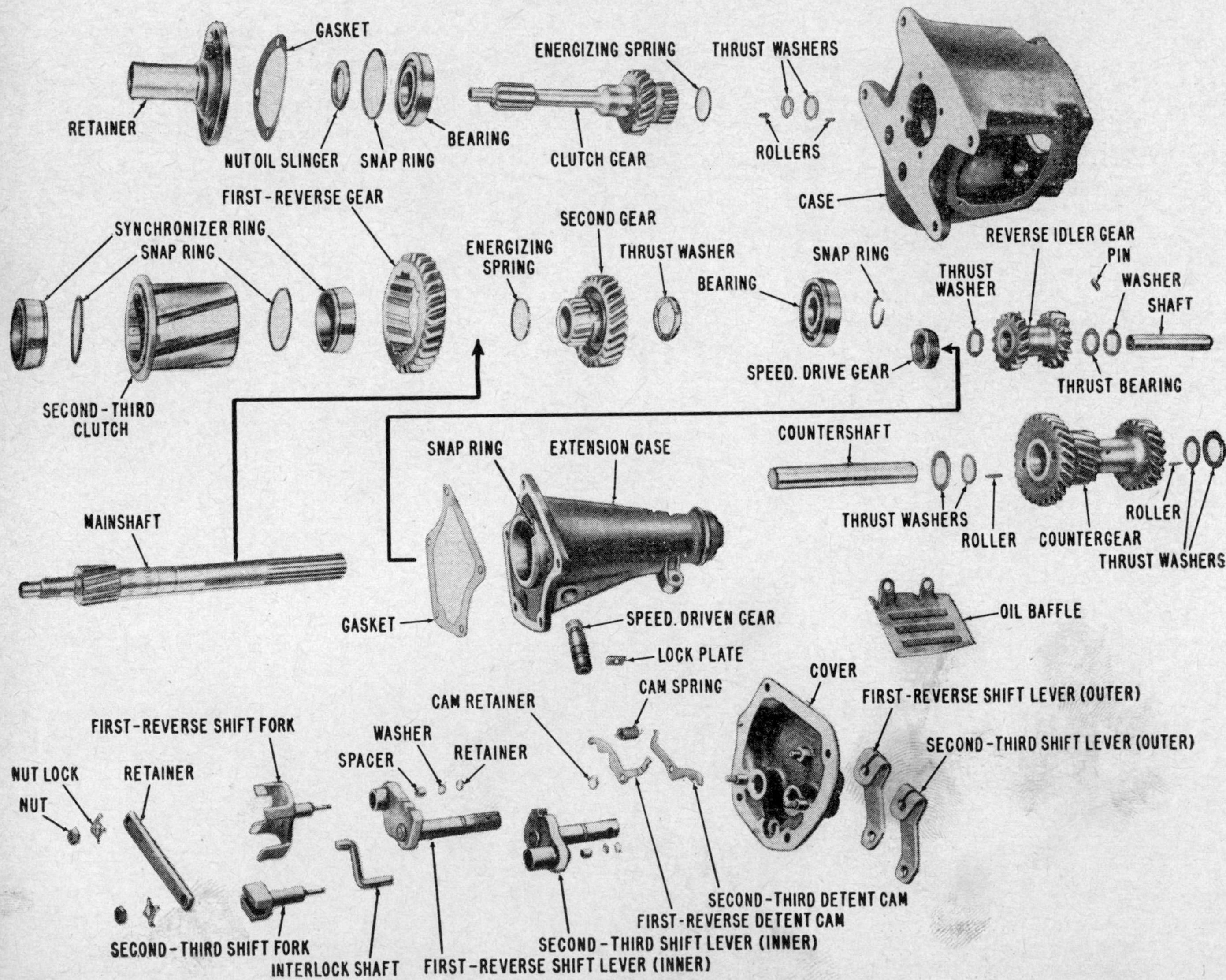

Fig. 1 Type 1 transmission disassembled. NOTE: Chevy II uses only one thrust washer at each end of cluster gear. Also some transmissions have needle bearings at each end of the reverse idler gear instead of bushings.

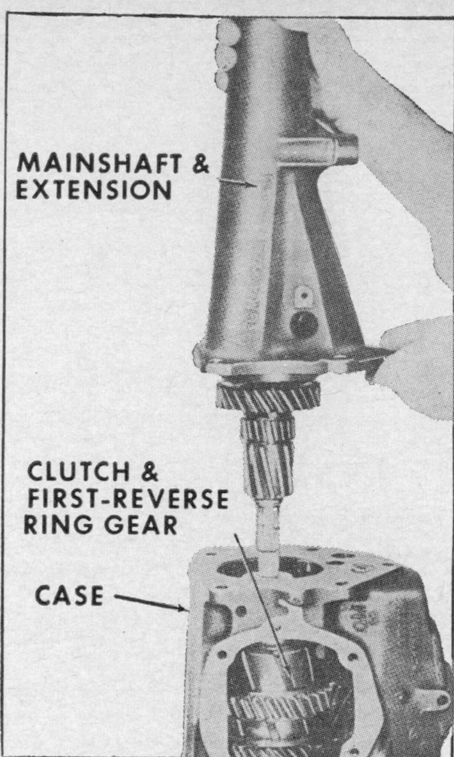

Fig. 2 Mainshaft and extension remove and install

Fig. 3 Countershaft remove and install

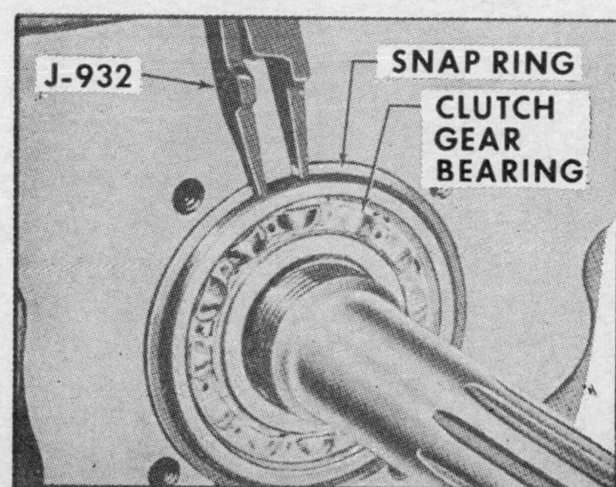

Fig. 4 Clutch gear snap ring remove and install

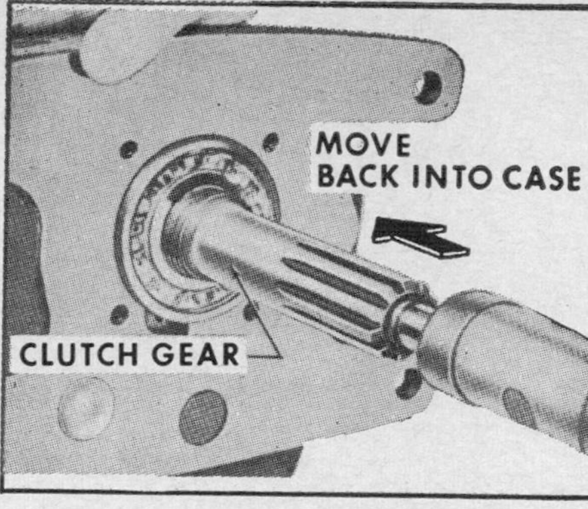

Fig. 5 Clutch gear bearing removal

Fig. 6 Idler shaft removal

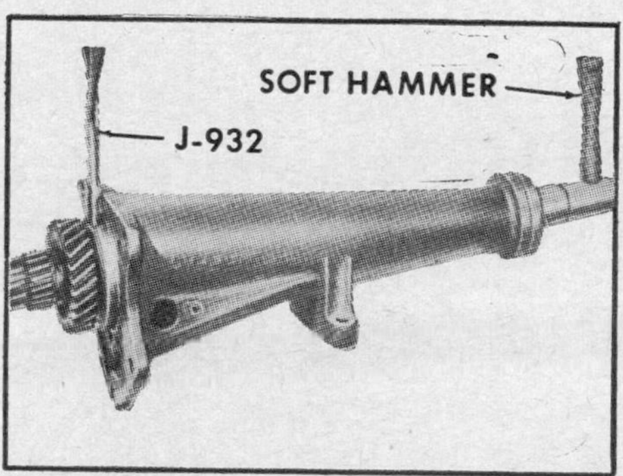

Fig. 7 Mainshaft removal

2. Install bearing, being certain groove in O. D. of bearing is toward 2nd gear.
3. Select and install a snap ring that gives no more than .004" end play between bearing and shaft.
4. Start speedometer drive gear on shaft with chamfered I. D. of gear toward bearing. Press gear on shaft until gear is positioned as shown in Fig. 8.

Clutch Gear Bearing

1. Remove bearing retainer nut and oil slinger, Fig. 9.
2. Install gear and bearing in transmission case. Then install snap ring on bearing.
3. Using a soft hammer, remove bearing from shaft by tapping clutch gear shaft back into case.
4. Remove bearing from case by tapping with soft hammer.
5. To assemble, place bearing on clutch shaft with snap ring groove to front.
6. Using tool shown in Fig. 9 or equivalent, install retainer nut and oil slinger. Tighten enough to permit free movement of bearing. Lock in place by staking into hole with a center punch.

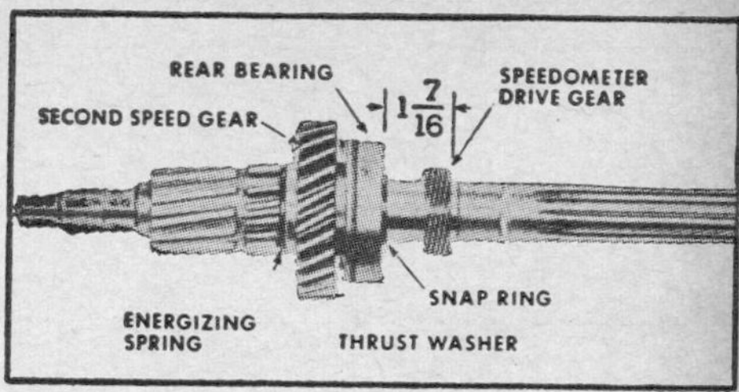

Fig. 8 Mainshaft identification

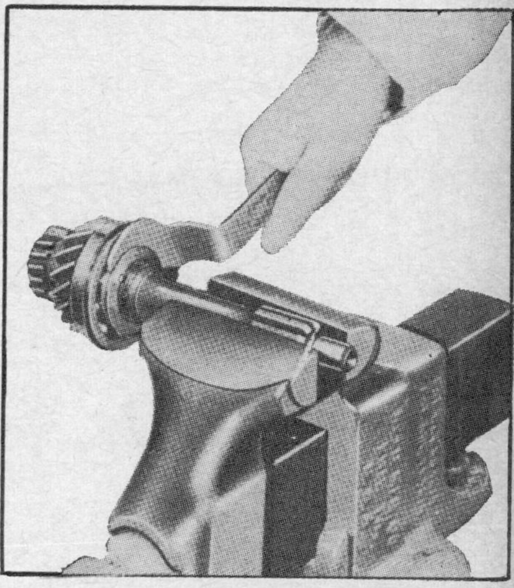

Fig. 9 Retainer nut and oil slinger removal

Clutch Sleeve & Synchronizer Ring

1. Remove low-reverse sliding gear from clutch.
2. Turn synchronizer ring in clutch sleeve until ends of ring retainer can be seen through slot in sleeve.
3. Using snap ring pliers, Fig. 10, expand retainer into counterbore in sleeve. This raises retainer from ring groove so that ring may be slipped out.

NOTE: Check rings for wear or looseness in clutch sleeve. If rings are damaged in any way, it will be necessary to replace sleeve and both synchronizer rings. Check each retainer in its respective ring. Check for any rocking or excessive looseness. Excessive rocking will not permit proper synchronization.

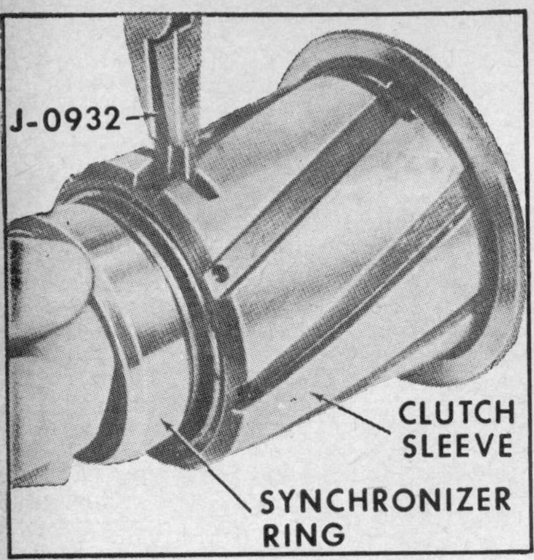

Fig. 10 Synchronizing ring removal

Fig. 12 Energizing spring location

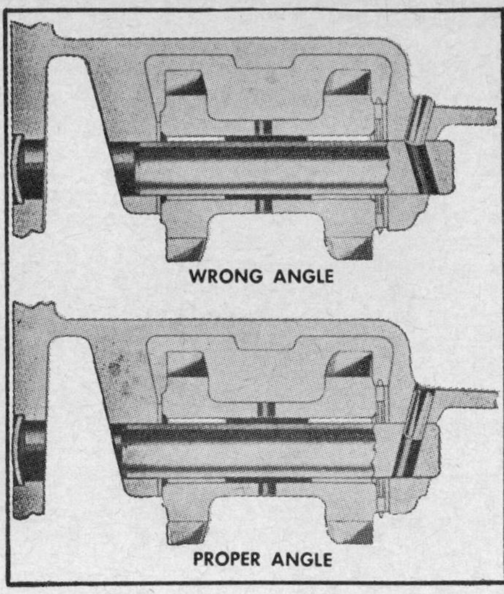

Fig. 13 Reverse idler shaft alignment

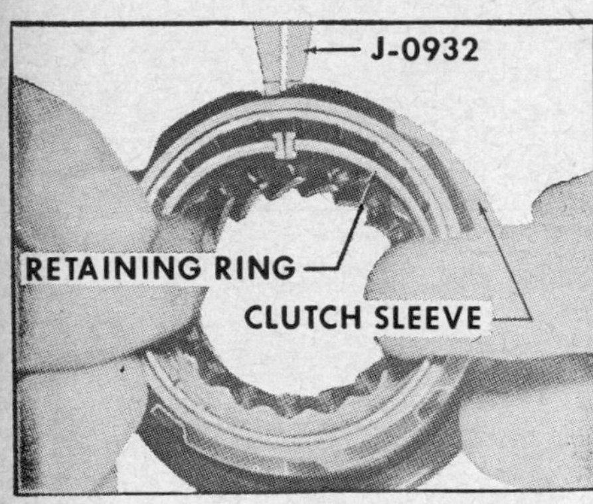

Fig. 11 Synchronizing ring installation

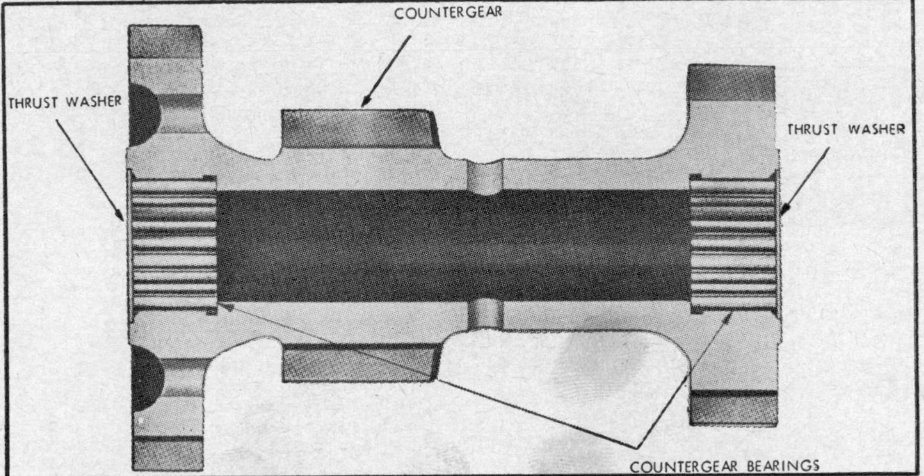

Fig. 14 Cluster gear and bearings assembled. NOTE: Chevy II uses only one thrust washer at each end of cluster gear

4. To assemble, install ring retainer in counterbores in ends of clutch sleeve.
5. Insert snap ring pliers, Fig. 11, in clutch sleeve opening. Expand retainer with fingers just enough to catch tips of tool jaws. Then open tool jaws enough to expand retainer back into counterbore and allow ring to slip in sleeve. Install both rings in same manner.

CAUTION: Be certain retainers are seated in groove all the way around ring so ring can turn freely.

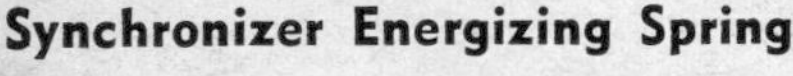

Synchronizer Energizing Spring

Under normal operation, it should never be necessary to replace the energizing springs. However, should a spring be removed for any reason, a new spring should be used for replacement. Locate springs as indicated in Fig. 12.

Side Cover Repair

DISASSEMBLE:

1. Remove shifter shaft retainer.
2. Remove detent cam spring, retaining ring and cams.
3. Using a soft hammer, remove shifter shaft and fork assemblies.
4. Remove interlock shaft.

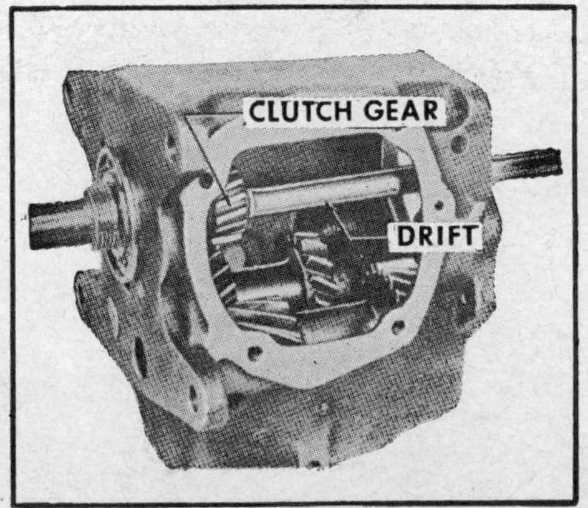

Fig. 15 Clutch gear installation

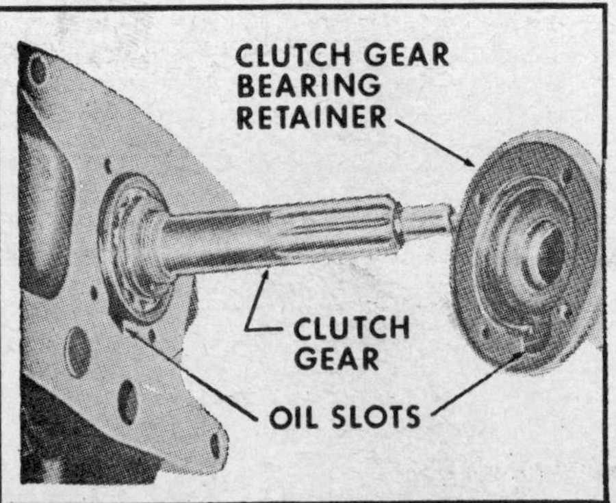

Fig. 16 Clutch gear bearing retainer oil slots

ASSEMBLE:
1. Install interlock shaft.
2. Lube shafts with transmission oil. Align low-reverse shaft in hole and tap in place. Position interlock so as to clear shaft.
3. Install 2-3 shaft and fork in same manner.
4. Install detent cams with low-reverse cam on top of 2-3 detent cam. Install retaining ring.
5. Install detent cam spring.
6. Install shifter shaft retainer and torque nuts to 3-5 ft-lbs.

REASSEMBLE TRANS.

1. Coat with grease and install reverse idler thrust washers and bearing. Coat bushings with transmission lube.
2. Place gear assembly in position in case with thrust bearing toward rear.
3. Install idler shaft, making sure lock pin hole in shaft lines up with hole in case at same angle, Fig. 13.
4. Coat new lock pin with Permatex No. 2 or equivalent. Drive it in about $\frac{1}{16}$" beyond flush with case and peen hole slightly.
5. Install idler shaft expansion plug in case.
6. Assemble bearings and thrust washers to cluster gear as shown in Fig. 14, using cup grease to hold parts in place. Use tool shown in Fig. 3 or a dummy shaft when installing bearings and thrust washers.

Fig. 17 Installation of clutch and low-reverse sliding gear

7. Set cluster gear in bottom of case.
8. Place cup grease in mainshaft pilot hole in clutch gear. Then install larger group of 14 rollers, then the washer with the small I. D. Next install washer with large I. D. and then group of 24 smaller roller bearings.
9. Insert clutch gear from inside of case and, using a soft drift, tap outer race of clutch gear bearing until bearing locating ring groove is outside front of case, Fig. 15.
10. Install snap ring on bearing and tap clutch gear rearward until snap ring is firmly against case.
11. Install clutch gear bearing retainer and gasket. Make sure oil slot in retainer lines up with oil slot in front face of case, Fig. 16. Do not allow gasket to protrude beyond edge of retainer.
12. Coat retainer screws with Permatex No. 2 or equivalent and install in retainer, using the special shakeproof washers. Torque screws to 12-15 ft-lbs.
13. Lube and insert countershaft in case. Align countergear with shaft and tap shaft through, pushing dummy shaft out through front of case. Be certain flat on end of countershaft is horizontal and to bottom of case.
14. After countershaft is aligned, drive it into case until flat on shaft is flush with case.

CAUTION: Flat on shaft must be horizontal and at bottom of case in order to allow rear extension to fit properly.

15. Assemble low-reverse gear on clutch sleeve. Insert this assembly into side cover opening by tipping front end of unit into opening first. Align lug of synchronizing ring with slot in clutch sleeve when positioning assembly on clutch sleeve, Fig. 17.
16. Install mainshaft in extension and secure with snap ring.
17. With gasket installed on rear face of case, align lugs on synchronizer rings with slot in mainshaft so that lugs slide in slots on gear. Push mainshaft into clutch sleeve until extension is tight against case (see Fig. 2). Install bolts and lock washers and torque to 40-45 ft-lbs.

Type Two

DISASSEMBLE TRANS.

1. Referring to Fig. 1, remove cover and rear bearing retainer.
2. Remove set screws from two shifter yokes, Fig. 2. Pull mainshaft rearward until mainshaft clears case. If fit between bearing and case is tight, tap 2nd speed gear, Fig. 3.
3. Remove synchronizer clutch, Fig. 4.
4. Remove 2nd gear snap ring, Fig. 5.
5. Remove keyed thrust washer, 2nd gear and rear thrust washer from mainshaft, Fig. 6.
6. Remove low-reverse retaining ring and slide gear off mainshaft, Fig. 7.
7. Pull mainshaft from rear of case.
8. Loosen outer shift lever bolt. Position lever so that inner shift levers are vertical and remove outer shift lever.
9. Remove set screws from inner shift levers (see Fig. 2).
10. Pull selector shaft away from 2-3 shifter shaft and remove interlock retainer, Fig. 8.
11. Drive selector shaft out through right side of case. Welch plug will be driven out by the shaft. Do not allow interlock levers to drop into case.
12. Push or tap low-reverse shifter shaft out through rear of case, taking care to prevent poppet ball and spring from flying out. Remove low-

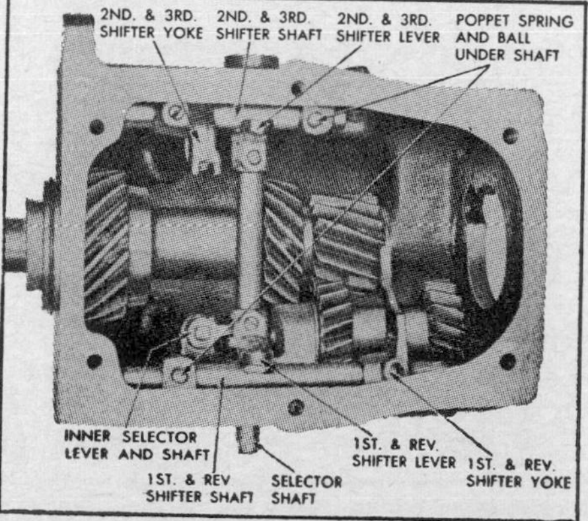

Fig. 2 Shift mechanism

Fig. 3 Freeing rear bearing from case

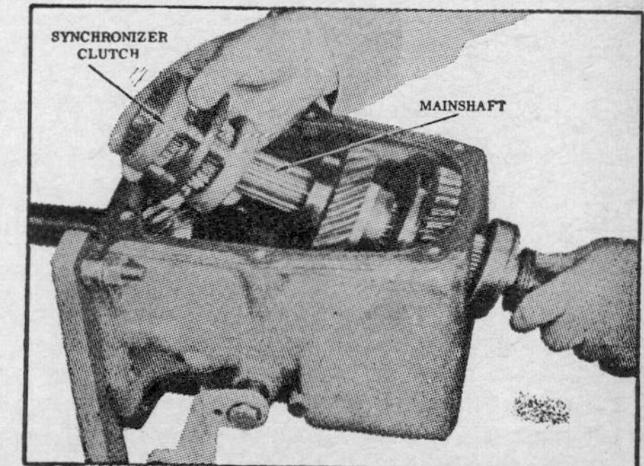

Fig. 4 Removing synchronizer clutch

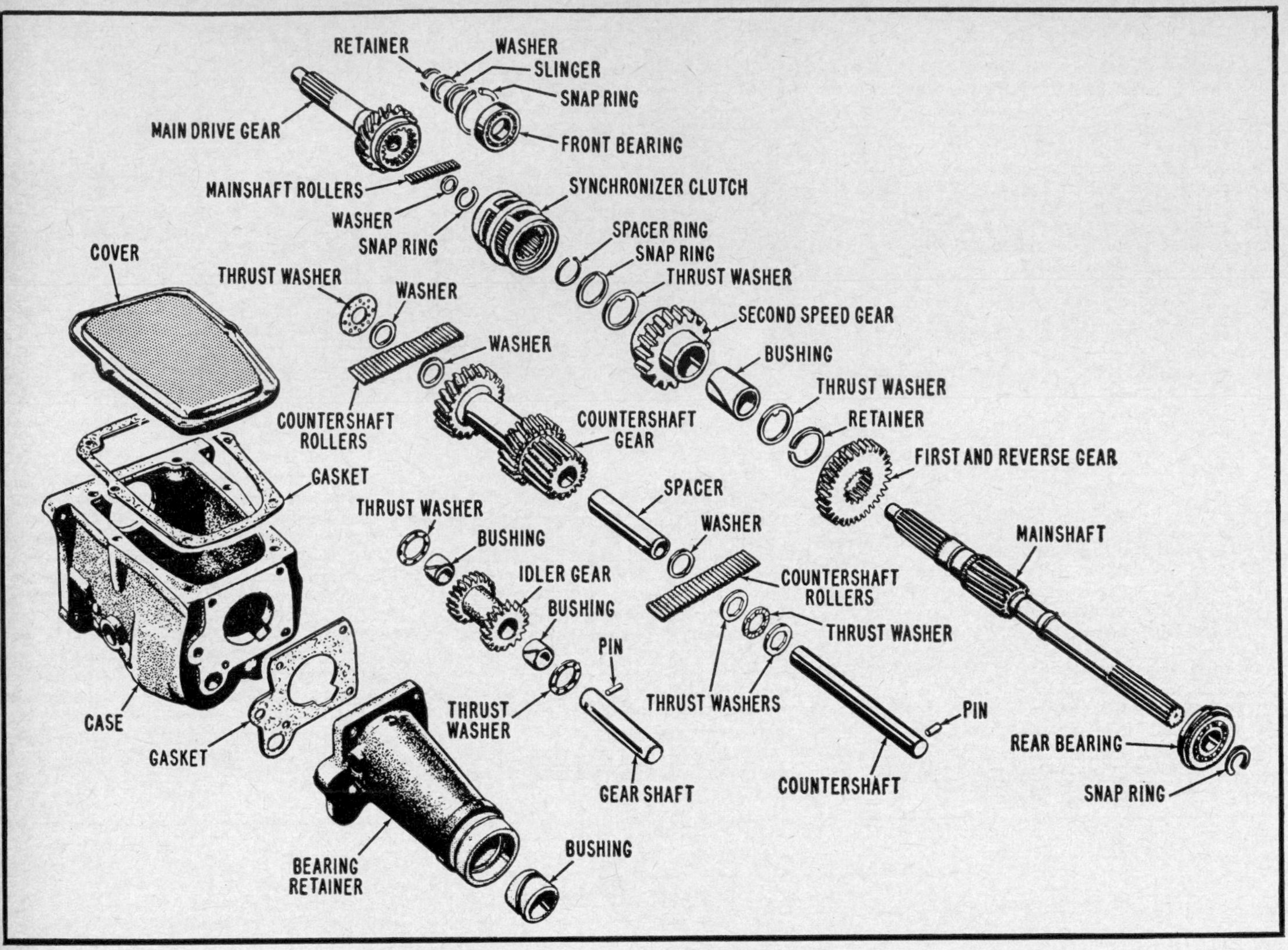

Fig. 1 Type 2 transmission disassembled. Note that low-reverse mainshaft gear has shift fork groove to rear

reverse shifter yoke, ball and spring.

13. Push or tap 2-3 shifter shaft out through front of case, then remove shifter yoke, ball and spring.
14. Remove low-reverse interlock pin from case, Fig. 9.
15. Drive countershaft lock pin into shaft, Fig. 10.
16. Remove retaining ring from main drive gear bearing outer race and tap drive gear and bearing assembly toward rear of case. Remove assembly from case.
17. Drive countershaft out through rear end of case, Fig. 11. Make sure loading tool being used follows shaft closely so that bearings and thrust washers will be held in place. Lift cluster gear from case.
18. Remove outer selector lever and seal, then remove inner selector shaft and lever.

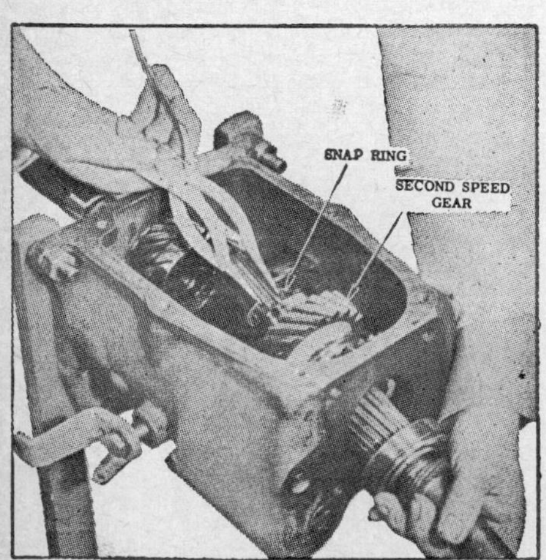

Fig. 5 Removing 2nd speed gear snap ring

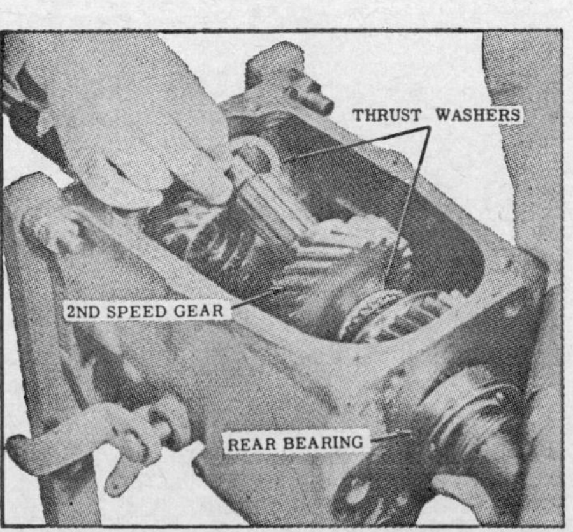

Fig. 6 Removing 2nd speed gear

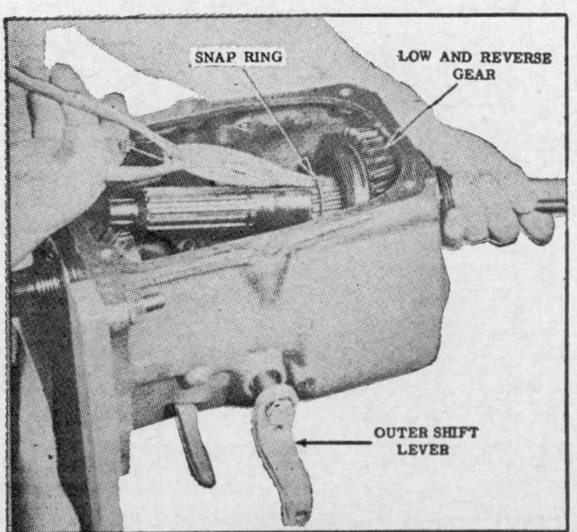

Fig. 7 Removing low-reverse snap ring

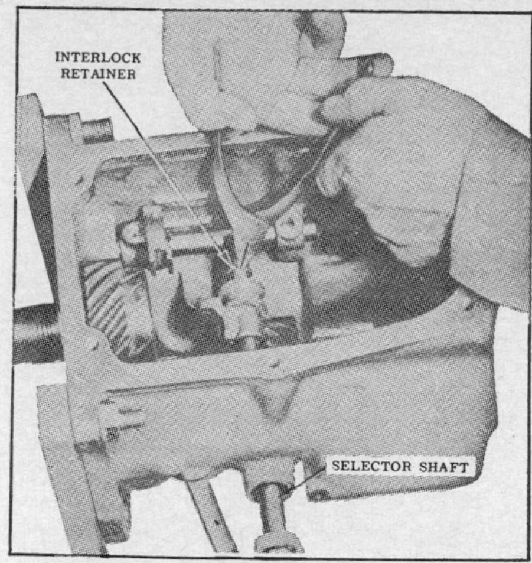

Fig. 8 Removing interlock retainer

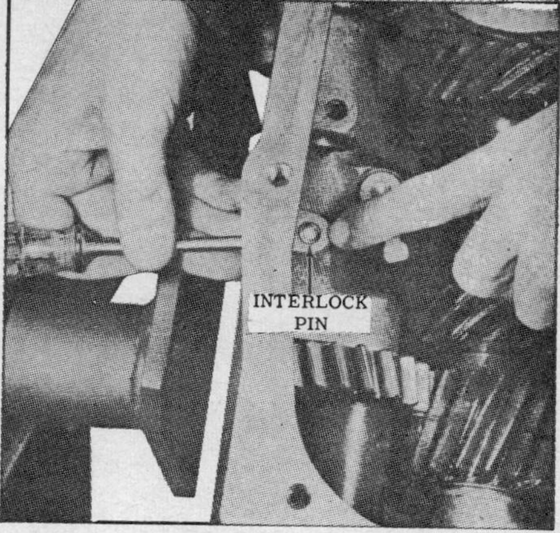

Fig. 9 Removing low-reverse interlock pin

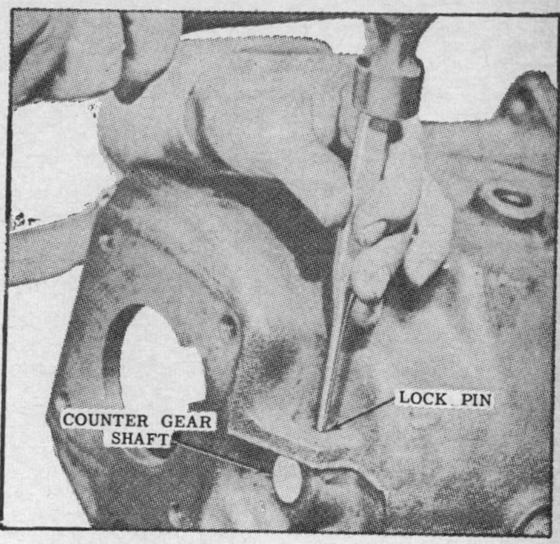

Fig. 10 Driving lock pin into countershaft

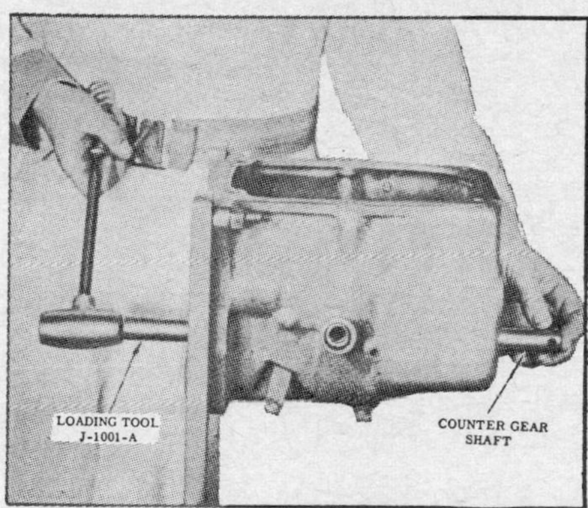

Fig. 11 Removing countershaft

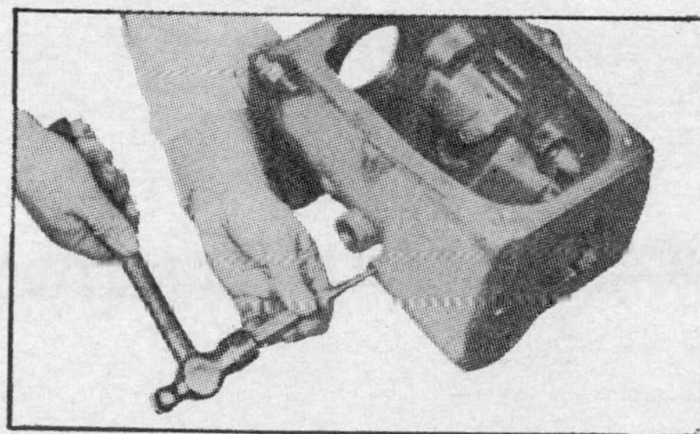

Fig. 12 Driving lock pin into idler shaft

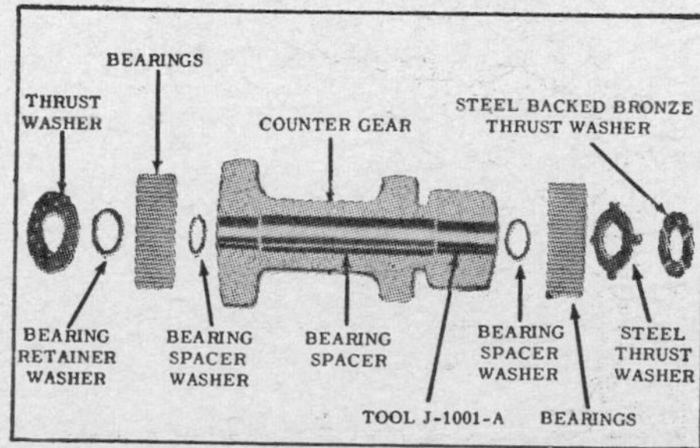

Fig. 14 Counter gear assembly

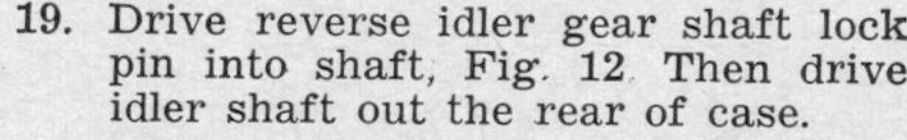

19. Drive reverse idler gear shaft lock pin into shaft, Fig. 12 Then drive idler shaft out the rear of case.

NOTE: A ½" x 8" brass drift should be used to remove the shaft by driving on the idler gear shaft through the countershaft boss in front of case

20. Remove idler shaft, gear and thrust washer from case, Fig 13.

UNIT REPAIRS

Countershaft & Gear

Assemble the unit as suggested by Fig. 14, using a suitable loading tool for the installation of bearings and washers. Use grease to hold washers in place. Be sure to place the steel side of thrust washer toward case.

When the unit is completely assembled, leave the loading tool in place until the assembly is installed in the case.

Main Drive Gear

1. To remove the bearing from the shaft, Fig. 15, remove the retaining ring and washer. Then remove the bearing by jarring the shaft on a block of wood.
2. Pry the wire lock ring from the bore of the gear, then remove retaining washer and 14 needle bearings.
3. To assemble, hold shaft in a vertical position and install needle bearings, using grease to hold them in place. Install retaining washer and lock ring.
4. Install bearing on shaft with shielded side of bearing toward gear.
5. Install washer (dished side toward bearing), then install retaining ring on shaft against washer.

Mainshaft

1. To remove the speedometer drive gear and bearing, bend the speedometer gear spacer and remove from shaft
2. Remove retaining ring from groove and slide it along shaft toward speedometer gear, Fig 16.
3. Place low-reverse gear on mainshaft with flat side of gear toward bearing. Using the low-reverse gear as a slide hammer, remove speedometer gear, retaining ring and bearing.
4. To assemble, install bearing on mainshaft with its shielded side toward shoulder of low-reverse splines on mainshaft and seat bearing against splines.
5. Install retaining ring against inner race of bearing.

NOTE. On late model Oldsmobiles it is not necessary to install the spacer or speedometer drive gear as the speedometer is driven by the left front wheel.

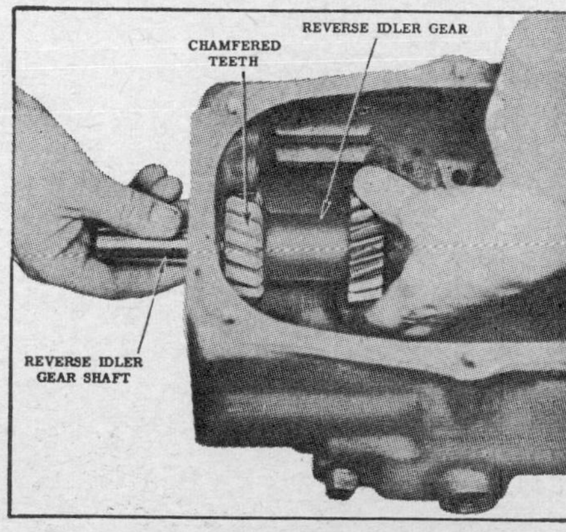

Fig 13 Removing reverse idler gear shaft

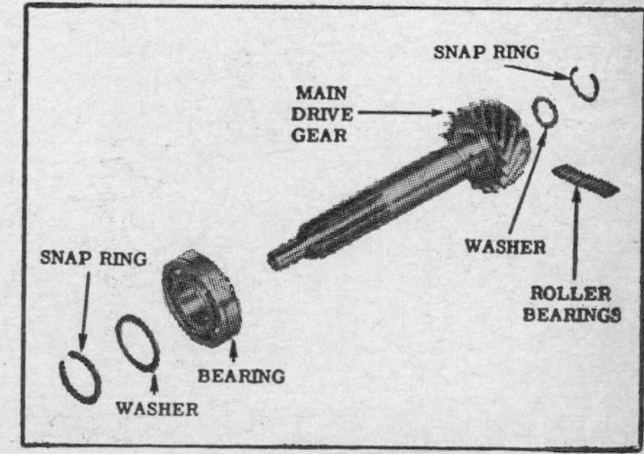

Fig. 15 Main drive gear assembly

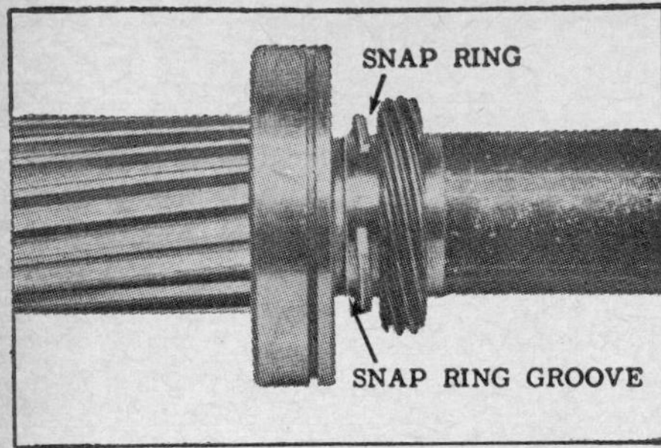

Fig. 16 Snap ring position prior to disassembly of mainshaft

Rear Bearing Retainer

The only item serviced in the rear bearing retainer is the seal. If the seal requires replacement, pry the old one out and install a new one as follows:

1. Apply a coating of lubricant to lip of seal.
2. Apply a light coating of sealer to outer diameter of seal.
3. Install seal in rear bearing retainer, using a suitable seal driver

Synchronizing Clutch

The clutch detent springs are serviced separately and replacement can be accomplished by prying each spring loose from the gear and pushing it out of the groove, Fig. 17. New springs can be installed by pushing them into position in the grooves.

Selector Shaft Seals

Pry out the old seals from the case. Coat the sealing lip of the new seals with lubricant, and coat outer diameter with sealer.

Install the seal without the garter spring in the case, using a tool such as a socket until it bottoms in the case. Install the seal with the garter spring toward the transmission until it is flush with the case.

REASSEMBLE TRANS.

Reverse Idler Gear

1. Position reverse idler gear and bronze thrust washers into case with chamfered teeth to rear of gear, Fig. 18.

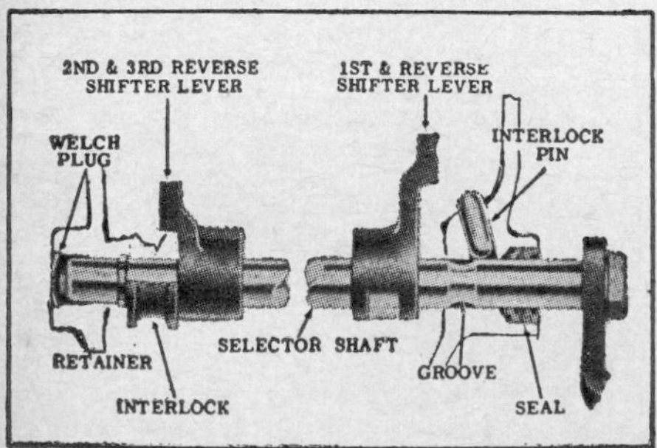

Fig. 20 Selector shaft and related parts

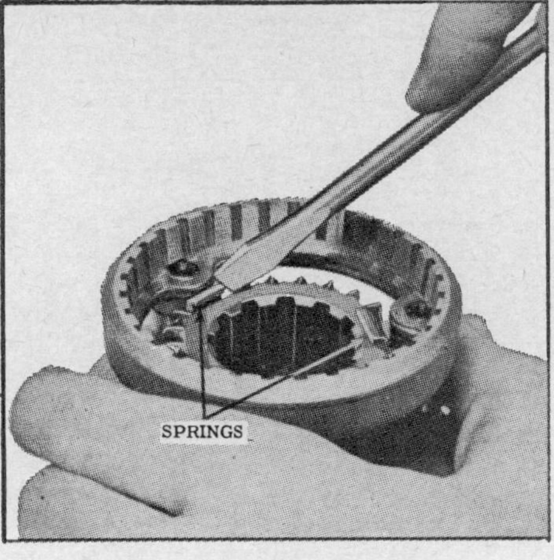

Fig. 17 Removing synchronizing clutch springs

2. Install idler gear shaft (slotted end out) until front of shaft picks up front thrust washer and just starts into inner support in case.
3. Coat slotted end of shaft with sealer. Make sure lock pin hole in shaft is in line with lock pin hole in case.
4. Finish driving shaft into case, using a brass drift and hammer.
5. Coat lock pin with sealer and drive it in 1" below surface of boss on case.

Countershaft & Gear

1. Position cluster gear assembly in case with large bronze thrust washer toward front of case.
2. Align cluster gear with shaft holes in case. Tang of combination steel-bronze thrust washer must index with case.
3. Install countershaft (small end first) from rear of case until front end of shaft just enters bore in front wall of case. Make sure shaft closely follows bearing loader tool so that bearings and washers are held in place.
4. Line up lock pin hole in shaft with lock pin hole in case, then coat protruding end of shaft with sealer.
5. Finish driving shaft into case with a brass drift and hammer.
6. Coat lock pin with sealer and drive pin flush with case.

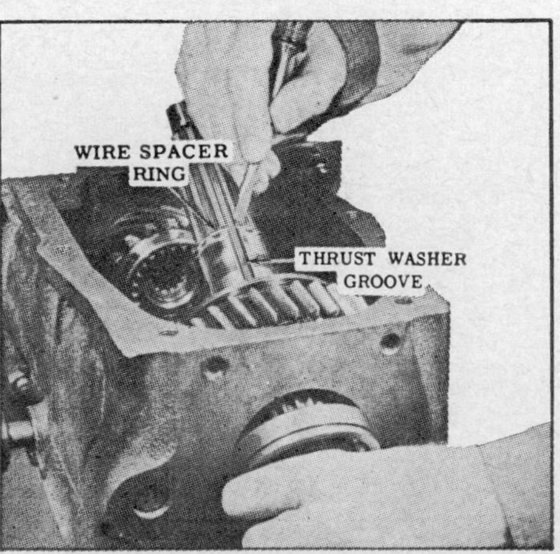

Fig. 21 Lining up wire spacer ring

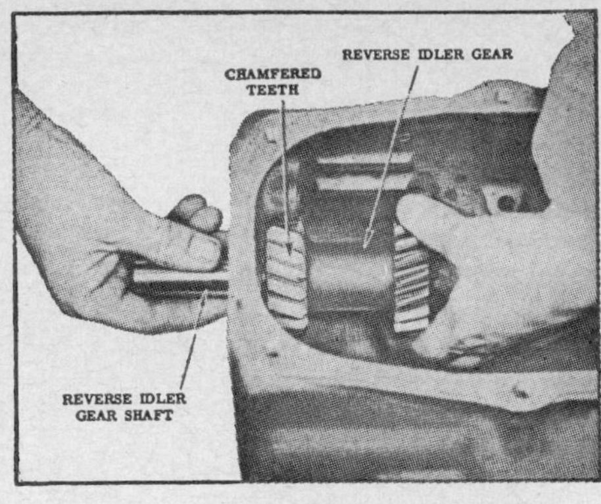

Fig. 18 Installing reverse idler shaft

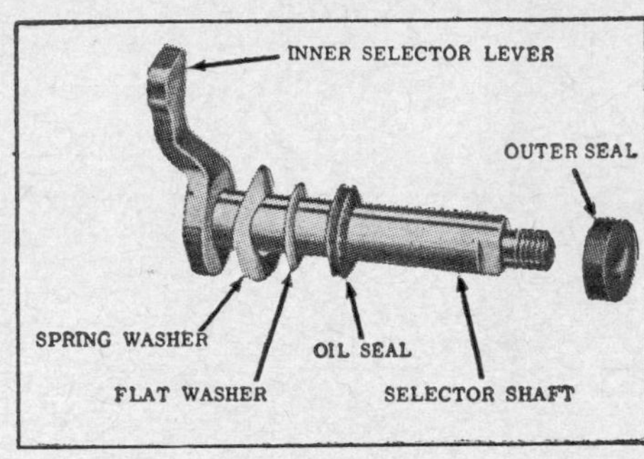

Fig. 19 Inner selector lever and shaft

Inner Selector Shaft & Main Drive Gear

1. Install parts on inner selector shaft as shown in Fig. 19
2. Apply lubricant to shaft and insert shaft into transmission case. Then install outer seal, outer selector lever, washer and nut so that bend of lever is down.
3. Install main drive gear shaft into front of case. Install bearing retainer ring.
4. Install a new welch plug coated with sealer in side of case opposite select-

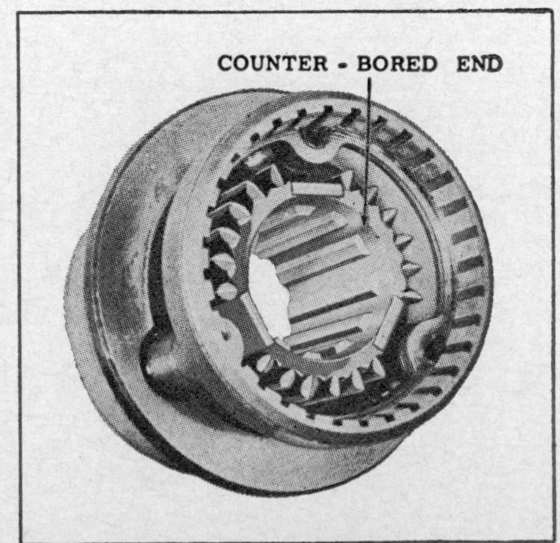

Fig. 22 Synchronizing drum

or shaft seals. Welch plug is seated when it bottoms in bore of case.

Selector Shaft & Shifter Levers

1. Coat sealing lips of seals with lubricant, then insert selector shaft through seals until it just protrudes inside of case.
2. Engage low-reverse shifter lever with inner selector lever in case. Then depress inner selector lever while sliding selector shaft through low-reverse shifter lever. *Flat ground surface of shifter lever must face left side of case.*
3. Install 2-3 shifter lever on selector shaft, with flat ground surface of lever toward right side of case.
4. Place 2-3 interlock on selector shaft.
5. Install new interlock retainer on shaft but do not tighten set screws at this time. The retainer can be installed and clinched with needle nose pliers.
6. Install selector shaft interlock pin in case. Move selector shaft until interlock pin engages groove in selector shaft, Fig. 20.
7. Install spring and poppet ball for low-reverse shifter shaft in case. Then install shifter shaft from rear of case with grooved end rearward. Place low-reverse shifter yoke on shaft with set screw hole facing up. Use a punch to depress poppet ball and spring when installing shaft. Do not install set screws at this time.
8. Install spring and poppet ball for 2-3 shifter shaft in case. Move selector shaft so that 2-3 interlock will be directly under 2-3 shifter shaft. Install shaft from front of case with three notched detents rearward. Place 2-3 shifter yoke on shaft with set screw hole facing up. Do not install set screws at this time.
9. Position low-reverse and 2-3 shifter shafts so that notch in each shaft is directly above selector shaft (this is neutral position).
10. Install new set screws and tighten to 15-20 ft-lbs. Stake screws to prevent loosening.
11. Install outer shift lever, lock washer and bolt on selector shaft.

Mainshaft & Rear Bearing Retainer

1. Install mainshaft through rear of case, then slide low-reverse gear on shaft with flat side of gear rearward. Install low-reverse gear retaining ring (thin) in groove in spline.
2. Line up small wire spacer ring in groove in mainshaft with machined thrust washer keyway groove on 2nd speed gear bearing surface, Fig. 21.

NOTE: There are two grooves machined for full length of 2nd speed gear bearing surface of mainshaft. The shallow angle groove is for lubrication purposes only and should not be obstructed. The deep groove, similar to a spline, is designed to receive the tangs of the 2nd speed gear thrust washers.

3. Install 2nd speed gear inner thrust washer with proper groove on mainshaft.
4. Place 2nd speed gear on shaft with cone clutch surface facing forward. Install outer thrust washer and retain with *new* retaining ring.
5. Install synchronizing drum on shaft with counterbored end toward 2nd speed gear, Fig. 22. Engage synchronizing drum with 2-3 shifter yoke and index low-reverse shifter yoke. Then tap mainshaft forward until it pilots in main drive gear, and rear bearing pilots to case.
6. Install rear bearing retainer ring.
7. Install new set screws in shifter yokes and torque to 15-20 ft-lbs. Stake screws to prevent loosening.

CAUTION: These screws are deformed at the slotted end to provide a self-locking feature to prevent screws from loosening. This feature is lost if screws are used a second time.

8. Coat rear bearing retainer bushing with transmission lube. Position a new gasket on rear of case. Apply sealer to rear bearing retainer screws, install screws and torque to 28-33 ft-lbs.
9. Coat sealing lip of rear bearing retainer oil seal with lubricant. Coat outer diameter of seal with sealer.
10. Install seal in rear bearing retainer.
11. Install top cover with new gasket and torque screws to 10-12 ft-lbs.
12. Install toggle spring and extension between spring clip and outer shift lever.

Type Three

DISASSEMBLE TRANS.

Mainshaft & Main Drive Gear

1. Remove top cover, Fig. 1.
2. Remove front bearing retainer.
3. Remove speedometer driven gear and sleeve.
4. Pull companion flange from mainshaft.
5. Remove lock plate, Fig. 2.
6. Drive countershaft rearward until shaft is just free in front bore of case. Use loading tool, Fig. 3, to push out countershaft.
7. Allow cluster gear to drop to bottom of case with loading tool in place to keep bearings and washers intact.
8. Remove main drive gear and bearing. Pull drive gear shaft forward and remove 14 pilot rollers from rear end of shaft.
9. Remove front bronze blocking ring from synchronizer. Remove snap ring, Fig. 4.
10. Move mainshaft rearward until rear bearing is free of case. Then move shaft to extreme right in case and remove 2-3 shift fork.
11. Slide mainshaft rearward out of case, picking off synchronizer, 2nd speed gear and low-reverse gear as shaft is being withdrawn, Fig. 5.
12. Remove low-reverse shift shoe from shift shaft. Drive reverse idler shaft out of case, Fig. 6, and lift out idler gear.
13. Lift out cluster gear.
14. If bearings on mainshaft and main drive gear are to be replaced, remove

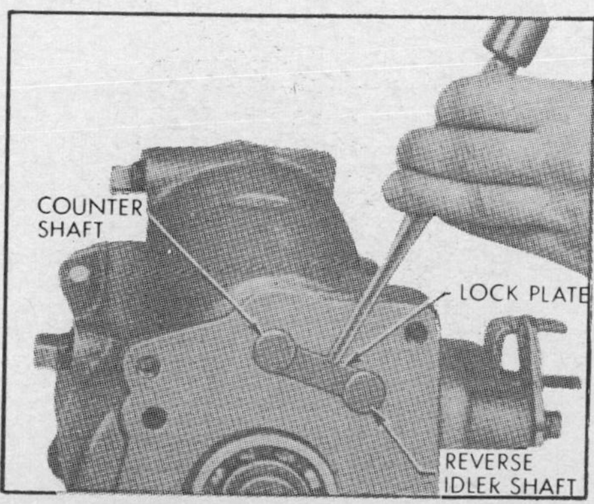

Fig. 2 Removing countershaft-idler shaft lock plate

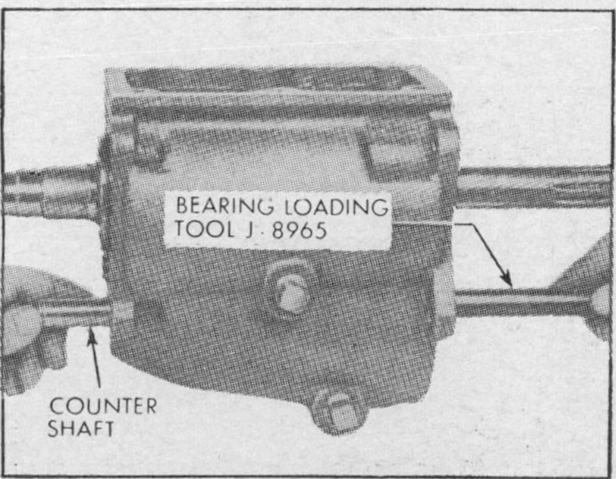

Fig. 3 Installing counter gear bearing loading tool

Fig. 4 Removing snap ring from front of mainshaft

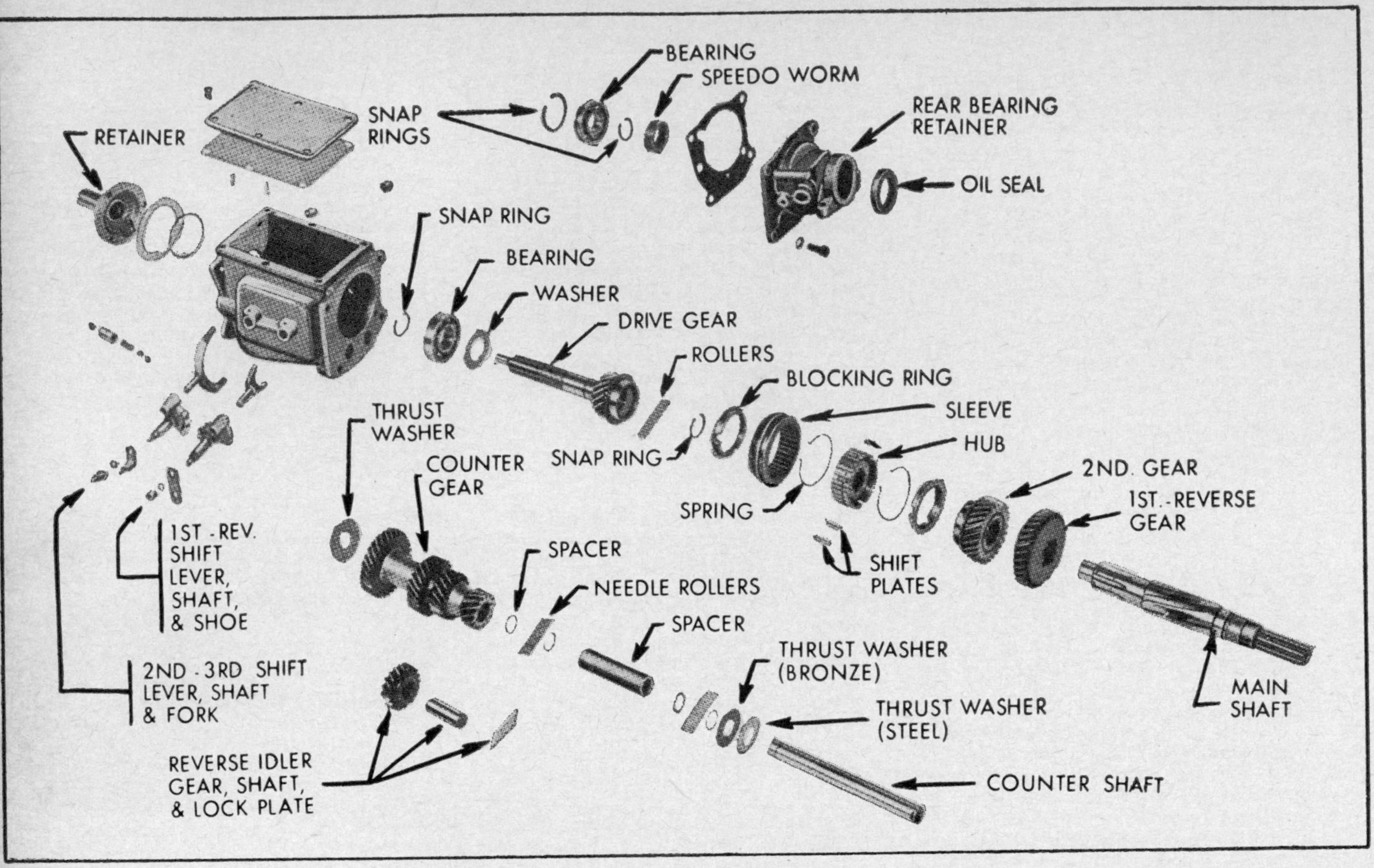

Fig. 1 Type 3 transmission disassembled. Note that low-reverse mainshaft gear has shift fork groove to the front

shaft snap ring and drive bearing off shaft. Remove slinger washer from drive gear shaft and outer snap rings from bearings.

Shift Levers & Interlock

1. If these parts are badly worn, remove shift levers, noting their positions.
2. Drive tapered shaft lock pins upward until shafts are free.
3. Remove shafts from inside case, being careful to catch two interlock balls. Pry oil seals from shaft grooves.
4. Remove interlock sleeve, spring and pin.

Synchronizer

1. Remove rear bronze blocking rings.
2. Remove spring from recess in both ends of hub.
3. Slide sleeve off hub; shift plates will fall from position.

Counter Gear Assembly

1. Remove thrust washers, noting their position.
2. Remove loading tool to free four bearing spacers, 44 needle rollers and a tubular spacer.

REASSEMBLE TRANS.

Counter Gear, Assemble

1. Install bearing loading tool.
2. Insert tubular spacer.
3. Hold counter gear in a vertical position and, while supporting loading tool from below, insert inner bearing spacer (washer) and place 22 rollers in position around loading tool, using

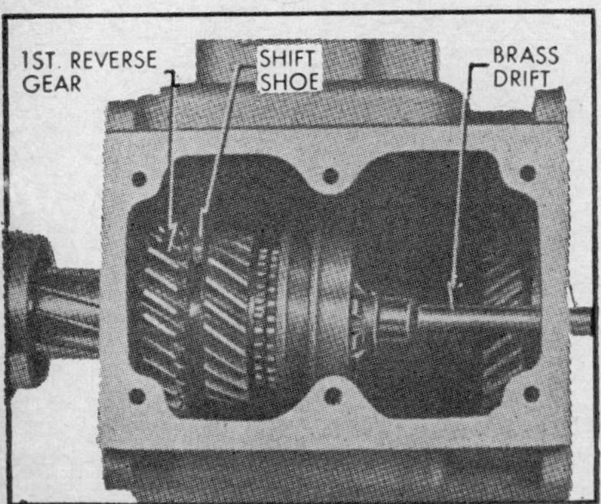

Fig. 5 Removing mainshaft

Fig. 6 Removing reverse idler shaft

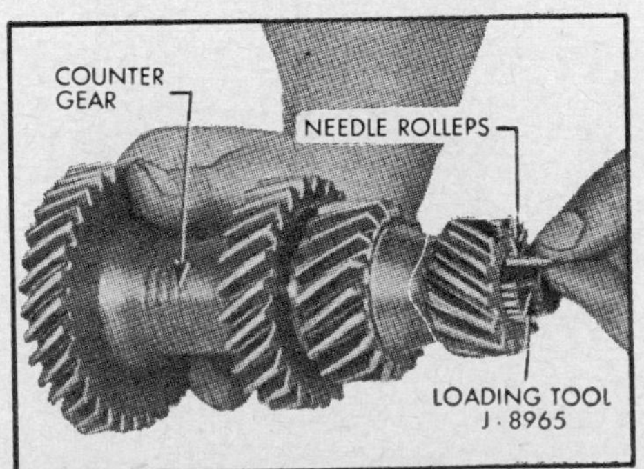

Fig. 7 Loading needle rollers in counter gear

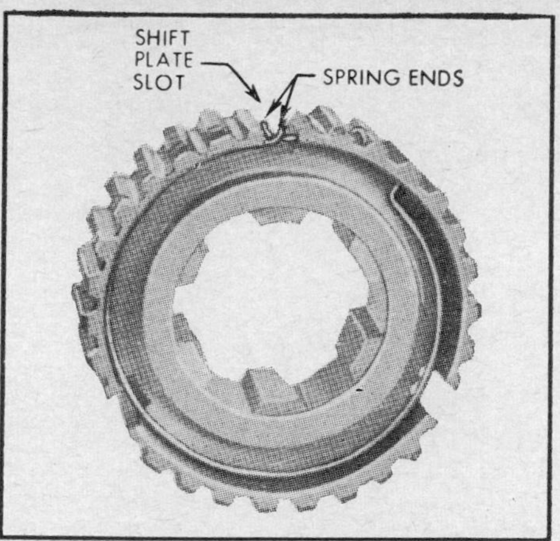

Fig. 8 Installing synchronizer springs

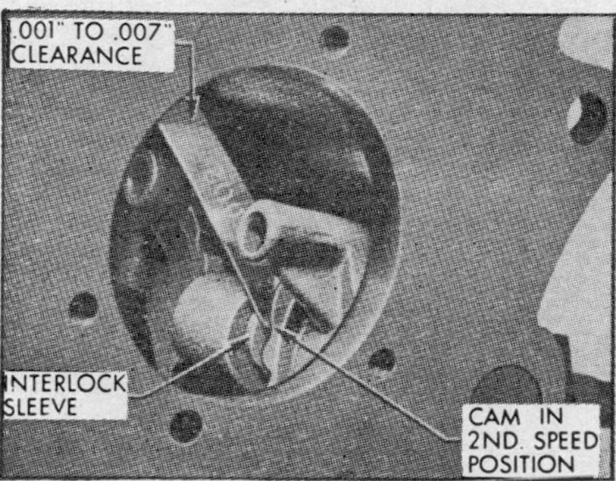

Fig. 11 Checking interlock sleeve end clearance

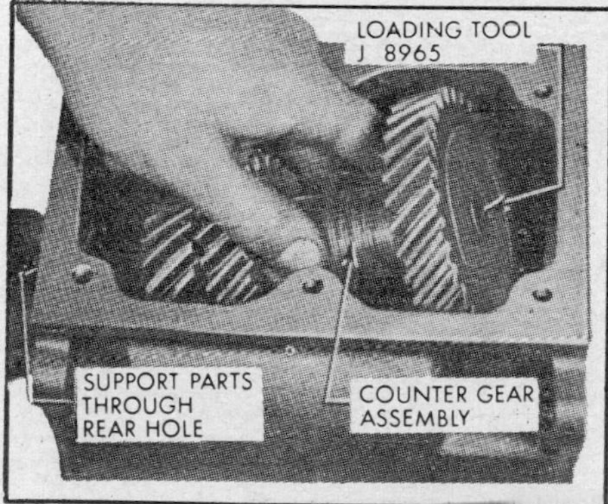

Fig. 12 Installing counter gear

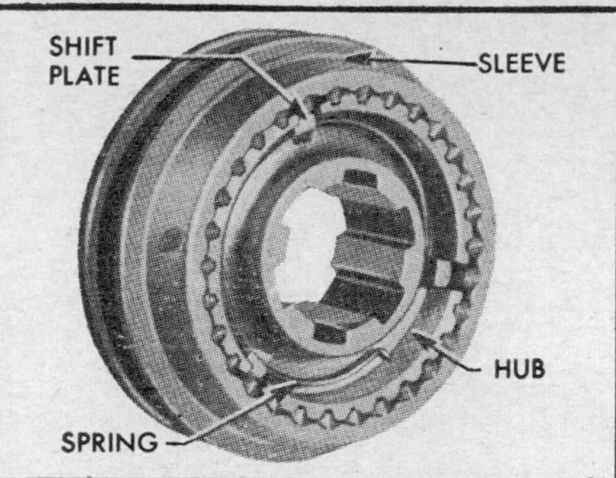

Fig. 9 Synchronizer assembled

grease to hold them in place.

4. Insert outer bearing spacer and repeat procedure at opposite end, Fig. 7.
5. Install inner bronze thrust washer so that lugs engage notches in counter gear.
6. Install outer rear steel washer. *Large front thrust washer should not be installed at this time.*

Synchronizer, Assemble

1. Install springs solidly in recesses on both ends of synchronizer hub, Fig. 8. One end of both springs should be located in same shift plate slot as shown so that springs will extend in opposite directions from each other. Install shift plate directly over these ends.
2. While holding shift plates in grooves on hub, slide sleeve over hub until detent is felt. The extended tapered portion of sleeve faces same direction (front) as long extended portion at center of hub, Fig. 9.
3. Place rear blocking ring in position at rear end of hub and rotate until shifting plates match notches in blocking ring.

Shift Levers & Interlock, Install

1. Insert new seals. Apply transmission lube to seals and shaft holes.
2. Install 2-3 shifter shaft and cam. This shaft has shorter cam ramps between detent notches on cam.
3. Insert interlock sleeve, spring and pin in case.

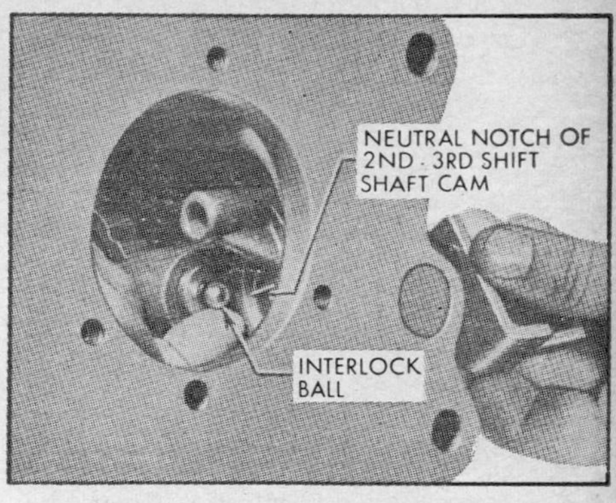

Fig. 10 Installing interlock ball

4. Install low-reverse shifter shaft and cam. Install levers, flat washers, lock washers and nuts on both shafts. The offset lever and equalizer pivot nut are installed on 2-3 shift shaft.
5. Move low-reverse cam toward case. Install interlock ball and move cam back to normal position, allowing neutral notch (center) of cam to retain ball. Install tapered shift shaft lock pin, Fig. 10.
6. Using procedure in Step 5, install interlock ball at 2-3 cam.
7. Shift 2-3 shift lever into 2nd gear position. With one end of interlock sleeve against low-reverse cam, clearance between sleeve and 2-3 cam should be .001-.007", Fig. 11. If clearance is greater than specified, and it seems possible that transmission can be forced into two gears at once, old interlock sleeve should be measured with a micrometer and replaced with a new longer sleeve. Sleeves are available in five lengths: 1.287", 1.291", 1.295", 1.299" and 1.303".

Transmission, Assemble

1. If front bearing was removed, locate slinger washer on drive gear shaft with raised center portion toward front. Press bearing on shaft with outer snap ring groove toward front. Install bearing outer snap ring and thickest shaft snap ring that will

Fig. 13 Checking end clearance of counter gear

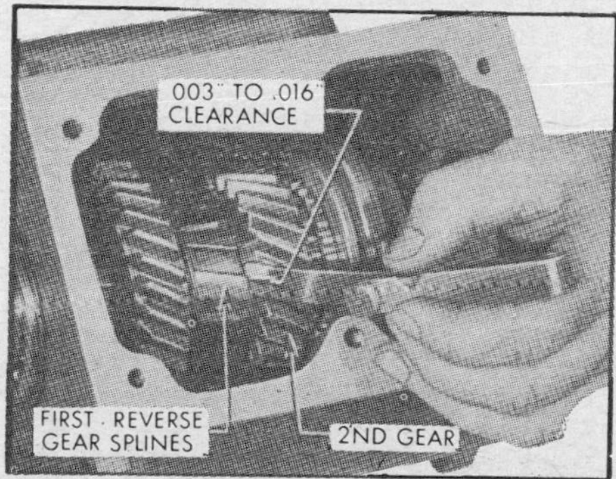

Fig. 14 Checking end clearance of 2nd speed gear

Fig. 15 Loading bearing rollers in main drive gear pocket

properly seat in snap ring groove (snap ring is available in 3 thicknesses).

2. If rear bearing was removed, press new bearing on mainshaft with outer snap ring groove toward rear. Install bearing outer snap ring and shaft snap ring.
3. Place counter gear assembly in bottom of case, Fig. 12.
4. Locate counter gear in normal position with lug on outer rear thrust washer up. Insert large front thrust washer with lug to front so as to engage slot in case. Align hole in washer with bore in counter gear and move bearing loading tool forward allowing counter gear to drop to bottom of case.
5. Check end clearance of counter gear using feeler gauge between two rear thrust washers, Fig. 13. Replace thrust washers if clearance exceeds .017″ (limits are .005″ to .017″).
6. Locate reverse idler gear in position with hub section and chamfered teeth forward. Drive idler shaft in through rear of case with lock plate slot toward countershaft bore. Leave shaft projecting about $\frac{1}{16}$″ from fully installed position.
7. Insert low-reverse shift shoe into its shift shaft and install mainshaft and bearing through rear of transmission. As shaft is being installed, slide low-reverse gear onto splines with groove on gear toward front; slide 2nd speed gear on shaft with extended portion toward front. With blocking ring in position, slide synchronizer on splines with extended portion of synchronizer sleeve toward front.

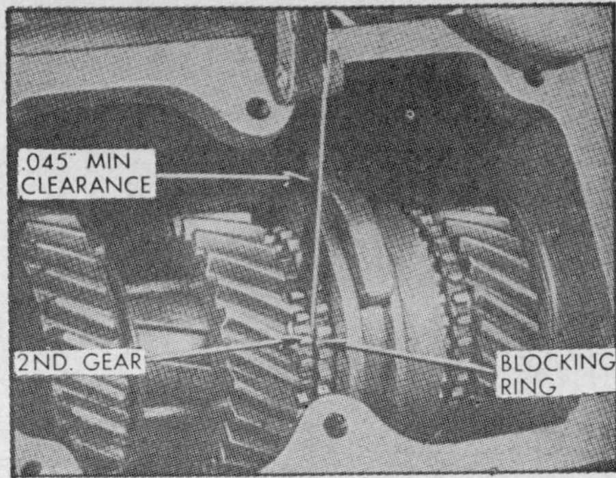

Fig. 16 Checking blocking ring clearance

8. Install mainshaft snap ring.
9. Insert 2-3 shift fork in 2-3 shift shaft and engage fork in groove on synchronizer sleeve.
10. With low-reverse shift shoe offset toward front, engage shift shoe in groove of low-reverse gear.
11. Move complete mainshaft assembly forward until rear bearing is fully installed in rear of case.
12. With synchronizer hub and 2nd gear pressed forward against snap ring, there should be .003-.016″ end clearance between 2nd gear and front face of low-reverse splines. If clearance is found to be excessive, replace worn parts, Fig. 14.
13. Place front blocking ring at front of synchronizer hub and rotate until shift plates match notches in blocking ring.
14. Insert 14 rollers in drive gear pocket, Fig. 15, using heavy grease to hold them in place.
15. Install drive gear and bearing through front of case, sliding bearing rollers over pilot end of mainshaft.
16. Check clearance between front blocking ring teeth and drive gear teeth by lightly seating blocking ring on contacting surface of gear. Minimum clearance should be .045″. Replace blocking ring if clearance is less than specified. Use same procedure to check between rear blocking ring teeth and 2nd gear teeth, Fig. 16.
17. Turn transmission upside down to allow counter gear and loading tool to drop to normal position. Install countershaft through rear of case with lock plate slot facing reverse idler shaft. Leave countershaft projecting about $\frac{1}{16}$″ from fully installed position.
18. Install lock plate. Drive reverse idler shaft and countershaft forward until lock plate is tight against case.
19. Install front bearing retainer and gasket. Oil return hole in retainer and gasket should match oil return hole in case.
20. Install new oil seal in rear bearing retainer. Lightly coat seal with gear lube.
21. Slide speedometer worm gear over rear end of mainshaft and install rear bearing retainer and gasket.
22. Install front companion flange.

Type Four

DISASSEMBLE TRANS.

1. Remove extension housing, Fig. 1.
2. Remove top cover and gasket.
3. Remove snap ring from mainshaft groove at rear of case.
4. Drive out clutch gear and bearing by driving on mainshaft.
5. Continue to drive or press mainshaft out of case and remove thrust washer. *Be sure synchronizer ring tangs are aligned with mainshaft splines prior to driving out shaft, otherwise damage to ring and shaft splines will occur.*

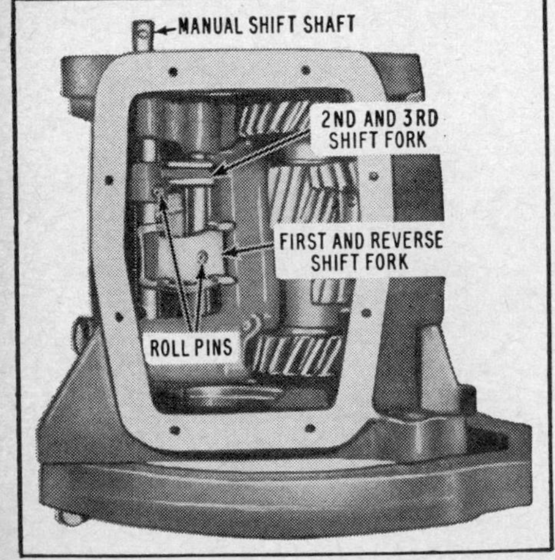

Fig. 2 Transmission shifter mechanism

6. Strip mainshaft parts by lifting them out through top cover opening.
7. Expand retaining ring and start mainshaft bearing out by tapping on outer race; then drive bearing out of case.
8. Remove detent cover plug and remove 2nd-3rd gear detent spring and ball.
9. With suitable punch, drive out roll pin securing 2-3 shift fork to shaft, Fig. 2, then tap shaft toward front with a drift and remove fork, shaft and roll pin.
10. Remove interlock from detent cavity. Then remove low-reverse shift fork and shaft in same manner as 2-3 fork.
11. Remove shift finger, Fig. 3.
12. Remove manual shift shaft seal from rear lower left corner of case.
13. Drive countershaft out from front of case, using a dummy shaft (or tool J-5777) to hold needle bearings in place.
14. If necessary, drive reverse idler shaft lock pin into shaft, then drive shaft out of case through hole at rear of case. Remove caged needle bearing and thrust washer used at rear of reverse idler gear.
15. Remove mainshaft bearing retainer ring from case.

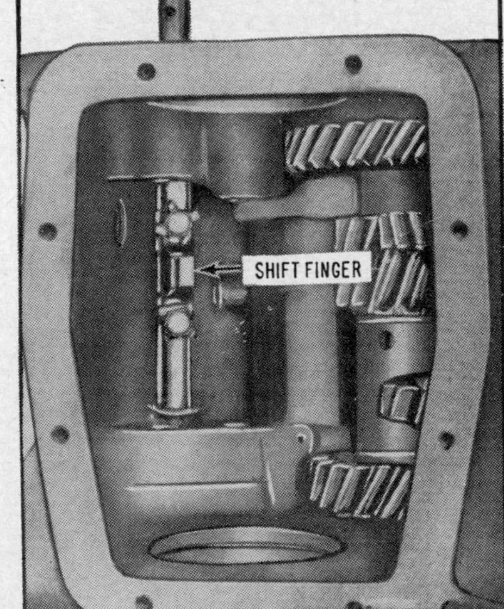

Fig. 3 Transmission shift finger

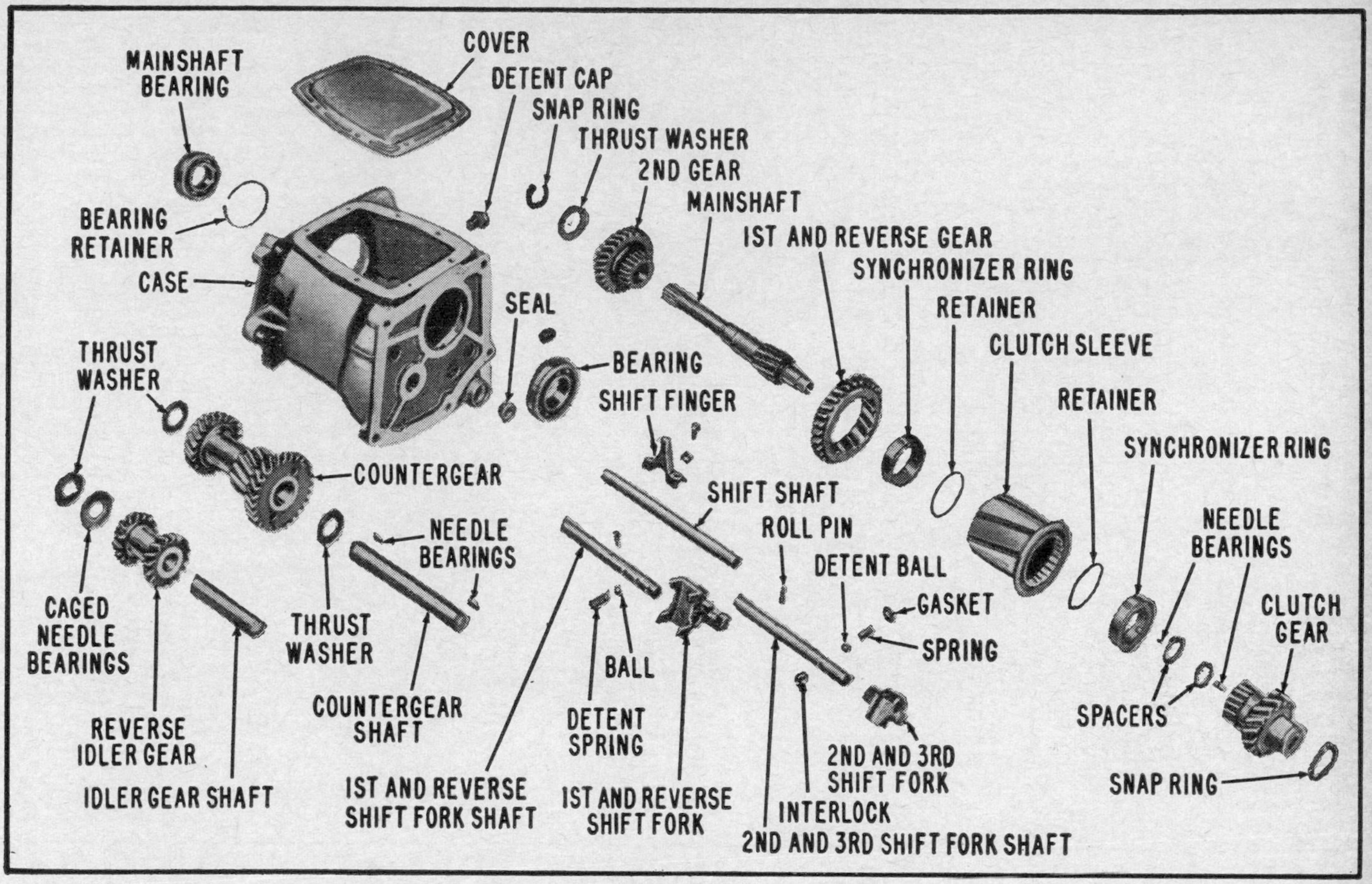

Fig. 1 Type 4 transmission disassembled

Assemble

1. Install manual shaft seal.
2. Install assembled countergear, Fig. 3.
3. Install reverse idler gear, Fig. 4.
4. Insert manual shift shaft through seal in case. Position actuating finger and secure to shaft (see Fig. 3) with two lock tabs and capscrews, tightening to 5-7 ft. lbs. Bend lock tabs over screw heads. Install detent ball and spring (in that order) through hole in side of case. Tap ball and spring to be sure spring is resting on bottom of cavity.
5. Start roll pin into low-reverse fork. Insert fork shaft through lower hole at front of case with three detents facing detent ball and slip fork on shaft. Depressing ball, press shaft over ball to the center detent position. Secure fork to shaft with roll pin. Coat interlock with oil and install in detent cavity. *Be sure* shift finger is engaged with low-reverse shift fork prior to installing 2-3 shift fork, Fig. 2.
6. Start roll pin into fork. Insert 2-3 fork shaft through front of case with three detents facing away from interlock and slip fork onto shaft. Secure with roll pin.
7. Insert detent ball and spring (in that order) for 2-3 shift fork and install detent cavity cover and gasket. Torque cover bolts to 25-35 ft. lbs. After installing detent plug, check for free movement of manual shift shaft in all gear positions.
8. Place assembled clutch sleeve, low-reverse sliding gear and 2nd gear in case, Fig. 5. Make sure low-reverse gear and shoulder on clutch sleeve are in proper forks.

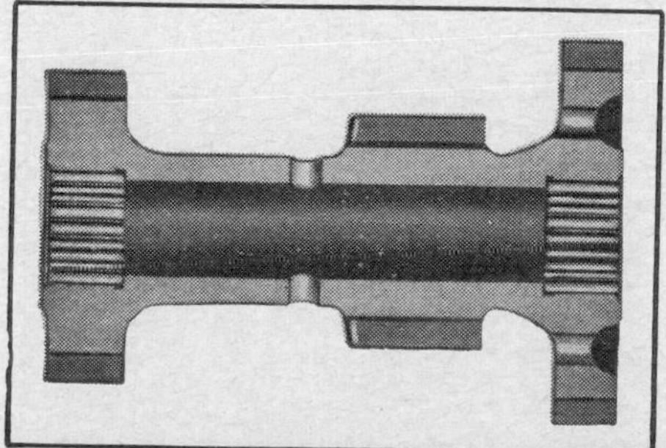

Fig. 4 Counter gear needle bearings installed

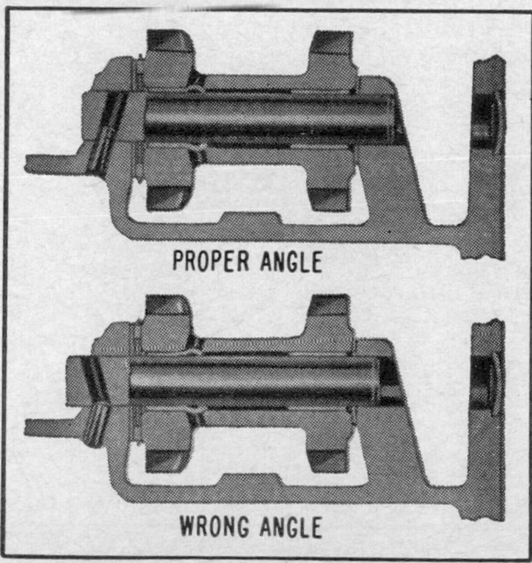

Fig. 5 Reverse idler gear lock pin

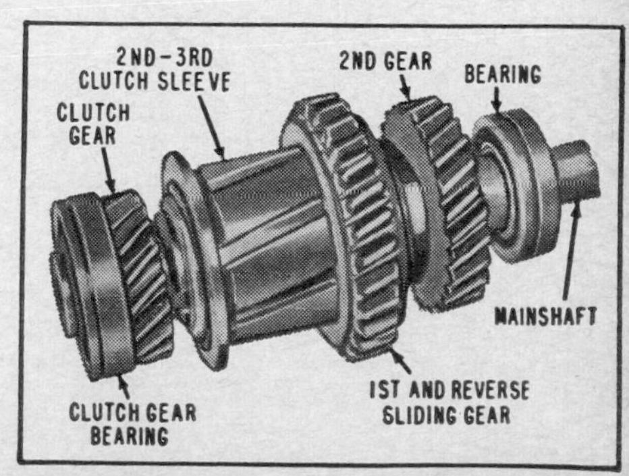

Fig. 6 Mainshaft components assembled

9. Place mainshaft in clutch gear and, from front of case, insert mainshaft through clutch sleeve and 2nd speed gear. *Be sure tangs of synchronizer ring are aligned with mainshaft splines before installing mainshaft and that clutch gear slots, Fig. 6, are properly aligned with larger tangs on synchronizer ring.*
10. Drive clutch gear bearing into place.
11. Install thrust washer on mainshaft with its oil grooves toward 2nd gear. Install mainshaft bearing retainer ring. Install mainshaft bearing with ring groove toward case and, with retainer ring expanded, drive bearing onto mainshaft.
12. Install a ½" deep socket in clutch gear and continue to drive on mainshaft bearing until snap ring groove is accessible. Install snap ring.
13. Check end play of mainshaft by inserting feeler gauge between snap ring and bearing inner race. Final end clearance must be .004" maximum. Use a snap ring of a size that will establish this clearance. Snap rings are available in four thicknesses ranging from .086" to .097". After making this check, drive mainshaft forward into case until snap ring contacts inner bearing race.
14. Check for free movement of shift shaft to be sure each gear position may be easily obtained. Install top cover, filler plug and extension housing.

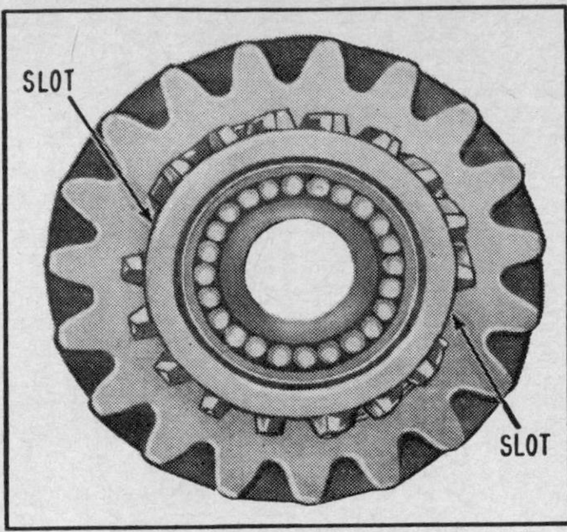

Fig. 7 Clutch gear needle bearings installed

Types Five & Six

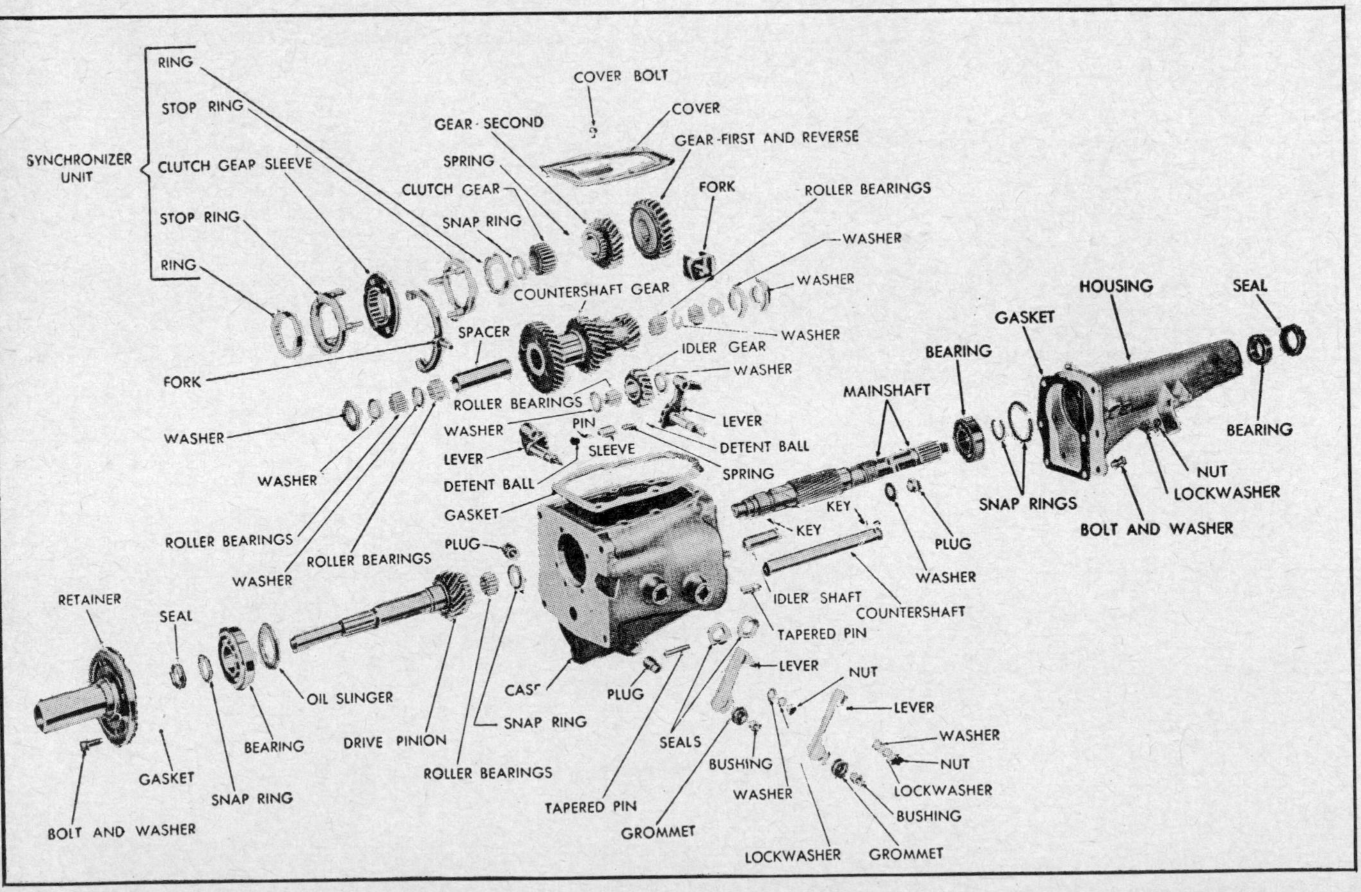

Fig. 1 Type 5 heavy duty transmission disassembled

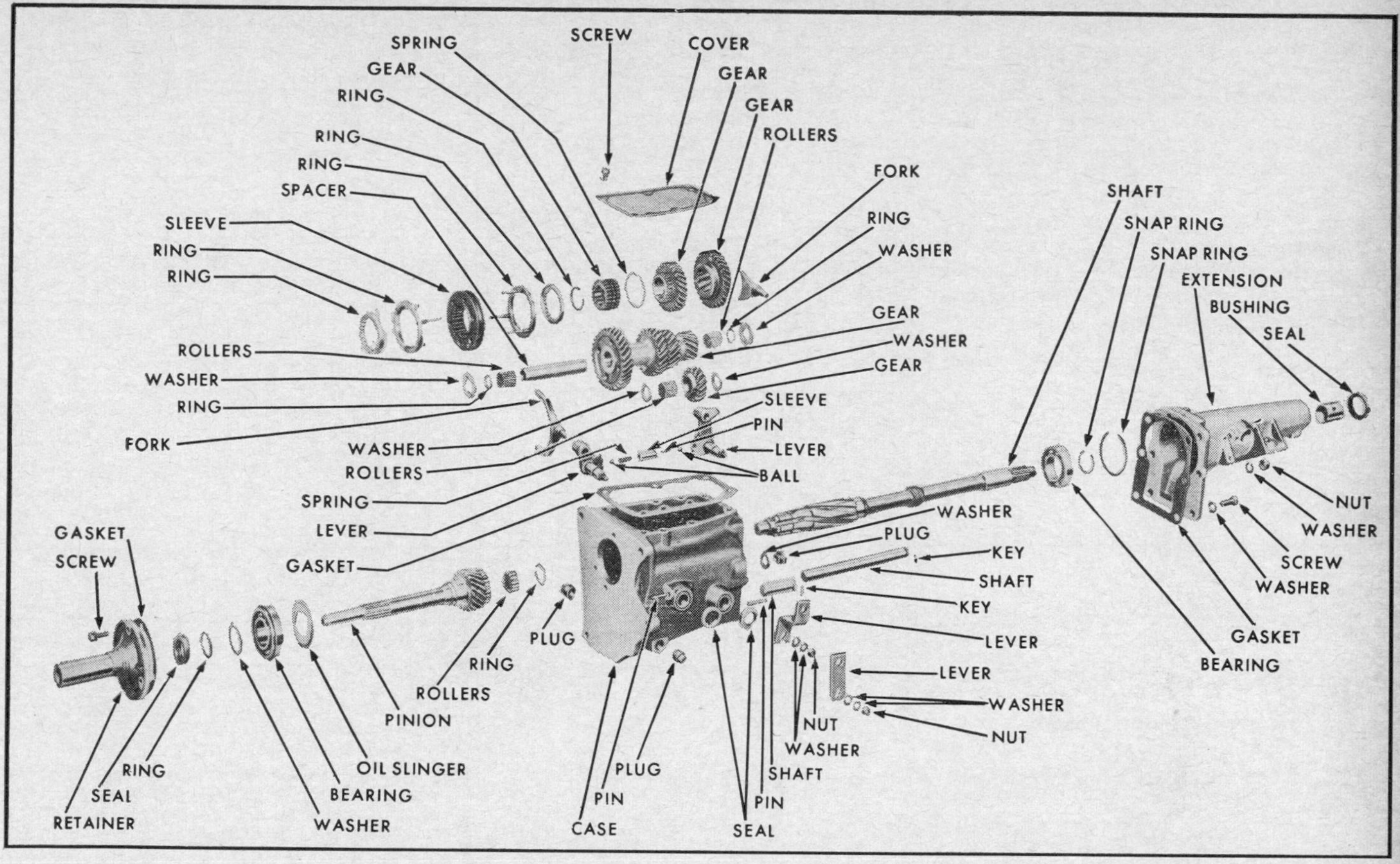

Fig. 2 Type 6 standard duty transmission disassembled. Note that low-reverse mainshaft gear shift fork groove goes to the front

NOTE

These transmissions, Figs. 1 and 2, are quite similar, the chief difference being the cut of the mainshaft splines and the double set of counter gear needle bearings used in the heavy duty unit, Fig. 1. Note that in Fig. 2 there are only one set of needle bearings at each end of the counter gear. The procedure which follows apply to both units unless otherwise indicated.

DISASSEMBLE TRANS.

1. Pull flange from rear of mainshaft.
2. Slide extension housing off mainshaft.
3. Remove transmission cover.

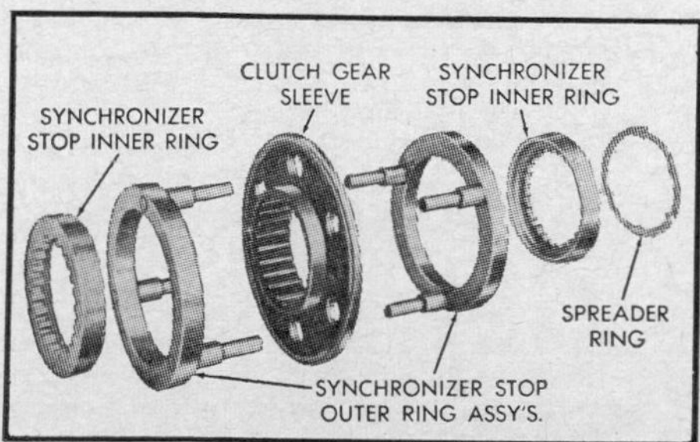

Fig. 3 Type 5 synchronizer unit

Main Drive Gear

1. Remove drive gear bearing retainer.
2. On H.D. models, Fig. 1, when removing drive gear from transmission, slide front synchronizer inner stop ring from short splines on gear as assembly is being removed from case.
3. On S.D. models, Fig. 2, grasp drive gear shaft and pull assembly out of case. *Be careful not to bind inner synchronizer ring on drive gear clutch teeth.*
4. Remove bearing rollers from drive gear pocket, using a hook or flat blade.

Counter Gear

1. Use a suitable bearing loading tool to drive countershaft toward rear of case until key can be removed from countershaft. Then drive countershaft all the way out, keeping loading tool tight against end of countershaft to keep needle bearings in place.

Mainshaft

1. With transmission in reverse, remove outer center bearing snap ring, using a hook or flat blade, then partially remove mainshaft.
2. Cock mainshaft, then remove clutch sleeve, outer synchronizer rings, front inner ring and 2-3 shift fork, Figs. 3 and 4.
3. Remove clutch gear snap ring. Slide clutch gear off end of mainshaft.
4. Slide 2nd speed gear, stop ring and synchronizer spring off mainshaft.
5. Remove low-reverse sliding gear and shift fork as mainshaft is withdrawn from case.
6. Lift counter gear assembly from case.

Reverse Idler Gear

1. Drive reverse idler shaft towards rear and out of case. Remove key from end of shaft.

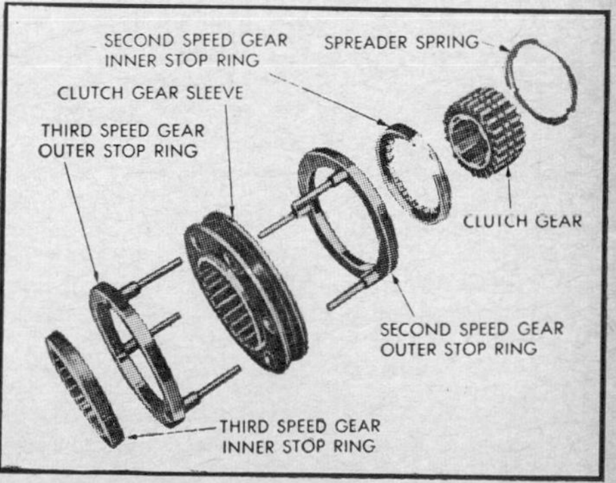

Fig. 4 Type 6 synchronizer unit

2. Lift out idler gear, thrust washers and needle bearings from case.

Gearshift Mechanism

HEAVY DUTY UNIT, Fig. 5

1. Remove both lever shaft seals.
2. Drive tapered lock pins from lever shafts, driving from bottom toward top of transmission.
3. Remove lever shafts from transmission, being careful not to lose spring-loaded detent balls.
4. Remove interlock sleeve, spring, pin and balls.

STANDARD DUTY UNIT, Fig. 6

1. Remove operating levers from shafts.
2. Drive out tapered pin from either of two lever shafts, then withdraw shaft from inside of case. The detent balls are spring-loaded; as the shaft is being withdrawn, ball will drop to bottom of case.
3. Remove interlock sleeve, spring, pin and both balls from case. Then drive out remaining tapered pin and slide shaft out of transmission.
4. Drive out shaft seals and discard.

REASSEMBLE TRANS.

Gearshift Mechanism

1. Center two new seals over holes in case, then drive both seals into case.
2. Slide low-reverse shaft into rear boss of case, through seal and into position. Lock with tapered pin. Turn lever until center (neutral) detent is in line with interlock bores. Use sealer on pins.
3. Slide interlock sleeve in its bore, followed by one interlock ball. Install interlock spring and pin.
4. Place remaining interlock ball on top of spring. Depress interlock ball and at the same time install 2-3 lever into fully seated position with center (neutral) detent aligned with detent ball. Secure shaft with tapered pin.

Counter Gear

1. Slide bearing spacer over bearing loading tool. Coat bore of gear with lubricant. Then slide tool and spacer into gear bore.
2. Lubricate needle bearings and install half the total of bearings at each end of gear around loading tool (Type 6 transmission uses a total of 88 bearings, Type 7 uses 44 total).
3. Install bearing retainer rings at each end of gear. Apply grease to hold bearings in place.
4. Thrust washers are available in two sizes, marked A and B. Make a selection to obtain .004-.012" total end play of counter gear.
5. Install thrust washers at each end of assembly and over loading tool, using grease to hold washers in place.
6. Install counter gear assembly in case, making sure tabs on thrust washers slide into grooves in case.

Reverse Idler Gear

1. Coat bore of gear with grease and slide a suitable bearing loading tool into bore.
2. Lubricate 22 needle bearings and in-

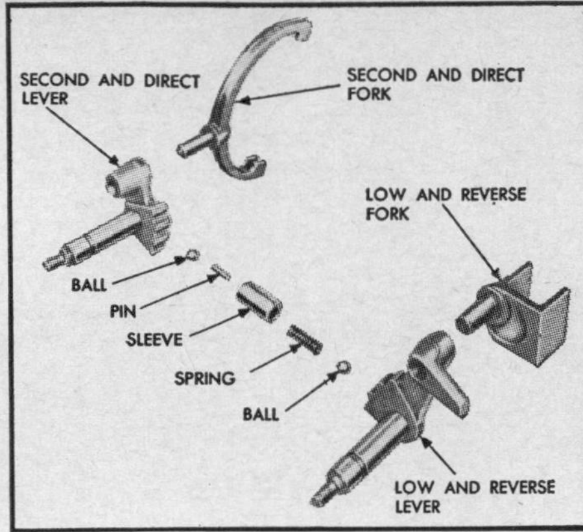

Fig. 5 Type 5 gearshift mechanism

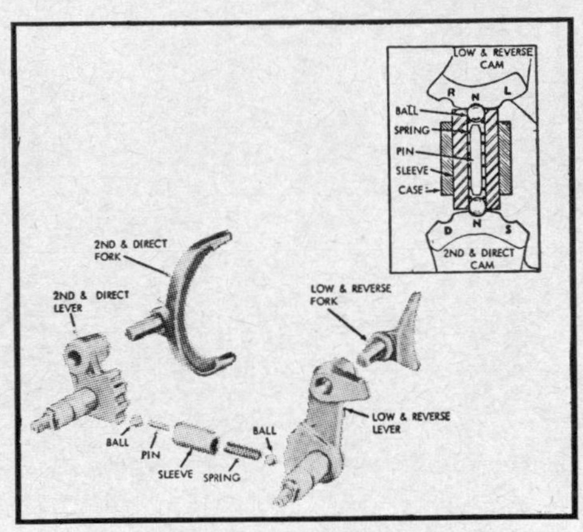

Fig. 6 Type 6 gearshift mechanism

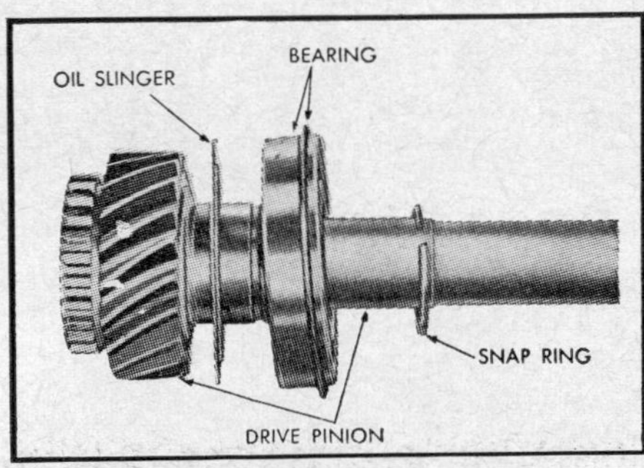

Fig. 7 Main drive gear components

stall around loading tool.

3. Install new thrust washer at each end of gear and over loading tool, using grease to hold washers in place.
4. With bevelled ends of gear teeth forward, slide gear down into position in case.
5. Install gear shift in its opening at rear of case.
6. Install key in shaft, and position shaft with keyway.
7. Raise idler gear slightly to align with shaft, then drive shaft into case through thrust washer and gear until end of shaft is about $\frac{1}{64}$" below surface of case.

Mainshaft

1. If new bearing is to be installed, press it on mainshaft and install snap ring.
2. Install low-reverse fork with offset to rear. Engage fork in low-reverse sliding gear. Position in case by shifting into reverse.
3. Slide mainshaft into case and through low-reverse gear.
4. Install 2-3 shift fork with offset toward rear.
5. Install 2nd speed gear and spreader spring on mainshaft.

NOTE: Synchronizer float should be .050" to .090" when measured between end of synchronizer outer ring pin and opposite synchronizer outer ring. This measurement must be made 180 degrees apart with equal gap on both pin ends for float determination. To be acceptable, the gauge should be a snug fit between pins and outer rings. In cases where float dimension is over .090", synchronizer shims (part no. 2464724) should be installed to reduce float to .090" or less. This shim is to be installed on the 2nd speed gear before the energizing spring is installed. In cases where float is below .050", material should be removed from ends of all six synchronizer pins, using a magnetic grinder or other suitable equipment.

---

6. Install 2nd gear inner stop ring and outer stop ring assembly. Engage synchronizer clutch sleeve with 2-3 shift fork.
7. Slide clutch gear over end of mainshaft and down against 2nd speed gear. Select a snap ring of the correct thickness and install. This snap ring eliminates end play and must be a snug fit.
8. Measure clearance between clutch gear and 2nd speed gear. Limits are .002-.011". If clearance is in excess of .011", "gear jump-out" may result.
9. Position mainshaft further in case by tapping on outer bearing race until bearing bottoms. Install a snap ring of the correct thickness in case.

Main Drive Gear

1. Slide oil slinger (if removed) over shaft and down against gear, Fig. 7.
2. Slide bearing over shaft with snap ring groove away from gear end. Seat bearing on shaft with a press. *Be sure slinger does not hang up in snap ring groove during pressing operation.*
3. Install keyed washer. Then secure bearing and washer with the correct thickness snap ring. Four snap rings are available to eliminate end play. If large snap ring around bearing was removed, install at this time.
4. Install rollers in drive gear pocket using grease to hold them in place, and retain with lock ring (14 rollers used with Fig. 2 unit, 15 with Fig. 1 unit).
5. Install 3rd gear outer stop ring and inner stop ring. Guide drive gear through front of case and engage inner stop ring with clutch teeth. Then seat bearing. Bearing is fully seated when snap ring is in full con-

tact with case.

6. Install new seal in drive gear bearing retainer. Slide bearing retainer (less gasket) down against case.
7. Hold retainer against case and measure clearance between case and retainer, using a feeler gauge. Select a gasket .003" to .004" thicker than the clearance to eliminate all end play in bearing.
8. Install gasket selected and reinstall bearing retainer. Install attaching bolts and tighten to 23 ft-lbs. torque.
9. Install the countershaft, driving the bearing loading tool forward and out of counter gear until key can be inserted in shaft. Continue to drive shaft into case until about $\frac{1}{64}$" below surface of case.

Extension Housing & Cover

1. Slide extension housing over mainshaft and down against case, at the same time guiding mainshaft into oil seal. Torque attaching bolts to 50 ft-lbs.
2. Install companion flange and torque nut to 175 ft-lbs.
3. Install cover with new gasket and torque attaching bolts to 12 ft-lbs.

Type Seven

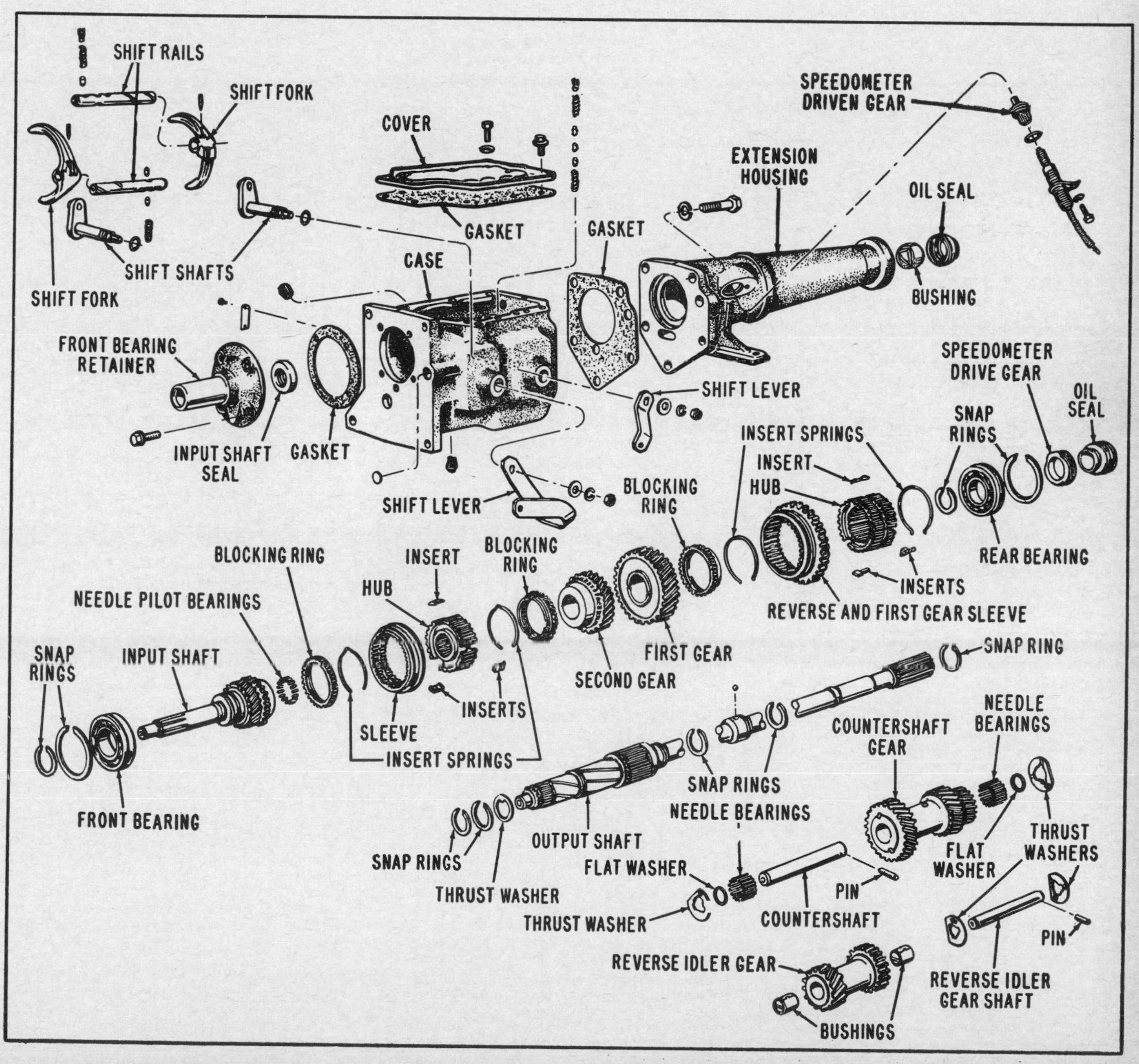

Fig. 1 Type 7 transmission disassembled

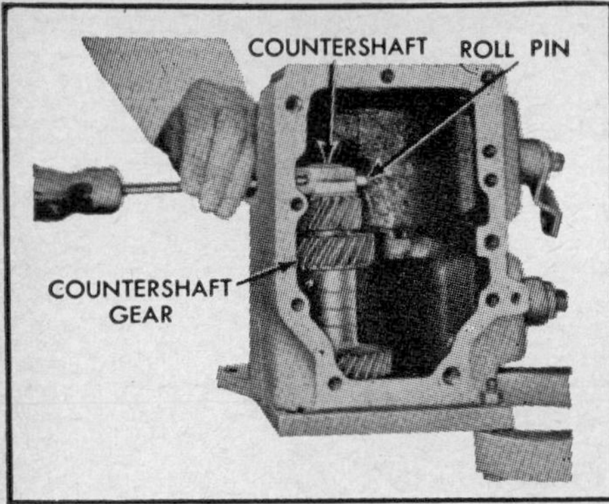

Fig. 2 Removing countershaft roll pin

Fig. 3 Removing countershaft

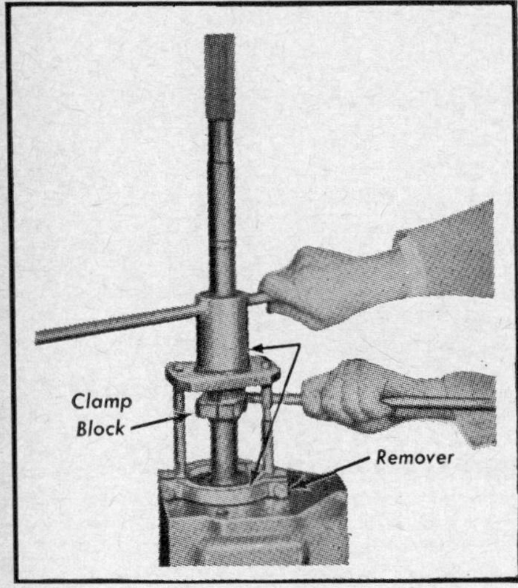

Fig. 4 Removing mainshaft bearing

DISASSEMBLE TRANS.

1. Remove transmission cover, Fig. 1.
2. Remove extension housing. To prevent mainshaft from following housing (with resultant loss of needle bearings) tap end of mainshaft while withdrawing housing.
3. Remove front bearing retainer.
4. Remove filler plug from right side of case. Then working through plug opening, drive roll pin out of case and countershaft with small punch, Fig. 2.
5. Hold counter gear with a hook and, with a dummy shaft, push countershaft out rear of case until counter gear can be lowered to bottom of case, Fig. 3.
6. Pull main drive gear forward until gear contacts case, then remove large snap ring.

NOTE: It is necessary to move gear forward to provide clearance when removing mainshaft assembly. This applies to transmissions used with V8-352 and 390 engines. On all other models, the drive gear is removed from front of case.

7. Remove snap ring and slide speedometer drive gear off mainshaft. Remove lock ball from shaft.
8. Remove snap ring and remove mainshaft rear bearing from shaft and case, Fig. 4.
9. Place both shift levers in neutral (central) position.
10. Remove a set screw that retains detent springs and plugs in case. Remove one spring and plug, Fig. 5.
11. Remove low-reverse set screw and slide shift rail out through rear of case.
12. Rotate low-reverse shift fork upward and lift it from case.
13. Remove 2-3 set screw and rotate 2-3 shift rail 90 degrees with pliers.
14. Lift interlock plug from case with a magnet rod.
15. Tap inner end of 2-3 shift rail to remove expansion plug from front of case. Remove shift rail.
16. Remove 2-3 detent plug and spring from detent bore.
17. Rotate 2-3 shift fork upward and lift from case.
18. Lift mainshaft assembly out through top of case.
19. On transmissions used with V8-352 and 390 engines, push main drive gear into case until bearing is free of bore; then lift gear and bearing out through top of case.
20. Working through front bearing opening, drive reverse idler gear shaft out through rear of case with a drift, Fig. 6.
21. Lift reverse idler gear and two thrust washers from case.
22. Lift counter gear and thrust washers from case, Fig. 7. Be careful not to allow dummy shaft and needle bearings to fall out of gear.
23. Remove countershaft-to-case retaining pin and any needle bearings that may have fallen into case.
24. Unfasten and lift shift levers off shafts. Slide each lever and shaft out of case. Discard O-ring seal from each shaft, Fig. 8.

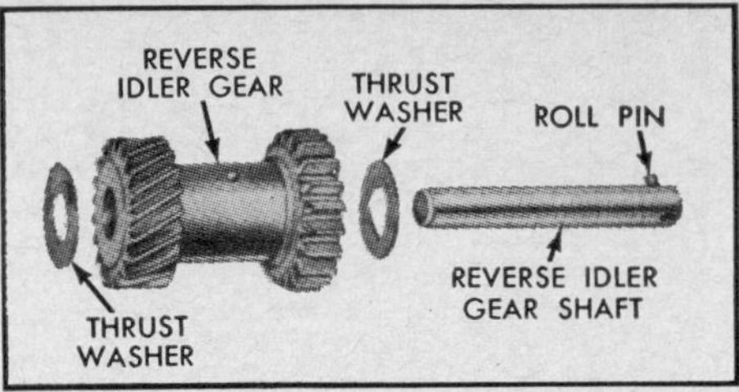

Fig. 6 Reverse idler gear disassembled

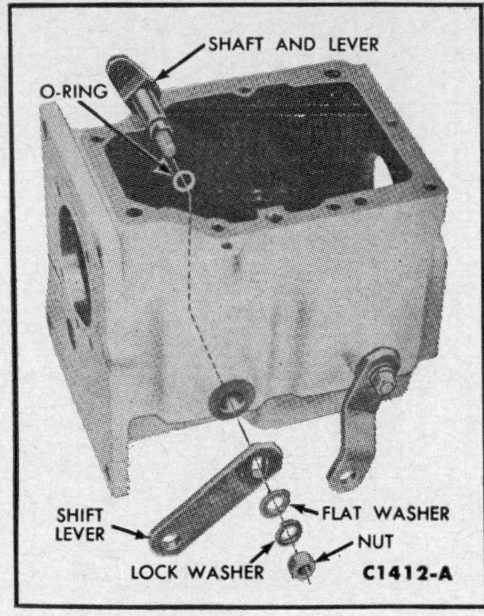

Fig. 8 Shift lever and related parts

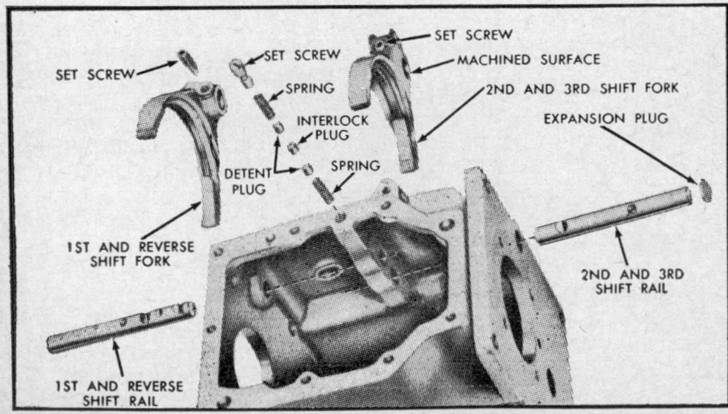

Fig. 5 Shift rails and forks disassembled

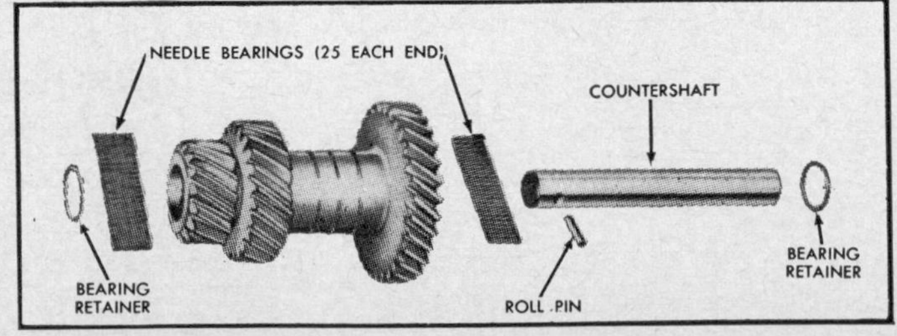

Fig. 7 Counter gear disassembled

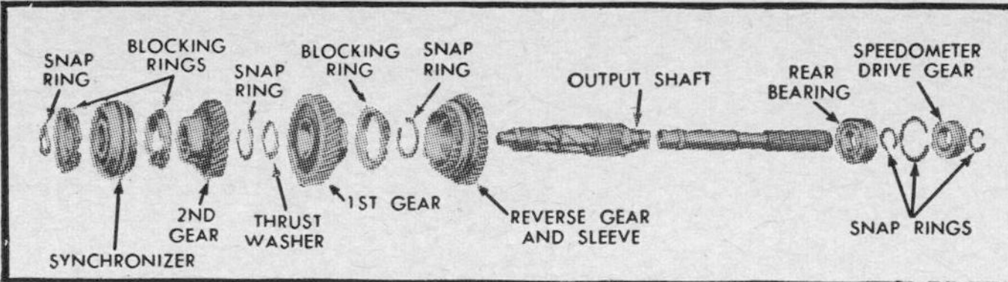

Fig. 9 Mainshaft disassembled

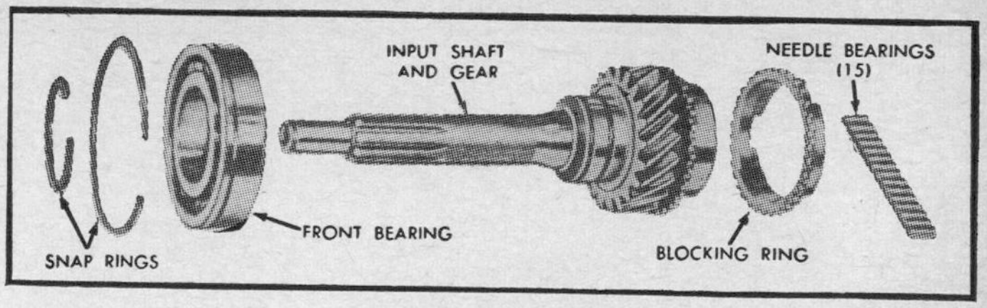

Fig. 10 Main drive gear disassembled

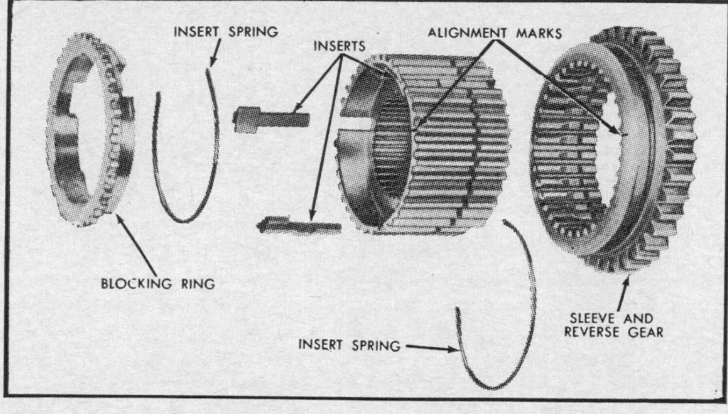

Fig. 11 Low-reverse synchronizer disassembled

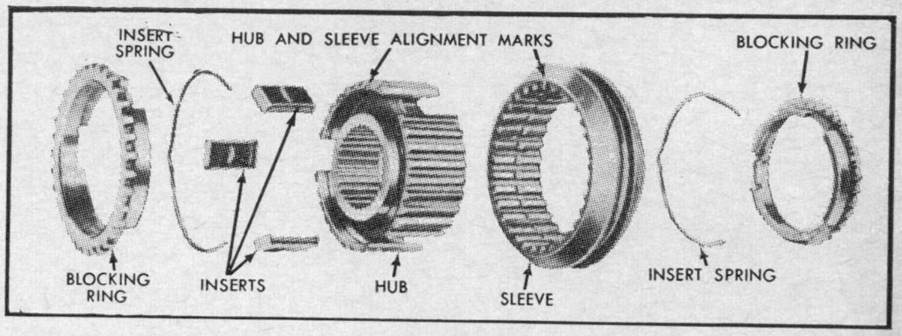

Fig. 12 Second-high synchronizer disassembled

25. Remove snap ring from front end of mainshaft and remove synchronizers, gears and related parts, Fig. 9.
26. If main drive gear is to be disassembled, refer to Fig. 10.

REASSEMBLE TRANS.

Counter Gear

1. Coat bore at each end of counter gear with grease.
2. Hold appropriate dummy shaft in gear and install 25 needle bearings and a retainer washer in each end of gear, Fig. 7.
3. Install counter gear, thrust washers and countershaft in case.
4. Place transmission case in vertical position and check end play with a feeler gauge as shown in Fig. 13. If end play exceeds .018", replace thrust washers as required to obtain .004-.018" end play.
5. Once end play has been established, remove countershaft with dummy shaft.
6. Allow counter gear assembly to remain in case.

Reverse Idler Gear

1. Install idler gear, thrust washers and shaft in case.
2. Make sure that thrust washer with flat side is at the web end, and that the spur gear is toward the rear of case, Fig. 6.
3. Check reverse idler gear end play in same manner and to the same clearance as the counter gear. If end play is within limits of .004-.018" leave gear in case.

Low-Reverse Synchronizer

1. Install an insert spring, Fig. 11, in groove of low-reverse synchronizer hub. Make sure spring covers all insert grooves.
2. Start hub in sleeve, making sure that alignment marks are properly indexed.
3. Position three inserts in hub, making sure that small end is over spring and that shoulder is on inside of hub.
4. Slide sleeve and reverse gear onto hub until detent is engaged.
5. Install other insert spring in front of hub to hold inserts against hub.

Second-Third Synchronizer

1. Install one insert spring, Fig. 12, into a groove of synchronizer hub, making sure that all three insert slots are fully covered.
2. With alignment marks on hub and sleeve aligned, start hub into sleeve.
3. Place three inserts on top of retaining spring and push assembly together.
4. Install remaining insert spring so that spring ends cover same slots as do other spring. Do not stagger springs.
5. Place a synchronizer blocking ring in each end of sleeve.

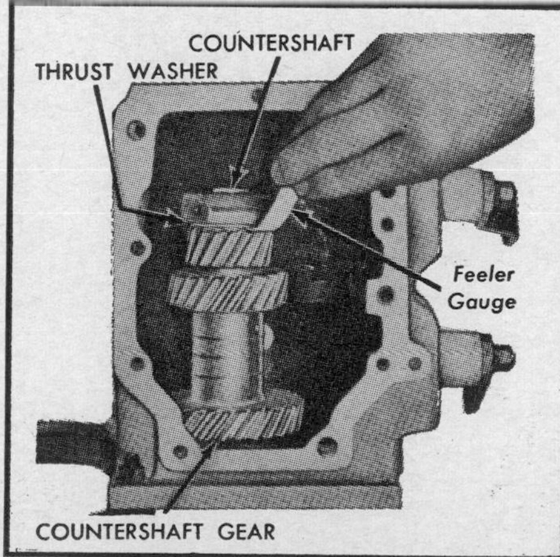

Fig. 13 Checking counter gear end play

Main Drive Line

1. Lubricate mainshaft splines and machined surfaces with transmission lube.
2. Slide low-reverse synchronizer, Fig. 9, onto mainshaft with teeth end of gear facing toward rear of shaft. Secure in place with snap ring.
3. Coat tapered machined surface of low gear with grease. Place blocking ring on greased surface.
4. Slide low gear onto mainshaft with blocking ring toward rear of shaft. Rotate gear as necessary to engage the three notches in blocking ring with synchronizer inserts. Secure low gear with thrust washer and snap ring.
5. Coat tapered machined surface of 2nd gear with grease and slide blocking ring onto it. Slide 2nd gear with blocking ring and 2-3 synchronizer onto mainshaft. Tapered machined surface of 2nd gear must be toward front of shaft. Make sure that notches in blocking ring engage synchronizer inserts. Secure synchronizer with snap ring.
6. Install new O-ring on each of two shift lever shafts, Fig. 8. Lubricate shafts with transmission lube and install them in case. Secure each lever on its shaft with a flat washer, lock washer and nut.
7. Coat bore of main drive gear shaft with thick coat of grease. Install 15 needle bearings in gear pocket, Fig. 10.
8. Position drive gear assembly into case.
9. Place a detent spring and plug in case, Fig. 5. Place 2-3 shift fork in synchronizer groove. Rotate fork into position and install 2-3 shift rail. It will be necessary to depress detent plug to enter rail in bore. Move rail inward until detent plug engages center (neutral) notch. Secure fork to shaft with set screw.

10. Install interlock plug in case. If 2-3 shift rail is in neutral position, top of interlock will be slightly lower than surface of low-reverse shift rail bore.
11. Place low-reverse shift fork in groove of synchronizer. Rotate fork into position and install low-reverse shift rail. Move rail inward until center (neutral) notch is aligned with detent bore. Secure fork to shaft with set screw.
12. Install remaining detent plug and spring. Secure spring with slotted head set screw. Turn set screw in until head is flush with case.
13. Install new expansion plug in case.
14. Install large snap ring on drive bearing. Work drive gear into case and onto mainshaft until snap ring is seated against case. Make sure that needle bearings do not fall out of place and that notches in blocking ring engage inserts in synchronizer.

NOTE: The foregoing applies only to transmissions used with V8-352 and 390 engines. On all other models, the drive gear is installed through front of case with bearing in place on shaft.

15. Position new front bearing retainer gasket on case. Place bearing retainer on case, making sure oil return groove is at the bottom. Install and tighten attaching screws to 19-25 ft-lbs.
16. Install large snap ring on mainshaft rear bearing. Place bearing on mainshaft with snap ring end toward rear of shaft. Press bearing into place and secure with snap ring.
17. Hold speedometer drive gear lock ball in detent and slide gear into place. Secure gear with snap ring.

Final Assembly

1. Place transmission in vertical position. Working through drain hole in bottom of case, align bore of counter gear and thrust washers with bore of case, using a screwdriver.
2. Working through rear of case, push dummy shaft out with countershaft. Before countershaft is completely inserted, make sure the hole that accommodates roll pin is aligned with hole in case.
3. Working through lubricant filler hole, install roll pin (Fig. 2) in case and countershaft.
4. Install filler and drain plugs, making sure magnetic plug is installed in bottom of case.
5. Install extension housing with new gasket and torque attaching cap screws to 42-50 ft-lbs.
6. Place transmission in gear, pour lubricant over entire gear train while rotating input and output shafts.
7. Install cover with new gasket and torque attaching screws to 14-19 ft-lbs. Coat gasket and cover screws with sealer.

Type Eight

DISASSEMBLE TRANS.

1. Referring to Fig. 1, remove cover.
2. Remove extension housing. *To prevent mainshaft from following housing (with resultant loss of needle bearings) tap end of mainshaft while withdrawing extension housing.*
3. Remove speedometer drive gear snap ring, gear and drive ball from mainshaft.
4. Remove idler gear shaft and countershaft retainer. If necessary tap front ends of both shafts to free retainer.
5. Using a suitable bearing loading tool, drive countershaft rearward out of gear and case. Then carefully lower counter gear to bottom of case, Fig. 2.
6. After removing main drive gear bearing retainer, remove drive gear and front synchronizer blocking ring from case, Fig. 3.
7. Remove synchronizer retaining snap ring from mainshaft. Then, while holding synchronizer together, pull mainshaft out of case. Lift synchronizer, gears and shift forks from case. *For reference on reassembly, note which end of synchronizer hub faces forward.*
8. Drive reverse idler shaft out of case and lift out idler gear, shaft and counter gear.
9. Remove shift levers.
10. From underside of case, drive out tapered pins, Fig. 4. Using a plastic hammer, drive 2-3 shift cam and shaft toward outside of case and separate balls and springs from plunger. Push out cam and shaft assemblies and remove plunger.
11. If necessary, shift lever oil seals may be removed with a slide hammer type hooked tool.
12. Remove snap ring and press main drive gear out of bearing and oil slinger.
13. Remove snap ring and press bearing from mainshaft.

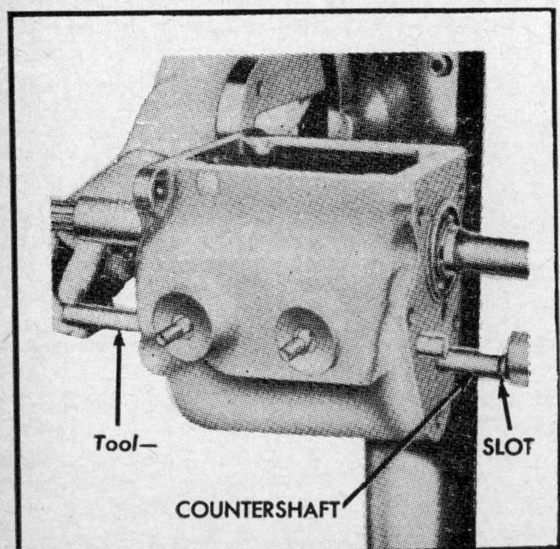

Fig. 2 Countershaft removal and installation

REASSEMBLE TRANS.

1. Press main drive gear bearing and oil slinger on shaft, securing with snap ring.
2. Press mainshaft bearing on shaft and secure with snap ring.
3. Insert spacer and dummy shaft, Fig. 2, into counter gear. Position one flat washer at each end of spacer. Apply grease to needle bearings and assemble them around dummy shaft at each end of gear. Apply grease to other two flat washers and thrust washers and assemble at each end of counter gear. Note position of tangs on thrust washers, Fig. 1.
4. Position counter gear assembly in bottom of case with larger gear toward front.
5. Install low-reverse shift cam through case opening. Assemble spacer and spring in plunger. Hold plunger in position and install 2-3 cam and shaft in case opening, allowing balls to register in cam detents.
6. Align cam and shaft grooves with openings in shaft bosses, and install retaining pins, Fig. 4. Check cam action; bent pins may restrict movement.
7. Position reverse idler gear, and insert shaft (from rear) through case just far enough to hold gear.
8. After assembling three inserts in synchronizer hub and securing them with two spring retainers, insert hub into 2-3 synchronizer sleeve. Install one blocking ring in rear side of hub. Coat blocking rings with grease.
9. Using a coating of grease, assemble needle bearings in drive gear pocket

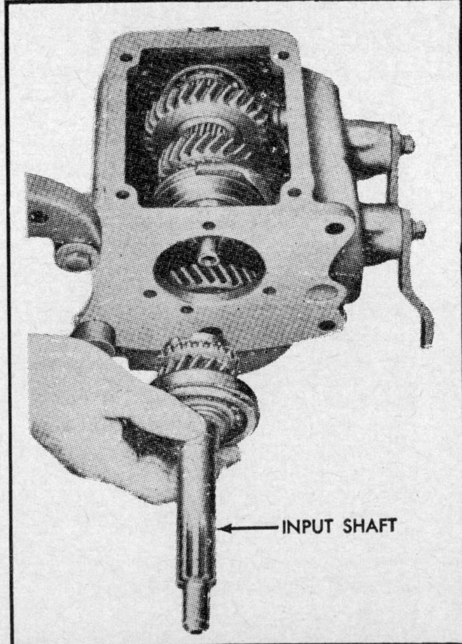

Fig. 3 Removing main drive gear

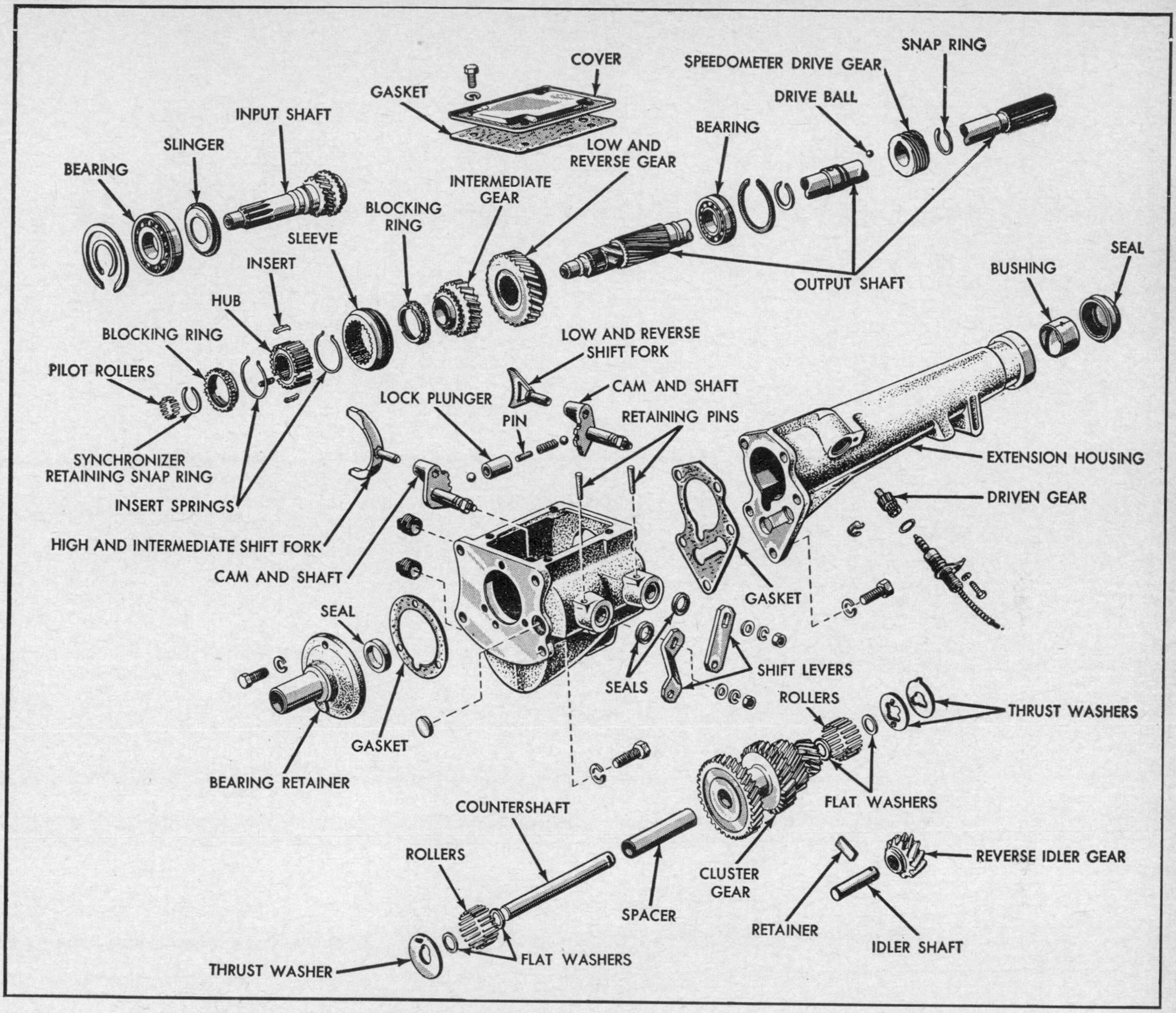

Fig. 1 Type 8 transmission. Note that longer end of synchronizer hub goes to the front. CAUTION: On some models the shift fork groove for low-reverse sliding gear goes to rear as shown; on other models fork goes to front. Check position after cover is removed

and install front synchronizer blocking ring on drive gear shaft.

10. Install shift forks in shift lever shafts with large fork in 2-3 shaft. Web of low-reverse fork must be to rear of shaft center.
11. Start mainshaft through rear of case. Place low-reverse gear on shaft, followed by 2nd speed gear. Tilt mainshaft enough to allow rear shift fork to engage sliding gear groove.
12. *With longer hub forward,* slide synchronizer onto mainshaft and engage synchronizer sleeve in 2-3 shift fork.
13. Install synchronizer hub and snap ring.
14. Position main drive gear and front synchronizer blocking ring.
15. Place a new gasket on drive gear bearing retainer. If shaft oil seal was removed from retainer, install a new seal. Install bearing retainer, using sealer on bolts. Line up oil drain groove in retainer with oil hole in case.
16. Raise counter gear assembly and align dummy shaft with countershaft opening in case. Start countershaft into case from rear, and carefully drive shaft into position.
17. Install idler gear shaft and retainer.
18. Secure speedometer drive gear and ball with snap ring.
19. Using a new gasket, install extension housing.
20. Start new seal over each cam and shaft and drive in seals.
21. Fill transmission to proper level with lubricant. Then, using a new gasket and sealer on bolts, install transmission cover.

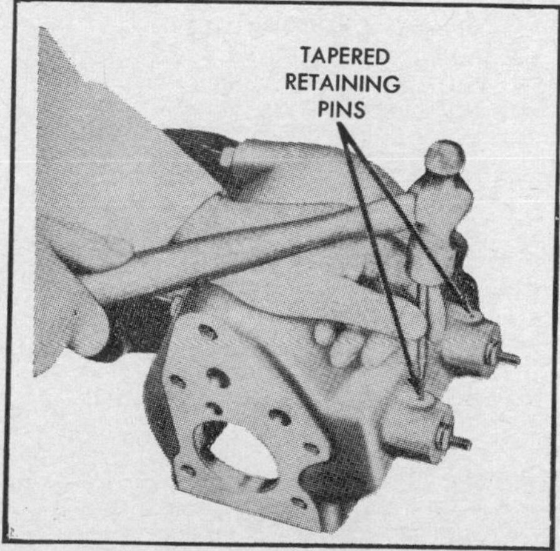

Fig. 4 Removing shift shaft retaining pins. Note that pins are driven out from the bottom

NOTE: Cover gasket vent holes must be toward rear and cover vent hole must be toward front.

Type Nine

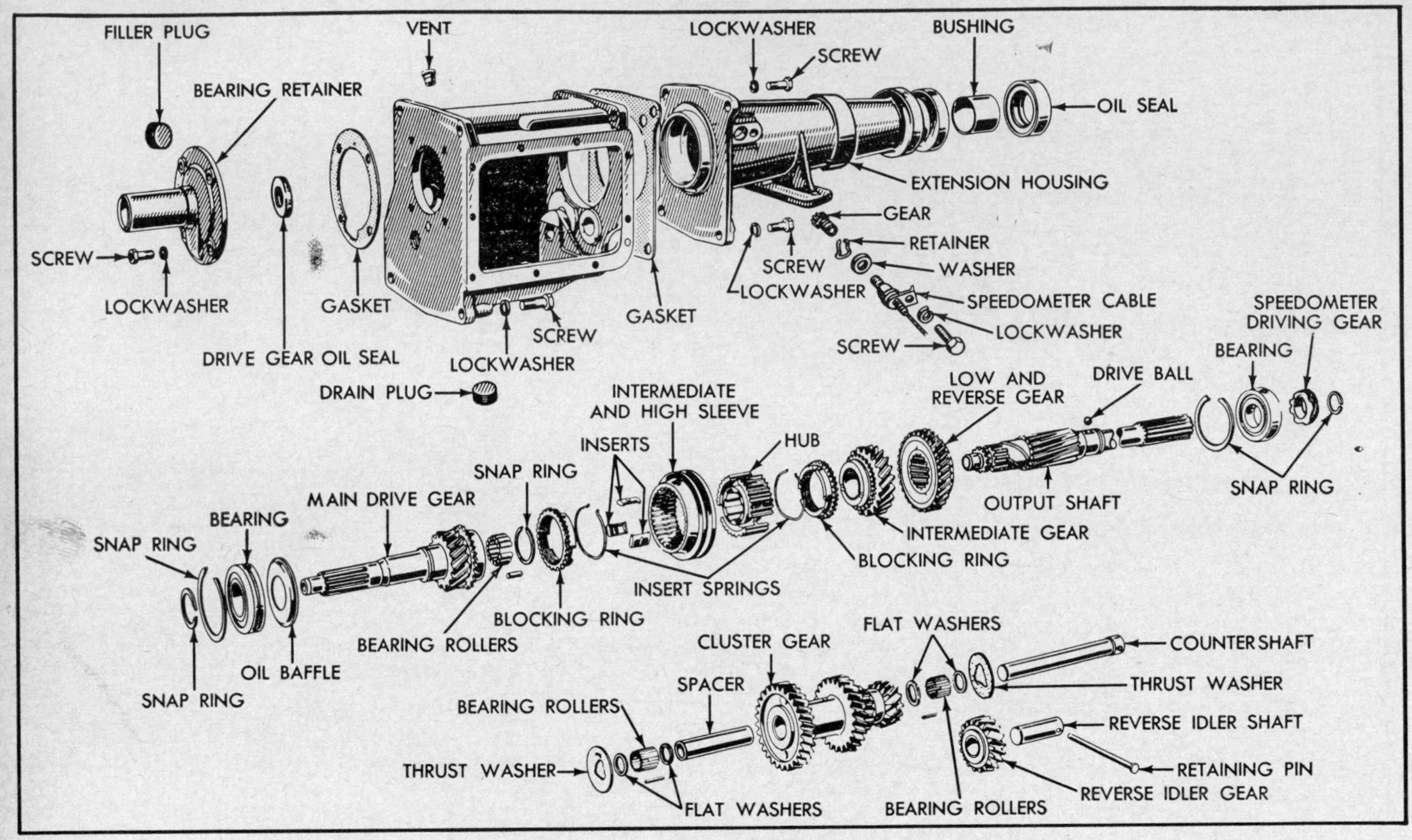

Fig. 1 Type 9 transmission disassembled. Note that shift fork groove on low-reverse sliding gear goes toward rear of case

DISASSEMBLE TRANS.

1. Remove gear shift housing.
2. Unfasten extension housing from case and turn housing to expose end of countershaft, Fig. 1.
3. Remove countershaft-idler shaft retaining pin and drive countershaft out through rear of case with a pilot tool (dummy countershaft), Fig. 2. When tool has been driven in far enough to clear hole in front of case, allow counter gear to drop to bottom of case.
4. Remove extension housing and mainshaft as a unit. Some mainshaft pilot bearing rollers may drop to bottom of case when shaft is pulled rearward.
5. Remove snap ring from front end of mainshaft and strip shaft of synchronizer, 2nd gear and low-reverse gear.
6. To remove mainshaft from extension housing, remove snap ring that holds bearing outer race in housing, then tap bearing and shaft out of housing together.
7. Remove main drive gear bearing retainer. Tap drive gear and bearing out of front of case. Remove pilot roller bearings.
8. Drive reverse idler gear shaft out rear of case and lift out idler gear.
9. Lift counter gear assembly from case.

UNIT REPAIRS

Synchronizer

Disassemble synchronizer by sliding sleeve off hub and removing three inserts, wave washer and spring.

When assembled, the overlapping ends of the wave washer must be underneath the lip of one of the inserts, and the ends must also be flush against front face of hub.

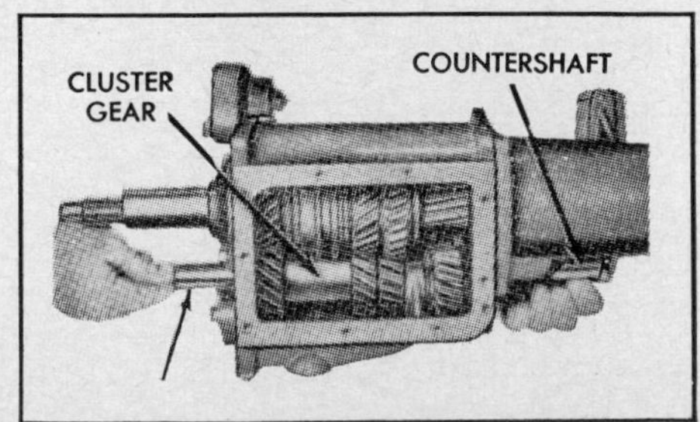

Fig. 2 Countershaft removal

Main Drive Gear

If the main drive gear bearing is to be replaced, make the substitution with a suitable press. If the bearing does not have a built-in shield, a baffle, which spins with the mainshaft, is used at the rear of the bearing. The baffle must be installed with the dished side away from the bearing so it does not rub the outer face of the bearing.

Mainshaft

The bearing can be removed from the mainshaft by removing the speedometer gear snap ring, gear and driving ball. The bearing is then pressed off the shaft.

Gear Shift Housing

The gear shift housing, Fig. 3, does not need to be disassembled to inspect parts. Check the condition of the forks and levers. If there is any binding or possibility of shifting into two gears at once when lever is operated, disassemble housing as follows:

1. Remove levers from cam and shaft assemblies.
2. Pull fork and cams out of housing. As cams are removed, interlock balls, retainer and spring will fall out of housing.

3. Pull shift forks out of cams and remove seal rings from cams.
4. Reverse removal procedure to assemble, using new seal rings on cams.

Counter Gear

1. Place bearing loading tool (dummy shaft), Fig. 2, in counter gear.
2. Center spacer in gear.
3. Using cup grease, install flat washer, 25 needle bearings and a second flat washer at each end of counter gear.
4. Apply a thin film of grease and place thrust washers on each end of gear with flat side next to gear.

REASSEMBLE TRANS.

1. Place counter gear assembly in bottom of case.
2. Place reverse idler gear in case with chamfered teeth ends toward front.
3. Install reverse idler shaft from rear of case.

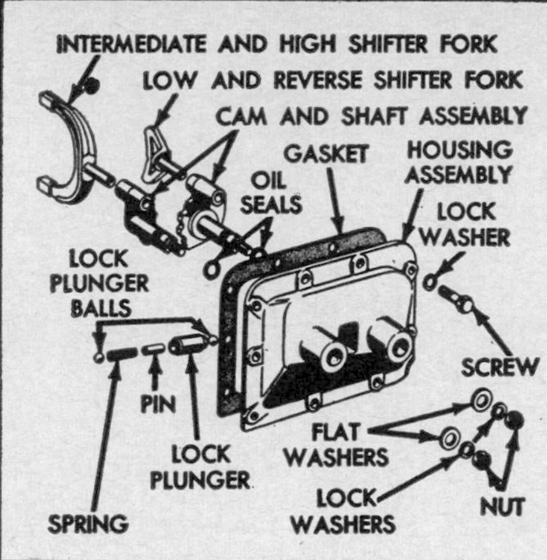

Fig. 3 Gear shift housing

4. Install pilot roller bearings in drive gear pocket, then install drive gear in front of case.
5. Install drive gear bearing retainer with new gasket, and with drain hole in retainer aligned with hole in case. Apply sealer to retaining bolts before installation.
6. Install low-reverse gear on mainshaft with shift fork groove to rear.
7. Install 2nd speed gear and synchronizer on shaft and secure with snap ring.
8. Place mainshaft in extension housing and secure with snap ring.
9. Install extension housing with new gasket (coated with sealer). Turn extension housing to provide access to countershaft hole in case.
10. Work counter gear into position.
11. Install countershaft from rear of case, pushing dummy shaft out through front.
12. Turn extension housing to normal position and secure to case.
13. Install gear shift housing to case.

Type Ten

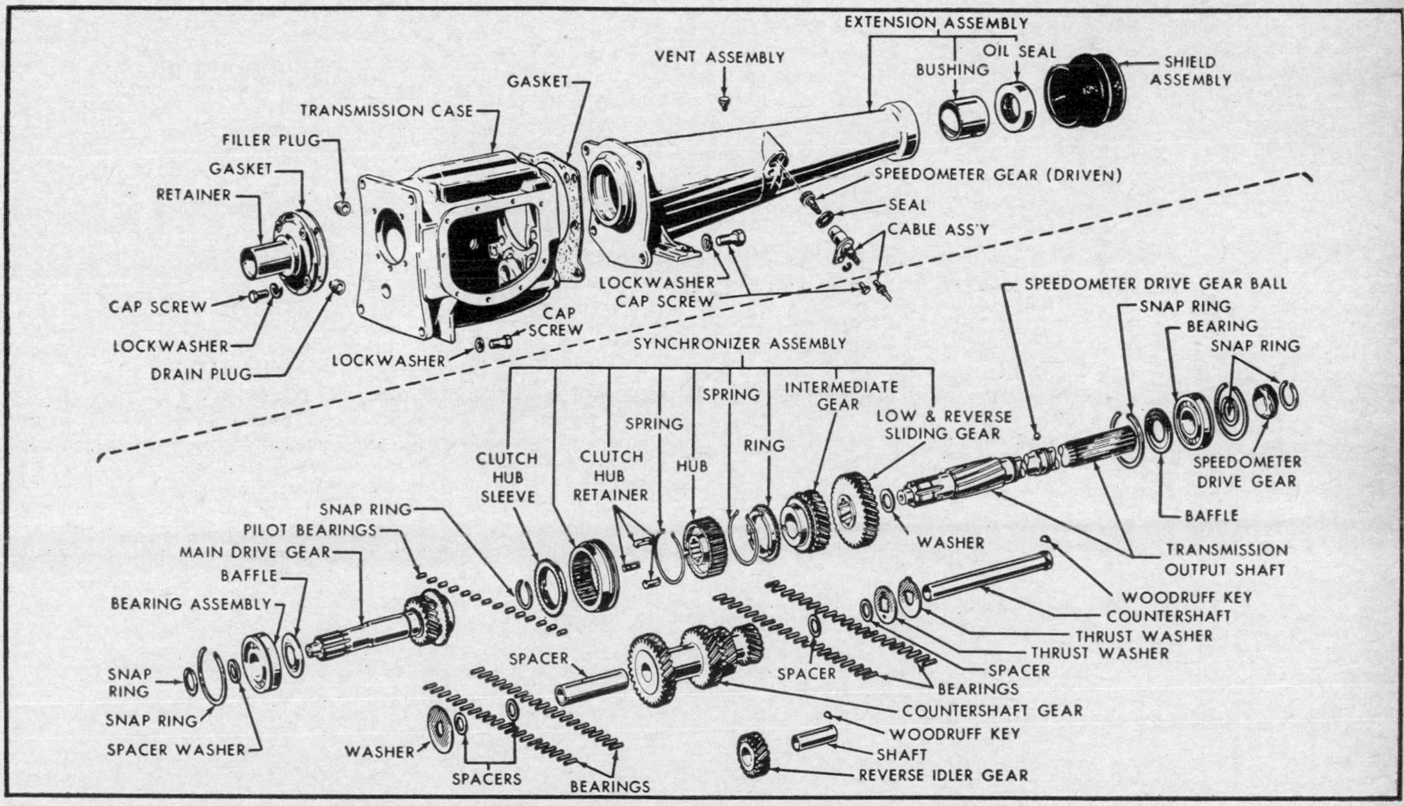

Fig. 1 Type 10 transmission disassembled. Note that shift fork groove on low-reverse sliding gear goes toward front of case

DISASSEMBLE TRANS.

1. Remove gearshift housing.
2. Remove drive gear bearing retainer, Fig. 1. Remove snap ring and washer from drive gear shaft.
3. Unfasten and pull extension housing to the rear. Pull drive gear shaft forward.
4. Slide synchronizer sleeve forward. Tilt case and mainshaft so that mainshaft gears clear counter gear and remove mainshaft and extension housing as a unit.
5. Remove main drive gear through cover opening and remove rollers from drive gear pocket.
6. Using a suitable bearing loading tool, Fig. 2, remove countershaft.

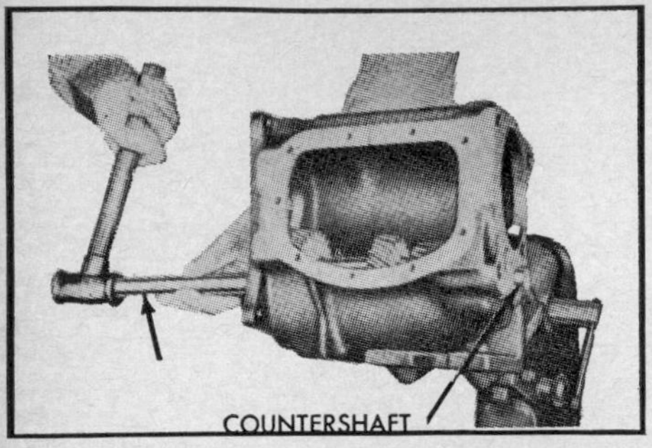

Fig. 2 Countershaft removal

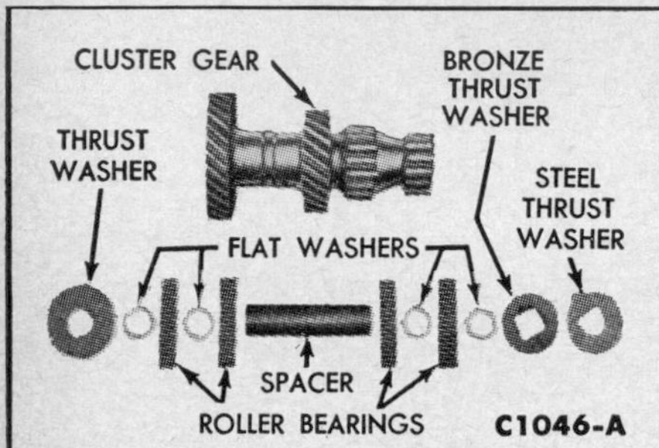

Fig. 4 Counter gear disassembled

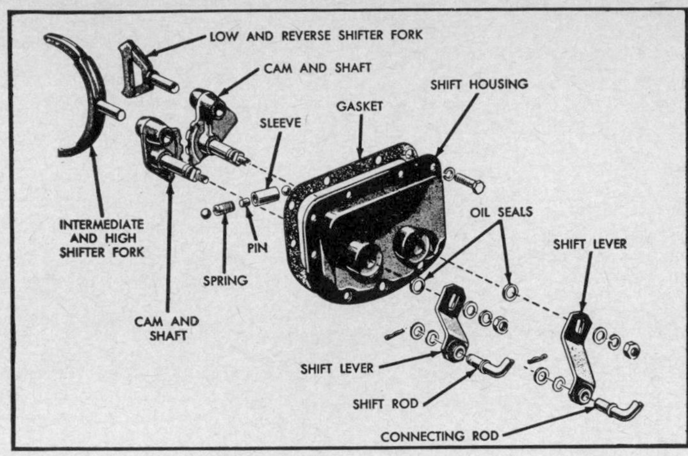

Fig. 3 Gearshift housing disassembled

As front end of shaft clears rear of case, counter gear will drop to bottom of case. Take counter gear out of case.

6. Drive out idler gear shaft.
7. Remove snap ring and slide synchronizer and gears from mainshaft.
8. Remove mainshaft rear bearing snap ring and remove mainshaft from extension housing.
9. Remove speedometer drive gear snap ring, gear and driving ball from mainshaft.
10. If gearshift housing requires service, refer to Fig. 3. Install new seals on reassembly.

REASSEMBLE TRANS.

1. Install speedometer drive gear front snap ring. Position gear and ball, holding them in place with lubricant. Install retaining snap ring.
2. Tap mainshaft into extension housing and install snap ring that holds shaft in housing.
3. Coat mainshaft with transmission lube and position low-reverse gear (shift fork groove to front) on shaft. Place 2nd gear on shaft with synchronizer teeth and taper to the front.
4. Assemble synchronizer by placing spring at each end of hub, with ends of springs between same two inserts. Position inserts in hub grooves and slide sleeve (with shift fork groove to rear) onto hub.
5. Slide synchronizer with shoulder of hub forward onto shaft and install snap ring. Use a snap ring that will provide .003-.012" clearance between rear side of ring and synchronizer hub when hub is forced as far back as possible.
6. Assemble counter gear as suggested by Fig. 4, using dummy shaft in gear to hold bearings and thrust washer in place.
7. Coat front thrust washer with grease and place it in front of case with washer tab in its slot.
8. Coat countershaft rear inner thrust washer with grease and place in counter gear pocket.
9. Position counter gear assembly in case. Start countershaft in case, center gear and thrust washers and continue to slide shaft into gear. Before rear end of shaft enters case, place key in shaft slot, making sure key lines up with keyway in case. Drive shaft rest of the way until it is flush with or slightly inside machined surface of case.
10. Install reverse idler gear with large shoulder to rear and install gear shaft.
11. Install pilot rollers in drive gear pocket and install drive gear into case.
12. Install bearing retainer, using new gasket. Line up oil drain hole in retainer with oil hole in case. Secure retainer with attaching bolts.
13. Install extension housing (with new gasket) and mainshaft into case. Secure extension housing with attaching bolts.
14. Install gear shift housing.

Type Eleven

DISASSEMBLE TRANS.

1. After draining transmission and overdrive, remove solenoid retaining screw and rotate solenoid about ¼ turn to remove it.
2. Remove governor and transmission cover.
3. With a sharp punch, pierce snap ring hole cover and remove cover, Fig. 2.
4. Remove overdrive housing-to-transmission case bolts and overdrive control shaft pin.
5. Pull overdrive control lever and shaft out as far as possible. Spread snap ring that retains overdrive output shaft bearing and remove overdrive housing, Fig. 2. It may be necessary to tap output shaft to free bearing from housing.
6. Remove overdrive output shaft. Catch any free wheel unit rollers that drop out. Remove rest of rollers.
7. Remove snap ring and take off speedometer gear and drive ball.
8. Remove free wheel unit retainers. Then remove clutch, planet carrier, sun gear and shift rail.
9. Remove snap ring from adapter and remove plate and trough, balk ring gear and pawl.
10. Remove input shaft bearing retainer.
11. Rotate overdrive adapter to expose countershaft lock and remove lock.
12. With a drift, drive countershaft toward rear until it just clears hole at front of case. Support countershaft gear with a hook, then push countershaft out of rear with a special mandrel or a spare countershaft cut to the length of the countershaft gear to hold the roller bearings and thrust washers in place, Fig. 3.
13. Lower countershaft gear assembly to bottom of case to provide clearance for removal of input shaft and bearing. Tap input shaft and bearing out of front of case.
14. Remove shift lever shaft retaining pins, Fig. 4.

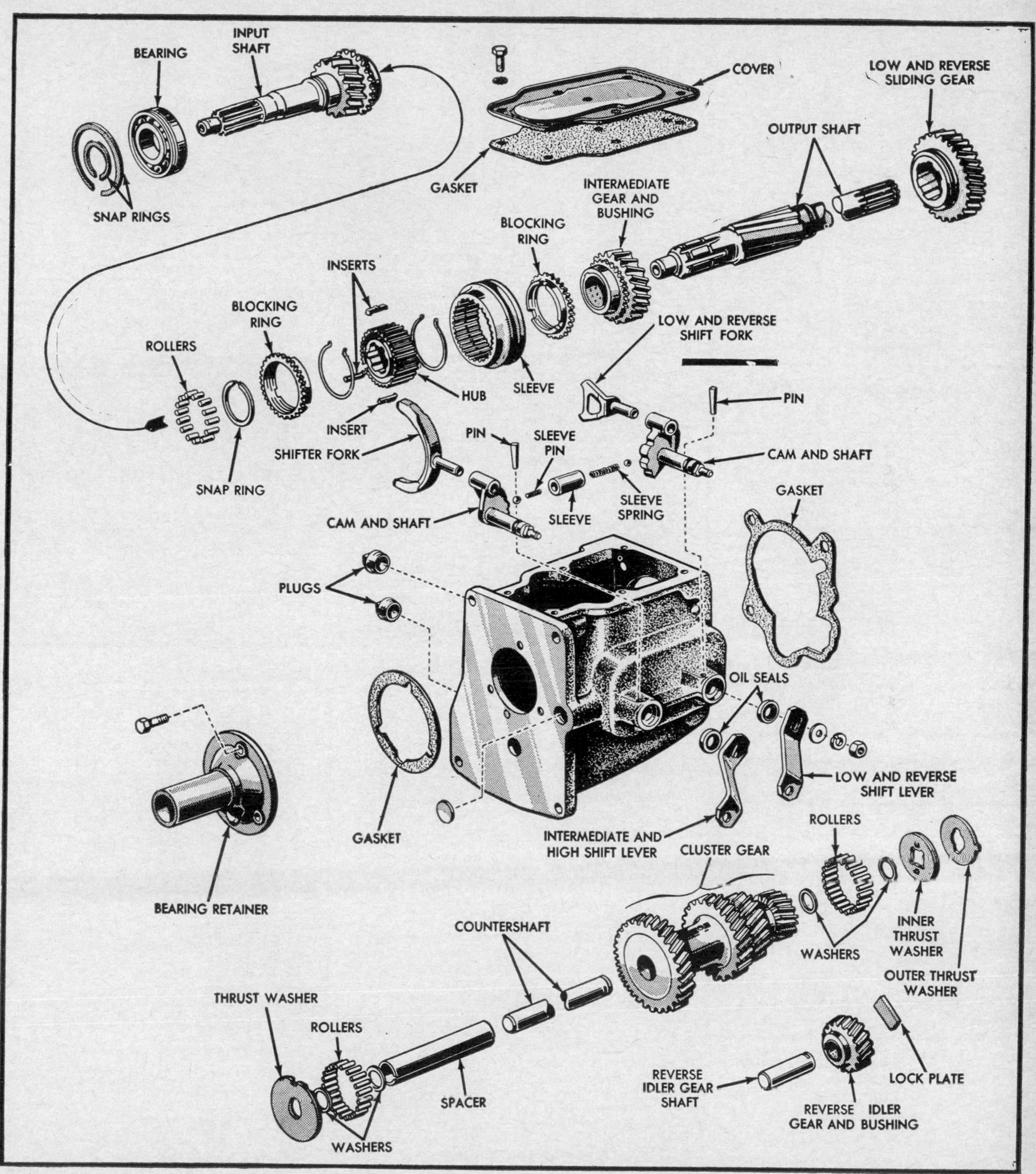
BEARING
INPUT SHAFT
COVER
LOW AND REVERSE SLIDING GEAR
OUTPUT SHAFT
GASKET
SNAP RINGS
INTERMEDIATE GEAR AND BUSHING
BLOCKING RING
INSERTS
BLOCKING RING
LOW AND REVERSE SHIFT FORK
ROLLERS
HUB
SLEEVE
PIN
INSERT
PIN
SLEEVE PIN
SHIFTER FORK
CAM AND SHAFT
SNAP RING
SLEEVE SPRING
GASKET
CAM AND SHAFT
SLEEVE
PLUGS
OIL SEALS
LOW AND REVERSE SHIFT LEVER
GASKET
INTERMEDIATE AND HIGH SHIFT LEVER
ROLLERS
CLUSTER GEAR
BEARING RETAINER
COUNTERSHAFT
INNER THRUST WASHER
WASHERS
OUTER THRUST WASHER
THRUST WASHER
ROLLERS
LOCK PLATE
REVERSE IDLER GEAR SHAFT
SPACER
REVERSE IDLER GEAR AND BUSHING
WASHERS

Fig. 1 Type 11 overdrive transmission disassembled

Fig. 2 Removing overdrive housing

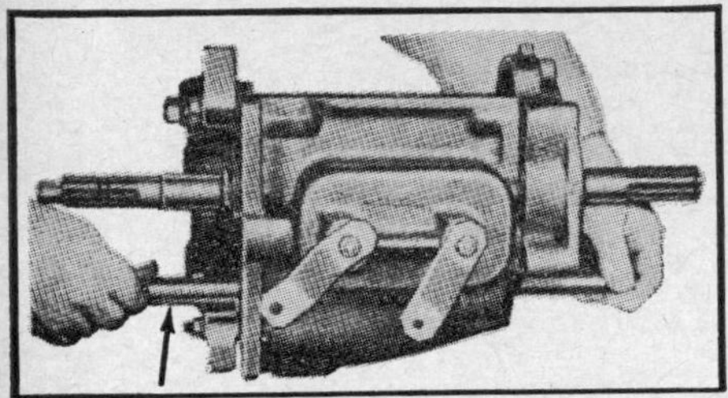

Fig. 3 Removing countershaft

Fig. 4 Removing shift lever retaining pin

Fig. 5 Removing output shaft and overdrive adapter

15. Pull low-reverse shift lever out as far as it will go, then remove low-reverse fork.
16. Remove output shaft and overdrive adapter, Fig. 5.
17. Remove snap ring at front of transmission output shaft, then strip shaft of gears.
18. While holding washers and bearing retainer tool at small end of countershaft gear, lift gear assembly from case.
19. Drive reverse idler gear shaft out of rear of case and remove idler gear from case.
20. Remove lock plunger, spring, pin and detent balls from case, Fig. 6.

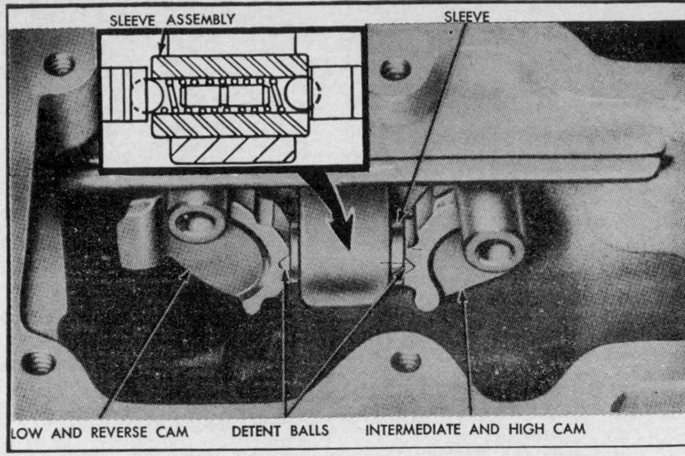

Fig. 6 Cams and detent balls installed

Synchronizer Repairs

1. Disassemble synchronizer, Fig. 1, by sliding 2-3 sleeve off hub. Remove three inserts and two springs from hub.
2. Assemble synchronizer unit by installing the two springs on hub and placing three inserts in hub. Hook one spring end in an insert as shown in Fig. 7.
3. After lining up etched marks on sleeve and hub splines, slide sleeve into place on hub.

Cam & Shaft Seals

1. Remove levers from shafts and cams.
2. Remove cams and shafts, detent balls, pin, spring and sleeve from case.
3. Remove seals with suitable puller.
4. Install new seals with suitable driver.
5. Install 2-3 shift fork and shaft in case.
6. Insert a detent ball, sleeve, spring and pin in bore of case. Move cam and shaft so that detent ball seats in neutral (center) notch.
7. Install low-reverse cam and shaft, then install levers on shafts with nuts and lockwashers.
8. Install detent ball in sleeve at low-reverse end. Then push low-reverse cam toward detent ball far enough to hold ball in place in neutral notch. Ball must seat in notch in cam.
9. Install shift lever shaft retaining pins, Fig. 4.
10. In order to assure positive shifting and eliminate the possibility of engaging more than one set of gears at the same time, the clearance between ramp of one cam and sleeve must be checked.

Countershaft Rollers

1. Remove thrust washers from end of countershaft.
2. Remove dummy shaft, retainer washers, rollers and spacer from gear.

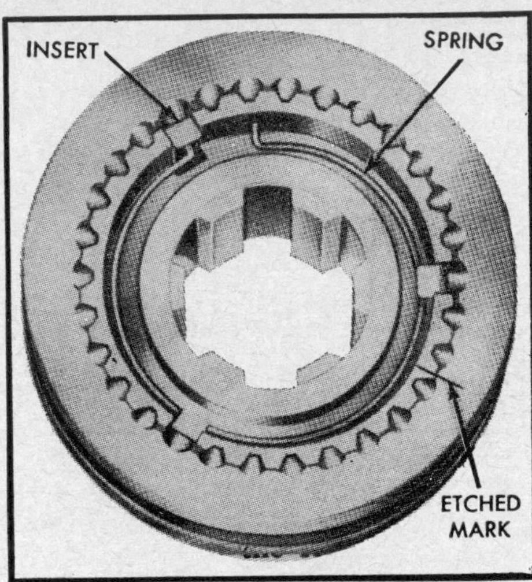

Fig. 7 Synchronizer

Fig. 8 Installing balk ring gear and pawl

3. Position spacer and dummy shaft in gear.
4. Place a retainer washer in each end of gear.
5. Coat bore in each end of gear with grease. Hold dummy shaft in gear and install roller bearings and retainer washer in each end of gear.
6. Apply grease to two remaining retainer washers and to the contact surface of thrust washers. Install retainer washers and thrust washers on each end of gear.

Assemble Trans.

Use new gaskets and gasket sealer during assembly. To provide initial lubrication, apply a thin coating of grease on all parts before installation.

1. Place countergear with dummy shaft and roller bearings in case.
2. With case in vertical position, align countershaft gear bore and thrust washers with bores in case and install countershaft.
3. With case in horizontal position, check countergear end play with a feeler gauge. End play should be .004-.018". If not within these limits, replace thrust washers.
4. After establishing correct end play, install dummy shaft in countershaft gear and allow gear to remain in bottom of case.
5. Install reverse idler gear in case with chamfered teeth ends toward front.
6. Drive reverse idler shaft in case with locking notch aligned with countershaft hole.
7. Install low-reverse sliding gear on mainshaft with shifter fork groove toward front.
8. Install intermediate gear on mainshaft with clutch teeth toward front.
9. Place a blocking ring on intermediate gear and install synchronizer on mainshaft with hub thrust surface toward rear, Fig. 1. Rotate intermediate gear as necessary to line up notches in blocker ring with synchronizer inserts. Install snap ring that retains synchronizer.
10. Install shift forks in cams inside case. The offset in low-reverse fork goes toward front.
11. Install new solenoid seal in overdrive adapter.
12. Place a new gasket on adapter, using gasket sealer to hold it in place.
13. Install overdrive adapter and transmission output shaft assembly in transmission.
14. Engage shift forks with 2-3 synchronizer sleeve and with low-reverse sliding gear.
15. Seat overdrive adapter squarely against transmission case and secure with a capscrew.

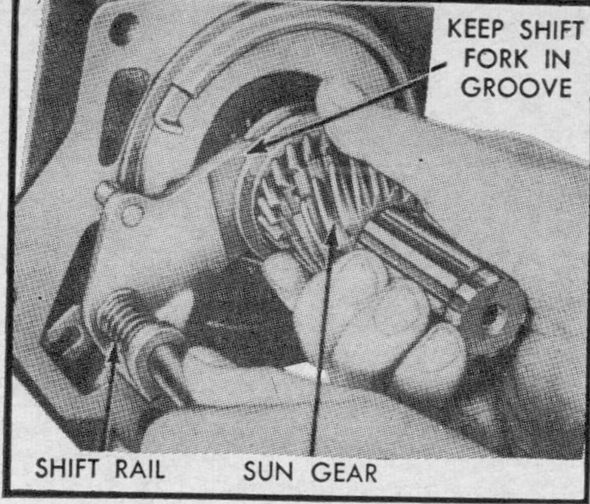

Fig. 9 Installing sun gear and shift rail

16. Insert pilot roller bearings in input shaft and retain with grease.
17. Place a blocking ring on input shaft gear.
18. Tap input shaft and bearing into case, and at the same time line up slots in blocking ring with synchronizer inserts.
19. Place a new gasket on input shaft bearing retainer, holding it in place with gasket sealer.
20. Install input shaft bearing retainer in case.
21. Invert transmission and remove capscrew from overdrive adapter. Pull adapter out about ¼" and rotate it to expose countershaft hole.
22. Work countershaft gear into normal position by rotating input and output shafts.
23. Push countershaft into case from rear.
24. Align slots in countershaft with slot in reverse idler shaft and install lock plate.
25. Rotate adapter to its normal position and set it squarely against transmission case. Check blocking rings to make sure slots are aligned with synchronizer inserts.
26. With input shaft pointing down, place balk ring gear and pawl in adapter, Fig. 8.
27. Place plate and trough in adapter and install snap ring.
28. Install sun gear and shift rail, Fig. 9.
29. Install planet carrier and clutch cam, and retainers.
30. Install 12 clutch rollers and hold them in position with a rubber band.
31. Rotate roller cage counterclockwise (from rear) until rollers are off cam surfaces (rubber band will hold them there).
32. Slide overdrive output shaft over clutch rollers (rubber band will not affect overdrive operation).
33. Align shift rail spring with holes in overdrive housing.
34. Place a new gasket on overdrive adapter and hold it in place with gasket sealer.
35. Install overdrive housing over output shaft and shift rail. Secure housing to transmission case with four bolts.
36. Engage overdrive shaft lever by pushing it inward. Lever is correctly engaged when a spring load is apparent as lever is pushed forward.
37. Install retaining pin in overdrive housing to hold control shaft in place.
38. Thread governor into overdrive housing.
39. Rotate solenoid ¼ turn from normal position so that half ball on solenoid stem can engage pawl. Install solenoid screws.

NOTE: If solenoid stem is properly engaged, solenoid cannot be removed from overdrive in its normal position. Any attempt to pull it out will merely compress the engaging spring in solenoid.

40. Install transmission cover with new gasket.
41. Install drain plugs in transmission case and overdrive housing.
42. Check gear operation in all positions.

Type Twelve

DISASSEMBLE TRANS.

Case Components

1. Remove side cover and shift forks.
2. Unfasten attaching screws and rotate extension housing clockwise to expose reverse idler gear shaft.
3. Drive reverse idler shaft and its woodruff key out through rear of case, Fig. 2.
4. Rotate extension housing counterclockwise to expose countershaft and use a brass drift at front of shaft to drive shaft and its woodruff key out rear of case, Fig. 3.
5. With countergear dropped to bottom of case remove entire mainshaft and extension assembly through rear of case, Fig. 4. Remove mainshaft pilot roller bearings from clutch gear.
6. Expand snap ring in extension and remove extension from rear bearing and mainshaft by tapping on end of mainshaft, Fig. 5.
7. Remove clutch gear bearing retainer, bearing snap ring and washer from mainshaft, Fig. 6.
8. Drive clutch gear through its bearing into case, Fig. 7, and remove bearing by tapping out from inside of case.
9. Remove countergear assembly from case.

Mainshaft Disassembly

1. Remove snap ring and strip front of mainshaft, Fig. 8.
2. Remove rear bearing snap ring, Fig. 9.
3. Support reverse gear with press plates and press on rear of mainshaft to remove reverse gear, rear bearing, special washer, snap ring and speedometer drive gear from rear of mainshaft.

CAUTION: When pressing rear bearing be sure special washer is clear of snap ring groove. Also, be careful to center gear, bearing, washer and snap ring on mainshaft before attempting to press off speedometer drive gear.

4. Remove low-reverse sliding clutch hub snap ring from mainshaft, Fig. 10, and remove clutch assembly, blocker ring and low gear from mainshaft.

Synchronizer Clutch Keys & Springs

NOTE: The clutch hubs and sliding sleeves are a selected assembly and

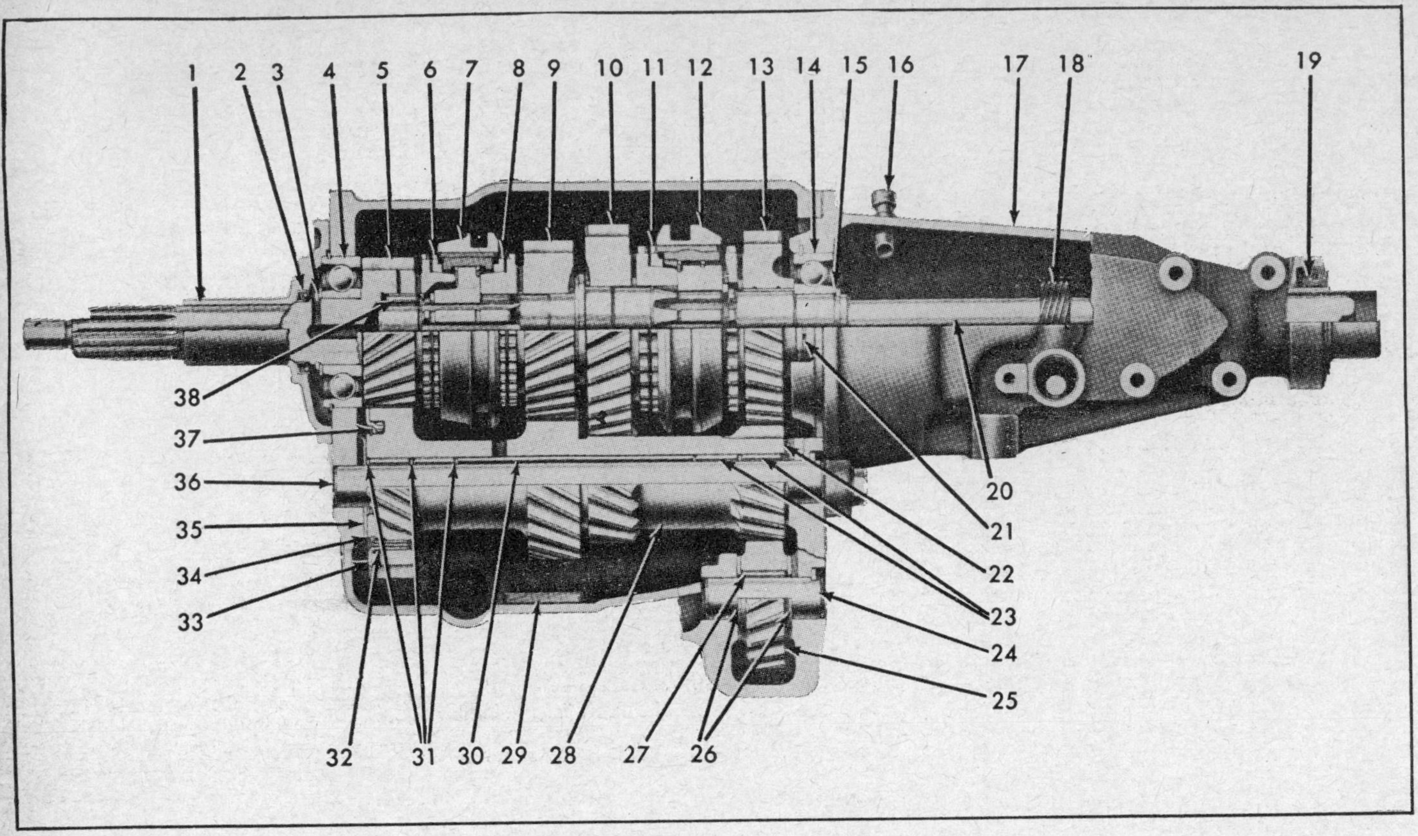

Fig. 1 Type 12 three speed fully synchronized transmission

1. Bearing Retainer
2. Lip Oil Seal
3. Snap Ring and Special Washer
4. Clutch Gear Bearing
5. Clutch Gear
6. 3rd Speed Blocker Ring
7. 2-3 Sliding Clutch Sleeve
8. 2nd Speed Blocker Ring
9. Second Speed Gear
10. First Speed Gear
11. 1st Speed Blocker Ring
12. 1st and Reverse Sliding Clutch Sleeve
13. Reverse Gear
14. Mainshaft Rear Bearing
15. Snap Ring and Special Washer
16. Vent
17. Extension
18. Speedo Drive Gear
19. Extension Oil Seal
20. Mainshaft
21. Extension to Bearing Retainer Ring
22. Countergear Thrust Washer
23. Roller Bearings
24. Reverse Idler Shaft
25. Reverse Idler Gear
26. Thrust Washer
27. Roller Bearings
28. Countergear
29. Magnet
30. Tube Spacer
31. Washers
32. Roll Pin
33. Dampener Plate
34. Spiral-Lox Retainer
35. Countergear Thrust Washer
36. Countergear Shaft
37. Dampener Spring
38. Mainshaft Pilot Bearings

Fig. 2 Removing reverse idler shaft

should be kept together as originally assembled. However, the two keys and springs may be replaced if worn or broken.

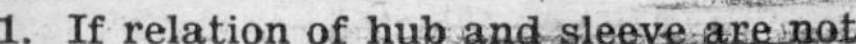

1. If relation of hub and sleeve are not already marked, mark for assembly purposes.
2. Push hub from sliding sleeve. Keys will fall free and springs may easily be removed.
3. Place two springs in position (one on each side of hub) so all three keys are engaged by both springs,

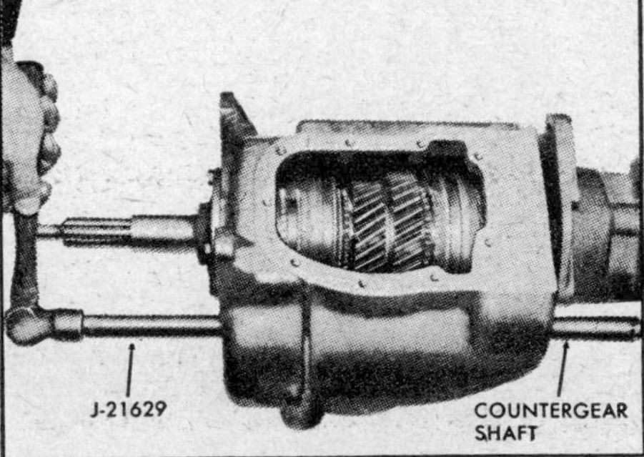

Fig. 3 Removing countershaft

Fig. 4 Removing mainshaft and extension from case

Fig. 11. Place keys in position and, holding them in place, slide sleeve onto hub, aligning marks made previously.

Mainshaft Reassemble

1. Referring to Fig. 12, install 1st gear on rear of mainshaft with gear clutching teeth to rear.
2. Install 1st gear blocking ring over 1st gear tapered cone end area with

Fig. 5 Extension-to-rear bearing snap ring

Fig. 6 Clutch gear bearing-to-gear snap ring

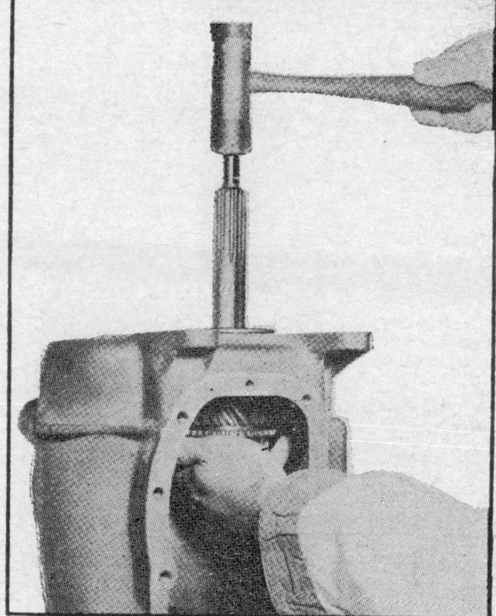

Fig. 7 Removing clutch gear from bearing and case

clutch key notches toward rear.

3. Install 1st-reverse sliding clutch assembly over rear of mainshaft, being careful to engage three keys with notches of blocker ring. Properly installed, straightest side of clutch hub and taper of sliding sleeve should both be toward rear of mainshaft (see Fig. 1).
4. Install snap ring in front of 1st-reverse clutch hub, Fig. 10.

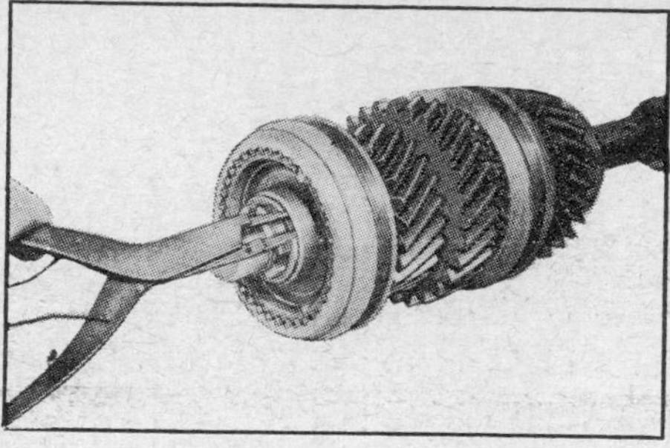

Fig. 8 2nd-3rd clutch hub snap ring

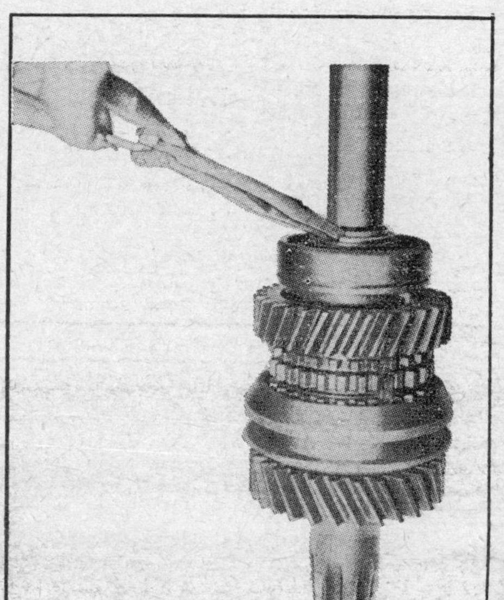

Fig. 9 Rear bearing-to-mainshaft snap ring

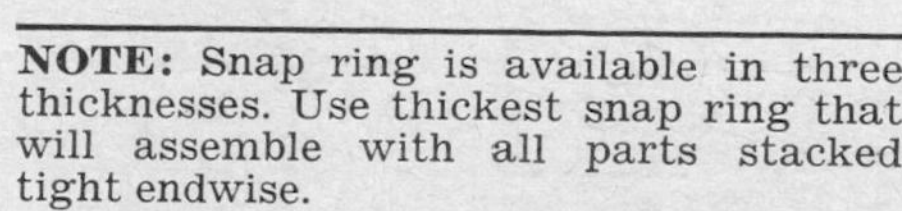

Fig. 10 First-reverse clutch hub snap ring

NOTE: Snap ring is available in three thicknesses. Use thickest snap ring that will assemble with all parts stacked tight endwise.

5. Install reverse gear over mainshaft with gear clutch teeth toward front.
6. Press rear bearing on mainshaft with its outer race snap ring groove closest to reverse gear.

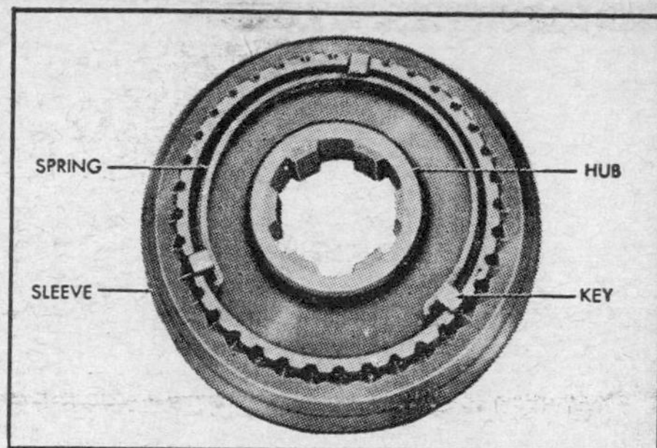

Fig. 11 2nd-3rd synchronizer clutch

Fig. 14 Loading countershaft bearings

Fig. 15 Installing countershaft

7. Install rear bearing special washer and snap ring to mainshaft, Fig. 9.

NOTE: This snap ring is available in six thicknesses. Use thickest snap ring that will assemble with all parts stacked tight endwise.

8. Press speedometer drive gear on rear of mainshaft until centered on shaft boss.
9. Install 2nd speed gear over front of mainshaft with gear clutch teeth toward front.
10. Install blocker ring over 2nd gear tapered cone end with clutch key notches toward front.
11. Install 2-3 sliding clutch assembly

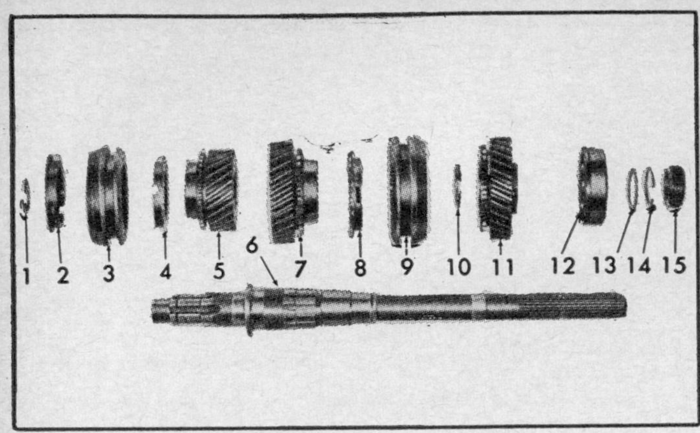

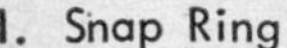

Fig. 12 Mainshaft disassembled

1. Snap Ring
2. 3rd Speed Blocker Ring
3. 2-3 Clutch Assembly
4. 2nd Speed Blocker Ring
5. 2nd Speed Gear
6. Mainshaft
7. 1st Speed Gear
8. 1st Speed Blocker Ring
9. 1st Reverse Clutch Assembly
10. Snap Ring
11. Reverse Gear
12. Rear Bearing
13. Special Washer
14. Snap Ring
15. Speedo Drive Gear

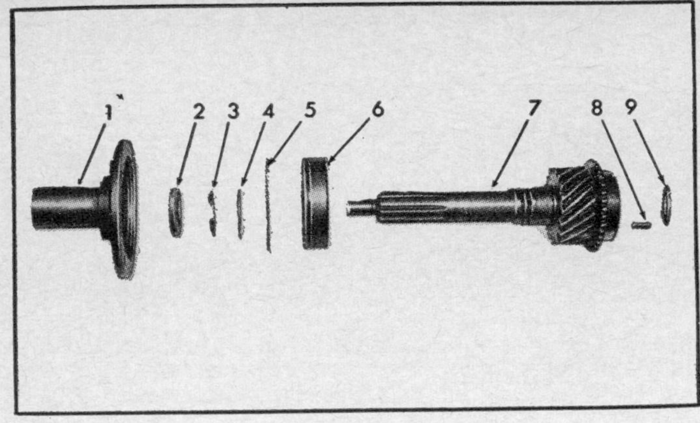

Fig. 13 Clutch gear components

1. Retainer
2. Lip Seal
3. Snap Ring
4. Special Washer
5. Snap Ring
6. Clutch Gear Bearing
7. Clutch Gear
8. Mainshaft Pilot Bearings
9. Bearing Spacer

Fig. 16 Checking countergear end play

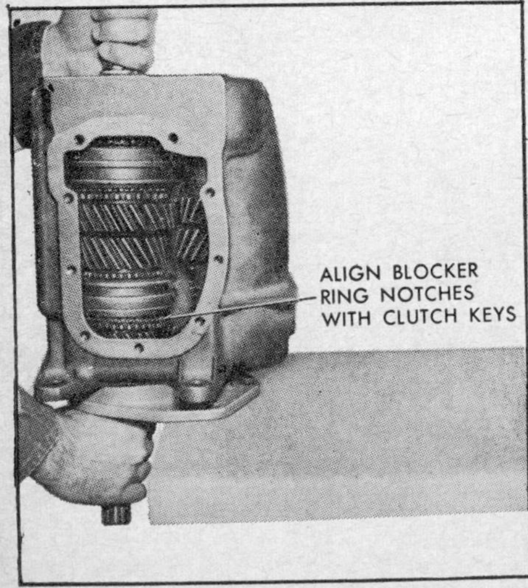

Fig. 17 Installing mainshaft assembly

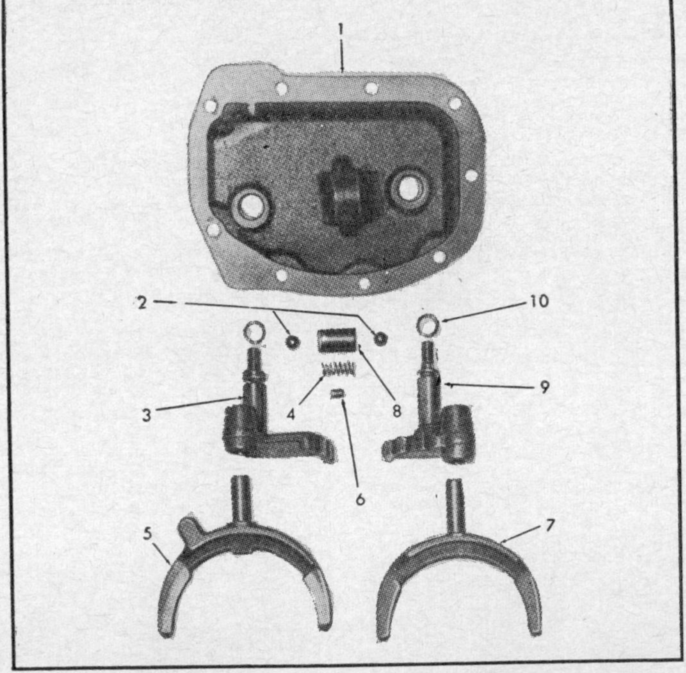

Fig. 19 Side cover disassembled

1. Side Cover
2. Poppet
3. 1st and Reverse Shifter Lever and Shaft
4. Poppet Spring
5. 1st and Reverse Shifter Fork
6. Interlock Pin
7. 2nd and 3rd Shifting Fork
8. Interlock Sleeve
9. 2nd and 3rd Shifter Lever and Shaft
10. "O" Ring Seal

over front of mainshaft, engaging clutch keys with notches of 2nd gear blocker ring. Properly installed the straightest side of clutch hub should be toward rear and clutch sliding sleeve taper should be toward front of mainshaft (see Fig. 1).

12. Install 2-3 clutch hub snap ring to mainshaft, Fig. 8.

NOTE: This snap ring is available in four

thicknesses. Use thickest snap ring that will assemble with all parts stacked tight endwise.

ASSEMBLE TRANS.

Case Components

1. Insert tube spacer and a double row of roller bearings and bearing retainer washers at each end of countergear, using grease to hold them in place, Fig. 14.
2. Place countergear assembly through case rear opening along with a tanged thrust washer (tang away from gear) at each end (large washer at front). Install countershaft and woodruff key from rear of case, Fig. 15.

CAUTION: Be sure countershaft picks up both thrust washers and that washer tangs are aligned with their notches in case.

3. Attach a dial indicator as shown in Fig. 16 and check end play of countergear. If end play is greater than .025" new thrust washers must be installed.
4. Use grease to hold 25 reverse idler gear roller bearings in position and place gear and bearings along with a thrust washer on each end into position inside case so that bevelled edge of gear teeth face toward front of case.
5. Load pilot bearing rollers and spacer into clutch gear with grease to hold them in place and position gear in case. *Do not install clutch gear bearing at this time.*
6. Stand case on end with clutch gear shaft through hole in bench or stand, and place 3rd gear blocker ring over clutch gear.
7. Install mainshaft assembly through rear of case, picking up spacer, pilot bearings and 3rd gear blocker rings, Fig. 17.
8. Install reverse idler gear shaft and woodruff key. *Be sure shaft picks up both thrust washers during installation.*

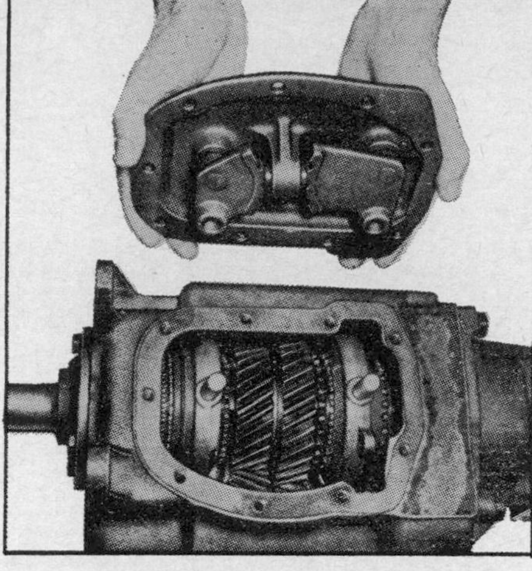

Fig. 18 Installing side cover assembly

9. Install extension gasket on rear of case and, using snap ring pliers, expand snap ring, Fig. 5, and install extension over mainshaft and rear bearing. Be sure snap ring has started over bearing, then install and tighten extension case bolts. *Use graphite sealer on the two lower bolts.*
10. Tap on front of clutch gear shaft to force rear bearing snap ring to seat in its groove.

NOTE: This snap ring is available in five thicknesses. Use thickest snap ring that will assemble with all parts stacked tight endwise.

11. Install snap ring in outer race of clutch gear bearing. If snap ring groove is partially inside case opening, tap on inside bearing outer race with a long drift used through side cover opening.

NOTE: If mainshaft does not turn freely, check clutch sliding sleeves for neutral positions and that blocker rings are free on their gear cone surfaces.

12. Install gaskets and clutch gear bearing retainer and lip seal with oil drain passages at bottom and tighten. *Use graphite sealer on threads of retainer bolts.*

NOTE: Install two retainer-to-case gaskets (one .010" and .015") to replace the one .025" production gasket removed.

13. Install shift forks to clutch sleeve grooves with 1st-reverse fork "hump" toward bottom of case, Fig. 18.
14. Install side cover and gasket. *The two rear side cover-to-case bolts have special oil sealing splines and must be used at these two "through" hole locations.*

SIDE COVER

Disassemble

1. Referring to Fig. 19, remove shift forks from shift levers.
2. Remove outer shift levers and lightly tap shift lever shafts from assembly.
3. Remove two steel balls, poppet spring, interlock pin and sleeve from cover.
4. Remove O-ring seals from shafts.

Reassemble

1. Install new O-ring seals on shafts.
2. Install low-reverse shaft and plate to cover.
3. Place shift shaft and plate in neutral (middle detent) and install interlock sleeve, ball, spring and interlock pin.
4. Install remaining ball and then install 2-3 shift shaft and plate.
5. Check clearance between end of interlock sleeve and cams when one plate is in neutral and the other is shifted into gear position. Clearance should be .002" to .008". Sleeves are available in four sizes to give the proper clearance.
6. Install outer shift levers. Install forks to levers with 1st-reverse fork "hump" toward bottom.

Type 13 Saginaw

This transmission, Fig. 1, is fully synchronized in that all forward speed changes are accomplished with synchronizer sleeves. The synchronizers permit quicker shifts, greatly reduce gear clash, and permit down shifting from third to second between 40 and 20 mph, and from second to first below 20 mph.

Disassemble

1. Drain lubricant.
2. Remove side cover and gasket.
3. Remove front bearing retainer.
4. Remove front bearing snap ring, pull main drive gear out of case as far as possible and remove bearing.
5. Remove rear bearing retainer-to-case bolts.
6. Remove reverse idler shaft-to-gear "E" ring, Fig. 2.
7. From front of case, remove rear bearing retainer and mainshaft assembly.
8. Remove main drive gear, 14 needle rollers and 3rd speed gear blocking ring from mainshaft.
9. Expand snap ring and remove rear bearing retainer, Fig. 3.
10. Remove countershaft through rear of case, Fig. 4, and remove two tanged thrust washers.
11. Use a long brass drift or punch and drive reverse idler shaft and key through rear of case.
12. Remove reverse idler gear tanged thrust washer.

Disassemble Mainshaft

1. Referring to Fig. 5, remove 2-3 synchronizer sleeve.
2. Remove rear bearing snap ring.
3. Using a ram or arbor press, remove

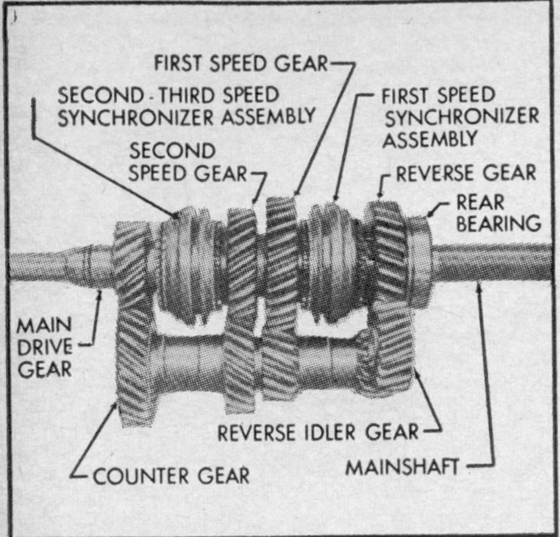

Fig. 1 Type 13 Saginaw three speed transmission

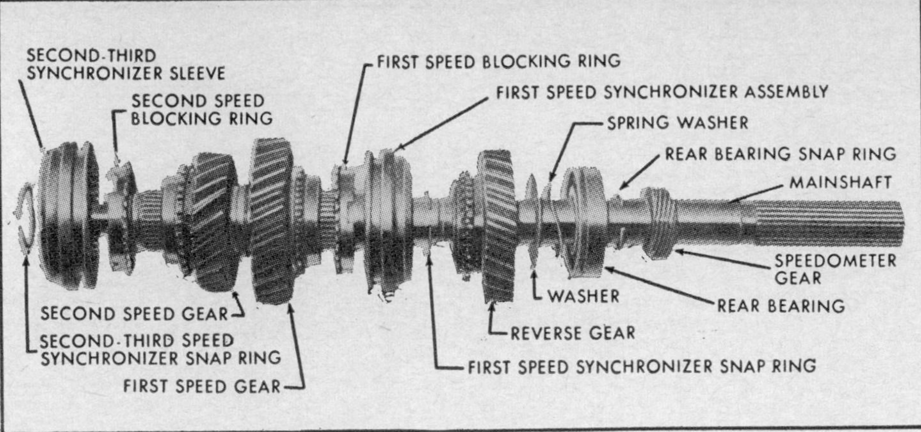

Fig. 5 Mainshaft and related parts assembled loosely to show location of parts

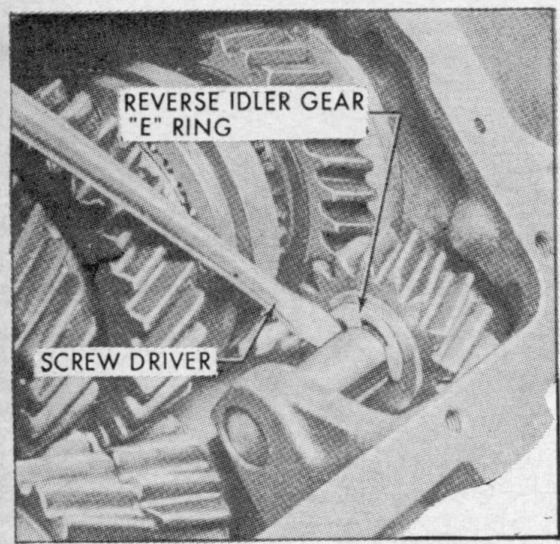

Fig. 2 Removing reverse idler "E" ring

Fig. 3 Removing rear bearing retainer after spreading snap ring as shown

rear bearing, spring washer, thrust washer and reverse gear.

4. Remove speedometer drive gear.
5. Remove first speed synchronizer snap ring. Support first gear on a press and remove first gear and its synchronizer.
6. Remove 2-3 synchronizer snap ring and press off synchronizer and second speed gear.

Synchronizers

NOTE: The synchronizer hubs and sliding sleeves are a selected assembly and should be kept together as originally assembled. The keys and springs may be replaced if worn or broken.

1. Mark hub and sleeve so they can be reassembled in same position.
2. Remove sleeve from synchronizer hub.
3. Remove keys and springs from hub.
4. Place three keys and two springs in position (one on each side of hub) so all three keys are engaged by both springs, Fig. 6. The tanged end of each synchronizer spring should be installed in different key cavities on either side of hub. Slide sleeve onto hub, aligning marks made before disassembly.

NOTE: A chamfer around outside of synchronizer hub splines identifies end that must be opposite shift fork slot in sleeve, Fig. 7.

Mainshaft, Assemble

1. Install second speed and synchronizer on mainshaft. Using a ram or arbor press, press 2-3 synchronizer (with chamfer toward rear) onto mainshaft, Fig. 8.
2. Install first speed gear and synchronizer on mainshaft, Fig. 9, and install snap ring. *Make certain notches in blocking ring align with keys in synchronizer.*
3. Install reverse gear, thrust washer, spring washer and rear bearing. Grooves on bearing must be toward reverse gear.
4. Install speedometer drive gear on mainshaft. Press gear until its rear face is 6 inches from rear bearing, Fig. 10.
5. Install 2-3 synchronizer sleeve.

Fig. 4 Removing counter shaft, using aligning arbor to hold needle bearings in place

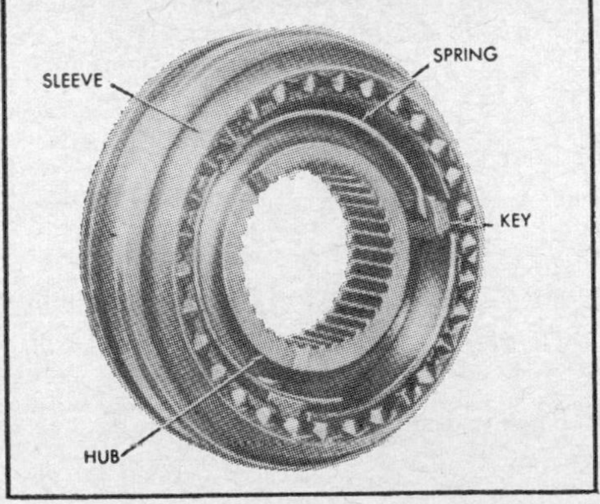

Fig. 6 Synchronizer assembly

Assemble Transmission

1. Install countergear-to-case thrust washers. Install countergear into case from rear. Make certain woodruff key is in place. Note that anti-rattle gear is riveted to countergear in four places and is not serviced separately, Fig. 11.

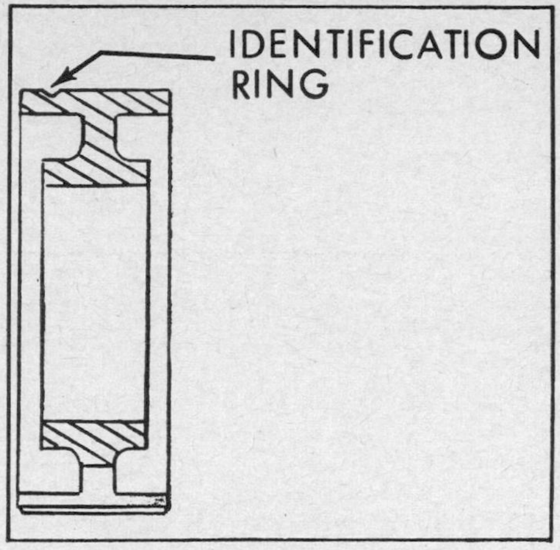

Fig. 7 Identification chamfer around synchronizer hub

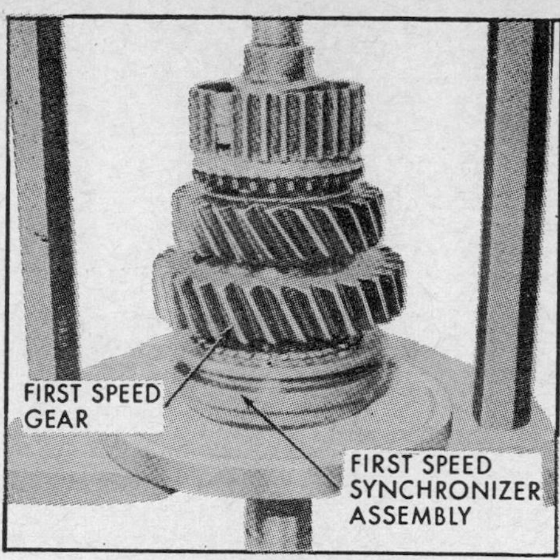

Fig. 9 Installing first speed gear

Fig. 11 Anti-rattle gear is riveted to countergear

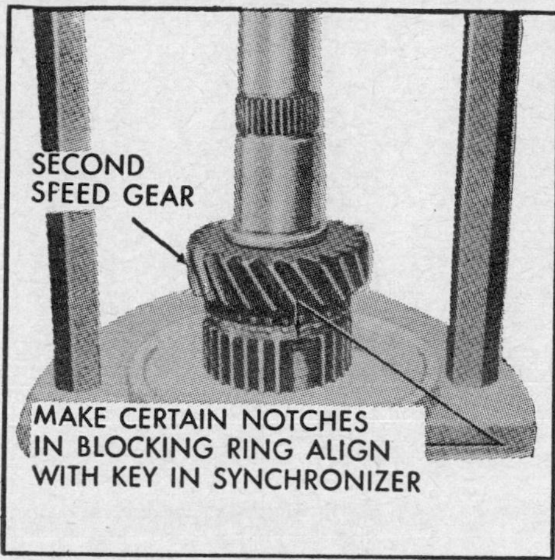

Fig. 8 Installing second speed gear

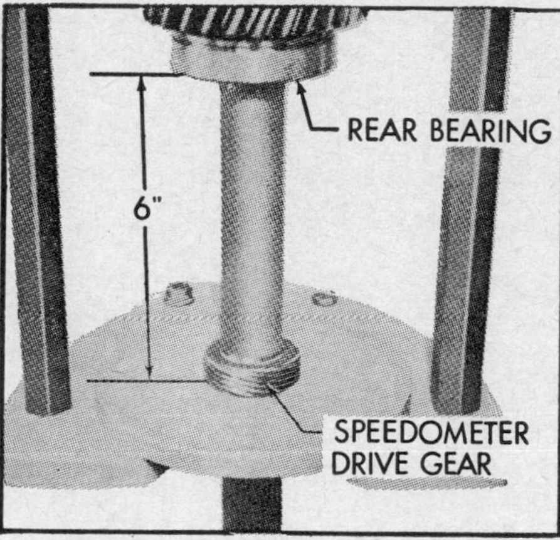

Fig. 10 Installing speedometer drive gear (6" from bearing)

2. Install reverse idler gear tanged steel thrust washer. Install idler gear, shaft and woodruff key. *Reverse idler gear snap ring will be installed after installation of mainshaft.*
3. Install rear bearing retainer. Spread snap ring in retainer to allow snap ring to drop around rear bearing. Press on end of mainshaft until snap ring engages groove in rear bearing.
4. Install 14 needle rollers in main drive gear pocket, using grease to hold them in place. Assemble third speed blocking ring on main drive gear. Pilot main drive gear and blocking ring over front of mainshaft. Make certain notches in blocking ring align with keys in 2-3 synchronizer.
5. Install rear bearing retainer-to-case gasket, using heavy grease to hold gasket in place.
6. Install rear bearing retainer and mainshaft assembly into case. Torque bearing retainer-to-case bolts to 35-55 ft-lbs. torque.
7. Install bearing on main drive gear. Outer snap ring groove must be toward front of gear. Install snap ring.
8. Install front bearing retainer and gasket.
9. Install reverse idler gear "E" ring.
10. If repairs are required to the side cover, refer to Fig. 12.
11. Install side cover gasket. Place transmission gears in neutral and install side cover. Install attaching bolts and tighten evenly to avoid cover distortion.

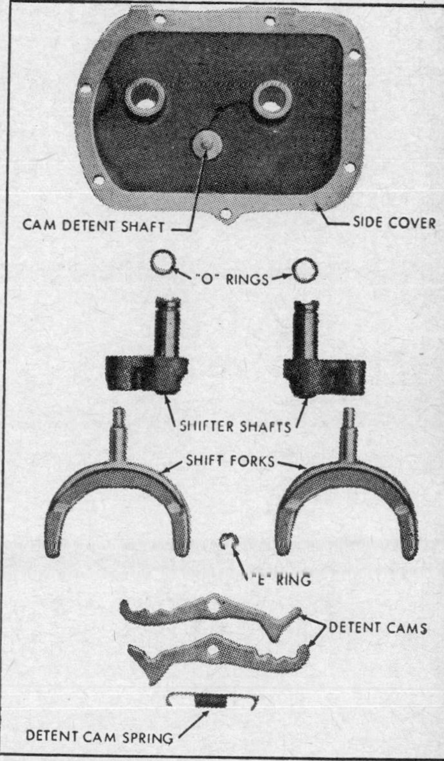

Fig. 12 Disassembled view of side cover

Type 14

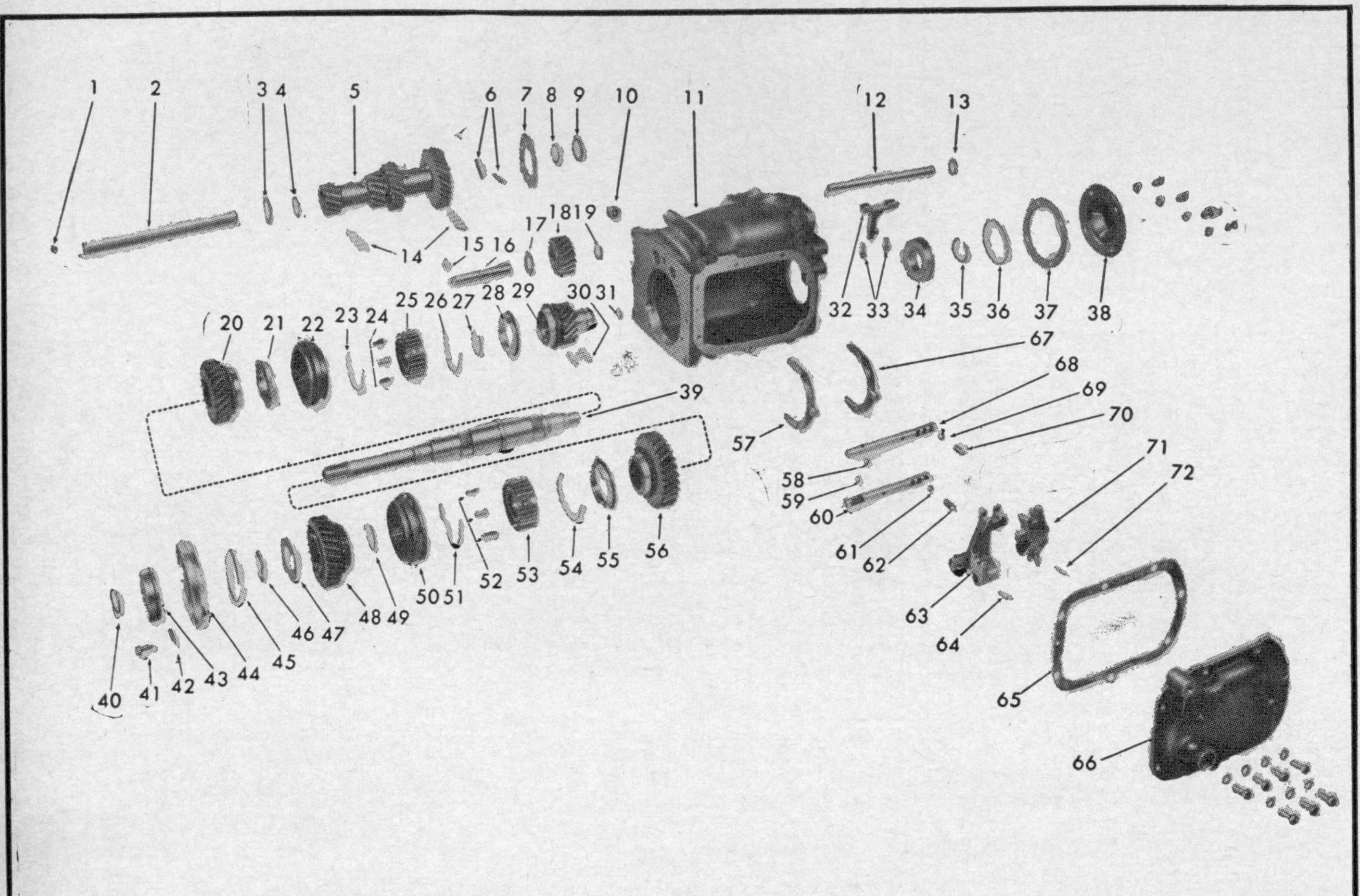

1. Woodruff Key
2. Countershaft
3. Thrust Washer
4. Needle Washer
5. Countergear
6. Spring—N.S.S.
7. Anti-Rattle Plate—N.S.S.
8. Needle Washer
9. Thrust Washer
10. Filler Plug
11. Case
12. Shift Selector Shaft
13. Seal
14. Needle Bearings
15. Woodruff Key
16. Reverse Idler Shaft
17. Thrust Washer (Tanged)
18. Reverse Idler Gear
19. Retainer "E" Ring
20. 2nd Speed Gear
21. 2nd Speed Blocker Ring
22. 2-3 Synchronizer Sleeve
23. Synchronizer Key Retainer
24. Synchronizer Keys
25. Synchronizer Hub
26. Synchronizer Key Retainer
27. Snap Ring
28. 3rd Speed Blocker Ring
29. Clutch Gear
30. Pilot Bearings
31. Snap Ring
32. Shifter Finger
33. Screws & L. Washers
34. Clutch Gear Bearing
35. Snap Ring—Bearing to Gear
36. Snap Ring—Bearing to Case
37. Gasket
38. Clutch Gear Retainer
39. Mainshaft
40. Snap Ring—Bearing to Shaft
41. Retainer Bolt
42. Retainer Strap
43. Mainshaft Rear Bearing
44. Bearing Retainer
45. Snap Ring—Bearing to Retainer
46. Spring Washer
47. Thrust Washer
48. Reverse Gear
49. Snap Ring
50. 1st & Reverse Synch. Sleeve
51. Synchronizer Key Retainer
52. Synchronizer Keys
53. Synchronizer Hub
54. Synchronizer Key Retainer
55. 1st Speed Blocker Ring
56. 1st Speed Gear
57. 1st & Reverse Shift Fork
58. Interlock Ball
59. Interlock Ball
60. 1st & Reverse Shift Rail
61. Detent Ball
62. Detent Spring
63. 1st & Reverse Shifter Head
64. Roll Pin
65. Gasket
66. Side Cover
67. 2nd & 3rd Shift Fork
68. 2nd & 3rd Shift Rail
69. Detent Ball
70. Detent Spring
71. 2nd & 3rd Shifter Head
72. Roll Pin

Fig. 1 Type 14 Corvair transmission

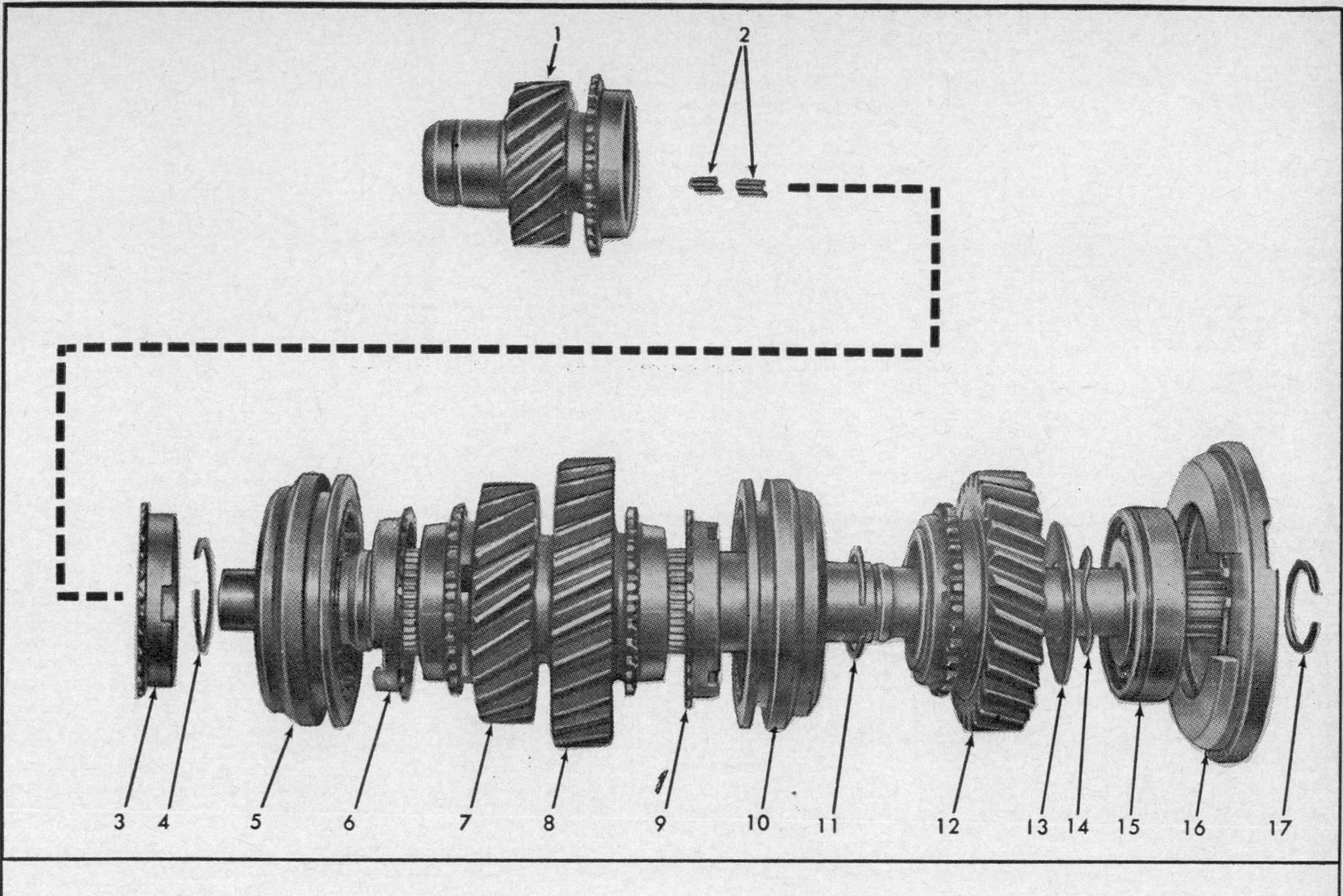

1. Clutch Gear
2. Mainshaft Pilot Bearings (76)
3. 3rd Speed Blocker Ring
4. Snap Ring
5. 2-3 Synchronizer Assembly
6. 2nd Speed Blocker Ring
7. 2nd Speed Gear
8. 1st Speed Gear
9. 1st Speed Blocker Ring
10. 1st Speed Synchronizer Assembly
11. Snap Ring
12. Reverse Gear
13. Reverse Gear Thrust Washer
14. Spring Washer
15. Rear Bearing
16. Rear Bearing Retainer & Snap Ring
17. Snap Ring

Fig. 2 Clutch gear and mainshaft assembled loosely to show location of parts

This transmission, Fig. 1, is a conventional synchromesh transmission except for the use of concentric input and output shafts and its mounting on the differential carrier. Because of its attachment to the differential carrier, the mainshaft is hollow to permit passage of the clutch shaft to the clutch gear at the front of the transmission. The clutch gear drives a countergear and the remaining power flow sequence is identical to the conventional three speed transmission. All drive gears have helical teeth and all forward gears are synchronized. A spring-loaded dampener plate (anti-rattle) on the countergear loads the clutch gear to eliminate torsional rattle.

Disassembly

1. Remove side cover and shift forks.
2. Remove clutch gear bearing cover.
3. Remove clutch gear bearing snap ring.
4. Use a brass drift and tap clutch gear bearing out of case bore, tapping through side cover opening.
5. Remove reverse idler gear retainer "E" ring and rear bearing retainer strap and bolt.
6. Remove rear bearing retainer, mainshaft, pilot bearings, and clutch gear as an assembly through rear of case. *Move synchronizer sleeves forward as necessary to allow clearance between mainshaft and countergear assemblies.*
7. Using a long drift through clutch gear bearing case bore, drive out reverse idler shaft and its woodruff key. Remove reverse idler gear and tanged thrust washer.
8. Using a suitable arbor, drive countershaft and its woodruff key out rear of case. Remove countergear, roller bearings and tanged thrust washers through rear case bore.
9. If necessary, remove two screws attaching shift finger to selector shaft and remove shaft out front of case. The shaft seal may now be pryed from case and replaced if necessary.

Disassemble Mainshaft

1. Remove 2-3 sliding clutch hub snap ring from mainshaft and remove clutch assembly, 2nd speed blocker ring and 2nd speed gear from front of mainshaft.
2. Remove mainshaft rear bearing snap ring.
3. Support reverse gear in a press and press on rear of mainshaft to remove reverse gear, thrust washer, spring washer, rear bearing and bearing retainer assembly.

Synchronizers

1. Clutch hubs and sliding sleeves are a selected assembly and should be kept together as originally assembled but the keys and two springs may be replaced if worn or broken. Mark hub and sleeve so they can be matched on reassembly.
2. When assembling, place three keys and two springs in position (one on each side of hub) so all three keys are engaged by both springs. The tanged end of each synchronizer spring should be installed into different key cavities on either side. Slide the sleeve into the hub, align-

Fig. 3 Loading bearings into countergear

ing the marks made before disassembly.

NOTE: A groove around the outside of the synchronizer hub identifies the end that must be opposite the fork slot in the sleeve when assembled. This groove indicates the end of the hub with a .07" greater recess depth.

Assemble Mainshaft

1. Referring to Fig. 2, turn front of mainshaft upward and install 2nd speed gear with clutching teeth upward; rear face of gear will butt against flange on mainshaft.
2. Install blocking ring with clutching teeth downward over synchronizing surface of 2nd speed gear.
3. Install 2-3 synchronizer assembly with fork slot downward; press it onto splines on mainshaft until it bottoms out. *Be sure notches of blocker ring align with synchronizer keys.*
4. Install synchronizer hub-to-mainshaft snap ring.
5. Turn rear of mainshaft upward and install 1st speed gear with clutching teeth upward; front face of gear will butt against flange on mainshaft.
6. Install blocker ring with clutching teeth downward over synchronizing surface of 1st speed gear.
7. Install 1st-reverse synchronizer with fork slot downward, pressing it onto splines of mainshaft. *Be sure notches of blocker ring align with synchronizer keys.*
8. Install synchronizer hub-to-mainshaft snap ring.
9. Install reverse gear with clutching teeth downward. Install reverse gear thrust washer (steel), and reverse spring washer.
10. Using snap ring pliers, expand rear bearing retainer snap ring and assemble rear bearing into retainer so snap ring groove is toward chamfered edge of retainer. Be sure to seat retainer snap ring into bearing groove.
11. Press rear bearing and retainer assembly onto rear of mainshaft so that chamfered retainer edge is toward gears.
12. Install rear bearing-to-mainshaft snap ring.

Assemble Transmission

1. Load countergear with 27 rollers and a thrust washer at each end, Fig. 3. Use heavy grease to hold them in place.
2. Place countergear through rear of case with a tanged thrust washer (tang away from gear) at each end and install countershaft and woodruff key from rear of case. *Be sure countershaft picks up both thrust washers and that tangs are aligned with their notches in case.*
3. Install reverse idler gear thrust washer, gear and shaft with woodruff key from rear of case. Be sure thrust washer is between gear and rear of case with its tang toward notch in case. *Do not install idler shaft "E" ring at this time.*
4. Load two rows of mainshaft pilot bearings (74) into clutch gear cavity and assemble 3rd speed blocker ring onto clutch gear clutching surface with its teeth toward gear.

Fig. 4 Rear bearing, retainer and strap

5. Place clutch gear, pilot bearings and 3rd speed blocker ring assembly over front of mainshaft. *Do not assemble bearing to gear at this time. Be sure notches in blocker ring align with keys in the 2-3 synchronizer assembly.*
6. From rear of case, assemble clutch gear and mainshaft assembly into case and install rear bearing retainer strap and bolt to case, Fig. 4.
7. Install front bearing outer snap ring to bearing and position bearing over hub of clutch gear and into front case bore.
8. Install snap ring to clutch gear hub, and bearing retainer and gasket to case. *Retainer oil hole should be at bottom.*
9. Install reverse idler gear retainer "E" ring to shaft. Be sure thrust washer tang engages notch in case.
10. Install selector shaft and shift finger so the 90-deg. finger projection is facing clutch gear end of transmission.
11. Shift synchronizer sleeves to neutral positions and install cover, gasket and fork assembly to case. *Be sure forks align with their synchronizer sleeve grooves and selector finger with shifter heads.*

TYPE 15

DISASSEMBLE TRANS.

1. Remove transmission cover and shift levers.
2. Remove front retainer and gasket and front bearing snap rings.
3. Align notch in clutch shaft with 3rd speed gear and use suitable puller to remove clutch shaft using care not to lose rollers.
4. Remove front bearing with puller.
5. Remove extension case and remove snap rings that retain speedometer drive gear.
6. Remove speedometer gear using care not to lose drive ball.
7. Remove rear bearing snap rings and remove rear bearing with a puller.
8. Move mainshaft to side and remove shift forks.
9. Place front synchronizer in 2nd speed position and remove mainshaft by tilting front of shaft up and lifting through top of case, Fig. 3.
10. Use a punch to remove roll pins from shift shafts and push shafts into case. Detent assembly may now be removed from case.
11. Using a brass drift drive reverse idler gear shaft out of rear of case and remove idler gear. Do not lose rollers.
12. To retain rollers in countershaft gear, use a dummy shaft to drive countershaft out of rear of case.
13. After disassembling mainshaft carefully inspect all bearings and gears.

REASSEMBLE TRANS.

Mainshaft Assemble

1. Place low speed and rear synchronizer on mainshaft and install rear synchronizer snap ring. **NOTE:** Snap rings are available in select thicknesses. Clearance between first gear and collar on mainshaft must be .003-.012".
2. Place 2nd speed gear and 2nd & 3rd synchronizer on shaft and install snap ring. **NOTE:** Snap rings are available in select thicknesses. Clearance between 2nd speed gear and collar on mainshaft must be .003-.018".

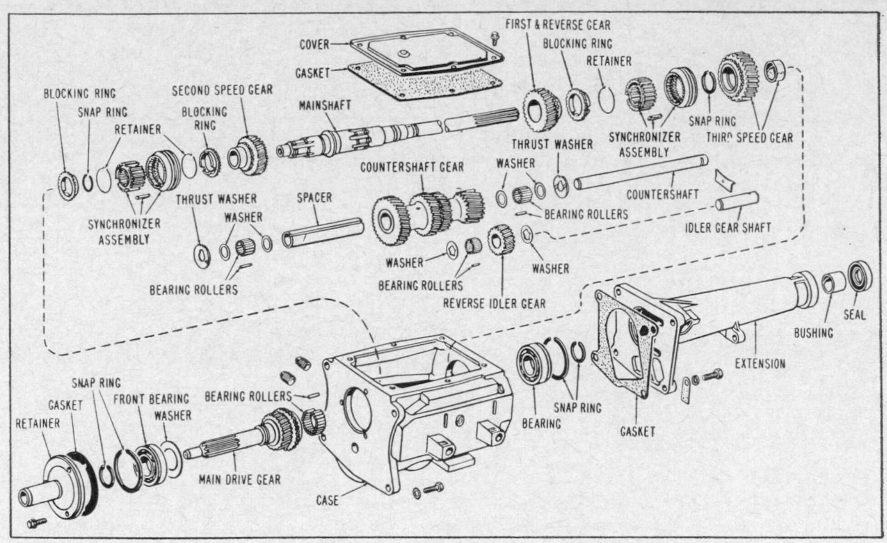

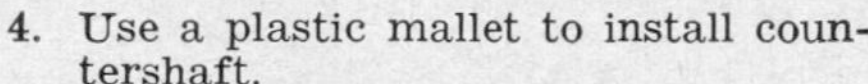
Fig. 1 Type 15 fully synchronized transmission exploded

Fig. 3 Removing mainshaft

3. Slide reverse speed gear on mainshaft and set assembly aside to be installed later.

Counter Gear

1. Coat bore at each end of counter gear with grease to hold rollers in place.
2. Install dummy shaft in countergear and install spacher, washers and rollers.
3. Place countergear in transmission case and position thrust washers at each end so tabs align with slots in case.
4. Use a plastic mallet to install countershaft.

Reverse Idler Gear

1. Coat bore of idler gear with grease to retain rollers.
2. Install idler gear in case and position thrust washers.
3. Use plastic mallet to install idler gear shaft.

Shifter Shafts

1. Partially install shifter shafts in transmission case.
2. Align detent assembly with shifter shafts and case stud.
3. Push shift detent assembly and shift shafts into place and install roll pins.

Mainshaft Installation

1. Place front synchronizer in 2nd speed position and place mainshaft in case.
2. Move mainshaft to side and install shift forks by pulling detent lever up and placing forks in the shifting assembly.
3. Position mainshaft assembly in center of case and install Pilot End Support J-22994, Fig. 4.
4. Place rear bearing on mainshaft and drive bearing into position and install snap ring.
5. Install speedometer gear and snap ring.

Final Assembly

1. Install rollers in clutch shaft using grease to retain them.
2. Slide clutch shaft into position through front of case.
3. Install front bearing, snap rings, gasket and retainer.
4. Replace seal if necessary and install extension housing, shift levers and case cover.
5. Fill transmission with lubricant and check operation.

Fig. 2 Removing clutch shaft with puller

Fig. 4 Installing mainshaft with Pilot End Support J-22994

FOUR SPEED MANUAL SHIFT TRANSMISSIONS

See Car Chapters for Linkage Adjustments and Removal Procedures

APPLICATION INDEX

Car Make	Transmission Type	Page
BUICK—Seniors		
1963-66	1	1-299
BUICK—Intermediates		
1963-66	1	1-299
1967-69	4	1-311
CAMARO		
1967-69	4	1-311
CHEVELLE		
1964-69 Muncie	4	1-311
1966-69 Saginaw	4	1-311
CHEVROLET		
1963 Warner	1	1-299
1964-69 Muncie	4	1-311
1966-69 Saginaw	4	1-311
CHEVY II		
1964-69 Muncie	4	1-311
1966-69 Saginaw	4	1-311
CHRYSLER		
1964-65	5	1-314
COMET & MONTEGO		
1964-65 V8 (Warner)	1	1-299
1963 Six	2	1-303
1964-69 V8 (Ford)	6	1-316
CORVAIR		
1963-65	3	1-307
1966-69	7	1-319
CORVETTE		
1963-69	4	1-311
COUGAR		
1967-69	6	1-316
DODGE		
1963	1	1-299
1964-69	5	1-314

Car Make	Transmission Type	Page
FAIRLANE		
1963-65 V8 (Warner)	1	1-299
1964-69 V8 (Ford)	6	1-316
FALCON		
1963-64 Six	2	1-303
1963-65 V8 (Warner)	1	1-299
1964-68 V8 (Ford)	6	1-316
FORD		
1963-64 V8 (Warner)	1	1-299
1964-69 V8 (Ford)	6	1-316
MERCURY		
1963-64 V8 (Warner)	1	1-299
1964-68 V8 (Ford)	6	1-316
MUSTANG		
1965-66 Six	2	1-303
1965-69 V8 (Ford)	6	1-316
1965 V8 (Warner)	1	1-299
OLDSMOBILE—Seniors		
1964-66	1	1-299
OLDS—Intermediates		
1963	1	1-299
1964-69 Saginaw	4	1-311
PLYMOUTH		
1963	1	1-299
1964-69	5	1-314
PONTIAC—Seniors		
1963-69 Muncie	4	1-311
1965-69 Saginaw	4	1-311
PONTIAC—Intermediates		
1963	3	1-307
1964-69 Muncie	4	1-311
1966-69 Saginaw	4	1-311
1967-69 Firebird (Saginaw)	4	1-311
1967-69 Firebird (Muncie)	4	1-311
RAMBLER		
1965-69	1	1-299

Type One Warner T-10

THIS TRANSMISSION is a fully synchronized unit with all forward speeds in constant mesh. Forward speed gear changes are made by moving synchronizer sleeves. The reverse gear is contained in the extension housing and is the only sliding gear in the transmission, Fig. 1.

Service Bulletin

DRIVE JUMPS OUT OF GEAR: If a Borg-Warner four-speed manual transmission on a 1962-64 Ford, Fairlane or Falcon jumps out of gear, and the cause lies in the transmission, excessive end play of the gear train on the output shaft will likely be found. This end play is controlled by snap rings located on the output shaft at the front and rear of the gear train.

In addition to the standard-size snap ring, five snap rings of different thicknesses are now available in a package so that a selective fit can be made to provide minimum end play. This recommendation should be followed either to correct a condition of jumping out of gear, or as standard overhaul procedure to eliminate the possibility of its happening.

At the front, select a snap ring to provide a .003 to .008 in. clearance between the snap ring and synchronizer hub. At the rear, use the thickest snap ring that can be installed.

Side Cover, Remove

1. Disconnect control rods from levers.
2. Remove cover assembly from transmission and allow oil to drain.
3. Remove outer shift lever nuts and lockwashers and pull levers from shaft.
4. Carefully push shifter shafts into cover, allowing detent balls to fall free, then remove both shifter shafts.
5. Remove interlock sleeve, pin and poppet spring.
6. Replace necessary parts, Fig. 2.

Side Cover, Install

1. Install interlock sleeve and one shifter shaft. Place detent ball into sleeve followed by poppet spring and interlock pin.
2. Start second shifter shaft into position and place second detent ball on poppet spring. Compress ball and spring with screwdriver and push shifter shaft fully in.

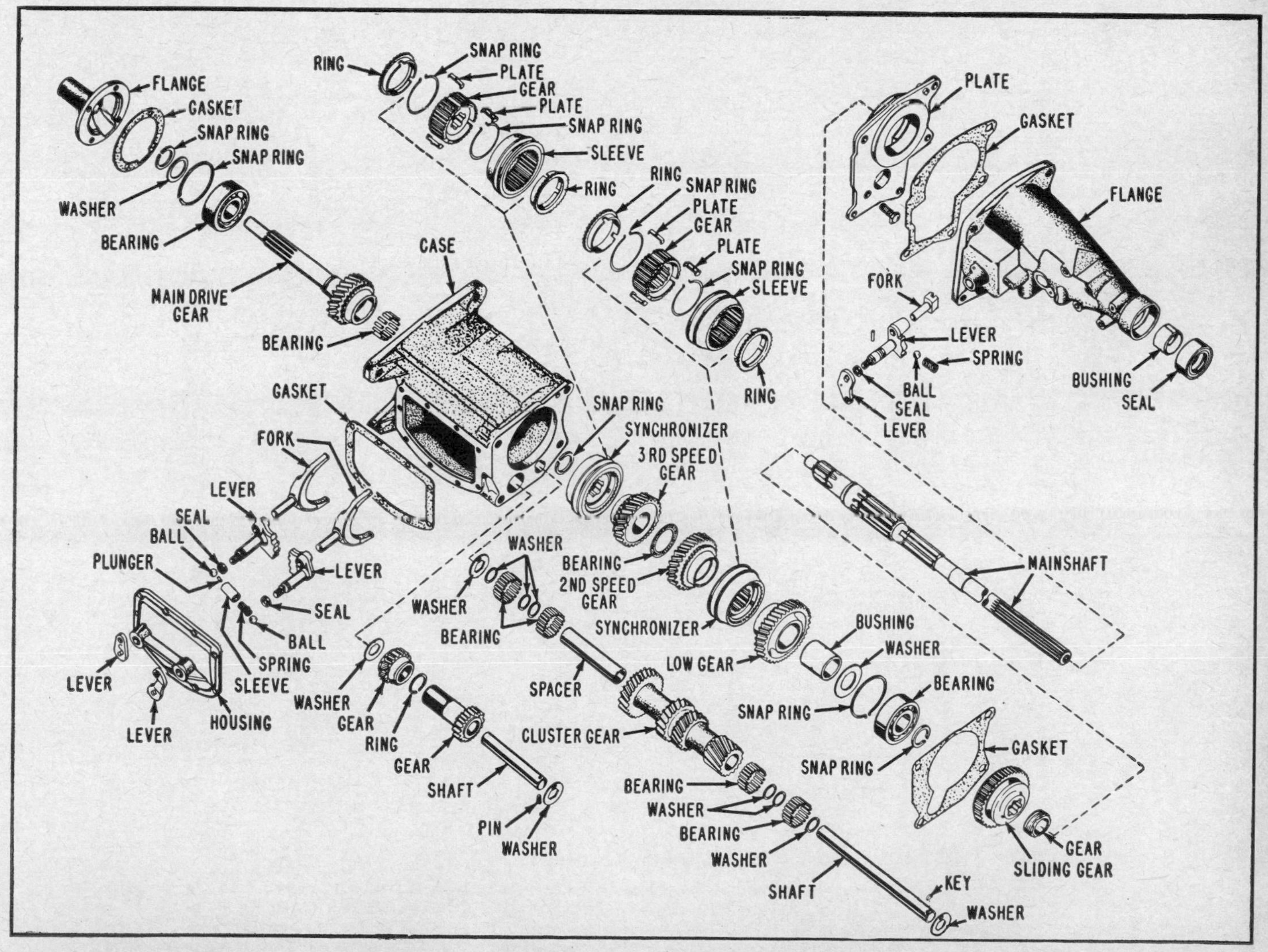

Fig. 1 Type 1 Warner T-10 four speed transmission. Some units do not have the mainshaft low gear bushing shown

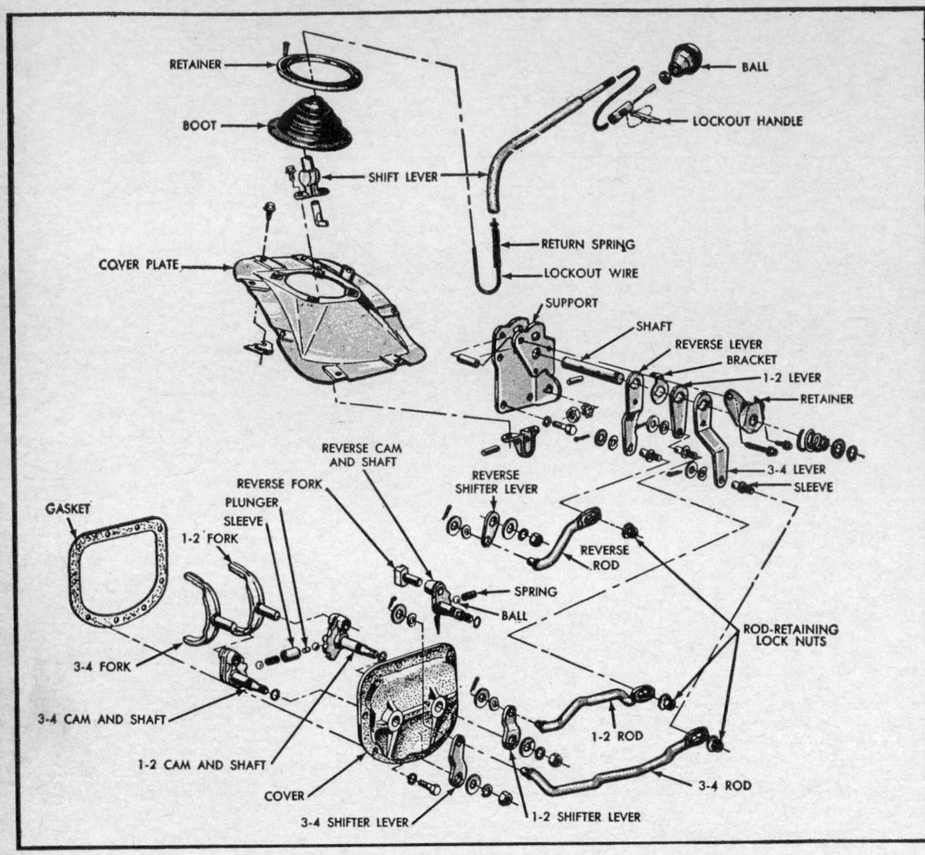

Fig. 2 Disassembled view of shift linkage and cover

Fig. 3 Removing reverse shifter lock pin

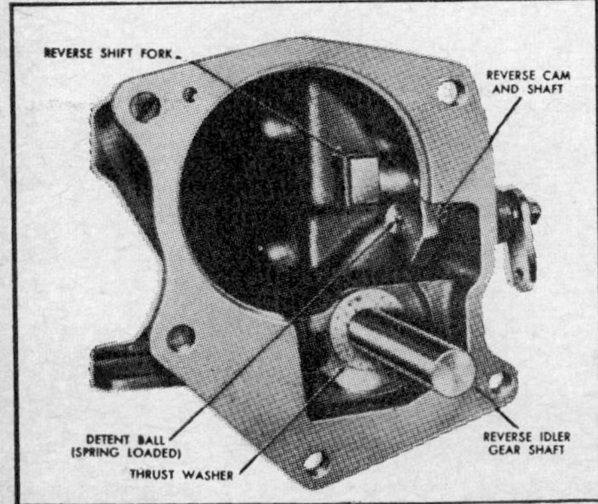

Fig. 4 Reverse idler shaft and reverse shifter

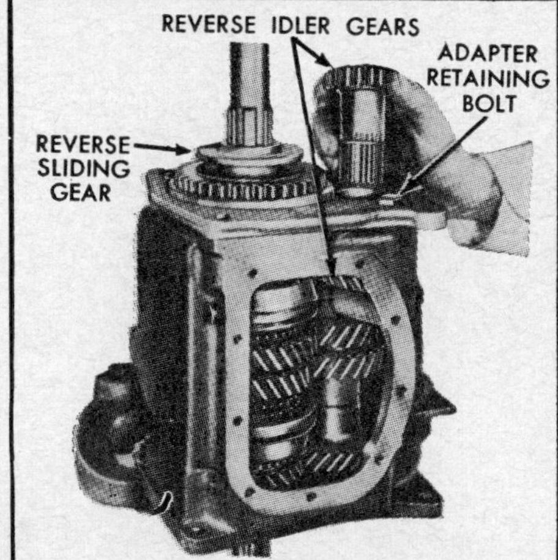

Fig. 5 Reverse gear rear idler removal

3. With transmission in neutral and shifter forks and levers in place, lower side cover into place. Install attaching bolts, using sealer on bolts to prevent leakage. Tighten bolts evenly.

Disassemble Transmission

1. Remove side cover as outlined above.
2. Remove front bearing retainer.
3. Drive lock pin from bottom side of reverse shifter lever boss, Fig. 3, and pull shifter out about ⅛". This disengages reverse shift fork from reverse gear.
4. Unfasten extension housing from rear bearing retainer (adapter). Tap extension with soft hammer in rearward direction to start. When reverse idler shaft is out as far as it

Fig. 6 Reverse gear front idler removal

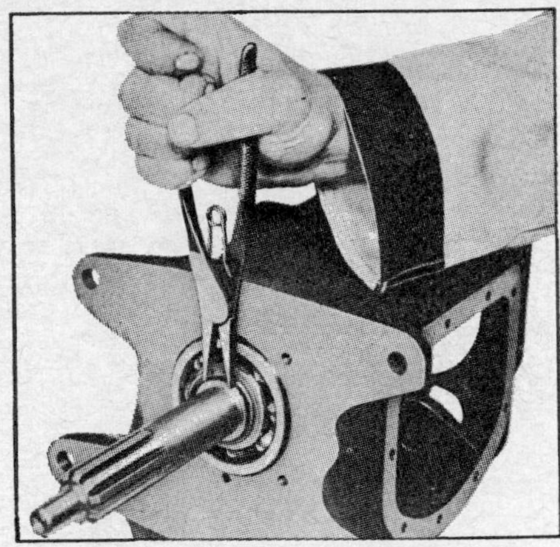

Fig. 7 Removing main drive gear snap ring

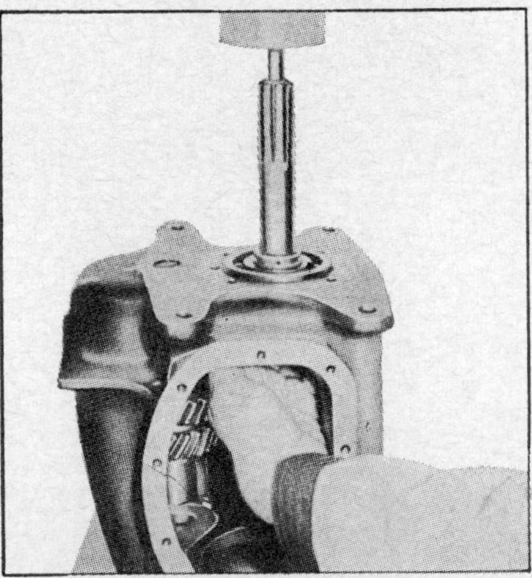

Fig. 8 Removing main drive gear from front bearing

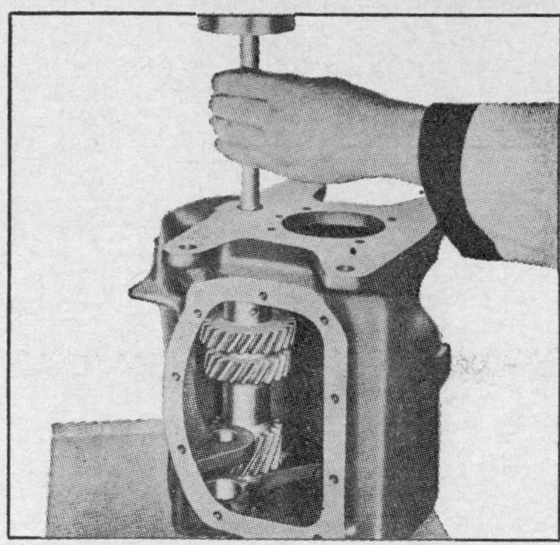

Fig. 9 Removing countershaft

Fig. 10 Removing mainshaft front snap ring

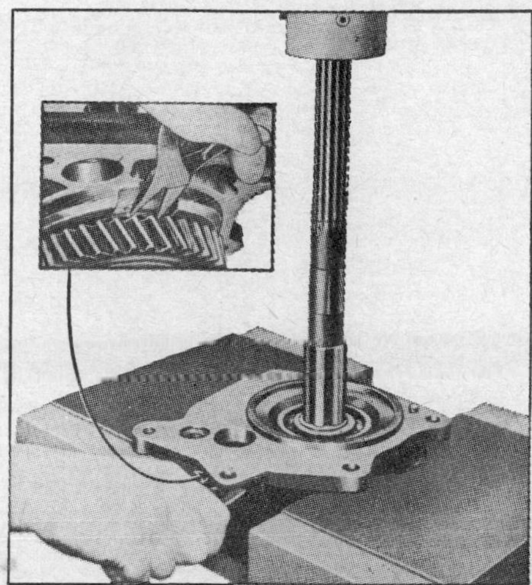

Fig. 11 Removing mainshaft from rear bearing retainer

will go, move extension to left so reverse fork clears reverse gear, and remove extension and gasket.

5. Remove speedometer drive gear with a suitable puller.
6. The rear reverse idler gear, tanged thrust washer and reverse gear may now be removed, Figs. 4 and 5.
7. Remove self-locking bolts attaching rear bearing retainer (adapter) to transmission case. Then carefully remove entire mainshaft assembly.
8. Lift front reverse idler gear and thrust washer from case, Fig. 6.
9. Unload bearing rollers from main drive gear and remove 4th speed synchronizing ring.
10. Remove main drive gear snap ring, Fig. 7, and remove spacer washer.
11. With soft hammer, tap main drive gear down from front bearing, Fig. 8.
12. From inside case, tap out front bearing and snap ring.
13. From front of case, tap out countershaft, Fig. 9, using a dummy shaft as shown. Remove countergear and both tanged thrust washers.
14. Remove dummy shaft, all 80 rollers and six spacers from countergear.
15. Remove mainshaft front snap ring, Fig. 10, and slide 3-4 speed synchronizer, 3rd speed gear and synchronizing ring, 2-3 speed gear thrust washer (needle roller bearing), 2nd speed gear and synchronizing ring from front of mainshaft.
16. Spread rear bearing snap ring and press mainshaft out of retainer, Fig. 11.
17. Remove mainshaft rear snap ring. Support 1-2 speed synchronizer assembly Fig. 12, and press on rear of mainshaft to remove shaft from remaining parts on shaft.

Cleaning & Inspection

1. Wash transmission case inside and out with cleaning solvent and inspect for cracks. Inspect front face of case for burrs and, if present, dress them off with a fine cut mill file.
2. Wash front and rear bearings in cleaning solvent. Blow out bearings with compressed air. *Do not allow bearings to spin; turn them slowly by hand. Spinning bearings will damage race and balls.*
3. Make sure bearings are clean, then lubricate them with light engine oil and check them for roughness. Roughness may be determined by turning outer race by hand.
4. All main drive gear and countergear bearing rollers should be inspected closely and replaced if they show wear. Inspect countershaft and replace if necessary. Replace all worn spacers.
5. Inspect all gears and first speed gear bushing (or sleeve) and, if necessary, replace all that are worn or damaged.

Synchronizers

Clutch hubs and sliding sleeves are a selected assembly and should be kept together as originally assembled, but the three keys and two springs may be replaced if worn or broken.

Push hub from sliding sleeve. Keys will fall free and springs may be easily removed. To assemble, place the two springs in position (one on each side of hub) so tanged end of each spring falls into same keyway in hub. Place keys in position and, holding them in place, slide hub into sleeve.

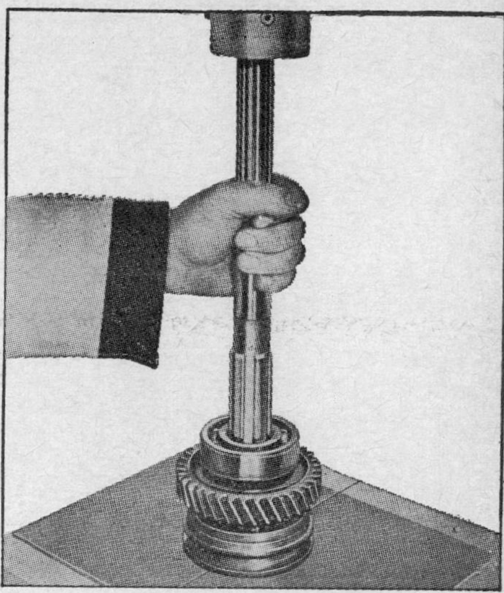

Fig. 12 Removing mainshaft from rear bearing and synchronizer

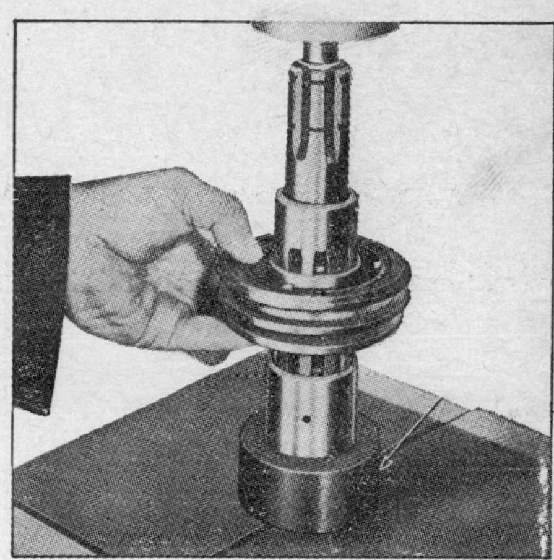

Fig. 13 Installing first speed gear bushing

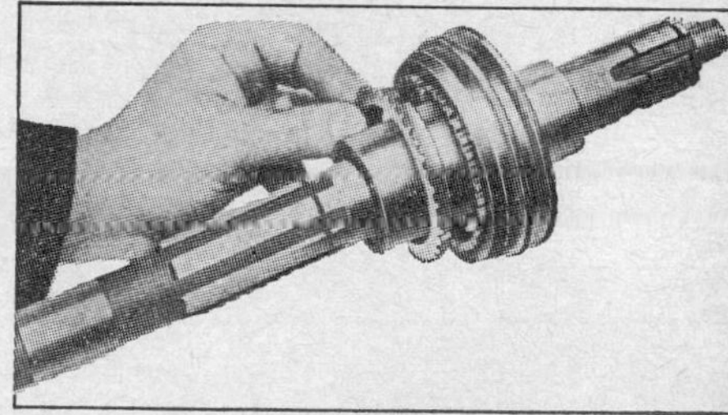

Fig. 14 Installing synchronizer ring

Assemble Mainshaft

1. From rear of mainshaft, assemble 1-2 speed synchronizer to mainshaft with sleeve taper toward rear. Press 1st gear bushing on shaft, Fig. 13.
2. Install 1st gear synchronizing ring so that notches in ring correspond to keys in hub, Fig. 14.
3. Install 1st gear with hub toward front, and 1st gear thrust washer. Make certain that grooves in washer are facing 1st gear.
4. Press on rear bearing with snap

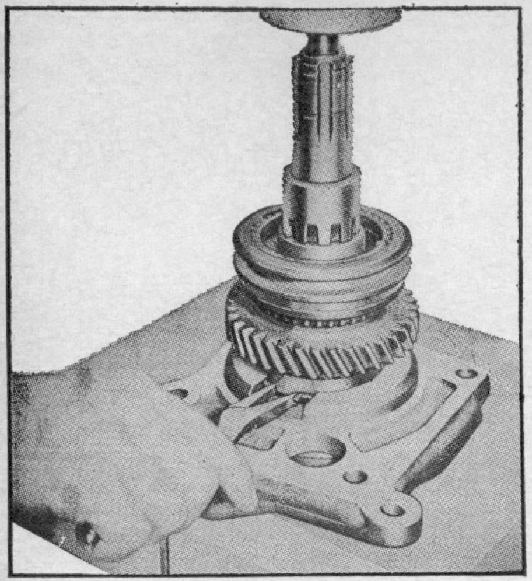

Fig. 15 Installing rear bearing retainer

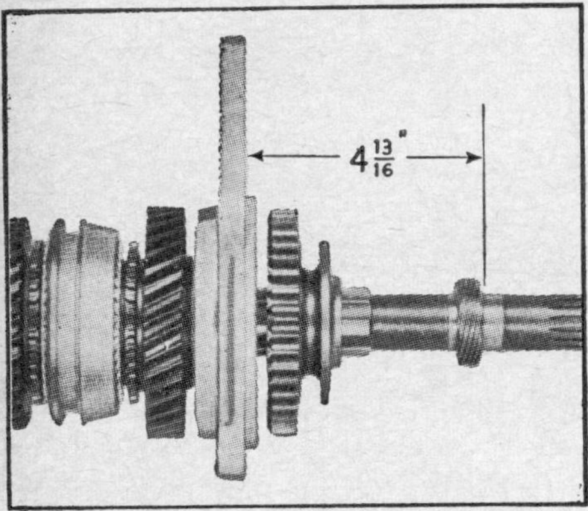

Fig. 16 Installing speedometer drive gear. Note: On Ford and Mercury units, take measurement from rear end of shaft to rear face of speedometer gear; Ford 9 1/4", Mercury 8 7/8"

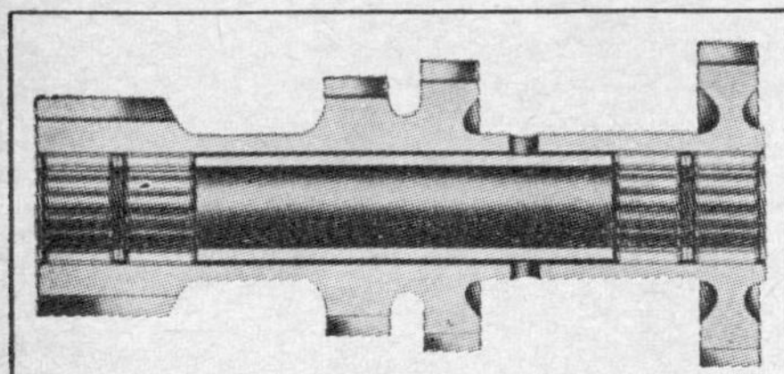

Fig. 17 Cross section of countergear assembly

ring groove toward front of transmission.

5. Choose correct selective fit snap ring and install it in groove in mainshaft behind rear bearing. *Always use new snap ring and do not expand it further than necessary for assembly.*
6. From front of mainshaft, install 2nd gear synchronizing ring so notches in ring correspond to keys in hub.
7. Install 2nd gear with hub of gear toward back of transmission. Install 2-3 speed gear thrust washer (needle roller bearing).
8. Install 3rd gear with hub to front of transmission, and 3rd gear synchronizing ring with notches to front of transmission.
9. Install 3-4 synchronizer with sleeve taper toward front, making sure keys in hub correspond to notches with 3rd gear synchronizing ring.
10. Install snap ring in groove in mainshaft in front of 3-4 synchronizer. *With the correct size snap ring, 3rd speed gear will have .010-.015" end play with 3-4 synchronizer hub forward against snap ring.*
11. Install rear bearing retainer, Fig. 15. Spread selective fit snap ring in plate to allow snap ring to drop around rear bearing and press end of mainshaft until snap ring engages groove in rear bearing (use largest size snap ring that will fit into groove).
12. Install reverse gear with shift collar to rear.
13. Press speedometer drive gear onto mainshaft. Position speedometer gear as shown in Fig. 16 for all units except those used on Ford and Mercury. *On Ford and Mercury units, take measurement from rear end of shaft to rear face of speedometer gear; Ford 9¼", Mercury 8⅞".*

Assemble Countergear

1. Install roller spacer in countergear.
2. Using heavy grease to retain rollers, install 20 rollers in either end of countergear, two spacers, 20 more rollers, then one spacer, Fig. 17.
3. Assemble rollers and spacers in the same manner in other end of countergear. Then insert dummy shaft in countergear to retain rollers.

Assemble Transmission

1. Rest case on its side with side cover opening toward you. Place countergear tanged thrust washers in place, retaining them with heavy grease, making sure that tangs are resting in notches in case.
2. Place countergear assembly in bottom of case, making sure that tanged thrust washers are not knocked out of place.
3. Press bearing onto main drive gear with snap ring groove to front.
4. Install spacer washer and selective fit snap ring in groove on gear stem.
5. Install main drive gear assembly through side cover opening and into position in transmission front bore. Tap lightly into place with a soft hammer, if necessary. Place snap ring in groove in front bearing.
6. With transmission resting on its front face, move countergear into mesh with main drive gear, making sure thrust washers remain in place. Install key in end of countershaft and, from front of case, tap or press shaft, Fig. 18, until end of shaft is flush with rear of case and dummy shaft is displaced.
7. Attach dial indicator as shown in Fig. 19 and check end play of countergear. End play must not be more than .025".
8. Install 14 rollers into main drive

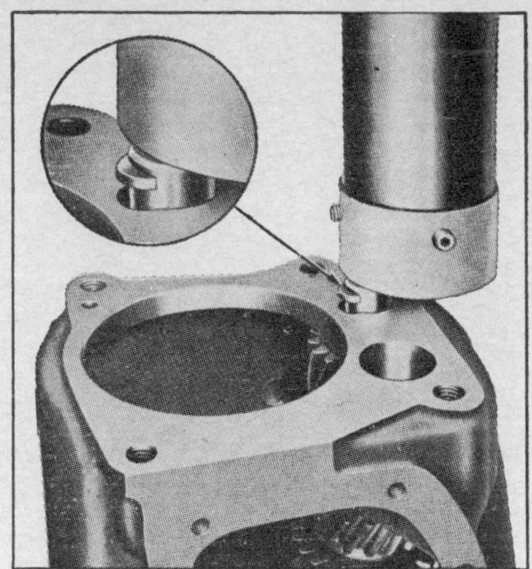

Fig. 18 Installing countershaft

Fig. 19 Checking countershaft end play

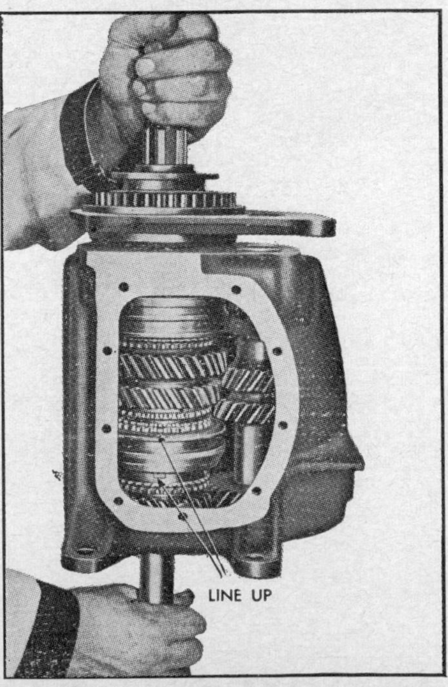

Fig. 20 Installing mainshaft assembly

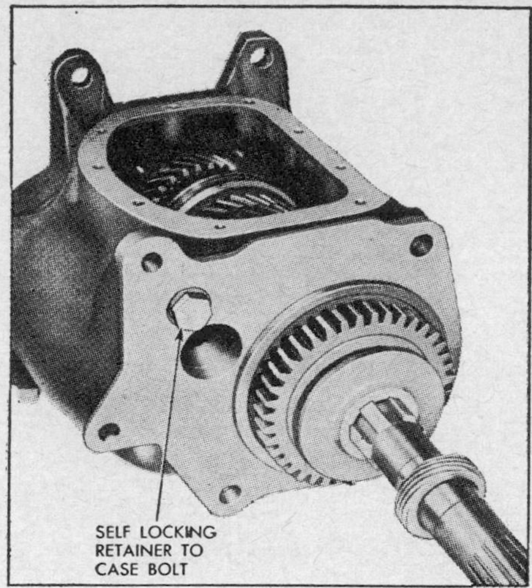

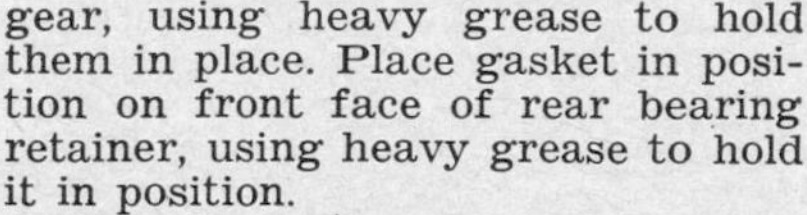

Fig. 21 Self-locking bearing retainer-to-case bolt

gear, using heavy grease to hold them in place. Place gasket in position on front face of rear bearing retainer, using heavy grease to hold it in position.

9. Install 4th gear synchronizing ring on main drive gear with clutch key notches toward rear of case.
10. Position reverse idler gear thrust washer (untanged) on machined face of ear cast in case for reverse idler shaft. Position front reverse idler gear on top of thrust washer, with hub facing toward rear of case.
11. Lower mainshaft assembly into case, making certain that notches on 4th gear synchronizing ring correspond to keys in synchronizer, Fig. 20.
12. Install self-locking bolt attaching rear bearing retainer to case, Fig. 21.

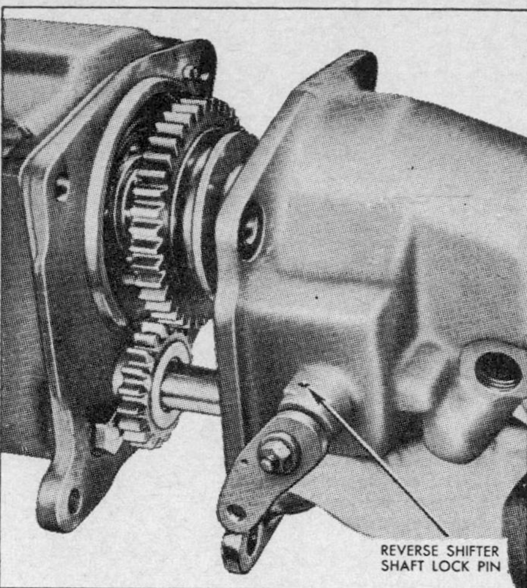

Fig. 22 Installing extension housing on transmission case

13. From rear of case, insert rear reverse idler gear, engaging splines with portion of gear within case.
14. Using heavy grease, place gasket into position on rear face of rear bearing retainer.
15. Install remaining tanged thrust washer into place on reverse idler shaft, being sure tang on washer is in notch in idler thrust face of extension.

---

16. Place two synchronizers in neutral position. *If locking-up of gears is encountered, a small amount of petrolatum may be applied to the 1st speed gear synchronizing ring, enabling it to turn freely on 1st speed gear hub.*

---

17. Pull reverse shifter shaft to left side of extension and rotate shaft to bring reverse shift fork to extreme

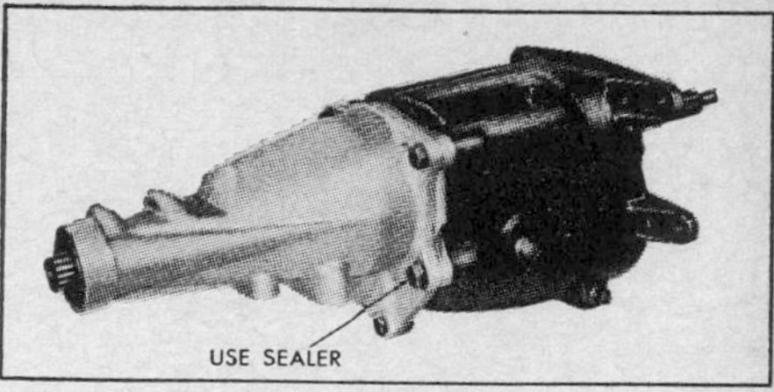

Fig. 23 Sealing lower right attaching bolt

forward position in extension. Line up front and rear reverse idler gears, making sure front thrust washer is in place.

18. Start extension into case. Fig. 22, by carefully inserting reverse idler shaft through reverse idler gears. Slowly push it on shifter shaft until shift fork engages reverse gear shift collar. When fork engages, rotate shifter shaft to move reverse gear rearward, permitting extension to slide onto transmission case.
19. Install extension and retainer to case attaching bolts, and extension to retainer attaching bolts. Use suitable sealer on the bolt indicated in Fig. 23.
20. Adjust reverse shifter shaft so that groove in shaft lines up with hole in boss and drive in lock pin from top of boss, Fig. 22.
21. Install main drive gear bearing retainer and gasket, being sure oil well lines up with oil outlet hole.
22. Install shift fork in each synchronizer sleeve. With both synchronizers in neutral, install side cover with gasket. Use suitable sealer when installing lower right cover bolt.
23. Install shifter levers, lock washers and nuts.

Type Two

This transmission, Fig. 2-1, has four forward speeds, all synchronized, and a reverse gear. The forward speed gears are in constant mesh. Gears used in the reverse train are spur cut and not synchronized. The gearshift pattern is engraved on the shifter knob. A safety latch prevents accidental engagement of reverse gear.

Disassemble Transmission

1. Disconnect the three shift rods from shift levers. Reverse shift lever nut must be loosened to free reverse rod.
2. Remove selector assembly from extension housing.
3. Unhook retainer that secures clutch release lever to retainer bracket, Fig. 2-2.
4. Detach clutch housing from transmission.
5. Remove cover from transmission.
6. Remove main drive gear bearing retainer.

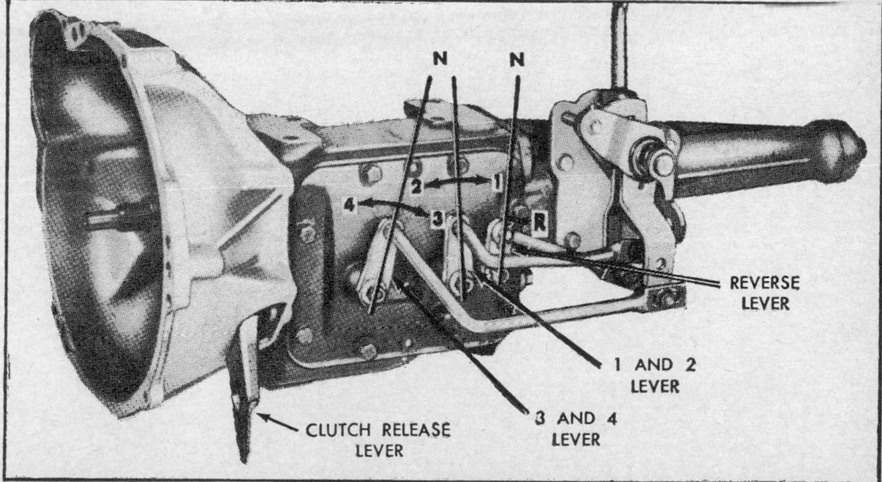

Fig. 2-1 Type Two transmission and clutch housing

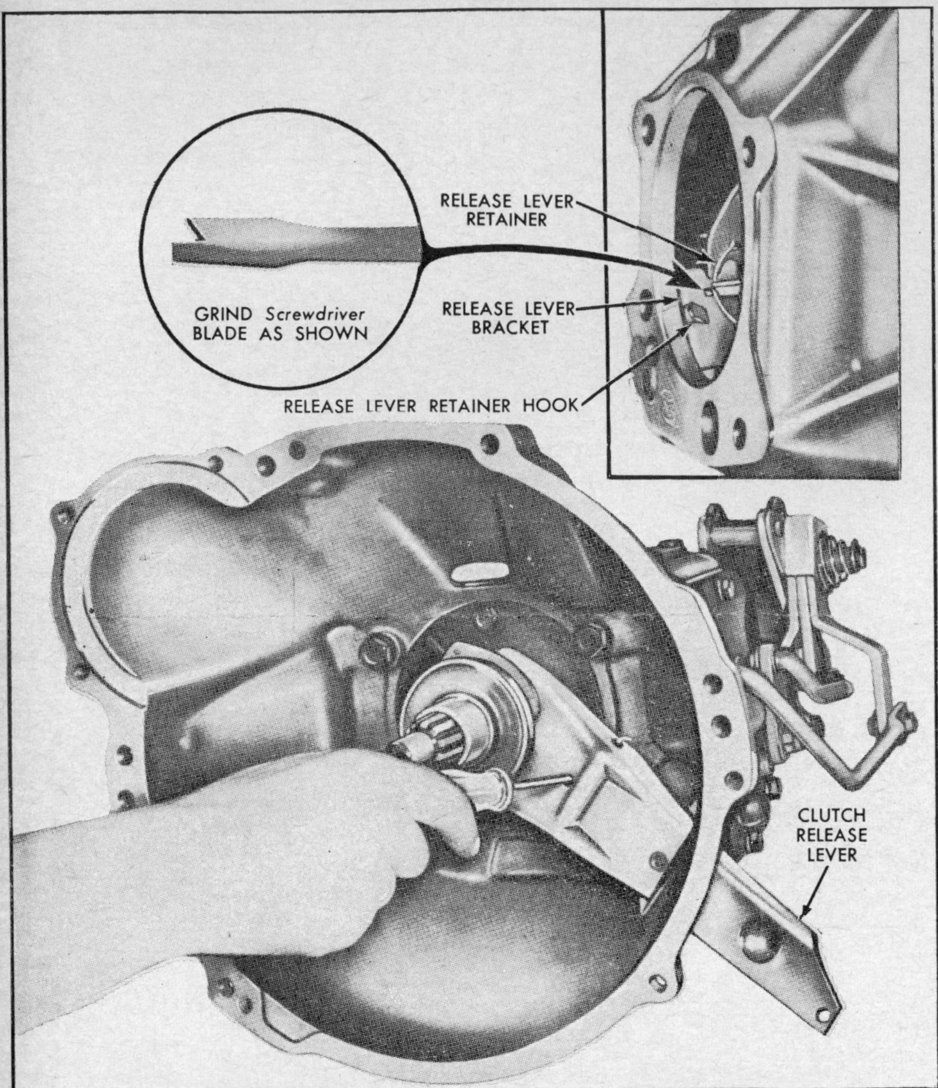

Fig. 2-2 Clutch release lever retainer attachment and disengagement

Fig. 2-3 Countershaft removal and installation

7. Remove extension housing and rear bearing retainer.
8. Drive countershaft out from front of case toward rear until it just clears front wall of case. Then using a dummy shaft, Fig. 2-3, push countershaft out until tool and countergear drop out of position.

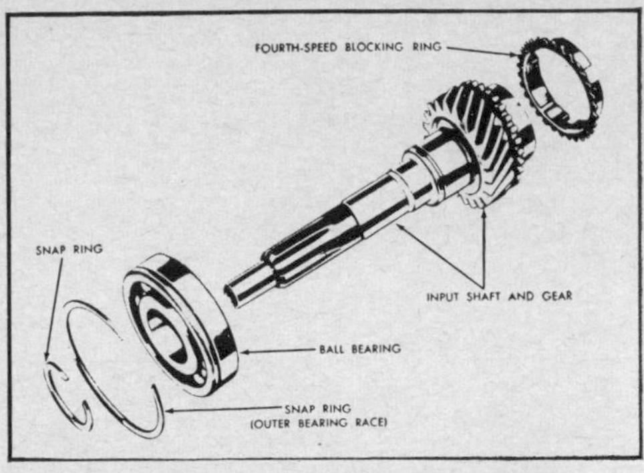

Fig. 2-5 Main drive gear and bearing

9. Remove mainshaft assembly, Fig. 2-4.
10. Remove main drive gear and bearing from front of case, Fig. 2-5.
11. Lift countergear assembly out through cover opening.
12. Install a $\frac{5}{16}$-24 bolt into rear end of reverse idler gear shaft and pull out shaft. Remove idler gear.
13. Remove nut from mainshaft and strip shaft of all parts, Fig. 2-6.
14. If necessary, disassemble, inspect and reassemble shift selector and gearshift housing assemblies, replacing all worn or damaged parts. Refer to Figs. 2-7, 2-8, 2-9.
15. Clean and air-dry all parts except bearings. Rotate bearings in solvent until all lube is removed. Then hold bearing to keep it from rotating and dry with compressed air. After inspection, lubricate bearing with transmission lube and protect from dirt until ready for use.

Synchronizers

1. When assembling synchronizers, Fig. 2-10, place long inserts into slots in 1-2 synchronizer hub and slide combination sleeve and reverse

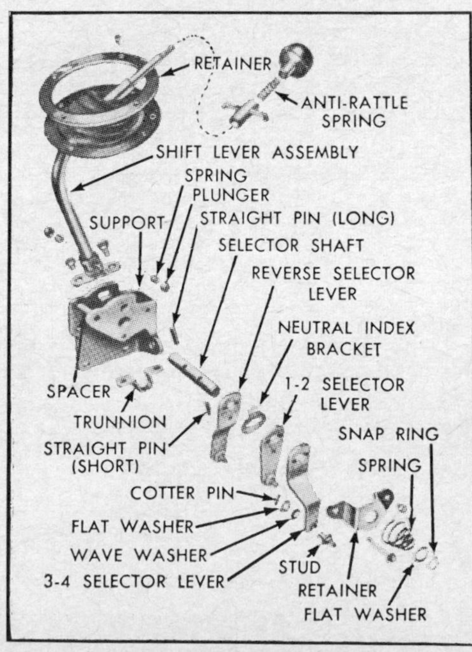

Fig. 2-7 Shift selector components

gear over it with the etch marks on hub and sleeve aligned.

2. Snap insert springs in place. The tab on each spring must set into the underside of an insert.
3. Position short inserts into slots in 3-4 synchronizer hub and slide sleeve over it with etch marks aligned. Install insert springs in same manner as with 1-2 synchronizer.

Assemble Mainshaft

1. Assemble mainshaft and related parts in the sequence shown in Fig. 2-6, and observe the following precautions:
2. Be sure 2nd speed blocking ring is not cocked on gear and that the three index slots align with the synchronizer inserts.
3. Assemble mainshaft ball bearing into recess in bearing adapter. Position adapter and bearing onto rear of mainshaft with adapter forward. Hold 1st gear and sleeve (bushing) forward and place assembly in a press with the tool (or equivalent) shown in Fig. 2-11 resting against rear of bearing inner race. Press into place until bearing is seated firmly against 1st gear bushing.
4. When installing the speedometer drive gear and related parts, be sure to install the driving ball into recess in gear and mainshaft, Fig. 2-6.

Assemble Transmission

1. Place dummy shaft into countergear. Then starting on either end, Fig. 2-12, drop a steel washer over tool and into gear. Coat each needle bearing with grease and install 22 of them into gear. Lay another steel washer on ends of needle bearings and the proper (greased) thrust washer or washer as shown.
2. Repeat foregoing operation for other end of gear. Do not lose bearings and spacer in the initially assembled end when inverting the gear to assemble opposite end.
3. Install countergear assembly in case with the two thrust washers at the front. Allow gear and dummy shaft assembly to rest in bottom of case until main drive gear and mainshaft assemblies are installed.
4. Assemble main drive gear as suggested by Figs. 2-5 and 2-13. Then, using grease to hold them in place, install 17 roller bearings in bore of main drive gear.
5. Stick the extension housing gasket to rear of transmission case with a non-drying sealer.
6. Install main drive gear into front case bore. Place 4th gear blocking ring onto rear end of main drive gear with clutch teeth forward.
7. Enter mainshaft assembly through rear of case and guide the shaft front pilot into the main drive gear bore. Be sure 4th gear blocking ring slots index with slots on synchronizer.

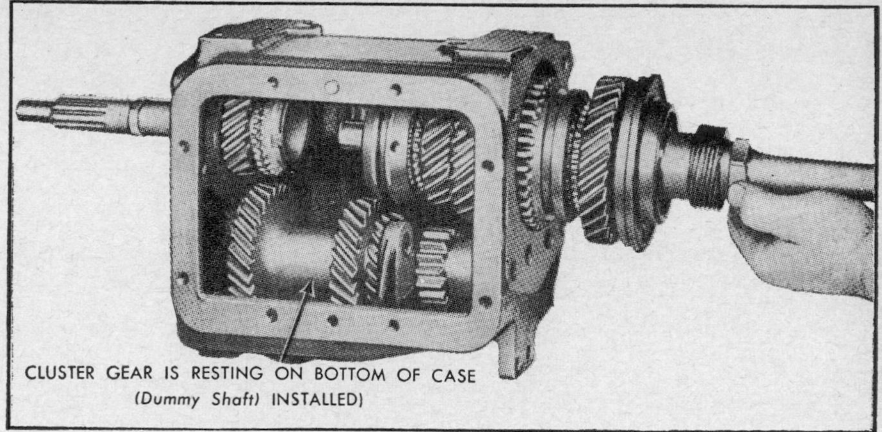

Fig. 2-4 Mainshaft removal and installation

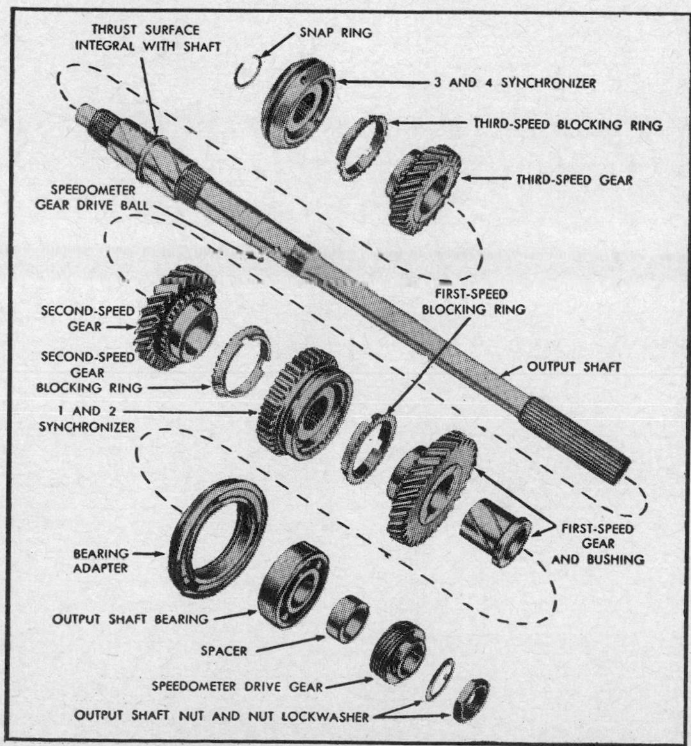

Fig. 2-6 Mainshaft components

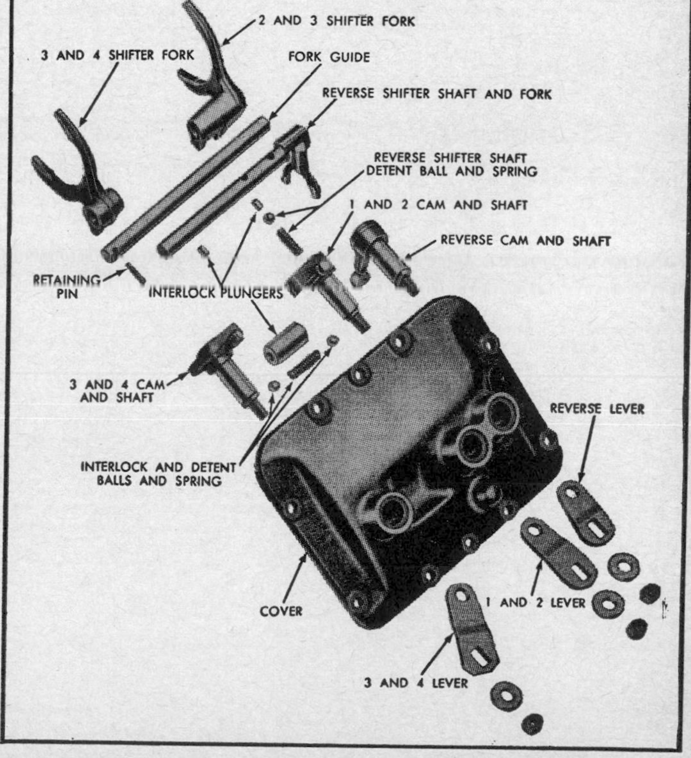

Fig. 2-8 Gearshift housing details

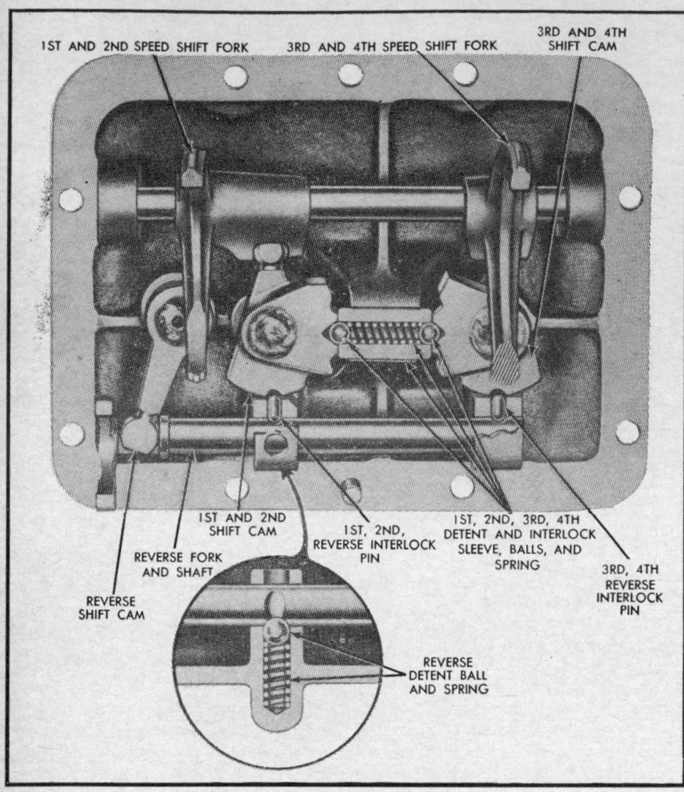

Fig. 2-9 Transmission shift mechanism details

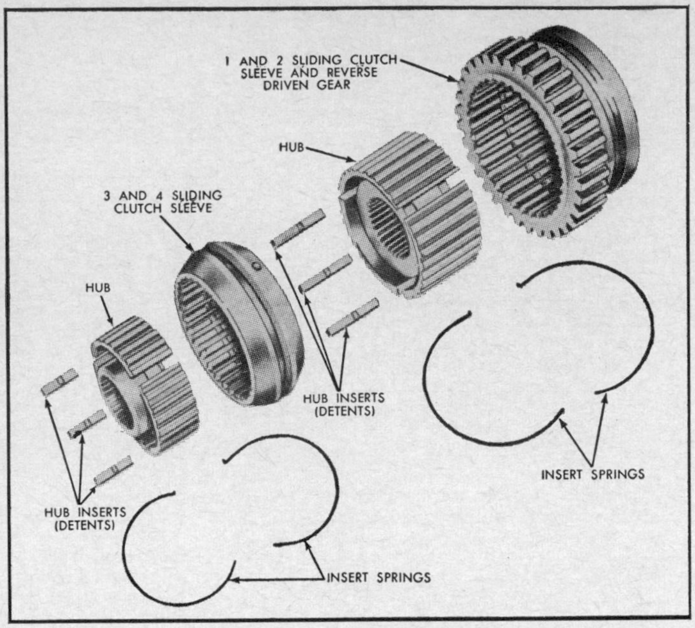

Fig. 2-10 Synchronizer details

8. Raise countergear assembly and insert countershaft through the rear. Shaft should push through, easily displacing tool, until front of case is contacted, Fig. 2-3.
9. Position flat on rear end of countershaft in horizontal plane so it will align with slot in extension housing. Tap shaft into place.
10. Install reverse idler gear with fork groove toward rear and with idler shaft flat horizontal and parallel with countershaft flat.

11. Install extension housing. Align dowel in housing with hole in rear bearing adapter, Fig. 2-14. Be sure housing is sealed squarely on case, bearing and adapter before tightening bolts. *If two long and two shorter bolts are used, install the two long bolts in the upper right and lower left holes.*

12. Install new bearing retainer gasket, using sealer. Install bearing retainer with drain slot facing downward. Seal and tighten bolts.
13. Place 1-2 and 3-4 synchronizers in neutral and reverse idler gear into reverse (forward) position. Set shift housing into reverse. Install new shift housing gasket on case, using sealer. Install shift housing, using sealer on bolts and tighten.
14. Install clutch housing. Use sealer on retaining bolts.
15. Install clutch release bearing onto clutch release lever. Position release lever through housing from inside housing and clip lever retainer onto its hook, Fig. 2-2.
16. Install shift selector assembly on extension housing, Fig. 2-1.
17. Install shift rods to cam levers and secure them with spring washers and cotter pins or clips. Tighten reverse cam lever nut.
18. Loosely assemble shift rods to linkage levers. Insert a ¼" drill or rod through three linkage levers and into the support. Move levers until gauge rod will enter all three alignment holes and tighten lock nuts.
19. Assemble shield over shift selector assembly.

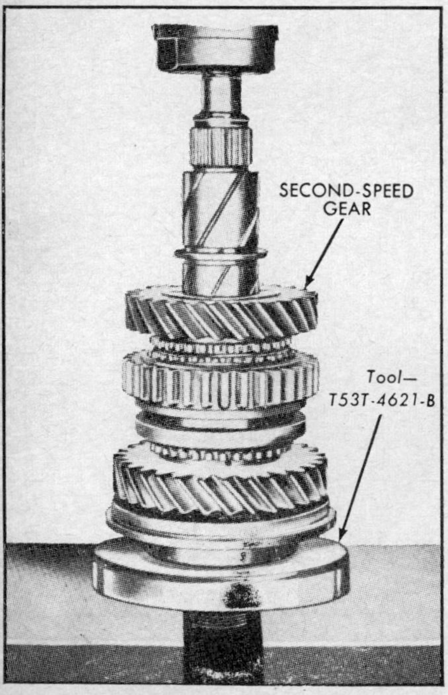

Fig. 2-11 Mainshaft bearing installation

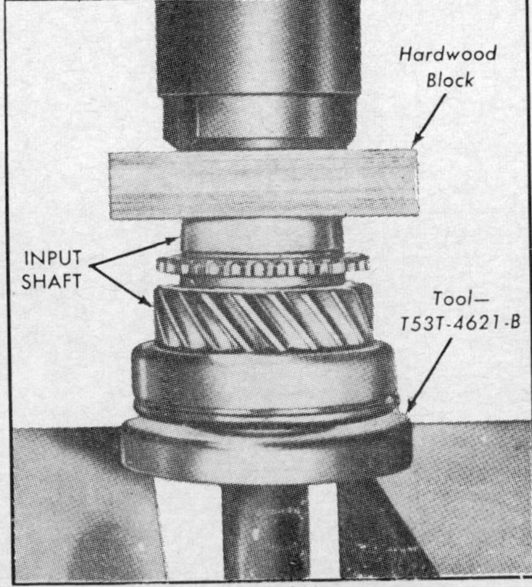

Fig. 2-13 Installation of main drive gear bearing

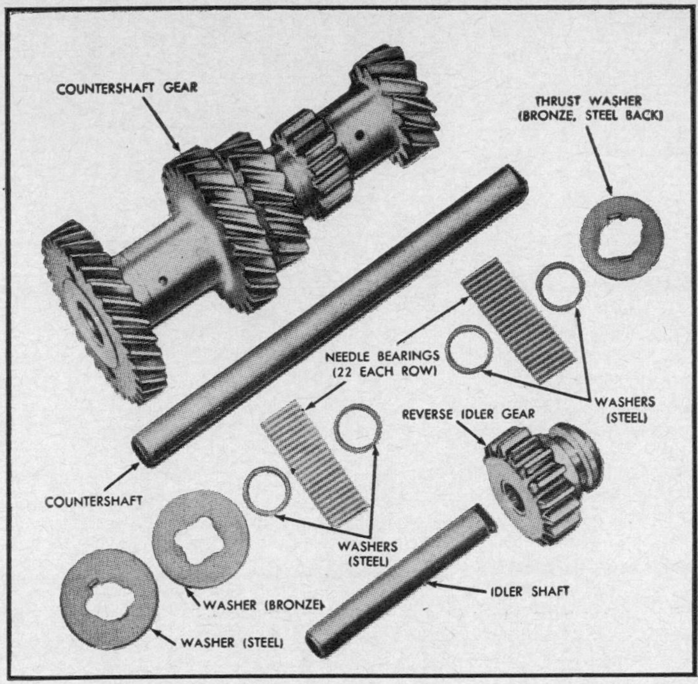

Fig. 2-12 Countergear and idler gear assemblies

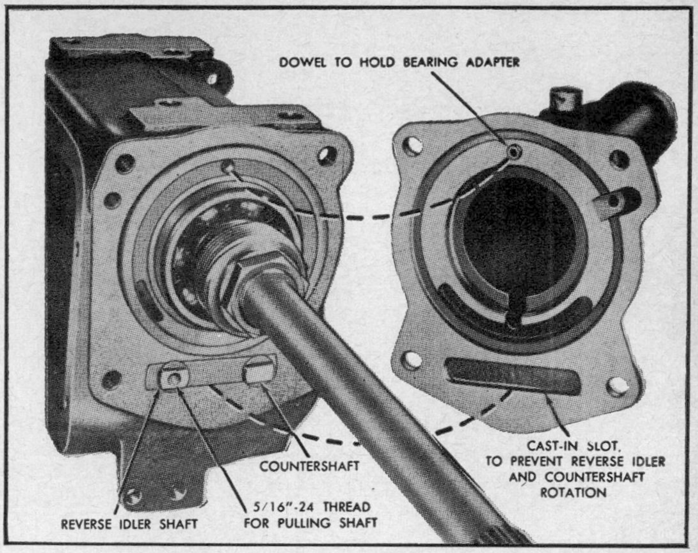

Fig. 2-14 Extension housing installation

Type Three

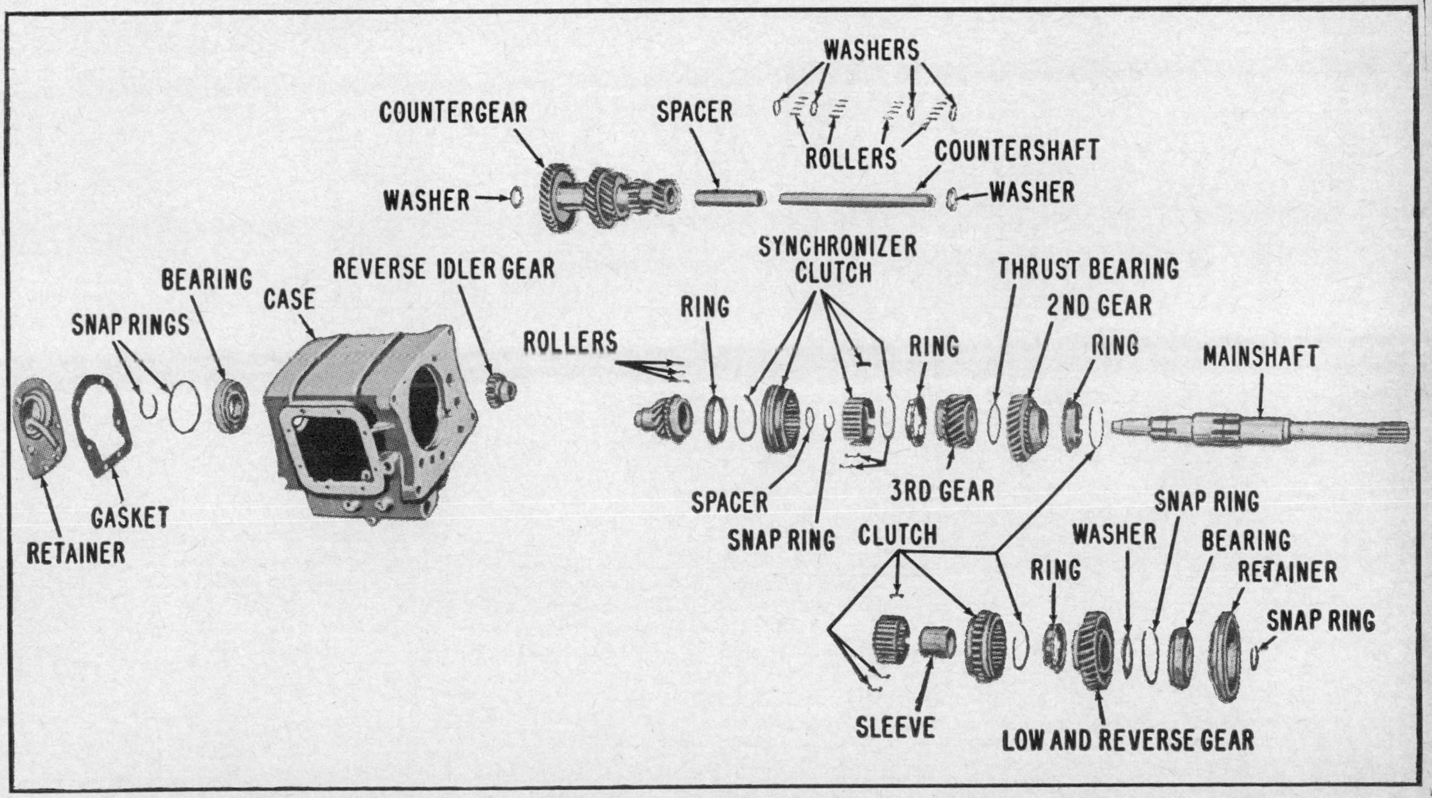

Fig. 3-1 Disassembled view of Corvair and Tempest four speed synchromesh transmission. NOTE: The 1964 mainshaft has a shoulder to act as a thrust surface for the 2nd speed gear. This shoulder eliminates need for the needle thrust bearing between 2nd and 3rd speed gears used formerly. Also the reverse idler lever pins have been eliminated in 1964 transmissions

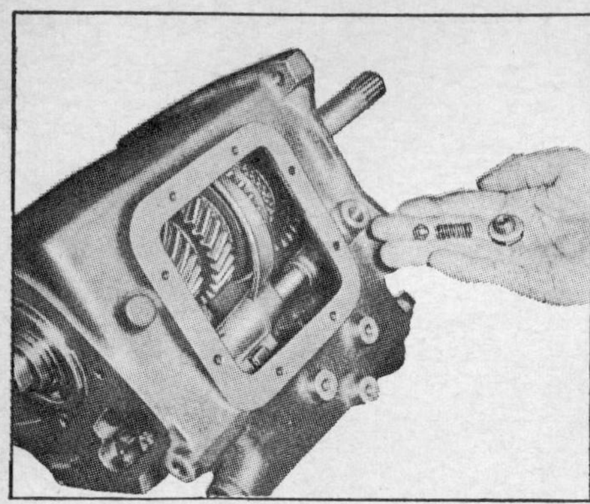

Fig. 3-2 Removing 3-4 shift fork detent parts

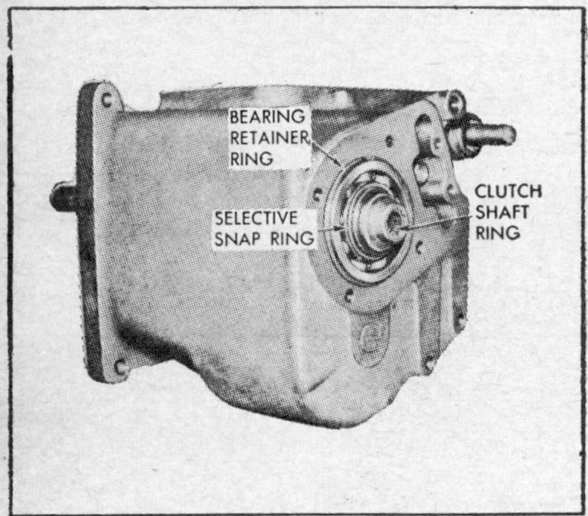

Fig. 3-3 Clutch gear and bearing snap rings

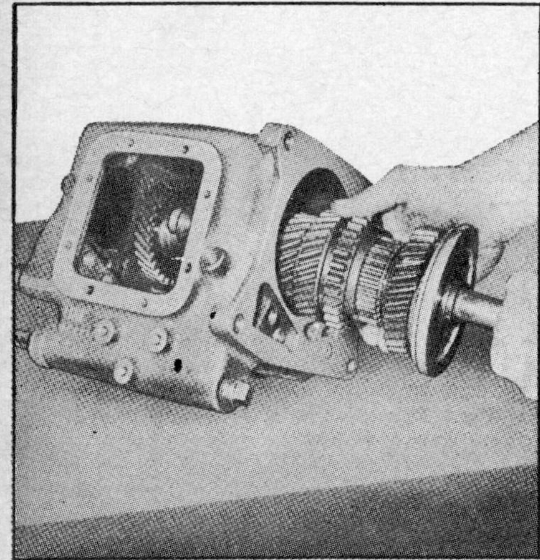

Fig. 3-4 Removing mainshaft assembly

TYPE 3

This transmission, Fig. 3-1, is a four-speed, constant mesh type to provide full synchronization in all forward speeds. Spur gears on the mainshaft and countershaft are engaged by a small sliding spur gear to provide reverse. The mainshaft is hollow to permit passage of the clutch shaft forward to the clutch gear.

Disassemble Transmission

1. Remove front and side covers.
2. Remove 3-4 shift fork detent, Fig. 3-2.
3. Shift 3-4 fork into 4th gear (forward), then drive roll pin from fork with pin punch. Remove 3-4 shift shaft with a drift and remove fork. Shaft can be driven from case in either direction.
4. Remove plug, spring and detent ball from 1-2 detent channel at front of case adjacent to shifter shaft.
5. Move 1-2 shift fork into 2nd gear (forward), then remove roll pin securing fork to shaft with a pin punch. Remove shift fork and shaft by tapping shaft out of case in either direction.
6. Remove snap rings located in clutch gear bore, Fig. 3-3, between clutch gear and bearing, and between clutch gear bearing and case.
7. Use suitable puller to remove clutch gear bearing.
8. Remove mainshaft assembly, Fig. 3-4. It may be necessary to jiggle the mainshaft, making sure clutch gear does not separate from mainshaft. With mainshaft removed, shift synchronizer sleeves to neutral.
9. With a pin punch, drive roll pin from reverse shifter head, Fig. 3-5, then remove shifter head and shaft from case by tapping shaft out in either direction with a drift.
10. Drive out reverse idler gear and reverse shifter fork shafts from the case by driving rearward with a drift. Use care not to lose key used in reverse idler gear shaft. Remove idler gear and reverse shifter fork from case, Fig. 3-5.
11. Remove reverse shifter lever by lifting off its pin in case.
12. To remove countershaft, improvise a dummy shaft by cutting a 7″ length of ⅝″ roll stock. Then drive countershaft rearward, using the dummy shaft until the countershaft is fully disengaged from the case and the dummy shaft is fully within the countergear. Carefully remove the countergear and dummy shaft from case, using care not to tip countergear to prevent needle bearings from falling out.
13. Remove two countergear thrust washers from case.
14. Using a magnet or by tipping the case, remove two interlocks and the detent ball and spring remaining in the 3-4 detent channel.
15. Remove shift finger from selector shaft by first flattening lock tabs securing the two retaining screws. Then remove shifter shaft plug in rear of case. Tap shaft rearward out through hole in case with a drift.
16. Remove two screws securing reverse inhibitor to case and remove inhibitor.

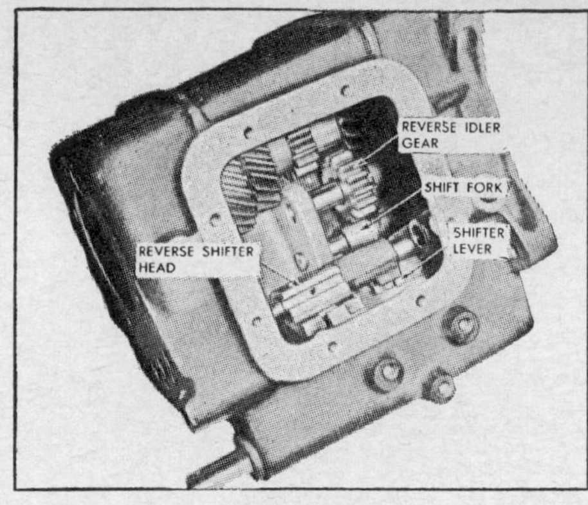

Fig. 3-5 Reverse components installed

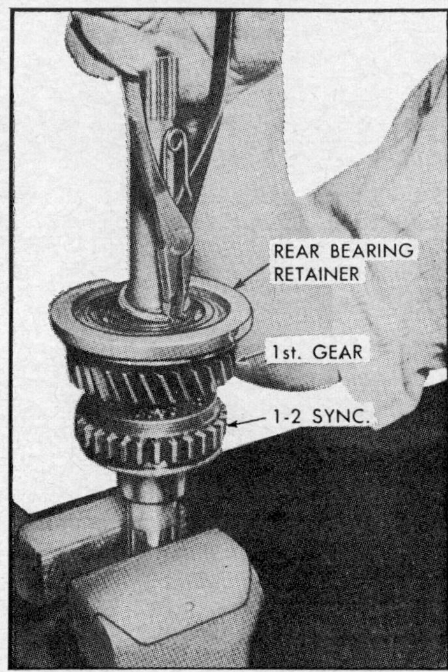

Fig. 3-6 Mainshaft rear components

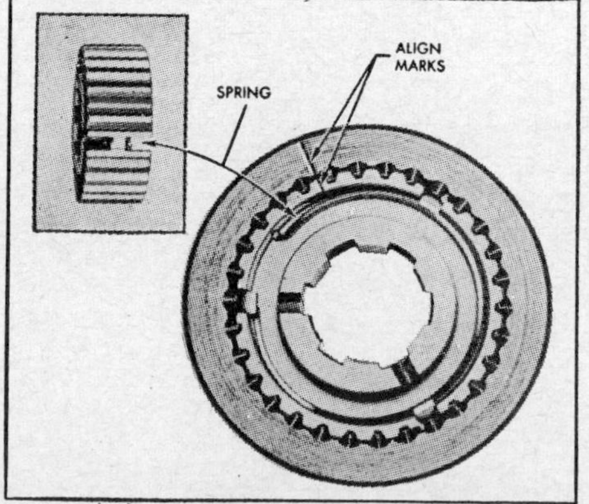

Fig. 3-7 Synchronizer spring and hub installation

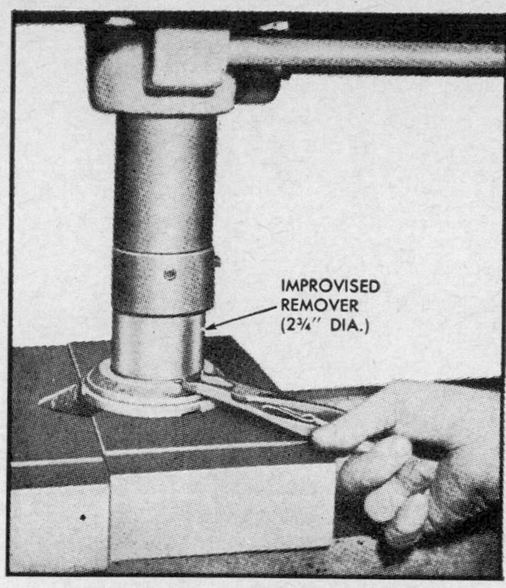

Fig. 3-8 Pressing rear bearing from bearing retainer

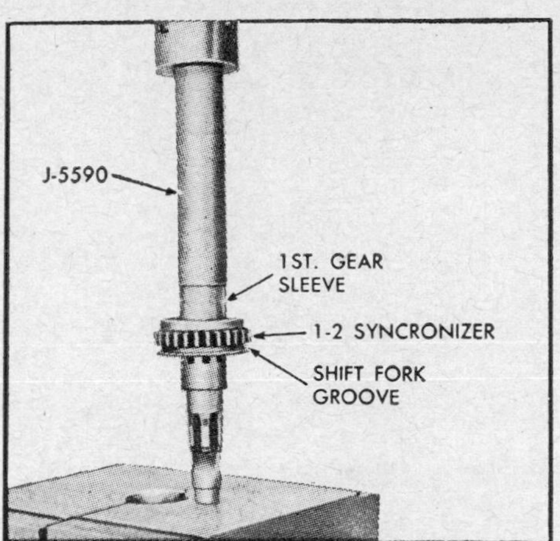

Fig. 3-9 Installing 1st gear sleeve and 1-2 synchronizer on mainshaft

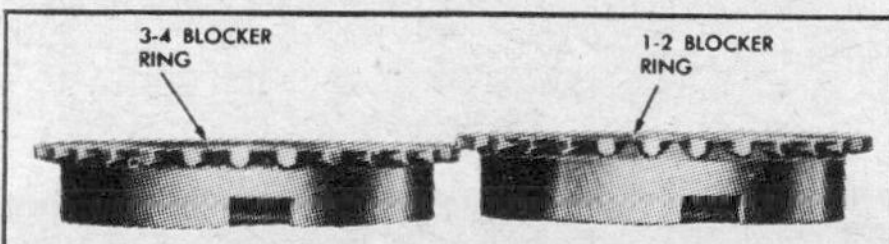

Fig. 3-10 Blocker ring length comparison

Disassemble Mainshaft

1964 MODELS

1. Place clutch gear down against work bench and lift mainshaft out of clutch gear to prevent disturbing clutch gear roller bearings.
2. Remove snap ring from front of mainshaft, then slide 3-4 synchronizer unit with blocker rings and 3rd gear from mainshaft.
3. Remove rear bearing snap ring, then remove rear bearing and retainer as a unit.
4. Remove 1st gear thrust washer, 1st gear and 1-2 blocker ring.
5. Press mainshaft out of 1-2 synchronizer unit and 1st gear sleeve. Remove 1-2 blocker ring and 2nd gear.

1963 MODELS

1. Place clutch gear downward against work bench and carefully lift mainshaft out of clutch gear to prevent disturbing clutch gear roller bearings.
2. Remove special snap ring from front of mainshaft, then slide 3-4 synchronizer unit with blocker rings, 3rd gear, radial needle bearing and 2nd gear from mainshaft.
3. Remove rear bearing selective snap ring, Fig. 3-6, then remove bearing and retainer as an assembly.
4. Remove 1st gear thrust washer, 1st gear and 1-2 blocker rings, Fig. 3-6.
5. Press mainshaft out of 1-2 synchronizer unit and 1st gear sleeve.

Inspection & Repair

1. Wash transmission inside and out with cleaning solvent and inspect for cracks. Inspect rear face which fits against differential carrier for burrs and, if any are present, dress them off with a fine mill file.
2. Check condition of shifter shaft seal and replace if necessary.
3. Wash bearings thoroughly and air-dry. Do not allow bearings to spin but turn them slowly by hand. Spinning bearings will be damaged.
4. Make sure bearings are clean, then lubricate them with light engine oil and check them for roughness. Roughness may be determined by slowly turning outer race by hand.
5. All clutch gear and countergear bearing rollers should be inspected and replaced if worn. Inspect countershaft, thrust washers and spacers and replace if necessary.
6. The synchronizer hubs and sliding sleeves are a matched assembly and should be kept together as originally assembled, but the three keys and two springs may be replaced if worn or broken as follows:
7. Push hub from sliding sleeve. Keys will fall free and springs may be easily removed. Place the two springs in position (one on each side of hub) so a tanged end of each spring falls into the same keyway in the hub, Fig. 3-7. Holding keys in position, align etched marks in hub and sleeve, then slide hub in sleeve.
8. If rear bearing requires replacement, place bearing and retainer in a press, Fig. 3-8. Expand retainer ring and press out bearing. Install a new bearing by reversing the procedure.

Mainshaft, Assemble

1964 MODELS

1. Install 2nd speed gear with clutching teeth toward 1-2 synchronizer, then place 1-2 blocker ring on 2nd gear.
2. Install 1-2 synchronizer hub on mainshaft with shift fork groove toward 2nd gear, being sure to engage blocker ring notches with keys in synchronizer unit.
3. Place 1st gear on mainshaft. Then press sleeve, synchronizer hub and 2nd gear onto mainshaft until they bottom.
4. Install blocker ring in rear of synchronizer, being sure that notches in blocker ring engage keys in synchronizer unit. Then slide 1st gear and its thrust washer onto mainshaft. Note that blocker rings in 1-2

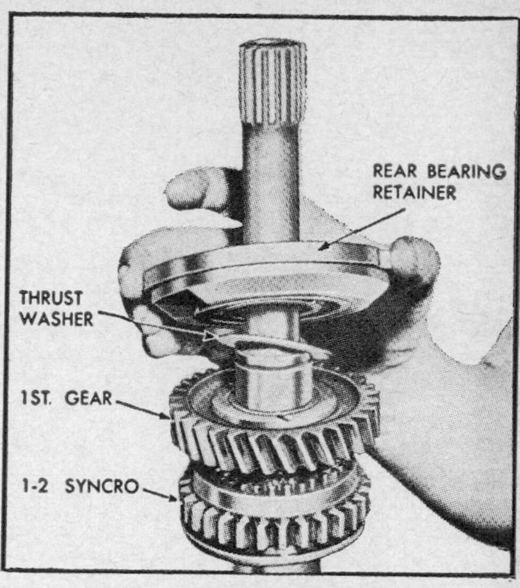

Fig. 3-11 Installing 1-2 synchronizer, 1st gear and rear bearing retainer on mainshaft

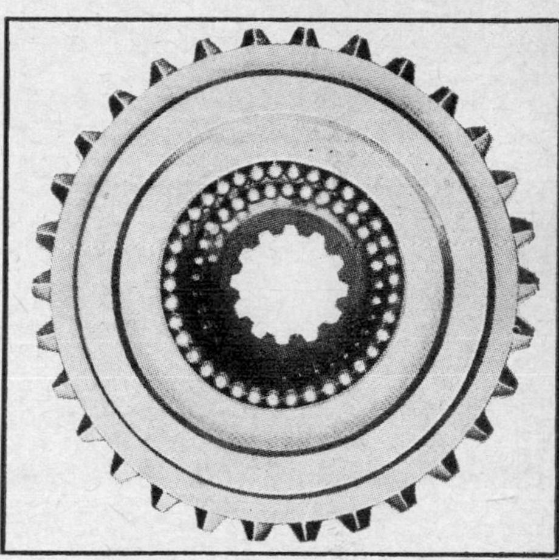

Fig. 3-12 Clutch gear roller bearings installed

Fig. 3-13 Reverse inhibitor and shift finger installation

Fig. 3-14 Istalling countergear shaft

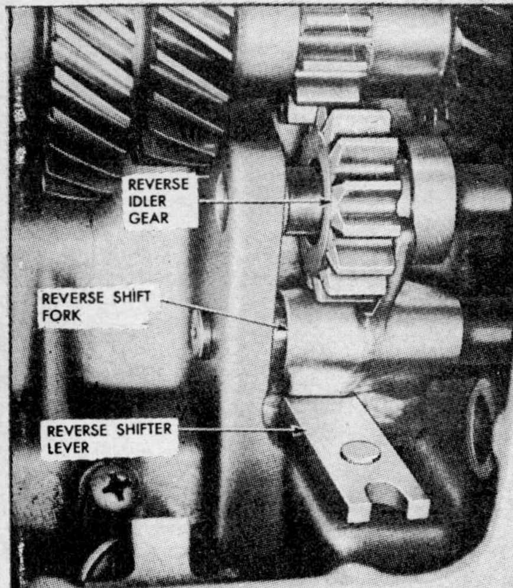

Fig. 3-15 Installation of reverse shifter lever, shift fork and reverse idler gear

synchronizer have longer hubs than those used in 3-4 synchronizer.

5. Install assembled rear bearing retainer and bearing onto mainshaft and secure with selective fit snap ring. With proper snap ring installed (3 sizes available) maximum end play between rear face of rear bearing and snap ring will be .005".
6. Invert mainshaft and install 3rd gear with clutching teeth upward onto mainshaft and seat it against mainshaft shoulder.
7. Place 3-4 blocker ring on cone surface of 3rd gear, then slide 3-4 synchronizer onto blocker ring. Be sure notches in blocker ring engage clutch keys in synchronizer unit. Install other blocker ring onto 3-4 synchronizer.
8. Install special snap ring on front of mainshaft.
9. If clutch gear rollers have become displaced, load 34 needle bearings into innermost diameter and 38 into outermost diameter, using petroleum jelly to hold them in place.
10. Slide clutch gear onto mainshaft. It is good practice (to prevent disturbing clutch gear rollers) to place clutch gear on bench with its pilot bore upward and insert mainshaft into clutch gear.

1963 MODELS

1. Install 1-2 synchronizer hub onto mainshaft with shift fork groove of hub downward, Fig. 3-9. Place 1st gear sleeve on mainshaft. Press sleeve and synchronizer hub on shaft until they bottom, using tool shown or its equivalent.
2. Install blocker ring in rear of 1-2 synchronizer, being sure that notches in ring engage keys in synchronizer. It should be noted that 1-2 blocker rings have slightly longer hubs than those used in 3-4 synchronizer, Fig. 3-10. Then slide 1st gear and its thrust washer onto mainshaft, Fig. 3-11.
3. Install assembled rear bearing retainer, Fig. 3-11, and rear bearing onto mainshaft and secure with selective fit snap ring as shown in Fig. 3-6. With proper snap ring installed (3 thicknesses available) maximum end play between rear face of rear bearing and snap ring will be .005".
4. Invert mainshaft, then install second blocker ring (long hub) on front side of 1-2 synchronizer, again being sure to engage blocker ring notches with keys in synchronizer.
5. Install 2nd gear with clutching teeth toward 1-2 synchronizer, then place radial needle bearing on 2nd gear.
6. Install 3rd gear with clutching teeth upward onto mainshaft and seat it against radial needle bearing.
7. Place 3-4 blocker ring on cone surface of 3rd gear, then slide 3-4 synchronizer onto blocker ring. Be sure notches in blocker ring engage clutch keys in synchronizer. Install second blocker ring onto 3-4 synchronizer.
8. If clutch gear roller bearings have become dislodged, load 33 needle bearings into innermost diameter and 37 needle bearings into outermost diameter, using a generous amount of petroleum jelly to hold bearings in place, Fig. 3-12.
9. Carefully slide clutch gear onto mainshaft. It is good practice to place clutch gear on workbench with its pilot bore upward and insert mainshaft into clutch gear. Set assembled mainshaft aside for later installation in transmission case.

Assemble Transmission

1. Position reverse inhibitor body, Fig. 3-13, in case with its dowel pin and secure with two screws and lockwashers. Be sure to install plunger in inhibitor body.
2. Coat selector shaft with grease, then insert through seal from inside of case. Do not install shaft from front of case as notches in selector shaft will damage seal lips.
3. Attach shift finger to selector shaft, using two bolts and lock tabs, Fig. 3-13. Bend tabs onto bolt heads after tightening bolts, then install drain plug in case at rear of selector shaft.

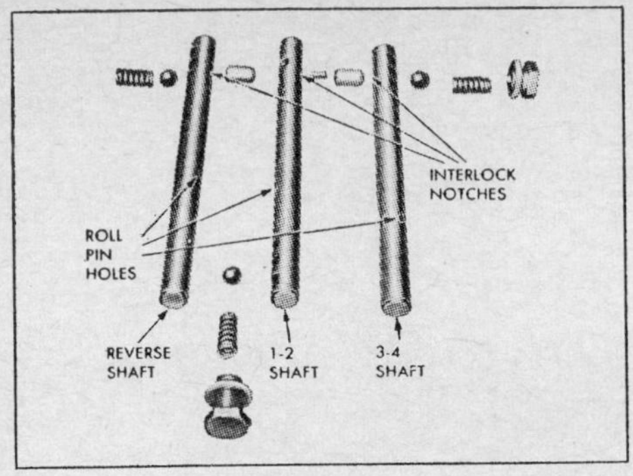

Fig. 3-16 Shift fork shaft identification

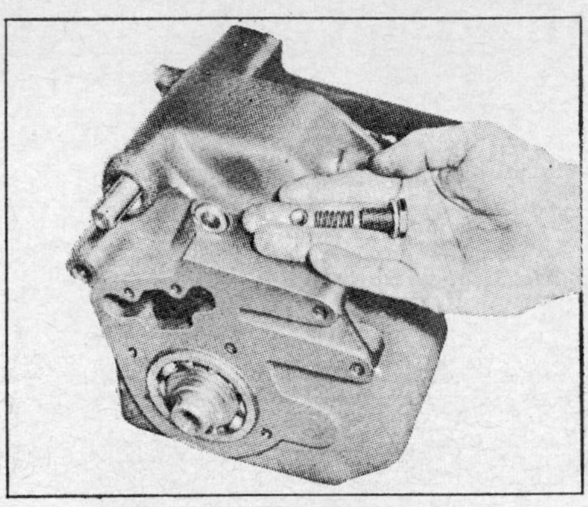

Fig. 3-17 Installing 1-2 shift fork detent components

4. Using a generous amount of petroleum jelly, position countergear thrust washers in case, being sure tabs on washers engage grooves in case.
5. Insert countergear with its bearings and dummy shaft into case through the rear bearing hole. Carefully lift countergear into alignment with countershaft holes in case, then tap countershaft into gear from rear of case, Fig. 3-14. Tap countershaft until it is flush with rear face of case. The countershaft is a light press fit at front of case.
6. Place reverse shifter lever, Fig. 3-15, on pin (1962-63 only) in case with tapered end away from reverse inhibitor.
7. Place reverse idler gear shift fork in case with its pin toward front. Engage fork pin with reverse shifter lever, then insert shift fork shaft.
8. With reverse idler gear shaft to the rear, engage reverse idler gear to shift fork. Then align key groove in idler gear shaft with keyway in rear face of case and slide shaft almost fully in case. Install key in shaft, then fully bottom shaft.
9. Tap both reverse idler and shift fork shafts to insure full seating, then stake each shaft bore in two places below rear face of case adjacent to shaft chamber. Be sure stakes do not protrude above rear face as this would disrupt mating surface for the axle.

10. Insert detent spring and ball in 3-4 detent channel, checking that spring goes fully to bottom of channel and that detent ball does not roll out of reverse shifter head shaft hole in detent channel.
11. Lay out shift fork shafts as shown in Fig. 3-16 to prevent mixing during installation.
12. Depress detent ball and spring in 3-4 detent channel slightly with a small drift and insert reverse shifter head shaft partially into case to compress detent (see Fig. 3-5). Then engage pin in reverse shifter head with yoke of reverse shift lever. Check that shaft pin hole is aligned with pin hole in shifter head and push shaft through until pin holes in head and shaft align. Secure shifter head to shaft with roll pin.
13. To install assembled mainshaft in case, shift synchronizers into 2nd and 4th speed simultaneously (full forward) to provide clearance to pass countergear. Insert mainshaft through rear of case. Align rear bearing retainer portion of clearance hole with portion of clearance hole located at 2 o'clock position on rear face of case. Then tap rear bearing retainer into case until flush with rear face.
14. With large snap ring installed in outer diameter of front bearing, tap bearing into front of case and over clutch gear hub until large snap ring seats against front of case.
15. Retain clutch gear in bearing with selective snap ring (see Fig. 3-3). With proper snap ring installed, maximum end play between bearing and snap ring will be .005".
16. Install small snap ring in inner diameter of clutch gear. This snap ring acts as a bottoming stop for clutch shaft.
17. Prior to installing 1-2 shift fork, shift both synchronizers to neutral. Then install one interlock in 3-4 detent channel.
18. With interlock pin in hole in interlock notch end, push 1-2 shift fork shaft partially into case. The interlock end (two opposite notches) of shaft goes to rear of case. Engage 1-2 shift fork with 1-2 synchronizer. Align pin holes in shaft and fork, then tap shaft rearward until it engages interlock. Secure shaft with roll pin.
19. Install detent ball, spring, gasket and cap in 1-2 detent channel, Fig. 3-17. Cap used at this location has longer shank.
20. Drop remaining interlock into 3-4 detent channel, then push 3-4 shift fork shaft partially through hole in front of case. Engage 3-4 shift fork in 3-4 synchronizer, align pin hole in fork and shaft, then push shaft fully to rear of case until it engages interlock. Secure shaft with roll pin.
21. Install remaining detent ball, spring, nylon washer and cap in 3-4 detent channel at left rear of case.
22. Prior to installing front bearing retainer and side cover, test operation of shift forks by actuating shift lever with a small pin punch inserted in hole in shifter shaft. If transmission shifts satisfactorily, install front bearing retainer and new gasket and tighten bolts to 15-20 ft. lbs. Install side cover with new gasket and tighten bolts to 3-4 ft. lbs.

Type Four Muncie & Saginaw

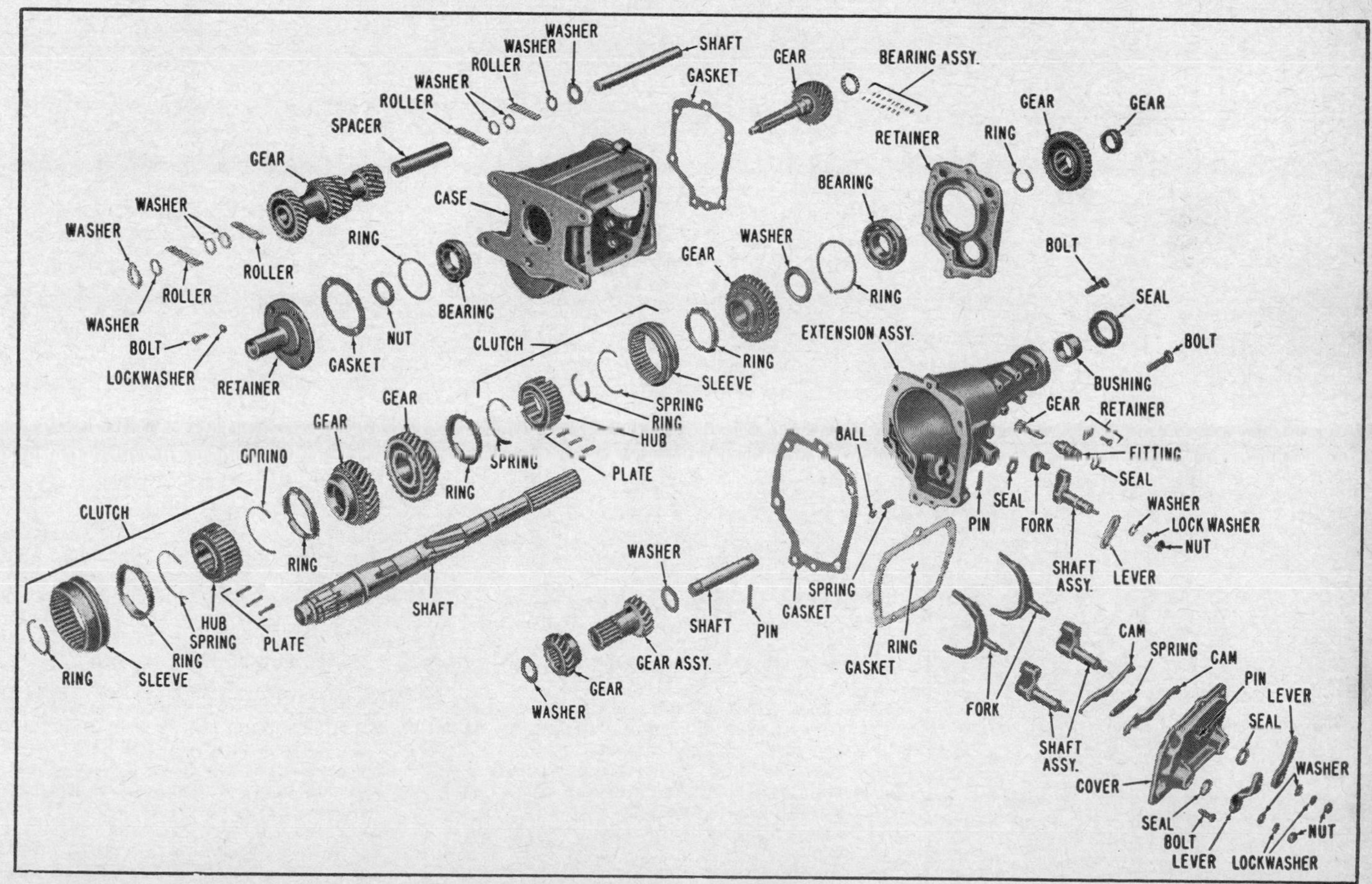

Fig. 4-1 Type 4 Saginaw (from 1966) and Muncie four-speed transmissions. These units have the reverse gears located in the extension housing. The Muncie design uses spur-cut gears whereas the Saginaw unit have helical cut gears

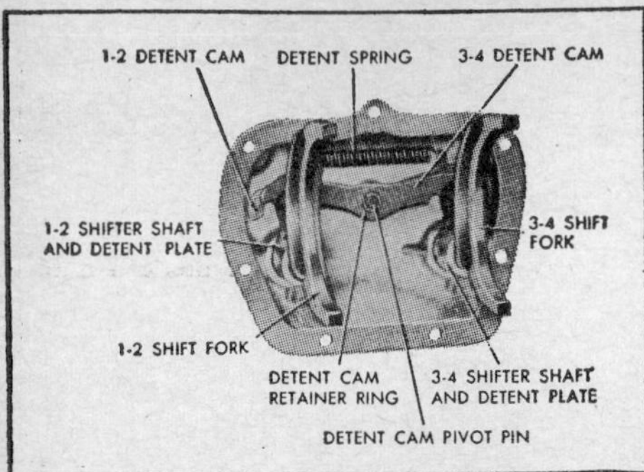

Fig. 4-2 Transmission side cover

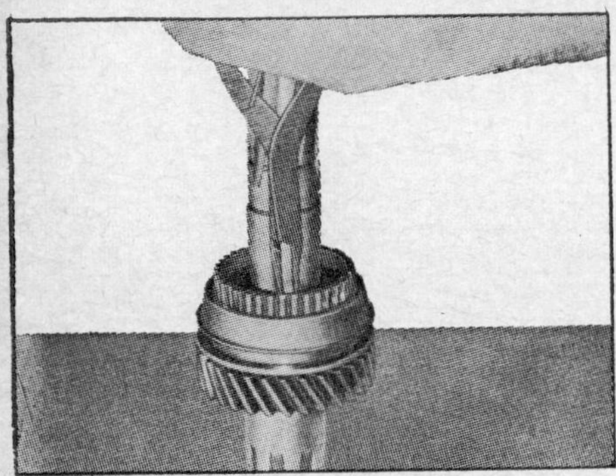

Fig. 4-3 Removing 1-2 synchronizer clutch snap ring

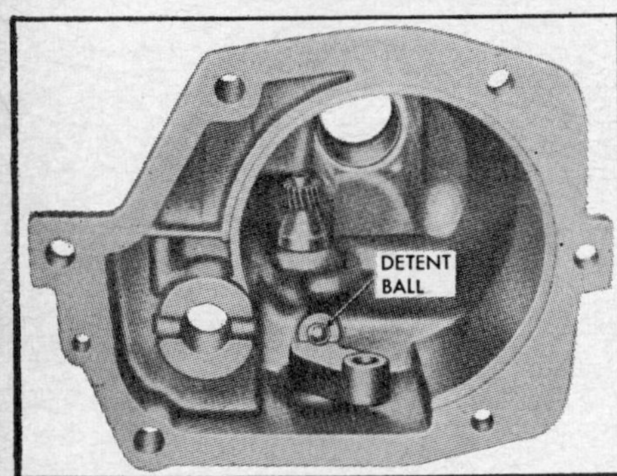

Fig. 4-4 Installing reverse shifter shaft and detent ball

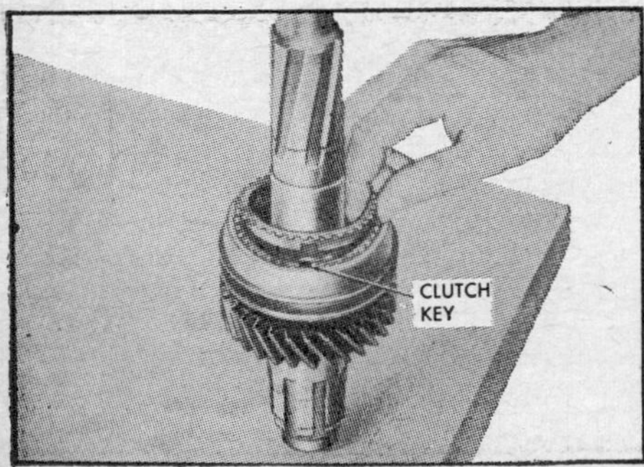

Fig. 4-5 Installing synchronizer ring

This four speed transmission, Fig. 4-1, incorporates helical gears throughout. All four forward gears are fully synchronized. Reverse is not synchronized, although it uses a helical gear for quiet operation. Shafts, bearings, high capacity clutches and other precision parts are held to close limits, providing proper clearances necessary for durability during extended heavy usage.

SIDE COVER, REPLACE

1. Referring to Fig. 4-2 disconnect control rods from levers.
2. Shift transmission into 2nd speed before removing cover by moving 1-2 shifter lever into forward detent position.
3. Remove cover from case.
4. Reverse procedure to install the cover, being sure first to shift the transmission into 2nd gear. Make sure shift forks are aligned with their respective grooves in synchronizer sliding sleeves.

DISASSEMBLE TRANSMISSION

1. Remove side cover.
2. Remove front bearing retainer.
3. Shift transmission into two gears at once to keep mainshaft from turning, then remove retaining nut from main drive gear.
4. With gears in neutral, drive lock pin from reverse shifter lever boss and pull shifter shaft out about ⅛". This disengages reverse shift fork from reverse gear.
5. Unfasten extension case from main case. Tap extension case rearward with a soft hammer to start. When reverse idler shaft is out as far as it will go, move extension to left so reverse fork clears reverse gear. Then remove extension and gasket.
6. Now remove rear reverse idler gear, shaft and plate thrust washer.
7. Use a suitable puller to remove speedometer gear from mainshaft, after which remove reverse gear.
8. Slide 3-4 synchronizer clutch sleeve to 4th gear position before trying to remove mainshaft assembly from case.
9. Remove rear bearing retainer and mainshaft assembly from case by tapping retainer with soft hammer.
10. Unload bearing rollers from main drive gear and remove 4th gear synchronizer blocking ring.
11. Lift front half of reverse idler gear and its tanged washer from case.
12. Press main drive gear down into case and remove. From inside of case, tap out front bearing and snap ring.
13. From front of case, press out countershaft. Then remove countergear and both tanged washers.
14. Remove mainshaft front snap ring and strip mainshaft of loose parts.
15. Spread rear bearing retainer snap ring and press mainshaft out of retainer.
16. Remove mainshaft rear snap ring. Support 1st gear in a press and press against rear of shaft to remove it from rear bearing, 1st gear thrust washer, 1st gear and synchronizing ring.
17. Remove 1-2 synchronizer snap ring and remove 1-2 synchronizer unit, 2nd gear synchronizer ring and 2nd gear from shaft, Fig. 4-3.

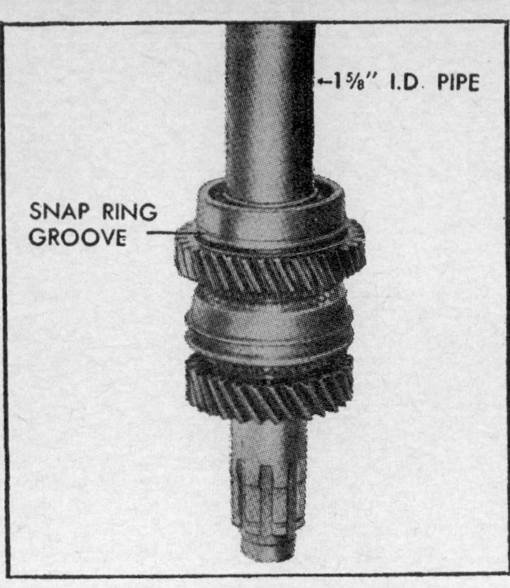

Fig. 4-6 Installing mainshaft rear bearing

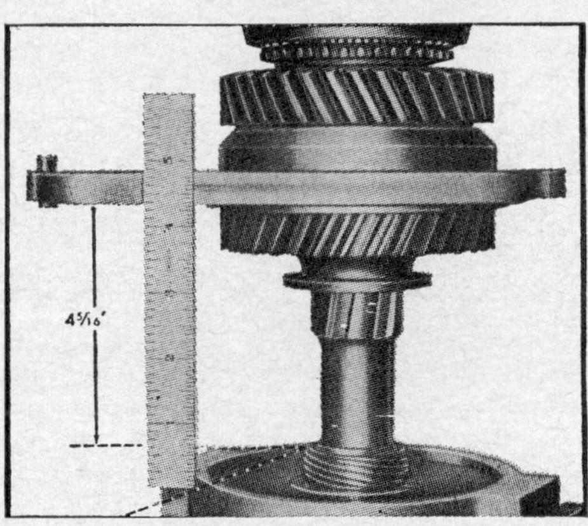

Fig. 4-7 Installing speedometer drive gear

UNIT REPAIRS

Reverse Idler

Because of the high degree of accuracy to which the reverse idler gear bushings are machined, the bushings are not serviced separately. Check bushings for excessive wear by using a narrow feeler gauge between shaft and bushing. Proper clearance is from .003 to .005".

Reverse Shifter Shaft & Seal

1. With extension case removed as outlined previously, remove shift fork.
2. Drive shifter shaft into case extension, allowing ball detent to drop into case. Remove shaft and ball detent spring.
3. Place ball detent spring into its hole and, from inside extension, install shifter shaft fully into its opening until detent plate is butted against

inside of extension housing.

4. Place detent ball on spring, Fig. 4-4, and, holding ball down with thumb or a suitable tool, push shifter shaft back in, away from case until it is directly over ball and turn until ball drops into detent on shaft detent plate.
5. Install shift fork.

NOTE: Do not drive shifter shaft lock pin into place until extension has been installed on transmission case.

Extension Oil Seal or Bushing

If bushing in rear of extension requires replacement, remove oil seal and drive bushing into case extension. Drive new bushing in from the rear. Coat I.D. of bushing with transmission lubricant, then install new oil seal.

Clutch Keys & Springs

NOTE: The clutch hubs and sliding sleeves are a selected assembly and should be kept together as originally assembled. However, the three keys and two springs may be replaced if worn or broken.

1. To replace, push hub from sliding sleeve. Keys will fall free and springs easily removed.
2. Place the two springs in position (one on each side of hub) so all three keys are engaged by both springs. Place keys in position and, holding them in place, slide hub into sleeve.

Assemble Mainshaft

1. From rear of mainshaft, assemble 2nd gear with hub of gear toward rear of shaft.
2. Install 1-2 synchronizer clutch to mainshaft (with clutch sleeve taper toward rear and hub to front) together with a synchronizer ring on either side so their keyways line up with clutch keys, Fig. 4-5. Install smaller of two synchronizer retainer snap rings to mainshaft with ends of snap ring behind spline teeth.
3. Install 1st gear (hub toward front) and 1st gear thrust washer.
4. Press rear bearing on mainshaft, Fig. 4-6, being sure to seat bearing firmly.
5. Choose correct selective fit snap ring and install it in groove of mainshaft behind rear bearing. (Snap rings of .084", .087", .090", .093", .096" are available.) With proper snap ring, maximum distance between ring and rear face of bearing will be from zero to .005".
6. Install 3rd gear (hub to front) and 3rd gear synchronizing ring (notches to front).
7. Install 3-4 clutch assembly with both sleeve taper and hub toward front, making sure keys in hub correspond to notches in 3rd gear synchronizing ring.
8. Install snap ring in mainshaft groove in front of 3-4 synchronizer clutch with ends of snap ring seated behind spline teeth.
9. Install rear bearing retainer. Spread snap ring in plate to allow ring to drop around rear bearing and press on end of mainshaft until snap ring engages groove in rear bearing.
10. Install reverse gear with shift collar to rear.
11. Press speedometer drive gear on mainshaft to distance shown in Fig. 4-7.

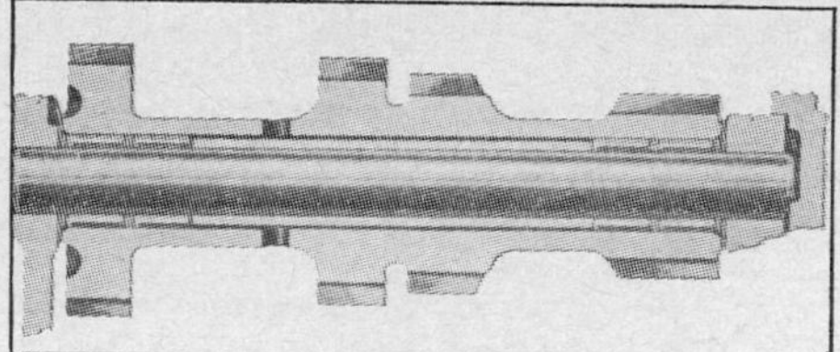

Fig. 4-8 Sectional view of countergear assembly

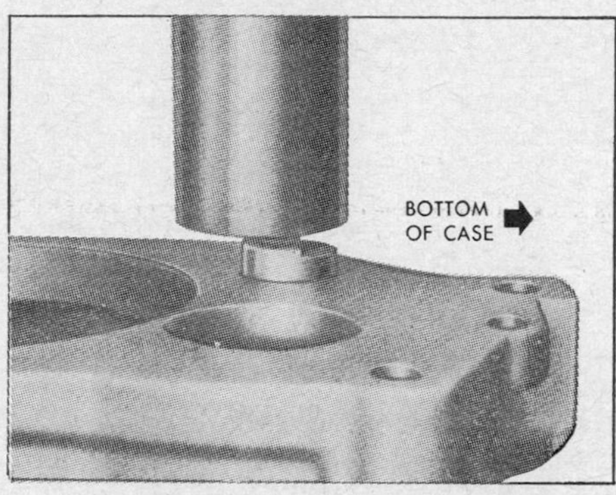

Fig. 4-9 Installing countershaft

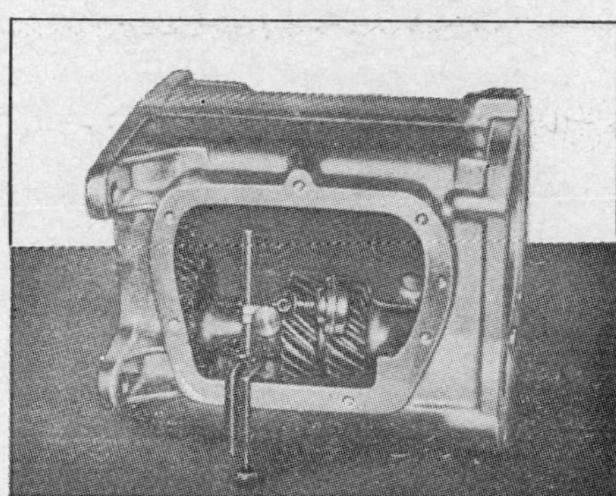

Fig. 4-10 Checking countergear end play

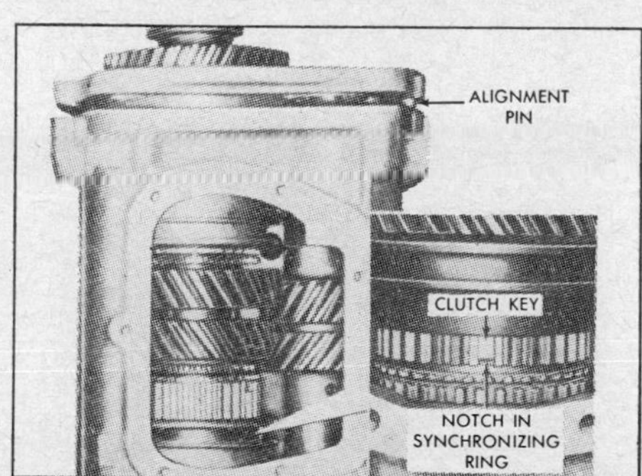

Fig. 4-11 Installing mainshaft assembly

Assemble Countergear

1. Install roller spacer in countergear.
2. Using heavy grease to retain rollers, install 20 rollers in either end of countergear, two .050" spacers, 20 more rollers, then one .050" spacer. Make same installation at other end of countergear, Fig. 4-8.

ASSEMBLE TRANS.

1. With transmission case on its side, put countergear tanged thrust washers in place, retaining them with heavy grease, and making sure tangs are resting in notches in case.
2. Set countergear in bottom of case.
3. Position transmission so it is resting on its front face.
4. Lubricate and insert countershaft through rear of case. Turn countershaft so flat on end of shaft is horizontal and facing bottom of case.
5. Align countergear with shaft in rear and hole in front of case. Press countershaft into case until flat on shaft is flush with rear of case, Fig. 4-9. Be sure thrust washers remain in place.
6. Attach a dial indicator as shown in Fig. 4-10 and check end play of countergear. If end play is greater than .025", new thrust washers must be installed.
7. Install 17 roller bearings in main drive gear, using heavy grease to hold bearings and cage in place.
8. Install main drive gear and pilot bearings through side cover opening and into transmission front bore.
9. Place gasket in position of front face of rear bearing retainer.
10. Install 4th gear synchronizing ring on main drive gear with notches toward rear.
11. Position tanged reverse idler gear thrust washer on machined face of ear cast in case for reverse idler shaft and hold with heavy grease. Position front reverse idler gear next to thrust washer, with hub facing toward rear. **NOTE:** Before attempting to install mainshaft assembly in case, slide 3-4 synchronizer clutch sleeve forward into 4th speed detent position.
12. Lower mainshaft into case making certain notches in 4th speed synchronizing ring correspond to keys in clutch, Fig. 4-11.
13. Tap rear bearing into position.
14. Insert rear reverse idler gear.
15. Install remaining flat thrust washer on reverse idler shaft. If new idler shaft is being used, drive out roll pin and press it into new shaft.
16. Install reverse idler shaft, making sure to pick up rear tanged thrust washer. *Roll pin should be in a vertical position.*
17. Pull reverse shifter shaft to left side of extension and rotate shaft to bring reverse shift fork forward in extension (reverse detent position). Start extension onto transmission case, while slowly pushing in on shifter shaft to engage shift fork with reverse gear shift collar. Then pilot reverse idler shaft into extension housing, permitting extension to slide into transmission case.

18. Install extension attaching bolts. Torque upper three bolts to 15-25-ft-lbs, and lower three bolts to 25-35 ft-lbs.
19. Push or pull reverse shifter shaft to line up holes and drive in lock pin. Then install shifter lever.
20. Press bearing onto main drive gear (snap ring groove to front) and into case until several main drive gear retaining nut threads are exposed.
21. Lock transmission by shifting into two gears. Install main drive gear retaining nut. Be sure bearing fully seats against shoulder of gear. Torque nut to 40 ft-lbs and lock it in place by staking securely into shaft hole with center punch.
22. Install main drive gear bearing retainer, using sealer on bolts. Torque to 15-20 ft-lbs.
23. Shift 3-4 sliding sleeve into neutral and 1-2 sliding sleeve into 2nd gear position. Shift side cover 3-4 shift lever into neutral and 1-2 shift lever into 2nd gear.
24. Install side cover with gasket. Torque attaching bolts evenly to avoid cover distortion and torque to 15-20 ft-lbs.

Type Five Chrysler

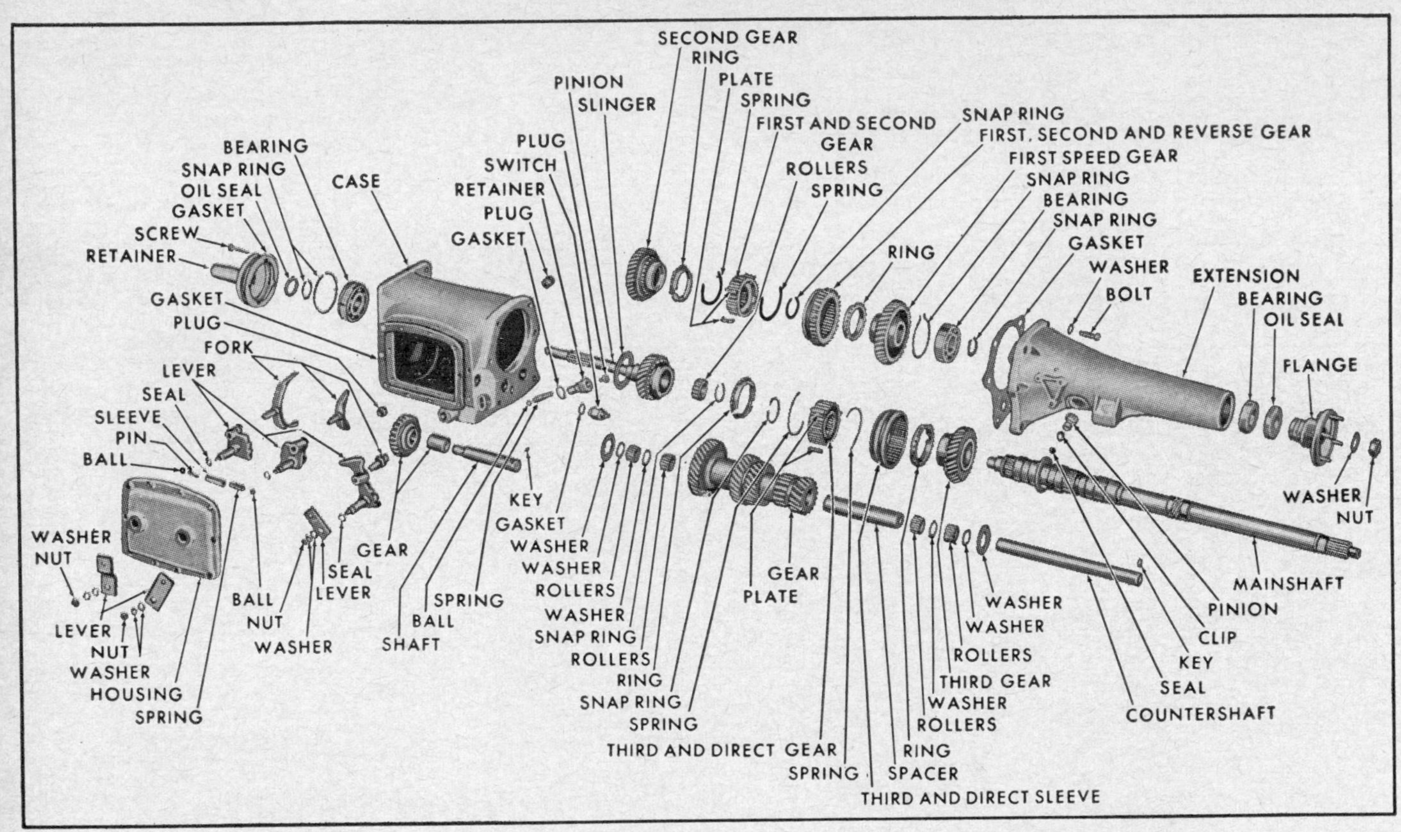

Fig. 5-1 Type Five Chrysler four-speed transmission. NOTE: The drive pinion bearing oil slinger shown has been eliminated with the release of new drive pinions which do not use an oil slinger. The new drive pinions were incorporated into production on September 1, 1964

This transmission, Fig. 5-1, consists of a series of helical gears with synchronization in all forward speeds. The shafts, bearings, synchronizers and other precision parts are held to close tolerances to provide durability during extended heavy operation.

DISASSEMBLE TRANS.

1. Disconnect shift control rods from shift levers and operating levers.
2. Shift transmission into two gears at once to prevent mainshaft from turning and remove flange from end of mainshaft.
3. Unfasten shift housing and, with all levers in neutral position, Fig. 5-2, pull housing out and away from case. Work shift forks out of synchronizer sleeves and remove from case.
4. Remove main drive gear bearing retainer.
5. Unfasten extension housing from transmission case.
6. Slide 3-4 synchronizer slightly forward and slide housing and mainshaft assembly out of case, Fig. 5-3.

Disassemble Mainshaft

1. Remove snap ring in front of 3-4 synchronizer and slide off synchronizer.
2. Slide off 3rd gear and stop ring.
3. While holding center bearing snap ring compressed, Fig. 5-4, pull mainshaft assembly and bearing out of extension housing.
4. Remove rear bearing from mainshaft by inserting steel plates on front side of 1st speed gear. Then, using an arbor or hammer, press or drive bearing from mainshaft.
5. Remove mainshaft rear bearing snap ring and remove bearing, retainer ring, 1st gear and its stop ring.
6. Remove snap ring and slide 1-2 clutch from mainshaft.

NOTE: Fig. 5-6 shows mainshaft bearing surfaces. Inspect these surfaces for any condition that would warrant the use of a new mainshaft. Fig. 5-7 shows details of reverse gearing and related parts.

7. With a feeler gauge, Fig. 5-8, measure countergear end play by inserting gauge between thrust washer and gear. Measurement should not exceed .0045" to .028". If greater than specified, new thrust washers should be used upon reassembly.

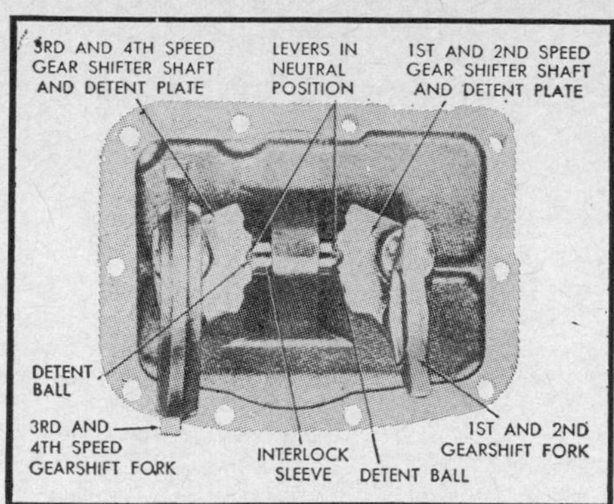

Fig. 5-2 Shift housing assembly

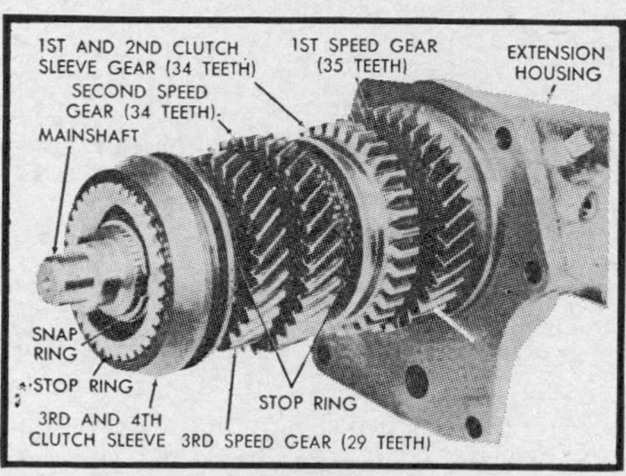

Fig. 5-3 Mainshaft assembly

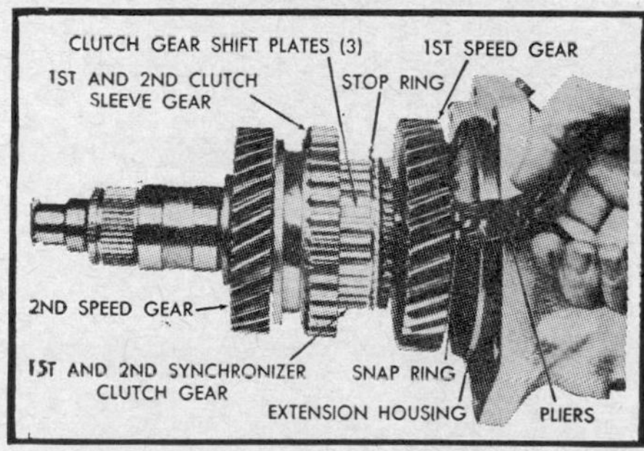

Fig. 5-4 Compressing center bearing snap ring so mainshaft can be pulled from bearing housing

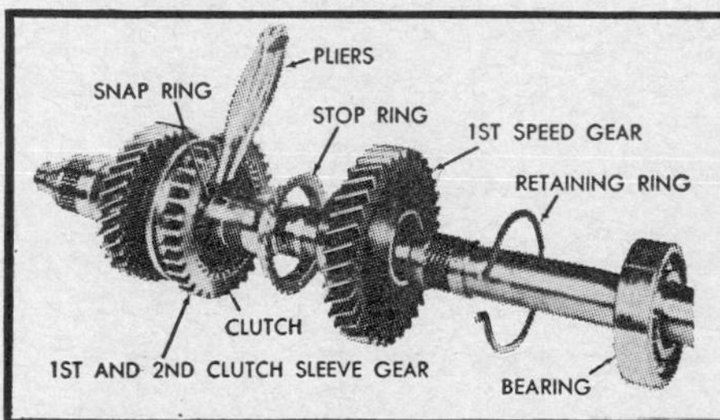

Fig. 5-5 Removing clutch gear snap ring

8. Drive reverse slider gear shaft (from front to rear) far enough out of case to remove slider gear. Remove key from shaft and shaft from case, Fig. 5-9.
9. Remove reverse lever detent parts.
10. Push reverse lever shaft into case and remove as shown in Fig. 5-10. Lift out detent ball from bottom of case, and remove shift fork from shaft and detent plate.
11. Using a suitable arbor, drive countershaft out of case, allowing cluster gear to rest in bottom of case to permit removal of main drive gear.
12. Remove snap ring and remove main drive gear by driving it into case. Remove snap ring and press bearing from main drive gear.
13. Lift cluster gear from case.

REASSEMBLE TRANS.

Countergear

1. Using heavy grease, coat inside of gear bore at each end, then center bearing spacer. Insert arbor through gear and spacer.
2. Grease needle rollers and, at each end of gear, install 19 rollers, followed by a spacer ring, 19 more rollers and a spacer ring.
3. Coat thrust washers with grease and install them over arbor with tang side toward case boss.
4. Install countergear into case, Fig. 5-11. Allow assembly to rest in bottom of case until after main drive gear is installed.

Mainshaft

1. Slide 2nd gear over mainshaft (synchronizer cone toward front) and down into position against shoulder on shaft (see Fig. 5-5).
2. Slide 1-2 clutch sleeve gear including 2nd gear stop ring over mainshaft with shift fork slot toward front, and down into position against 2nd gear. Be sure stop ring is indexed with shift plates and install snap ring.
3. Slide low gear stop ring over shaft and down into position and index with shift plates.
4. Slide 1st gear synchronizer (synchronizer cone toward clutch gear sleeve just installed) over mainshaft and down against clutch sleeve gear.
5. Install mainshaft bearing retainer ring followed by center bearing. Using an arbor and a suitable tool, drive or press bearing down into position, and secure with snap ring.
6. Install mainshaft rear bearing.
7. Install partially assembled mainshaft into extension housing far enough to engage retaining ring in slot in extension housing. Compress retaining ring and at same time rest mainshaft in extension housing (see Fig. 5-4). Be sure retaining ring is seated all around slot.
8. Slide 3rd gear on shaft synchronizer cone toward front followed by 3rd gear stop ring.
9. Install 3-4 synchronizer clutch assembly with shift fork slot toward rear. Be sure to index rear stop ring with clutch gear shift plates (see Fig. 5-4). Install snap ring.

Service Bulletin

QUIETS GEAR RATTLE: A gear rattle, or neutral noise, having automatic transmission fluid in the case can be quieted by changing the lubricant. Drain the automatic transmission fluid and replace it with SAE-140 multipurpose gear lube. If the SAE-140 causes hard or stiff shifting during cold weather operation, change to SAE-80 or 90. This will lessen the effort required for shifting.

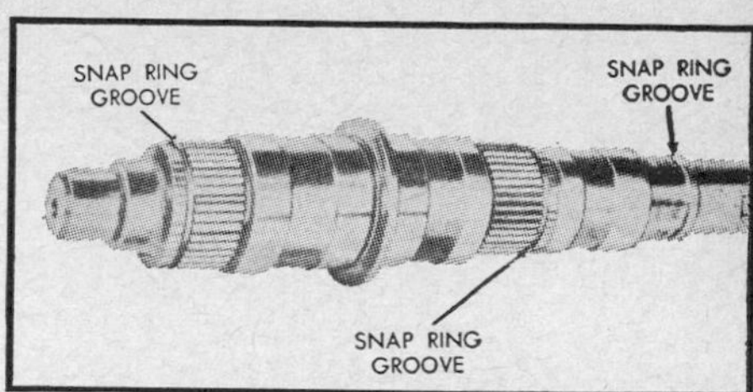

Fig. 5-6 Mainshaft bearing surfaces

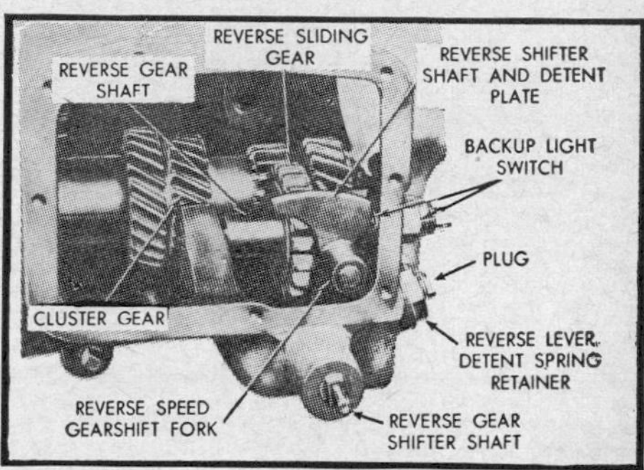

Fig. 5-7 Reverse gearing and countergear

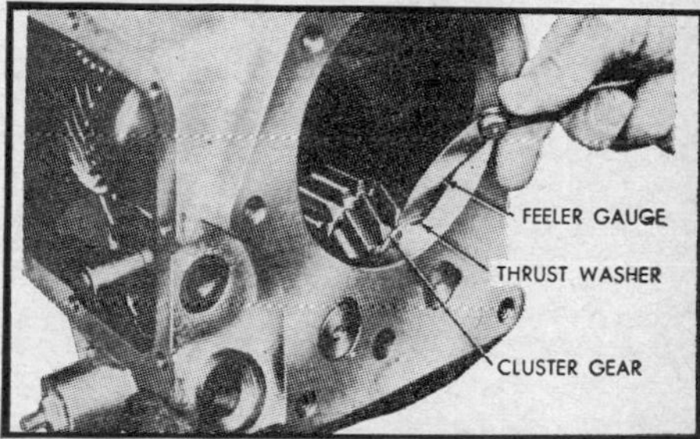

Fig. 5-8 Measuring countergear end play

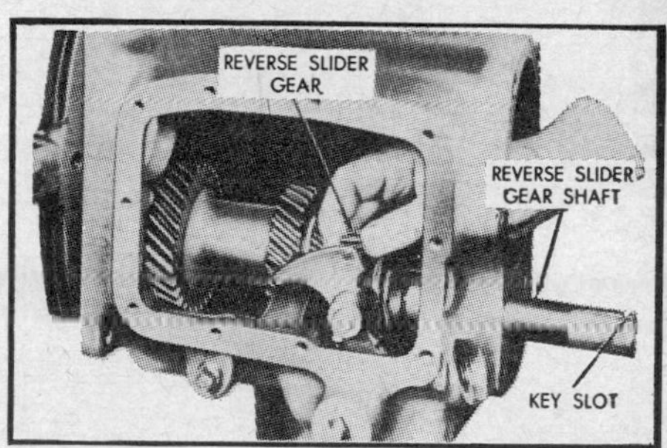

Fig. 5-9 Removing reverse slider gear

10. Using heavy grease, position front stop ring over clutch gear, indexing ring slots with shift plates.

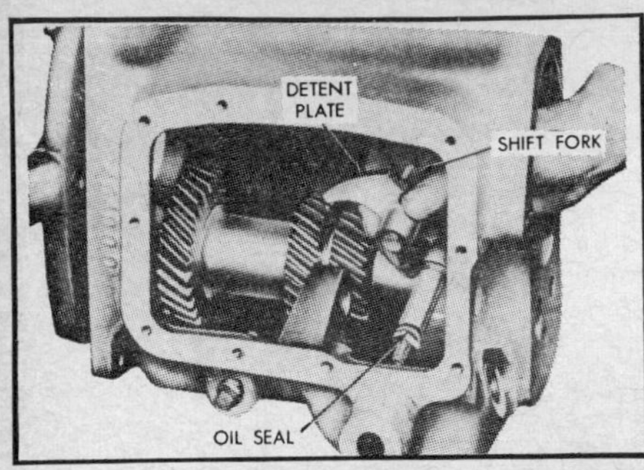

Fig. 5-10 Removing reverse shift fork and lever

Caution: It is very important that indexing of all stop rings and positioning of gears and clutches on mainshaft be correct, or the mating of the extension housing to the case will not be possible without damage.

Main Drive Gear & Countershaft

1. Slide oil slinger over shaft, then press bearing on shaft. Be sure outer snap ring groove is toward front. Seat bearing fully against shoulder of gear.
2. Install new inner snap ring into groove to retain bearing.
3. Install gear and bearing into case and position in front bore. Tap lightly into place. Install outer snap ring in bearing groove.
4. Start countershaft in its bore at rear of case. Raise countergear to mesh with main drive gear. Be sure thrust washer tangs are aligned with slots in case.
5. Drive or press countershaft into gear. Install woodruff key. Continue to press shaft into case until end of shaft is flush with rear face of case.
6. Measure countergear end play (see Fig. 5-8). If end play is greater than .028" install new thrust washers.

Reverse Gearing

1. Install reverse shaft detent and spring. Install spring retainer gasket and retainer (see Fig. 5-7).
2. Position reverse slider gear shaft in end of case and drive it far enough to position slider gear on protruding end of shaft with shift slot toward rear (see Fig. 5-9). At same time engage slot with reverse shift fork.
3. Drive reverse gear shaft into case far enough to permit installation of woodruff key. Drive shaft flush with end of case.

Mainshaft & Extension Housing

1. Grease both sides of extension housing gasket and stick it on case.
2. Center reverse slider gear on its shaft, then insert mainshaft into case. Be sure 3-4 speed stop ring is indexed with shifter plates.
3. Move 3-4 speed clutch sleeve slightly toward front and at same time align front of mainshaft with main drive gear. Push in on extension housing and bottom against case and housing.
4. Install bolts and tighten securely.
5. Move reverse slider gear ahead to neutral position and install shift housing.

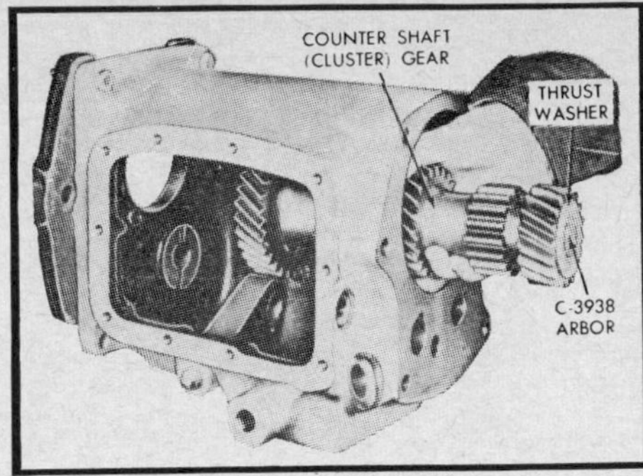

Fig. 5-11 Installing countergear

Service Bulletin

CURES HARD SHIFTING: Hard shifting can result if there is a binding of the shifter shafts in the case or in the cover. This happens when moisture enters between the shaft and bore and causes a build-up of corrosion.

To restore normal shifting, remove the external shift levers from the transmission, leaving the levers attached to the shift rods. It is not necessary to drain oil from the unit.

Place a $\frac{3}{4}$" diameter hole saw over the shifting shaft protruding from the case and cut a $\frac{1}{8}$" deep counterbore in the case. After blowing out the cuttings, apply to the shaft a penetrating oil that will not damage the "O" ring, and work the shaft until it is free. Now apply a liberal amount of multi-purpose grease to the shaft and counterbore, and then insert an "O" ring, available for the purpose, in the counterbore.

Type Six Ford

This transmission, Fig. 6-1, is of the fully synchronized type with all gears except the reverse sliding gear being in constant mesh. All forward speed changes are accomplished with synchronizer sleeves instead of sliding gears. The synchronizers will enable quicker shifts, greatly reduce gear clash, and permit down-shifting into any forward speed gear while the car is moving.

DISASSEMBLE TRANS.

1. Remove shift linkage and control bracket.
2. Remove transmission cover.
3. Remove extension housing.
4. Remove input shaft bearing retainer.
5. Support countergear with a wire hook. Then working from front of case, push countershaft out rear of case and lower countergear to bottom of case.
6. Place 1-2 shift lever and reverse shift lever in neutral. Place 3-4 shift lever in 3rd speed position.
7. Remove bolt that retains 3-4 shift rail detent spring and plug in left side of case, Fig. 6-2. Remove spring and plug with a magnet.
8. Remove detent mechanism set screw from top of case and take out detent spring and plug with a magnet.
9. Remove attaching screw from 3-4 speed shift fork. Tap on inner end of shift rail to unseat expansion plug from front of case. Then withdraw 3-4 shift rail from front of case. Do not lose interlock pin from shift rail.
10. Remove attaching screw from 1-2 shift fork. Slide 1-2 shift rail out of rear of case.
11. Remove interlock plug and detent plug from top of case with a magnet.
12. Remove snap ring that secures speedometer drive gear to output shaft. Slide gear off shaft and remove speedometer drive gear ball.
13. Remove snap ring that secures output shaft bearing to shaft and use a suitable puller to remove bearing.
14. Remove input shaft and bearing and blocking ring from front of case.
15. Move output shaft to right side of case to provide clearance for shift forks. Rotate forks as shown in Fig. 6-3 and lift them from case.
16. Support 1st gear to prevent it from sliding off shaft, then lift output shaft assembly from case, Fig. 6-4.
17. Remove reverse gear shift fork attaching screw. Rotate reverse shift rail 90 deg. as shown in Fig. 6-5. Slide shift rail out rear of case and lift fork from case.
18. Remove reverse detent plug and spring from case with a magnet.
19. Remove reverse idler gear shaft from case, Fig. 6-6.
20. Lift reverse idler gear and thrust washers from case.
21. Lift countergear and thrust washers from case.

Disassemble Output Shaft

1. Remove snap ring from front of output shaft. Slide 3-4 synchronizer blocking ring and 3rd gear off shaft, Fig. 6-7.
2. Remove next snap ring and 2nd gear thrust washer. Slide 2nd gear and blocking ring from shaft.

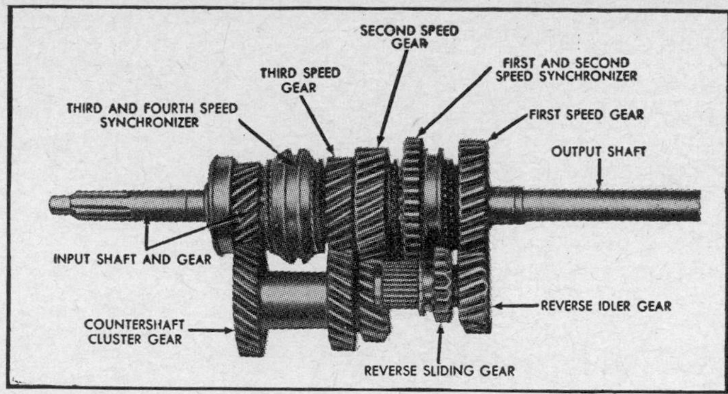

Fig. 6-1 Type Six Ford four speed transmission

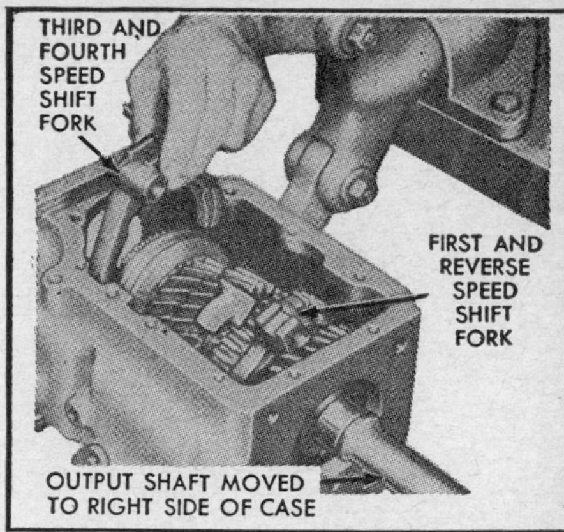

Fig. 6-3 Removing shift forks from case

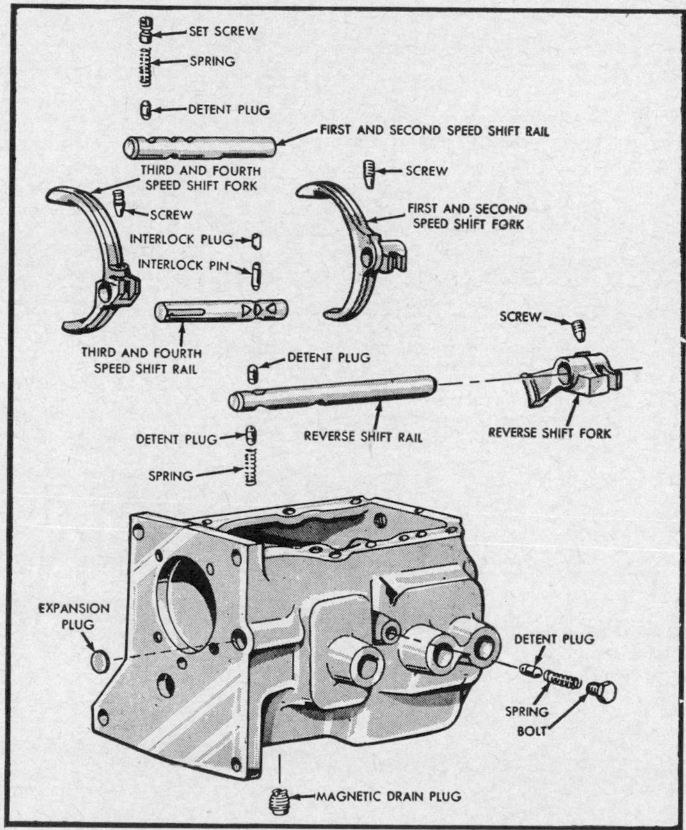

Fig. 6-2 Shift rails and forks disassembled

Fig. 6-4 Removing output shaft assembly

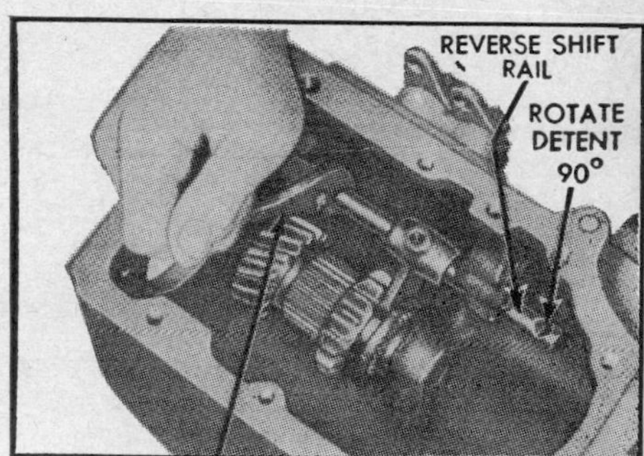

Fig. 6-5 Rotating reverse shift rail

3. Remove next snap ring and slide 1-2 speed synchronizer, blocking ring and 1st gear off shaft. Remove thrust washer from rear of shaft.

UNIT REPAIRS

Cam & Shaft Seals

1. Referring to Fig. 6-8, remove three shift levers.
2. Remove three cams and shafts from inside of case.
3. Remove O-ring from each cam and shaft.
4. Dip new O-rings in gear lubricant and install them on cam and shafts.
5. Slide each cam and shaft into its respective bore in case.
6. Secure each shift lever.

Input Shaft Bearing

1. Referring to Fig. 6-9, remove snap ring that secures bearing to shaft.
2. Press input shaft gear out of bearing.
3. Press new bearing onto shaft and secure bearing with snap ring.

Synchronizers

1. Referring to Fig. 6-10, push synchronizer hub from each sleeve.
2. Separate inserts and springs from hubs. Do not mix parts from one synchronizer to another.
3. Position hub in sleeve, being sure that alignment marks are properly indexed.
4. Place three inserts into hub. Install insert springs, making sure that irregular surface (hump) is seated in one of inserts. Do not stagger springs.

Countergear

1. Referring to Fig. 6-11, and with unit disassembled, coat bore in each end of countergear with grease.
2. Hold a suitable dummy shaft in gear and insert 21 rollers and a retainer washer in each end of gear.

Reverse Idler Gear

1. With unit disassembled, Fig. 6-12, coat bore at each end of gear with grease.
2. Hold a suitable dummy shaft in gear and insert 22 rollers and retainer

Fig. 6-6 Removing reverse idler gear shaft

washer at each end of gear.

3. Install sliding gear on reverse idler gear, making sure that shift fork groove is toward front.

REASSEMBLE TRANS.

Countergear

1. Coat countergear thrust surfaces in case with a film of grease and position a thrust washer at each end of case.
2. Place assembled countergear in case.

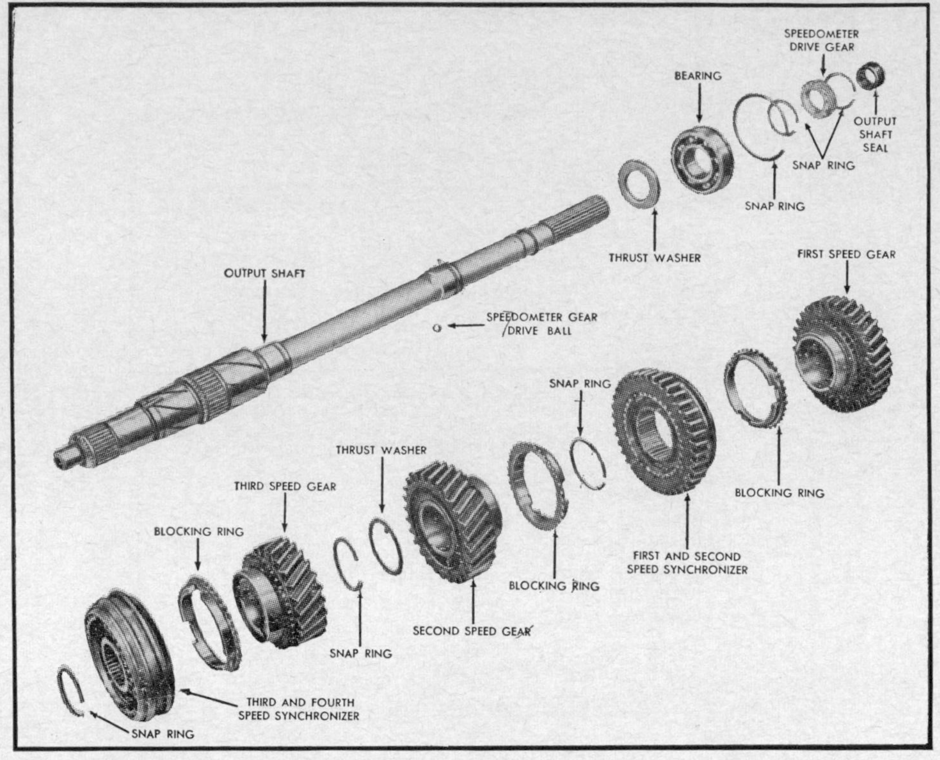

Fig. 6-7 Output shaft disassembled

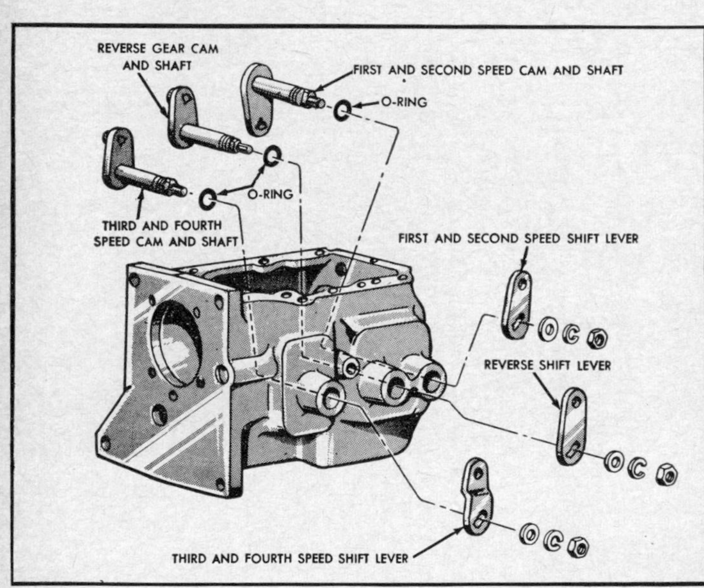

Fig. 6-8 Cam and shafts and levers disassembled

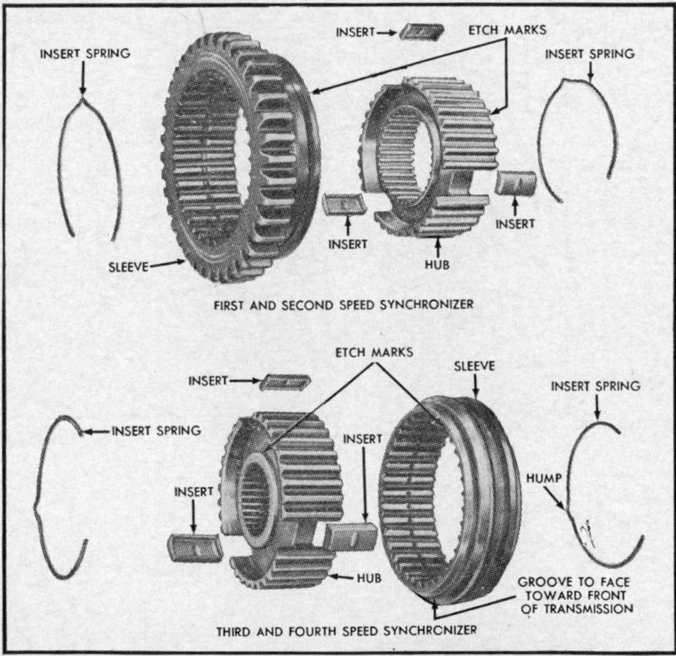

Fig. 6-10 Synchronizers disassembled

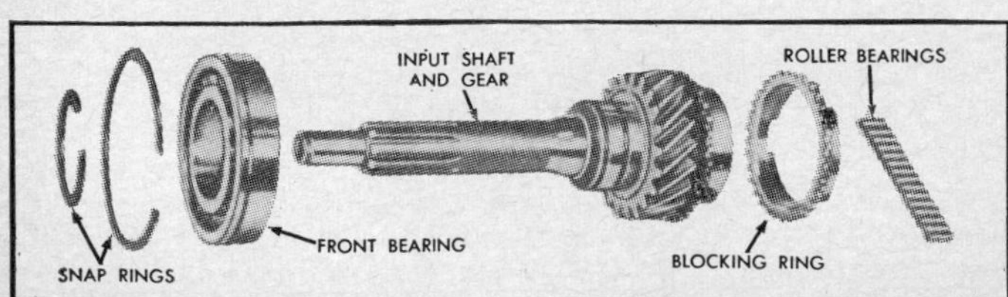

Fig. 6-9 Input shaft gear disassembled

3. With case in a vertical position, align gear bore and thrust washers with bores in case and install countershaft.
4. With case in horizontal position, check countergear end play with a feeler gauge. If not within limits of .004″ to .018″, install new thrust washers.

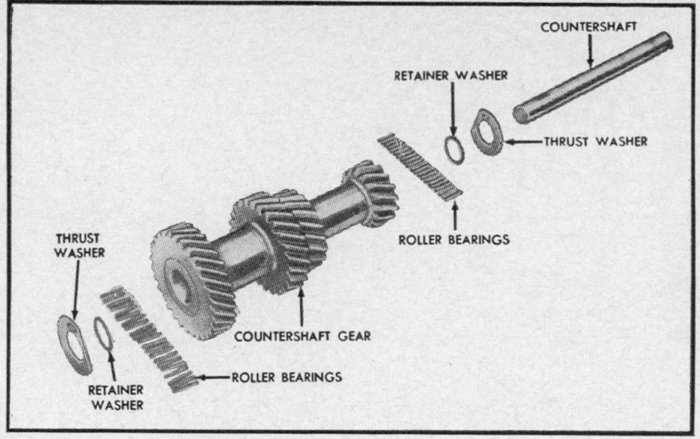

Fig. 6-11 Countergear disassembled

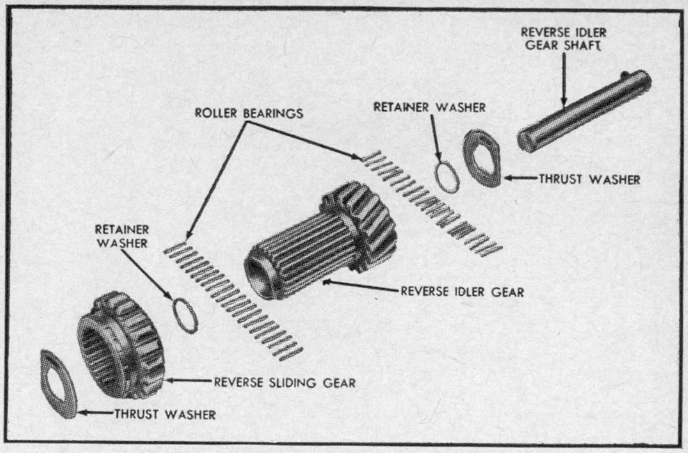

Fig. 6-12 Reverse idler gear disassembled

5. After establishing correct end play, install dummy shaft in countergear and allow gear to remain in bottom of case.

Reverse Gearing

1. Coat gear thrust surfaces in case with a film of grease and position two thrust washers in place, Fig. 6-12.
2. Position idler gear, sliding gear, dummy shaft and roller bearings in place, making sure that shift fork groove in sliding gear is toward front of case.
3. Align gear bore and thrust washers with case bores and install reverse idler shaft.
4. Measure reverse idler gear end play with feeler gauge. If not within the limits of .004″ to .018″, install new thrust washers.
5. Position reverse gear shift rail detent spring and plug in case. Hold reverse shift fork in place on sliding gear and install shift rail from rear of case. Secure fork to rail with set screw.

Output Shaft

1. Referring to Fig. 6-7, install 1-2 synchronizer on shaft.
2. Slide 2nd gear onto front of shaft with synchronizer coned surface facing to rear.
3. Install 2nd gear thrust washer and snap ring.
4. Slide 3rd gear on shaft with synchronizer coned surface to front.
5. Coat coned surface of 3rd gear with grease and place blocking ring on gear.
6. Slide 3-4 synchronizer onto shaft making sure inserts in synchronizer engage notches in blocking ring. Install snap ring on front of shaft.
7. Coat coned surface of 2nd gear with grease and place blocking ring on gear.
8. Slide 1-2 synchronizer on rear of shaft, making sure that inserts engage notches in blocking ring and that shift fork groove is toward rear.
9. Coat coned surface of 1st gear with grease and place blocking ring on it.
10. Slide 1st gear onto rear of shaft, making sure notches in blocking ring engage synchronizer inserts.
11. Install thrust washer on rear of shaft and lower output shaft assembly into case, Fig. 6-4.

Shift Rails & Forks

1. Referring to Fig. 6-2, position 1-2 shift fork and 3-4 shift fork in place on their respective gears and rotate them in place.
2. Place detent plug in its bore and place reverse shift rail into neutral position.
3. Coat 3-4 shift rail interlock pin with grease and place it in shift rail.
4. Align 3-4 shift fork with shift rail bores and slide rail into place, making sure three detents are facing outside of case.
5. Place front synchronizer into 3rd gear position and install set screw in 3-4 shift fork. Move synchronizer to neutral position. Install 3-4 rail detent plug, spring and bolt in left side of case. Place interlock plug (tapered ends) in detent bore.
6. Align 1-2 shift fork with case bores and slide shift rail into place. Secure fork with set screw. Install detent plug and spring in detent bore. Thread set screw into case until its head is flush with case.

Final Assembly

1. Coat input gear bore with just enough grease to hold roller bearings in place, then install 15 roller bearings.
2. Install input gear in case, making sure output shaft pilot enters roller bearings in input gear.
3. Stick a new gasket on input shaft bearing retainer. Dip attaching bolts in sealing compound and install and tighten.
4. Install output shaft bearing and secure with snap ring.
5. Put speedometer gear ball in output shaft and slide gear into place. Secure gear with snap ring.
6. With transmission in vertical position, align countergear bore and thrust washers with bore in case and install countershaft.
7. Use a new gasket and secure extension housing to case. Use sealing compound on attaching screws.
8. Poor specified gear lube over entire gear train while rotating output shaft. Then install cover and shift linkage and adjust as outlined in the car chapters.

Type 7 Corvair

A great deal of similarity and interchangeability exists between this transmission, Fig. 1, and the Type 14 Corvair three-speed transmission shown before. Therefore, the following material deals only with the differences in service between the 3 and 4 speed units. Other 4 speed service procedures are similar to the 3 speed unit and are not repeated here.

Mainshaft Assembly

Assembly procedures described for the Type 14 Corvair 3 speed transmission also apply to this transmission. However, the synchronizer assembly at the front of the mainshaft is used for the 3rd and 4th rather than the 2-3 shift. The synchronizer assembly at the rear of the mainshaft is used for the 1st and 2nd rather than the 1st and reverse shifts. Gear teeth cut in the 1st and 2nd synchronizer sleeve distinguish it from the 3rd and 4th synchronizer sleeve.

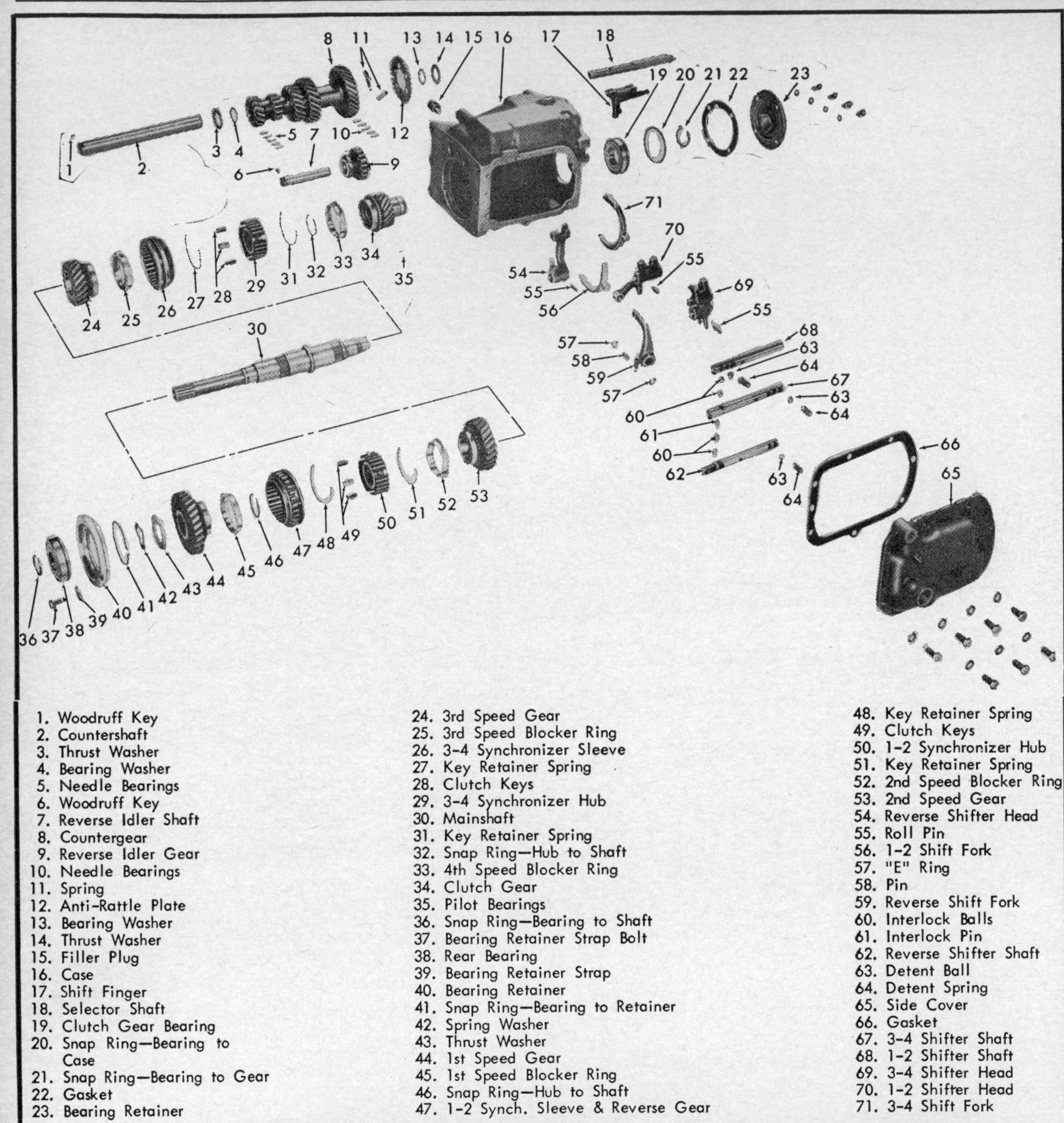

Type 7 Corvair four speed transmission

All parts except the gears and the 1st and 2nd synchronizer sleeve in this 4 speed transmission mainshaft assembly are also used in the Type 14 Corvair 3 speed mainshaft assembly. However, starting from the front, gears on the mainshaft are 3rd, 2nd and 1st rather than 2nd, 1st and reverse. A fourth blocker ring is used between the 1-2 synchronizer assembly and 1st gear on the 4 speed transmission.

Reverse Idler Gear Parts

There is a sliding reverse idler gear and shaft retained by a woodruff key. Elimination of the thrust washer between the gear and case, and removal of the snap ring groove to allow movement of the reverse idler gear, distinguishes this shaft from the 3 speed transmission reverse idler shaft. Otherwise service procedures are the same as for the 3 speed transmission.

AUTOMATIC TRANSMISSIONS

NOTE: — This chapter deals only with maintenance, adjustments and "in car" repairs. For major service work, Motor's Automatic Transmission Manual is available. Current edition is a 740 page volume that includes 240 pages of oil circuit diagrams mostly in full color.

INDEX

NOTE: For 1969 linkage adjustment information, see car chapters.

CHRYSLER UNITS

Torqueflite with Aluminum Case 1-382

FORD UNITS

C4 Dual Range Automatic 1-390
C6 Dual Range Automatic 1-395
Cruise-O-Matic 1-407
Ford-O-Matic Three-Speed Unit 1-407
Ford-O-Matic Two-Speed Unit 1-401
Lincoln Turbo-Drive 1-407
Merc-O-Matic Three-Speed Unit 1-407
Merc-O-Matic Two-Speed Unit 1-401

GENERAL MOTORS UNITS

Buick Special Dual Path Drive 1-344
Buick Super Turbine "400" 1-322
Buick Super Turbine "300" 1-353
Buick Twin Turbine Transmission 1-339
Cadillac Eldorado Turbo Hydra-Matic 1-332
Chevrolet Powerglide with Aluminum Case 1-376
Chevrolet Torque-Drive 1-352
Corvair Powerglide 1-371
Dual Coupling Hydra-Matic 1-346
Oldsmobile F-85 Hydra-Matic 1-364
Oldsmobile Jetaway, 1964-68 1-353
Olds Toronado Turbo Hydra-Matic 1-332
Pontiac Tempestorque, 1963 1-367
Pontiac Automatic Transmission, 1964-68 1-353
Roto Hydra-Matic 375 1-359
Turbo Hydra-Matic 1-322

MISCELLANEOUS

Jeep Automatic Transmission 1-413
Rambler Flash-O-Matic 1-413

HOW TO PUSH AND TOW AUTOMATIC DRIVE CARS—Inside Back Cover

BUICK SUPER TURBINE "400" & GM TURBO HYDRA-MATIC

NOTE: — This chapter deals only with maintenance, adjustments and "in car" repairs. For major service work, Motor's Automatic Transmission Manual is available. Current edition is a 740 page volume that includes 240 pages of oil circuit diagrams mostly in full color.

TRANSMISSION IDENTIFICATION

An identification plate is attached to the transmission. The plate indicates year of production, code letters, and serial number.

BUICK	CODE
1964 LeSabre, V8-300	BU
V8-401 with Column Shift	BJ
V8-401 with Console Shift	BK
V8-425 with Column Shift	BL
V8-425 with Console Shift	BN
V8-425 Two Carbs., Column	BP
V8-425 Two Carbs., Console	BQ
1965 LeSabre, V8-300	BU
V8-401 with 3.07 Axle	BJ
V8-401 with 3.23 Axle	BR
V8-425 with 3.07 Axle	BN
V8-425 with 3.23 Axle	BT
V8-425 Two Carbs, 3.07 Axle	BQ
V8-425 Two Carbs, 3.42 Axle	BS
1966 V8-401	BR
V8-425 Wildcat, Riviera, G.S.	BS
V8-425 Exc. Above, V8-430	BT
V8-400 G.S. 400	BA
V8-340 Sport Wagon 400	BW
V8-340 LeSabre	BU
1967 V8-430 Wildcat, Electra, Riviera	BT
V8-400 G. S. 400	BA
V8-430 Sport Wagon 400	BW
V8-340 LeSabre 400	BU
1968 V8-430 Wildcat, Electra, Riviera	BT
V8-400 G.S. 400	BA
V8-400 Sport Wagon 400	BW
V8-350 Le Sabre	BU

CADILLAC	
1964 Series 60, 63 & Convertible	CD
1965-67 75 Sedan & Limousine	AC
Commercial Chassis	AB
All Others	AA
1968 75 and Commercial Chassis	AB
All Others	AA

CHEVROLET	
1965	A
1966 V8-396	CA
V8-427	CB
1967-68 V8-396 Chevrolet	A
V8-427	B
V8-396 Chevelle, Camaro	C
V8-327	D
1968 V8-396 High Performance	E
V8-396	H
V8-327 Corvette	K
V8-327 Except Corvette	L

OLDSMOBILE	
1965 Two-Bar. Carb, Hi Comp	OA
Four-Bar. Carb.	OB
Two-Bar. Carb, Lo Comp	OC
Heavy Duty Unit	OE
1966 Standard Unit	OB
Ultra Hi Perf. Engine	OD
Jetstar 88	OF
Heavy Duty Unit	OE
1967 Vista Cruiser	OA
Senior Models 2 & 4 Bar. Carbs.	OB
Senior Models with Low Comp. Eng.	OC
Starfire Engine	OD
Heavy Duty Transmission	OE
Delmont 88	OF
F-85 with V8-400 and 4 Bar. Carb.	OG
F-85 with V8-400 and 2 Bar. Carb.	OH
1968 V8-400 with 2 Barrel Carburetor	OG
V8-400 with 4 Barrel Carburetor	OH
Vista Cruiser except V8-400	OA
Vista Cruiser with V8-400	OP
V8-350	OF
V8-455 with 2 Barrel Carburetor	OC
V8-455 with 4 Barrel Carburetor	OB

PONTIAC	
1965-66 With 3 Carburetors	PA
With V8-389	PB
With V8-421	PC
Heavy Duty Unit	PH
V8-421 Except 2+2	PG
1967 V8-400 2 Bar. Carb	PB
V8-428 4 Bar. Carb	PC
V8-400 4 Bar. Carb	PD
V8-400 4 Bar. Carb. (GP)	PG
V8-400 for Heavy Duty	PH
GTO V8-400 4 Bar. Carb	PS
GTO V8-400 2 Bar. Carb	PT
1968 V8-428 with Single Exhaust	PA
V8-400 with 2 Barrel Carburetor	PB
V8-428 with 4 Bar. Carb. and High Perf.	PC
V8-400 with 4 Bar. Carb. (Grand Prix)	PG
V8-400, 428 Heavy Duty	PH
V8-400 Ram Air (GTO, Firebird)	PQ
V8-400 with 2 Bar. Carb. (GTO)	PT
V8-400 with 4 Bar. Carb. (GTO, Firebird)	PX
V8-400 with 4 Bar. Carb. (Firebird with A/C)	PY

JEEP WAGONEER	
1966-68	

BUICK SUPER TURBINE "400" & GM TURBO HYDRA-MATIC

GENERAL DESCRIPTION

This transmission, Fig. 1, is a fully automatic unit consisting primarily of a three-element hydraulic torque converter and a compound planetary gear set. Three multiple-disc clutches, two one-way clutches, and two bands provide the friction elements required to obtain the desired functions of the planetary gear set.

NOTE: On early units, the two one-way clutches mentioned above consist of an intermediate sprag and a low sprag. In late 1965 a roller clutch was substituted for the low sprag.

The torque converter, the multiple-disc clutches and the one-way clutches couple the engine to the planetary gears through oil pressure, providing three forward speeds and reverse. The torque converter, when required, supplements the gears by multiplying engine torque.

Torque Converter

The torque converter is of welded construction and is serviced as an assembly. The unit is made up of two vaned sections, or halves, that face each other in an oil-filled housing. The pump half of the converter is connected to the engine and the turbine half is connected to the transmission.

When the engine makes the converter pump revolve, it sends oil against the turbine, making it revolve also. The oil then returns in a circular flow back to the converter pump, continuing this flow as long as the engine is running.

Stator

The converter also has a smaller vaned section, called a stator, that funnels the oil back to the converter pump through smaller openings, at increased speed. The speeded up oil directs additional force to the engine-driven converter pump, thereby multiplying engine torque. In other words, without the stator, the unit is nothing more than a fluid coupling.

The stator assembly in some transmissions is a variable pitch unit. The stator blades are operated at either of two positions: maximum or high angle, and minimum or low angle.

Maximum or high angle means greater redirection of the oil and increased engine speed, and torque multiplication for maximum performance. At engine idle, it reduces the converter's efficiency, reducing "creep". Minimum or low angle results in a more efficient converter for cruising operation.

External Controls

The external control connections to the transmission are:

1. Manual linkage to select the desired operating range.
2. Engine vacuum to operate the vacuum modulator unit.
3. An electrical signal to operate an electric detent solenoid.
4. A stator solenoid (to 1967) to "switch the pitch" or stator angle. *This device is used only with transmissions having a variable pitch stator.*

Vacuum Modulator

A vacuum modulator is used to sense engine torque input to the transmission automatically. The vacuum modulator transmits this signal to the pressure regulator, which controls line pressure, so that all torque requirements of the transmission are met and proper shift spacing is obtained at all throttle openings.

Detent Solenoid

The detent solenoid is activated by an

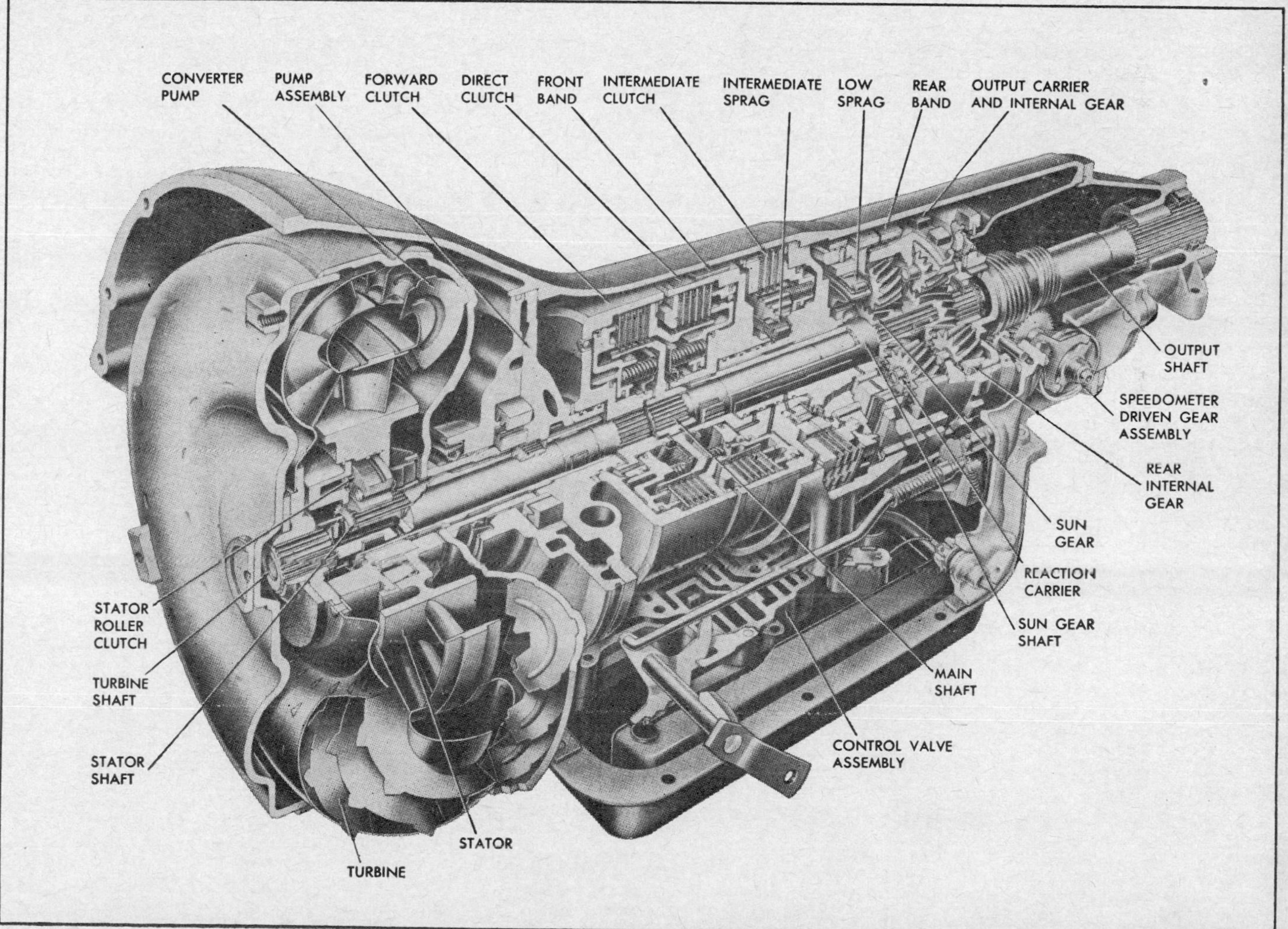

Fig. 1 Cutaway view of transmission assembly

electric switch at the carburetor. When the throttle is opened sufficiently to close this switch, the solenoid in the transmission is activated, causing a downshift at speeds below 70 mph. At lower speeds, downshifts will occur at lesser throttle openings without use of the electric switch.

Stator Solenoid

Used only with 1965-67 transmissioons having the variable pitch stator, the solenoid is activated in several ways:

On 1965-67 Buick and Oldsmobile, the solenoid is activated by a signal from a switch on the carburetor linkage at idle speed which changes the stator blade angle from low to high. It is also energized at 40° and over of carburetor opening (48° on Buick) by a switch on the throttle linkage to change the blade angle from low to high.

On 1965 Cadillac, the solenoid is activated by a signal from a switch at the carburetor, a relay at the radiator cradle, and a switch in the speedometer. The stator relay and speedometer switch change the stator blade from low to high below a speed of about 6 mph. The switch on the carburetor changes the blade angle from low to high at 40° throttle opening.

On 1966-67 Cadillac, the stator solenoid is activated by a signal from a switch at the carburetor or by the brake light switch. The brake light switch changes the blade angle from low to high whenever the brake pedal is applied. The switch at the carburetor changes the angle from low to high above 40° throttle opening.

TROUBLE SHOOTING GUIDE

Oil Pressure High or Low

1. Vacuum line or fittings clogged or leaking.
2. Vacuum modulator.
3. Modulator valve.
4. Pressure regulator.
5. Oil pump.
6. Governor.

No Drive In Drive Range

1. Low oil level (check for leaks).
2. Manual control linkage not adjusted properly.
3. Low oil pressure. Check for blocked strainer, defective pressure regulator, pump assembly or pump drive gear. See that tangs have not been damaged by converter.
4. Check control valve assembly to see if manual valve has been disconnected from manual lever pin.
5. Forward clutch may be stuck or damaged. Check pump feed circuits to forward clutch, including clutch drum ball check.
6. Sprag or roller clutch assembled incorrectly.

1 - 2 Shift At Full Throttle Only

1. Detent switch may be sticking or defective.
2. Detent solenoid may be stuck open, loose or have leaking gasket.
3. Control valve assembly may be leaking, damaged or incorrectly installed.

1st Speed Only - No 1-2 Shift

1. Governor valve may be sticking.
2. Driven gear in governor assembly loose, worn or damaged.
3. The 1-2 shift valve in control valve assembly stuck closed. Check governor feed channels for blocks, leaks, and position. Also check control valve body gaskets for leaks and damage.
4. Intermediate clutch plug in case may be leaking or blown out.
5. Check for porosity between channels and for blocked governor feed channels in case.
6. Check intermediate clutch for proper operation.

No 2 - 3 Shift - 1st & 2nd Only

1. Detent solenoid may be stuck open.
2. Detent switch may not be properly adjusted.
3. Control valve assembly may be stuck, leaking, damaged, or incorrectly installed.
4. Check direct clutch case center support for broken, leaking or missing oil rings.
5. Check clutch piston seals and piston ball check in clutch assembly.

Moves Forward In Neutral

1. Manual control linkage improperly adjusted.
2. Forward clutch does not release.

No Drive In Reverse or Slips In Reverse

1. Check oil level.
2. Manual control linkage improperly adjusted.
3. Vacuum modulator assembly may be defective.
4. Vacuum modulator valve sticking.
5. Strainer may be restricted or leaking at intake.
6. Regulator or boost valve in pump assembly may be sticking.
7. Control valve assembly may be stuck, leaking or damaged.
8. Rear servo and accumulator may have damaged or missing servo piston seal ring.
9. Reverse band burned out or damaged. Determine that apply pin or anchor pins engage properly.
10. Direct clutch may be damaged or may have stuck ball check in piston.
11. Forward clutch does not release.
12. Low-reverse ball check missing from case.

Slips In All Ranges & On Starts

1. Check oil level.
2. Vacuum modulator defective.
3. Modulator valve sticking.
4. Strainer assembly plugged or leaking at neck.
5. Pump assembly regulator or boost valve sticking.
6. Leaks from damaged gaskets or cross leaks from porosity of case.
7. Forward and direct clutches burned.

Slips 1 - 2 Shift

1. Incorrect oil level.
2. Vacuum modulator valve sticking.
3. Vacuum modulator defective.
4. Pump pressure regulator valve defective.
5. Porosity between channels in case.
6. Control valve assembly.
7. Pump-to-case gasket may be mispositioned.
8. Intermediate clutch plug in case may be missing or leaking excessively.
9. Intermediate clutch piston seal missing or damaged.
10. Intermediate clutch plates burned.
11. Front or rear accumulator oil ring may be damaged.

Slips 2 - 3 Shift

1. Items 1 through 6 under Slips 1-2 Shift will also cause 2-3 shift slips.
2. Direct clutch plates burned.
3. Oil seal rings on direct clutch may be damaged permitting excessive leaking between tower and bushing.

Rough 1 - 2 Shift

1. Modulator valve sticking.
2. Modulator assembly defective.
3. Pump pressure regulator or boost valve stuck or inoperative.
4. Control valve assembly loosened from case, damaged or mounted with wrong gaskets.
5. Intermediate clutch ball missing or not sealing.
6. Porosity between channels in case.
7. Rear servo accumulator assembly may have oil rings damaged, stuck piston, broken or missing spring or damaged bore.

Rough 2 - 3 Shift

1. Items 1, 2 and 3 under Rough 1-2 Shift will also cause rough 2-3 shift.
2. Front servo accumulator spring broken or missing. Accumulator piston may be sticking.

No Engine Braking In Second Speed

1. Front servo or accumulator oil rings may be leaking.
2. Front band may be broken or burned out.
3. Front band not engaged on anchor pin and/or servo pin.

No Engine Braking In Low Range

1. Low-reverse check ball may be missing from control valve assembly.
2. Rear servo may have damaged oil seal ring, bore or piston; leaking, apply pressure.
3. Rear band broken, burned out or not engaged on anchor pins or servo pin.

No Part Throttle Downshifts

1. Vacuum modulator assembly.
2. Modulator valve.
3. Regulator valve train.
4. Control valve assembly has stuck 3-2 valve or broken spring.

No Detent Downshifts

1. Detent switch needs fuse, connections tightened or adjustment.
2. Detent solenoid may be inoperative.
3. Detent valve train in control valve assembly malfunctioning.

Low or High Shift Points

1. Oil pressure. Check vacuum modu-

lator assembly, vacuum line connections, modulator valve, and pressure regulator valve train.
2. Governor may have sticking valve or feed holes that are leaking, plugged or damaged.
3. Detent solenoid may be stuck open or loose.
4. Control valve assembly. Check detent, 3-2, and 1-2 shift valve trains, and check spacer plate gaskets for positioning.
5. Check case for porosity, missing or leaking intermediate plug.

Won't Hold In Park

1. Manual control linkage improperly adjusted.
2. Internal linkage defective; check for chamfer on actuator rod sleeve.
3. Parking pawl broken or inoperative.

Excessive Creep At Idle

NOTE: Transmissions having the variable pitch stator.

1. High idle speed.
2. Stator switch inoperative or defective.
3. Stator solenoid defective.
4. Pump may have stator valve train stuck.
5. Pump lead wires disconnected or grounded out.
6. Pump feed circuit to stator may be restricted or blocked.
7. Converter out check valve may be broken or stuck.
8. Turbine shaft may have defective oil seal ring.
9. Stator orifice plug in case may be blocked.
10. Converter assembly defective.

Poor Performance - ¾ Throttle

NOTE: Transmissions having the variable pitch stator.

1. Stator and detent switch inoperative.
2. Items 3 through 10 above will also cause poor performance at ¾ throttle.

Noisy Transmission

1. Pump noises caused by high or low oil level.
2. Cavitation due to plugged strainer, porosity in intake circuit or water in oil.
3. Pump gears may be damaged.
4. Gear noise in low gear of Drive Range - transmission grounded to body.
5. Defective planetary gear set.
6. Clutch noises during application can be worn or burned clutch plates.

MAINTENANCE

Checking & Adding Fluid

Fluid level should be checked at every engine oil change. The full ("F") and "ADD" marks on the transmission dipstick are one pint apart and determine the correct fluid level at normal operating temperature (170°F.). *Careful attention to transmission oil temperature is necessary as proper fluid level at low operating temperatures will be below the "ADD" mark on the dipstick. Proper fluid level at higher operating temperatures will rise above the "F" mark.*

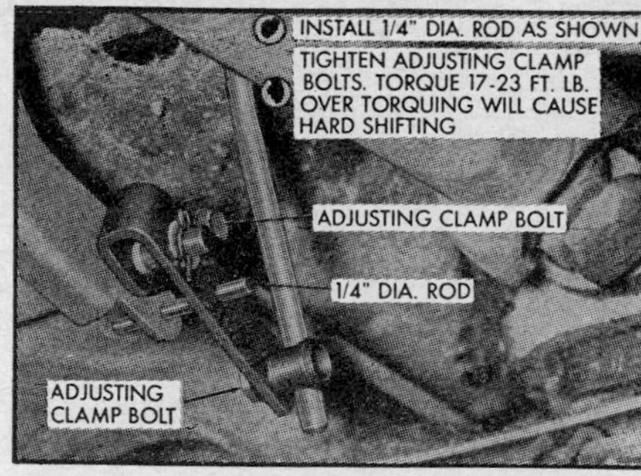

Fig. 2 Manual linkage adjustment. Buick Wildcat and Riviera 1964-68

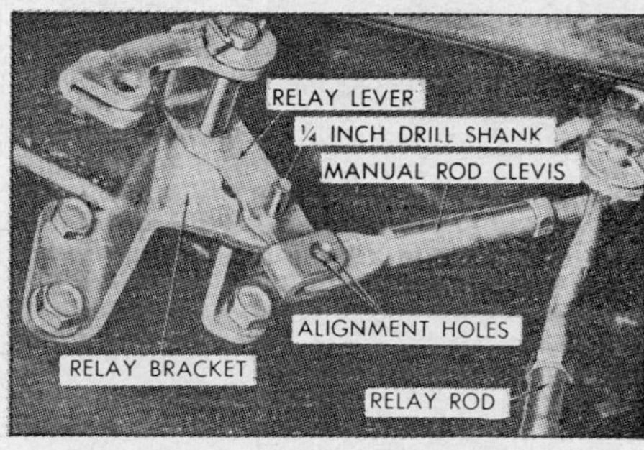

Fig. 3 Manual linkage adjustment. Cadillac 1964 and Fleetwood 1965

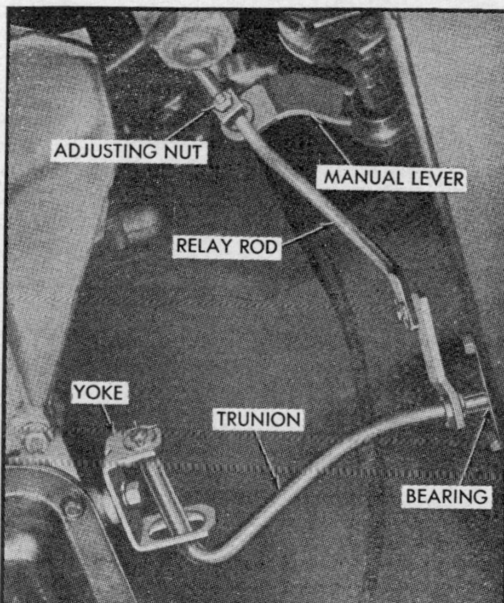

Fig. 4 Manual linkage adjustment. Cadillac 1965-68 (except '65 Fleetwood)

Fluid level must always be checked with the car on a level surface, and with the engine running to make certain the converter is full. To determine proper fluid level, proceed as follows:

1. Operate engine at a fast idle for about 1½ minutes with selector lever in park ("P") position.
2. Reduce engine speed to slow idle and check fluid level.
3. With engine running, add fluid as required to bring it to the proper level.

CAUTION: Do not overfill as foaming might occur when the fluid heats up. If fluid level is too low, especially when cold, complete loss of drive may result after quick stops. Extremely low fluid level will result in damage to transmission.

Draining Bottom Pan Only

1. Disconnect filler tube at bottom pan and allow fluid to drain. Remove and discard filler tube O-ring.
2. Use a new O-ring on filler tube and install tube on pan.
3. Lower car and add three quarts of transmission fluid through filler tube when replacing intake pipe and strainer assembly. When just draining bottom pan, add only two quarts.
4. Operate engine at a fast idle for about 1½ minutes with selector lever in park ("P") position.
5. Reduce engine speed to slow idle and check fluid level. Then add fluid as required to bring it to the proper level.

Adding Fluid to Fill Dry Transmission and Converter

1. Add seven quarts of fluid through filler tube.
2. Operate engine at a fast idle for about 1½ minutes with selector lever in park ("P") position.
3. Reduce engine speed to slow idle and add three more quarts of fluid.
4. Check fluid level and add as required to bring it to the proper level.

MANUAL LINKAGE, ADJUST

1967-68 Buick

1. Loosen trunnion nut (1968) or adjusting clamp bolt (1967).
2. Set selector lever against Drive stop.
3. Place transmission in Drive.
4. Tighten trunnion nut to 6-9 ft-lbs (1968) or adjusting clamp bolt to 17-23 ft-lbs (1967).

Column Shift, Senior Models

1. Loosen adjusting clamp bolt.
2. Place control lever against Drive stop.
3. Place selector lever in Drive.
4. Tighten clamp bolt to 17-23 ft-lbs.

Console Shift, Wildcat & Riviera

1. Place selector lever in Park.
2. Loosen adjusting clamp bolt.
3. Place transmission in Park.
4. Adjust as directed in Fig. 2.

Buick 1964-66

Wildcat (console)

1. Place selector lever in Park and loosen adjusting clamp bolt.
2. Place transmission in Park.
3. Adjust as directed in Fig. 2.

All Other Models

1. Place selector lever in Park and loosen adjusting strap bolt.

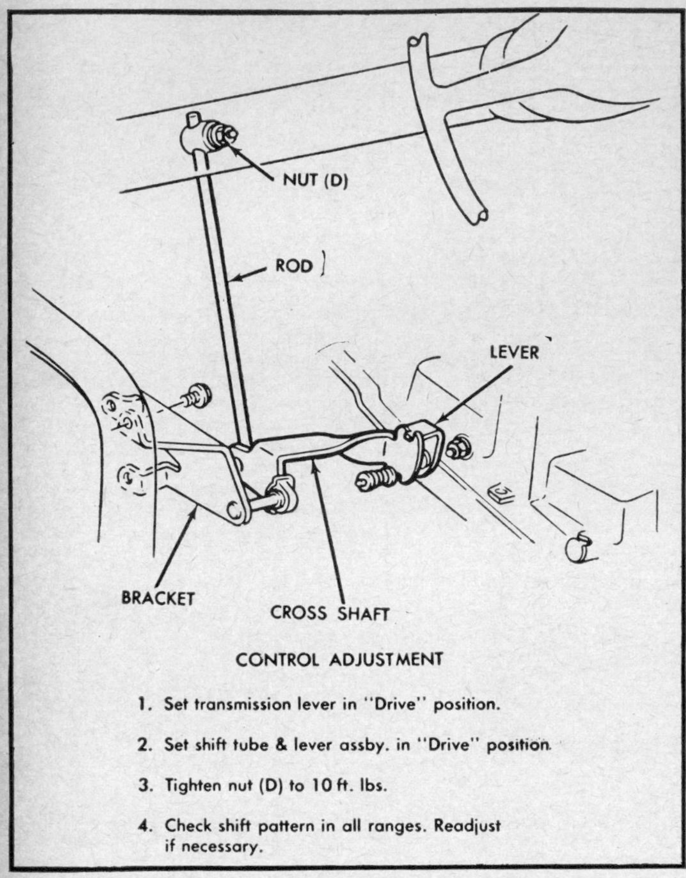

NUT (D)
ROD
LEVER
BRACKET
CROSS SHAFT
CONTROL ADJUSTMENT
1. Set transmission lever in "Drive" position.
2. Set shift tube & lever assby. in "Drive" position.
3. Tighten nut (D) to 10 ft. lbs.
4. Check shift pattern in all ranges. Readjust if necessary.

Fig. 5 Manual linkage adjustment. Chevrolet 1965-68 column shift

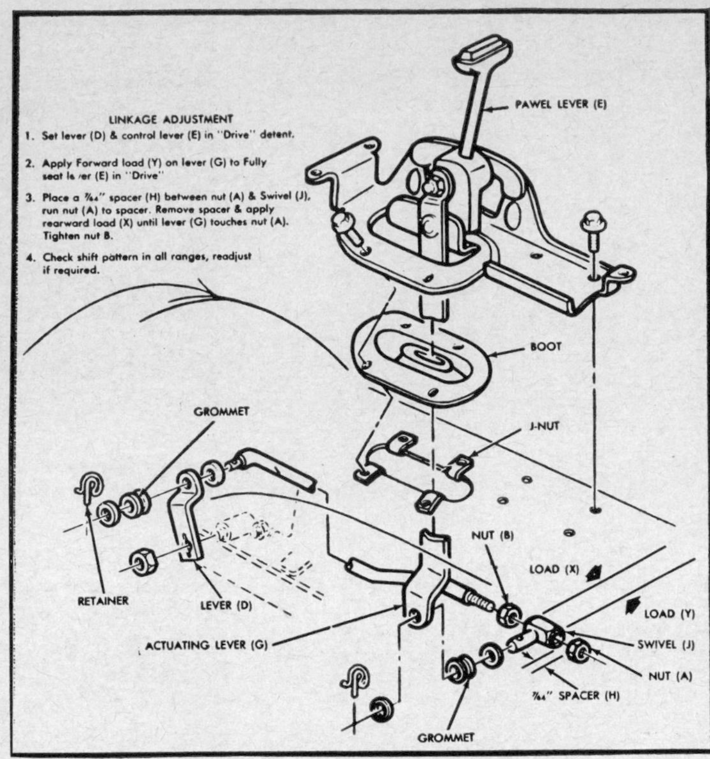

2. Apply Forward load (Y) on lever (G) to Fully seat lever (E) in "Drive"
3. Place a 7/64" spacer (H) between nut (A) & Swivel (J), run nut (A) to spacer. Remove spacer & apply rearward load (X) until lever (G) touches nut (A). Tighten nut B.

ACTUATING LEVER (G)

Fig. 6 Manual linkage adjustment. Chevrolet 1965-67 console shift

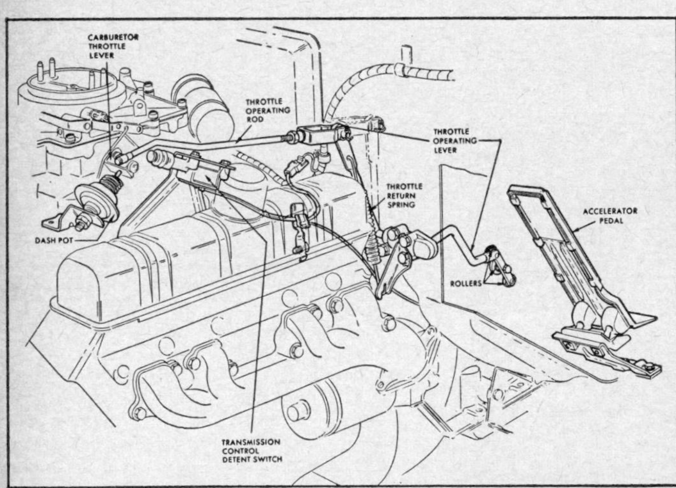

Fig. 8 Throttle linkage adjustment. Buick 1964

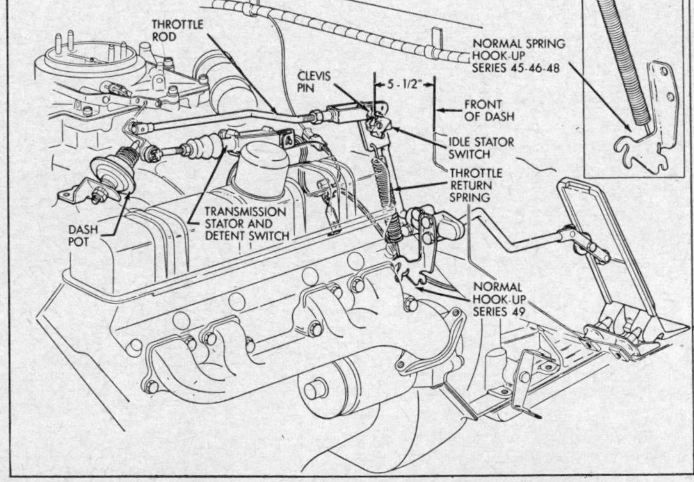

Fig. 7 Throttle linkage adjustment. Buick 1965-67

2. Place transmission in Park.
3. Tighten swivel clamp bolt at transmission to 17-23 ft-lbs.

Cadillac 1964 & Fleetwood 1965

CAUTION: Do not attempt to align shift indicator pointer by changing adjustment of manual linkage. Manual linkage must be properly adjusted first, and then, if necessary, align indicator pointer.

1. Referring to Fig. 3, disconnect relay rod from relay lever.
2. Disconnect manual rod from relay lever.
3. Place manual lever on transmission in Drive position.
4. Align gauging hole in relay lever with gauging hole in relay bracket and insert a ¼" drill through holes.
5. Adjust length of relay rod until hole in clevis lines up with hole in relay lever.
6. Install relay rod on relay lever and tighten locknut.
7. Place selector lever on steering column in Drive position against stop.
8. Adjust length of manual rod until hole in clevis lines with hole in relay lever.
9. Connect manual rod to relay lever and tighten locknut.
10. Remove gauging drill from gauging holes and check operation of selector lever. It should be free to enter Park position.
11. Make certain indicator pointer in-

dexes in Drive position when selector lever is at Drive stop. Align if necessary.

1965-68 Cadillac Except 1965 Fleetwood

1. Referring to Fig. 4, loosen nut on steering column manual lever-to-relay rod clamp.
2. Pull relay rod up to position transmission shift valve in PARK, then push rod down to third (neutral) step.
3. Position selector lever in neutral.
4. Tighten clamp nut. Selector lever should enter all positions and indicator pointer should index correctly.

Chevrolet Line 1965-68

When properly adjusted the following conditions must be met for manual operation of the steering column shift lever, Fig. 5.

1. From reverse to drive position travel the transmission detent feel must be noted and related to indicated position on dial.
2. When in drive and reverse positions, pull lever rearward (toward steering wheel) and then release. It must drop back into position with no restrictions.

Console Shift, Chevrolet Line

On 1965-67 models, adjust shift linkage as outlined in Fig. 6.

On 1968 models, obtain Drive position by moving transmission lever counterclockwise to Low detent, then clockwise two positions for Drive. Secure in this position.

Console Shift, 1968 Corvette

Place selector lever in Drive, then place transmission control lever in Drive position. Install cable and secure with retaining clip and cotter pin.

Jeep

1. Loosen nut on adjusting swivel clamp.
2. Set transmission selector lever in Park.
3. Set shift lever in Park.
4. Tighten nut on adjusting swivel clamp to 6-12 ft-lbs.

Oldsmobile

Column Shift, 1966-68

1. Use enough washers to obtain zero clearance at upper shift lever and shift rod.
2. Set outer shift lever in "D".
3. Loosen swivel bolt.
4. Push up on shift rod until selector lever is against the "D" position stop in upper steering column.
5. Tighten swivel bolt to 20 ft-lbs.
6. Check neutral switch adjustment.

Column Shift, 1965

Set transmission outer shift lever in "D" position. Hold upper shift lever against "D" position stop in upper steering column. Adjust shift rod by means of swivel to maintain adjustment.

Console Shift, 1965-66

1. Place selector lever in "D".
2. Disconnect manual rod from transmission manual lever.

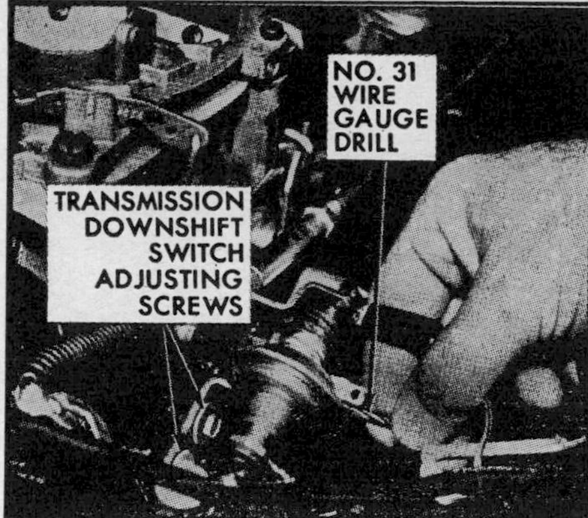

Fig. 9 Downshift switch adjustment. Cadillac 1967

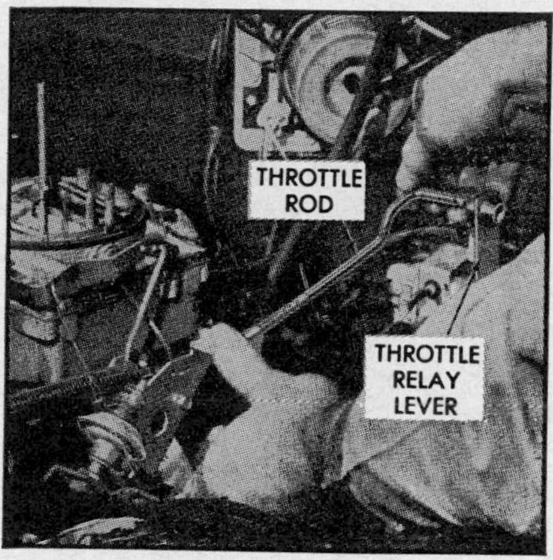

Fig. 10 Throttle linkage adjustment. Cadillac 1965-67

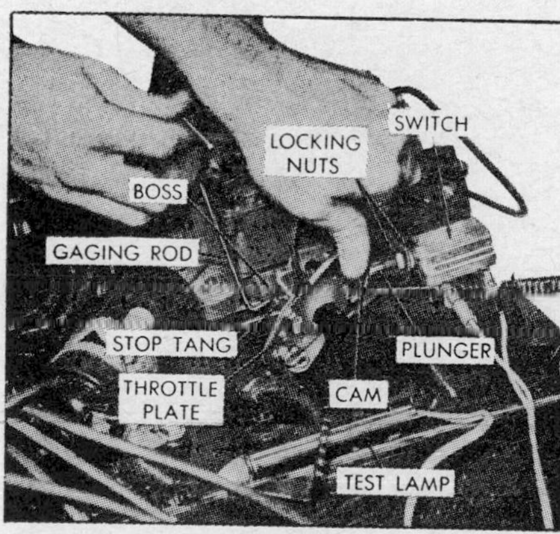

Fig. 11 Downshift switch adjustment Cadillac 1964

3. Place transmission manual lever in "D" detent position.
4. Loosen lock nut on manual rod.
5. With selector lever held against its stop in "D" position and transmission manual lever in "D" detent position, adjust manual rod until it enters transmission manual lever.
6. Shorten manual rod three turns.

Console Shift, 1967

1. Place shift lever in Park.
2. Set transmission outer shift lever in Park position.
3. Set pin to just enter hole in shift cable.
4. Tighten nut and check through all detent positions and recheck adjustment.

Pontiac

Column Shift, 1967-68

1. Loosen screw or nut on adjusting swivel clamp.
2. Set transmission selector lever in Drive detent.

NOTE: Obtain Drive position by rotating transmission lever clockwise to Park position, then counterclockwise three positions to Drive detent.

3. Set upper gearshift lever against Drive stop.
4. Tighten screw in adjusting swivel clamp to 20 ft-lbs (Pontiac and GTO) or tighten nut on adjusting swivel clamp on Firebird to 30 ft-lbs.

Console Shift, 1966-68

1. Disconnect shift cable from transmission selector lever pin.
2. Rotate transmission selector lever clockwise to Park position and adjust pin on selector lever to obtain smooth shifting through all detents.
3. Torque selector pin nut to 30 ft-lbs, set the gearshift lever in Park and connect shift cable to pin.

Column Shift, 1965-66

1. Loosen nut on adjusting swivel clamp.
2. Set transmission selector lever in park detent.
3. Set shift lever in park position.
4. Tighten nut on adjusting swivel.

THROTTLE LINKAGE, ADJUST

Buick

1968

1. Remove air cleaner. Make sure that linkage is free in all positions and that nothing touches or interferes with the linkage. Hold choke open and make sure that return spring fully closes throttle, even though throttle is released very slowly.
2. With throttle linkage in hot curb idle position, measurement from throttle rod pin horizontally to dash must be 6½" on 45-46-48000 Series or 6¼" on Series 49000. If measurement is off, shorten or lengthen throttle rod as required to correct.
3. Operate linkage to open carburetor and make sure carburetor wide open stop is contacting.
4. As a final check, have a helper depress accelerator pedal and check to make sure wide open stop contacts at carburetor.

1965-67

1. Remove air cleaner.
2. Make sure linkage is free in all positions.
3. Hold choke open and make sure that

return spring fully closes throttle, even though throttle is released very slowly.
4. Adjust engine idle speed and mixture.
5. With throttle linkage at hot idle position, measurement from throttle rod clevis pin to dash must be 5½", Fig. 7.
6. If measurement is off, shorten or lengthen operating rod as required.
7. Operate linkage to open carburetor and make sure carburetor wide open stop is contacting. If carburetor does not reach wide open position and nothing is interfering with throttle linkage, transmission stator and detent switch must be adjusted as outlined below.

1964

1. Remove air cleaner.
2. Make sure linkage is free in all positions and that return spring fully closes throttle, even though throttle is released very slowly.
3. Unsnap front end of throttle operating rod from carburetor throttle lever, Fig. 8.
4. While another person presses accelerator pedal against floor mat, hold carburetor throttle lever in wide open position and hold throttle rod socket in alignment with ball on throttle lever. Socket must be approximately $\frac{1}{16}$" (2 turns) short of ball. If adjustment is necessary, loosen lock nut, adjust throttle rod length as required, and tighten lock nut.
5. With accelerator pedal released, reinstall throttle rod on throttle lever. With accelerator pedal depressed again to floor mat, recheck throttle for wide open position.

Cadillac

1967-68

1. Remove air cleaner. Check linkage for free movement in all positions and see that the return spring fully closes the throttle.
2. Remove cotter pin that holds end of throttle rod in relay lever and remove rod from lever.
3. On cars with Cruise Control, detach Cruise Control linkage at its power unit end.
4. While a helper presses accelerator pedal against floor mat, hold carburetor throttle lever in wide open throttle position. Make sure choke valve is wide open.
5. Loosen lock nut and throttle rod end in either direction as necessary to allow free entry into bushing on relay lever.
6. With accelerator pedal released, reinstall washer on throttle rod and install rod into bushing in relay lever.
7. Install other washer and then cotter pin. Recheck for fully closed throttle when accelerator pedal is against floor mat.
8. Install Cruise Control linkage (if equipped). If adjustment on throttle rod was changed, it will be necessary to adjust Cruise Control linkage.

1965-66

1. Remove air cleaner. Check linkage for free movement in all positions,

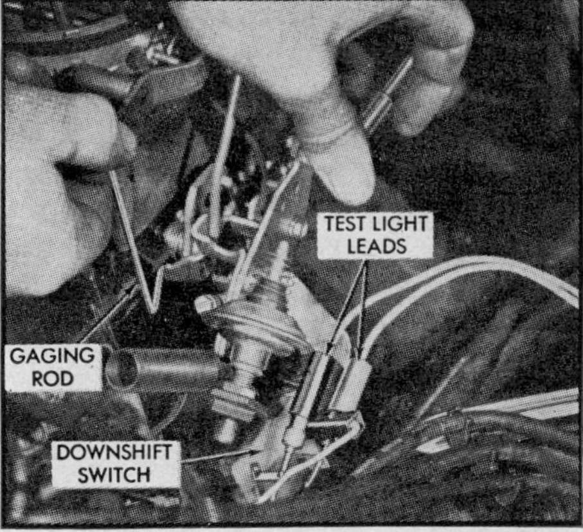

Fig. 12 Downshift switch adjustment. Cadillac 1965

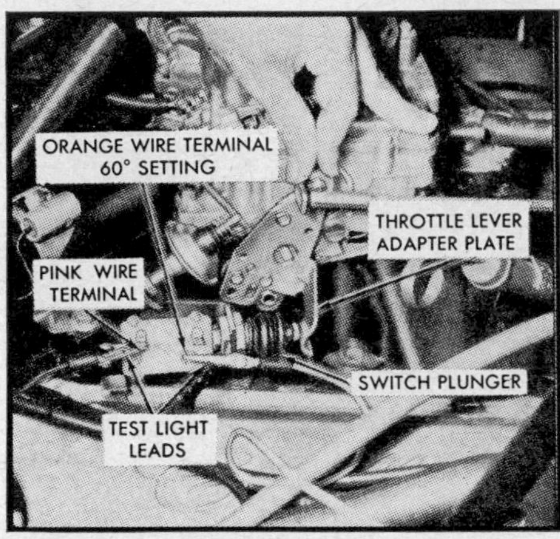

Fig. 13 Downshift switch adjustment. Cadillac 1966

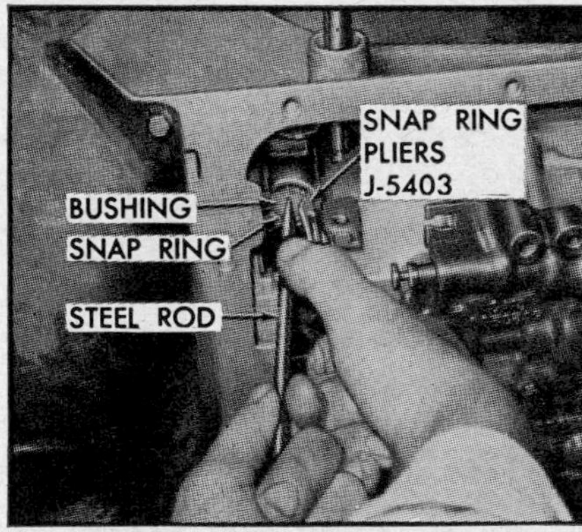

Fig. 14 Removing and installing pressure regulator valve

and check to see that return spring fully closes the throttle.
2. Remove cotter pin that holds end of throttle rod in relay lever and remove washers and rod from lever.
3. If equipped with Cruise Control, detach linkage at Cruise Control power unit end.
4. While a helper presses accelerator pedal to the floor, hold carburetor throttle lever in full throttle (wide open) position. Make sure choke valve is wide open.
5. Turn throttle rod end in either direction as necessary to allow free entry into bushing on relay lever, Fig. 9.
6. With accelerator pedal released, reinstall washer on throttle rod and install rod into bushing in relay lever.
7. Install other washer and then the cotter pin.
8. With accelerator pedal pressed again to floor mat, recheck throttle for wide open position.
9. Install Cruise Control linkage (if equipped) and adjust if necessary.

1964

1. Remove throttle rod trunnion from relay lever bracket lever. If equipped with Cruise Control, the control rod is also detached.
2. Place a ¼" drill shank through gauging hole in dash relay lever and into dash relay bracket.
3. With engine running, set carburetor throttle lever in hot idle position (A/C off). Throttle valves should be seated in bores.
4. Adjust carburetor rod trunnion to allow free entry into dash relay lever.
5. Install washers and cotter pin in trunnion.
6. Install Cruise Control rod and adjust if necessary.

Chevrolet

1968

1. Disconnect throttle rod swivel at throttle lever on carburetor.
2. On Corvette only, hold accelerator pedal to floor against stop. Move carburetor throttle lever to wide open position, then tighten clamp bolt to 45 inch-lbs.
3. Disconnect throttle rod at throttle lever.
4. Hold carburetor throttle wide open, push throttle rod rearward to position accelerator pedal to floor mat and adjust swivel so it just enters hole in throttle lever.
5. Connect swivel to throttle lever and install accelerator return spring.
6. Hold throttle lever in full open position, pull throttle rod to full detent position and adjust rod so it just enters hole in throttle lever.

1965-67

1. Disconnect throttle rod swivel at throttle lever on carburetor.
2. Disconnect TV rod at throttle lever.
3. Hold carburetor throttle valve in wide open position and pull throttle forward to position accelerator pedal at floor mat. Then adjust swivel so it enters hole in throttle lever.
4. Connect swivel to throttle lever and hook up accelerator return spring.
5. Hold throttle rod in full throttle position, push TV rod to full detent position and adjust TV rod to just enter hole in throttle lever. Connect TV rod to throttle lever.

Jeep

With choke valve wide open and accelerator pedal pressed to floor mat throttle valve should be wide open. If it is not, adjust throttle linkage as necessary to obtain this condition.

Oldsmobile

Equalizer Rod, 1965

Disconnect carburetor rod and adjust equalizer rod to obtain $\frac{1}{2}$" clearance between equalizer bracket and dash.

Carburetor Rod, 1966-67

With slow idle properly adjusted and carburetor in slow idle position, engine shut off, transmission stator must be in high angle position (test lamp on). To adjust, lengthen carburetor rod until test goes off. Slowly shorten rod until test lamp just comes on. Then shorten rod two more complete turns and tighten lock nut.

Carburetor Rod, 1965

With carburetor slow idle properly adjusted, adjust carburetor rod so that a $\frac{1}{4}$" diameter pin can be freely inserted through hole in throttle switch lever and bottom of hole in throttle switch boss.

Accelerator Pedal Height

With slow idle and carburetor rod properly adjusted adjust accelerator rod so the distance from pedal lever to floor carpet is $5\frac{1}{16}$".

Throttle Switch, 1965-67

With slow idle, carburetor rod and accelerator pedal height properly adjusted, disconnect carburetor rod and rotate lever until it hits stop. Connect carburetor rod (without moving lever) to wide open throttle position. Depress accelerator pedal through detent and release.

Pontiac

1967-68 Intermediate Models

There are no throttle linkage adjustments. A reference dimension of $1\frac{9}{16}$" between bottom of accelerator pedal roller and floor pan should be used only as a check for bent bracket assemblies.

1967-68 Full Size Models

With carburetor set at hot idle position, line up throttle rod socket with attaching ball stud on carburetor extension lever, turn rod counterclockwise five turns and snap into place.

1965-66

1. Check accelerator pedal height.
2. If necessary, adjust linkage to obtain $4\frac{11}{16}$" between accelerator pedal and floor pan with carburetor set at hot idle speed.
3. Depress accelerator pedal to floor and check to see that carburetor throttle valves are wide open.

DOWNSHIFT SWITCH

1968 Transmission

The detent solenoid is activated by a downshift switch at the carburetor or throttle linkage. When the throttle is opened sufficiently to close this switch the solenoid in the transmission is activated, causing a downshift at speeds below approximately 70 mph. At lower speeds, downshifts will occur at lesser throttle openings without the use of the switch. To adjust, proceed as follows:

Buick

The downshift switch is connected to the throttle linkage. To adjust, fully depress the switch plunger to insure proper setting. Then fully depress the accelerator pedal.

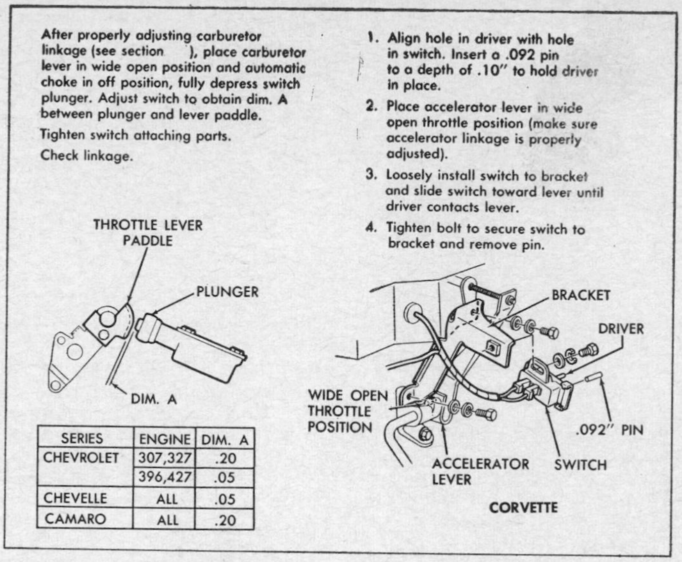

After properly adjusting carburetor linkage (see section), place carburetor lever in wide open position and automatic choke in off position, fully depress switch plunger. Adjust switch to obtain dim. A between plunger and lever paddle.

Tighten switch attaching parts.

Check linkage.

THROTTLE LEVER PADDLE

PLUNGER

DIM. A

SERIES	ENGINE	DIM. A
CHEVROLET	307,327	.20
	396,427	.05
CHEVELLE	ALL	.05
CAMARO	ALL	.20

1. Align hole in driver with hole in switch. Insert a .092 pin to a depth of .10" to hold driver in place.
2. Place accelerator lever in wide open throttle position (make sure accelerator linkage is properly adjusted).
3. Loosely install switch to bracket and slide switch toward lever until driver contacts lever.
4. Tighten bolt to secure switch to bracket and remove pin.

BRACKET

DRIVER

WIDE OPEN THROTTLE POSITION

.092" PIN

ACCELERATOR LEVER

SWITCH

CORVETTE

Fig. 15 Downshift switch adjustment. 1968 Chevrolet Line

Cadillac

1. Remove air cleaner.
2. Make certain that carburetor is adjusted properly and that throttle linkage is at low idle speed setting.
3. If downshift switch is properly adjusted, a No. 31 drill shank can be inserted through the calibrating hole below the wire terminal extending through to carburetor side of switch.
4. If adjustment is necessary, loosen the two 7/16" mounting screws and position switch for proper alignment. Tighten mounting screws and remove drill gauge from calibrating hole in switch.

Chevrolet Line

Refer to Fig. 15 for switch adjustment on the various Chevrolet line of cars equipped with this transmission.

Oldsmobile

Push plunger of downshift switch forward until it is flush with switch housing. Push accelerator pedal to wide open position to set switch.

STATOR & DETENT SWITCHES

Buick

Idle Stator Switch, 1965-67

1. Referring to Fig. 7, adjust switch with throttle at closed position and return spring attached.
2. With attaching screws loose, rotate switch until the switch **stop screw** bottoms against case.
3. Hold screw in this position and tighten attaching screws.

Stator & Detent Switch, 1965-67

1. With carburetor throttle wide open and switch plunger bottomed, adjust link until it will slip over carburetor lever pin.
2. Then screw link into plunger $1\frac{1}{2}$ turns.
3. Install washer and retainer.

1964 Detent Switch

The transmission detent switch is mounted at the full throttle position of the carburetor throttle lever, Fig. 8. When throttle linkage is moved to wide open throttle position, the switch contacts are closed to cause the transmission to downshift.

To adjust detent switch, hold carburetor at wide open throttle and adjust switch plunger so that it is about .050" from bottom.

Cadillac

1967

1. Remove carburetor air cleaner.
2. Make sure that low idle speed is properly adjusted.
3. If downshift switch is properly adjusted, a $\frac{1}{8}$" drill or rod can be inserted through calibrating hole below wire terminal extending through carburetor side of switch, Fig. 9.

NOTE: With this adjustment the stator should break contact $5\frac{1}{2}$° to $7\frac{1}{2}$° from closed hot idle throttle and make contact at 40° throttle. The downshift should make contact above 60° throttle.

4. If adjustment is necessary, loosen the two $\frac{7}{16}$" switch mounting screws and position switch for proper alignment as in Step 3.
5. With switch positioned, tighten mounting screws and remove drill or rod from calibrating hole through switch.

1964-66

1. Remove carburetor air cleaner.
2. Referring to Figs. 10 to 13 disconnect throttle rod from throttle plate and attach spring to fast idle cam

to hold choke open. This will facilitate movement of throttle plate when adjusting switch.
3. Disconnect leads from terminals under switch. Note color code of leads.
4. Connect a test lamp to switch terminals.
5. Loosen front and rear locking nuts that hold switch on mounting bracket.

NOTE: A gauge for adjusting the switch can be made out of an 8" length of 1/8" rod. Bend one end of the rod at a right angle 3/4" from end. Insert angled end of gauge rod between machined boss on carburetor base and wide open throttle stop tang on throttle plate as shown and hold stop tang against rod. This will set primary throttle opening at about 60 degrees, the setting at which switch must energize.

CAUTION: Make certain gauge rod is properly located, otherwise setting of primary throttle opening will be incorrect.

6. Continue to hold stop tang against gauge rod and move switch fore and aft until cam surface on throttle plate depresses switch plunger sufficiently to close circuit and light test lamp.
7. Tighten locknuts securely to prevent loss of adjustment.
8. Recheck adjustment by moving throttle plate stop tang back and forth against gauge rod to make certain switch energizes at proper setting.

NOTE: Make certain switch plunger does not impede wide open throttle. If carburetor will not reach wide open throttle, reposition switch mounting bracket and readjust switch.

9. Remove test lamp and connect electrical leads. Connect throttle rod and return spring to throttle plate. Install air cleaner.

IN CAR REPAIRS

Services outlined in this section can be performed without removing the transmission from the vehicle.

Pressure Regulator Valve

1. Remove bottom pan and strainer.
2. Using a screwdriver or steel rod, compress regulator boost valve bushing against pressure regulator spring, Fig. 14.

CAUTION: Pressure regulator spring is under extreme pressure and will force valve bushing out of bore when snap ring is removed if valve bushing is not held securely.

3. Continue to exert pressure on valve bushing and remove snap ring. Gradually release pressure on valve bushing until spring force is exhausted.
4. Carefully remove regulator boost valve bushing and valve, and pressure regulator spring. Be careful not to drop parts as they will fall out if they are not held.
5. Remove pressure regulator valve and spring retainer. Remove spacers if present.
6. Reverse procedure to install.

Control Valve Body

1. Remove bottom pan and strainer.
2. Remove control valve body attaching screws and detent roller spring assembly. *Do not remove solenoid attaching screws.*
3. Remove control valve body and governor pipes. If care is used in removing control valve body, the six check balls will stay in place above spacer plate.
4. Remove governor pipes and manual valve from control valve body.
5. Reverse procedure to install.

Governor

1. Remove governor cover and discard gasket.
2. Withdraw governor from case.
3. Reverse procedure to install, using a new gasket.

Modulator & Modulator Valve

1. Remove modulator attaching screw and retainer.
2. Remove modulator assembly from case and discard O-ring seal.
3. Remove modulator valve from case.
4. Reverse procedure to install, using a new O-ring seal.

Parking Linkage

1. Remove bottom pan and oil strainer.
2. Unthread jam nut holding detent lever to manual shaft.
3. Remove manual shaft retaining pin from case.
4. Remove manual shaft and jam nut from case.
5. Remove O-ring seal from manual shaft.
6. Remove parking actuator rod and detent lever assembly.
7. Remove parking pawl bracket, pawl return spring and pawl shaft retainer.
8. Remove parking pawl shaft, O-ring seal and parking pawl.
9. Reverse procedure to install, using new seals and gasket.

Rear Seal

1. Remove propeller shaft.
2. Pry out seal with screwdriver.
3. Install new seal with a suitable seal driver.
4. Install propeller shaft.

TRANSMISSION, REPLACE

Buick 1966-68

1. Raise and support front and rear of car.
2. Disconnect front exhaust crossover pipe if necessary. Remove propeller shaft.
3. Place suitable jack under transmission.
4. Remove vacuum line from vacuum modulator.
5. Separate cooler lines from transmission.
6. Remove transmission crossmember.
7. On models to 1967 disconnect stator and detent solenoid wires from transmission. Starting with 1968, stator wire is not used.
8. Disconnect speedometer cable.
9. Disconnect shift linkage from transmission.
10. Remove transmission filler pipe.
11. Support engine at oil pan.
12. Remove flywheel cover pan.
13. Mark flywheel and converter pump for reassembly in same position, then remove three converter pump-to-flywheel bolts.
14. Remove transmission-to-engine bolts.
15. Move transmission rearward to provide clearance between converter pump and crankshaft. Install a suitable holding tool to secure converter. Then lower and remove transmission.
16. Reverse above procedure to install.

Buick 1964-65

1. With front and rear of car supported off floor, disconnect front exhaust pipe bolts at exhaust manifold and at connection of intermediate exhaust pipe location (single exhaust only). On dual exhaust jobs, exhaust pipes need not be removed.
2. Support propeller shaft out of the way to prevent damage to center joint caused by weight of shaft.
3. Support transmission with a jack.
4. Remove vacuum line-to-vacuum modulator hose from modulator.
5. Separate cooler lines from transmission.
6. Remove transmission support crossmember.
7. Disconnect speedometer cable.
8. Loosen shift linkage adjusting swivel clamp nut and remove equalizer from outer range selector lever.
9. Remove transmission filler pipe.
10. Support engine at oil pan.
11. Remove flywheel cover pan.
12. Mark flywheel and converter pump for reassembly in same position.
13. Unfasten converter pump from flywheel (3 bolts) and transmission to engine bolts. Secure converter in place before removing transmission.
14. Move transmission rearward to provide clearance between converter pump and crankshaft. Then lower transmission from vehicle.

Cadillac 1965 Fleetwood & All 1964

1. Disconnect negative battery cable.
2. Raise car on hoist or jack stands.
3. Remove intermediate frame crossmember yaw bumpers.
4. Remove intermediate crossmember.
5. Disconnect relay rod from manual lever.
6. Disconnect manual rod from relay lever. Rotate relay lever upward toward floor pan and wire relay lever and relay rod out of the way to prevent damaging linkage when raising and lowering transmission jack.
7. Remove transmission filler tube bracket screw from exhaust manifold.
8. Remove filler tube from bottom pan and allow fluid to drain.

9. Remove three screws that hold starter to adapter ring. Remove two starter mounting bracket screws at engine oil pan and slide starter forward.
10. Remove transmission case front and lower covers.
11. Disconnect parking brake cable from relay lever.
12. Remove propeller shaft.
13. Remove speedometer cable and disconnect detent switch wire from left side of transmission.
14. Remove three converter-to-flex plate attaching bolts.

NOTE: This is done by inserting a heavy screwdriver in open slot under one of the weld nuts on the converter, and rotating converter and flex plate until bolts can be reached for removal. Do not pry on flex plate ring gear to rotate converter, otherwise flex plate may be damaged.

15. Place jack or other suitable device under rear of engine oil pan. Use a wood block to prevent damage to oil pan.
16. Position transmission jack under transmission and raise it just enough to take load off rear engine support bracket.
17. Remove rear engine mount-to-support bracket screws and plate. Remove shims (if present) between rear cushion and support bracket.
18. Remove support bracket from frame.
19. Disconnect oil cooler pipes at transmission. Cap pipes and plug connector holes in transmission to prevent drainage of fluid. Position oil cooler pipes out of the way.
20. Disconnect vacuum pipe hose from vacuum modulator and position vacuum pipe out of the way.
21. Remove six transmission-to-adapter ring attaching screws. It may be necessary to lower engine and transmission slightly to gain access to upper screws.
22. Move transmission toward rear of car, disengaging transmission case from locating dowels on adapter ring. Install a suitable converter holding clamp and lower transmission from car.
23. Reverse removal procedure to install transmission.

Cadillac 1965-68 Except 1965 Fleetwood

1. Disconnect negative battery cable.
2. Raise car on hoist or place on jack stands.
3. Disconnect relay rod from trunnion lever and wire relay rod up out of the way to prevent damage while removing transmission.
4. Remove two screws and bearing from frame side rail.
5. Disconnect trunnion from manual yoke on left side of transmission.
6. Remove speedometer drive cable and disconnect detent solenoid wire and, on models to 1967, disconnect stator wire.
7. Remove transmission filler tube bracket screw from right exhaust manifold.
8. Remove filler tube from transmission case and plug hole in case.
9. Disconnect oil cooler pipes at transmission. Cap pipes and plug connector holes in transmission. Position cooler pipes out of the way.
10. Disconnect vacuum pipe hose from vacuum modulator and position pipe out of the way.
11. Remove resonator support bracket from extension housing.
12. Remove propeller shaft.
13. Unfasten and remove two starter motor brackets and slide starter forward.
14. Remove lower flywheel housing cover and two engine-to-transmission struts.
15. Remove three converter-to-flex plate screws.

NOTE: This is done by inserting a heavy screwdriver in open slot under one of weld nuts on converter, and rotating converter and flex plate until bolts can be reached for removal. Do not pry on flex plate ring gear to rotate converter as flex plate might be damaged.

16. Support rear of engine.
17. Position jack under transmission and raise it just enough to take load off rear engine support.
18. Remove two rear engine mount-to-extension housing screws.
19. Remove rear engine support (4 bolts).
20. Remove six transmission case-to-engine screws. It may be necessary to lower engine and transmission slightly to gain access to upper screws.
21. Move transmission toward rear, disengaging case from locating dowels on engine. Install a holding clamp on front of case and lower transmission from car.
22. Remove holding clamp and converter from transmission, using care not to drop it as it weighs about 50 pounds.
23. Reverse removal procedure to install transmission assembly.

Chevrolet Line, 1965-68

1. Disconnect battery ground cable and release parking brake.
2. Place vehicle on hoist.
3. On Camaro models, disconnect parking brake cables. Remove underbody reinforcement plate (convertible). Disconnect left exhaust pipe from manifold for clearance.
4. On Corvette models, remove both exhaust pipes.
5. Remove propeller shaft.
6. Disconnect speedometer cable, electrical lead to case connector, vacuum line modulator, and oil cooler pipes.
7. Disconnect shift control linkage.
8. Support transmission with jack.
9. Disconnect rear mount from frame crossmember.
10. Remove two bolts at each end of frame crossmember and remove crossmember. On Corvette also remove through bolt at inside of frame and parking brake pulley.
11. Remove oil cooler lines, vacuum modulator line, speedometer cable, and downshift solenoid wire at transmission.
12. Remove converter under pan.
13. Remove converter to flywheel bolts.
14. Loosen exhaust pipe to manifold bolts about ¼" (Chevrolet and Chevelle). Lower transmission until jack is barely supporting it.
15. Remove transmission to engine mounting bolts and oil filler tube.
16. Raise transmission to its normal position, support engine with jack and slide transmission rearward and lower it away from vehicle.
17. Use a converter holding tool when lowering transmission or keep rear of transmission lower than front so as not to lose converter.
18. Reverse procedure to install. However, before installing flex plate to converter bolts, make certain that weld nuts on converter are flush with flex plate and converter rotates freely by hand in this position. Then hand start three bolts and tighten finger tight before the final tightening.

Oldsmobile 1965-68

1. Remove flywheel cover and torque converter attaching bolts.
2. Mark flywheel and converter so they can be installed in same position.
3. Support engine at rear.
4. Disconnect solenoid wires and manual shift linkage at side of transmission.
5. Disconnect oil cooler lines, vacuum modulator line and oil filler pipe.
6. Disconnect parking brake cable.
7. Before removing propeller shaft, scribe marks on drive shaft and companion flange for correct assembly.
8. Disconnect exhaust pipe bracket at rear of crossmember.
9. Support transmission, then remove crossmember.
10. Unfasten transmission from engine.
11. Move transmission away from engine, then, before removing transmission, fasten a suitable piece of strap iron to housing to prevent converter from falling out as transmission is removed.

Pontiac 1965-68

1. Disconnect battery and release parking brake. Then raise car.
2. Remove propeller shaft.
3. Disconnect speedometer cable, electrical lead to case connector, vacuum line at modulator, and oil cooler pipes.
4. Disconnect shift control linkage.
5. Support transmission with jack.
6. Disconnect rear mount from transmission and crossmember.
7. Remove crossmember (2 bolts at each end).
8. Remove converter dust shield.
9. Remove converter-to-flex plate bolts.
10. Loosen exhaust pipe to manifold about ¼", and lower transmission until jack is barely supporting it.
11. Remove transmission-to-engine mount bolts.
12. Raise transmission to its normal position, slide it rearward and lower it away from vehicle.
13. Reverse procedure to install.

GM FRONT WHEEL DRIVE TURBO HYDRA-MATIC

NOTE: — This chapter deals only with maintenance, adjustments and "in car" repairs. For major service work, Motor's Automatic Transmission Manual is available. Current edition is a 740 page volume that includes 240 pages of oil circuit diagrams mostly in full color.

TRANSMISSION IDENTIFICATION

CADILLAC ELDORADO

1967-68 .... AJ

OLDSMOBILE TORONADO

1966-68 With Std. Engine .... OJ

1968 With High Perf. Eng. .... OM

DESCRIPTION

This transmission is a fully automatic unit used for front wheel drive applications, Fig. 1. It consists primarily of a three-element hydraulic torque converter, dual sprocket and chain link assembly, compound planetary gear set, three multiple disc clutches, a sprag clutch, a roller clutch, two band assemblies, and a hydraulic control system.

Torque Converter

The torque converter consists of a pump or driving member, a turbine or driven member, and a variable stator or reaction member.

The stator is mounted on a one-way roller clutch which allows the stator to overrun when not used as a reaction member. The stator is a variable type that allows the blades to change from low to high angle.

The torque converter couples the engine to the planetary gear set through the use of a drive sprocket, a chain link assembly, and a driven sprocket. Clockwise engine torque turns the drive sprocket clockwise. This, in turn, drives the driven sprocket in a clockwise direction. This in effect is a reverse in the direction of engine torque due to the side mounting of the gear unit.

Planetary Gear Set

The gear set provides three forward ratios and reverse. The approximate gear ratios are: First 2½ to 1, second 1½ to 1, third 1.1 to 1, reverse 2.1 to 1. Second and third are also multiplied by a lesser degree.

Converter stall ratio, first gear (2½ x 2) equals 5 to 1. Converter stall ratio, reverse (2.1 x 2) equals 4.2 to 1.

External Controls

External control connections to the transmission are: a) Engine vacuum, b) 12-volt electrical signals, c) manual linkage control.

Engine vacuum is used to operate the vacuum modulator assembly. The vacuum modulator automatically senses any change in torque input to the transmission that the driver induces through a change in accelerator position.

On all models an electrical signal is used to operate an electrical solenoid. The solenoid is activated by a switch at the carburetor. When the throttle is opened sufficiently to close this switch, the solenoid in the transmission is activated, causing a downshift at speeds below approximately 70 mph. At lower speeds, downshifts will occur at lesser speeds without use of the switch.

On 1966-67 models, a stator solenoid is also activated by an electrical switch on the carburetor. The stator is activated at small throttle openings to reduce creep, and at larger throttle openings and high speeds to increase engine output.

TROUBLE SHOOTING GUIDE

NOTE: In many of the following diagnosis procedures, it is recommended that air pressure be applied to help in determining if the seal, rings or pistons are stuck, missing or damaged. Therefore, when air is applied, listen carefully for escaping air and piston action as air is applied to a particular area.

No Drive In "D" Range

1. Low oil level. Check for external leaks or vacuum modulator diaphragm leaking.
2. Manual linkage maladjusted. Correct alignment in manual lever shift quadrant.
3. Low oil pressure.
4. Oil strainer O-ring seal missing or damaged, neck weld leaking, strainer blocked.
5. Oil pump pressure regulator stuck or inoperative. Pump drive gear tangs damaged by converter.
6. Case porosity in intake bore.
7. Control valve. Manual valve disconnected from manual lever pin. (Other shift lever positions would also be affected.)
8. Forward clutch does not apply. Piston cracked; seals missing or damaged. These defects can be checked by removing the valve body and applying air pressure to the drive cavity in the case valve body face. Missing, damaged or worn oil rings on driven support housing can also be checked in this manner at the same time because they can also cause the forward clutch not to apply. Clutch plates burned.
9. Roller clutch inoperative. Rollers worn, damaged springs, or damaged races. May be checked by placing selector lever in "L" range.

No Drive In "R" or Slips In Reverse

1. Low oil level.
2. Manual linkage.
3. Oil pressure. Vacuum modulator defective, modulator valve sticking.
4. Restricted strainer, leak at intake pipe or O-ring seal. Pressure regulator or boost valve sticking.
5. Control valve body gaskets leaking or damaged (other malfunctions may also be indicated). Low-reverse check ball missing from case (this will cause no overrun braking in low range). The 2-3 valve train stuck open (this will also cause 1-3 upshifts in drive range). Reverse feed passage not drilled; also check case passages. Apply air to reverse passage in case valve body face.
6. Rear servo and accumulator. Servo piston seal ring broken or missing. Apply air pressure to drilled hole in intermediate clutch passage of case valve body face to check for piston operation and excessive leakage. Band apply pin too short (this may also cause no overrun braking or slip in overrun braking in low range).
7. Rear band burned, loose lining, apply pin or anchor pin not engaged; band broken.
8. Direct clutch outer seal damaged or missing. Clutch plates burned (may be caused by stuck ball check in piston).
9. Forward clutch does not release (will also cause drive in neutral range).

Drive In Neutral

1. Manual linkage maladjusted.
2. Forward clutch does not release (this condition will also cause no reverse).

1st Speed Only—No 1-2 Upshift

1. Governor valve sticking; driven gear loose, damaged or worn. If driven gear shows signs of wear or damage, check output flange drive gear for nicks or rough finish.
2. Control valve. The 1-2 shift valve train stuck closed. Dirt, chips or

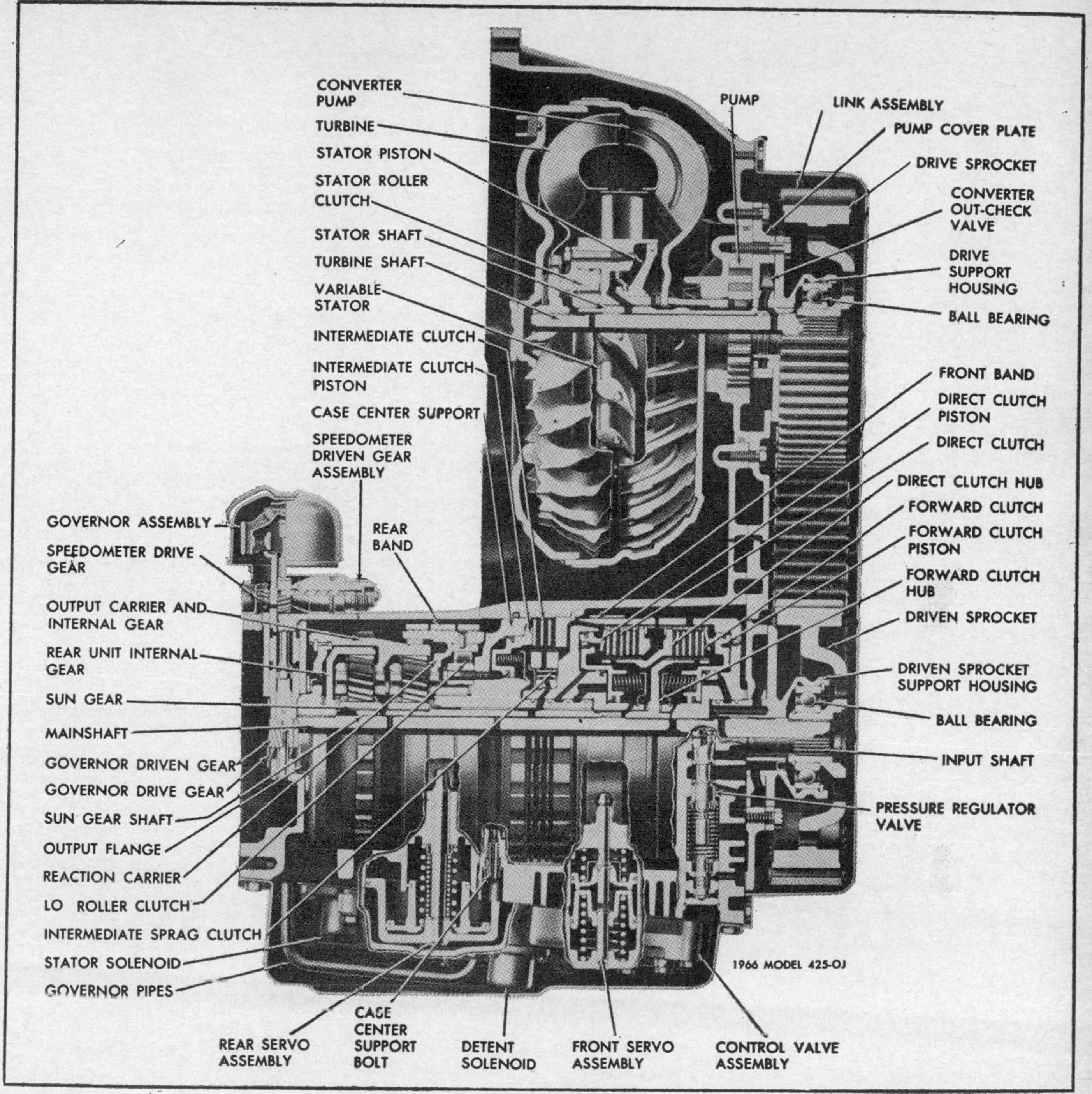

Fig. 1 General Motors Front Wheel Drive Turbo Hydra-Matic

damaged valve in 1-2 shift valve train. Governor feed channels blocked or leaking; pipes out of position. Valve body gaskets leaking or damaged. Case porosity between oil channels. Governor feed passage blocked.

3. Intermediate clutch. Case center support oil rings missing, broken or defective. Clutch piston seals missing, improperly assembled, cut or damaged. Apply air to intermediate clutch passage located in case valve body face to check for these defects.

1-2 Shift Obtained Only At Full Throttle

1. Detent switch sticking or defective.
2. Detent solenoid loose, gasket leaking, sticks open, electrical wire pinched between cover and casting.
3. Control valve body gasket leaking or damaged. Detent valve train stuck.

1st & 2nd Speeds Only No 2 - 3 Shift

1. Detent solenoid stuck open (the 2-3 shift would occur at very high speeds) may be diagnosed as no 2-3 shift.
2. Detent switch sticking or defective.
3. Control valve body. The 2-3 valve train stuck with dirt or foreign material. Valve body gaskets leaking or damaged.

4. Direct clutch. Case center support oil rings missing or broken. Clutch piston seals missing, improperly assembled, cut or damaged; piston ball check stuck or missing. Apply air to direct clutch passage in case valve body face to check these conditions.

Slips In All Ranges

1. Oil level incorrect.
2. Low oil pressure. Vacuum modulator defective or valve sticking. Oil strainer plugged or leaks at neck; O-ring (case to strainer) missing or damaged. Pressure regulator or boost valve sticking.
3. Case cross channel leaks; porosity.
4. Forward, intermediate and direct clutches slipping. Clutch plates burned. Always look for a primary defect that would cause clutch plates to burn. (Missing feed holes, seals and oil rings, etc., are primary defects).
5. Roller clutch rollers worn; springs or cage damaged, and worn or damaged races (operates normally in low and reverse ranges).

Slips 1-2 Shift

1. Oil level incorrect.
2. Low oil pressure. Look for defective vacuum modulator or valve sticking. Pump pressure regulator valve stuck.
3. Front servo accumulator piston cracked or porous, oil ring damaged or missing.
4. Control valve. The 1-2 accumulator valve train (may cause a slip-bump shift). Porous valve body or case valve body face.
5. Rear servo accumulator oil ring missing or damaged; case bore damaged; piston cracked or damaged.
6. Case porous between oil passages.
7. Intermediate clutch lip seals missing, cut or damaged. Apply air pressure to intermediate clutch passage in case valve body face to check. Clutch plates burned. Case center support leaks in feed circuits (oil rings damaged or grooves damaged) or excessive leak between tower and bushing.

Rough 1-2 Shift

1. Oil pressure. Check vacuum modulator for loose fittings, restrictions in line; defective vacuum modulator. Modulator valve stuck. Pressure regulator boost valve stuck.
2. Control valve. 1-2 accumulator valve train; valve body-to-case bolts loose; gaskets inverted, off location, or damaged.
3. Case. Intermediate clutch passage check ball missing or not seating. Case porous between channels.
4. Rear servo accumulator piston stuck. Apply air pressure to 1-2 accumulator passage in case valve body face (you should hear the servo piston move). Broken or missing spring; bore scored or damaged.

Slips 2-3 Shift

1. Oil level high or low.
2. Low oil pressure. Modulator defective or valve sticking. Pump pressure regulator valve or boost valve sticking.
3. Control valve. Accumulator piston pin leak at valve body end.
4. Direct clutch piston seals leaking. Case center support oil seal rings damaged or excessive leak between tower and bushing. Apply air to direct clutch passage in case valve body face. If air comes out intermediate passage, center support is defective.

Rough 2-3 Shift

1. Oil pressure high. Vacuum modulator defective or valve sticking. Pump pressure regulator valve or boost valve stuck or inoperative.
2. Front servo accumulator spring missing or broken; accumulator piston stuck.

Shifts Occur at too High or too Low Car Speed

1. Oil pressure. Vacuum modulator defective or valve sticking. Leak in vacuum line (engine to transmission). Vacuum modulator line fitting on carburetor blocked. Pump pressure regulator valve or boost valve train stuck.
2. Governor valve stuck or sticking. Feed holes restricted or leaking; pipes damaged or mispositioned.
3. Detent solenoid stuck open or loose on valve body (will cause late shifts).
4. Control valve. Detent valve train sticking; 3-2 valve train sticking; 1-2 shift valve stuck; 1-2 detent valve sticking open (will probably cause early 2-3 shift).
5. Spacer plate gaskets inverted or mispositioned; orifice holes missing or blocked; check balls missing or mislocated.
6. Case porous in channels or foreign material blocking channels.

No Detent Downshift

1. Detent switch mispositioned or electrical connections loose.
2. Solenoid defective or electrical connections loose.
3. Control valve detent valve train stuck.

No Engine Braking—Super Range 2nd Speed

1. Front servo or accumulator piston rings broken or missing. Case or valve body bores worn oversize, causing excessive leakage.
2. Front band worn or burned (check for cause); band end lugs broken or damaged; band lugs not engaged on anchor pins or servo apply pin (check for cause).

No Engine Braking—Low Range 1st Speed

1. Control valve low-reverse check ball missing from case.
2. Rear servo oil ring damaged or missing; piston damaged or porous, causing a leak in apply pressure.
3. Rear band lining worn or burned (check for cause); band end lugs broken; band ends not engaged on anchor pin or servo apply pin. These items will also cause slip in reverse or no reverse.

Will Not Hold Car In Park Position

1. Manual linkage maladjusted (external).
2. Parking brake lever and actuator rod assembly defective (check for proper actuator spring action). Parking pawl broken or inoperative.

Poor Performance or Rough Idle

1. Stator switch defective or maladjusted.
2. Stator solenoid defective or wire ground to solenoid housing; electrical connection loose; stator valve train stuck (located in valve body); oil feed circuit to stator restricted or blocked (check feed hole in stator shaft); converter-out check valve broken or missing (reed valve located in cover plate under drive support housing).
3. Turbine shaft converter return passage not drilled; oil seal rings broken, worn or missing.
4. Case porous in feed circuit channels or foreign material blocking feed circuit.
5. Converter assembly defective.

Transmission Noise

1. Pump noise. Oil level high or low; water in oil, driving gear assembled upside down; driving or driven gear teeth damaged.
2. Gear noise (1st gear drive range). Check planetary pinions for tooth damage. Check sun gear and front and rear internal gears for tooth finish or damage.
3. Clutch noise during application. Check clutch plates.
4. Sprocket and chain link assembly. Chain link too long (sounds similar to popcorn popping). There will be a rough burr along teeth of drive sprocket if chain link is too long; replace chain link and drive sprocket. Drive or driven sprocket teeth damaged. Engine mounts worn or damaged.

MAINTENANCE

Adding Oil

The fluid level should be checked at every engine oil change interval, and should be changed at 24,000 mile intervals. The fluid level should be checked with the selector lever in PARK position, engine running at idle speed and car on a level surface. The oil indicator and filler tube are located under the hood at the left front corner of the engine. *The filler tube comes out from the final drive housing but it is for the transmission.*

NOTE: If any work is performed on the transmission, it will require the following amounts of oil to bring the oil to the correct level:
1. Pan removed 5½ qts.
2. Drive cover sprocket housing ½ qt.

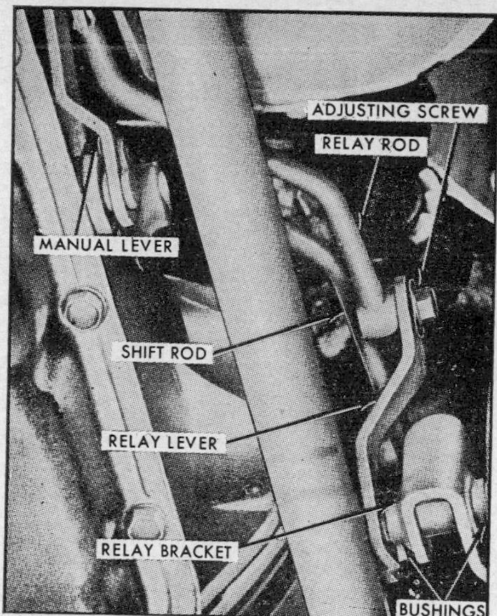

Fig. 2 Manual control linkage adjustment. Cadillac Eldorado

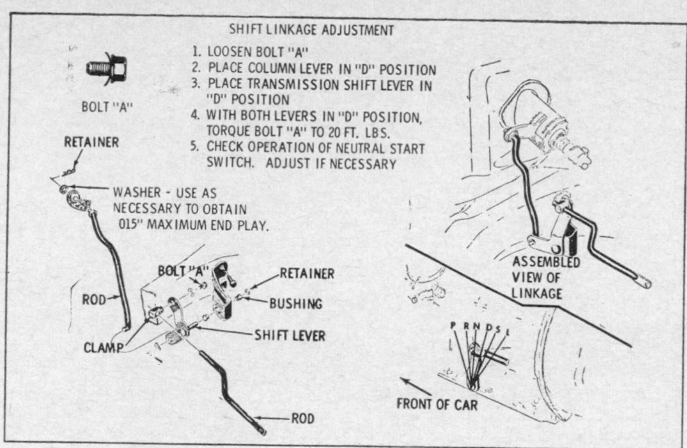

Fig. 3 Shift linkage adjustment. Toronado column shift

3. Converter changed 3½ qts.
4. Total overhaul (total capacity) 13 qts.

Changing Oil

When changing transmission oil, first add 4 quarts, start the engine, and add oil to bring the fluid level to the FULL mark on the dipstick. Use only the recommended automatic transmission oil.

MANUAL LINKAGE, ADJUST

Cadillac Eldorado

1. Referring to Fig. 2, loosen adjusting screw on relay bracket.
2. Pull relay rod up to position transmission shift valve in Park, then push rod down to the third (Neutral) step. Make sure rod is centered in this detent position.
3. Position selector lever in Neutral against quadrant stop in steering column.
4. Tighten relay rod adjusting screw, making sure shift lever is held against Neutral stop while this operation is being performed.

Olds Toronado

Make the adjustment as directed in Figs. 3 and 4.

DOWNSHIFT SWITCH, ADJUST

Cadillac Eldorado

1. Remove carburetor air cleaner.
2. Make sure that carburetor is properly adjusted and that throttle linkage is at low speed idle setting.
3. If the downshift switch is properly adjusted, a #31 (wire gauge size) drill can be inserted in the calibrating hole below lower wire terminal extending through to carburetor side of switch.
4. If adjustment is necessary, loosen the two switch mounting screws and position the switch for proper alignment.
5. With switch positioned, tighten mounting screws, remove drill gauge and install air cleaner.

Olds Toronado

1. With slow idle and carburetor rod properly adjusted, engine off, proceed as follows:
2. Disconnect carburetor rod and move switch lever towards closed throttle position until lever hits stop.
3. Connect carburetor rod without moving switch lever to wide open throttle position.
4. Push accelerator pedal to wide open throttle through the detent. This moves the internal switch contacts to the proper position.

NOTE: Trailer Hauling Switch (Y-73 option) is bronze colored. When checking the special throttle switches with a test lamp, the test lamp *should light* only when the throttle valves are at idle or at

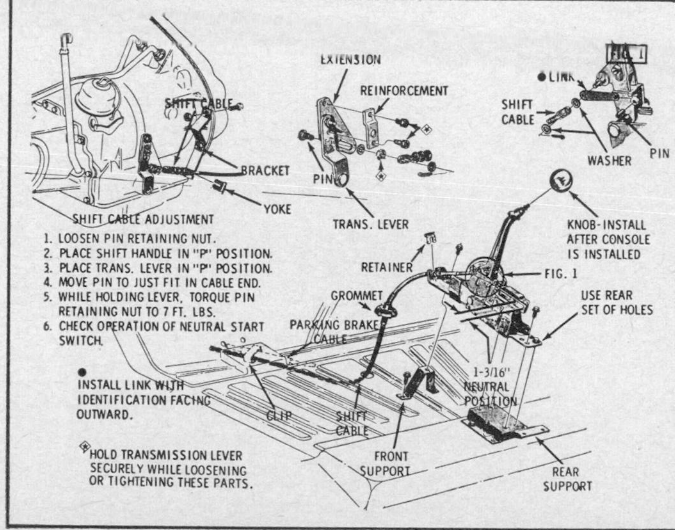

Fig. 4 Shift linkage adjustment. Toronado console shift

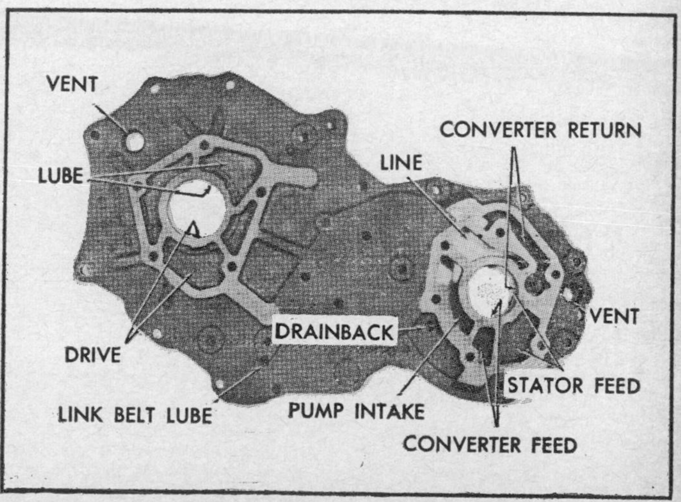

Fig. 5 Location of check balls

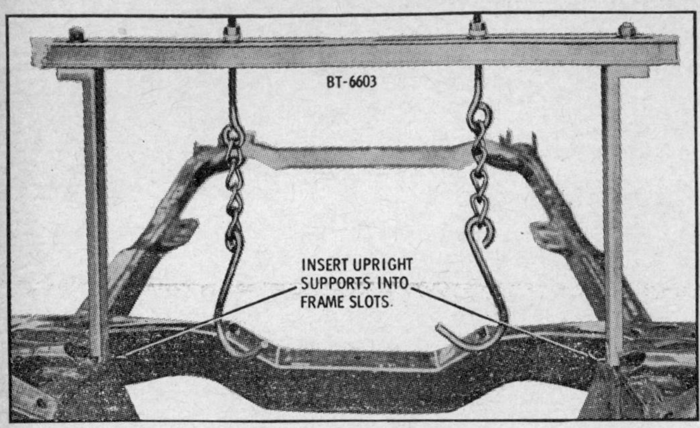

Fig. 6 Installing support bar. Olds Toronado

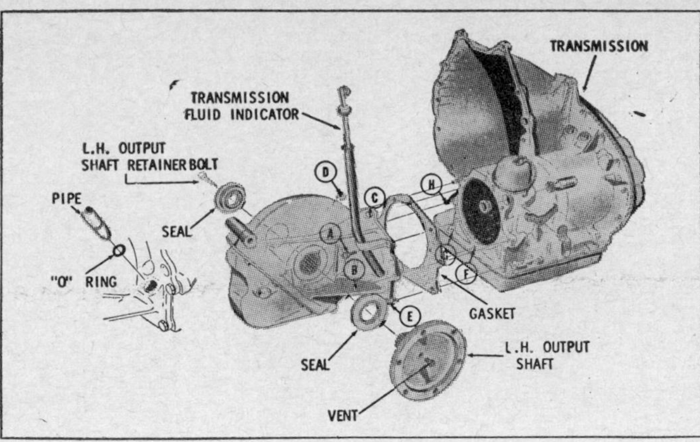

Fig. 7 Transmission attachment

wide open throttle position. The test lamp *will not light* at the 40° throttle opening as it does when checking a regular switch.

IN CAR REPAIRS

Operations Not Requiring Transmission Removal

1. Oil cooler fitting replacement or adjustment.
2. Governor assembly service.
3. Vacuum modulator, bushing and valve service.
4. Speedometer drive gear service.
5. Cruise Control service.
6. Oil level check.
7. Oil pressure check with oil pressure gauge.

Units That Can Be Serviced After Oil Pan Removal

1. Oil pan and pan-to-case gasket.
2. Pressure regulator valve assembly.
3. Valve body assembly.
4. Rear servo and accumulator assembly.
5. Front servo and accumulator assembly.
6. Governor pipes.
7. Detent solenoid.
8. Stator solenoid.
9. Solenoid connector.
10. Manual linkage.
11. Parking linkage.
12. Valve body-to-case spacers and gaskets.
13. Check balls for proper location (7 balls), Fig. 5.
14. Detent roller and spring assembly.

TRANS. REPLACE

1966-68 Olds Toronado

Removal

1. Disconnect battery.
2. Disconnect oil cooler lines at transmission and speedometer cable at governor.
3. Install a suitable engine support bar, such as shown in Fig. 6.
4. Remove nut D and bolts A, B and C, Fig. 7.
5. Remove bolts A, B, C, D, Fig. 8.
6. Remove flywheel cover plate bolt, A, Fig. 10.
7. Hoist car and remove starter.
8. Remove bolts B, C and D from flywheel cover plate, Fig. 9.
9. Remove flywheel to converter bolt E, Fig. 9. Rotate flywheel until bolts are removed.
10. Disconnect vacuum modulator line and stator wiring.
11. Install transmission lift.
12. Remove shift linkage.
13. Remove bolts E, F, G and nut H, Fig. 7.
14. Remove bolts A and B, Fig. 10.
15. Remove two upper engine mount bracket-to-transmission bolts.
16. Remove four bracket-to-engine mount bolts.
17. Slide transmission rearward and down.
18. Attach converter holding strap to housing to prevent converter from falling out when transmission is being removed.
19. After transmission is removed from vehicle, the link assembly cover insulator can be removed or installed.

Installation

When installing the transmission the engine mount bracket must be positioned loosely on the link assembly cover until the transmission is in place. Then reverse removal procedure and torque bolts to ft-lb values as follows:

Engine to converter housing	25
Engine bracket to transmission	55
Engine bracket to rubber mount	55
Oil cooler lines to transmission	25
Final drive to transmission	25

1967-68 Cadillac Eldorado

Removal—Figs. 11 and 12

1. Disconnect ground cable at battery.

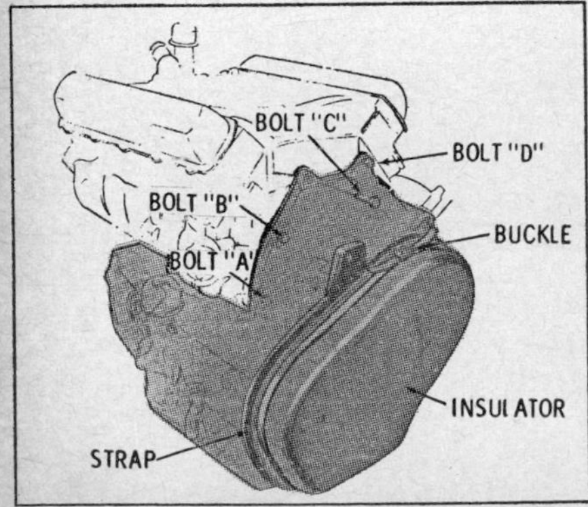

Fig. 8 Transmission to engine attachment

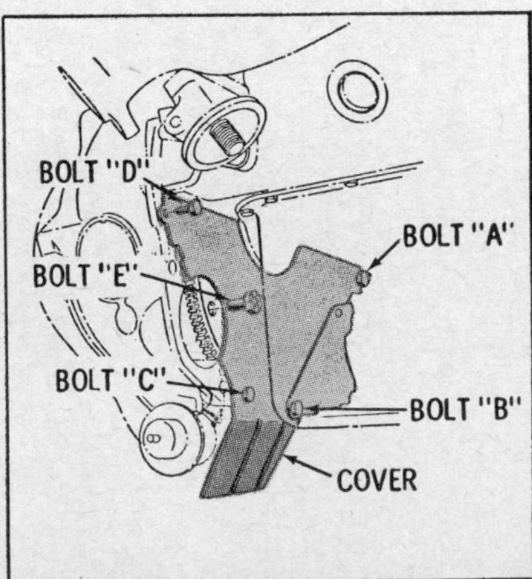

Fig. 9 Converter attachment

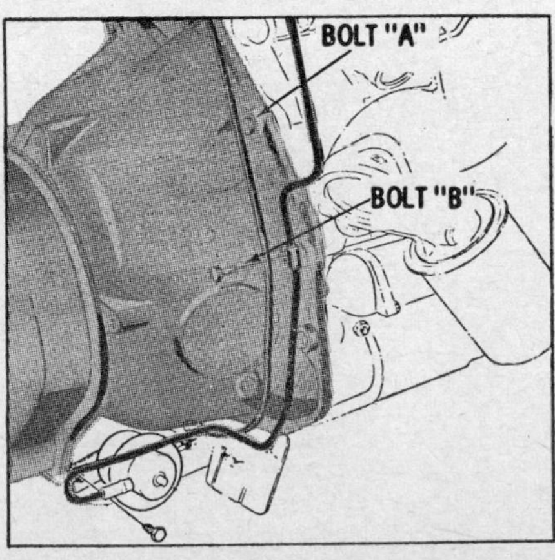

Fig. 10 Transmission to engine attachment

Fig. 11 Transmission attaching bolt locations. Cadillac Eldorado

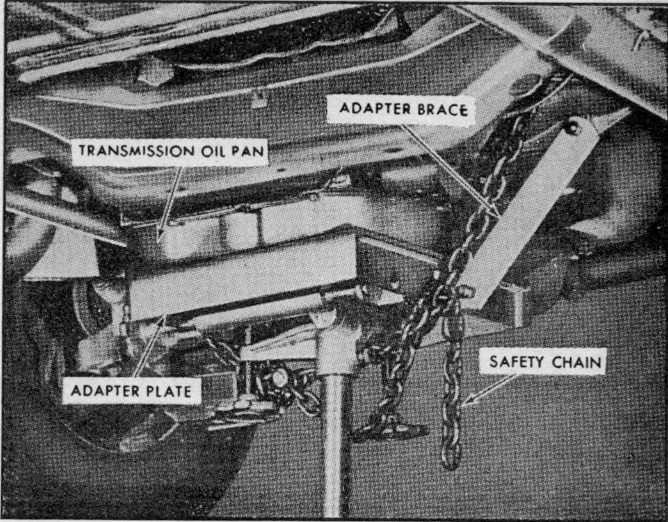

Fig. 12 Positioning transmission jack to transmission. Cadillac Eldorado

2. Remove hood.
3. Remove transmission dipstick.
4. Remove filler tube.
5. Remove bolts at locations A, B and C, securing final drive case to transmission.
6. Disconnect speedometer cable at governor.
7. Disconnect oil cooler pipes at transmission and at radiator. Cap pipes and plug connector holes in transmission and radiator.
8. Remove bolt securing cooler pipe bracket to final drive bracket and position pipes away from governor.
9. Remove nut at location H, securing final drive case to transmission.
10. Remove bolts at locations I, J, K and L, securing transmission to engine and adapter plate.
11. Remove upper left bolt securing rear engine mount bracket to transmission.
12. Remove ground strap from cowl.
13. Remove upper left nut securing converter cover plate to transmission.

NOTE: Use a $\frac{7}{16}$" universal socket and extension and reach underneath left exhaust manifold. Removal of this screw can be facilitated by having a helper under the car, verbally guiding socket onto nut.

14. Position cable (with looped ends) under engine intake manifold and hook looped ends to chain fall. Take up slack in chain fall and cable, putting engine mounts under tension.
15. Position safety chain over top of transmission.
16. Raise car and place on jack stands, adjusting chain fall as required.
17. Disconnect leads from starter motor.
18. Remove bolt at location O, securing starter motor to transmission case and remove ground strap from bolt.
19. Remove bolt at location P and remove starter.
20. Remove three remaining screws securing converter cover plate to transmission and remove cover plate.
21. Position transmission jack.
22. Disconnect electrical connector from transmission connector.
23. Remove pipe from vacuum modulator.
24. Secure transmission to transmission jack adapter plate with safety chain.
25. Remove three flex plate-to-converter attaching bolts.

NOTE: This can be done by installing a 9/16-18 bolt and washer into end of crankshaft at vibration damper, after removing cork plug, and rotating converter and flex plate until bolts are accessible for removal. Do not pry on flex plate ring gear to rotate flex plate and converter as flex plate may be damaged.

26. Remove bolts at locations M and N securing transmission to engine and adapter plate.
27. On left side of transmission, separate relay rod from manual yoke.
28. Remove bolts at locations D, E and F, and nut at location G, securing final drive to transmission.

NOTE: Position drain pan under point where transmission and final drive meet as approximately 1½ quarts of transmission fluid will be lost when transmission and final drive are separated.

29. Remove five bolts and washers securing wear of acromat (cushion) to front cross bar and frame horns and allow acromat to hang free.
30. Through access holes in bottom of front cross bar, remove left bolt and loosen right bolt securing front engine mount to front cross bar.
31. Have a helper, using a large pry bar, shift engine forward, while you use a small pry bar to help separate transmission from engine and final drive. *Select pry points with care to avoid damaging any components.*
32. After initial separation has been made, allow transmission oil to drain at final drive junction.
33. Remove two bolts on right side securing rear engine mount bracket to transmission.
34. Through access hole in bottom of transmission support bar, remove two bolts, one each side, securing rear mounts to transmission support bar, and position mounts and bracket rearward to underbody.
35. While a helper pries and holds engine forward, move transmission rearward to disengage transmission case from dowels on engine adapter and to disengage final drive from studs on transmission case. Top of transmission should be tilted slightly rearward.
36. Slowly lower transmission, making certain top of transmission case clears flex plate ring gear and splined input shaft of final drive, until converter is approximately half-way exposed from flex plate.
37. Install a suitable clamp to transmission case at location N to avoid possibility of converter becoming disengaged when transmission is removed.
38. Lower transmission from car.

CAUTION: Rear engine mount bracket will follow transmission from car; to avoid damage or injury, remove bracket as soon as there is sufficient clearance.

39. Remove and discard final drive gasket and clean mounting surface of final drive.

Installation

1. Position transmission, on jack, under car.
2. Install new gasket on final drive, after first soaking gasket with transmission fluid.
3. Position rear engine mount bracket on top of transmission support bar against underbody.
4. Raise transmission in place until

converter is approximately half-way covered by flex plate, then remove converter holding clamp.

5. While a helper assists in holding engine forward with pry bar, continue raising transmission, making certain top of transmission case clears splined input shaft of final drive, and position to engine.
6. Position transmission to engine and final drive by aligning following points in the order listed, while a helper assists:
   a. Studs on transmission case to mounting holes in final drive.
   b. Guide holes in transmission case to dowels on adapter.
   c. Internal flange on final drive to transmission.

NOTE: As engagement of splined final drive input shaft to transmission is hidden, extreme care must be taken to avoid damaging transmission and final drive.

To facilitate engagement of final drive splines, rotate one front wheel while a helper holds the other. When alignment is complete and proper, gap between final drive case and transmission should not exceed ¼".

7. Loosely install bolts (3/8 x 1¼) at locations D and F attaching transmission to final drive and bolt (3/8 x 2½) at location N attaching transmission to engine adapter, alternately tightening bolts to avoid cocking transmission. *Do not torque bolts at this time.*
8. Working in engine compartment, loosely install bolt (3/8 x 1 3/8 at location J attaching transmission to adapter. *Do not torque bolt at this time.*
9. Install bolt (3/8 x 1 3/8) at location M attaching transmission to adapter plate. *Do not torque bolt at this time.*
10. Position rear engine mount bracket to transmission and loosely install three bolts securing bracket to transmission. *Upper left bolt is installed from engine compartment.*
11. Position rear engine mounts and bracket to transmission support bar and loosely install bolts through access holes in bottom of bar, attaching mounts to bar.
12. Reposition engine as necessary and install left bolt securing front engine mount to front cross bar. Tighten both front mount bolts to 90 ft-lbs.
13. Remove transmission jack.
14. Torque rear engine mounts to transmission support bar bolts to 55 ft-lbs. Torque rear engine mounts to transmission bolts (2 on right side) to 55 ft-lbs. Torque transmission to adapter to engine bolts (location N) to 30 ft-lbs. Torque transmission to adapter bolts (location M) to 30 ft-lbs.

CAUTION: The procedure for attaching the converter to the flex plate as described above must be strictly followed. Any deviation from this procedure will result in improper installation and damage to flex plate and transmission.

15. Rotate converter until two of the three weld nuts on converter line up with two of the three bolt holes in flex plate. Position converter so that weld nuts are flush with flex plate. making certain converter is not cocked and that pilot in center of converter is properly seated in crankshaft.
16. Install two flex plate-to-converter attaching bolts through accessible holes in flex plate and tighten to 28 ft-lbs. *Bolts must be tightened at this time to assure proper alignment of converter.*
17. Rotate flex plate and converter by rotating bolt previously installed in forward end of crankshaft until third bolt hole is accessible. Install bolt in this hole and tighten to 28 ft-lbs. Remove bolt from crankshaft and install cork plug.
18. Install hose on vacuum modulator.
19. Install electrical connector to transmission connector.
20. Position converter cover plate to transmission case and install two lower and one upper right bolts securing cover plate to transmission, tightening to 5 ft-lbs.
21. Position starter to transmission case and install bolt at location P.
22. Position ground strap to transmission and install bolt securing ground strap and starter to transmission at location O. Tighten bolts at locations O and P to 25 ft-lbs.
23. Install leads on starter motor.
24. Install bolts at locations C and E and nut at location G, securing transmission to final drive.
25. Torque bolts at locations C through F to 25 ft-lbs.
26. Position acromat (cushion) to front cross bar and frame horns and install five bolts and washers.
27. Connect relay rod to manual yoke with cotter pin.
28. Check operation of manual linkage and adjust.
29. Disconnect chain fall and lower car.
30. Install bolts at locations A and B and nut at location H, securing transmission to final drive. Tighten bolts to 25 ft-lbs.
31. Install upper left bolt securing converter cover plate to transmission in the manner described for removing it in Step 13.
32. Install bolts at locations I, J, K and L, securing transmission to engine and adapter. Torque to 25 ft-lbs.
33. Tighten brass cooler pipe connectors at case to 28 ft-lbs. Clean ends of cooler pipes with solvent, connect pipes to transmission and tighten fittings to 28 ft-lbs.
34. Connect cooler pipes to radiator and tighten fittings to 40 ft-lbs.
35. Install cooler pipe clamp.
36. Install speedometer cable to governor.
37. Install new O-ring seal on transmission oil filler tube through hole in final drive case. Fasten filler tube bracket to exhaust manifold.
38. Install body ground strap to firewall.
39. Connect battery cable, fill transmission with fluid and install hood.

BUICK TWIN TURBINE

NOTE: — This chapter deals only with maintenance, adjustments and "in car" repairs. For major service work, Motor's Automatic Transmission Manual is available. Current edition is a 740 page volume that includes 240 pages of oil circuit diagrams mostly in full color.

TRANSMISSION IDENTIFICATION

A production identification number is stamped into the lower edge of the reaction shaft flange directly to the rear of the high (left) accumulators. The identification is as follows:

1963 .... H 031

DESCRIPTION

The complete transmission, Fig. 1, consists of a combination torque converter combined with an auxiliary gear box. The torque converter constitutes a complete automatic transmission within itself, the gear box being used solely for the purpose of providing a neutral position, a reverse gear, a parking brake and a rarely used emergency low gear. During all normal driving the gear box is inactive.

The major feature of this torque converter is a stator with variable pitch blades. The stator gives the equivalent of a passing gear with no gear change, and is accomplished by changing the angle (or pitch) of the stator blades.

The gear box consists primarily of a planetary gear set and multiple disc clutch. The clutch locks the planetary gears to give direct drive when the control lever is in Drive. In Neutral and Parking the free turning gears and dis-

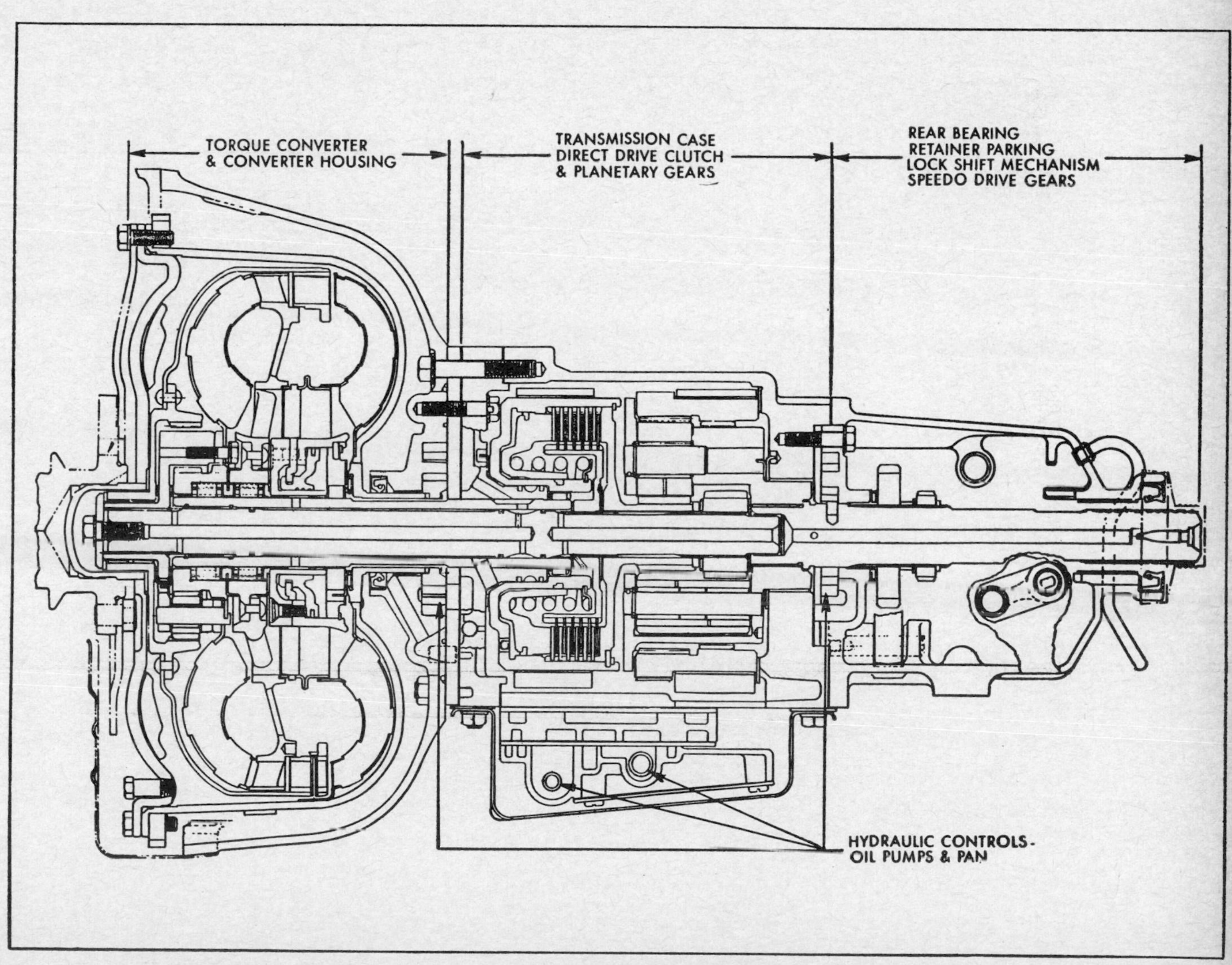

Fig. 1 Sectional view of Buick Twin Turbine transmission

engaged clutch provide a condition in which the engine is disconnected from the propeller shaft.

Two oil pumps are used to provide oil circulation and pressure, and valves are used to regulate and control the oil pressure. The hydraulic system performs the following functions: (1) Keeps torque converter filled with oil; (2) provides lubrication to all working parts; (3) applies clutch in direct drive; (4) applies low band in low range; (5) applies reverse band in reverse range.

Additional controls are used to change the angle of the stators when the transmission is in direct drive.

The transmission is provided with two accumulators. An accumulator is simply a surge chamber which cushions the application of hydraulic pressure (somewhat on the order of a hydraulic door check.) The high accumulator cushions the engagement of the multiple disc clutch for direct drive, whereas the low accumulator cushions the application of the low band.

Torque Converter

The torque converter is connected to the engine flywheel and serves as an hydraulic coupling through which engine torque is transmitted to drive the car. In addition, it automatically provides torque multiplication as required under all ordinary driving conditions.

Operation of the torque converter is the same in Direct Drive, Low and Reverse. The two-position stator is in the low angle position at part throttle and in the high angle position at full throttle. The converter transmits torque to the direct drive clutch and planetary gears through the transmission input shaft. The range of operation is determined by control of the clutch and gears.

Planetary Gears & Direct Drive Clutch

The planetary gears and related parts, Fig. 6, provide reverse and an emergency low driving range. The direct drive clutch locks the planetary gears to provide direct drive without gear action when transmission is in Direct Drive. In Neutral and Parking, the free turning planetary gears and disengaged clutch provide a condition in which the engine is completely disconnected from the propeller shaft and rear wheels.

TROUBLE SHOOTING GUIDE

Engine Stalls While Decelerating Car with Brakes Applied

1. Improper adjustment of throttle dashpot.
2. Engine not properly tuned up.

Transmission Oil Foams and Spews Out of Breather

1. Transmission overfilled. If transmission is overfilled, check for blackened condition of oil, indicating leakage of rear axle lubricant into transmission due to defective propeller shaft seals. Check for low oil level in rear axle housing. Correct cause of leakage and completely drain and refill transmission.
2. Water in transmission, indicated by overfilled condition and brown color of transmission oil. Water in transmission usually comes from a leaking oil cooler. In this case there may be excessive oil accumulation in top tank of engine radiator. Correct cause of leakage and completely drain and refill transmission.
3. Air leak into hydraulic system at rear oil pump gaskets.

Car Will Not Move In Any Range—Rear Wheels Free

1. If car will not move for 1 to 8 minutes after standing overnight, park car for several hours with engine stopped and then check front oil pump pressure. A zero reading until such time as car will move indicates that front pump loses its prime due to excessive clearances. Inspect front pump. If condition has existed for some time it is advisable to inspect clutch and bands for excessive wear due to slippage at low apply pressure.
2. If car will not move in any range after extended operation in Reverse it indicates air leakage into pump suction line and suction and excessive clearance at front oil pump. Front oil pump pressure will be very low during period when car will not move. Inspect for air leaks at rear oil pump gaskets. Inspect front oil pump and cover for excessive clearances.
3. Converter one-way clutch slipping.
4. Defective stator shaft.

Car Will Not Move In Any Range—Rear Wheels Locked

1. Parking lock engaged or parking brake applied.
2. Lock up due to broken part in rear axle or transmission.

Car Will Not Move In Direct Drive Only

1. If front oil pump and high accumulator pressures are okay, remove and inspect clutch assembly.
2. If front oil pump pressure is okay but high accumulator pressure is low and accumulator body gasket is not leaking internally, inspect for leaks in reaction flange gasket. If gasket is satisfactory, inspect clutch piston outer seal and ball check, also oil sealing rings on hubs of reaction shaft flange and low drum.

Car Will Not Move In Reverse Only

1. Reverse servo inoperative.
2. Band improperly adjusted or band operating strut has dropped out of place.
3. Reverse ring gear.

Excessive Slip In All Ranges

1. If condition occurs only after operation in Reverse, see Condition 2 under *Car Will Not Move in Any Range—Rear Wheels Free.*
2. Low oil level.
3. Manual control linkage improperly adjusted.
4. If front oil pump pressure is low, remove and inspect pressure regulator valve and all valve and servo body gaskets. If cause is not found remove and inspect front oil pump for wear or excessive clearances. Inspect pump cover and reaction shaft flange gaskets for leaks.
5. Defective sun gear and sprag assembly.

Excessive Slip In Direct Drive Only

1. Manual control linkage improperly adjusted.
2. Leak at high accumulator gasket, indicated by low oil pressure at high accumulator.
3. If above items are okay, remove and inspect clutch plates, sealing rings and clutch piston. Inspect for stuck check ball in piston.

Excessive Slip In Low Only

1. Manual control linkage improperly adjusted.
2. Low band improperly adjusted.
3. If pressure at low accumulator is low, check for leak at accumulator body gasket. If gasket is okay remove valve and servo body and check for gasket leaks and condition of low servo piston seal.
4. Low band and drum scored or worn.

Excessive Slip In Reverse Only

1. Manual control linkage improperly adjusted.
2. Reverse band improperly adjusted. Check for strut out of place or broken anchor.
3. If front oil pump pressure is low remove valve and servo body and check for gasket leaks and condition of reverse servo piston seal.
4. Reverse band and ring gear scored or worn.

Car Creeps In Neutral

1. Manual control linkage improperly adjusted.
2. Remove valve and servo body and check for low servo piston sticking up.
3. Remove clutch and inspect for sticking, warped or improperly assembled clutch plates. Note whether "dish" of steel plates is in same direction on all plates. If creep occurs only when engine is accelerated to about 2500 rpm, pay particular attention to condition of check balls at vents in clutch piston and reaction shaft flange.

Car Creeps Forward In Reverse or Backward In Low

Manual control linkage improperly adjusted.

Low-To-Direct Shift Abnormally Rough, or Slip Occurs

1. If high accumulator pressure is low, remove accumulator and check body gaskets. Check for accumulator piston sticking down. Top land of piston must be fully visible through top port in body.
2. If accumulator and gasket are okay, inspect for leaks in valve and servo body gaskets.

3. Low band improperly adjusted.
4. Binding or worn clutch plates.

Excessive Chatter or Clunk When Starting In Low or Reverse

NOTE—A very slight chatter just as car starts to move in reverse, which disappears as soon as car is in motion, may be considered normal. A slight clunk when shifting into Low or Reverse is also normal.

1. Check engine and transmission mountings for tightness. Inspect for broken rubber thrust pad at transmission mounting.
2. Low or Reverse band improperly adjusted.
3. If conditions 1 and 2 do not correct the trouble, direct drive clutch may be dragging. Remove clutch and inspect for sticking, warped, or improperly assembled clutch plates. Note whether "dish" of steel plates is in same direction on all plates.
4. Inspect for excessive wear of reverse ring gear bushing. Check for foreign matter in planet pinion needle bearings.

Hard Shifting Out of Parking

This condition is caused by binding of transmission shift rod in shift idler lever. If a burr exists on shift rod where it enters idler lever, remove burr with a file. If idler lever is distorted, replace the lever.

TRANSMISSION NOISES

When diagnosing abnormal noises in the transmission, consideration should be given to the parts that are in motion when the noise occurs. The presence or absence of noise in each range should be noted so that the parts which cause the noise can be determined by a process of elimination.

Hum or Low Whine In Neutral or Parking

A hum or low whine in neutral or parking is normal since all planetary gears are free to rotate without the steadying effect of a load. Some hum also may be expected in Low and Reverse.

Low Growl In Transmission

A low growl in transmission which disappears in several minutes after engine is started, following extended parking in extremely cold weather is caused by cavitation of the cold oil. This is a normal condition which requires no correction.

Buzzing Noise

A buzzing noise can be caused by low oil level, or by the front pump delivery check valve seating on the edge of the gasket between valves and servo bodies.

A buzzing noise, noticeable in Parking and Neutral, may be caused by excessive clearance of pressure regulator valve in valve body or an oversize orifice in valve land. Correction requires replacement of valve.

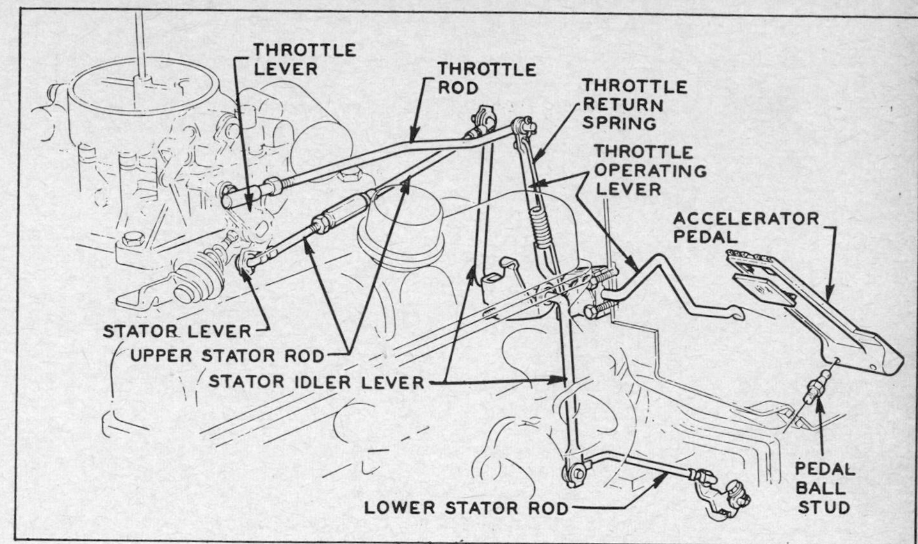

Fig. 2 Throttle and stator linkage. 1963

Clicking Noise In All Ranges

This may be caused by a foreign object going through the converter. A clicking noise only when car is in motion may be caused by the parking lock pawl contacting the ratchet wheel due to improper manual control linkage adjustment.

Abnormal Hum or Whine In All Ranges

This condition may be attributed to worn parts or excessive clearances in the front oil pump. Noise caused by the front pump will increase in Low and will diminish at car speeds above 45 mph in Direct Drive. It increases and decreases with engine speed in all ranges. When excessive clearances exist in front oil pump, a pressure test will usually indicate low front pump pressure.

Abnormal Hum or Whine In All Ranges but Direct Drive

This may be attributed to conditions in the planetary gear train since these gears are locked in Direct Drive but either idling or transmitting power in all other ranges.

Squealing or Screeching

Squealing or screeching immediately following installation of front oil pump parts indicates that the driving gear has been installed backwards. This condition should be corrected without further operation of the transmission as severe damage will result.

Whistling Noise

A whistling noise which occurs during low speed acceleration in Drive, Low and Reverse, accompanied by unsatisfactory transmission performance indicates cavitation of oil due to incomplete filling of torque converter. Remove valve and servo body assembly and check for restrictions in passages leading to torque converter. If these passages are clear, check passages in reaction shaft flange.

A whistling noise during low speed acceleration in Drive, Low and Reverse but with otherwise satisfactory transmission performance may be caused by thin, weak, or cracked turbine vanes, or vanes which are bent over at the exit edges. Such vanes will vibrate under load, causing a whistle. Replacement of the turbine is required for correction.

MAINTENANCE

Adding Fluid

Check the oil level with the transmission oil warm, selector lever in Parking position and with engine idling. Remove the oil gauge rod, wipe dry and reinstall to its full depth. Remove gauge rod again and check oil level.

If the oil level is more than one inch below the "Full" mark on the gauge rod, add Automatic Transmission Fluid as required to bring the level up to (but not above) the "Full" mark. The distance between the "Full" mark and the "Add Oil" mark is one inch and represents approximately one pint.

Changing Fluid

1. Warm up transmission.
2. Remove bell housing cover.
3. Loosen one converter drain plug (through opening in flywheel).
4. Turn flywheel until opposite drain plug is straight down.
5. Remove this plug and drain converter.
6. Remove drain plug from oil pan and drain transmission.
7. Put three quarts of oil in transmission.
8. With engine idling and transmission in Park position, complete the refilling to bring the oil level 1¾" below "Full" mark on gauge rod. When transmission oil is warmed up, the level should then be at the "Full" mark on the rod.

Fig. 3 Band adjustment

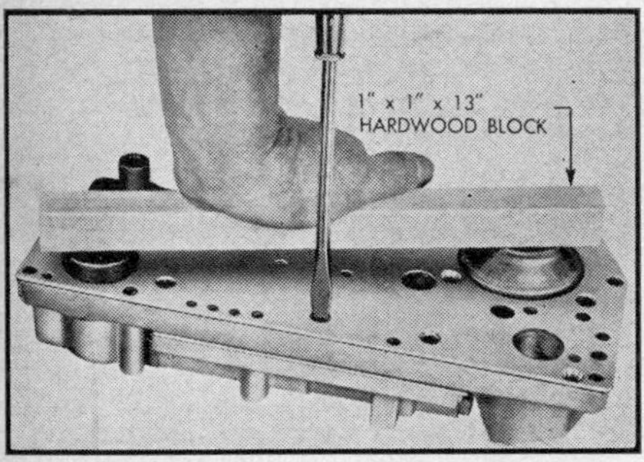

Fig. 5 Removing servo body spacer plate

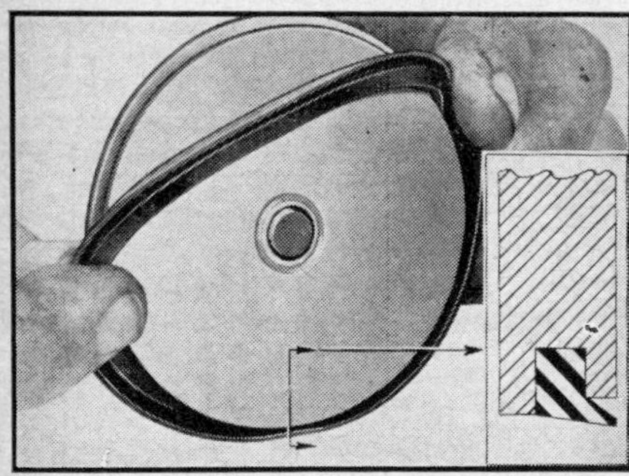
Fig. 6 Installing servo piston seal

MANUAL LINKAGE, ADJUST

When the transmission does not operate properly it is advisable to first check the shift control linkage adjustment, after checking to see if oil is at the proper level.

1. With manual control lever in Park position, raise car to allow access to lower linkage.

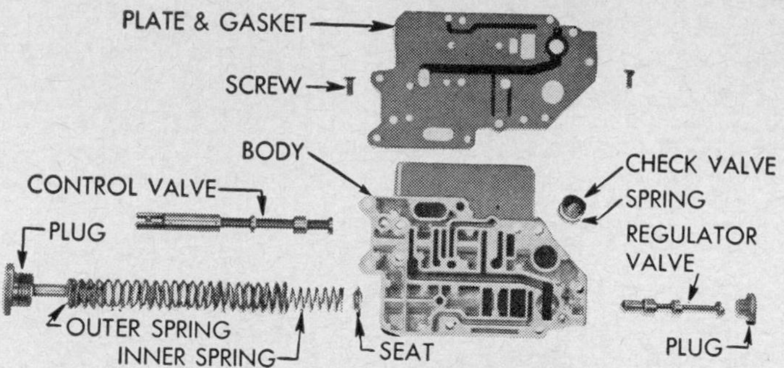

Fig. 4 Valve body disassembled

2. Loosen clamp nut at lower end of upper rod. Move lever several times to be sure it is in the "Park" detent.
3. Tighten clamp bolt.

THROTTLE LINKAGE, ADJUST

1. Remove air cleaner.
2. Move throttle lever to wide open position and check to make sure stator linkage does not prevent throttle from opening completely. If it does, make stator linkage adjustment first as outlined below.
3. Disconnect throttle rod from throttle operating lever, Fig. 2.
4. While a helper presses accelerator firmly against floor mat, hold throttle in wide open position, and hold rear end of throttle rod at hole in throttle operating lever. Rod end must be approximately 1/16" short of entering hole in lever. Adjust throttle rod length as required to obtain this condition.
5. Connect throttle rod to operating lever.
6. Hold choke valve tightly closed and move throttle lever to wide open position and check adjustment of choke unloader. If choke unloader does not operate properly, adjust as outlined in *Carburetor Section.*
7. Finally, check for smooth operation of linkage from fully closed to wide open position of throttle.

BANDS, ADJUST

The reverse band adjusting screw is located on the left side of the transmission and the low band on the right. To adjust, proceed as follows:

1. Loosen lock nut and turn adjusting screw clockwise until considerable resistance is felt, indicating that the band is in full contact with the low drum or reverse ring gear.
2. Back off the screw until just a trace of play can be felt by prying up on the lock nut with a screwdriver, Fig. 3.
3. Back off the screw 6 complete turns and tighten lock nut.
4. After noting position of adjusting screw slot, tighten lock nut. Remove wrench and check to make sure adjusting screw did not turn during the tightening process.
5. Install band adjusting covers with new gaskets.

VALVE & SERVOS

Removal

When removing the assembly from the transmission (after removing oil pan), slightly loosen all valve and servo body attaching screws but do not loosen the slotted safety nuts on the valve-to-servo body studs. Remove all screws, turning each a little at a time in succession until pressure of anchor pin spring is relieved.

Push shift control valve and lower operating lever inward to align lower lever with opening in transmission case. As the assembly is lifted from the case, reach under to hold the anchor piston to prevent it from falling out and getting damaged.

Remove reverse band operating strut by extending a finger through adjustment hole to prevent strut from falling into transmission case. Then release the strut by raising the operating lever.

Valve Body, Disassemble

1. Remove safety nuts and washers from studs, then lift valve body and gasket from servo body. Remove shift control valve from valve body. Check gasket for evidence of oil leakage, Fig. 4.
2. Remove rear pump delivery check valve and spring from servo body.
3. Remove large pressure regulator valve plug from valve body, using care because of the heavy spring pressure behind the plug. Remove the two springs and spring seat.
4. Remove the small valve plug and remove pressure regulator valve from body.
5. Remove valve body plate and gasket; then remove the front pump delivery check valve and spring. Check gasket for evidence of oil leakage.

Servo Body, Disassemble

Remove nut and washer which attaches the lower valve operating lever and linkage adjusting lever to lever shaft and remove levers.

When removing servo body spacer plate, use wood block as shown in Fig. 5. Hold block down firmly while remov-

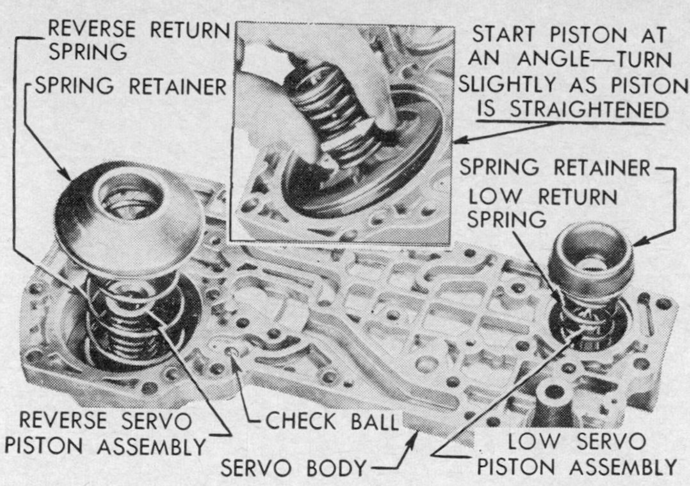

Fig. 7 Parts installed in servo body

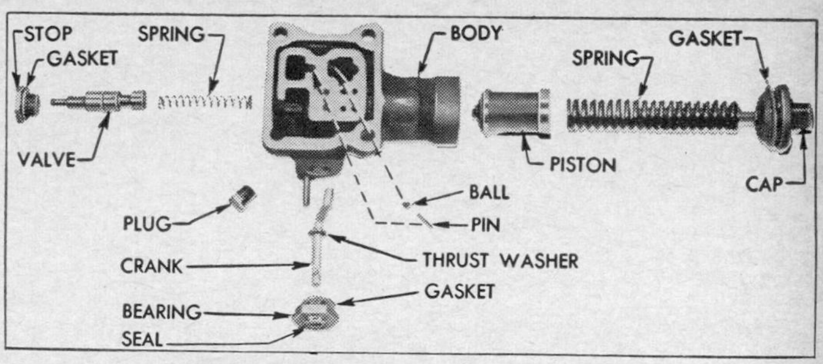

Fig. 8 High accumulator disassembled

ing spacer plate screws. Then carefully release pressure on block to allow servo springs to expand.

Inspect Valve & Servo Parts

1. Wash parts, dry and blow out all passages with air pressure.
2. Inspect bodies for cracks, damage to gasket surfaces, scores in piston and valve bores, or other damage which would render these parts unfit for use.
3. Inspect surfaces and shoulders of shift control valve, pressure regulator valve and anchor piston. Surfaces must be free of nicks, scores or deep scratches.
4. A valve or piston must be replaced if sharp edges are marred or rounded because such conditions will permit fine particles of foreign matter to work in between part and body and cause sticking.
5. Check valves on surface plate and replace if bent.
6. Worn or damaged piston seals should be replaced. When a new seal is installed on a piston, be sure the lip fits over the smaller diameter land, Fig. 6.

Servo Body, Assemble

1. Oil and install low and reverse piston assemblies in servo body. To avoid curling or damaging edge of piston seal, start each piston into cylinder at an angle then turn piston slightly as it is straightened and pushed into cylinder. Check pistons for free movement in cylinders, Fig. 7.
2. Install small return spring with small end against low servo piston. Install large return spring with large end against reverse servo piston. Place spring seats on upper ends of both springs.
3. Place check ball in reverse servo feed channel.
4. Install spacer plate with the aid of the wood block shown in Fig. 5. Tighten screws uniformly to avoid distorting spacer plate.
5. Insert valve operating upper lever shaft through bearing in servo body. With upper lever pointing toward reverse servo, place lower lever with linkage adjusting lever on shaft so that forked end of lower lever points to the low servo; then install lockwasher and nut.

Valve Body, Assemble

1. Place front pump delivery check valve spring in body with large end down and place check valve on spring with ridged side up.
2. Install valve body plate and new gasket, making sure that check valve is seated against plate and is not caught under gasket.
3. Place pressure regulator spring seat on the inner spring; then install spring seat, inner and outer springs and large plug in valve body.
4. See that oil orifice in pressure regulator valve end land is clear, then install valve with this land outward. Install plug and tighten.
5. Install shift control valve with slotted end on same end of valve body as the large pressure regulator plug.
6. Install rear pump delivery check valve in its seat in servo body, ridged face inward, and place valve spring on valve with large end up.
7. Install a new gasket and valve body on servo body, using care to keep pump delivery check valve spring below gasket; then install plain washers and safety nuts on two studs adjacent to control valve. Tighten stud nuts evenly.

ACCUMULATORS

1. Remove retaining pin and check valve from high accumulator body (no check ball on low accumulator).
2. Remove pipe plug, cap, gasket, spring (2 in low) and piston from accumulator body. Keep parts separated so same parts will be installed in same body, Fig. 8.
3. *On high accumulator only,* remove clamp bolt, lever, bearing with seal, gasket, thrust washer and control valve crank from body; then remove valve stop with gasket, control valve and spring.
4. Wash all parts, air dry and blow out all passages. Examine all parts for excessive wear, scoring or other damage.
5. With all parts clean and dry, install pistons and check for free sliding as body is tipped back and forth.
6. Check mounting surface of body with straightedge. If necessary, body may be trued up by moving body in a circular motion on emery cloth placed on a surface plate. Be sure to wash body to remove all traces of emery.
7. If body or piston is worn or damaged or piston does not slide freely in body after all burrs are removed, replace accumulator assembly.
8. Lubricate each piston and install it in body from which it was removed. Start piston squarely (do not tap or force) in body.
9. Install proper piston springs in each body. The high accumulator uses one heavy spring approximately $4\frac{5}{16}$" long. The low accumulator uses one shorter heavy spring and one inner spring. Install caps with new gaskets but tighten caps later.
10. *On high accumulator only,* install spring, control valve and stop; then install crank with thrust washer, bearing with new gasket and seal (grooved side inward), operating lever and clamp bolt.
11. Adjust operating lever on crank so that lever contacts its stop and the crank contacts the valve with valve in extreme upper position, Fig. 9; then tighten clamp bolt.
12. Install pipe plugs in both accumulator bodies and install check valve and retaining pin in high accumulator body.

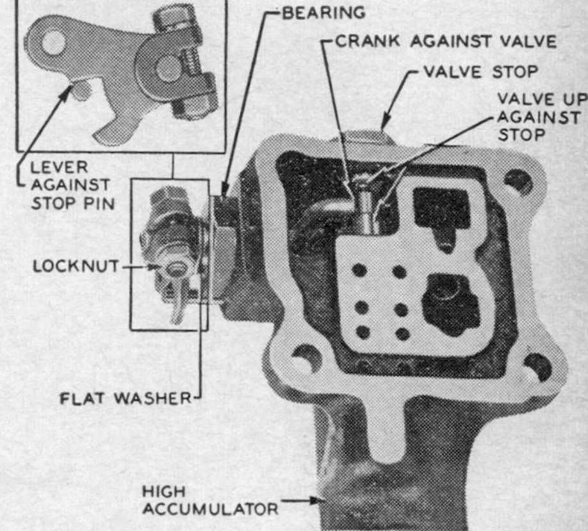

Fig. 9 High accumulator valve operating lever adjustment

TRANSMISSION, REPLACE

1. Raise car front and rear.
2. Disconnect exhaust pipe (s).
3. Remove converter housing cover.
4. Drain converter and oil pan.
5. Disconnect oil cooler pipes. *If transmission is being removed to correct clutch or band difficulties, the cooler and lines must be flushed with air and, if possible, oil to remove residue.*
6. Remove three flywheel-to-converter bolts.
7. Disconnect speedometer cable, stator control rod at accumulator and lower shift rods at equalizer.
8. Disconnect equalizer bracket at accumulator bolts. Slide equalizer out of bushing in frame rail. Remove equalizer and bracket.
9. Disconnect propeller shaft at rear companion flange. Mark flange and shaft so parts may be reassembled in the same relative position. Support shaft up out of the way to prevent damage to center joint caused by weight of shaft.
10. Support transmission with jack.
11. Remove two center support frame bolts and slide propeller shaft rearward until shaft is disengaged from transmission.
12. Remove bolts attaching mounting pad to rear bearing retainer.
13. Raise engine and transmission just enough to relieve load on transmission support. Remove bolts attaching support to frame rail and remove support and pad as an assembly. *Shims may be used between support and frame. If so, note number and location so they may be reinstalled in original position.*
14. Support rear of engine with jack.
15. Lower transmission just enough so that converter housing bolts can be reached. Disconnect converter housing from engine crankcase.
16. Move transmission rearward to disengage hub of converter pump cover from crankshaft, lower transmission and remove from car.
17. Reverse procedure to install.

BUICK SPECIAL DUAL PATH DRIVE

NOTE: — This chapter deals only with maintenance, adjustments and "in car" repairs. For major service work, Motor's Automatic Transmission Manual is available. Current edition is a 740 page volume that includes 240 pages of oil circuit diagrams mostly in full color.

TRANSMISSION IDENTIFICATION

A production identification number is stamped on the raised surface of the case, forward of the oil pan on the left side. The identification consists of a letter followed by one or more digits.

DESCRIPTION

This transmission, Fig. 1, provides five different control or operating ranges which may be manually selected by the driver through movement of the control lever. Letters on the stationary dial on the control panel identify each range as follows: P for parking; N for neutral; D for drive; L for low, and R for reverse.

The transmission case is bolted to the engine crankcase through the converter housing section of the case. The transmission case, converter housing and rear bearing retainer are one integral cast aluminum part.

TROUBLE SHOOTING GUIDE

Upshifts Below Normal Speed

1. Governor valve not adjusted properly or sticking.
2. Shift valve or shift regulator valve sticking.
3. Throttle valve pressure too low. Could be worn or broken spring or sticking valve.

Upshifts Above Normal Speed

1. Governor valve not adjusted properly or sticking.
2. Shift valve or shift regulator sticking.
3. Throttle valve pressure too high, valve sticking.

Slow, Lagging Upshift

1. Converter pressure regulator valve sticking. This results in a slower lowering of converter pressure and a slow engagement of converter clutch.

Harsh Upshift

1. Converter pressure regulator valve sticking and creating a low converter pressure at all times. This results in a harsh, fast engagement of the converter clutch.

Car Won't Move or Slips In Reverse

1. Coast clutch slipping, burned out or not engaged.
2. Reverse clutch slipping, burned out or not engaged.
3. Front overrunning clutch slipping.
4. Forward clutch locked up or not releasing.

Car Won't Move or Slips on Take-Off In Drive or Low

1. Forward clutch slipping, burned out or not engaged.

Car Won't Upshift In Drive Range

1. Throttle valve stuck in high pressure position or throttle valve linkage may be binding holding throttle valve open.
2. Converter clutch slipping, burned out or not engaged.
3. Converter pressure regulator valve stuck keeping converter pressure high at all times.
4. Governor valve stuck in "Off" position or improperly adjusted.
5. Shift valve stuck in "Off" position or shift regulator valve stuck.

Car Coasts on Deceleration In Low

1. Coast clutch slipping, burned out or not engaged.

Car Locks Up When It Upshifts In Drive Range

1. Coast clutch locked up or not releasing.
2. Rear overrunning clutch locked up.

Car Backs Up In Neutral

1. Reverse clutch locked up or not releasing.

Car Pulls Forward In Neutral

1. Forward clutch locked up or not releasing.
2. Converter clutch locked up or not releasing.

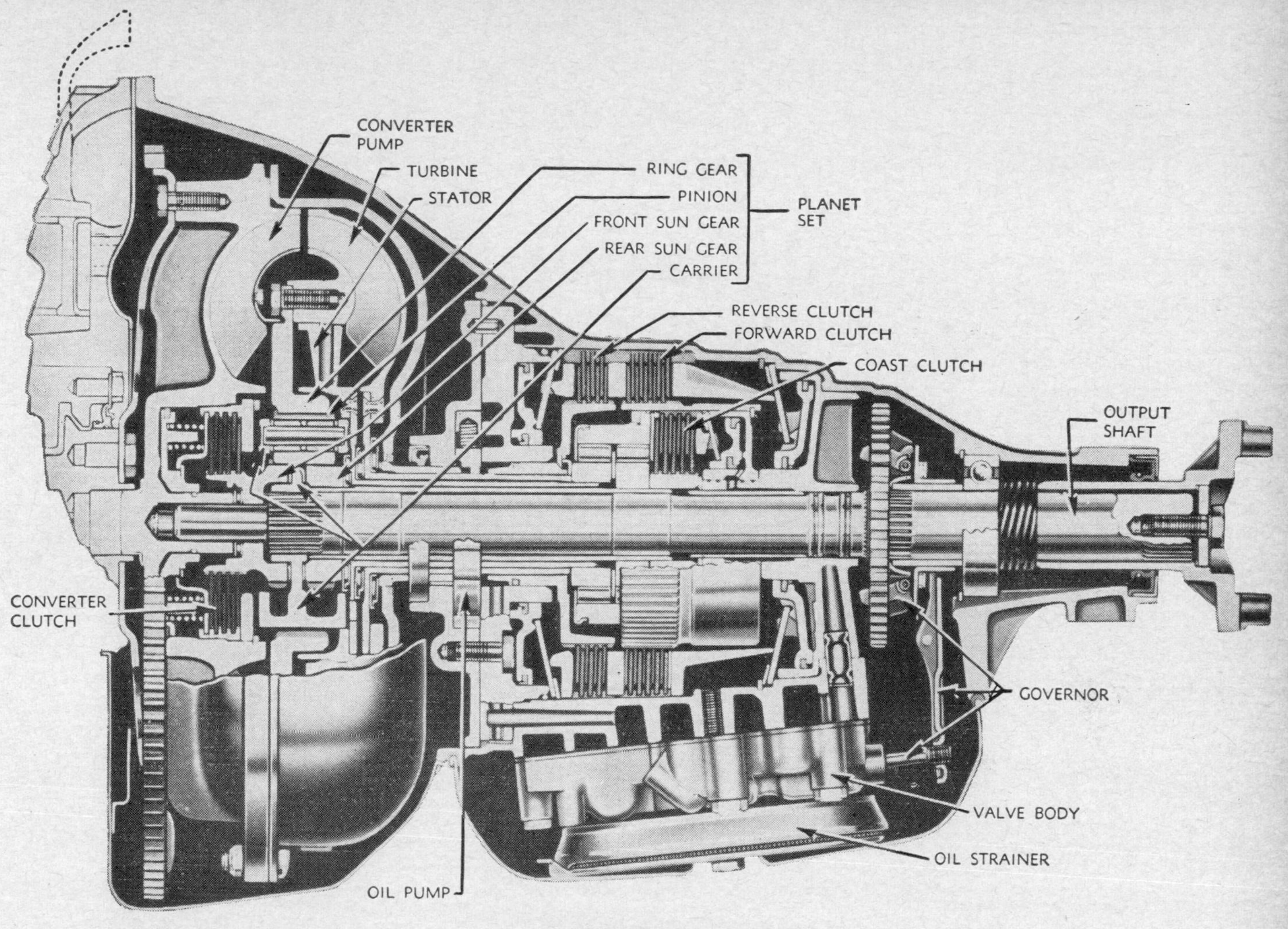

Fig. 1 Sectional view of Buick Special Dual Path Drive

Car Labors On Take-Off or Stalls

1. Converter clutch locked up or not releasing.

Car Slips On Take-Off In Drive or Low

1. Front overrunning clutch slipping.

Engine Labors When Approaching Cruising Speed

1. Front overrunning clutch locked up.

Upshifts Early but Will Not Downshift

1. Throttle valve stuck in "Off" position.

Upshifts Only at High Speed

1. Throttle pressure regulator valve stuck causing throttle pressure to be too high.
2. Throttle detent valve stuck wide open.

Upshifts Early except At Wide Open Throttle

1. Shift regulator stuck.

MAINTENANCE

Adding Oil

Check transmission oil level with transmission oil warm, transmission in Park and engine idling. Remove the oil level dipstick, wipe dry with a clean cloth and reinstall to full depth. Remove dipstick and note level.

If oil level is below "ADD" mark on dipstick, add automatic transmission oil as required but do not fill above the "FULL" mark. The distance between the "FULL" and "ADD" marks represents approximately one pint.

Changing Oil

At 24,000 mile intervals, the transmission oil pan should be removed and cleaned. The oil strainer should be replaced and fresh oil added to the transmission. *This operation should not be attempted unless accurate foot pound and inch pound torque wrenches are available and the operator is fully qualified in their use.*

1. Remove bolt and seal attaching oil pan to transmission.
2. Remove oil pan and case seal.
3. Remove oil strainer and O-ring seal.
4. Install new strainer and O-ring seal. Torque strainer bolts (strap not used after 1962).
5. Clean oil pan. Install new seal on pan using care not to stretch seal.
6. Install oil pan and seal, oil pan bolt and bolt seal. Torque oil pan bolt.
7. Add two quarts of oil to transmission. Start engine and allow to idle in Park range. Then add oil to bring level to the "FULL" mark on dipstick with transmission warmed up.

MANUAL LINKAGE, ADJUST

1. Referring to Fig. 2, loosen adjusting swivel clamp bolt.
2. Set transmission selector lever in neutral detent.
3. Move shift lever against neutral stop.
4. Tighten adjusting swivel clamp nut.

THROTTLE LINKAGE, ADJUST

1. Referring to Fig. 2, hold throttle rod

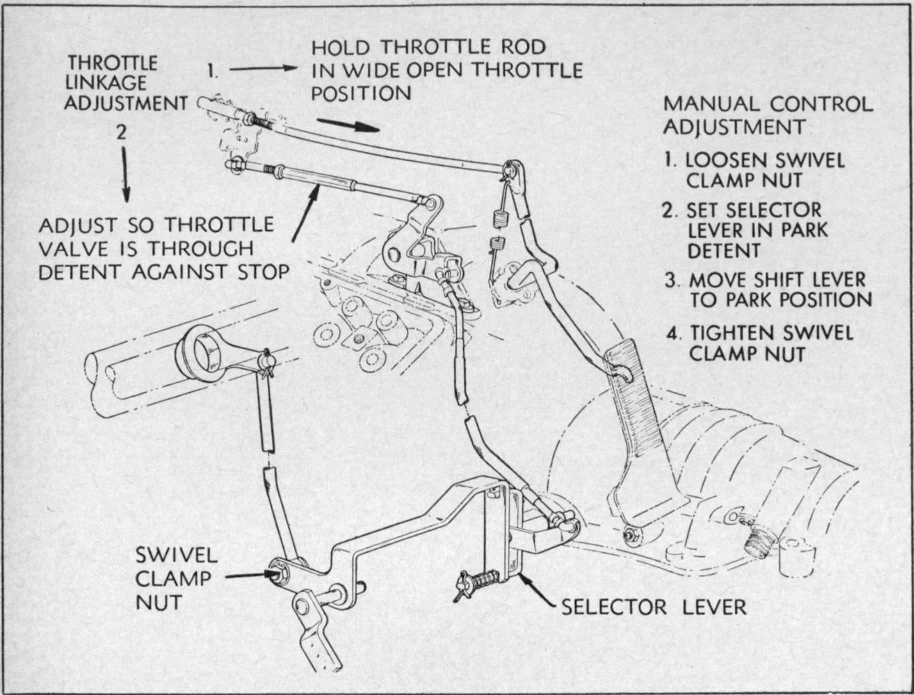
THROTTLE LINKAGE ADJUSTMENT
1.
HOLD THROTTLE ROD IN WIDE OPEN THROTTLE POSITION
2
ADJUST SO THROTTLE VALVE IS THROUGH DETENT AGAINST STOP
MANUAL CONTROL ADJUSTMENT
1. LOOSEN SWIVEL CLAMP NUT
2. SET SELECTOR LEVER IN PARK DETENT
3. MOVE SHIFT LEVER TO PARK POSITION
4. TIGHTEN SWIVEL CLAMP NUT
SWIVEL CLAMP NUT
SELECTOR LEVER

Fig. 2 Buick Dual Path Drive transmission linkage

in wide open position (against stop on carburetor).

2. Hold idler lever in full throttle valve position (through detent to stop). *Do not confuse detent position of throttle valve with stop position. Increased resistance will be felt as the throttle valve reaches detent position. The idler lever should be pushed through detent to stop.*
3. Adjust turnbuckle so no lost motion exists in slide link (wide open throttle and throttle valve stop reached simultaneously).
4. Tighten lock nut on turnbuckle.

PARKING PAWL, REPLACE

Transmission In Car

1. Remove oil pan and seal.
2. Remove parking lock pawl engaging spring.
3. Remove parking lock bracket-to-case bolts.
4. Drive lock pawl shaft pin out of case with punch or drift.
5. Pull pawl shaft and O-ring seal out of case, and remove pawl.
6. Install and lube O-ring seal on lock pawl shaft. Align pawl with shaft and install shaft with slots lined up with hole in case. Install roll pin.
7. Install parking lock bracket loosely.
8. Shift transmission to "Park" position and turn output shaft so pawl engages wheel. Now tighten parking lock bracket bolts.
9. Check for freedom of travel between park and neutral ranges. If a bind exists, place a .001″ shim under parking lock bracket at both bolts.
10. Install lock pawl disengaging spring and install oil pan.

TRANSMISSION, REPLACE

1. Raise car and support front and rear.
2. Remove exhaust crossover pipe.
3. Remove front U-joint bolts and slide propeller shaft rearward to separate U-joint at transmission. Support propeller shaft to avoid weight of shaft damaging center U-joint.
4. Place suitable jack under transmission and fasten jack to transmission.
5. Remove transmission crossmember.
6. Disconnect speedometer cable.
7. Loosen shift linkage swivel clamp nut. Remove cotter pin, spring and washer attaching equalizer to range selector outer lever and remove equalizer.
8. Remove oil filler pipe.
9. Support engine at oil pan.
10. Remove transmission cover pan.
11. Mark flywheel and converter pump for reassembly in same position and remove three converter-to-flywheel bolts.
12. Remove transmission-to-engine bolts.
13. Move transmission rearward to provide clearance between converter pump and crankshaft.
14. Lower transmission out of car. *Wire converter to transmission case or otherwise suitably retain it. If not retained, converter will fall out if transmission is tilted forward even slightly.*
15. Reverse removal procedure to install the transmission.

DUAL COUPLING HYDRA-MATIC

NOTE: — This chapter deals only with maintenance, adjustments and "in car" repairs. For major service work, Motor's Automatic Transmission Manual is available. Current edition is a 740 page volume that includes 240 pages of oil circuit diagrams mostly in full color.

TRANSMISSION IDENTIFICATION

Each transmission may be identified by a name plate located on the lower left corner of the transmission case rear face. Car model application is designated by a prefix letter or letters followed by the serial number of the unit.

CADILLAC HYDRA-MATIC		CODE
1963	All except Series 75—black plate	C
	Series 75—orange plate	CA
1964	All except Series 75—red plate	C
	Series 75—blue plate	CA

PONTIAC SUPER HYDRA-MATIC		
1963-64	With two-barrel carburetor	PS
	With three carburetors	PAS
	With four-barrel carburetor	PBS
	Economy engine	PES
1964	With 421 High Output engine	PCS

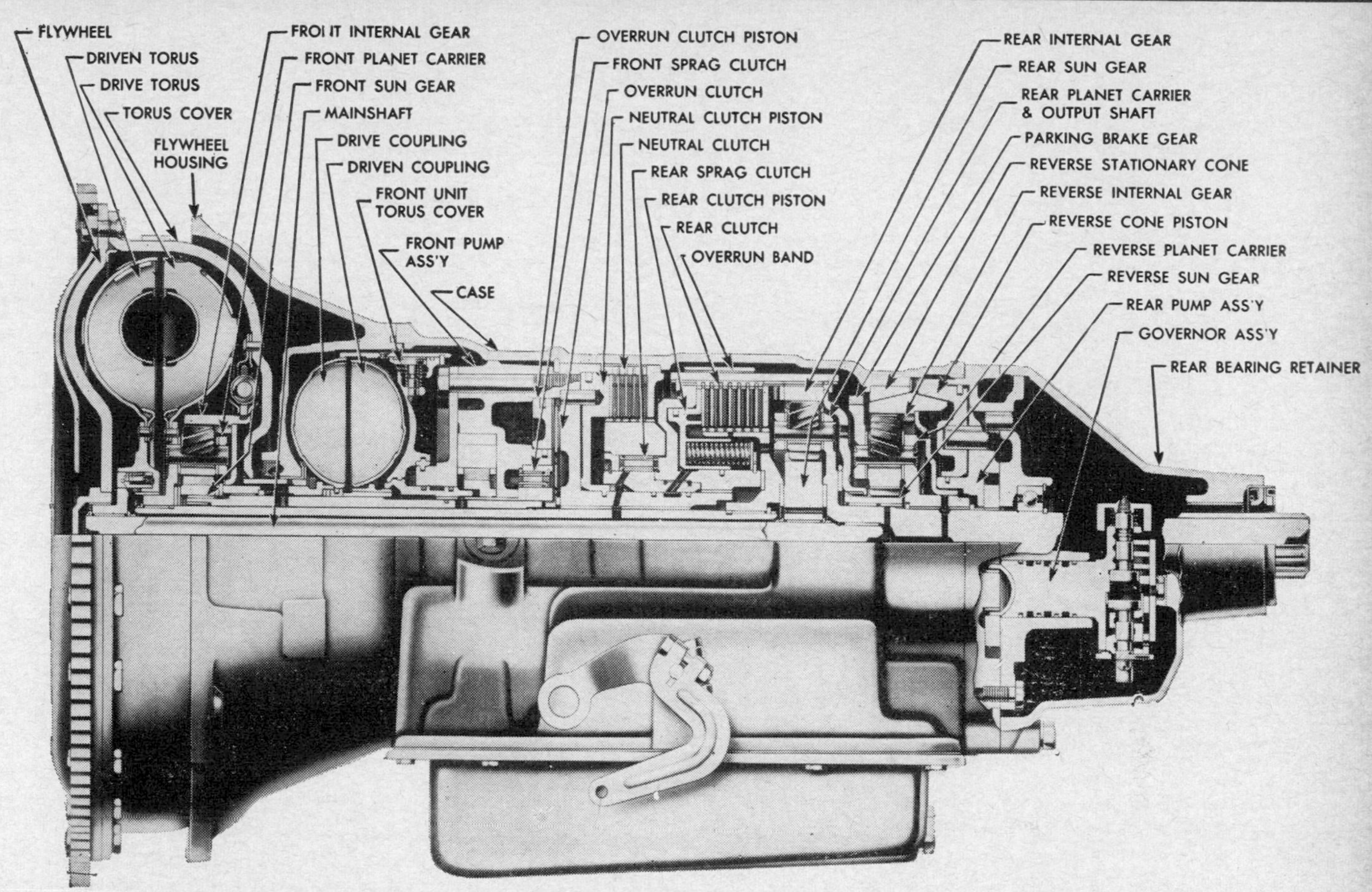

Fig. 1 Cutaway view of two coupling Hydra-Matic featuring sprag (one way) clutches and a small fluid coupling in place of the multiple disc clutches and servo applied bands used formerly. Rear pump not used after 1958

DESCRIPTION

The Dual Coupling Hydra-Matic has four forward speeds and one reverse, Fig. 1. A "Park" position is provided which mechanically locks up the propeller shaft. The gear reductions required to obtain the various speeds are provided by planetary gearsets.

The fluid coupling acts as a hydraulic clutch which is used to transmit engine torque to the transmission. The use of the fluid coupling eliminates the need for a manual (mechanical) clutch and it also provides a cushioning effect of the gear changes between the engine and the transmission.

In order to create the understanding of fundamentals which is required for effective trouble shooting and repair work, here is an outline of the operating principles of the Dual Coupling Hydra-Matic, along with a summary of the power flow in chart form:

The main working units of the transmission are the front unit, rear unit and the reverse unit. The front and rear units both consist of an individual planetary gear reduction and means for locking up these planetary gear trains for direct drive, depending on driving requirements.

The reverse unit operates through its own gearset, which when coupled to the reduction in the front unit changes the direction of output shaft rotation at near maximum reduction.

The front and rear units in the transmission are controlled hydraulically by selector lever position, the governor (car speed) and throttle pressure (load requirements). The reverse unit is controlled hydraulically by selector lever position only.

TROUBLE SHOOTING GUIDE

Slips In 1st & 3rd

1. Front sprag clutch slipping.
2. Front sprag clutch broken.

Slips In or Misses 2nd & 4th

1. Front unit torus cover seals leaking.
2. Front unit torus cover exhaust valves sticking or missing.
3. Front unit torus cover feed restriction or leak.
4. Front unit torus cover signal restriction or leak.
5. Low oil pressure.
6. Coupling valve sticking.
7. Sticking valves or dirt in valve body.
8. Coupling snap ring improperly installed or missing.
9. Limit valve.
10. Coupling passage restricted or leaking.
11. Front unit torus vanes damaged.

Slips In All D Ranges

1. Manual linkage.
2. Neutral clutch slipping or burned.
3. Neutral clutch apply restricted or leaking (case support or valve body).
4. Incorrect number of neutral clutch plates.
5. Low oil pressure.
6. Control valve.
7. Torus members (check valve).
8. Intake pipe O-ring damaged or missing.
9. Pressure regulator valve stuck in pump.
10. Pump slide stuck.

Slips In 1st & 2nd (D Range)

1. Rear sprag clutch slipping or improperly assembled.
2. Rear sprag clutch broken.
3. Neutral clutch burned, restricted, piston sticking.

Slips In 3rd & 4th

1. Rear unit clutch slipping or burned.
2. Rear unit clutch apply restricted or O-ring leaking.

3. Incorrect number of clutch plates (rear).
4. Accumulator.
5. Center support, leak at 2-3 passage.
6. Low oil pressure.
7. Accumulator valve stuck (3rd only).

Slips In 3rd In Drive Right On Coast

1. Overrun clutch slipping or burned.
2. Overrun clutch apply restricted or leaking.
3. Sticking valves or dirt in valve body.
4. Overrun clutch passages restricted or leaking.

Slips In 1st & 2nd In Low Range On Coast

1. Low servo apply restricted or leaking.
2. Low band not anchored to case or broken.
3. Low servo piston and rod binding in case or servo and accumulator body.
4. Band facing worn or loose.
5. Anchor dowel pin missing or loose in case.

No Drive In D Range

1. Manual linkage incorrectly adjusted.
2. Manual valve not engaged with drive pin.
3. Low oil pressure.
4. Pressure regulator stuck.
5. Pump intake pipe improperly installed.
6. Front sprag broken, pump bushing, front unit drive torus shaft.
7. Front and/or rear sprag incorrectly installed.
8. Rear sprag broken.
9. Front sprag inner race broken.
10. Rear sprag outer race broken.
11. Neutral clutch plates burned.
12. Neutral clutch piston.
13. Control valve.
14. Pump.

Erratic or No Upshifts

1. Governor valves stuck.
2. Broken governor rings.
3. Sticking valves or dirt in valve body.
4. G-2 bushing turned.

Misses In 2nd

1. Governor boost valve stuck closed.
2. Transition valve stuck away from plate.
3. Sticking valves or dirt in valve body.
4. Governor sticking.

Misses In 3rd

1. Transition valve sticking.
2. Sticking valves or dirt in valve body.
3. TV adjustment—too long.
4. Rear clutch.
5. Transition valve spring.

Locks Up In 2nd & 4th

1. Front sprag clutch broken or reversed.
2. Overrun clutch applied or sticking.

Locks Up In 3rd & 4th

1. Rear sprag clutch broken.
2. Low band not releasing.

Rough 2-3 Shift

1. Accumulator valve stuck.
2. Accumulator piston stuck.
3. Accumulator gasket broken or missing.
4. Restricted or leaking oil passages.
5. Broken accumulator spring.
6. Broken or leaking piston oil seal rings.
7. Control valve.
8. TV adjusted incorrectly.
9. Rear clutch pack.
10. Case passages; TV oil, 2-3 oil, leaks or restrictions.

Upshifts High

1. Throttle linkage adjusted short.
2. Governor valves sticking.
3. Broken governor rings.
4. Sticking valves or dirt in valve body.
5. Leaking or restricted main line feed to governor.

Upshifts Low

1. Throttle linkage adjusted long.
2. Governor valves sticking.
3. Broken governor rings.
4. Sticking valves or dirt in valve body.
5. Leaking TV oil.

No Reverse, Slips or Locks Up

1. Manual linkage incorrectly adjusted.
2. Manual valve not engaged with drive pin.
3. Reverse piston apply restricted or leaking.
4. Low oil pressure.
5. Pressure regulator.
6. Neutral clutch not released.
7. Flash restricting neutral clutch exhaust port on manual body.

Selector Lever Won't Go In Reverse

1. Governor valves sticking.
2. Broken governor rings.
3. Reverse blocker piston stuck.
4. Manual linkage interference.

Reverse Drive In Neutral

1. Reverse stationary cone sticking.

Delayed 1-2 Shift

1. Coupling valve sticking.
2. Governor boost valve sticking.
3. G-1 valve sticking.
4. Wrong spring on coupling valve.

Drive In Low Range Only

1. Rear sprag broken.
2. Neutral clutch not applying.

No Forced Downshifts 4-3 or 3-2

1. Control valve.
2. Linkage.

2-3 Runaway

1. 2-3 passage in center bearing support.
2. Plug out of accumulator.
3. Rear clutch burned.
4. Valve body; transition valve, case passages (2-3 circuit).

Won't Go Into Park

1. Parking links broken.
2. Mechanical interference.
3. Manual linkage.
4. Parking pawl.

Starts In 2nd Speed

1. Valves sticking.
2. Governor sticking.
3. Governor boost valve stuck.

Drives Forward In Reverse & Neutral

1. Neutral clutch piston stuck in applied position.

Lunges Forward Before Back Up When Placing Selector In Reverse

1. G-2 plunger stuck in outward position.
2. Restricted neutral clutch release oil.

NOISE DIAGNOSIS

P, R, N, D 1st and 3rd

1. Front unit planetary gears.

P, R, N, D 1st and 2nd

1. Rear unit planetary gears.

All Ranges, especially during warm up

1. Pump noisy; cut O-ring on intake pipe, cut O-ring on cooler sleeves.

1-2 and 3-4 With Hot oil

1. Front unit coupling leaks.

All Ranges—Loaded only in Reverse

1. Reverse planetary gears.

Clicking—Low Speed Forward

1. Pressure regulator.
2. Low oil pressure or level.
3. Coupling valve.
4. Governor.

Buzzing

1. Pressure regulator.
2. Oil pressure.
3. Throttle valve.
4. Rear bearing (at about 35 mph).

Rattle or Buzz under light load in 3rd and 4th

1. Torus cover; damper spring.

Squeak When Engaging Reverse

1. Low oil pressure or leak in front clutch overrun piston.
2. Rear pump (prior to 1959).

Vibration

1. Flywheel balance.
2. Torus cover balance.
3. Front unit assembly balance.
4. Rear brake drum balance.

MAINTENANCE

Adding Fluid

Due to the smaller size of this transmission, it is extremely important that the proper fluid level be maintained. A one pint tolerance is marked on the level indicator. Checking or changing the fluid should never be attempted when the transmission is extremely hot or cold because of fluid expansion and contraction.

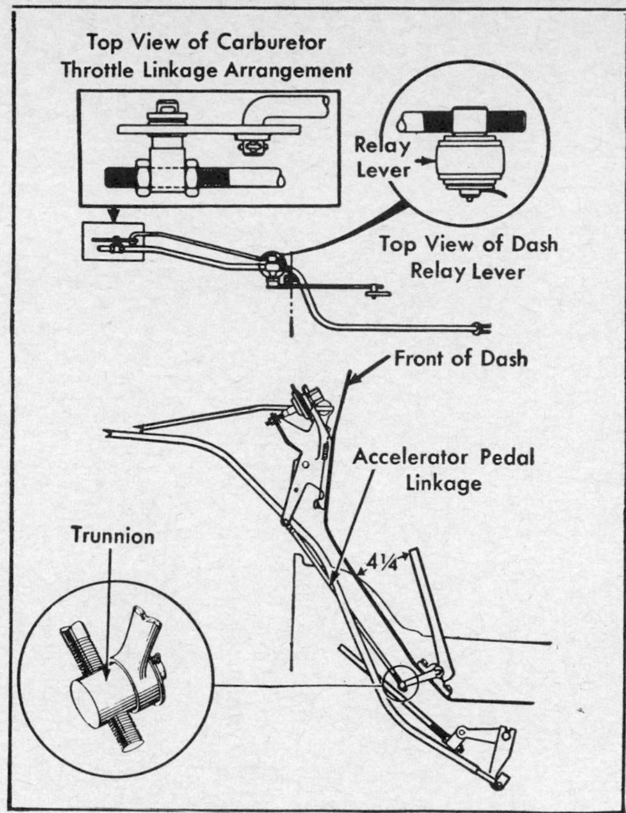

Fig. 2 Manual and throttle linkage. Cadillac

CARBURETOR THROTTLE ROD
T.V. UPPER CONTROL ROD
APPROX. 3¾" TO CARPET
GEARSHIFT UPPER CONTROL ROD
T.V. LOWER CONTROL ROD
GEARSHIFT LOWER CONTROL ROD

Fig. 4 Throttle linkage. Pontiac

Throttle Rod
Trunnion
TV Rod
Adjusting Nuts

Fig. Throttle linkage adjustment. Cadillac

The fluid level should be checked at every chassis lubrication. Add fluid, if necessary, until the proper level is indicated on the dipstick. Check the level after the engine has been running to make certain the fluid coupling is full. Run the engine with the selector lever in "N" or "P" at a fast idle (800 rpm) for 1½ minutes.

Reduce engine speed to slow idle. Remove and wipe dipstick and check fluid level. With engine still running, add fluid to bring it to the proper level. At normal operating temperature, from low mark (bottom dimple) to "F" requires one pint of fluid.

Changing Fluid

Transmission fluid should be changed as directed by the manufacturer as follows:

Cadillac: For normal use change after the first 30,000 miles and every 16,000 miles thereafter. For commercial cars (ambulances) and cars subjected to unusually hard use, first 16,000 miles and every 9,000 miles thereafter.

Oldsmobile: Every 26,000 miles.

Pontiac: Every 30,000 miles.

1. Remove lower flywheel housing cover plate.
2. Remove drain plugs from transmission oil pan and front face of flywheel or torus cover.
3. When fluid has drained, reinstall drain plugs.
4. Pour 7 quarts of fluid into filler tube.
5. Run engine at a fast idle speed (800 rpm) for 1½ minutes with selector lever in "N".
6. Reduce engine speed to slow idle and add 1½ to 2 quarts to bring level to the "F" mark on dipstick provided transmission is at normal operating temperature (160-200°).

MANUAL LINKAGE, ADJUST

Cadillac

1. Remove slush deflector.
2. Remove clevis from manual lever on transmission, Fig. 2.
3. Loosen adjusting nuts on transmission manual rod.
4. Place manual lever on transmission in DR 4 position.
5. Place selector lever on steering column in DR-4 position.
6. Adjust length of manual rod until hole in manual lever lines up with hole in clevis and then *increase length one more turn.*
7. Install clevis and tighten adjusting nuts.
8. Check manual selector lever; it should be free to enter "Park" position, and DR-4 stop in steering column should correspond to DR-4 detent position in transmission. Readjust if these conditions are not met.

Pontiac

1. Place upper shift lever and transmission lever in Park position and, with transmission outer shift lever trunnion nuts backed clear of trunnion, pull shift rod down toward transmission as far as possible.

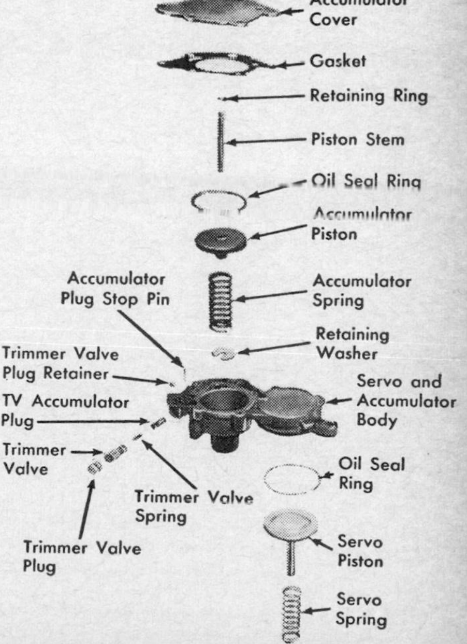

Fig. 5 Servo and accumulator

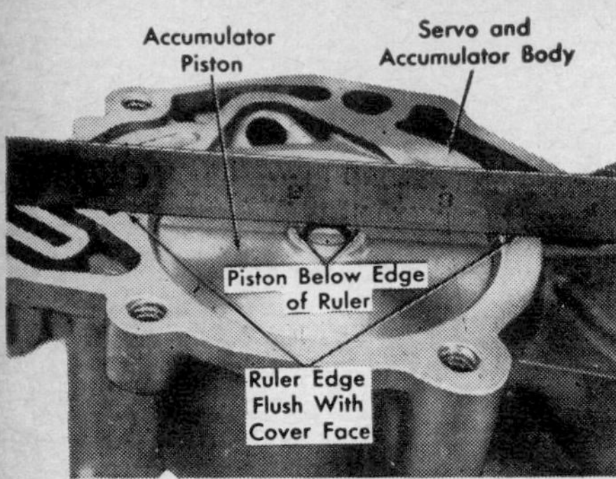

Fig. 6 Accumulator piston installed. Pontiac

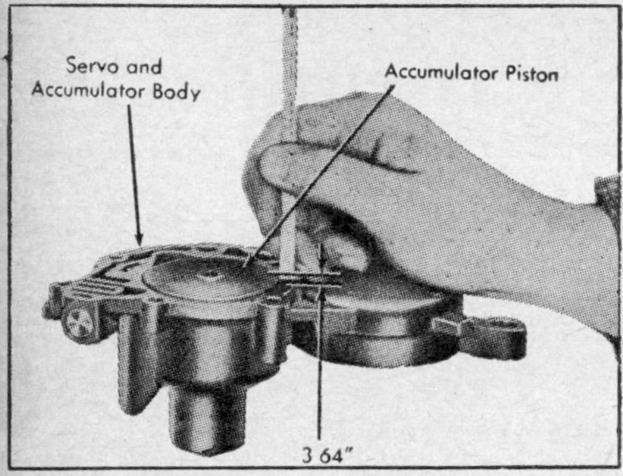

Fig. 7 Accumulator piston installed. Cadillac

While holding rod in this position, run trunnion upper nut down to just contact trunnion. Run lower nut up to contact trunnion and lock nuts securely.

2. After completing above adjustments, check transmission parking lock with car on ramp or grade for positive lock.
3. Place upper shift lever in Drive Right position and check indicator pointer index. If necessary to adjust, loosen check nut above ball stud, adjust index by rotating rod and lock check nut securely.

THROTTLE LINKAGE, ADJUST

Cadillac

1. Remove spring clip from carburetor throttle rod trunnion and remove trunnion from relay bracket lever.
2. Place ¼" drill shank through gauging hole in dash relay lever and into dash relay bracket, Fig. 2.
3. With engine running, set throttle lever in hot idle position (Air Conditioner off).
4. Adjust carburetor throttle rod trunnion to allow free entry into dash relay lever.
5. Install spring clip in trunnion.
6. Using two wrenches, back off both jam nuts on T.V. rod at carburetor to allow free movement of rod in trunnion, Fig. 3.
7. Push end of T.V. rod toward rear of car to position transmission throttle lever against its stop.
8. Turn front jam nut against the trunnion until all slack is taken up. Tighten nut 3 full turns for both one and two-carburetor engines.
9. Turn rear jam nut into contact with trunnion and use two wrenches to tighten nuts, being careful not to put any binding force on the carburetor plate.

Pontiac

1. Refer to Fig. 4. Remove carburetor air cleaner.
2. Loosen two throttle control rod trunnion nuts.
3. Adjust engine idle speed to specifications.
4. Shut off engine and install a suitable pin through holes in throttle control lever and bracket. *Four barrel carburetors are equipped with an anti-stall dashpot (throttle return check). Before installing pin, either remove dashpot or install tool J-6324-01 over dashpot so that it will not interfere with linkage adjustment.*

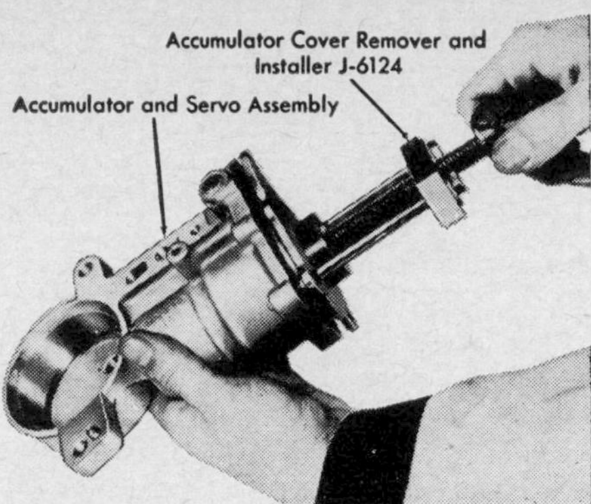

Fig. 8 Removing accumulator cover

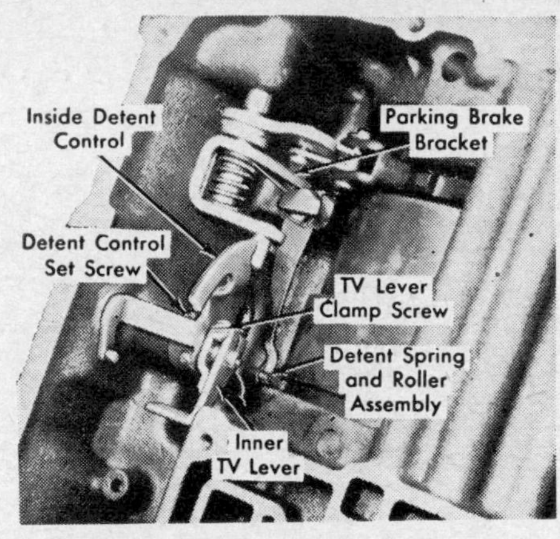

Fig. 9 Inside control levers

5. With throttle valves fully closed, loosen lock nut and adjust length of transmission control rod to carburetor so that gauge pin is free in holes. Leave pin installed and tighten lock nut securely. Recheck freeness of pin in holes.
6. Push throttle valve upper control rod

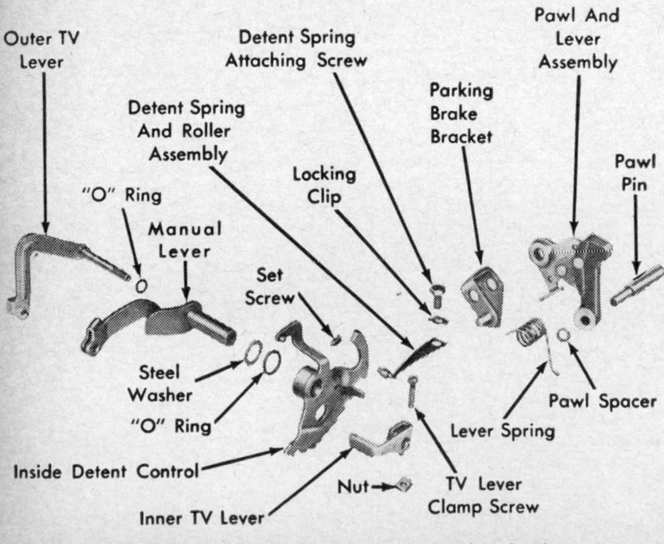

Fig. 10 Control lever and parking brake

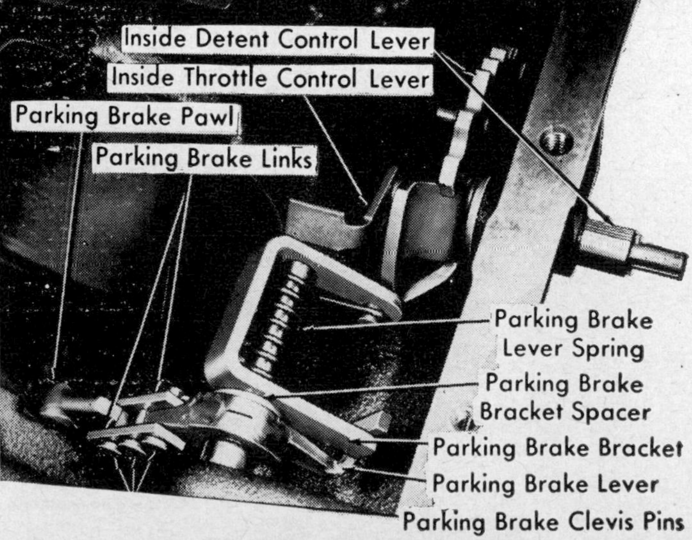

Fig. 11 Inside control levers and parking brake bracket (typical)

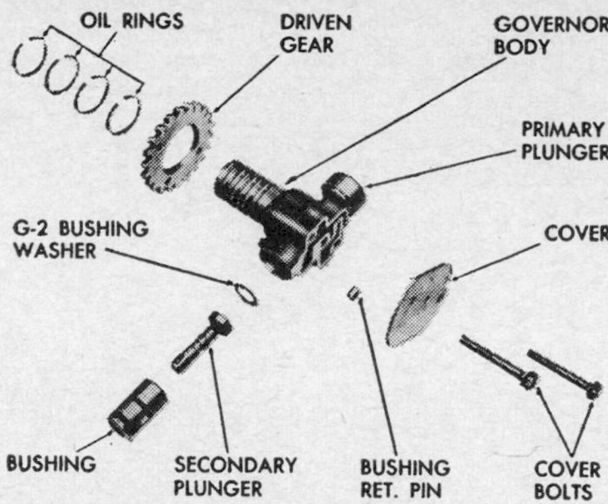

Fig. 12 Governor assembly

downward until outer throttle valve lever is felt to touch end of travel. Make sure that when lever is in this position, upper lock nut is not touching trunnion.

7. While holding throttle valve upper control in this position, tighten upper and lower trunnion lock nuts finger tight. Shorten upper control rod by backing off lower trunnion 4½ turns and tighten upper lock nut securely. Remove gauge pin.
8. Loosen lock nut on carburetor throttle rod. Then adjust this rod to obtain 4.55″ clearance from underside of attaching boss on pedal-to-body toe pan, Fig. 6, (approximately 3¾″ to carpet).
9. Tighten lock nut on carburetor throttle rod securely.

SERVO & ACCUMULATOR

After removing oil pan, oil strainer and intake pipe, remove two screws holding unit to case and lift off.

Disassemble the unit as indicated in Fig. 5. When installing the TV accumulator plug have the slotted end out and align the slot in the plug with the vent passage. Use small screwdriver to align plug in bore.

When installing the accumulator piston, install stem end first, being careful not to damage accumulator piston oil ring. Stem must be seated in recess of bottom of accumulator body. If stem is properly seated, piston will be in the correct position in the accumulator body as shown in Figs. 6 and 7.

CONTROL VALVE

Remove oil pan, oil strainer and intake pipe. Remove servo and accumulator assembly. Then remove five attaching capscrews and take off the control valve assembly. Do not allow the assembly to rest on the channel plate-to-case spacer, and do not allow the manual valve to drop out from its bore.

PARKING BRAKE & PAWL

NOTE—These units Figs. 9 and 10, can be removed with the transmission in the car. The operation involves the removal of the oil pan and strainer, intake pipe, control valve and servo-accumulator assemblies.

1. After above units have been removed, loosen inner TV lever-to-TV shaft clamp screw. Withdraw outer TV lever and shaft from case. Discard O-ring seal.
2. Remove inner TV lever.
3. Loosen inside detent control set screw.
4. Withdraw manual lever and shaft from case. Remove steel washer and discard seal ring, Fig. 10.
5. To remove the parking pawl, it will be necessary to remove the extension housing and reverse clutch housing retaining bolt, then rotate the reverse clutch housing to expose the parking pawl pin for removal. Do not damage the reverse clutch housing-to-case gasket as it must be re used.

CAUTION—On some Pontiac models, there is a governor feed screen protruding from the case into the reverse clutch housing. On these models it will not be possible to rotate the reverse clutch housing; therefore it will be necessary to remove this unit entirely to gain access to the parking pawl pin. Whether or not such a screen is used on any given transmission can be determined by removing the pipe plug at the bottom of the reverse clutch housing; if a screen is used it will be visible through the plug opening.

6. Install a ⅜″ bolt into parking pawl pin and remove pin and spacer. Remove lever and pawl as a unit.

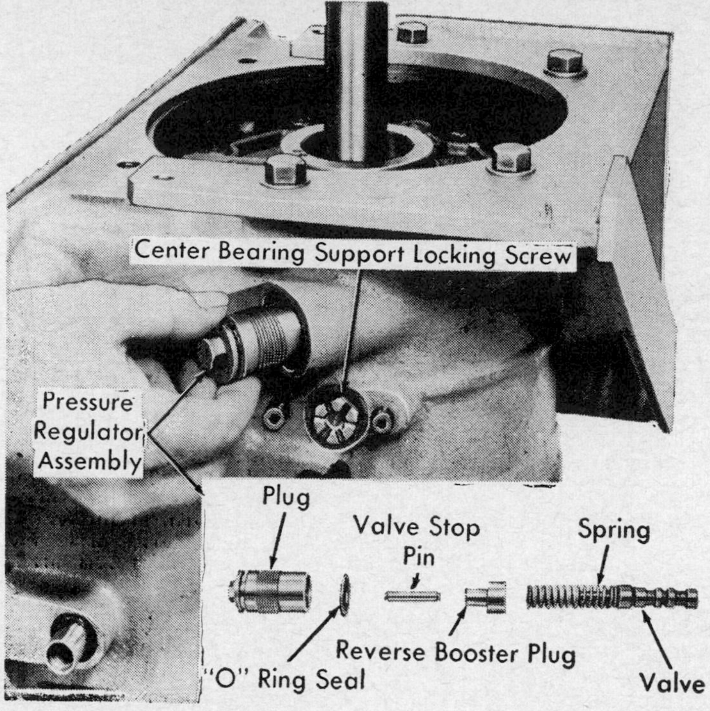

Fig. 13 Pressure regulator assembly. Center bearing support lock screw not used on 1962-64 units

Installation

1. Referring to Figs. 9 and 10, install steel washer and O-ring seal on manual lever shaft.
2. Position detent lever in place against detent spring and roller with dowel pin on parking brake bracket outside detent lever.
3. Install manual lever and shaft through case, aligning serrations on shaft with serrations in detent lever.

As an aid in aligning serrations, note recess in manual shaft which mates with set screw in detent lever.

4. Press detent lever on manual shaft as far as possible and tighten set screw securely.
5. Install new O-ring seal on TV lever shaft.
6. Install TV shaft through manual shaft.
7. Install inside TV lever on TV shaft, aligning serrations on shaft with serrations in lever. *Tang on inside TV lever points toward side of transmission case.*
8. Press inside TV lever on TV shaft as far as possible and then back off slightly to provide .005″ to .010″ clearance between inside TV lever and inside detent lever. Tighten clamp screw.
9. Pull on outside TV lever to be sure inside TV lever is secure on shaft. Recheck clearance and adjust if necessary.
10. Install parking brake lever and pawl as a unit and install spacer and parking pawl pin.
11. Reposition or install reverse clutch housing and install extension housing.

GOVERNOR

After removing the extension housing, remove the governor from the rear pump by pulling rearward.

When disassembling, refer to Fig. 12. When disassembled, see that all parts are free of dirt. Inspect valves and bushings for burrs or other damage; remove burrs with fine crocus cloth and light oil. Test valves and bushing in their respective bores for free movement. If valves stick, replace governor assembly. Inspect ring lands and rings for freedom in grooves. If lands are damaged or worn, replace governor assemby.

PRESSURE REGULATOR

Remove pressure regulator from side of transmission, Fig. 13.

To disassemble, remove the valve stop pin from the reverse booster plug and remove plug from regulator plug. Remove O-ring seal from regulator plug.

Inspect all passages to determine whether they are blocked with dirt or metal chips. Inspect parts for burrs or other damage; burrs may be removed with fine crocus cloth and light oil. Check pressure regulator spring for distortion and collapsed coils.

Assemble the pressure regulator, referring to Fig. 13 and install in side of transmission case.

TRANSMISSION, REPLACE

Cadillac

1. Disconnect battery and raise car.
2. Remove starter motor and slush deflector.
3. Remove front and lower flywheel housing covers.
4. Drain transmission and torus cover.
5. Remove transmission filler pipe bracket bolt.
6. Slide filler pipe out of sleeve in transmission.
7. Disconnect brake cables from parking brake relay lever. Remove retracting spring and remove relay from frame.
8. Remove propeller shaft.
9. Remove intermediate frame crossmember from below flywheel housing.
10. Disconnect speedometer cable.
11. Disconnect TV and manual rods.
12. Remove four nuts from flywheel-to-drive plate screws.
13. Support engine with jack under oil pan.
14. Raise transmission enough to take strain off rear engine support.
15. Disconnect rear engine mount at transmission extension housing.
16. Remove six screws and remove rear engine support from frame.
17. Disconnect oil cooler pipes.
18. Remove six screws holding flywheel housing to engine.
19. Remove transmission and flywheel housing as a unit by moving assembly toward rear of car, disengaging flywheel housing from locating dowels on engine, and then tilting front of unit downward to lower it from car.
20. Reverse removal procedure to install transmission.

Pontiac

1. Remove oil filler tube and drain transmission.
2. Remove propeller shaft and disconnect speedometer cable.
3. Disconnect shift linkage from transmission.
4. Remove parking brake guide hook from crossmember.
5. Remove oil cooler lines.
6. Loosen exhaust pipe-to-manifold nuts about ¼″.
7. Remove starter and cover from bottom of case.
8. Remove flywheel front cover plate.
9. Support transmission with a jack.
10. Remove transmission crossmember.
11. Remove breather pipe (if equipped).
12. Unfasten transmission from engine and remove from car.
13. Reverse removal procedure to install the unit. Add fluid and adjust linkage as outlined previously.

CHEVROLET TORQUE DRIVE

GENERAL DESCRIPTION

The "Torque-Drive" transmission is basically a modified Powerglide consisting of a torque converter and a two-speed planetary gear set. As the automatic shifting provisions have been removed the transmission can only be shifted manually.

The selector lever positions are PARK-R-N-Hi-1st. 1st speed should be used for speeds up to 20 mph but never exceeding 55 mph. When in Hi position, do not downshift to 1st at speeds above 55 mph.

LUBRICATION & MAINTENANCE

Lubrication, maintenance and service information as it is covered in the Aluminum Case Powerglide section of this manual will also apply to the "Torque-Drive" with the exception of the following operation.

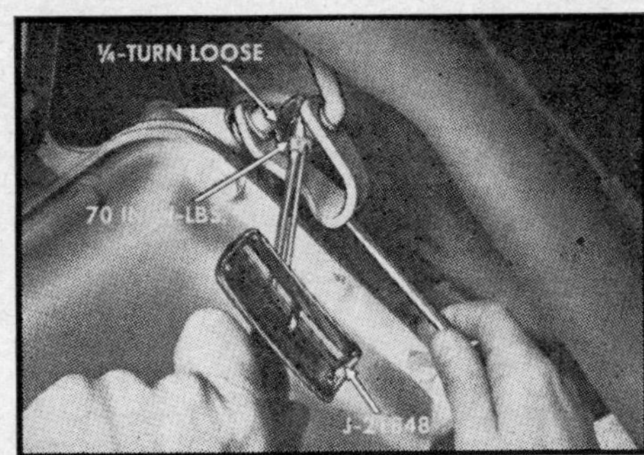

Fig. 1 Low band adjustment (in vehicle)

LOW BAND, ADJUST

Band adjustment should be performed at the first transmission oil change and sooner if slipping is evident.

1. With the selector in Neutral, back off the locknut ¼ turn. Tighten the adjusting screw to 70 in. lbs., Fig. 1.
2. Next, back off the adjusting screw exactly four turns if the band has more than 6,000 miles on it, or three turns if the band has less than 6,000 miles of use.

CAUTION: Be sure to hold the locknut at ¼ turn loose during the adjusting procedure. Then tighten locknut. The amount of back off is not an approximate figure; it must be exact.

BUICK SUPER TURBINE 300
OLDS JETAWAY, 1964-68
PONTIAC TWO SPEED, 1964-68

NOTE: — This chapter deals only with maintenance, adjustments and "in car" repairs. For major service work, Motor's Automatic Transmission Manual is available. Current edition is a 740 page volume that includes 240 pages of oil circuit diagrams mostly in full color.

TRANSMISSION IDENTIFICATION

The transmissions can be identified by either the metal tag or the stamping on the low servo cover. The metal tag is used on all 1964 and early 1965 units. For later 1965 and all 1966-67 the data is stamped on the low servo cover. The identification data includes the year of production, code letters or numbers followed by the transmission serial number. The model application is as follows:

BUICK		CODE
1964	V6-225 engine	25
	V8-300 except Sportwagons	35
	V8-300 Sportwagon	36
1965	V6-225 engine	LJ
	V8-300 except Sportwagons	MJ
	V8-300 Sportwagon	MR
	V8-400 Skylark Gran Sports	NK
1966-67	V6-225 engine	LJ
	V8-300 except Sportwagon	MJ
	V8-340 Sportwagon	MR
	V8-340 except Sportwagon	ML
	V8-400 Skylark Gran Sports	NK
1968	All Sportwagons	MH
	All V8-350 engines except Sportwagons	ME
	All models with 6-250 engine	LC

OLDSMOBILE INTERMEDIATE MODELS		
1964	F-85 with V6 engine	25
	F-85 with V8 engine	35
	Jetstar 88 with two barrel carburetor	37
	Jetstar 88 with four barrel carburetor	39
	Jetstar 88 for export	38
1965	F-85 with V6 engine	LJ
	F-85 with V8 engine	MJ
	F-85 with V8 and four barrel carburetor	MK
	Jetstar 88	MT
	V8 with four barrel carburetor	MU
1966	F-85 with V6 engine	LC
	F-85 with V8-330 and two barrel carburetor	ML
	F-85 with V8-330 and four barrel carburetor	MK
	V8-400 and four barrel carburetor	NJ
	Jetstar 88 with V8-330 engine	MT
1967	F-85 with V6 engine	LC
	Others with two-barrel carburetor	ML
	Others with four-barrel carburetor	MK
	Delmont 88	MT
1968	All models with 6-250 engine	LC
	Cutlass with V8-350 engine	MM
	Delmont 88 with V8-350 engine	MT

PONTIAC INTERMEDIATE MODELS		
1964	V6 engine with air cooled transmission	20
	V8 engine with water cooled transmission	30
1965	V6 with air cooled transmission	20
	V8 with water cooled transmission	30
	V8-326 High Output engine	31
	V8 G.T.O.	40
1966	L-6 engine with one barrel carburetor	LA
	L-6 engine with four barrel carburetor	LB
	V8 with two barrel carburetor	MA
	V8 with four barrel carburetor	MB
	V8 G.T.O.	NA
	V8 with A/C and A.I.R.	MC
1967	L-6 with 1 barrel carburetor	LA
	L-6 with 4 barrel carburetor	LB
	L-6 with 1 barrel carburetor and A/C	LD
	V8-326 with 2 barrel carburetor	MA
	V8-326 with 4 barrel carburetor	MB
	V8-326 with A/C and A.I.R.	MC
1968	6-250 engine with 1 barrel carburetor	LA
	6-250 engine with 4 barrel carburetor	LB
	6-250 engine with 1 barrel carburetor and A/C	LD
	6-250 engine with 1 barrel carburetor, Firebird	LF
	6-250 engine with 4 barrel carburetor, Firebird	LG
	V8-350 with 2 barrel carburetor	MA
	V8-350 with 4 barrel carburetor	MB
	V8-350 with 2 barrel carburetor and A/C	MC

DESCRIPTION

This transmission, Fig. 1, is a combination torque converter and two-speed planetary geared unit. Torque multiplication is obtained hydraulically through the converter and mechanically through the compound planetary gear set. The gear set, in combination with the torque converter, provides a high starting ratio for acceleration from a stop, up steep grades, etc. The torque converter provides torque multiplication for performance and exceptionally smooth operation. It functions as a fluid coupling at normal road load conditions and at higher speeds.

Torque Converter

The torque converter is connected to the engine flywheel and serves as a hydraulic coupling through which engine torque is transmitted to the input shaft. The converter steps up or multiplies engine torque whenever operating conditions demand greater torque than the engine alone can supply.

Converter Pump

The function of the converter pump is to convert engine torque into an energy transmitting a flow of oil to drive the converter turbine into which the oil is projected. The converter pump operates as a centrifugal pump, picking up oil at its center and discharging the oil at its rim. However, the converter is shaped to discharge the oil parallel to its axis in the form of a spinning hollow cylinder.

Variable Pitch Stator

Used on all Buick and V8 Oldsmobile, this type stator is located between the converter pump and converter turbine, and is supported by the stator shaft. The stator is equipped with an overrunning clutch. When the clutch is held stationary, it changes the direction of oil flow from the turbine to the proper angle for smooth entrance into the converter pump. As the turbine approaches pump speed, the direction of oil flow changes until the stator no longer opposes pump rotation. The stator then free wheels so that it will not interfere with the flow of oil between turbine and converter pump. For normal operation in Drive Range the stator blades are set at low angle. For

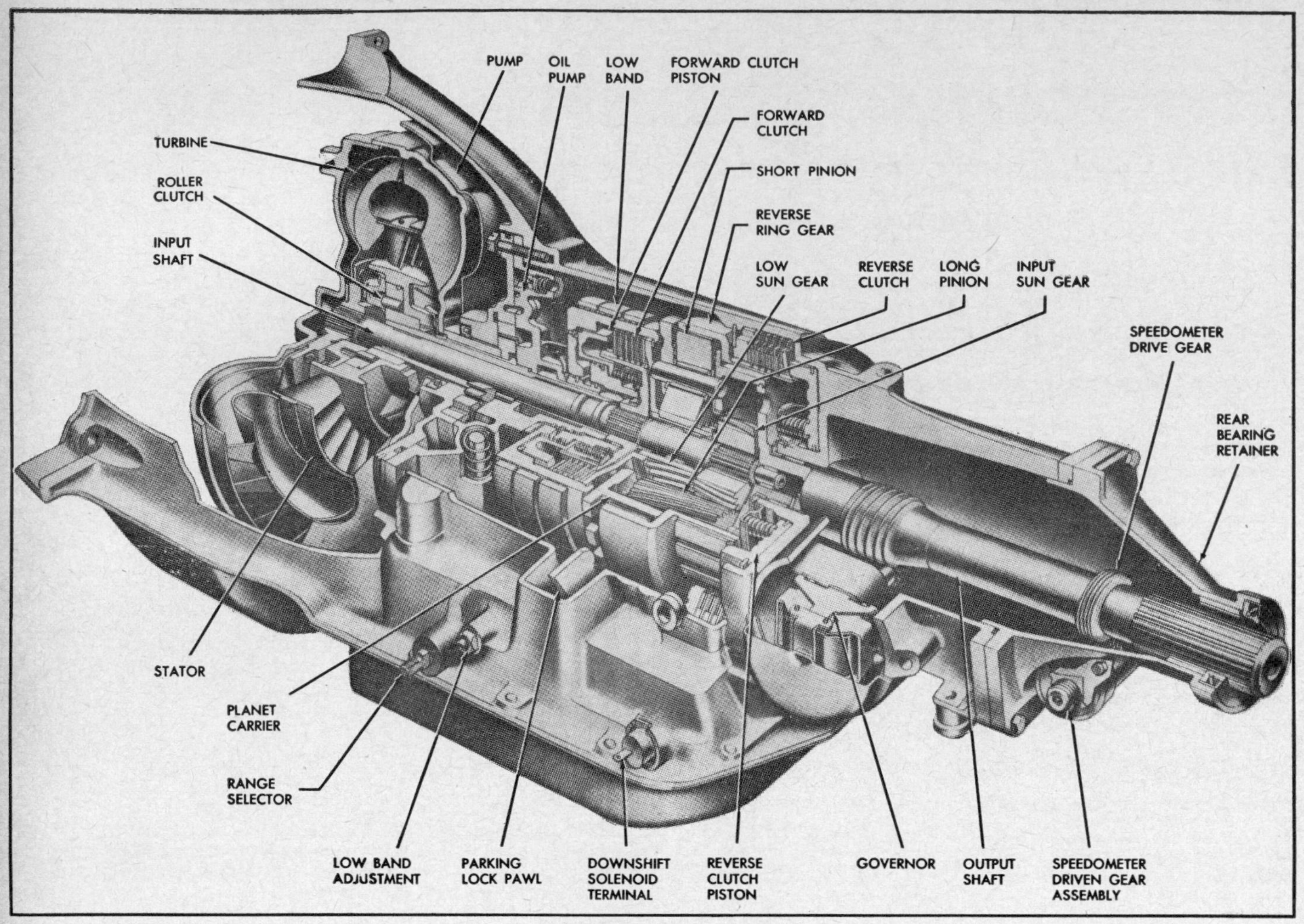

Fig. 1 Cutaway view of transmission

increased acceleration and performance, torque is obtained by setting the stator blades at high angle.

Fixed Stator

Used on all Pontiac Tempest and 6-cylinder Oldsmobile, the performance of the fixed stator is the same as the variable pitch type except that stator remains at a pre-set angle.

Converter Turbine

The function of the converter turbine is to absorb energy from the oil projected into it by the converter pump and convert the energy into torque and transmit that torque to the input shaft.

External Controls

Vacuum Modulator

The vacuum modulator is used to sense automatically any change in the torque input to the transmission. The vacuum modulator transmits this signal to the pressure regulator, which controls line pressure, so that all torque requirements of the transmission are met and smooth shifts are obtained at all throttle openings.

Stator Control Solenoid

Used only on Oldsmobile V8's and Buick up to and including 1967, with the variable pitch stator, the stator control solenoid is activated by a signal from the idle stator switch on the throttle linkage which changes the blade angle from low to high. The stator and detent switch is also energized at ¾ throttle openings to change the stator blades from low to high angle.

Detent Solenoid

On 1968 Buicks the detent solenoid is activated by the detent switch in the throttle linkage. When the throttle is fully open, the switch is closed, activating the detent solenoid and causing the transmission to downshift at speeds below approximately 60 mph.

Oil Pump

A positive displacement internal-external gear type oil pump is used to supply oil to fill the converter, for engagement of forward and reverse clutches, for application and release of the low band and to provide oil for lubrication and heat transfer.

Planetary Gear Set

The planetary gear set consists of an input sun gear, low sun gear, long and short pinions, a reverse ring gear and a planet carrier.

The input sun gear is splined to the input shaft. The low sun gear, which is part of the forward clutch assembly, may revolve freely until the low band or high clutch is applied.

The input sun gear is in mesh with three long pinions and the long pinions are in mesh with three short pinions. The short pinions are in mesh with the low sun gear and reverse ring gear.

The input sun gear and short pinions always rotate in the same direction. Application of either the low band or the reverse clutch determines whether the output shaft rotates forward or backward.

Forward Clutch

The forward clutch assembly consists of a drum, piston, cushion ring, springs, piston seals, and a clutch pack. These parts are retained inside the drum by the low sun gear and the flange assembly and retainer ring.

When oil pressure is applied to the piston, the clutch plates are pressed together, connecting the clutch drum to the input shaft through the clutch hub. Engagement of the clutch causes the low sun gear to rotate with the input shaft.

Low Band

The low band is a double-wrap steel band faced with a bonded lining which surrounds the forward clutch drum. The band is hydraulically applied by the low servo piston, and released by spring pressure.

Reverse Clutch

The reverse clutch consists of a piston, cushion ring, inner and outer seal, coil springs, clutch pack, and reaction plate. These parts are retained inside the case by a retaining snap ring.

When oil pressure is applied to the piston, the clutch plates are pressed together, holding the reverse ring gear stationary. This engagement of the clutch causes reverse rotation of the output shaft.

Governor

The governor is located to the rear of the transmission case on the left side and is driven off the output shaft. The purpose of the governor is to generate a speed sensitive modulating oil pressure that increases up to a point with output shaft or car speed.

Valve Body

The valve body assembly is bolted to the bottom of the transmission case and is accessible for service by removing the oil pan. The valve body assembly consists of manual valve, shift valve, modulator limit valve, and high speed downshift timing valve.

TROUBLE SHOOTING GUIDE

Oil Forced Out Of Filler Tube

1. Oil level too high; foaming caused by planet carrier running in oil.
2. Water in oil.
3. Leak in pump suction circuits.

Oil Leaks

1. Check extension oil seal.
2. Check outer shift lever oil seal.
3. Check speedometer driven gear fitting.
4. Check oil cooler pipe connections.
5. Check vacuum modulator assembly and case.

No Drive In Any Position

1. Low oil level.
2. Clogged oil strainer screen or suction pipe loose.
3. Defective pressure regulator valve.
4. Front pump defective.
5. Input shaft broken.

Erratic Operation and Slippage Light to Medium Throttle

1. Low oil level.
2. Clogged oil strainer screen.
3. Servo piston seal leaking.
4. Band facing worn.
5. Low band apply struts disengaged or broken.
6. Vacuum modulator.

Engine Speed Flares On Upshifts

1. Low oil level.
2. Improper band adjustment.
3. Clogged oil strainer screen.
4. Forward clutch not fully engaging.
5. Forward clutch plates worn.
6. Forward clutch piston hanging up.
7. Forward clutch drum relief ball not sealing.
8. Vacuum modulator.

Upshifts Harsh

1. Vacuum modulator line broken or disconnected.
2. Vacuum modulator diaphragm leaks.
3. Vacuum modulator valve stuck.

Closed Throttle (Coast) Downshift Harsh

1. High engine idle speed.
2. Improper low band adjustment.
3. Downshift timing valve malfunction.
4. High main line pressure. Check the following: a) vacuum modulator line broken or disconnected, b) modulator diaphragm ruptured, c) sticking pressure regulator coast valve, pressure regulator valve or vacuum modulator valve.

Car Creeps Excessively In Drive

1. Idle speed too high.
2. Closed throttle stator switch improperly adjusted (except Tempest and Oldsmobile 6-cylinder models).

Car Creeps In Neutral

1. Forward clutch not released.
2. Low band not released.

No Drive In Reverse

1. Reverse clutch piston stuck.
2. Reverse clutch plates worn out.
3. Reverse clutch seal leaking excessively.
4. Blocked reverse clutch apply orifice.

MAINTENANCE

Checking Oil Level

The transmission oil level should be checked every 6000 miles. Oil should be added only when the level is near the ADD mark on the dipstick with oil at normal operating temperature. *NOTE: The difference in oil level between FULL and ADD is one pint.*

To check oil level accurately, the car should be level, the engine should be idled with the transmission oil at normal temperature, and the control lever in Park position.

It is important that the oil level be maintained no higher than the FULL mark. *Do not overfill,* for when the oil level is at the full mark on the dipstick, it is just slightly below the planetary gear unit. If oil is added which brings the level above the full mark, the planetary unit will run in the oil foaming and aerating the oil. This will cause malfunctioning of the transmission assembly due to improper application of the band or clutches and excessive temperature.

If the transmission is found to be consistently low on oil, a thorough inspection should be made to find and correct all external oil leaks. All mating surfaces, such as the oil pan rail, filler tube, governor and modulator should be carefully examined for signs of leakage. The modulator must also be checked to insure that the diaphragm has not ruptured as this would allow transmission oil to be drawn into the intake manifold of the engine. Usually, the exhaust will be excessively smoky if the diaphragm ruptures, due to transmission oil being drawn into the combustion chambers of the engine.

Draining & Refilling

Draining the transmission oil at 24,000 mile intervals is recommended. Drain the oil by removing the oil pan (no drain plug is provided). Clean oil strainer.

To refill the transmission, replace the oil pan, using a new gasket, and add five (5) pints of transmission fluid, using filler tube and funnel. Start and allow engine to idle in Park position three to five minutes to warm the oil, then check oil level and add as required to bring the level to the Full mark. Assuming that the converter has not been drained (since it is welded) and allowing for normal spillage or drain-down, approximately six pints will be required for refill.

MANUAL LINKAGE, ADJUST

Buick

1967-68 Column Shift

1. Loosen swivel clamp bolt.
2. Place selector lever against Drive stop.
3. Place transmission lever in Drive detent (2nd from rear).
4. Torque swivel clamp bolt to 17-23 ft-lbs.

1967-68 Console Shift

1. Loosen shift rod adjusting clamp bolt (to '67) or trunnion nut (1968).
2. Place selector lever against Drive stop.
3. Place transmission in Drive detent (2nd from rear).
4. Tighten adjusting clamp bolt to 17-23 ft-lbs or trunnion nut to 6-9 ft-lbs.

1964-66 Buick Special Column Shift

1. Place selector lever in Drive.
2. Loosen swivel clamp bolt.
3. Place transmission in Drive detent (2nd from rear).
4. Tighten swivel clamp bolt to 17-23 ft-lbs.

1964-66 Le Sabre Column Shift

1. Place selector lever in Park.
2. Loosen adjusting clamp bolt.
3. Set transmission lever in Park.
4. Tighten swivel clamp bolt to 17-23 ft-lbs.

1964-66 Console Shift

1. Place selector lever in Park.
2. Loosen shift rod adjusting clamp bolt.
3. Place transmission lever in Park.
4. Tighten adjusting clamp bolt to 17-23 ft-lbs.

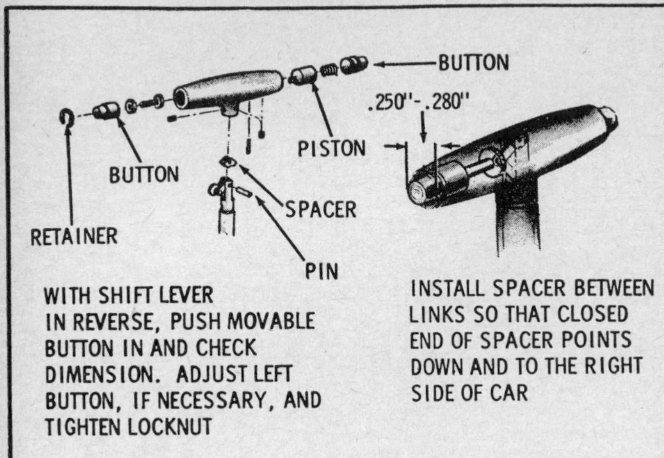

BUTTON
.250"-.280"
PISTON
BUTTON
SPACER
RETAINER
PIN
WITH SHIFT LEVER IN REVERSE, PUSH MOVABLE BUTTON IN AND CHECK DIMENSION. ADJUST LEFT BUTTON, IF NECESSARY, AND TIGHTEN LOCKNUT
INSTALL SPACER BETWEEN LINKS SO THAT CLOSED END OF SPACER POINTS DOWN AND TO THE RIGHT SIDE OF CAR

Fig. 1 Console shift lever. Oldsmobile 1965-66

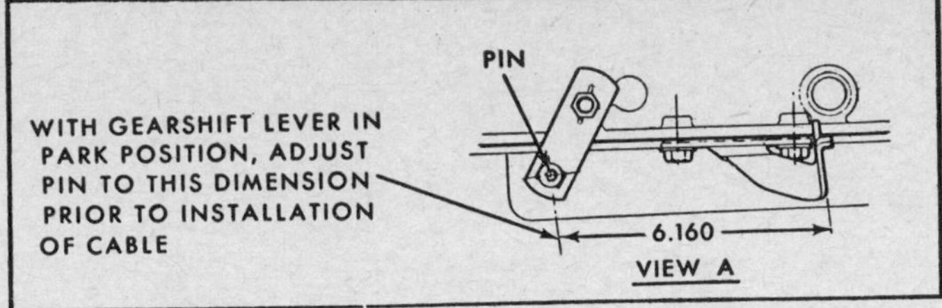

Fig. 2 Console shift adjustment. Pontiac 1967. Dimension for 1968 is 7.260

Oldsmobile

1967-68 Column Shift

1. Set outer shift lever at transmission to "D" position.
2. Loosen swivel bolt.
3. Hold down on shift rod to seat upper shift lever against "D" position stop in upper steering column.
4. Tighten swivel bolt to 20 ft-lbs.

1967-68 Console Shift

1. Place shift lever in Park.
2. Set transmission outer shift lever in Park.
3. Set pin to just enter hole in shift cable.
4. Tighten nut and check adjustment.

1965-66 Column Shift

1. Set transmission outer shift lever in Drive detent.
2. Loosen swivel nut.
3. Hold manual rod up against Drive position stop.
4. Be sure outer shift lever is in Drive position detent, then tighten swivel nut.

1965-66 Console Shift

Adjust as directed in Fig. 1.

1964 Models

1. To adjust, place selector lever in "D" against the stop.
2. Place manual lever at transmission in the "D" detent.
3. Adjust swivel on manual rod to a free pin fit at manual lever.
4. If pin will not enter freely, adjust rod ½ turn short.

NOTE: The shift indicator can be adjusted by removing the snap-on cover and loosening the set screw. Position indicator properly and tighten set screw.

Pontiac

Column Shift, 1968

1. Loosen screw (nut on Firebird) on adjusting swivel clamp.
2. Set transmission selector lever in Drive. Obtain Drive position by rotating transmission lever clockwise to Park position, then counterclockwise three positions to Drive position.
3. Set upper gearshift lever against Drive stop.
4. Tighten screw on swivel clamp to 20 ft-lbs (Tempest) or tighten nut on swivel clamp to 30 ft-lbs. (Firebird).

Console Shift, 1968

1. Disconnect shift cable from transmission selector lever pin.
2. Rotate transmission selector lever clockwise to Park position and adjust pin on selector lever to 7-260", Fig. 2.

1967 Column Shift

1. Set transmission lever in Drive.
2. Set selector lever in Drive.
3. Tighten screw on adjusting swivel clamp.

1964-66 Column Shift

1. Set transmission lever in Park.
2. Set selector lever in Park.
3. Tighten clamp on adjusting swivel.

1966-67 Console Shift

With shift lever in Park position, adjust pin to the dimension shown, Fig. 2, prior to installation of cable.

1964-65 Console Shift

1. Place selector lever in Reverse and set transmission shift lever in Reverse detent.
2. Pull forward lightly on lever to make certain that lever assembly is against stop between Reverse and Park.
3. Screw sleeve forward until it is finger tight and all axial clearance between sleeve and trunnion has been removed.
4. Holding sleeve from turning tighten locknut.
5. With shift lever in Park, check to be sure that transmission pawl is in Park position.

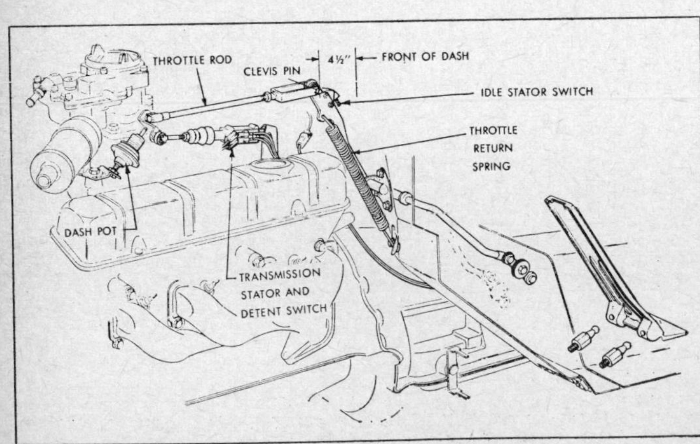

Fig. 3 Throttle linkage adjustment. Buick 1965-67. On LeSabre models, dimension is 5½"

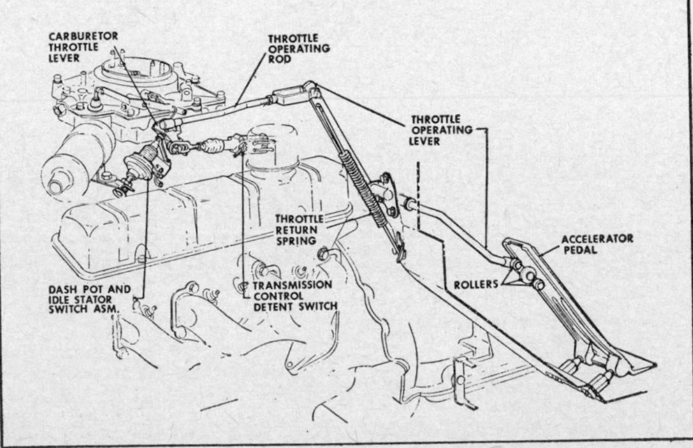

Fig. 4 Throttle linkage and transmission control switches. Buick 1964

THROTTLE LINKAGE

Buick 1968

Intermediate Models

The flexible cable type linkage is used and is not adjustable.

Le Sabre

Follow procedure outlined for 1967 models except that dimension from throttle rod pin to dash should be 6 1/8″.

Buick 1965-67

1. Remove air cleaner.
2. Make sure linkage is free in all positions.
3. Hold choke open and make sure that return spring fully closes throttle, even though throttle is released very slowly.
4. Adjust engine idle speed and mixture.
5. With throttle linkage at hot idle position, measurement from throttle rod clevis pin to dash must be 4½″, (5½″ on Le Sabre), Fig. 3.
6. If measurement is off, shorten or lengthen operating rod as required.
7. Operate linkage to open carburetor and make sure carburetor wide open stop is contacting. If carburetor does not reach wide open position and nothing is interfering with throttle linkage, transmission stator and detent switch must be adjusted as outlined below.

Buick 1964

1. Remove air cleaner.
2. Make sure linkage is free in all positions and that return spring fully closes throttle, even though throttle is released very slowly.
3. Unsnap front end of throttle operating rod from carburetor throttle lever, Fig. 4.
4. While another person presses accelerator pedal against floor mat, hold carburetor throttle lever in wide open position and hold throttle rod socket in alignment with ball on throttle lever. Socket must be approximately $\frac{1}{16}$″ (2 turns) short of ball. If adjustment is necessary, loosen lock nut, adjust throttle rod as required, and tighten lock nut.
5. With accelerator pedal released, reinstall throttle rod on throttle lever. With accelerator pedal depressed again to floor mat, recheck throttle for wide open position.

Oldsmobile

Carburetor Rod, 1966-67

With slow idle properly adjusted and carburetor in slow idle position, engine shut off, transmission stator must be in high angle position with test lamp on. (Stator with 6-250 engine has fixed angle). To adjust, lengthen carburetor rod until test lamp goes off. Slowly shorten rod until test lamp just comes on. Then shorten rod two more complete turns and tighten lock nut.

Carburetor Rod, 1965

With slow idle properly adjusted, adjust carburetor rod so that a ¼″ diameter pin can be freely inserted through hole in throttle switch lever and to bottom of hole in switch boss.

Accelerator Pedal, 1965-66

With slow idle and carburetor rod properly adjusted, adjust accelerator rod so the distance from accelerator pedal lever to floor carpet on Jetstar 88 is $5\frac{1}{16}$″. For F-85 models, distance is $4\frac{11}{16}$″.

Accelerator Pedal, 1964

Adjust height of pedal to $4\frac{15}{32}$″ on V6 and $4\frac{3}{32}$″ on V8s.

Pontiac

Firebird, 1968

The throttle control system is of the rod and lever type. The throttle control rod which is threaded at the carburetor end is attached to the carburetor linkage by means of a threaded trunnion.

Check linkage adjustment with carburetor set at hot idle position and also check for full throttle opening with accelerator depressed. Adjust as necessary by removing cotter pin and turning trunnion to obtain correct opening and closing positions.

1965-68 Tempest

Throttle linkage adjustments cannot be made. A reference dimension of $1\frac{9}{16}$″ between the bottom of the accelerator pedal roller and floor pan can be used only as a check for bent bracket assemblies.

1964 Models

1. Depress accelerator pedal to floor and check to see that carburetor throttle valves are wide open.
2. On six-cylinder models, adjust carburetor rod length so that the bottom of the accelerator rod roller is 1⅞″ from floor. This adjustment is made with carburetor lever in full open position.
3. On V8 models, retain the throttle control lever so that the bottom of the accelerator rod roller is $1\frac{9}{16}$″ from the floor. With the carburetor held full open, pull lightly on the carburetor end of the cable and insert a stud on carburetor lever into hole with which it aligns, or the next rearward hole.

DOWNSHIFT SWITCH

Buick, Olds, Pontiac 1968

The downshift switch is in the throttle linkage. To adjust, depress the switch plunger fully to insure proper setting, then depress the accelerator pedal fully.

STATOR & DETENT SWITCHES, ADJUST

Buick

Idle Stator Switch, 1965-67

1. Referring to Fig. 3, adjust switch with throttle at closed position and return spring attached.
2. With attaching screws loose, rotate switch until the switch stop screw bottoms against case.
3. Hold screw in this position and tighten attaching screws.

Stator & Detent Switch, 1965-67

1. With carburetor throttle wide open and switch plunger bottomed, adjust link until it will slip over carburetor lever pin.
2. Then screw link into plunger 1½ turns.
3. Install washer and retainer.

1964 Detent Switch

The transmission detent switch is mounted at the full throttle position of the carburetor throttle lever, Fig. 4. When throttle linkage is moved to wide open throttle position, the switch contacts are closed to cause the transmission to downshift.

The switch also has a second set of contacts which close slightly before wide open throttle position to cause the stator blades in the transmission to "switch-the-pitch" to high performance angle.

To adjust either type of detent switch, hold carburetor at wide open throttle and adjust switch plunger so that it is about .050″ from bottom.

1964 Idle Stator Switch

This switch closes just before the throttle reaches slow idle position, Fig. 4. This causes a solenoid valve in the transmission to operate which, in turn, causes the stator blades to "switch-the-pitch" to high angle. This reduces the transmission load on the engine at idle, thereby reducing the tendency of the car to creep.

Before adjusting idle stator switch, engine idle speed and mixture must be adjusted.

1. With engine at normal operating temperature, adjust idle speed and mixture as outlined in the *Carburetor Section.*
2. Shut engine off. Unplug idle stator switch connector and plug prods of a test lamp into end of connector.
3. Turn stator switch adjuster nut to back switch away from throttle lever until test lamp is out.
4. Turn adjusting nut to move stator switch toward throttle lever until test lamp just lights. Then turn ten flats (notches) in addition to make sure switch always closes at idle speed.
5. Remove test lamp and connect switch connector.

Oldsmobile

Throttle Switch, 1966-67

Disconnect carburetor rod and rotate switch lever forward until it hits stop. Connect carburetor rod without moving switch lever to wide open throttle position. Depress accelerator pedal through detent and release.

NOTE: Trailer Hauling Switch (Y-73 option) is bronze colored. When checking this switch with a test lamp, the test lamp should light only when the throttle valves are at closed or wide open position. The test lamp will NOT light at the 40° throttle opening as it does when checking a regular switch.

Throttle Switch, 1965

With slow idle, carburetor rod and accelerator rod properly adjusted, move lever under tension spring on switch to extreme forward position.

Throttle Switch, 1964

1. Adjust throttle switch and link assembly short.
2. Turn on ignition switch.
3. Connect test lamp to white lead terminal on throttle switch and ground.
4. Hold a .040" wire gauge in front of wide open throttle stop on throttle body.
5. Open carburetor by pulling on accelerator lever-to-auxiliary bellcrank rod until tang on carburetor lever stops against gauge.
6. With carburetor held in this position, turn switch plunger until test lamp lights. Tighten lock nut.

NOTE: This adjustment can only be made by lengthening the switch assembly. If necessary to shorten switch, let carburetor return to idle, shorten beyond the necessary amount and repeat the lengthening procedure.

Pontiac Tempest

Throttle Downshift Switch

If a forced downshift cannot be obtained it may be caused by an improperly set downshift switch. To re-set the switch, push the plunger all the way forward toward the firewall. Now, when the accelerator is fully depressed, the switch will automatically adjust itself to the linkage travel.

IN CAR REPAIRS

The following operations can be performed without removing the transmission from the car.

1. Oil pan and strainer.
2. Rear bearing retainer.
3. Vacuum modulator.
4. Valve body.
5. Governor.
6. Low servo.
7. Selector and parking mechanism.
8. Pressure regulator valve.

LOW BAND, ADJUST

The low band adjusting screw is located on the left side of the transmission adjacent to the range selector lever. Adjustment is made as follows:

Remove protective cap, loosen lock nut and tighten adjusting screw 35 to 45 inch pounds with a torque wrench. Then back off *exactly four full turns.* While holding adjusting screw stationary, tighten lock nut securely and replace cap.

TRANSMISSION, REPLACE

Buick 1966-68

1. Raise and support front and rear of car.
2. Disconnect front exhaust crossover pipe if necessary.
3. Remove propeller shaft.
4. Support transmission with suitable jack.
5. Remove line from vacuum modulator.
6. Separate cooler lines from transmission.
7. Remove cross member.
8. Disconnect speedometer cable.
9. Disconnect solenoid wire from case connector (1968).
10. Disconnect shift linkage from transmission.
11. Remove oil filler pipe.
12. Support engine at oil pan.
13. Remove flywheel cover pan.
14. Mark flywheel and converter for reassembly in same position and remove flywheel to converter bolts.
15. Unfasten transmission from engine.
16. Move transmission rearward to provide clearance between converter pump and crankshaft.
17. Install holding tool to retain converter, then lower transmission from car.
18. Reverse procedure to install.

Buick, 1964-65

1. With front and rear of car supported off floor, disconnect front exhaust pipe bolts at exhaust manifold and at connection of intermediate exhaust pipe location (single exhaust only). On dual exhaust jobs, exhaust pipes need not be removed.
2. Remove pinion flange U-bolts and slide propeller shaft toward transmission as far as possible to separate universal joint from pinion flange. Remove propeller shaft.
3. Support transmission with a jack.
4. Remove vacuum line-to-vacuum modulator hose from modulator.
5. Separate cooler lines from transmission.
6. Remove transmission support crossmember.
7. Disconnect speedometer cable.
8. Loosen shift linkage adjusting swivel clamp nut and remove equalizer from outer range selector lever.
9. Remove transmission filler pipe.
10. Support engine at oil pan.
11. Remove flywheel cover pan.
12. Mark flywheel and converter pump for reassembly in same position.
13. Unfasten converter pump from flywheel (3 bolts) and transmission to engine bolts. Secure converter in place before removing transmission.
14. Move transmission rearward to provide clearance between converter pump and crankshaft. Then lower transmission from vehicle.

Oldsmobile

1. Remove transmission oil filler pipe. Hoist car.
2. Disconnect control wires at transmission, and manual rod from transmission lever.
3. Remove propeller shaft.
4. Remove flywheel dust cover.
5. Support engine with a suitable jack or support bar.
6. Remove transmission cross support bar. *On models with dual exhaust, it may be necessary to disconnect the left hand exhaust pipe at exhaust manifold to provide clearance.*
7. Disconnect and cap oil cooler lines.
8. Disconnect speedometer cable (or speed adapter if so equipped) from speedometer driven gear.
9. Remove three flywheel-to-converter attaching bolts. Mark flywheel and converter so they can be assembled in the same relationship.

CAUTION: On 1964 models, if a support strap is not installed on cars with V8 engine and air conditioning, the engine may tip forward and damage the radiator.

10. Support transmission with a suitable lift and remove transmission-to-flywheel housing bolts. *It may be necessary to lower engine slightly to permit removal of the upper bolts.*
11. Carefully move transmission rearward and out of car.
12. Reverse removal procedure to install the unit and adjust the shift linkage as outlined below.

Pontiac

1. Disconnect speedometer cable and remove speedometer driven gear to allow oil to drain during removal procedure.
2. Remove propeller shaft.
3. Disconnect vacuum line and downshift switch lead.
4. Disconnect shift linkage from outer shift lever.
5. Support transmission and remove frame crossmember.
6. Remove flywheel housing bottom cover.
7. After removing flywheel-to-converter bolts, make sure converter hub is free of crankshaft.
8. Lower transmission and engine assembly to gain access to cooler line fittings (V8 only). Disconnect cooler lines, using a crowfoot adapter and a suitable extension. *On some cars it may be necessary to loosen exhaust system.*
9. With transmission in lowered position, remove case-to-engine bolts.
10. Move transmission down and to the rear and install a suitable strap across the converter housing to hold the converter in position until transmission is to be disassembled.
11. Reverse removal procedure to install the unit and adjust shift linkage.

ROTO HYDRA-MATIC 375

NOTE: — This chapter deals only with maintenance, adjustments and "in car" repairs. For major service work, Motor's Automatic Transmission Manual is available. Current edition is a 740 page volume that includes 240 pages of oil circuit diagrams mostly in full color.

TRANSMISSION IDENTIFICATION

Each transmission may be identified by the serial number plate attached to the left side of the transmission. The serial number includes a prefix letter or letters, followed by the year of production, followed by the serial number of the unit.

OLDSMOBILE

		CODE
1963	88 Series Low Compression Engine	O
	88 Series Standard Compression Engine	OC
	88, S88 With Four Barrel Carburetor	OA
	Starfire and 98	OCH
	Starfire and 98 (Heavy Duty)	OHC
1964	Dynamic 88 Low Compression Engine	O
	Dynamic 88 Standard Compression Engine	OC
	Dynamic 88, S88, 98 Four Barrel Carb.	OA
	Jetstar I, Starfire, 98 Custom Sport Coupe	OB
	Dynamic 88 (Heavy Duty)	OCH
	Heavy Duty with Four Barrel Carburetor	OBH

PONTIAC CATALINA & GRAND PRIX

		CODE
1963	Tri-Power and Four Barrel Carburetor	PA
	Catalina with Four Barrel Carburetor	PB
	With Two Barrel Carburetor	PE
	Tri-Power and Four Barrel Carb. (Heavy Duty)	PAH
	With Two Barrel Carburetor (Heavy Duty)	PEH
	Low Compression Engine (Export)	P
1964	389 Engine, Two Barrel Carb. (Hi Comp)	P
	389 Engine, Two Barrel Carb. (low Comp)	PE
	389 Engine, Four Barrel Carb. Catalina	PB
	389 Engine, Four Barrel Carb. Grand Prix	PG
	421 Engine, Catalina	PAH
	421 High Output Engine, Catalina	PC
	Two Barrel Carb., Low Comp. (Heavy Duty)	PEH
	Heavy Duty, All Others	PAH

DESCRIPTION

The transmission, Fig. 1, consists of a fluid coupling and torque multiplier combined with a hydraulically controlled automatic transmission having four speeds forward and one reverse. Gear shifting is automatic and is controlled by the requirements of road conditions and the wishes of the driver.

As a greater variation of speed ratios is required to satisfactorily operate the vehicle, the transmission contains two planetary gear trains arranged to provide three forward speeds and one reverse.

Direct drive or reduction in each of the units is obtained hydraulically by controlling the front clutch and the fluid coupling as will be explained in the power flow section.

The overrun band, neutral clutch and reverse cone clutch are also applied, when necessary, by hydraulic pressure. Hydraulic pressure is maintained by a pump that is driven by the input shaft whenever the engine operates.

Oil pressure is directed to the proper places in the transmission by means of a control valve assembly. When the driver places the selector lever in the desired range, the control valve automatically directs oil to the proper places in the transmission.

Operation in Drive Range

The transmission provides three selective drive ranges: D or D (left); D (right) or S, and L. In D or D (left), the transmission starts in first speed and shifts automatically to second, third and fourth.

With the selector lever in the D (right) or S range, the transmission will shift to third and remain in third until approximately 70 to 82 mph regardless of throttle opening. This provides additional acceleraton for long hills and congested traffic conditions, as well as engine braking power when descending long grades. When car speed reaches approximately 70 to 82 mph, the transmission automatically shifts to fourth speed. If the car speed decreases to approximately 65 to 78 mph, the transmission will automatically downshift to third.

With the selector lever in the L range, the transmission will not shift beyond second speed regardless of throttle opening or car speed. L range is designed for engine braking when descending steep grades. It may also be used to hold the car in second speed for maximum pulling power.

Part Throttle Downshift—4th to 3rd

A part throttle downshift can be made any time the transmission is in fourth and the car speed is below approximately 35 mph. Since this downshift will occur at part throttle opening, the advantage of third stage power is obtained with a wide open throttle. This feature is desirable in congested traffic conditions where a wide open throttle would be unnecessary.

Forced (Detent) Downshifts

In D or D (left) the transmission can be downshifted from fourth to third, and from third to second within set speed ranges. In D (right) or S range a third to second forced downshift can be made within a set speed range. A warning "feel" on the accelerator pedal makes it possible for the driver to obtain full throttle performance with or without downshift, as desired.

Closed Throttle Downshifts

D or D (Left) Range

When the transmission is in this range and the driver takes his foot off the accelerator, the transmission will automatically downshift from fourth to second when coming to a stop.

D (Right) or S Range

When the transmission is in fourth in this range (over 75 mph) and the driver takes his foot off the accelerator, the transmission will automatically downshift from fourth to third at approximately 75 mph and downshift from third to second when coming to a stop.

Low Range

If the car is being driven in the D (right) or S range and the selector lever is moved to L range and the driver takes his foot off the accelerator, the transmission will automatically downshift from third to second at approximately 30 to 40 mph.

If the car is being driven in D or D (left) range (above 75 mph) and the driver moves the selector lever to L

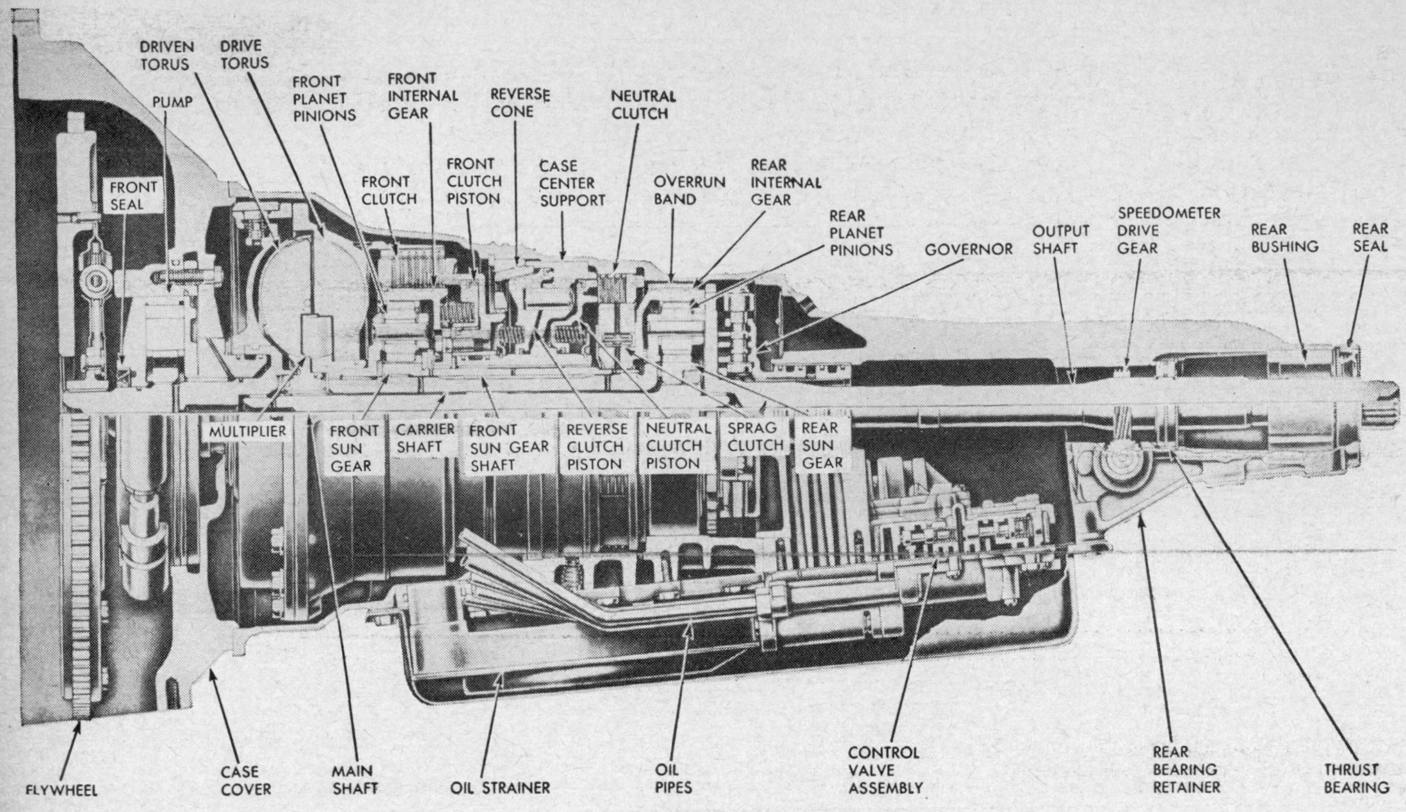

Fig. 1 Cross section of transmission

range and takes his foot off the accelerator, the transmission will automatically downshift from fourth to third at approximately 70 mph and from third to second at 30 to 40 mph.

Reverse
Reverse is accomplished through the use of a friction clutch applied by oil pressure and designed for ease in "rocking" the car. A reverse blocker piston prevents movement of the selector lever to the "R" position above 13 mph.

Park Position
The selector quadrant has a "P" position which is desirable for parking and starting the car when on an incline. The engine can also be started with the selector lever in the "N" position.

With the selector lever in P position, a parking pawl engages with lugs on the output shaft flange and locks the output shaft to the transmission case. A detent in the shift selector quadrant prevents accidental movement of the selector lever in the P position.

TROUBLE SHOOTING GUIDE

High Oil Pressure

1. Pressure regulator valve stuck or damaged.
2. Boost plug sticking.
3. Manual valve misaligned with pin.
4. Sticking valve in control valve body.
5. Pump slide sticking; cover-to-slide clearance too great.

Low Oil Pressure

1. Oil level low.
2. Boost plug stuck.
3. Pressure regulator valve stuck or spring damaged.
4. Strainer O-ring seal damaged.
5. Manual valve misaligned with pin.
6. Internal leaks.
7. Sticking valves in control valve body.
8. Leak in pump suction circuit.
9. Front pump defective.
10. Ball check valve in control valve assembly defective.

No Drive In Drive Range

1. Low oil level.
2. Low oil pressure.
3. Manual control linkage.
4. Control valve assembly.
5. Leaking or restricted circuit in coupling, neutral clutch, case cover, governor.
6. Reverse clutch.
7. Sprag or race.

First Speed Only

1. Governor.
2. Control valve assembly.
3. Front clutch.

Drive In Third Only

1. Governor.
2. Control valve assembly.

Drive 3rd and 4th Only

1. Control valve assembly.
2. Governor.

No Fourth

1. Governor.
2. Control valve assembly.
3. Oil passages in clutch, accumulator, compensator, drive passages or TV passages.

Drive In Neutral—Forward or Reverse

1. Manual linkage improperly adjusted.
2. Neutral clutch.
3. Reverse clutch.

No Reverse

1. Manual linkage improperly adjusted.
2. Low oil pressure.
3. Reverse clutch.
4. Governor.

Slipping All Ranges

1. Low oil level.
2. Low oil pressure.
3. Coupling.

Slipping 2-3 Shift

1. Throttle linkage improperly adjusted.
2. Low oil level.
3. Low oil pressure.
4. Leaking or restricted circuit in front clutch, accumulator, compensator, TV passage, drive passage.
5. Control valve assembly.

Rough 1-2 Shift

1. Neutral clutch by-pass valve broken.

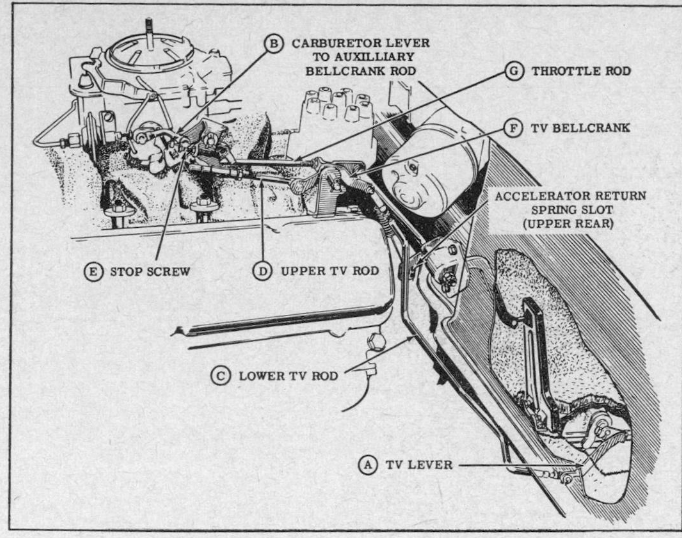

Fig. 2 Oldsmobile throttle linkage (typical)

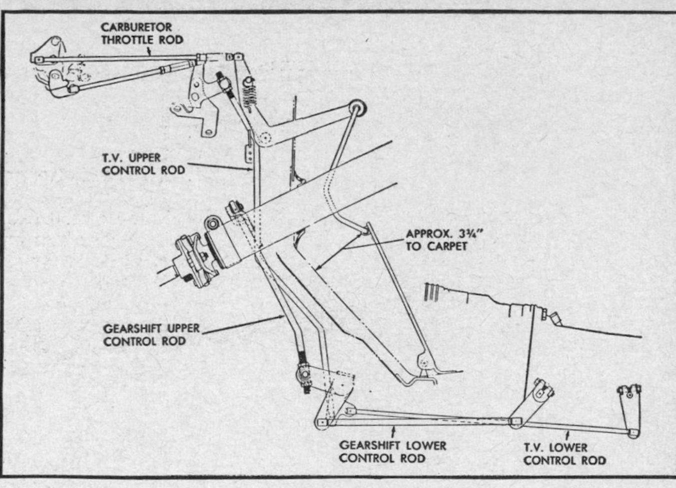

Fig. 3 Pontiac throttle linkage

Rough 2-3 Shift

1. Throttle linkage improperly adjusted.
2. Control valve assembly.
3. Leaking or restricted circuit in front clutch, accumulator, compensator, TV passage, drive passage.

Slipping 3-4 Shift

1. Control valve assembly.
2. Leaking or restricted circuit in coupling, front clutch, accumulator, compensator, TV passage, drive passage.

No Engine Braking—3rd or Low

1. Control valve assembly.
2. Overrun band servo.

No Part Throttle or Detent Downshifts

1. Throttle linkage improperly adjusted; accelerator pedal height.
2. Control valve assembly.
3. Governor.

Selector Lever Won't Go Into Reverse

1. Manual linkage improperly adjusted.
2. Reverse blocker piston.
3. Governor.

Selector Lever Won't Go Into Park

1. Manual linkage improperly adjusted.
2. Parking linkage (internal).

Forward Drive In Reverse

1. Manual linkage improperly adjusted.
2. Manual valve.
3. Neutral clutch.

Low or High Upshifts

1. Throttle linkage improperly adjusted.
2. TV pressure high.
3. Governor.

MAINTENANCE

Adding Oil

With engine idling and warmed up to normal operating temperature and with selector lever in Park position, check oil level on dipstick. Add automatic transmission fluid to bring the level up to the "Full" mark on dipstick.

Since this transmission is very sensitive to oil level, special precautions should be taken when checking the level, otherwise valve buzz or shift malfunctions may be experienced.

Changing Oil

1. Remove flywheel housing bottom cover.
2. Remove hex head pipe plug from torus cover. Disconnect filler pipe from right side of oil pan.
3. Remove oil pan and discard strainer.
4. Install new strainer using new "O" ring on pump intake pipe if necessary.
5. Install oil pan with new gasket.
6. Connect filler pipe and install torus cover drain plug.
7. Install flywheel housing bottom cover.
8. Pour 5 quarts of Hydra-Matic fluid into transmission.
9. Set selector lever in Park position and set hand brake. Run engine at a fast idle for about 1½ minutes to fill fluid coupling.
10. Reduce engine speed to slow idle and add fluid to bring the oil level up to the "Full" mark. *Do not overfill as foaming will result.*

MANUAL LINKAGE, ADJUST

Oldsmobile

Floor Shift

The manual lever adjustment provides for proper clearance between neutral detent in transmission and the stop for the selector lever in the console.

1. Place selector lever in neutral.
2. Disconnect rod from manual lever at transmission.
3. Place transmission manual lever in neutral.
4. Loosen locknut on manual rod.
5. With selector lever held against its stop in neutral position and transmission manual lever in neutral detent position, adjust manual rod until it enters transmission manual lever.
6. Lengthen manual rod four turns and check alignment. Readjust if necessary.
7. Connect rod to manual lever and tighten locknut.

Steering Post Shift

This adjustment provides proper clearance between neutral detent in transmission and stop for manual shift lever in upper steering column mast jacket.

1. Loosen both swivel locknuts on manual rod. Set transmission manual lever in neutral detent position.
2. Hold lower shift lever upward so selector lever is positioned against stop in upper steering column. Do not raise lever.
3. Tighten rear nut finger tight against swivel.
4. Adjust manual rod short by tightening rear nut two turns.
5. Lock swivel in position by tightening front nut.

Pontiac

1. Place upper shift lever and transmission lever in Park position and, with transmission outer shift lever trunnion nuts backed clear of trunnion, pull shift rod down toward transmission as far as possible. While holding rod in this position, run trunnion upper nut down to just contact trunnion. Run lower nut up to contact trunnion and lock nuts securely.
2. After completing above adjustments, check transmission parking lock with car on ramp or grade for positive lock.

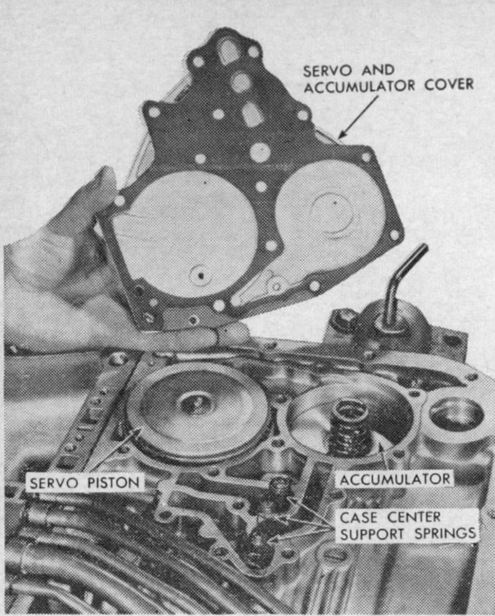

Fig. 4 Servo and accumulator cover

3. Place upper shift lever in Drive Right position and check indicator pointer index. If necessary to adjust, loosen check nut above ball stud, adjust index by rotating rod and lock check nut securely.

THROTTLE LINKAGE, ADJUST

Oldsmobile

Before making any checks or adjustments of the linkage, check the performance of the engine. The transmission is often blamed for poor operation of the vehicle when the engine is not tuned to deliver maximum power.

1. Throttle linkage must be adjusted so that when the carburetor throttle valves are fully closed (hot idle) the transmission throttle valve lever must be all the way toward the rear of the transmission against the internal stop, Fig. 2.
2. In order to assure kickdown operation, the accelerator pedal linkage must be adjusted so that when it is fully depressed, the carburetor throttle valves are in wide open position.

Fig. 5 Case center support seals and springs

Pontiac

1. Refer to Fig. 3. Remove carburetor air cleaner.
2. Loosen two throttle control rod trunnion nuts.
3. Adjust engine idle speed to specifications.
4. Shut off engine and install a suitable pin through holes in throttle control lever and bracket. *Four barrel carburetors are equipped with an anti-stall dashpot (throttle return check). Before installing pin, either remove dashpot or install tool J-6324-01 over dashpot so that it will not interfere with linkage adjustment.*
5. With throttle valves fully closed, loosen lock nut and adjust length of transmission control rod to carburetor so that gauge pin is free in holes. Leave pin installed and tighten lock nut securely. Recheck freeness of pin in holes.
6. Push throttle valve upper control rod downward until outer throttle valve lever is felt to touch end of travel. Make sure that when lever is in this position, upper lock nut is not touching trunnion.
7. While holding throttle valve upper control in this position, tighten upper and lower trunnion lock nuts finger tight. Shorten upper control rod by backing off lower trunnion nut 3½ turns on 1963, and 4½ turns on 1964 and tighten upper lock nut securely. Remove gauge pin.
8. Loosen lock nut on carburetor throttle rod. Then adjust this rod to obtain 4.55″ clearance from underside of attaching boss on pedal-to-body toe pan, Fig. 3. (approximately 3¾″ to carpet).
9. Tighten lock nut on carburetor throttle rod securely.

PRESSURE REGULATOR VALVE

1. To remove, take off left-hand inspection cover on case cover.
2. Remove valve plug, stop, spring and valve from pump body.

Installation

1. Replace "O" ring on plug, if necessary.
2. Place line boost plug in valve plug with hollow end facing out, and then set valve stop on top of plug.
3. With spring attached to regulator valve, place spring through plug stop and into plug.
4. Feed assembly through inspection hole and into pump. Some manipulation may be required to get valve and plug stop properly into their bores. Tighten plug and replace inspection cover.

LINE BOOST PRESSURE CHECK

The line boost plug in the pressure regulator valve is supplied in three different bore depths which provide different line boost pressures. The plugs are distinguished by either a plain side, a

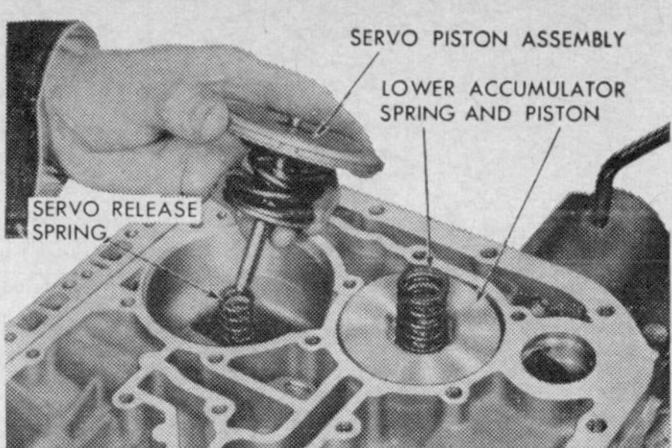

Fig. 6 Servo and accumulator pistons

ring, or a groove on the side of the cap at the end of the plug. The plain side plug creates normal pressure, the ring plug a higher pressure, and the groove plug creates the highest pressure. If replacement of a plug is necessary, the same size should be used unless a pressure test shows otherwise. To check line boost pressure:

1. Disconnect control rod at T.V. outer lever.
2. Secure T.V. lever in full T.V. position with a length of wire.
3. Install oil pressure gauge in upper of two test holes in rear bearing retainer.
4. Start engine and run at 1500 rpm in Park position. Main line pressure should be 176-183 psi.
5. Change line boost plug if necessary to obtain correct pressure.

COUPLING FEED LIMIT VALVE

1. To remove, take off inspection plate on right-hand side of case cover.
2. Coupling feed valve plug is located in lower portion of pump and may be removed with a ¾″ socket and suitable extension.
3. The valve plug and pin will come out with the socket. The spring and valve will usually remain in the pump body and may be removed with long nose pliers.

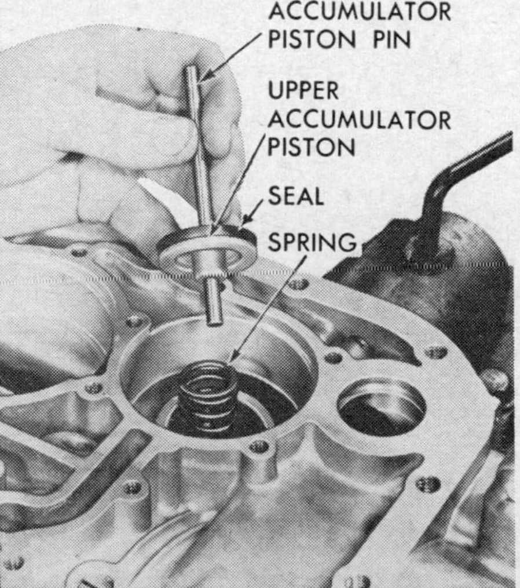

Fig. 7 Accumulator piston

Installation

1. Using long nose pliers, carefully insert spring and valves together into pump.
2. Replace "O" ring on plug if necessary.
3. Place valve plug into wrench socket and then place pin into plug.
4. Insert plug and pin into inspection hole and, with pin in center of spring, screw plug into pump. A speed handle wrench works best for starting the plug. Tighten plug and replace inspection plate.

REAR SEAL & BUSHING

To remove the rear seal it is necessary only to remove the propeller shaft and then the seal from the rear bearing retainer with a screwdriver.

To replace the seal, coat the outer casing with gasket sealing compound and drive it into the rear extension housing.

If removal of both the rear bushing and sleeve assembly and the rear seal is necessary, remove the bushing retaining bolt from the left side of the rear bearing retainer and remove the propeller shaft. Bushing remover (J-8845) with slide hammer (J-2619) is then fitted into the bushing and tightened. The slide hammer will then remove the bushing and seal in one operation.

To replace the bushing, install it, chamfered end first, into rear bearing retainer, aligning retaining bolt slot with bolt hole. Install with a soft hammer and drift. Coat the casing of the seal with gasket sealing compound and install it. Then replace propeller shaft.

CONTROL VALVE BODY

1. Remove filler pipe and drain transmission.
2. Remove outer throttle lever.
3. Remove throttle lever seal, using a small screwdriver behind flange.
4. Remove oil pan and gasket.
5. Unfasten valve body from rear bearing retainer (5 bolts).
6. Slide valve body off pipe assembly and remove from transmission. *Do not let manual valve drop out of valve body during removal.*

Installation

1. Install manual valve in valve body.
2. Apply petrolatum (vaseline) to valve body pipe ports to prevent damage to "O" rings during assembly.
3. Install valve body in rear bearing retainer by guiding throttle shaft through its opening and then positioning manual valve on pick-up pin (detent lever). Guide valve body over pipe assembly and slide forward to seat seals. Attach with five screws.
4. Install seal over throttle shaft and into case. Install oil pan gasket, using petrolatum and tighten pan bolts.
5. Install oil filler pipe and refill transmission.

GOVERNOR

1. To remove, take off oil filler tube and drain transmission.
2. Remove oil pan.
3. Remove T.V. lower control rod from T.V. outside lever, remove T.V. outside lever and gearshift control rod from outside shift lever.
4. Remove speedometer cable.
5. Remove hand brake cable guide rod and return spring from frame crossmember.
6. Remove propeller shaft.
7. Place jack under front of transmission.
8. Remove crossmember.
9. Remove control valve (5 bolts).
10. Remove breather pipe.
11. Reach into rear bearing retainer and remove the four governor and output shaft attaching bolts. Hold outside manual lever forward to engage parking brake when loosening bolts. Rotate shaft as necessary to remove all four bolts.
12. Mark edge of output shaft flange and a corresponding spot on inside of case with a grease pencil to match output shaft with planet carrier when reassembling. *Do not rotate carrier after removing output shaft or guide marks will become meaningless.*
13. Remove rear bearing retainer-to-case attaching bolts (2 are inside) and remove retainer.
14. Remove bearing retainer cover.
15. Reach through access hole with 90° snap ring pliers and unseat snap ring from output shaft. Remove output shaft from front of retainer. *Do not strike inner sleeve of rear bearing retainer with speedometer drive gear when removing shaft.*
16. Press off speedometer drive gear and remove governor.

Installation—Reverse removal procedure to install the governor, observing the following:

1. Install speedometer drive gear on shaft so that its rear side is 6 9/32" from end of shaft.
2. Be sure to align guide marks on output shaft flange and case.
3. When installing rear bearing retainer, use a short bolt in the center hole on each side and one inside rear bearing retainer.
4. Install and tighten governor attaching bolts.
5. When installing frame crossmember, brake cables go above crossmember.

PARKING PAWL, REPLACE

NOTE—Proceed with Steps 1 through 15 above for Governor Removal only so far as necessary to remove output shaft and rear bearing retainer. Then proceed as follows:

Push parking pawl pin from case with a small rod. Remove pin and spacer from case. The remainder of the linkage may be removed as a unit from the rear of the case.

Reverse the procedure to install, completing the job by performing Steps 2 to 5 for Governor Installation.

SERVO & ACCUMULATOR

1. To remove, take off filler pipe and drain transmission.
2. Remove oil pan and compensator valve body (3 screws and 1 bolt).
3. Remove servo and accumulator cover, Fig. 4. *The servo release spring pushes the servo piston against the cover, so care is required to prevent dropping servo piston when cover is removed.* Accumulator lower spring and possibly case center support springs will be removed with cover, Figs. 5 and 6.
4. Use accumulator pin to remove both accumulator pistons and remaining spring, Fig. 7.
5. Remove case center support seal springs and seals if they did not previously fall free.

Installation

1. It will be necessary to make a retainer to hold servo piston in place while cover is being installed. *A rectangular piece of sheet metal can be cut so it will hold servo piston in its bore when bolted to right rear oil pan bolt hole.*
2. Place upper accumulator piston on pin and place tapered spring over pin with large end of spring against piston and seal facing away from spring, Fig. 7.
3. Install tapered spring, pin and upper piston into case with small end of spring up. Hold these parts in case and install lower accumulator piston with pocket side down.
4. Screw ends of case center support seal springs into seals far enough so they will not fall off easily and install seals into case so springs are suspended below them. Petrolatum may be needed to help hold seals and springs in place.
5. Place servo return spring over servo pin and install assembly in case. Retain it in bore using previously mentioned retaining tool bolted to an oil pan hole.
6. Place remaining accumulator spring in position over pin and hold in place while installing servo and accumulator cover. Attach cover with three bolts and leave just loose enough to remove servo retaining tool. Make sure three seal springs enter case straight.
7. Remove servo retaining tool and install remaining cover bolts except strainer attaching bolt.
8. Install compensator, oil strainer, oil pan (with new gasket), oil filler pipe and refill transmission.

TRANSMISSION, REPLACE

Oldsmobile

1. Disconnect transmission vent pipe from rear of right-hand exhaust manifold.
2. Raise car and remove oil filler pipe from transmission and drain fluid.
3. Disconnect speedometer cable (not 1963-64) and shift rods from transmission.
4. Remove propeller shaft.
5. Support rear of engine.
6. Support transmission with transmission lift.
7. Raise engine enough to relieve weight from rear engine mounts and

remove bolts attaching mounts to crossmember.
8. Remove crossmember.
9. Lower engine enough to gain access to upper transmission attaching bolts.
10. Disconnect oil cooler lines and cap lines immediately.
11. Pry vent pipe from transmission case.
12. Remove remaining transmission attaching bolts.
13. Lower transmission from car.
14. Reverse removal operations to install transmission and adjust shift linkage.

Pontiac

1. Remove oil filler tube and drain transmission.
2. Remove propeller shaft and disconnect speedometer cable.
3. Disconnect shift linkage from transmission.
4. Remove parking brake guide hook from crossmember.
5. Remove oil cooler lines.
6. Loosen exhaust pipe-to-manifold nuts about ¼".
7. Remove starter and cover from bottom of case.
8. Remove flywheel front cover plate.
9. Support transmission with a jack.
10. Remove transmission crossmember.
11. Remove breather pipe (if equipped).
12. Unfasten transmission from engine and remove from car.
13. Reverse removal procedure to install the unit. Add fluid and adjust linkage as outlined previously.

OLDS F-85 HYDRA-MATIC

NOTE: — This chapter deals only with maintenance, adjustments and "in car" repairs. For major service work, Motor's Automatic Transmission Manual is available. Current edition is a 740 page volume that includes 240 pages of oil circuit diagrams mostly in full color.

TRANSMISSION IDENTIFICATION

Each transmission is identified by a metal plate attached to the right side of the unit above the filler tube boss. The plate includes a prefix code letter or letters, followed by a 5, year of production and the serial number of the unit.

OLDSMOBILE F-85		CODE
1963	Two barrel carburetor, column shift	O563
	Four barrel carburetor, column shift	OD563
	Four barrel carburetor, console shift	OE563
	Turbo Rocket, console shift	OX563

DESCRIPTION

The transmission provides three selective drive ranges: "D", "S" and "L". *For 1961 models, in "D" range the transmission starts in first gear and shifts automatically to second and third. For 1962-63 models the transmission starts in first and shifts automatically to second, third and fourth.*

With the selector lever in the "S" range, the transmission starts in first, shifts to second and third and remains in third until approximately 60-65 mph, regardless of throttle opening.

On all models the "S" range provides additional acceleration for long hills or traffic driving as well as engine braking power when descending long grades. When car speed increases above approximately 60-65 mph, the transmission automatically shifts to fourth. If car speed decreases to approximately 60-65 mph, the transmission will downshift to third.

On all models when the selector lever is in the "L" range, the transmission will remain in first regardless of throttle opening or car speed. "L" range is designed for engine braking when descending steep grades. It may also be used to hold the car in first for maximum pulling power.

Part Throttle Downshift

A part throttle downshift can be made anytime the transmission is in fourth gear and the car speed is below approximately 38 mph. Since this downshift will occur at part throttle, the advantage of third gear power is obtained without a wide open throttle. This feature is desirable in traffic conditions where a wide open throttle would be unnecessary.

Forced (Detent) Downshifts

With selector lever in "D" range the transmission can be down-shifted from fourth to third and third to second within set speed ranges.

With selector lever in "S" range, a third to second forced down-shift can be made within a set speed range. A warning "feel" on the accelerator pedal makes it possible for the driver to obtain full throttle performance with or without downshift, as desired.

Reverse

Reverse is accomplished through use of a friction clutch applied by oil pressure and designed for ease in "rocking" the car to get out of mud or snow. A reverse blocker piston prevents movement of the selector lever to reverse position above 13 mph.

Parking

With the selector lever in "P" position, a parking pawl engages with lugs on the reverse planet carrier and locks the output shaft to the transmission case. A detent in the selector quadrant prevents accidental movement of the selector lever to the park position.

TROUBLE SHOOTING GUIDE

Low Oil Pressure

1. Boost plug stuck.
2. Pressure regulator valve stuck or spring damaged.
3. Strainer O-ring damaged.
4. Manual valve misaligned with pin.
5. Internal leaks.
6. Control valve assembly may have sticking valves.
7. Leak in pump suction circuit.
8. Front pump defective.
9. Ball check valve in control valve assembly defective.

High Oil Pressure

1. Pressure regulator valve may be stuck or damaged.
2. Boost plug sticking.
3. Manual valve misaligned with pin.

4. Sticking valve in control valve assembly.
5. Pump slide sticking; cover-to-slide clearance too great.

No Drive In Drive Range

1. Low oil level.
2. Low oil pressure.
3. Manual control linkage improperly adjusted.
4. Adjust or replace servo band.
5. Sticking valve in valve body.
6. Leaking or restricted circuit in servo, coupling, case cover, governor.
7. Reverse clutch.

Missing All Shifts

1. Sticking governor valve.
2. Sticking valve in control valve assembly.
3. Clutch not applying.

Drive In 2nd and 3rd Only

1. Sticking valve in control valve assembly.
2. Clutch locked—too many plates.

Drive In 1st Only

1. Sticking valve in control valve assembly.
2. Inspect front clutch and accumulator for leaks.

3. Governor rings broken, worn ring lands, sticking valves.

Drive In 1st and 2nd Only

1. G-2 governor valve sticking.
2. Sticking valve in control valve assembly.

Drive In 3rd Only

1. Sticking valve in control valve assembly.
2. Governor valves sticking.

Drive In Neutral (Reverse or Forward)

1. Internal linkage (manual) engaging.
2. Mispositioned front clutch.
3. Reverse cone clutch not applying.

No Reverse

1. Manual linkage (internal) mispositioned.
2. Low oil pressure.
3. Reverse cone clutch not engaging.
4. Restricted passage.
5. Band not releasing.

Rough 1-2 Shift

1. TV linkage maladjusted.
2. Stuck valves in control valve assembly.
3. Defective accumulator (sticking parts).

4. Coupling not emptying fast enough.
5. Front clutch slipping.
6. 1-2 oil passages restricted.

Rough 2-3 Shift

1. Band not releasing quickly.
2. Sticking servo parts.

Slipping In All Ranges

1. Low oil pressure.

Slipping 1-2 Shift

1. TV linkage adjusted too long.
2. Low oil pressure.
3. Check for restrictions or sticking accumulator parts.
4. Stuck valves in control valve assembly.
5. Slipping band.
6. Front clutch (check number of plates).
7. Restricted 1-2 oil passages.

Slipping 2-3 Shift

1. Stuck valves in control valve assembly.
2. Coupling not filling fast enough (1961).
3. Front clutch slipping.

Slipping 3-4 Shift

1. Stuck valves in control valve assembly.
2. Front clutch slipping.

No Engine Braking

1. Stuck valves in control valve assembly.
2. Slipping band.
3. Servo not applying.

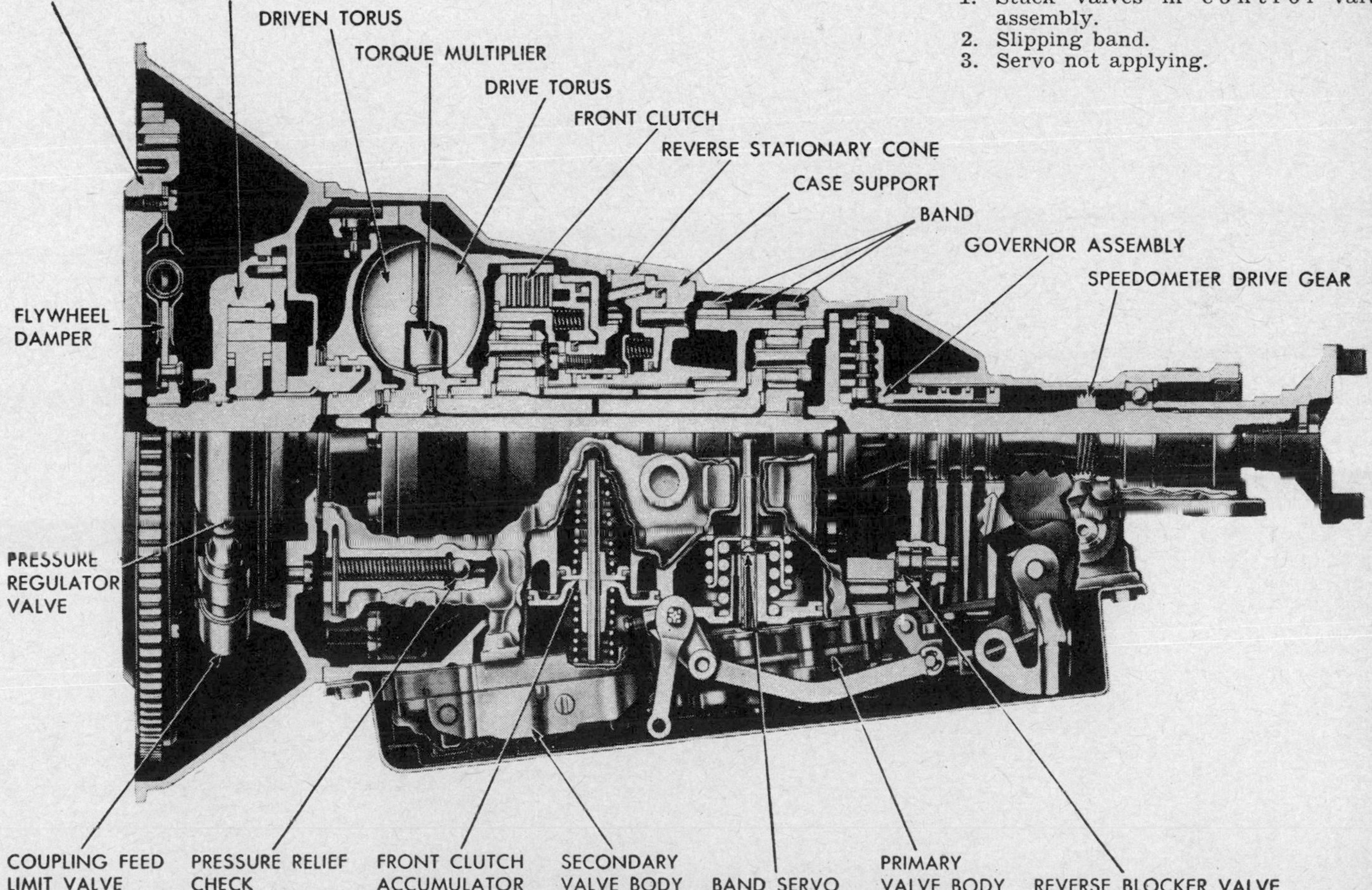

Fig. 1 Sectional view of Olds F-85 Hydra-Matic transmission

No Part Throttle or Detent Downshifts

1. TV linkage adjusted too long.
2. Stuck valves in control valve assembly.
3. Accelerator travel short.
4. Governor valves sticking.

Selector Valve Won't Go Into Reverse

1. Manual linkage (internal) mispositioned.
2. Reverse blocker valve stuck open.
3. Governor G-2 valve sticking.

Selector Lever Won't Go Into Park

1. Parking linkage broken, improperly assembled, distorted.
2. Manual linkage maladjusted.

Drives Forward In Reverse

1. Manual linkage (internal) improperly assembled or distorted.

High Upshifts

1. TV linkage adjusted short.
2. Stuck valve in control valve assembly.
3. Sticking governor valve.
4. TV lever bent.
5. TV pressure high.
6. Line pressure high.
7. Governor oil passage restricted.

Upshifts Low

1. TV linkage adjusted long.
2. Stuck valve in control valve assembly.
3. Governor valve sticking.
4. TV lever bent.
5. TV pressure low.
6. Line pressure low.
7. Governor oil passage restricted.

Hanging In 2nd—Engine Stall Upon Stop

1. Sticking governor valve.
2. Sticking valve in control valve assembly.
3. TV linkage adjusted short.
4. Clutch not releasing.

MAINTENANCE

Fluid Level

Fluid level in the transmission should be checked every 2000 miles and changed every 26,000 miles. Check the level with the selector lever in "Park" and with engine running at hot idle speed.

Approximately 4 quarts of oil are required to fill the transmission after it has been drained; 5 quarts if the oil pan has been removed; and 7 quarts if the transmission has been overhauled.

When changing the oil, add 4 quarts, start the engine and add oil to bring the level up to the "Full" mark on the dipstick. Use only approved automatic transmission oil and do not overfill as this causes aeration and foaming.

MANUAL LINKAGE, ADJUST

1. Place selector lever in Neutral.
2. Loosen front and rear lock nuts at manual lever at transmission.
3. Hold manual rod and shift lever upward so selector lever is positioned against the neutral stop.
4. Tighten rear lock nut until it just contacts swivel, then tighten it two additional turns.

THROTTLE LINKAGE, ADJUST

1. Throttle linkage must be adjusted so that when the carburetor throttle valves are fully open (hot idle) the transmission throttle valve lever must be all the way toward the rear of the transmission against the internal stop.
2. In order to insure kickdown operation, the accelerator pedal linkage must be adjusted so that when the pedal is fully depressed the carburetor throttle valves are in wide open position.

BAND, ADJUST

Every 24,000 miles remove the oil pan and screen and adjust the band. Use an inch-pound torque wrench and an Allen wrench extension to torque the adjusting screw to 20 inch lbs.; then back off screw two turns. Tighten adjusting screw lock nut.

IN CAR REPAIRS

Units that may be removed from an installed transmission are as follows: Limit valve, pressure regulator valve, companion flange, rear oil seal, oil filler pipe, oil pan, and rear bearing retainer.

Units that can be removed after oil pan removal are: Control valve assembly, parking linkage, control valve channel plate, band adjusting screw and nut, accumulator, servo, throttle and manual control levers and related parts, oil cleaner, oil pump intake pipe and "O" ring seals.

Units that can be serviced after extension housing removal are: Speedometer drive gear, governor, reverse blocker valve, rear bearing and parking pawl.

TRANSMISSION, REPLACE

1. Support engine.
2. Remove oil filler and breather tubes.
3. Remove propeller shaft and disconnect shift and throttle linkage, cooler lines and speedometer cable.
4. Remove exhaust pipe and transmission rear cross support bar.
5. Support transmission. Then remove attaching bolts and remove transmission from car.
6. Install in reverse order of removal. Lubricate transmission-to-engine attaching bolts and torque to 30-35 ft. lbs. Fill transmission with approved fluid and adjust linkage.

PONTIAC TEMPESTORQUE 1963

NOTE: — This chapter deals only with maintenance, adjustments and "in car" repairs. For major service work, Motor's Automatic Transmission Manual is available. Current edition is a 740 page volume that includes 240 pages of oil circuit diagrams mostly in full color.

TRANSMISSION IDENTIFICATION

1963 Units

The transmission used with the V8-326 engine is of a different calibration than that used with the four cylinder engine. Under no circumstances should the V8 transmission or transmission-axle assembly be interchanged with the four cylinder unit. The primary differences found in these two units are in the number of plates in the clutch packs, the valve body and the modulator.

DESCRIPTION

This transmission, Fig. 1, consists of an air cooled, three element torque converter and a two speed planetary transmission. The transmission is attached to the differential carrier assembly to form a transmission-axle assembly. As a result, the torque converter is mounted on the opposite side of the carrier from the transmission. Two shafts run axially through the differential pinion shaft, transmitting torque from the engine to the converter and back to the transmission.

Torque multiplication is obtained both hydraulically through the converter and mechanically through the planetary gear set. The transmission provides neutral, low range, direct drive and reverse. Gear ratios are 1.76 to 1 in low and reverse and 1 to 1 in direct drive. The components of the transmission are shown schematically in Fig. 2.

Torque Converter Operation

The torque converter is a device that multiplies engine torque when required. The assembly has three members: a driving member called the converter pump, a driven member called the turbine, and a stator located between the pump and turbine. The three components are immersed in oil.

The converter pump is mechanically connected, through the converter pump and propeller shafts to the engine. When the engine is running, oil within the converter cavity is maintained under pressure by the oil pump. Oil is then picked up at the inner section of the converter pump and directed to its outer edges where it is thrown against the curved blades in the turbine. This causes the turbine to rotate, driving the turbine shaft.

As the oil leaves the turbine blades it is traveling in a direction opposite to the pump rotation. The blades of the stator, curved in the opposite direction to those in the turbine, change the direction of oil flow so that the oil strikes the back side of the converter pump blades, helping to drive the pump. Therefore, the total torque transmitted to the drive line is the combination of engine torque plus the additional torque supplied by the redirected oil striking the back side of the converter pump blades.

Stator Operation

The stator is mounted on a sprag (one way) clutch which holds the stator from moving in a reverse direction when the unit is acting to multiply torque. As the turbine speed approaches pump speed there is progressively less torque multiplication. The stator, which in the beginning was standing still, is picked up by the rapidly rotating oil and accelerates until the pump, turbine and stator are turning at almost the same speed. When the stator rotates, interference in the oil flow between the turbine and pump is minimized. When all three members are turning together there is no torque multiplication in the converter and it is acting as a fluid coupling.

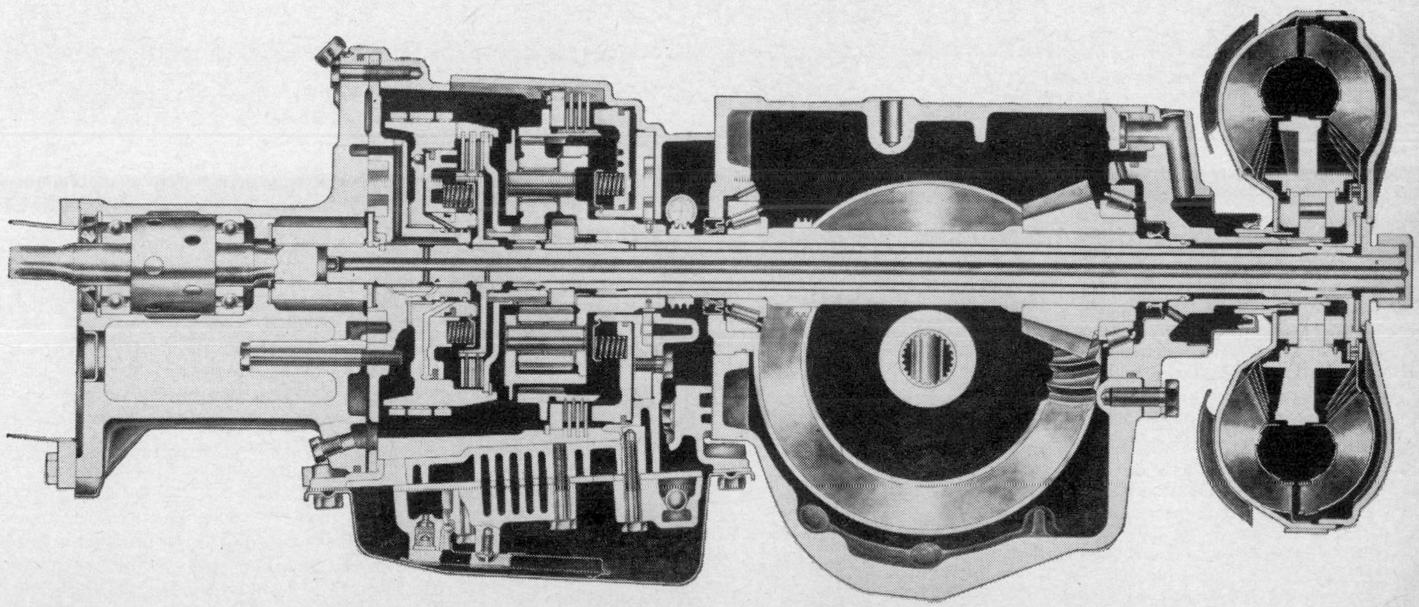

Fig. 1 Tempest Torque transmission and differential carrier (transaxle)

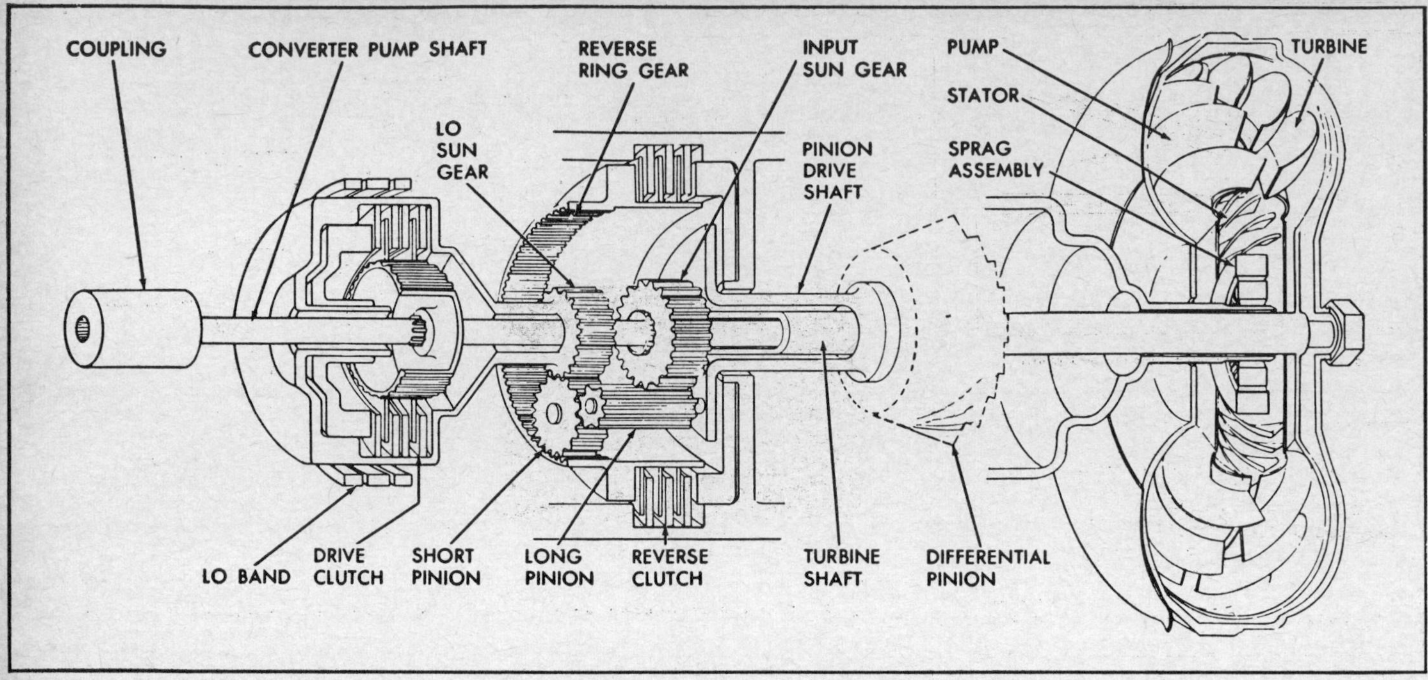

Fig. 2 Schematic drawing of transaxle

TROUBLE SHOOTING GUIDE

Oil Forced Out of Filler Tube

1. Oil level too high causing planet carrier to run in oil and cause foam.
2. Oil pickup pipe split or not sealed, causing air entrapment.

No Drive In Any Position

1. Low oil level.
2. Clogged oil suction pipe screen.
3. Broken or disconnected manual valve cable.
4. Defective pressure regulator valve.
5. Defective line pressure limit valve.
6. Front pump defective.
7. Front pump shaft disengaged at either converter or pump gear.
8. Front pump priming ball not seating.

Erratic Operation and Slippage—Light to Medium Throttle

1. Low oil level.
2. Clogged pickup pipe screen.
3. Band facing worn.
4. Low band apply linkage disengaged or broken.
5. Servo piston apply passage blocked.
6. Servo piston ring broken or leaking.
7. Converter stator not holding (rare).

Engine Speed Flares On Upshift

1. Low oil level.
2. Improper band adjustment.
3. Clogged oil suction screen.
4. High clutch partially applied—blocked feed orifice.
5. High clutch plates worn.
6. High clutch seals leak.
7. High clutch piston hung up.
8. High clutch drum relief ball not seating.
9. Vacuum modulator hose plugged.
10. Defective vacuum modulator.

Will Not Upshift

1. Maladjusted manual valve lever.
2. Throttle valve stuck or maladjusted.
3. Defective governor.
4. Stuck low-drive valve.

Harsh Upshifts

1. Throttle valve linkage improperly adjusted.
2. Vacuum modulator hose broken or disconnected.
3. Vacuum modulator diaphragm leaks.
4. Vacuum modulator valve stuck.
5. Improper low band adjustment.

Harsh Closed Throttle Downshifts

1. High engine idle speed.
2. Improper low band adjustment.
3. Vacuum modulator hose disconnected or broken.
4. Vacuum modulator diaphragm ruptured.
5. Vacuum modulator valve stuck.
6. Sticking valves in valve body.

Car Creeps In Neutral

1. Manual linkage improperly adjusted.
2. High clutch or low band not released.

No Drive In Reverse

1. Manual linkage improperly adjusted.
2. Reverse clutch piston stuck.
3. Reverse clutch plates worn out.
4. Reverse clutch leaking excessively.
5. Blocked reverse clutch apply orifice.

Improper Shift Points

1. Throttle linkage improperly adjusted.
2. Incorrectly adjusted TV valve.

MAINTENANCE

Adding Oil

Oil should be added only when the level is near the "ADD" mark on the dipstick with oil at normal operating temperature. The difference in oil level between "FULL" and "ADD" is one pint.

In order to check the oil level accurately, the engine should be idled with the transmission oil at normal operating temperature and the selector lever in neutral (N) position.

It is important that the oil level be maintained no higher than the "FULL" mark. Do not overfill. If oil is added which brings the level above the full mark, the planetary unit will run in the oil, foaming and aerating the oil. This will cause malfunction of the transmission due to improper application of the band or clutches and excessive temperature.

Changing Oil

No periodic draining of the transmission oil is recommended. When transmission requires repair, drain the oil by loosening the filler tube attaching nut in the oil pan and allow oil to drain (no drain plug is provided).

To refill the transmission, tighten the filler tube nut and add 2 quarts of approved automatic transmission oil, using filler tube and funnel. Start engine and allow it to idle in neutral 3 to 5 minutes to warm the oil. Then check the level and add as required to raise the level to the "FULL" mark. Assuming that the converter is not drained (since it is welded) and allowing for nominal spillage or draindown, approximately 3 quarts of oil will be required for refill.

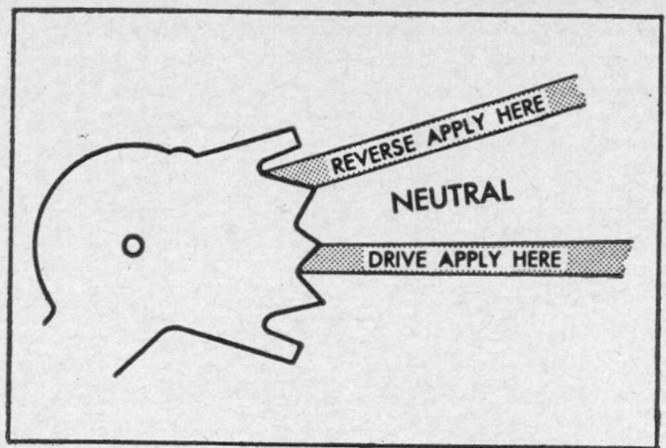

Fig. 3 Shift linkage check diagram

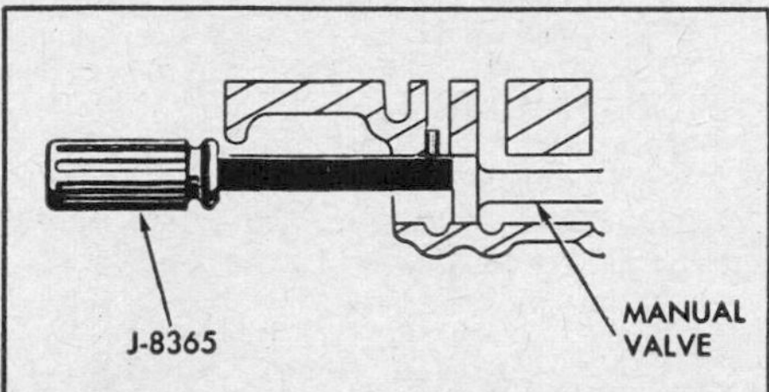

Fig. 4 Gauging manual valve

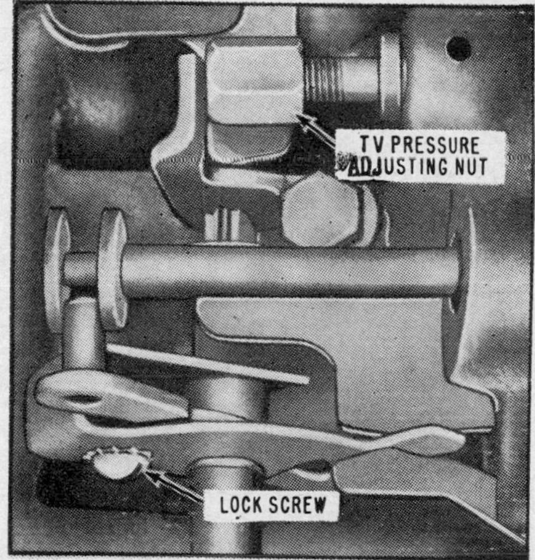

Fig. 5 Throttle valve pressure adjusting nut and manual valve lever lock screw

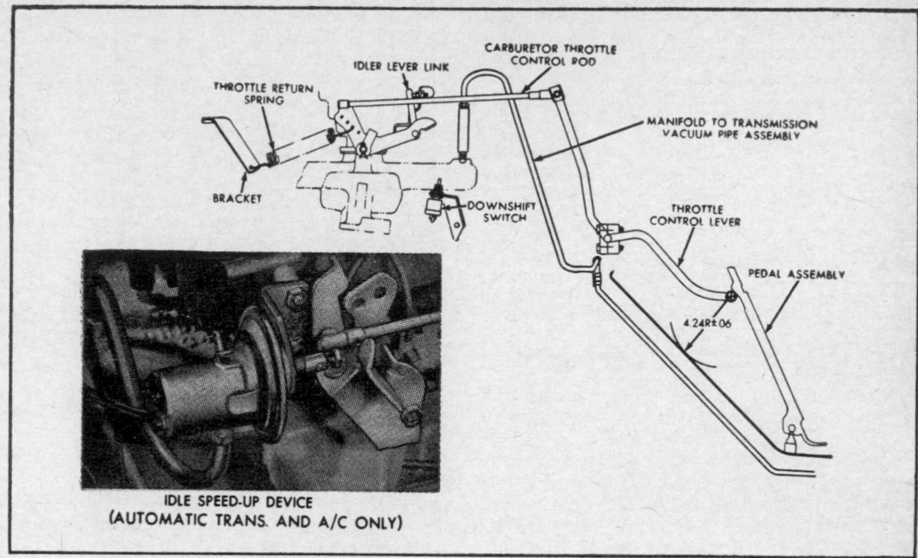

Fig. 6 Accelerator linkage on 4 cylinder model with single-barrel carburetor

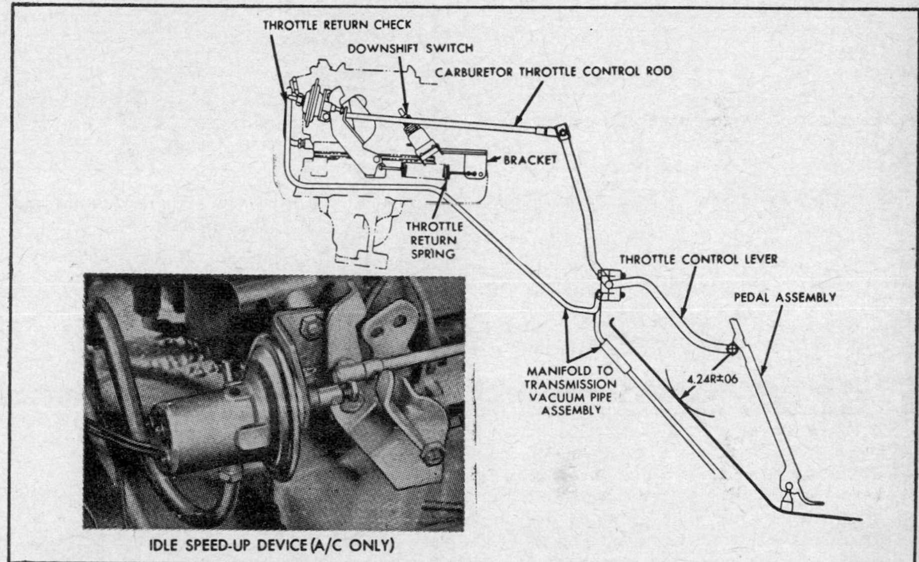

Fig. 7 Accelerator linkage on 4 cylinder model with 4-barrel carburetor

MANUAL LINKAGE

Check

1. Start engine. If cold, allow 2 to 3 minutes for transmission oil to warm up.
2. With engine at normal idle speed, move selector lever up from "N" toward "R" and note by feel the point at which reverse clutch applies. Properly adjusted, reverse clutch should apply within band from tooth peak to full Reverse detent, **Fig. 3.**
3. Make same check while moving selector lever from "N" to "D". Properly adjusted, the low band should apply as selector lever indicator is felt to be between tooth peak separating Neutral from Drive and full Drive Detent.
4. Unless shifts are obtained at points illustrated in Fig. 3, the shift linkage should be adjusted as follows:

Adjust

1. Drain oil from transmission and remove oil pan.
2. Place selector lever in driving compartment in "D".
3. Insert gauge (J-8365), Fig. 4, into manual valve bore with tab of gauge upward so it engages forward part of valve body.
4. With gauge in place, push forward on manual valve levers. Properly adjusted, the gauge will be held in place horizontally without being supported.
5. If readjustment is required, loosen lock screw, Fig. 5, push manual valve levers forward so that gauge is held in position. Retighten lock screw.

THROTTLE LINKAGE, ADJUST

1. Check accelerator pedal height and adjust as indicated in Figs. 6 and 7.
2. Depress accelerator pedal to the floor and check to see that the throttle valves are wide open.
3. Adjust carburetor throttle rod as required to obtain full throttle opening when accelerator pedal is pushed to the floor.

DOWNSHIFT SWITCH

1. Check and adjust carburetor throttle rod as outlined above.
2. With throttle valve in wide open position, use adjusting nuts to adjust downshift switch, Figs. 6 and 7.

Clearance between lever extension and lever should be .030-.100". Tighten nuts securely.

DOWNSHIFT SOLENOID

To replace the downshift solenoid, remove the oil pan, disconnect the solenoid lead wire from its terminal and remove the two screws attaching the solenoid to the valve body. *NOTE — It may be necessary to remove one reinforcement plate screw to remove the screw nearer the plate.*

LOW BAND, ADJUST

No periodic adjustment of the band is recommended. However, if necessary it may be adjusted as follows:

The transmission must be lowered to gain access to the adjusting screw. To adjust, loosen lock nut and tighten adjusting screw to 35-45 inch lbs. torque, then back off 4 full turns exactly. While holding screw, tighten lock nut securely.

EXTENSION OIL SEAL

1. Remove torque tube and propeller shaft.
2. Pry out old oil seal and tap new seal into position.
3. Install torque tube and propeller shaft.

EXTENSION BEARINGS

1. Remove torque tube and propeller shaft.
2. Remove oil seal and bearing snap ring.
3. Insert tool in extension housing, Fig. 8, so that it picks up inner race of bearing.
4. Using slide hammer as shown, tap out front bearing, spacer sleeve and rear bearing.
5. Using suitable socket, tap new rear bearing into position. Install spacer sleeve and tap in new front bearing.
6. Install new oil seal, torque tube and propeller shaft.

VACUUM MODULATOR

When removed check the valve for nicks or burrs; if such cannot be repaired with a slip stone, replace the valve. The modulator can be checked with a vacuum source for leakage. However, leakage normally results in transmission oil pullover, oil smoky exhaust and continually low transmission oil.

1. Referring to Fig. 9, remove vacuum hose and modulator retainer plate, after which remove modulator and valve from transmission case.
2. Install valve and modulator with a new O-ring seal on modulator. Tighten retainer plate firmly and install vacuum hose.

GOVERNOR

Referring to Fig. 10, remove lock screw securing governor tab to case and pull governor from transmission.

The only part replaceable is the driven gear. To remove, drive out roll pin with

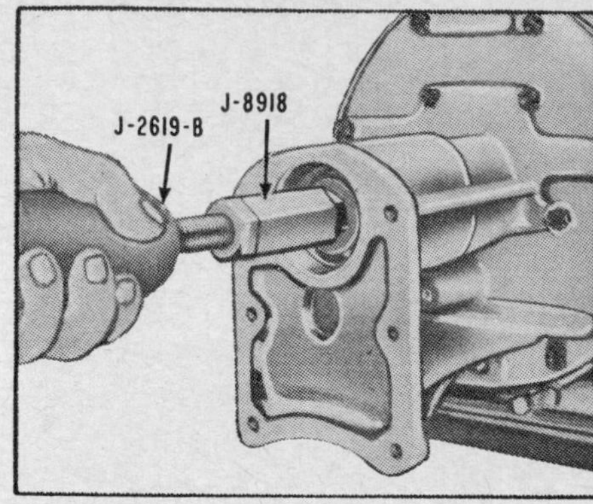

Fig. 8 Removing extension housing bearings

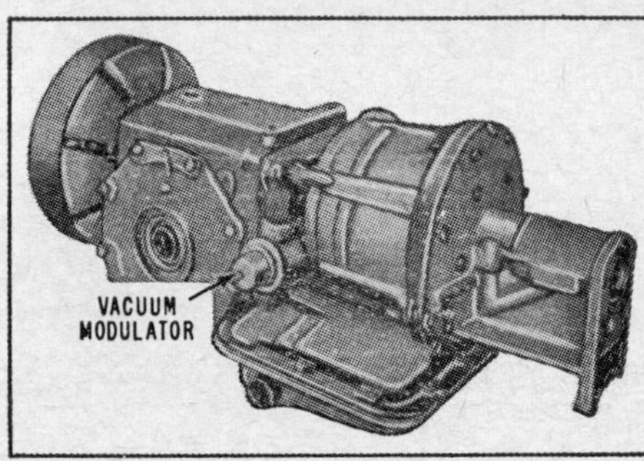

Fig. 9 Location of vacuum modulator

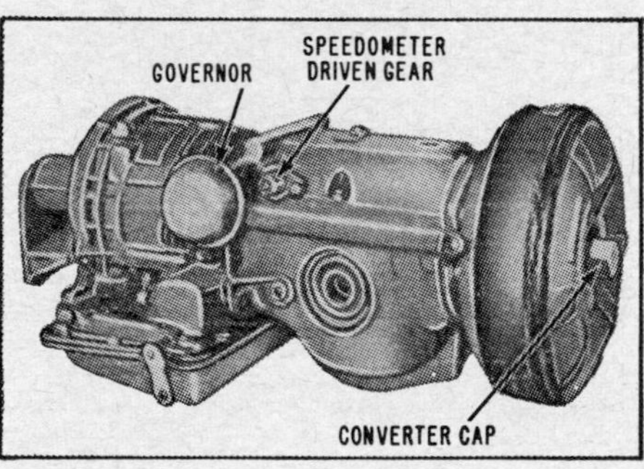

Fig. 10 Location of governor

Fig. 11 Servo piston retainer. Downshift timing valve location shown is for 1962 only

a punch and pull out old gear. Drill a new hole in the governor 90° from the original, insert new gear and install roll pin.

To install, use O-ring on governor and install governor into transmission with a slight twist to engage gear teeth. Secure with lock bolt.

VALVE BODY & LOW SERVO

1. To remove valve body, loosen oil filler nut in order to drain transmission oil and remove filler pipe.
2. Disconnect throttle valve rods from transmission levers.
3. Remove oil pan and gasket.
4. Remove retainer screw, oil screen and O-ring.
5. Loosely install retainer, Fig. 11, in pan screw hole. Retainer can be made from a piece of sheet metal.
6. Remove valve body attaching screws and tap valve body lightly to loosen from its dowels; then carefully lower body about $\frac{1}{16}$". Rotate retainer into place so it secures servo piston hub and tighten with oil pan screw. This eliminates the possibility of servo piston slipping out of its bore and loss of low band engagement with its apply components.
7. Remove valve body and gasket.
8. If necessary to remove low servo, tighten low band adjusting screw fully. Remove retainer and pull downward on piston shaft with screwdriver.
9. When disassembling the valve body the modulator body should be held during removal of screws as it is under spring pressure from pressure regulator valve spring.

Valve Body & Low Servo, Install

1. Install low servo piston and return spring in transmission bore and engage notch in piston shaft with low band apply strut, loosening low band screw slightly to permit piston ring to seat in case bore and allow installation of valve body.
2. Install retainer to hold servo piston in bore (see Fig. 11).
3. Position new gasket on valve body.
4. Position valve body in transmission, indexing on dowels and remove retainer. Be sure manual valve indexes properly with pin on inner shaft lever.
5. Secure valve body screws and tighten them to specified torque.
6. Install oil pick-up screen and O-ring in valve body and secure with screw.
7. Position manual valve lever in full reverse position so it is held securely by wedging device in transfer plate. Engage shift control cable and secure.
8. Using a new oil pan gasket, install oil pan and torque bolts to specified torque. It is important that an even torque be applied to the pan bolts to prevent leakage between pan and pan rail.
9. Tighten filler tube attaching nut; then refill transmission with oil.

10. Readjust band as previously directed.

PARKING PAWL, REPLACE

1. Remove screw securing parking lock control cable to cover and pawl.
2. Remove cover and pawl mounting screws and take off assembly with gasket.
3. Inspect pawl for damage. Check to see if actuator rollers turn freely. Replace any worn or damaged parts.
4. Using new gasket, install cover and pawl assembly.
5. Install new O-ring seal on end of cable. Seat O-ring seal and secure installation with screw and lockwasher.

TRANSAXLE, REPLACE

1. Raise car so that rear wheels hang free. Support torque tube and transaxle separately. Drain lube from transaxle.
2. Remove rear wheels and brake drums.
3. Remove bolts securing axle shaft bearing retainer to brake backing plate. Pull axle shafts out far enough to remove U-joint flanges from differential carrier.
4. On manual transmission jobs, disconnect speedometer cable and parking brake spring from differential carrier. On automatic transmission cars, disconnect vacuum line, parking brake return spring, T.V. rod, transmission control cable and speedometer cable. Remove oil filler tube.
5. Disconnect torque tube from transmission extension.
6. Unfasten differential carrier from rear crossmember. Remove bolt from bracket.
7. On manual transmission cars, remove muffler support bracket from torque tube.
8. Separate transaxle from torque tube and lower transaxle from car.
9. To install, reverse removal procedure.

CORVAIR POWERGLIDE

NOTE: — This chapter deals only with maintenance, adjustments and "in car" repairs. For major service work, Motor's Automatic Transmission Manual is available. Current edition is a 740 page volume that includes 240 pages of oil circuit diagrams mostly in full color.

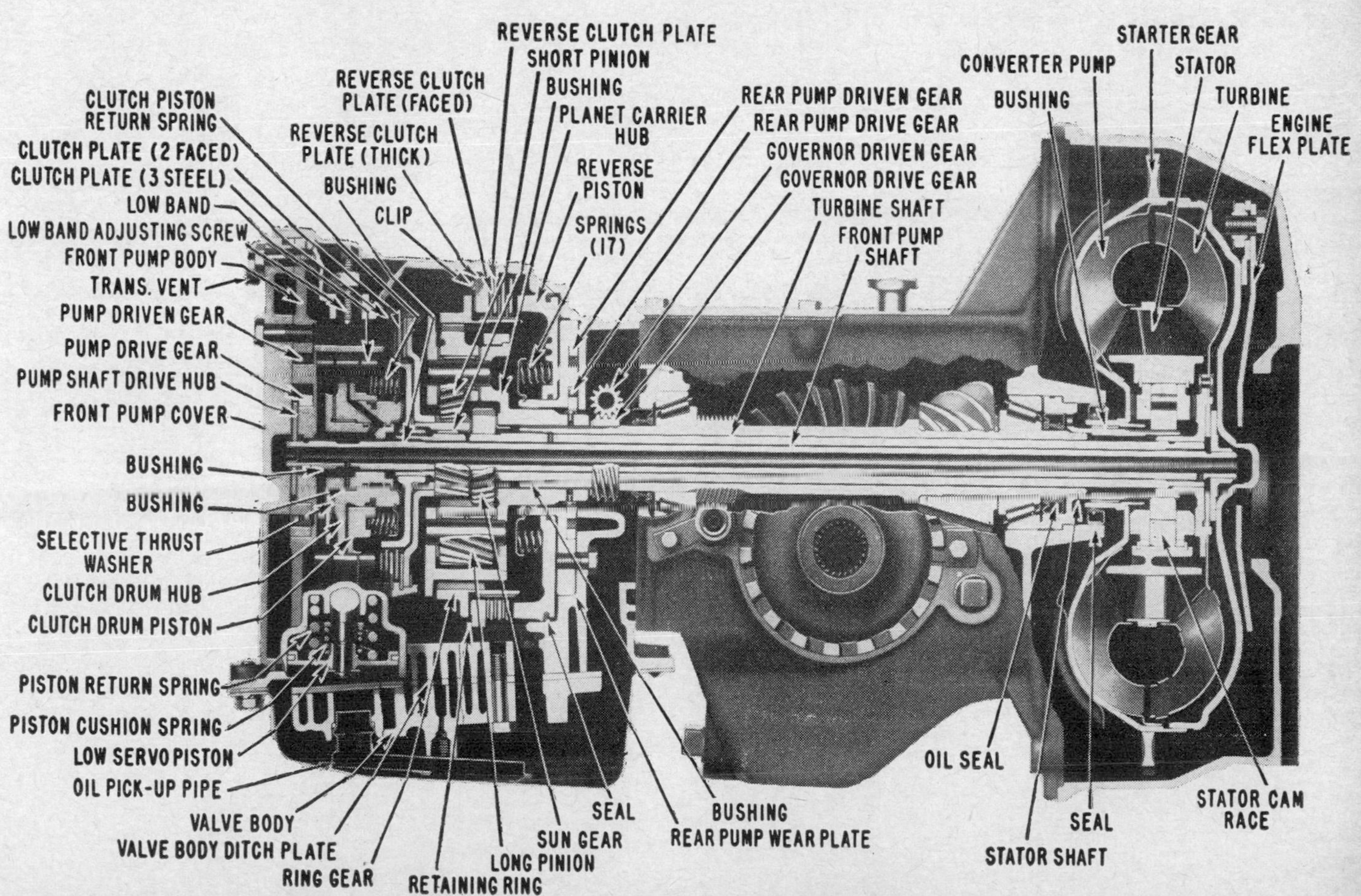

Fig. 1 Corvair Powerglide

TRANSMISSION IDENTIFICATION

All transmissions carry the unit number B-706-D. This number is stamped on the right hand side of the transmission case between the forward and middle pan mounting bosses. From 1964 the number is stamped on the oil pan at the shallow end.

DESCRIPTION

This transmission is similar to that described for the 1963 Pontiac Tempest. Like the Tempest transmission it consists of an air cooled three element torque converter which drives through an automatic shift, two-speed planetary transmission.

As shown in Fig. 1, the transmission is integrated with the differential carrier to form a transaxle. As a result, the converter is remote from the main transmission assembly, being separated by the differential carrier. Two shafts run axially through the hollow pinion shaft; one from the converter cover hub to the front pump and the other from the turbine to the input sun gear to transmit converter torque to the transmission gear box.

Construction

This transmission, Fig. 1, consists of an air-cooled, three-element torque converter driving a two-speed planetary gear set. The selector lever has four positions providing Drive, Neutral, Low and Reverse. No Park Range is provided.

The torque converter is attached through a flex plate to the engine crankshaft. From the converter the transmission input shaft goes through the hollow hypoid pinion and transmission output shafts.

Inside the transmission the compound planetary gear set is employed to provide a 1.82 reduction for Low and Reverse. A double-wrap band provides the reaction for Low, and a multiple plate clutch connects the input and output for Direct Drive. A multiple plate clutch supplies the reaction for Reverse operation.

The torque converter features an all welded cover to facilitate air cooling and provide a positive seal. Maximum torque multiplication is 2.6 to 1.

Special provision is made to drive the transmission front pump. A special shaft is splined to the converter front cover and runs through the hollow input shaft to the transmission front pump. The front pump shaft also serves as the bearing support for the input shaft under the drive clutch.

Drive Range performance features a smooth upshift from the 1.82 to 1 geared reduction to Direct Drive. The shift speed is determined by the combined influence of an engine vacuum modulator, output shaft driven governor and accelerator linkage controlled throttle valve.

TROUBLE SHOOTING

Oil Forced Out Filler Tube

1. Oil level too high causing planet carrier to run in oil and cause foam.
2. Oil pickup pipe split or not sealed, allowing air in system.

No Drive In Any Position

1. Low oil level.
2. Clogged oil suction pipe screen.
3. Broken or disconnected manual valve cable.
4. Defective pressure regulator valve.
5. Front pump defective.
6. Rear pump check valve, check valve poppet, or rear pump priming ball not seating. Both must occur for possible malfunction.
7. Defective line pressure limit valve.
8. Front pump shaft disengaged at either converter or pump gear.
9. Front pump priming ball not seating.

Erratic Operation or Slippage (Light to Medium Throttle)

1. Low oil level.
2. Clogged pickup pipe screen.
3. Improper band adjustment.
4. Band facing worn.
5. Low band apply linkage disengaged or broken.
6. Servo piston apply passage blocked.
7. Servo piston ring broken or missing.
8. Converter stator not holding (rare).

Engine Speed Flares on Upshift

1. Low oil level.
2. Improper band adjustment.
3. Clogged oil suction screen.
4. High clutch partially applied (blocked feed orifice).
5. High clutch plates worn.
6. High clutch seals leak.
7. High clutch piston hung up.
8. High clutch relief ball not seating.
9. Vacuum modulator hose plugged.
10. Vacuum modulator defective.

Will Not Upshift

1. Maladjusted manual valve lever.
2. Throttle valve stuck or maladjusted.
3. No rear pump output caused by stuck priming valve, sheared pin or defective pump.
4. Defective governor.
5. Stuck low-drive valve.

Harsh Upshifts

1. Throttle valve linkage improperly adjusted.
2. Vacuum modulator hose broken or disconnected.
3. Vacuum modulator diaphragm leaks.
4. Vacuum modulator valve stuck.
5. Hydraulic modulator valve stuck.
6. Improper low band adjustment.

Harsh Closed Throttle Downshifts

1. High engine idle speed.
2. Improper low band adjustment.
3. Vacuum modulator hose disconnected or broken.
4. Vacuum modulator diaphragm ruptured.
5. Vacuum modulator valve stuck.
6. Sticking valves in valve body (pressure regulator or hydraulic modulator valves).

Creeps In Neutral

1. Manual linkage improperly adjusted.
2. High clutch or low band not released.

No Drive In Reverse

1. Manual valve linkage improperly adjusted (cable).
2. Reverse clutch piston stuck.
3. Reverse clutch plates worn out.
4. Reverse clutch leaking excessively.
5. Blocked reverse clutch apply orifice.

Improper Shift Points

1. Throttle valve linkage improperly adjusted.
2. Incorrectly adjusted TV valve.
3. Governor defective.
4. Rear pump priming valve stuck.

Unable to Push Start

1. Rear pump drive gear not engaged with drive pins on planet carrier hub.
2. Drive pin sheared off or missing.
3. Rear pump priming ball not seating.
4. Rear pump defective.

MAINTENANCE

Adding Oil

Oil level should be checked every 1000 miles. Oil should be added only when the level is near the "ADD" mark on the dipstick with oil at normal operating temperature. The oil level dipstick is located in the right front of the engine compartment. *The difference in oil level between "FULL" and "ADD" is one pint.*

To check oil level accurately, the engine should be idled with the transmission oil at normal operating temperature and the control lever in Neutral position. Oil level should be maintained no higher than the "FULL" mark on the dipstick. Do not overfill as foaming and aerating of the oil will result because the planetary unit will be running in oil, causing improper application of the band or clutches.

Draining and Refilling

SERVICE NOTE: Periodic draining of the oil pan on all 1964 and later transmissions every 12,000 miles under normal operation and more frequently under extreme service usage is now recommended. It is realized that only a portion of the fluid can be drained at the oil pan. However, the addition of even this volume of fresh fluid will replenish the additives in the remaining fluid to increase transmission durability.

To drain the oil, loosen the filler tube attaching nut in the oil pan and allow the oil to drain. When drained, tighten filler tube nut and add 3 quarts of approved transmission fluid to the transmission.

Set the parking brake and operate the transmission through all ranges. Then with engine idling, selector lever in neutral and transmission at operating temperature, recheck the fluid level and add fluid as necessary to bring the level up to the "Full" mark on the dipstick. Do not overfill as damage to the transmission can result.

Refilling After Repairs

To refill the transmission, tighten the filler tube nut and add 4 pints of transmission fluid, using a suitable filler tube and funnel. Start engine and allow it to idle in Neutral for 3 to 5 minutes to warm the transmission fluid. Then add oil as required to bring the level to the "FULL" mark on the dipstick. Assuming that the converter was not drained

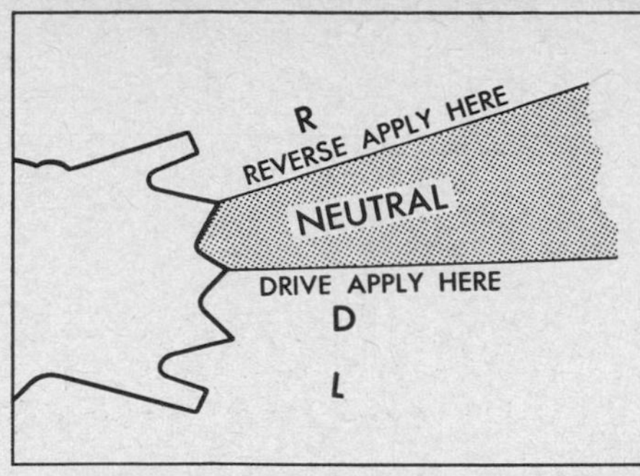

Fig. 2 Shift linkage check diagram

(since it is welded) and allowing for nominal spillage or draindown, approximately 3 quarts are required for a refill.

MANUAL LINKAGE

Check Operation

If improper shift linkage adjustment is suspected, a check can be made quickly without any disassembly as follows:

1. Start engine and allow to run for 2 to 3 minutes to warm up the transmission fluid.
2. With engine at normal idle speed, very slowly move range selector lever up from "N" to "R" and note by feel the point at which the reverse clutch applies. Properly adjusted, the reverse clutch should apply at the peak of the tooth separating Neutral and Reverse detents, Fig. 2.
3. Make the same check as in Step 2 while moving the selector lever from "N" toward "D". Properly adjusted, the low band should apply as the selector lever follower is felt to be at the tooth peak separating Neutral from Drive and full Drive detent.
4. Unless the shifts are obtained at the points illustrated, the shift linkage should be adjusted with Gauge J-8365, Fig. 3.

Adjustment

1. Drain oil and remove oil pan.
2. Place selector lever in "D".
3. Insert Gauge J-8365 into manual valve bore as shown in Fig. 3 with tab of gauge upward so it engages to forward port of valve body as shown in inset.
4. With gauge in place, push forward on manual valve levers. Properly adjusted, the gauge will be held in place horizontally without being supported.
5. If readjustment is required, loosen lock screw and push manual valve levers forward so that gauge is held in this attitude. Recheck adjustment as in Step 4.
6. When satisfactory adjustment is obtained, install oil pan and filler tube; then refill transmission with oil as described above.

THROTTLE LINKAGE

1966-68

NOTE: Accelerator linkage should be adjusted to get simultaneous full throttle position at the accelerator pedal, the linkage idler lever and the carburetor throttle lever. The pedal downward travel stop (at idler lever at transmission) is adjustable to furnish a pedal angle comfortable to the driver.

1. To adjust, disconnect accelerator pull rod swivel from rear idler lever.
2. Disconnect carburetor pull-back spring. Remove carburetor cross shaft actuating rod swivel from cross shaft.
3. Pull carburetor cross shaft actuating rod rearward until rear idler lever hits stop on its bracket. Rotate carburetor cross shaft to move L.H. primary carburetor into wide open throttle position (thru detent on Powerglide).
4. With carburetor cross shaft and its actuating rod held in the foregoing positions, align actuating rod swivel until it freely engages its mating hole in cross shaft lever. Remove swivel and back it off five full turns and replace it in lever hole.
5. Connect pull-back spring.
6. Depress pedal to within 1⅛" of floor carpet and block pedal in this position. *This pedal setting is measured from the underside of the rubber flange at the top of the pedal.*
7. Rotate rear idler lever into wide open throttle position and reconnect accelerator pull rod after adjusting rod swivel so it freely engages its mating hole in idler lever.
8. Remove pedal block and check complete accelerator control linkage adjustment by depressing pedal and inspecting carburetor throttle valve to be sure it is at wide open position.

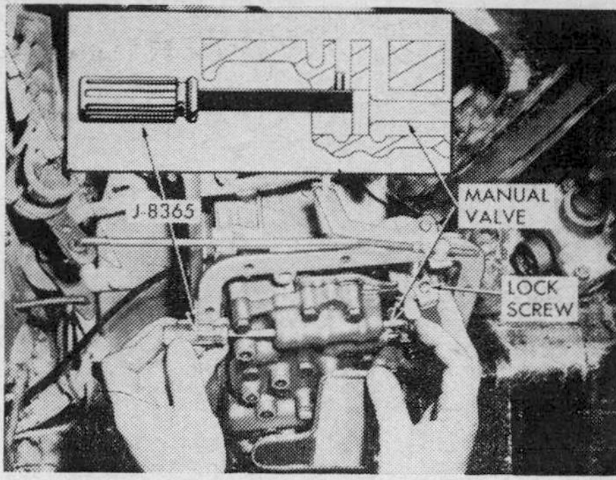

Fig. 3 Adjusting manual valve linkage

1963-65

1. Disconnect accelerator rod swivel.
2. Disconnect actuating rod swivel at L.H. carburetor lever.
3. Pull cross shaft actuating rod to wide open position and turn cross shaft lever to wide open throttle position (carburetor throttle lever against stop). Adjust actuating rod swivel to align with hole in cross shaft lever, then lengthen accelerator rod by backing off swivel five full turns.
4. Position accelerator pedal one inch from the floor mat (1¼" on Powerglide) by placing a block of wood between pedal and floor mat.
5. Hold rear idler lever in wide open throttle position and turn swivel to align with hole in lever.

LOW BAND ADJUST

As no periodic adjustment of the low band is recommended, access to the adjusting screw has been provided from inside the vehicle via the parcel compartment area behind the rear seat.

To gain access to the low band, remove the parcel shelf and the plug covering the access hole in the floor pan.

Adjustment of the low band requires an improvised tubular hex ¾" socket approximately 4½ to 6" long. Probably the simplest way to fabricate this tool would be to weld two ¾" tubular stamped steel spark plug wrenches together.

To adjust, loosen the lock nut and tighten the adjusting screw *to 35 to 45 inch lbs., then back off 4 complete turns exactly.* While holding the adjusting screw stationary by means of the socket, inserted through the improvised wrench, tighten the lock nut securely.

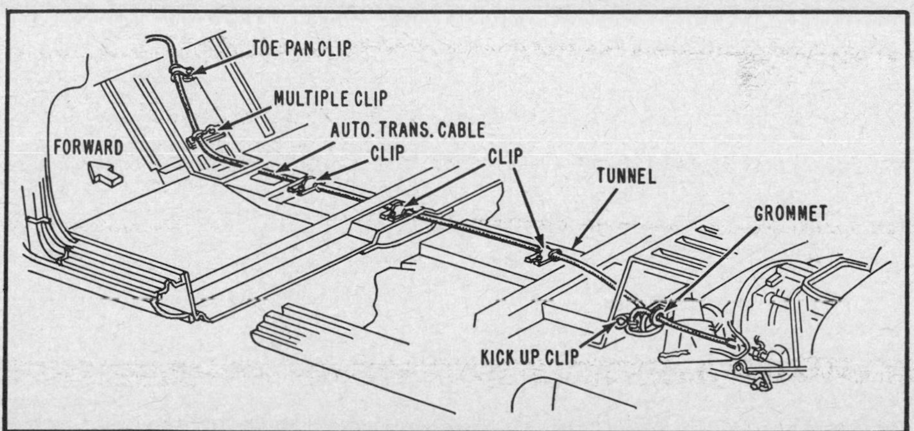

Fig. 4 Shift control cable routing. 1963-64

CONTROL CABLE REPLACE

1963-64

Remove tunnel covers and detach cable as suggested by Fig. 4. Install new cable as follows:

1. Lay cable out beneath car in its correct relationship.
2. Insert cable up into passenger compartment. Cable must then be routed *under* parking brake cable and then *over* parking brake pipe to prevent possibility of brake cable riding against shift cable.
3. Connect shift cable to range selector.
4. Shift range selector to "D" and secure cable to base of toe-pan.
5. Complete installation as shown in Fig. 4, being sure to bow cable to center line of vehicle to guide cable through hole in engine front support.

Cable-to-Transmission Installation

Fig. 5—Install O-ring seal on cable, having lubricated it with Lubriplate. With throttle rods disconnected from throttle valve lever on transmission, rotate throttle valve lever its full limit counterclockwise and insert cable ball into slot of manual valve lever. Fully seat O-ring and secure installation by installing capscrew and lockwasher.

Checking Installation, Fig. 6—Once fully tightened, exert a slight hand pressure in the counterclockwise direction and check that the hole in the notched arm of the throttle valve lever is *below* the transmission oil pan rail and dimension indicated by the arrows, Fig. 6 (3/8" plus or minus 1/16"). If hole is above pan rail, cable installation is faulty and must be rechecked.

1965-68

Removal

1. Remove instrument cluster.
2. Disconnect control cable from range selector.
3. Remove tunnel covers.
4. At front of vehicle remove cable from dash clip, Fig. 7, and from beneath parking brake pulley shaft.
5. Remove cable from three body harness clips in tunnel.
6. Remove grommet plate at rear of tunnel, free cable sheath from plate, and remove clip in underbody kick-up area.
7. Disconnect throttle rods from TV lever on transmission.
8. Complete cable removal by rotating transmission TV lever its full limit to free cable ball from inner manual valve lever slot in transmission and withdraw cable. Bow cable towards center line of vehicle to guide cable through hole in engine front support.

Installation

1. With tunnel covers removed, lay cable out beneath car in its correct relationship.
2. Insert front of cable up into passenger compartment. Cable must then be routed under parking brake cable and then over brake pipe to prevent brake cable riding against shift cable and establishing a sawing action.
3. After cable routing is satisfactory, connect shift cable to range selector.
4. Shift range selector to Drive position, then route cable through upper dash clip and close clip. Continue routing cable through underbody opening and under parking brake pulley shaft at base of toe pan. Be sure rubber protector is installed on cable sheath.
5. Secure cable with two clips provided in tunnel area. Bow cable towards center line of vehicle to guide cable through hole in engine front support.
6. Install O-ring seal on cable, Fig. 8, applying lubriplate lightly on seal.
7. With throttle rods disconnected from TV lever on transmission, rotate TV lever its full limit counter-clockwise and insert cable ball into slot of manual valve lever.
8. Fully seat O-ring seal and secure installation by installing cap screw and lock washer.
9. Correctness of installation is easily checked. Once fully tightened, exert a slight hand pressure in counter-clockwise direction and check that the hole in the notched arm of the TV lever is below the transmission oil pan rail, Fig. 6. If hole is above pan rail, cable installation is faulty and must be re-checked.
10. Install cable rear grommet, Fig. 7, in grommet plate, then install grommet plate in rear of tunnel and pull cable through grommet until white tape or paint mark is visible outside grommet.
11. Install clip on cable in rear kick-up area.
12. Check shift linkage for proper operation.

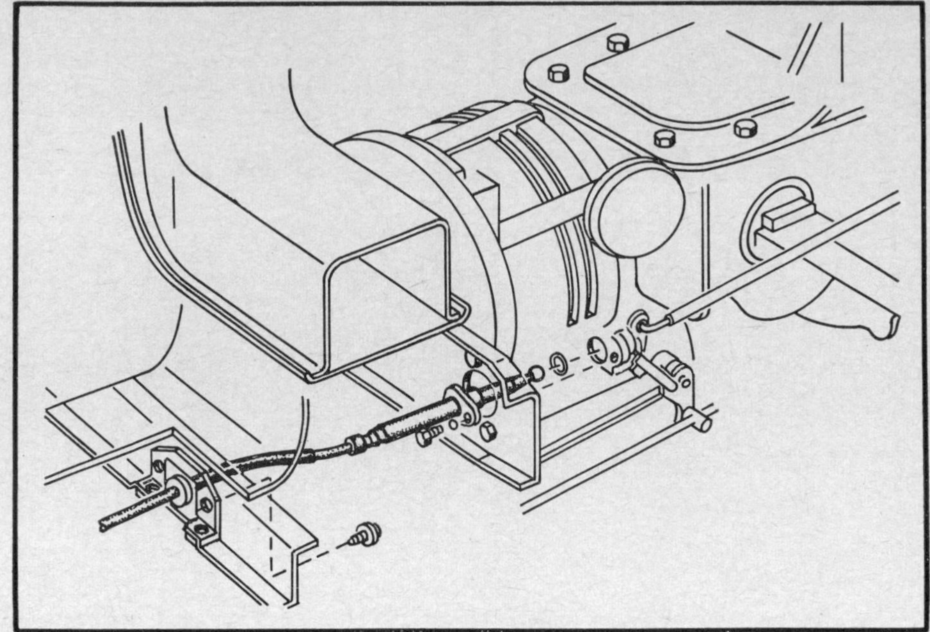

Fig. 5 Cable-to-case installation. 1963-64

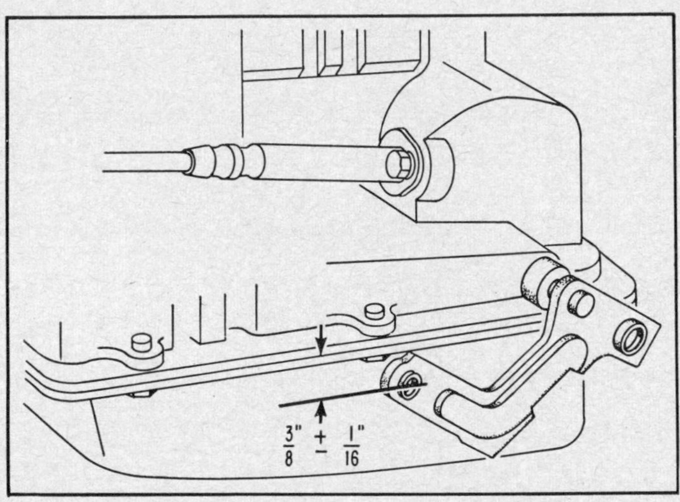

Fig. 6 Cable installation check diagram. 1963-68

VACUUM MODULATOR

The vacuum modulator is mounted on the right side of the transmission and can be serviced from beneath the vehicle. Disconnect the vacuum hose and unscrew the modulator from the transmission with channel lock pliers or a thin one-inch wrench.

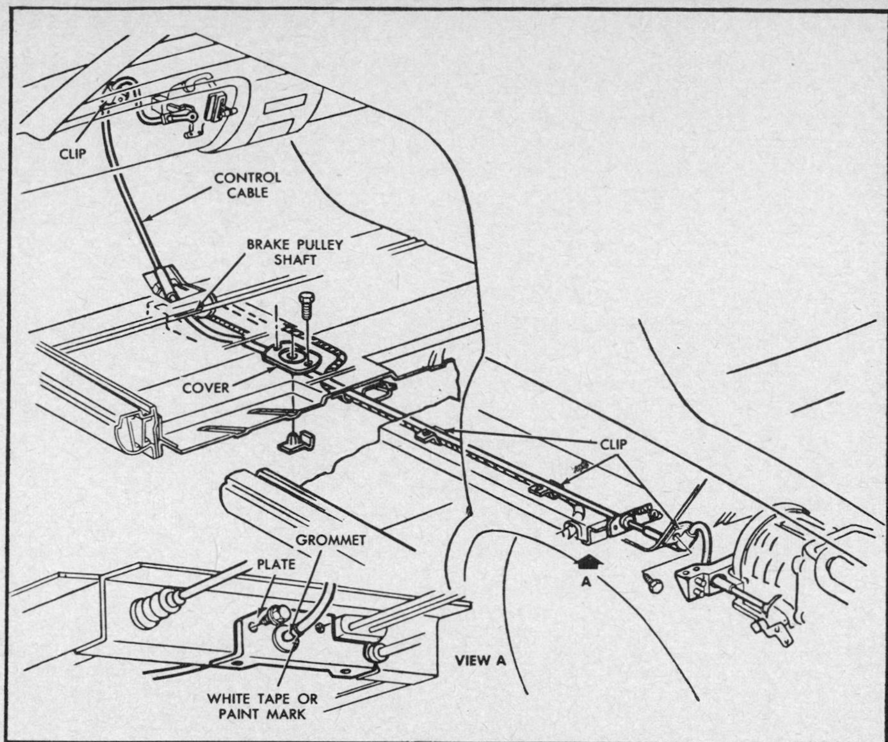

Fig. 7 Shift control cable routing. 1965-68

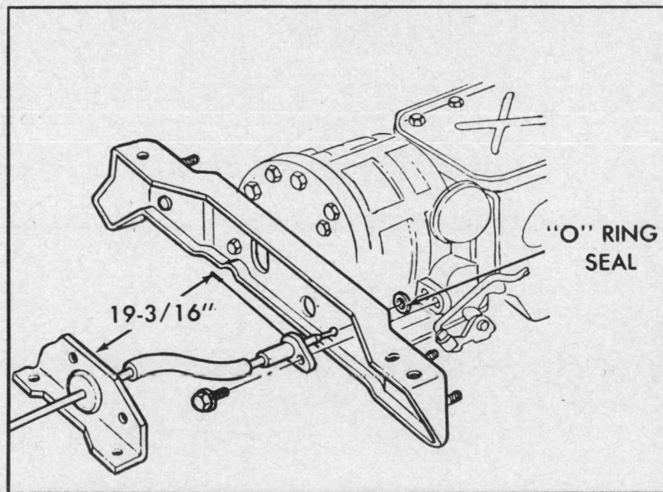

Fig. 8 Cable to case installation. 1965 68

The vacuum modulator can be checked with a vacuum source for leakage. However, leakage normally results in transmission oil pull-over and results in oil smoky exhaust and continually low transmission oil level. No repairs are possible on the modulator; replace with new unit.

When installing, center the gasket in place with vaseline and hold it centered during installation to prevent an external oil leak.

GOVERNOR

Governor is accessible from beneath the vehicle and is mounted on the left side of the transmission. To remove, unscrew lock screw and pull the unit out of the transmission.

VALVE BODY & LOW SERVO

Removal

1. Drain oil pan and disconnect throttle valve rods from TV lever on transmission.
2. Remove oil pan and oil pick-up pipe.
3. Make an improvised sheet metal strap, Fig. 9, and loosely install with one pan bolt.
4. Remove bolts securing valve body to transmission, tap valve body lightly with a soft hammer to loosen from its dowels in transmission case, then carefully lower the valve body about $\frac{1}{16}$", rotate improvised strap into place so it spans the servo piston hub and secure strap with pan bolt. This eliminates possibility of servo piston slipping down out of its bore and the loss of low band engagement with its apply components.
5. To remove the low servo piston, pull downward on the hub of the piston shaft with a screwdriver. *Do not remove piston in vehicle unless low band screw is first tightened fully.*

Fig. 9 Removing valve body

Low Servo Piston Repairs

Disassemble the servo piston by removing the hairpin clip. Remove ring from piston and install it in low servo bore to measure the ring gap which should be .002" to .012".

Assemble ring to piston and measure clearance between ring and one wall of piston groove which should be .0005" to .005".

Installation

1. Install low servo piston and return spring in transmission bore and engage notch in piston shaft with low band apply strut, loosening low band screw slightly to permit piston ring to seat in case bore.
2. Install valve body in transmission while simultaneously loosening low band screw until it is possible to index valve body on dowels in case. If manual valve is installed, index it with a manual valve lever in case; then secure valve body with 20 bolts to a torque of 9 11 ft. lbs.
3. Install O-ring in valve body and install oil pick-up pipe and secure with screw.
4. Complete installation and adjust low band as outlined previously.

POWER TRAIN, REPLACE

1. Remove shrouds and shields as required.
2. Back car into place so that rear bumper is under a chain hoist.
3. Use holes provided to attach a chain to bumper.
4. Raise car with hoist and install jack stands.
5. Disconnect all necessary wires, hoses, pipes, linkage, etc.
6. Loosen (do not remove) bolts attaching engine to mounts.
7. Lower car so that engine rests absolutely flat on two 6 x 6 inch blocks.
8. Reach under car and remove loosened bolts from mounts.
9. Raise car body to clear engine.
10. Slide power train out under car.
11. Reverse procedure to install.

CHEVROLET POWERGLIDE
(Aluminum Case)

NOTE: — This chapter deals only with maintenance, adjustments and "in car" repairs. For major service work, Motor's Automatic Transmission Manual is available. Current edition is a 740 page volume that includes 240 pages of oil circuit diagrams mostly in full color.

TRANSMISSION IDENTIFICATION

On 1963-68 models the unit number is located on the right rear vertical surface of oil pan. There is no particular code with which a transmission may be identified. Therefore, when ordering parts use the transmission serial number.

DESCRIPTION

This Powerglide is essentially a torque converter coupled to a two-speed transmission, Fig. 1. The gear portion of the transmission is a two-speed compound planetary gear set, permitting a gear reduction of 1.82 to 1 on the light duty version and 1.76 to 1 on the heavy duty version. The shift from low gear to direct drive is automatic, and the vehicle speed at which the shifts occur is determined by the interaction of a governor driven by the output shaft and a throttle valve controlled by the accelerator pedal. Thus, the transmission starts with both the torque converter and the gear box multiplying torque. As vehicle speed increases, the gear box section upshifts to direct drive, leaving only the torque converter for any speed-torque changes required. The torque multiplication ability of the converter multiplied by the planetary gear reduction allows an overall torque multiplication of approximately 4.55 to 1.

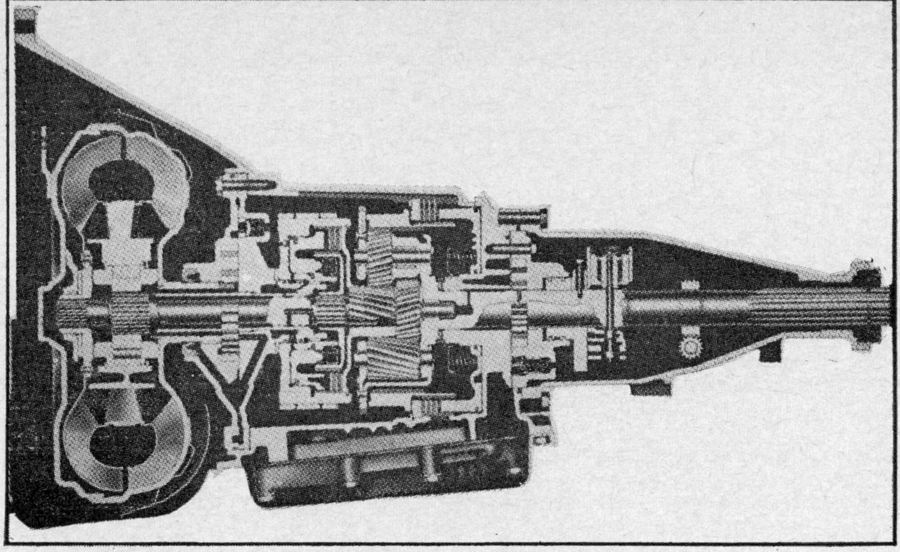

Fig. 1 Sectional view of Powerglide with aluminum case

TROUBLE SHOOTING

Oil Forced Out Filler Tube

1. Oil level too high; aeration and foaming caused by planet carrier running in oil.
2. Water in oil.
3. Leak in pump suction circuits.

Oil Leaks

1. Transmission case and extension: extension oil seal, shifter shaft oil seal, speedometer driven gear fitting, pressure taps, oil cooler pipe connections, vacuum modulator and case, transmission oil pan gasket.
2. A very smoky exhaust indicates a ruptured vacuum modulator diaphragm.
3. Converter cover pan; front pump attaching bolts, pump seal ring, pump oil seal, plugged oil drain in front pump, porosity in transmission case.

No Drive In Any Position

1. Low oil level.
2. Clogged oil suction screen.
3. Defective pressure regulator valve.
4. Front pump defective.
5. Input shaft broken.
6. Front pump priming valve stuck.

Erratic Operation and Slippage—Light to Medium Throttle

1. Low oil level.
2. Clogged oil suction screen.
3. Improper band adjustment.
4. Band facing worn.
5. Low band apply linkage disengaged or broken.
6. Servo apply passage blocked.
7. Servo piston ring broken or leaking.
8. Converter stator not holding (rare).

Engine Speed Flares On Upshift

1. Low oil level.
2. Improper band adjustment.
3. Clogged oil suction screen.
4. High clutch partially applied—blocked feed orifice.
5. High clutch plates worn.
6. High clutch seals leak.
7. High clutch piston hung up.
8. High clutch drum relief ball not sealing.
9. Vacuum modulator line plugged.
10. Vacuum modulator defective.

Will Not Upshift

1. Maladjusted manual valve lever.
2. Throttle valve stuck or maladjusted.
3. No rear oil pump output caused by stuck priming valve, sheared drive pin or defective pump.
4. Defective governor.
5. Stuck low-drive valve.

Harsh Upshifts

1. Throttle valve linkage improperly adjusted.
2. Vacuum modulator line broken or disconnected.
3. Vacuum modulator diaphragm leaks.
4. Vacuum modulator valve stuck.
5. Hydraulic modulator valve stuck.
6. Improper low band adjustment.

Harsh Closed Throttle (Coast) Downshifts

1. High engine idle speed.
2. Improper band adjustment.
3. Vacuum modulator line broken or disconnected.
4. Modulator diaphragm ruptured.
5. Sticking hydraulic modulator valve, pressure regulator valve or vacuum modulator valve.
6. Downshift timing valve malfunction.

No Downshift (Direct-to-Low) Accelerator Floored

1. Throttle control linkage improperly adjusted.
2. Sticking shifter valve or throttle and detent valve.

Car Creeps In Neutral

1. Manual control linkage improperly adjusted.
2. High clutch or low band not released.

No Drive In Reverse

1. Manual control linkage improperly adjusted.
2. Reverse clutch piston stuck.
3. Reverse clutch plates worn out.
4. Reverse clutch leaking excessively.
5. Blocked reverse clutch apply orifice.

Improper Shift Points

1. Throttle valve linkage improperly adjusted.
2. Incorrectly adjusted throttle valve.
3. Defective governor.
4. Rear pump priming valve stuck.

Unable To Push Start

1. Rear pump drive gear not engaged with drive pin on output shaft.
2. Drive pin sheared off or missing.
3. Rear pump priming valve not sealing.
4. Rear pump defective.

MAINTENANCE

Powerglide Fluid Deterioration

The deterioration of transmission fluid has in some instances caused clutch failure and adversely affected other transmission components. Once such a condition has been encountered the only solution is to overhaul the transmission. It is also necessary to clean all parts that are not replaced.

One component that may not be replaced in the overhaul operation, because visual inspection, after cleaning, does not reveal the need for replacement is the oil intake suction screen. Although inspection of the screen leads one to believe that it can still perform its function, the screen in almost every instance is partially clogged with varnish (even after cleaning). If the transmission is reassembled with a partially clogged screen, oil passage through it is impeded, resulting in starvation of the rear pump. This lack of sufficient oil to the rear pump results in an objectionable siren-type noise and eventual failure. Consequently, due to the possible damage caused by a partially clogged screen versus the cost of the screen, it is recommended that the oil pump suction screen be replaced whenever a Powerglide is overhauled due to fluid deterioration.

Oil Level

The transmission oil level should be checked every 1000 miles. Oil should be added only when the level is near the "Add" mark on the dipstick with oil hot or at operating temperature.

In order to check oil level accurately, the engine should be idled with the transmission oil hot and the control lever in neutral "N" position.

It is important that the oil level be maintained no higher than the "Full" mark on the oil level gauge. *Do not overfill for when the oil level is at the full mark on the dipstick, it is just slightly below the planetary gear unit. If additional oil is added, bringing the level above the full mark, the planetary unit will run in the oil, foaming and aerating the oil. This aerated oil carried through the various oil pressure passages may cause malfunction of the transmission assembly, resulting in cavitation noise in the converter and improper band or clutch application.*

Changing Oil

SERVICE NOTE: Starting with April 1, 1964, all transmissions will be equipped with a drain plug in the oil pan. This change was introduced in production on a limited basis during February 1964.

Periodic draining of the oil pan when equipped with a drain plug is recommended every 12,000 miles under normal operating conditions and more frequently under extreme service usage. It is realized that only a portion of the total transmission fluid can be drained at the oil pan. However, the addition of even this volume of fresh fluid will replenish the additives in the remaining fluid sufficiently to increase transmission durability.

After draining the oil pan, pour two quarts of approved transmission fluid into the transmission. Then set the parking brake and operate the transmission through all ranges. With engine idling, transmission selector lever in neutral, and transmission at operating temperature, recheck the fluid level and add fluid as necessary to bring the level to the "Full" mark on the dipstick. Do not overfill as damage to the transmission can result.

Units Without Drain Plug:
When the transmission is to be removed for repairs, drain and refill as follows:

To drain the transmission, carefully loosen the oil pan bolts. Position a receptacle to catch the draining oil. If the transmission is to be removed for repairs, the draining operation may be performed after removal, if desired.

To refill the transmission, remove the dipstick from the filler tube and refill the transmission with approved fluid. The engine should then be run at a fast idle speed with the transmission in neutral until the oil warms up. Then add oil as required to raise the fluid level on the dipstick to the "Full" mark. Refill capacity is 1½ quarts.

MANUAL LINKAGE, ADJUST

CAUTION: Shift linkage adjustment must be accurately made. Any inaccuracies may result in premature failure of the transmission due to operation without controls in full detent. Such operation results in reduced oil pressure and in turn partial engagement of the affected clutches. Partial engagement of the clutches with sufficient pressure to cause apparent normal operation of the vehicle will result in failure of the clutches or other internal parts after only a few miles of operation.

1967-68

1. Shift tube and lever assembly must be free in mast jacket.
2. To check for proper adjustment, lift selector lever toward steering wheel. Allow selector lever to be positioned in D by transmission detent.

NOTE: Do NOT use the indicator pointer as a reference to position the selector lever. When performing linkage adjustment, pointer is adjusted last.

3. Release selector lever. Lever should be inhibited from engaging low range unless the lever is lifted.
4. Lift selector lever towards steering wheel and allow lever to be positioned in N by the transmission detent.
5. Release selector lever. Lever should now be inhibited from engaging reverse range unless lever is lifted.

NOTE: A properly adjusted linkage will prevent the selector lever from moving from beyond both the neutral detent and the drive detent unless the lever is lifted to pass over the mechanical stop in the steering column.

6. If an adjustment is required, place the selector lever in D as determined by the transmission detent (see Steps 2 and 3).
7. Loosen adjusting swivel at cross shaft and rotate the transmission lever so that it contacts the drive stop in the steering column.
8. Tighten swivel and recheck adjustment.
9. Readjust indicator needle if required.

1964-66

1. Tube and lever must be free in mast jacket.
2. Assemble swivel and related parts loosely.
3. Set transmission lever in DRIVE position. Obtain drive position by moving lever counter-clockwise to LOW detent, then clockwise one detent to drive position.
4. Place tube and lever assembly in reverse position and then bring lever down to insert rod in swivel and retainer.
5. Set tube and lever assembly in drive position and tighten swivel nut.

CAUTION: Any inaccuracies in the foregoing adjustment may result in premature failure of the transmission due to operation without controls in full detent.

1963

1. Check transmission shift linkage for proper adjustment as follows: With engine stopped, lift up on range selector lever and move lever to the position where transmission DRIVE detent is felt. Slowly release lever to feel if shaft lever tang freely enters lock plate. Check REVERSE range in similar manner. If tang does not freely enter lock plate in both DRIVE and REVERSE ranges, adjust linkage as follows:

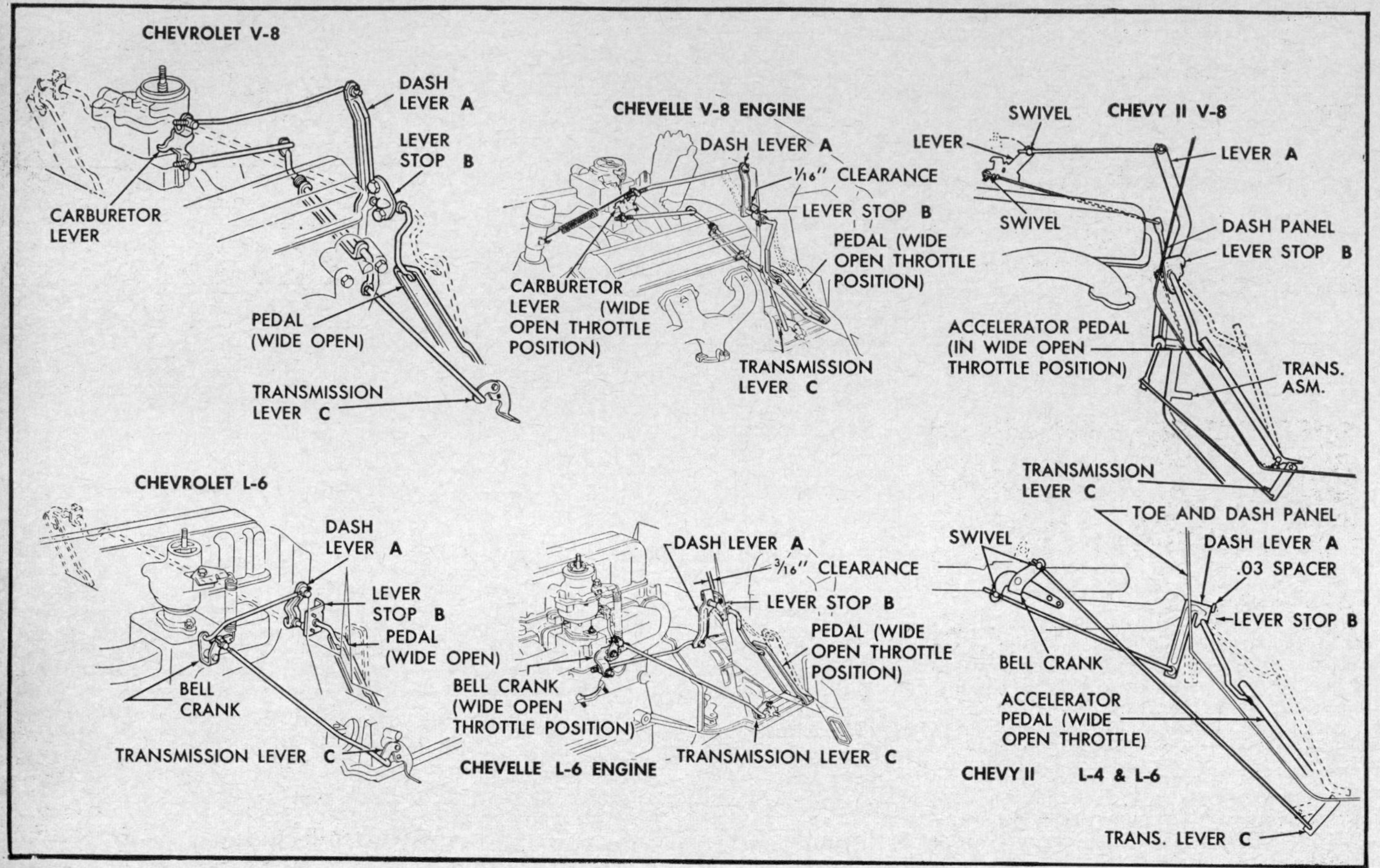

Fig. 2 Throttle valve linkage adjustments. Typical of all models

2. Position range selector lever in "D". Disconnect shift control rod at its swivel attachment to shift control lever and lower end of mast jacket by loosening clamp nut.
3. Place transmission shift control outer lever in DRIVE position.

NOTE: Drive detent in transmission is first clockwise detent position from fully counter-clockwise detent ("L") position.

4. Hold shift control lever (at lower end of mast jacket) against DRIVE stop of range selector lock plate and, with control rod through swivel, tighten clamp nut.

THROTTLE LINKAGE, ADJUST

1968

1. Disconnect throttle rod swivel at throttle lever on carburetor.

NOTE: Cable controls do not require adjustment except on Corvette. TV controls used with cable throttle linkages are adjusted same as in Step 5.

2. On Corvette only, hold accelerator pedal to floor against stop. Move carburetor throttle lever to wide open position. Tighten cable clamp bolt to 45 inch-lbs of torque.
3. Disconnect TV rod at throttle lever.
4. Hold carburetor throttle in wide open position, push throttle rod rearward (to push accelerator pedal to floor mat) and adjust swivel so it just enters hole in throttle lever.
5. Connect swivel to throttle lever and install accelerator return spring.
6. Hold throttle lever in full open position, pull TV rod to full detent position and adjust TV rod so it just enters hole in throttle lever.

1966-67

1. Disconnect throttle rod swivel at throttle lever on carburetor.
2. Disconnect TV rod at throttle lever.
3. Hold carburetor throttle in wide open position, push throttle rod rearward (to position accelerator pedal at floor mat) and adjust swivel so it just enters hole in throttle lever.
4. Connect swivel to throttle lever and install accelerator return spring.
5. Hold throttle rod in full throttle position, pull TV rod to full detent position and adjust TV rod so it just enters hole in throttle lever.

1963-65 In Line Engines

1. Disconnect throttle rod at bellcrank lever on manifold.
2. Disconnect TV rod at bellcrank.
3. Hold carburetor throttle rod in wide open position, then pull throttle rod forward (to position accelerator pedal at floor mat) and adjust rod so it just enters hole in bellcrank lever.
4. Connect rod to bellcrank lever and install retainer.
5. Hold throttle rod in full throttle position, then push TV rod to full detent position and adjust swivel on TV rod so it just enters hole in throttle bellcrank.
6. Connect TV rod swivel at bellcrank.

1963-65 V8s

1. Disconnect throttle rod swivel at throttle lever on carburetor.
2. Disconnect TV rod at throttle lever.
3. Hold carburetor throttle valve in wide open position. Pull throttle rod forward (to position accelerator pedal at floor mat) and adjust swivel so it just enters hole in throttle lever.
4. Connect swivel to throttle lever and install accelerator return spring.
5. Hold throttle rod in full throttle position. Push TV rod to full detent position and adjust TV rod to just enter hole in throttle lever.
6. Connect TV rod to throttle lever.

THROTTLE VALVE, ADJUST

No provision is made for checking TV pressures. However, if operation of the

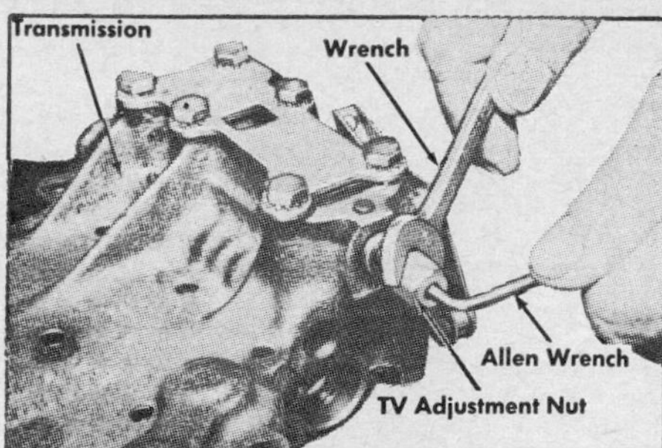

Fig. 3 Adjusting throttle pressure (on bench)

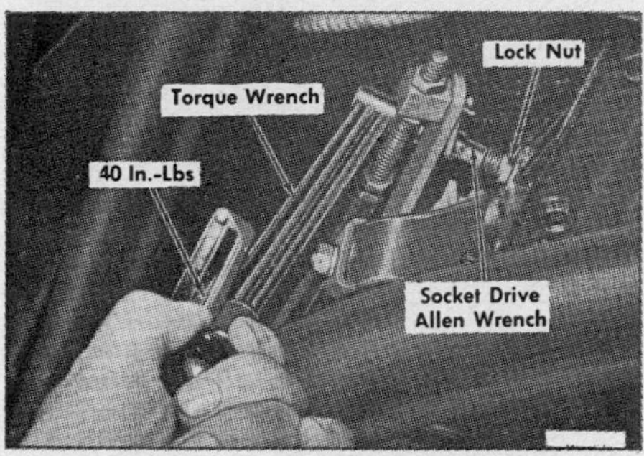

Fig. 4 Adjusting low band (in vehicle)

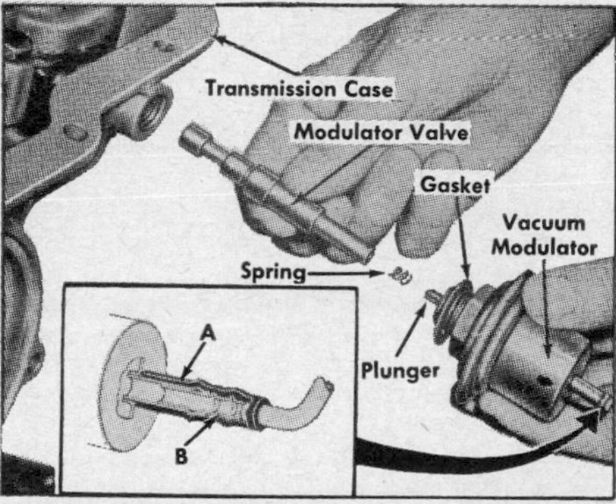

Fig. 5 Vacuum modulator, gasket and valve

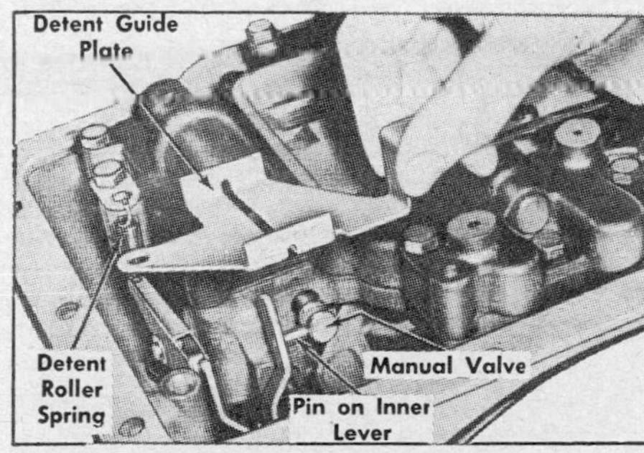

Fig. 6 Detent guide plate installation

transmission is such that some adjustment of the throttle valve is indicated, pressures may be raised or lowered by adjusting the position of the jam nut on the throttle valve assembly, Fig. 3.

To raise TV pressure 3 psi, back off the jam nut one full turn. This increases the dimension from the jam nut to the TV valve stop. Conversely, tightening the jam nut one full turn lowers TV pressure 3 psi.

A difference of 3 psi in TV pressure will cause a change of approximately 2 to 3 mph in the wide open throttle upshift point. Smaller pressure adjustments can be made by partial turns of the jam nut. The end of the TV adjusting screw has an Allen head so the screw may be held stationary while the jam nut is moved. *Use care when making this adjustment since no pressure tap is provided to check TV pressure.*

LOW BAND, ADJUST

Low band adjustment should be performed at 12,000 mile intervals, or sooner if operating performance indicates low band slippage.

1. Raise vehicle and place selector lever in Neutral.
2. Remove protective cap from transmission adjusting screw.

NOTE: On Corvette models it may be necessary to drop the left exhaust pipe for clearance. On Chevelle models, to gain clearance between underbody and transmission, it may be necessary to remove rear mount bolts from crossmember and move transmission slightly toward passenger side of vehicle.

Loosen adjusting screw locknut ¼ turn and hold in this position with a wrench, Fig. 4.

Using a suitable inch-pound torque wrench as shown, adjust band to 70 inch-lbs and back off four complete turns for a band that has been in operation for 6000 miles or more, or three turns for one in use less than 6000 miles.

CAUTION: Be sure to hold the locknut at ¼ turn loose during the adjusting procedure. Then tighten locknut. The amount of back off is not an approximate figure; it must be exact.

VACUUM MODULATOR VALVE

1. To remove, disconnect line from vacuum modulator, Fig. 5.
2. Unscrew vacuum modulator from oil pan.
3. Remove vacuum modulator, gasket and valve.
4. Reverse removal procedure to install.

LOW SERVO

1. Remove servo cover and gasket (3 screws).
2. Remove cover oil seal, servo piston and return spring.
3. Reverse removal procedure to install.

NOTE: If low servo is not functioning properly, overhaul servo as directed in the repair section of this chapter.

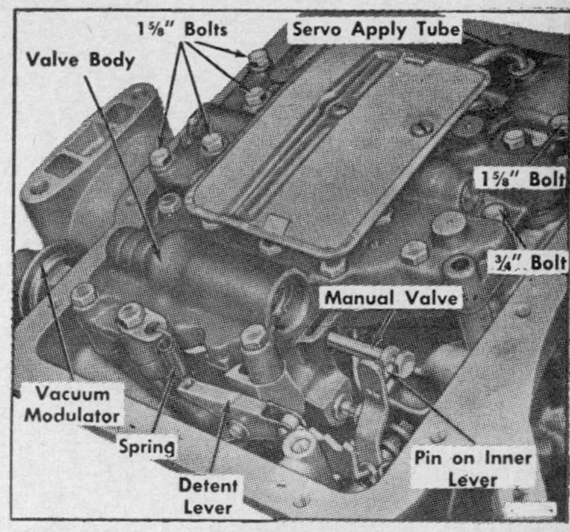

Fig. 7 Control valve assembly installed

Fig. 8 Inner control levers, parking pawl and bracket

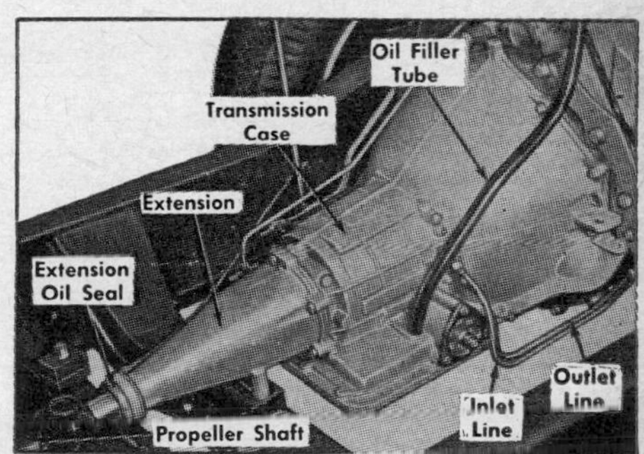

Fig. 9 Exterior of transmission

CONTROL VALVE BODY

1. To remove control valve, remove vacuum modulator valve as outlined above.
2. Remove oil pan and gasket.
3. Remove two bolts attaching detent guide plate to valve body and transmission case. Remove guide plate and range selector detent roller spring, Fig. 6.
4. Remove remaining control valve bolts, Fig. 7.
5. Carefully remove valve body and gasket, disengaging servo apply tube from transmission case as valve body is removed.

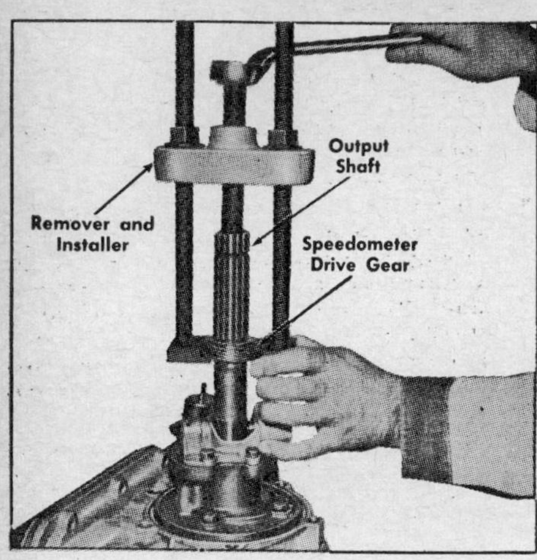

Fig. 10 Removing speedometer drive gear

6. Reverse removal procedure to install valve body, being sure range selector detent lever is in position shown in Fig. 7 and that pin on parking lock and range selector inner lever is engaged in slot in manual valve.

PARKING PAWL

After removing the control valve assembly as outlined above, remove the parking pawl, bracket and inner control levers. To make the installation, proceed as follows:

1. Install parking lock pawl and shaft. Install a new "E" ring on shaft.
2. Install parking lock pawl pull-back spring over its boss to rear of pawl. Short leg of spring should locate in hole in parking pawl, Fig. 8.
3. Install parking lock pawl reaction bracket (2 bolts). Fit actuator assembly between parking lock pawl and bracket.
4. Insert outer shift lever into case, making sure to pick up inner shift lever and parking lock assembly. Tighten Allen head nut.
5. Insert outer TV lever and shaft special washer and O-ring seal into case and pick up inner TV lever. Tighten Allen head nut.
6. Install selector lever detent roller.
7. Install valve body as directed above.

EXTENSION HOUSING SEAL

1. Referring to Fig. 9, disconnect propeller shaft from transmission.
2. Use a suitable puller to remove extension rear oil seal.
3. With a suitable installer, drive new seal into bore of extension. Sealing cement should be used at outer diameter of seal to prevent leakage. Wipe off excess cement. Reconnect propeller shaft.

EXTENSION BUSHING

1. Remove extension oil seal as outlined above. Then, using a suitable remover tool, pull bushing from rear of extension.
2. Place new bushing in pilot end of a suitable installer and drive bushing into bore of extension. Install rear oil seal.

SPEEDOMETER DRIVEN GEAR

1. Disconnect speedometer drive cable fitting. Remove cap screw and retainer clip holding driven gear in extension and remove gear.
2. Reverse removal procedure to install.

EXTENSION CASE

1. Disconnect propeller shaft from transmission output shaft.
2. Disconnect speedometer cable fitting.
3. Install transmission lift to support transmission and engine.
4. Unfasten extension from support crossmember (2 studs).
5. Unfasten extension from transmission case (5 bolts.)

NOTE: Remove any shims found between extension and crossmember. Tie shims together as it is vital that exactly the same number of shims be used when the extension is reinstalled as these shims affect the drive line angle.

6. Reverse removal procedure to install.

SPEEDOMETER DRIVE GEAR

1. Remove extension case as outlined above. Remove speedometer drive gear from output shaft, Fig. 10.
2. Using a suitable installer, install gear on output shaft and replace extension case.

GOVERNOR

1. Remove extension case and speedometer drive gear as outlined above.
2. Remove "C" clip from governor shaft on weight side of governor.
3. Remove shaft and governor valve from opposite side of governor. Remove two Belleville springs, Fig. 11.
4. Loosen governor drive screw and lift governor from output shaft.
5. Reverse removal procedure to install governor. However, be sure concave side of Belleville springs are against transmission output shaft.

REAR OIL PUMP TO '65

1. Remove extension case, speedometer drive gear and governor as outlined above.
2. Unfasten pump from case.
3. Remove pump body, drain back baffle, seal ring and drive and driven gears.

NOTE: When drive gear is removed, drive pin may fall out when output shaft is horizontal and hole in shaft is at bottom.

4. Remove drive pin and pump wear plate.

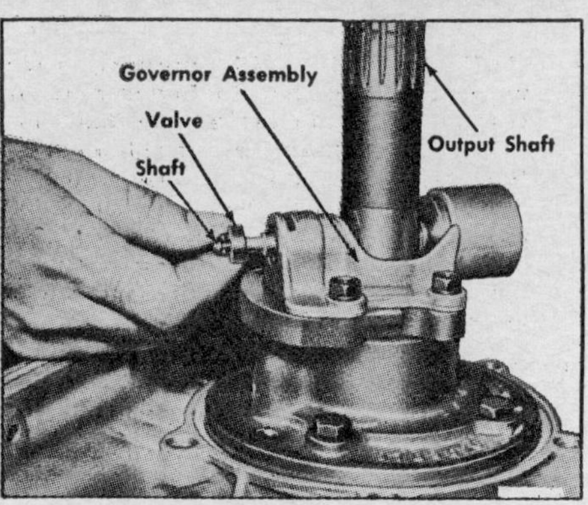

Fig. 11 Removing governor valve and shaft

5. Reverse removal procedure to install.

TRANSMISSION, REPLACE

1965-68

1. Disconnect oil cooler lines (external cooled models), vacuum modulator line and speedometer drive cable fitting at transmission. Tie lines out of the way.
2. Disconnect manual and TV rods from transmission.
3. Disconnect propeller shaft from transmission.
4. Attach transmission jack on transmission.
5. Disconnect engine rear mount on transmission extension, then disconnect transmission support crossmember and slide rearward.

NOTE: On Camaro models, moving the crossmember rearward is not possible because the crossmember is mounted in a recess in the frame which is enclosed by the underbody of the car. Consequently, rather than moving the crossmember rearward, it must be completely removed during transmission assembly removal.

6. Remove converter underpan. Scribe flywheel-converter relationship for reassembly, then remove flywheel-to-converter bolts.

NOTE: The "light" side of the converter is denoted by a "blue" stripe painted across the ends of the converter cover and housing. This marking should be aligned as closely as possible with the "white" stripe painted on the engine side of the flywheel outer rim (heavy side of engine) to maintain balance during assembly.

7. Support engine at oil pan rail with a jack or other suitable brace capable of supporting engine when transmission is removed.
8. Lower rear of transmission slightly so that upper transmission housing-to-engine attaching bolts can be reached, using a universal socket and a long extension. Remove upper bolts.

CAUTION: On V8 engines, care must be taken not to lower rear of transmission too far as the distributor housing may be forced against the dash, causing damage to the distributor. It is best to have an assistant observe clearance of all upper engine components while transmission rear end is being lowered.

9. Remove remainder of transmission-to-engine bolts.
10. Remove transmission by moving it slightly to the rear and downward, then remove from under vehicle.

NOTE: Observe converter when moving transmission rearward. If it does not move with the transmission, pry it free of flywheel before proceeding.

CAUTION: Keep front of transmission upward to prevent converter from falling out. Install a suitable holding strap or length of strong wire across the housing to keep the converter in place.

11. Reverse procedure to install.

1963-64

1. Disconnect oil cooler lines, vacuum modulator line and speedometer drive cable at transmission. Tie lines out of the way.
2. Disconnect linkage at transmission.
3. Disconnect propeller shaft.
4. Attach suitable lifting equipment to transmission.
5. On Chevelle, disconnect engine rear mount on transmission extension, then disconnect transmission support crossmember and slide it rearward.
6. On Chevrolet and Chevy II, remove transmission support crossmember.

NOTE: Use care to remove shims that may be present between extension mounting boss and crossmember. It is vital that the same number of shims be reinstalled as these effect drive line angles.

7. Remove converter underpan, scribe flywheel-converter relationship for assembly, then remove attaching bolts. *This is important to maintain balance on assembly.*
8. Support engine at oil pan rail with a jack or other suitable brace capable of supporting engine while transmission is removed.
9. Lower rear of transmission slightly so that upper transmission housing-to-engine bolts can be reached using a universal socket and long extension. Remove upper bolts. *Caution: On V8 engines, use care when lowering rear of transmission to see that distributor housing is not forced against dash.*
10. Remove remaining attaching bolts. Then move transmission slightly to the rear and downward out of chassis. *When moving transmission rearward observe converter; if it does not move with the transmission, pry it free of flywheel before proceeding. Keep front of transmission upward to prevent converter from falling out. Use a length of strong wire to keep it attached to the transmission while being removed.*
11. Reverse foregoing procedures to install transmission.

CHRYSLER TORQUEFLITE

NOTE: — This chapter deals only with maintenance, adjustments and "in car" repairs. For major service work, Motor's Automatic Transmission Manual is available. Current edition is a 740 page volume that includes 240 pages of oil circuit diagrams mostly in full color.

IDENTIFICATION

Transmission identification markings shown in the following application chart are cast in raised letters and numerals on the lower left side of the ball housing. NOTE: There are sufficient variations within each of the main categories listed below to make it necessary to service them by serial number—a stamped 7-digit number appearing on the oil pan side rail.

Year	Engine	Transmission
1968-69	6-170, 6-225 engines	A-904-G
	V8-273 engine	A-904-A
	V8-318 engine	A-904-LA
	6-225 police and taxi	A-727-RG
	V8-318, V8-340 engines	A-727-A
	V8-383, V8-426, V8-440 engines	A-727-B
1965-67	6-170, 6-225 engines	A-904-G
	V8-273 engine	A-904-LA
	V8-318 engine	A-727-A
	V8-361, 383, 413, 426, 440	A-727-B
1963-64	All six cylinder	A-904
	All V8 engines	A-727

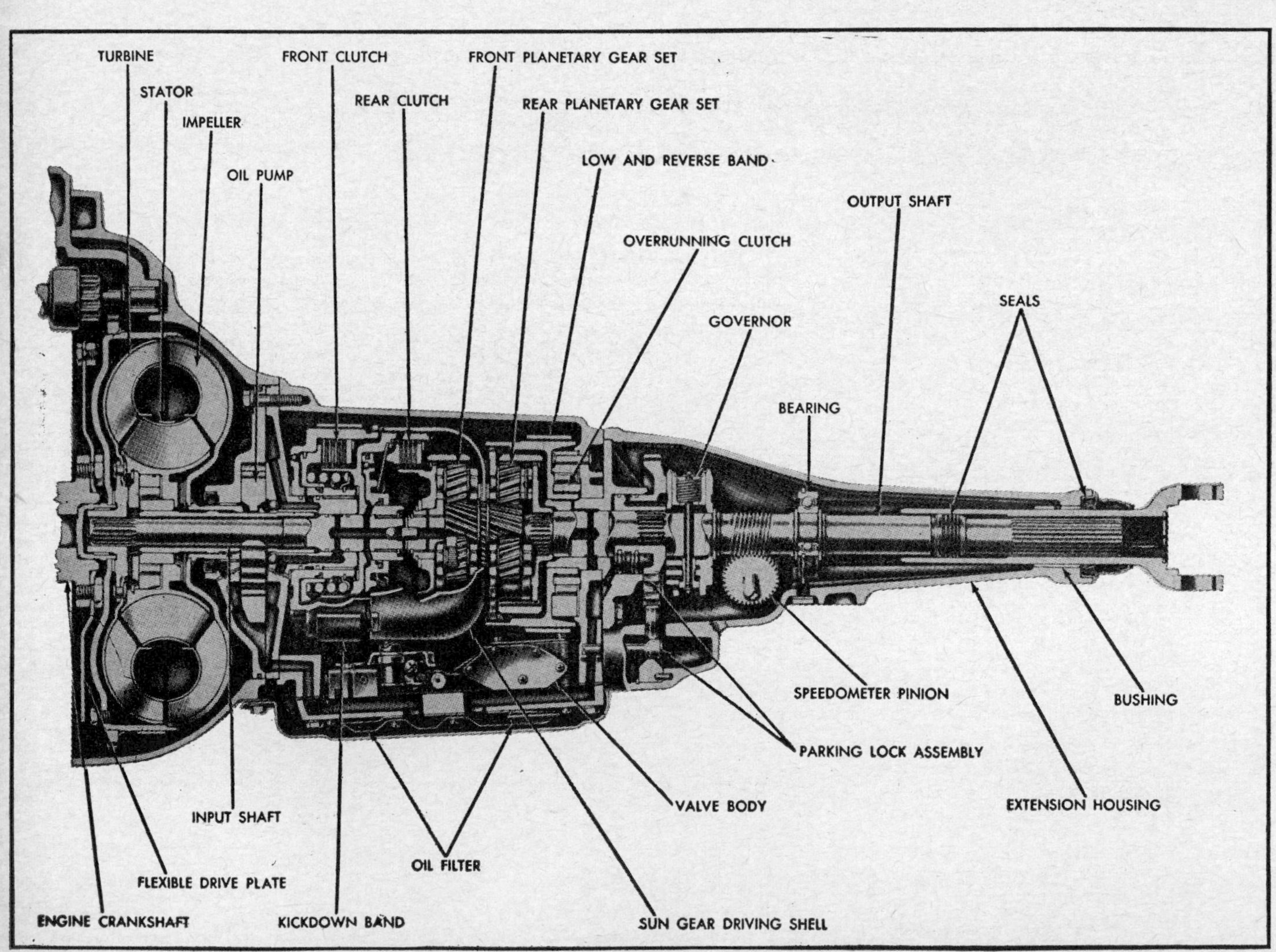

Fig. 1 Series 904 Torqueflite transmission used on 1966-68. Earlier models have a rear pump

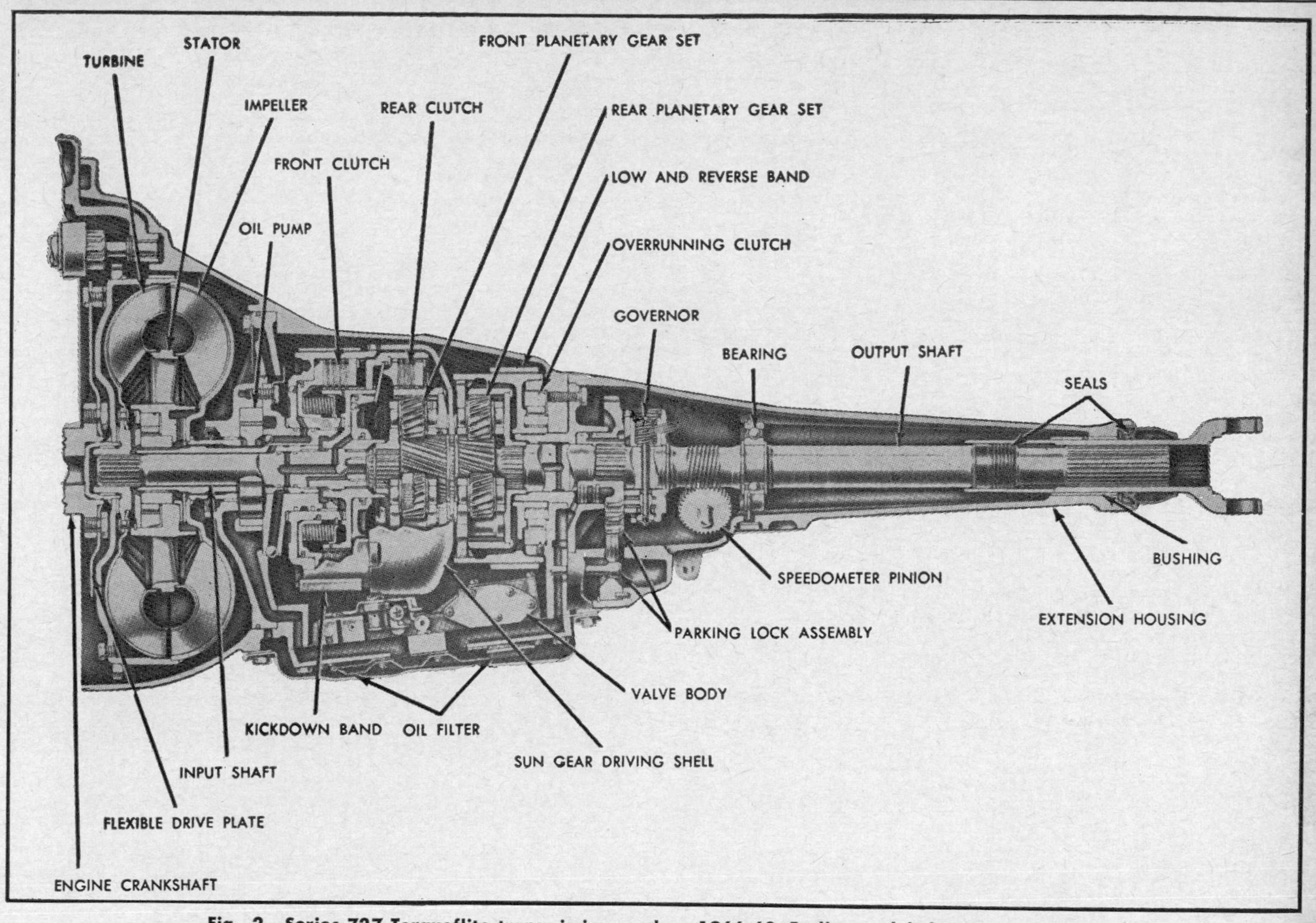

Fig. 2 Series 727 Torqueflite transmission used on 1966-68. Earlier models have a rear pump

DESCRIPTION

These transmissions, Figs. 1 and 2, combine a torque converter with a fully automatic three speed gear system. The converter housing and transmission case are an integral aluminum casting. The transmission consists of two multiple disc clutches, an overrunning (one-way) clutch, two servos and bands and two planetary gear sets to provide three forward speeds and reverse.

The common sun gear of the planetary gear sets is connected to the front clutch by a driving shell that is splined to the sun gear and to the front clutch retainer.

On 1965 and earlier models the hydraulic system consists of a front and rear pump and a single valve body that contains all of the valves except the governor valve.

On 1966 and later models the hydraulic system consists of a single oil pump and a valve body that contains all the valves except the governor valve.

Venting of the transmission is accomplished by a drilled passage through the upper part of the front pump housing.

The torque converter is attached to the engine crankshaft through a flexible driving plate. The converter is cooled by circulating the transmission fluid through an oil-to-water type cooler located in the radiator lower tank. The converter is a sealed assembly that cannot be disassembled.

TROUBLE SHOOTING GUIDE

Harsh Engagement In D-1-2-R

1. Engine idle speed too high.
2. Hydraulic pressures too high or too low.
3. Low-reverse band out of adjustment.
4. Accumulator sticking, broken rings or spring.
5. Low-reverse servo, band or linkage malfunction.
6. Worn or faulty front and/or rear clutch.

Delayed Engagement In D-1-2-R

1. Low fluid level.
2. Incorrect manual linkage adjustment (from 1966) or incorrect control cable adjustment (to 1965).
3. Oil filter clogged.
4. Hydraulic pressures too high or low.
5. Valve body malfunction or leakage.
6. Accumulator sticking, broken rings or spring.
7. Clutches or servos sticking or not operating.
8. Faulty front oil pump.
9. Worn or faulty front and/or rear clutch.
10. Worn or broken input shaft and/or reaction shaft support seal rings.
11. Aerated fluid.

Runaway or Harsh Upshift and 3-2 Kickdown

1. Low fluid level.
2. Incorrect throttle linkage adjustment.
3. Hydraulic pressures too high or low.
4. Kickdown band out of adjustment.
5. Valve body malfunction or leakage.
6. Governor malfunction.
7. Accumulator sticking, broken rings or spring.
8. Clutches or servos sticking or not operating.
9. Kickdown servo, band or linkage malfunction.
10. Worn or faulty front clutch.
11. Worn or broken input shaft and/or reaction shaft support seal rings.

No Upshift

1. Low fluid level.
2. Incorrect throttle linkage adjustment.
3. Kickdown band out of adjustment.
4. Hydraulic pressures too high or low.
5. Governor sticking.
6. Valve body malfunction or leakage.
7. Accumulator sticking, broken rings or spring.
8. Clutches or servos sticking or not operating.
9. Faulty oil pump (from 1966).
10. Faulty rear oil pump (to 1965).
11. Kickdown servo, band or linkage malfunction.

12. Worn or faulty front clutch.
13. Worn or broken input shaft and/or reaction shaft support seal rings.

No Kickdown or Normal Downshift

1. Incorrect throttle linkage adjustment.
2. Incorrect gearshift linkage adjustment (from 1966).
3. Incorrect control cable adjustment (to 1965).
4. Kickdown band out of adjustment.
5. Hydraulic pressure too high or low.
6. Governor sticking.
7. Valve body malfunction or leakage.
8. Accumulator sticking, broken rings or spring.
9. Clutches or servos sticking or not operating.
10. Kickdown servo, band or linkage malfunction.
11. Overrunning clutch not holding.

Erratic Shifts

1. Low fluid level.
2. Aerated fluid.
3. Incorrect throttle linkage adjustment.
4. Incorrect gearshift control linkage adjustment (from 1966).
5. Incorrect control cable adjustment (to 1965).
6. Hydraulic pressures too high or low.
7. Governor sticking.
8. Oil filter clogged.
9. Valve body malfunction or leakage.
10. Clutches or servos sticking or not operating.
11. Faulty oil pump (from 1966).
12. Faulty front and/or rear oil pump (to 1965).
13. Worn or broken input shaft and/or reaction shaft support seal rings.

Slips In Forward Drive Positions

1. Low oil level.
2. Aerated fluid.
3. Incorrect throttle linkage adjustment.
4. Incorrect gearshift control linkage adjustment (from 1966).
5. Incorrect control cable adjustment (to 1965).
6. Hydraulic pressures too low.
7. Valve body malfunction or leakage.
8. Accumulator sticking, broken rings or spring.
9. Clutches or servos sticking or not operating.
10. Worn or faulty front and/or rear clutch.
11. Overrunning clutch not holding.
12. Worn or broken input shaft and/or reaction shaft support seal rings.

Slips In Reverse Only

1. Low fluid level.
2. Aerated fluid.
3. Incorrect gearshift control linkage adjustment (from 1966).
4. Incorrect control cable adjustment (to 1965).
5. Hydraulic pressures too high or low.
6. Low-reverse band out of adjustment.
7. Valve body malfunction or leakage.
8. Front clutch or rear servo sticking or not operating.
9. Low-reverse servo, band or linkage malfunction.
10. Faulty oil pump (front to 1965).

Slips In All Positions

1. Low fluid level.
2. Hydraulic pressures too low.
3. Valve body malfunction or leakage.
4. Faulty oil pump (front to 1965).
5. Clutches or servos sticking or not operating.
6. Worn or broken input shaft and/or reaction shaft support seal rings.

No Drive In Any Position

1. Low fluid level.
2. Hydraulic pressures too low.
3. Oil filter clogged.
4. Valve body malfunction or leakage.
5. Faulty oil pump (front to 1965).
6. Clutches or servos sticking or not operating.

No Drive In Forward Drive Positions

1. Hydraulic pressures too low.
2. Valve body malfunction or leakage.
3. Accumulator sticking, broken rings or spring.
4. Clutches or servos, sticking or not operating.
5. Worn or faulty rear clutch.
6. Overrunning clutch not holding.
7. Worn or broken input shaft and/or reaction shaft support seal rings.

No Drive In Reverse

1. Incorrect gearshift control linkage adjustment (from 1966).
2. Incorrect control cable adjustment (to 1965).
3. Hydraulic pressures too low.
4. Low-reverse band out of adjustment.
5. Valve body malfunction or leakage.
6. Front clutch or rear servo sticking or not operating.
7. Low-reverse servo, band or linkage malfunction.
8. Worn or faulty front clutch.

Drives In Neutral

1. Incorrect gearshift control linkage adjustment (from 1966).
2. Incorrect control cable adjustment.
3. Valve body malfunction or leakage.
4. Rear clutch inoperative.

Drags or Locks

1. Kickdown band out of adjustment.
2. Low-reverse band out of adjustment.
3. Kickdown and/or low-reverse servo, band or linkage malfunction.
4. Front and/or rear clutch faulty.
5. Planetary gear sets broken or seized.
6. Overrunning clutch worn, broken or seized.

Grating, Scraping or Growling Noise

1. Kickdown band out of adjustment.
2. Low-reverse band out of adjustment.
3. Output shaft bearing and/or bushing damaged.
4. Governor support binding or broken seal rings.
5. Oil pump scored or binding (either pump (to 1965).
6. Front and/or rear clutch faulty.
7. Planetary gear sets broken or seized.
8. Overrunning clutch worn, broken or seized.

Buzzing Noise

1. Low fluid level.
2. Pump sucking air (both pumps to 1965).
3. Valve body malfunction.
4. Overrunning clutch inner race damaged.

Hard to Fill, Oil Flows Out Filler Tube

1. High fluid level.
2. Breather clogged.
3. Oil filter clogged.
4. Aerated fluid.

Transmission Overheats

1. Low fluid level.
2. Kickdown band adjustment too tight.
3. Low-reverse band adjustment too tight.
4. Faulty cooling system.
5. Cracked or restricted oil cooler line or fitting.
6. Faulty oil pump (either pump to 1965).
7. Insufficient clutch plate clearance in front and/or rear clutches.

Starter Will Not Energize In Neutral or Park

1. Incorrect gearshift control linkage adjustment (from 1966).
2. Incorrect control cable adjustment (to 1965).
3. Faulty or incorrectly adjusted neutral starting switch.
4. Broken lead to neutral switch.

Impossible to Push Start, To 1965

1. Low fluid level.
2. Low-reverse band slipping.
3. Valve body malfunction or leakage.
4. Rear oil pump faulty.
5. Low-reverse servo, band or linkage malfunction.
6. Worn or faulty rear clutch.
7. Worn or broken input shaft and/or reaction shaft support seal rings.

MAINTENANCE

Service Note

It has been found that an occasional "no-drive" condition, generally occurring after making the first stop when a car is cold can be caused by incorrect transmission oil level. In cases where this condition is encountered, it is essential that the transmission oil level be checked and corrected as outlined below.

On 1963-64 models, oil should be at the "Add 1 Pint" mark when *cold* and between the "Full" and "Add 1 Pint" mark when *hot*.

If the no-drive condition still exists with the correct oil level, the push button cable adjustment should be checked.

After the above corrections have been made, if the no-drive condition still exists, it is suggested that the transmission be removed and the front pump disassembled for inspection before attempting any further repairs. Inspect the pump inner rotor and front support for wear, especially where the pinion rubs the support. The clearance specified for the front pump rotors and the face of the

tate adjustment wheel clockwise until it just contacts case squarely.

2. Turn wheel clockwise just enough to make the next adjustment hole in wheel line up with screw hole in case.
3. Counting this hole as number one, continue turning wheel clockwise until the fifth hole lines up with screw hole in case.
4. Install lock screw and torque it to 75 inch pounds.
5. Refill transmission.

Wheel-Type Cable

Removal

1. To remove the cable, drain approximately three quarts of oil from the transmission.
2. Engage "1" push button.
3. Remove adjusting wheel lock screw, Fig. 10.
4. Remove neutral starter switch, cupped washer and seal.
5. With a screwdriver inserted through neutral starter switch opening, push gently against the upward projecting portion of the control cable adapter lock spring and pull outward on cable to remove cable assembly from case.

Install & Adjust

1. Engage "R" push button. *Have an assistant hold this button firmly until the transmission end of the cable has been adjusted and locked.*
2. Back off the cable adjustment wheel (turn counter-clockwise) on cable housing until only two or three threads are showing. *Caution: do not back the wheel entirely off the guide threads because it serves as a stop prevent the "O" ring from going too far into the case and becoming caught inside the case when the cable is installed.*
3. Push cable control housing into the transmission case with just enough force to overcome the "O" ring friction and to bottom the assembly. While holding the cable firmly into the bottomed position, rotate adjusting wheel clockwise *to just contact the transmission case.*
4. Release the inward pressure on the cable and then turn the adjusting wheel until the next adjustment hole in the wheel lines up with the lock screw hole in the case. Counting this hole as number one, continue turning the wheel clockwise until the fifth hole lines up with the screw hole in the case. Check cable adjustment to be sure of full detent in all shift ranges.
5. Install neutral starter switch and refill transmission with oil.

THROTTLE LINKAGE, ADJUST

All Models

The throttle linkage must be adjusted so that when the accelerator pedal is pressed down to the floor the carburetor throttle valve(s) will be wide open.

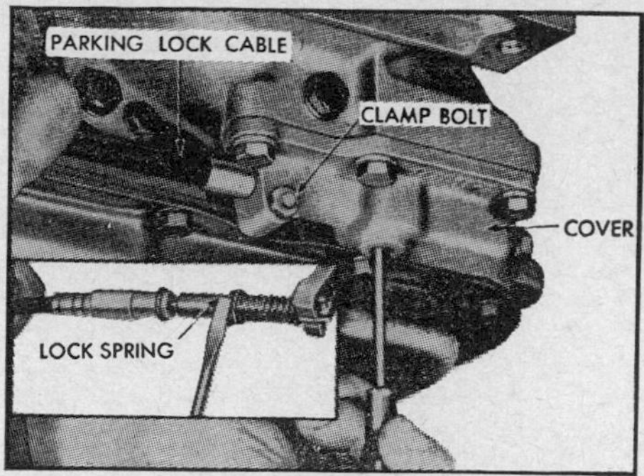

Fig. 11 Removing parking lock cable. 1963-65

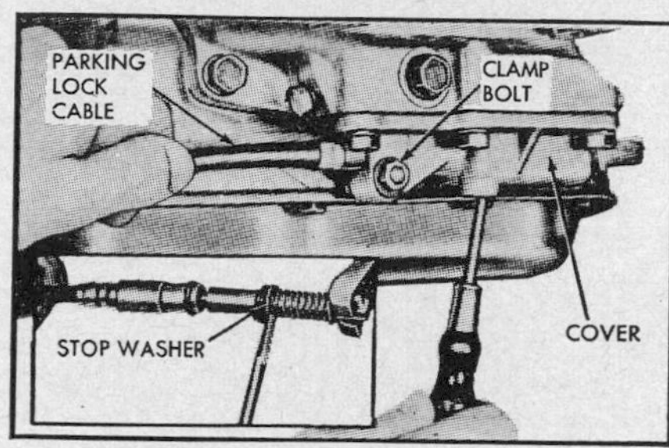

Fig. 12 Installing parking lock cable. 1963-65

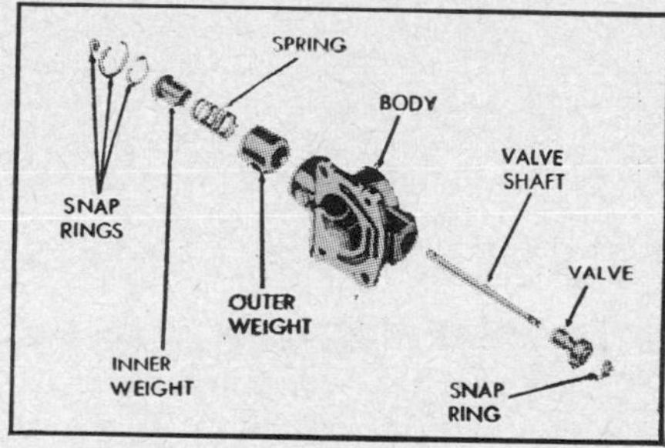

Fig. 13 Governor disassembled

GEARSHIFT CONTROL CABLE REPLACE

1963-64

1. Place parking lock lever in "off" position and drain approximately 2 quarts of fluid from transmission.
2. Remove gearshift control cable-to-transmission adjusting wheel lock screw. Pull gearshift cable out of transmission case as far as possible, back off adjusting wheel a few turns if necessary.
3. Insert a small screwdriver above and slightly to right of gearshift cable. Disengage cable adapter lock spring by pushing screwdriver handle to right while pulling outward on cable.

Installation, 1963-64

1. To install cable, have an assistant engage the "R" button and hold it firmly engaged until the cable attachment operation is completed.
2. Back the adjusting wheel off the cable housing (counterclockwise) until only two or three threads are showing behind the wheel on the guide.
3. Lubricate cable housing with transmission fluid, insert cable in case, push inward on cable, making sure lock spring engages cable. Then adjust cable as outlined below.

GEARSHIFT CONTROL CABLE ADJUST

1. Have an assistant hold the "R" button firmly depressed.
2. Remove cable adjustment wheel lock screw.
3. Back off adjusting wheel on cable guide (counterclockwise) until only two or three threads are showing behind wheel on guide. *Check wheel for free turning on guide; remove any burrs or dirt in threads of cable guide that may interfere. Lubricate threads with a few drops of transmission fluid.*
4. Hold cable guide centered in hole of case and apply only enough inward force to bottom assembly at reverse detent. While holding cable bottomed, rotate adjustment wheel clockwise until it just contacts the case squarely.
5. Turn wheel clockwise just enough to make the next adjustment hole in the wheel line up with the screw hole in the case.
6. Counting this hole as number one, continue turning the wheel clockwise until the fifth hole lines up with the screw hole in the case.
7. Install lock screw.

PARKING LOCK CABLE, REPLACE 1963-65

1. Loosen parking lock cable clamp bolt where cable enters housing cover. Remove housing cover lower plug.
2. With screwdriver inserted through plug opening, push gently against projecting portion of cable lock-spring, then withdraw lock cable. Do not use pliers or similar tool to withdraw cable from adapter cover as cable may be damaged, causing an oil leak, Fig. 11.
3. To install cable, have an assistant hold parking lock lever on instrument panel in "off" position.
4. Insert screwdriver through plug opening and position it behind cable adapter stop washer. Hold adapter outward while pushing cable in as far as possible, making sure lock-spring engages cable, Fig. 12.
5. Gently pull outward on cable housing to its limit of travel, release and then tighten clamp bolt. Reinstall plug in cover and tighten to proper torque.

PARKING LOCK CABLE, ADJUST 1963-65

1. Operate parking lock lever from one end of slot in instrument panel to the other. The lever should have clearance at both ends. One hole in

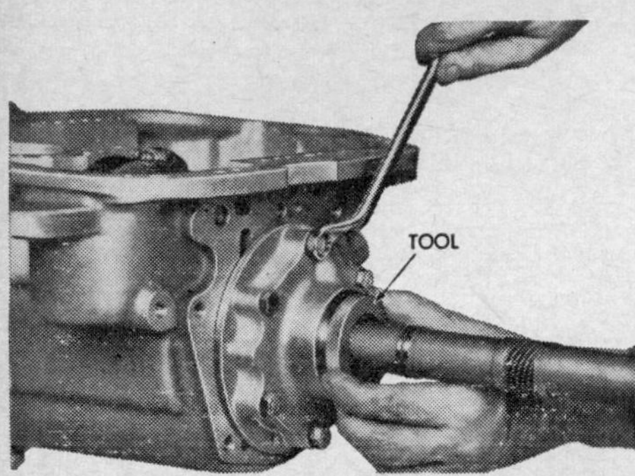

Fig. 14 Aligning rear oil pump cover

the parking lock arm is slotted to permit parking lock lever adjustment. If adjustment of lever is required, first loosen cable clamp bolt on transmission, making sure that cable housing is free to move in parking sprag cover hole.

2. To adjust, move lever to fully "off" position. Loosen two nuts attaching lock arm to pushbutton housing. Loosen nuts just enough to free up lock arm.
3. Block locking lever $\frac{1}{16}$" from "off" end of lever slot, then tighten the two nuts on pushbutton housing. Recheck lever travel to be certain that clearance exists at both ends of lever travel.
4. Place parking lock lever on instrument panel in "off" position.
5. Gently pull outward on cable housing at transmission to its limit of travel in sprag lever cover. Release cable and tighten clamp bolt. *NOTE: Do not use pliers or similar tool to pull outward on cable as cable cover might be damaged, causing an oil leak.*
6. Check adjustment by allowing vehicle to roll slowly on a slight incline. The parking sprag should fully engage gear with lever in "on" position. There should be no ratcheting noise in "off" position.

PARKING PAWL, REPLACE

Extension Housing In Car

1. Remove parking lock cable adapter cover from bottom of extension housing.
2. Remove plug from extension housing, slide out shaft to remove parking lock lever, shim and cable adapter. Replace cable adapter spring if it is distorted.
3. Slide bushing sleeve out of housing to remove the parking pawl and spring.

OUTPUT SHAFT OIL SEAL

1. To remove seal, disconnect propeller shaft at transmission.
2. Remove transmission flange or brake drum.
3. Removal seal.
4. Install new seal with lip side facing in.
5. Install transmission flange and tighten nut to proper torque.
6. Connect propeller shaft.

EXTENSION HOUSING

1. Remove speedometer drive pinion and sleeve assembly.
2. Remove transmission flange or parking brake drum and cable (if so equipped).
3. Drain about two quarts of fluid from transmission.
4. On models with parking lock lever, loosen parking brake cable clamp bolt where cable enters the housing cover. Remove housing cover lower plug. Insert screwdriver through hole, then, while exerting pressure against projecting portion of cable lock spring, withdraw brake cable.
5. Remove bolts securing extension housing insulator to crossmember.
6. With a suitable jack, raise transmission slightly to clear crossmember.
7. Remove crossmember. If parking brake cable to rear wheels interferes with removal, first disconnect cable and housing.
8. Unfasten and remove extension housing from transmission.
9. If necessary, the extension housing bushing may be replaced at this time. However, when installing the new bushing, make sure the oil hole in the bushing lines up with the slot in the housing.

NOTE: On 6 Cyl. it is necessary to burnish bushing for proper fit.

10. Install the extension housing in the reverse order of its removal.

GOVERNOR

1. To remove the governor, take off the extension housing.
2. Using a screwdriver, carefully pry the snap ring from the weight end of the governor valve shaft, Fig. 13. Slide the valve and shaft out of governor housing.
3. Remove large snap ring from weight end of governor housing, and lift out weight assembly.
4. Remove snap ring from inside governor weight and remove inner weight and spring from outer weight.
5. Remove snap ring from behind governor housing, then slide governor housing and parking brake sprag assembly off input shaft. If necessary, separate governor housing from sprag (4 screws).
6. The primary cause of governor operating failure is due to a sticking governor valve or weights. Rough surfaces may be removed with crocus cloth. Thoroughly clean all parts and check for free movement before assembly.
7. Reverse above operations to assemble and install governor.

REAR PUMP

1. To remove pump, remove extension housing, governor and parking sprag.

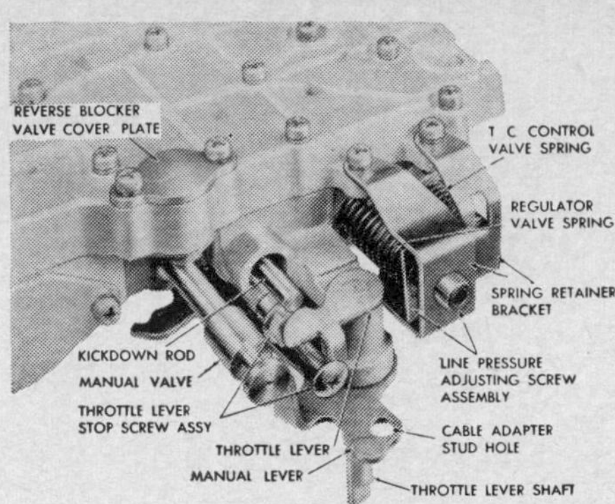

Fig. 15 Valve body external parts

2. Remove oil pump cover.
3. Mark a line across the face of the inner and outer pump rotors with dye so they may be reinstalled in the same relation to each other.
4. *The oil pump inner rotor is keyed to output shaft by a small ball. Therefore, use care in sliding out inner rotor so as not to lose the ball.* Remove outer rotor from pump body.

Inspection

If rear oil pump body requires replacement, it will be necessary to disassemble the transmission as the pump body must be driven rearward out of the case with a wood block.

Inspect pump body and pump cover machined surfaces for nicks or burrs. Inspect rotors for scoring or pitting. With gears cleaned and installed in pump body, place a straightedge across face of rotors and pump body. Using a feeler gauge check clearance between straightedge and face of rotors. Clearance limits are from .0015-.003" for V8s and 6 cyl.

Installation

Reverse removal procedure to install pump, being sure to align the rotors as marked at disassembly if same rotors are being used. When installing pump cover, thread retaining bolts in a few turns. Then slide aligning tool, Fig. 14, all the way in until it bottoms against rotors. Then tighten cover bolts.

VALVE BODY

1. To remove valve body and accumulator piston, drain transmission fluid and remove oil pan.
2. Loosen clamp bolt and lift throttle lever, washer and seal off transmission throttle lever shaft, Fig. 15.
3. Shift manual control into "L" position to expose the nut securing the cable adapter to the manual lever. Remove nut and disengage cable adapter from lever.
4. Place drain pan under transmission; then remove ten hex-head valve body-to-transmission case bolts.
5. Lower valve body down out of transmission, being careful not to cock

throttle lever shaft in case hole or lose the accumulator spring.

6. Withdraw accumulator piston from transmission case. Inspect piston for scoring, and check rings for wear or breakage.

TRANSMISSION, REPLACE

1965-68

CAUTION: The transmission and converter must be removed as an assembly, otherwise, the converter drive plate, front pump bushing and oil seal will be damaged. The drive plate will not support the load; therefore, none of the weight of the transmission should be allowed to rest on the plate during removal.

NOTE: On 1965 Chrysler, Polara, Monaco, 880 as well as Plymouth Station Wagons, it will be necessary first to remove the torsion bar rear anchor crossmember and rubber isolators before the transmission is removed from the vehicle.

1. Disconnect high tension wire from distributor cap or coil.
2. Place selector lever in Park.
3. Remove cover plate from in front of converter to provide access to converter drain plug and mounting bolts.
4. Using a remote control starter switch, rotate engine to bring drain plug to "6 o'clock" position. Then drain converter and transmission.
5. Mark converter and drive plate to aid in reassembly.
6. Rotate engine to locate two converter-to-drive plate bolts at "5 and 7 o'clock" positions. Remove the two bolts, rotate engine and remove other two bolts.

   CAUTION: Do not rotate converter or drive plate by prying with a screwdriver or similar tool as the drive plate might become distorted. Also, the starter should never be engaged if the drive plate is not attached to the converter with at least one bolt or if the transmission case-to-engine bolts have been loosened.

7. Disconnect battery ground cable.
8. Remove starting motor.
9. Disconnect wire from neutral starting switch.
10. On 1966-68 models, disconnect gearshift rod from transmission lever. Remove gearshift torque shaft from transmission housing and left side rail. On Console shift, remove two bolts securing torque shaft lower bracket to extension housing. Swing bracket out of the way for transmission removal. Disconnect gearshift rod from transmission lever. On earlier models, remove gearshift control cable-to-transmission adjusting wheel lock screw. Pull cable out of case as far as possible, backing off adjusting wheel a few turns if necessary.
11. Insert a small screwdriver above and slightly to the right of the control cable. Disengage cable adapter lock spring by pushing screwdriver handle to the right while pulling outward on cable.
12. Disconnect throttle rod from lever on transmission.
13. Disconnect oil cooler lines at transmission and remove oil filler tube.
14. Remove speedometer pinion and sleeve from transmission.
15. Loosen transmission parking lock cable clamp bolt. Remove housing cover lower plug. Insert screwdriver through hole, then gently exert pressure against projecting portion of cable lock spring and withdraw lock cable.
16. On cars with 6-170, 6-225 and V8-273 engines, disconnect front universal joint and secure propeller shaft out of the way. On all other V8 models, disconnect propeller shaft at rear universal joint and carefully pull shaft out of extension housing.
17. Remove two bolts securing extension housing to crossmember insulator.
18. Install engine support fixture and raise engine slightly.
19. Unfasten and remove crossmember.
20. Support transmission with a jack.
21. Attach a small "C" clamp to edge of converter housing to hold converter in place during removal of transmission.
22. Remove converter housing retaining bolts. Work transmission rearward off engine dowels and disengage converter hub from end of crankshaft.
23. Lower transmission jack and remove converter and transmission as a unit.
24. To remove converter, release "C" clamp and slide converter out of transmission.
25. Reverse procedure to install.

1963-64

1. Disconnect battery ground cable.
2. Depress "L" button to position control cable for removal from transmission.
3. Remove starting motor.
4. Raise vehicle on a hoist or support with stands.
5. Remove cover plate from in front of converter to provide access to converter drain plugs and mounting bolts.
6. Drain converter and transmission.
7. Remove neutral starter switch.
8. Remove cable adjusting wheel lock screw at transmission.
9. Insert screwdriver through neutral starting switch opening. Push screwdriver gently against upper projecting portion of cable lock spring, and pull cable out of transmission.
10. Loosen clamp screw and remove throttle link and lever from throttle shaft.
11. Disconnect oil cooler lines at transmission and remove oil filler tube.
12. Remove speedometer driven gear and sleeve.
13. Loosen transmission parking brake cable clamp bolt where cable enters cover. Remove housing cover lower plug. Insert screwdriver through hole, then gently exert pressure against projecting portion of cable lock spring and withdraw brake cable.
14. Disconnect front universal joint and secure out of the way.
15. Remove nut securing extension housing insulator to crossmember.
16. Raise engine slightly.
17. Disconnect rear wheel brake cable from lever and crossmember. Then remove crossmember.
18. Support transmission with a jack.
19. Mark converter and flex driving plate so they can be assembled in the same relative position. Remove converter to flex plate screws.
20. Attach a small "C" clamp to edge of bell housing to hold converter in place during transmission removal.
21. Remove bell housing retaining bolts.
22. Carefully work transmission rearward off engine block dowels and to disengage converter hub from end of crankshaft.
23. Lower transmission jack and remove transmission and converter.
24. Reverse above procedure to install the assembly.

C4 DUAL RANGE AUTOMATIC

NOTE: — This chapter deals only with maintenance, adjustments and "in car" repairs. For major service work, Motor's Automatic Transmission Manual is available. Current edition is a 740 page volume that includes 240 pages of oil circuit diagrams mostly in full color.

TRANSMISSION IDENTIFICATION

Each transmission may be identified by the tag attached to the low-reverse servo cover bolt. The tag includes the model prefix and suffix, a service identification number and a build date code. The service identification number indicates changes to service details which affect interchangeability when the transmission model is not changed. For interpretation of this number the Ford Master Parts Catalog should be consulted.

YEAR	CAR MODEL	TRANS. MODEL	ENGINE MODEL
1964	Comet	PCW-Y	V8-260①
	Comet	PCW-Z	V8-289②
	Fairlane	PCW-Y	V8-289
	Falcon	PCW-Y	V8-260①
	Falcon	PCW-Z	V8-289②
	Ford	PCV-D	6-223
	Ford	PCW-V	V8-289①
1965	Comet	PCS-G	6-200
	Comet	PCW-AA	V8-289
	Fairlane③	PCS-J	6-200
	Fairlane④	PCS-M	6-200
	Fairlane③	PCW-M	V8-289
	Fairlane④	PCW-AD	V8-289
	Fairlane③	PCW-AC	V8-289⑤
	Fairlane④	PCW-AF	V8-289⑤
	Falcon	PCS-E	6-170
	Falcon	PCS-G	6-200
	Falcon	PCW-AA	V8-289
	Ford③	PCV-B	6-240
	Ford③	PCW-AG⑥	6-240
	Ford④	PCW-R	V8-289
	Ford③	PCW-S	V8-289
	Mustang	PCF-F	6-200
	Mustang	PCW-J	V8-289
1966	Comet③	PCS-W	6-200
	Comet④	PCS-AA	V8-289
	Comet③	PCW-AN	V8-289
	Comet④	PCW-AR	V8-289
	Fairlane③	PCS-W	6-200
	Fairlane④	PCS-AA	6-200
	Fairlane③	PCW-AN	V8-289
	Fairlane④	PCW-AR	V8-289
	Fairlane⑦	PCW-AY	6-200
	Fairlane⑥	PCW-AZ	V8-289
	Falcon	PCS-V	6-170
	Falcon	PCS-W	6-200
	Falcon	PCW-AN	V8-289
	Ford	PCV-E	6-240
	Ford③	PCW-AW	V8-289
	Ford④	PCW-AV	V8-289
	Ford⑥	PDA-D	6-240
	Ford⑦	PDA-D	V8-289
	Mustang	PCS-Y	6-200
	Mustang	PCW-AS	V8-289
1967	Comet④	PEE-B	V8-289
	Comet③	PEE-J	V8-289
	Cougar	PEE-C	V8-289
	Fairlane③	PEB-F	6-200
	Fairlane③	PEE-J	V8-289
	Fairlane③	PEE-A	V8-289
	Fairlane④	PEB-E	6-200
	Fairlane④	PEE-B	V8-289
	Fairlane⑦	PEE-D	6-200
	Fairlane⑦	PEE-E	V8-289
	Falcon	PEB-A	6-170
	Falcon	PEB-H	V8-289
	Falcon	PEB-C	6-200
	Ford③	PEA-A	6-240
	Ford④	PEA-B	V8-289
	Ford③	PEA-C	V8-289
	Mustang	PEE-C	V8-289
	Mustang	PEB-B	6-200
1968	Cougar①	PEE-N	V8-302
	Cougar②	PEE-S	V8-302
	Fairlane④	PEB-A1	6-200
	Fairlane③	PEB-F2	6-200
	Fairlane④	PEE-M	V8-302
	Fairlane③	PEE-V	V8-302
	Falcon	PEB-A2	6-170
	Falcon	PEB-C2	6-200
	Falcon	PEE-H2	V8-289
	Falcon	PEE-R	V8-302
	Ford	PHA-B	V8-302
	Ford	PHB-A	V8-302
	Ford	PFA-B-1	V8-302
	Ford⑧	PFA-D-1	6-240
	Ford⑧	PFA-F	V8-302
	Montego④	PEB-E1	6-200
	Montego③	PEB-F2	6-200
	Montego①④	PEE-M	V8-302
	Montego②④	PEE-U	V8-302
	Montego②③	PEE-R	V8-302
	Montego①③	PEE-V	V8-302
	Mustang	PEB-B1	6-200
	Mustang②	PEE-S	V8-302

①—Two-barrel carburetor.
②—Four-barrel carburetor.
③—Column shift.
④—Floor shift.
⑤—High performance engine.
⑥—Taxi.
⑦—Police.
⑧—Police, Taxi, Fleet

DESCRIPTION

Starting with 1967 the unit is basically the same as the 1966 C4 unit except that the main control assembly has been revised to incorporate a manually selected first and second gear range. The transmission features a drive range that provides for fully automatic upshifts and downshifts, and manually selected low and second gears.

As shown in Fig. 1 the transmission consists essentially of a torque converter, a compound planetary gear train, two multiple disc clutches, a one-way clutch and a hydraulic control system.

For all normal driving the selector lever is moved to the green dot under "Drive" on the selector quadrant on the steering column or on the floor console. As the throttle is advanced from the idle position, the transmission will upshift automatically to intermediate gear and then to high.

The driver can force downshift the transmission from high to intermediate at speeds up to 65 mph. A detent on the downshift linkage warns the driver when the carburetor is wide open. Accelerator pedal depression through the detent will bring in the downshift.

With the throttle closed the transmission will downshift automatically as the car speed drops to about 10 mph. With the throttle open at any position up to the detent, the downshifts will come in automatically at speeds above 10 mph and in proportion to throttle opening. This prevents engine lugging on steep hill climbing, for example.

When the selector lever is moved to "L" with the transmission in high, the transmission will downshift to intermediate or to low depending on the road speed. At speeds above 25 mph, the downshift will be from high to intermediate. At speeds below 25 mph, the downshift will be from high to low. With the selector lever in the "L" position the transmission cannot upshift.

TROUBLE SHOOTING GUIDE

The items to check for each trouble symptom are arranged in a logical sequence that should be followed for quickest results.

Rough Initial Engagement In D1 or D2

1. Engine idle speed.

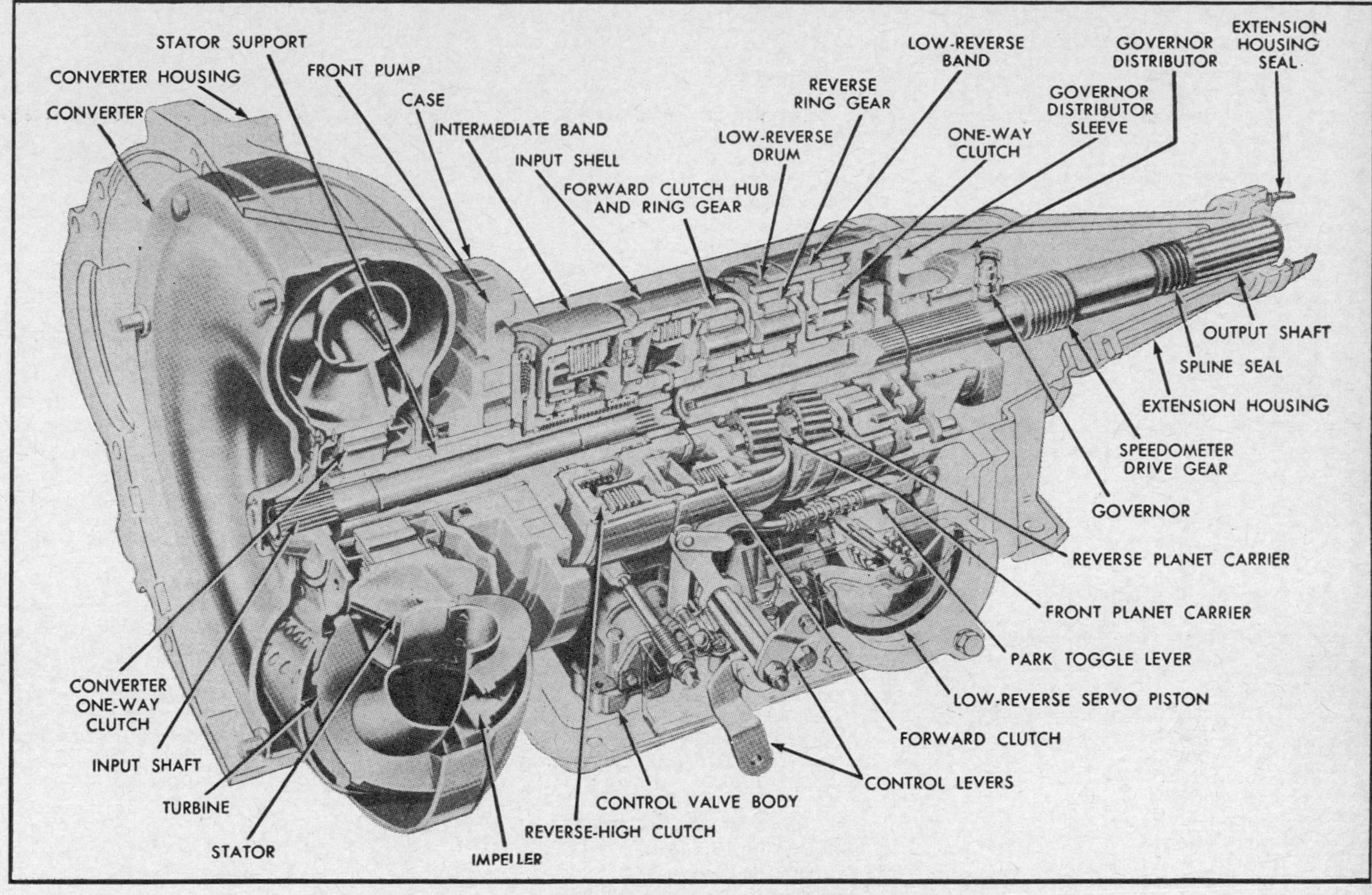

Fig. 1 C4 Dual Range Automatic

2. Vacuum diaphragm unit or tubes restricted, leaking or maladjusted.
3. Check control pressure.
4. Pressure regulator.
5. Valve body.
6. Forward clutch.

1-2 or 2-3 Shift Points Erratic

1. Check fluid level.
2. Vacuum diaphragm unit or tubes restricted, leaking or maladjusted.
3. Intermediate servo.
4. Manual linkage adjustment.
5. Governor.
6. Check control pressure.
7. Valve body.
8. Make air pressure check.

Rough 1-2 Upshifts

1. Vacuum diaphragm unit or tubes restricted, leaking or maladjusted.
2. Intermediate servo.
3. Intermediate band.
4. Check control pressure.
5. Valve body.
6. Pressure regulator.

Rough 2-3 Upshifts

1. Vacuum diaphragm unit or tubes restricted, leaking or maladjusted.
2. Intermediate servo.
3. Check control pressure.
4. Pressure regulator.
5. Intermediate band.
6. Valve body.
7. Make air pressure check.
8. Reverse-high clutch.
9. Reverse-high clutch piston air bleed valve.

Dragged Out 1-2 Shift

1. Check fluid level.
2. Vacuum diaphragm unit or tubes restricted, leaking or maladjusted.
3. Intermediate servo.
4. Check control pressure.
5. Intermediate band.
6. Valve body.
7. Pressure regulator.
8. Make air pressure check.
9. Leakage in hydraulic system.

Engine Overspeeds on 2-3 Shift

1. Manual linkage.
2. Check fluid level.
3. Vacuum diaphragm unit or tubes restricted, leaking or maladjusted.
4. Reverse servo.
5. Check control pressure.
6. Valve body.
7. Pressure regulator.
8. Intermediate band.
9. Reverse-high clutch.
10. Reverse-high clutch piston air bleed valve.

No 1-2 or 2-3 Shift

1. Manual linkage.
2. Downshift linkage, including inner lever position.
3. Vacuum diaphragm unit or tubes restricted, leaking or maladjusted.
4. Governor.
5. Check control pressure.
6. Valve body.
7. Intermediate band.
8. Intermediate servo.
9. Reverse-high clutch.
10. Reverse-high clutch piston air bleed valve.

No 3-1 Shift in D1 or 3-2 Shift in D2

1. Governor.
2. Valve body

No Forced Downshifts

1. Downshift linkage, including inner lever position.
2. Valve body.
3. Vacuum diaphragm unit or tubes restricted, leaking or maladjusted.

Runaway Engine on Forced 3-2 Downshift

1. Check control pressure.
2. Intermediate servo.
3. Intermediate band.
4. Pressure regulator.
5. Valve body.
6. Vacuum diaphragm unit or tubes restricted, leaking or maladjusted.
7. Leakage in hydraulic system.

Rough 3-2 or 3-1 Shift at Closed Throttle

1. Engine idle speed.
2. Vacuum diaphragm unit or tubes restricted, leaking or maladjusted.
3. Intermediate servo.
4. Valve body.
5. Pressure regulator.

Shifts 1-3 in D1 and D2

1. Intermediate band.
2. Intermediate servo.
3. Vacuum diaphragm unit or tubes restricted, leaking or maladjusted.
4. Valve body.
5. Governor.
6. Make air pressure check.

No Engine Braking In 1st Gear —Manual Low

1. Manual linkage.
2. Reverse band.
3. Reverse servo.
4. Valve body.
5. Governor.
6. Make air pressure check.

Slips or Chatters in 1st Gear—D1

1. Check fluid level.
2. Vacuum diaphragm unit or tubes restricted, leaking or maladjusted.
3. Check control pressure.
4. Pressure regulator.
5. Valve body.
6. Forward clutch.
7. Leakage in hydraulic system.
8. Planetary one-way clutch.

Slips or Chatters in 2nd Gear

1. Check fluid level.
2. Vacuum diaphragm unit or tubes restricted, leaking or maladjusted.
3. Intermediate servo.
4. Intermediate band.
5. Check control pressure.
6. Pressure regulator.
7. Valve body.
8. Make air pressure check.
9. Forward clutch.
10. Leakage in hydraulic system.

Slips or Chatters in R

1. Check fluid level.
2. Vacuum diaphragm unit or tubes restricted, leaking or maladjusted.
3. Reverse band.
4. Check control pressure.
5. Reverse servo.
6. Pressure regulator.
7. Valve body.
8. Make air pressure check.
9. Reverse-high clutch.
10. Leakage in hydraulic system.
11. Reverse-high piston air bleed valve.

No Drive in D1 Only

1. Check fluid level.
2. Manual linkage.
3. Check control pressure.
4. Valve body.
5. Make air pressure check.
6. Planetary one-way clutch.

No Drive in D2 Only

1. Check fluid level.
2. Manual linkage.
3. Check control pressure.
4. Intermediate servo.
5. Valve body.
6. Make air pressure check.
7. Leakage in hydraulic system.
8. Planetary one-way clutch.

No Drive in L Only

1. Check fluid level.
2. Manual linkage.
3. Check control pressure.
4. Valve body.
5. Reverse servo.
6. Make air pressure check.
7. Leakage in hydraulic system.
8. Planetary one-way clutch.

No Drive in R Only

1. Check fluid level.
2. Manual linkage.
3. Reverse band.
4. Check control pressure.
5. Reverse servo.
6. Valve body.
7. Make air pressure check.
8. Reverse-high clutch.
9. Leakage in hydraulic system.
10. Reverse-high clutch piston air bleed valve.

No Drive in Any Selector Position

1. Check fluid level.
2. Manual linkage.
3. Check control pressure.
4. Pressure regulator.
5. Valve body.
6. Make air pressure check.
7. Leakage in hydraulic system.
8. Front pump.

Lockup in D1 Only

1. Reverse-high clutch.
2. Parking linkage.
3. Leakage in hydraulic system.

Lockup in D2 Only

1. Reverse band.
2. Reverse servo.
3. Reverse-high clutch.
4. Parking linkage.
5. Leakage in hydraulic system.
6. Planetary one-way clutch.

Lockup in L Only

1. Intermediate band.
2. Intermediate servo.
3. Reverse-high clutch.
4. Parking linkage.
5. Leakage in hydraulic system.

Lockup in R Only

1. Intermediate band.
2. Intermediate servo.
3. Forward clutch.
4. Parking linkage.
5. Leakage in hydraulic system.

Parking Lock Binds or Won't Hold

1. Manual linkage.
2. Parking linkage.

Maximum Speed Too Low, Poor Acceleration

1. Engine performance.
2. Brakes bind.
3. Converter one-way clutch.

Noisy in N or P

1. Check fluid level.
2. Pressure regulator.
3. Front pump.
4. Planetary assembly.

Noisy in All Gears

1. Check fluid level.
2. Pressure regulator.
3. Planetary assembly.
4. Forward clutch.
5. Front pump.
6. Planetary one-way clutch.

Car Moves Forward in N

1. Manual linkage.
2. Forward clutch.

MAINTENANCE

Checking Oil Level

1. Make sure car is standing level.
2. Firmly apply parking brake.
3. If transmission fluid is at normal operating temperature, run engine at normal idle speed. If transmission fluid is cold, run engine at a fast idle until fluid reaches normal operating temperature. Then reduce engine speed to slow idle.
4. Shift selector lever through all positions, then place the lever in reverse.
5. With engine idling, remove dipstick and check fluid level. It should be at the full dot to ⅜″ above the full dot. This ⅜″ position above the center of the full dot is halfway between the letter "F" and "T" of the word transmission on the dipstick.
6. Add fluid as required to bring the fluid to the proper level.

Drain & Refill

NOTE: Normal maintenance and lubrication requirements do not necessitate periodic fluid changes. If a major failure has occurred in the transmission, it will have to be removed for service. At this time the converter must be thoroughly flushed to remove any foreign matter.

When filling a dry transmission and converter, install five quarts of fluid. Start engine, shift the selector lever through all ranges and place it at R position. Check fluid level and add enough to raise the level in the transmission to the "F" (full) mark on the dipstick.

When a partial drain and refill is required due to front band adjustment or minor repair, proceed as follows:

1. Loosen and remove all but two oil pan bolts and drop one edge of the pan to drain the oil.
2. Remove and clean pan and screen.
3. Place a new gasket on pan and install pan and screen.
4. Add three quarts of fluid to transmission.
5. Run engine at idle speed for about two minutes.
6. Check oil level and add oil as necessary.
7. Run engine at a fast idle until it reaches normal operating temperature.
8. Shift selector lever through all ranges and then place it in P position.
9. Add fluid as required to bring the level to the full mark.

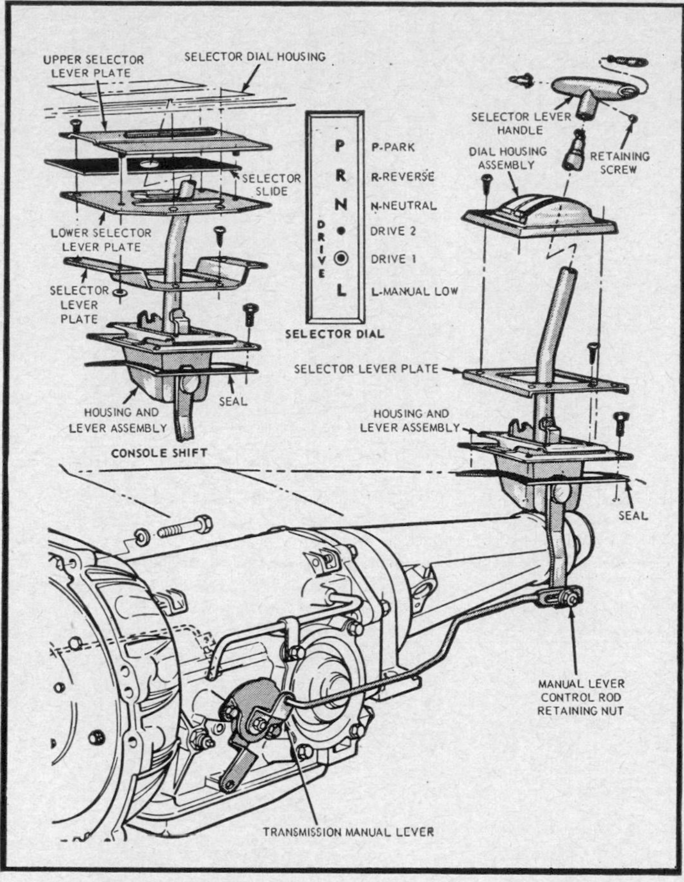

Fig. 2 Manual linkage. 1965-66 floor shift (except Ford)

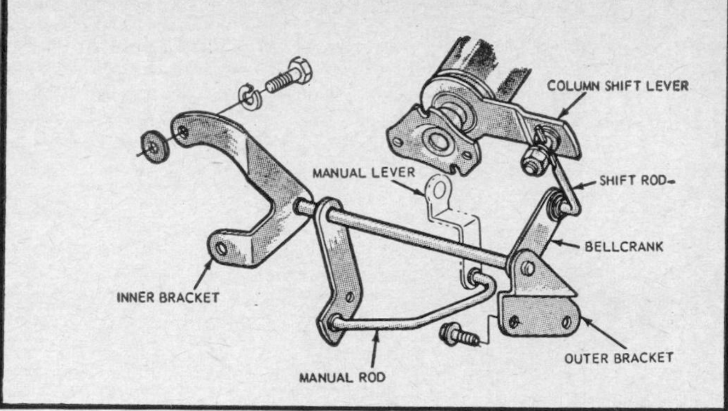

Fig. 4 Manual linkage. 1965-66 Ford column shift

NOTE: Ford recommends the use of an automatic transmission fluid with Ford Qualification No. M2C-33D (on container) instead of the conventional Type A fluid. The recommended fluid is said to have a higher coefficient of friction and greater ability to handle maximum engine torques without band or clutch slippage.

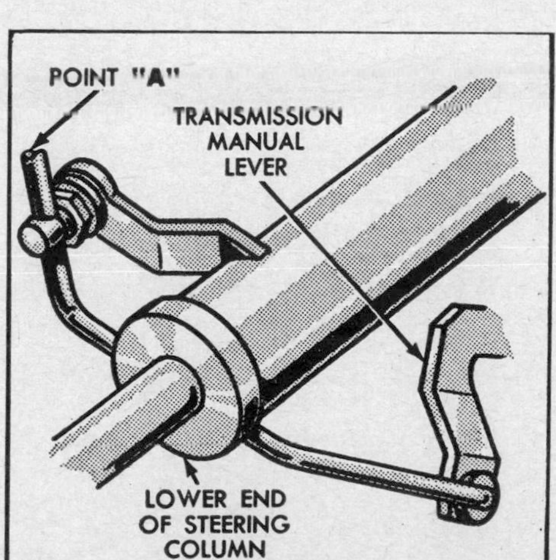

Fig. 3 Manual linkage. 1964-66 column shift (except Ford)

MANUAL LINKAGE, ADJUST

1967-68

Column Shift

1. Place selector lever in D position tight against the D stop.
2. Loosen nut at column shift lever enough to permit shift lever to slide on shift rod.
3. Shift manual lever on transmission into D detent position (3rd from rear).
4. Make sure that selector lever has not moved from the D stop, then tighten nut to secure shift rod to shift lever.

Floor Shift

1. Position selector lever in D position.
2. Raise vehicle and loosen manual lever shift rod retaining nut.
3. Move manual lever at transmission in D position (4th from rear).
4. With selector lever and manual lever in D position, tighten retaining nut.

1965-66 Except Ford

Floor Shift

1. Referring to Fig. 2, position selector lever in D-1 (large dot) position.
2. Raise car and loosen manual control lever rod retaining nut.
3. Move manual lever to D-1 position (2nd detent from back of transmission). The last detent position is manual low.
4. With selector lever and manual lever in D-1 position, tighten retaining nut.
5. Check operation in all positions.

Column Shift

1. With engine stopped, loosen clamp at shift lever at point "A" so that shift rod is free to slide in the clamp, Fig. 3.
2. Place transmission selector lever into the D1 (large dot) position.
3. Shift manual lever at transmission into D1 detent position (second from rear).
4. Tighten clamp on shift rod at point "A".

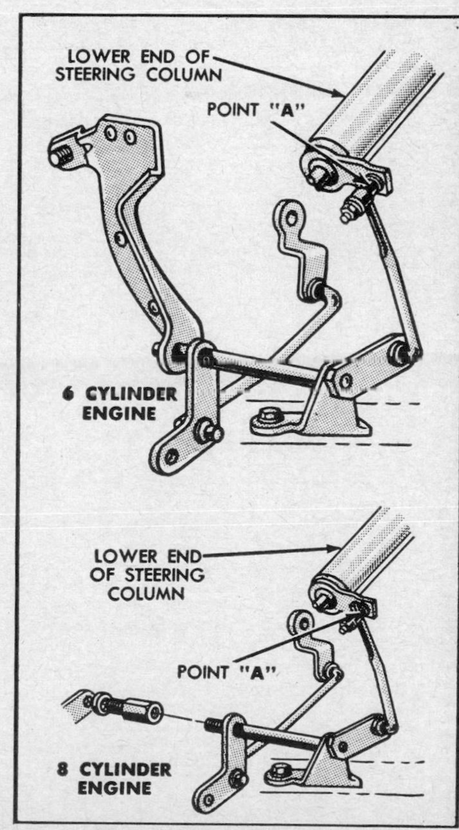

Fig. 5 Manual linkage. 1964 Ford

Fig. 7 Intermediate band adjustment

5. Check pointer alignment and transmission operation for all ranges.

1965-66 Ford

1. Place selector lever in the D1 (circle) position tight against D stop.
2. Loosen nut at column shift lever enough to permit lever to slide on shift rod, Fig. 4.
3. Shift manual lever at transmission into D1 detent position (second from rear).
4. Make sure that selector lever has not moved from the D1 stop, then tighten nut at column shift lever.
5. Check pointer alignment and transmission operation for all selector lever positions.

1964 Ford

1. With engine stopped, loosen clamp at shift lever at point "A" so that shift rod is free to slide in clamp, Fig. 5.
2. Position selector lever in D1 (large dot) position.
3. Shift manual lever at transmission into D1 detent (second from rear).
4. Tighten clamp at point "A".
5. Check pointer alignment and transmission operation in all ranges.

THROTTLE LINKAGE, ADJUST

1. Apply parking brake and place selector lever in "N".
2. Run engine at normal idle speed.
3. Connect tachometer to engine.
4. Adjust engine idle speed to specified rpm with selector lever in Drive position.

NOTE: The carburetor throttle lever must be against the hot idle speed adjusting screw at the specified idle speed.

5. Adjust the throttle linkage so that when the accelator pedal is depressed to the floor, the carburetor throttle valve(s) will be wide open.

BANDS, ADJUST

NOTE: The intermediate and low-reverse bands from 1967 are basically the same as 1966 except that the adjusting screw locknut must be discarded and a new one installed each time a band is adjusted.

Intermediate Band

1. Loosen lock nut several turns.
2. With tool shown in Fig. 7, tighten adjusting screw until tool handle clicks. *This tool is a pre-set torque wrench which clicks and overruns when the torque on the adjusting screw reaches 10 ft-lbs.*
3. Back off adjusting screw exactly 1¾ turns (1½ on 1964).
4. Hold adjusting screw from turning and tighten lock nut.

Low-Reverse Band

1. Loosen lock nut several turns.
2. Tighten adjusting screw until tool handle clicks, Fig. 8. *Tool shown is a pre-set torque wrench which clicks and overruns when the torque on the adjusting screw reaches 10 ft-lbs.*
3. Back off adjusting screw exactly 3 full turns.
4. Hold adjusting screw from turning and tighten lock nut.

"IN CAR" REPAIRS

The following operations may be performed without removing the transmission from the vehicle.

1. Oil pan remove and replace.
2. Valve body replacement.
3. Intermediate servo repair.
4. Low-reverse servo piston replace.
5. Extension housing bushing and rear seal.
6. Extension housing and governor replace.

TRANSMISSION, REPLACE

All Except Ford

1. Raise car and remove converter cover at lower front side of converter housing.
2. Remove both drain plugs and drain oil from converter. Replace plugs.
3. Remove drive shaft.
4. Remove vacuum hose from transmission vacuum unit.
5. Remove speedometer cable from extension housing.
6. Disconnect exhaust pipe from manifold.
7. Remove parking brake cable from equalizer lever.
8. Loosen the transmission oil pan bolts and drain oil at one corner of oil pan. Tighten bolts.
9. Disconnect oil cooler lines from transmission case. Remove oil filler tube from case.
10. Remove manual and kickdown rods from transmission shift levers.
11. Remove transmission outer downshift lever and neutral start switch. On Mustang and Cougar, disconnect neutral start switch wires from retaining clamps and connectors.

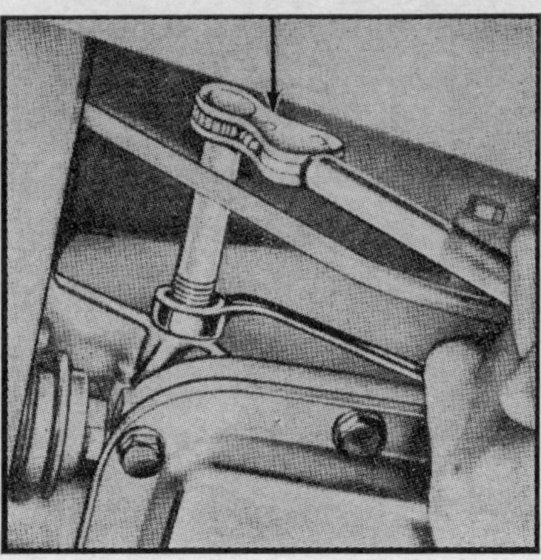

Fig. 8 Low-reverse band adjustment

12. Remove starting motor.
13. Remove four converter-to-flywheel retaining bolts.
14. Support transmission with a jack.
15. Unfasten and lower crossmember.
16. Remove five converter housing-to-engine bolts and lower transmission.
17. Reverse removal procedure to install transmission.

Ford

1. On 1965-66 models, disconnect neutral switch wires in engine compartment.
2. Raise car and remove converter cover at lower front side of converter housing.
3. Drain converter.
4. Remove propeller shaft.
5. Remove vacuum line hose from transmission vacuum unit. Disconnect vacuum line from clip.
6. Remove two extension housing-to-crossmember bolts.
7. Remove speedometer cable from extension housing.
8. Disconnect exhaust pipe from manifold.
9. Remove parking brake cable from equalizer lever.
10. Remove filler tube from oil pan and drain transmission fluid.
11. Disconnect cooler lines from transmission case.
12. Remove manual and kickdown linkage rods from transmission control levers.
13. Disconnect neutral safety switch wires from clips.
14. Remove starting motor.
15. Remove four-converter-to-flywheel nuts.
16. Support transmission with a jack.
17. Remove crossmember.
18. Remove five converter housing-to-engine bolts.
19. Lower transmission and remove it from car.

C6 DUAL RANGE AUTOMATIC

> **NOTE: — This chapter deals only with maintenance, adjustments and "in car" repairs. For major service work, Motor's Automatic Transmission Manual is available. Current edition is a 740 page volume that includes 240 pages of oil circuit diagrams mostly in full color.**

TRANSMISSION IDENTIFICATION

YEAR	CAR MODEL	TRANS. MODEL	ENGINE MODEL
1966	Comet①	PDD-J	V8-390③
	Comet②	PDD-P	V8-390③
	Comet①	PDD-E	V8-390④
	Comet②	PDD-R	V8-390④
	Fairlane same as Comet.		
	Ford①	PDD-B	V8-390③
	Ford②	PDD-W	V8-390③
	Ford①	PDD-C	V8-390④
	Ford②	PDD-K	V8-390④
	Ford①	PDD-H	V8-428
	Ford②	PDD-N	V8-428
	Lincoln	PDE-A	V8-462
	Mercury⑤	PDD-D	V8-410
	Mercury⑥	PDD-L	V8-410
	Mercury⑦	PDD-U	V8-410
	Mercury⑧	PDD-T	V8-410
	Mercury①	PDD-H	V8-428
1967	Comet①	PGA-B	V8-390③
	Comet②	PGA-C	V8-390③
	Comet②	PGA-M	V8-390④
	Cougar	PGA-P	V8-390
	Fairlane①	PGA-B	V8-390③
	Fairlane②	PGA-C	V8-390③
	Fairlane①	PGA-F	V8-390④
	Fairlane②	PGA-G	V8-390④
	Fairlane①	PGA-R	V8-390④
	Fairlane②	PGA-M	V8-390④
	Ford①	PGA-A	V8-390③
	Ford②	PGA-L	V8-390③
	Ford①	PGB-F	V8-428
	Ford⑨	PGB-G	V8-390
	Ford⑨	PGB-H	V8-428
	Ford①	PGA-H	V8-390④
	Ford②	PGA-J	V8-390④
	Ford①	PGB-A	V8-428
	Ford②	PGB-B	V8-428

An identification tag attached to the servo cover bolt, includes the model prefix and suffix, as well as the service identification number and serial number. The service identification number indicates changes to service details which affect interchangeability when the transmission model IS NOT CHANGED. For interpretation of this number the Ford Master Parts Catalog should be consulted.

YEAR	CAR MODEL	TRANS. MODEL	ENGINE MODEL
	Lincoln	PGC-A	V8-462
	Mercury①	PGA-A	V8-390③
	Mercury⑦	PGA-H	V8-410
	Mercury⑥	PGB-A	V8-410
	Mercury⑥	PGB-A	V8-428
	Mercury②	PGB-B	V8-428
	Mercury⑨	PGB-F	V8-428
	Mercury①	PGB-G	V8-390③
	Mercury⑧	PGB-G	V8-410
	Mercury⑤	PGB-H	V8-410
	Mercury⑤	PGB-H	V8-428
	Mustang	PGA-P	V8-390
	Thunderbird	PGA-K	V8-390
	Thunderbird	PGB-C	V8-428
1968	Cougar②	PGA-S	V8-390③
	Cougar②	PGA-P2	V8-390④
	Cougar①	PGB-W	V8-427
	Fairlane①	PGA-B3	V8-390③
	Fairlane②	PGA-C2	V8-390③
	Fairlane②	PGA-M2	V8-390④
	Fairlane①	PGA-R2	V8-390④
	Fairlane①	PGB-Y	V8-427
	Fairlane②	PGB-2	V8-427

YEAR	CAR MODEL	TRANS. MODEL	ENGINE MODEL
	Ford①	PGA-A-2	V8-390③
	Ford①	PGB-G-1	V8-390
	Ford②	PGA-L-2	V8-390③
	Ford①	PGA-H-2	V8-390④
	Ford②	PGA-J-2	V8-390④
	Ford①	PGB-A-2	V8-428
	Ford①⑨	PGB-H-1	V8-428
	Ford②	PGB-B-2	V8-428
	Ford①	PGB-AA	V8-427
	Ford②	PGB-AB	V8-427
	Lincoln	PGC-B	V8-460
	Lincoln	PGC-A3	V8-462
	Mercury	PGA-A-2	V8-390③
	Mercury	PGB-G-1	V8-390
	Mercury	PGA-H-2	V8-390
	Mercury	PGB-A-2	V8-428
	Mercury	PGB-F-1	V8-428
	Montego①	PGA-B3	V8-390③
	Montego②	PGA-C2	V8-390③
	Montego②	PGA-M2	V8-390④
	Montego①	PGA-R2	V8-390④
	Montego①	PGB-Y	V8-427
	Montego②	PGB-2	V8-427
	Thunderbird	PGA-K3	V8-390
	Thunderbird	PGB-J	V8-429

①—Column shift.
②—Floor shift.
③—Two barrel carburetor.
④—Four barrel carburetor.
⑤—Column shift, dual exhaust.
⑥—Floor shift, dual exhaust.
⑦—Floor shift, single exhaust.
⑧—Column shift, single exhaust.
⑨—Fleet and heavy duty.

DESCRIPTION

As shown in Fig. 1, the transmission consists essentially of a torque converter, a compound planetary gear train controlled by one band, three disc clutches and a one-way clutch, and a hydraulic control system.

The transmission is made so that in the first design (1966) the shifting is fully automatic from the "D" position. In the later design (some Comets and Fairlanes in 1966 and in all models from 1967) a system of manual and automatic shifting is provided.

Fully Automatic Type, 1966

The shift selector has six positions: Park, Reverse, Neutral, D2 (small dot), D1 (large dot), and manual low.

In the normal driving range (D1), the car starts in low gear, with automatic upshifts to second and high as road speed increases. With the throttle closed, the transmission downshifts from high to low in D1 at about 10 mph.

D2 range provides a second gear start and upshift to high. The coasting or closed throttle downshift to second gear occurs at about 10 mph.

Manual low (L) range is designed primarily for engine braking. Starting in this position, the car is in low gear and there is no upshift. If the transmission is in high gear in D2 or D1 and the driver moves the selector lever to L, a downshift to second occurs, and the transmission stays in second down to 10 mph. Then it downshifts to low.

Automatic & Manual Shifting 1966-68

This unit has a shift pattern which is indicated on the selector as P-R-N-D-2-1. This refers respectively to Park, Reverse, Neutral, Full Automatic, Second Gear (manual), Low Gear (manual).

In this unit an overriding control is provided which enables the driver to exercise his own judgement with regard to the gear ratios to be selected and an understanding of what is possible greatly enhances the pleasure to be derived from driving the car. No automatic mechanism has the power of anticipation, but the driver can see ahead and has the means for over-riding the automatic mechanism.

Automatic Shift

In "D" position the shift sequence is

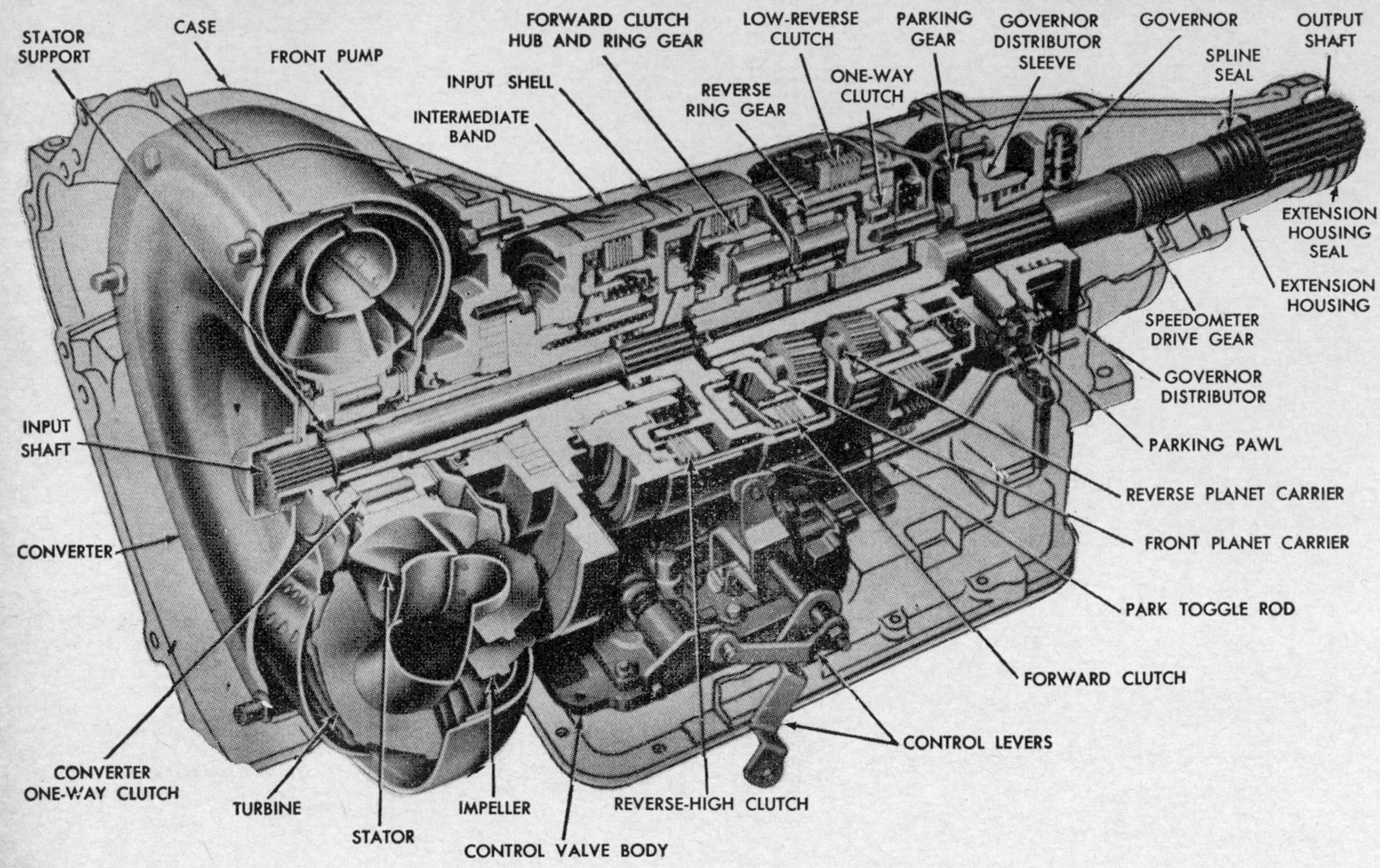

Fig. 1 Sectional view of C6 transmission

fully automatic in that the transmission starts in low gear and upshifts through second gear to third or high gear.

Manual Shifting

The shift to 2 or 1 is done manually by shifting the lever from neutral to either position. In "1" position, the transmission starts in 1st (low gear) and is retained. In "2" position it starts in 2nd gear and remains in 2nd gear, regardless of road speed.

Manual Shift To "1"

Manual shifting from "D" to "1" can also be accomplished any time. Here the transmission immediately shifts to second and remains in second until the predetermined governor control speed allows it to shift down to low gear where it remains. The governor speed control at this point eliminates the possibility of a direct down shift to low gear until the road speed is reduced.

Shift Lever Controls

A shift lever button control is used to shift from neutral to reverse or park, also when shifting from "D" to "2" or "1" position. However, the button control function is not required when shifting from neutral to "D", or to shift forward from "1" to "2" position.

Parking Pawl

The transmission gear train is in neutral in both P and N positions. There is no pressure to any clutch and only the transmission input shaft turns. In park, a pawl engages a parking gear which is splined to the transmission output shaft, Fig. 1, to lock the rear wheels to the transmission main case.

A neutral start switch, mounted on the transmission and operated by the selector linkage, completes the engine cranking circuit in P and N only so that the engine cannot be started in any drive gear.

Forced Downshifts

Forced downshifts (kickdown shifts) from high to second gear are possible at speeds as high as 65 mph in D1 or D2. In D1 it is possible to force a downshift to 1st gear up to 30 mph.

The carburetor is at full throttle before the accelerator is floored. Up to full throttle, a "torque demand" downshift to 2nd is possible up to 40 mph. "Kickdown" shifts require depressing the accelerator to the floor to actuate the downshift valve in the transmission.

TROUBLE SHOOTING GUIDE

No Drive In Forward Speeds

1. Manual linkage adjustment.
2. Check control pressure.
3. Valve body.
4. Make air pressure check.
5. Forward clutch.
6. Leakage in hydraulic system.

Rough Initial Engagement in D, D1, D2 or 2

1. Engine idle speed too high.
2. Vacuum diaphragm unit or tubes restricted, leaking or maladjusted.
3. Check control pressure.
4. Valve body.
5. Forward clutch.

1-2 or 2-3 Shift Points Incorrect or Erratic

1. Check fluid level.
2. Vacuum diaphragm unit or tubes restricted, leaking or maladjusted.
3. Downshift linkage, including inner lever position.
4. Manual linkage adjustment.
5. Governor defective.
6. Check control pressure.
7. Valve body.
8. Make air pressure check.

Rough 1-2 Upshifts

1. Vacuum diaphragm unit or tubes restricted, leaking or maladjusted.
2. Intermediate servo.
3. Intermediate band.
4. Check control pressure.
5. Valve body.

Rough 2-3 Shifts

1. Vacuum diaphragm or tubes restricted, leaking or maladjusted.
2. Intermediate servo.
3. Check control pressure.
4. Intermediate band.
5. Valve body.
6. Make air pressure check.
7. Reverse-high clutch.
8. Reverse-high clutch piston air bleed valve.

Dragged Out 1-2 Shift

1. Check fluid level.
2. Vacuum diaphragm unit or tubes restricted, leaking or maladjusted.
3. Intermediate servo.
4. Check control pressure.
5. Intermediate band.
6. Valve body.
7. Make air pressure check.
8. Leakage in hydraulic system.

Engine Overspeeds on 2-3 Shift

1. Manual linkage adjustment.
2. Check fluid level.
3. Vacuum diaphragm unit or tubes restricted, leaking or maladjusted.
4. Intermediate servo.
5. Check control pressure.
6. Valve body.
7. Intermediate band.
8. Reverse-high clutch.
9. Reverse-high clutch piston air bleed valve.

No 1-2 or 2-3 Shift

1. Manual linkage adjustment.
2. Downshift linkage including inner lever position.
3. Vacuum diaphragm unit or tubes restricted, leaking or maladjusted.
4. Governor.
5. Check control pressure.
6. Valve body.
7. Intermediate band.
8. Intermediate servo.
9. Reverse-high clutch.
10. Leakage in hydraulic system.

No 3-1 Shift In D1, 2 or 3-2 Shift In D2 or D

1. Governor.
2. Valve body.

No Forced Downshifts

1. Downshift linkage, including inner lever position.
2. Check control pressure.
3. Valve body.

Runaway Engine on Forced 3-2 Shift

1. Check control pressure.
2. Intermediate servo.
3. Intermediate band.
4. Valve body.
5. Vacuum diaphragm unit or tubes restricted, leaking or maladjusted.
6. Leakage in hydraulic system.

Rough 3-2 Shift or 3-1 Shift at Closed Throttle

1. Engine idle speed.
2. Vacuum diaphragm unit or tubes restricted, leaking or maladjusted.
3. Intermediate servo.
4. Check control pressure.
5. Valve body.

Shifts 1-3 in D, D1, 2, D2

1. Intermediate band.
2. Intermediate servo.
3. Valve body.
4. Governor.
5. Make air pressure check.

No Engine Braking in 1st Gear—Manual Low Range

1. Manual linkage adjustment.
2. Low-reverse clutch.
3. Valve body.
4. Governor.
5. Make air pressure check.
6. Leakage in hydraulic system.

Creeps Excessively

1. Engine idle speed too high.

Slips or Chatters In 1st Gear, D1

1. Check fluid level.
2. Vacuum diaphragm unit or tubes restricted, leaking or maladjusted.
3. Check control pressure.
4. Valve body.
5. Forward clutch.
6. Leakage in hydraulic system.
7. Planetary one-way clutch.

Slips or Chatters In 2nd Gear

1. Check fluid level.
2. Vacuum diaphragm unit or tubes restricted, leaking or maladjusted.
3. Intermediate servo.
4. Intermediate band.
5. Check control pressure.
6. Valve body.
7. Make air pressure check.
8. Forward clutch.
9. Leakage in hydraulic system.

Slips or Chatters In Reverse

1. Check fluid level.
2. Vacuum diaphragm unit or tubes restricted, leaking or maladjusted.
3. Manual linkage adjustment.
4. Low-reverse clutch.
5. Check control pressure.
6. Valve body.
7. Make air pressure check.
8. Reverse-high clutch.
9. Leakage in hydraulic system.
10. Reverse-high clutch piston air bleed valve.

No Drive In D1 or 2

1. Manual linkage adjustment.
2. Check control pressure.
3. Valve body.
4. Planetary one-way clutch.

No Drive In D, D2

1. Check fluid level.
2. Manual linkage adjustment.
3. Check control pressure.
4. Intermediate servo.
5. Valve body.
6. Make air pressure check.
7. Leakage in hydraulic system.

No Drive In L or 1

1. Check fluid level.
2. Check control pressure.
3. Valve body.
4. Make air pressure check.
5. Leakage in hydraulic system.

No Drive In R Only

1. Check fluid level.
2. Manual linkage adjustment.
3. Low-reverse clutch.
4. Check control pressure.
5. Valve body.
6. Make air pressure check.
7. Reverse-high clutch.
8. Leakage in hydraulic system.
9. Reverse-high clutch piston air bleed valve.

No Drive In Any Selector Position

1. Check fluid level.
2. Manual linkage adjustment.
3. Check control pressure.
4. Valve body.
5. Make air pressure check.
6. Leakage in hydraulic system.
7. Front pump.

Lockup In D1 or 2

1. Valve body.
2. Parking linkage.
3. Leakage in hydraulic system.

Lockup In D2 or D

1. Low-reverse clutch.
2. Valve body.
3. Reverse-high clutch.
4. Parking linkage.
5. Leakage in hydraulic system.
6. Planetary one-way clutch.

Lockup In L or 1

1. Valve body.
2. Parking linkage.
3. Leakage in hydraulic system.

Lockup In R Only

1. Valve body.
2. Forward clutch.
3. Parking linkage.
4. Leakage in hydraulic system.

Parking Lock Binds or Does Not Hold

1. Manual linkage adjustment.
2. Parking linkage.

Transmission Overheats

1. Oil cooler and connections.
2. Valve body.
3. Vacuum diaphragm unit or tubes restricted, leaking or maladjusted.
4. Check control pressure.
5. Converter one-way clutch.
6. Converter pressure check valves.

Maximum Speed Too Low, Poor Acceleration

1. Engine performance.
2. Car brakes.
3. Forward clutch.

Transmission Noisy In N and P

1. Check fluid level.
2. Valve body.
3. Front pump.

Noisy In 1st, 2nd, 3rd or Reverse

1. Check fluid level.
2. Valve body.
3. Planetary assembly.
4. Forward clutch.
5. Reverse-high clutch.
6. Planetary one-way clutch.

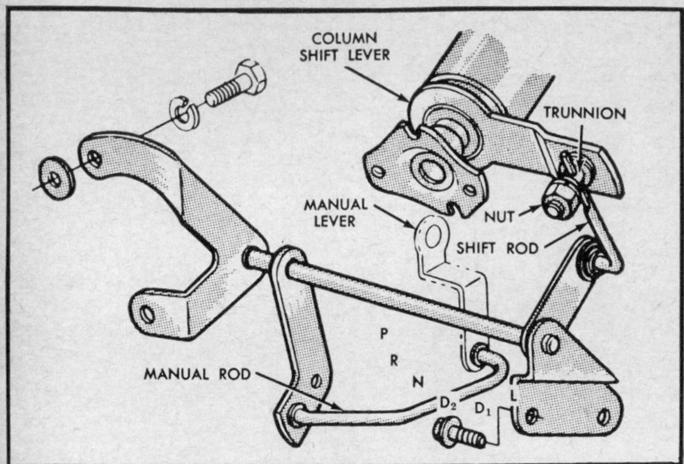

Fig. 2 Manual linkage (column shift)

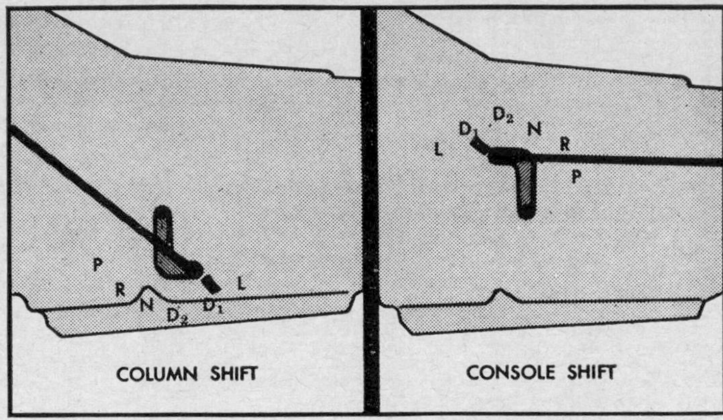

Fig. 3 Manual valve lever positions for 1966 fully automatic transmissions. For 1966-68 units with manual override feature, the corresponding positions are P-R-N-D-2-1

Car Moves Forward In N

1. Manual linkage adjustment.
2. Forward clutch.

Fluid Leak

1. Check fluid level.
2. Converter drain plugs.
3. Oil pan gasket, filler tube or seal.
4. Oil cooler and connections.
5. Manual or downshift lever shaft seal.
6. 1/8" pipe plugs in case.
7. Extension housing-to-case gasket.
8. Extension housing rear oil seal.
9. Speedometer driven gear adapter seal.
10. Vacuum diaphragm unit or tubes.
11. Intermediate servo.
12. Engine rear oil seal.

MAINTENANCE

Checking Oil Level

1. Make sure car is on a level floor.
2. Apply parking brake firmly.
3. Run engine at normal idle speed. If transmission fluid is cold, run engine at a fast idle until fluid reaches normal operating temperature. When fluid is warm, slow engine to normal idle speed.
4. Shift selector lever through all positions, then place lever at "P". Do not shut down engine during fluid level checks.
5. Clean all dirt from dipstick cap before removing dipstick from filler tube.
6. Pull dipstick out of tube, wipe it clean and push it all the way back in tube.
7. Pull dipstick out of tube again and check fluid level. If necessary, add enough fluid to raise the level to the "F" mark on dipstick. Do not overfill.

Drain & Refill

NOTE: The Ford Motor Company recommends the use of an automatic transmission fluid with Qualification No. M2C-33D (on container) instead of the conventional Type A fluid. The recommended fluid is said to have a greater coefficient of friction and greater ability to handle maximum engine torques without band or clutch slippage.

Normal maintenance and lubrication requirements do not necessitate periodic fluid changes. If a major failure has occured in the transmission, it will have to be removed for service. At this time the converter must be thoroughly flushed to remove any foreign matter.

1. To drain the fluid, loosen pan attaching bolts and allow fluid to drain.
2. After fluid has drained to the level of the pan flange, remove pan bolts, working from rear and both sides of pan to allow it to drop and drain slowly.
3. When fluid has stopped draining, remove and clean pan and screen. Discard pan gasket.
4. Using a new gasket, install pan.
5. Add 3 quarts of recommended fluid to transmission through filler tube.
6. Run engine at idle speed for 2 minutes, and then run it at a fast idle until it reaches normal operating temperature.
7. Shift selector lever through all positions, place it at "P" and check fluid level.
8. If necessary, add enough fluid to transmission to bring it to the "F" mark on the dipstick.

MANUAL LINKAGE, ADJUST

1967-68

Column Shift

1. Place selector lever in D position tight against D stop.
2. Loosen nut at column shift lever enough to permit shift lever to slide on shift rod.
3. Shift manual lever on transmission into D detent position (3rd from rear).
4. Make sure that selector has not moved from the D stop, then tighten nut to secure shift rod to shift lever.

Floor Shift

1. Position selector lever in D position.
2. Raise vehicle and loosen manual lever shift rod retaining nut.
3. Move manual lever at transmission in D position (4th from rear).
4. With selector lever and manual lever in D position, tighten retaining nut.

1966

Column Shift

1. Move the selector to D1.
2. Loosen the nut on the shift rod trunnion, Fig. 2, to permit the column shift lever to slide on the rod.
3. Shift the manual lever on the transmission to D1, Fig. 3.
4. Check that the selector lever is against the gate stop in D1, then tighten the nut on the trunnion.
5. Check the other positions and for starting in park and neutral. If necessary, adjust the neutral start switch.

Console Shift

1. Move the selector to D1.
2. Loosen the nut, Fig. 4, that holds the manual lever control rod to the shift lever link.
3. Move the manual-shift lever on the transmission to the D1 position, Fig. 3.
4. Tighten the nut while the selector and shift lever are both in D1.
5. Check the other selector positions, and for starting in neutral and park. If necessary, adjust the neutral start switch.

THROTTLE LINKAGE

Adjusting the throttle linkage is important to be certain the throttle and kickdown systems are properly adjusted. The kickdown system should come in when the accelerator is pressed through detent, and not before detent.

The throttle linkage should be adjusted so that when the accelerator pedal is pressed to the flooor the carburetor throttle valve(s) will be wide open.

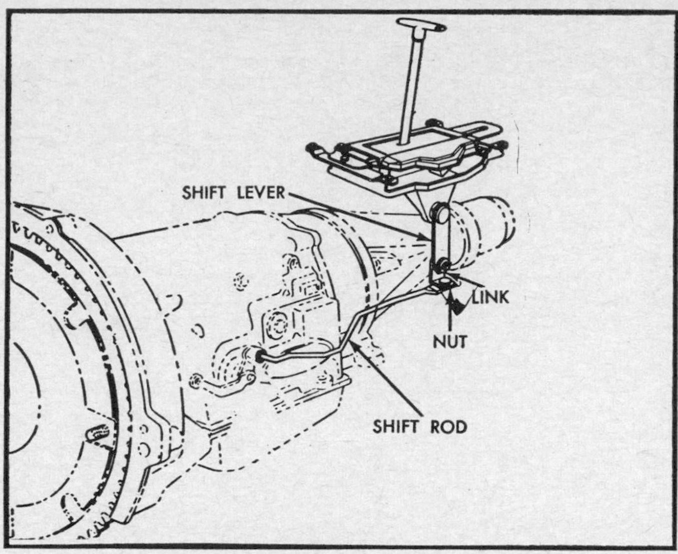

Fig. 4 Manual linkage (console shift)

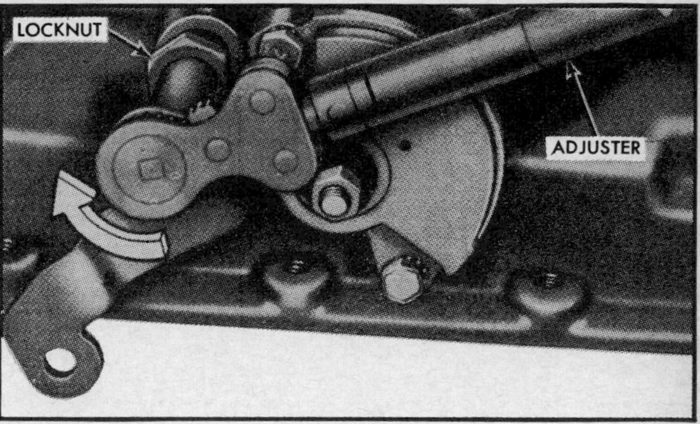

Fig. 5 Band adjustment.

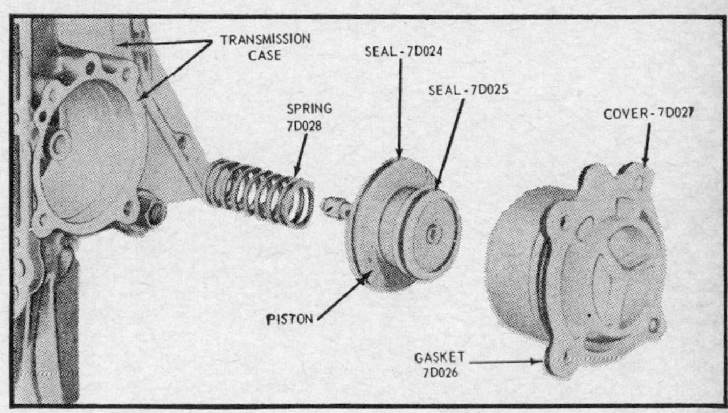

Fig. 6 Intermediate servo disassembled

BAND ADJUSTMENT

NOTE: The intermediate band adjustment from 1967 is basically the same as 1966 with the exception of the adjusting screw lock nut. The lock nut must be discarded and a new one installed each time the band is adjusted.

If you have any difficulty with intermediate gear on the road test, a band adjustment is in order.

Some possible indications of a slipping band are:

First gear start in D2.
Upshift directly from first to high.
Bump on 1-2 upshift or dragged-out shift.

Besides adjusting the band, look for any evidence of leakage around the servo cover seal.

Adjusting Procedure

1. Loosen the locknut on the adjusting screw several turns, Fig. 5.
2. Torque the screw to 10 ft-lbs, or until the adjuster wrench overruns.
3. Back the screw off exactly one turn.
4. Hold the adjustment and torque the locknut to the 35-45 ft-lbs.

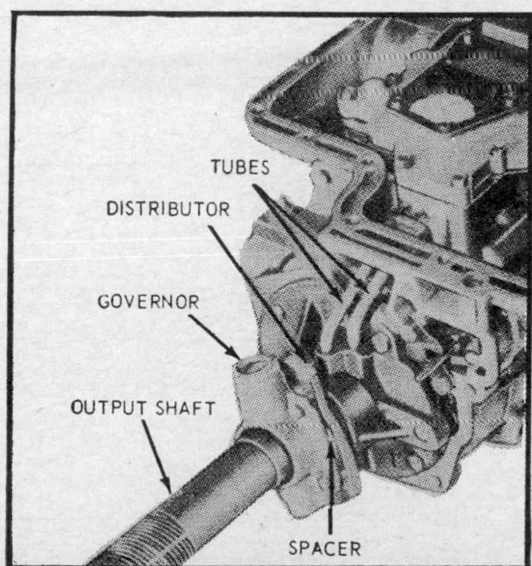

Fig. 7 Governor installed

OIL PAN & CONTROL VALVE

Removal

1. Raise car on hoist or jack stands.
2. Loosen and remove all but two oil pan bolts from front of case and drop rear edge of pan to drain fluid. Remove and clean pan and screen.
3. Unfasten and remove valve body.

Installation

1. Position valve body to case, making sure that selector and downshift levers are engaged, then install and torque attaching bolts to specifications.
2. Using a new pan gasket, secure pan to case and torque bolts to specifications.
3. Lower car and fill transmission to the correct level with specified fluid.

INTERMEDIATE SERVO

Removal

1. Raise car and remove engine rear support-to-extension housing bolts.
2. Raise transmission high enough to relieve weight from support.
3. Remove support (1 bolt).
4. Lower transmission.
5. Place drain pan beneath servo.
6. Remove servo cover-to-case bolts.
7. Loosen band adjusting screw locknut.
8. Remove servo cover, piston, spring and gasket from case, *screwing band adjusting screw inward as piston is removed. This insures that there will be enough tension on the band to keep the struts properly engaged in the band end notches while the piston is removed.*

Replacing Seal, Fig. 6

1. Apply air pressure to port in servo cover to remove piston and stem.
2. Remove seals from piston.
3. Remove seal from cover.
4. Dip new seals in transmission fluid.
5. Install seals in piston and cover.
6. Dip piston in transmission fluid and install in cover.

Installation

1. Position new gasket on servo cover and spring on piston stem.
2. Insert piston stem in case. Secure cover with bolts, taking care to back off band adjusting screw while tightening cover bolts. Make sure that vent tube retaining clip is in place.
3. Raise transmission high enough to install engine rear support. Secure support to extension housing. Lower transmission as required to install

support-to-crossmember bolt.
4. Remove jack and adjust band.
5. Lower car and replenish fluid as required.

EXTENSION HOUSING & GOVERNOR

Removal

1. Raise car and drain transmission.
2. Disconnect parking brake cable at equalizer.
3. Remove torque plate.
4. Disconnect drive shaft from rear axle flange and remove from transmission.
5. Disconnect speedometer cable from extension housing.
6. Remove two nuts that secure engine rear mount to crossmember.
7. Raise transmission with a jack just high enough to relieve weight from crossmember. Remove crossmember.
8. Remove engine rear support.
9. Lower transmission to permit access to extension housing bolts. Remove bolts and slide housing off output shaft.
10. Disconnect governor from distributor (4 bolts) and slide governor off output shaft.

Installation, Fig. 7

1. Secure governor to distributor flange.
2. Position new gasket on transmission.
3. Secure extension housing to case.
4. Secure engine rear support to case.
5. Install crossmember.
6. Lower transmission and remove jack. Then install and torque engine rear support-to-extension housing bolts.
7. Install speedometer cable, connect parking brake cable to equalizer and install drive shaft.
8. Install torque plate to floor pan.
9. Replenish transmission fluid.

TRANSMISSION, REPLACE

Compact & Intermediates

1. On Cougar, Mustang and 1966 Comet, disconnect neutral switch wires from harness connector and retaining clip on dash.
2. Remove bolt that secures filler tube to rear of right cylinder head.
3. Raise car on hoist or stands.
4. Drain converter and oil pan.
5. Remove drive shaft.
6. Disconnect shift rods from transmission levers.
7. Disconnect speedometer cable from extension housing.
8. Disconnect hose from vacuum diaphragm at rear of transmission. Remove vacuum tube from clip at transmission.
9. Remove starter.
10. Lift filler tube from case.
11. Remove four converter-to-flywheel nuts.
12. Remove two nuts that attach engine rear support to crossmember.
13. Raise transmission to take weight off crossmember.
14. Remove crossmember.
15. Remove rear engine support.
16. Lower transmission and disconnect oil cooler lines.
17. Secure transmission to jack with a chain.
18. Remove six converter housing-to-cylinder block bolts.
19. Move jack rearward until transmission clears engine, tip it forward to provide clearance. Then lower and remove transmission.
20. Reverse procedure to install.

Ford & Mercury 1967-68

1. Raise vehicle on a hoist and drain fluid from transmission and converter.
2. Remove propeller shaft.
3. Remove starter motor.
4. Remove four converter-to-flywheel nuts. Use a wrench on crankshaft pulley bolt to turn converter to gain access to nuts.
5. Disconnect parking brake front cable from equalizer.
6. Remove two crossmember-to-frame bolts.
7. Remove two engine rear support-to-extension housing bolts.
8. Disconnect downshift and selector rods from transmission levers.
9. Separate exhaust pipes from manifolds.
10. Remove exhaust thermostat and gaskets.
11. Raise transmission to provide clearance to remove crossmember.
12. Disconnect parking brake rear cables from equalizer.
13. Remove crossmember from side supports.
14. Lower transmission to gain access to cooler lines.
15. Disconnect oil cooler lines from transmission.
16. Disconnect vacuum line from diaphragm at right rear of transmission.
17. Remove metal line from clip on transmission.
18. Disconnect speedometer cable from extension housing.
19. Remove filler tube from transmission.
20. Remove converter housing-to-engine bolts.
21. Remove transmission away from engine and, at the same time, lower it to clear underside of vehicle.
22. Reverse procedure to install.

Ford & Mercury, 1966

Closed Cars

1. Drive car on hoist but do not raise it at this time.
2. Remove two upper converter housing-to-engine bolts.
3. Raise car and remove cover from lower side of converter housing.
4. Drain converter now or wait until unit is removed from car.
5. Disconnect filler tube from transmission oil pan.
6. Disconnect vacuum hose from vacuum diaphragm unit and tube from extension housing clip.
7. Install converter housing front plate to hold converter in place when transmission is removed.
8. Remove starting motor.
9. Disconnect oil cooler lines from transmission, and remove transmission vent tube.
10. Disconnect shift linkage from transmission.
11. Disconnect speedometer cable from extension housing.
12. Remove propeller shaft.
13. Support transmission on a jack or stand.
14. Remove engine rear support-to-transmission bolts and raise transmission slightly to take weight off crossmember.
15. Support rear of engine.
16. Remove remaining converter housing-to-engine bolts.
17. Move assembly rearward and out of car.
18. Reverse procedure to install.

Convertibles

The frame construction of these models will not permit the transmission to be moved rearward enough to clear the turbine shaft from the converter. For this reason the converter and transmission must be removed as a unit.

After removing the crossmember, remove the four transmission-to-converter housing bolts. Support the engine. Tilt rear of transmission slightly upward, then move the assembly toward the rear until it is clear of the turbine shaft. Lower the assembly and remove it from the car.

Lincoln

1. Raise hood and disconnect neutral switch wires.
2. Remove nut attaching transmission filler tube to manifold.
3. Raise car on a hoist and remove bolts from reinforcement plate at rear of transmission oil pan and remove plate.
4. Loosen all transmission oil pan bolts and allow fluid to drain. Remove pan entirely to completely drain transmission. Remove pan with four bolts.
5. Drain converter after removing lower cover from converter housing.
6. Unfasten converter from drive plate.
7. Lift filler tube from case.
8. Remove starting motor.
9. Disconnect cooler lines from transmission, and vacuum hose from diaphragm.
10. Disconnect manual and downshift rods from transmission.
11. Disconnect speedometer cable from extension housing.
12. Remove downshift control rod splash shield from side rail.
13. Remove lower bellcrank bracket bolt and loosen upper bolt. Pivot bracket to permit bellcrank to hang free.
14. Pry upper bellcrank from converter housing and allow it to hang free.
15. Remove propeller shaft.
16. Remove converter housing-to-engine lower bolts.
17. Loosen parking brake adjusting nut at equalizer and remove retracting spring. Disconnect rear brake cables and remove equalizer from bracket.
18. Remove two nuts attaching engine rear mounts to crossmember.
19. Support transmission with a jack and raise it just enough to remove weight from crossmember. Then remove crossmember.
20. Remove engine rear support from extension housing.

21. Lower transmission and remove upper converter housing-to-engine bolts.
22. Move transmission back and down out of vehicle.
23. Reverse procedure to install.

Thunderbird

1. Unfasten and remove fluid filler tube.
2. Remove starting motor upper bolt.
3. Remove two converter housing upper bolts.
4. Remove dust shield from front lower end of converter housing.
5. Drain converter.
6. Remove propeller shaft.
7. Disconnect exhaust pipe from manifolds, and tailpipe and resonator supports from underbody.
8. Remove frame side rail support brace.
9. Drain transmission oil pan by loosening several bolts. Then remove pan to drain completely.
10. Remove converter-to-flywheel nuts.
11. Disconnect downshift lever from transmission.
12. Unfasten and place neutral safety switch to one side.
13. Separate selector rod from lever.
14. Remove shift rod bellcrank bracket from converter housing.
15. Disconnect hose from upper end of vacuum diaphragm tube.
16. Disconnect speedometer cable from extension housing.
17. Remove starting motor.
18. Disconnect oil cooler lines from transmission.
19. Remove engine rear support-to-extension housing bolts.
20. Support transmission with a jack and raise it enough to take weight off support. Then unfasten and remove support.
21. Remove four remaining converter housing-to-engine bolts, and accelerator linkage stop from left side of housing.
22. Lower transmission and remove it from vehicle.
23. Reverse procedure to install.

FoMoCo TWO-SPEED TRANS.

NOTE: — This chapter deals only with maintenance, adjustments and "in car" repairs. For major service work, Motor's Automatic Transmission Manual is available. Current edition is a 740 page volume that includes 240 pages of oil circuit diagrams mostly in full color.

TRANSMISSION IDENTIFICATION

The model data is on a tag attached to the rear servo cover bolt.

COMET MODELS

YEAR	ENGINE	TRANS. MODEL
1963	6-144	PCL-E
	6-144⑤	PCL-D
	6-170	PCM-F
	6-170⑤	PCM-E
	8-260	PCP-G
1964	6-200	PCY-D, F
	6-200⑤	PCY-C, E

FALCON MODELS

YEAR	ENGINE	TRANS. MODEL
1963	6-144	PCL-D
	6-170	PCM-E, K
	6-170	PCM-S, S1
	8-260	PCP-G
1964	6-144	PCL-D
	6-144	PCL-J
	6-170	PCM-K, M
	6-170	PCM-S, S1
	6-200	PCY-C, E
	8-260	PCP-J, J1
	8-260	PCP-M

FAIRLANE MODELS

YEAR	ENGINE	TRANS. MODEL
1963	6-170	PCM-G
	6-200	PCY-A
	8-221	PCN-B
	8-260	PCP-B
	8-260	PCP-L, L1
1964	6-170	PCM-G
	6-200	PCY-A
	6-200	PCY-B
	8-260	PCP-H
	8-260	PCP-L, L1

FORD MODELS

YEAR	ENGINE	TRANS. MODEL
1963	6-223	PCH-B
	6-260	③PCP-C
	6-260	④PCP-D
	8-289	③PCP-E
	8-289	④PCP-F

③—Column shift.
④—Floor shift.
⑤—Station wagon.

DESCRIPTION

These transmissions, Fig. 1, have two forward speeds and one reverse speed. A park device is employed to lock-up the transmission output shaft for the purpose of parking.

Two forward ratios are provided. Low ratio allows for continued operation in low gear without any automatic shifts. Drive ratio provides for a low gear start and automatic shifts between low and high, depending upon throttle opening and road speed.

A single-stage, three-element torque converter is incorporated between the engine and transmission. Two hydraulic pumps, a front pump and a rear pump, are utilized to provide oil under pressure to the transmission hydraulic control system.

The front pump, driven by the converter hub, supplies all operating pressure (except governor pressure) at speeds below approximately 40 mph. The rear pump, driven by the rear wheels, supplies the governor below 40 mph. Above 40 mph, the rear pump supplies all hydraulic pressure, and the front pump merely recirculates fluid.

TROUBLE SHOOTING GUIDE

The items to check for each trouble symptom are arranged in a logical sequence which should be followed for quickest results.

Harsh Initial Engagement in D, L and R

1. Engine idle speed.
2. Vacuum unit or tube leaking.
3. Throttle linkage.
4. Check control pressure.

Slips or Chatters in D or L

1. Fluid level.
2. Check control pressure.
3. Control valve body.
4. Low band adjustment.
5. Make air pressure check.
6. Leakage in low servo apply circuit.
7. Engine-transmission mounts.
8. Low servo and band.
9. Planetary gears.

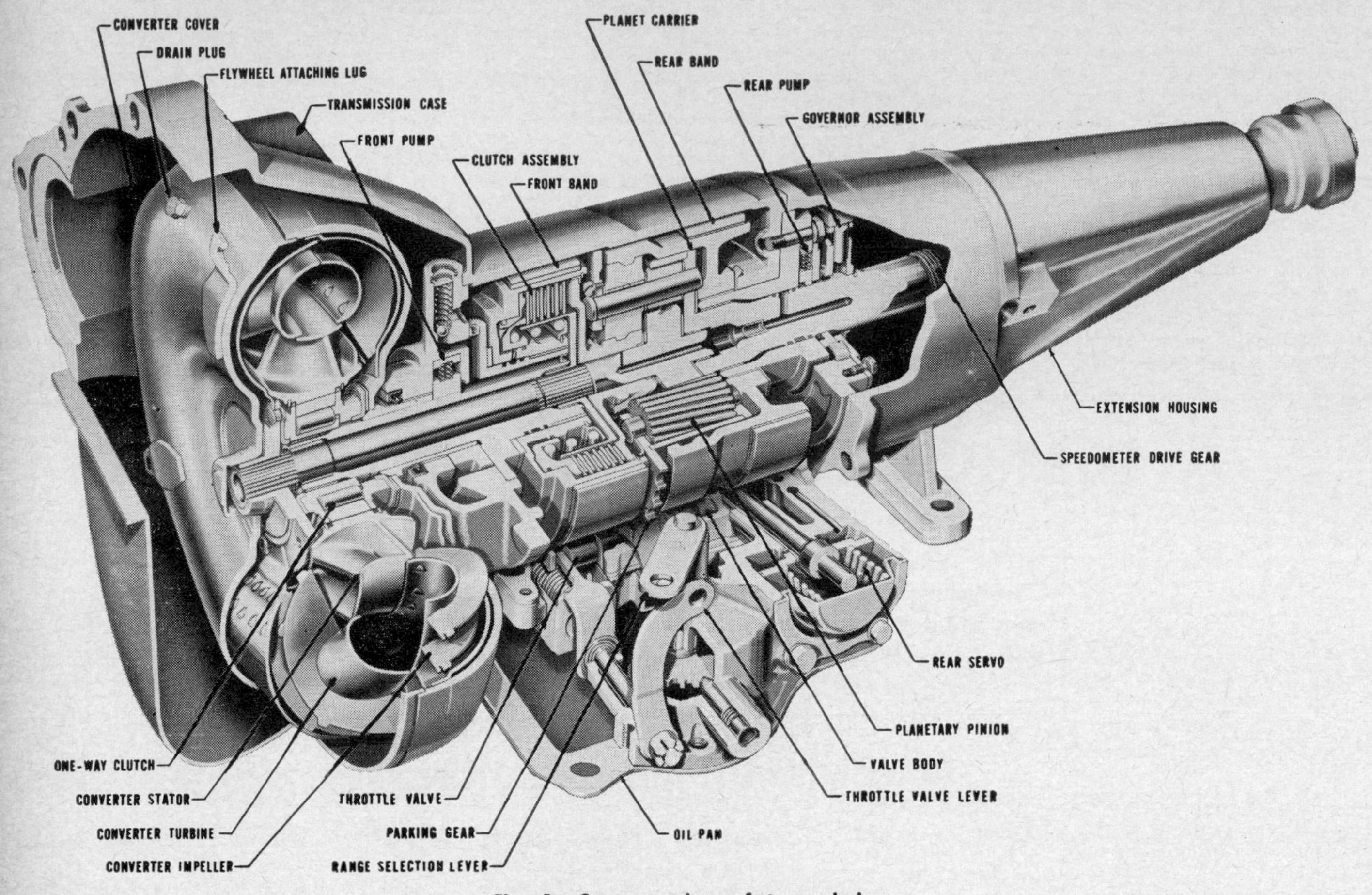

Fig. 1 Cutaway view of transmission

Car Won't Move in D but Will in L

1. Low servo piston check valve.

Slips or Chatters in R

1. Fluid level.
2. Check control pressure.
3. Manual linkage.
4. Control valve body.
5. Reverse band adjustment.
6. Air pressure check.
7. Leakage in reverse servo apply circuit.
8. Engine-transmission mounts.
9. Reverse servo and band.
10. Cracked or broken rear band anchor.

Engine Overspeeds During 1-2 Shift

1. Fluid level.
2. Check for burned clutch plates if there is fluid odor.
3. Check control pressure.
4. Low band adjustment.
5. Air pressure check.
6. Control valve body.
7. Leakage in clutch apply or low servo release circuit.
8. High clutch.

Momentary Lock-Up During 1-2 Shift

1. Fluid level.
2. Control pressure check.
3. Control valve body.
4. Low band adjustment.
5. Low servo and band.
6. High clutch.
7. Low servo piston return spring.

Severe 2-1 Shift During Coast-Down

1. Engine idle speed.
2. Throttle linkage.
3. Control valve body.
4. Control pressure check.
5. Low band adjustment.

No 1-2 Shift in D

1. Fluid level.
2. Check for burned clutch plates if there is fluid odor.
3. Manual linkage.
4. Governor.
5. High clutch piston.
6. Low servo and band.
7. Leakage in control pressure main circuit.
8. High clutch.
9. High clutch piston.
10. Rear pump.

Delayed or Severe 1-2 Shift

1. Vacuum diaphragm or tube leakage.
2. Throttle linkage.
3. Governor.
4. Control valve body.
5. Leakage in control pressure main circuit.
6. Low servo piston check valve.

Slips Continuously After 1-2 Shift

1. Check for burned clutch plates if there is fluid odor.
2. Fluid level.
3. Check control pressure.
4. Air pressure check.
5. Control valve body.
6. High clutch.
7. Leakage in clutch apply or low servo release circuit.

No 2-1 Forced Downshift

1. Downshift linkage.
2. Control valve body.
3. Leakage in control pressure main circuit.

No 2-1 Shift During Coast-Down

1. Control valve body.
2. Governor.

Fluid Forced Out Vent

1. Fluid level.
2. Transmission external vent.
3. Fluid aeration.
4. Fluid contaminated with engine coolant.
5. Cooler flow check.

Transmission Overheats

1. Fluid level.
2. Control pressure check.
3. Converter cooler air passages.

4. Cooler flow check.
5. Converter one-way clutch.
6. Fluid check for engine coolant contamination.
7. Transmission external vent.

Acceleration Normal—Maximum Speed About 50 mph

1. Converter one-way clutch.

Acceleration Poor—Operation Above 30 mph Normal with Steady Throttle

1. Converter one-way clutch.

Engine Won't Push Start

1. Fluid level.
2. Manual linkage.
3. Control valve body.
4. Low band adjustment.
5. Low servo piston check valve.
6. Rear pump.
7. Leakage in control pressure main circuit.
8. Low servo and band.
9. Leakage in low servo apply circuit.

Parking Lock Doesn't Hold or Binds

1. Manual linkage.
2. Parking linkage.
3. Front band installed backwards, strut out of position.

MAINTENANCE

Adding Oil

1. Every 1000 miles, check oil level. Make sure car is standing level. Apply parking brake.
2. Run engine at normal idle speed. If transmission oil is cold, run engine at fast idle until oil reaches its normal operating temperature. When oil is warm, slow engine to normal idle speed.
3. Shift selector lever to all positions; then place lever in P.
4. Clean all dirt from transmission dipstick cap before removing stick from filler tube.
5. Wipe dipstick clean and push it all the way back in the tube.
6. Remove stick and check level. Add automatic transmission oil to bring the level up to the "Full" mark on dipstick.

Changing Oil

NOTE: The Ford Motor Company recommends the use of an automatic transmission fluid with Qualification No. M2C-33D (on container) instead of the conventional Type A fluid. The recommended fluid is said to have a higher coefficient of friction and greater ability to handle maximum engine torques without band or clutch slippage.

1. Every 24,000 miles, remove cover from lower front side of converter housing.
2. Remove one of the converter drain plugs.
3. Rotate converter 180 deg. and remove other drain plug.
4. Remove drain plug from transmission oil pan. On models without drain plug, loosen front of oil pan carefully and allow oil to drain out.

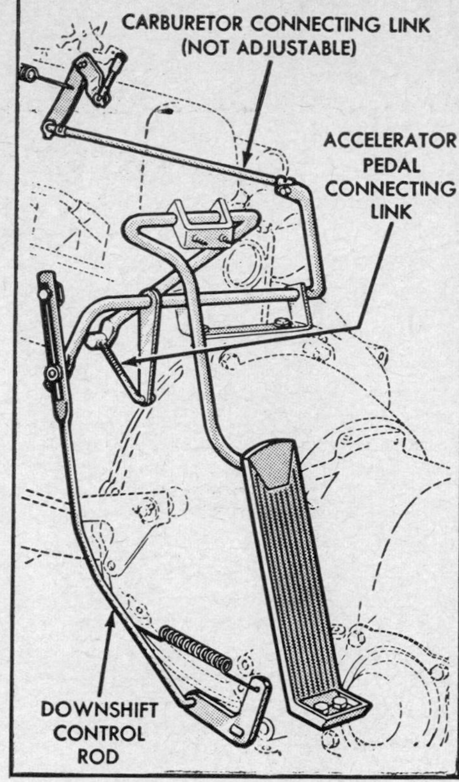

Fig. 2 Six-cylinder throttle linkage. Comet, Falcon and Fairlane

5. Remove, clean and replace transmission oil pan and screen, using new pan gasket.
6. Install converter drain plugs.
7. Install converter housing cover.
8. Pour 4 quarts of fluid in transmission.
9. Run engine at idle speed for about 2 minutes; then pour 5 more quarts (2 qts. on Comet and Falcon) of oil in transmission. Then run engine at a fast idle until it reaches normal operating temperature.
10. Shift selector lever through all positions. Place lever at P. Then add fluid as necessary to bring level to "Full" mark on dipstick.

MANUAL LINKAGE, ADJUST

Comet, Falcon, Fairlane

1. With engine stopped, loosen clamp at shift lever so that shift rod is free to slide in clamp.
2. Position selector lever so that pointer lines up in D position.
3. Shift manual lever at transmission into D detent position (second from rear).
4. Tighten clamp on shift rod.
5. Check pointer alignment for all lever detent positions.

Ford & Mercury

1. With engine stopped, loosen clamp at shift lever so that shift rod is free to slide in clamp.
2. Position selector lever in D position against steering column stop.
3. Shift manual lever at transmission into D detent position (second from rear).
4. Tighten clamp on shift rod.
5. Check pointer alignment for all selector lever positions.

THROTTLE LINKAGE, ADJUST

Comet, Falcon, Fairlane

1. Apply parking brake and place selector lever at N.
2. Run engine until it reaches normal operating temperature, then adjust hot idle speed to specifications.

NOTE: The carburetor throttle lever must be against the idle adjusting screw at the specified slow idle speed with selector in D.

3. Attach a tachometer to engine.
4. If necessary, adjust dashpot plunger.

6 Cyl. Models

1. After performing Steps 1 through 4 above, and with engine stopped, adjust carburetor throttle rod length to obtain an accelerator pedal height to the following dimensions, measured from top front corner of pedal to floor mat.
   1964 All Models .... 4¼″
   1963 Falcon .... 4½″
   1963 Comet .... 4 5/16″
   1963 Fairlane .... 3 15/16″
2. Disconnect throttle return spring and downshift linkage return spring.
3. Loosen adjusting screw on downshift control rod, Fig. 2.
4. Pull downshift control rod and throttle linkage Z bar up to limit of its travel.
5. Hold them in this position, then slide adjusting screw down against Z bar and tighten adjusting screw.
6. Install return springs and check throttle and downshift linkage for full travel.

V8 Models

1. Perform Preliminary Steps 1 through 4.
2. With engine stopped, check and, if necessary, adjust accelerator connecting link to obtain a pedal height to the following dimensions, measured from either top front corner of pedal to floor mat:
   1964 .... 4 15/16″
   1963 .... 3 15/16″
3. With accelerator pedal at proper height, and carburetor lever off fast idle setting, adjust carburetor connecting link rod between carburetor and bellcrank to allow a free fit of a ¼″ drill gauging pin through gauge pin holes in bellcrank, Fig. 3. Downshift control rod is not adjustable.

Ford & Mercury

Vacuum-Controlled V8s

Referring to Fig. 3, apply parking

brake and place selector lever in "N". Then adjust as follows:

1. With engine at normal operating temperature, adjust idle speed to 485 rpm.
2. With throttle in hot idle position, bottom dashpot plunger and adjust dashpot so there is 5/64" clearance between plunger and throttle lever.
3. With engine stopped, disconnect carburetor connecting link from accelerator assembly.
4. Insert a ¼" drill rod through gauging holes shown at "A", Fig. 3. Hold carburetor connecting link forward and adjust sleeve until link assembly fits freely in accelerator assembly. Then rotate sleeve counterclockwise one full turn. Remove drill rod.
5. Measure accelerator pedal height as indicated in dimension "C", Fig. 3. If height is not 3¾", turn threaded trunnion on accelerator pedal link until correct height is obtained.

Vacuum-Controlled 6-Cyl.

1. Measure accelerator pedal height as shown in dimension "C", Fig. 3 (top view). If not 3¾", turn threaded trunnion on accelerator connecting link until correct height is obtained.
2. Disconnect downshift control rod from bellcrank.
3. Block accelerator pedal to floor.
4. Push downshift control rod down to the limit of its travel. Then adjust sleeve on rod until end of rod enters bellcrank freely. Connect linkage and tighten lock nut.

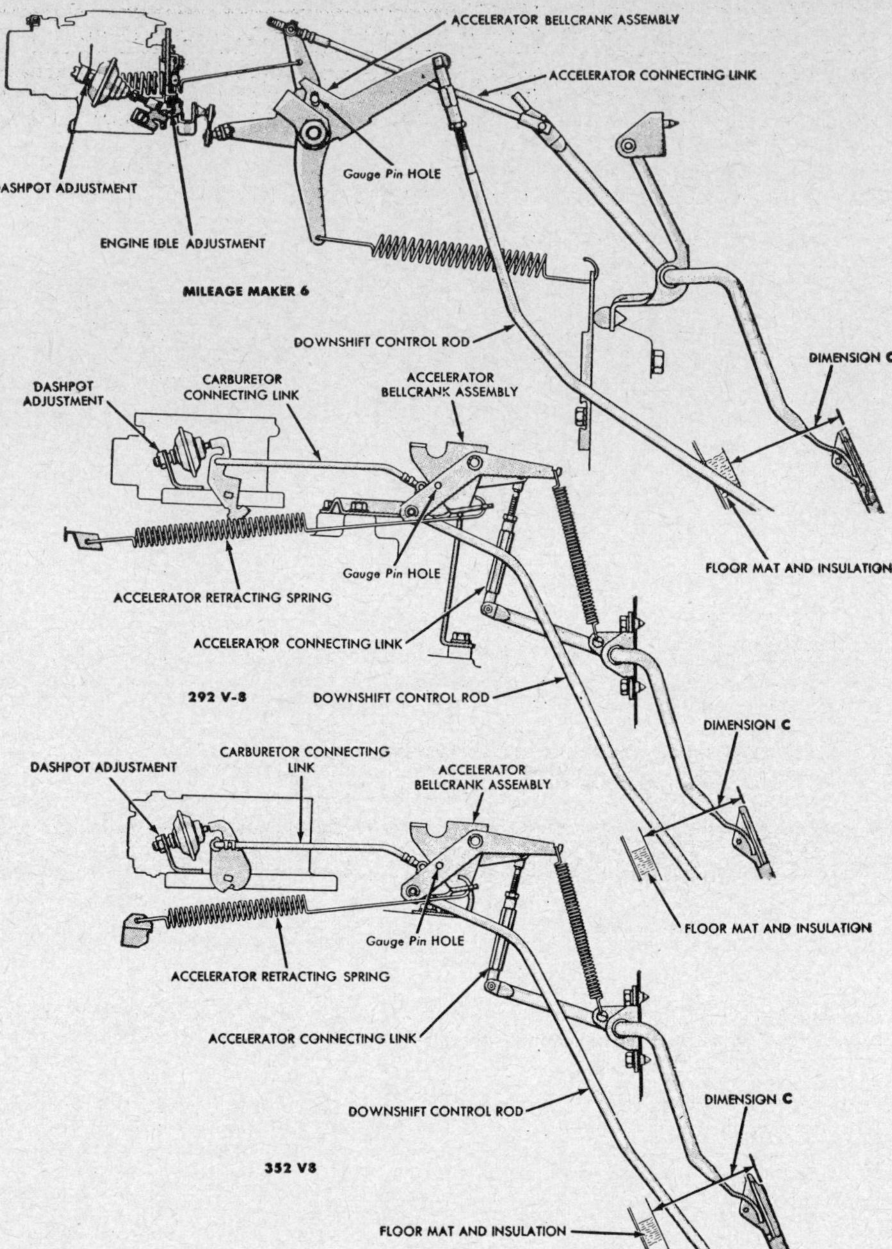

Fig. 3 Vacuum-controlled throttle linkage. Ford and Mercury

VALVE BODY COMPENSATOR SPRING ADJUSTMENT

Some Models

Due to repair operations it may be necessary to adjust the compensator spring tension, Fig. 4. To make an initial adjustment of the screw before installing the control valve body, remove the lower body right front cover plate and turn the adjusting screw until it protrudes through the cover plate approximately .060" as shown. This will require 1½ turns when starting from a flush position.

In Car Adjustment

1. Attach pressure gauge to transmission.
2. Attach a vacuum gauge to the vacuum diaphragm line. This is necessary to check for a vacuum leak which would cause a false line pressure reading.
3. Start the engine and allow transmission to reach its operating temperature.
4. After transmission has reached normal operating temperature, record the idle line pressure. If pressure is not within specifications (see charts) remove transmission oil pan.
5. To increase line pressure turn adjusting screw counterclockwise which lowers compensator pressure. To decrease line pressure, turn adjusting screw clockwise which increases compensator pressure. One complete turn of the adjusting screw will change line pressure approximately 10 psi.
6. After adjustment has been made, install oil pan and fill transmission with oil.
7. Start engine and move selector lever to all ranges several times before reading pressure gauge.

FRONT BAND, ADJUST

The low band adjusting screw is threaded through the front left side of the case. When making the adjustment, it is recommended that the special tool shown in Fig. 5 be used. This is a pre-set torque wrench that clicks or overruns when the torque on the screw reaches 10 lbs. ft.

To make the adjustment, loosen the lock nut several turns. Tighten the adjusting screw until the wrench clicks and back it off exactly two turns. Hold the adjusting screw in this position and tighten the lock nut.

If the special wrench is not available, an emergency adjustment may be made by turning the adjusting screw in until a resistance is felt, which indicates that the band is snug against the drum. Then back it off two full turns.

REAR BAND, ADJUST

Fig. 6 illustrates the special tools required to make this adjustment. With the oil pan removed, place the tool on the rear servo piston rod so that the two

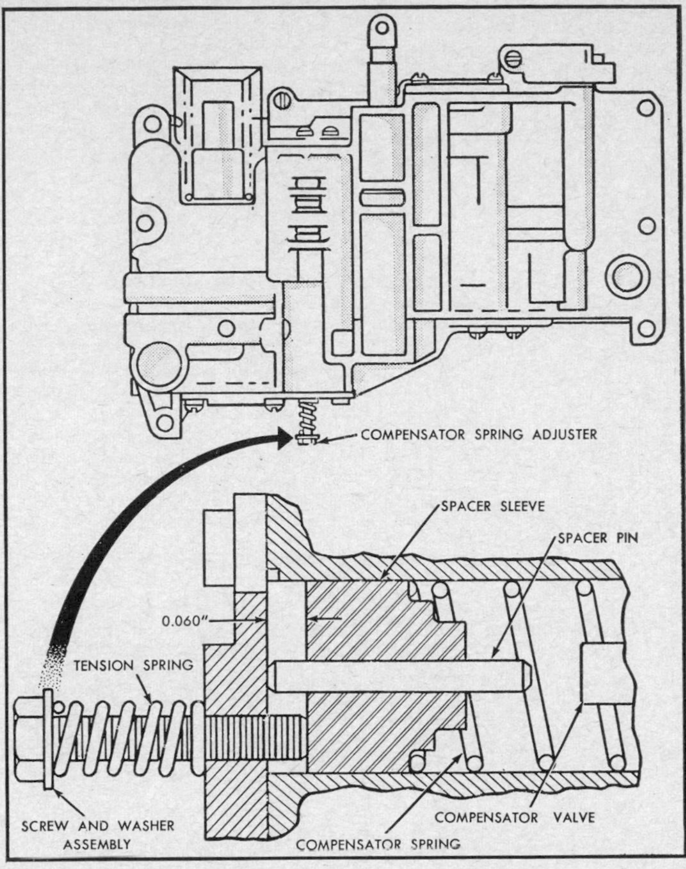

Fig. 4 Valve body compensator spring adjustment. Some models

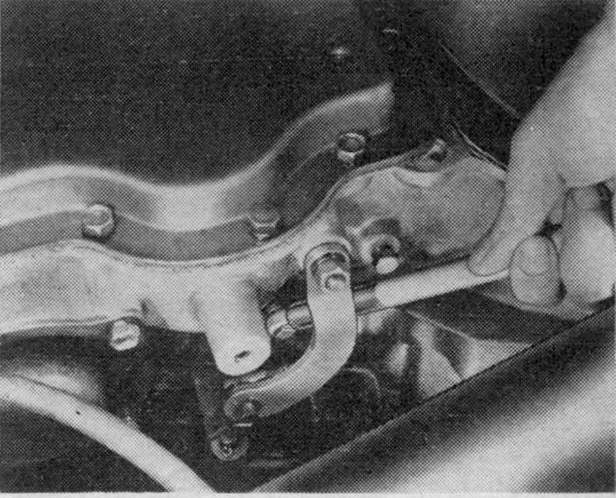

Fig. 5 Adjusting front band

Fig. 6 Adjusting rear band

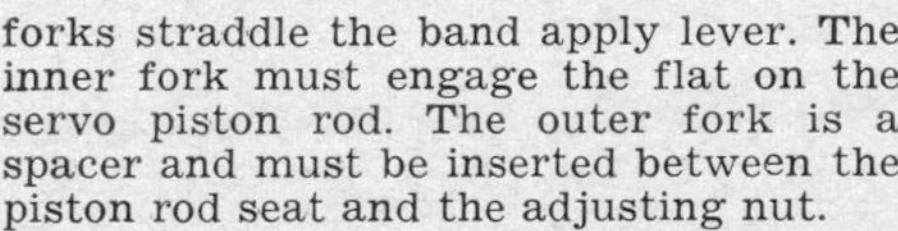

forks straddle the band apply lever. The inner fork must engage the flat on the servo piston rod. The outer fork is a spacer and must be inserted between the piston rod seat and the adjusting nut.

Loosen the piston rod lock nut and adjusting nut. Tighten the adjusting nut until the tool is felt to ratchet and heard to click as it overruns (the wrench is set to overrun at 45-50 inch-lbs). Then back off adjusting nut exactly two turns and tighten lock nut while holding adjusting nut against rotation.

IN CAR REPAIRS

The following units can be replaced with the transmission in the vehicle:

1. Control valve body.
2. Low servo piston and cover seal.
3. Reverse servo cover seal.
4. Extension housing bushing and seal.

TRANSMISSION, REPLACE

Ford & Mercury

NOTE: Since the transmission and converter are housed in a single casting, the assembly can only be removed as a unit.

1. Remove converter housing bottom cover.
2. Drain transmission and converter.
3. Remove drive shaft.
4. Disconnect linkage, speedometer cable and oil cooler lines at transmission.
5. Disconnect oil filler tube.
6. On 1961 models, disconnect pressure test line from transmission.
7. Remove starter.
8. Disconnect parking brake cable at equalizer.
9. Remove rear engine support bolts.
10. Support transmission with a jack and remove crossmember.
11. Unfasten converter from flywheel, and converter housing from engine.
12. Secure converter to transmission so it will not fall out when transmission is separated from engine.
13. Work transmission off engine block dowel pins and toward rear until converter pilot clears crankshaft.
14. Lower transmission from car.
15. Reverse procedure to install.

1964 Comet, Falcon, Fairlane

1. Drive car on hoist. Before raising hoist, and working under hood, remove cable from starter. Then raise hoist.
2. Drain transmission fluid. If transmission oil is water cooled, disconnect oil cooler lines from transmission.
3. Disconnect drive shaft at rear and remove it.
4. Remove manual and downshift linkage from transmission.
5. Remove starting motor.
6. On some models it may be necessary to remove exhaust pipe from manifolds and from muffler inlet pipe.
7. Disconnect speedometer cable.
8. Disconnect vacuum line from diaphragm.
9. Disconnect oil filler tube.
10. Remove parking brake front cable from equalizer bar.
11. Raise transmission with a jack until it is supporting the transmission.
12. Remove crossmember.
13. Lower transmission and support rear of engine.
14. Remove converter lower cover and the four stud nuts that retain converter to flywheel.
15. Remove converter housing-to-engine bolts.
16. Remove transmission from car.
17. Reverse removal procedure to install transmission.

1963 Comet & Falcon

1. Pull back floor mat and remove converter housing-to-engine bolt access hole covers. Remove two upper bolts which attach converter housing to engine.
2. From under hood, remove two bolts attaching throttle linkage bracket to converter housing.

3. Remove starter. Then raise car on hoist.
4. Remove converter housing bottom cover.
5. Drain converter and transmission.
6. Remove propeller shaft.
7. Disconnect linkage at transmission.
8. Disconnect oil filler tube.
9. Remove engine rear support-to-extension housing bolt.
10. Disconnect parking brake cable rod at equalizer lever.
11. Place jack under transmission and raise it slightly to take weight off engine rear support member.
12. Unfasten support member from underbody (2 bolts) and remove support member.
13. Lower transmission and support engine.
14. Detach converter from flywheel (4 nuts) and remove converter away from flywheel as far as it will go.
15. Remove two lower converter housing-to-engine bolts.
16. Work converter housing off engine block dowel pins and work converter pilot out of engine crankshaft.
17. Secure converter to its housing and lower transmission.
18. Reverse above procedure to install.

1963 Fairlane

1. Disconnect cable from starter.
2. Drain transmission fluid.
3. Disconnect oil cooler lines from transmission.
4. Disconnect drive shaft at rear and remove it.
5. Remove shift linkage at transmission.
6. Remove starter.
7. On V8's, remove exhaust pipe from manifolds and from muffler inlet pipe.
8. Disconnect speedometer cable at extension housing and vacuum line from diaphragm. If transmission is to be overhauled, remove diaphragm assembly.
9. Disconnect oil filler tube from case.
10. Remove parking brake front cable from equalizer bar.
11. Support transmission with a jack.
12. Remove crossmember.
13. Lower transmission and support rear of engine.
14. Remove converter lower cover and remove four stud nuts that retain converter to flywheel.
15. Remove converter housing-to-engine bolts.
16. Remove transmission from vehicle.
17. Reverse removal procedure to install. Install transmission fluid. Then, with engine running at idle speed, shift selector lever from N to D and from D back to N at least 20 times. This repeated shifting will fill low servo release cavity with fluid and expel trapped air. Adjust manual and downshift linkage.

CRUISEOMATIC, MERCOMATIC, TURBO-DRIVE
WITH CAST IRON CASE

NOTE: — This chapter deals only with maintenance, adjustments and "in car" repairs. For major service work, Motor's Automatic Transmission Manual is available. Current edition is a 740 page volume that includes 240 pages of oil circuit diagrams mostly in full color.

TRANSMISSION IDENTIFICATION

The identification tag is attached to the right side of the transmission case. It includes the model prefix and suffix as well as a service identification number and serial number. The service identification number indicates changes to service details which affect interchangeability when the transmission model is not changed. For details of this number, the manufacturer's Parts Catalog should be consulted. The tag must be kept with the individual transmission it was originally installed on. If the tag was removed during disassembly, reinstall it on the same unit.

FORD MODELS

Year	Engine Model	Trans. Model
1963	8-260, 289④	⑦PCT-A
	8-260, 289	⑧PCT-B
	8-260, 289	⑧PCT-F
	8-352	⑦PCD-E
	8-352	⑧PCD-G
	8-352	⑧PCD-L
	8-390	⑦PCE-M
	8-390	⑦PCE-C
	8-390	⑧PCE-U
	8-390	⑧PCE-AD
	8-390	⑧PCE-AL
1964	8-289④	⑦PCT-G
	8-289	⑧PCT-H
	8-352	⑦PCD-P
	8-352	⑧PCD-R
	8-390	⑦PCE-AU-AU1
	8-390	⑧PCE-AV-AV1
1965	8-289④	⑦PCT-J2-J3
	8-289	⑦PCT-J1
	8-352	⑦PCD-U
	8-352	⑦PCD-Z
	8-352	⑧PCD-V
	8-352	⑧PCD-AA
	8-390	⑦PCE-BC
	8-390	⑦PCE-BK
	8-390	⑧PCE-BD
	8-390	⑧PCE-BL
1966	8-289④	⑦PCT-J3
	8-289	⑦PCT-K
	8-352	⑦PCD-Z
	8-352	⑦PCD-AB
	8-352	⑧PCD-AA
	8-352	⑧PCD-AC
	8-390	⑦PCE-BK
	8-390	⑦PCE-BR
	8-390	⑧PCE-BL
	8-390	⑧PCE-BS
1967	8-390	⑥PFA-B
	6-240	PFA-D
	8-289	PFA-E
1968	8-289	PHA-A
	8-302	PHA-B
	8-390	PHB-A
	8-390	PFA-B-1
	6-240	⑭PFA-D-1
	8-302	⑭PFA-F

LINCOLN MODELS

Year	Engine Model	Trans. Model
1963-64	8-430	PCA-E
1965	8-430	PCA-E-1

THUNDERBIRD MODELS

Year	Engine Model	Trans. Model
1963	8-390	④PCE-L
	8-390	④PCF-Y

Year	Engine Model	Trans. Model
	8-390	⑤PCE-R
	8-390	⑤PCE-AC
1964	8-390	PCE-AT-AT-1
	8-390	⑤PCE-R
	8-390	⑤PCE-AC
1965	8-390	PCE-BB
	8-390	PCE-BJ
1966	8-390	PCE-BJ
	8-390	PCE-BT

MERCURY MODELS

Year	Engine Model	Trans. Model
1963	8-390⑥	⑦PCE-AF-AG
	8-390⑦	⑦PCE-M-Z
	8-390	⑧PCE-U-AD
1964	8-390	⑧PCE-AZ-AU
	8-390	⑧PCE-AV
1965	8-390⑥	⑦PCE-BG-BP
	8-390⑦	⑦PCE-BC-BK
	8-390⑦	⑧PCE-BD-BL
1966	8-390⑥	⑦PCE-AK
	8-390⑥	⑧PCE-BL
	8-410⑫	⑦PDD-T
	8-410⑫	⑧PDD-U
	8-410, 428⑬	⑦PDD-D-H
	8-410, 428⑬	⑧PDD-H-N
1967	8-390	⑥PFA-B

④—Dual range unit.
⑤—With 4 barrel carburetor.
⑥—With 2 barrel carburetor.
⑦—With column shift.
⑧—With floor shift.
⑫—Single exhaust.
⑬—Dual exhaust.
⑭—Police, Taxi and Fleet.

DESCRIPTION

Dual Range Operation to 1966

D1 Range

This range is used for a high degree of maneuverability in traffic. It features maximum performance and flexibility by incorporating a low gear start. For fast acceleration, press the accelerator pedal as far as it will go and the transmission will downshift into low gear at speeds below approximately 30 mph.

To obtain maximum acceleration from a standstill, press the accelerator pedal to the floor and the car will move forward in low gear under wide open throttle. With the accelerator all the way to the floor, the transmission will shift from low to intermediate gear at approximately 50 mph and then into high gear at approximately 75 mph.

D2 Range

Most normal city and highway driving can be accomplished by using the position marked "D2". This range is economically desirable when on long trips, driving in open country, or in light city traffic. Simply position the selector at "D2" and push down on the accelerator for a smooth getaway. To go faster, press the accelerator down further.

For faster acceleration at speeds below approximately 70 mph, press the accelerator down as far as it will go and the transmission will automatically downshift to intermediate gear. For maximum acceleration from a standstill, position the selector at "D1" and then press accelerator to the floor. The selector can be alternated from "D2" and "D1" positions as desired.

Dual Range Operation From 1967

This transmission features a drive range that provides for fully automatic upshifts and downshifts, and manually selected low and second gears. The six selector lever positions provided are P (park), R (reverse), N (neutral), D (automatic drive range), 2 (second gear hold) and 1 (low gear hold).

D is a fully automatic range providing for a first gear start with automatic up-

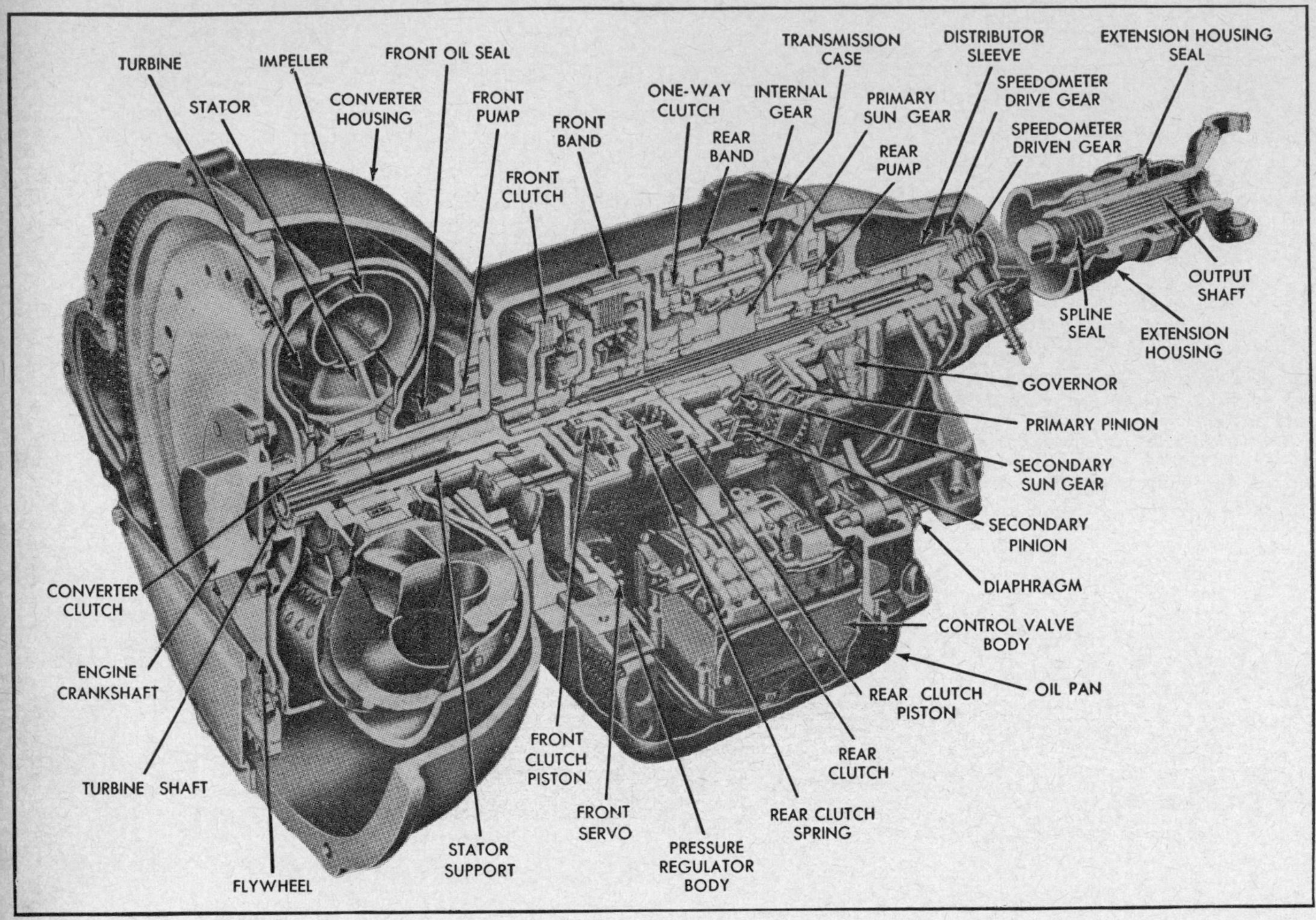

Fig. 1 Cruiseomatic and Mercomatic three speed dual range unit with cast iron case

shifts to second and high gear occurring at appropriate intervals, similar to operation in D1 in the 1966 transmission.

Second gear (2) is a manually selected second gear hold. When the selector lever is moved to 2, the transmission will engage and remain in second gear, regardless of throttle opening or road speed.

Low gear (1) is similar to manual low range in the 1966 transmission.

D—Drive

The normal automatic driving range is indicated by D. In this range the car starts off in first gear and gives the best combination of automatic gear shifts to provide for economy and full power starts. As the accelerator is depressed and the car picks up speed, automatic shifts to second and high gears will occur. The transmission will automatically downshift as speed decreases. Forced downshifts in D are made by pressing the accelerator pedal all the way to the floor.

2—Second Gear Hold

When the car is started and the shift lever is moved to 2, the car will start off and remain in second gear, regardless of throttle opening or road speed. This range is especially useful for starting the car on icy pavements or other slippery surfaces. Similarly, when engine braking is required and the shift lever is moved from D to 2, the transmission will engage and remain in second gear.

Selector lever position 2 is not a cruising range in the usual sense of the term. While the transmission is capable of limited cruising in second gear, maximum fuel economy and best all-around performance are realized in D range.

1—Low Gear Hold

This range is identical in operation to manual low range on the 1966 transmission except that when the shift lever is moved to 1 to provide engine braking, the automatic shift from second to low gear will occur between 22 and 39 mph (exact shift point will vary with axle ratio and tire size).

TROUBLE SHOOTING GUIDE

Rough Initial Engagement

1. Idle speed.
2. Vacuum unit or tubes.
3. Front band.
4. Check control pressure.
5. Pressure regulator.
6. Valve body.

Shift Points High, Low or Erratic

1. Fluid level.
2. Vacuum unit or tubes.
3. Manual linkage.
4. Governor.
5. Check control pressure.
6. Valve body.
7. Downshift linkage.

Rough 2-3 Shift

1. Manual linkage.
2. Front band.
3. Vacuum unit or tubes.
4. Pressure regulator.
5. Valve body.
6. Front servo.

Engine Overspeeds, 2-3 Shift

1. Vacuum unit or tubes.
2. Front band.
3. Valve body.
4. Pressure regulator.

No 1-2 or 2-3 Shifts

1. Governor.
2. Valve body.
3. Manual linkage.
4. Rear clutch.
5. Front band.
6. Front servo.

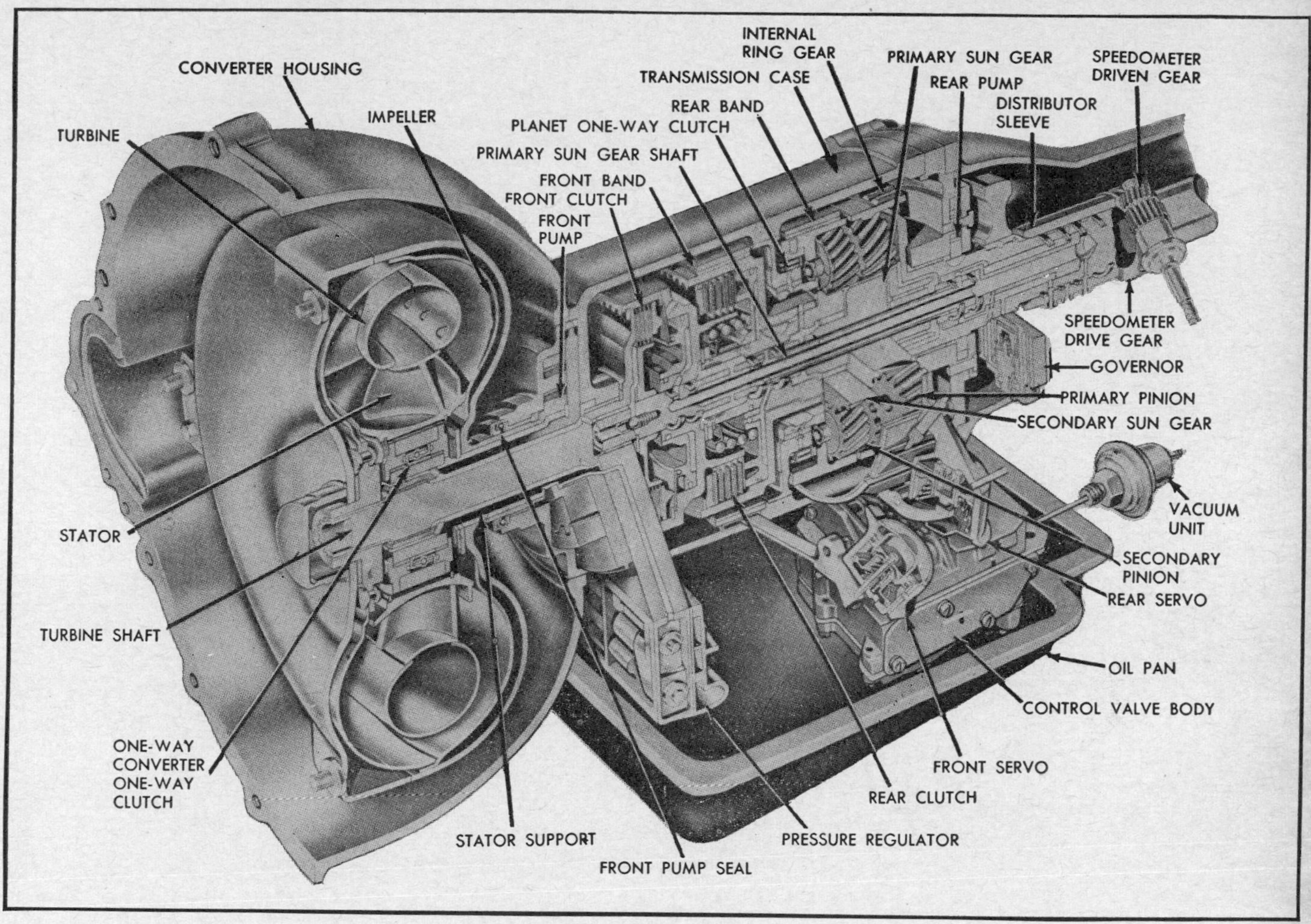

Fig. 2 Lincoln Turbo-Drive three speed dual range transmission with cast iron case

7. Leakage in hydraulic system.
8. Pressure regulator.

No Forced Downshifts

1. Downshift linkage.
2. Check control pressure.
3. Valve body.

Rough 3-2 or 3-1 Shifts

1. Engine idle speed.
2. Vacuum unit or tubes.
3. Valve body.

Slips or Chatters in 2nd

1. Fluid level.
2. Vacuum unit or tubes.
3. Front band.
4. Check control pressure.
5. Pressure regulator.
6. Valve body.
7. Front servo.
8. Front clutch.
9. Leakage in hydraulic system.

Slips or Chatters in 1st

1. Fluid level.
2. Vacuum unit or tubes.
3. Check control pressure.
4. Pressure regulator.
5. Valve body.
6. Front clutch.
7. Leakage in hydraulic system.
8. Fluid distributor sleeve in output shaft.
9. Planetary one-way clutch.

Slips or Chatters in Reverse

1. Fluid level.
2. Rear band.
3. Check control pressure.
4. Pressure regulator.
5. Valve body.
6. Rear servo.
7. Rear clutch.
8. Vacuum unit or tubes.
9. Leakage in hydraulic system.
10. Fluid distributor sleeve in output shaft.

No Drive in D or D2

1. Valve body.
2. Make air pressure check.
3. Manual linkage.
4. Front clutch.
5. Leak in hydraulic system.
6. Fluid distributor sleeve in output shaft.

No Drive in D1

1. Manual linkage.
2. Valve body.
3. Planetary one-way clutch.

No Drive in L

1. Manual linkage.
2. Front clutch.
3. Valve body.
4. Make air pressure check.
5. Leak in hydraulic system.
6. Fluid distributor sleeve in output shaft.

No Drive in R

1. Rear band.
2. Rear servo.
3. Valve body.
4. Make air pressure check.
5. Rear clutch.
6. Leak in hydraulic system.
7. Fluid distributor sleeve in output shaft.

No Drive in Any Range

1. Fluid level.
2. Manual linkage.
3. Check control pressure.
4. Pressure regulator.
5. Valve body.
6. Make air pressure check.
7. Leak in hydraulic system.

Lockup in D or D1

1. Manual linkage.
2. Rear servo.
3. Front servo.
4. Rear clutch.
5. Parking linkage.
6. Leak in hydraulic system.

Lockup in D2

1. Manual linkage.
2. Rear band.
3. Rear servo.
4. Rear clutch.
5. Parking linkage.
6. Leak in hydraulic system.
7. Planetary one-way clutch.

Lockup in R

1. Front band.
2. Front servo.
3. Front clutch.
4. Parking linkage.
5. Leak in hydraulic system.

Lockup In L

1. Front band.
2. Pressure regulator.
3. Valve body.
4. Rear clutch.
5. Parking linkage.
6. Leak in hydraulic system.

Parking Lock Binds or Won't Hold

1. Manual linkage.
2. Parking linkage.

Unable to Push Start

1. Fluid level.
2. Manual linkage.
3. Pressure regulator.
4. Valve body.
5. Rear pump.
6. Leak in hydraulic system.

Transmission Overheats

1. Oil cooler and connections.
2. Pressure regulator.
3. Converter one-way clutch.

Engine Runaway on Forced Downshift

1. Front band.
2. Pressure regulator.
3. Valve body.
4. Front servo.
5. Vacuum unit or tubes.
6. Leak in hydraulic system.

Maximum Speed Below Normal, Acceleration Poor

1. Converter one-way clutch.

No 3-1 Downshift

1. Engine idle speed.
2. Vacuum unit or tubes.
3. Valve body.

Noise in Neutral

1. Pressure regulator.
2. Front clutch.
3. Front pump.

Noise in 1-2-3 or R

1. Pressure regulator.
2. Planetary assembly.
3. Front clutch.
4. Rear clutch.
5. Front pump.

Noise in Reverse

1. Pressure regulator.
2. Front pump.

Noise on Coast in Neutral

1. Rear pump.

MAINTENANCE

Adding Fluid

The fluid level in the transmission should be checked at 1000-mile intervals. Make sure that the car is standing level, and firmly apply the parking brake.

Run the engine at normal idle speed. If the transmission fluid is cold, run the engine at fast idle speed until the fluid reaches normal operating temperature. When the fluid is warm, slow the engine down to normal idle speed, shift the transmission through all ranges and then place the lever or button a P.

Clean all dirt from the transmission fluid dipstick cap before removing the dipstick from the filler tube. Pull the dipstick out of the tube, wipe it clean and push it all the way back into the tube.

Pull the dipstick out again and check the fluid level. If necessary, add enough Automatic Transmission Fluid to the transmission to raise the fluid level to the F (full mark) on the dipstick.

Changing Fluid

NOTE: The Ford Motor Company recommends the use of an automatic transmission fluid with Qualification No. M2C-33D (on container) instead of the conventional Type A Fluid. The recommended fluid is said to have a higher coefficient of friction and greater ability to handle maximum engine torques without band or clutch slippage.

The transmission fluid should be changed at 24,000-mile intervals. The procedure for changing fluid is as follows:

1. Remove cover from lower front side of converter housing.
2. Remove one of the converter drain plugs. Then rotate the converter 180 deg. and remove the other plug. *Do not attempt to turn the converter with a wrench on the converter stud nuts as there is danger of stripping threads as well as skinning your knuckles on the bell housing.*
3. When all fluid has drained, remove and clean the oil pan and screen.
4. Using a new pan gasket, install screen and pan.
5. Connect filler tube to oil pan and tighten fitting securely.
6. Install both converter drain plugs.
7. Install converter housing cover.
8. Install 5 quarts of Automatic Transmission Fluid.
9. Run engine at idle speed for about 2 minutes; then add the additional quantity of oil required for the particular transmission being serviced.
10. Run engine at a fast idle until it reaches normal operating temperature.
11. Shift the transmission through all positions; then place it at P and check fluid level. If necessary, add enough fluid to bring the level to the F mark on the dipstick.

MANUAL LINKAGE, ADJUST

Ford & Mercury

Column Shift, 1967-68

1. Place selector lever in D.
2. Loosen nut on column shift lever to permit this lever to slide on shaft rod.
3. Shift manual lever on transmission into D position.
4. Tighten nut to secure shift rod to lever.

Column Shift, 1963-66

1. Place selector lever in D or D1.
2. Loosen nut on column shift lever to permit this lever to slide on shift rod.
3. Shift manual lever at transmission into D or D1 position (2nd from rear).
4. Tighten nut to secure shift rod to shift lever.

Floor Shift, 1964-66

NOTE: On 1964 models, first check the adjustment of the button on top of the shift knob. The button should be flush to .030" above the knob. To establish this clearance, loosen the screw in the center of the button and rotate the button to the proper height and tighten the screw. This adjustment positions the detent rod to obtain proper alignment and detent travel of the rod.

1. Move shift lever to D1 position.
2. Raise car and loosen manual linkage retaining nut and move transmission manual lever to D1 position (2nd from rear).
3. With selector and manual levers in D1 position, tighten rod lock nut.

Lincoln

1963-65 Models

1. Place selector lever against stop in D1 position.
2. Raise car and remove linkage splash shield.
3. Disconnect adjustable link from transmission manual shift lever.
4. Place transmission shift lever in D1 position (2nd from bottom).
5. Loosen lock nut on adjustable link. Pull downward on link to hold selector lever against its stop.
6. Lengthen or shorten link by rotating its lower end until hole in link aligns with stud on transmission manual lever.
7. Lengthen link ½ additional turn and connect it to transmission shift lever.

CAUTION: Do not make compensating adjustments in the manual control linkage to overcome misalignment of the selector lever indicator or the neutral safety switch. Adjustment or necessary corrections must be made to these com-

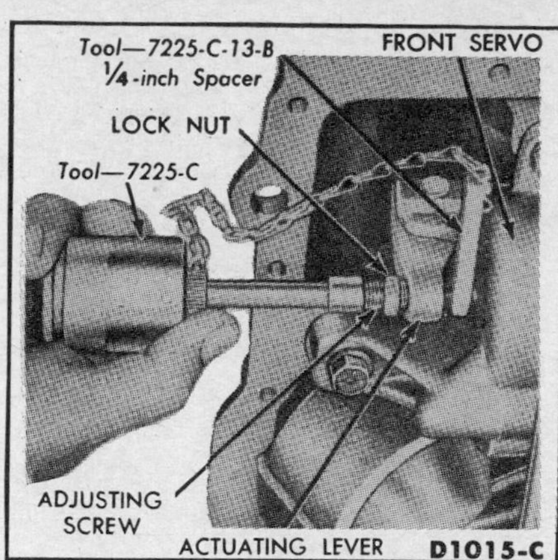

Fig. 3 Front band adjustment Ford, Mercury and Thunderbird

ponents without disturbing the correct manual linkage adjustment.

1963 Thunderbird

1. With engine stopped, loosen nut at lower end of manual shift rod on transmission shift lever.
2. Position manual selector lever so that pointer is down against steering column stop in D1 (large green dot) position.
3. Move shift lever on transmission to D1 detent (2nd from bottom) position and tighten nut on shift rod and lever.

1964-66 Thunderbird

1. With engine stopped, loosen nut at lower end of manual shift rod on transmission shift lever.
2. With steering column in straight ahead (locked in place) position, move manual selector lever so that pointer is down against steering column stop in D1 (large green dot) position.
3. Move shift lever on transmission to D1 position (2nd detent from bottom) and tighten nut on shift rod and shift lever.

THROTTLE LINKAGE, ADJUST

Connect tachometer to engine and adjust slow idle speed with selector lever in Drive position. Throttle linkage should be adjusted so that when the accelerator pedal is depressed to the floor the carburetor throttle valve(s) will be wide open.

BAND ADJUSTMENTS

The front and rear bands of the transmission should be adjusted at 15,000 mile intervals or as operation of the transmission dictates. *On Lincoln both bands are adjusted from outside of the transmission case.*

Front Band

1967-68 Ford and Mercury

1. Drain fluid from transmission, remove and clean oil pan and screen.
2. Loosen front servo adjusting screw locknut.
3. Pull back on actuating rod and insert a 1/4 inch spacer between adjusting screw and servo piston stem, Fig. 3.
4. Tighten adjusting screw to 10 inch-lbs torque. Remove spacer and tighten adjusting screw an additional 3/4 turn. Hold adjusting screw stationary and tighten locknut securely.
5. Install oil pan with new gasket and add fluid to transmission.

1963-66 Ford, Mercury, Thunderbird

The tool shown in Fig. 3 is especially made for this adjustment. However, by using a piece of 1/4" thick metal block and an ordinary end or box wrench a satisfactory adjustment can be made.

With the transmission oil pan removed, back off the adjusting screw lock nut and screw far enough to permit the 1/4" block to be inserted between the servo piston rod and adjusting screw. Turn adjusting screw in until it contacts the 1/4" block. Then tighten the adjusting screw a little more (equivalent to 10 inch-lbs) and back off one full turn. *Severe damage to the transmission may result if the adjusting screw is not backed off exactly one full turn.*

1963-65 Lincoln

Loosen the lock nut and back off the adjusting screw. Retighten adjusting screw to a torque of 10 ft-lbs, then back it off three full turns. Tighten lock nut to the proper torque. *Severe damage to the transmission may result if the adjusting screw is not backed off exactly three full turns.*

Rear Band

All Models

The tool shown in Fig. 4 is especially made for this adjustment. However, a satisfactory adjustment may be made by using a conventional torque wrench. Loosen the lock nut and tighten the adjusting screw to a torque of 10 ft-lbs. Then back off the screw exactly 1 1/2 turns and tighten lock nut. *Severe damage may result to the transmission if the adjusting screw is not backed off exactly 1 1/2 turns.*

OIL PRESSURE REGULATOR

Remove oil pan and screen. Maintain constant pressure on spring retainer to prevent damage to springs and remove retainer from bosses on oil pressure regulator body. Remove springs and pilots. Remove the three pipes. Unfasten and remove the oil pressure regulator for the transmission case.

CONTROL VALVE

To remove the assembly, loosen the adjustment on the front and rear bands 5 or 6 turns. Loosen front servo attaching screws. Remove cap screws and washers which attach control valve to case. Align throttle and manual levers to permit removal of control valve. Disengage front

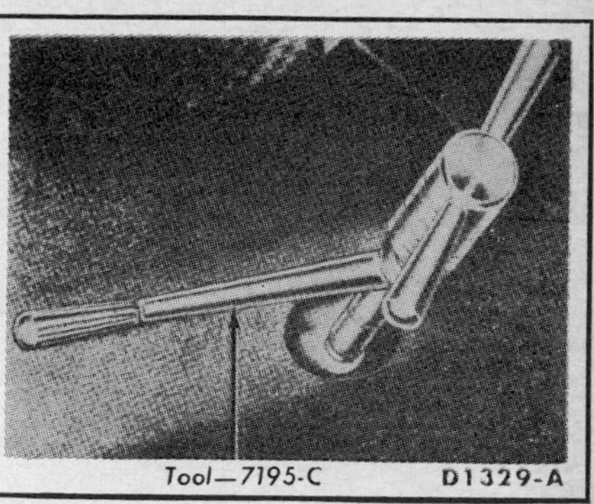

Fig. 4 Rear band adjustment

servo tubes from control valve and lift valve assembly from case.

FRONT & REAR SERVOS

Except Lincoln

To remove the front servo, remove the cap screw which holds it to the case. Hold the actuating lever strut with one hand and lift the servo from the case.

To remove the rear servo, take out the attaching cap screws. Then hold the anchor strut and lift the servo from the case.

EXTENSION HOUSING SEAL

NOTE: On 1963-65 Lincoln, mark the drive shaft with the location of the rear axle companion flange before removing the drive shaft so that it can be replaced in the same position.

After removing the drive shaft and telescopic shield, the seal may be pulled out of the extension housing.

Before installing the new seal, inspect the sealing surface of the universal joint yoke for scores. If scores are evident, replace the yoke. Inspect the counterbore in the housing for burrs. Polish all burrs with crocus cloth.

To install the new seal, position it in the bore of the extension housing with the felt side of the seal to the rear. The seal may be driven into the housing with a special tool designed for the purpose.

OIL DISTRIBUTOR

With Bolted Distributor & Sleeve

After removing the extension case remove the spacer from the transmission output shaft and slide the distributor toward the rear of the transmission. Note that the tube spacer is located in the center tube.

Remove the three tubes and spacer from the distributor. Remove the screws which attach the distributor to the sleeve and separate these parts.

Inspect the distributor and sleeve for burrs on the mating surfaces and obstructed fluid passages. Check the fit of the tubes in the distributor. Inspect the distributor sleeve for wear and scores in the sleeve bore.

To assemble, align the distributor and sleeve and install the cap screws. Install the tubes in the distributor with the spacer installed on the center tube.

With One Piece Distributor & Sleeve

After removing the extension housing, remove the distributor drive gear snap ring. Remove distributor gear, taking care not to lose the gear drive ball. Remove distributor sleeve and pipes from the transmission. Inspect the 4 seal rings on the output shaft for wear or breakage, and replace if necessary. Inspect the distributor sleeve for wear and the tubes for proper alignment and fit into the distributor sleeve.

With tubes installed in the distributor sleeve, install distributor on output shaft (chamfer forward) sliding the distributor over the seal rings and at the same time guiding tubes into the case. Install speedometer drive ball and gear and install snap ring.

GOVERNOR

Remove the governor inspection cover from the extension housing. Rotate the drive shaft to bring the governor body in line with the inspection hole. Remove the two screws which attach the governor body to the counterweight, and remove the body.

Remove the valve from the new governor body. Lubricate the valve with automatic transmission fluid. Install the valve in the body, making sure the valve moves freely in the bore. Install the body in the counterweight making sure the fluid passages in the counterweight and body are aligned.

PARKING PAWL, REPLACE

Transmission In Car

1. Remove oil pan and screen, pressure regulator and control valve. Disconnect speedometer cable.
2. Completely tighten rear band to prevent movement of planetary assembly and dislocation of thrust washers on transmission shaft. Disconnect drive shaft from transmission.

NOTE: On 1963-65 Lincoln, mark the drive shaft with the location of the rear axle companion flange before removing the drive shaft so that it can be replaced in the same position.

3. Remove extension housing-to-case bolts and move extension housing rearward far enough to permit removal of snap ring which retains speedometer gear.
4. Slide oil delivery sleeve back far enough so that oil distributor tubes clear transmission case. *NOTE: On models with bolted on oil delivery tubes, the tubes may be removed without sliding sleeve back.*
5. Rotate rear oil pump housing until parking pawl pin in case is exposed.

NOTE: Care should be taken to avoid damaging gaskets as they will have to be re-used.

6. Disconnect link (parking pawl torsion rod) located between detent lever and torsion lever.
7. Remove hairpin clip retaining torsion lever and remove from shaft.
8. Tap toggle lever pin toward rear of transmission to remove plug and pin; then remove parking pawl pin by working pawl back and forth.
9. Remove toggle lever and parking pawl from transmission and replace any damaged parts.
10. Reverse the above procedure to reassemble.

TRANSMISSION, REPLACE

Ford & Mercury

Closed Cars & Wagons

The transmission can be disconnected from the converter and removed from the car, leaving the converter in place.

1. Disconnect hose from vacuum diaphragm unit. Disconnect oil filler tube from oil pan and drain fluid.
2. Remove drive shaft.
3. Disconnect oil cooler lines from transmission. Remove vent tube.
4. Disconnect manual and downshift linkage at transmission.
5. Disconnect speedometer cable.
6. Remove two engine rear support-to-transmission bolts.
7. Place jack under transmission and raise it slightly to take weight off crossmember.
8. Unfasten and remove crossmember. With jack in position, remove four transmission-to-converter housing bolts.
9. Support engine. Tilt rear of transmission slightly upward, and with jack, move transmission toward rear until it is clear of turbine shaft. Lower assembly and remove from car.

Soft Top Convertibles

The frame construction of these models will not permit the transmission to be moved rearward enough to clear the turbine shaft from the converter. For this reason the transmission and converter must be removed as a unit as follows:

1. Drive car on hoist but do not raise it. Remove two upper bolts that attach converter housing to engine.
2. Raise car and remove converter lower cover.
3. Remove one converter drain plug. Rotate converter 180 degrees and remove other drain plug. Drain oil. Replace plugs. If desired, converter may be drained after unit has been removed from car.
4. Disconnect oil filler tube from oil pan. Disconnect vacuum hose from vacuum diaphragm.
5. Remove flywheel-to-converter nuts. Install converter housing front plate to hold converter in place when transmission is removed.
6. Remove starter.
7. Disconnect oil cooler lines from transmission. Remove transmission vent tube.
8. Disconnect manual and downshift linkage from transmission.
9. Disconnect speedometer cable and remove drive shaft.
10. On some cars it may be necessary to drop exhaust system to allow converter to clear exhaust pipe.
11. Support transmission. Remove engine rear support-to-transmission bolts and raise transmission slightly to take weight off crossmember. Remove crossmember and support rear of engine.
12. Remove remaining converter housing-to-engine bolts and remove transmission.
13. Reverse removal procedure to install the assembly.

Lincoln

It is necessary to remove the complete transmission and converter housing as a unit as there is one additional attaching bolt located behind the converter where it is not accessible until after the converter has been removed.

1. Drain transmission oil pan. Remove converter access cover from front of converter housing. Remove transmission linkage splash shield.
2. *Mark rear universal joint flange and pinion flange before removing drive shaft so it can be reinstalled in same position, thus maintaining original balance.*
3. Disconnect parking brake cables and equalizer.
4. Disconnect linkage from transmission levers and vacuum hose at vacuum diaphragm. Disconnect speedometer cable.
5. Remove three upper converter housing-to-engine bolts. Remove nuts attaching converter to flywheel.
6. Turn front wheels to right and remove starter motor. Raise transmission slightly with a jack. Remove crossmember.
7. Detach vacuum line at converter housing. Remove manual linkage equalizer mounted between transmission and underbody.
8. Remove remaining transmission-to-engine bolts and remove transmission and converter assembly from car.
9. Reverse removal procedure to install. Adjust linkage as outlined previously.

RAMBLER & JEEP "J" SERIES

NOTE: — This chapter deals only with maintenance, adjustments and "in car" repairs. For major service work, Motor's Automatic Transmission Manual is available. Current edition is a 740 page volume that includes 240 pages of oil circuit diagrams mostly in full color.

TRANSMISSION IDENTIFICATION

An identification plate is attached to the left side of the transmission case. Included on the plate is the transmission model and the serial number of the unit.

DESCRIPTION

These transmissions combine a three-element torque converter and a hydraulically-controlled three speed and reverse planetary gear train. The drive is always through the torque converter and one of the planetary gear ranges.

The torque converter consists of an impeller (pump), a turbine and stator. All these parts operate in a fluid-filled housing which is sealed. The torque converter cannot be serviced and must be replaced as a unit in case of a malfunction.

The planetary gear train in all units transmits power from the torque converter turbine shaft to the transmission output shaft. Hydraulic clutches and servo-operated bands drive or hold certain gears to provide the various output ratios.

Single range transmissions of this type start in 2nd gear and shift to direct drive. However, single range transmissions using a one-way clutch in the pinion carrier start in 1st gear when the selector lever is in D position. In dual range transmissions, when shifted into the D1 position, the transmission starts in 1st, shifts into 2nd and then into direct drive. When the selector lever is placed in the D2 position the transmission starts in 2nd and shifts into direct drive.

When maximum acceleration is desired in order to pass a slow moving vehicle or to ascend a steep grade, the transmission may be downshifted from 3rd to 2nd by pushing the accelerator to the floor. If pressure is released on the pedal the transmission will automatically upshift to high.

Low range is used for going up very steep grades or driving in deep mud, sand or snow. This position is also used for descending steep grades in order to take advantage of engine braking. There is no automatic upshift in the L position regardless of car speed or throttle position. The selector lever may be moved from low to drive at any car speed and the transmission will then accomplish all the automatic upshifts.

Rambler Command Shift

Used on 1964-68 cars with floor shift, this arrangement permits manual shifting through all speed ranges. In short, whichever range the shift lever is placed in, the transmission will remain in that range until a manual shift is made to another range.

Initial start is made by placing the lever in range "1". It is then moved to range "2", then to "D" as the driver wishes.

TROUBLE SHOOTING GUIDE

Engine Won't Push Start

1. Check fluid level.
2. Adjust control linkage.
3. Check valve body.
4. Check front and rear bands.
5. Check converter drive plate.
6. Check pressure regulator.
7. Check rear pump.

Transmission Overheats

1. Check fluid level.
2. Check oil cooler.
3. Check oil cooler lines.
4. Check converter or one-way clutch.
5. Check for fluid leakage.
6. Check front pump.
7. Adjust front and rear bands.
8. Check pressure regulator.
9. Check front and rear clutches.

Severe Shift in D, L or R

1. Check linkage.
2. Check front band.
3. Check front and rear clutches.
4. Check one-way clutch.
5. Check engine idle speed.
6. Perform pressure checks.
7. Check pressure regulator.
8. Check valve body.

2-3 Shift Low, High or Erratic

1. Check fluid level.
2. Adjust control linkage.
3. Check governor.
4. Perform pressure checks.
5. Check valve body.
6. Check vacuum-solenoid unit.
7. Check engine idle speed.
8. Output shaft oil rings.

Severe 2-3 Shift

1. Check linkage.
2. Check vacuum-solenoid unit.
3. Check rear clutch.
4. Adjust front band.
5. Check pressure regulator.
6. Check valve body.
7. Check front servo.

Engine Overspeeds, 2-3 Shift

1. Check linkage.
2. Perform pressure checks.
3. Adjust front band.
4. Check valve body.
5. Check governor.
6. Check for fluid leaks.

No 2-3 Shift

1. Check governor.
2. Check valve body.
3. Check rear clutch.
4. Check for fluid leaks.
5. Leak in primary sun gear shaft.

No 3-2 Kickdown

1. Check kickdown switch and wiring.
2. Check valve body.
3. Perform pressure checks.

Severe 3-2 Shift, Closed Throttle

1. Check vacuum-solenoid unit.
2. Check governor.
3. Check valve body.

Engine Races on Kickdown

1. Check pressure regulator.
2. Check linkage.
3. Adjust front band.
4. Perform pressure checks.
5. Check valve body.
6. Check for internal fluid leaks.

Slips or Chatters in 2nd

1. Check fluid level.
2. Check governor.
3. Adjust front band.
4. Perform pressure checks.
5. Check pressure regulator.
6. Check valve body.
7. Check front clutch.
8. Check for fluid leaks.

Slips or Chatters in 1st

1. Check fluid level.
2. Check vacuum-solenoid unit.
3. Adjust rear band.
4. Perform pressure checks.
5. Check pressure regulator.
6. Check valve body.
7. Check rear servo.
8. Check front clutch.
9. Check for fluid leaks.
10. Leak in primary sun gear shaft.

Slips in Reverse

1. Check fluid level.
2. Check vacuum-solenoid unit.
3. Perform pressure checks.

4. Check valve body.
5. Check rear servo.
6. Check rear clutch.
7. Check for fluid leak.
8. Leak in primary sun gear shaft.

No Drive in D Range

1. Perform pressure checks.
2. Check front clutch.
3. Adjust both bands.
4. Check front pump.
5. Check for fluid leak.
6. Leak in primary sun gear shaft.

No Drive in Reverse

1. Perform pressure check.
2. Check linkage.
3. Check rear clutch.
4. Check for fluid leak.
5. Leak in primary sun gear shaft.

No Drive in Low

1. Perform pressure checks.
2. Check linkage.
3. Check front clutch.
4. Adjust both bands.
5. Check valve body.
6. Check for fluid leaks.
7. Leak in primary sun gear shaft.

No Drive in Any Range

1. Check fluid level.
2. Check governor.
3. Adjust linkage.
4. Perform pressure checks.
5. Adjust rear band.
6. Check front pump.
7. Check for fluid leaks.

Locked in Any Range

1. Adjust front band.
2. Check linkage.
3. Check front clutch.
4. Check rear clutch.
5. Check front pump.
6. Check valve body.
7. Check for fluid leak.

MAINTENANCE

The fluid level in the transmission should be checked at 1000-mile intervals. Make sure that the car is standing on a level floor, and firmly apply the parking brake.

Run the engine at normal idle speed. If the transmission fluid is cold, run the engine at a fast idle speed until the fluid reaches normal operating temperature. When the fluid is warm, slow the engine to normal idle speed, shift the transmission through all ranges and then place the lever or button at "P".

Clean all dirt from the transmission fluid dipstick cap before removing the dipstick from the filler tube. Pull the dipstick out of the tube, wipe it clean and push it all the way back into the tube.

Pull the dipstick out again and check the fluid level. If necessary, add enough automatic transmission fluid to the transmission to raise the level to the "F" or "Full" mark on the dipstick.

Changing Fluid

The transmission fluid should be changed at 24,000-mile intervals. The procedure is as follows:

1. Turn converter until one drain plug is visible through the converter bell housing opening.
2. Remove the converter drain plug. Then rotate the converter 180 degrees and remove the other plug.

NOTE—Do not attempt to turn the converter with a wrench on the converter stud nuts as there is danger of stripping threads as well as skinning your knuckles on the bell housing.

3. As the oil is draining out of the converter, remove the transmission oil pan drain plug and allow oil to drain from transmission. If no drain plug is provided, remove oil filler tube.
4. When all oil is drained, remove and clean oil pan and screen. Then, using a new oil pan gasket, install oil pan and screen.
5. Install oil pan drain plug or connect filler tube and tighten securely. Then install both converter drain plugs.
6. Install converter housing cover.
7. Install 5 quarts of approved automatic transmission fluid.
8. Run engine at idle speed for about 2 minutes; then add the additional quantity of oil required for the particular transmission being serviced.
9. Run engine at a fast idle speed until it reaches normal operating temperature.
10. Shift transmission through all ranges; then place it in "P" and check fluid level. If necessary, add enough fluid to bring the level up to the "F" or "Full" mark on the dipstick.

MANUAL LINKAGE, ADJUST

Jeep J Series

1. Loosen the two adjusting nuts at steering shift lever.
2. Set transmission control lever and transmission selector lever in neutral.
3. Retighten adjusting nuts, making sure neutral settings are maintained.

Note: If equipped with power steering, check for clearance between selector linkage bellcrank and either converter housing or power steering valve body. If there is interference at either point, it will be necessary to provide clearance. In some cases this will mean the installation of a new bellcrank and shift rods.

Rambler

1968 Javelin, Rebel & Ambassador

1. With transmission selector lever in N position, pull shift rod against shifter gate.
2. Push selector lever forward to remove any free play and adjust the clevis for a free pin fit in the transmission outer lever.

1968 American

1. With transmission selector lever in "1" position, pull shift rod against shifter gate.
2. Pull selector lever forward to remove any free play and adjust the clevis for a free pin fit in the transmission outer lever.

1966-68 Column Shift

1. Turn ignition off. Then place selector lever in "N" position.
2. Disconnect manual lever from transmission outer lever. Move transmission outer lever to extreme rear notch or low range position. Move lever forward 3 notches to "N" (neutral) position.
3. Hold selector lever linkage against neutral stop.
4. On 1966 six-cylinder and all 1967-68 models, adjust linkage for a free fit in transmission outer lever and connect linkage.
5. On 1966 V8s, adjust linkage for a free fit. Then shorten linkage three full turns and connect to transmission outer lever.

1966-67 Console Shift

1. Place selector lever in "N".
2. Disconnect linkage rod from shift lever.
3. Move transmission outer lever to extreme forward notch (1 range position). Move lever to rear 3 notches to neutral position.
4. Adjust linkage for a free pin fit and connect linkage.

1963-65

1. Place selector lever in "L" position.
2. Disconnect shift rod trunnion from operating shaft lever.
3. Make certain transmission lever is in the extreme rear position.
4. Adjust trunnion so it enters freely into lever on transmission.
5. Install trunnion in hole and secure in place.
6. Check selector lever in all positions.

THROTTLE LINKAGE, ADJUST

The linkage is in correct adjustment when the carburetor throttle lever obtains full throttle position properly and also returns to the idle position when the accelerator pedal is released.

The kickdown switch is actuated when the accelerator pedal is fully depressed. Adjustments are made by varying the length of the adjustable linkage rod at its threaded end.

VACUUM-SOLENOID, ADJUST

Rambler 1963-65 & Jeeps

The vacuum-solenoid must be properly adjusted for proper operation of the transmission. Loosen the lock nut and, with a gauge, check the distance between the transmission case and the solenoid, Fig. 2. Set this clearance at ⅜" within half a turn of the solenoid valve, depending on the shift quality.

Turning the solenoid valve into the transmission case causes a harder shift; turning it out causes a softer shift.

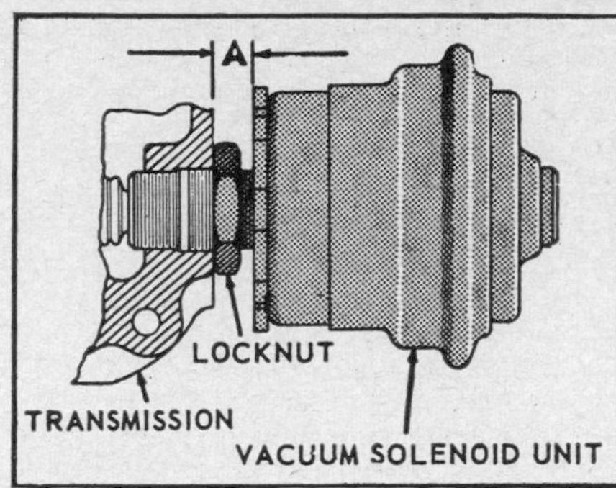

Fig. 2 Vacuum-solenoid adjustment. Rambler 1963-65 and Jeeps

FRONT BAND

Rambler 6 Cyl. and V8-290, Jeeps

Remove transmission oil pan. Loosen locknut on front servo adjusting screw and insert a .250" metal block between end of adjusting screw and servo piston rod, Fig. 3.

With metal block in place, tighten adjusting screw to a torque of 10 inch-pounds and tighten locknut to 23 ft-lbs torque. If a special adapter is used, torque adjusting screw to 9 inch-pounds.

Rambler V8s Except 290

Adjusting Tool J-5880-01 should be used to make the adjustment. Tighten the adjusting screw until the tool over-rides, then tighten locknut to 23 ft-lbs torque and remove gauge block.

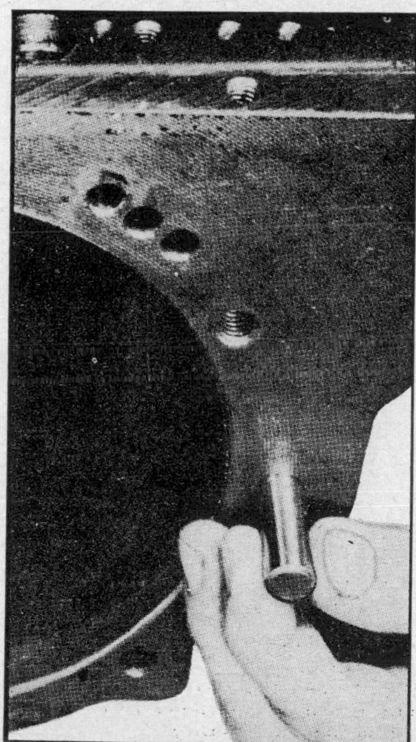

Fig. 4 Removing parking pawl shaft

REAR BAND, ADJUST

Rambler 6 Cyl. and V8-290, Jeeps

Loosen locknut and tighten adjusting screw to a torque of 10 ft-lbs. Then back off the adjusting screw ¾ turn and tighten locknut to 28 ft-lbs. torque.

Rambler V8s Except 290

Loosen locknut and tighten adjusting screw to 10 ft-lbs torque. Then back off the adjusting screw 1½ turns and tighten locknut.

OIL PRESSURE REGULATOR

Remove oil pan and screen. Maintain constant pressure on spring retainer to prevent damage to springs and remove retainer from bosses on oil pressure regulator body. Remove springs and pilots. Remove the three pipes. Unfasten and remove the oil pressure regulator from the transmission case.

CONTROL VALVE

To remove the assembly. loosen the adjustment on the front and rear bands 5 to 6 turns. Loosen front servo attaching screws. Remove cap screws and washers which attach control valve to case. Align throttle and manual levers to permit removal of control valve. Disengage front servo tubes from control valve and lift valve assembly from case.

FRONT & REAR SERVOS

To remove the front servo, remove the cap screw which holds it to the case. Hold the actuating lever strut with one hand and lift the servo from the case.

To remove the rear servo, take out the attaching cap screws. Then hold the anchor strut and lift the servo from the case.

EXTENSION HOUSING SEAL

Remove propeller shaft or torque tube and propeller shaft from transmission. Pull seal out of extension housing.

Before installing the new seal, inspect the sealing surface of the universal joint yoke for scores. If scores are evident, replace the yoke. Inspect the counter bore in the housing for burrs. Polish all burrs with crocus cloth.

To install the new seal, position it in the bore of the extension housing with the felt side of the seal to the rear. The seal may be driven into the housing with a special tool designed for the purpose.

OIL DISTRIBUTOR

NOTE: On Rambler 1963-66 Six, oil distribution is handled through the rear pump body, and oil distributor sleeve is therefore not used.

With Bolted Distributor & Sleeve

After removing the extension case remove the spacer from the transmission output shaft and slide the distributor toward the rear of the transmission. Note that the tube spacer is located in the center tube.

Remove the three tubes and spacer from the distributor. Remove the screws which attach the distributor to the sleeve and separate these parts.

Inspect the distributor and sleeve for burrs on the mating surfaces and obstructed fluid passages. Check the fit of the tubes in the distributor. Inspect the distributor sleeve for wear and scores in the sleeve bore.

To assemble, align the distributor and sleeve and install the cap screws. Install the tubes in the distributor with the spacer installed on the center tube.

With One Piece Distributor & Sleeve

After removing the extension housing,

Fig. 3 Adjusting front servo band

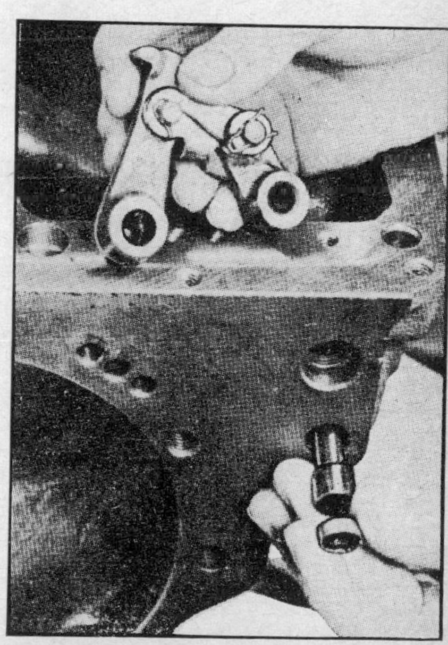

Fig. 5 Removing toggle lever

remove the distributor drive gear snap ring. Remove distributor gear, taking care not to lose the gear drive ball. Remove distributor sleeve and pipes from the transmission. Inspect the 4 seal rings on the output shaft for wear or breakage, and replace if necessary, Inspect the distributor sleeve for wear and the tubes for proper alignment and fit into the distributor sleeve.

With tubes installed in the distributor sleeve, install distributor on output shaft (chamfer forward) sliding the distributor over the seal rings and at the same time guiding tubes into the case. Install speedometer drive ball and gear and install snap ring.

GOVERNOR

Remove the governor inspection cover from the extension housing, Rotate the drive shaft to bring the governor body in line with the inspection hole. Remove the two screws which attach the governor body to the counterweight, and remove the body.

Remove the valve from the new governor body. Lubricate the valve with automatic transmission fluid. Install the valve in the body, making sure the valve moves freely in the bore. Install the body in the counterweight. Be sure the fluid passages in the counterweight and body are aligned.

PARKING PAWL, REPLACE

Transmission In Car

Rambler 1963-67 Six and V8-290

1. Support engine at rear.
2. Support torque tube with jack.
3. Remove speedometer cable and remove exhaust pipe clamp from lower bracket.
4. Unfasten and remove rear crossmember over exhaust pipe by pulling down on exhaust pipe.
5. Remove oil pan and control valve.
6. Remove parking brake toggle roll pin and remove toggle pin.
7. Unfasten rear extension housing from torque tube adapter and rotate housing clockwise until governor inspection plate is almost level to the bottom. The parking brake anchor pin will then clear extension housing.
8. Remove parking brake anchor pin with a magnet or remove pin from inside of case with needle nose pliers.
9. Remove parking brake toggle link and pawl assembly.
10. Reverse procedure to install.

Rambler 1963-67 V8 (Except 290), All Jeeps

1. Remove oil pan and screen, pressure regulator and control valve. Disconnect speedometer cable.
2. Completely tighten rear band to prevent movement of planetary assembly and dislocation of thrust washers on the transmission shaft. Disconnect drive shaft or drive shaft and torque tube from the transmission.
3. Remove extension housing-to-case bolts and move housing rearward far enough to permit removal of snap ring which retains speedometer gear.
4. Slide oil delivery sleeve back just far enough so that the oil distributor tubes clear the transmission case.
5. Rotate oil pump housing until parking pawl pin in case is exposed.
6. Disconnect link (parking pawl torsion rod) located between detent lever and torsion lever assembly.
7. Remove hair pin clip retaining torsion lever assembly and remove from shaft.
8. Tap toggle lever pin toward rear of transmission to remove plug and pin, then remove parking pawl pin by working pawl back and forth, Fig. 4.
9. Remove toggle lever and parking pawl assembly from transmission and replace any damaged parts, Fig. 5.
10. Reverse above procedure for reassembly.

TRANSMISSION, REPLACE

Jeep J Series

1. Remove floor mat and access cover.
2. Disconnect battery positive cable.
3. Raise vehicle on hoist.
4. Drain converter.
5. Drain transmission by disconnecting oil filler tube.
6. Drain and remove transfer case, if so equipped, as outlined previously.
7. Disconnect propeller shaft from flange on transmission and tie shaft out of way.
8. Disconnect wire and vacuum line from transmission diaphragm solenoid.
9. Remove exhaust pipe.
10. Disconnect transmission control rod from control lever.
11. Disconnect emergency brake cable.
12. Disconnect oil cooler lines from transmission, if so equipped, and tie out of way.
13. Disconnect speedometer cable from transmission and tie out of way.
14. Disconnect hand brake cable plate from crossmember.
15. Position a transmission lift under transmission.
16. Support engine at converter end.
17. Remove bolts that attach crossmember to frame.
18. Remove two nuts and one remaining bolt that attach transmission to converter. *Note: A standard 5/8" open end crowfoot wrench is required when removing lower left transmission-to-converter housing bolt on 4-wheel drive vehicles.*
19. Slide transmission away from engine and lower it.
20. Remove crossmember from transmission.
21. Reverse removal procedure to install.

Rambler 1967-68

1. Disconnect battery.
2. Raise car and support with car stands. *Car weight must be on rear springs, therefore, place stands under rear axle tubes.*
3. Disconnect the following:
4. Oil filler tube and drain transmission.
5. Selector linkage at transmission outer manual lever.
6. Speedometer cable at transmission.
7. Vacuum hose and solenoid wire.
8. Exhaust pipe and remove pipe bracket from converter housing.
9. Position transmission hoist under transmission.
10. On American, remove body crossmember tie plate on Convertibles.
11. On models other than American, disconnect rear support crossmember from body side sill brackets and transmission.
12. With 199 and 232 engines, remove converter housing lower cover.
13. Remove converter access cover (in spacer plate on 290 engine).
14. Mark converter and drive plate to assure original location upon assembly.
15. Remove converter-to-drive plate capscrews (6-cyl.) stud nuts on V8s.
16. Remove starter mounting bolts and converter housing-to-cylinder block bolts.
17. Push converter housing and converter to rear a sufficient distance to clear crankshaft.

NOTE: Rear of engine tends to raise when transmission weight is removed and may bind the converter in the crankshaft pilot bushing. Blocking the engine up at the front will assist separating converter from crankshaft.

---

18. Maintain pressure against converter housing and lower assembly until converter housing is clear of engine. Then disconnect propeller shaft and remove transmission from vehicle.
19. Reverse procedure to install.

1966 Rambler

1. Disconnect battery.
2. Disconnect throttle valve control cable at throttle linkage bracket on engine.
3. Raise car and support with floor stands. *Car weight must be on rear springs; therefore, support rear of car with stands placed under rear axle tubes.*
4. Disconnect oil filler tube and drain transmission.
5. Disconnect selector linkage at transmission outer manual lever.
6. Disconnect speedometer cable at transmission.
7. Disconnect exhaust pipe from manifold and remove exhaust pipe bracket from converter housing.
8. Position transmission hoist with a suitable cradle under transmission.
9. Disconnect rear support crossmember from body side sill brackets and transmission. Remove body crossmember tie plate on Convertible models.
10. Lower transmission and rear of engine for access to upper converter housing-to-engine bolts.
11. Remove converter housing lower cover.
12. Mark converter and drive plate to assure original location upon reassembly.

13. Remove converter-to-drive plate capscrews.
14. Remove starter mounting bolts and converter housing-to-engine bolts.
15. Push converter housing and converter rearward a sufficient distance to clear crankshaft.

NOTE: Rear of engine tends to raise when transmission weight is removed and may bind converter in crankshaft pilot bushing. Blocking the engine up at the front will assist separating converter from crankshaft.

16. Maintain pressure against converter housing and lower transmission, converter housing and converter as an assembly until housing is clear of engine.
17. Disconnect transmission from propeller shaft and torque tube.

1965 Rambler

1. Disconnect battery cable.
2. On V8 models, disconnect vacuum and solenoid vacuum line (if equipped). If transmission is cable controlled, disconnect cable at transmission.
3. On 6 cylinder models, disconnect throttle cable at throttle shaft on carburetor and at cable bracket.
4. Raise car on hoist and place stand jacks under rear of car at body sills.
5. On 6 cylinder models, disconnect oil filler tube at transmission oil pan and drain transmission. Remove oil pan and loosen valve body to drain converter.
6. On V8 models, remove oil pan and pressure regulator valve retainer and drain converter through regulator valves.
7. After converter is drained, replace oil pan temporarily with four screws.
8. Disconnect speedometer cable and manual shift rod from transmission.
9. On American with 6-196 engine, disconnect rear brake line and parking brake cable.
10. On Rambler models, disconnect rear brake hose bracket from floor panel.
11. On American with 6-196 engine, loosen rear axle and move it toward rear to separate propeller shaft from transmission.
12. On American with 6-232 engine, remove propeller shaft by separating rear U-joint and sliding the U-joint from transmission mainshaft.
13. On Rambler models, disconnect shock absorbers from rear axle and stabilizer bar from left rear axle tube. Disconnect torque tube and parking brake cable. Then lower rear axle and move it rearward to separate torque tube and propeller shaft from transmission.
14. On V8 models, disconnect exhaust pipes from engine and left side at muffler pipe.
15. Support transmission with a suitable jack or hoist. Support engine at rear, being careful not to damage engine oil pan.
16. Unfasten transmission from converter.
17. Disconnect rear crossmember from side sills.
18. Pull transmission to rear to disengage it from housing and converter.
19. Lower transmission and remove it from vehicle.

NOTE: An additional body crossmember is used on Convertible models. Therefore, it is also necessary to remove crossmember tie plate when removing transmission.

20. Reverse foregoing procedure to install transmission.

1963-64 Rambler

1. Disconnect battery cable.
2. Drain transmission.
3. Disconnect vacuum line and wire terminal at vacuum unit at rear of transmission.
4. Disconnect speedometer cable.
5. Disconnect rear brake hose bracket from floor panel.
6. Disconnect linkage from transmission lever.
7. Disconnect rear shock absorbers from rear axle.
8. Ser. 10, 20, 80: Disconnect torque tube, drive shaft and hand brake cable.

8a. American: Disconnect rear spring front brackets from body floor pan and disconnect hand brake cable. On convertible models the "U" bolts on the rear axle must be removed instead of the rear spring front brackets.

9. Ser. 10, 20, 80: Lower rear axle and move rearward to separate torque tube and propeller shaft from transmission.

9a. American: Slide rear axle rearward to remove front universal joint from transmission output shaft. On convertible models axle should be moved rearward on springs.

10. Support transmission with suitable hoist or jack.
11. Remove transmission-to-converter housing upper cap screws and install two guide pins in screw holes.
12. Remove lower cap screws.
13. Remove transmission from converter.
14. Reverse the foregoing procedure to install the transmission and adjust the shift linkage as outlined above.

UNIVERSAL JOINTS

SERVICE NOTES

Before disassembling any universal joint, examine the assembly carefully and note the position of the grease fitting (if used). Also, be sure to mark the yokes with relation to the propeller shaft so they may be reassembled in the same relative position. Failure to observe these precautions may produce rough car operation which results in rapid wear and failure of parts, and place an unbalanced load on transmission, engine and rear axle.

When universal joints are disassembled for lubrication or inspection, and the old parts are to be reinstalled, special care must be exercised to avoid damage to universal joint spider or cross and bearing cups.

NOTE: Some late model cars use an injected nylon retainer on the universal joint bearings. When service is necessary, pressing the bearings out will sheer the nylon retainer. Replacement with the conventional steel snap ring type is then necessary.

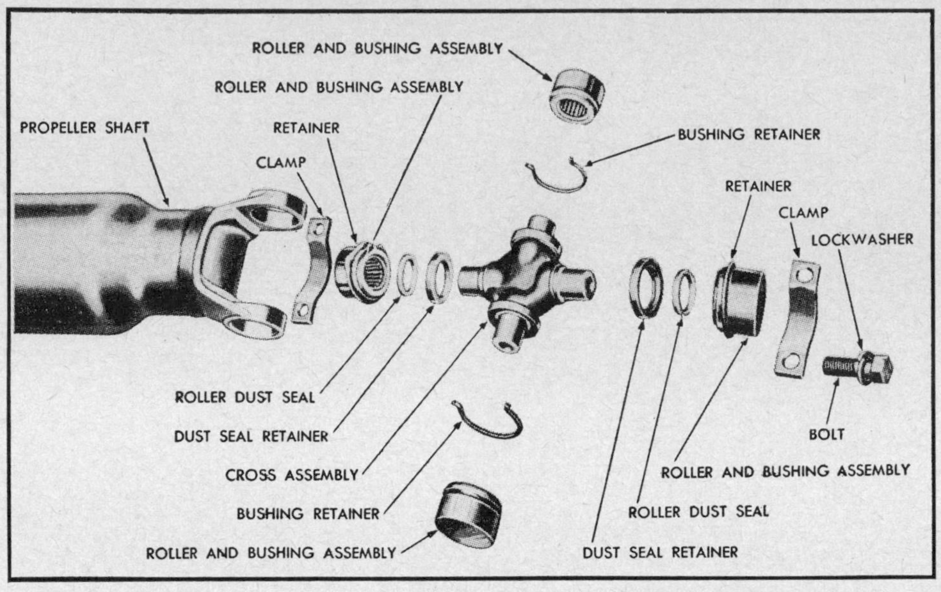

Fig. 1 Cross and roller type universal joint. Chrysler-built cars

CROSS & ROLLER TYPE

Figs. 1, 2 and 3 illustrate typical examples of universal joints of this type. They all operate on the same principle and similar service and replacement procedures may be applied to all.

Disassembly

1. Remove snap rings (or retainer plates) that retain bearings in yoke and drive shaft.
2. Place U-joint in a vise.
3. Select a wrench socket with an outside diameter slightly smaller than the U-joint bearings. Select another wrench socket with an inside diameter slightly larger than the U-joint bearings.
4. Place the sockets at opposite bearings in the yoke so that the smaller socket becomes a bearing pusher and the larger socket becomes a bearing receiver when the vise jaws come together, Fig. 4. Close vise jaws until both bearings are free of yoke and remove bearings from the cross or spider.
5. If bearings will not come all the way out, close vise until bearing in receiver socket protrudes from yoke as much as possible without using excessive force. Then remove from vise and place that portion of bearing which protrudes from yoke between vise jaws. Tighten vise to hold bearing and drive yoke off with a soft hammer.
6. To remove opposite bearing from yoke, replace in vise with pusher socket on exposed cross journal with receiver socket over bearing cup. Then tighten vise jaws to press bearing back through yoke into receiving socket.
7. Remove yoke from drive shaft and again place protruding portion of bearing between vise jaws. Then tighten vise to hold bearing while driving yoke off bearing with soft hammer.
8. Turn spider or cross ¼ turn and use the same procedure to press bearings out of drive shaft.

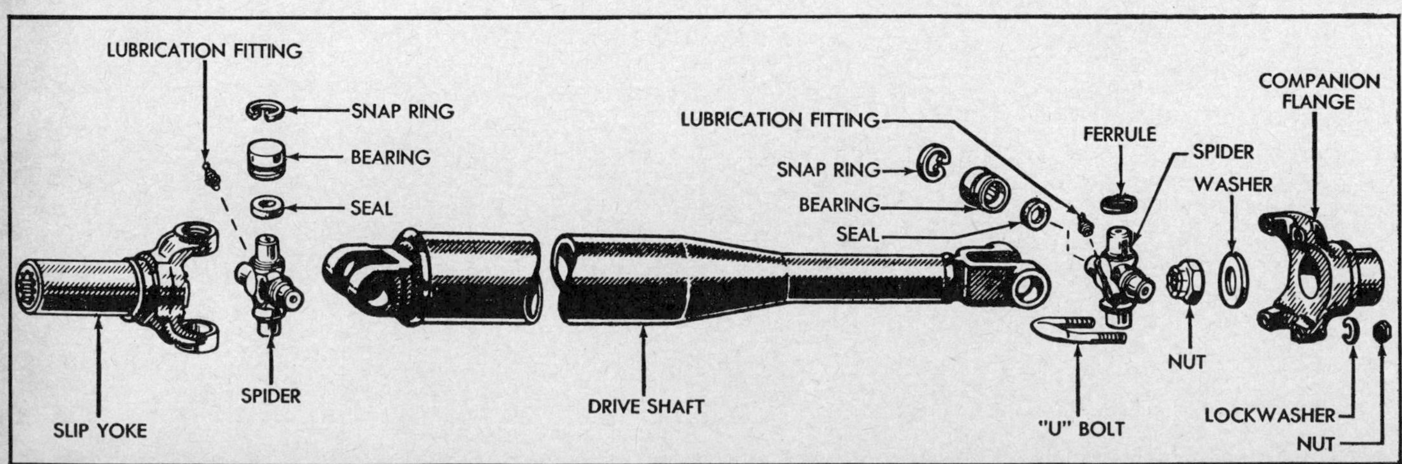

Fig. 2 Cross and roller universal joints and propeller shaft. Ford-built cars

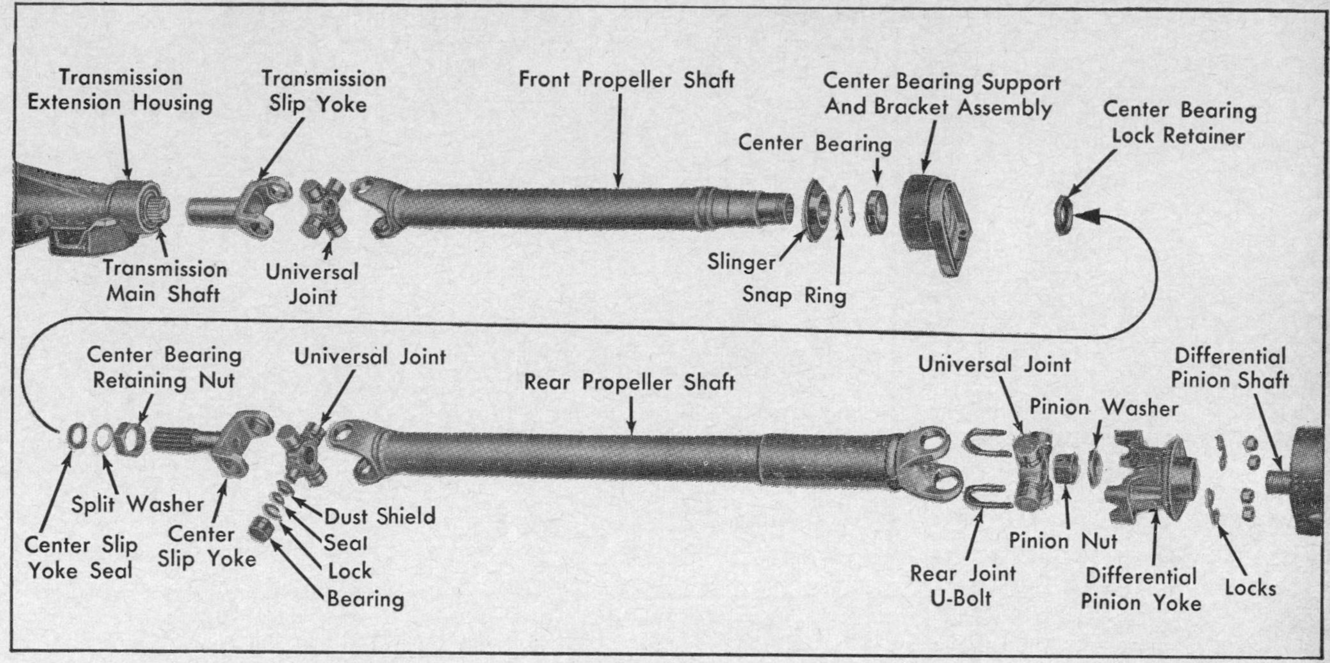

Fig. 3 Example of a two-piece propeller shaft with three cross and roller universal joints and center bearing support assembly. Cadillac

Reassembly

1. If old parts are to be reassembled, pack bearing cups with universal joint grease. *Do not fill cups completely or use excessive amounts as over-lubrication may damage seals during reassembly.* Use new seals.
2. If new parts are being installed, check new bearings for adequate grease before assembling.
3. With the pusher (smaller) socket, press one bearing part way into drive shaft. Position spider into the partially installed bearing. Place second bearing into drive shaft. Fasten drive shaft in vise so that bearings are in contact with faces of vise jaws, Fig. 5. *Some spiders are provided with locating lugs which must face toward drive shaft when installed, Fig. 6.*
4. Press bearings all the way into position and install snap rings or retainer plates.
5. Install bearings in yoke in same manner. When installation is completed, check U-joint for binding or roughness. If free movement is impeded, correct the condition before installation in vehicle.

BALL & TRUNNION TYPE

Disassembly

1. Referring to Fig. 7, straighten tabs and remove grease cover and gasket.
2. Push body back and remove thrust button, spring, ball, rollers and thrust washer from each end of pin.
3. Remove clamps and loosen dust cover. Remove and save breather located between shaft and cover.
4. Clean and examine trunnion and raceways in body for roughness and wear. If either part is to be replaced, press out pin. Care must be exercised to support end of drive shaft properly to avoid damage during pressing operation.

Reassembly

When the trunnion pin and body have not been removed, a new boot may be installed and the U-joint may be repacked. Coat all parts with universal joint grease and, without using tools, stretch boot over pin and work it through body into position on the shaft. Lubricate and complete boot installation as directed further on.

1. To assemble the U-joint, place boot clamps, boot and U-joint body on drive shaft.

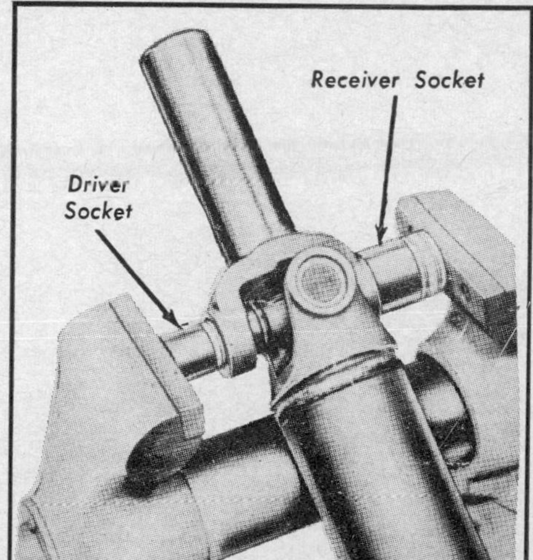

Fig. 4 Removing bearings from yoke using small and large wrench sockets as pusher and receiver tools, respectively

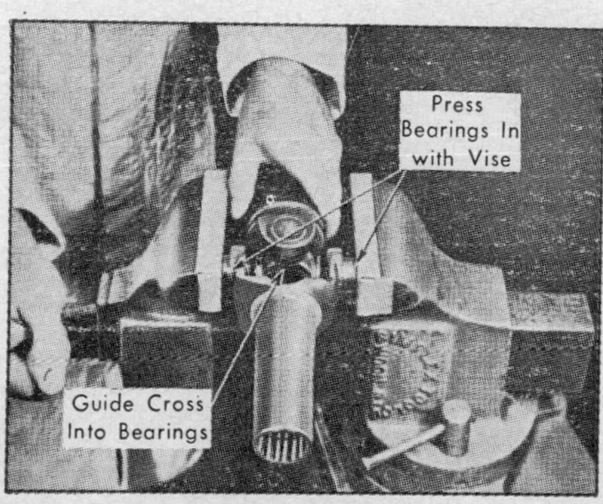

Fig. 5 Installing bearings into drive shaft yoke

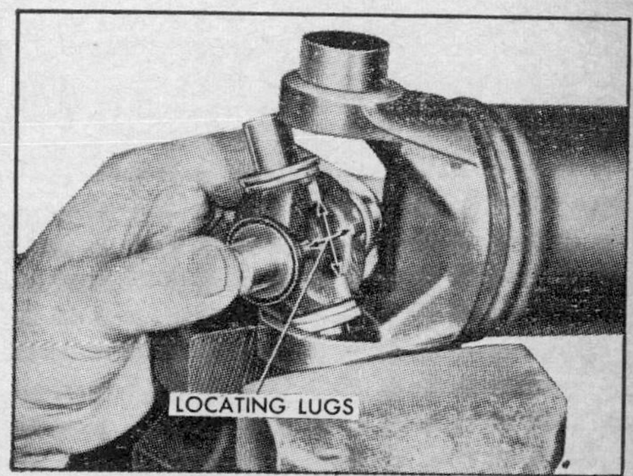

Fig. 6 Some units have locating lugs which must face propeller shaft when installed

2. Press pin through end of propeller shaft so that pin is exactly centered.
3. Assemble parts on pin in the order shown in Fig. 7, then position U-joint body over pin assembly.
4. Position boot on propeller shaft, with breather parallel to shaft. Install and tighten clamp.
5. Place boot on U-joint body and install clamp.
6. Lubricate U-joint with two ounces of fibrous U-joint grease applied evenly in both raceways, one half in back of the trunnion pin and one half between pin and cover.
7. Install grease cover and gasket on body with tabs at grooves in body. Bend tabs to tighten in place.

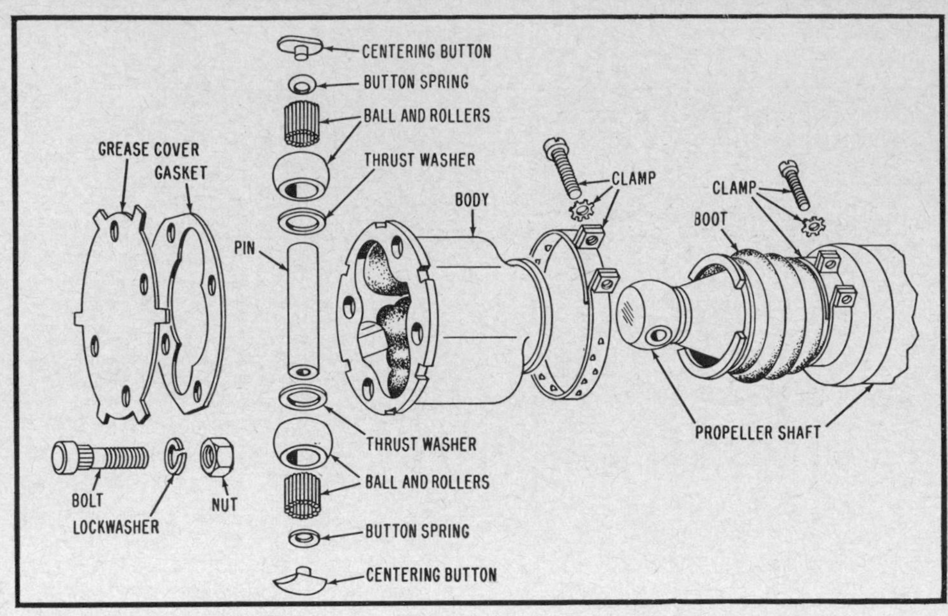

Fig. 7 Ball and trunnion type universal joint. Chrysler-built cars

CONSTANT VELOCITY TYPES

This type of U-joint, Fig. 8, is composed of two conventional cross and roller joints connected with a special link yoke. Because the two joint angles are the same, even though the usual U-joint fluctuation is present within the unit, the acceleration of the front joint (within the yoke) is always neutralized by the deceleration of the rear joint (within the yoke) and vice versa. The end result is the front and rear propeller shafts always turn at a constant velocity.

Buick, Buick Special, Olds F-85

For ease of handling and to prevent damage to the constant velocity U-joints, the front and rear propeller shafts must be separated at the slip joint before any service is attempted.

Disassemble Slip Joint

1. Pry lockwasher from flats on bearing locknut.
2. Loosen locknut until free of threads and slide locknut and seal against constant velocity joint.
3. Slide rear propeller shaft from front propeller shaft, making sure that index spring wire in splines is not lost.

Disassemble Constant Velocity U-Joint

1. Mark yokes before disassembly to be sure reassembly is made in same relative position of components.
2. Disassemble rear section of constant velocity U-joint first as follows:
3. Remove snap rings from bearings using a punch.
4. Place rear propeller shaft yoke in a vise. Shaft must be supported horizontally and link yoke must be free to move vertically, Fig. 9.
5. Using a pipe coupling or a wrench socket with the inside diameter slightly larger than outside diameter of bearing, Fig. 9, drive link yoke downward until about a ¼″ of bearing projects from yoke. *Do not attempt to drive yoke down farther than ball socket will allow easily.*
6. Rotate shaft 180 degrees and repeat Steps 3, 4 and 5.
7. Clamp ¼″ projecting portion of either bearing in vise and remove bearing by driving link yoke upward. Remove other bearing in same manner, Fig. 10.
8. Separate spider, shaft yoke and shaft from link yoke.
9. To remove bearings from shaft yoke, clamp spider in vise with its jaws bearing against ends of spider journals. Yoke must be free to move vertically between jaws of vise.
10. Using the same bearing remover tool as in Step 5, apply force on shaft yoke around bearing. Drive yoke downward until bearing is free of yoke.

Reassemble Constant Velocity U-Joint—

All yokes must be carefully assembled using the marks made before disassembly for reference. Assemble front section of constant velocity joint first.

1. Position spider inside splined yoke. Install bearings by pressing between vise jaws. Make sure that spider journals enter bearings squarely to avoid damage, Fig. 11.

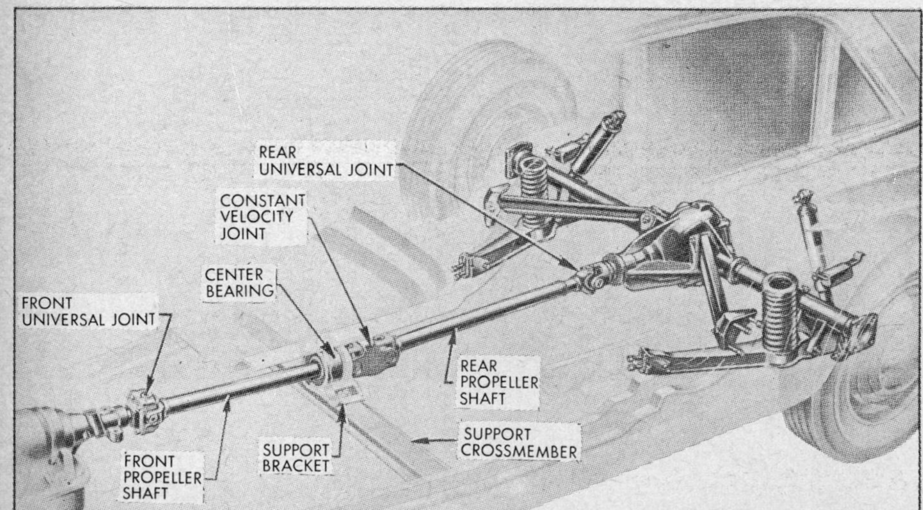

Fig. 8 Two-piece propeller shaft with constant velocity universal joint connected between front and rear propeller shafts. Buick, Buick Special and Olds F-85

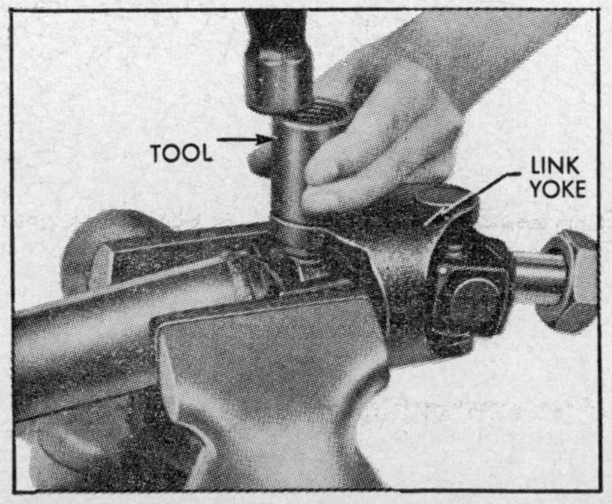

Fig. 9 Driving bearing from link yoke

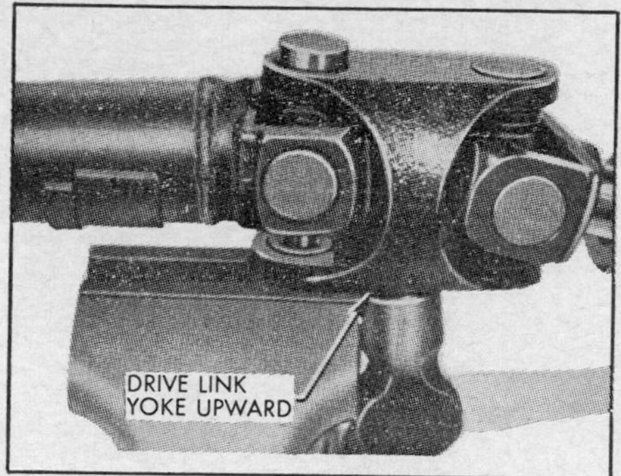

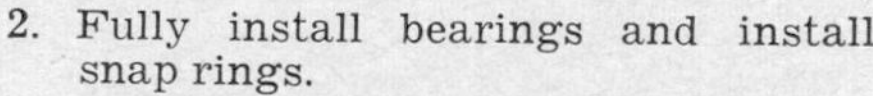
Fig. 10 Removing bearing

Fig. 11 Installing bearings

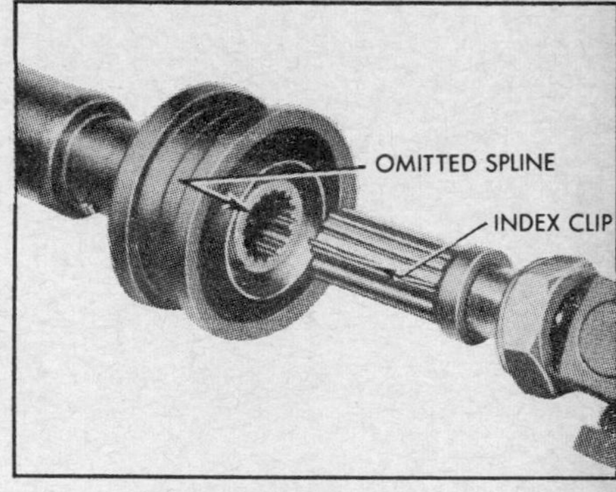

Fig. 12 Aligning index spring with missing internal spline on propeller shaft

2. Fully install bearings and install snap rings.
3. Position splined yoke and spider inside link yoke and install bearings into link yoke in same manner as for splined yoke.
4. Position spider inside rear propeller shaft yoke and install bearings.
5. Lubricate ball and socket with a high grade of extreme pressure grease.
6. Position spider of rear propeller shaft assembly in link yoke.
7. Engage socket with ball of splined yoke assembly. *Make sure that all reference marks are properly aligned.*
8. Install bearings into link yoke in same manner as above while holding spring loaded ball and socket assembly together to make sure that spider journals enter bearings squarely.

Reassemble Slip Joint

1. Make sure locknut, seal and split washer are in place on smooth part of spline shaft. Also make sure that index spring wire is in place in splines and that spacer washer and large lockwasher are in place on rear end of front propeller shaft.
2. Align index spring with missing internal spline in rear end of propeller shaft and slide slip joint together, Fig. 12.
3. Install locknut and tighten securely. Bend in rim of lockwasher to engage flat of locknut firmly.

Lincoln & Rambler

This type, Figs. 13 and 14, is similar in construction to the GM type shown in Fig. 8 except that no center bearing support is used. Also, the transmission mainshaft extension serves the same purpose as the front propeller shaft on GM cars.

Disassemble Constant Velocity U-Joint

1. Mark position of spiders, center yoke and centering socket yoke as related to yoke that is welded to the drive shaft tube. Also, note the position of the grease fittings as they must be assembled in the same position to provide proper clearance.
2. Remove grease fittings. Apply pressure on centering socket yoke and remove one bearing cup. Remove opposite bearing cup in same manner.
3. Remove snap rings which retain bearing cups in front of center yoke. As a remover tool, use a wrench socket or a piece of pipe with an outside diameter slightly smaller than the bearing cup. As a receiver tool, use a wrench socket or a piece of pipe with an inside diameter slightly larger than the bearing cup. Clamp center yoke in vise with driver and receiver tools in place as shown in Fig. 15.
4. Close vise to press bearing cup about ⅜" out of center yoke and into receiver tool. *The bearing cup cannot be pressed out more than this without causing damage.*
5. Tightly clamp exposed bearing cup in vise and drive yoke from cup, using a brass drift.
6. Remove opposite bearing from center yoke, using above procedure.
7. Pull centering socket yoke assembly off entering stud. Remove rubber seal from centering ball stud.
8. Remove snap rings from rear of center yoke and drive shaft yoke. Start disassembly by pressing bearing cups from drive shaft yoke, being careful to stop pressing operation when inside of center yoke almost contacts slinger ring at front of drive shaft yoke. Pressing bearing beyond this point will distort the ring, Fig. 16.
9. Removing remaining bearing cups from center yoke.

Reassembly

1. Position spider in drive shaft yoke. Make sure that grease fitting will be in same position as originally installed. Press in bearing cups and seals and install snap rings.
2. Position center yoke over spider ends, making sure that reference marks made before disassembly are properly aligned. Press bearing cups into center yoke and install snap rings.
3. Install new seal on centering ball stud and position centering socket yoke on the stud.
4. Place front spider, with grease fitting properly positioned, in center yoke. Press bearing cups into center yoke and install remaining bearing cups and seals.

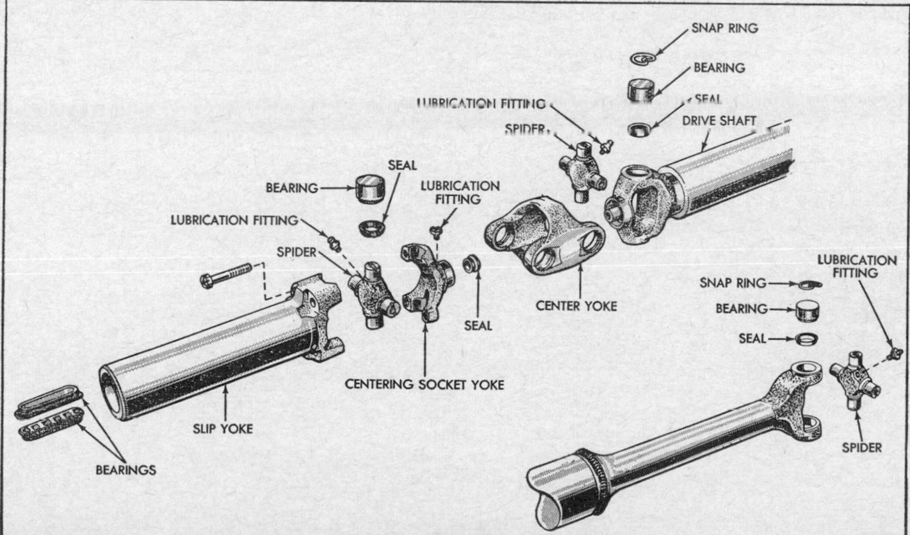

Fig. 13 Constant velocity universal joint used on Lincoln

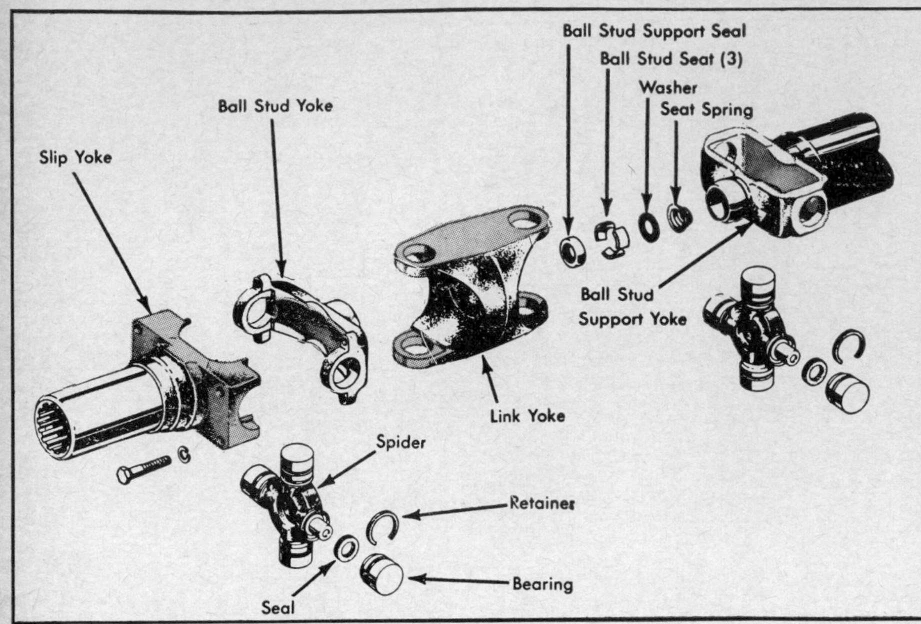

Fig. 14 Rambler Ambassador constant velocity universal joint

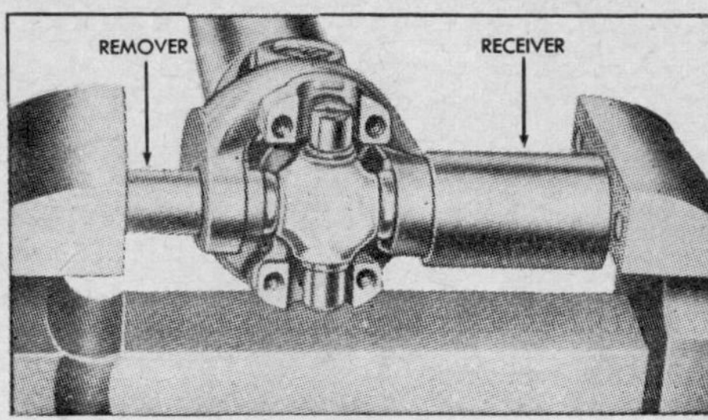

Fig. 15 Partially removing bearing cup from center yoke

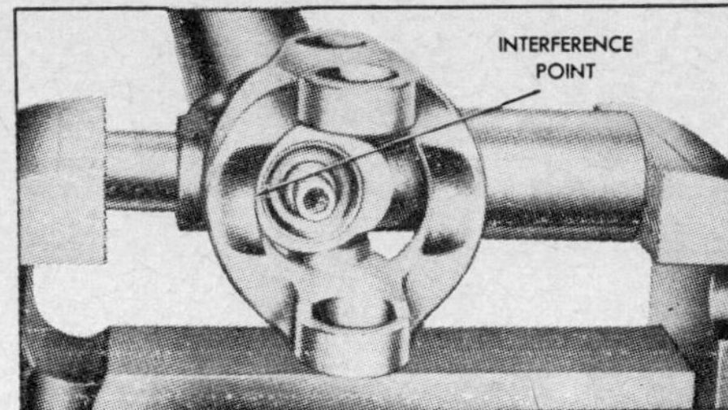

Fig. 16 Bearing cup removal and interference

HYDRAULIC BRAKE SYSTEM

For Brake Adjustments, see Car Chapters

SINGLE MASTER CYLINDER SYSTEM

Depressing the brake pedal moves the master cylinder push rod and piston, forcing hydraulic fluid out through a check valve, Fig. 1. This fluid flows through the hydraulic lines into the wheel cylinders, forcing the wheel cylinder pistons outward from the center of the cylinder and expanding the brake shoes and linings against the brake drums.

When the brake pedal is quickly released, the master cylinder piston returns to the released position faster than fluid returns from the lines. Holes in the piston head allow fluid to pass from the rear to the front of the piston head, past the primary cup to fill the space.

At the same time (when the pedal is released) the brake shoe return springs force the wheel cylinder pistons to return toward the center of the wheel cylinder (released position). Fluid forced out of the wheel cylinders by this action returns to the master cylinder by overcoming the pressure of the master cylinder piston spring which holds the check valve closed. As this fluid returns, the excess portion will return to the reservoir through the compensating port which is uncovered when the master cylinder piston is in the released position. The piston spring will close the check valve when the pressure in the lines is reduced to 8 to 12 lbs, maintaining a slight pressure in the lines at all

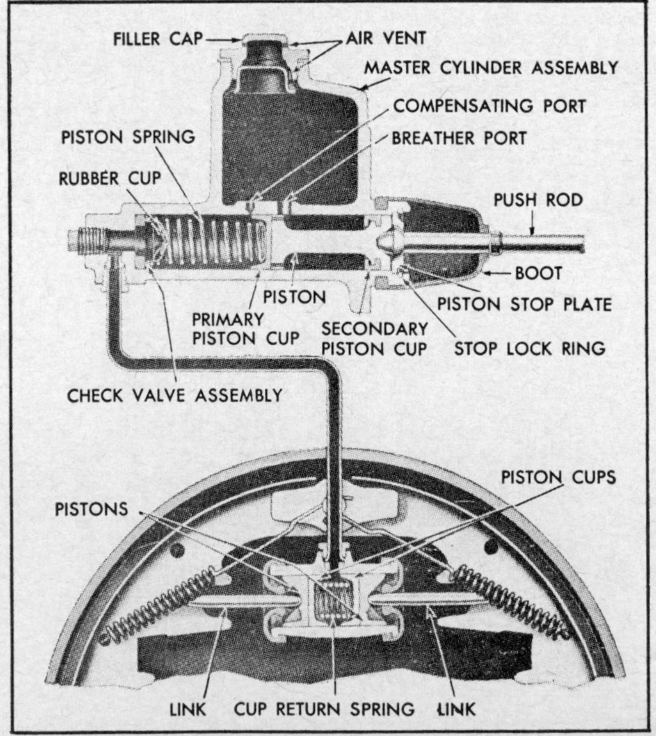

Fig. 1 Schematic diagram of a typical hydraulic brake system

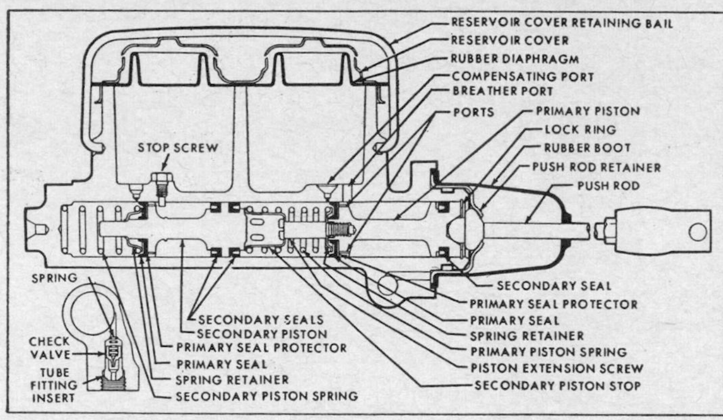

Fig. 2 Delco-Moraine dual master cylinder used with drum brakes (typical)

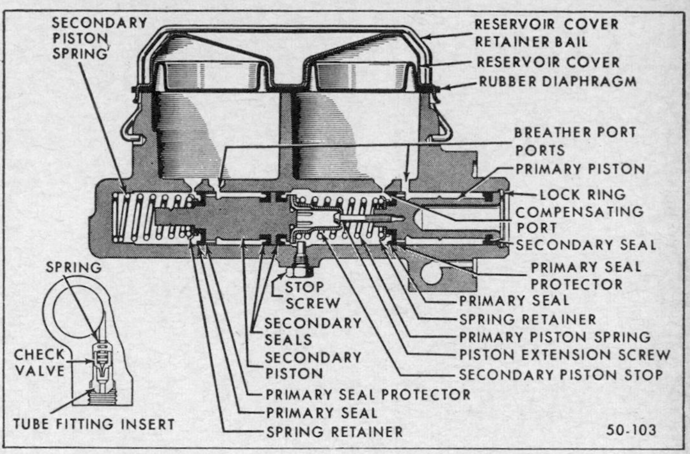

Fig. 3 Bendix dual master cylinder used with drum brakes (typical)

times. The purpose of this pressure is to keep the wheel cylinder cups from leaking fluid and to reduce the possibility of air entering the system.

DUAL MASTER CYLINDER SYSTEM

When the brake pedal is depressed, both the primary (front brake) and the secondary (rear brake) master cylinder pistons are moved simultaneously to exert hydraulic fluid pressure on their respective independent hydraulic system. The fluid displacement of the two master cylinders is proportioned to fulfill the requirements of each of the two independent hydraulic brake systems, Figs. 2 and 3.

If a failure of a rear (secondary) brake system should occur, initial brake pedal movement causes the unrestricted secondary piston to bottom in the master cylinder bore. Primary piston movement displaces hydraulic fluid in the primary section of the dual master cylinder to actuate the front brake system.

Should the front (primary) brake system fail, initial brake pedal movement causes the unrestricted primary piston to bottom out against the secondary piston. Continued downward movement of the brake pedal moves the secondary piston to displace hydraulic fluid in the rear brake system to actuate the rear brakes.

The increased pedal travel and the increased pedal effort required to compensate for the loss of the failed portion of the brake system provides a warning that a partial brake system failure has occurred. When the ignition switch is turned on, a brake warning light on the instrument panel provides a visual indication that one of the dual brake systems has become inoperative.

Should a failure of either the front or rear brake hydraulic system occur, the hydraulic fluid pressure differential resulting from pressure loss of the failed brake system forces the valve toward the low pressure area to light the brake warning lamp.

Brake Warning Light Switches

There are three basic types of brake warning light switches as shown in Figs. 5, 6 and 7, and usually they form a common electrical circuit with the parking brake light.

When a pressure differential occurs between the front and rear brake systems, the valves will shuttle toward the side with the low pressure.

As shown in Fig. 5, movement of the differential valve forces the switch

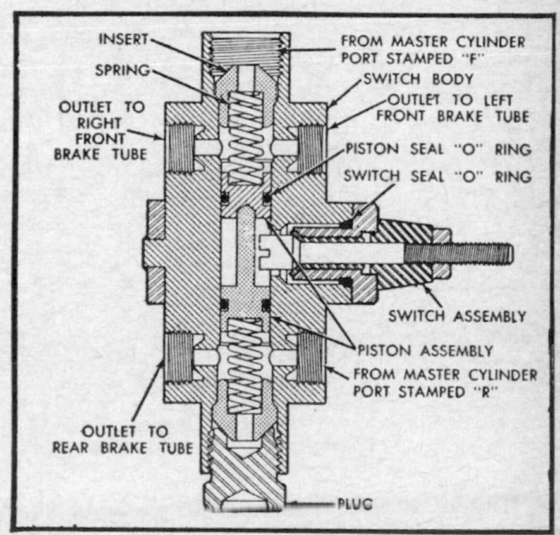

Fig. 7 Pressure differential valve and brake warning light switch

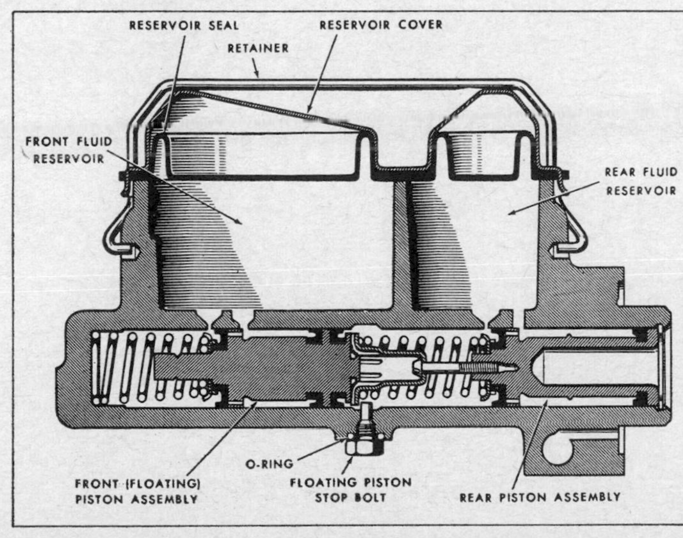

Fig. 4 Bendix dual master cylinder used with disc brakes (typical)

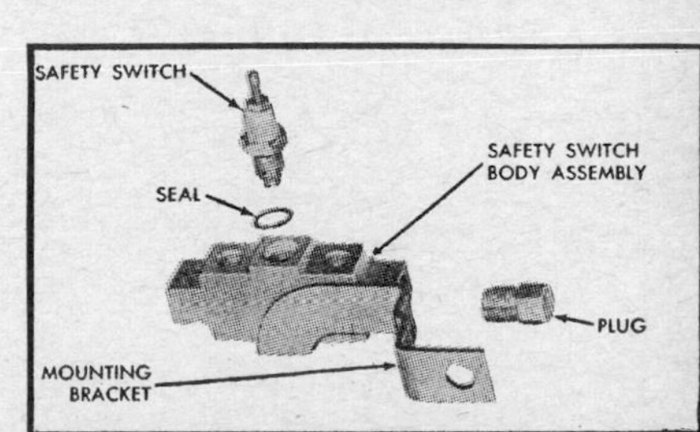

Fig. 8 Typical pressure valve and brake warning light switch. These switches are usually mounted on the left frame side rail

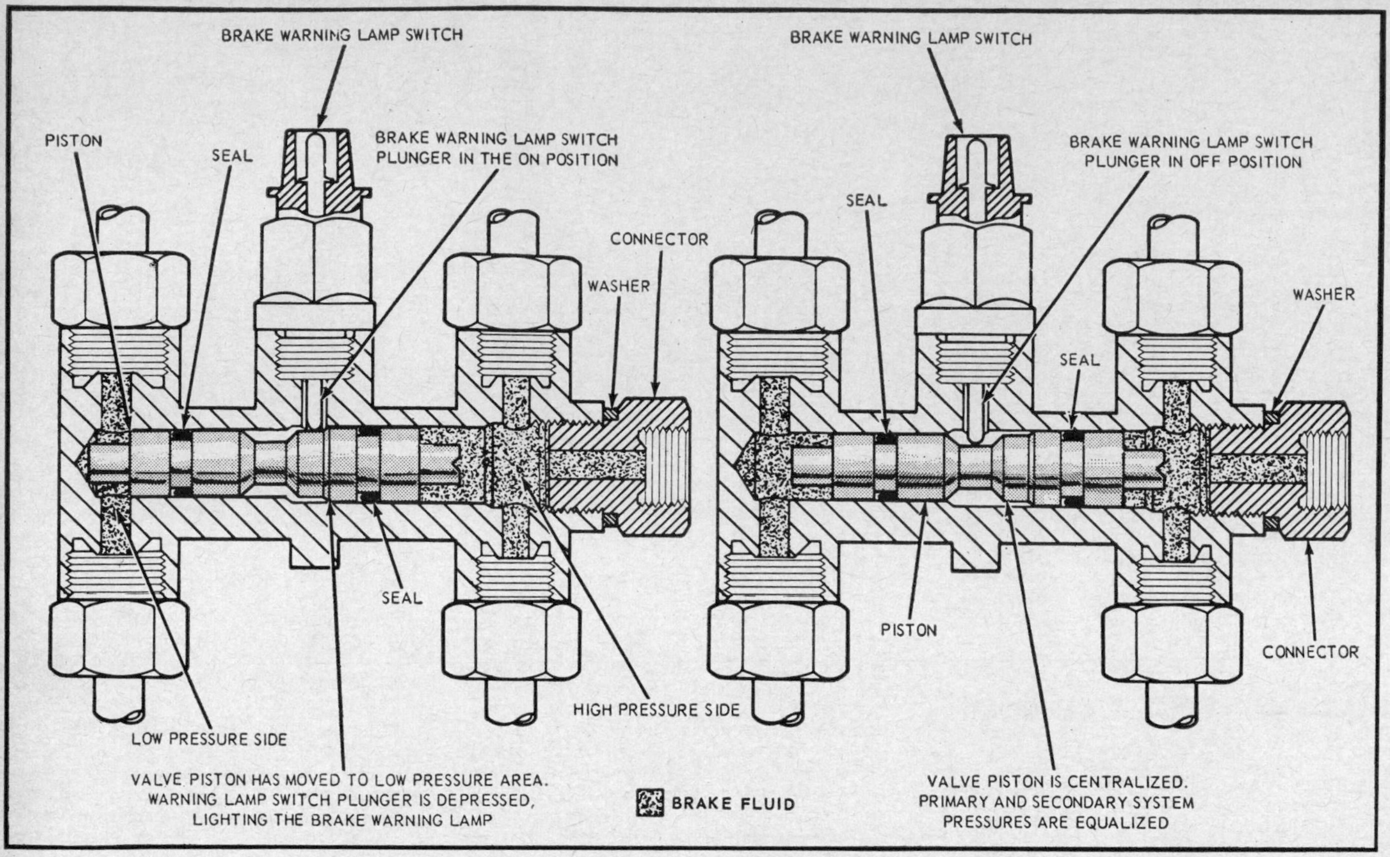

Fig. 5 Pressure differential valve and brake warning light switch

plunger upward over the tapered shoulder of the valve to close the switch contacts and light the dual brake warning lamp, signaling a brake system failure.

In Fig. 6 the valve assembly consists of two valves in a common bore that are spring loaded toward the centered position. The spring-loaded switch contact plunger rests on top of the valves in the centered position (right view). When a pressure differential occurs between the front and rear brake systems, the valves will shuttle toward the side with the low pressure. The spring-loaded switch plunger is "triggered" and the ground circuit for the warning light is completed, lighting the lamp (left view).

In Fig. 7, as pressure falls in one system, the other system's normal pressure forces the piston to the inoperative side, contacting the switch terminal, causing the warning light on the instrument panel to glow.

Testing Warning Light System

If the parking brake light is connected into the service brake warning light system, the brake warning light will flash only when the parking brake is applied with the ignition turned ON. The same light will also glow should one of the two service brake systems fail when the brake pedal is applied.

To test the system, turn the ignition ON and apply the parking brake. If the lamp fails to light, inspect for a burned out bulb, disconnected socket, a broken or disconnected wire at the switch.

Fig. 8 is an exterior view of one of these switches. They are usually mounted on the left frame side rail or on the brake pedal bracket.

To test the brake warning system, raise the car and open a wheel bleeder valve while a helper depresses the brake pedal and observes the warning light on the instrument panel. If the bulb fails to light, inspect for a burned out bulb, disconnected socket, or a broken or disconnected wire at the switch. If the bulb is not burned out, and the wire continuity

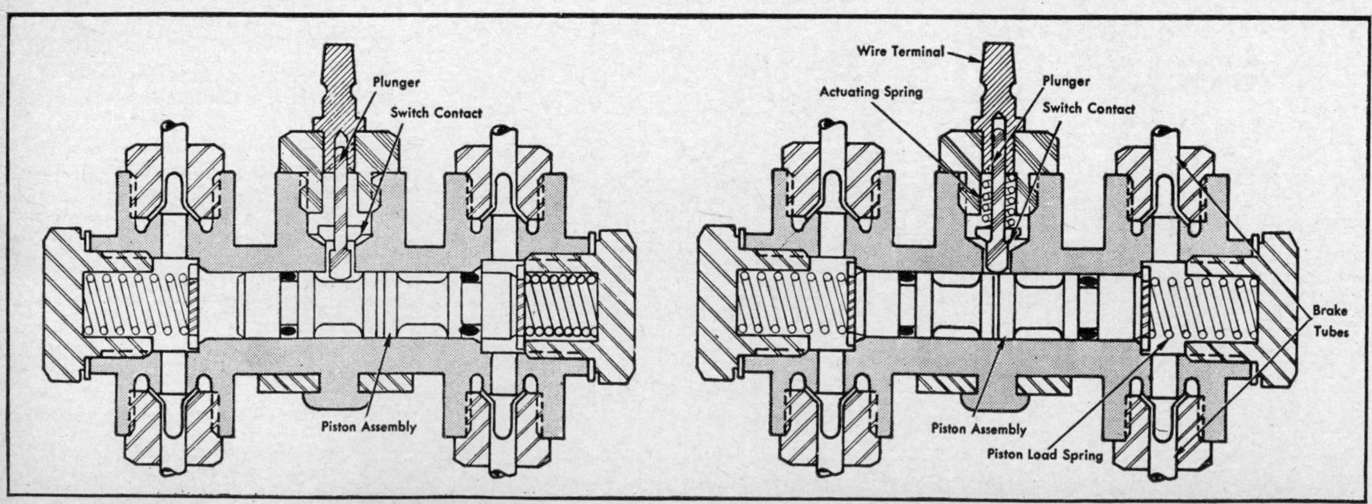

Fig. 6 Pressure differential valve and brake warning light switch

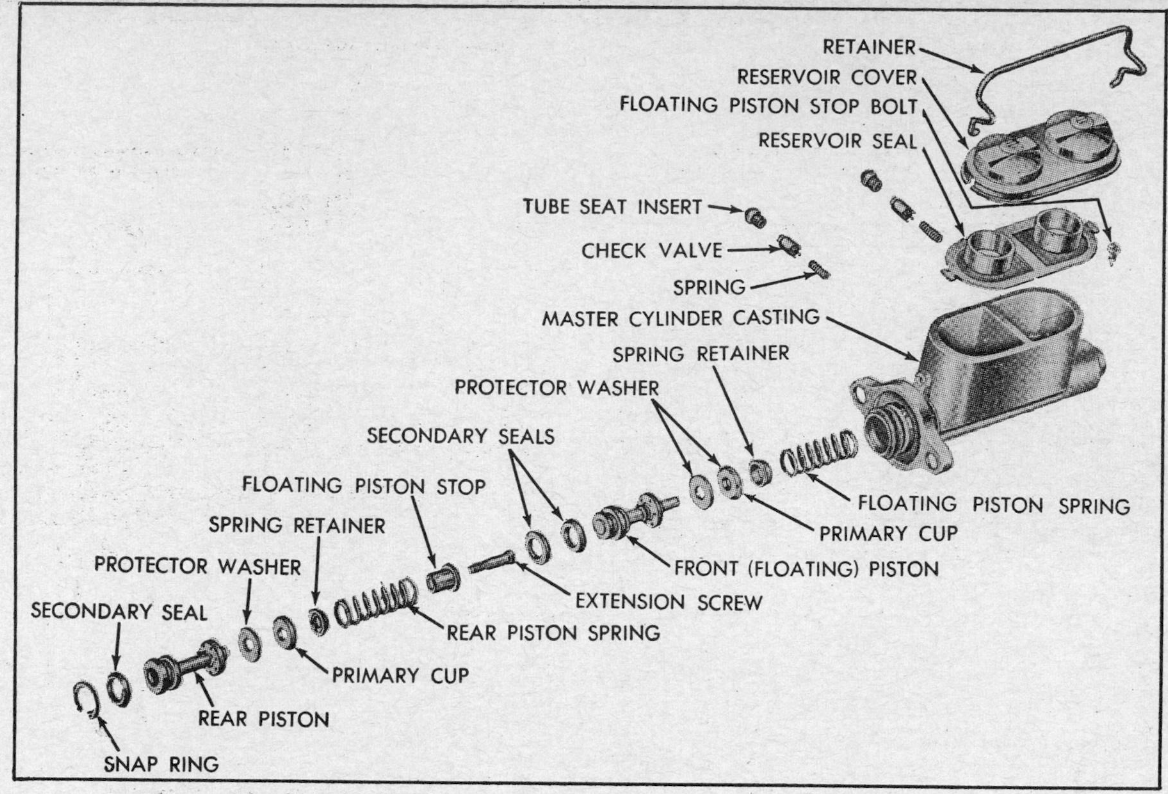

Fig. 9 Delco-Moraine dual master cylinder disassembled (GM cars)

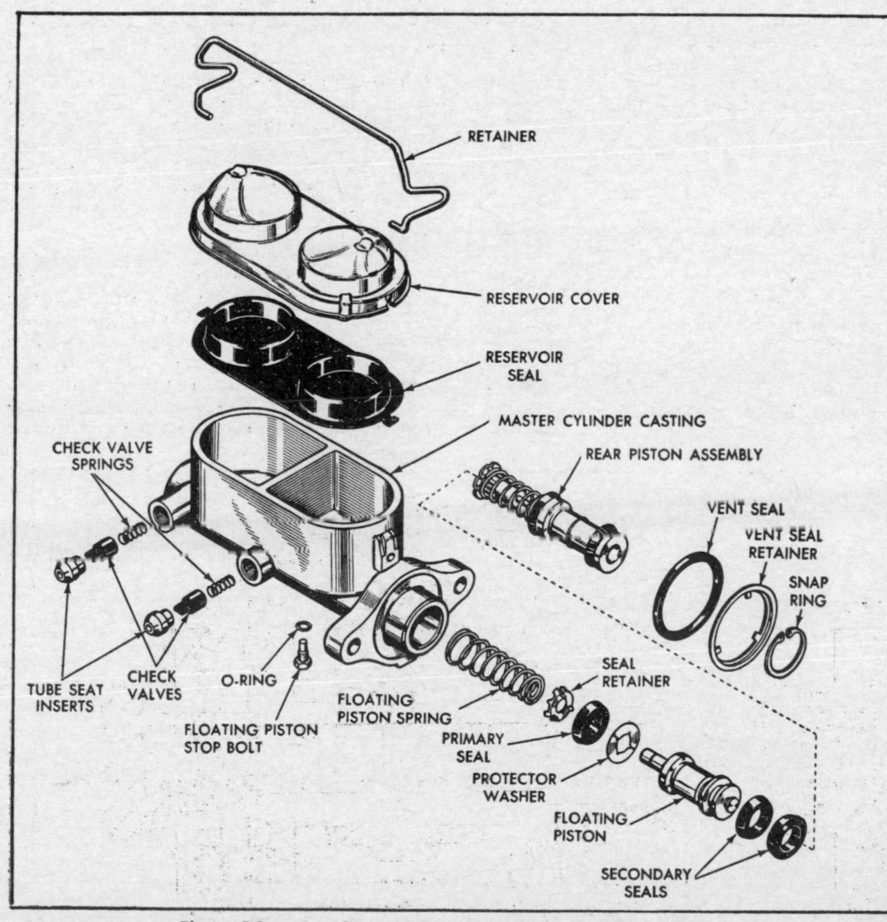

Fig. 10 Bendix dual master cylinder disassembled used with drum brakes (GM and Rambler)

is proven, replace the brake warning switch.

Master Cylinder Service

Figs. 9-14 shows an array of dual and single master cylinders. With cylinder removed from vehicle, and from brake booster if so equipped, remove the covers and disassemble the unit as suggested by the illustration of the unit being serviced.

When disassembled, wash all parts in alcohol *only.* Use an air hose to blow out all passages, orifices and valve holes. Air dry and place parts on clean paper or lint-free cloth. Inspect master cylinder bore for scoring, rust, pitting or etching. Any of these conditions will require replacement of the housing. Inspect master cylinder pistons for scoring, pitting or distortion. Replace piston if any of these conditions exist.

If either master cylinder housing or piston is replaced, clean new parts with alcohol and blow out all passages with air hose.

Examine reservoirs for foreign matter and check all passages for restrictions. If there is any suspicion of contamination or evidence of corrosion, completely flush hydraulic system as outlined below.

When overhauling a master cylinder, use all parts contained in repair kit. Before starting reassembly, dip all cups, seals, pistons, springs, check valves and retainers in alcohol and place in a clean pan or on clean paper. *Wash hands with soap and water only to prevent contamination of rubber parts from oil, kerosene or gasoline.* During assembly, dip all parts in clean, heavy duty brake fluid.

Inspect through side outlet of dual master cylinder housing to make certain

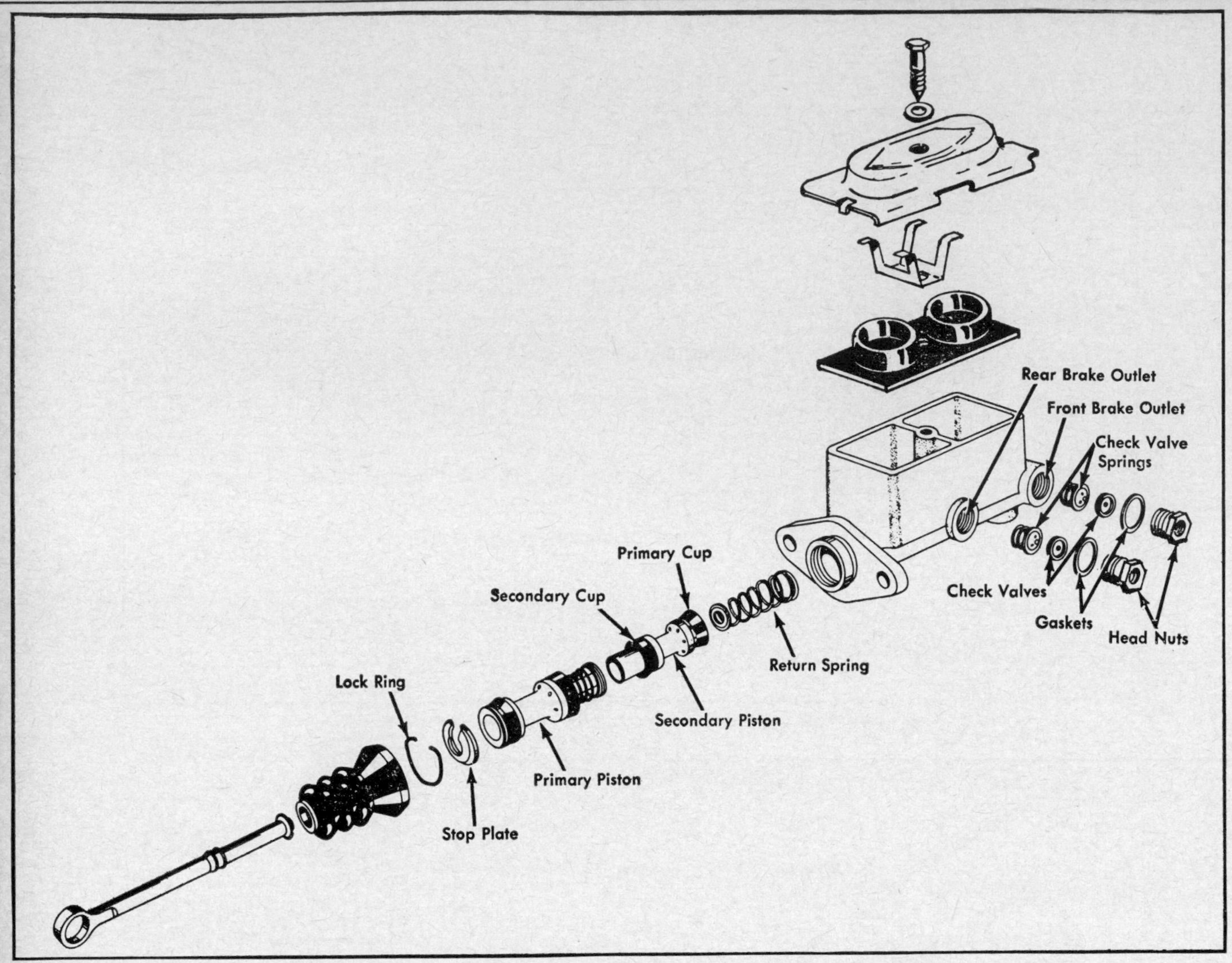

Fig. 12 Wagner dual master cylinder disassembled (Rambler American)

cup lips do not hang up on edge of hole or turn back, which would result in faulty operation. A piece of $\frac{3}{16}$" rod with an end rounded off will be helpful in guiding cups past hole.

BLEEDING BRAKES

The bleeding operation itself is fairly well standardized. First step in all cases is cleaning the dirt from the filler cap before removing it from the master cylinder. This should be done thoroughly.

Pressure bleeding is fastest because the master cylinder doesn't have to be refilled several times, and the job can be done by one man. To prevent air from the pressure tank getting into the lines, do not shake the tank while air is being added to the tank or after it has been pressurized. Set the tank in the required location, bring the air hose to the tank, and do not move it during the bleeding operation. The tank should be kept at least one-third full.

If air does get into the fluid, releasing the pressure will cause the bubbles to increase in size, rise to the top of the fluid, and escape. Pressure should not be greater than about 35 lb. per sq. in.

When bleeding without pressure, open the bleed valve three-quarters of a turn, depress the pedal a full stroke, then allow the pedal to return slowly to its released position. Some makers suggest that after the pedal has been depressed to the end of its stroke, the bleeder valve should be closed before the start of the return stroke. On cars with power brakes, first reduce the vacuum in the power unit to zero by pumping the brake pedal several times with the engine off before starting to bleed the system.

Pressure bleeding, of course, eliminates the need for pedal pumping. Chrysler Corp. suggests that, when pressure is used, the bleeder valve should be opened and closed intermittently at about four-second intervals. This gives a whirling action to the fluid in the wheel cylinder, and helps expel the air.

At one time, some car makers recommended that a clean container be used for the drained fluid, so that the fluid could be reused. All now agree that drained fluid should be discarded. Care should be taken not to spill brake fluid, since this can damage the finish of the car.

Flushing is essential if there is water, mineral oil or other contaminants in the lines, and whenever new parts are installed in the hydraulic system. Fluid contamination is usually indicated by swollen and deteriorated cups and other rubber parts.

Wheel cylinders on disc brakes are equipped with bleeder valves, and are bled in the same manner as wheel cylinders for drum brakes.

Bleeding is necessary on all four wheels if air has entered the system because of low fluid level, or the line or lines have been disconnected. If a line is disconnected at any one wheel cylinder, that cylinder only need be bled. Of course, on brake reline jobs, bleeding is advisable to remove any air or contaminants.

Master cylinders equipped with bleeder valves should be bled first before the wheel cylinders are bled. In all cases where a master cylinder has been overhauled, it must be bled. Where there is no bleeder valve, this can be done by leaving the line (or lines) loose, actuating the brake pedal to expel the air and then tightening the line (or lines).

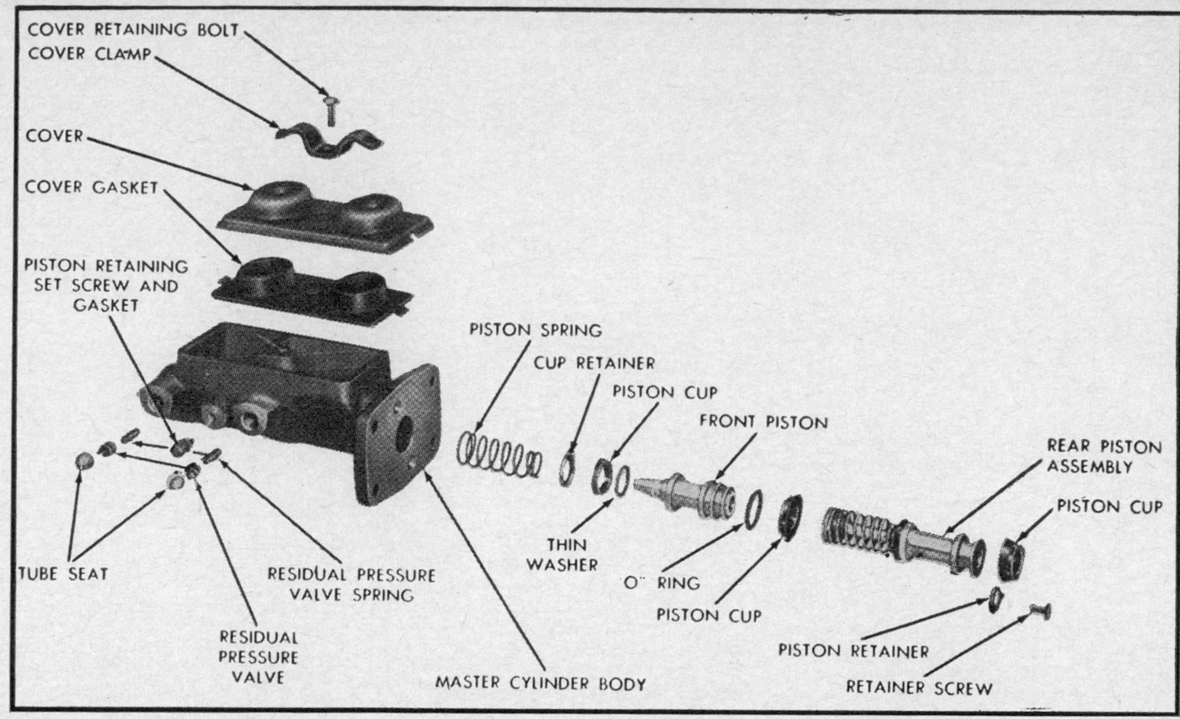

Fig. 11 Bendix dual master cylinder disassembled used with drum brakes (Chrysler Line)

NOTE: After overhauling a dual master cylinder used in conjunction with disc brakes, it is advisable to bleed the cylinder before installing it on the car. The reason for this recommendation is that air may be trapped between the master cylinder pistons because there is only one residual pressure valve (check valve) used in these units.

The recommended procedure for Chrysler Line cars is as follows:

1. Clamp master cylinder in a vise and attach the special Bleeding Tubes (Tool No. C-4029) Fig. 16. *Be sure that the residual pressure valve is on the end of the tube in the large capacity reservoir as shown. This*

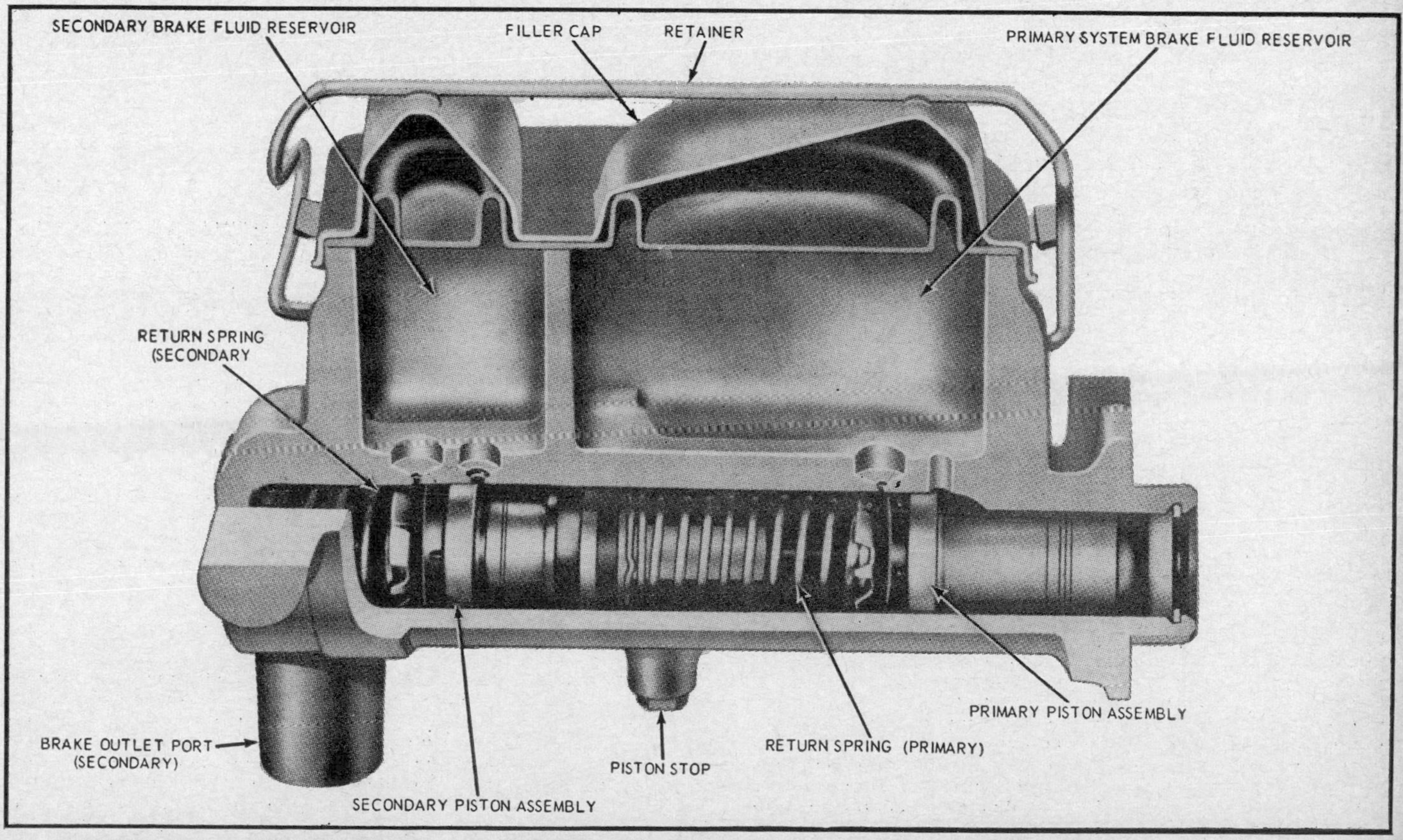

Fig. 13 Cutaway view of Bendix dual master cylinder used with disc brakes (typical)

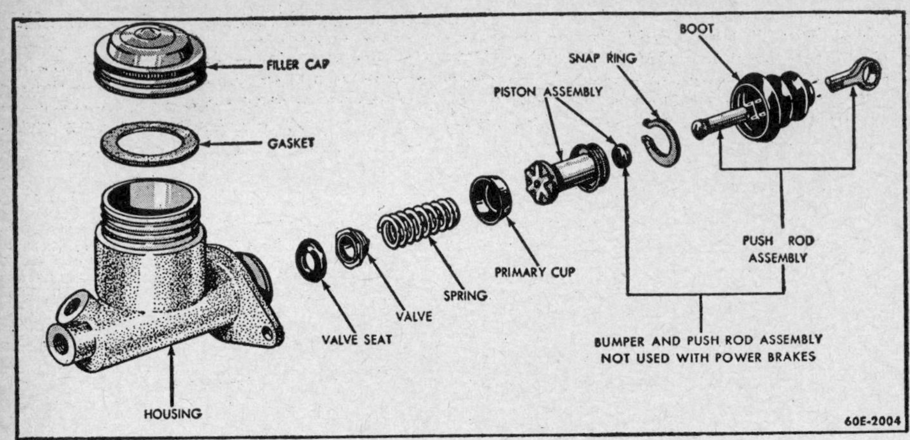

Fig. 14 Typical single brake master cylinder

keeps the brake fluid from being syphoned out of the reservoir while bleeding.

2. Fill both reservoirs with approved brake fluid.
3. Using a wooden stick or dowel (cars with power brakes) depress push rod slowly and allow the pistons to return under pressure of the springs. Do this several times until all air bubbles are expelled.
4. Remove bleeding tubes from cylinder and install cover and gasket.
5. Install master cylinder on car and bleed wheel cylinders, preferably with a pressure bleeder.

Alternate Method

1. Support assembly in a vise and fill both reservoirs with brake fluid.
2. Loosely install a plug in each outlet port of the cylinder. Depress push rod several times until air bubbles cease to appear in the brake fluid.
3. Tighten plugs and attempt to depress the piston. Piston travel should be restricted after all air is expelled.
4. Install master cylinder on car and bleed wheel cylinders, preferably with a pressure bleeder.

Testing Dual Master Cylinders

Be sure that the master cylinder compensates in both ports. This can be done by applying the brake pedal lightly (engine running with power brakes), and observing for brake fluid squirting up in the reservoirs. This may only occur in the front chamber. To determine if the rear compensating port is open, pump up the brakes rapidly and hold the pedal down. Have an observer watch the fluid in the rear reservoir while the pedal is raised. A disturbance in the fluid indicates that the compensating port is open.

Wheel Bleeding Sequence

Difference of opinion as to whether the longest or shortest line should be bled first still exists. To be safe, use the sequence given below, recommended by the car manufacturers.

Chrysler Corp. cars ..... RR-LR-RF-LF
Ford Company cars ..... RR-LR-RF-LF
General Motors cars:
All except Chevrolet .. LF-RF-LR-RR
Chevrolet Division .... LR-RR-LF-RF
Rambler .... RR-LR-RF-LF

Dual Master Cylinder Bleeding Notes

Ford Motor Co. Cars

After the normal bleeding operation has been completed, note that the brake warning light will be ON because the pressure differential valve has moved off center, and must be returned to the central position. To do this, loosen the valve's inlet tube on the side opposite the wheel cylinder that was bled last. Apply the brake pedal slowly until the warning light goes out, and tighten fitting. Replace any fluid that has leaked out during the operation.

General Motors Cars

On cars with combined drum and disc brakes, the spring-loaded end of the pressure differential valve must be held in its open position while bleeding. This is done by depressing and holding in the plunger in the end of the valve either by hand or by taping. If pressure bleeding equipment is used, pressure must be below 30 psi.

Corvette

On Corvette models with disc brakes on all four wheels, there are two bleeder valves on each rear wheel disc brake. Remove the rear wheels to bleed. A single valve is used on front disc brakes.

Rambler

Before bleeding brakes, disconnect the switch terminal wire and remove nylon switch terminal, contact plunger actuating spring, and nylon plunger with contact.

In the event the valve has "triggered", the valve centering spring pressure may hold the switch plunger. If this happens, apply a slight amount of brake pedal pressure while releasing the plunger from the valve body.

After the bleeding operation, assemble the plunger spring and install valve with contact down. Install the nylon terminal and connect warning light wire to valve terminal. In the event brake fluid leaks from the center terminal body opening when the terminal is removed, replace the valve assembly.

Imperial 1967

Cars produced at approximately December 17, 1966 are equipped with a front disc brake pressure metering valve which is located on the left frame rail directly under the battery.

The purpose of the metering valve is to provide a better match of the front disc brakes with the rear drum brakes, resulting in improved braking balance *in light pedal applications.*

Gravity bleed and pedal methods are not affected by the presence of the metering valve. However, pressure bleeding is influenced by the metering valve. Bleed pressure, which is normally about 35 psi, is high enough to cause the metering valve to close, which stops the flow of fluid to the front brakes. However, the valve can be held open manually by depressing the pressure release plunger (located at the bottom of the valve) in its uppermost position by hand or secured with masking tape while bleeding the brakes.

CAUTION: Under no conditions should a rigid clamp, wedge or block be used to secure the plunger as this can cause an internal failure in the valve. It should be

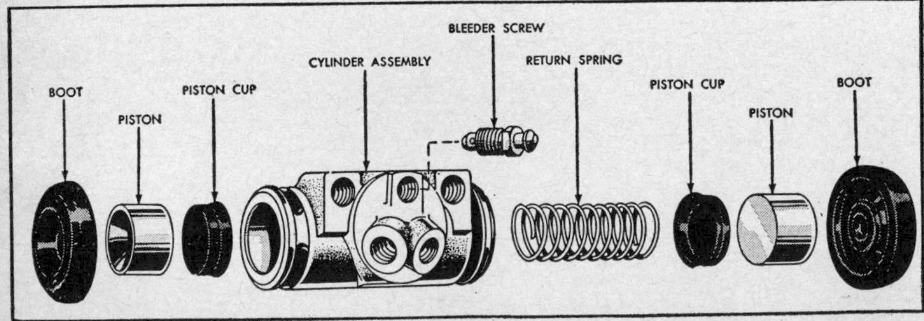

Fig. 15 Disassembled view of typical wheel cylinder

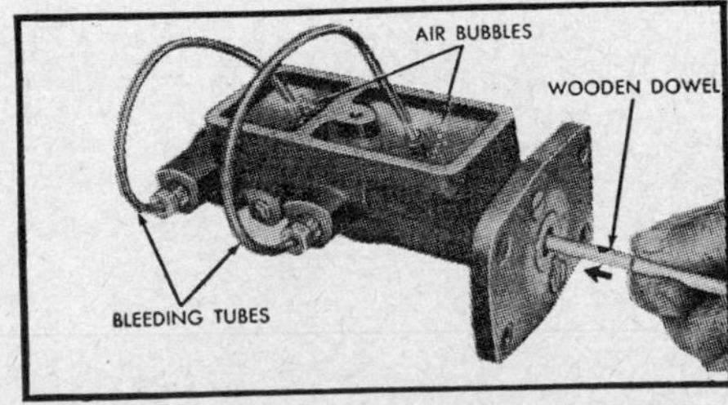

Fig. 16 Bleeding master cylinder used in conjunction with disc brakes

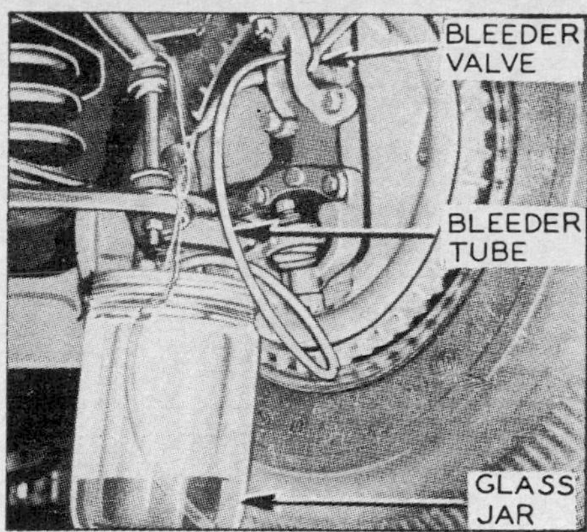

Fig. 17 Bleeding wheel cylinder

noted that the pressure release plunger of the valve is already in its uppermost position when there is no pressure present.

WHEEL CYLINDERS

1. Remove wheel, drum and brake shoes.
2. Disconnect hydraulic line at wheel cylinder. *Do not pull metal line away from cylinder as the cylinder connection will bend metal line and make installation difficult. Line will separate from cylinder when cylinder is moved away from brake backing plate.*
3. Remove screws holding cylinder to brake plate and remove cylinder.

Overhaul

1. Referring to Fig. 15 as a guide, remove boots, pistons, springs and cups from cylinder.
2. Place all parts, except cylinder casting, in alcohol. Wipe cylinder walls with alcohol.
3. Examine cylinder bore. A scored bore may be honed providing the diameter is not increased more than .005". Replace worn or damaged parts from the repair kit.
4. Before assembling, wash hands with soap and water only as oil, kerosene or gasoline will contaminate rubber parts.
5. Lubricate cylinder wall and rubber cups with brake fluid.
6. Install springs, cups, pistons and boots in housing.
7. Wipe end of hydraulic line to remove any foreign matter.
8. Place hydraulic cylinder in position. Enter tubing into cylinder and start connecting fitting.
9. Secure cylinder to backing plate and then complete tightening of tubing fitting.
10. Install brake shoes, drum and wheel.
11. Bleed system as outlined previously, and adjust brakes.

FLUSHING HYDRAULIC SYSTEM

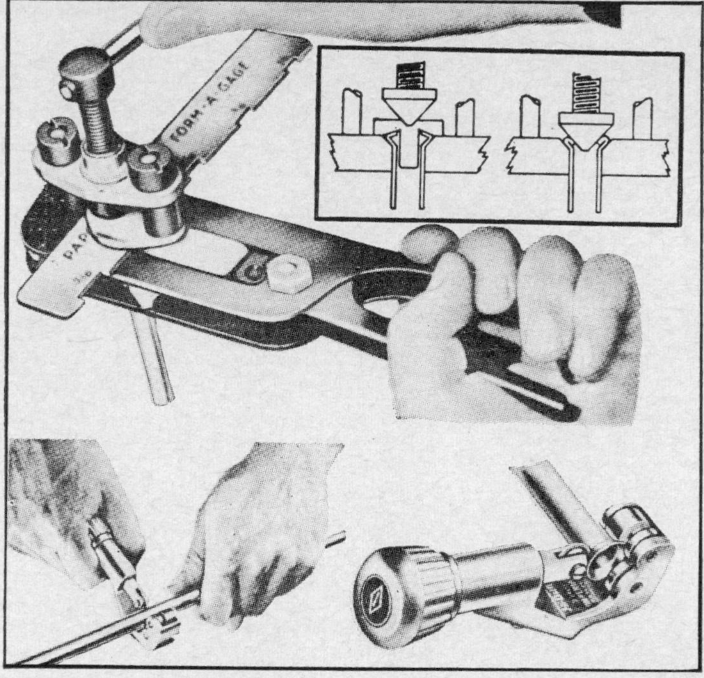

Fig. 18 Flaring hydraulic brake tubing

It may sometime become necessary to flush out the system due to the presence of mineral oil, kerosene, gasoline, etc., which will cause swelling of rubber piston cups and valves so they become inoperative. The procedure is as follows:

1. Attach bleeder tube and open bleeder valve at left front wheel, Fig. 17.
2. Flush out system thoroughly with clean denatured alcohol, pumping the fluid from the master cylinder reservoir and out of the wheel cylinder bleeder valve.
3. Repeat Steps 1 and 2 at remaining wheel cylinders. To ensure thorough flushing, about ½ pint of alcohol should be bled through each wheel cylinder.
4. Replace all rubber parts in master and wheel cylinders. Thoroughly clean cylinders and pistons in alcohol before installing new parts.
5. After installing parts, fill system with recommended brake fluid and flush system of cleaning solution and then bleed brakes. In doing this, pump brake fluid from wheel cylinder bleeder valves until clear fluid flows from bleeder tube and then, if necessary, continue until no air bubbles emerge from bleeder tube.

HYDRAULIC TUBING

Steel tubing is used to conduct hydraulic pressure to the brakes. All fittings, tubing and hose should be inspected for rusted, damaged or defective flared seats. The tubing is equipped with a double flare or inverted seat to insure more positive seating in the fitting. To repair or reflare tubing, proceed as follows:

1. Using the tool shown in Fig. 18 or its equivalent, cut off the damaged seat or damaged tubing.
2. Ream out any burrs or rough edges showing on inside edges of tubing. This will make the ends of the tubing square and insure better seating of the flared end. *Before flaring tubing, place a compression nut on tubing.*
3. Open handles of flaring tool and rotate jaws of tool until mating jaws of tubing size are centered in the area between vertical posts.
4. Slowly close handles with tubing inserted in jaws but do not apply heavy pressure to handle as this will lock tubing in place.
5. Referring to Fig. 18, place gauge on edge over end of tubing and push tubing through jaws until end of tubing contacts recessed notch of gauge matching size of tubing.
6. Squeeze handles of flaring tool and lock tubing in place.
7. Place proper size plug of gauge down in end of tubing. Swing compression disc over gauge and center tapered flaring screw in recess in disc.
8. Lubricate taper of flaring or screw and screw in until plug gauge has seated in jaws of flaring tool. This action has started to invert the extended end of tubing.
9. Remove gauge and apply lubricant to tapered end of flaring screw and continue to screw down until tool is firmly seated in tubing.
10. Remove tubing from flaring tool and inspect the seat. If seat is cracked, cut off cracked end and repeat flaring operation.

DISC BRAKES

CONTENTS

BENDIX With Opposed Pistons . I-431

Buick, 1967-69 Senior Cars
Cadillac, 1967-68
Dodge Coronet and Charger, 1966-69
Plymouth Belvedere and Satellite, 1966-69
Rambler, 1965-69

BUDD With Opposed Pistons . . I-434

Chrysler, 1967-68
Dodge Polara and Monaco, 1965-68
Plymouth Fury & V.I.P., 1965-68
Plymouth Seniors, 1965-68

DELCO-MORAINE Opposed Pistons I-436

Buick, 1967-68 Intermediate Cars
Chevrolet Line, 1967-68
Corvette, 1965-69
Oldsmobile & F-85, 1967-68
Pontiac Line, 1967-68

KELSEY-HAYES Opposed Pistons . . I-436

Dodge Charger, Coronet & Dart, 69
Dodge Dart, 1965-69
Ford, 1965-67
Lincoln Continental, 1965-69
Mercury, 1965-67
Mustang, 1965-67
Plymouth Valiant and Barracuda, 1965-69
Thunderbird, 1965-67
Toronado, 1967-68

KELSEY-HAYES Single Piston I-438

Dodge Polara and Monaco, 1969
Ford Line, 1968-69
Mark III, 1969
Mercury Line, 1968-69
Plymouth, 1969
Thunderbird, 1968-69

TROUBLE SHOOTING

Excessive Pedal Travel

1. Shoe and lining knock back after violent cornering or rough road travel.
2. Piston and shoe and lining assembly not properly seated or positioned.
3. Air leak or insufficient fluid in system or caliper.
4. Loose wheel bearing adjustment.
5. Damaged or worn caliper piston seal.
6. Improper booster push rod adjustment.
7. Shoe out of flat more than .005".
8. Rear brake automatic adjusters inoperative.
9. Improperly ground rear brake shoe and lining assemblies.

Brake Roughness or Chatter; Pedal Pumping

1. Excessive lateral run-out of rotor.
2. Rotor excessively out of parallel.

Excessive Pedal Effort

1. Frozen or seized pistons.
2. Brake fluid, oil or grease on linings.
3. Shoe and lining worn below specifications.
4. Proportioning valve malfunction.
5. Booster inoperative.
6. Leaking booster vacuum check valve.

Pull, Uneven or Grabbing Brakes

1. Frozen or seized pistons.
2. Brake fluid, oil or grease on linings.
3. Caliper out of alignment with rotor.
4. Loose caliper attachment.
5. Unequalized front tire pressure.
6. Incorrect front end alignment.
7. Lining protruding beyond end of shoe.

Brake Rattle

1. Excessive clearance between shoe and caliper or between shoe and splash shield.
2. Shoe hold-down clips missing or improperly positioned.

Heavy Brake Drag

1. Frozen or seized pistons.
2. Operator riding brake pedal.
3. Incomplete brake pedal return due to linkage interference.
4. Faulty booster check valve holding pressure in hydraulic system.
5. Residual pressure in front brake hydraulic system.

Caliper Brake Fluid Leak

1. Damaged or worn caliper piston seal.
2. Scores in cylinder bore.
3. Corrosion build-up in cylinder bore or on piston surface.
4. Metal clip in seal groove.

No Braking Effect When Pedal is Depressed

1. Piston and shoe and lining assembly not properly seated or positioned.
2. Air leak or insufficient fluid in system or caliper.
3. Damaged or worn caliper piston seal.
4. Bleeder screw open.
5. Air in hydraulic system or improper bleeding.

SERVICE PRECAUTIONS

Brake Lines & Linings

Remove one of the front wheels and inspect the brake disc, caliper and linings. (The wheel bearings should be inspected at this time and repacked if necessary).

Do not get any oil or grease on the linings. If the linings are worn to within .030" of the surface of the shoe, replace both sets of shoe and lining assemblies. It is recommended that both front wheel sets be replaced whenever a respective shoe and lining is worn or damaged. Inspect and, if necessary, replace rear brake linings also.

If the caliper is cracked or fluid leakage through the casting is evident, it must be replaced as a unit.

Shoe & Lining Wear

If a visual inspection does not adequately determine the condition of the lining, a physical check will be necessary.

To check the amount of lining wear, remove a wheel from the car, the caliper from the steering knuckle, and the shoe and lining assemblies. Three thickness measurements should be taken (with a micrometer) across the middle section of the shoe and lining; one reading at each side and one reading in the center.

When a shoe and lining assembly has worn to a thickness of .180", it should be replaced. If shoes do not require replacement, reinstall them in their original inner and outer positions.

Brake Roughness

The most common cause of brake chatter on disc brakes is a variation in thickness of the disc. If roughness or vibration is encountered during highway operation or if pedal pumping is experienced at low speeds, the disc may have excessive thickness variation. To check for this condition, measure the disc at 12 points with a micrometer at a radius approximately one inch from edge of disc. If thickness measurements vary by more than .0005" inch the disc should be replaced with a new one.

Excessive lateral runout of braking disc may cause a "knocking back" of the pistons, possibly creating increased pedal travel and vibration when brakes are applied.

Before checking the runout, wheel bearings should be adjusted. The readjustment is very important and will be required at the completion of the test to prevent bearing failure. Be sure to make the adjustment according to the recommendations given under *Front Wheel Bearings, Adjust* in the car chapters.

Brake Disc Service

Servicing of disc brakes is extremely critical due to the close tolerances required in machining the brake disc to insure proper brake operation. In manufacturing brake discs, tolerances of the rubbing surfaces for flatness is .001" and usually for parallelism .0005". Lateral runout of the faces should not exceed .004 to .005" in most cases although the limit on Ford Company cars is only .002".

The maintenance of these close controls of the shape of the rubbing surfaces is necessary to prevent brake roughness. In addition, the surface finish must be non-directional and maintained at a micro inch finish. This close control of the rubbing surface finish is necessary to avoid pulls and erratic performance and promote long lining life and equal lining wear of both left and right brakes.

In light of the foregoing remarks, refinishing of the rubbing surfaces should not be attempted unless precision equipment, capable of measuring in micro inches (millionths of an inch) is available. This equipment is expensive (about $300.00) and it is safer and less expensive

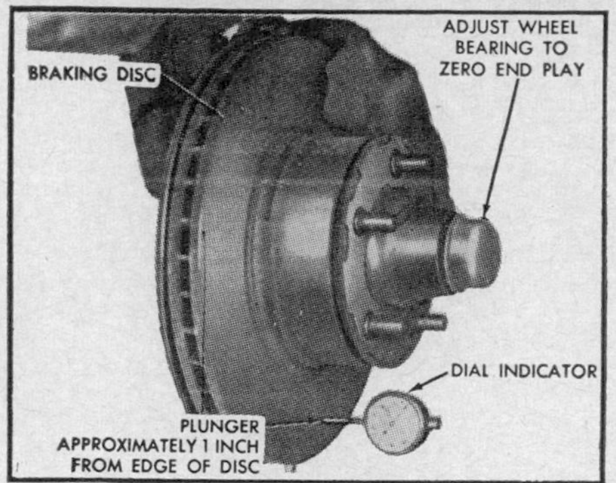

Fig. 1 Checking brake disc for runout

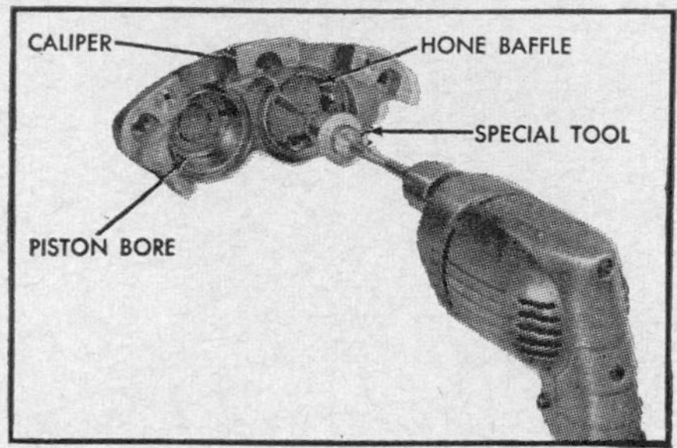

Fig. 2 Honing caliper piston bore

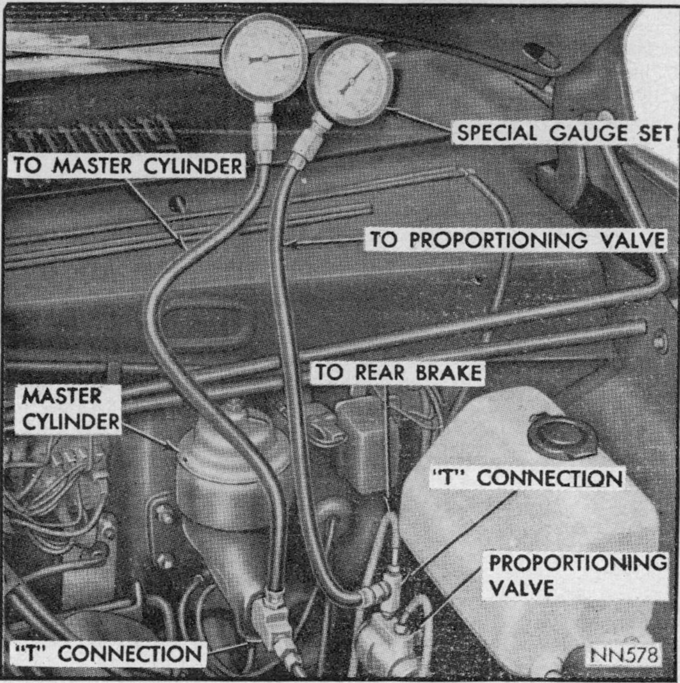

Fig. 3 Gauge hook-up for testing proportioning valve (typical)

to install a new disc when the runout exceeds the specifications mentioned above.

To check runout of a disc, mount a dial indicator on a convenient part (steering knuckle, tie rod, disc brake caliper housing) so that the plunger of the dial indicator contacts the disc at a point one inch from the outer edge, Fig. 1. If the total indicated runout exceeds specifications, install a new disc.

General Precautions

1. Grease or any other foreign material must be kept off the caliper, surfaces of the disc and external surfaces of the hub, during service procedures. Handling the brake disc and caliper should be done in a way to avoid deformation of the disc and nicking or scratching brake linings.
2. If inspection reveals rubber piston seals are worn or damaged, they should be replaced immediately.
3. During removal and installation of a wheel assembly, exercise care so as not to interfere with or damage the caliper splash shield, the bleeder screw or the transfer tube.
4. Front wheel bearings should be adjusted to specifications.
5. Be sure vehicle is centered on hoist before servicing any of the front end components to avoid bending or damaging the disc splash shield on full right or left wheel turns.
6. Before the vehicle is moved after any brake service work, be sure to obtain a firm brake pedal.
7. The assembly bolts of the two caliper housings should not be disturbed unless the caliper requires service.

Inspection of Caliper

Should it become necessary to remove the caliper for installation of new parts, clean all parts in alcohol, wipe dry using lint-free cloths. Using an air hose, blow out drilled passages and bores. Check dust boots for punctures or tears. If punctures or tears are evident, new boots should be installed upon reassembly.

Inspect piston bores in both housings for scoring or pitting. Bores that show light scratches or corrosion can usually be cleaned with crocus cloth. However, bores that have deep scratches or scoring may be honed, provided the diameter of the bore is not increased more than .002". If the bore does not clean up within this specification, a new caliper housing should be installed (black stains on the bore walls are caused by piston seals and will do no harm).

When using a hone, Fig. 2, be sure to install the hone baffle before honing bore. The baffle is used to protect the hone stones from damage. Use extreme care in cleaning the caliper after honing. Remove all dust and grit by flushing the caliper with alcohol. Wipe dry with clean lint less cloth and then clean a second time in the same manner.

Bleeding Disc Brakes

The disc brake hydraulic system can be bled manually or with pressure bleeding equipment. On vehicles with disc brakes the brake pedal will require more pumping and frequent checking of fluid level in master cylinder during bleeding operation.

Never use brake fluid that has been drained from hydraulic system when bleeding the brakes. Be sure the disc brake pistons are returned to their normal positions and that the shoe and lining assemblies are properly seated. Before driving the vehicle, check brake operation to be sure that a firm pedal has been obtained.

Proportioning Valve

The proportioning valve (when used), Fig. 3, provides balanced braking action between front and rear brakes under a wide range of braking conditions. The valve regulates the hydraulic pressure applied to the rear wheel cylinders, thus limiting rear braking action when high pressures are required at the front brakes. In this manner, premature rear wheel skid is prevented.

Testing Proportioning Valve

When a premature rear wheel slide is obtained on a brake application, it usually is an indication that the fluid pressure to the rear wheels is above the 50% reduction ratio for the rear line pressure and that a malfunction has occurred within the proportioning valve.

To test the valve, install gauge set shown in Fig. 3 in brake line between master cylinder and proportioning valve, and at output end of proportioning valve and brake line as shown. Be sure all joints are fluid tight.

Have a helper exert pressure on brake pedal (holding pressure). Obtain a reading on master cylinder output of approximately 800 psi. While pressure is being held as above, reading on valve outlet should be 530-570 psi. If the pressure readings do not meet these specifications, the valve should be removed and a new valve installed.

BENDIX OPPOSED PISTONS

The front wheel disc brake, Fig. 4, consists of a fixed caliper (inner and outer housing), two friction pads (brake lining) molded to steel shoes, four pistons, piston return springs, piston seals and dust boots. The brake disc is made from

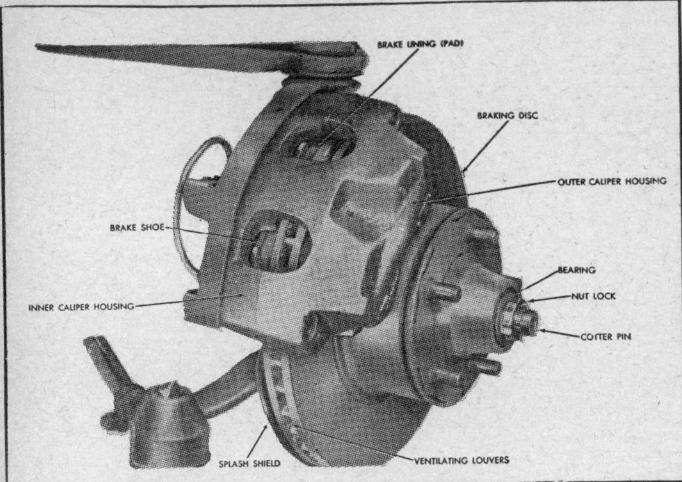

Fig. 4 Bendix opposed piston disc brake

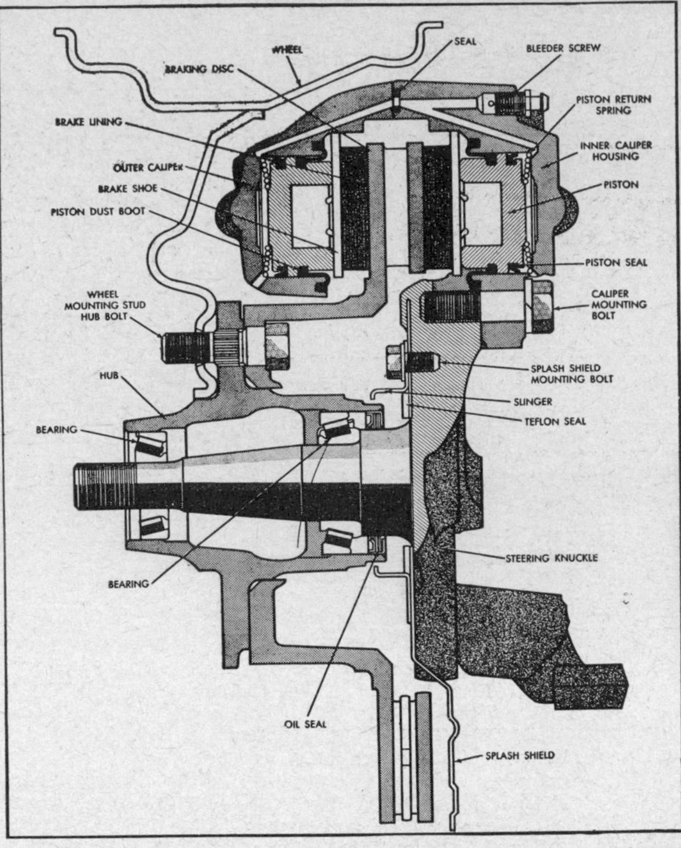

Fig. 5 Sectional view of Bendix opposed piston disc brake

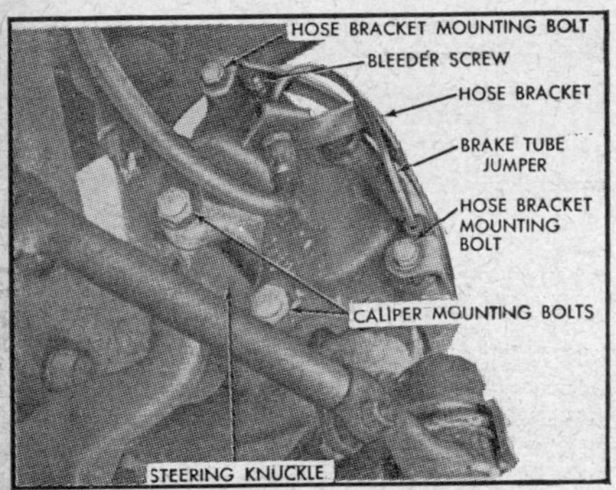

Fig. 6 Caliper mounting

high grade cast iron and has a series of air vent louvers to provide for cooling of the disc. The splash shield that is bolted to the spindle is used to prevent road contaminants from contacting the inboard side of the disc and lining surfaces, Fig. 5. The wheel itself provides for the outboard surface of the disc.

The brake disc is mounted on the front wheel hub by five bolts, and is straddled by the caliper which is attached to the steering knuckle by two bolts. Inserted between the pistons and the disc are the shoe and lining assemblies, which are held in position by parallel machined abutments within the caliper.

Brake Shoe Removal

1. Remove wheel assemblies.
2. Remove caliper-to-steering knuckle bolts, Fig. 6.
3. Remove caliper from disc by sliding it up and away from disc, Fig. 7.
4. Remove brake shoes and lining assemblies one at a time through bottom opening, Fig. 8.

Brake Shoe Installation

1. Referring to Fig. 8, slide shoe and lining assemblies into position in caliper, one at a time, with curved portion (with tabs) entering first and metal shoe against open ends of pistons. Using fingers, spread linings apart until pistons are seated in their bores.
2. Slide caliper down into position over brake disc and align mounting holes.

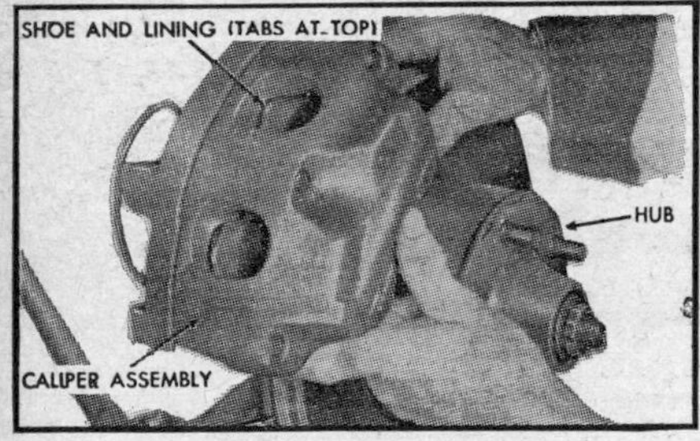

Fig. 7 Removing or installing caliper

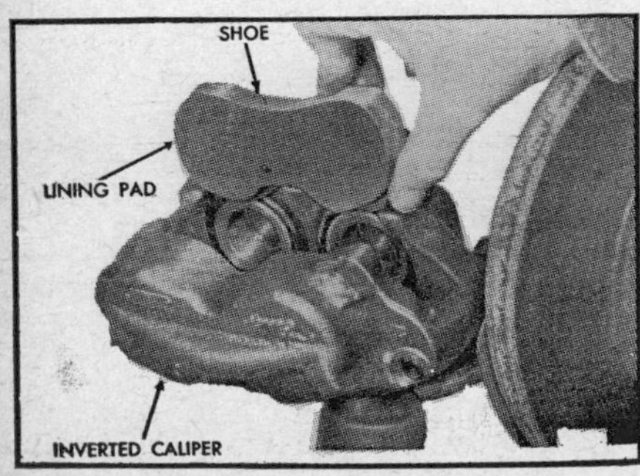

Fig. 8 Removing or installing brake shoe and lining

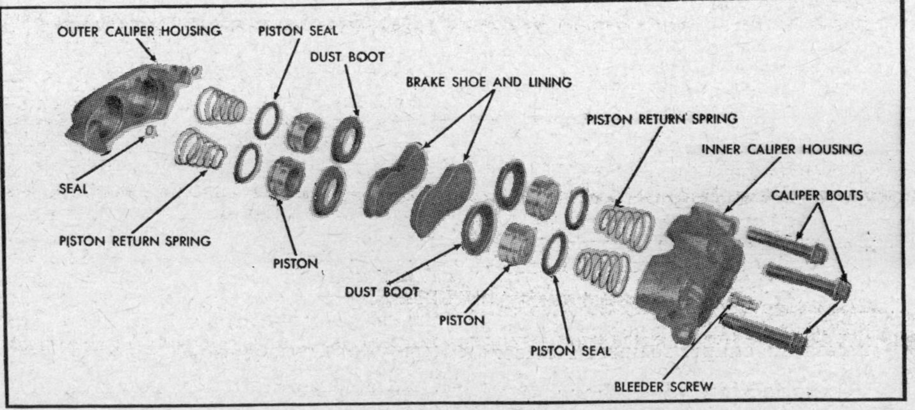

Fig. 9 Exploded view of caliper assembly

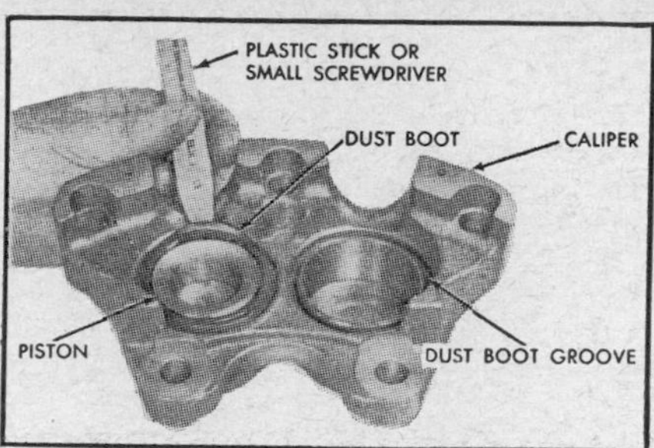

Fig. 10 Removing piston dust boot

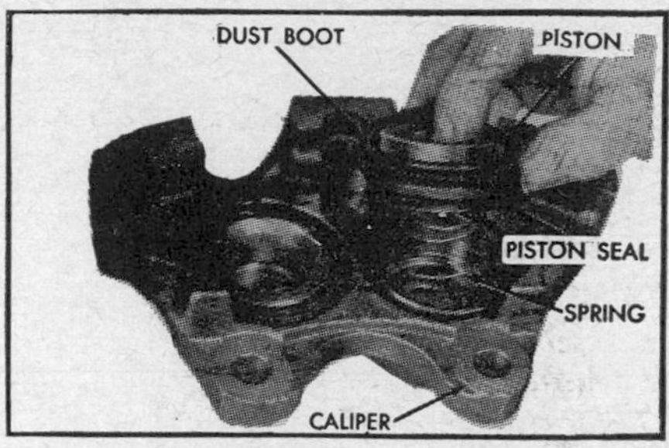

Fig. 11 Removing piston, boot, seal and return spring

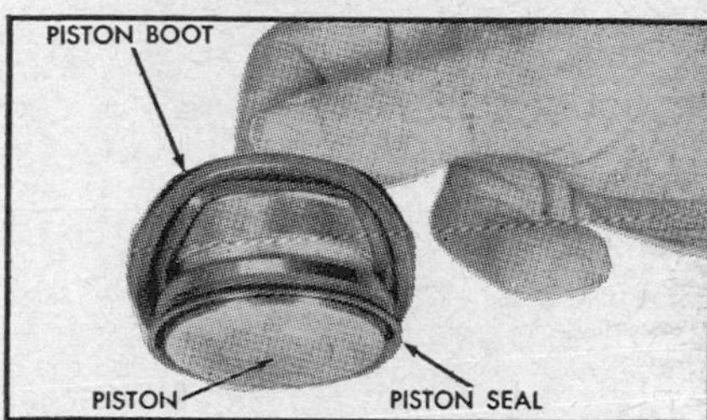

Fig. 12 Removing or installing piston boot

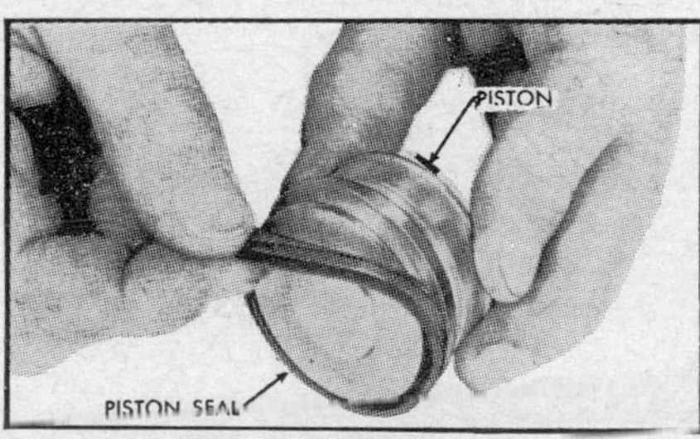

Fig. 13 Removing or installing piston seal

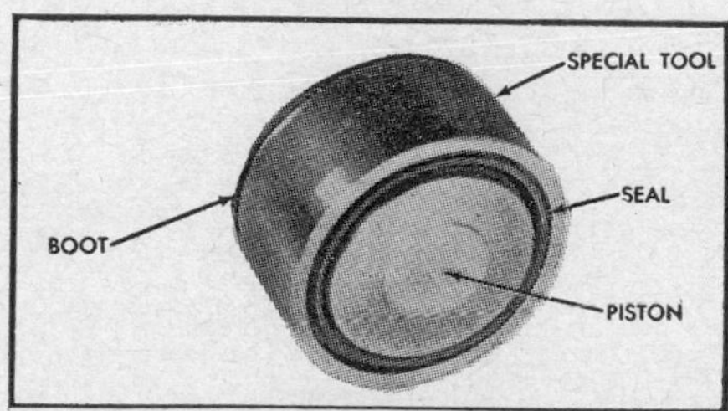

Fig. 14 Piston and seal installing tool

As caliper is being lowered, be sure that lining slides easily along brake disc.

3. Install caliper mounting bolts and torque to 85-90 ft-lbs.
4. Make sure disc rotates freely and with minimum drag.
5. Install wheel assembly.

CAUTION: Road test vehicle and make several heavy 40 mph stops to wear off any foreign material on the brakes and to seat the linings. The vehicle may pull to one side if this is not done.

Removing Caliper

1. Remove wheels.
2. Disconnect brake line at caliper housing and install a pipe plug in the tube opening.
3. Remove bolts that attach hose bracket to caliper.
4. Remove bolts that attach caliper to steering knuckle.
5. Remove caliper from brake disc by slowly sliding it up and away from disc.

Disassembling Caliper

1. Referring to Fig. 9, drain caliper, then place it in a vise.
2. Separate caliper halves and remove two crossover seals.
3. Using a screwdriver, pry exposed dust boot out of groove, Fig. 10. Be sure to hold piston compressed during this operation.
4. Remove piston, seal and dust boot from caliper, Fig. 11. Remove piston return spring.
5. Remove piston dust boot by grasping edge and pulling out of its groove, Fig. 12.
6. Using fingers, roll piston seal out of its groove and discard seal, Fig. 13.
7. Remove remaining pistons in same manner.
8. Remove bleeder screw from inner caliper.

Assembling Caliper

1. Clamp caliper housing in vise and coat cylinder bores with silicone grease, then install piston return spring with large diameter down and seated in recess at bottom of bore.
2. Coat outside diameter and fill inner diameter of a new piston seal with silicone grease and work over piston land and down into position in groove, using fingers only.
3. Install dust boot on piston with lip of seat toward piston.
4. Using a suitable tapered sleeve, Fig. 14, install piston, seal and boot in sleeve, with lip of seal towards taper. Push in on assembly until seal lip is even with knife edge of sleeve, Fig. 14.
5. Place installing tool over bore opening and return spring. Index with boot in caliper, Fig. 15. Press down on piston, sliding piston out of tool and into caliper bore until bottomed. Remove sleeve tool.
6. Position piston boot sealing lip over groove evenly. Using the tool shown in Fig. 16 or its equivalent, press down on tool, forcing boot sealing lip into caliper groove. Remove tool and install remaining pistons in same manner, Fig. 17.
7. Test pistons for smooth operation in their bores by depressing with fingers.
8. Lightly clamp outer caliper half in vise and install new crossover passage seals in position in recess of caliper mating surface, Fig. 17.
9. Place mating caliper half over one clamped in vise, install attaching bolts and torque to 120-140 ft-lbs.
10. Install brake shoes in caliper with

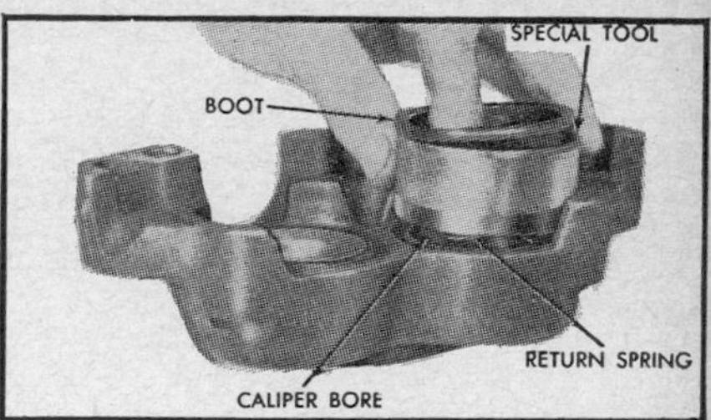

Fig. 15 Installing piston, seal and dust boot

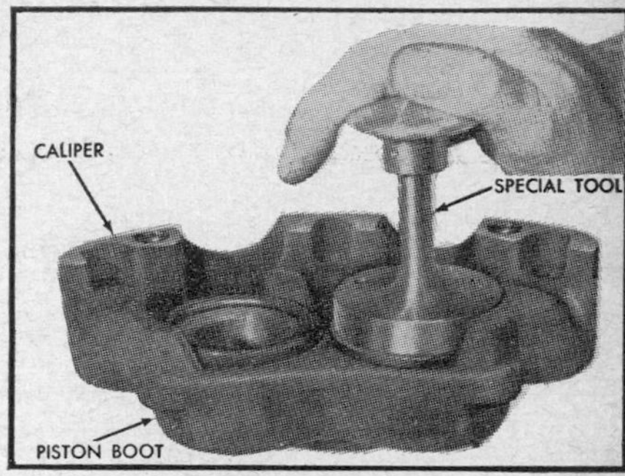

Fig. 16 Installing piston dust boot in caliper groove

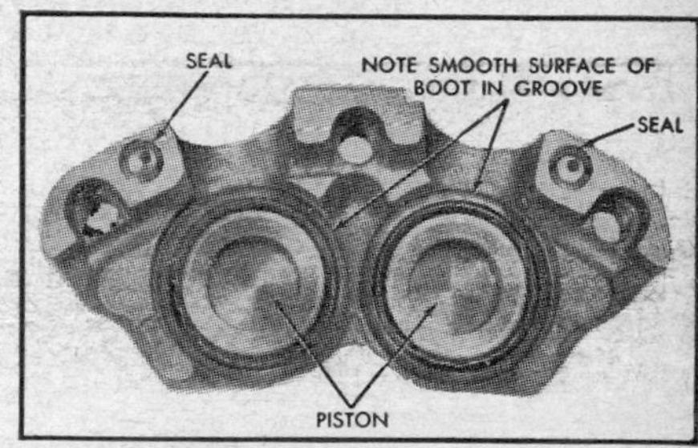

Fig. 17 Pistons and boots installed in caliper

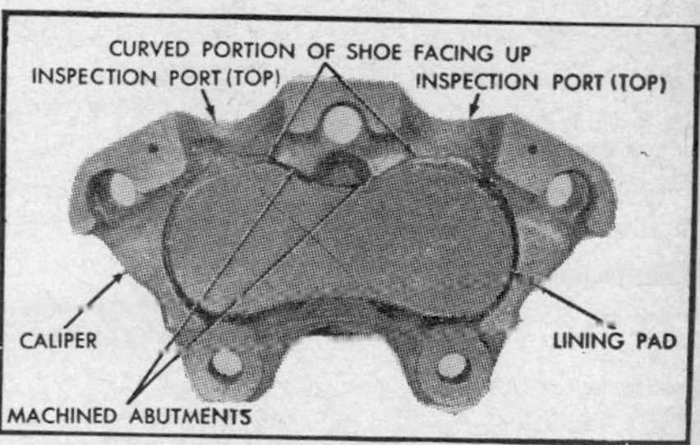

Fig. 18 Shoes and linings correctly positioned in caliper

curved portion (with tabs) entering first and metal shoe against open ends of pistons. Using fingers, spread linings apart until pistons are seated in their bores, Fig. 18.

11. Install bleeder screw and tighten lightly.

Installing Caliper

1. Check runout of brake disc with dial indicator as outlined previously.
2. Install caliper over disc and align mounting holes. Install bolts and torque to 85-90 ft-lbs. (As caliper is being lowered into place, be sure that linings ride freely over disc.)
3. Connect brake line at caliper housing, then position brake hose bracket. Install bracket and attaching bolts and tighten securely.
4. Follow normal bleeding procedure, being sure all air bubbles have escaped.
5. Replenish brake fluid in master cylinder.
6. Install wheels and road test as suggested previously.

BUDD OPPOSED PISTONS

The Budd Disc brake, Fig. 19, consists of a fixed caliper (inner and outer housing), two friction pads (brake lining) bonded to steel shoes, four pistons, piston return springs, piston seals, dust boots and retainers. The brake disc is made from high grade cast iron and has a series of air vent louvers to provide cooling for the brake assembly. The splash shield has a series of stamped vents so designed as to supply additional air for cooling.

Removing Lining

1. Remove wheels.
2. Remove brake shoe anti-rattle spring.
3. Slide piston compression tools, Fig. 20, between brake shoes and piston insulator and snap in place. This will hold pistons in a retracted position during removal and installation of brake lining units.
4. Remove bolts that attach caliper assembly to steering knuckle and knuckle arm.
5. Slowly slide caliper up and away from brake shoe.
6. Carefully invert caliper and remove brake shoe assembly (one at a time).

Installing Lining

1. Slide brake disc shoe and lining assembly into position in caliper (one at a time).
2. Slide caliper down into position over brake disc and align mounting holes.
3. Install caliper mounting bolts and torque to 65 ft-lbs.
4. Remove piston compression tools.
5. Install wheels.

CAUTION: Road test vehicle and apply several heavy 40 mph stops to wear off any foreign material on brakes and to seat units. The vehicle may pull to one side or the other if this is not done. This condition will be more noticeable if only one wheel was worked on.

Removing Caliper

1. Remove wheels.
2. Slide piston compression tools, Fig. 20, between brake shoes and piston pads and snap in place.

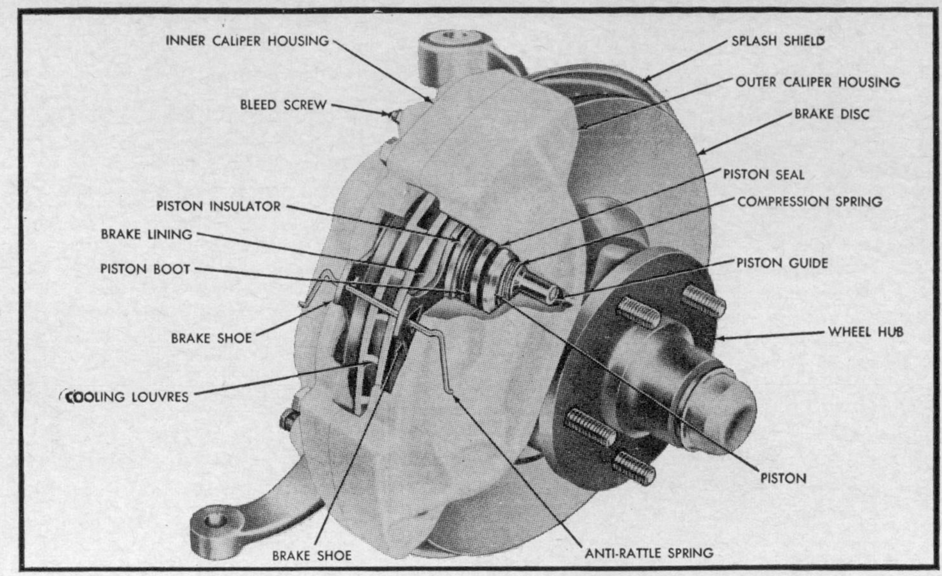

Fig. 19 Budd opposed piston Disc Brake assembly

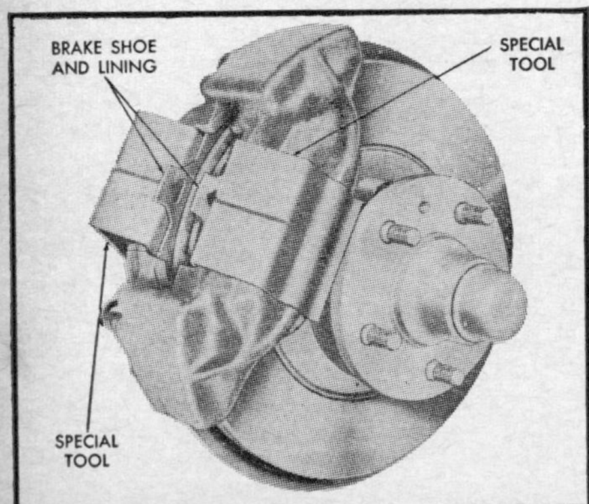

Fig. 20 Piston compression tools installed

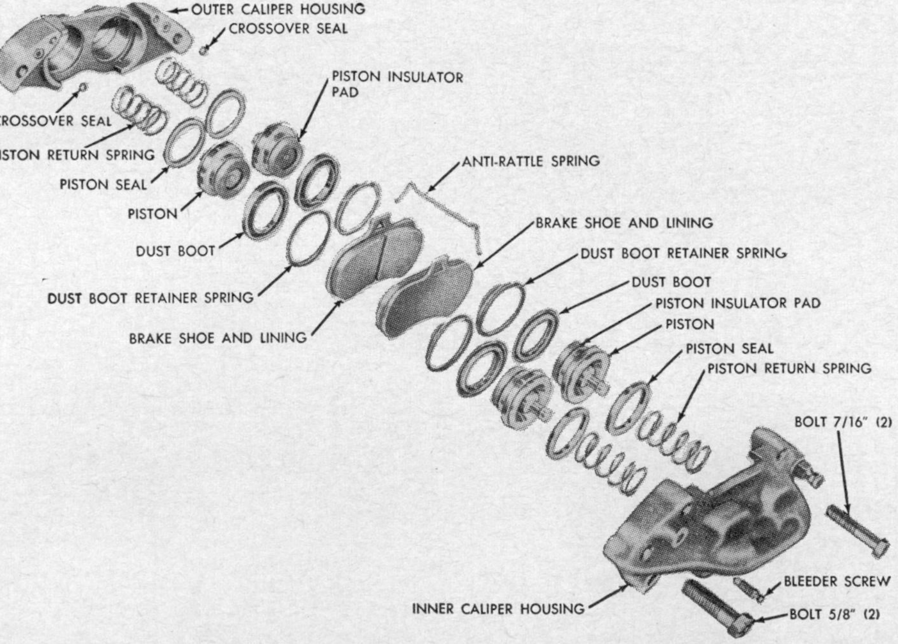

Fig. 21 Budd disc brake caliper disassembled

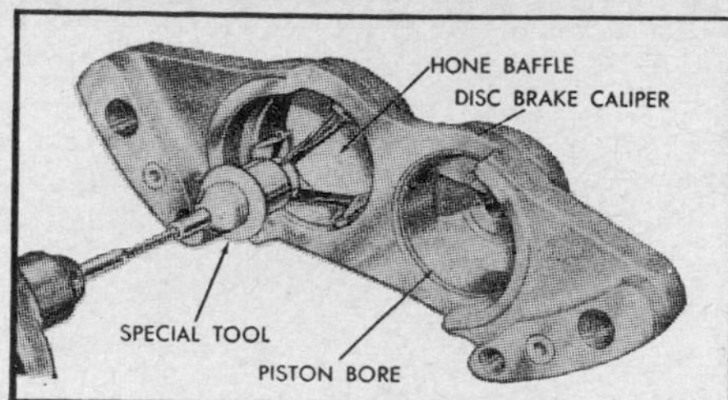

Fig. 22 Honing piston bore

3. Disconnect brake line at caliper housing and install a ⅛" pipe plug.
4. Unfasten caliper and slowly slide it up and away from brake disc.

Disassembling Caliper

1. Referring to Fig. 21, remove piston compression tools and four bolts that hold two halves of caliper together.
2. Separate halves and remove two crossover seals.
3. Using a small screwdriver, pry out exposed end of piston dust boot retainer spring and uncoil from its groove to release dust boot.
4. Using same screwdriver, work dust boot out of groove. Be sure to hold piston compressed during this operation.
5. Remove piston, seal and dust boot from caliper. Remove piston return spring.
6. Remove piston dust boot by grasping edge and pulling out of its groove.
7. Pry piston seal out of its groove and discard.
8. Remove remaining three pistons in same manner.
9. Remove bleeder screw from inner caliper housing.

Cleaning & Inspection

1. Clean all parts in brake fluid and wipe dry. Using an air hose, blow out drilled passages and bores.
2. Check dust boots for punctures and tears. If punctures or tears are evident, new boots should be installed.
3. Inspect piston bores in both housings for scoring or pitting. Bores that show light scratches or corrosion can usually be cleaned with crocus cloth. However, bores that have deep scratches or scoring may be honed, Fig. 22, providing the diameter of bore is not increased more than .002". If the bore does not clean up within this specification, a new caliper housing must be installed. Black stains on bore walls are caused by the piston seals and will do no harm.
4. When honing, Fig. 22, be sure to install the hone baffle before honing bore. The baffle is used to protect hone stones from damage.
5. Use extreme care in cleaning the caliper after honing. Remove all dust and grit by flushing caliper with brake fluid. Wipe dry with clean, lintless cloth and then clean a second time in like manner.

Assembling Caliper

1. Referring to Fig. 21, clamp caliper in a vise, then install piston return spring. Be sure spring is seated in recess in bottom of bore.
2. Coat outside diameter and fill inner diameter of a new piston seal with silicone grease and work over piston land and down into position in groove, using fingers only.
3. Install dust boot on piston with lip of boot toward piston pad.
4. Install piston over return spring and press down until piston bottoms in bore.
5. Using a small, blunt screwdriver, work lip of boot into groove, around diameter of bore. Use care so as not to puncture boot during this operation, or a new boot will have to be installed.
6. Install coil spring by inserting one end in position in groove and continue to install around diameter of bore until retainer is fully seated. Be sure boot is completely locked in position by retainer and that retainer is fully seated in groove.
7. Install remaining pistons in same manner, then test pistons for smooth operation in their bores by depressing with fingers.
8. Install piston compression tool over each caliper half to hold pistons in retracted position.
9. Install new crossover passage seals in recess of caliper mating surface.
10. Install brake shoe in caliper and place mating caliper half over one clamped in vise.
11. Install attaching bolts and torque to 55 ft-lbs ($\frac{7}{16}$") and 150 ft-lbs for ½" bolts.
12. Install bleeder screw but do not tighten.

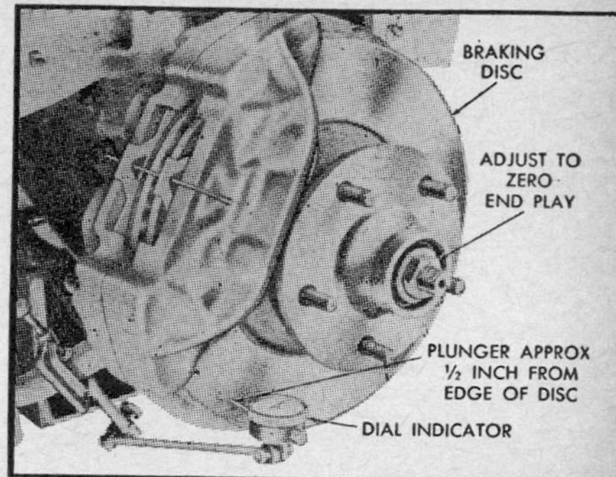

Fig. 23 Checking brake disc for runout

Installing Caliper

1. Before installing caliper over disc, check disc for runout with a dial gauge as shown in Fig. 23. Lateral runout should not exceed .003": if runout is excessive, remove disc and check its mounting surface on wheel hub. Runout of hub should not exceed .004".
2. Install caliper over disc and torque $\frac{7}{16}$" bolts to 65 ft-lbs, and 150 ft-lbs for ½" bolts. Remove piston compression tools.
3. Connect brake line at caliper housing and allow caliper to fill with

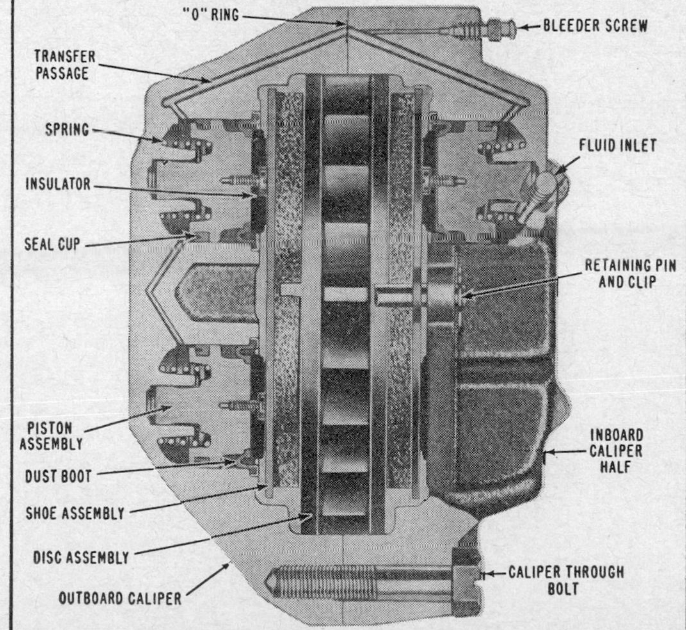

Fig. 24 Delco-Moraine disc brake assembly

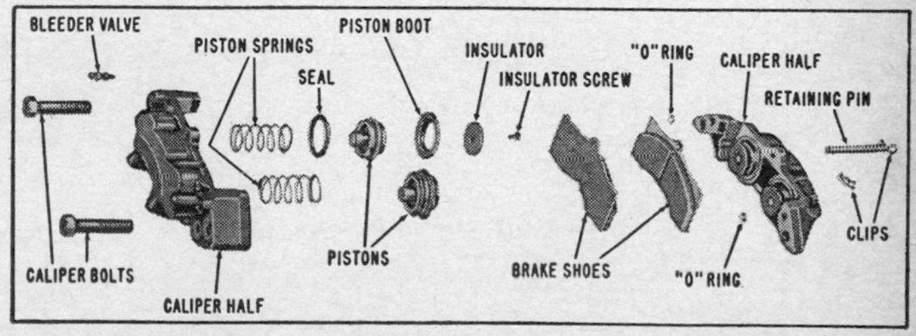

Fig. 27 Delco-Moraine disc brake caliper components

Fig. 25 Installing Delco-Moraine disc brake shoes

brake fluid then close bleeder screw. Be sure all air bubbles have escaped when bleeding the caliper. Replenish brake fluid in master cylinder.

4. Install wheels and road test vehicle as outlined previously.

DELCO-MORAINE

These brakes are used on all four wheels. The components of the disc brake system are shown in Fig. 24. The caliper assemblies replace the conventional wheel cylinder, brake shoes and linings, and the disc replaces the brake drum.

The caliper assembly contains four pistons, two acting on each shoe with one shoe on each side of the disc.

The brake disc is riveted to the hub flange at the front wheel and to the spindle flange at the rear wheel. The disc rotates through the caliper assembly, which is bolted to a support that is attached to the steering knuckle at the front wheel and the spindle support bolts at the rear wheel. The disc has cooling fins between the two shoe reacting surfaces. When a disc must be replaced, the rivets can be drilled out and then the wheel studs will be used for disc retension purposes.

A miniature set of brake shoes, mounted on a flange plate and shield assembly attached to the rear wheel spindle support bolts, are used for vehicle parking, Fig. 25.

Brake Shoes, Replace

To avoid overflow of the master cylinder reservoir, the manufacturer recommends removing only about two-thirds of the fluid in the reservoir when replacing brake shoe pads.

If all the hydraulic fluid is removed, as previously directed, air can enter the master cylinder when pistons are moved toward the discs, making it necessary to bleed the system.

When replacing brake shoes, Fig. 25, siphon about two-thirds of the brake fluid from the master cylinder (see above) and remove the wheel assembly. Then remove the shoe guide pin and clip after which the shoes can be lifted out.

Before the new shoes can be replaced, the cylinder pistons must be pushed back into their bores and retained with a thin clip to allow clearance for the new shoes to be installed. Pushing the pistons back into the cylinders causes the brake fluid to be forced backward into the master cylinder reservoir. The amount of brake fluid pushed back would overflow the master cylinder, causing fluid spillage around the engine fire wall.

Calipers

The caliper assembly, Fig. 27 comes in two halves assembled by strong bolts at the flange end. The two halves contain fluid crossover passages from one to the other, sealed with "O" rings.

The bleeder screw is threaded into a passage drilled to intersect the fluid crossover passage. The bleeder screws are located at the front of each caliper. There are two bleeder screws, one inboard, one outboard at the rear wheels, and one bleeder screw at the inboard side at the front wheel. It is necessary, therefore, to remove the rear wheel when bleeding the rear caliper.

Service Summary

1. There is no brake shoe adjustment on the disc brakes.
2. The groove in the brake shoe is an indicator of brake wear. When the groove is just about gone it is time for shoe replacement.
3. When replacing shoes it is necessary to siphon fluid from master cylinder reservoir to make room for fluid return to the reservoir when pushing the caliper pistons back into their bores to make room for the thickness of the new shoes.
4. The shoes have a directional arrow on the back of the shoe plate. This arrow points to the forward rotation of the disc, and the purpose is for aligning the grain of the lining material in relation to the disc.
5. When bleeding the calipers, the rear wheel must be removed to reach the outboard bleeder screw.
6. A retaining clip of thin metal is used to hold the pistons into the bores while installing the new brake shoes.
7. The caliper assembly is removable, after disconnecting the brake line, by removing the two mounting bolts and lifting the assembly off the disc.

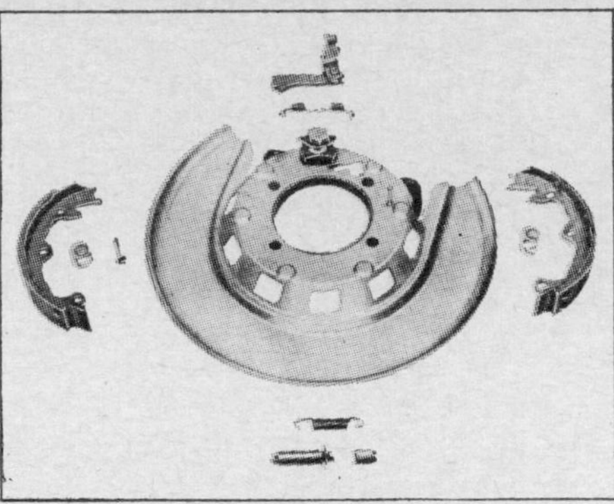

Fig. 26 Delco-Moraine parking brake components

8. The disc is riveted to the spindle flange in production. However, the rivets may be drilled out and the wheel studs and nuts are sufficient to hold the new disc in place when replacing the disc.
9. The rear wheel spindle must be removed to gain access to the parking brake shoes. It is necessary then to remove the caliper, the axle drive shaft, the spindle drive shaft yoke and remove the spindle and disc as an assembly from the wheel support. You now have access to the parking brake shoes the same as any other conventional bendix type brake shoe, Fig. 26.
10. If the car is equipped with the special optional knock-off hub assemblies, the adapters must be removed to gain access to the parking brake adjustment.

KELSEY-HAYES OPPOSED PISTON TYPE BRAKE

This type brake, Fig. 28, is a fixed caliper, opposed piston, non-energized, ventilated type, actuated by the hydraulic system. There is no lateral movement of either the disc or the caliper. The caliper assembly consists

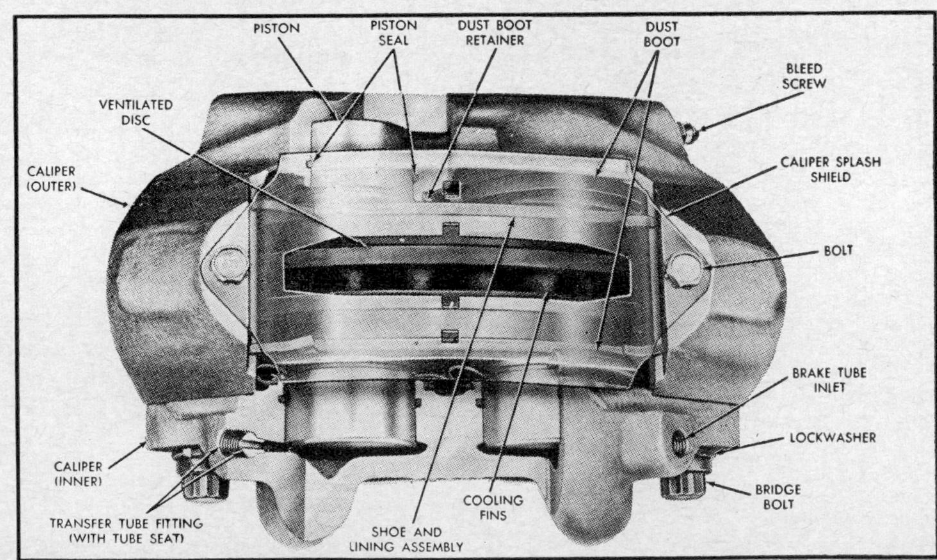

Fig. 28 Kelsey-Hayes opposed piston disc brake

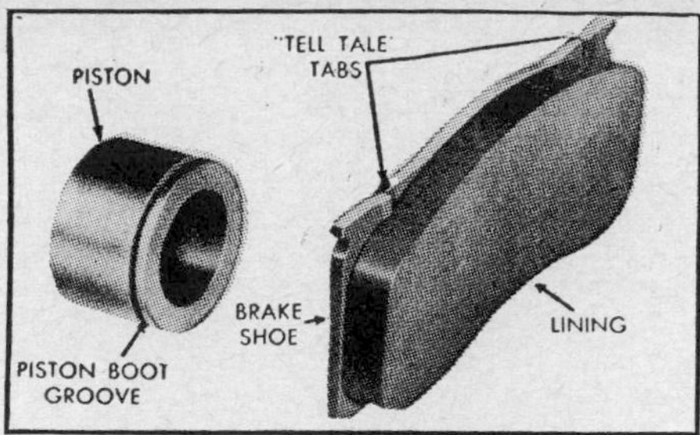

Fig. 29 Brake piston, shoe and lining assembly

Fig. 30 Removing brake shoe and lining

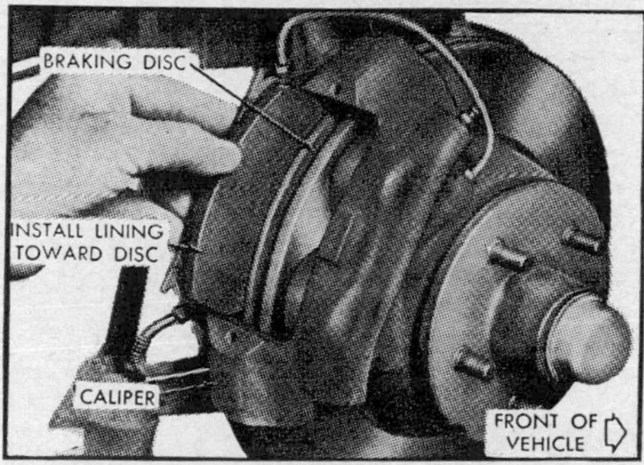

Fig. 31 Installing brake shoe and lining

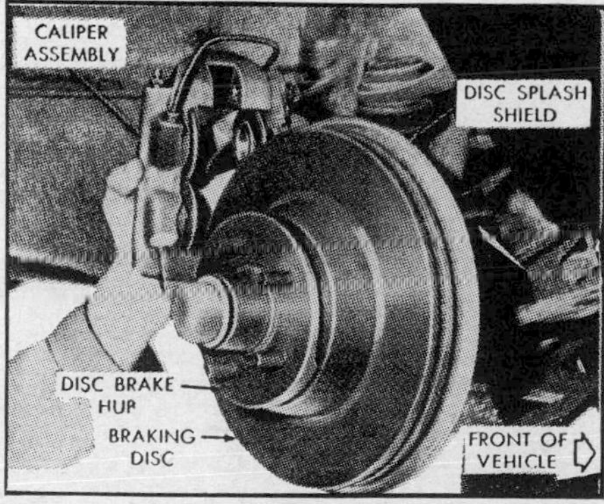

Fig. 32 Replacing brake disc caliper

of two caliper housings bolted together. Each half contains two cylinder bores. Each cylinder contains a seal, piston and externally attached molded rubber dust boot to seal the cylinder bore from contamination. The pistons are sealed by rubber piston seals positioned in grooves machined in the cylinder bores which provide hydraulic sealing between pistons and cylinder bores.

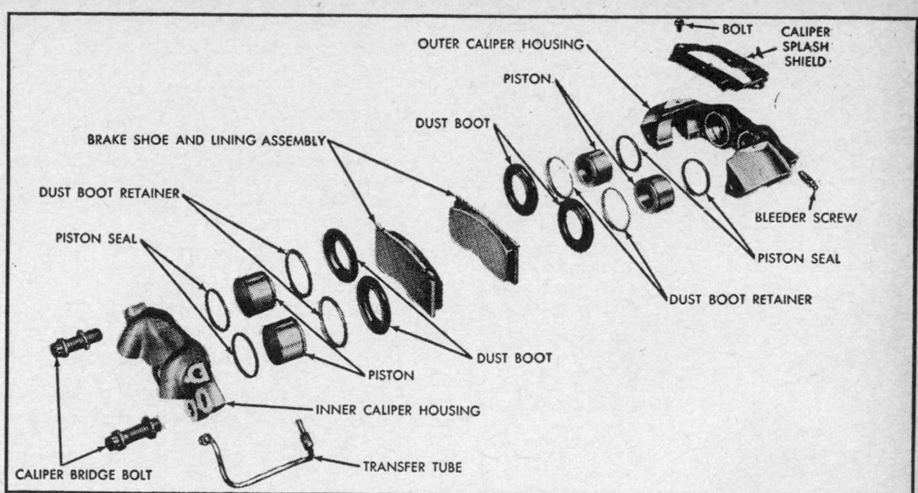

Fig. 33 Caliper disassembled

An additional feature of this brake system is a "tell-tale" tab sounding device which indicates when replacement of the shoe and lining assemblies are required, Fig. 29. The tabs on the shoes create an audible metallic scraping noise from the brake by metal-to-metal contact on the braking disc. This warns the driver that the lining has worn to a minimum thickness, at which time it should be replaced.

Checking Running Clearance

To check the lining-to-disc running clearance, remove wheel and caliper splash shield. Insert a feeler gauge between lining and disc. Clearance ordinarily should be .003-.006". However, if the vehicle was stopped by a brake application just prior to checking the clearance, it is considered normal for the brakes to drag slightly.

Brake Shoe Replace

1. Raise vehicle on hoist or stands.
2. Remove wheel assembly.
3. Remove caliper splash shield and anti-rattle spring.
4. Using two pairs of pliers, grasp tabs on outer ends of shoes and remove shoe and lining by pulling outward, Fig. 30.

NOTE: Due to a ridge of rust that may have formed on the disc surface outside of lining contact area, it may be necessary to force the piston back slightly into its bore. This is done by forcing the shoe back with water pump pliers placed on corner of shoe and caliper housing as shown, Fig. 30.

INSTALLATION

1. Push all pistons back into their bores until bottomed to allow for installation of new shoes. This can be done by placing a flat-sided metal bar against piston and exerting a steady force until bottomed.
2. Slide new shoe and lining into caliper with ears of shoe resting on bridges of caliper, Fig. 31. Be sure shoe is fully seated and lining is facing disc.
3. Slide remaining shoe and lining into caliper, using same procedure as above.
4. Place caliper splash shield and anti-rattle spring in position on caliper and install attaching bolts securely.
5. Pump brake pedal several times until a firm pedal has been obtained and shoe and linings have been properly seated.
6. Install wheel. Replenish master cylinder fluid as required.

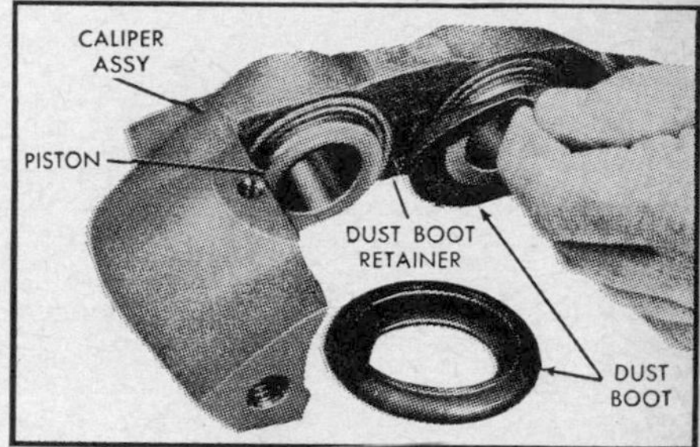

Fig. 34 Removing dust boot from piston and caliper

CAUTION: Road test vehicle and make several heavy 40 m.p.h. stops to wear off any foreign material on the brakes and to seat the units. The vehicle may pull to one side or the other if this is not done. It should not be necessary to bleed the system after replacing linings.

Servicing Caliper

REMOVAL

1. Raise car on hoist or stands.
2. Remove wheel assembly.
3. Disconnect front brake flexible hose from brake tube at frame mounting bracket. Plug tube to prevent loss of fluid.
4. Remove bolts that attach caliper to steering knuckle.

NOTE: Should it become necessary to install a new flexible brake hose, scribe

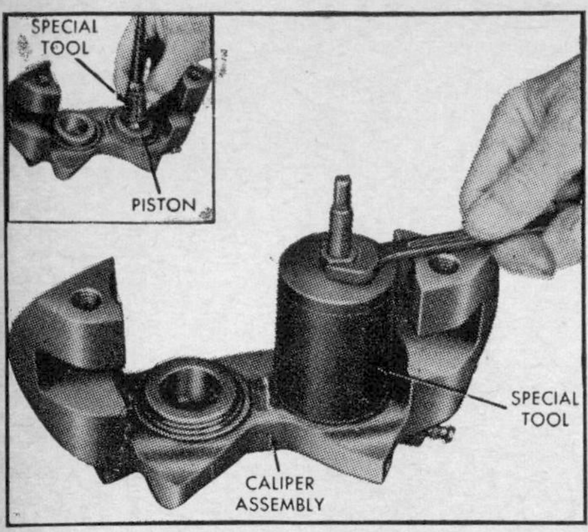

Fig. 35 Removing pistons from caliper

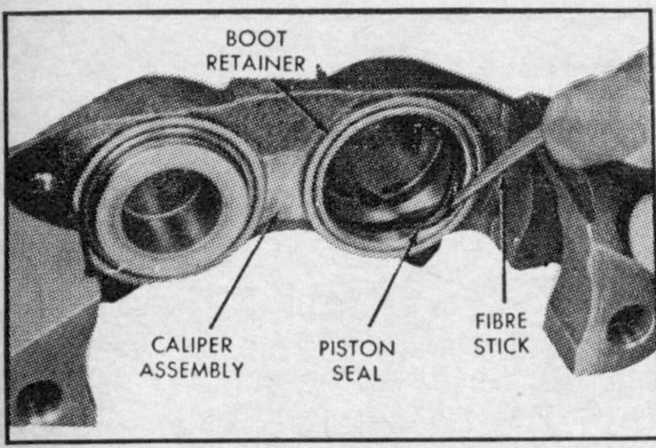

Fig. 36 Removing piston seals from caliper

a mark on hose bracket on side where hose enters, and position of hose retaining clip underneath. When reassembling, be sure open end of retaining clip is facing out and away from caliper.

5. Slowly slide caliper up and away from brake disc, Fig. 32.

DISASSEMBLY

1. Referring to Fig. 33, remove splash shield and anti-rattle spring.
2. Remove jumper tube at caliper.
3. Mount caliper in a vise with soft jaws and remove transfer tube.
4. Remove shoe and lining units.
5. Remove bridge bolts and separate caliper halves.
6. Peel dust boot out and away from caliper housing retainer and out of piston groove, Fig. 34. Remove remaining boots in same manner.
7. Using Tool C-3999, remove each piston, Fig. 35.

CAUTION: Care must be used so as not to scratch, burr or otherwise damage piston on outside diameter. To do so effects sealing qualities of piston. Draw piston straight out of its bore. If a piston becomes cocked, removal is more difficult and piston or bore may be damaged.

8. Using a small pointed wooden or plastic tool, remove piston seals from grooves in cylinder bore, Fig. 36. Discard old seals.

ASSEMBLING CALIPER

1. Clamp inner caliper half in a vise (with protector jaws) by mounting lugs.
2. If it was necessary to install a new dust boot retainer ring, contact area on housing should be cleaned and Loctite Sealant Grade H (or equivalent) applied to retainer ring on surface where it seats in housing, then install retainer ring.
3. Dip new piston seals in brake fluid and install in caliper grooves. Seal should be positioned at one area in groove and gently worked around cylinder bore with a finger until properly seated. *Be sure seals are not twisted or rolled.*
4. Coat outside diameter of pistons with brake fluid and install them in cylinder bores, Fig. 37, with open end of piston and boot retaining groove facing out of cylinder.
5. Position piston squarely in bore and apply slow steady pressure. *If piston will not position itself, remove it and check seal for proper position in groove.*
6. Install new dust boot over caliper retaining ring and in piston groove. Install remaining boots in same manner.
7. Install caliper half on one clamped in vise. Assemble with bridge bolts and torque to 70-80 ft-lbs.

CAUTION: Under no circumstances should the bridge bolts be substituted or replaced by inferior bolts as this could cause caliper failure, resulting in an accident.

8. Install and tighten transfer tube.
9. Install bleeder screw loosely.

INSTALLATION

1. Before installing caliper, check brake disc for runout. Mount a dial indicator as shown in Fig. 38 and check lateral runout, which should not exceed .0025″. If runout is excessive, install a new disc. *Be sure wheel bearings are adjusted to zero end play during this check. Readjust wheel bearings after checking runout.*
2. Install caliper over disc. Install mounting bolts and torque to 45-60 ft-lbs.

NOTE: A check should be made to be sure that brake disc runs squarely and

Fig. 39 Single piston disc brake (typical)

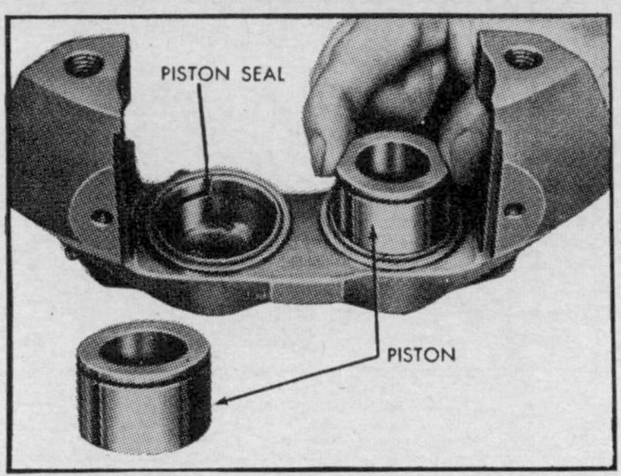

Fig. 37 Installing piston in caliper

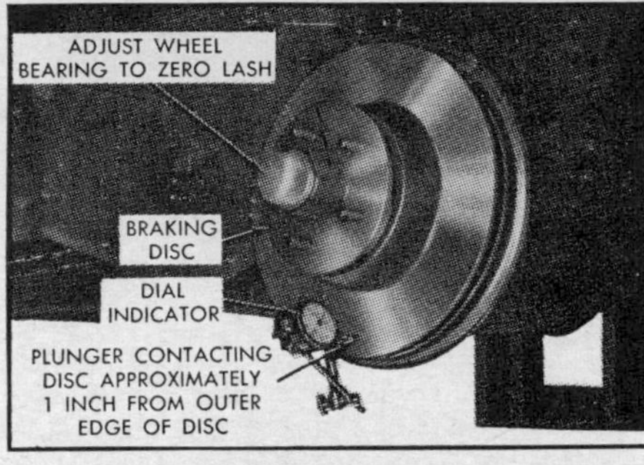

Fig. 38 Checking brake disc runout

centrally within caliper opening. There should be .090″ to .120″ clearance between outside diameter of disc and caliper. There should also be a minimum of .050″ from either disc face to machined groove in outboard caliper.

3. Install shoe and lining units.
4. Install caliper splash shield.
5. Open bleeder screw, then connect brake line to caliper housing. Allow caliper to fill with brake fluid, then close bleeder screw. Be sure all air bubbles have escaped when bleeding caliper. Replenish fluid in master cylinder.
6. Pump brake pedal several times to actuate piston seals and to position linings.
7. Road test vehicle as outlined previously.

KELSEY-HAYES SINGLE PISTON TYPE

This type brake is a floating caliper, single piston, ventilated unit, actuated by the hydraulic system, Fig. 39. The caliper assembly, Fig. 40, is made up of a floating caliper assembly and an anchor plate. The anchor plate is bolted to the wheel spindle arm by two bolts. The caliper is attached to the anchor plate through two spring steel stabilizers. The caliper slides on two guide pins which also attach to the stabilizers. A single piston is used. The cylinder bore contains a piston with a molded rubber dust boot to seal the cylinder bore from contamination and also to return the piston to the released position when hydraulic pressure is released. Also a rubber piston seal is used to provide sealing between cylinder and piston.

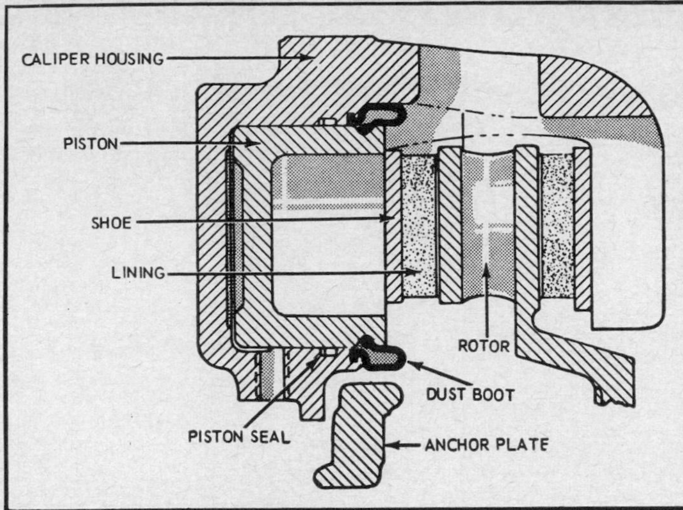

Fig. 40 Single piston disc brake caliper (typical)

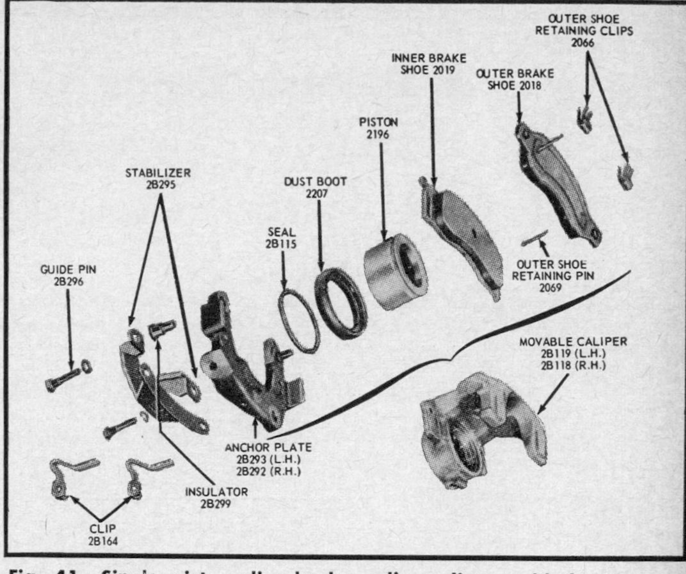

Fig. 41 Single piston disc brake caliper disassembled (typical)

Service Precautions

In addition to the precautions described at the beginning of this chapter, the following must be observed.

1. If the piston is removed for any reason the piston seal must be replaced.
2. During removal and installation of a wheel assembly, use care not to interfere with and damage the caliper splash shield or the bleeder screw fitting.
3. Be sure the vehicle is centered on the hoist before servicing any front end components to avoid bending or damaging the rotor splash shield on full right or left wheel turns.
4. The proportioning valve should not be disassembled or adjustments attemped on it.
5. The wheel and tire must be removed separately from the brake rotor.
6. The caliper assembly must be removed from the spindle prior to removal of shoe and lining assembly.
7. Do not attempt to clean or restore oil or grease soaked brake linings. When contaminated linings are found, linings must be replaced in complete axle sets.

Remove & Disassemble Caliper

1. Remove wheel and tire assembly.
2. Unfasten caliper from spindle (2 bolts).
3. To facilitate removal and installation of shoe and lining assemblies, piston must be pushed into its bore. Apply a steady inward pressure against the inner shoe and lining assembly. Maintain pressure for at least one minute.
4. Slide the two outer shoe retaining clips off retaining pins, Fig. 41.
5. Remove the two retaining pins from outer shoe, then remove shoe from caliper.
6. Slide inner brake shoe outward until it is free of hold-down springs, then remove brake shoe.
7. Remove caliper guide pins and stabilizer attaching bolts, then remove stabilizers.
8. Remove guide pin insulators from anchor plate.

NOTE: If necessary to remove the piston, apply air pressure to the fluid port in the caliper, Fig. 42, to remove the piston. Place a cloth over the piston to prevent damage to the piston. If the piston is seized and cannot be forced from the caliper, tap lightly around the piston before applying air pressure. Care should be taken because the piston can develop considerable force due to pressure build-up.

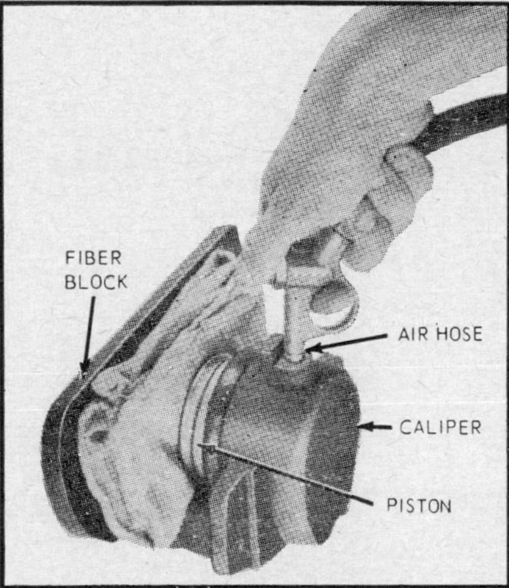

Fig. 42 Removing piston with air pressure

9. Remove dust boot from caliper.
10. Remove rubber piston seal from cylinder and discard it.

Assemble & Install Caliper

1. Apply a film of clean brake fluid to the new caliper piston seal and install it in cylinder bore. Be sure seal does not become twisted and that it is seated fully in the groove.
2. Install a new dust boot by setting the flange squarely in the outer groove of the caliper bore.
3. Coat piston with brake fluid and install in cylinder bore. Spread dust boot over piston as it is installed. Seat dust boot in piston groove.
4. Position inner brake shoe so that ears of shoe rests on top of anchor plate bosses and beneath hold-down springs.
5. Install new caliper guide pin insulators in anchor plate.
6. Position caliper on anchor plate.
7. Install guide pins loosely in anchor plate, being sure guide pins are free of oil, grease or dirt.
8. Install caliper on spindle.

Brake Shoes & Linings, Install

NOTE: When new shoe and lining assemblies are being installed to replace worn linings it will be necessary to push the piston all the way into the caliper bore. This will displace fluid from the caliper into the master cylinder reservoir. Check the primary (front) brake system reservoir level and remove fluid to approximately half full before replacing brake shoes. This will prevent overflow. Do not reuse the removal fluid.

1. Install new caliper guide pin insulators in anchor plate.
2. Position caliper in anchor plate.
3. Install caliper guide pins loosely in anchor plate, being sure they are free of oil, grease or dirt.
4. Position outer brake shoe on caliper and install two retaining pins and clips.
5. Install inner brake shoe so that ears of shoe are on top of anchor plate bosses and under shoe hold-down springs.
6. Position shoe and lining assemblies so that caliper can be placed over rotor. Rotate hammer handle between linings to provide proper clearance.
7. Install caliper over rotor and on spindle. Install and tighten the two caliper bolts, tightening the upper bolt first. Install safety wire and twist ends at least five turns. With moderate pressure applied to brake pedal, tighten stabilizer attaching screws and caliper guide pins.

POWER BRAKE UNITS

A Picture Guide to Power Unit Overhaul

INDEX

BENDIX MASTERVAC — PAGE NO.

Fig. BM-1 Piston type 1-442

Fig. BM-2 Single diaphragm type 1-442

Fig. BM-3 Tandem diaphragm type 1-442

DELCO-MORAINE — PAGE NO.

Fig. DM-1 Air suspended type 1-443

Fig. DM-2 Vacuum suspended type 1-445

KELSEY-HAYES

Fig. KH-1 Bellows type 1-446

Fig. KH-2 Diaphragm type 1-448

MIDLAND-ROSS — PAGE NO.

Fig. MR-1 Diaphragm type 1-449

Fig. MR-2 Diaphragm type 1-449

APPLICATION

	Fig. No.
BUICK	
1963	DM-1
1964-68	DM-2
1967-69	BM-2
BUICK SPECIAL	
1963	KH-1
1964	KH-2
1964-69	DM-2
CADILLAC	
1963-69	DM-2
1963-68	BM-2
CAMARO	
1967	DM-2
1968	BM-2
CHEVROLET	
1963-67	BM-2
1963-67	DM-2
1968	BM-3
CHEVY II	
1963-67	DM-2
1968	BM-3
CHEVELLE	
1964-67	BM-2
1968	BM-3
CHRYSLER	
1963-68	BM-2
1965-66	KH-2
1965-68	MR-2
COMET	
1964-67	MR-2
CORVETTE	
1963-67	DM-2
1968	BM-3
COUGAR	
1967-68	MR-2
DART	
1963-66	BM-1
1967-68	MR-2
DODGE	
1963-68	BM-2
1965-68	KH-2
1966-68	MR-2
FAIRLANE	
1963-64	MR-1
1965-68	MR-2
FALCON	
1964-68	BM-2
FORD	
1963-64	MR-1
1965-68	MR-2
IMPERIAL	
1963	BM-2
1964-68	BM-3
JEEP	
1963-68	BM-3
LINCOLN	
1963-64	BM-1
1965-68	BM-3
MERCURY	
1963	BM-2
1963-64	MR-1
1964-68	MR-2
MONTEGO	
1968	MR-2
MUSTANG	
1965-68	MR-2
OLDSMOBILE	
1963	BM-1
1963	DM-1
1964-67	BM-2
1964-67	DM-2
1964-67	KH-2
OLDS F-85	
1963	KH-1
1964-68	BM-2
1964-68	DM-2
1964-67	KH-2
PLYMOUTH	
1963-68	BM-2
1965-66	KH-2
1966-68	MR-2
PONTIAC	
1963-69	BM-2
1963-69	DM-2
RAMBLER	
1963-69	BM-2
1969	BM-3
THUNDERBIRD	
1963-64	MR-1
1963-68	MR-2
1965-68	BM-3
VALIANT	
1963-66	BM-1
1967-68	MR-2

THE SECRET of power brake service and repair work is a good understanding of the operation of the different brakes available on today's cars.

Mechanical assist units employ a power unit that is connected only to the brake pedal or linkage and helps push the pedal down. Hydraulic assist types, on the other hand, are inserted in the hydraulic system and directly increase hydraulic fluid pressure. In the hydraulic assist unit known as the integral type, the power unit is attached to the master cylinder; in the other, it is attached to an auxiliary slave cylinder.

Power units are similar in operation and get their energy by opposing engine vacuum to atmospheric pressure. A piston and cylinder, flexible diaphragm or bellows utilize this energy to provide brake assistance. The fundamental difference between the different types lies simply in how the power unit is suspended when the brakes are not in use.

It is obviously important to know whether a power unit is air suspended or vacuum suspended. Air-suspended units are under atmospheric pressure until the brakes are applied. Then engine vacuum is admitted, causing the piston or diaphragm to move or the bellows to collapse. Vacuum-suspended types are balanced with engine vacuum until the brake pedal is depressed, allowing atmospheric pressure to unbalance the unit and apply force to the brake system.

General Service

Regardless of whether the brakes are air or vacuum suspended, or have integral or auxiliary hydraulic cylinders, certain general service procedures apply. Only top quality, clean brake fluid should be used in power brakes. More seals and valves are used with power brake systems than with ordinary brakes, so an inferior brake fluid will do much more damage. For the same reason, be sure all dirt is kept out of the system.

The fact that brakes will operate even if the power unit fails gives us a clue to successful power brake service. This means the conventional brake system is left intact and a power unit is simply added to the existing system. Troubleshooting is then exactly the same until we get to the power unit. As with conventional hydraulic brakes, a spongy pedal with power brakes still means air in the system and grease on the linings will still make the brakes grab. Keep in mind, however, that power brakes give a higher line pressure, thus making leaks more critical.

Power units do not require adjustment. Either they work or they don't. If they don't, the various valves and connections are simply replaced. The only exception is that the power units themselves sometimes have an adjustable connection to the brake pedal or linkage.

Another thing that is helpful in power brake overhaul is the manner in which the units wear. Repairs are infrequent until the unit has been in service for a long time. Then, when a malfunction does occur, it means the whole unit should be overhauled. Complete overhaul kits are available and all the parts in the kit should be used in the overhaul.

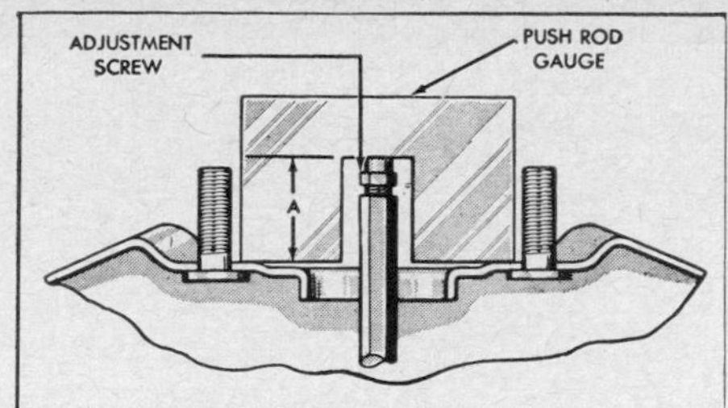

Fig. 1. Typical push rod screw adjustment

PRECAUTIONS

After disassembling a power brake unit, soak all metal parts in a suitable solvent. Use only alcohol on rubber parts or parts containing rubber. After the parts have been thoroughly cleaned and rinsed in solvent, the metal parts that come in contact with hydraulic brake fluid or rubber parts should be rewashed in clean alcohol before assembly. Use an air hose to blow dirt and cleaning fluid from the recesses and internal passages. *Always use all the parts furnished in the repair kit. Discard all old rubber parts.*

Push Rod Adjustment

Most power units of the integral type (unit combined with master cylinder) are provided with a means of adjusting the position of the push rod. This adjustment is necessary to be sure the master cylinder compensating port is open when the brakes are released.

There are two methods that can be used when making this adjustment: gauge method and air method. Usually, if the power unit push rod requires an adjustment the Power Unit Repair Kit for the unit being serviced includes a gauge. The gauge measures from the end of the push rod to the power unit shell, Fig. 1.

Air Method

1. Be sure master cylinder attaching nuts are tight.
2. Remove master cylinder filler cap.
3. With brake released, force compressed air into the hydraulic outlet of the master cylinder.
4. If air passes through the compensating port, which is the smaller of the two holes in the bottom of the master cylinder reservoir, the adjustment is satisfactory.
5. If air does not flow through the compensating port, adjust the push rod as required, either by means of the adjustment screw (if provided) or by adding shims between the master cylinder and power unit shell until the air flows freely.

Checking Complaints

Complaints about power brake operation should be handled as if two separate systems exist. Check for faults in the regular brake system first. If it is O.K., start looking over the power brake circuit. For a quick check of proper power unit operation, press the brake pedal firmly and then start the engine. The pedal should fall away slightly and less pressure should be needed to maintain the pedal in any position. On vacuum-suspended power units, air will rush into the air intake when the brakes are applied.

Another check begins with removal of the stoplight switch and installation of a pressure gauge. Take a reading with the engine off and the power unit not operating. Maintaining the same pedal height, start the engine and take another reading. There should be a substantial pressure increase in the second reading.

Pedal free travel and total travel are critical on cars equipped with power brakes. As a general rule, brakes should be adjusted or relined if the pedal is closer than 1½ in. from the floor with the brakes applied. Free travel should be kept strictly to specifications.

Take a manifold vacuum reading if the power unit isn't giving enough assistance. Remember, though, that some of the new V-8's have less than 15 in. of vacuum at idle. If manifold vacuum is abnormally low, tune the engine and then try the power brakes again. Naturally, loose vacuum lines and clogged air intake filters will cut down power brake efficiency. Most units have a check valve that retains some vacuum in the system when the engine is off. A vacuum gauge check of this valve will tell you when it is restricted or stuck open or closed.

Failure of the brakes to release in nine out of 10 cases is caused by a tight or misaligned connection between the power unit and the brake linkage. If this connection is free, look for a broken piston, diaphragm or bellows return spring. The power unit will have to be disassembled for this check and, if the spring is in good condition, continue going through the power unit, checking the fluid, air and vacuum valves.

A simple check of the hydraulic system should be made before proceeding. Loosen the connection between the power unit and the wheel cylinder lines. If the brakes release, the trouble is in the power unit hydraulic circuit. If the brakes still will not release, look for a restricted brake line or similar difficulties in the regular hydraulic circuit.

A residual pressure check valve is usually included immediately under the brake line connection on hydraulic assist power brakes. This valve maintains a slight hydraulic pressure on the brake lines and wheel cylinders to give better pedal response. If it is sticking, the brakes may not release.

Power brakes that have a hard pedal are usually suffering from a milder form of the same ills that cause complete power unit failure. Collapsed or leaking vacuum lines or insufficient manifold vacuum, as well as punctured diaphragms or bellows and leaky piston seals, all lead to weak power unit operation. A steady hiss when the brake is held down means a vacuum leak that will cause poor power unit operation.

Do not immediately condemn the power unit if the brakes grab. First look for all the usual causes, such as greasy linings or scored drums. Then investigate the power unit. When the trouble has been traced to the power unit, check for a damaged reaction control. The reaction control is usually made up of a diaphragm, spring and valving that tends

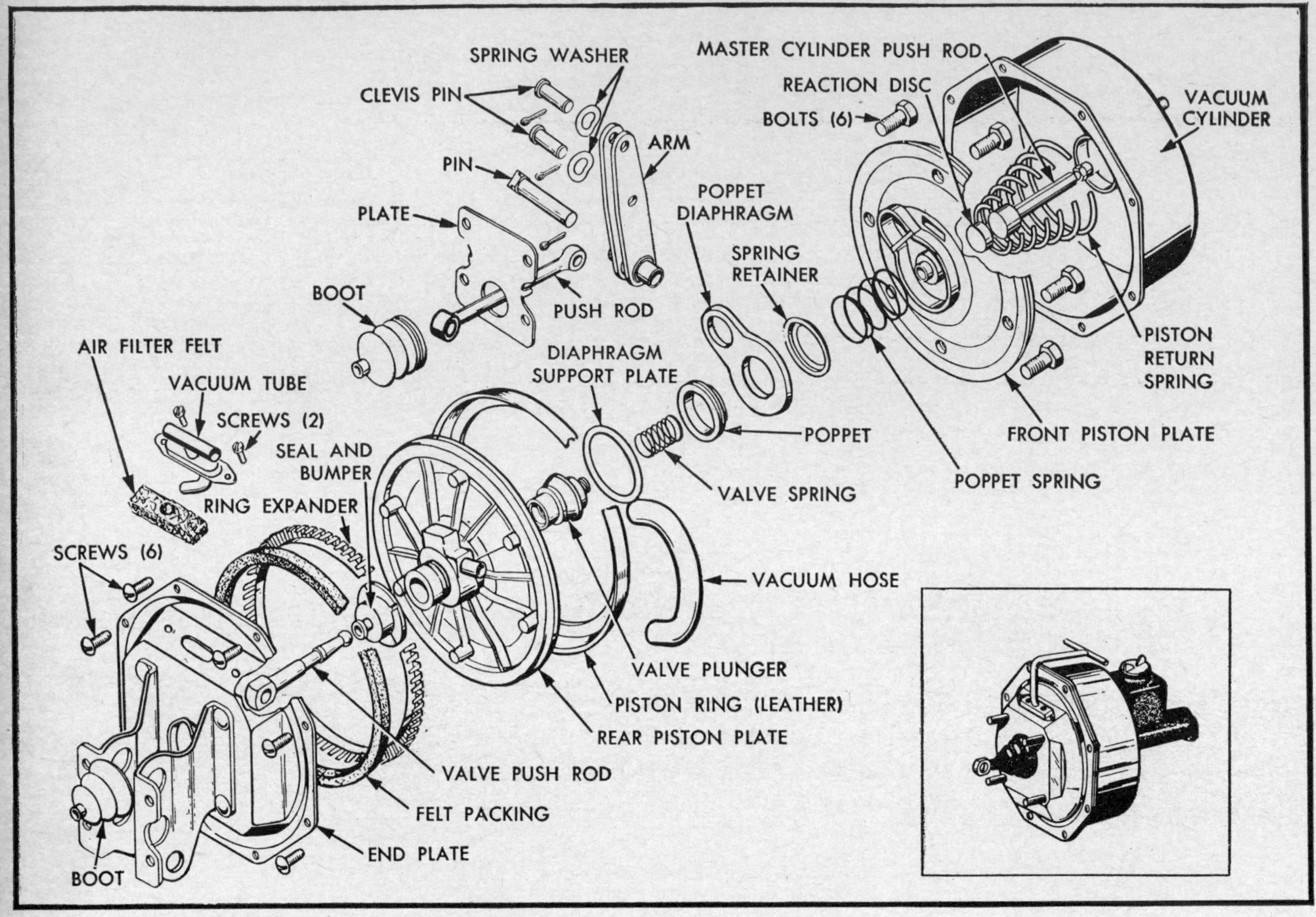

Fig. BM-1 Bendix piston type power brake

to resist pedal action. It is put in the system to give the pedal "feel" and deceive your foot into believing it is doing all the work.

BENDIX PISTON TYPE

Fig. BM-1

These power brake units are of the air suspended type which utilizes intake manifold vacuum and atmospheric pressure for power. They consist of three basic elements combined into a single unit.

1. A vacuum power cylinder that contains a cylinder, a vacuum power piston, and hydraulic push rod, and a vacuum piston return spring.
2. A mechanically actuated control valve, integral with the vacuum power piston, controls the degree of power brake application or release in accordance with the foot pressure applied to the valve operating rod through the brake pedal linkage. The control valve consists of a single poppet with an atmospheric port and a vacuum port. The atmospheric port seat is part of the valve plunger which moves within the vacuum power piston. The vacuum port seat is part of the rear piston plate.
3. An hydraulic cylinder that contains all the elements of the conventional brake master cylinder except the hydraulic push rod.

Operation

As the brake pedal is depressed, the valve operating rod and plunger move forward against the poppet valve to close the atmospheric port. Further travel of the rod and plunger moves the poppet away from the vacuum seat to open the vacuum port and establish direct connection between the intake manifold (or reservoir) through the porting in the valve and piston to the forward chamber. As vacuum removes air from the forward chamber, atmospheric pressure behind the booster piston exerts the force against the hydraulic push rod and piston that supplies the power assist. The amount of assist supplied by the power unit is always directly proportional to the amount of pressure being supplied to the pedal. Gradual application of the brakes is thus possible.

Push Rod Adjustment

Adjust push rod as outlined in the *General Service* section of this chapter.

Bleeding The System

The bleeding operation is accomplished in the same manner as outlined for conventional brakes in the *Hydraulic Brake System* chapter.

Trouble Shooting

Hard Pedal

1. Internal vacuum hose loose or restricted.
2. Jammed vacuum cylinder piston.
3. Vacuum leaks from loose piston plate screws.
4. Faulty piston seal.
5. Leak between power and master cylinders.
6. Control valve jammed.

Brakes Grab

1. Counter reaction spring broken.
2. Sticking poppet valves.

Slow or No Release

1. Piston return spring broken.
2. Valve plunger sticking.
3. Air passage restricted.
4. Piston stroke interference.

BENDIX DIAPHRAGM TYPES

Figs. BM-2 & BM-3

These units are of the vacuum suspended type. Some units are of the single diaphragm type while others are of the tandem diaphragm type. Both single piston and double piston or split system type master cylinders are used.

The vacuum suspended diaphragm type units utilize engine manifold vacuum and atmospheric pressure for its power. It consists of three basic elements combined into a single power unit. The three basic elements of the single diaphragm type are:

1. A vacuum power section which includes a front and rear shell, a power diaphragm, a return spring and a push rod.

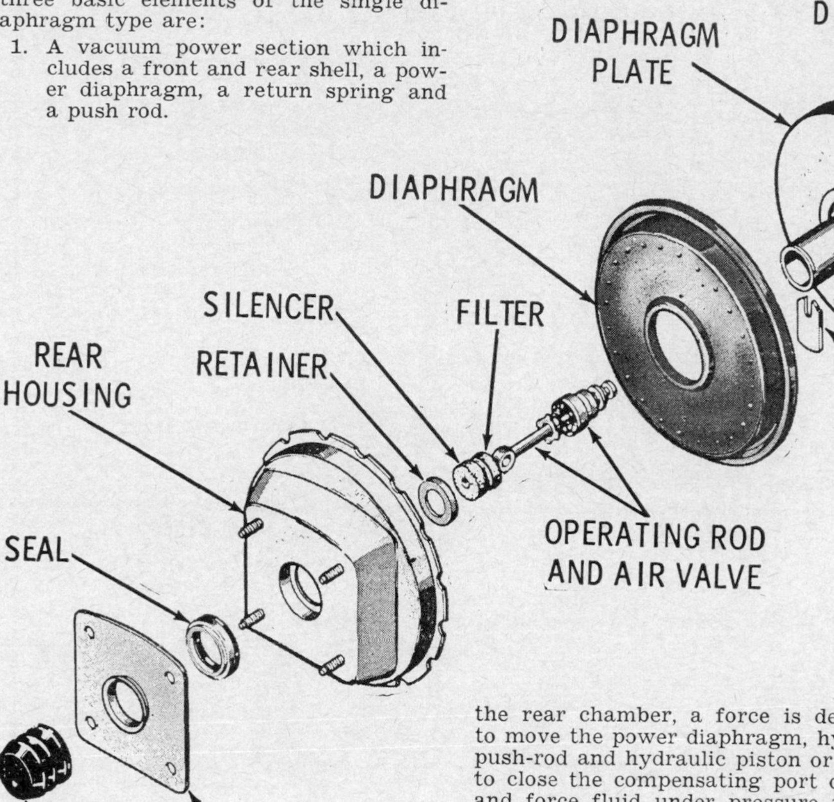

Fig. BM-2 Bendix single diaphragm power brake

2. A control valve, built integral with the power diaphragm and connected through a valve rod to the brake pedal, controls the degree of brake application or release in accordance with the pressure applied to the brake pedal.
3. A hydraulic master cylinder, attached to the vacuum power section which contains all of the elements of the conventional brake master cylinder except for the push rod, supplies fluid under pressure to the wheel brakes in proportion to the pressure applied to the brake pedal.

Operation

Upon application of the brakes, the valve rod and plunger move to the left in the power diaphragm to *close* the vacuum port and *open* the atmospheric port to admit air through the air cleaner and valve to the rear diaphragm chamber. With vacuum present in the front chamber and atmospheric pressure in the rear chamber, a force is developed to move the power diaphragm, hydraulic push-rod and hydraulic piston or pistons to close the compensating port or ports and force fluid under pressure through the residual check valve or valves and lines into the front and rear wheel cylinders to actuate the brakes.

As pressure is developed within the master cylinder a counter force acting through the hydraulic push-rod and reaction disc against the vacuum power diaphragm and valve plunger sets up a reaction force opposing the force applied to the valve rod and plunger. This reaction force tends to *close* the atmospheric port and *reopen* the vacuum port. Since this force is in opposition to the force applied to the brake pedal by the driver it gives the driver a "feel" of the amount of brake applied. The proportion of reactive force applied to the valve plunger thru the reaction disc is designed into the Master-Vac to assure maximum power consistent with maintaining pedal feel. The reaction force is in direct proportion to the hydraulic pressure developed within the brake system.

Push Rod Adjustment

Adjust the push rod as outlined in the *General Service* section of this chapter.

Trouble Shooting

Hard Pedal or No Assist

1. Air cleaner element clogged.
2. Control valve faulty.
3. Defective diaphragm.
4. Worn or distorted reaction plate or levers.
5. Cracked or broken power piston or levers.
6. Internal or external leaks.

Brakes Grab

1. Control valve defective or sticking.
2. Bind in linkage.
3. Reaction diaphragm leaking.
4. Worn or distorted levers or plate.

No or Slow Release

1. Push rod adjustment incorrect.
2. Linkage binding.
3. Return spring defective.

DELCO MORAINE

Air Suspended Diaphragm Type Fig. DM-1

This unit consists of a vacuum power section cylinder and a hydraulic master cylinder. Some units have mounting brackets with linkage.

The vacuum power section contains a power piston with a rolling diaphragm which houses the control valve, the reaction mechanism and power piston return spring. The control valve is made up of an air valve and a floating vacuum control valve assembly. The reaction mechanism consists of a hydraulic piston reaction plate.

A tube is used to connect the vacuum source with an air filter, both of which are mounted on the outside of the rear power chamber. The pedal push rod, which connects to the air valve, operates the air valve and floating vacuum control valve.

The master cylinder attaches to the front housing of the vacuum power section. A rubber seal between the master cylinder and front power chamber prevents air leaks. Secondary cups or seals on the master cylinder piston prevents leakage of hydraulic fluid in the master cylinder and reservoir from entering the vacuum power chamber. The master cylinder also contains a primary piston cup, a check valve spring and retainer, a check valve and check valve seat washer. A compensating port in the casting connects the fluid reservoir with the master cylinder bore when the hydraulic piston is in the fully released position to compensate for loss of fluid (or expansion of fluid) from within the hydraulic brake system. A second or larger (fuel inlet) port connects the fluid reservoir with the space between the primary and secondary hydraulic piston cups at all times.

Operation

As the brake pedal is depressed, the push rod forces the air valve forward until its seat contacts the floating control valve to seal off atmosphere from the vacuum chamber side of the power piston. Continued movement of the air valve forces the floating control valve away from its seat on the power piston and admits vacuum to the vacuum chamber side of the power piston and evacuates air from the vacuum chamber side of the power piston.

The atmospheric pressure on the air chamber side moves the power piston toward the master cylinder bore. As the master cylinder primary cup passes the compensating port, the reservoir is sealed off from the hydraulic system to permit a hydraulic pressure build up in the hydraulic system and applying the brakes.

The pressure acting against the end of the master cylinder piston moves the piston reaction plate away from its stop and forces the reaction levers to turn on their pivots and push the valve reaction plate back to the rubber snubbers of the reaction diaphragm. The opposing force on the hydraulic piston is transmitted through the air valve and valve operating rod to the brake pedal giving the driver "feel" as well as position control of brake application.

Push Rod Adjustment

Adjust the push rod as outlined in the *General Service* section of this chapter.

Bleeding The System

The bleeding operation is accomplished in the same manner as outlined in the *Hydraulic Brake System* chapter for conventional brakes. However, if pressure bleeding equipment is not available do not use any vacuum assist. The engine should be running and the vacuum reserve should be used up by repeatedly applying the brake before starting the bleeding operation.

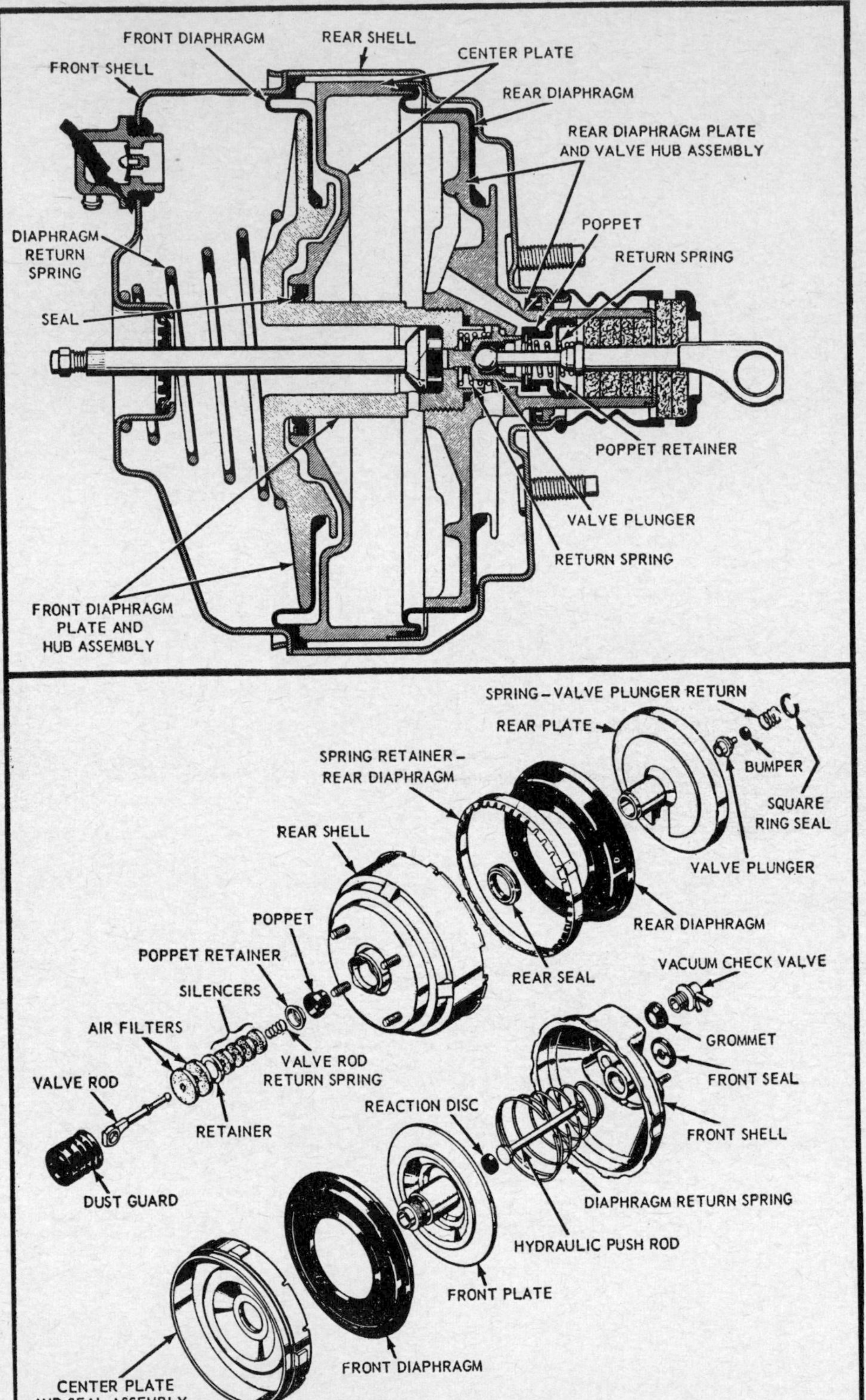

Fig. BM-3 Bendix tandem diaphragm power brake

Trouble Shooting

Hard Pedal

1. Vacuum hose in unit loose or restricted.
2. Restricted air cleaner.
3. Internal vacuum leak.
4. Jammed sliding valve.

Brakes Grab

1. Floating valve diaphragm leakage due to faulty rubber bumper pad in valve.
2. Improper number of shims on air valve.

Slow or No Release

1. Broken vacuum piston return spring.
2. Restricted air cleaner.
3. Bent or dented vacuum cylinder.

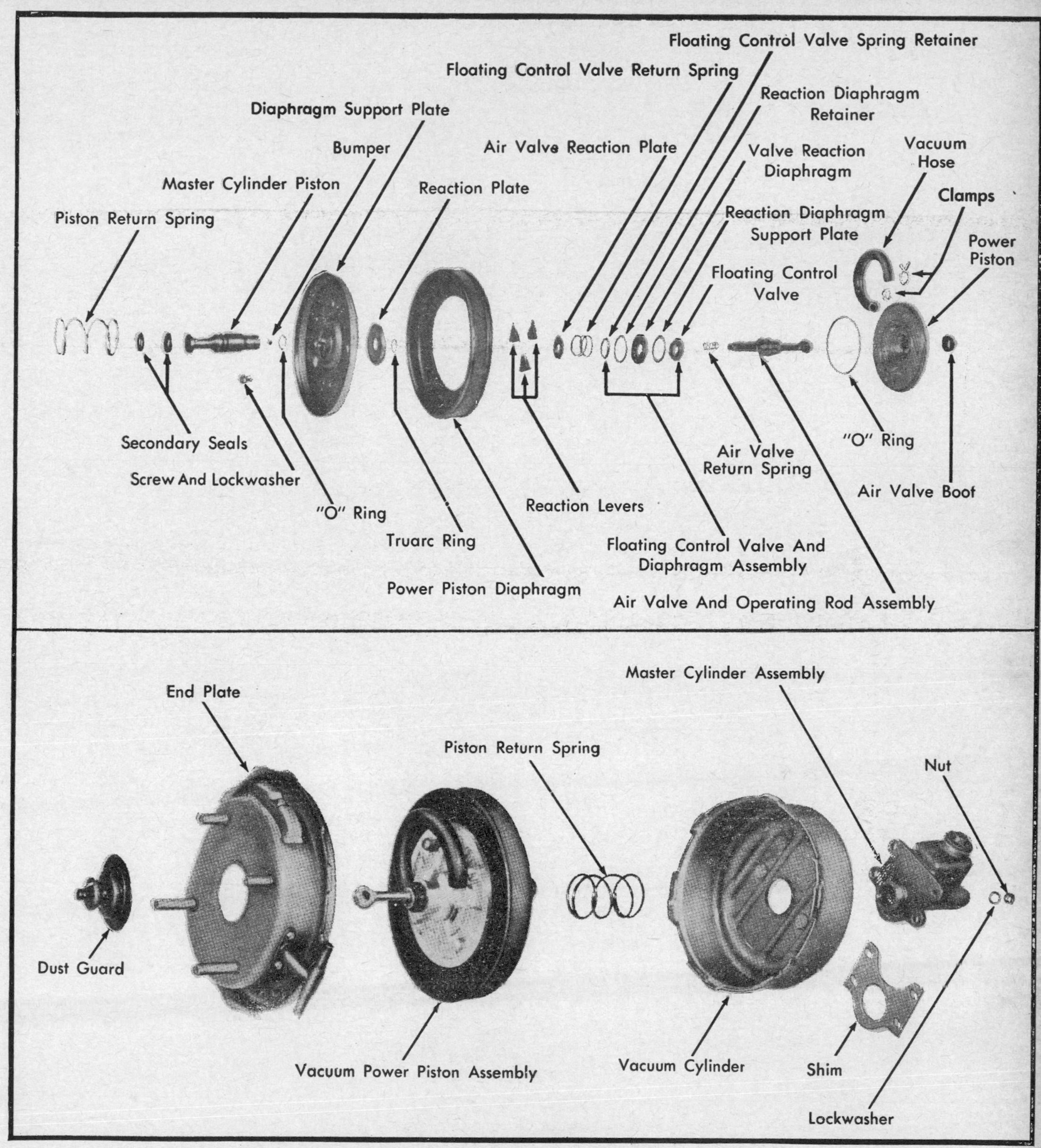

Fig. DM-1 Delco Moraine Air Suspended Diaphragm type

DELCO MORAINE

Vacuum Suspended Diaphragm Type—Fig. DM-2

This power brake unit is a combination vacuum-hydraulic brake booster of the vacuum suspended type which utilizes engine intake manifold vacuum and atmospheric pressure for its power.

The unit consists of a vacuum power section and a hydraulic master cylinder section. The vacuum power section contains a power piston with rolling diaphragm and houses the control valve, the reaction mechanism and power piston return spring.

The control valve is made up of an air valve and floating vacuum control valve assembly. The reaction mechanism consists of a hydraulic piston, reaction plate and a series of levers. The valve operating rod, which operates the air valve, projects from the power section and is

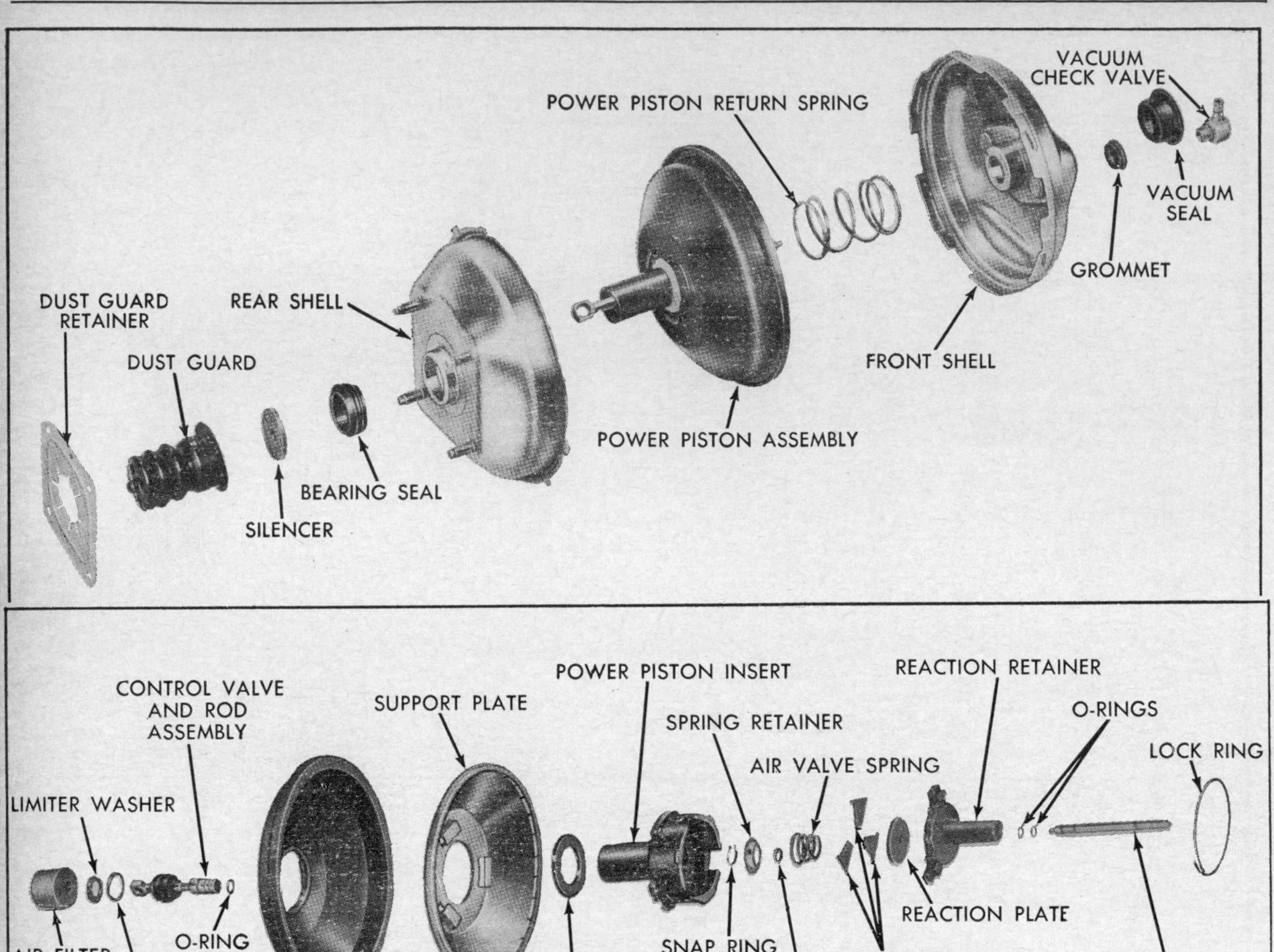

Fig. DM-2 Delco Moraine Vacuum Suspended Diaphragm type

connected to the brake pedal linkage.

The hydraulic push rod operates against the master cylinder piston. A split system (tandem piston) type master cylinder is incorporated into some units. The front half of the master cylinder in the split system operates the rear brakes while the rear half of the master cylinder operates the front brakes (see HYDRAULIC BRAKE SYSTEM chapter).

A vacuum check valve, attached to the front vacuum chamber and connected to the intake manifold, traps vacuum in the power unit at the highest level of vacuum.

Operation

As the brakes are applied by the driver the valve operating rod and control piston move forward in the power piston assembly to compress the valve return spring and bring the poppet valve into contact with the vacuum valve seat in the valve housing to *close* the vacuum port. Any additional movement of the valve operating rod in the applied direction moves the control valve away from the poppet valve to *open* the atmospheric port and admit air through the air filter and passages to the chamber at the right of the vacuum power piston assembly. With vacuum on the left side of the diaphragm and atmospheric pressure on the right side of the diaphragm, a force is developed to move the vacuum power piston assembly, hydraulic push rod, and hydraulic piston to the left to close the compensating port and force hydraulic fluid under pressure through the residual check valve and brake tubes into the brake wheel cylinders.

Push Rod Adjustment

Adjust the push rod as outlined in the *General Service* section of this chapter.

Trouble Shooting

Hard Pedal

1. Internal vacuum leak.
2. Faulty control valve.

Brakes Grab

1. Faulty control valve.

Slow or No Release

1. Faulty push rod adjustment.
2. Bind in linkage.

KELSEY-HAYES

Bellows Type—Fig. KH-1

The Kelsey-Hayes Round Bellows pedal assist type power brake unit is mounted on the driver side of the dash and is mechanically linked to the brake pedal and master cylinder to reduce the pedal

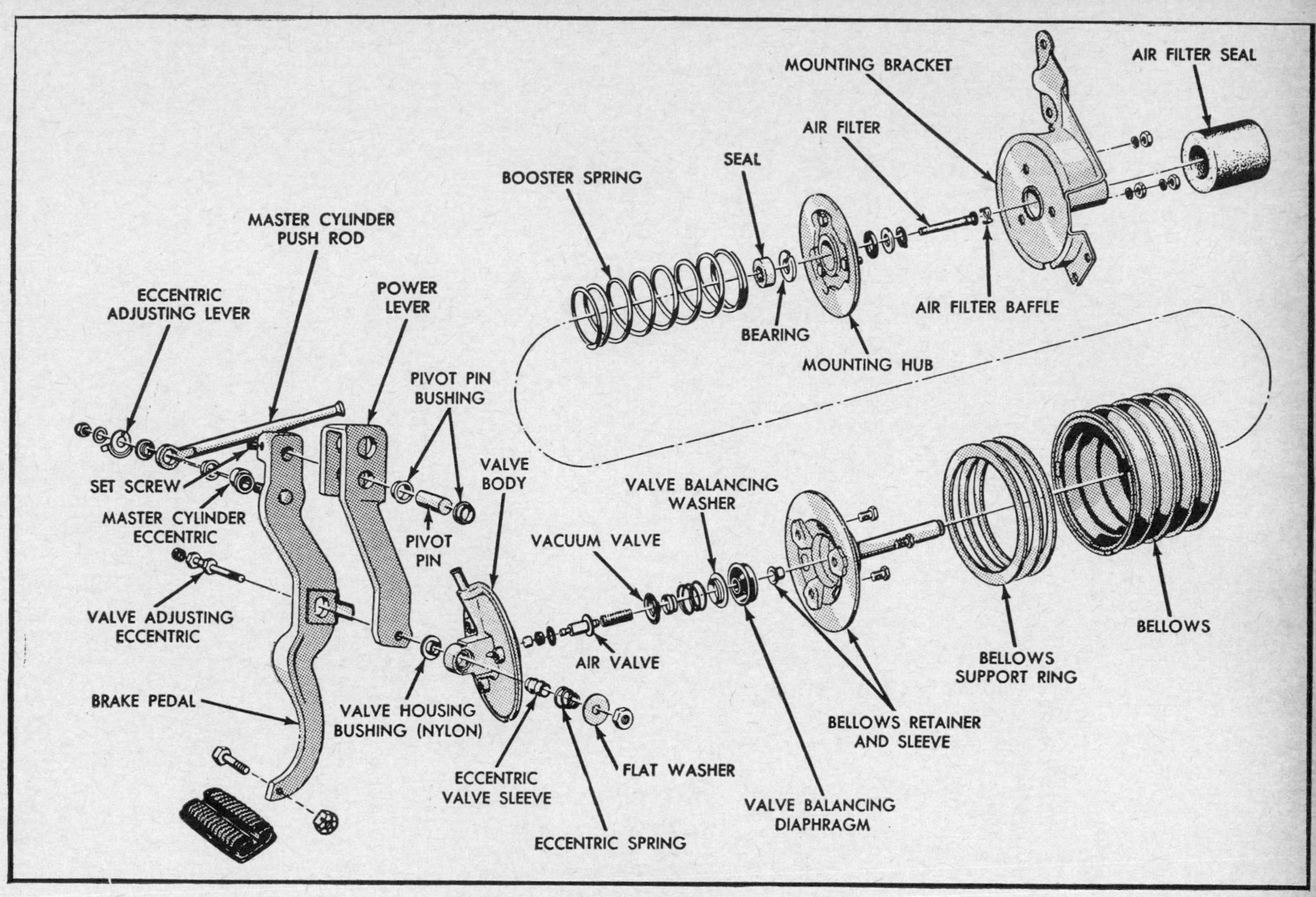

Fig. KH-1 Kelsey-Hayes Bellows type

pressure required by the driver when applying the brakes.

The power unit is of the air suspended type with a bellows that contracts to apply the brakes and expands upon release of the brakes. It derives its power from the engine intake manifold vacuum through a vacuum reservoir mounted in the engine compartment.

A trigger mechanism attached to the brake pedal mechanism controls the degree of brake application and release through an air valve and a vacuum valve built integral with the power unit. The application of power is transmitted to the master cylinder piston through a push rod attached to the power lever of the brake pedal linkage.

In the event of engine failure, there is enough vacuum in the reservoir to make two or three power applications. When the reserve vacuum is used, the brakes can still be applied but considerably more brake pedal pressure will be required.

Operation

As the brake pedal is depressed by the driver, the trigger lever moves the air valve button to overcome the air valve return spring compression and *close* the air valve. Further movement of the brake pedal starts to open the vacuum valve and begin evacuating the bellows of the air. As air is removed from the bellows, the bellows begins to contract and apply a pull on the power lever to force the push rod into the master cylinder and apply pressure to the brakes. As soon as the bellows starts to contract, the air valve button starts to move away from the trigger lever unless pressure is maintained on the brake pedal. As pressure is maintained on the brake pedal the vacuum valve remains open to continue evacuating the bellows until the point of "full power" or maximum manifold vacuum is attained.

Valve Eccentric Adjustment

Start the engine. Turn the valve-adjusting eccentric until the unit chatters when the pedal is depressed in the applying movement. Then turn the eccentric until the chatter disappears. *Do not turn the eccentric more than necessary or the unit will "cut-in" will be excessively high.* If the eccentric cannot be adjusted satisfactorily, the pedal trigger may be bent.

Master Cylinder Push Rod Adjustment

1. Loosen the push rod eccentric lock nut enough to rotate the eccentric.
2. Rotate the eccentric in a clockwise direction to its maximum travel. This will shorten the push rod and allow the master cylinder piston to return to full *unapplied* position.
3. Rotate eccentric counterclockwise until the master cylinder piston starts to resist movement of the push rod. Hold the eccentric and tighten the lock nut securely.
4. Check the master cylinder at the compensator port for bubbles or spurt which indicates push rod is properly adjusted.

Bleeding The System

The bleeding operation is accomplished in the same manner as outlined in the HYDRAULIC BRAKE SYSTEM chapter for conventional brakes.

Trouble Shooting

Hard Pedal

1. Valve eccentric or push rod incorrectly adjusted.
2. Bent pedal trigger.

Brake Pedal Chatter

1. Valve eccentric or push rod incorrectly adjusted.

Slow or No Release

1. Clogged air filter.
2. Push rod incorrectly adjusted.

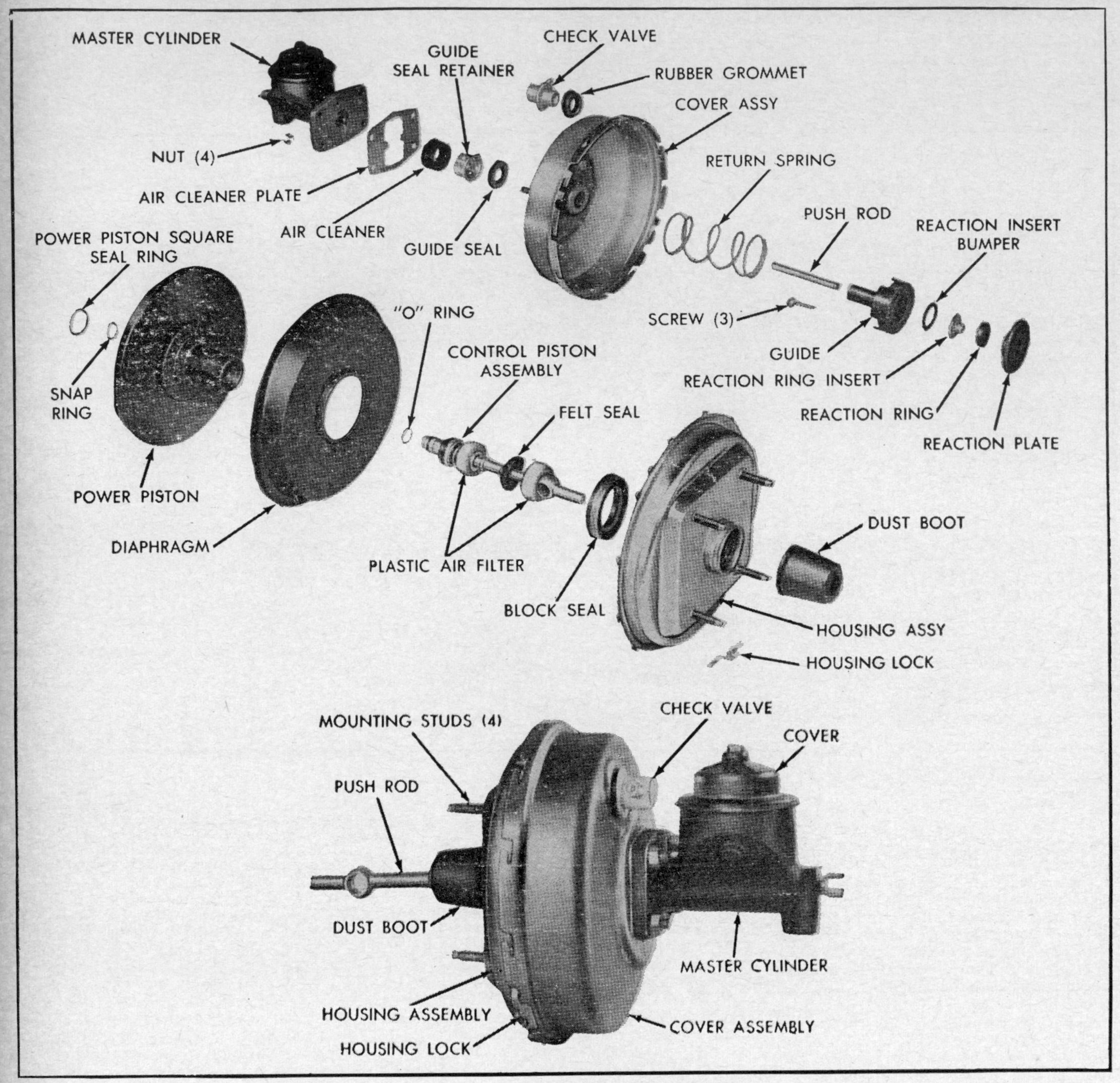

Fig. KH-2 Kelsey-Hayes Diaphragm type

KELSEY-HAYES

Diaphragm Type—Fig. KH-2

This power unit is a combined vacuum and hydraulic unit which utilizes engine intake manifold vacuum and atmospheric pressure to provide power assisted application of the vehicle brakes. The power unit provides lighter pedal pressures.

The power brake unit, which is self-contained and eliminates external rods and levers, mounts on the engine side of the dash. The unit is externally connected to the rest of the system at three points. 1) It is connected by a pedal push rod to the brake pedal; 2) it is connected by a vacuum line to the intake manifold (through a vacuum check valve); 3) a hydraulic connection. From the hydraulic master cylinder connection outward to the wheel cylinders there is no other difference in the brake system from the conventional system.

The vacuum check valve, which is connected to the vacuum line at the front of the housing, prevents loss of vacuum when manifold vacuum falls below that in the power brake system. In case of engine failure and consequent loss of engine vacuum, several applications of the brakes are possible by using vacuum retained in the power unit. When vacuum reserve is exhausted, brakes can be applied manually in the conventional manner except that more pedal pressure is required.

Push Rod Adjustment

Adjust the push rod as outlined in the *General Service* section of this chapter.

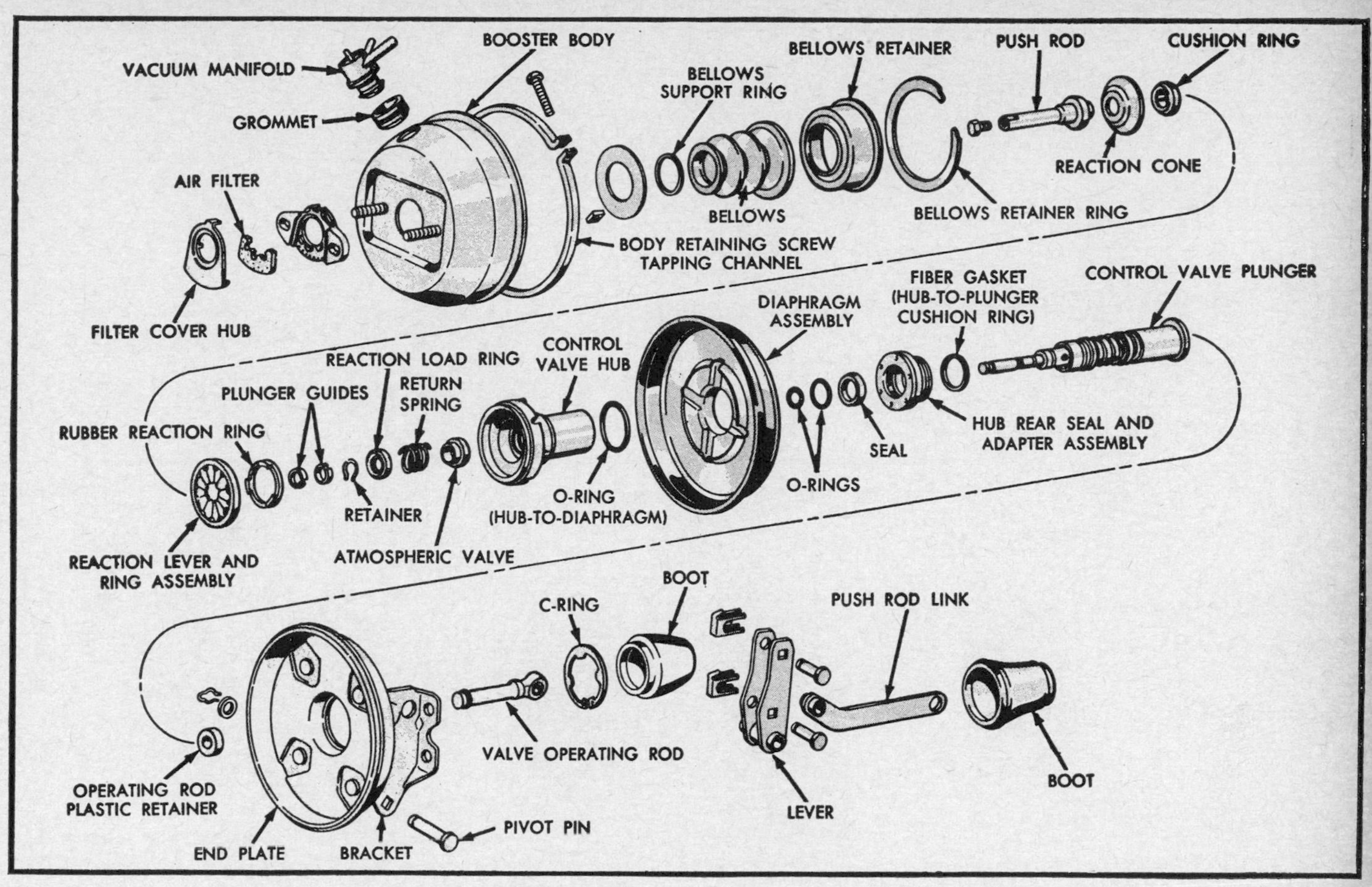

Fig. MR-1 Midland-Ross Diaphragm type

Bleeding The System

The bleeding operation is accomplished in the conventional manner as outlined in the HYDRAULIC BRAKE SYSTEM chapter.

NOTE: On Buick Special 1964 the master cylinder and power brake unit is mounted at an angle on the cowl. A bleeder valve is located at the upper end of the master cylinder. Because of the mounting angle, it will be necessary to bleed the master cylinder first and then the wheel cylinders whenever the master cylinder reservoir has become empty or whenever the master cylinder is removed from the car.

Trouble Shooting

Hard Pedal

1. Faulty vacuum check valve.
2. Vacuum hose or pipe collapsed, plugged, kinked or disconnected.
3. Internal leaks.
4. Vacuum leaks in unit caused by improper assembly, missing parts, damaged parts or foreign matter.
5. Cups swollen by improper fluid.
6. Improper push rod adjustment.
7. Badly dented vacuum cylinder.
8. Bound up pedal linkage.
9. Improperly adjusted stop light switch.
10. Scored valve plunger.
11. Broken or missing springs.

Brake Grab

1. Faulty pedal linkage.
2. Dented vacuum cylinder.
3. Sticking control piston.
4. Defective vacuum check valve.
5. Loose vacuum connections.

MIDLAND-ROSS

Diaphragm Type—Figs. MR-1 & MR-2

This power unit is installed on the engine side of dash and connected to the brake pedal through a lever assembly and push rod link.

The power unit consists of a vacuum chamber, air valve, control valve plunger assembly, diaphragm and an air chamber.

Atmospheric pressure is present at all times in the air chamber at the front side of the air valve. The air intake to the air chamber is protected by a filter. The air chamber is separated from the vacuum chamber by the bellows assembly within the vacuum chamber.

Vacuum is present at all times in that area of the vacuum chamber forward of the diaphragm. Vacuum is supplied through a hose from the engine intake manifold to the vacuum manifold and check valve on the power unit body. With this integral check valve and vacuum chamber, it is possible to obtain several assisted brake applications with the engine shut off. This arrangement makes a vacuum reservoir unnecessary.

Either vacuum from the forward side of the diaphragm or air from the bellows (air chamber) can be connected to the rear side of the diaphragm through porting in the control valve hub and plunger assembly.

Operation

As the brakes are applied by the driver, the valve operating rod and control valve plunger move forward to compress the valve plunger return spring and close the vacuum port. Further movement of the actuating valve opens the atmospheric port to admit atmospheric pressure to the rear side of the power diaphragm. With vacuum on the front side of the diaphragm and atmospheric pressure on the rear side of the diaphragm, the diaphragm, push rod and master cylinder piston move forward to close the compensating port and force hydraulic fluid under pressure through the residual check valve and brake lines to the wheel brakes. As hydraulic pressure is developed within the hydraulic system, an opposing force (counter force) through the reaction levers and ring assembly transmits the reaction force back through the actuating control valve assembly and valve operating rod

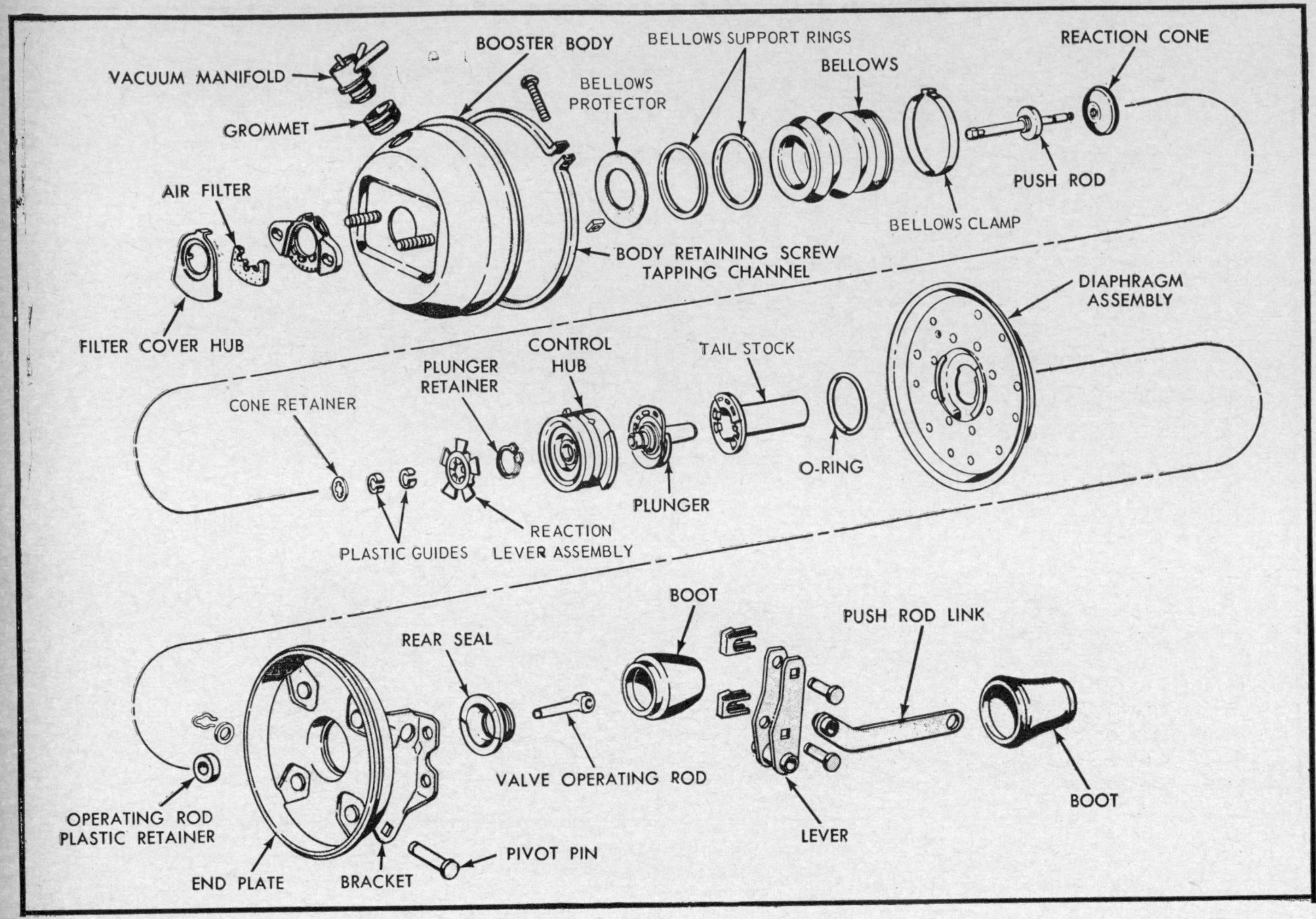

Fig. MR-2 Midland-Ross Diaphragm type

to the brake pedal. This reaction force tends to reduce the power application and is the means of providing the proper "pedal feel" to the driver.

Push Rod Adjustment

Adjust the push rod as outlined in the *General Service* section of this chapter.

Bleeding The System

The bleeding operation is accomplished in the same manner as outlined in the *Hydraulic Brake System* chapter for conventional brakes. However, some units have a bleeder valve on the power brake master cylinder. In bleeding the brakes, first bleed the master cylinder, then proceed with the wheel cylinders.

Trouble Shooting

Hard Pedal

1. Leak in bellows.
2. Diaphragm out of place in housing.

Brakes Grab

1. Sticking actuating valve.

Brakes Self-Apply when Engine is Started

1. Leak in rear housing.
2. Diaphragm out of position in housing allowing air into rear chamber.
3. Sticking or unseated air valve.

MANUAL STEERING GEARS

STEERING GEAR ADJUSTMENT SPECIFICATIONS

CAR MAKE	GEAR TYPE	WORM BEARING PRELOAD	CROSS SHAFT PRELOAD
BUICK			
1965	Ball & Nut	5 to 9①	10 to 18①
1963-64, 66, 67	Ball & Nut	2 to 7①	6 to 15①
1968-69	Ball & Nut	5 to 9①	10 to 20①
BUICK SPECIAL			
1963-67	Ball & Nut	2 to 7①	6 to 15①
1968-69	Ball & Nut	5 to 9①	10 to 20①
CAMARO & CHEVELLE			
1964	Ball & Nut	6 to 10②	14 to 24②
1965-66	Ball & Nut	4 to 7①	8 to 17①
1967-69	Ball & Nut	5 to 8①	9 to 18①
CHEVROLET			
1963-64	Ball & Nut	6 to 10②	14 to 24②
1965-66	Ball & Nut	4 to 7①	8 to 17①
1967-69	Ball & Nut	5 to 8①	9 to 18①
CHEVY II			
1963-64	Ball & Nut	8 to 14②	8 to 20②
1965	Ball & Nut	1½-5½①	4½-12½①
1966	Ball & Nut	8 to 14①	8 to 20①
1967-69	Ball & Nut	5 to 8①	9 to 18①
CHRYSLER			
1963-64	Worm & Roller	6 to 12②	16 to 32②
1965-69	Ball & Nut	1 to 4①	8 to 11①
COMET & COUGAR			
1963-64	Ball & Nut	4 to 7①	9 to 14①
1965-68	Ball & Nut	4 to 5①	9 to 10①
CORVAIR			
1963-64	Ball & Nut	7 to 11②	18 to 24②
1965-69	Ball & Nut	3½-4½①	11½-14½①
CORVETTE			
1963-65	Ball & Nut	6 to 10②	14 to 24②
1966	Ball & Nut	8 to 14①	8 to 20①
1967-69	Ball & Nut	5 to 8①	9 to 18①
DODGE & DART			
1965-69	Ball & Nut	1 to 4①	8 to 11①
1963-64	Ball & Nut	2 to 6①	11 to 15①
FAIRLANE			
1963-64	Ball & Nut	4 to 7①	9 to 14①
1965-69	Ball & Nut	4 to 5①	9 to 10①
FALCON			
1963-64	Ball & Nut	4 to 7①	9 to 14①
1965-69	Ball & Nut	4 to 5①	9 to 10①
FORD			
1963-64	Ball & Nut	4 to 12②	16 to 26②
1965-69	Ball & Nut	4 to 5①	9 to 10①
JEEP			
1963-65	Cam & Lever	③	④
1965-68	Worm & Roller	2 to 5	7 to 12
1966-68	Ball & Nut	8	18
MERCURY			
1963-64	Ball & Nut	4 to 12②	16 to 26②
1965-69	Ball & Nut	4 to 5①	9 to 10①
MONTEGO			
1968-69	Ball & Nut	4 to 5①	9 to 10①
MUSTANG			
1964	Ball & Nut	4 to 7①	9 to 14①
1965-69	Ball & Nut	4 to 5①	9 to 10①
OLDSMOBILE			
1963-69	Ball & Nut	4 to 7①	8 to 17①
1965	Ball & Nut	1½- 8①	5½-16 ①
OLDS F-85			
1963-69	Ball & Nut	4 to 7①	8 to 17①
1965	Ball & Nut	1½- 8①	5½-16 ①
PLYMOUTH			
1965-69	Ball & Nut	1 to 4①	8 to 11①
1963-64	Ball & Nut	2 to 6①	11 to 15①
PONTIAC			
1968-69	Ball & Nut	7①	16①
1966-67	Ball & Nut	5 to 9①	9 to 18①
1965	Ball & Nut	5 to 9①	10 to 20①
1964	Ball & Nut	5 to 9①	9 to 14①
1963	Ball & Nut	6 to 10①	8 to 16①
PONTIAC TEMPEST & FIREBIRD			
1963-64	Ball & Nut	5 to 9①	9 to 14①
1965-67	Ball & Nut	5 to 9①	9 to 14①
1968-69	Ball & Nut	7①	16⑤
RAMBLER			
1963-64	Ball & Nut	8 to 12②	16 to 20②
1965-67	Ball & Nut	2 to 6②	12 to 18②
1968-69	Ball & Nut	1/8 to 3/8①	3/4 to 1 1/8①
RAMBLER AMERICAN			
1965-68	Worm & Roller	4 to 10②	16 to 18②
1968	Ball & Nut	1/8 to 3/8①	3/4 to 1 1/8①
VALIANT			
1965-69	Ball & Nut	1 to 4①	8 to 11①
1963-64	Ball & Nut	2 to 6①	11 to 15①

①—Measured with inch-pound torque wrench attached to steering wheel nut.

②—Measured in ounces pull on spring scale attached to rim of steering wheel.

③—Adjust to slight drag but steering wheel must turn freely.

④—Adjust to slight drag through mid-position only.

⑤—Firebird with V8 engine and A/C. Others 14 in-lbs.

Saginaw Recirulating Ball Worm & Nut Gear

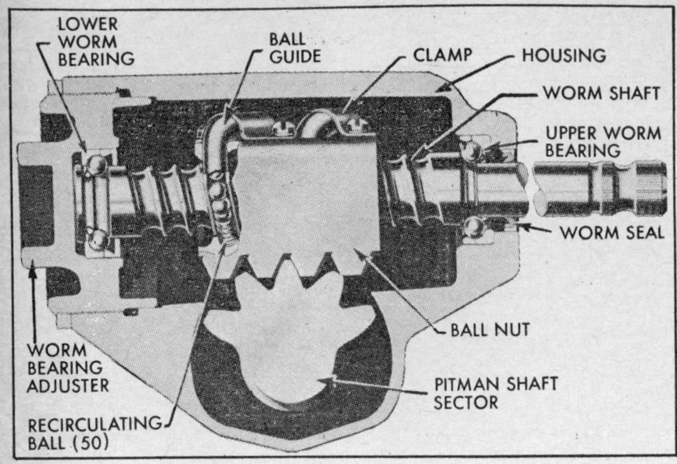

Fig. 1 Recirculating ball-worm and nut steering gear

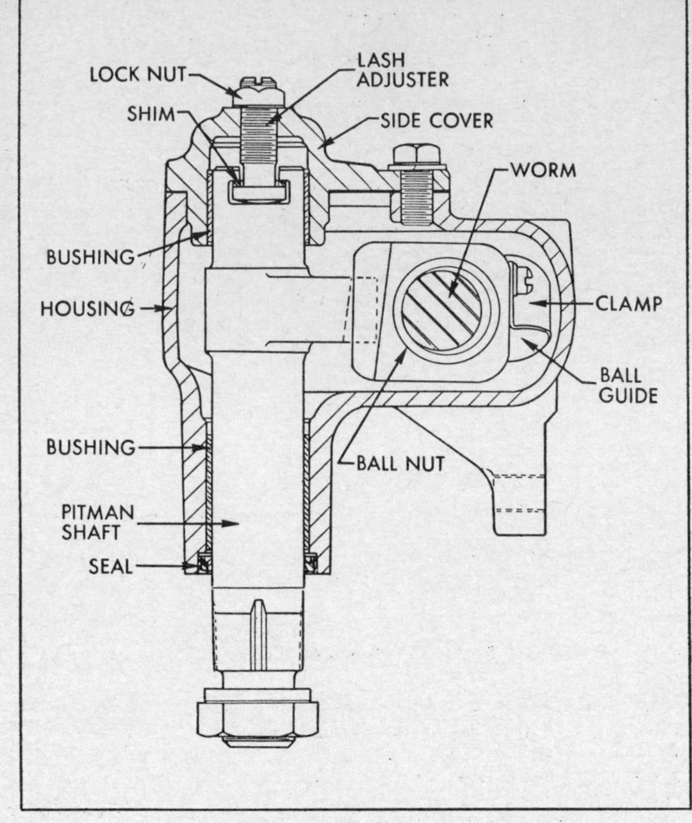

Fig. 2 Recirculating ball-worm and nut and pitman (cross) shaft

DESCRIPTION

As shown in Fig. 1, the worm on the lower end of the steering shaft and the ball nut which is mounted on the worm have mating spiral grooves in which steel balls circulate to provide a low friction drive between worm and nut.

Two sets of balls are used, ranging in number from approximately 20 to 30 to a set, depending upon the size of the steering gear unit. Each set of balls operate independently of the other. The circuit through which each set of balls circulates includes the grooves in the worm and ball nut and a ball return guide attached to the outer surface of the nut.

When the wheel and steering shaft turn to the left, the ball nut is moved downward by the balls which roll between the worm and nut. As the balls reach the outer surface of the nut they enter the return guides which direct them across and down into the ball nut where they enter the circuit again.

When a right turn is made the ball nut moves upward and balls circulate in the reverse direction.

The teeth on the ball nut engage teeth on the sector which is forged integral with the pitman shaft, Fig. 2. The teeth on the ball nut are made so that a "high point" or tighter fit exists between the ball nut and pitman shaft sector teeth when the front wheels are in the straight-ahead position. The teeth on the sector are tapered slightly so that a proper lash may be obtained by moving the pitman shaft endwise by means of a lash adjuster screw which extends through the gear housing side cover. The head of the lash adjuster and the selectively fitted shim fit snugly into a T-slot in the end of the pitman shaft so that the screw also controls end play of the shaft. The screw is locked by an external lock nut.

GEAR ADJUSTMENTS

There are two adjustments on the steering gear: worm bearing preload and pitman shaft overcenter preload, Fig. 3.

Important: Never attempt to adjust the steering gear while it is connected to the steering linkage. The gear must be free of all outside load in order to properly make any steering gear adjustment.

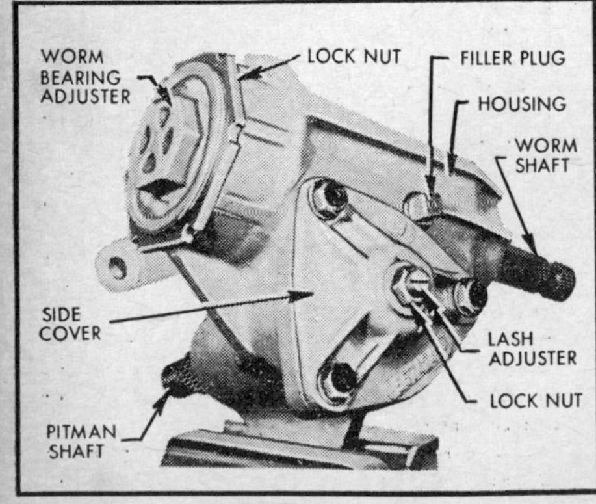

Fig. 3 Steering gear adjustments

Fig. 4 Checking adjustments with inch-pound torque wrench

Fig. 5 Checking adjustments with spring scale

Preliminary

1. Tighten steering gear mounting bolts.
2. Disconnect steering linkage from steering arm or gear.
3. Turn wheel slowly from one extreme to the other.
   Caution: Never turn the wheel hard against the stopping point in the gear as damage to the ball nut assembly may result.
4. Steering wheel should turn freely and smoothly throughout its entire range.
   Note: Roughness indicates faulty internal parts requiring disassembly of gear unit. Hard pull or binding indicates an excessively tight adjustment of the worm bearings, or excessive misalignment of the steering shaft. Any excessive misalignment must be corrected before the gear can be properly adjusted.

NOTE: Specifications in the Steering Gear Adjustment Specifications chart are given in inch pounds as measured with a torque wrench pulling on steering wheel nut, Fig. 4, or with a spring scale, measured in ounces, attached to rim of steering wheel, Fig. 5.

Checking Worm Bearing Preload

1. Turn steering wheel gently in one direction until it stops. This positions gear away from "high point" load.
2. Attach torque wrench or spring scale and check the torque or pull required to turn the wheel steadily in the range where lash exists between ball nut and pitman shaft sector.
3. If adjustment is not within specified limits, adjust worm bearing preload.

Adjust Worm Bearing Preload

1. Loosen worm bearing adjuster lock nut, using a drift, Fig. 3.
2. Turn bearing adjuster as required to bring the adjustment within specified limits.
3. Tighten lock nut and recheck preload.

Checking Pitman Shaft Over-Center Preload

1. Turn steering wheel from one extreme to the other while counting the total turns, then turn wheel back ½ the number of turns. This positions steering gear on "high point" where a preload should exist between ball nut and pitman shaft teeth.
2. Attach torque wrench or spring scale and check torque or pull required to turn the wheel through the "high point" range.
3. If adjustment is not within the specified limits, adjust as follows:

Adjust Pitman Shaft Overcenter Preload

1. Loosen lock nut and turn pitman shaft lash adjuster screw as required to bring the adjustment within specified limits.
2. After tightening lock nut, rotate steering wheel back and forth through the "high point" and through the entire range to check for tight spots.

NOTE: If lash cannot be removed at the "high point", or if gear load varies greatly and feels rough, the gear should be removed for inspection of internal parts.

3. Attach linkage to steering gear when adjustments have been completed.

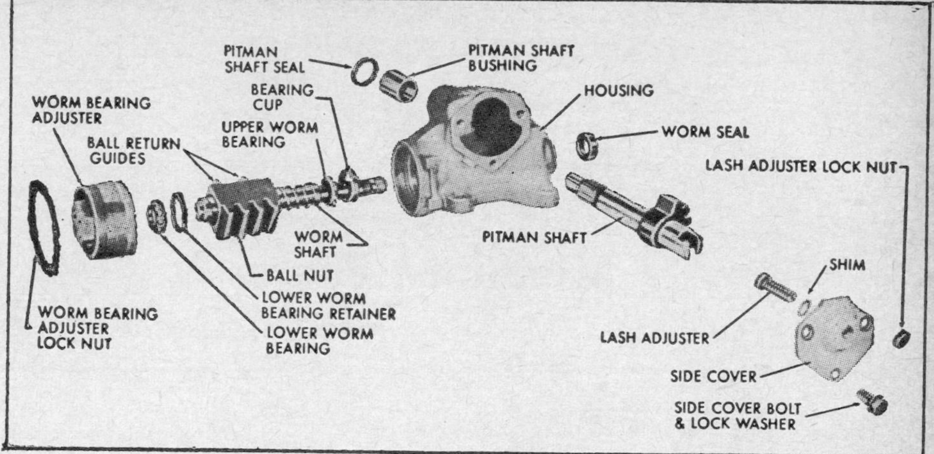

Fig. 6 Recirculating ball-worm and nut gear disassembled

STEERING GEAR REPAIRS

1. Referring to Fig. 6, loosen adjusting screw lock nut and remove housing side cover by unscrewing adjusting screw.
2. Loosen lock nut and back off worm bearing adjuster several turns, then remove housing end cover and gasket.
3. Remove lower thrust bearing, steering shaft and upper bearing from housing.
4. Remove ball return guide clamps and guides from ball nut, turn ball nut over to remove balls and remove ball nut from steering shaft worm.

Inspection of Parts

1. Clean and inspect all ball and roller bearings and races, including race in housing.
2. Inspect pitman shaft bushings in gear housing and end cover. Replace bushings in housing and replace end cover if bushings are worn excessively.
3. It is advisable to replace pitman shaft grease seal in housing to avoid possible leakage of lubricant. Seal must be installed with feather edge toward inside of housing.
4. Inspect steering shaft for wear or pits in bearing races, which would require replacement of shaft.
5. Check shaft for straightness.
6. Inspect teeth of ball nut and pitman shaft. If scored or excessively worn it is advisable to replace both parts to insure proper mating of teeth.
7. Check serrations of pitman shaft; if twisted, replace shaft.
8. Check fit of pitman shaft adjusting screw and shim in slot in end of pitman shaft. *With shim in place, screw head must be free to turn in slot with zero to .002" end play.* If end play is excessive, selectively fit a new shim, which are furnished in four different thicknesses.
9. Inspect steering column jacket for distortion. A ripple or wavy feeling of jacket surface, particularly at lower end, will usually indicate a sprung jacket. Replace jacket if sprung or otherwise damaged.
10. Inspect control shaft bearing in tube of gear housing, and steering shaft upper bearing in control lever housing support. Replace worn or damaged parts.

Reassemble

Note: Lubricate all seals, bushings, bearings and gears with multi-purpose gear lube prior to installation.

1. Position ball nut over worm shaft so that deep side of teeth will be toward side cover when installed in gear housing.
2. Install exactly ½ the total number of balls in each circuit, rocking worm shaft slightly to aid in installing balls.
3. Place about six balls in each return guide, using grease to hold balls in place.
4. Install return guides, clamp and screw.
5. Rotate worm through its complete travel several times to be sure balls are installed correctly and rotate freely.
6. Place upper bearing on worm shaft and slide worm shaft assembly into housing.
7. Place lower bearing in worm bearing adjuster and install bearing retainer.
8. Install adjuster assembly and lock nut in housing. Tighten adjuster only enough to hold worm bearings in place. Final adjustment will be made later.
9. Turn worm shaft until center groove in ball nut lines up with center of pitman shaft bushing.
10. Install pitman shaft and lash adjuster with shim so that center

tooth meshes with center groove in ball nut.
11. Install side cover with gasket on lash adjuster by turning adjuster counterclockwise.
12. Install side cover bolts and washers.
13. Turn lash adjuster so that teeth on shaft and ball nut engage but do not bind.
14. Install lash adjuster lock nut loosely.
15. To protect pitman shaft seal from damage, cover shaft splines with masking tape. Slide new seal into place and seat it against shoulder in housing.
16. Install new worm shaft seal flush with surface of housing.
17. Fill gear housing with multi-purpose lubricant and adjust gear assembly as outlined previously.

Gemmer Worm & Roller Gear

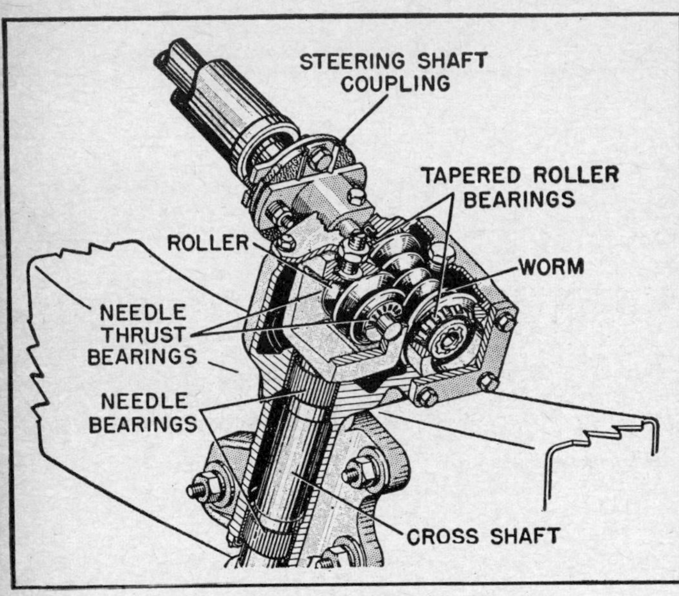

Fig. 7 Worm and roller steering gear

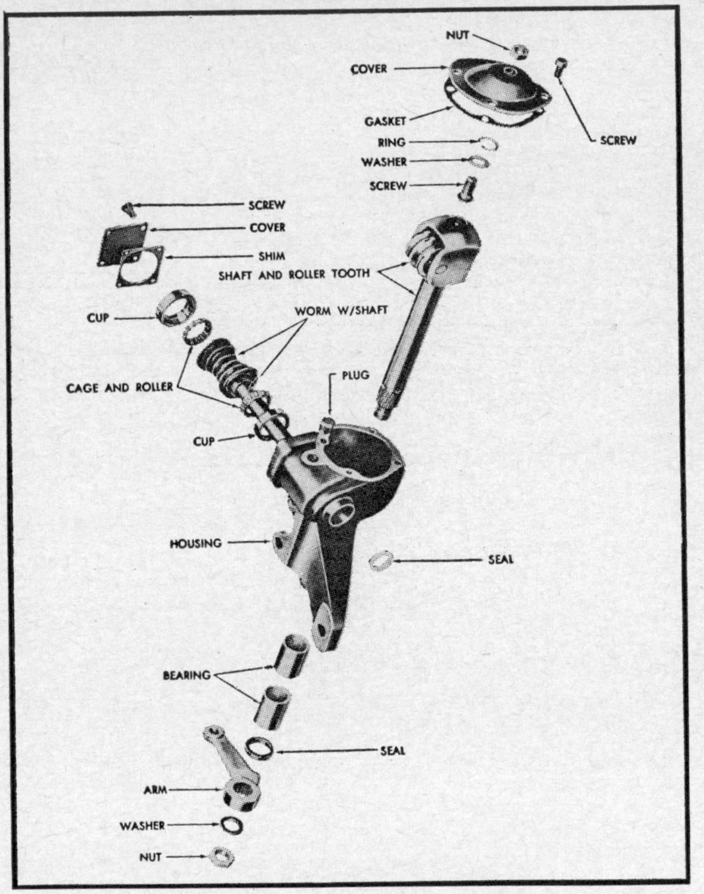

Fig. 8 Worm and roller gear unit disassembled

DESCRIPTION

In this type steering gear, Fig. 7, the worm is integral with the steering shaft and is supported on each end by opposed tapered roller bearings. The triple tooth roller is attached to the roller shaft by means of a steel shaft. Two needle bearing assemblies are installed between this shaft and the roller.

The roller shaft is mounted in the steering gear housing on two needle bearing assemblies which are pressed into the housing. The housing cover is attached to the housing by four cap screws. An adjustment screw, mounted in the cover, controls roller shaft end play and worm and roller mesh adjustment.

The steering wheel and roller shaft arm (pitman arm) are splined to the steering shaft and roller shaft respectively. Both the pitman arm and steering wheel have master splines to insure correct installation.

ADJUSTMENTS

Worm End Play, Adjust

1. Free the steering gear of all load by disconnecting the linkage and loosening the steering column braces.
2. Loosen the four cover screws about ⅛".
3. Use a knife to separate the top shim, passing the blade all the way around between the shims, being careful not to damage the remaining shims.
4. Remove one shim at a time between inspections to remove the end play.
5. The adjustment is correct when there is no end play and no stiffness in the steering gear throughout the complete range of its travel.

Roller Shaft End Play, Adjust

1. Turn the steering gear to either extreme and back off ⅛ of a turn.
2. Gripping the pitman arm at the hub, the roller shaft should rotate freely without a particle of end play.
3. If end play exists, adjust as required by means of the roller shaft adjusting screw in the side cover.
4. Be sure to tighten the lock nut securely and inspect for end play and free rotation throughout the entire range of steering gear travel.

Worm & Roller Mesh, Adjust

1. Loosen the roller shaft adjusting screw lock nut.
2. With the steering gear in its central position (linkage disconnected) tighten the roller shaft adjusting screw just enough to remove play between the roller shaft roller tooth and worm.
3. Check this by the amount of play felt at the pitman arm. It is better to leave a slight amount of play at this point than to tighten too much.

4. If tightened beyond the point where the lash is removed, serious results will occur which will cause poor steering operation.
5. Tighten the adjusting screw lock nut.

GEAR REPAIRS

1. Referring to Fig. 8, use a suitable puller to remove gear oil seal from housing. If shaft is corroded or dirty, clean the portion between oil seal and serrations to avoid binding in bearings.
2. Place a suitable arbor over cross shaft threads while withdrawing cross shaft, following with the arbor. This arbor will keep bearing rollers from dropping out of their cages.
3. Remove cross shaft adjusting screw lock nut. Remove cover and shims from bottom cover gasket and cross shaft.
4. Remove shaft-worm, bearings and cups.
5. If necessary, drive needle bearings from housing.
6. Clean all parts and inspect for wear.
7. Assemble parts without lubrication. Lubrication should be done after adjustments are completed. The needle bearings are grease-packed at the factory.
8. If either of the worm thrust bearings is damaged, replace both bearings. Use new oil seals.

Ross Cam & Lever Gear

DESCRIPTION

This type steering gear, Fig. 9, can be identified by the location of the filler hole plug which is at the upper end of the housing.

Two adjustments are provided for the steering gear assembly: steering post end play and cam lever shaft stud clearance. Before making adjustments, free the steering gear of all load by disconnecting the steering gear from the steering linkage.

ADJUSTMENTS

Steering Post End Play

Loosen the cam lever shaft adjusting screw lock nut and back off the adjusting screw. Using a spring scale that is calibrated in ounces, measure the amount of pull required to turn the steering wheel. The scale should be hooked to a tag wire or string which is wrapped around the rim of the steering wheel at the spoke. A steady pull of the specified drag (see table), should turn the steering wheel smoothly. If the pull is not within limits, loosen the steering post jacket clamp, remove the top cover cap screws and add or remove shims as required to secure the proper scale reading.

Cam Lever Shaft Stud Clearance

With the steering post end play adjusted correctly, locate the center of travel (high spot) of the steering gear. While turning the steering wheel back and forth over the high spot, turn the lever shaft adjusting screw. Keep the lock nut snug until a slight drag is felt. Then tighten the lock nut.

To check the adjustment, hook the spring scale to the steering wheel rim and check the amount of effort required to turn the wheel in either direction through the high spot. The scale reading should be as specified in table.

GEAR REPAIRS

Disassemble

1. Referring to Fig. 9, loosen lock nut and back off adjusting screw.

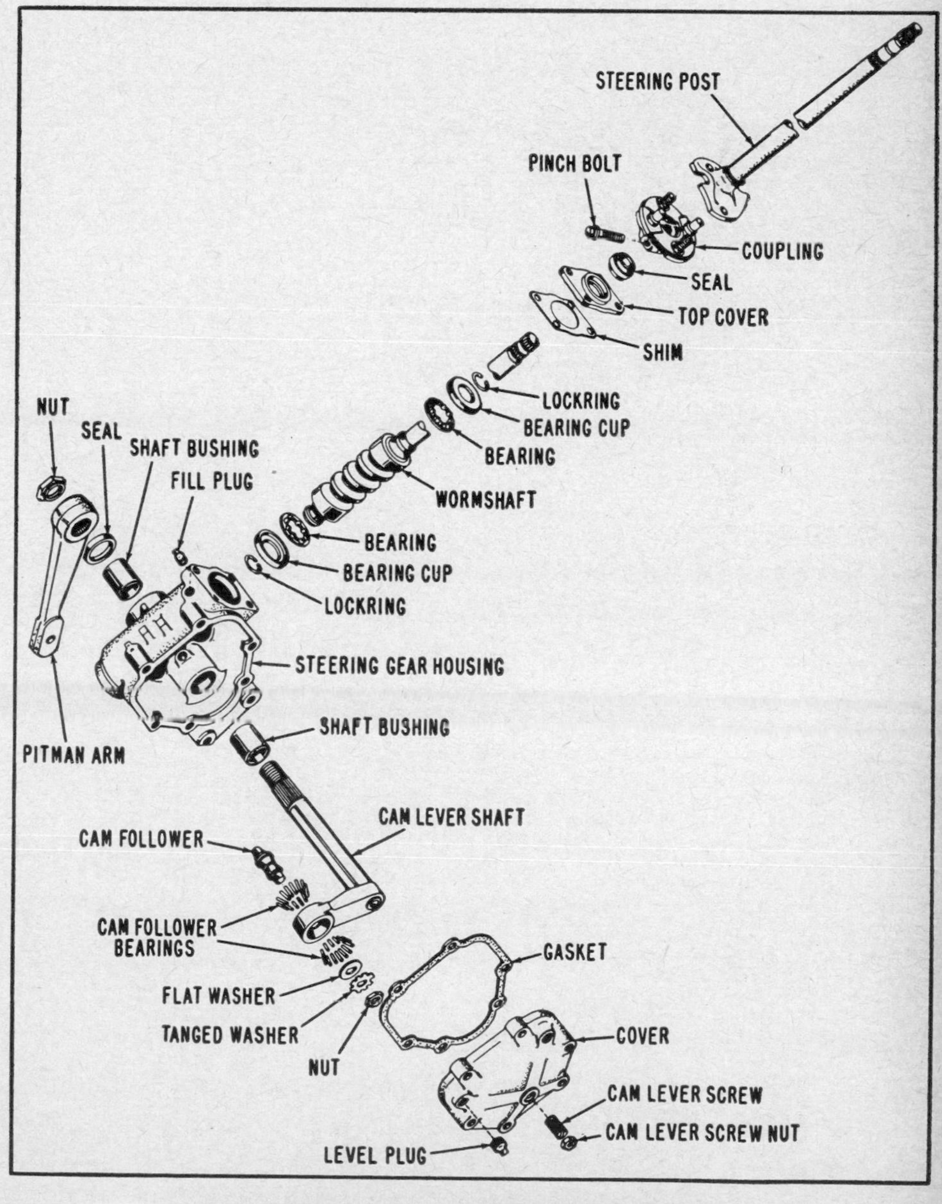

Fig. 9 Cam and lever steering gear disassembled. Some twin lever units are used on Jeep vehicles

2. Remove side cover and gasket.
3. Clean serrated end of cam lever shaft to prevent seal and/or bushing damage. Then pull cam lever shaft assembly from housing.
4. Remove top cover and adjusting shims from housing. Then remove post and cam assembly from housing.
5. Remove lower cam bearing retainer ring and slip lower bearing cup and ball retainer assembly off shaft. Remove upper bearing in same manner.
6. Remove cam lever shaft oil seal from gear housing. If cam lever bushings are to be replaced, use a suitable arbor and press inner and outer bushings from housing.
7. Remove cam follower from lever shaft by bending down locking tang. Then remove tanged washer and retainer washer and slip bearings and stud out of lever.

Reassembly

1. If cam lever bushings were removed from housing, install new bushings, using an arbor press and a suitable arbor. The bushings should then be line reamed to fit the cam lever shaft. Use a suitable arbor and install a new cam lever shaft oil seal.
2. Place the inner set of bearing rollers around cam follower stud. Hold rollers in place with heavy grease.
3. Carefully insert stud and assembled rollers into lever and assemble outer set of rollers, using heavy grease. Then install retainer washer, a new tanged lockwasher and nut.
4. Adjust gear unit as outlined above and fill housing with specified lubricant.

BUICK

All Intermediate & Full Size Models

OLD CAR SPECIFICATIONS: For 1946-62 Tune Up and Wheel Alignment Specifications see back of book.

INDEX OF SERVICE OPERATIONS

PAGE NO.

ACCESSORIES

Automatic Level Controls 1-41
Clock Troubles 1-11
Heater Core, Replace 2-19
Power Top Troubles 1-18
Power Window Troubles 1-18
Radio, Replace 2-17
Speed Controls, Adjust 2-19

BRAKES

Brake Troubles, Mechanical 1-17
Disc Brake Service 1-430
Hydraulic System Service 1-422
Master Cylinder, Replace 2-36
Parking Brake, Adjust 2-36
Power Brake Unit, Replace 2-37
Power Brake Service 1-440
Power Brake Troubles 1-440
Service Brakes, Adjust 2-35

CLUTCH

Clutch Pedal, Adjust 2-27
Clutch, Replace 2-28
Clutch Troubles 1-12

COOLING SYSTEM

Cooling System Troubles 1-6
Variable Speed Fans 1-39
Water Pump, Replace 2-26

ELECTRICAL

Alternator Service 1-63
Back-up Light Switch, Replace 2-14
Clutch Start Switch 2-13
Dash Gauge Service 1-117
Distributor, Replace 2-12
Distributor Service:
Standard 1-53
Transistorized 1-47
Electrical Troubles 1-8
Flasher Location Chart .... Back of Book
Generator Service 1-91
Headlamps, Concealed Type 1-40
Horn Sounder, Remove 2-14
Ignition Coils and Resistors 1-24
Ignition Switch, Replace 2-12
Ignition Timing 2-12
Instrument Cluster Removal 2-15
Light Switch, Replace 2-12
Neutral Start Switch, Replace 2-14
Radio, Replace 2-17
Spark Plug Condition Chart 2-647
Starter Service 1-101
Starter, Replace 2-12
Starter Switch Service 1-114
Stop Light Switch, Replace 2-13
Turn Signal Switch, Replace 2-13
Turn Signal Troubles 1-11
Windshield Wiper Motor, Replace 2-17
Windshield Wiper Troubles 1-20

PAGE NO.

ENGINE

Camshaft, Replace 2-25
Crankshaft Rear Oil Seal 2-25
Cylinder Head, Replace 2-20
Engine Identification 2-3
Engine, Replace 2-20
Engine Troubles 1-1
Main Bearings 2-25
Oil Pan, Replace 2-25
Piston Pins 2-25
Piston Rings 2-25
Piston and Rod, Assemble 2-25
Pistons 2-25
Rocker Arm Service 2-22
Rod Bearings 2-25
Timing Case Cover, Replace 2-23
Timing Chain, Replace 2-24
Valve Arrangement 2-22
Valve Guides 2-23
Valve Lifters 2-23
Valve Lift Specs. 2-23
Valve Timing Specs. 2-23

ENGINE LUBRICATION

Crankcase Ventilation (PCV) 1-29
Exhaust Emission Controls 1-30
Oil Pump 2-26

FUEL SYSTEM

Carburetor Adjustments and Specs. 1-124
Crankcase Ventilation (PCV) 1-29
Exhaust Emission Controls 1-30
Fuel Pump, Replace 2-26
Fuel Pump Service 1-120
Fuel System Troubles 1-2

PROPELLER SHAFT & U JOINTS

Propeller Shaft 2-34
Universal Joint Service 1-418

REAR AXLE

Axle Shaft, Bearing and Seal 2-32
Rear Axle, Replace 2-32
Rear Axle Description 2-31
Rear Axle Specifications 2-10
Rear Axle Troubles 1-17

SPECIFICATIONS

Alternator 2-9
Brakes 2-10
Capacities 2-11
Carburetors 1-124
Cooling System 2-11
Crankshaft and Bearings 2-8
Distributors 2-6

PAGE NO.

Engine Tightening Torque 2-9
General Engine Specs. 2-3
Generators 2-9
Ignition Coils and Resistors 1-24
Pistons, Rings and Pins 2-8
Rear Axle 2-10
Starting Motor 2-6
Tune Up 2-4
Valves 2-8
Valve Lift 2-23
Valve Timing 2-23
Wheel Alignment 2-7

STEERING GEAR

Horn Sounder Removal 2-14
Manual Gear, Replace 2-40
Manual Gear Service 1-451
Manual Gear Troubles 1-18
Power Gear, Replace 2-40
Steering Wheel, Replace 2-14

SUSPENSION, FRONT

Ball Joints, Replace 2-39
Ball Joints, Check for Wear 2-39
Coil Spring, Replace 2-40
Shock Absorber, Replace 2-39
Suspension, Description of 2-37
Tire Wear Chart 2-648
Toe-In, Adjust 2-38
Wheel Alignment, Adjust 2-38
Wheel Bearings, Adjust 2-39
Wheel Bearings, Replace 2-39

TRANSMISSIONS

Three Speed Manual:
Replace 2-29
Repairs 1-261
Linkage, Adjust 2-29
Four Speed Manual:
Replace 2-30
Repairs 1-298
Linkage, Adjust 2-30
Automatic Units 1-321
Linkage, 1969 2-31

TUNE UP

Service 1-21
Specifications 2-4

WINDSHIELD WIPER

Wiper Motor, Replace 2-17
Wiper Linkage, Replace 2-17
Wiper Switch, Replace 2-17
Wiper Troubles 1-20

BUICK – All Intermediate & Full Size Models

1963 Special

1963 Le Sabre, Electra, Invicta

1963 Wildcat

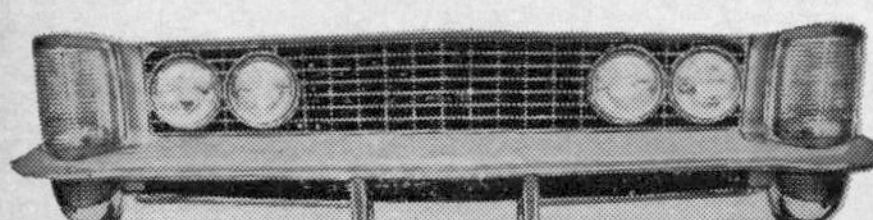
1963-64 Riviera

1964 Special

1964 Le Sabre and Electra

1964 Wildcat

1965 Special

1965 Le Sabre

1965 Wildcat

1965 Electra

1965 Riviera

1966 Special & Std. Skylark

1966 Skylark Gran Sport

1966 LeSabre

1966 Electra

1966 Wildcat

1966 Riviera

1967 Sportwagon, Special

1967 Gran Sport

1967 LeSabre & Electra

1967 Wildcat

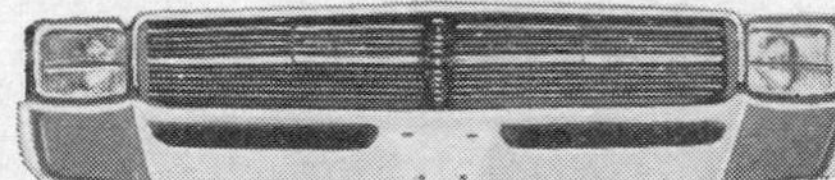
1967 Riviera

1968 Sportwagon, Special, Skylark

1968 Gran Sport

1968 LeSabre

1968 Electra

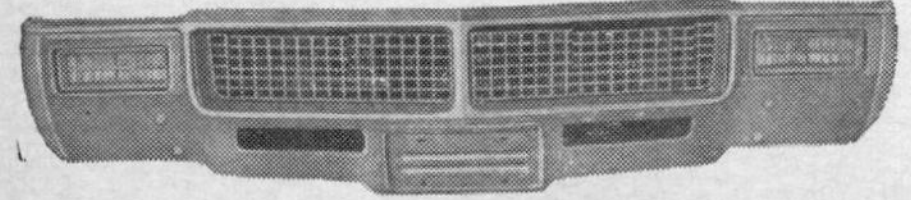
1968 Riviera

1968 Wildcat

1969 Sportwagon, Special

1969 Gran Sport

1969 LeSabre & Wildcat 4 Dr. Sed.

1969 Wildcat exc. 4 Dr. Sed.

1969 Skylark

1969 Electra

1969 Riviera

ENGINE IDENTIFICATION

Buick engines are stamped with two different sets of numbers. One is the engine production code which identifies the engine and its approximate production date. The other is the engine serial number which is the same number that is found on the vehicle identification plate attached to the left body hinge pillar. To identify an engine, look for the production code prefix letters, then refer to the following table for its identification.

On 1968-69 V8-350, 400, 430 on left bank cylinder head.

On V8-215, 400, 401, 425 engines the code is stamped upside down on front of cylinder block when viewed from front of engine.

On V6-225, V8-300 and 340 engines the code is stamped on right side of crankcase between middle branches of right exhaust manifold.

On V6-198 engines, code is stamped on front of crankcase below left cylinder head.

ENGINE	CODE PREFIX
1963 V6-198	JL
V8-215 Std. Eng.	JM
V8-215 Hi. Comp	JN
V8-401 2 Bar. Carb.	JR
V8-401 4 Bar. Carb.	JT
1964 V6-225	KH
V8-300 Std. Eng.	KL
V8-300 Hi. Perf.	KP
V8-401	KT
V8-425 One Carb.	KW
V8-425 Two Carbs.	KX
1965 V6-225	LH
V8-300 Std. Eng.	LL
V8-300 Hi. Perf.	LP
V8-400	LR
V8-401	LT
V8-401 Riviera	LW
V8-425	LX
1966 V6-225	MH
V8-300	ML
V8-340 2 Bar. Carb.	MA
V8-340 4 Bar. Carb.	MB
V8-400	MR
V8-401	MT
V8-425	MW
1967 V6-225	NH
V8-300	NL
V8-340 2 Bar. Carb.	NA
V8-340 4 Bar. Carb.	NB
V8-400	NR
V8-430	MD, or ND
1968 6-250	
V8-350 2 Bar. Carb.	PO
V8-350 4 Bar. Carb.	PP
V8-400	PR
V8-430	PD
1969 6-250	
V8-350 2 Bar. Carb.	RO
V8-350 4 Bar. Carb.	RP
V8-400	RR
V8-430	RD

GENERAL ENGINE SPECIFICATIONS

Year	Engine	Carburetor	Bore and Stroke	Piston Displacement, Cubic Inches	Compression Ratio	Maximum Brake H.P. @ R.P.M.	Maximum Torque Lbs. Ft. @ R.P.M.	Normal Oil Pressure Pounds
1963	135 Horsepower.............V6-198	2 Barrel	3.625 x 3.20	198	8.80	135 @ 4600	205 @ 2400	33
	155 Horsepower.............V8-215	2 Barrel	3.500 x 2.80	215	9.00	155 @ 4600	220 @ 2400	33
	200 Horsepower.............V8-215	4 Barrel	3.500 x 2.80	215	11.00	200 @ 5000	240 @ 3200	33
	265 Horsepower.............V8-401	2 Barrel	4.1875 x 3.64	401	9.00	265 @ 4400	412 @ 2400	40
	280 Horsepower.............V8-401	2 Barrel	4.1875 x 3.64	401	10.25	280 @ 4400	424 @ 2400	40
	325 Horsepower.............V8-401	4 Barrel	4.1875 x 3.64	401	10.25	325 @ 4400	445 @ 2800	40
	340 Horsepower.............V8-425	4 Barrel	4.3125 x 3.64	425	10.25	340 @ 4400	465 @ 2800	40
1964–65	155 Horsepower.............V6-225	1 Barrel	3.750 x 3.40	225	9.00	155 @ 4400	225 @ 2400	33
	210 Horsepower.............V8-300	2 Barrel	3.750 x 3.40	300	9.0	210 @ 4600	310 @ 2400	33
	250 Horsepower.............V8-300	4 Barrel	3.750 x 3.40	300	11.0	250 @ 4800	335 @ 3000	33
	325 Horsepower "400"........V8-401	4 Barrel	4.1875 x 3.64	401	10.25	325 @ 4400	445 @ 2800	40
	340 Horsepower.............V8-425	4 Barrel	4.3125 x 3.64	425	10.25	340 @ 4400	465 @ 2800	40
	360 Horsepower.............V8-425	Two 4 Bar.	4.3125 x 3.64	425	10.25	360 @ 4400	465 @ 2800	40

Continued

GENERAL ENGINE SPECIFICATIONS—Continued

Year	Engine	Carburetor	Bore and Stroke	Piston Displacement, Cubic Inches	Compression Ratio	Maximum Brake H.P. @ R.P.M.	Maximum Torque Lbs. Ft. @ R.P.M.	Normal Oil Pressure Pounds
1966	160 Horsepower............V6-225	2 Barrel	3.750 x 3.40	225	9.0	160 @ 4200	235 @ 2400	33
	210 Horsepower............V8-300	2 Barrel	3.750 x 3.40	300	9.0	210 @ 4600	310 @ 2400	33
	220 Horsepower............V8-340	2 Barrel	3.750 x 3.85	340	9.0	220 @ 4000	340 @ 2400	33
	260 Horsepower............V8-340	4 Barrel	3.750 x 3.85	340	10.25	260 @ 4000	365 @ 2800	33
	325 Horsepower............V8-401	4 Barrel	4.1875 x 3.64	401	10.25	325 @ 4400	445 @ 2800	40
	340 Horsepower............V8-425	4 Barrel	4.3125 x 3.64	425	10.25	340 @ 4400	465 @ 2800	40
	360 Horsepower............V8-425	Two 4 Bar.	4.3125 x 3.64	425	10.25	360 @ 4400	465 @ 2800	40
1967	160 Horsepower............V6-225	2 Barrel	3.750 x 3.40	225	9.0	160 @ 4200	235 @ 2400	33
	210 Horsepower............V8-300	2 Barrel	3.750 x 3.40	300	9.0	210 @ 4400	310 @ 2400	33
	220 Horsepower............V8-340	2 Barrel	3.750 x 3.85	340	9.0	220 @ 4200	340 @ 2400	33
	260 Horsepower............V8-340	4 Barrel	3.750 x 3.85	340	10.25	260 @ 4200	365 @ 2800	33
	340 Horsepower............V8-400	4 Barrel	4.040 x 3.90	400	10.25	340 @ 5000	440 @ 3200	30
	360 Horsepower............V8-430	4 Barrel	4.1875 x 3.90	430	10.25	360 @ 5000	475 @ 3200	30
1968	155 Horsepower............(1)6-250	1 Barrel	3.875 x 3.53	250	8.5	155 @ 4200	235 @ 1600	30-45
	230 Horsepower............V8-350	2 Barrel	3.800 x 3.85	350	9.0	230 @ 4400	350 @ 2400	37
	280 Horsepower............V8-350	4 Barrel	3.800 x 3.85	350	10.25	280 @ 4800	375 @ 3200	37
	340 Horsepower............V8-400	4 Barrel	4.040 x 3.90	400	10.25	340 @ 5000	440 @ 3200	30
	360 Horsepower............V8-430	4 Barrel	4.1875 x 3.90	430	10.25	360 @ 5000	475 @ 3200	30
1969	155 Horsepower............(1)6-250	1 Barrel	3.875 x 3.53	250	8.5	155 @ 4200	235 @ 1600	30-45
	230 Horsepower............V8-350	2 Barrel	3.800 x 3.85	350	9.0	230 @ 4400	350 @ 2400	37
	280 Horsepower............V8-350	4 Barrel	3.800 x 3.85	350	10.25	280 @ 4600	375 @ 3200	37
	340 Horsepower............V8-400	4 Barrel	4.040 x 3.90	400	10.25	340 @ 5000	440 @ 3200	40
	360 Horsepower............V8-430	4 Barrel	4.1875 x 3.90	430	10.25	360 @ 5000	475 @ 3200	40

(1)— See Chevrolet chapter for service procedures on this engine.

TUNE UP SPECIFICATIONS

OLD CAR SPECIFICATIONS: For 1946-62 Tune Up Specifications see back of book.

★ When using a timing light, disconnect vacuum tube or hose at distributor and plug opening in hose or tube so idle speed will not be affected.

Year	Engine	Spark Plug		Distributor		Firing Order	Ignition Timing★		Hot Idle Speed		Comp. Press. Lbs. (3)	Fuel Pump Press. Lbs.
		Type AC	Gap Inch	Point Gap Inch	Dwell Angle Deg.		BTDC (1)	Mark	Std. Trans.	Auto. Trans. (2)		
1963	401, 425 Std. Tr.	44S	.035	.016(5)	30	Fig. D	5°	Fig. A	500(4)	...	180	4¼-6½
	401, 425 Auto. Tr.	44S	.035	.016(5)	30	Fig. D	12°	Fig. A	...	500D(4)	180	4¾-6½
	V6-225	44S	.035	.016(5)	30	Fig. G	5°	Fig. E	500(4)	550D(4)	165	4½-5¼
1964	V6-225	44S	.035	.016(5)	30	Fig. G	5°	Fig. E	550(4)	550D(4)	165	4½-5¾
	V8-300	44FFS	.035	.016(5)	30	Fig. C	2½°	Fig. E	550(4)	550D(4)	180	4-5¼
	V8-401, 425	44S	.035	.016(5)	30	Fig. D	2½°(6)	Fig. A	500(4)	500D(4)	180	4¾-6½
1965	V6-225	44S	.035	.016(5)	30	Fig. G	5°	Fig. E	550(4)	550D(4)	165	4½-5¾
	V8-300	44S	.035	.016(5)	30	Fig. C	2½°	Fig. E	550(4)	550D(4)	180	4-5¼
	V8-401, 425	44S	.035	.016(5)	30	Fig. D	2½°(6)	Fig. A	500(4)	500D(4)	180	4¾-6½
1966	V6-225	44S	.035	.016(5)	30	Fig. G	5°	Fig. E	550(4)	550D(4)	165	4¼-5¾
	V8-300, 340 2 B.C.	44S	.035	.016(5)	30	Fig. C	2½°	Fig. E	550(4)	550D(4)	165	4¼-5¾
	V8-340 4 Bar. Carb.	44S	.035	.016(5)	30	Fig. C	2½°	Fig. E	550(4)	550D(4)	180	5½-7
	V8-401, 425	44S	.035	.016(5)	30	Fig. D	2½°(6)	Fig. A	500(4)	500D(4)	180	5½-7
1967	6-225 Except Cal.	44S	.035	.016(5)	30	Fig. G	5°	Fig. E	550(4)	550D(4)	165	4¼-5¼
	6-225 California(7)	44S	.035	.016(5)	30	Fig. G	5°	Fig. E	650(4)	600D(4)	165	4¼-5¼
	8-300 Except Cal.	44S	.035	.016(5)	30	Fig. B	2½°	Fig. E	550(4)	550D(4)	165	4¼-5¼
	8-300 California(7)	44S	.035	.016(5)	30	Fig. B	2½°	Fig. E	650(4)	600D(4)	165	4¼-5¼
	8-340 Except Cal.	44S	.035	.016(5)	30	Fig. B	2½°	Fig. E	550(4)	550D(4)	165	4¼-5¾

Continued

TUNE UP SPECIFICATIONS—Continued

OLD CAR SPECIFICATIONS: For 1946-62 Tune Up Specifications see back of book.

★When using a timing light, disconnect vacuum tube or hose at distributor and plug opening in hose or tube so idle speed will not be affected.

Year	Engine	Spark Plug		Distributor		Firing Order	Ignition Timing★		Hot Idle Speed		Comp. Press. Lbs. (3)	Fuel Pump Press. Lbs.
		Type AC	Gap Inch	Point Gap Inch	Dwell Angle Deg.		BTDC (1)	Mark	Std. Trans.	Auto. Trans. (2)		
1967	8-340 California(7)	44S	.035	.016(5)	30	Fig. B	2½°	Fig. E	650(4)	600D(4)	165	4¼–5¾
	8-400 Except Cal.	44TS	.035	.016(5)	30	Fig. B	2½°	Fig. E	500(4)	500D(4)	180	5½–7
	8-400 California(7)	44TS	.035	.016(5)	30	Fig. B	2½°	Fig. E	600(4)	550D(4)	180	5½–7
	8-430 Except Cal.	44TS	.035	.016(5)	30	Fig. B	2½°	Fig. E	550(4)	550D(4)	180	5½–7
	8-430 California(7)	44TS	.035	.016(5)	30	Fig. B	2½°	Fig. E	600(4)	550D(4)	180	5½–7
1968	6-250(8) Std. Tr.	46N	.030	.019	32	153624	TDC	Damper	700(4)	—	130	4–5
	6-250(8) Auto. Tr.	46N	.030	.019	32	153624	4°	Damper	—	600D(4)	130	4–5
	V8-350	45TS	.030	.016	30	Fig. B	TDC	Fig. E	700(4)	550D(4)	165	4¼–5¾
	V8-400	44TS	.030	.016	30	Fig. B	TDC	Fig. E	700(4)	600D(4)	180	5½–7
	V8-430	44TS	.030	.016	30	Fig. B	TDC	Fig. E	—	550D(4)	180	5½–7
1969	6-250(8) Std. Tr.	R46N	.035	.019	32	153624	TDC	Damper	700	—	130	4–5
	6-250(8) Auto. Tr.	R46N	.035	.019	32	153624	4°	Damper	—	500D(4)	130	4–5
	V8-350	R45TS	.030	.016	30	Fig. B	TDC(9)	Fig. E	700	600D	165	4¼–5¾
	V8-400 Std. Tr.	R44TS	.030	.016	30	Fig. B	2½ ATDC	Fig. E	700	—	180	5½–7
	V8-400 Auto. Tr.	R44TS	.030	.016	30	Fig. B	TDC	Fig. E	—	600D	180	5½–7
	V8-430	R44TS	.030	.016	30	Fig. B	TDC	Fig. E	—	550D	180	5½–7

(1)—BTDC: Before top dead center.

(2)—D: Drive. N: Neutral.

(3)—Plus or minus 20 lbs.

(4)—If air conditioned, turn A/C switch to "Full On" position.

(5)—Turn adjusting screw in (clockwise) until engine misfires; then turn screw out ½ turn.

(6)—12° BTDC for V8-425 with 2 carbs and automatic transmission.

(7)—Air Injector Reactor (A.I.R.).

(8)—See Chevrolet chapter for service procedures on this engine.

(9)—5° BTDC for LeSabre.

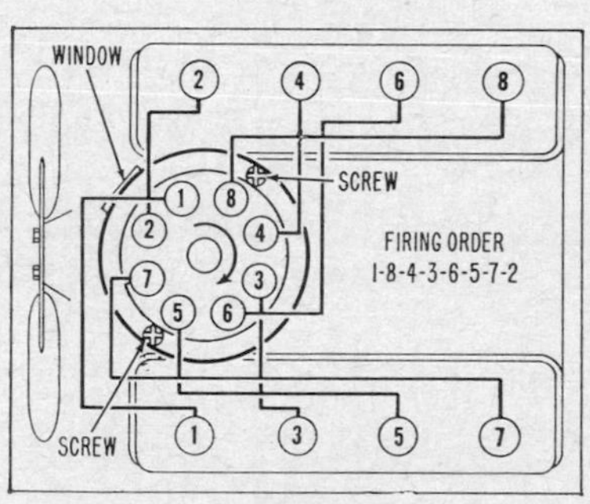

Fig. B

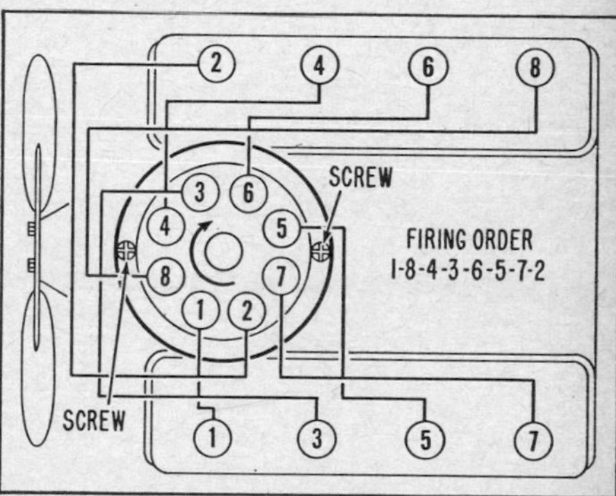

Fig. C

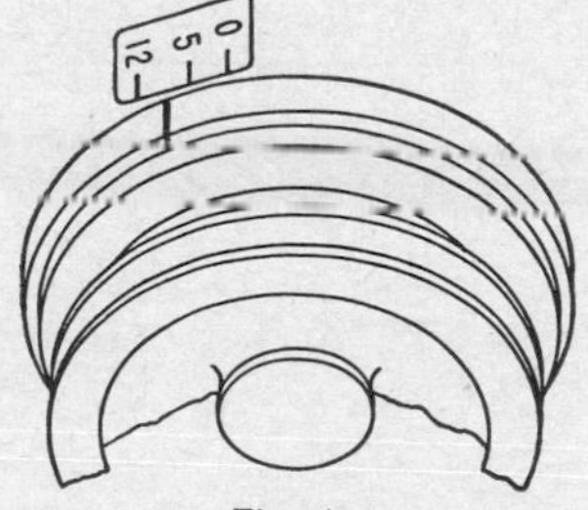

Fig. A

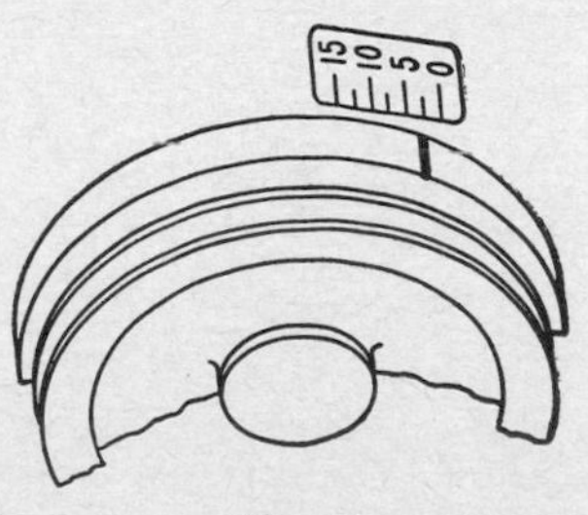

Fig. E

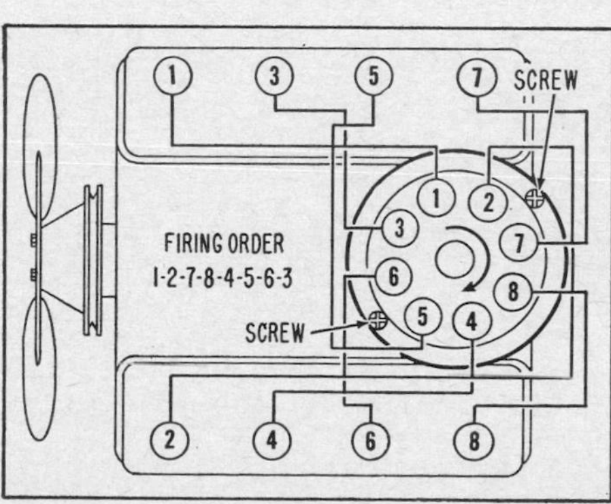

Fig. D

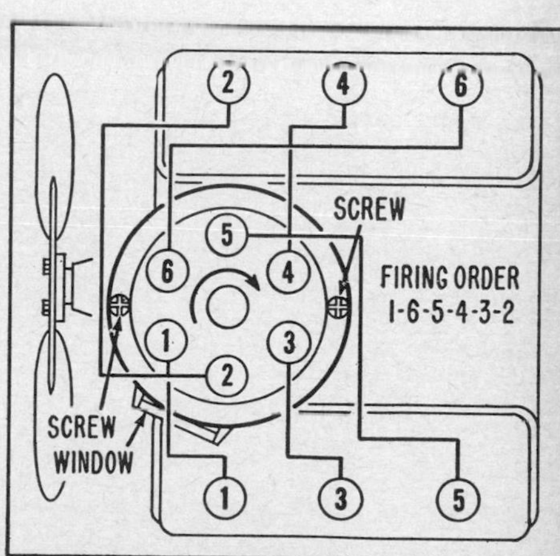

Fig. G

BUICK – All Intermediate & Full Size Models

DISTRIBUTOR SPECIFICATIONS

★NOTE: If advance is checked on the vehicle, double the R.P.M. and degrees advance to get crankshaft figures.

Year	Model	Distributor Part No.(1)	Rotation (2)	Breaker Gap	Dwell Angle Deg.	Breaker Arm Spring Tension	Centrifugal Advance Degrees @ R.P.M. of Distributor★		Vacuum Advance	
							Advance Starts	Full Advance	Inches of Vacuum To Start Plunger	Max. Adv. Dist. Deg. @ Vacuum
1963	V6-198	1110291	C	.016(3)	30	19–23	1 @ 500	12 @ 2100	6 to 8	8 @ 15
	V8-215-2 Bar. Carb.	1110977	C	.016(3)	30	19–23	1 @ 525	14 @ 1850	6 to 8	8 @ 15
	V8-215-4 Bar. Carb.	1111007	C	.016(3)	30	19–23	1 @ 550	13 @ 1900	6 to 8	8 @ 15
	Std. Trans.(4)	1111030	C	.016(3)	30	19–23	1 @ 400	14 @ 1975	7 to 9	8½ @ 18
	Std. Trans.(5)	1111031	C	.016(3)	30	19–23	1 @ 400	14 @ 1975	6 to 8	10 @ 12
	Auto. Trans.(4)	1110993	C	.016(3)	30	19–23	1 @ 450	10 @ 1900	7 to 9	8 @ 18
	Auto. Trans.(5)	1110999	C	.016(3)	30	19–23	1 @ 450	10 @ 1900	6 to 8	10 @ 13
1964–65	V6-225	1110322	C	.016(3)	30	19–23	1 @ 500	13 @ 2100	6 to 8	8 @ 15
	V8-300 (1964)	1111050	C	.016(3)	30	19–23	1 @ 400	14 @ 2100	6 to 8	8 @ 15
	V8-300 (1965)	1111083	C	.016(3)	30	19–23	1 @ 400	16 @ 2300	6 to 8	8 @ 15
	V8-401, 425	1111055	C	.016(3)	30	19–23	1 @ 400	15 @ 1950	6 to 8	8 @ 16
	425 Two Carbs.	1111058	C	.016(3)	30	19–23	1 @ 450	10 @ 1900	6 to 8	8 @ 16
1966	V6-225	1110342	C	.016(3)	30	19–23	1 @ 500	13 @ 2100	6 to 8	8 @ 15
	V8-300	1111147	C	.016(3)	30	19–23	1 @ 325	17 @ 2300	6 to 8	8 @ 16
	V8-340	1111144	C	.016(3)	30	19–23	1 @ 325	16 @ 2300	6 to 8	9 @ 15
	V8-401, 425	1111055	C	.016(3)	30	19–23	1 @ 400	15 @ 1950	6 to 8	8 @ 16
	V8-425 Two Carbs.	1111058	C	.016(3)	30	19–23	1 @ 450	10 @ 1900	6 to 8	8 @ 16
1967	V6-225	1110342	C	.016(3)	30	19–23	1 @ 500	13 @ 2100	6 to 8	8 @ 15
	V8-300	1111147	C	.016(3)	30	19–23	1 @ 325	17 @ 2300	6 to 8	8 @ 16
	V8-340	1111144	C	.016(3)	30	19–23	1 @ 325	16 @ 2300	6 to 8	9 @ 15
	V8-400, 430	1111149	C	.016(3)	30	19–23	1 @ 425	16 @ 1850	6 to 8	8 @ 15
1968	6-250 Std. Tr.	1110439	C	.019	32	19–23	1 @ 450	16 @ 2100	6 to 8	11 @ 17
	6-250 Auto. Tr.	1111339	C	.019	32	19–23	1 @ 450	15 @ 2100	6 to 8	11 @ 17
	V8-350	1111330	C	.016(3)	30	19–23	1 @ 550	14 @ 2300	6 to 8	8 @ 16
	V8-400, 430	1111285	C	.016(3)	30	19–23	1 @ 550	16 @ 2300	6 to 8	8 @ 16
1969	6-250 Std. Tr.	1110463	C	.019	32	19–23	1 @ 400	17 @ 2100	6 to 8	12 @ 17
	6-250 Auto. Tr.	1110464	C	.019	32	19–23	1 @ 400	15 @ 2100	6 to 8	12 @ 17
	V8-350-2 Bar. Carb.	1111938	C	.016(3)	30	19–23	1 @ 375	17 @ 2300	6 to 8	9 @ 16
	V8-350-4 Bar. Carb.	1111334	C	.016(3)	30	19–23	1 @ 500	15 @ 2300	6 to 8	9 @ 16
	V8-400, 430	1111335	C	.016(3)	30	19–23	1 @ 500	17 @ 2300	6 to 8	9 @ 16

(1)—Located on distributor housing plate.

(2)—As viewed from above.

(3)—Turn adjusting screw in (clockwise) until engine misfires. Then turn screw ½ turn in opposite direction.

(4)—Full size Buick with premium fuel.

(5)—Full size Buick with regular fuel.

STARTING MOTOR SPECIFICATIONS

Year	Model	Starter Number	Brush Spring Tension Oz(1)	Free Speed Test			Resistance Test(3)	
				Amps.	Volts	R.P.M.	Amps. (1)	Volts
1963	V6-198	1108303	35	58–80(2)	10.6	6750–10500	280–320(2)	4.0
	V8-215	1107266	35	65–100(2)	10.6	3600–5100	300–360(2)	3.5
	V8-401, 425	1107221	35	120	10.6	4700	290(2)	2.0
1964–65	V6-225 ('64)	1107307	35	49–76(2)	10.6	6200–9400	270–310	4.3
	V6-225 ('65)	1107260	35	58–80	10.6	6700–10500	280–320	4.0
	V8-300	1107306	55	65–100(2)	10.6	3600–5100	300–360	3.5
	V8-401, 425	1107313	35	70–105(2)	10.6	3800–6200	480–540	3.0
1966	V6-225	1107259	35	65–100(2)	10.6	3600–5100	300–360	3.5
	V8-300, 340	1107374	35	65–100(2)	10.6	3600–5100	300–360	3.5
	V8-401	1107361	35	70–105(2)	10.6	3800–6200	480–540	3.0
	V8-401, 425	1107313	35	70–105(2)	10.6	3800–6200	480–540(2)	3.0

Continued

STARTING MOTOR SPECIFICATIONS—Continued

Year	Model	Starter Number	Brush Spring Tension Oz①	Free Speed Test			Resistance Test③	
				Amps.	Volts	R.P.M.	Amps. ①	Volts
1967	V6-225, V8-300	1107596	35	49–87②	10.6	6200–10700	—	—
	V8-340	1107374	35	65–100②	10.6	3600–5100	300–360	3.5
	V8-400, 430	1107385	35	70–105②	10.6	3800–6200	480–540	3
1968	6-250	1108365	35	49–87②	10.6	6200–10700	290–425②	4.2
	V8-350	1108380	35	65–100②	10.6	3600–5100	300–360②	3.5
	V8-400, 430	1108354	35	70–105②	10.6	3800–6200	480–540②	3.0
1969	6-250	1108365	35	49–87②	10.6	6200–10700	—	—
	V8-350	1108391	35	55–85②	9	3100–4900	—	—
	V8-400, 430	1108392	35	48–74②	9	4100–6300	—	—

①—Minimum. ②—Includes solenoid.

③—Check capacity of motor by using a 500 ampere meter and a carbon pile rheostat to control voltage. Apply volts listed across motor with armature locked. Current should be as listed.

WHEEL ALIGNMENT SPECIFICATIONS

OLD CAR SPECIFICATIONS: For 1946-62 Wheel Alignment Specifications see back of book.

Year	Model	Caster Angle, Degrees		Camber Angle, Degrees				Toe-In. Inch	Toe-out on Turns, Deg.	
		Limits	Desired	Limits Left	Limits Right	Desired Left	Desired Right		Outer Wheel	Inner Wheel
1963	Special	—1½ to —2½	—2	—¼ to +1	—¼ to +1	—⅝	—⅝	7/32–5/16	20	23⅔
	Others	—1½ to +½	—½	—½ to +1	—½ to +1	+⅓	+⅓	7/32–5/16	20	22½
1964	Special	—1 to 0	—½	0 to +1	0 to +1	+½	+½	7/32–5/16	20	21¼
	Others	—1½ to +½	—½	—½ to +1	0 to +1	+¼	+¼	7/32–5/16	20	22½
1965–66	Special, Skylark	—1 to 0	—½	0 to +1	0 to +1	+½	+½	⅛–¼	20	21¼
	Le Sabre	+½ to +1½	+1	0 to +1	0 to +1	+½	+½	7/32–5/16	20	①
	Wildcat	+½ to +1½	+1	0 to +1	0 to +1	+½	+½	7/32–5/16	20	②
	Electra 225	+½ to +1½	+1	0 to +1	0 to +1	+½	+½	7/32–5/16	20	21° 47′
	Riviera	+½ to +1½	+1	0 to +1	0 to +1	+½	+½	7/32–5/16	20	22° 50′
1967	Special, Skylark	—1 to 0	—½	0 to +1	0 to +1	+½	+½	⅛–¼	18° 38′	20
	G.S. 400	—1 to 0	—½	0 to +1	0 to +1	+½	+½	⅛–¼	18° 38′	20
	Le Sabre	+½ to +1½	+1	0 to +1	0 to +1	+¼	+¼	7/32–5/16	18° 9′	20
	Wildcat	+½ to +1½	+1	0 to +1	0 to +1	+¼	+¼	7/32–5/16	16° 58′	20
	Electra 225	+½ to +1½	+1	0 to +1	0 to +1	+¼	+¼	7/32–5/16	16° 58′	20
	Riviera	+½ to +1½	+1	0 to +1	0 to +1	+¼	+¼	7/32–5/16	17° 5′	20
1968	Intermediates	—1 to 0	—½	0 to +1	0 to +1	+½	+½	⅛–¼	18° 8′	20
	Le Sabre	+½ to +1½	+1	—¼ to +¾	—¼ to +¾	+¼	+¼	7/32–5/16	18° 9′	20
	Wildcat	+½ to +1½	+1	—¼ to +¾	—¼ to +¾	+¼	+¼	7/32–5/16	16° 58′	20
	Electra 225	+½ to +1½	+1	—¼ to +¾	—¼ to +¾	+¼	+¼	7/32–5/16	16° 58′	20
	Riviera	+½ to +1½	+1	—¼ to +¾	—¼ to +¾	+¼	+¼	7/32–5/16	17° 5′	20
1969	Intermediates	—1 to 0	—½	0 to +1	0 to +1	+½	+½	⅛–¼	18½	20
	Le Sabre	+¼ to +1¼	+¾	—½ to +½	—½ to +½	0	0	7/32–5/16	19½	20
	Wildcat	+¼ to +1¼	+¾	—½ to +½	—½ to +½	0	0	7/32–5/16	19½	20
	Electra 225	+¼ to +1¼	+¾	—½ to +½	—½ to +½	0	0	7/32–5/16	19½	20
	Riviera	+½ to +1½	+1	—¼ to +¾	—¼ to +¾	+¼	+¼	5/32–¼	16¾	20

①—Manual steering 23° 32′, power steering 22° 46′.

②—Manual steering 23°, power steering 21° 47′.

VALVE SPECIFICATIONS

Year	Model	Valve Lash		Valve Angles		Valve Spring Installed Height ③	Valve Spring Pressure Lbs. @ In.	Stem Clearance		Stem Diameter	
		Int.	Exh.	Seat	Face			Intake	Exhaust	Intake	Exhaust
1963	V6-198	Hydraulic⑥		45	45	1.64	168 @ 1.26	.0015-.002①	.002-.0025①	.3407-.3412②	.3402-.3407②
	V8-215	Hydraulic⑥		45	45	1.64	168 @ 1.26	.0015-.002①	.002-.0025①	.3407-.3412②	.3402-.3407②
	V8-401, 425	Hydraulic⑥		45	45	1.59	101 @ 1.16	.002-.003①	.0025-.0035①	.3720-.3730②	.3715-.3725②
1964-65	V6-225, V8-300	Hydraulic⑥		45	45	1.64	168 @ 1.26	.002-.0025①	.0025-.003①	.3407-.3412②	.3402-.3407②
	V8-401, 425	Hydraulic⑥		45	45	1.60	101 @ 1.16	.002-.003①	.0025-.0035①	.3720-.3730②	.3715-.3725②
1966	V6-225	Hydraulic⑥		45	45	1.727	164 @ 1.34	.002-.0025①	.0025-.003①	.3407-.3412②	.3402-.3407②
	V8-300, 340	Hydraulic⑥		45	45	1.727	164 @ 1.34	.0012-.0032	.0025-.003①	.3405-.3415②	.3402-.3407②
	V8-401, 425	Hydraulic⑥		45	45	1.60	101 @ 1.16	.002-.003①	.0025-.0035①	.3720-.3730②	.3715-.3720②
1967	V6-225	Hydraulic⑥		45	45	1.727	168 @ 1.25	.0012-.0032	.0015-.0035①	.3405-.3415	.3402-.3407②
	V8-300, 340	Hydraulic⑥		45	45	1.727	164 @ 1.34	.0012-.0032	.0015-.0035①	.3405-.3415	.3402-.3407②
	V8-400, 430	Hydraulic⑥		45	45	1.89	177 @ 1.45	.0015-.0035	.0015-.0035①	.3720-.3730	.3720-.3730②
1968-69	6-250④	1 Turn⑤		46	45	1.66	185 @ 1.27	.001-.0027	.001-.0027	.3410-.3417	.3410-.3417
	V8-350	Hydraulic⑥		45	45	1.72	180 @ 1.34	.0015-.0035	.0015-.0035①	.3720-.3730	.3720-.3730②
	V8-400, 430	Hydraulic⑥		45	45	1.89	177 @ 1.45	.0015-.0035	.0015-.0035①	.3720-.3730	.3720-.3730②

①—Plus or minus .001″. Guide tapers top to bottom with larger dimension at bottom.
②—Plus or minus .0005″. Guide tapers top to bottom with larger dimension at top.
③—Outer spring.
④—See Chevrolet chapter for service procedures on this engine.
⑤—Turn rocker arm stud nut until all lash is eliminated, then tighten nut the additional turn listed.
⑥—No adjustment.

PISTONS, PINS, RINGS, CRANKSHAFT & BEARINGS

Year	Engine	Piston Clearance	Ring End Gap ①		Wrist-pin Diameter	Rod Bearings		Main Bearings			
			Comp.	Oil		Shaft Diameter	Bearing Clearance	Shaft Diameter	Bearing Clearance	Thrust on Bear. No.	Shaft End Play
1963	V6-198	.001-.0016	.010	.015	.8748	2.000	.0002-.0022	2.2992	.0005-.0021	2	.004-.008
	V8-215	.001-.0016	.010	.015	.8748	2.000	.0002-.0022	2.2992	.0005-.0021	3	.004-.008
	V8-401, 425	.001-.0016	.015	.015	.9995	2.249-2.250	.0002-.0023	2.498-2.499	.0005-.0021	3	.004-.008
1964	V6-225	.0002-.0023	.010	.015	.9394	2.000	.0002-.0023	2.2992	.0005-.0021	2	.004-.008
	V8-300	.0002-.0023	.010	.015	.9394	2.000	.0002-.0023	2.2992	.0005-.0021	3	.004-.008
	V8-401, 425	.001-.0016	.015	.015	.9995	2.249-2.250	.0002-.0023	2.498-2.499	.0005-.0021	3	.004-.008
1965	V6-225	.0002-.0023	.010	.015	.9394	2.000	.0002-.0023	2.498-2.499	.0005-.0021	2	.004-.008
	V8-300	.0002-.0023	.010	.015	.9394	2.000	.0002-.0023	2.498-2.499	.0005-.0021	3	.004-.008
	V8-401, 425	.001-.0016	.015	.015	.9995	2.249-2.250	.0002-.0023	2.498-2.499	.0005-.0021	3	.004-.008
1966	V6-225	.0005-.0011	.010	.015	.9394	2.000	.0002-.0023	2.4995	.0004-.0015	2	.004-.008
	V8-300, 340	.0005-.0011	.010	.015	.9394	2.000	.0002-.0023	2.9995	.0004-.0015	3	.004-.008
	V8-401	.001-.0016	.015	.015	.9995	2.2495	.0002-.0023	2.4985	.0001-.0019	3	.004-.008
	V8-425	.0013-.0019	.015	.015	.9995	2.2495	.0002-.0023	2.4985	.0001-.0019	3	.004-.008
1967	V6-225	.0011-.0027	.010	.015	.9394	2.000	.0002-.0023	2.4995	.0004-.0015	2	.004-.008
	V8-300	.0011-.0017	.010	.015	.9394	2.000	.0002-.0023	2.4995	.0004-.0015	3	.004-.008
	V8-340	.0011-.0017	.010	.015	.9394	2.000	.0002-.0023	2.9995	.0004-.0015	3	.004-.008
	V8-400, 430	.0007-.0023	.013	.015	.9994	2.249-2.250	.0002-.0023	3.2500	.0007-.0018	3	.003-.009
1968-69	6-250②	.0005-.0011	.010	.015	.9271	1.999-2.000	.0007-.0027	2.3004	.0003-.0029	7	.002-.006
	V8-350	.0008-.0014	.010	.01	.9394	2.0000	.0002-.0023	2.9995	.0004-.0015	3	.003-.009
	V8-400, 430	.0007-.0013	.013	.015	.9994	2.249-2.250	.0002-.0023	3.2500	.0007-.0018	3	.003-.009

①—Fit rings in tapered bores for clearance given in tightest portion of ring travel.
②—See Chevrolet chapter for service procedures on this engine.

ALTERNATOR & REGULATOR SPECIFICATIONS

Year	Alternator					Regulator						
	Model	Rated Hot Output Amps.	Field Current 12 Volts @ 80 F.	Cold Output @ 14 Volts		Model	Field Relay			Voltage Regulator		
				2000 R.P.M. Amps.	5000 R.P.M. Amps.		Air Gap In.	Point Gap In.	Closing Voltage	Air Gap In.	Point Gap In.	Voltage @ 125° F.
1963	1100633	55	1.9–2.3	32	50	1119512	.015	.030	1.5–2.7	.057	.014	13.5–14.4
1964	1100624	42	1.9–2.3	28	40	1119515	.015	.030	1.5–2.7	.067	.014	13.5–14.4
	1100679	55	2.2–2.6	32	50	1119515	.015	.030	1.5–2.7	.067	.014	13.5–14.4
	1100623	42	1.9–2.3	28	40	1119515	.015	.030	1.5–2.7	.067	.014	13.5–14.4
	1100661	55	2.2–2.6	32	50	1119515	.015	.030	1.5–2.7	.067	.014	13.5–14.4
	1100663	37	1.9–2.3	25	35	1119515	.015	.030	1.5–2.7	.067	.014	13.5–14.4
1965–66	1100691	42	2.2–2.6	28	40	1119515	.015	.030	1.5–2.7	.067	.014	13.5–14.4
	1100705	37	2.2–2.6	25	35	1119515	.015	.030	1.5–2.7	.067	.014	13.5–14.4
	1100708	42	2.2–2.6	28	40	1119515	.015	.030	1.5–2.7	.067	.014	13.5–14.4
	1100709	55	2.2–2.6	32	50	1119515	.015	.030	1.5–2.7	.067	.014	13.5–14.4
	1100710	55	2.2–2.6	32	50	1119515	.015	.030	1.5–2.7	.067	.014	13.5–14.4
1967	1100691	42	2.2–2.6	28	40	1119515	.015	.030	1.5–2.7	.067	.014	13.5–14.4
	1100761	37	2.2–2.6	25	35	1119515	.015	.030	1.5–2.7	.067	.014	13.5–14.4
	1100774	55	2.2–2.6	32	50	1119515	.015	.030	1.5–2.7	.067	.014	13.6–14.4
1968–69	1100762	37	2.2–2.6	25	35	1119515	.015	.030	1.5–3.2	.067	.014	13.6–14.4
	1100761	37	2.2–2.6	25	35	1119515	.015	.030	1.5–3.2	.067	.014	13.6–14.4
	1100802	55	2.2–2.6	32	50	1119515	.015	.030	1.5–3.2	.067	.014	13.6–14.4
	1100691	42	2.2–2.6	28	40	1119515	.015	.030	1.5–3.2	.067	.014	13.6–14.4
	1100774	55	2.2–2.6	32	50	1119515	.015	.030	1.5–3.2	.067	.014	13.6–14.4

ENGINE TIGHTENING SPECIFICATIONS★

★Torque specifications are for clean and lightly lubricated threads only. Dry or dirty threads produce increased friction which prevents accurate measurement of tightness.

Year	Engine	Spark Plugs Ft. Lbs.	Cylinder Head Bolts Ft. Lbs.	Intake Manifold Ft. Lbs.	Exhaust Manifold Ft. Lbs.	Rocker Arm Shaft Bracket Ft. Lbs.	Rocker Arm Cover Ft. Lbs.	Connecting Rod Cap Bolts Ft. Lbs.	Main Bearing Cap Bolts Ft. Lbs.	Flywheel to Crankshaft Ft. Lbs.	Vibration Damper or Pulley Ft. Lbs.
1963	V6-198	25–35	65–70	25–30	10–15	30–35	3–5	30–35	100–125①	50–60	140–160
	V8-215	15–20	50–55	25–30	10–15	25–30	3–5	30–35	50–55②	50–60	140–160
	V8 364	25–35	65–75	25–30	10–15	30–35	3–5	40–45	100–110	50–60	200 min.
	V8-401	25–35	65–80	25–35	10–15	30–35	3–5	40–50	100–110	50–65	200 min.
	V8-425	25–35	65–80	25–35	10–15	30–35	3–5	40–50	100–110	50–65	200 min.
1964	V6-225	25–35	60–70	25–35	10–15	25–30	3–5	30–40	65–70	50–60	140 min.
	V8-300	25–35	60–70	25–35	10–15	25–35	3–5	30–40	50–55③	50–60	140 min.
	401, 425	25–35	65–75	25–30	10–15	30–35	3–5	40–45	100–110	50–60	200 min.
1965	V6-225	25–35	65–80	25–35	10–15	25–35	3–5	30–40	95–120	50–65	140 min.
	V8-300	25–35	65–80	25–35	10–15	25–35	3–5	30–40	95–120	50–65	140 min.
	401, 425	25–35	65–80	25–35	10–15	25–35	3–5	40–50	95–120	50–65	200 min.
1966	V6-225	25–35	65–80	45–55	10–15	25–35	3–5	30–40	95–120	50–65	—
	300, 340	25–35	65–80	45–55	10–15	25–35	3–5	30–40	95–120	50–65	140 min.
	400, 401, 425	25–35	65–80	25–35	10–15	25–35	3–5	40–50	80–110	50–65	200 min.
1967	V6-225	25–35	65–80	45–55	15–20	25–35	3–5	30–40	95–120	50–65	—
	300, 340	25–35	65–80	45–55	15–20	25–35	3–5	30–40	95–120	50–65	140 min.
	400, 430	15	100–120	45–55	15–20	25–35	3–5	45–50	80–115	50–65	200 min.
1968–69	6-250	25	95	④	④	—	5	35	65	60	⑤
	V8-350	15	75	55	1	3[illegible]	4	35	95	60	140 min.
	V8-400, 430	15	100	55	18	30	4	45	110	60	200 min.

①—Rear bearing cap 100–110 ft.-lbs. ②—Rear bearing cap 65–70 ft. lbs. ③—Rear bearing cap 60–70 ft. lbs.

④—End clamps 20, center bolts 30. ⑤—Pressed on.

BRAKE SPECIFICATIONS

Year	Model	Brake Drum Inside Diameter	Wheel Cylinder Bore Diameter			Master Cylinder Bore Diameter		
			Front Disc Brake	Front Drum Brake	Rear Drum Brake	With Disc Brakes	With Drum Brakes	With Power Brakes
1963–64	Senior Models	11.997–12.007	—	1 1/8	1.00	—	1.00	1.00
1963	Special Models	9.495–9.505	—	1.00	7/8	—	1.00	1.00
1964	Special Models	9.495–9.505	—	1 1/16	15/16	—	1.00	1.00
1965–66	Special (Except Below)	9.495–9.505	—	1 1/16	15/16	—	1.00	1.00
	Sportwagon	9.495–9.505	—	1 1/16	1.00	—	1.00	1.00
	Skylark Gran Sport	9.495–9.505	—	1 1/8	15/16	—	1.00	1.00
	Senior Models	11.997–12.002	—	1 1/8	1.00	—	1.00	1.00
1967	Le Sabre, Wildcat, Electra	11.997–12.002	—	1 3/16	1.00	1 1/8	1.00	1.00
	Riviera	11.997–12.002	—	①	15/16	1 1/8	1.00	1.00
	Special, Skylark	9.495–9.505	—	1 1/8	15/16	1 1/8	1.00	1.00
	G.S. 400	9.495–9.505	—	1 1/8	7/8	1 1/8	1.00	1.00
	Sportwagon	9.495–9.505	—	1 1/8	1.00	1 1/8	1.00	1.00
1968	Special, Skylark	9.495–9.505	—	1 1/8	7/8	1 1/8	1.00	1.00
	Sportwagon	9.495–9.505	—	1 1/8	1.00	1 1/8	1.00	1.00
	GS-350, GS-400	9.495–9.505	—	1 1/8	7/8	1 1/8	1.00	1.00
	Le Sabre, Wildcat, Electra	11.997–12.022	—	1 3/16	1.00	1 1/8	1.00	1.00
	Riviera	11.997–12.022	—	1 3/16	15/16	1 1/8	1.00	1.00
1969	Special, Skylark	9.495–9.505	—	1 1/8	7/8	1 1/8	1.00	②
	Sportwagon	9.495–9.505	—	1 1/8	1.00	1 1/8	1.00	②
	GS-350, GS-400	9.495–9.505	—	1 1/8	7/8	1 1/8	1.00	②
	LeSabre, Wildcat, Electra	11.997–12.022	—	1 3/16	1.00	1 1/8	1.00	②
	Riviera	11.997–12.022	—	1 3/16	15/16	1 1/8	1.00	②

①—First type 1 1/8″, second type 1 3/16″.

②—Drum brakes 1″, disc brakes 1 1/8″.

REAR AXLE SPECIFICATIONS

Year	Model	Carrier Type	Ring Gear & Pinion Backlash		Pinion Bearing Preload			Differential Bearing Preload		
			Method	Adjustment	Method	Adjustment New Bearings Inch-Lbs.	Adjustment Used Bearings Inch-Lbs.	Method	Adjustment New Bearings Inch-Lbs.	Adjustment Used Bearings Inch-Lbs.
1963	Seniors	Removable	Shims	.007–.009	Spacer	15–35④	15–35④	Shims	③	③
	Specials	Integral	Shims	.007–.009	Spacer	25–35①	15–25①	Shims	20–30⑤	10–20⑤
1964	Seniors	Removable	Shims	.007–.009	Spacer	15–35④	15–35④	Shims	③	③
	Specials	Integral	Shims	.007–.009	Spacer	20–30①	12–20①	Shims	30–40⑤	20–30⑤
1965	Special	Integral	Shims	.007–.009	Spacer	20–30①	12–20①	Shims	30–40⑤	20–30⑤
	Le Sabre	Integral	Shims	.007–.009	Spacer	20–30①	12–20①	Shims	30–40⑤	20–30⑤
	Others	Removable	Shims	.007–.009	Spacer	20–30①	12–20①	Shims	30–40⑤	20–30⑤
1966–67	43-44-45000	Integral	Shims	.007–.009	Spacer	20–30①	12–20①	Shims	35–40⑥	20–25⑥
	46-48-49000	Integral	Shims	.007–.009	Spacer	25–30①	10–15①	Shims	35–40⑥	25–30⑥
1968–69	43-44-45000	Integral	Shims	.006–.008	Spacer	20–25①	10–15①	Shims	35–40⑥	20–25⑥
	46-48-49000	Integral	Shims	.007–.009	Spacer	25–30①	10–15①	Shims	35–40⑥	25–30⑥

①—Measured with torque wrench at pinion flange nut.
③—Preload .004″ (.002″ each side).
④—Measured with torque wrench with seal installed.
⑤—Measured with torque wrench at ring gear bolt.
⑥—Total preload measured with torque wrench at pinion flange nut with new seal installed.

COOLING SYSTEM & CAPACITY DATA

★Caution: Aluminum engines should have year-round protection of an ethylene glycol-water solution plus about 4 oz. of a soluble oil corrosion inhibitor (Bar's Leak or equivalent). Once a year the system should be drained and refilled with the foregoing ingredients. Plain water or alcohol-water solutions should never be used as corrosion and eventual clogging of the cooling system will develop from their use.

Year	Model or Engine	Cooling Capacity, Qts.			Radiator Cap Relief Pressure, Lbs.		Thermo. Opening Temp. (1)	Fuel Tank Gals.	Engine Oil Refill Qts. (3)	Transmission Oil			Rear Axle Oil Pints
		No Heater	With Heater	With A/C	With A/C	No A/C				3 Speed Pints	4 Speed Pints	Auto. Trans. Qts. (13)	
1963	Senior Models	17	18½	18½	15	15	180	20	4	2¼	2½	12	4½
	V6-198	10½	12	12	15	15	170	16	4	2¼	2½	6	2
	V8-215	12	13½	13½	15	15	170	16	4	2¼	2½	6	2
1964	V6-225	11½	13	13	15	15	180	20	4	2	2½	9¼	2
	V8-300	13½	15	15	15	15	180	20	4	2(8)	2½	9¼(8)	4½
	V8-401, 425	17	18½	18½	15	15	180	20	4	3½(9)	2½	11½(9)	4½
1965	V6-225	10	10.7	11.2	15	15	180	20	4	2	2½	9½	2½
	V8-300(11)	12.7	13.7	15	15	15	180	20	4	2	2½	9½	2½
	V8-300(10)	12.7	13.7	15	15	15	180	25	4	2	2½	9½(8)	2½
	V8-401(4)	16¾	17½	18¼	15	15	180	25	4	2	...	9½(2)	2½
	V8-425(4)	17¼	18	18¼	15	15	180	25	4	...	2½	11½	4½
	Riviera	17	18½	18½	15	15	180	20	4	...	2½	11½	4½
1966	V6-225	10½	11.2	11.2	15	15	180	20	4	...	...	11½	4½
	V8-300	12.2	12.7	14.0	15	15	180	20	4	3⅜	...	(5)	2½
	V8-340(11)	12.2	12.7	14.7	15	15	180	20	4	3⅜	...	(5)	2½
	V8-340(10)	13.7	14.5	14.5	15	15	180	20	4	3⅜	...	(5)	2½
	V8-401(6)	17½	18½	18½	15	15	180	25	4	3⅜	...	(5)	2½
	V8-401(4)	17	18	18.3	15	15	180	20	4	3½	...	(5)	2½
	Riviera	17	18	18.3	15	15	180	25	4	3½	...	(7)	2
1967	V6-225	10½	11.2	11.2	15	15	180	21	4	...	...	(7)	2
	V8-300	12.2	12.7	14.0	15	15	190	20	4	3⅜	...	(12)	2¾
	V8-340(11)	12.2	12.7	14.7	15	15	190	20	4	3⅜	...	(12)	2¾
	V8-340(10)	12.2	12.7	14.7	15	15	190	20	4	3⅜	...	(12)	2¾
	V8-400(6)	17.0	18.0	18¼	15	15	190	25	4	3⅜	...	(12)	2¾
	V8-430(4)	17.0	18.0	18¼	15	15	190	20	4	3½	3	(7)	2¾
	Riviera	17.0	18.0	18¼	15	15	190	25	4	...	...	(7)	4¼
1968	6-250	10.00	11.30	13.00	15	15	190	21	4	...	...	(7)	4¼
	V8-350(11)	12.62	13.50	13.52	15	15	195	20	4	3⅜	...	(12)	2.9
	GS-350	12.62	13.45	13.52	15	15	190	20	4	3⅜	...	(12)	2.9
	GS-400	15.34	16.17	16.67	15	15	190	20	4	3.4	3	(12)	2.9
	V8-350(10)	12.34	13.20	13.55	15	15	190	20	4	3.5	3	(7)	2.9
	V8-430(4)	15.84	16.70	17.00	15	15	190	25	4	3⅛	...	(12)	2.9
	Riviera	15.84	16.70	17.00	15	15	190	25	4	3½	...	(7)	4¼
1969	6-250	10.0	11.3	13.0	15	15	190	21	4	...	...	(7)	4¼
	V8-350(11)	12.6	13.5	13.5	15	15	195	20	4	3¾		(12)	2.9
	GS-350	12.6	13.5	13.5	15	15	190	20	4	3¾	...	(14)	2.9
	GS-400	15.3	16.2	16.7	15	15	190	20	4	3.4	3	(15)	2.9
	V8-350(10)	12.3	13.2	13.6	15	15	190	20	4	3.5	3	(16)	2.9
	V8-430	16.0	16.7	17.0	15	15	190	25	4	3.5	...	(17)	2.9
	Riviera	16.0	16.7	17.0	15	15	190	25	4	...	...	(16)	4¼
							190	21	4	...	...	(16)	4¼

(1)—For permanent type anti-freeze. If alcohol is used, install a 160° unit.

(2)—Super Turbine 400, 11½ qts.

(3)—Add one quart with filter change.

(4)—Wildcat and Electra.

(5)—Total 9½ qts.; oil pan only 4 qts.

(6)—Skylark Gran Sport.

(7)—Total 11½ qts.; oil pan only 2½ qts.

(8)—Buick Special and LeSabre passenger cars.

(9)—LeSabre Station Wagon, Wildcat and Electra.

(10)—LeSabre.

(11)—Special, Skylark and Sportwagon.

(12)—Total 9½ qts. Oil pan only 2½ qts.

(13)—Approximate. Make final check with dip-stick.

(14)—Two speed unit 9½ qts. total. Oil pan only 2½ qts.
Three speed unit 10 qts. total. Oil pan only 3 qts.

(15)—Total 10 qts. Oil pan only 3 qts.

(16)—Total 11½ qts. Oil pan only 3½ qts.

(17)—Two speed unit 9½ qts. total. Oil pan only 2½ qts.
Three speed unit 11½ qts. total. Oil pan only 3½ qts.

Electrical Section

IGNITION TIMING

If a timing light is to be used to set ignition timing, disconnect the vacuum advance pipe to the carburetor and place a piece of tape over open end of pipe. *This is important as carburetor trouble can affect timing adjustments.*

Lacking a power timing light, an accurate method of setting ignition timing with the engine stopped is with the aid of a jumper light. Be sure to use a light bulb that corresponds with the system voltage of the vehicle.

1. Remove distributor cap and rotor and see that the breaker gap is set according to specifications.
2. Rotate engine until No. 1 cylinder is at the ignition timing point as indicated by the timing pointer and timing mark being lined up with each other.
3. Connect the jumper light between distributor ignition terminal and ground.
4. Turn on ignition switch.
5. Loosen distributor and turn it in the direction of normal rotation until the points just close (light out). Then slowly turn distributor in the opposite direction just to the exact point that the light goes on. Tighten distributor in this position.

DISTRIBUTOR, REPLACE

1. Disconnect primary wire from distributor and disconnect pipe from vacuum control unit.
2. Remove distributor cap.
3. Crank engine until distributor rotor is in position to fire No. 1 cylinder and the timing mark (see *Tune Up Chart*) is aligned with the timing indicator.
4. Remove distributor clamp and lift the distributor out of the crankcase.

NOTE: Before installation of either a new or repaired distributor apply a few drops of engine oil to the drain hole near the lower end of the housing and apply oil to the oiler on the housing. Rotate the distributor shaft several times by hand to distribute the oil and to make sure that the shaft turns freely.

---

1. Check to make sure that the timing mark is aligned with the timing indicator with No. 1 piston on the compression stroke in position to fire.
2. Place a new seal on distributor housing.
3. Rotate distributor cam in direction of arrow on cam until rotor is in position to fire No. 1 cylinder.
4. Rotate oil pump shaft with screwdriver to align slot in shaft with tongue on lower end of distributor shaft.
5. Install distributor in crankcase with vacuum control pointing to right side of engine, in position to connect to vacuum pipe.
6. Install distributor clamp and bolt with lockwasher, leaving bolt just loose enough to permit movement of distributor.
7. Rotate distributor housing until breaker points just start to open and tighten clamp bolt. This will permit starting engine for setting timing.
8. Connect pipe to vacuum control and primary wire to terminal stud.
9. Install distributor cap. If spark plug wires are disconnected from cap make certain that wires are connected in accordance with firing order.
10. Check and set ignition timing as given below.

Fig. 1 Ignition switch in "Lock" position. 1969

STARTER, REPLACE

To remove the starter, disconnect battery cable from battery. Disconnect cable and solenoid lead wire from solenoid switch. Remove starter attaching bolts and take off starter.

LIGHT SWITCH, REPLACE

1963-69

1968-69 Special and Skylark

If air conditioned, remove two screws at left A/C duct and remove duct. Then remove switch as outlined below.

1963-65 Senior Models

Remove left access door from instrument panel. Then remove switch as outlined below.

1966-67 Riviera

1. Remove ash receiver.
2. Remove instrument panel molding.
3. Remove steering column lower cover.
4. Lower steering column.
5. Remove instrument panel lower housing.
6. Remove switch as directed below.

All Models

1. After performing the necessary preliminary operations given above, pull switch knob out to the last notch, then depress latch button and pull knob and rod assembly out of switch.
2. Remove switch escutcheon.
3. Pull switch down and unplug from connector.
4. Reverse procedure to install.

IGNITION SWITCH, REPLACE

1969

The ignition switch is located on the top of the steering column under the instrument panel. To replace it the steering column must be lowered as follows:

1. Disconnect shift indicator link.
2. Remove nuts securing bracket to dash panel and carefully lower column.
3. Unplug connectors from switch and be sure switch is in "accessory" position.
4. Remove two screws securing switch and remove switch.
5. When installing switch, it must be positioned in "Lock", Fig. 1, as well as the lock cylinder.

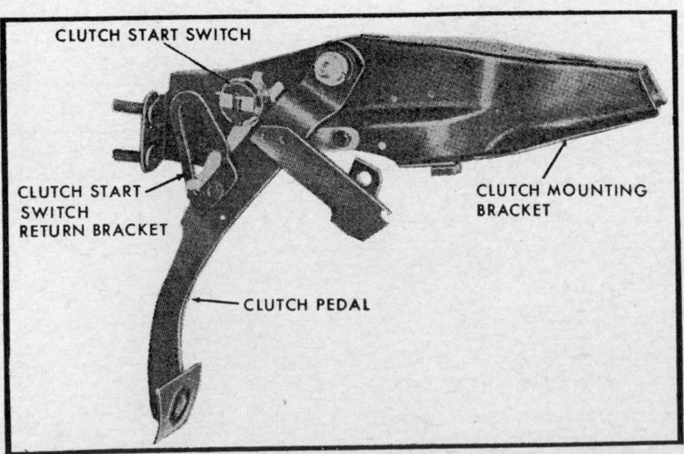

Fig. 2 Clutch start switch in start position. 1969

6. Fit actuator rod into switch and assemble to column.
7. Complete assembly in reverse of removal procedure.

1968

1. Except Riviera, if air conditioned, remove left A/C distribution duct.
2. On all models, remove lock cylinder (in accessory position).
3. Remove switch retaining nut.
4. Lower switch and unplug from connector by depressing retainer tabs.
5. Reverse procedure to install.

1966-67 Special, Skylark, G.S. 400

1. Turn key to accessory position and remove lock cylinder.
2. Remove switch retaining nut and pull switch down and unplug from connector.
3. Reverse procedure to install.

1966-67 LeSabre, Wildcat, Electra

1. Remove ash receiver.
2. Turn key to accessory position and remove lock cylinder.
3. Remove switch retaining nut.
4. Lower switch into ash receiver hole and unplug from connector.
5. Reverse procedure to install.

1966-67 Riviera

1. Remove ash receiver.
2. Remove instrument panel molding.
3. Remove column lower cover.
4. Lower steering column.
5. Remove instrument panel lower housing.
6. Turn key to accessory position and remove lock cylinder.
7. Remove switch retaining nut.
8. Lower switch and unplug connector.
9. Reverse procedure to install.

1963-65

1. Disconnect battery ground cable.
2. Insert key and turn ignition switch to "ACC" position. Insert a paper clip in small hole in face of lock cylinder to depress pin which locks the cylinder. Turn cylinder counterclockwise and pull it out.
3. On 1963-64 Senior models, remove right access door from instrument panel.
4. Remove switch nut or escutcheon.

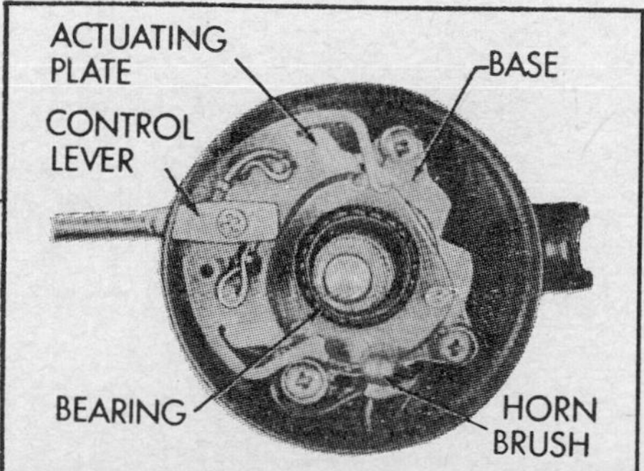

Fig. 4 Top view of turn signal switch control. 1965-66 all, 1964 Special

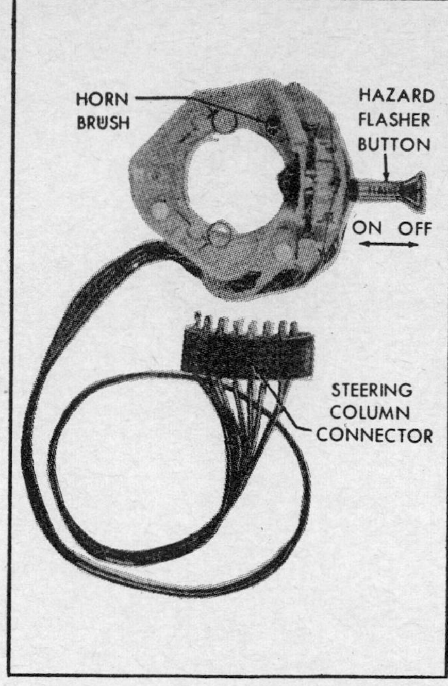

Fig. 3 Turn signal and hazard warning flasher switch assembly. 1967-69

5. Unplug connector from switch and remove switch.
6. Reverse above procedure to install. When installing lock cylinder, insert key, place cylinder in switch slightly counterclockwise from "ACC" position, press inward and turn cylinder clockwise.

STOP LIGHT SWITCH, REPLACE

1964-69

The stop lights are controlled by a mechanical switch mounted on the brake pedal bracket. This spring loaded switch makes contact whenever the brake pedal is applied. When the brake pedal is released it depresses the switch to open the contacts and turn brake lights off.

1963

The stop lights are controlled by an hydraulic switch mounted on the brake master cylinder. When replacing the switch have the new switch ready to install as soon as the old switch is removed from the master cylinder to keep brake fluid loss to a minimum. Before changing switch make sure area around switch is clean before making the change. Always fill master cylinder reservoir after new switch is installed.

Service Bulletin

FUSE CHANGE: On pre-1965 Senior models, a fuse protected the parking-brake warning light and the safety buzzer or cruise-control circuits. The fuel gauge and the indicator lights in the instrument cluster were fed directly from the ignition switch, and there was no fuse in these circuits.

This is different on 1965 LeSabre, Wildcat, Riviera and Electra 225 models. The fuse which protects the parking-brake warning light and safety buzzer or cruise control, now also serves the fuel gauge, water temperature lights, generator and oil pressure lights. Since the one fuse protects all indicator lights, if none of these lights operates it is probable that the fuse is defective. This fuse, marked "Cruise Cluster", is located in the fuse block, as in earlier models.

CLUTCH START SWITCH

1969

A clutch start switch is installed on all manual transmission cars. The switch is mounted on the clutch pedal bracket and it prevents the car from being started until the clutch pedal is depressed, Fig. 2.

TURN SIGNAL SWITCH, REPLACE

1967-69

As shown in Fig. 3, the assembly is a turn signal switch and hazard warning switch. It is mounted in a housing at the upper end of the steering column mast jacket, just below the steering wheel. Therefore to get at the switch the steering wheel will have to be removed.

1965-66 All, 1964 Special

The turn signal switch is mounted in a housing at the upper end of the steering column mast jacket just below the steering wheel. Therefore to get at the switch the steering wheel will have to be removed, Figs. 4 and 5.

1963 All, 1964 Senior Models

The turn signal switch is mounted on the steering mast jacket under the instrument panel. Its actuating mechanism is enclosed in a housing on the jacket just below the steering wheel. Movement of the actuating mechanism is transmitted to the signal switch through an actuating rod which runs down the inside of the jacket.

The upper end of the actuating rod is crank shaped and fits in a slot in the lever plate, Fig. 5A. The lower end of the rod is attached to the signal switch by a

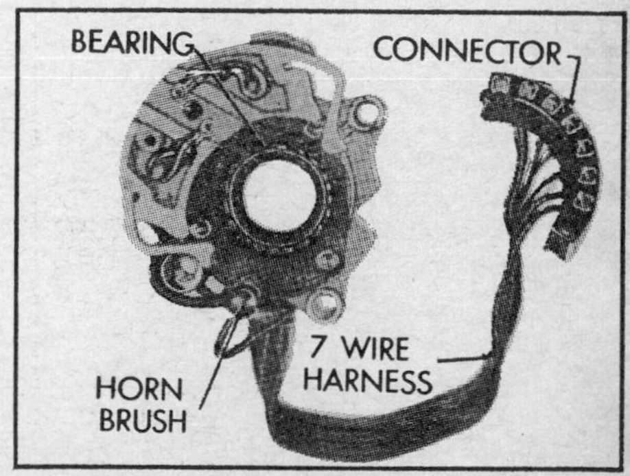

Fig. 5 Turn signal switch plate and wiring. 1965-66, 1964 Special

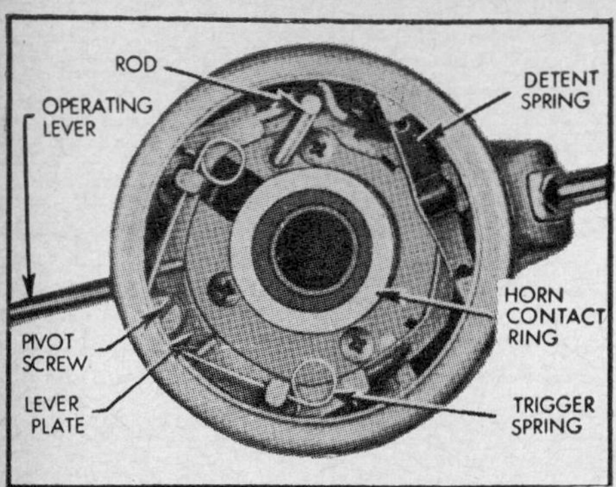

Fig. 5A Top view of turn signal switch actuator. 1964 Senior models and all 1963

spring pin which is installed around the switch operating pin and through a hole in the rod. An anti-rattle spring holds the rod (or cable) in place, Fig. 5B.

The movement of the rod (or cable) is not adjustable, therefore, any adjustment must be made by moving the switch on the mast jacket as follows:

1. Place control lever in center position.
2. Loosen two switch mounting screws and move switch sideways on mast jacket until operating pin projecting from switch is centered. Tighten screws.
3. To recheck adjustment, turn on ignition switch, place turn signal control lever in each position and check all signal lights.

NEUTRAL START & BACK-UP LIGHT SWITCH

To check operation of switch after adjustments are made as outlined below, proceed as follows:

1. With shift lever in Park starter should operate.
2. With shift lever in Reverse back-up lights should light but starter should not operate.
3. With shift lever in Neutral starter should operate but back-up lights should be out.
4. With shift lever in Drive, starter should not operate and back-up lights should be out.

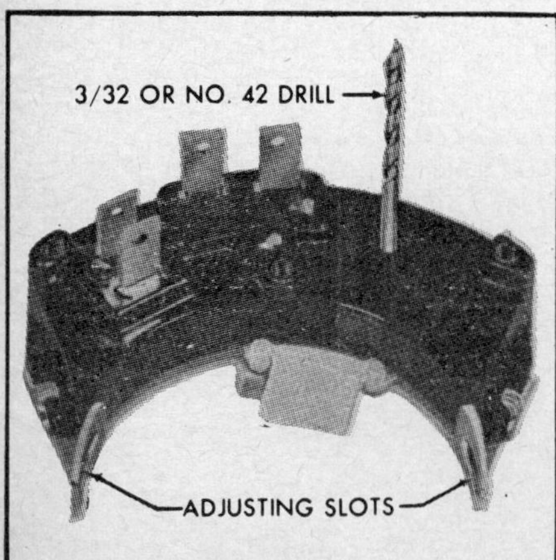

Fig. 6 Adjusting neutral safety switch. 1967-68

1967-69

1. Place shift lever in Drive.
2. Attempt to insert a 3/32" or a No. 42 drill through gauging hole in switch body into inner hole in sliding part of switch, Fig. 6.
3. If drill does not enter inner hole, loosen two switch mounting screws and slide switch body as required to allow drill to enter inner hole. Tighten screws and remove drill.

1963 All & 1964-66 Senior Cars

1. Referring to Fig. 7, place shift control lever in *Park* position.
2. Insert a 3/32" rod through gauging hole in operating lever and through gauging hole in switch body.
3. If gauging rod will not go through holes or is not parallel, loosen two switch mounting screws and move switch sidewise until gauge is parallel. Then retighten screws.

1964-66 Special Series

1. Place shift control lever in *Drive.*
2. Insert a 3/32" rod through gauging hole in right forward face of switch and into gauging hole in center of switch slide.
3. If gauging rod will not enter hole in switch slide, loosen two switch mounting screws and move switch sidewise until gauge enters hole. Tighten switch screws.

HORN SOUNDER & STEERING WHEEL

1968-69

1. Remove horn cap or actuator bar.
2. On deluxe wheels, pull horn wire from steering wheel and back off wheel nut flush with top of steering shaft.
3. Use a suitable puller to remove wheel.

1967

1. Unplug curved connector from switch on lower end of steering column.
2. On 43000 and 44000 Series with standard steering wheel, pry off cap, remove three screws and take off bushing spacer, receiver cup and Belleville spring.
3. On all other Series cars, remove screws from underside of steering wheel that secure horn actuator bar, partially lift off bar, pull lead connector from canceling cam, then fully lift off bar.
4. Remove nut and pull off steering wheel.

1966

1. Unplug large curved connector on mast jacket to prevent horn from blowing. Connector has locking tabs on outside edges; lift tabs to release.
2. On standard Special series wheels, pry off cap, remove three screws and take off spacer bushing receiver cup and Belleville spring.
3. On 43000 and 44000 Series, remove actuator bar cap and pull out lead plug in steering wheel.
4. On 45-46 and 48000 Series, remove actuator bar cap, bushing and screw assembly, adapter springs and contact plate.
5. On 49000 Series, remove cap and lens assembly and pull out lead plug in steering wheel. On 49000 Series with optional wheel, remove cap and lens assembly.
6. On all Series, loosen steering wheel nut several turns (do not remove). Attach a puller to wheel hub and pull wheel up to nut. Then remove nut and lift off wheel.

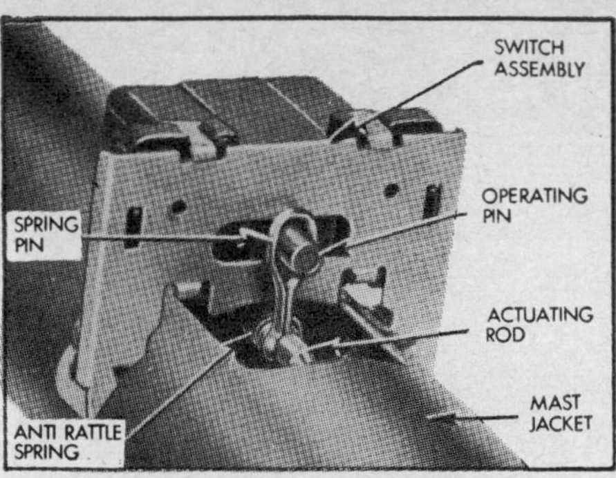

Fig. 5B Bottom view of turn signal switch installation. 1964 Senior models and all 1963

NOTE: Location marks for proper installation of steering wheel are provided to insure a straight-ahead position when front wheels are in straight-ahead position. When installing Belleville spring on standard wheels, be sure concave side of spring faces inward. Also locate receiver cup so that slot in cup is uppermost.

1965 Senior Series

1. Unplug horn ground wire connector at mast jacket to prevent horn from sounding.
2. Remove horn bar cap, bushing and screw assembly, adapter assembly springs and contact plate.

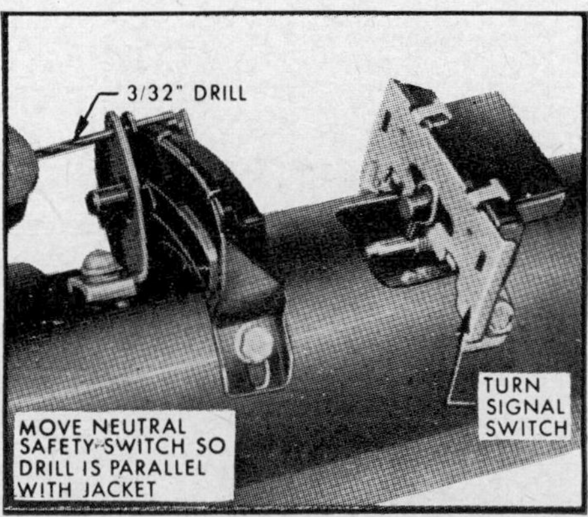

Fig. 7 Checking neutral safety switch adjustment. 1963 all and 1964-66 Senior cars

3. Loosen steering wheel retaining nut several turns (do not remove).
4. Use a suitable puller to loosen wheel from hub. Then remove nut and take off wheel.

1964-65 Special Series

1. Unplug large curved connector on mast jacket to prevent horn from sounding. Connector has locking tabs on outside edges; lift tab to release.
2. On deluxe wheels, remove actuator cap and pull out lead plug in wheel.
3. On standard wheels, pry off cap, remove three screws and take off spacer bushing, receiver cup and spring.
4. Loosen wheel retaining nut several turns. Then loosen wheel with a puller, remove nut and pull off wheel.

1963-64 Senior Series

The steering wheel has an actuator bar mounted across it. Fastened to the base of the actuator bar, but insulated from it, is a contact plate which is "hot" at all times. When the actuator bar is rocked, the contact plate contacts a ground plate on the steel hub of the steering wheel to sound the horn.

1. To remove horn contact, remove two screws from actuator bar cap, and four clutch head screws from actuator bar. Remove four plastic rivets from actuator plate.
2. To remove horn connector brush, remove actuator bar cap and bar and lift ground plate and horn connector brush from steering wheel.

1963 Special Series

1. Unplug horn ground wire connector at mast jacket to prevent horn from sounding.
2. On deluxe wheels, remove actuator cap, bar, springs and ground plate from wheel.
3. On standard wheels, remove cap assembly by inserting a screwdriver through hole in cap and loosening retaining screw. Unplug horn connector brush wire from cap.
4. Loosen wheel retaining nut several turns (do not remove).
5. Attach puller to wheel hub and pull wheel up to nut. Then remove puller, nut and wheel.
6. When installing wheel, note that location marks on wheel and shaft are provided to insure straight ahead position of wheel when front wheels are pointing straight ahead.

INSTRUMENT CLUSTER

1969 Special & Skylark

CAUTION: If equipped with Cruise Control, disconnect speedometer cable from transducer to prevent damage when cluster housing is pulled back.

1. Remove glove box (9 screws).
2. Remove instrument panel upper cover (2 screws thru cluster housing and 2 nuts above glove box opening). Pull cover rearward to disengage three guide pine from clips.
3. Remove steering column opening filler (4 screws). On air conditioned units, drop left plastic duct by removing 2 screws and disconnecting inner end from center distribution duct.
4. Lower steering column by removing 2 nuts and disconnecting shift indicator link. Pad column to avoid marring paint.
5. Pull cluster housing back after removing eight screws. Rest housing on column and rotate so back of cluster is visible.
6. Disconnect speedometer cable and wires from cluster. On air conditioned units, disconnect left air hose from left outlet by twisting "quick-connect" coupling counterclockwise. Disconnect heater control panel.
7. Remove cluster by removing four cluster to housing screws.
8. Reverse above procedure to install.

1969 LeSabre, Wildcat & Electra

CAUTION: If equipped with Cruise Control, disconnect speedometer cable from transducer to prevent damage when cluster housing is pulled back

1. Remove lower instrument panel filler (4 screws), then slide filler forward and down.
2. Remove glove box (5 screws).

NOTE: Do not remove glove box door as it comes off with cover along with ash tray assembly.

3. Remove instrument panel cover (2 nuts above glove box opening and 3 screws thru cluster housing) and remove all screws along bottom edge of cover.
4. Lower steering column by removing two nuts and disconnecting shift indicator link. Pad column to avoid marring paint.
5. Pull cluster housing back after removing eight screws. Rest housing on column and rotate so back of housing is visible.
6. Disconnect speedometer cable and wires.
7. Disconnect heater-air conditioner control panel.

NOTE: Do not disturb cables and vacuum hoses or adjustment will be required after reassembly.

8. Remove instrument cluster (6 cluster to housing screws).
9. Reverse procedure to install.

1968 Special & Skylark

CAUTION: If equipped with Cruise Control, the upper speedometer cable must be disconnected from the transducer before cluster housing is pulled back.

1. Remove instrument panel compartment body (6 screws).
2. Remove radio knobs and escutcheons.
3. Remove radio filler plate (2 nuts and 2 screws). *Do not remove radio.*
4. Remove four hex nuts at top underside of dash and two screws at housing. Pull instrument panel upper cover rearward to remove.
5. Remove steering column filler (4 screws). If air conditioned, remove one screw at left A/C duct and remove duct from instrument panel housing.
6. Remove four nuts from lower edge of instrument panel housing.
7. Remove four screws across upper edge of instrument panel housing.
8. Remove two nuts from steering column mounting bracket and disconnect shift quadrant link wire at steering column. Lower steering column.
9. Pull instrument panel rearward and rotate it so back of cluster is visible.
10. Remove two nuts from heater control installation and separate front instrument panel housing.
11. Disconnect speedometer cable (from below).
12. Disconnect wiring harness clip, printed circuit connector and clock connector from instrument cluster.
13. Disconnect accessory switch and Cruise Control switch wires from top side of instrument panel housing.
14. Disconnect headlight switch connector.
15. Disconnect W/S wiper-washer switch connector.
16. Disconnect cigar lighter connector.
17. Remove instrument panel housing.
18. Remove cluster from panel housing (4 screws).
19. Reverse procedure to install.

1968 LeSabre, Wildcat & Electra

CAUTION: If equipped with Cruise Control the upper speedometer cable must be disconnected from transducer before cluster housing is pulled back.

1. Remove instrument panel compartment body (8 screws).
2. Remove three hex nuts at top underside of dash and four screws at instrument panel housing. Pull instrument panel upper cover rearward to remove.
3. Remove steering column filler (2 screws). Disconnect shift quadrant link wire at steering column. Remove two nuts from steering column mounting bracket and one bolt from column wedge. Lower steering column.
4. Remove two nuts from lower edge of instrument panel housing at steering column.
5. Remove four screws across upper edge of instrument panel housing.
6. Remove two screws at heater control installation and separate from instrument panel housing.
7. Remove ash receiver (4 screws).
8. Remove one nut at lower right side of instrument housing.
9. Remove headlight switch from instrument panel housing; do not unplug connector.
10. Remove one nut at lower left side of instrument panel housing.
11. Protect steering column so that instrument panel housing will not mar column when housing is tilted back.
12. Remove two screws at center A/C duct (lower) and remove duct.
13. Disconnect from instrument cluster the speedometer cable (from below), printed circuit connector (from above), wiring harness clip (from below), clock connector and two clock bulbs (from above), Cruise

Control switch connector (from above), courtesy light connector (from above), W/S wiper-washer switch connector (from below), antenna and accessory switch connectors (from above), and cluster ground wire (from above).
14. Remove complete instrument panel housing, then separate cluster from panel housing (6 screws).
15. Reverse procedure to install.

1968-69 Riviera

CAUTION: If equipped with Cruise Control the upper speedometer cable must be disconnected from the transducer before cluster housing is pulled back.

1. Remove instrument panel compartment body (8 screws).
2. Remove four nuts at right underside of dash and four screws at housing. Pull instrument panel upper cover rearward to remove.
3. Remove steering column filler (2 screws). If column shift, disconnect shift quadrant link wire at steering column. Remove two nuts from column mounting bracket and one nut from column wedge. Lower steering column.
4. Remove two nuts from lower edge of instrument panel housing at steering column. Remove four screws across upper edge of instrument panel housing.
5. Remove one nut at lower left side of instrument housing.
6. Remove ash receiver (4 screws).
7. Remove one nut at lower right side of instrument housing.
8. Remove two screws at heater control installation and separate from instrument panel housing.
9. Protect steering column so panel housing will not mar column when housing is tilted back.
10. Disconnect from cluster the speedometer cable, two wiring harness clips, printed circuit connector (all from above).

NOTE: If equipped with Cruise Control, disconnect speedometer cable at Cruise Control transducer located at rear of engine compartment. This will allow instrument housing to be pulled rearward.

11. Disconnect from instrument housing the clock connector and two clock bulbs, Cruise Control switch connector, courtesy light connector, W/S wiper-washer switch connector, antenna and accessory switch connectors, cluster ground wire, A/C hose and headlight connector (all from above).
12. Remove instrument panel housing.
13. Separate panel housing from cluster (6 screws).
14. Reverse procedure to install.

1966-67 Special, Skylark, G.S. 400

1. Disconnect battery ground strap.
2. Remove five screws and pull instrument panel upper cover rearward to remove.
3. Lower steering column and remove ¼″ hex screw (in column cutout) from lower edge of instrument panel housing.
4. Remove one ¼″ hex screw from lower edge of instrument panel housing through glove box hole.
5. Remove four remaining ¼″ hex screws from lower edge of instrument panel housing.
6. Remove six screws across upper edge of instrument panel housing.
7. Disconnect speedometer cable.
8. Pull instrument panel rearward and rotate it so back of cluster is visible.
9. Disconnect from cluster: printed circuit connector, clock connector, shift quadrant light.
10. Remove four ¼″ hex screws and remove instrument panel cluster.

NOTE: To remove speedometer or printed circuit, first remove instrument cluster. The fuel gauge is accessible from below without removing any other parts. Bulbs in the left half of the cluster can be removed from below without removing any other parts. To remove bulbs from the right half of the cluster, however, the left defroster duct must be removed to provide working clearance.

1966-67 LeSabre, Wildcat, Electra

1. Disconnect battery ground strap.
2. Remove two windshield side garnish moldings.
3. Remove six screws and pull instrument panel upper cover rearward. Disconnect radio speaker wire and remove cover.
4. Remove ash receiver.
5. Remove one ⅜″ hex nut through hole in glove box.
6. Remove either radio bracket screw.
7. Remove two ⅜″ hex head bolts from outer ends of instrument panel housing.
8. Remove A/C hose from center distribution duct and push hose to left of steering column.
9. Remove light switch from instrument panel housing (do not unplug connector).
10. Protect steering column. Then tilt instrument panel housing back and place 1½″ spacer blocks (⅞″ on 1966) under each end of housing at attaching points.
11. Disconnect from cluster: shift indicator link, printed circuit connector, clock connector, Cruise switch connector, Cruise speedometer connector, and speedometer cable.
12. From below, remove two ¼″ hex head screws from bottom edge of instrument cluster.
13. From above, remove three ¼″ hex head screws from bottom edge of cluster, being careful not to lose two spacers.
14. Disconnect ground wire from upper edge of cluster.
15. Shift cluster to the right and lift out. It may be necessary to depress Cruise engage knob for clearance.

NOTE: To remove speedometer or printed circuit the cluster must first be removed. To remove the fuel gauge, perform Steps 1, 2 and 3 above, then remove gauge (3 screws).

1966-67 Riviera

1. Disconnect battery ground strap.
2. Remove ash receiver.
3. Remove center air outlet and duct.
4. Remove radio.
5. Remove upper cover by removing three screws at cluster housing and two ⅜″ nuts at glove box opening.
6. Pry out instrument panel molding.
7. Remove steering column lower cover.
8. Remove two $\frac{11}{16}$″ nuts and lower steering column.
9. Remove instrument panel lower housing by removing five ¼″ screws across bottom and six across top. Electro-Cruise amplifier connector must be unplugged (if equipped).
10. To loosen upper housing, protect steering column, then remove two ⅜″ nuts from below (one from each end of housing). Remove four ¼″ screws across top of housing. Pull housing out to rest on steering column and knees.
11. Rotate upper housing so that cluster retaining screws can be seen. Disconnect speedometer cable, unplug cluster connector, Cruise connector, courtesy light and clock connectors. Remove two wiring harness clamp screws.
12. Remove five ¼″ screws across bottom of cluster and five ⅜″ nuts across top of cluster. Then remove cluster assembly.

NOTE: To remove speedometer or printed circuit, the cluster assembly must first be removed.

To remove oil pressure or temperature gauge, pry off instrument panel molding, remove steering column lower cover and lower steering column, remove ash receiver, instrument panel lower housing (5 screws), light switch, and gauges as required.

To remove ammeter or fuel gauge, remove ash receiver, center air outlet and duct, radio, and gauges as required.

1965 Senior Series

NOTE: The speedometer, clock and "telltale" lights, or the fuel gauge can each be removed without disturbing the instrument cluster. Each of these three units can be removed by simply removing one or two screws and pulling the assembly out of the housing. When removing the speedometer from the cluster housing, it is not necessary to disconnect the speedometer cable. Only when the entire cluster assembly is to be removed is it necessary to disconnect the cable.

1. To remove the cluster assembly, first disconnect battery.
2. Remove instrument panel cover.
3. Remove radio control knobs and center cove moulding from left and right cove mouldings since these overlap.
4. Disconnect wiring from ignition, light and wiper switches, and from printed circuit.
5. Disconnect speedometer cable.
6. Disconnect left vent control cable from left cove moulding.

7. Remove six nuts that attach left cove moulding to instrument panel frame.
8. Remove four screws on underside of cluster housing that attach housing to instrument panel frame.
9. Drop steering column down by removing two U-clamp bolts.
10. Pull out cluster housing.

NOTE: On air conditioned cars it is necessary to disconnect clamped end of left air hose and pull out of the way to gain access to wiper switch.

1963-64 Senior Series

The complete instrument cluster seldom needs to be removed unless the printed circuit is defective. The speedometer, clock or gas gauge can each be removed without disturbing the cluster housing. However, when cluster must be removed, proceed as follows:

1. Remove control panel and trim plate from center of instrument panel.
2. Remove right and left lower access doors.
3. Disconnect wiring from light switch, wiper switch, ignition switch, ignition switch light, clock, clock light, multiple cluster connector and parking brake warning light.
4. Disconnect speedometer cable, left and right vent control cables, buzzer wire or cruise control wiring (if equipped).
5. Disconnect speedometer reset knob.
6. Remove upper left moulding by snapping from cluster. Remove exposed screws.
7. Remove nuts from studs along lower edge of cluster. Remove screws from Riviera cluster lower edge.
8. Remove two nuts from steering column support and lower complete steering column.
9. Remove cluster assembly.

1964-65 Special Series

1. Remove cover extension assembly by removing four screws across the bottom. Then raise entire extension to disengage it from four clips across top.
2. Remove heater control trim bezel by removing four screws from corners.
3. Remove four screws from cluster and pull cluster out as far as connections allow.
4. Disconnect speedometer cable and all electrical connections and remove cluster.

NOTE: Observe direction of keyway in printed circuit to make blind installation of cluster plug easier.

1963 Special Series

1. Remove cluster hood and then from under instrument panel, remove three nuts from studs that retain cluster.
2. Disconnect speedometer cable and printed circuit plug.
3. Unplug clock connector and clock light. Disconnect clock ground wire.
4. Remove cluster. *When installing the cluster, the projection on the disconnect plug must be lined up with the keyway in the printed circuit when assembling plug on connector pins.*

W/S WIPER MOTOR, REPLACE

1963-64 Senior Series

1. Disconnect wire connectors from motor and pump.
2. Pull washer hoses loose from pump.
3. Remove left side air intake grille.
4. Remove spring retainer clip from motor shaft lever.
5. Lift transmission drive links off motor shaft lever.
6. Unfasten and remove motor (3 bolts).

1963-67 Special Series

The wiper motor is held to the upper cowl by means of three bolts which fasten through three rubber bushings on the motor mounting plates and then into three weld nuts located in the cowl. The wiper motor is located on the engine side of the dash.

1965 Senior Series

1. Disconnect wire connectors from motor and pump.
2. Pull washer hoses loose from pump.
3. Remove air intake grille.
4. Remove grommet from hole over wiper motor lever and loosen two nuts at end of drive link.
5. Lift transmission drive link off crank arm ball.
6. Remove three wiper motor bolts and lift out motor.

W/S WIPER TRANSMISSION

1965 Senior Series

1. Remove wiper arms and blades, and escutcheon.
2. Unfasten and slide air intake grille out from under reveal moulding.
3. Remove grommet from hole over wiper motor lever and loosen two nuts at end of drive link. Lift drive link off crank arm ball.
4. Remove nine transmission retaining screws.
5. Slide transmission to the right until transmission and drive link can be lifted through left opening.

1963-64 Senior Series

1. Remove wiper arm and blade, shaft and escutcheon. Remove escutcheon from transmission shaft.
2. Unfasten and slide air intake grille out from under reveal molding.
3. Unclip and lift drive links off motor shaft.
4. Unfasten and slide transmission and drive link toward opposite side of car. Then lift transmission out through opening.
5. Reverse above procedure to install.

1963-65 Special Series

The wiper transmission arms are located on the passenger compartment side of the dash directly forward of the instrument panel. One transmission assembly operates both the right and left side arms in a tandem wiper pattern. The tubular drive link attaches to the drive crank arm on the wiper motor shaft by means of a clip.

W/S WIPER SWITCH, REPLACE

1969 LeSabre, Wildcat & Electra

1. Pry wiper-washer switch from cluster housing.
2. Remove switch by unplugging switch connector.
3. Reverse procedure to install.

1968-69 Special & Skylark

1. If air conditioned, remove two screws at left A/C distribution duct and remove duct.
2. Remove steering column filler (4 screws).
3. Unplug connectors from wiper-washer switches.
4. Remove two screws from switches and pull switches down.
5. Reverse procedure to install.

1968 LeSabre, Wildcat & Electra

1. Remove steering column filler (2 screws).
2. Disconnect shift quadrant link wire at steering column. Remove two nuts from steering column mounting bracket and one bolt from column wedge. Lower steering column to gain access to switch attaching screw.
3. Unplug connectors from wiper-washer switches.
4. Unfasten and pull switches down (2 screws).
5. Reverse procedure to install.

1968-69 Riviera

1. Pull instrument panel housing assembly out to rest on column and knees.
2. Unplug connectors from wiper-washer switches.
3. Unfasten and pull switches out (2 screws).
4. Reverse procedure to install.

1963-67 Except Riviera

1. Loosen set screw and remove knob.
2. Unscrew switch escutcheon.
3. Pull switch down and unplug from connector.

1964-67 Riviera

The windshield wiper and washer switches are removed together by prying with a small screwdriver in a notch at the bottom edge of the switch housing. The faulty switch can then be disconnected and removed from the assembly.

RADIO, REPLACE

NOTE: When installing radio, be sure to adjust antenna trimmer for peak performance.

1969 Special & Skylark

1. Remove radio knobs, escutcheons and two hex nuts.

2. Remove filler plate (2 screws).
3. Remove ash tray and slide (4 screws).
4. Remove radio support (2 screws). If air conditioned, remove center distributor duct.
5. Remove two nuts attaching radio face to instrument panel and move radio downward.
6. Disconnect antenna lead and wiring and remove radio.
7. Reverse procedure to install.

1969 LeSabre, Wildcat & Electra

1. Remove instrument panel lower filler (4 screws) and slide filler forward and down.
2. Remove radio ground strap screws.
3. Remove radio knobs, escutcheons and hex nuts and lower radio downward. In air conditioned cars, remove center distributor duct for clearance.
4. Disconnect antenna lead and wires.
5. Reverse procedure to install.

1969 Riviera

1. Remove ash tray assembly (4 screws).
2. Remove radio knobs, escutcheons and hex nuts.
3. Unplug antenna and leads from radio.
4. Remove radio downward through ash tray opening.
5. Reverse procedure to install.

1968 Special & Skylark

1. Remove radio knobs and escutcheons.
2. Remove radio filler plate (2 nuts and 2 screws).
3. Remove ash receiver.
4. If air conditioned, remove two screws at lower center A/C duct and remove duct.
5. Remove radio bracket-to-radio screw and two bracket screws at instrument panel and remove bracket.
6. Remove two instrument panel attaching nuts at radio face.
7. Disconnect radio wiring and remove radio downward.
8. Reverse procedure to install.

1968 Senior Models

1. Remove ash receiver.
2. If air conditioned (except Riviera), remove two screws at center A/C duct and remove duct.
3. Remove radio knobs and escutcheons.
4. Remove two hex nuts.
5. Unplug antenna lead from radio.
6. Unplug three wire and single wire connector from radio.
7. Remove radio downward.
8. Reverse procedure to install.

1967 Special & Skylark

Without Air Conditioning

1. Disconnect ground strap from battery.
2. Pull off radio control knobs and unscrew two nuts holding radio to instrument panel.
3. Disconnect radio and speaker lead connectors and antenna cable.
4. Remove screw holding support to radio and remove radio from underside of dash.

With Air Conditioning

1. Disconnect ground cable from battery.
2. Pull off radio control knobs and unscrew nuts securing radio to instrument panel.
3. Remove clamps connecting A/C outlet hoses to distribution duct. Remove two screws securing duct to heater and lower out duct.
4. Pry open two spring clips holding center duct to instrument panel and remove center duct.
5. Disconnect radio and speaker leads and antenna cable.
6. Remove screw holding support to radio and remove radio.

1967 LeSabre, Wildcat & Electra

1. Pull off radio control and unscrew nuts securing radio to instrument panel.
2. Unfasten instrument panel cover to panel (6 screws). Then pull cover rearward and raise it enough so that any connectors attached to underside of cover may be disengaged. Complete removal of cover.
3. Remove left and right radio mounting bracket screws. Disengage radio-speaker lead and antenna cable at rear of radio and remove radio.

1967 Riviera

1. Open and remove three screws from upper portion of ash tray and three screws from underside of assembly. Partially withdraw ash tray and disconnect lamp and cigar lighter leads, then complete removal of ash tray.
2. Pry out chrome trim strip at center of instrument panel.
3. Remove two screws securing center outlet, lift off center outlet and pull out plastic duct.
4. Pull off radio knobs, unscrew two nuts holding radio to instrument panel and take off escutcheon.
5. Disconnect radio-speaker lead and antenna cable.
6. Remove radio support (2 nuts and two screws).
7. Lower radio through ash tray opening.

1966 Special & Skylark

1. Remove ash receiver.
2. Remove radio-to-bracket screw.
3. Remove knobs and escutcheons and two ⅝" nuts.
4. Remove radio downward.

1966 LeSabre, Wildcat & Electra

1. Remove two windshield side garnish moldings.
2. Remove six screws and pull instrument panel upper cover rearward. Disconnect speaker wire and remove cover.
3. Remove ash receiver.
4. Remove A/C center outlet and duct.
5. Remove radio-to-bracket screw.
6. Remove knobs and escutcheons and two ⅝" nuts.
7. Remove radio upward.

1966 Riviera

1. Remove ash receiver.
2. Remove center air outlet and duct.
3. Remove brace from underside of radio.
4. Remove radio knobs and escutcheons and two ⅝" nuts.
5. Unplug feed and speaker wire connector and antenna cable from radio.
6. Remove radio through ash receiver opening.

1964-65 Special Series

Without Air Conditioning

1. Disconnect battery ground cable.
2. Pull off radio control knobs.
3. Disconnect radio, speaker and antenna lead connectors.
4. Remove screw holding support to radio and withdraw from underside of dash.

With Air Conditioning

1. Disconnect battery ground cable.
2. Remove exterior cover (5 screws).
3. Remove control trim bezel (4 screws).
4. Remove ash tray and screw holding support to radio.
5. Unfasten and partially withdraw instrument panel insert (4 screws).
6. Disconnect radio and antenna lead connectors and remove radio.
7. Further disassembly and separation of radio from insert is obvious upon inspection.

1963 Special Series

1. On air conditioned cars it is necessary to lower the evaporator assembly by removing both right and left bolts that retain assembly to underside of instrument panel. Then remove the brace that supports radio, the screw that holds the two right sections of the air duct together and the glove box. Radio and speaker may then be removed through glove box opening.
2. Disconnect antenna lead-in wire, speaker wire and battery wire from radio.
3. Remove knobs, escutcheons and retaining nuts from radio control shafts.
4. Remove support bracket-to-radio cap screw located at right side of radio and lower radio from under instrument panel.
5. Installation is made in the reverse order of removal.

1963 Senior Series

1. Remove control knobs, felt washers, inner knobs and hex nuts from radio.
2. Remove screws that retain trim plate and remove trim.
3. Remove two bolts holding radio to instrument panel.
4. Pull radio out and disconnect wires and connectors.

1964 Senior Series (Except Riviera)

1. Remove ash receiver (4 screws).
2. On air conditioned cars, detach center air outlet from radio trim plate (2 screws) and lift off outlet

assembly, also duct located directly under outlet assembly.
3. Remove 2 nuts holding bottom corner of radio trim plate.
4. Unfasten radio from cross support (2 screws) and partially withdraw radio trim plate and radio.
5. Further disassembly of trim plate from radio will be obvious upon inspection.

1964-65 Riviera

1. Remove 2 screws from center console front trim plate and partially lift up trim plate.
2. Disconnect lamp socket and lighter lead connector and complete removal of trim plate.
3. If air conditioned, remove 2 screws holding air conductor outlet to radio trim plate and lift off center outlet and duct.
4. Remove 4 screws and lower air conditioner control.
5. Remove 2 screws from lower corner of trim plate and 2 screws securing underside of radio to cross support. Partially withdraw radio and trim plate.
6. Remove all lead connectors attached to radio and complete removal of radio and trim plate. Further disassembly of trim plate from radio will be obvious upon inspection.

HEATER CORE REMOVAL

After draining radiator and disconnecting heater hoses, proceed as follows:

1969 Special & Skylark

1. Remove right front fender skirt.
2. Disconnect control cables from lever of defroster door and outside air inlet door on heater.
3. Disconnect temperature control cable from lever of temperature door on heater.
4. Remove attaching nuts from heater studs.
5. Remove connector from blower motor resistor.
6. Remove screws from lower part of defroster outlet to top of heater.
7. Work heater rearward until studs clear dash and remove.
8. Reverse procedure to install.

1969 LeSabre, Wildcat & Electra

1. Disconnect vacuum hoses from defroster door and outside air inlet door actuator diaphrams and control cable from temperature door lever.
2. Unfasten connector from blower motor resistor.
3. Remove nuts securing heater to dash.
4. Remove screws securing defroster outlet adapter to heater and raise adapter away from heater.
5. Work heater rearward until studs clear dash and remove.
6. Reverse procedure to install.

1969 Riviera

1. Remove right front fender.
2. Disconnect blower motor wire and resistor connectors.
3. Disconnect temperature door cable.
4. Disconnect vacuum hoses attached to outside door and vent heater door vacuum diaphrams.
5. Remove screws securing blower and heater assembly to dash and remove.
6. Reverse procedure to install.

1965-68 Full Size Cars

1. Remove nuts securing heater-defroster assembly to cowl.
2. Disconnect all control cables from defroster door, outside air door and temperature door levers.
3. Disconnect electrical connector from blower motor resistor.
4. Remove screws securing the defroster outlet adapter-to-heater core and raise adapter away from heater.
5. Heater core can now be worked away from cowl and removed.

1965-68 Intermediate Cars

NOTE: On 1968 models, the right front fender skirt must be removed before all attaching nuts can be taken off heater core studs. The balance of the removal procedure is the same as previous models as outlined below. The screw securing the defroster to the top of the heater may have to be removed as for 1967 models.

1. Remove right front wheel and draw an arc on the inside of the fender skirt 11" from the upper bolt of the wheel opening. Then draw another arc 16¾" from the lower wheel opening bolt. Drill a ¾" hole at the intersection of the two arcs and remove the lower right attaching nut from the heater core through this hole.
2. Disconnect all control wires from levers of defroster door, outside air door and the lever of the temperature control door.
3. Remove connector from blower resistor and take off nuts from remaining studs that retain heater core to cowl.
4. On 1967 models, remove the screw securing defroster outlet to top of heater. Heater core may now be worked rearward until studs clear cowl and lifted out.

1963-64 Intermediate Cars

Heater assembly is located in engine compartment. On 1964 models only, it is necessary to remove the battery, battery support and fender skirt to permit removal of the heater core case. Disconnect water hoses at heater, then remove air inlet case from engine side of dash.

1963-64 Full Size Cars

1. Remove blower and air inlet case as an assembly.
2. To gain access to mounting screws on blower side, remove right-hand hood hinge and antenna access hole cover.
3. Remove cover plate on rear face of heater and disconnect flapper valve cables.
4. Inside car, remove adapter between floor duct and heater, then pull heater away from dash. Heater core is then accessible by removing right-hand end of heater case.

SPEED CONTROLS

1969 Cruise Master

Bead Chain Adjustment

1. Adjust engine hot idle speed and mixture, then shut off engine.
2. Check slack in chain by unsnapping swivel from ball stud and holding chain taut at ball stud; center of swivel should extend ⅛" beyond center of ball stud.
3. Adjust bead chain slack by sliding sleeve back on chain and removing loose rivet. Move swivel on ball chain until slack is correct. Then reinstall rivet and slide sleeve over rivet.

Cruise Speed Adjustment

The cruise speed adjustment can be set as follows:
1. If car cruises below engagement speed, screw orifice tube on transducer outward.
2. If car cruises above engagement speed, screw orifice tube inward.

NOTE: Each ¼ turn of the orifice tube will change cruise speed about one mile per hour. Snug up lock nut after each adjustment.

Brake Release Switch Adjustment

1. Turn on ignition switch and connect a test light between one terminal of brake release switch and ground; select terminal where light goes out when pedal is depressed.
2. Loosen screw that retains switch to pedal support bracket. Position switch so circuit opens (light goes out) when pedal is depressed ¼". Tighten screw and recheck.

1968 Cruise Master

Servo Unit Adjustment

Adjust the bead chain so that it is as tight as possible without holding the throttle open when the carburetor is set at its lowest idle throttle position.

When connecting the bead chain (engine stopped) manually set the fast idle cam at its lowest step and connect the chain so that it does not hold the idle screw off the cam. If the chain needs to be cut, cut it three beads beyond the bead that pulls the linkage.

Regulator Unit Adjustment

To remove any difference between engagement and cruising speed, one adjustment is possible. However, no adjustment should be made until the following items have been checked or serviced.
1. Bead chain properly adjusted.
2. All hoses in good condition, properly attached, not leaking, pinched or cracked.
3. Regulator air filter cleaned and properly oiled.
4. Electric and vacuum switches properly adjusted.

Engagement - Cruising Speed Zeroing

If the cruising speed is lower than the

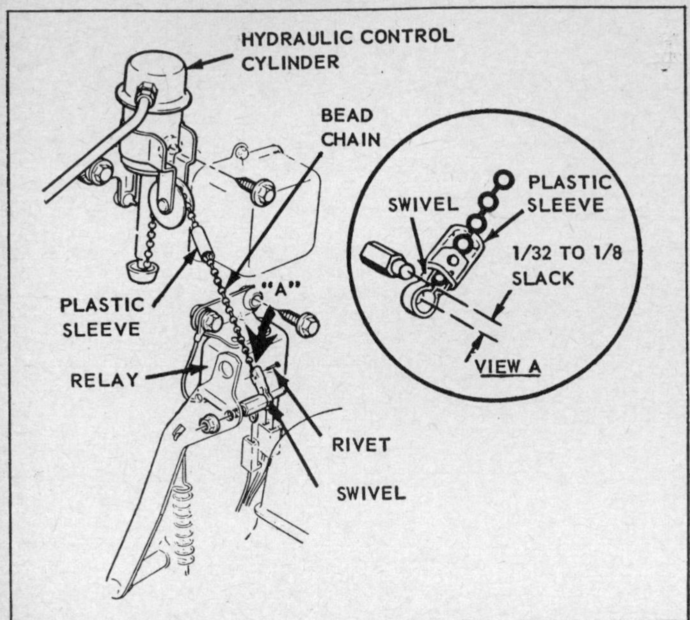

Fig. 8 Auto Cruise bead chain adjustment

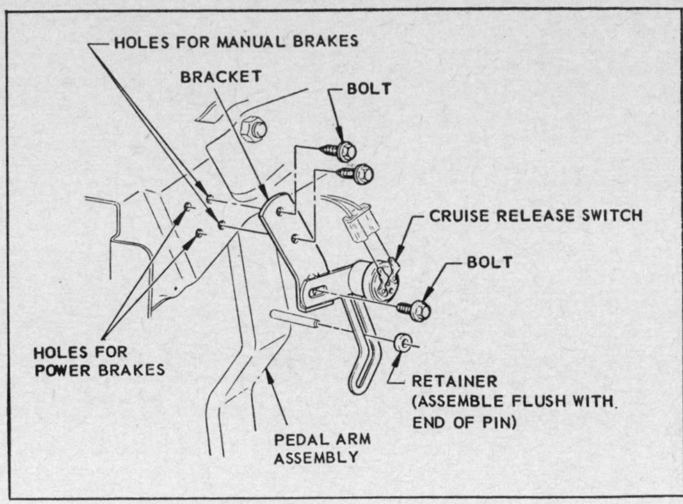

Fig. 9 Auto Cruise brake release switch adjustment

engagement speed, loosen the orifice tube locknut and turn the tube outward; if higher turn the tube inward. Each ⅛ turn will alter the engagement-cruising speed difference one mph. Tighten locknut after adjustment and check the system operation at 50 mph.

1967 Auto Cruise

Bead Chain Adjustment

To check the bead chain adjustment, snap swivel off stud and check measurement shown in Fig. 8. If chain is too loose or too tight, adjustments can be made in ⅛" increments by sliding plastic sleeve off swivel, removing rivet, repositioning chain and inserting rivet in nearest open hole. Recheck adjustment. Snap swivel onto stud and slide plastic sleeve over swivel body to retain rivet.

Brake Release Switch Adjustment

Turn on ignition switch and connect a test lamp between one terminal of the brake release switch and ground. Select terminal where light goes out when brake pedal is depressed.
Loosen screw that retains brake release switch to brake pedal support bracket. Position switch so that circuit opens (light goes out) when brake pedal is depressed ¼", Fig. 9.

1963-67 AC Electro Cruise

Power Unit Ball Chain, Adjust

IMPORTANT: Do not lubricate power unit ball chain or its pulley.

1. Loosen jam nut on threaded stud attached to end of ball chain.
2. With carburetor set on slow idle cam, rotate threaded stud so that chain is just taut without advancing idle speed of engine with engine running, then back off one full turn.
3. Tighten jam nut against rivnut on throttle bracket.
4. This adjustment should always be checked whenever carburetor linkage is adjusted.

Brake Release Switch, Adjust

1. Disconnect wiring harness connector from brake release switch.
2. Connect test lamp across switch terminals.

NOTE: If desired, the cruise lamp in the engagement switch may be used as a test lamp by unplugging connector to speed transducer in speedometer and leaving release switch wiring connector on switch. Then turn ignition switch on and press control knob which will cause Cruise light to be on.

3. Loosen screw that retains switch to brake pedal support bracket. Position switch to open the circuit at ½ inch brake pedal travel. An open circuit will be indicated by an unlit test lamp. If Cruise lamp is used, an open circuit will be indicated when light goes out.
4. When brake pedal is at released position, the circuit must be closed for the Electro-Cruise to operate.
5. Tighten adjusting screw and recheck switch adjustment by depressing brake pedal several times with test lamp connected.

Engine Section

NOTE:—SEE CHEVROLET CHAPTER FOR SERVICE ON THE 6-250 ENGINE

ENGINE, REPLACE

1. Drain cooling system and remove radiator.
2. Disconnect linkage at transmission and clutch (if equipped).
3. Remove transmission.
4. Remove hood and battery.
5. Disconnect exhaust pipes from manifolds.
6. Disconnect usual items under hood such as fuel lines, radiator hoses, wires, etc.
7. If equipped with an oil cooler, disconnect cooler lines.
8. If engine lifting fixture is used, remove carburetor after disconnecting automatic choke tube and fuel lines as mentioned above.
9. Attach engine lifting fixture to carburetor flange studs on intake manifold.
10. Remove engine mounting bolts and lift engine from chassis.
11. To install, reverse foregoing procedure.

CYLINDER HEADS

Some cylinder head gaskets are coated with a special lacquer to provide a good seal once the parts have warmed up. Do not use any additional sealer on such gaskets. If the gasket does not have this lacquer coating, apply suitable sealer to both sides.

1967-69

1. Drain coolant and disconnect battery.

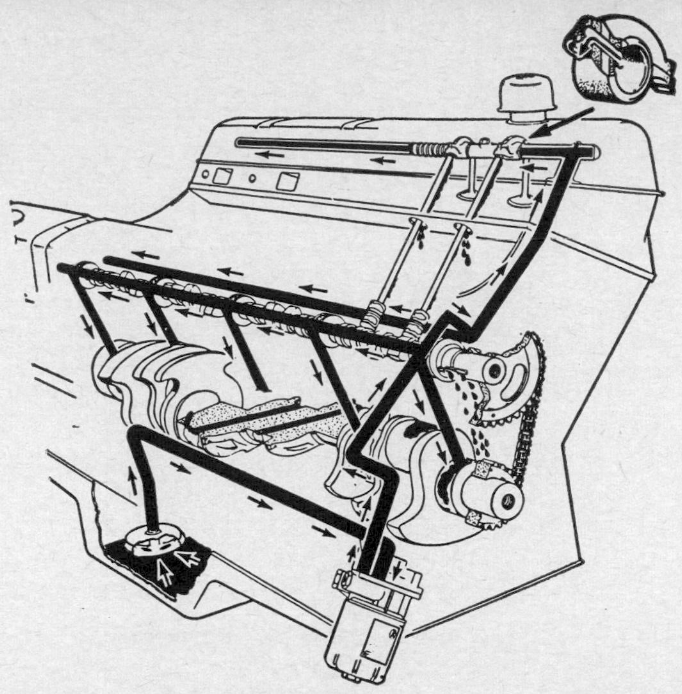

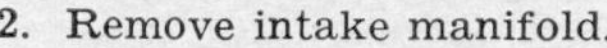

Engine lubrication system. 6-198, 225; 8-215, 300, 340, 350, 400, 430

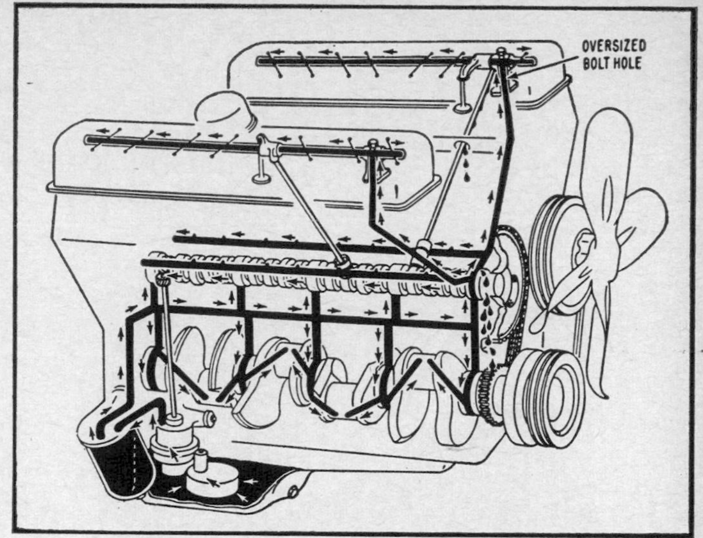

Engine oiling system. V8-401, 425

Fig. 2 Intake manifold tightening sequence. V8-350, 400, 430

2. Remove intake manifold.
3. When removing right cylinder head, remove Delcotron and/or A/C compressor with mounting bracket and move out of the way. *Do not disconnect hoses from air compressor.* Disconnect A.I.R. pipe assembly if so equipped.
4. When removing left cylinder head, remove oil dipstick, power steering pump and/or A.I.R. pump with mounting bracket (if equipped) and move out of the way with hoses attached. Disconnect A.I.R. pipe if so equipped.
5. Disconnect exhaust manifold from head to be removed.
6. Remove rocker arm shaft and lift out push rods.
7. Remove cylinder head.
8. Reverse procedure to install and tighten bolts gradually and evenly in the sequence shown in Figs. 1 through 6.

1963-66 V8-401, 425

1. Drain cooling system.
2. Remove air cleaner and disconnect all pipes from carburetor and intake manifold.
3. Disconnect wires from accelerator vacuum switch and remove throttle return spring.
4. Remove ignition coil and equalizer shaft bracket from engine.
5. Take off intake manifold and carburetor as an assembly.
6. When removing *right* cylinder head, remove air conditioning compressor (if equipped), exercising care.
7. When removing *left* cylinder head, remove power steering gear pump with mounting bracket (if equipped) and move it out of the way with hoses attached.
8. Disconnect wires from plugs.
9. Disconnect water manifold from both cylinder heads and disconnect exhaust manifold from head to be removed.
10. With air hose and cloths, clean dirt off cylinder head and adjacent area to avoid getting dirt into engine, and *particularly into the hydraulic valve lifters.*
11. Remove rocker arm cover and rocker arm and shaft assembly.
12. Lift out push rods. *Due to close tolerance in the engine compartment it is necessary to leave some of the bolts and push rods in the head during removal. The push rods should be pulled up and taped in position while cylinder is being removed. The same parts must be in the head during installation.*
13. Remove cylinder head attaching bolts and lift off head.
14. Installation is made in the reverse order of removal. Tighten head bolts in the sequence shown in Fig. 7.

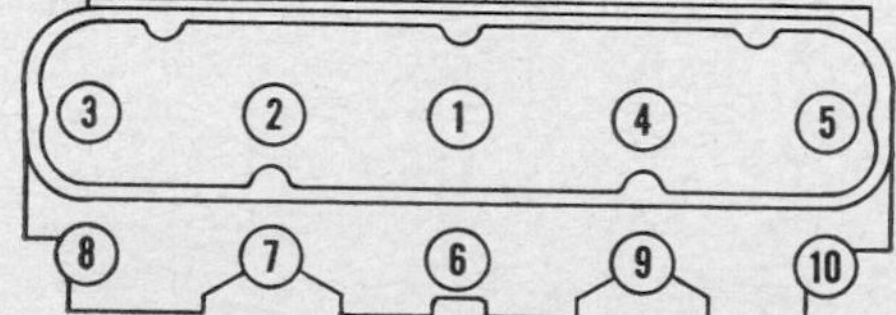

Fig. 1 Cylinder head tightening sequence. V8-350, 400, 430

1963-65 198, 215, 225, 300, 340

1. Drain cooling system.
2. Remove air cleaner. Disconnect all pipes and hoses from carburetor.
3. Remove ignition coil.
4. Disconnect temperature switch wire.
5. Disconnect accelerator and transmission linkage at carburetor.
6. Disconnect crankcase ventilator hose at valve.
7. Slide front thermostat by-pass hose clamp back on hose. Disconnect by-pass hose at timing chain cover to allow coolant to drain from manifold. Disconnect upper radiator hose at outlet.

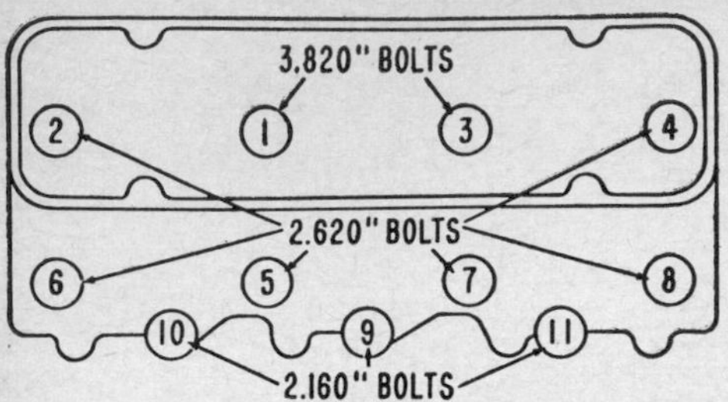

Fig. 3 Cylinder head tightening sequence. V6 engines

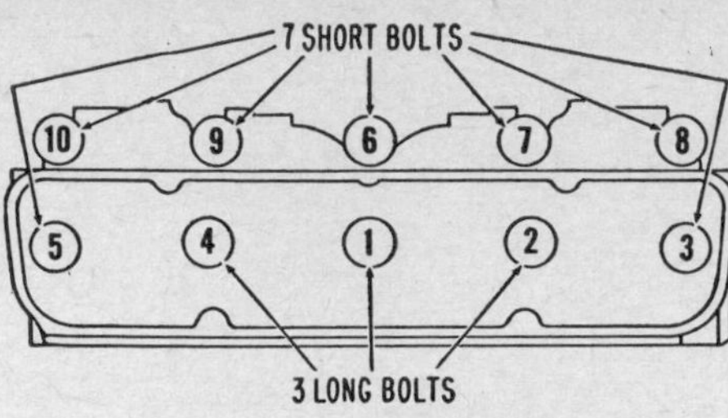

Fig. 5 Cyl. head tightening sequence. V8-300, 340

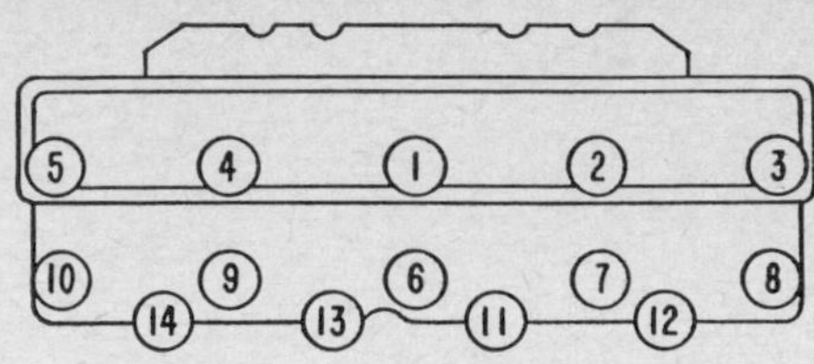

Fig. 7 Cylinder head tightening sequence. V8-401, 425

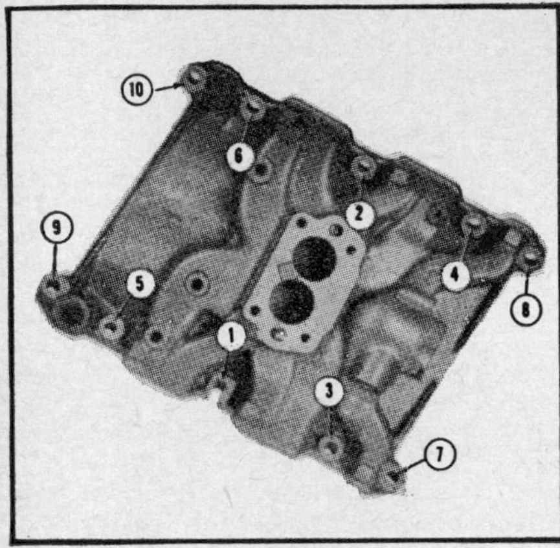

Fig. 4 Intake manifold tightening sequence. V6-225

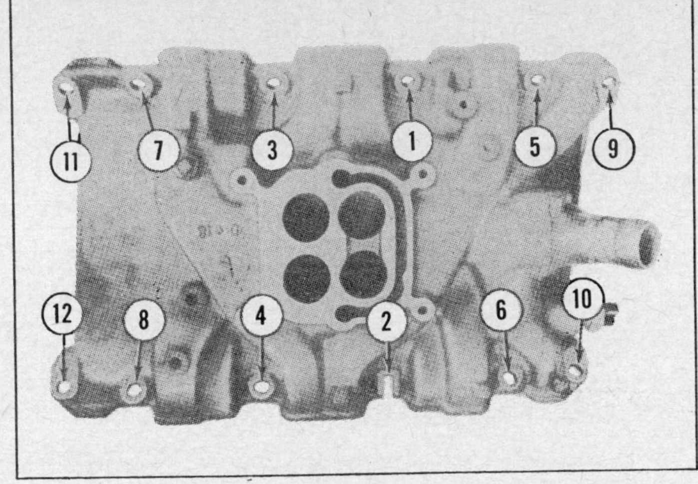

Fig. 6 Intake manifold tightening sequence. V8-300, 340

8. On V8 engines, disconnect heater hose at heater water temperature control valve inlet. Push end of hose down to allow coolant to drain from intake manifold.
9. On V6 engines, disconnect heater hose at intake manifold.
10. Remove intake manifold and carburetor as a unit.
11. Disconnect spark plug wires at plugs and swing wires and retainer out of the way.
12. On right side, remove crankcase ventilator valve.
13. Remove rocker arm cover. Unfasten and remove rocker arm and shaft assembly. Oil baffle is mounted under rear bolts on right head assembly.
14. Remove push rods. If valve lifters are to be serviced, remove them at this time. If not, protect the lifters and camshaft from dirt by covering area with clean cloths.
15. Remove alternator and power steering pump bracket.
16. Unfasten and remove cylinder head with exhaust manifold attached.
17. Reverse removal procedure to install heads. Refer to the illustrations for correct location of bolts and tightening sequence.

ROCKER ARMS

V8-350, 400, 430

When installing rocker arm shaft, be sure that drill mark is facing up and toward rear of left cylinder head and toward front on right cylinder head, Fig. 10.

6-198, 225; 8-215, 300, 340

1. To disassemble, remove cotter pin, plain washer and spring washer from each end of rocker arm shaft.
2. Remove bracket bolts and slide rocker arms and brackets off shaft.
3. Clean and inspect all parts, taking care to clean out all oil holes. Replace parts that are excessively worn.
4. Assemble springs, rocker arms and brackets. *Note that two different rocker arms are used and that the valve ends of rocker arms slant away from the brackets.*
5. Install spring washer, flat washer and cotter pin on each end of shaft in the order named.
6. Install bolts with plain washers through brackets and shaft so the notches are positioned as shown in Fig. 11.

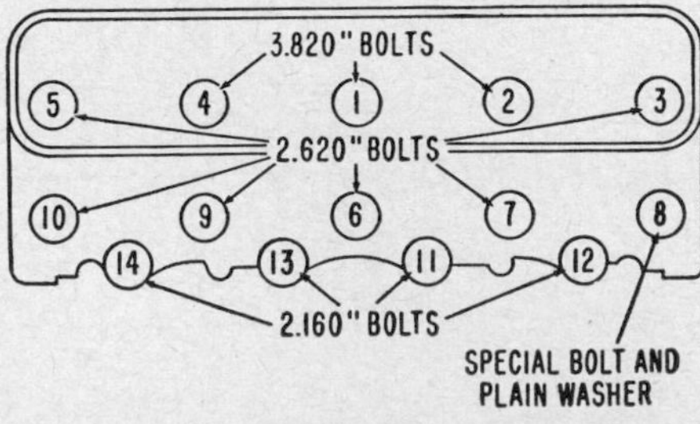

Fig. 8 Cylinder head tightening sequence. V8-215

V8-401, 425

1. To disassemble, remove cotter pin, flat washer and spring washer from each end of the rocker arm shaft and remove bolts from brackets. Remove rocker arms, springs and brackets from shaft.
2. Clean and inspect all parts and replace those that are excessively worn.
3. Assemble springs, rocker arms and brackets on shaft, Fig. 12. Note that the long spring is at the middle of the shaft, the valve ends of all rocker arms slant toward middle of shaft, and a bracket is located between each pair of rocker arms.
4. Install spring washer, flat washer and cotter pin on each end of the shaft in the order named.
5. Install bolts with plain washers through brackets and shaft so that the notch on one end of the shaft is *upward* in line with bolt heads. This places the oil holes on lower side of shaft in proper relationship to rocker arms.

VALVE ARRANGEMENT

Front to Rear

V6 Left Head	E-I-E-I-I-E
V6 Right Head	E-I-I-E-I-E
V8-350, 400, 430	E-I-I-E-E-I-I-E
Other V8s	E-I-E-I-I-E-I-E

VALVE LIFT SPECS.

Engine	Year	Intake	Exhaust
V6-198	1963	.385	.385
V8-215	1963	.383①	.383①
V6-225	1964	.391	.401
V6-225	1965-67	.401	.401
6-250	1968-69	.388	.388
V8-300	1964	.401	.401
V8-300	1965-67	.3931	.401
V8-340	1966-67	.3992③	.3992③
V8-350	1968-69	.3766	.384
V8-400	1967	.4214	.4498
V8-400	1968-69	.4187	.4482
V8-401	1963-66	.431②	.431②
V8-425	1964-66	.439	.441
V8-430	1967	.4214	.4498
V8-430	1968-69	.4187	.4482

①..1963 Skylark .401.
②..1963 Riviera .441.
③..1966 LeSabre; intake .393, exhaust .401.

VALVE TIMING

Intake Opens Before TDC

Engine	Year	Degrees
V6-198	1963	18
V8-215	1963	29
V6-225	1964-67	24
6-250	1968-69	62
V8-300	1964	26
V8-300	1965-67	30
V8-340	1966-67	32
V8-350	1968-69	24
V8-400	1967-69	14
V8-401	1963-66	28
V8-425	1964-66	29
V8-430	1967-69	14

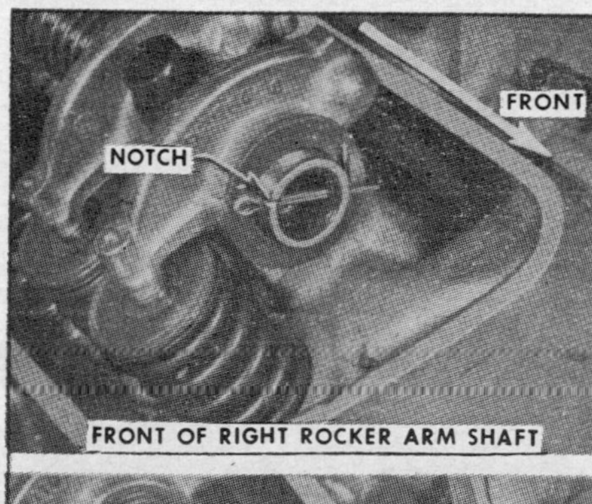

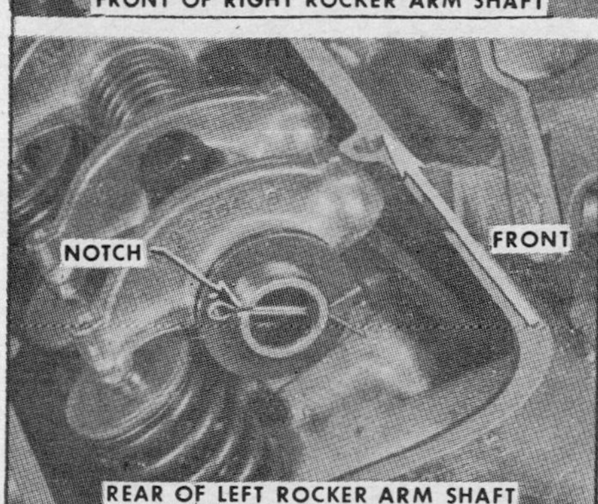

Fig. 11 Rocker arm shaft installation. 6-198, 225; 8-215, 300, 340

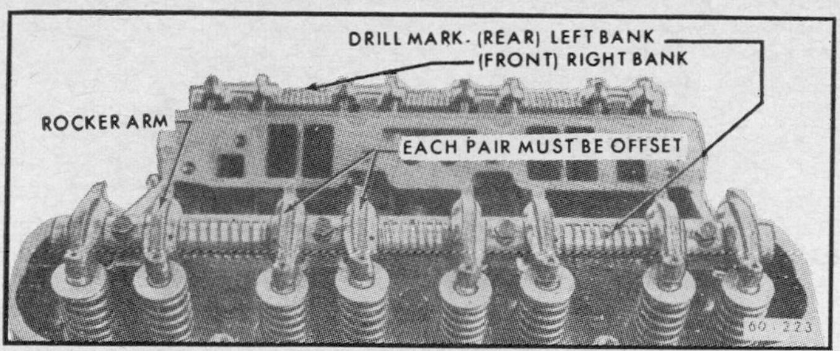

Fig. 10 Rocker arms positioned on shaft. V8-350, 400, 430

VALVE GUIDES

The valves operate in guides pressed into the cylinder head.

HYDRAULIC VALVE LIFTERS

Failure of an hydraulic valve lifter, Fig. 13, is generally caused by an inadequate oil supply or dirt. An air leak at the intake side of the oil pump or too much oil in the engine will cause air bubbles in the oil supply to the lifters, causing them to collapse. This is a probable cause of trouble if several lifters fail to function, but air in the oil is an unlikely cause of failure of a single unit.

The valve lifters may be lifted out of their bores after removing the rocker arms and push rods. Adjustable pliers with taped jaws may be used to remove lifters that are stuck due to varnish, carbon, etc. Fig. 13 illustrates the type of lifter used.

TIMING CHAIN COVER

V8-401, 425

1. To remove the timing chain, drain cooling system, then remove radiator, shroud, fan belt, fan and pulley, and vibration damper.
2. Remove all bolts that attach timing chain cover and water manifold to engine. *Do not remove five small bolts attaching water pump to chain cover.* Remove cover and manifold, using care to avoid damaging oil pan gasket.

V6-198, 225, V8-215-300-340-350-400-430

1. Drain cooling system and remove radiator.
2. Remove fan, pulleys and belts.
3. Remove crankshaft pulley and reinforcement.
4. If equipped with power steering, remove any pump bracket bolts attached to timing chain cover and loosen and remove any other bolts necessary that will allow pump and brackets to be moved out of the way.
5. Remove fuel pump.
6. Remove Delcotron and brackets.
7. Remove distributor cap and pull spark plug wire retainers off brackets on rocker arm cover. Swing distributor cap with wires attached out of the way. Disconnect distributor primary lead. On 400, 430, remove coil.
8. Remove distributor. *If chain and sprockets are not to be disturbed, note position of distributor rotor for installation in the same position.*
9. Loosen and slide clamp on thermostat by-pass hose rearward.
10. Remove bolts attaching chain cover to block.
11. On 198, 225, 300, 340, 350 engines, remove two oil pan-to-chain cover bolts and remove cover.
12. On 400, 430 engines, remove four oil pan-to-chain cover bolts. *Do not remove the five bolts attaching water pump to chain cover.* Remove cover, using care to avoid damaging oil pan gasket.
13. Reverse procedure to install, noting data shown in Figs. 14 and 15.

IMPORTANT

Remove the oil pump cover and pack

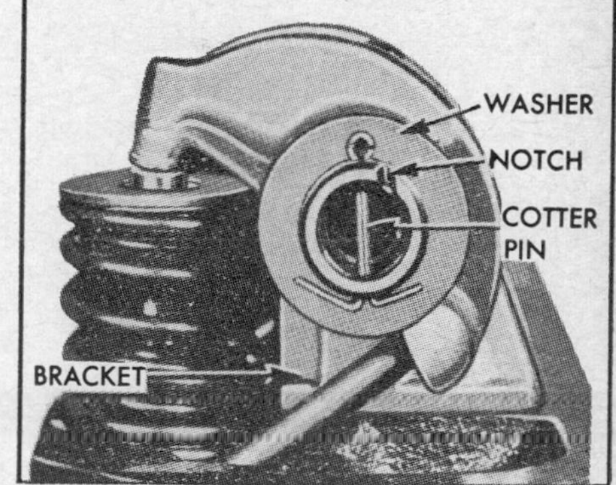

Fig. 12 Rocker arm shaft installation. V8-401, 425

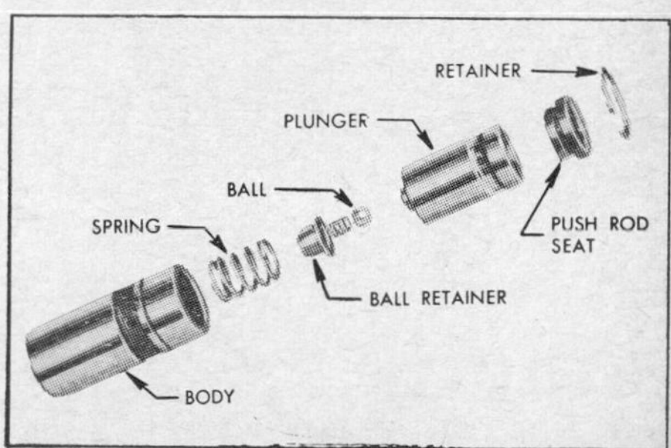

Fig. 13 Hydraulic valve lifter parts

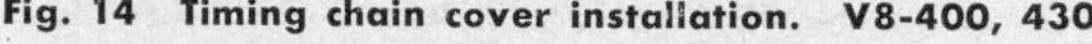
Fig. 14 Timing chain cover installation. V8-400, 430

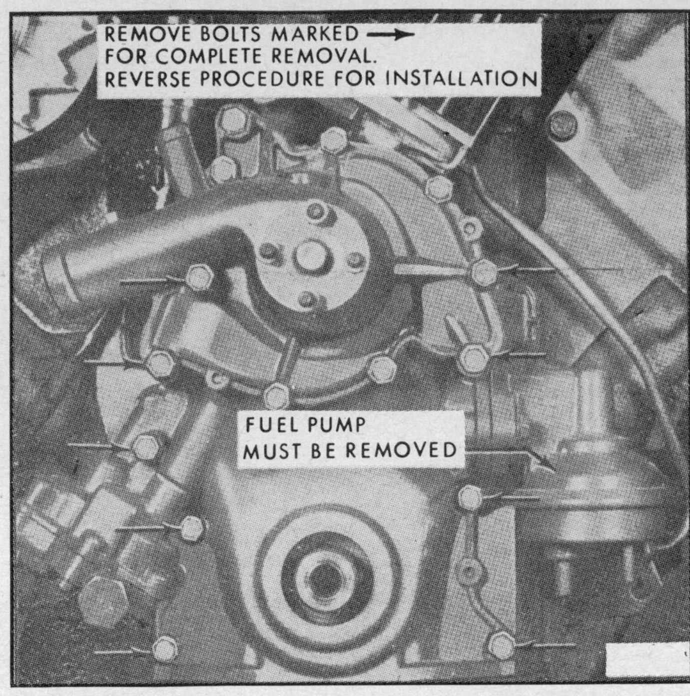

Fig. 15 Timing chain cover installation. 1968 V8-350, 1967 V6-225

the space around the oil pump gears completely full of vaseline. There must be no air space left inside the pump. Reinstall the cover using a new gasket. This step is very important as the oil pump may lose its prime whenever the pump, pump cover or timing chain cover is disturbed. If the pump is not packed it may not begin to pump oil as soon as the engine is started.

TIMING CHAIN

198, 215, 225, 300, 340, 350, 400, 430

1. With the timing case cover removed as outlined above, temporarily install the vibration damper bolt and washer in end of crankshaft.
2. Turn crankshaft so sprockets are positioned as shown in Figs. 17, 18. Use a sharp rap on a wrench handle to start the vibration damper bolt out without disturbing the position of the sprockets.
3. Remove front oil slinger.
4. Remove camshaft distributor drive gear and fuel pump eccentric.
5. Use two large screwdrivers to alternately pry the camshaft sprocket then the crankshaft sprocket forward until the camshaft sprocket is free. Then remove camshaft sprocket and chain, and crankshaft sprocket off crankshaft.
6. To install, assemble chain on sprockets and slide sprockets on their respective shafts with the "0" marks on the sprockets lined up as shown.
7. Complete the installation in the reverse order of removal.

V8-401, 425

1. Remove oil slinger from crankshaft and remove bolt, lockwasher and plain washer that attaches fuel pump operating eccentric and camshaft sprocket to camshaft.
2. If there has been doubt about the valve timing, turn the crankshaft until the camshaft sprocket keyway is straight down toward the crankshaft and the timing marks on both sprockets are as shown in Fig. 16.
3. Using two large screwdrivers, alternately work the sprockets outward until the camshaft sprocket is free of the camshaft. Remove this sprocket and chain, then remove the other sprocket from the crankshaft.

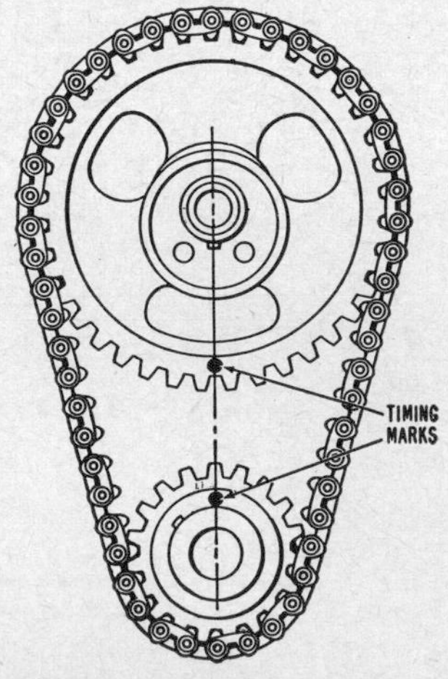

Fig. 16 Valve timing marks. V8-401, 425

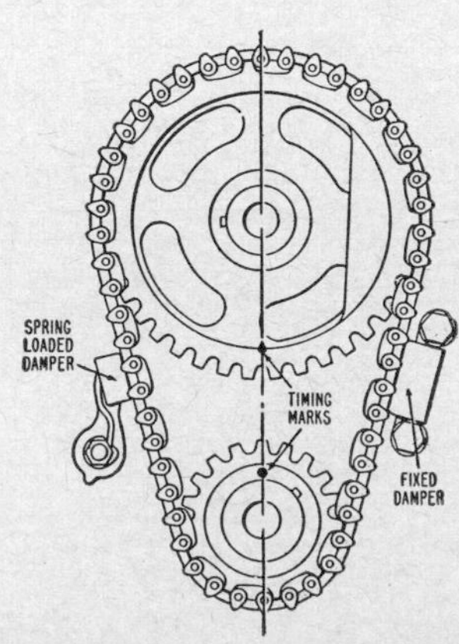

Fig. 17 Valve timing marks. V6-198, 225

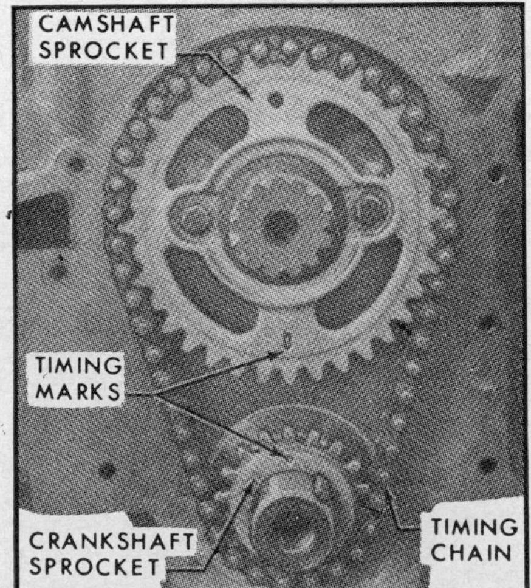

Fig. 18 Valve timing marks. V8-300, 340, 350, 400, 430

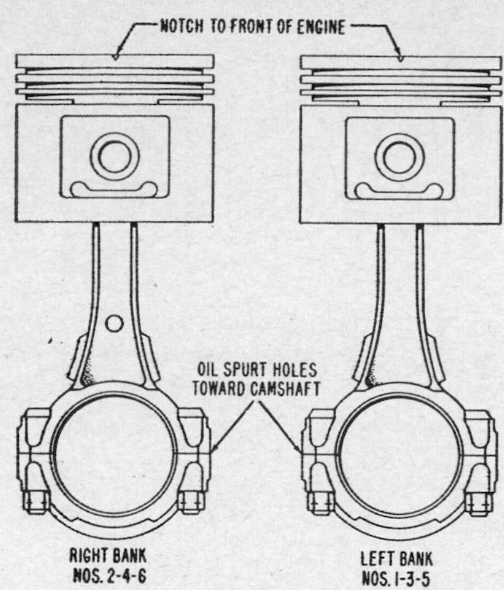

Fig. 19 Piston and rod assembly. V6-198, 225

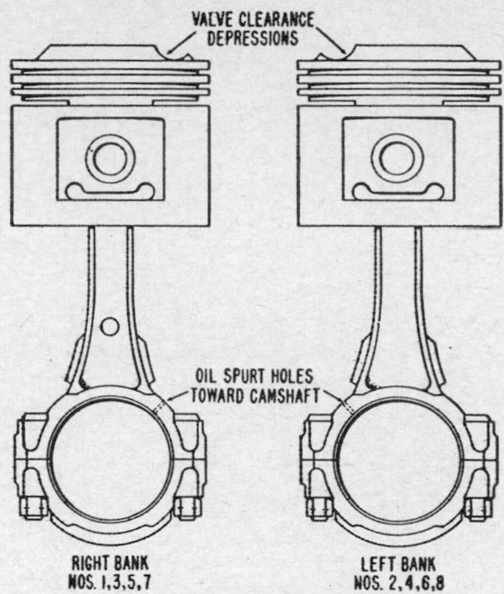

Fig. 20 Piston and rod assembly. V8-401, 425

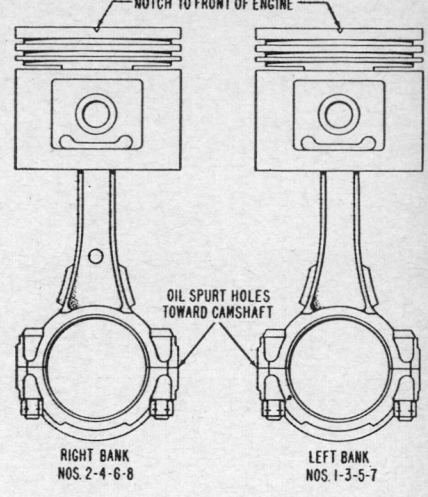

NOTCH TO FRONT OF ENGINE
OIL SPURT HOLES TOWARD CAMSHAFT
RIGHT BANK NOS. 2-4-6-8
LEFT BANK NOS. 1-3-5-7

Fig. 21 Piston and rod assembly. V8-215, 300, 340, 350, 400, 430

4. Thoroughly clean all sludge from cover and front face of crankcase. Inspect crankshaft oil seal in chain cover and replace if worn.
5. When ready to install the chain, turn crankshaft until Nos. 1 and 4 pistons are on top dead center. Turn camshaft so that sprocket key points straight down toward crankshaft.
6. Place timing chain over sprockets so that timing marks are located as shown in Fig. 7. Install sprockets with chain on the two shafts.
7. Install fuel pump eccentric and oil slinger. Then complete the installation in the reverse order of removal.

CAMSHAFT

1. To remove camshaft, remove rocker arm shaft assemblies, push rods and valve lifters.
2. Remove timing chain and sprockets.
3. Slide camshaft out of engine, using care not to mar the bearing surfaces.

PISTONS & RODS, ASSEMBLE

Rods and pistons should be assembled and installed as shown in Figs. 19, 20, 21.

PISTONS, PINS & RINGS

Pistons are available in standard sizes and oversizes of .001, .005, .010, .020 and .030 inch.

Rings are furnished in standard sizes and oversizes of .010, .020 and .030 inch.

Piston pins are supplied in standard sizes and oversizes of .003 and .005 inch.

MAIN & ROD BEARINGS

Main bearings are available in standard sizes and undersizes of .001, .002, .003 and .010 inch.

Rod bearings are furnished in standard sizes and undersizes of .001, .002 and .010", Fig. 22.

CRANKSHAFT OIL SEAL

A braided oil seal is pressed into the upper and lower grooves behind the rear main bearing.

OIL PAN

1968-69 V8-350, 400, 430

1. Disconnect battery and drain oil.
2. Raise and support car on stands.
3. With manual transmission, loosen clutch equalizer bracket-to-frame bolts. Remove exhaust crossover pipe, and front engine mounting bolts. Remove fan shroud-to-radiator tie bar screws.
4. With automatic transmission, remove lower flywheel housing. Remove shift linkage attaching bolts and swing out of the way (LeSabre only). Remove front engine mounting bolts. Remove fan shroud-to-radiator tie bar screws.
5. Raise engine by placing jack under crankshaft pulley mounting.

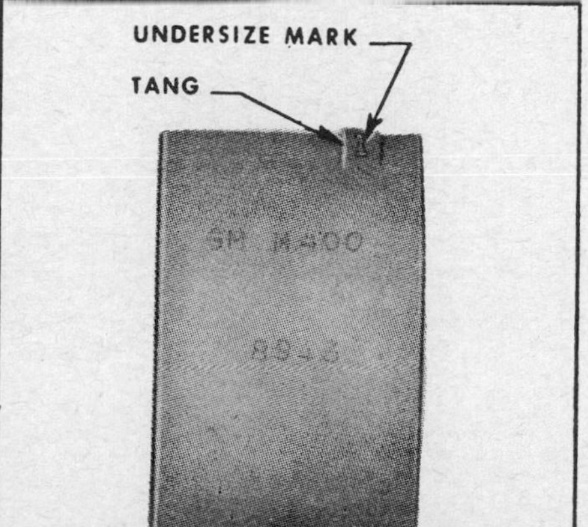

Fig. 22 Location of undersize mark on main and rod bearing shell

6. Unfasten and remove pan.
7. Reverse procedure to install.

1967 V8-400, 430

1. Disconnect ground strap at battery.
2. Raise car and drain oil.
3. With manual shift transmission, loosen clutch equalizer bracket-to-frame bolts. Remove lower flywheel housing, exhaust crossover pipe, front engine mount bolts and fan shroud-to-radiator tie bar screws.
4. With automatic transmission, remove lower flywheel housing, loosen shift linkage bolts, remove steering idler arm bracket-to-right front frame bolts, front engine mount bolts and fan shroud-to-radiator tie bar screws.
5. Raise engine with jack under crankshaft pulley mounting.
6. Unfasten and remove oil pan.

V8-401, 425

On single exhaust models the exhaust crossover pipe must be removed. On some models, it may be necessary to remove the flywheel housing lower cover and starter splash shield. It may also be necessary to disconnect the steering idler arm bracket from the right frame side rail and lower the steering linkage for clearance. *The idler arm bracket should be fastened in its relative position to the idler arm while disconnected from the frame. This will prevent turning and possible changing of toe-in adjustment.*

6-198, 225; 8-215, 300, 340

1. Remove air cleaner and drain oil from oil pan.
2. Loosen clutch equalizer bracket-to-frame bolts (if equipped).
3. Loosen shift linkage attaching bolts.
4. Remove steering idler arm bracket-to-suspension crossmember attaching bolts.
5. Support engine either with a jack under the oil pan or with chains around exhaust manifold.
6. Remove engine mounting bolts.

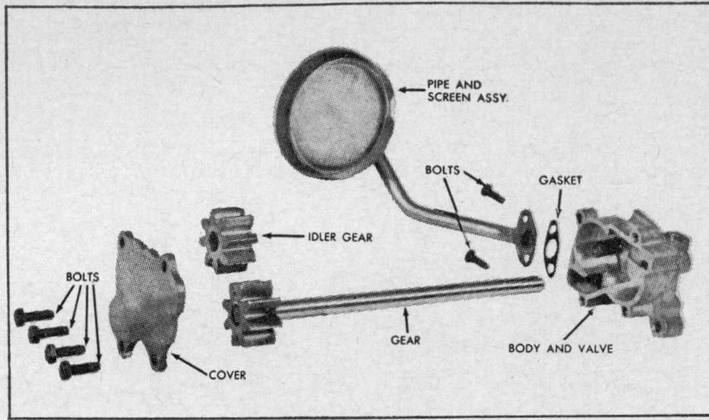

Fig. 23 Oil pump disassembled. V8-401, 425

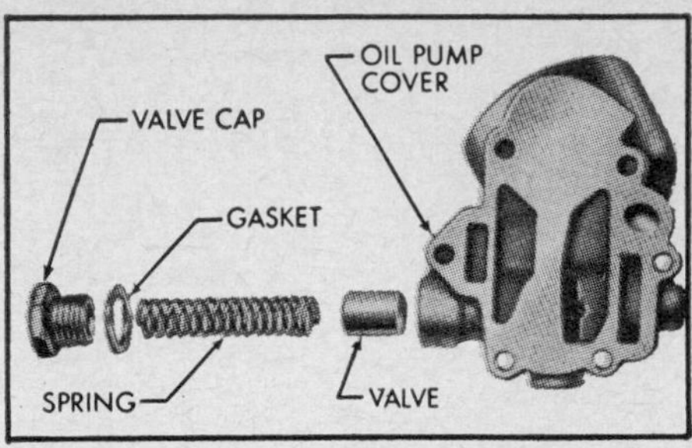

Fig. 24 Oil pump cover and by-pass valve. 198, 215, 225, 300, 340, 350, 400, 430

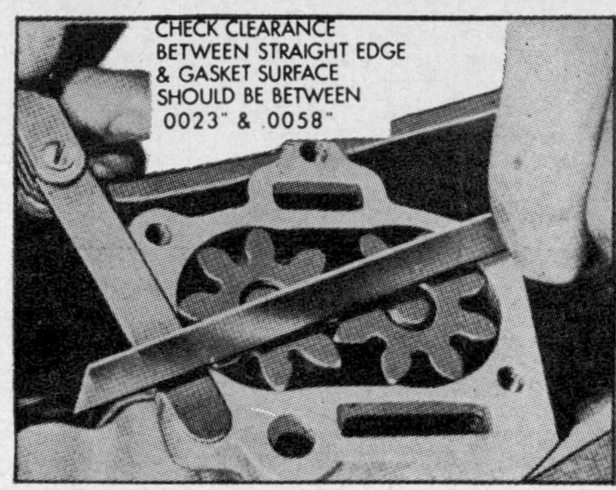

Fig. 25 Checking oil pump gear end clearance. 198, 215, 225, 300, 340, 350, 400, 430

7. Raise engine and insert bolts through engine mount bracket bolt holes, then lower engine so mounts rest on bolts.
8. Remove lower flywheel housing.
9. Remove oil pan bolts and lower pan enough to remove oil pump pipe and screen-to-cylinder block bolts.
10. Rotate crankshaft to provide maximum clearance at forward end of oil pan. Move front of pan to the right and lower through opening between crossmember and steering linkage intermediate shaft.
11. Reverse removal procedure to install pan.

OIL PUMP

V8-401, 425

1. Referring to Fig. 23, remove pipe and screen. Take off cover and slide gears out of body. Wash all parts and blow dry.
2. Replace any parts not serviceable.
3. Install gear and shaft and idler gear in body.
4. Check for clearance between gears and cover using a straightedge. Clearance should be .0005" to .005".
5. Pack cavity and space between gears and body with vaseline, not chassis lube.
6. Install pump cover with side having grooves toward gears.
7. Complete assembly and install pump.
8. Install pump with new gasket and tighten bolts a little at a time while turning pump shaft through gear lash. If pump shaft tends to bind when bolts are tightened, it may be freed up by tapping body with a mallet.

198, 215, 225, 300, 340, 350, 400, 430

1. To remove pump, take off oil filter.
2. Disconnect wire from oil pressure indicator switch in filter by-pass valve cap (if so equipped).
3. Remove screws attaching oil pump cover to timing chain cover. Remove cover and slide out pump gears. Replace any parts not serviceable.
4. Remove oil pressure relief valve cap, spring and valve, Fig. 24. Remove oil filter by-pass valve cap, spring and valve. Replace any parts of valve not serviceable.
5. Check relief valve in its bore in cover. Valve should have no more clearance than an easy slip fit. If any perceptible side shake can be felt, the valve and/or cover should be replaced.
6. The filter by-pass valve should be flat and free of nicks and scratches.

Assembly & Installation

1. Lubricate and install pressure relief valve and spring in bore of pump cover. Install cap and gasket. Torque cap to 30-35 ft-lbs.
2. Install filter by-pass valve flat in its seat in cover. Install spring, cap and gasket. Torque cap to 30-35 ft-lbs.
3. Install pump gears and shaft in pump body section of timing chain cover to check gear end clearance. Check clearance as shown in Fig. 25. If clearance is less than .0018" check timing chain cover for evidence of wear.
4. If gear end clearance is satisfactory, remove gears and pack gear pocket *full* of vaseline, not chassis lube.
5. Reinstall gears so vaseline is forced into every cavity of gear pocket and between teeth of gears. *Unless pump is packed with vaseline, it may not prime itself when engine is started.*
6. Install cover and tighten screws alternately and evenly. Final tightening is 10-15 ft-lbs. torque. Install filter on nipple.

WATER PUMP, REPLACE

Drain cooling system, being sure to drain into a clean container if anti-freeze solution is to be saved. Remove the fan belt and disconnect all hoses from water pump. Remove water pump.

FUEL PUMP, REPLACE

1969 Riviera Electric Pump

These models have a turbine type electric pump located at the lower end of the fuel pick-up pipe in the bottom of the tank, Fig. 26. This pump runs continuously whenever the engine is running thus maintaining a steady pressure whether fuel is needed or not. To replace, proceed as follows:

1. Raise car, disconnect two terminal connector at tank and remove ground wire screw.
2. Lower car and pull back trunk floor mat.
3. Remove five screws from access hole cover and remove cover.
4. Disconnect fuel hose from tank unit.
5. Unscrew retaining cam ring and remove fuel pump-tank unit assembly.
6. To remove pump from tank unit, remove flat wire conductor from plastic clip on fuel tube.
7. Squeeze clamp and pull pump straight back about 1/2".
8. Remove two nuts and washers from pump terminals.
9. Squeeze clamp and pull pump straight back-take care to prevent bending of circular support bracket.
10. Reverse procedure to install.

All Models Mechanical Pump

NOTE: Before installing the pump, it is good practice to crank the engine so that the nose of the camshaft eccentric is out of the way of the fuel pump rocker arm when the pump is installed. In this way there will be the least amount of tension on the rocker arm, thereby easing the installation of the pump.

1. Remove all gasket material from the pump and block gasket surfaces. Apply sealer to both sides of new gasket.

2. Position gasket on pump flange and hold pump in position against its mounting surface. Make sure rocker arm is riding on camshaft eccentric.
3. Press pump tight against its mounting. Install retaining screws and tighten them alternately.
4. Connect fuel lines. Then operate engine and check for leaks.

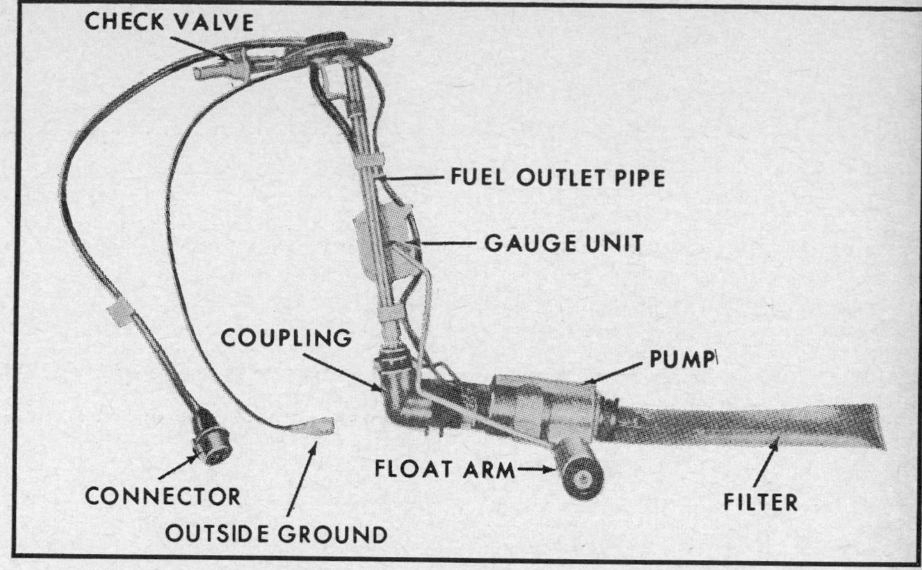

Fig. 26 Electric fuel pump and gauge tank unit assembly. 1969 Riviera

Clutch and Transmission Section

NOTE: 1969 linkage adjustment information is in this section. Repair procedures on both automatic and manual shift transmissions are covered elsewhere in this manual. Procedures for removing automatic transmissions as well as linkage adjustments on 1963-68 models are included in the automatic transmission chapters. See Chapter Index.

CLUTCH PEDAL, ADJUST

1969 LeSabre & Wildcat

With clutch pedal at full release position contacting rubber bumper stop, adjust clutch release rod to give zero lash at clutch pedal. Back off release rod about two turns to give ¾" lash at pedal pad. Tighten lock nut on release rod.

1967-69 Intermediates

With clutch pedal at full release position contacting rubber bumper stop, adjust clutch release rod to give zero lash at clutch pedal. Back off release rod approximately two turns to give ⅝ to ⅞ inch lash at pedal pad. Tighten lock nut on clutch release rod.

1967-68 LeSabre & Wildcat

With clutch pedal at full release position contacting rubber bumper stop, assemble all linkage parts except clutch release rod clevis so clevis pin will just assemble in equalizer inner lever with zero lash at clutch pedal. Lengthen release rod by turning clevis off rod approximately three turns to give ⅝ to ⅞ inch lash at pedal pad.

1966 Special, Skylark & LeSabre

1. Before making clutch adjustment, make certain clutch fork is on ball stud.
2. Unhook spring from clutch fork.
3. Push and hold equalizer and release rod toward front of car.
4. Pull and hold clutch fork toward rear of car.
5. If clutch is properly lashed there will be 1/16" to ⅛" clearance between clutch fork and rod.
6. To adjust clutch lash, loosen nut and turn clutch release rod as required.
7. Install spring to clutch fork.

1966 Skylark Gran Sport

1. Hold clutch pedal at full release position, contacting rubber bumper stop.
2. Adjust lower release rod clevis so clevis pin will just assemble into equalizer outer lever, with zero lash at clutch pedal.
3. Shorten lower clutch release rod by turning clevis on rod about two turns to give ⅝" to ⅞" lash at pedal.

1966 Wildcat

1. With clutch pedal at full release position, contacting rubber bumper stop and load removed from clutch overcenter spring, adjust turnbuckle to obtain zero lash at pedal.
2. Lengthen rod by turning turnbuckle about two turns to give ⅞" to 1⅛" lash at pedal pad.
3. Tighten lock nut on rod and on overcenter spring eyebolt.

1964-65 Senior Series

1. Check pedal at full release position, making sure it contacts rubber stop.
2. Adjust clutch release rod to give zero lash at pedal.
3. Back off release rod 3 full turns.
4. Check pedal lash. If not between ⅝" to ⅞" (¾" to 1" on 1964), adjust release rod further.
5. When lash is at desired dimension, tighten lock nut to a torque of 5-15 ft-lbs.

1964-65 Special Series

1. Check pedal at full release position, making sure it contacts rubber stop.
2. Adjust clutch release rod to give zero lash at pedal.
3. Back off release rod three full turns.
4. If pedal lash is not now between ⅝" to ⅞" (¾" to 1" on 1964), adjust release rod further.

1963 Special Series

1. Make certain that clutch pedal returns firmly against pedal bumper when pedal is released. If pedal does not contact bumper, check pedal and linkage for binding or lack of lubrication.

2. Pull outer end of clutch fork rearward until clutch release bearing contacts clutch release levers. Free movement at outer end of fork should be about 3/16".
3. If free movement is not approximately 3/16", remove clevis pin from rear end of clutch release rod and rotate rod as required. Reinstall clevis pin and retainer.
4. Check to make sure pedal lash is between 7/8" and 1".

1963 Senior Series

1. Make certain clutch pedal returns firmly against pedal bumper when pedal is released. If pedal does not contact bumper, check pedal and linkage for binding.
2. With car raised, lift outer end of clutch equalizer until release bearing contacts clutch release levers. Free movement at outer end of equalizer should be 3/16". This should give correct lash at pedal.
3. If free movement is not about 3/16", remove clevis pin from bottom end of clutch release rod and rotate rod as required.
4. Check to make sure pedal lash is 7/8" to 1".

CLUTCH, REPLACE

1969

1. Remove transmission.
2. Remove pedal return spring from clutch fork. *On LeSabre and Wildcat, disconnect rod assembly from clutch fork.*
3. Remove flywheel housing.
4. Remove clutch throw-out bearing from clutch fork.
5. Disconnect clutch fork from ball stud by moving it toward center of flywheel housing.
6. Mark clutch cover and flywheel so it can be installed in the same position.
7. Loosen clutch cover to flywheel bolts one turn at a time to avoid bending of clutch cover flange until spring pressure is released.
8. Support pressure plate and cover assembly while removing last bolts, then remove pressure plate and driven plate.
9. Reverse procedure to install being sure to line up marks made in removal.

1967-68 Special, Skylark, G.S. 350, 400, LeSabre & Wildcat

1. Remove transmission. *On LeSabre the equalizer assembly must be released first.*
2. Remove pedal return spring from clutch fork. *On LeSabre disconnect rod assembly from clutch fork.*
3. Remove flywheel housing.
4. Remove clutch release bearing.
5. Disconnect clutch fork from ball stud by forcing it toward center of flywheel housing.
6. Mark clutch cover and flywheel so that cover can be reinstalled in the same position on flywheel to preserve engine balance.
7. Loosen clutch cover-to-flywheel bolts one turn at a time each to avoid bending clutch cover flange until spring pressure is released.
8. Support pressure plate and cover assembly while removing last bolts, then remove assembly with driven disc.
9. Reverse procedure to install, being sure to align marks on clutch cover with mark made on flywheel during removal. Adjust pedal lash as directed above.

1966 Skylark Gran Sport

1. Remove transmission.
2. Disconnect lower clutch release rod from equalizer.
3. Loosen nut on frame side of equalizer and remove equalizer.
4. Remove ball stud from clutch release shaft.
5. Remove release lever and seal.
6. Remove flywheel housing.
7. Remove nylon bushing from flywheel housing.
8. Remove socket head capscrew on clutch release shaft; from same hole remove second socket head capscrew (cone point).
9. Pull clutch release shaft out about three inches. Slide release yoke, release bearing, woodruff key and return spring off end of release shaft. Remove release shaft.
10. Mark clutch cover and flywheel with a center punch so that cover can be reinstalled in same position on flywheel.
11. Loosen each clutch cover bolt one turn at a time in order to relieve clutch spring pressure evenly, thereby avoid distortion of cover.
12. Support clutch cover and pressure plate while removing last bolts, then remove cover and driven plate.
13. Reverse procedure to install.

1964-66 Wildcat

1. Remove propeller shaft and transmission.
2. Remove clutch equalizer shaft.
3. Remove ball stud from clutch release shaft.
4. Remove clutch release lever.
5. Remove clutch release seal.
6. Remove nylon bushing.
7. Remove socket head capscrew on clutch release shaft. From same hole remove second socket head (cone point).
8. Pull clutch release shaft out about three inches. Slide release yoke, key, release bearing and return spring off end of release shaft. Remove release shaft.
9. Mark clutch cover and flywheel with center punch for assembly purposes to preserve engine balance.
10. Loosen clutch cover bolts a little at a time until spring pressure is relieved, then completely remove bolts and take out clutch and driven plate.
11. Reverse procedure to install.

1965-66 Special, Skylark & LeSabre

1. Remove transmission.
2. Remove clutch release bearing.
3. Remove pedal return spring from fork.
4. Remove flywheel housing.
5. Disconnect fork from ball stud by forcing it toward center of vehicle.
6. Mark clutch cover and flywheel for assembly purposes in order to maintain engine balance.
7. Loosen clutch cover bolts a little at a time until spring pressure is released. Then completely remove bolts and take out clutch and driven plate.
8. Reverse procedure to install.

1964 Special, Skylark & LeSabre

1. Remove transmission.
2. Remove clutch release bearing from fork.
3. Remove tension spring from clutch fork and disconnect fork push rod.
4. Disconnect fork from ball stud by forcing it toward center of vehicle.
5. Mark clutch cover and flywheel with center punch so that cover can be reinstalled in the same position on flywheel to preserve engine balance.
6. Loosen clutch attaching bolts one turn at a time until diaphragm spring is released.
7. Support pressure plate and cover assembly while removing last bolts, then remove clutch and driven plate.
8. Reverse removal procedure to install clutch and adjust pedal lash.

1963 Senior Series

1. Remove propeller shaft from front companion flange.
2. Remove transmission.
3. Remove clutch equalizer shaft.
4. Disconnect clutch return spring.
5. Remove ball stud from clutch release shaft.
6. Remove clutch release lever.
7. Remove clutch release seal.
8. Remove nylon bushing.
9. Remove socket head capscrew on clutch release shaft. From same hole, remove second socket head (cone point).
10. Pull clutch release shaft out about 3". Slide release yoke and release bearing off end of release shaft and remove shaft.
11. Mark clutch cover and flywheel with a center punch so that the cover can be reinstalled in same position on flywheel in order to preserve engine balance.
12. Loosen each clutch cover bolt a turn or two at a time to relieve clutch spring pressure evenly and thus avoid distortion of cover. *Metal spacers (such as 1/4" nuts) placed between release levers and inner edge of clutch cover will aid removal and later installation by holding clutch springs partially compressed.*
13. Support pressure plate and cover assembly while removing last bolts, then remove cover and driven plate.
14. Reverse removal procedure to install and adjust pedal lash as outlined above.

1963 Special Series

1. Remove transmission.
2. Remove flywheel lower cover.
3. Remove clutch release bearing.
4. Disconnect release rod from fork.

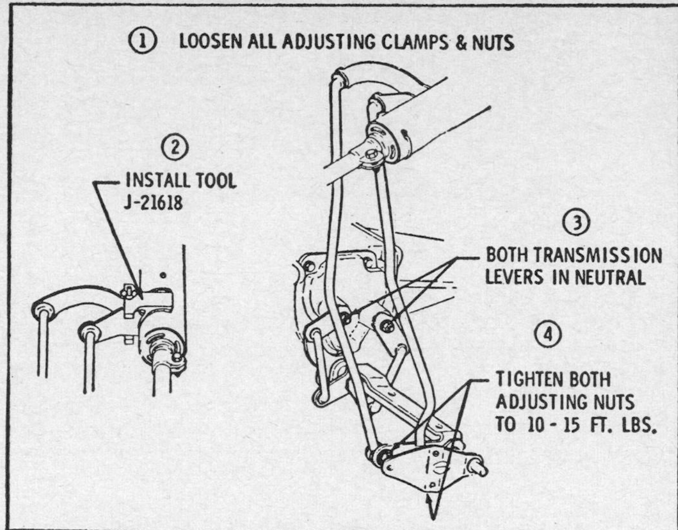

Fig. 2 Manual shift transmission linkage. 1964-65 Three Speed Units

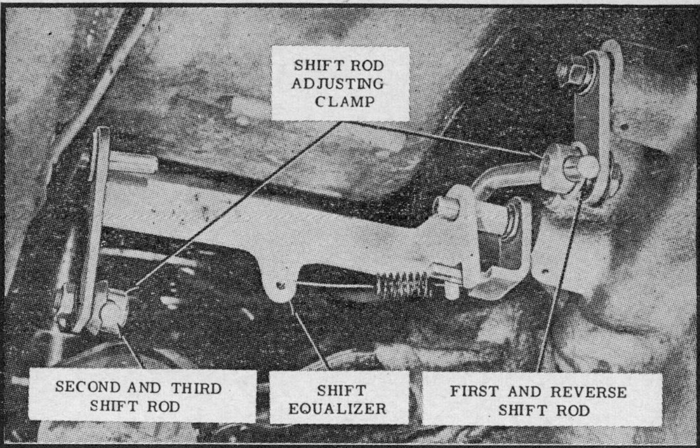

Fig. 3 Shift rod adjusting clamps. 1963 Special Series with three speed transmission

5. Unhook fork boot from opening in flywheel housing.
6. Push inward on release fork to free it from ball stud in flywheel housing and remove fork through bottom of housing.
7. Mark clutch cover and flywheel with a center punch so that cover can be reinstalled in same position on flywheel in order to preserve engine balance.
8. Loosen each clutch cover bolt a turn at a time in order to relieve clutch spring pressure evenly and thereby avoid distortion of cover. Metal spacers (such as ¼" nuts) placed between release levers and inner edge of cover will aid removal and later reinstallation by holding clutch springs partially compressed.
9. Support pressure plate and clutch cover assembly while removing last bolts, then remove clutch cover and driven plate.
10. Reverse removal procedure to install the clutch and adjust free pedal play as outlined previously.

3 SPEED TRANS. REPLACE

All 1966-69, 1964-65 Special, Skylark & LeSabre

1. Disconnect speedometer cable from driven gear fitting.
2. Disconnect shift control rods from shifter levers at transmission.
3. Remove propeller shaft.
4. Support rear of engine and remove transmission crossmember.
5. Remove two top transmission attaching bolts and insert guide pins in these holes.
6. Remove two lower bolts and slide transmission straight back and out of vehicle.
7. Reverse procedure to install.

1964-65 Wildcat, 1963 Special

1. Mark front companion flange and propeller shaft so that these parts can be reassembled in the same relative position.
2. Remove U-bolts attaching front companion flange to propeller shaft and slide front propeller shaft rearward as far as possible for working clearance.
3. Disconnect shift linkage from transmission by first removing the equalizer spring. Slide shift equalizer to full left position to disengage it from 2-3 shift lever, then slide equalizer to the right to remove from support pin.
4. Remove low-reverse shift lever from shaft. *NOTE: by disconnecting linkage in this manner, the linkage adjustment is not disturbed and should not require readjustment.*
5. Disconnect speedometer cable from transmission.
6. Loosen all three exhaust pipe joints so that transmission and rear end of engine can be lowered.
7. Disconnect clutch push rod.
8. Remove two bolts attaching transmission mounting pad to transmission support. Leave pad bolted to transmission.
9. With a wood block placed on jack, jack under engine oil pan until transmission mounting pad just clears transmission support.
10. Remove support (4 bolts), then lower jack so that transmission will clear underbody during removal.
11. Remove upper left transmission-to-clutch housing mounting bolts and install a guide pin in this hole. Remove lower right bolt and install a guide pin.
12. Remove other two transmission bolts and slide transmission straight back and out of vehicle.

3 SPEED TRANS. SHIFT LINKAGE

1969

Column Shift

1. Place column selector lever in Reverse detent, making sure the steering column selector plate engages lower most column lever (1st-reverse).
2. Loosen 1st-reverse adjusting clamp.
3. Shift transmission lever into reverse and tighten the 1st-reverse clamp to 17-23 ft-lbs.
4. Shift transmission levers into neutral and loosen 2nd-3rd clamp.
5. Install $\frac{3}{16}$" diameter rod through 2nd-3rd lever selector plate and the 1st-reverse lever and alignment plate.
6. Tighten 2nd-3rd shift rod clamp to 17-23 ft-lbs.

1968

Column Shift

1. Place transmission levers in neutral.
2. Loosen shift rod adjusting clamps.
3. Install a $\frac{3}{16}$" drill rod through 2-3 lever, selector plate and 1st-reverse lever and align plate.
4. Tighten shift rod clamp bolts to 17-23 ft-lbs.
5. To check the cross-over, find the neutral detent in the 1st-reverse position and mark the mast jacket.
6. Move shift lever down to the 2nd-3rd position and find the neutral detent position. Check to see if the two detents line up as shown by the mark made on the mast jacket.
7. If they do not line up, shorten the 1st-reverse rod by pulling it through the swivel by no more than $\frac{3}{16}$".

1968-69 G.S. 350 & 400

Floor Shift

1. Place transmission levers in neutral.
2. Loosen shift rod adjusting clamp bolts on shifter assembly.
3. Place a ¼" drill rod through shift assembly and shift levers.
4. Tighten clamp bolts to 17-23 ft-lbs.

1967 LeSabre

1. Place transmission levers in neutral.
2. Loosen shift rod adjusting clamp bolts.
3. Install a 3/16 diameter rod through 1st-reverse rod.
4. Tighten clamp bolts.

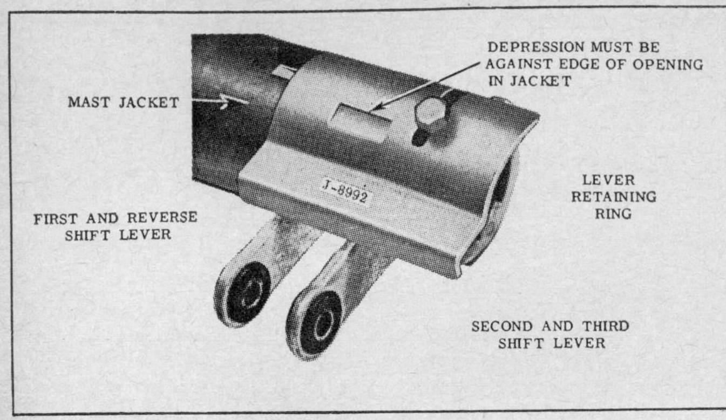

Fig. 4 Installation of tool. 1963 Special Series with three speed transmission

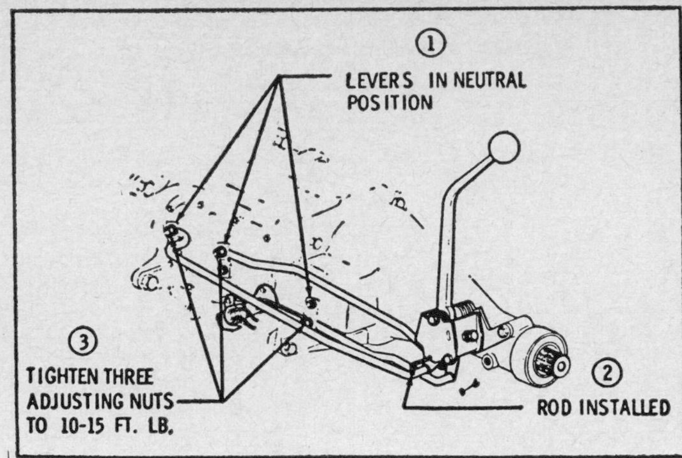

Fig. 5 Manual shift transmission linkage. 1963-65 Four Speed Units

1966-67 Special & Skylark

1. Place transmission levers in neutral.
2. Loosen shift rod adjusting clamps.
3. Install a $\frac{3}{16}$" diameter rod through low-reverse lever and selector plate.
4. Push 2-3 shift rod through adjusting clamp until ¼" exists from bottom of adjusting clamp to bottom of shift rod.
5. Tighten shift rod clamps.

1966-67 G.S. 400

1. Place transmission levers in neutral.
2. Loosen shift rod adjusting clamp bolts.
3. Place a $\frac{5}{16}$" bolt or drill rod in notch in rear portion of shift lever bracket.
4. Move both levers back against the $\frac{5}{16}$" tool.
5. Tighten adjusting clamp bolts.

1966 LeSabre & Wildcat

1. Place transmission levers in neutral.
2. Loosen shift rod adjusting clamp bolts.
3. Install a ¼" drill rod into bearing tab and low-reverse lever.
4. Place screwdriver beneath selector plate and the 2-3 lever until selector plate engages tang on both shift levers.
5. Tighten adjusting clamps.

1964-65

1. Place transmission in neutral.
2. Install all shift rod clamps.
3. Install tool shown in Fig. 2 on mast jacket.
4. Check levers on side of transmission, making sure they are positioned as shown.
5. Tighten shift rod clamps to 10-15 ft-lbs.
6. Remove tool from mast jacket and check for ease of shifting.

1963 Special

1. Place transmission in neutral.
2. Loosen shift rod adjusting clamps, Fig. 3.
3. Loosen lever ring bolt and install a holding tool on mast jacket, Fig. 4.
4. Position 2-3 shift lever against fixture. Tighten 2-3 adjusting clamp with lever held against fixture and torque to 10-12 ft-lbs.
5. Next, move low-reverse shift rod until a good cross-over point is obtained. This is done by lifting shift control lever at steering wheel location several times until no interference is felt when moving lever from 2-3 to low-reverse neutral position. When lever is released in low-reverse neutral position, it should spring down to the 2-3 neutral position. Hold lever midway in this cross-over position and tighten adjusting clamp.
6. Remove fixture and retighten ring bolt.
7. Tighten 2-3 shift rod adjusting clamp.
8. Lift manual control lever from 2-3 position into low-reverse range. Do this several times to align low-reverse lower control shaft lever, then tighten adjusting clamp.

4 SPEED TRANS. REPLACE

1966-69 G.S. 350, 400

1. Disconnect speedometer cable and remove driven gear.
2. Disconnect shift control rods from transmission.
3. Remove propeller shaft.
4. Support rear of engine and remove transmission support.
5. Remove two top transmission-to-flywheel housing bolts and insert guide pins.
6. Remove two lower bolts.
7. Slide transmission back and out.
8. Reverse procedure to install.

1964-65 All, 1963 Senior Series

1. Mark propeller shaft and front companion flange so that these parts can be reassembled in the same relative position.
2. Remove U-bolts attaching propeller shaft to front companion flange. Slide propeller shaft rearward as far as possible for working clearance.
3. Remove gearshift knob and floor shift trim bezel.
4. Disconnect speedometer cable and shift control rods from transmission.
5. Loosen all three exhaust pipe joints so transmission and rear end of car can be lowered.
6. Remove two bolts attaching transmission mounting pad to transmission support. Leave pad bolted to transmission.
7. Place a flat wood block on a jack. Place jack under engine pan until transmission mounting pad just clears transmission support.
8. Remove transmission support. Then lower jack so transmission will clear underbody during removal.
9. Remove upper left and lower right attaching bolts and install guide pins in these holes. Remove other two attaching bolts and slide transmission straight back until drive gear shaft is clear of flywheel housing.
10. Lower and remove transmission.
11. Reverse removal procedure to install transmission.

1963 Special Series

1. Disconnect speedometer cable and shift control rods from transmission levers.
2. Remove propeller shaft and support rear of engine with a jack stand.
3. Remove transmission mounting pad and support.
4. Remove two upper capscrews attaching transmission to clutch housing and install guide pins in these holes.
5. Remove the two lower capscrews and slide transmission back and out of vehicle.
6. Reverse removal procedure to install and check shift linkage.

4 SPEED TRANS. SHIFT LINKAGE

1968-69 G.S. 350, 400

Floor Shift

1. Place transmission in neutral.
2. Adjust all three shift rods so a ¼" drill rod can be installed through shifter assembly and shift levers.
3. Tighten swivel nuts to 17-23 ft-lbs.

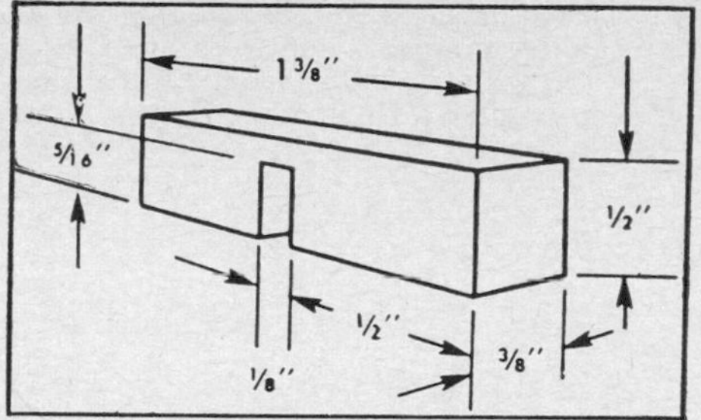

Fig. 6 Shift linkage gauge block dimensions. 1963

1966-67 G.S. 400

1. With transmission in neutral, loosen shift rod adjusting clamp bolts.
2. Place a 5/16″ bolt or drill rod in notch in rear lower portion of shift bracket.
3. Move all three shift levers back against the 5/16″ tool.
4. Tighten adjusting clamps.

1964-65 All, 1963 Senior Series

1. Referring to Fig. 5, install aligning rod shown in linkage at end of shift lever.
2. Loosen shift rod adjusting clamps to allow shift rods freedom of movement inside swivel.
3. Tighten all shift rod adjusting clamps to 10-15 ft-lbs torque.
4. Remove aligning rod.
5. After shift controls are adjusted to neutral position, hold shift lever in 4th gear by merely resting hand on lever to remove all lash in linkage. Then turn "stop" bolt until it contacts shift lever. Torque jam nut to 20-30 ft-lbs.
6. Repeat same procedure for 3rd gear.

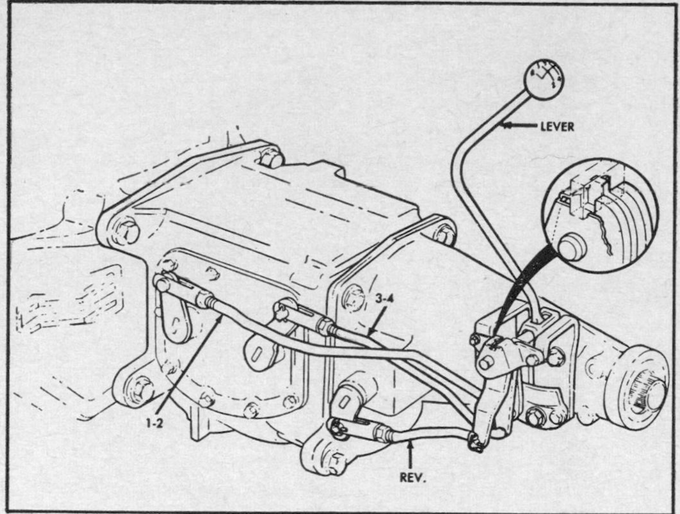

Fig. 7 Four speed manual shift linkage 1963. Insert shows gauge block (Fig. 6) in position

1963 Special Series

1. Remove floor pan chrome ring.
2. Unfasten and slide boot up shift rod.
3. Place transmission in neutral and install gauge block in position shown in Fig. 7 (also see Fig. 6).
4. Remove clevis pin at each of the three levers.
5. On each shift rod, adjust threaded clevis to permit free entry of clevis pin into hole in transmission shift lever.
6. Lubricate clevis pin before installing.
7. Connect clevises to levers.

1969 AUTO. TRANS. LINKAGE ADJUST

Column Shift Turbo-Hydramatic 400

This adjustment is the same as that for previous models and is described in the front section of this book.

Console Shift Turbo-Hydramatic 400

1. Place transmission shift lever in Drive detent.
2. Loosen trunnion bolt.
3. Set bar assembly against drive stop.
4. Tighten trunnion bolt against cable end to 72-108 inch-lbs.

Super Turbine 300 & Turbo-Hyd. 350

This adjustment is the same as that described for previous models and is found in the front section of this book in the Super Turbine 300 section.

Rear Axle, Propeller Shaft & Brakes

REAR AXLES

Figs. 1 and 2 illustrate the type rear axle assemblies used on Buicks. When necessary to overhaul any of these units, refer to the *Rear Axle Specifications* table in this chapter.

1963-64 Special & 1965 Special, Skylark, G.S. 350, 400 & LeSabre & 1966-69 All

In this rear axle, Fig. 1, the drive pinion is mounted in two tapered roller bearings which are preloaded by two selected spacers at assembly. The pinion is positioned by shims located between a shoulder on the drive pinion and the rear bearing. The front bearing is held in place by a large nut.

The differential is supported in the carrier by two tapered roller side bearings. These are preloaded by inserting shims between the bearings and the pedestals. The differential assembly is positioned for proper ring gear and pinion backlash by varying these shims. The ring gear is bolted to the case. The case houses two side gears in mesh with two pinions mounted on a pinion axle which is anchored in the case by a spring pin. The pinions and side gears are backed by thrust washers.

1963-65 Senior Series (Except 1965 LeSabre)

In this rear axle, Fig. 2, the drive pinion is mounted in two tapered roller bearings that are preloaded by two selected spacers. The pinion is positioned by a shim located between the head of the drive pinion and the rear pinion bearing. The front bearing is held in place by a large washer and a locking pinion nut. The differential carrier casting has an oil feed passage to the pinion bearings and an oil return hole so that oil will circulate and cool.

The differential is supported in the carrier by two tapered roller side bearings. These bearings are preloaded by inserting shims between the bearings and the pedestals. The differential assembly is positioned for proper ring gear and pinion backlash by varying these shims. The bearings are centered on the cross axis by lock taper cones secured in the pedestal bores by clamp bolts. The ring gear is bolted to the case. The case

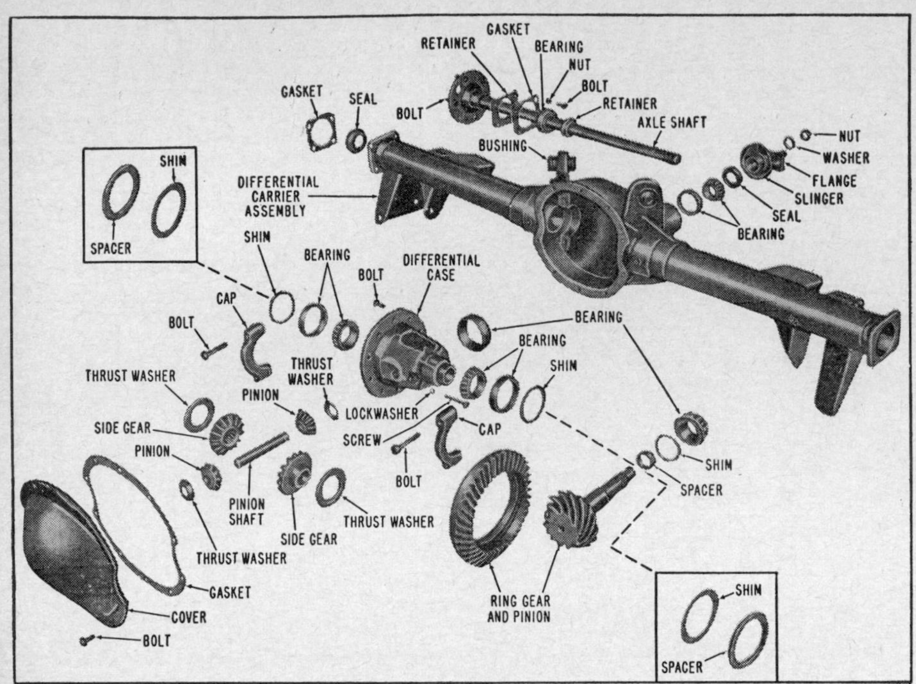

Fig. 1 Rear axle assembly. 1963-64 Special, Skylark, G.S. 350, 400 and LeSabre and 1966-69 All. The axle for 1964 Special is similar except that the pinion bearing preload spacers have been replaced with a collapsible spacer. Roller bearings are used in the 1969 Special and Skylark axle shafts.

houses two side gears in mesh with two pinions mounted on a pinion axle which is anchored to the case by a spring pin. The pinions and side gears are backed by bronze thrust washers.

REAR AXLE ASSEMBLY, REPLACE

1963-64 Special & 1965 Special, G.S. 350, 400, Skylark & LeSabre & 1966-69 All

It is not necessary to remove the rear axle assembly for any normal repairs. The axle shafts and carrier assembly can easily be removed from the vehicle, leaving the axle housing in place.

1. Raise rear end of car with rear axle hanging on shock absorbers.
2. Mark rear universal joint and pinion flange for proper reassembly. *These parts are carefully balanced in production and assembled with heavy sides opposite. For this reason they should be reassembled the same way.*
3. Disconnect rear universal joint from pinion flange by removing two U-bolts. Wire propeller shaft to exhaust pipe to support it out of the way.
4. Remove rear wheels and brake drums.
5. Remove axle shafts as outlined below.
6. Remove all cover bolts and break cover loose at the bottom to allow lubricant to drain.
7. Remove carrier assembly by prying or by use of a slide hammer.
8. Reverse foregoing procedure to install the carrier assembly, being sure to connect the rear universal joint to the pinion flange according to the alignment marks made previously.

1963-65 Senior Series (Except 1965 LeSabre)

It is not necessary to remove the rear axle assembly for any normal repairs. The axle shafts and carrier assembly can easily be removed from the vehicle, leaving the rear axle housing in place.

1. Mark rear universal joint and pinion flange for proper alignment at reassembly.
2. Disconnect rear universal joint by removing two U-bolts. Push propeller shaft forward as far as possible, then wire it to the upper control arm frame bracket to hold it out of the way.
3. Remove rear wheels and brake drums.
4. Remove axle shafts as outlined below.
5. Remove carrier-to-housing nuts except two opposite nuts. Back these two nuts out until they engage only a few threads.
6. Place drain pan under carrier flange and move carrier forward to drain lubricant.
7. Remove carrier, using a transmission jack if available.
8. Reverse foregoing procedure to install carrier, observing the following: Connect U-joint to pinion flange according to alignment marks made previously. Compress U-joint bearings with a C-clamp so that bearing snap rings will engage pinion flange without gouging.

AXLE SHAFT, REPLACE

1963-64 Special & 1965 Special, G.S. 350, 400, Skylark & LeSabre & 1966-69 All

IMPORTANT

Design allows for axle shaft end play up to .042" (.018" on 1969). This end play can be checked with the wheel and brake drum removed by measuring the difference between the end of the housing and the axle shaft flange while moving the axle shaft in and out by hand.

End play over this is excessive. Compensating for all the end play by inserting a shim inboard of the bearing in the housing is not recommended since it ignores the end play of the bearing itself, and may result in improper seating of the gasket or backing plate against the housing. If end play is excessive, the axle shaft and bearing assembly should be removed and the cause of the excessive end play determined and corrected.

Removing Axle Shaft

NOTE: For 1963, left side wheel bolts have left-hand threads (marked "LH"). For 1964-69 right-hand threads are used on both sides.

1. Remove wheels and brake drums.
2. Remove nuts holding retainer plates to brake backing plates. Pull retainers clear of bolts and reinstall two lower nuts finger tight to hold brake backing plate in position.
3. Use a slide hammer type puller to pull out axle shaft, if bearing is a tight fit in axle housing, using care not to cut lip of oil seal as shaft is being withdrawn from axle housing.

Replacing Shaft Bearings

1. Nick bearing retainer in three or four places with a chisel deep enough to spread ring, Fig. 4. Retainer will then slip off.
2. Press bearing off shaft.
3. Press new bearing against shoulder on axle shaft. *Retainer plate which retains bearing in housing must be on axle shaft before bearing is installed; retainer gasket can be installed after bearing.*
4. Press new retainer ring against bearing.

Replacing Oil Seal

1. Insert axle shaft so that splined end is just through seal.
2. Using axle shaft as a lever, push down on shaft until seal is pried from housing.
3. Apply sealer to outside diameter of new seal.

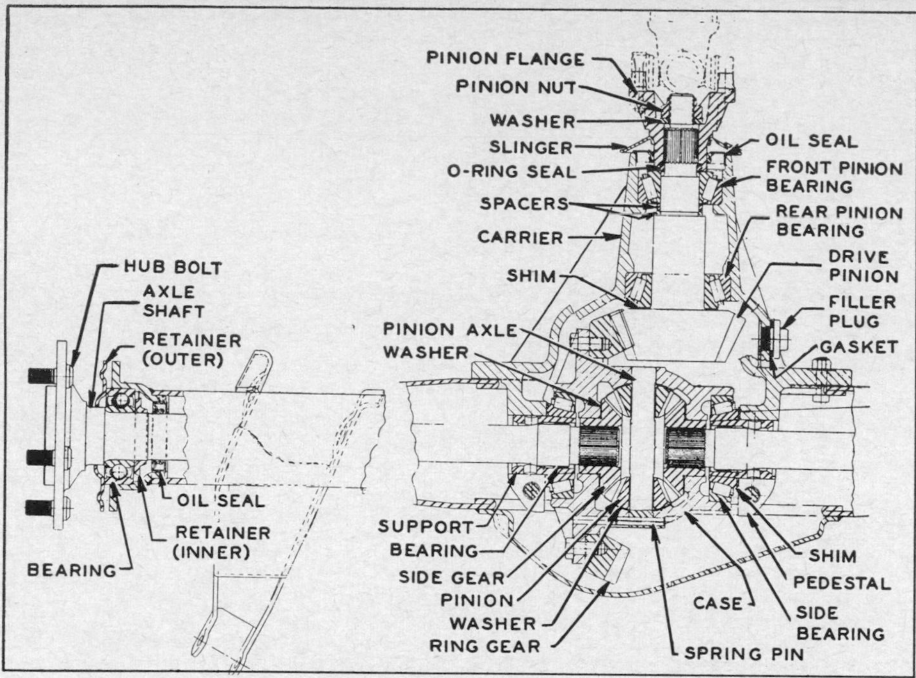

Fig. 2 Rear axle assembly. 1963-65 Senior Series (except 1965 LeSabre)

4. Position seal over a suitable installer and drive seal straight into axle housing until seated.

Axle Shaft, Install

1. Apply a coat of wheel bearing grease in bearing recesses of housing.
2. Install new outer retainer gaskets.
3. To help prevent damage to lip of oil seal when installing axle shaft and to ensure lubricant on seal lip during the first few miles of operation, the axle shaft should be lightly lubricated with axle lubricant from the sealing surface to about 6" inboard of the shaft.
4. Insert axle shafts carefully until splines engage in differential to avoid damage to seals.

1963-65 Senior Cars (Except 1965 LeSabre)

Removal

1. Place car stands solidly under rear axle housing so that rear wheels clear floor.
2. Remove rear wheel and brake drum. Note that left side wheel bolts have left hand threads.
3. Remove nuts holding wheel bearing retainer plate to brake backing plate, leaving bolts in place to support backing plate.
4. Use a slide hammer type puller to remove axle shaft if bearing is a tight fit in axle housing. *While pulling axle shaft out through seal, support shaft carefully in center of seal to avoid cutting seal lip.*
5. Replace two opposite retainer nuts finger tight to hold brake backing plate in position.

Replacing Bearing—The bearing and bearing retaining ring both have a heavy press fit on the axle shaft, Fig. 5. Because of this fit they should be removed and installed separately.

1. Notch bearing retaining ring in 3 or 4 places with a chisel, Fig. 4. Ring will expand so that it can be slipped off. *Do not cut ring all the way through as axle shaft may be nicked.*
2. Press off bearing.
3. Install bearing retainer plate.
4. Press new bearing against shoulder on axle shaft. *Bearing retainer plate must be on axle shaft before bearing is installed; gasket can be installed after bearing.*
5. Press new retainer ring against bearing.

Replacing Oil Seal—The oil seal is located inboard of the wheel bearing with its outside diameter tight in the axle housing and its sealing lip contacting a ground surface of the axle shaft.

1. Remove oil seal.
2. Apply sealer to outside diameter of new seal.
3. Install new seal with a suitable seal driver.

Replacing Axle Shaft—Axle shaft on right side is longer than the left axle. Also, wheel bolts in right shaft have right-hand threads; left shaft bolts have left-hand threads.

Fig. 4 Removing axle shaft bearing retainer

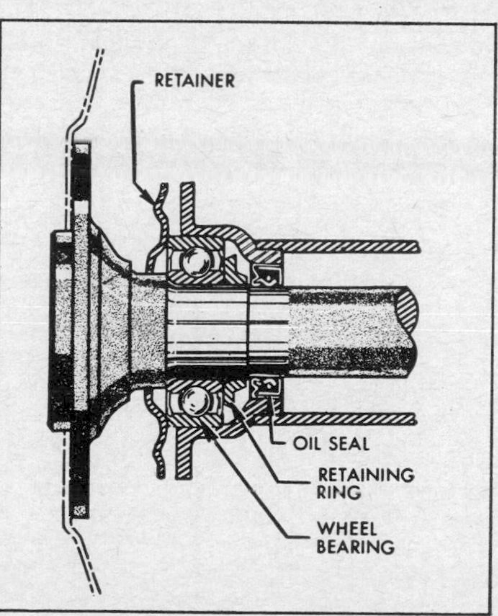

Fig. 5 Axle shaft bearing and oil seal. 1963-68 axle shaft. 1969 Senior Series

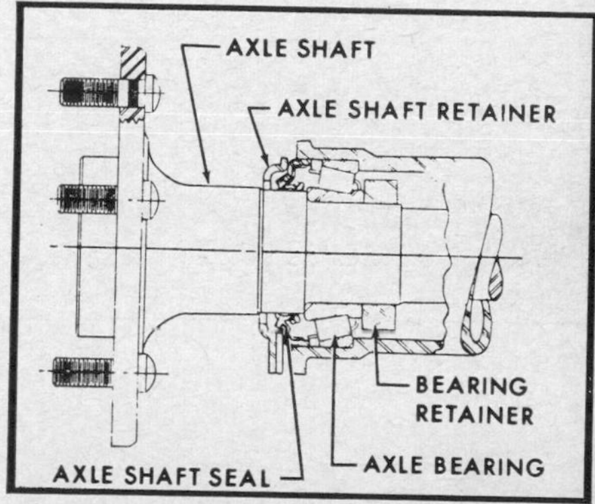

Fig. 5A Axle shaft, bearing and oil seal. 1969 Special and Skylark

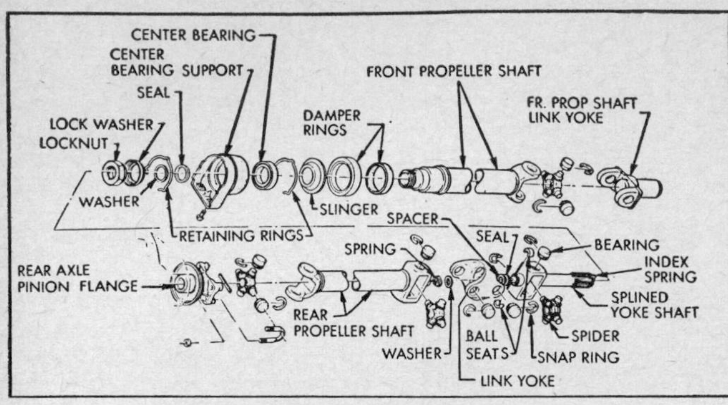

Fig. 11 Propeller shaft disassembled. 1963-64 Senior Series (Except Riviera)

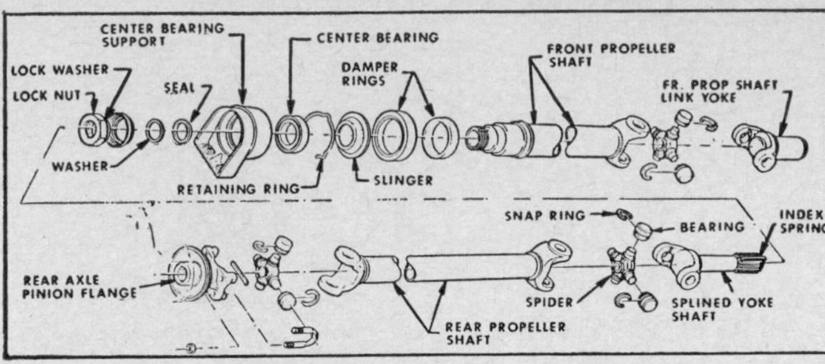

Fig. 12 Propeller shaft disassembled. 1963-64 Riviera

1. Apply coat of wheel bearing grease in bearing recess in housing. Install new outer retainer plate gasket over retainer bolts.
2. Apply gear lube to bearing surface and splines at inner end of axle shaft.
3. Apply coat of wheel bearing grease on seal surface of shaft to about 6″ inboard of shaft.
4. Install axle shaft through seal, carefully avoiding cutting seal lip.
5. Drive shaft into position. *If axle shaft is installed in a non-slip differential only special lube for this device should be used.*

PROPELLER SHAFT

SERVICE BULLETIN

U-Joint Lubrication: The universal joints on the 1964 Riviera should be lubricated every 6,000 miles with proper lubricant. On early models up to serial 7K 1005077, an access hole to permit lubrication was not provided in the mid-section of the frame tunnel. However, an access hold can be drilled in the following manner:

To locate the proper point for drilling the tunnel, use the two access holes for the center bearing support as a guide. First, mark a center line running between these holes and rearward on the tunnel. Then, on this line, mark the drilling point $2\frac{11}{16}$ in. back from the rear edges of the bearing-access holes.

After the drilling point has been marked with a center punch, drill a $\frac{1}{8}$ in. pilot hole. Then use a hole saw to make a $1\frac{1}{8}$ in. diameter access hole.

1963-68 Senior Series

NOTE

When service is required, the propeller shaft must be removed from the car as a complete assembly. While handling it out of the car, the assembly must be supported on a straight line as nearly as possible to avoid jamming or bending any of the parts. Figs. 11 to 14 show the components of the assemblies.

1. To remove the assembly, remove center bearing attaching bolts.
2. At rear pinion flange, remove U-bolt clamps from rear U-joint.
3. Mark both flange and shaft to assemble in the same position.

CAUTION: If rear U-joint bearings are not retained on the spider by a connecting strap, use tape or wire to secure bearings.

4. Support rear end of propeller shaft to avoid damage to constant velocity joint and slide complete assembly rearward until front yoke slips from transmission shaft splines.
5. Protect oil seal surface on front slip yoke by taping or wiring a cloth over the complete front U-joint.
6. Slide complete propeller shaft rearward through frame tunnel (if present). Do not bend constant velocity U-joint to its extreme angle at any time

Installation

The propeller shaft must be handled carefully during its installation to avoid bending any of the parts, Figs. 11 to 14.

1. Protect oil seal diameter on front slip yoke by taping or wiring a cloth over the entire front U-joint.
2. Slide complete propeller shaft forward through frame tunnel.
3. Remove protecting cover from front U-joint. Fill space between lips of transmission seal with wheel bearing grease and apply a thin coat of the same grease to the seal surface of the front U-joint.
4. Slide front U-joint yoke forward over splines of transmission shaft.
5. Compress two loose bearings of rear U-joint toward each other using a 4″ C-clamp. This allows the bearings to seat in the pinion flange without the snap rings gouging the locating surfaces of the pinion flange while entering.
6. Install U-bolt clamps, lock plates and nuts. Draw nuts up evenly and torque to 13 ft. lbs, using a ½″ extension. *Over-tightening U-bolt nuts distorts the bearings, causing a binding on the spider which can cause drive line shudder and also*

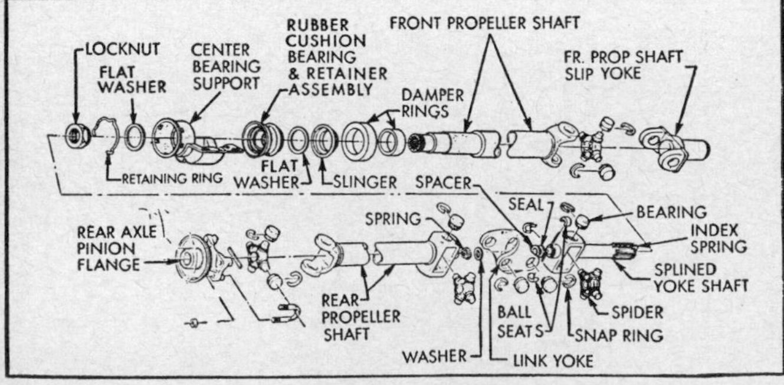

Fig. 13 Propeller shaft assembly. 1965-68 LeSabre, Wildcat and Electra. A one-piece propeller shaft is used in 1969

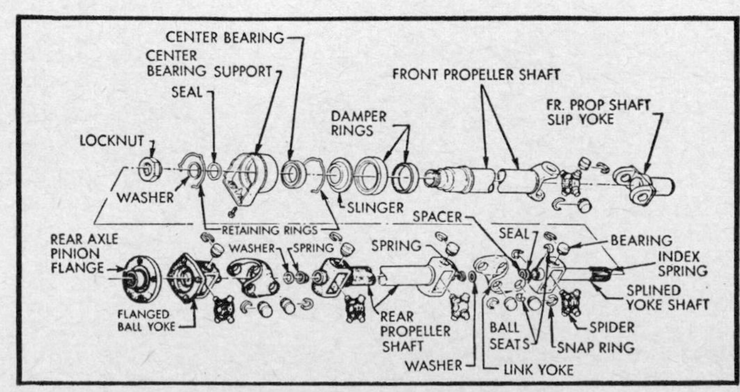

Fig. 14 Propeller shaft assembly. 1965-69 Riviera

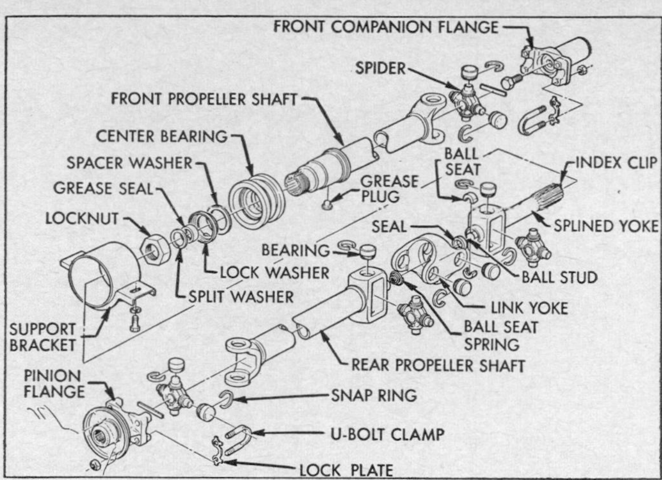

Fig. 15 Propeller shaft and universal joints. 1963 Special. A one-piece propeller shaft is used on 1964-69 Special. See Universal Joints Chapter for repairs on these units

reduce the life of bearings and spider.

7. Bend lock plate tabs against nuts.
8. Install two bolts in center bearing support and torque to 20 ft. lbs.
9. Make certain propeller shaft slip spline and center ball stud seat are fully lubricated.

CAUTION

If drive line shudder, roughness, vibration, or rumble is experienced, it may be due to incorrect rear universal joint angle and this angle should be checked. Also, if there is a severe rear end collision, or if the axle housing or any control arms are replaced, the rear universal joint angle should be checked and corrected if necessary. To make the check, however, special Alignment Set No. J-8973 must be used. Inasmuch as this equipment is not likely to be found in general repair shops, it is recommended that a Buick dealer having this equipment do the work.

1963 Special Series, Fig. 15

1. Attach center support crossmember to center bearing support bracket. Support complete assembly adequately to prevent excessive bending of propeller shaft and install to car underbody with four bolts attaching crossmember to body.
2. Make certain rear U-joint mark is aligned with pinion flange mark, then install U-bolts, lock plates and nuts.
3. The bearing and spider assembly must be started straight and seated in the companion flange so that no burr is formed by snap rings gouging locating surfaces of companion flange when entering.
4. Use a 4″ C-clamp if necessary to compress bearings so snap rings do not contact companion flange bearing surface. Replace flange if it has been gouged or burred. Torque nuts evenly to 15 ft. lbs., using a ½″ extension. Bend lock tabs against nuts.
5. Make sure front U-joint mark is aligned with front companion flange mark. Then install U-bolts, lock plates and nuts. Follow same precautions given above and torque nuts evenly to 15 ft. lbs. and bend lock plate tabs against nuts.
6. Lubricate slip spline by removing plug and installing grease fitting. Fill with proper grease, remove fitting and install plug.

REAR U-JOINT ANGLE

The rear universal joint angle is carefully adjusted to specifications at the factory. On 1963 models, this adjustment is made possible by shims between the forward ends of the lower control arms and the body. These shims cause the rear axle housing to rotate, thereby changing the angle of the drive pinion in relation to the angle of the propeller shaft. If for any reason this factory setting is changed, roughness and objectionable vibration could result.

On 1964-69 models this adjustment is made possible by cam bolts located in slotted holes at the rearward ends of each upper control arm, Fig. 16. Rotating the cam bolts causes the upper axle brackets to move forward or backward in the slotted upper control arm holes.

Therefore, if there is a very severe rear end collision, or if the rear axle housing or any control arms are replaced, the rear universal joint angle should be checked and corrected if necessary. To make this check, however, special Alignment Set No. J-8973 must be used. Inasmuch as this equipment is not likely to be found in general repair shops, it is recommended that a Buick dealer having this equipment do the work.

BRAKE ADJUSTMENTS

1963-69 Self-Adjusting Brakes

These brakes, Fig. 17, have self-adjusting shoe mechanisms that assure correct lining-to-drum clearances at all times. The automatic adjusters operate only when the brakes are applied as the car is moving rearward or when the car comes to an uphill stop.

Although the brakes are self-adjusting, an initial adjustment is necessary after the brake shoes have been relined or replaced, or when the length of the adjusting screw has been changed during some other service operation.

Frequent usage of an automatic transmission forward range to halt reverse vehicle motion may prevent the automatic adjusters from functioning, thereby inducing low pedal heights. Should low pedal heights be encountered, it is recommended that numerous forward and reverse stops be made until satisfactory pedal height is obtained.

NOTE

If a low pedal condition cannot be corrected by making numerous reverse stops (provided the hydraulic system is

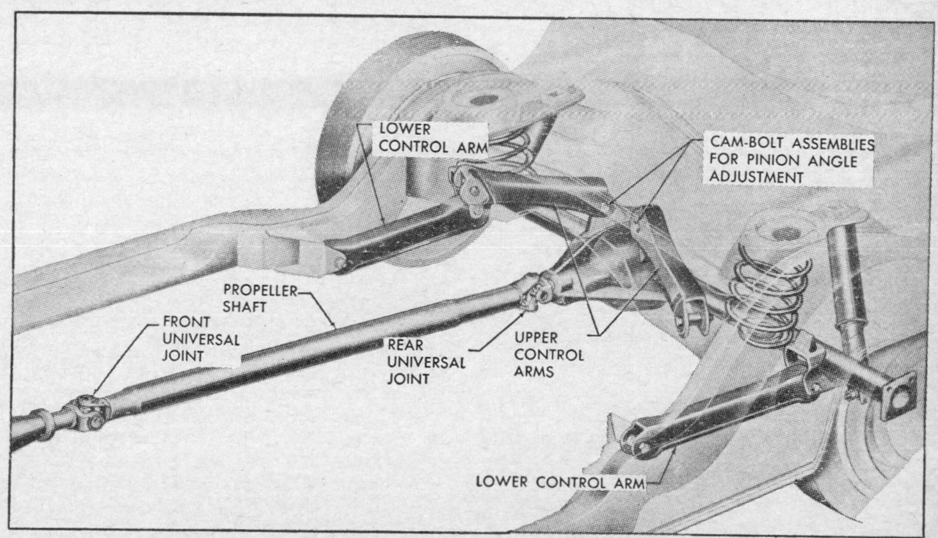

Fig. 16 Propeller shaft assembly. 1964-69 Special, G.S. 350, 400, Skylark and 1969 LeSabre, Wildcat and Electra

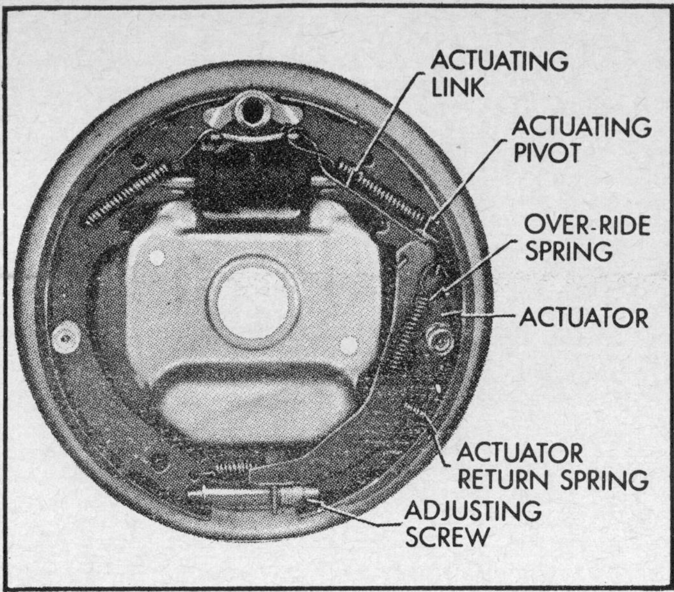

Fig. 17 Left front wheel brake. 1963-69

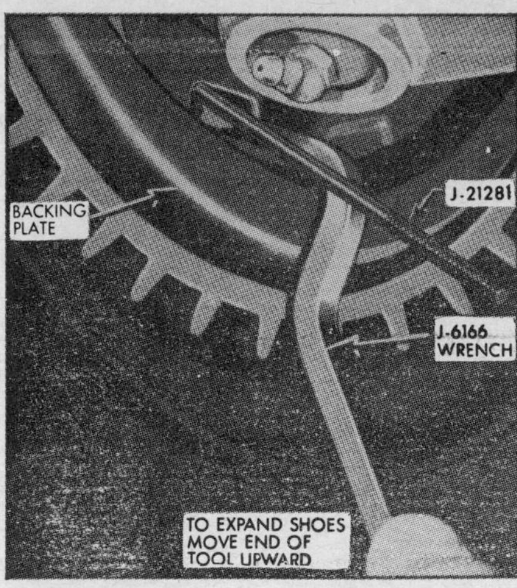

Fig. 18 Adjusting brakes. 1963-69

free of air) it indicates that the self-adjusting mechanism is not functioning. Therefore, it will be necessary to remove the brake drum, clean, free up and lubricate the adjusting mechanism. Then adjust the brakes as follows, being sure the parking brake is fully released.

Adjustment

1. Remove adjusting hole cover from brake backing plate and, from backing plate side, turn adjusting screw upward with a screwdriver or other suitable tool to expand the shoes until a slight drag is felt when the drum is rotated.
2. Remove the drum.
3. While holding the actuator out of engagement with the adjusting screw, Fig. 18, back off the adjusting screw one turn with fingers.

CAUTION

If finger movement will not turn the screw, free it up. If this is not done, the actuator will not turn the screw during subsequent vehicle operation. Lubricate the screw with oil and coat with wheel bearing grease. Any other adjustment procedure may cause damage to the adjusting screw with consequent self-adjuster problems.

4. Install wheel and drum, and adjusting hole cover. Adjust brakes on remaining wheels in the same manner.
5. If pedal height is not satisfactory, drive the vehicle and make sufficient reverse stops until proper pedal height is obtained.

PARKING BRAKE, ADJUST

1967-69 All; 1964-66 Special, Skylark, G.S. 350, 400

Need for parking brake adjustment is indicated if the service brake operates with good pedal reverse but the parking brake pedal can be depressed more than eight ratchet clicks under heavy foot pressure. After making certain that service brakes are properly adjusted, adjust parking brake mechanism as follows:

1. Depress parking brake pedal exactly three ratchet clicks.
2. Loosen jam nut located at rear of equalizer adjusting nut.
3. Tighten adjusting nut until rear wheels can just be turned rearward, using two hands, but are locked when forward motion is attempted.
4. Release parking brake ratchet one click. At this two-click engagement the rear wheels should rotate forward with a light drag and rearward freely.
5. Release mechanism one more click. At this engagement as well as with mechanism totally disengaged, rear wheels should turn freely in either direction.

1963-66 Senior Series

Adjustment of the parking brake is necessary whenever the rear brake cables have been disconnected or when the cables have stretched due to extended use. Also to insure proper functioning of the parking brake, the idler lever must have approximately ⅜ in. clearance in slot in frame when parking lever is fully released. Need for parking brake adjustment is indicated if service brake operates with a good pedal reserve but the parking brake ratchets more than eight clicks when depressed.

1. Make brake adjustment as outlined above.
2. Check for correct position of idler lever in frame with parking brake fully released. If necessary, adjust front cable clevis.
3. Depress parking brake pedal exactly two ratchet clicks.
4. Tighten rear cable adjusting nut until rear wheels can just be turned forward using both hands (heavy two-hand drag).
5. Release parking brake lever and check both rear wheels to make sure they turn freely in either direction.

1963 Special Series

Need of adjustment is indicated if service brakes operate with a good pedal reserve but the parking brake lever pulls out more than 15 ratchet clicks. After making certain that service brakes are properly adjusted, adjust parking brake as follows:

1. Pull out parking brake lever exactly eight ratchet clicks.
2. Hold threaded end of intermediate parking brake cable to prevent cable from twisting and tighten adjusting nut until left rear wheel can just be turned rearward using two hands.
3. Release parking brake lever and pull out exactly three notches. Check both rear wheels to make sure they turn freely in both directions.

MASTER CYLINDER, REPLACE

1967-69

1. Disconnect brake pipes from master cylinder and tape end of pipes to prevent entrance of dirt.
2. On manual brakes, disconnect brake pedal from master cylinder push rod.
3. Remove two nuts holding master cylinder to dash or power cylinder and remove master cylinder from car.

1963-66

1. Remove connector from stop light switch. Disconnect brake pipe from master cylinder and tape end of pipe to prevent entrance of dirt.
2. Disconnect brake pedal from master cylinder push rod by removing safety washer and retainer.
3. Remove nuts holding master cyl-

inder to dash panel and remove cylinder from car.

POWER BRAKE UNIT

1967-69

1. Disconnect brake pipes from master cylinder and tape ends of pipes to prevent entrance of dirt. Disconnect vacuum hose from cylinder.
2. Remove four nuts holding power unit to dash.
3. Remove retainer and washer from brake pedal pin and disengage push rod eye or clevis.
4. Remove power unit from car.

1963-66 Senior Series

1. Remove connector from stop light switch and disconnect brake pipe from master cylinder.
2. Remove retainer and special washer from brake pedal pin and disengage push rod eye.
3. On 1963, remove air silencer from power cylinder air intake.
4. Remove four nuts holding power cylinder to dash panel.
5. Disconnect vacuum hoses from tee.
6. Remove power cylinder.

1963-66 Special & Skylark

1. To remove unit, first remove stop light switch wires.
2. Disconnect hydraulic line. Plug or tape line to prevent dirt from entering hydraulic system.
3. Disconnect vacuum hoses from top of bellows unit.
4. Disconnect air supply hose from unit.
5. Disconnect pedal push rod from pedal.
6. Unfasten and remove brake nut from cowl.
7. Reverse removal procedure to install the unit and bleed the system in the conventional manner.

Front End and Steering Section

FRONT SUSPENSION

1964-69 G.S. 350, 400, Special, Skylark

Referring to Fig. 1, the upper control arms have threaded steel bushings that are screwed into the inner ends of the arms (1969 models use rubber bushings at these locations). A ball joint is riveted to the outer end of the upper arm and is spring loaded to insure proper alignment of the ball in the socket.

The inner end of the lower control arm has pressed-in bushings. Two bolts, passing through the bushings, attach the arm to the frame. The lower ball joint is a press fit in the arm and attaches to the steering knuckle with a castellated nut that is retained with a cotter pin.

Rubber seals are provided on upper and lower shafts and at ball socket assemblies to exclude dirt and moisture from bearing surfaces. Grease fittings are provided at all bearing locations.

1963 Special Series

Referring to Fig. 2, both upper and lower control arms are stamped steel. Hardened, replaceable threaded steel bushings are screwed solidly into the inner ends of the arms to provide thread-type bearings on the ends of the control arm shaft.

The lower control arm shaft is threaded through bushings welded to the front crossmember. The upper control arm shaft is attached to a bracket which is integral with the front crossmember.

The socket portion of the ball joint assembly is pressed into the outer end of each control arm to connect the steering knuckle to the control arm. The tapered shanks of the ball studs fit into matched tapered holes in the steering knuckles and are held in place by castellated nuts retained by cotter pins.

Rubber seals are provided on upper and lower control arm shafts and at ball joint sockets to exclude dirt and moisture from bearing surfaces. Grease fittings are provided at all bearing locations.

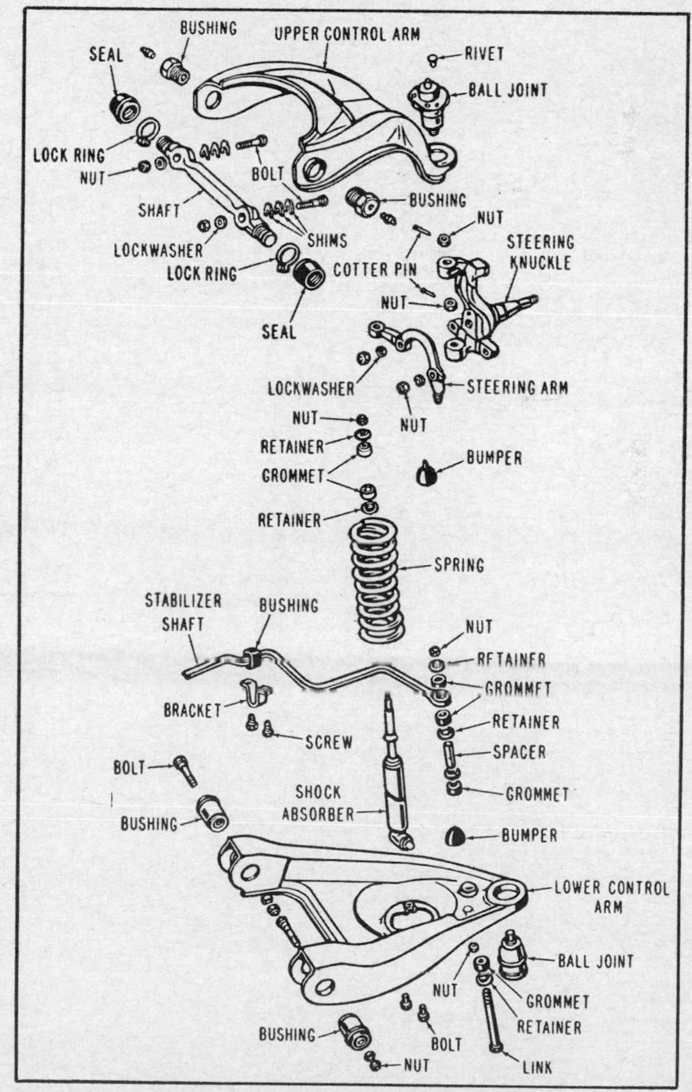

Fig. 1 Front suspension. 1964-68 Special, G.S. 350, 400 and Skylark. For 1969, rubber bushings are used at the upper shaft ends.

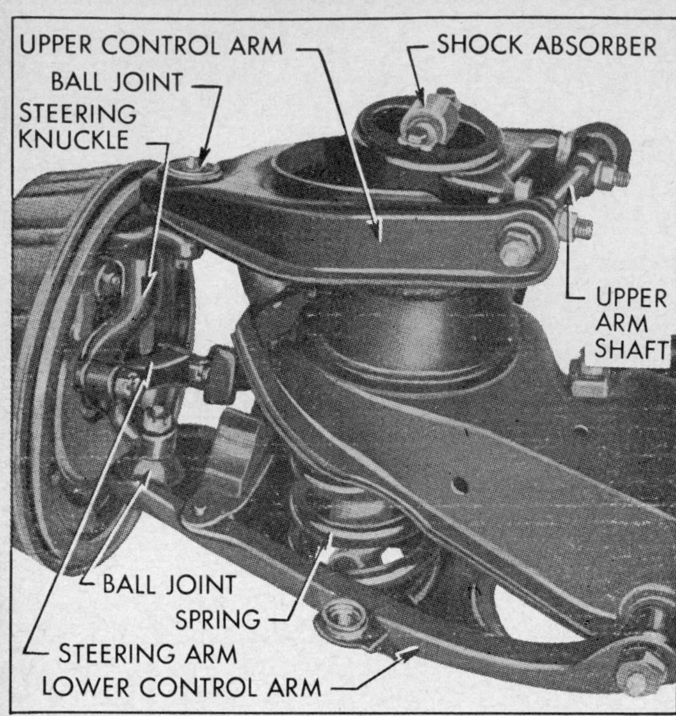

Fig. 2 Front suspension. 1963 Special & Skylark Series

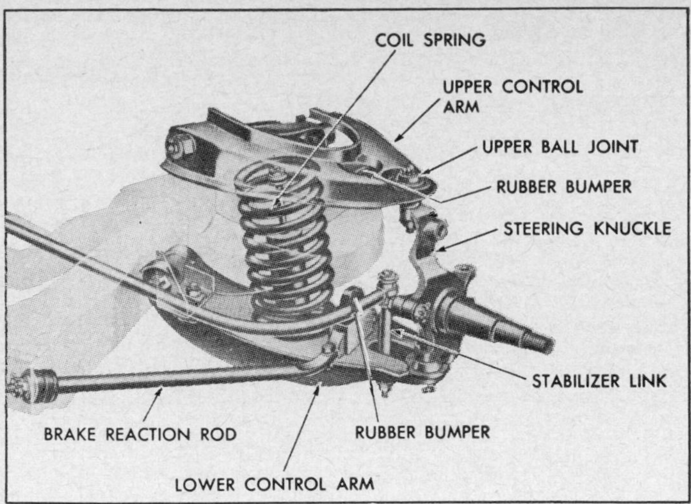

Fig. 3 Front suspension. 1963-69 Senior Series. Rubber bushings are used at upper shaft ends in 1969

SERVICE BULLETIN

Wheel Bolt Replaced: Wheel bolts should not be pressed out of a front hub when it is necessary to replace one or more of the bolts on a 1963-65 Special. A shoulder is formed on each bolt by a swaging operation when the bolts are pressed into the hub and drum during manufacture. Pressing out a swaged bolt enlarges the bolt hole in the hub and drum, making it impossible to install the new bolt tightly.

The method recommended to remove the bolt is to secure the hub and drum in a vise, and mark the center of the bolt head with a center punch. Drill a 1/8 in. pilot hole in the head of the bolt, and then redrill with a 5/16 in. bit. Use a chisel to cut off a portion of the bolt head, and then drive out the bolt with a drift. Press the new wheel bolt into place to complete the job.

1963-69 Senior Series

Referring to Fig. 3, the lower control arm assembly consists of two stamped steel plates welded together. The inner ends of the lower control arms are bolted to the frame front crossmember through rubber bushings. The outer end of each arm is connected to the steering knuckle with a ball joint assembly pressed into the lower control arm and bolted to the steering knuckle. The lower ball joint can be removed for service replacement. Position of the lower control arms is maintained by a brake reaction rod mounted between the lower control arm and frame.

To resist fore and aft movement of the lower control arm in relation to the frame, two solid steel brake reaction rods are positioned between the lower control arms and front of frame side rails. The forward ends of the rods are rubber mounted to hold securely to the frame bracket with nuts and cotter pins. The rearward end of the brake reaction rod attaches to the lower control arm with two bolts.

Special hardened flat washers are used under the bolts and nuts to aid in maintaining required torque. The brake reaction rod must be properly installed and secured prior to checking caster and camber.

The upper control arms consist of a single stamped steel plate. Two replaceable hardened steel bushings are threaded into the inner end of each assembly. 1969 models use rubber bushings at these locations. A ball joint is positioned through the outer end of each arm.

NOTE

For 1963-65 models the upper ball joint is pressed into the control arm and is serviced only as part of the control arm-ball joint assembly.

IMPORTANT

The front suspension is initially lubricated with a special lubricant (Buick Specification No. 742). Every 6000 miles or six months, whichever occurs first, this lubricant or its equivalent should be used. If lubricants other than this type is used the lubrication interval should be shortened and should not exceed 2000 miles.

WHEEL ALIGNMENT

1963-69 Special, Skylark, G.S. 350, 400

Caster and camber are adjusted by shimming at the upper control arm shaft attaching points. These shims are available in thicknesses of .030", .060" and .120"

Adding shims at the front locations will change caster toward negative with practically no change in camber. Adding shims at the rear locations will change caster toward positive and camber toward negative. Adding equal shims at both front and rear locations will not change caster but will change camber toward negative.

To adjust, loosen both front and rear bolts to free shims for removal or addition. After installing or removing shims (limit to .380" in any one stack) tighten and torque shaft bolts to 75 ft. lbs.

1963-69 Senior Series

Adjustments are performed by installing shims between the upper control arm and the mounting bracket on the frame. Installing or removing shims at either the front or rear bracket changes the *caster* setting. Installing or removing shims equally at both brackets changes the *camber*.

To adjust caster, remove shims at the front bracket or add shims at the rear bracket to increase caster. To decrease caster, add shims at the front bracket or remove shims at the rear bracket.

To adjust camber, remove shims at both brackets to increase camber. To decrease camber, add shims at both brackets.

TOE-IN, ADJUST

1963-69 Special, Skylark, G.S. 350, 400

IMPORTANT

Car must be at curb weight and running height; bounce front end and allow it to settle at running height. Steering gear and front wheel bearings must be properly adjusted with no looseness at tie rod ends. The car should be moved forward one complete revolution of the wheels before the toe-in check and adjustment is started and the car should never be moved backward while making the check and adjustment.

With front wheels in the straight ahead position, toe-in is adjusted by turning the tie rod adjusting sleeves as required. Left and right adjusting sleeves must be turned exactly the same amount but in opposite directions in order to maintain front wheels in straight ahead position when steering wheel is in straight ahead position.

IMPORTANT

The steering knuckle and steering arm "rock" or tilt as front wheel rises and falls. Therefore, it is vitally important to position the bottom face of the tie rod end parallel with the machined surface at the outer end of the steering arm when tie rod length is adjusted. Severe damage and possible failure can result unless this precaution is taken. The tie rod sleeve clamps must be straight down to 45° forward to provide clearance.

1963-69 Senior Series

Adjust tie rod sleeves at outer ends. With front wheels in straight ahead position, the lower indented spoke of the steering wheel should be in center position. If not shorten one tie rod and lengthen the other. When this is done, recheck toe-in.

The intermediate rod is maintained in position by the pitman and idler arms. This requires proper location of the idler arm on its support so that the idler arm ball stud will be approximately level with the pitman arm ball stud to insure good steering action. The support must be threaded into the idler arm bushing until the distance from the center of the support lower bolt hole to the nearest face of the idler arm is 2$\frac{21}{32}$" to 2¾" as shown. After any adjustment of the idler arm on its support, the front wheels should be checked to insure proper toe-in.

CAUTION

If the idler arm support is dismounted from the frame for other work, such as when the oil pan is removed, wire the support to the idler arm so that it cannot turn from its existing position and possibly change the toe-in of the front wheels.

WHEEL BEARINGS, ADJUST

1963-68 Sepcial, G.S. 350, 400, Skylark

1. Torque spindle nut to 19 ft-lb while rotating wheel. Back off nut and retorque to 11 ft-lb.
2. If spindle hole lines up a nut slot, back off nut 1/6 turn and insert cotter pin.
3. If neither spindle hole lines up with nut slot, back off nut a maximum of 3/12 of a turn and install cotter pin.
4. Before installation of grease cap in hub, make sure end of spindle and inside of cap are free of grease so that radio static collector makes good contact. Make sure that static collector is properly shaped to provide good contact between end of spindle and grease cap.

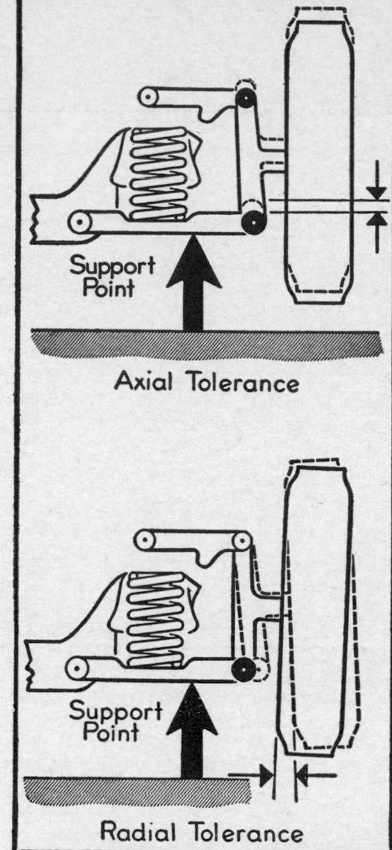

Fig. 5 Checking ball joints for wear

1969 All; 1963-68 Senior Series

1. Torque spindle nut to 19 ft-lb while rotating wheel.
2. Back off nut until bearings are loose.
3. Retighten nut to 11 ft-lb while rotating wheel.
4. If either cotter pin hole in spindle lines up with slot in nut, back off nut 1/12 turn and install cotter pin. *A 1/6 turn is maximum allowable backup to align hole with slot.*
5. Before installing grease cap in hub, make sure that end of spindle and inside of cap are free of grease so radio static collector makes good contact. Be sure static collector is properly shaped to provide good contact.

WHEEL BEARINGS, REPLACE

(Disc Brakes)

1. Raise car and remove front wheels.
2. Remove tube support bracket bolt. Do not disconnect hydraulic tube or hose.
3. Remove caliper to mounting bracket bolts. Hang caliper from upper suspension.

NOTE: Do not place strain on brake line.

4. Remove spindle nut and hub and disc assembly. Inner wheel bearing and grease retainer can now be removed.

CHECKING BALL JOINTS FOR WEAR

If loose ball joints are suspected, first be sure front wheel bearings are properly adjusted and that control arms are tight. Then check ball joints as follows:

Referring to Fig. 5, raise the wheel with a jack placed under the lower control arm at the point shown. Then test by moving the wheel up and down to check axial play, and rocking it at the top and bottom to measure radial play.

1. Upper ball joint should be replaced if there is any noticeable looseness at this joint.
2. Lower ball joint should be replaced if radial play exceeds .250".
3. Lower ball joint should be replaced if axial play between lower control arm and spindle exceeds the following tolerances:

1963-69 Senior Series	.100"
1963 Special Series	.080"
1964-69 Intermediate Models	.070"

BALL JOINTS, REPLACE

NOTE: On all models the upper ball joint is spring-loaded in its socket. If the ball stud has any perceptible shake or if it can be twisted with the fingers, the ball joint should be replaced.

The lower ball joint is not spring-loaded and depends upon car weight to load the ball. The lower ball joint should never be replaced merely because it "feels" loose when in an unloaded condition.

Ball joints are mounted in the control arms in three ways. On some models the ball joints are riveted to the control arms. All service ball joints, however, are provided with bolt and nut assemblies for replacement purposes.

Some ball joints are pressed into the control arms, in which case they may be pressed out and new ones installed. However, the upper ball joint is supplied only with the upper control arm.

SHOCK ABSORBER, REPLACE

Unfasten shock absorber top and bottom and remove it through the spring seat. Check shock absorber for obvious physical damage or oil leakage. Push and pull shock absorber in an upright position. If smooth hydraulic resistance is not present in both directions, replace shock absorber.

SPRING, REPLACE

1. Remove wheel with hub and drum.
2. Disconnect stabilizer link from lower control arm and remove shock absorber.
3. Disconnect lower control arm ball joint from steering knuckle.
4. Lower floor jack under spring until spring is fully extended and remove spring.
5. Complete the installation in the reverse order of removal.

MANUAL STEERING GEAR, REPLACE

1964-69 All Models 1963 Senior Series

1. Remove two nuts or pinch bolt securing lower coupling to steering shaft flange.
2. Use a suitable puller to remove pitman arm.
3. Unfasten gear (3 bolts) from frame and remove from car.

1963 Special Series

NOTE

Due to lack of clearance it is necessary to remove the steering gear from the car to remove pitman arm and nut from pitman shaft.

1. Remove lower coupling clamp bolt.
2. Loosen clamp that retains mast jacket to toe pan cover and U-bolt that retains jacket to instrument panel.
3. Pull mast jacket up to expose lower coupling.
4. Remove lower coupling.
5. Disconnect pitman arm from intermediate rod.
6. Unfasten steering gear from front crossmember (4 bolts) and remove gear from car. Do not remove pitman arm from gear unless pitman shaft or seal are to be removed.
7. Reverse removal procedure to install gear.

POWER STEERING, REPLACE

1967-69

1. Disconnect pressure and return line hoses at steering gear and elevate ends of hoses higher than pump to prevent oil from draining out of pump.
2. Remove pinch bolt securing coupling to steering gear.
3. Jack up car and remove pitman shaft nut, then use a suitable puller to remove pitman arm.
4. On Senior models, remove sheet metal baffle that covers frame-to-gear attaching bolts.
5. Loosen the three frame-to-steering gear bolts and remove steering gear.

1964-66 Special & Skylark

1. Disconnect pressure and return line hoses at steering gear and elevate ends of hoses higher than pump to prevent oil from draining out of pump.
2. Remove two nuts securing gear coupling lower flange to steering shaft coupling.
3. Jack up car and remove pitman shaft nut, then remove pitman arm with a puller.
4. Unfasten gear from frame and remove from car.

1963 Special Series

1. Disconnect hydraulic hoses from gear.
2. Remove two nuts that retain lower coupling to steering shaft flange.
3. Loosen clamp that retains mast jacket to toe pan cover and U-bolt that retains jacket to instrument panel.
4. Pull mast jacket up far enough to disengage steering shaft flange with flexible coupling.
5. Disconnect pitman arm from intermediate rod.
6. On cars with synchromesh transmission, remove lower coupling from gear stub shaft.
7. Remove steering gear from front suspension crossmember (4 bolts). *Do not remove pitman arm from housing unless pitman shaft or seals or rack piston nut are to be removed.*
8. Reverse removal procedure to install the gear. Tighten pitman arm nut to a torque of 95 ft. lbs. Torque gear attaching bolts to 55 ft. lbs.
9. On synchromesh cars, there must be at least $\frac{1}{16}$" clearance between lower coupling and adjuster plug.
10. When installing the mast jacket, see that flange on steering shaft is properly positioned on flexible coupling.

NOTE

Make sure coupling rivet heads are positioned in center of correct slots in flange. Small rivet goes in small slot and large rivet in large slot.

11. After hoses are connected to steering gear, fill pump reservoir to correct level with automatic transmission oil. Start engine and maintain oil level in reservoir while allowing engine to idle at least three minutes before turning steering wheel. Then rotate steering wheel throughout its entire range slowly a few times to bleed system of air. Recheck oil level and for leaks.

1963-66 Senior Series

1. To remove the assembly, disconnect pressure and return line hoses at steering gear and elevate ends of hoses higher than pump to prevent oil from draining out of pump.
2. Disconnect flexible coupling by removing two bolts which attach coupling to steering shaft or flanges. (For 1963-66, flexible coupling is installed on gear box spline and secured by one pinch bolt.)
3. Remove pitman arm.
4. Unfasten and remove steering gear from frame.
5. To install, reverse removal procedure.
6. Check toe-in after installation.
7. Bleed system by turning steering wheel throughout its range until all air bubbles cease to appear in power steering oil reservoir.

CADILLAC

OLD CAR SPECIFICATIONS: For 1946-62 Tune Up and Wheel Alignment Specifications see back of book.

INDEX OF SERVICE OPERATIONS

PAGE NO.

ACCESSORIES

Automatic Level Controls 1-41
Clock Troubles 1-11
Heater Core, Replace 2-54
Power Top Troubles 1-18
Power Window Troubles 1-18
Radio, Replace 2-52
Speed Controls, Adjust 2-54

BRAKES

Brake Troubles, Mechanical 1-17
Disc Brake Service 1-430
Hydraulic System Service 1-422
Parking Brake, Adjust 2-68
Power Brake, Replace 2-68
Power Brake Service 1-440
Power Brake Troubles 1-440
Service Brakes, Adjust 2-67
Vacuum Release Parking Brake 2-68

COOLING SYSTEM

Cooling System Troubles 1-6
Variable Speed Fans 1-39
Water Pump, Replace 2-63

ELECTRICAL

Alternator Service 1-63
Dash Gauge Service 1-117
Distributor, Replace 2-46
Distributor Service:
  Standard 1-53
  Transistorized 1-47
Electrical Troubles 1-8
Flasher Location Chart .... Back of Book
Generator Service 1-91
Headlamps, Concealed Type 1-40
Horn Sounder, Remove 2-51
Ignition Coils and Resistors 1-24
Ignition Switch, Replace 2-47
Ignition Timing 2-46
Instrument Cluster Removal 2-51
Light Switch, Replace 2-48
Neutral Start Switch, Replace 2-50
Radio, Replace 2-52
Spark Plug Condition Chart 2-647
Starter Service 1-101
Starter, Replace 2-46
Starter Switch Service 1-114
Stop Light Switch, Replace 2-49
Turn Signal Switch, Replace 2-50
Turn Signal Troubles 1-11
Windshield Wiper Motor, Replace 2-53
Windshield Wiper Troubles 1-20

ENGINE

Camshaft, Replace 2-59
Crankshaft Rear Oil Seal 2-61

PAGE NO.

Cylinder Head, Replace 2-56
Engine, Replace 2-55
Engine Troubles 1-1
Main Bearings 2-61
Piston Pins 2-61
Piston Rings 2-61
Piston and Rod, Assemble 2-60
Pistons 2-60
Rocker Arms 2-57
Rod Bearings 2-61
Timing Case Cover, Replace 2-57
Timing Case Oil Seal 2-58
Timing Chain, Replace 2-59
Valve Arrangement 2-57
Valve Guide 2-57
Valve Lifters 2-57
Valve Lift Specs. 2-57
Valve Timing Specs. 2-57

ENGINE LUBRICATION

Crankcase Ventilation (PCV) 1-29
Exhaust Emission Controls 1-30
Oil Pan, Replace 2-62
Oil Pump Repairs 2-63

FUEL SYSTEM

Carburetor Adjustment and Specs. 1-124
Crankcase Ventilation (PCV) 1-29
Exhaust Emission Controls 1-30
Fuel Pump, Replace 2-64
Fuel Pump Service 1-120
Fuel System Troubles 1-2

PROPELLER SHAFT & U JOINTS

Propeller Shaft 2-66
Universal Joint Service 1-418

REAR AXLE

Axle Shaft, Bearing and Seal 2-64
Rear Axle Troubles 1-17

SPECIFICATIONS

Alternator 2-44
Brakes 2-45
Capacities 2-45
Carburetors 1-124
Cooling System 2-45
Crankshaft and Bearings 2-45
Distributors 2-44
Engine Tightening Torque 2-46
General Engine Specs. 2-42
Generators 2-44
Ignition Coils and Resistors 1-24

PAGE NO.

Pistons, Rings and Pins 2-45
Starting Motors 2-44
Tune Up 2-43
Valves 2-43
Valve Lift 2-57
Valve Timing 2-57
Wheel Alignment 2-46

STEERING GEAR

Horn Sounder Removal 2-51
Mechanical Gear Service 1-451
Mechanical Gear Troubles 1-18
Power Gear, Replace 2-73
Steering Wheel, Replace 2-51

SUSPENSION, FRONT

Ball Joints, Replace:
  Standard Cars 2-70
  Eldorado 2-71
Ball Joints, Check for Wear:
  Standard Cars 2-70
  Eldorado 2-71
Coil Spring, Replace 2-70
Lubrication 2-69
Shock Absorber, Replace 2-70
Standing Height, Adjust 2-70
Suspension, Description of:
  Standard Cars 2-69
  Eldorado 2-71
Tie-Strut & Bushings, Replace 2-70
Tire Wear Chart 2-648
Toe-In, Adjust:
  Standard Cars 2-69
  Eldorado 2-71
Torsion Bar, Replace 2-72
Wheel Alignment, Adjust:
  Standard Cars 2-69
  Eldorado 2-71
Wheel Bearings, Adjust 2-70
Wheel Bearings, Replace 2-70

TRANSMISSIONS

Automatic Units 1-321
Linkage, 1969 2-64

TUNE UP

Service 1-21
Specifications 2-43

WINDSHIELD WIPER

Wiper Motor, Replace 2-53
Wiper Linkage, Replace 2-53
Wiper Switch, Replace 2-53
Wiper Troubles 1-20

SERIAL & ENGINE NUMBER LOCATION: 1963-64 On left side of block.

VEHICLE IDENTIFICATION NUMBER LOCATION: 1965-67 On rear portion of block behind intake manifold and on top surface of right frame side rail.

On 1968-69 models the Vehicle identification Number is located on rear upper portion of cylinder block, behind intake manifold and on left side of transmission.

ENGINE UNIT NUMBER LOCATION: 1965-67 Rear of left cylinder bank below cylinder head. On 1968-69 at rear of cylinder block.

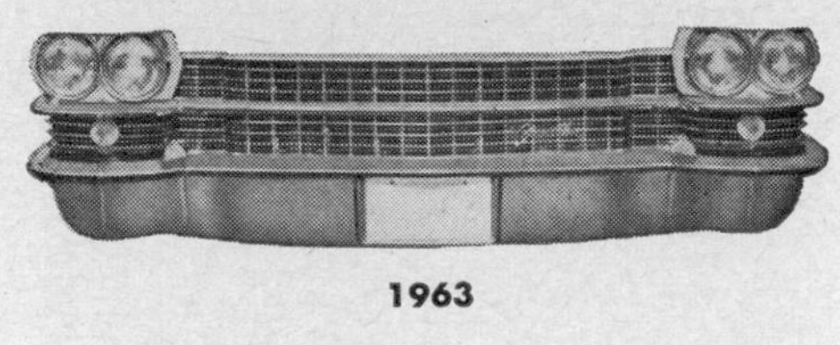

1963

1964

1965

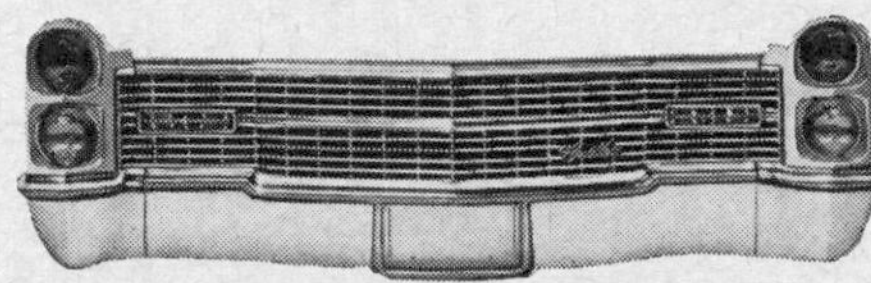

1966

1967 Eldorado

1967 Except Eldorado

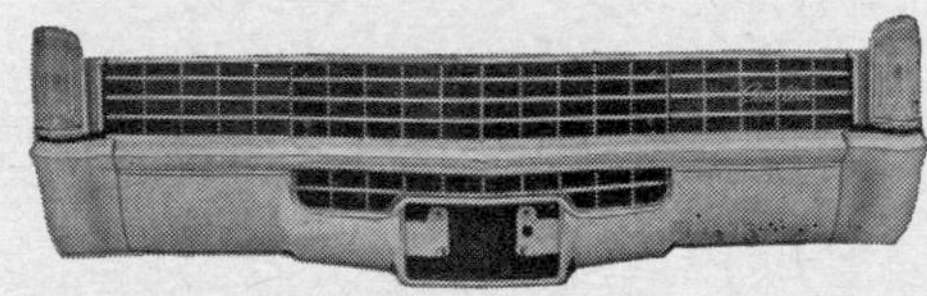

1968 Eldorado

1968 Except Eldorado

1969 Eldorado

1969 Except Eldorado

GENERAL ENGINE SPECIFICATIONS

Year	Engine	Carburetor	Bore and Stroke	Piston Displacement, Cubic Inches	Compression Ratio	Maximum Brake H.P. @ R.P.M.	Maximum Torque Lbs. Ft. @ R.P.M.	Normal Oil Pressure Pounds
1963	325 Horsepower.............V8-390	4 Barrel	4.0000 x 3.875	390	10.50	325 @ 4800	430 @ 3100	30–35
1964–67	340 Horsepower.............V8-429	4 Barrel	4.1300 x 4.000	429	10.50	340 @ 4600	480 @ 3000	30–35
1968–69	375 Horsepower.............V8-472	4 Barrel	4.3000 x 4.060	472	10.50	375 @ 4400	525 @ 3000	30–35

TUNE UP SPECIFICATIONS

OLD CAR SPECIFICATIONS: For 1946-62 Tune Up Specifications see back of book.

★When using a timing light, disconnect vacuum hose or tube at distributor and plug opening in hose or tube so idle speed will not be affected.

Year	Engine	Spark Plug		Distributor		Firing Order	Ignition Timing★		Hot Idle Speed		Comp. Press. Lbs. ③	Fuel Pump Press. Lbs.
		Type AC	Gap Inch	Point Gap Inch	Dwell Angle Deg.		BTDC ①	Mark	Std. Trans.	Auto. Trans. ②		
1963	V8-390	44⑥	.035	⑤	30	Fig. D	5°	Fig. C	—	480D⑦	175	5¼-6½
1964-65	V8-429	44	.035	⑤	30	Fig. D	5°	Fig. B	—	480D⑦	175	5¼-6½
1966	Standard Cars	44	.035	⑤	30	Fig. D	5°	Fig. B	—	480D④	175	5¼-6½
	With A.I.R.	44	.035	⑤	30	Fig. D	5°	Fig. B	—	550D④	175	5¼-6½
	With A.I.R. and A/C	44	.035	⑤	30	Fig. D	5°	Fig. B	—	550D④	175	5¼-6½
1967	Without A.I.R.	44	.035	⑤	30	Fig. D	5°	Fig. B	—	480D④	175	5¼-6½
	With A.I.R.	44	.035	⑤	30	Fig. D	5°	Fig. B	—	550D④	175	5¼-6½
	With A.I.R. and A/C	44	.035	⑤	30	Fig. D	5°	Fig. B	—	550D④	175	5¼-6½
1968	All	44N	.035	⑤	30	Fig. F	5°	Fig. B	—	550D④	175	5¼-6½
1969	All	R44N	.035	⑤	30	Fig. F	5°	Fig. B	—	550D④	175	5¼-6½

①—BTDC: Before top dead center.

②—D: Drive. N: Neutral.

③—Plus or minus 20 lbs.

④—When making adjustments, air conditioner must be turned off (if equipped). Also, hose must be disconnected at vacuum release cylinder. The hot idle compensator must be closed; this can be done by pressing finger or eraser end of pencil on compensator. On 1968 units, compensator pin is just in front of primary throttle bores; on 1967 compensator is located in air horn vent stack just to left rear of secondary metering rod hanger; on 1966 units brass valve located in secondary side of unit.

On 1966 models, to set stator blades for proper performance, remove pink wire from contact fitting on transmission downshift switch and connect to white wire fitting with alligator clip; this will activate stator switch.

⑤—Turn adjusting screw in (clockwise) until engine begins to misfire; then back screw out ½ turn.

⑥—Use R44 if equipped with AM/FM radio.

⑦—If equipped, adjust idle speed with air conditioner turned on. Also, the vacuum released parking brake hose from switch to engine must be disconnected and opening taped closed to prevent any air leak.

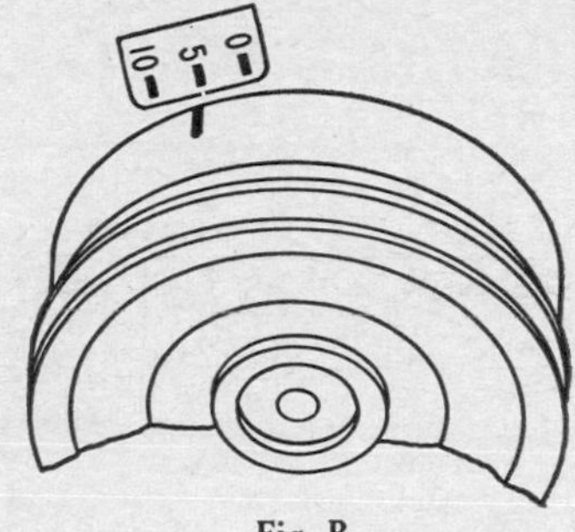

Fig. B

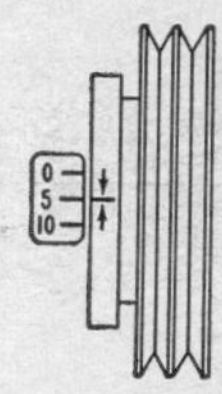

Fig. C

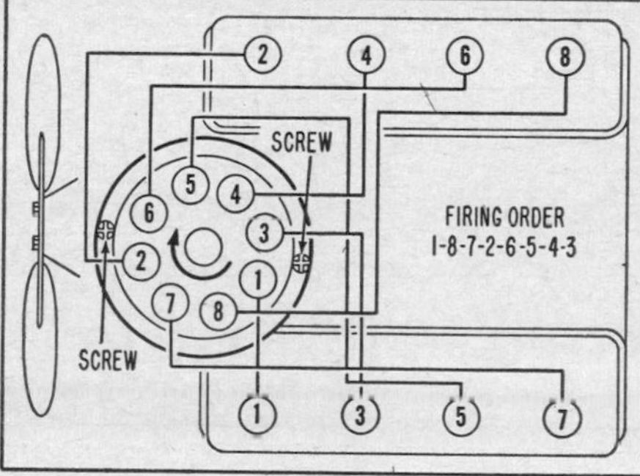

Fig. D

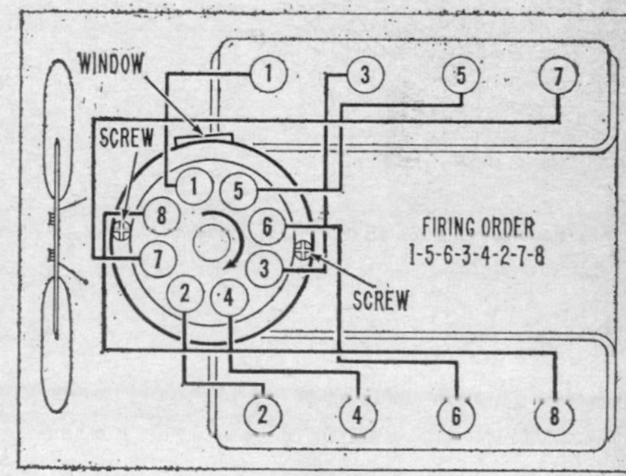

Fig. F

VALVE SPECIFICATIONS

Year	Model	Valve Lash	Valve Angles		Valve Spring Installed Height	Valve Spring Pressure Lbs. @ In.	Stem Clearance		Stem Diameter	
			Seat	Face			Intake	Exhaust	Intake	Exhaust
1963-69	All	Hydraulic①	45	44	1 15/16	160 @ 1½	.0005-.0025	.001-.0025	.3415-.3425	.3415-.3420

①—No adjustment

DISTRIBUTOR SPECIFICATIONS

★NOTE: If advance is checked on vehicle, double the R.P.M. and degrees advance to get crankshaft figures.

Year	Model	Distributor Part No.①	Rotation ②	Breaker Gap	Dwell Angle Deg.	Breaker Arm Spring Tension	Centrifugal Advance Degrees @ R.P.M. of Distributor★		Vacuum Advance	
							Advance Starts	Full Advance	Inches of Vacuum To Start Plunger	Max. Adv. Dist. Deg. @ Vacuum
1963		1111032	C	③	30	19–23	1 @ 400	9 @ 2000	8	11 @ 15
1964		1111061	C	③	30	19–23	1 @ 500	9 @ 2000	5–7	11 @ 20
1965		1111032	C	③	30	19–23	1 @ 400	9 @ 2000	6	12 @ 20
1966		1111131	C	③	30	19–23	1 @ 400	8 @ 2000	7.5–9.5	12 @ 15
1967	Early	1111259	C	③	30	19–23	1 @ 400	8 @ 2000	7.5–9.5	12 @ 15
	Late	1111262	C	③	30	19–23	1 @ 400	7 @ 2000	7.5–9.5	12 @ 15
1968	All	1111239	C	③	30	19–23	1 @ 400	13 @ 2000	8–10	12 @ 13
1969	All	1111939	C	③	30	19–23	1 @ 400	13 @ 2000	8–10	12 @ 13

①—Stamped on distributor housing plate.
②—As viewed from above.
③—Turn adjusting screw to the right until engine misfires. Then turn screw ½ turn to the left.

ALTERNATOR & REGULATOR SPECIFICATIONS

Year	Alternator					Regulator						
	Model	Rated Hot Output Amps.	Field Current 12 Volts @ 80° F.	Output @ 14 Volts		Model	Field Relay			Voltage Regulator		
				2000 R.P.M. Amps.	5000 R.P.M. Amps.		Air Gap In.	Point Gap In.	Closing Voltage	Air Gap In.	Point Gap In.	Voltage @ 125° F.
1963–69	1100742	63	2.8–3.2	35	59	1119519	.015	.030	1.5–2.7	.067	.014	13.5–14.3
1963–64	1100617	55	1.9–2.3	32	50	1119512	.015	.030	1.5–2.7	.057	.014	13.5–14.4
	1100624	42	1.9–2.3	28	40	1119512	.015	.030	1.5–2.7	.057	.014	13.5–14.4
1965 &	1100696	42	2.2–2.6	28	40	1119515	.015	.030	2.3–3.7	.060	.014	13.5–14.4
1967–69	1100694	55	2.2–2.6	32	50	1119515	.015	.030	2.3–3.7	.060	.014	13.5–14.4
1966	1100691	42	2.2–2.6	28	40	1119515	.015	.030	2.3–3.7	.060	.014	13.5–14.4
	1100692	55	2.2–2.6	32	50	1119515	.015	.030	2.3–3.7	.060	.014	13.5–14.4

STARTING MOTOR SPECIFICATIONS

Year	Model	Starter Number	Brush Spring Tension Oz①	Free Speed Test			Resistance Test③	
				Amperes	Volts	R.P.M.	Amperes	Volts
1963	All	1107799	40	65②	10.6	3600①	300②	3.5
1964	Hydramatic	1107311	35	70–105②	10.6	3800–6200	480–540②	3.0
1964–65	Turbo Hydramatic	1107314	35	70–105②	10.6	3800–6200	480–540②	3.0
1965	Series 75	1107340	35	70–105②	10.6	3800–6200	480–540②	3.0
1966–67	Exc. 75, Eldo.	1107367	35	70–105②	10.6	7800–12000	480–540②	3.0
1966	Series 75	1107368	35	70–105②	10.6	7800–12000	480–540②	3.0
1967	Eldorado	1107389	35	70–99②	10.6	7800–12000	435–535②	3.0
1968–69	Std. Cars	1108381	35	70–99②	10.6	7800–12000	435–455②	3.0
	Eldorado	1108352	35	70–99②	10.6	7800–12000	435–455②	3.0

①—Minimum.
②—Includes solenoid.
③—Check capacity of motor by using a 500-ampere meter and a carbon pile rheostat to control voltage. Apply volts listed across motor with armature locked. Current should be as listed.

PISTONS, PINS, RINGS, CRANKSHAFT & BEARINGS

Year	Model	Fitting Pistons		Ring End Gap (1)		Wrist-pin Diameter	Rod Bearings		Main Bearings			
		Shim To Use	Pounds Pull On Scale	Comp.	Oil		Shaft Diameter	Bearing Clearance	Shaft Diameter	Bearing Clearance	Thrust on Bear. No.	Shaft End Play
1963–67	All	(2)	(2)	.013	.015	.9995	2.2488–2.2493	.0005–.0021	3.000	.0008–.0029	3	.001–.007
1968–69	All	(2)	(2)	.013	.015	.9995	2.500	.0005–.0028	3.250	.0003–.0026	3	.002–.012

(1)—Fit rings in tapered bores for clearance given in tightest portion of ring travel.

(2)—See text under "Pistons".

BRAKE SPECIFICATIONS

Year	Model	Brake Drum Inside Diameter	Wheel Cylinder Bore Diameter			Master Cylinder Bore Diameter		
			Disc Brake	Front Drum Brake	Rear Drum Brake	Disc Brakes	Drum Brakes	Power Brakes
1963–66	All	12(4)	—	1 3/16	1	—	1	1
1967	Series 75	12	—	1 1/16	1	—	1	1
	Eldorado	11	1 15/16	1 1/8	7/8	1	1	1
	All Others	12	—	1 3/16	15/16	—	1	1
1968	Series 75	12	2 3/4	1 3/16	7/8(2)	1	1	1
	Eldorado	11	1 15/16	1 1/8	13/16(3)	1	1	1
	All Others	12	2 3/4	1 3/16	13/16(1)	1	1	1
1969	Series 75	12	2 3/4	—	7/8	1	—	1
	Eldorado	11	2 15/16	—	7/8	1	—	1
	All Others	12	2 3/4	—	13/16	1	—	1

(1)—Cars with front drums 15/16".
(2)—Cars with front drums 1".
(3)—Cars with front drums 7/8".
(4)—Plus or minus .005".

COOLING SYSTEM & CAPACITY DATA

Year	Model or Engine	Cooling Capacity, Qts.			Radiator Cap Relief Pressure, Lbs.		Thermo. Opening Temp. (1)	Fuel Tank Gals.	Engine Oil Refill Qts. (3)	Transmission Oil			Rear Axle Oil Pints
		No Heater	With Heater	With A/C	With A/C	No A/C				3 Speed Pints	4 Speed Pints	Auto. Trans. Qts. (10)	
1963	Series 60	...	17.2	18.3	15	15	175	26	4	...	...	9	5
	Series 62	...	17.2	18.3	15	15	175	26	4	...	...	9	5
	Series 75	...	19 3/4	20 3/4	15	15	175	26	4	...	...	9	5
1964	All	16 1/4	17 1/4	18 1/4	15	15	175	26	4	...	...	9	5
1965	All	17 1/2	18 1/2	19	15	15	175	26	4	...	...	(5)	5
1966	Except 75	...	17.2	18.2	15	15	175	26	4	...	...	(6)	5
	Series 75	...	...	20.7	15	15	175	26	4	...	...	(6)	5
1967	Eldorado	16	17	17 1/2	15	15	(7)	24	4	...	...	(6)	5
	Series 75	—	18	19	15	15	(7)	20	4	...	...	(9)	4 1/2
	Others	16	18	20 1/2	15	15	(7)	26	4	...	...	(6)	5
1968–69	Eldorado	...	20.3	20.8	15	15	195	24	5	...	...	(6)	4 1/2
	Series 75	...	23.8(13)	23.8(13)	15	15	195	20	4	...	...	(9)	4 1/2
	Others	...	20.3(11)	20.8(12)	15	15	195	26	4	...	...	(8)	5

(1)—For permanent anti-freeze.
(3)—Add one quart with filter change.
(5)—Hydramatic 9 qts. Turbo-Hydramatic 11 qts.
(6)—Oil pan 3 qts. Total capacity 11 qts.
(7)—With A/C 185° without A/C 195°
(8)—Oil pan 2 qts. Total capacity 12 1/2 qts.
(9)—Oil pan 5 qts. Total capacity 13 qts.
(10)—Approximate. Make final check with dipstick.
(11)—1969, 21.3 qts.
(12)—1969, 21.8 qts.
(13)—1969, 24.8 qts.

ENGINE TIGHTENING SPECIFICATIONS★

★Torque specifications are for clean and lightly lubricated threads only. Dry or dirty threads produce increased friction which prevents accurate measurement of tightness.

Year	Spark Plugs Ft. Lbs.	Cylinder Head Bolts Ft. Lbs.	Intake Manifold Ft. Lbs.	Exhaust Manifold Ft. Lbs.	Rocker Arm Shaft Bracket Ft. Lbs.	Rocker Arm Cover Ft. Lbs.	Connecting Rod Cap Bolts Ft. Lbs.	Main Bearing Cap Bolts Ft. Lbs.	Flex Plate to Crankshaft Ft. Lbs.	Vibration Damper or Pulley Ft. Lbs.
1963	25	75	②	60	75	28①	40	95	75	18③
1964–66	25	60	②	60④	75	28①	40	95	75	15③
1967	25	60	②	60④	—	28①	40	95	75	15③
1968–69	25	115	30	35	—	24①	40	90	75	17

①—Inch pounds. Retorque after engine has been run. ②—Bolt 30, nut 25. ③—Pulley to damper screws. ④—50 ft.-lbs. on engines with no gaskets.

WHEEL ALIGNMENT SPECIFICATIONS

OLD CAR SPECIFICATIONS: For 1946-62 Wheel Alignment Specifications see back of book.

Year	Model	Caster Angle, Degrees		Camber Angle, Degrees				Toe-In. Inch	Toe-Out on Turns, Deg.	
				Limits		Desired				
		Limits	Desired	Left	Right	Left	Right		Outer Wheel	Inner Wheel
1963–66	All	—1½ to —½	—1	—⅛ to +⅜	—⅜ to +⅛	Zero	—¼	3/16 to ¼	20	22° 11′
1967–68	Eldorado	—⅜ to +⅜	Zero	—1½ to —2½	—1½ to —2½	Zero	Zero	0 to ⅛	18⅙	20
	All Others	—½ to —1½	—1	+⅜ to —⅛	+⅛ to —⅜	Zero	—¼	3/16 to ¼	18⅙	20
1969	Eldorado	—1½ to —2½	—2	+⅜ to —⅜	+⅜ to —⅜	Zero	Zero	0 to ⅛	18⅙	20
	All Others	—½ to —1½	—1	+⅜ to —⅜	+⅜ to —⅜	Zero	Zero	⅛ to ¼	18⅙	20

Electrical Section

IGNITION TIMING

If a timing light is used to set ignition timing, disconnect the vacuum advance pipe to the carburetor and plug its open end. Also on cars with vacuum release parking brake mechanism, the vacuum line to the engine should be disconnected and its open end plugged to prevent air leaks. *Timing adjustments can be affected if these steps are not taken.*

Lacking a power timing light, an accurate method of setting ignition timing with the engine stopped is with the aid of a jumper light. Be sure to use a light bulb that corresponds with the system voltage of the vehicle.

1. Remove distributor cap and rotor and see that the breaker gap is set according to specifications.
2. Rotate engine until No. 1 cylinder is at the ignition timing point as indicated by the timing pointer and timing mark being lined up with each other.
3. Connect the jumper light between distributor ignition terminal and ground.
4. Turn on ignition switch.
5. Loosen distributor and turn it in the direction of normal rotation until the points just close (light out). Then slowly turn distributor in the opposite direction just to the exact point that the light goes on. Tighten distributor in this position.

DISTRIBUTOR, REPLACE

1. Remove distributor cap.
2. Disconnect primary wire from coil.
3. Disconnect vacuum advance pipe or hose from distributor.
4. Crank engine until rotor is pointing to No. 1 spark plug wire position on cap.
5. Remove distributor hold-down nut and clamp.
6. Lift distributor from engine.
7. Note that the rotor will turn slightly as the drive gear becomes disengaged from the camshaft gear. Therefore, when installing the distributor, the rotor should be turned slightly counter-clockwise on 1963 (clockwise on earlier models) from No. 1 spark plug position to insure proper engagement of gears. When properly installed, rotor should point directly to No. 1 spark plug position.

STARTER, REPLACE

1967 Eldorado, All 1968-69

1. Disconnect ground strap at battery.
2. Raise and support front end of car.
3. Disconnect battery lead at starter solenoid terminal.
4. Disconnect neutral safety switch wire and coil feed wire at starter solenoid.
5. Remove spring clip securing wires to solenoid housing.
6. Unfasten starter (2 screws) and remove starter by pulling it forward and then lowering it straight down.
7. Reverse procedure to install.

1966-67 Except Eldorado

1. Disconnect battery ground cable.
2. Raise front of car and place on jack stands.
3. Disconnect battery lead at starter solenoid.
4. Disconnect neutral safety switch wire and coil feed wire at starter solenoid terminals.
5. Remove spring clip securing wires to solenoid housing.

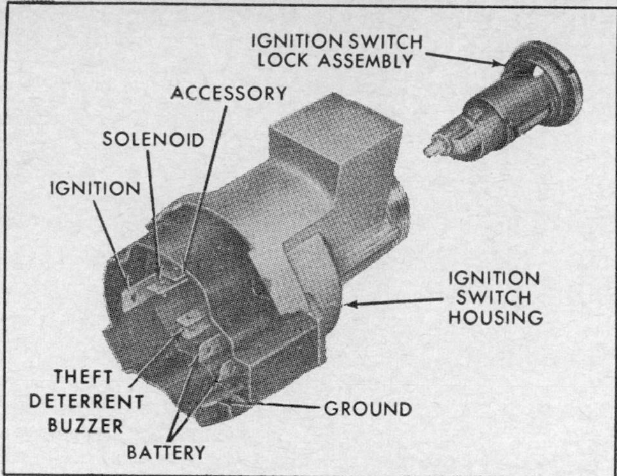

Fig. 1 Ignition switch. 1967-68

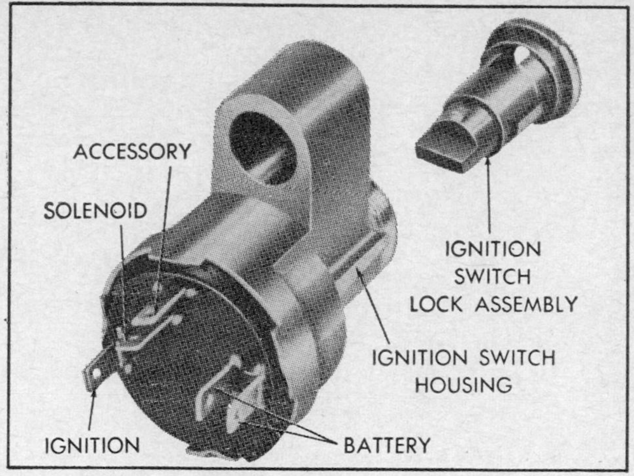

Fig. 2 Ignition switch. 1965-66

6. Remove two screws that hold starter motor lower brace between starter housing and transmission lower cover and remove brace.
7. Remove starter upper mounting bolt.
8. Remove two special screws that hold starter to engine.
9. Remove starter by pulling it forward and over transmission cooler pipes, then lower it between idler arm and frame. *It may be necessary to turn front wheels several times to allow starter to be lowered between idler arm and frame.*
10. Reverse procedure to install.

1965 Except Fleetwood Models

After disconnecting battery and wiring at starter, unfasten starter and pull it forward and over transmission cooler pipes. Then lower starter between steering idler arm and frame. It may be necessary to turn front wheels several times to allow starter to be lowered between idler arm and frame.

1965 Fleetwood & 1964 With Turbo-Hydra-Matic

After disconnecting battery and wiring at starter, turn front wheels to full left position. Unfasten clamp from transmission cooler pipes. Remove starter by pulling it forward and rotating it slightly counterclockwise end for end until gear end of starter faces downward. Then remove starter between exhaust pipe and idler arm support.

1964 With Hydra-Matic

After disconnecting battery and wiring at starter, unfasten clamp from transmission cooler pipes at bell housing. Remove starter by pulling it slightly forward and rotating it clockwise end for end until front of starter faces straight down. Then remove starter from car.

1963

1. Disconnect battery ground cable.
2. Disconnect wiring at starter.
3. Remove starter mounting bolts and pull starter forward and out.

IGNITION SWITCH, REPLACE

1969

1. Disconnect battery cable and position ignition key in "Lock".
2. Remove steering column lower cover.
3. Loosen two upper column support nuts and allow column to drop as far as possible without removing the nuts.

NOTE: Do not remove nuts as column may bend under its own weight.

4. Disconnect switch connector and remove switch. Fig. 1A.
5. When reassembling, make sure the ignition key is in the "Lock" position. Assemble switch on actuator rod. Hold rod stationary and move switch towards bottom of column then back off on detent. Install screws and torque to 35 inch lbs.

1967-68

1. Remove steering column lower cover.
2. Remove switch lock cylinder by using a paper clip to depress tumbler pin while turning ignition key to the left from accessory position and pulling outward, Fig. 1.

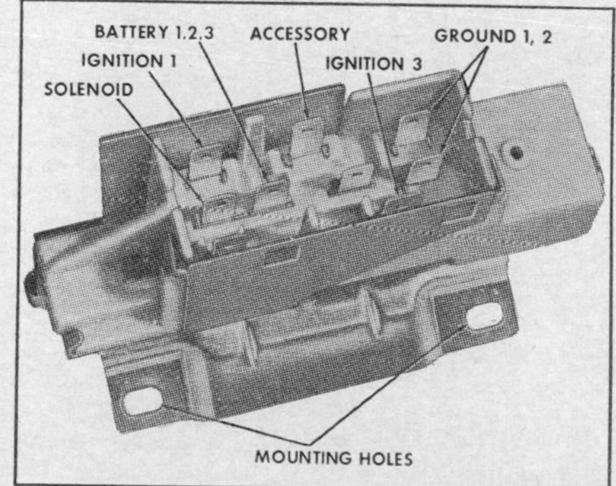

Fig. 1A Ignition switch. 1969

3. Disconnect connector at rear of switch housing.
4. Remove switch mounting nut.
5. Disconnect dial bulb socket at rear of ignition switch housing and remove switch through rear of instrument panel.
6. Reverse procedure to install.

1965-66

1. Disconnect battery ground cable.
2. Remove right and left windshield garnish moldings (4 screws each side).
3. Separate upper panel cover from upper panel (6 screws).
4. Raise upper panel high enough to disconnect wire connectors at radio speaker, courtesy lights, and for Twilight Sentinel Photocell and Comfort Control sensor (if so equipped).
5. Pull upper panel cover rearward to disengage three hooks at front of cover and remove cover.
6. Remove switch lock from switch housing, using a .035" diameter wire (paper clip) to depress tumbler pin while turning ignition key to the left and pulling outward.
7. Disconnect 4-way connector at rear of ignition switch housing.
8. Remove ignition switch spanner nut.
9. Disconnect dial bulb socket at rear of ignition housing and remove switch through rear of instrument panel.
10. Reverse above procedure to install.

SERVICE BULLETIN

New Ignition Lock Cylinder: To help reduce the possibility of car theft, a redesigned ignition lock cylinder and mounting nut are installed on 1965 cars beginning with Vehicle Identification No. 120500. The new lock cylinder and nut will not allow removal of the ignition switch, *unless the lock cylinder is removed first.*

1963-64

1. Disconnect battery ground cable.
2. On 1964 cars with tilt wheel, position wheel in maximum "up" posi-

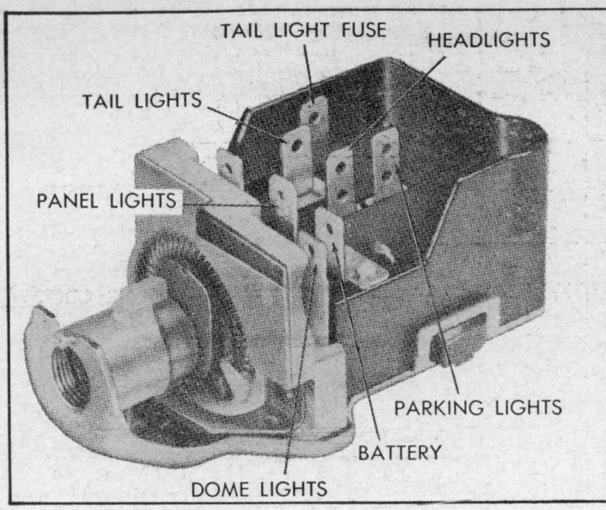

Fig. 3 Headlight switch. 1964-69

Fig. 4 Loosening headlight control set screw. 1965-66

tion for greater accessibility.

3. Remove one special larger screw from upper end of steering column lower cover.
4. Remove three screws from upper end of steering column lower cover.
5. Remove column lower cover (5 screws).

NOTE: On convertibles, it will be necessary to disconnect 3-way electric connector from rear of convertible top control switch. And on cars so equipped, disconnect multiple connector of Twilight Sentinel, and multiple connector for rear window defogger switch.

6. Disconnect left-hand cigar lighter jumper wire 3-way connector.
7. Remove ignition lock cylinder, using a paper clip to depress tumbler pin while turning ignition key to left and pulling outward.
8. Remove switch retaining ring.
9. Disconnect ignition switch 4-way connector from back of switch and remove light bulb socket.
10. Remove ignition switch through rear of instrument panel.
11. Reverse above procedure to install.

LIGHT SWITCH, REPLACE

1969

1. Remove instrument panel top cover and steering column lower cover.
2. Remove left A/C duct and outlet and disconnect wiring harness below headlight switch.
3. Depress button on top of switch and remove knob and rod assembly.
4. Remove attaching screws, pull switch rearward and disconnect bulbs and wires and remove switch, Fig. 3.

1967-68

1. Remove steering column lower cover.
2. On Eldorado, remove hoses at vacuum valve, which is integral with headlight valve.
3. Remove lower right screw securing switch housing to lower instrument panel. *This screw has a special ¾" head and may be removed with a ¼" socket.*
4. If equipped with Automatic Climate Control, remove left outlet hose at inboard side to gain access to upper left screw.
5. Remove upper left screw securing light switch housing to lower instrument panel. *This screw has a special ¾" head and may be removed with a ¼" socket.*
6. Pull light switch rearward, disconnect wiring harness connectors, two bulbs and remove switch, Fig. 3.
7. Reverse procedure to install.

1965-66

1. Disconnect battery ground cable.
2. Loosen set screw securing switch housing to cluster bezel, Fig. 4.
3. Lift upward on bottom of switch housing to disengage upper retainer clip from locating slot in bezel opening, then pull control switch straight out to remove.
4. Disconnect switch housing dial bulb socket from top of housing case.
5. Disconnect trunk warning lens dial bulb socket from bottom of case (if so equipped).
6. If equipped with Guide-Matic and/or Twilight Sentinel, disconnect switch lead connectors.
7. Disconnect multiple wire connector from top of switch and remove switch assembly, Fig. 3.
8. On cars *without* Guide-Matic or Twilight Sentinel, depress spring-loaded release button on bottom of headlight switch and remove switch operating shaft on knob assembly. Remove knob and sleeve from switch, Fig. 5.
9. On cars *with* Guide-Matic and/or Twilight Sentinel, depress spring-loaded release button on bottom of switch and remove switch operating shaft and knob. Remove upper retainer clip from housing case (2 screws). Remove housing case from housing (2 screws) with switch attached. Remove hex head sleeve securing switch to case and remove switch from case.
10. Reverse removal procedure to install.

CAUTION: Be sure that tang on switch is aligned with locating notch in housing case before tightening knob and sleeve assembly (hex head sleeve on cars with Guide-Matic and/or Twilight Sentinel). Be sure that Guide-Matic and/or Twilight Sentinel control switch leads extend through notch in side of case.

Fig. 5 Removing light switch knob and sleeve assembly. 1963-66

1964

1. Disconnect battery ground cable.
2. Remove right and left windshield garnish moldings (3 screws each molding).
3. If equipped with Cruise Control, remove press fit "slide switch" and separate Cruise Control escutcheon from upper instrument panel cover (2 screws).
4. Separate upper panel cover from lower panel. Three screws are located above instrument cluster and two screws at inside top of glove box.
5. Pry loose lower ends of vertical segments of top cover to disengage fasteners at lower panel.
6. Raise upper panel high enough to disconnect wire connectors for courtesy lights, map light (on 75 Series only), and for Twilight Sentinel Photocell and heater air-conditioner sensor (if so equipped).

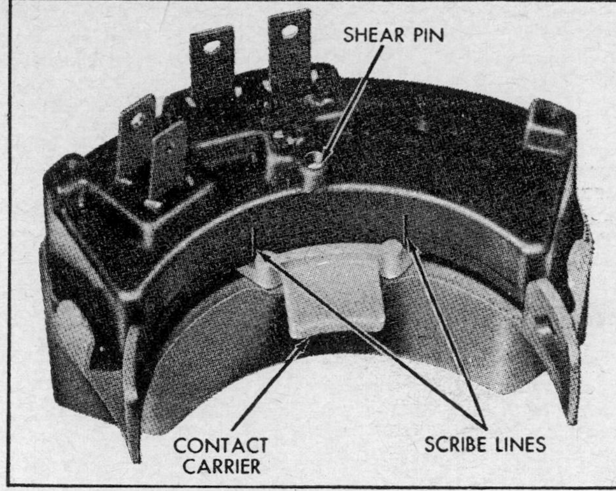

Fig. 6 Switch in neutral position. 1967-69

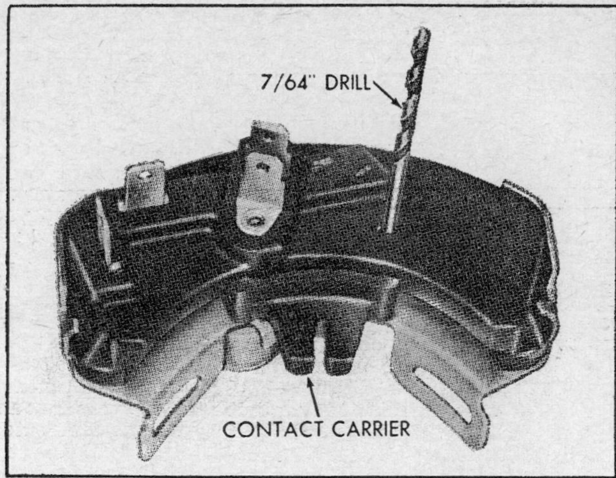

Fig. 7 Switch in neutral position. 1966

7. Pull cover rearward to disengage four hooks at front of cover from retainers on cowl and remove cover.
8. Disconnect multiple connector from headlight switch and (if so equipped) the two-way connector for Guide-Matic control.
9. Depress spring-loaded release button on bottom of switch housing and pull out switch operating rod.
10. On models without Guide-Matic control, remove knob and sleeve, Fig. 4. Then remove switch escutcheon and switch from instrument panel bezel.
11. On cars with Guide-Matic control, pry off spring-retained control knob. Remove spanner nut securing switch to instrument panel. Then remove escutcheon and switch from instrument panel bezel.
12. Reverse removal procedure to install.

1963

1. Disconnect battery ground cable.
2. Remove right and left windshield garnish moldings (3 screws each side).
3. If equipped with Cruise Control, remove press fit "on" and "off" button and remove escutcheon from instrument panel cover (2 screws).
4. Separate upper panel cover from lower panel (3 screws above instrument cluster and 2 screws at inside top of glove box).
5. Raise upper panel cover high enough to disconnect 3-way connector for map light and 3-way socket type connector for Guide-Matic Phototube unit (if so equipped).
6. Pull cover rearward to disengage four hooks at front of cover from retainers on cowl, and remove cover.
7. Disconnect one 6-way wire connector and one single connector from headlamp switch.
8. Depress spring-loaded knob and rod release button on bottom of switch housing and pull out rod and knob assembly.
9. Remove knob and sleeve, Fig. 4. Then remove switch escutcheon.
10. Reverse removal procedure to install.

NOTE: If car is equipped with Cruise Control, remove left end cover to upper cover screw and remove end cover. Align Cruise Control selector unit with screwdriver in unit mounting frame slots so upper cover can be installed over selector wheel.

STOP LIGHT SWITCH

1963-69

1. Disconnect two lead wires from switch on brake pedal flange.
2. Remove locking nut from switch.
3. Remove stop light switch.
4. Reverse procedure to install.

NOTE: Adjust switch action so that stop light is on when brake pedal is depressed ½". Loosen front and rear nuts that hold switch and move switch up or down until this action is obtained. Tighten switch lock nuts securely to prevent loss of adjustment.

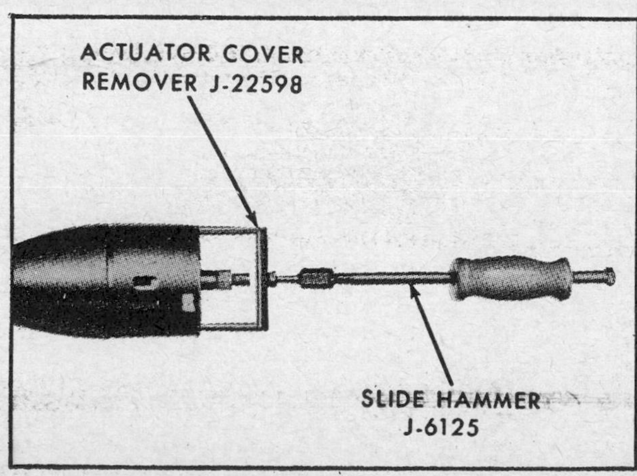

Fig. 8 Removing actuator cover. 1967-68

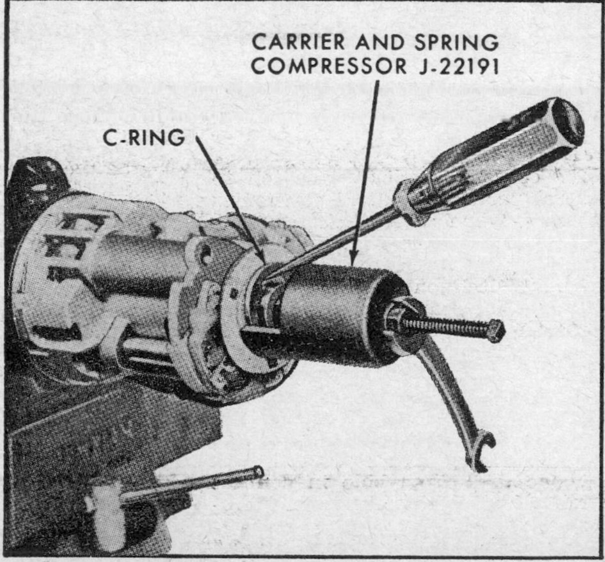

Fig. 9 Removing C-ring. 1967-69

NEUTRAL START SWITCH

NOTE: On all models the neutral switch, back-up light switch and parking brake vacuum release valve are combined into one unit mounted on the steering column under the instrument panel.

1967-69

Removal

1. Place transmission shift lever in neutral.
2. Remove switch from column, being careful not to disturb neutral position of contact carrier, Fig. 6.
3. Mark neutral position of contact carrier.
4. Mark top vacuum hose for identification and remove hoses.
5. Disconnect two wiring connectors from switch.

Installation

1. Place transmission shift lever in neutral detent.
2. Connect two wires to switch.
3. Move contact carrier on switch to neutral position as marked during removal.

NOTE: If necessary to install a new switch, the switch will be secured in neutral by a shear pin. Do not break pin.

4. Install switch on steering column, aligning contact carrier blade with slot in shift tube.
5. Secure switch to steering column with two mounting nuts, making sure that shift lever is in neutral detent while this operation is performed.
6. Connect vacuum hoses to switch as marked during removal.
7. Switch should now be properly adjusted. If new switch was installed, a slightly greater effort to position the shift lever in any position besides neutral will be necessary to break the shear pin.

1966

The removal procedure of the switch assembly is the same as outlined for later models. To install the switch, proceed as follows:

1. Place transmission shift lever in neutral detent.
2. Move contact carrier on switch to neutral position. Neutral position is obtained when a $\frac{7}{64}$" drill fits hole in contact carrier, Fig. 7.
3. Connect two wires to switch.
4. Install switch on steering column, aligning slot in contact carrier with blade on inner shift tube.
5. Secure switch with two screws, making sure shift lever is centered in neutral detent position while this operation is being performed.
6. Connect vacuum hoses to switch as marked during removal.
7. Remove drill from hole in contact carrier. Switch should now be properly adjusted.
8. Check adjustment by inserting $\frac{7}{64}$" drill into hole in contact carrier. Drill enters about ⅜" into housing when properly aligned. If drill does not enter about ⅜", move switch slightly until entry is obtained. Remove drill.

1964-65

Removal

1. Remove two mounting screws and switch from steering column.
2. Mark top vacuum hose for identification and remove hoses.
3. Disconnect two wires from switch.

Installation

1. Place transmission shift lever in PARK.
2. Connect two wires to switch.
3. Move contact carrier on switch to extreme counterclockwise position.
4. Install switch on steering column, aligning slot in contact carrier with blade on inner shift tube.
5. Secure switch with two screws.
6. Connect vacuum hoses to switch as marked during removal.

Adjustment

1. Loosen mounting screws on switch.
2. Place shift lever in NEUTRAL.
3. Adjust switch until engine starts in NEUTRAL. Tighten mounting screws.
4. Engine should start in PARK and NEUTRAL only.
5. Back-up lights should operate when shift lever is in REVERSE.
6. Parking brake should release in any drive range with engine running.

1963

Removal

1. Remove mounting screw and switch from steering column.
2. Mark top vacuum hose for identification and remove hoses.
3. Disconnect wires from switch.

Installation

1. Connect switch wires and install vacuum hoses on switch.
2. Install switch on steering column and secure with mounting screw.

Adjustment

1. Loosen switch mounting screw.
2. Place shift lever in NEUTRAL.
3. Insert a pin or rod (.090-.094" or #90 drill) in adjusting hole in switch cover.
4. Rotate switch counterclockwise until slider block inside switch bears against pin or drill.
5. Tighten adjusting screw, remove pin and test for operation.
6. Engine should start in PARK or NEUTRAL only.
7. Back-up lights should operate when shift lever is in REVERSE.
8. Parking brake should release in any drive range with engine running.

TURN SIGNAL SWITCH, REPLACE

1969

Standard Wheel

1. Remove battery cable.
2. Remove steering wheel.
3. Remove lock plate cover screws and cover.
4. With a suitable compressor, compress lock plate and spring and remove snap ring from shaft.
5. Remove lock plate, cancelling cam, preload spring and thrust washer.
6. Remove turn signal lever.
7. Disconnect switch wiring connector and wrap a piece of tape around connector and harness to facilitate removal.
8. Remove upper mounting bracket from column.
9. Remove three retaining screws and remove switch. Reverse procedure to install.

Tilt & Telescope Wheel

1. Disconnect battery cable and remove steering wheel and rubber bump stop.
2. With a suitable tool, compress upper steering shaft pre-load spring and remove C ring, Fig. 9.
3. Remove compressor, lock plate, horn contact, and upper shaft pre-load spring.
4. Disconnect switch wiring connector and wrap a piece of tape around connector and harness to facilitate removal.
5. Remove upper mounting bracket and switch wiring protector.
6. Position shift bowl in "Park" and remove turn signal lever.
7. On Eldorado, disconnect switch and Cruise Control connectors on column and attach a piece of piano wire to connector on Cruise Control harness, unscrew signal lever and gently pull Cruise Control harness up through and out of column. Secure piano wire in column to aid in reassembly.
8. Push hazard warning flasher button in then unscrew and remove button.
9. Remove retaining screws and remove switch.
10. Reverse procedure to install. On Eldorado, use the piece of piano wire previously installed to draw the Cruise Control harness through the column.

1968

Standard Wheel

1. Disconnect battery ground cable.
2. Remove lower steering column cover.
3. Disconnect turn signal switch and cornering switch multiple connectors at lower end of steering column.
4. Cut turn and cornering multiple connectors from wiring harnesses and harness strap on steering column.
5. Remove steering wheel.
6. Slide upper bearing preload spring and turn cancelling cam off steering shaft.
7. Remove turn signal lever.
8. Remove cap from hazard warning switch button. Push switch button in and, after removing screw remove button.
9. Remove snap ring from steering shaft.
10. Slide thrust washer and wave washer off shaft.
11. Loosen three switch mounting screws until assembly can be rotated counterclockwise. It may be necessary to push on top of screws to

loosen assembly.
12. Rotate cover counterclockwise and pull assembly off top of jacket.
13. Remove three screws from engagement with lock plate.
14. Remove switch and housing assemblies from cover and separate them.
15. Reverse procedure to install.

Tilt & Telescope Wheel

1. Perform Steps 1 through 5 above.
2. Remove tilt release lever and signal switch lever.
3. Remove cap from hazard warning switch knob.
4. Push in on hazard warning knob and remove screw and knob.
5. Remove actuator cover, using a suitable slide hammer. Rotate slide hammer after each hammer blow to distribute forces evenly around cover, Fig. 8.
6. Remove C-ring as shown in Fig. 9.
7. Remove carrier and spring compressor from column.
8. Remove horn contact carrier.
9. Remove signal switch and hazard warning switch screws.

1967

1. Disconnect battery ground cable.
2. Remove steering column lower cover.
3. Disconnect turn signal harness 9-way and cornering light 3-way "half-moon" connectors.
4. Remove steering wheel horn pad. On T & T column, also remove telescope lock lever.
5. Scribe mark for alignment of steering wheel when replacing, then remove steering wheel.
6. Remove turn signal lever and hazard warning knob. On T & T column, also remove tilt lever, shift lever and actuator cover, Fig. 8.
7. On standard column, remove "C" retaining ring and thrust and wave washers. On T & T column, snip wiring harness at switch, then remove "C" retaining ring, carrier, contact and bumper, and remove switch, Fig. 9.
8. Remove column mounting support bracket and carefully support column with a wood block.
9. Remove wire cover clips from column jacket. On T & T column, pull loose connector and harness out from below. On standard column, remove upper end assembly, pulling wiring up through top of column and remove switch from upper end assembly.
10. Reverse procedure to install.

1965-66

Standard Wheel

1. Remove steering column lower cover.
2. Remove transmission shift indicator.
3. Remove steering wheel.
4. Remove column lower cover plate.
5. Loosen column upper clamp.
6. Disconnect turn signal switch wires and horn contact wire at connectors under instrument panel.
7. Remove plastic cam from upper end of column shaft.
8. Remove wiring harness shield from jacket.
9. Remove six wires from turn signal-stop light connector by prying collapsible edge of each lead inboard until wire can be pulled through connector. Repeat procedure for three wires at cornering light connector.
10. Separate switch housing from lock plate (6 screws) and pull housing up to remove guide wires through carrier.

NOTE: When performing Step 10 it will be necessary to pull signal switch housing up on shaft until upper bearing seat is free from upper bearing and remove upper bearing seat.

---

11. Remove wire harness clamp on reverse side of turn signal switch housing.
12. Separate switch from housing (3 screws).
13. Reverse above procedure to install.

Tilt & Telescoping Wheel

1. Disconnect multiple connectors from turn signal switch on side of steering column jacket.
2. Remove turn signal switch from jacket.
3. Disconnect cable from switch by removing one self-tapping screw, and slip coil end of cable off post.

NOTE: When installing switch, raise tilt lever, place tilt mechanism in maximum "down" position and attach cable to switch. Coil end of cable should be slipped over post on switch with wire next to base of post and coil extending outward. Do not twist cable. Install cable in its natural position.

Insert clamp tang in mounting hole and install retaining screw through flag-shaped terminal into switch, locking them together. With turn signal lever in "off" position, install switch on steering column jacket, being certain that switch is centered properly and secured with two screws.

It is not necessary to apply extra tension on cable after switch is installed. Switch should function properly without further adjustment.

1963-64

Standard Wheel

1. Remove steering column lower cover and transmission shift indicator and holder.
2. Disconnect turn signal wires at connectors under dash.
3. Remove steering wheel.
4. Remove turn signal cancelling cam spacer.
5. Lower column and remove turn signal switch harness protector from column jacket.
6. Remove turn signal housing and switch from steering column.
7. Remove turn signal lever.
8. Remove turn signal switch and wires from switch housing.
9. Reverse above procedure to install.

Adjustable Wheel, 1964: Follow procedure outlined for 1965 models.

HORN SOUNDER & STEERING WHEEL

1967-69

1. Remove three screws from back of spokes and lift pad assembly from wheel.
2. On tilt and telescope wheels remove three screws securing lever and knob assembly to flange and screw assembly. Unscrew flange and screw assembly from steering shaft and remove. Remove lever and knob assembly.
3. On standard wheels, scribe an alignment mark on wheel hub in line with slash mark on steering shaft to be used upon installation.
4. Loosen steering shaft nut, apply a suitable puller to loosen wheel; then remove puller, nut and wheel.
5. Remove three screws securing three contact wires to wheel.
6. Reverse procedure to install.

1965-66

1. Remove cap from horn control shroud by prying it off carefully.
2. Remove steering shaft nut and washer.
3. Lift horn control shroud and switch assembly from steering wheel. If horn control shroud is to be replaced, remove three screws from underside of horn control and remove control, which is serviced only as an assembly.
4. Remove horn contact cartridge from wheel hub.
5. Scribe an alignment mark on wheel hub in line with slash mark on end of steering shaft to be used at installation.
6. Reinstall nut on steering shaft so that nut is flush with end of shaft.
7. Then use a suitable puller to remove wheel.

1963-64

1. Remove cap from horn control shroud by prying it off.
2. Disconnect horn wire from top of steering shaft.
3. Remove upper steering shaft nut.
4. Lift horn control shroud and switch assembly from wheel.
5. Scribe a line on wheel hub and end of steering shaft to be used at installation.
6. Use a suitable puller to remove wheel.

INSTRUMENT CLUSTER

1969

1. Disconnect battery cable.
2. Remove instrument panel top cover, clock, radio and steering column lower cover.
3. Remove shift indicator pointer.
4. Remove odometer reset knob by pulling it off shaft.
5. Remove four cluster-to-bezel screws.
6. Move cluster forward and to the right. Tip right hand corner of cluster downward and remove cluster from under panel.

1968

1. Remove instrument panel top cover.
2. Remove steering column lower cover.
3. Remove transmission shift indicator pointer with an Allen wrench. Locking screw is accessible through slot on lower edge of shift bowl.
4. Disconnect multiple connector at instrument panel cluster case and remove instrument panel harness from cluster attachment.
5. Disconnect speedometer cable from speedometer head by depressing risers on wave washer. Feed cable back through firewall to protect cable.
6. If equipped with Automatic Climate Control, remove the control left air outlet hose at outboard end.
7. Remove two upper screws that secure panel cluster to bezel.
8. If equipped with Automatic Climate Control, remove two screws securing center outlet duct to bezel and remove duct.
9. Remove two lower cluster-to-bezel screws. One screw is located below clock, the other is between headlight switch and left A/C air outlet duct.
10. Remove radio knobs, springs and rings. Remove radio control shaft nuts.
11. Remove screw on right side that secures radio to bracket.
12. Carefully pull radio out of bezel to disengage control shafts and lower radio slightly to permit removal of cluster.
13. If equipped with Rear Window Defogger, Seat Warmer or convertible top, disconnect connectors.
14. Loosen upper left and right bezel-to-bracket screws.
15. Pry left corner of bezel forward and pull cluster up to remove.

1967

1. Remove upper instrument panel cover.
2. Remove steering column lower cover.
3. Remove transmission shift indicator pointer.
4. Disconnect multiple connector at instrument panel cluster case and remove panel harness from cluster attachment.
5. Disconnect speedometer cable by depressing risers on wave washer. These risers are 180° apart.
6. Separate instrument panel cluster from bezel (3 screws).
7. Remove right and center lower screws that secure panel cluster to bezel. Center screw is located below clock.
8. If equipped with Automatic Climate Control, remove center air outlet boot.
9. Remove center air outlet (2 screws).
10. If equipped with Automatic Climate Control, remove left air outlet boot at inboard end.
11. Using a flexible hex driver, remove lower left instrument panel cluster-to-bezel screw.
12. If equipped with Rear Window Defogger, Seat Warmer or convertible top, disconnect connectors.
13. Disconnect map light switch connector.
14. Loosen upper left and right bezel-to-bracket screws.
15. Pry left corner of bezel forward and pull instrument panel cluster up to remove.
16. Reverse procedure to install.

1963-64

1. Remove upper instrument panel cover.
2. Remove steering column lower cover.
3. Remove front radio speaker.
4. Disconnect speedometer cable.
5. Disconnect trip odometer reset cable on lower flange of instrument panel.
6. Remove ignition switch light bulb.
7. Remove four instrument cluster mounting screws.
8. Remove four cluster bulb sockets.
9. Remove wire terminal and bulb retainer, and trunk lid tell-tale bulb socket (if equipped).
10. Remove cluster assembly.

1965-66

1. Remove upper instrument panel cover.
2. Remove headlamp switch, clock and steering column.
3. Remove steering column upper cover (2 screws).
4. Disconnect seven cluster bulb sockets, fuel gauge, temperature gauge and transmission stator switch connectors.
5. Disconnect cable from speedometer.
6. Working through headlamp switch opening in cluster bezel, remove screw that holds cluster bezel right lower mounting bracket to right mounting bracket on instrument panel center brace.
7. Remove two screws that hold cluster bezel to upper instrument panel center moulding and remove bezel and cluster from panel.
8. Remove trip odometer reset shaft knob.
9. Separate bezel from cluster panel (4 screws).

1965 Except Fleetwood Models

1. Disconnect negative battery cable.
2. Disconnect three washer hoses from washer control valve. Mark small outlet hoses and corresponding control valve nozzles for identification.
3. Disconnect two-way wire connector at washer unit and three-way wire connector at wiper.
4. Remove rubber grommet from opening in left side of cowl to gain access to wiper unit crank arm. Rubber grommet is located above wiper and washer assembly.
5. Loosen two lock nuts securing wiper crank arm to ball socket on end of transmission drive linkage, then disconnect crank arm from ball socket. Do not remove lock nuts from ball socket studs.
6. Remove three screws that hold wiper and washer assembly to cowl and remove from car.

RADIO, REPLACE

NOTE: When installing radio, be sure to adjust antenna trimmer for peak performance.

1968-69

1. On 1968, remove instrument panel top cover. On 1969, remove steering column lower cover. If necessary, remove defroster hose from behind radio.
2. On 1968, remove A/C center duct (2 screws).
3. Remove radio knobs, springs and rings.
4. Remove spanner nuts that hold radio control shafts to instrument panel.
5. Remove screw on right side that secures radio to bracket and loosen screw that secures bracket to brace.
6. Pull radio rearward to disengage control shafts and drop radio slightly to gain access to wiring connectors.
7. On AM/FM Stereo radio, disconnect audio-amplifier unit connector.
8. Disconnect antenna lead-in cable and connector at radio.
9. Disconnect light bulb socket from radio.
10. Disconnect foot control cable plug from radio if equipped.
11. On stereo radio, remove tape securing speaker leads: Two pieces on instrument panel cluster and two pieces at instrument panel frame above glove box door.
12. Remove radio by working it out through top of instrument panel.

1967

1. Remove upper instrument panel cover.
2. Remove ash tray housing.
3. Unfasten ash tray frame from retaining plate (4 screws), disconnect frame multiple connector and remove frame.
4. Remove radio knobs, springs and rings.
5. Remove spanner nuts that hold control shafts to instrument panel.
6. Unfasten radio bracket from frame (screw on right side).
7. Pull radio rearward to disengage control shafts and drop radio slightly to gain access to wiring connectors.
8. Remove radio through ash tray opening.
9. Reverse procedure to install.

1965-66

1. Remove upper instrument panel cover.
2. Remove radio knobs, springs and rings, using Allen wrench to loosen knob retainer screws.
3. Disconnect dial bulb socket from radio.
4. Disconnect antenna lead-in cable and five-way wire connector at radio.
5. Disconnect floor control cable plug from radio (if equipped).
6. Using spanner wrench, remove nuts that hold control shafts to upper panel right moulding and remove escutcheons.
7. Remove lock nut securing radio front side bracket to mounting stud.

8. Loosen screw securing radio rear side bracket to radio and remove screw securing rear side bracket to upper instrument panel.
9. Carefully pull radio rearward to disengage control shafts and front side bracket from upper panel.
10. Remove radio through opening in top of upper instrument panel.

1963-64

1. Disconnect battery ground cable.
2. Remove steering column lower cover.
3. Remove radio knobs, springs and rings.
4. Remove control shaft nuts.
5. Disconnect antenna lead-in cable and four-way electrical connector.
6. Disconnect floor control unit from bottom of radio (if equipped).
7. Remove glove box (7 screws).
8. Remove screw securing radio to rear support bracket through glove box opening.
9. Remove air conditioner center flange and duct boot (if equipped).
10. Lower radio, disconnect dial light and remove unit.

W/S WIPER MOTOR

1965-69

1. Disconnect battery ground cable.
2. Disconnect three washer hoses from washer control valve. *Mark small outlet hoses and corresponding control valve nozzles for identification.*
3. Disconnect two-way wire connector at washer unit and three-way wire connector at wiper unit.
4. Remove cover on 1967-69 from opening in left side of cowl to gain access to wiper crank arm. *Cover is located above wiper-washer assembly.*
5. Loosen two lock nuts securing wiper unit crank arm to ball socket on end of transmission drive linkage, then disengage crank arm from ball socket. *Do not remove lock nuts from ball sockets.*
6. Remove three screws that hold wiper-washer assembly to cowl and remove assembly.
7. Reverse procedure to install.

1965 Fleetwood & All 1963-64

1. Disconnect battery ground cable.
2. Disconnect three hoses from windshield washer. Mark hoses and pump valves for identification.
3. Disconnect multiple connectors at wiper unit.
4. Remove air intake grille.
5. Disconnect linkage by removing retainer.
6. Remove three screws and remove wiper motor from under hood.

W/S WIPER TRANSMISSION

1968-69 Except Eldorado

1. Remove both wiper arms.
2. Remove six clips securing rubber hood seal to cowl and position seal out of the way.
3. Remove cowl ventilator screen (12 screws).
4. Unfasten left wiper transmission from cowl (3 screws).
5. Repeat Step 4 for right side.
6. Allow transmissions, linkage and bellcrank to lie in cowl plenum.
7. Remove ball socket cover (2 screws). Cover is located on top of cowl directly behind wiper-washer assembly.
8. Loosen two lock nuts securing crank arm to ball socket on end of drive linkage, then disengage crank arm from ball socket. Do not remove locknuts from ball socket studs.
9. Slide linkage to one side to allow one end of linkage to be drawn out through opening in cowl and remove linkage.
10. Reverse procedure to install.

1968-69 Eldorado

1. Remove both wiper arms.
2. Remove cowl air inlet screen.
3. Remove access hole cover from opening in center of cowl to gain access to wiper unit crank arm.
4. Remove lock nut securing crank arm to ball socket stud.
5. Remove three transmission mounting screws on right and left transmissions.
6. Disengage ball socket stud at wiper unit and remove transmissions and linkages as a complete assembly.
7. Reverse procedure to install.

1965-67 Except Eldorado

1. Remove shroud top ventilator frame and grille assembly.
2. Remove rubber grommet (1965-66) or cover (1967) from opening in left side of cowl to gain access to wiper unit crank arm.
3. Loosen (do not remove) two retaining nuts that secure drive linkage ball socket to motor crank arm, then disengage linkage from crank arm ball.
4. Remove mounting screws from right and left transmissions.
5. Remove four screws at bellcrank, then remove transmissions and linkage as an assembly.
6. Reverse procedure to install.

1967 Eldorado

1. Remove top shroud ventilator frame and grille assembly.
2. Remove access hole cover (2 screws) from opening in center of cowl to gain access to wiper unit crank arm.
3. Remove lock nut securing crank arm to ball socket stud.
4. Remove mounting screws on right and left transmissions.
5. Disengage ball socket stud at wiper unit and remove transmissions and linkage as a unit.
6. Reverse procedure to install.

1963-64

1. Remove shroud top ventilator frame.
2. Remove clip retaining right-hand transmission and linkage to drive linkage.
3. Remove three transmission attaching screws on right side.
4. Remove right-hand transmission and linkage assembly as a unit.
5. Repeat Steps 2, 3 and 4 on left transmission.

SERVICE NOTE: To remove transmissions and linkages as a complete unit, remove clip retaining main drive linkage to wiper motor unit crank arm. Remove three transmission mounting screws on right and left sides. Then remove three screws securing linkage at pivot area and carefully remove entire linkage assembly.

Installation

1. Position transmissions and linkages in shroud top and install transmission mounting screws.
2. Install retaining screws at pivot area and all retaining clips.
3. Install shroud top ventilator frame.

IMPORTANT: When installing wiper arm and blade assemblies, be sure to "overpark" the arms and blades enough below the windshield so that a proper return to park position always results. Make certain that left blade assembly is above right blade assembly in park position.

W/S WIPER SWITCH

1969

1. Open left front door to gain access to screw securing control switch to instrument panel extension on door.
2. Loosen screw securing control switch to extension. *Screw is trapped and cannot be removed.*
3. Pull control switch out and disconnect electrical connector.

1967-68

1. Remove steering column lower cover.
2. Remove two screws and clip securing switch to panel.
3. Pull switch rearward to disengage from instrument panel.
4. Disconnect dial bulb socket and wiring harness connector from back of switch.
5. Reverse procedure to install.

1965-66

1. Disconnect negative battery cable.
2. Using a screwdriver, carefully pry frame and switch assembly from lower instrument panel to disengage snap-in mounting studs on frame from stud retainers in lower instrument panel.
3. Disconnect dial bulb socket and four-way wire harness connector from back of switch, then remove frame and switch assembly.
4. Remove switch from frame.

1965 Fleetwood & All 1963-64

1. Disconnect negative battery cable.
2. On 1964-65, remove steering column lower cover.

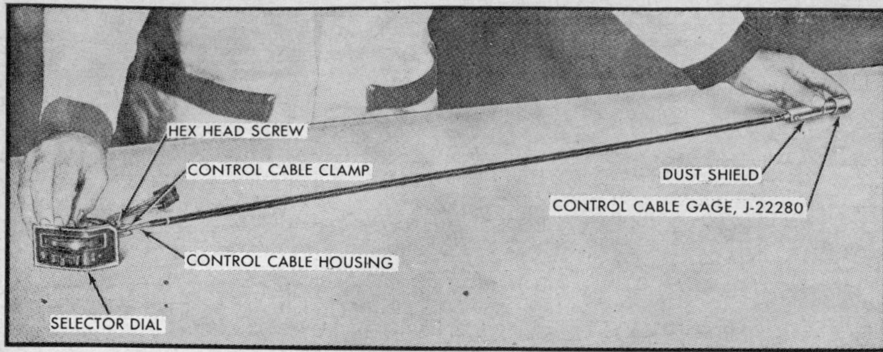

Fig. 10 Control cable adjustment for Slide Switch Speedostat

3. Disconnect three-way wire connector from wiper switch and pry switch from instrument panel.
4. Remove two screws and take switch from escutcheon.
5. Reverse above procedure to install.

HEATER CORE REMOVAL

1965-69 Except Eldorado

1. Blower motor and heater-blower assembly must be removed to get at the heater core. To do this, first disconnect electrical connector to blower on cowl in engine compartment. Then remove five screws securing blower motor to its case and remove motor.
2. Disconnect cable at temperature valve at pivot point on heater and remove cable clamp.
3. Remove screw securing vacuum manifold to heater and move manifold and hoses out of the way.
4. Remove seven screws securing bottom of heater to cowl and six screws securing top of heater to cowl, and take out heater assembly.
5. To remove heater core, remove four screws (two each side) that secure wire retaining clamp to heater blower case and remove clamps.

Fig. 11 Accelerator linkage adjustment for Slide Switch type Speedostat

6. Heater core can now be pulled out of case and rubber grommets removed from inlet and outlet fittings.

1967-69 Eldorado

1. Before removing heater blower and motor, disconnect rubber cooling hose from nipple on blower motor.
2. The left cowl-to-fender shield strut rod must also be removed before taking out heater-blower assembly.

1963-64

1. Remove glove box from instrument panel, then disconnect cables and defroster hoses at heater assembly.
2. Remove right and left kick pads and floor duct connector, then disconnect coolant hoses at heater.
3. At this point, blower and air inlet assembly must be removed from engine side of dash. To permit removal of this assembly, it is necessary to partially disconnect radio antenna and move it out of the way.
4. Remove heater from car. Slide heater core toward defroster outlets and lift out.

SPEED CONTROL

Control Cable Adjustment, Prior to 1966

1. Rotate selector dial rearward as far as it will turn without forcing.
2. Loosen set screw on cable dust shield.
3. Again try to rotate selector dial rearward only in order to make certain it is against the stop.
4. Push in lightly on control cable at dust shield, making certain cable is against stop (do not force cable beyond stop).
5. Hold cable against stop and tighten set screw on dust shield securely.

Control Cable Adjustment, 1966-69

The cable is preset at the factory and should not require adjustment unless a new cable is installed. This adjustment must be performed off the car as follows:

1. Remove the selector assembly.
2. Rotate selector dial to low speed position until it is positioned against its stop but do not force beyond its stop.
3. Position assembly flat on workbench and make certain there are no kinks in cable.
4. Loosen hex head set screw at cable clamp on selector control.
5. Pull cable housing until it is approximately half-way out of cable clamp. Position control cable gauge shown in Fig. 10 in end of dust shield. Hold dust shield and gauge and push toward selector control assembly until gauge bottoms. While holding in this position, tighten set screw at cable clamp.

Accelerator Linkage

1. Adjust throttle rod.
2. Start engine and operate at slow idle with transmission lever in "Park".
3. Separate linkage from exterior arm.
4. Adjust trunnion so that when it is installed through exterior arm, the stop stud will be aligned with locating notch and throttle valves will be closed.
5. Install washer on trunnion and secure with cotter pin.

NOTE: Due to the angle at which the trunnion enters hole in exterior arm, it is necessary to rotate the exterior arm slightly forward when inserting the trunnion. Repeat this operation until proper alignment is obtained. Be careful not to turn trunnion too far back or throttle valves will unseat and cause an incorrect adjustment. Insert the gauge shown in Fig. 11 (or small diameter pipe) over stop stud to check alignment.

Brake Release Switch

1. Turn on ignition but do not start engine.
2. Momentarily move slide switch to AUTO position until red indicator light glows.
3. Using a test lamp, ground one lead and touch the other lead to terminal No. 4, Fig. 12.
4. Loosen mounting screw securing release switch to brake pedal mounting bracket.
5. Adjust release switch so that lamp will light when brake pedal is fully released, and will go out when brake pedal is depressed about ¼ inch. Tighten switch mounting screw. If switch cannot be adjusted, it is defective and should be replaced.

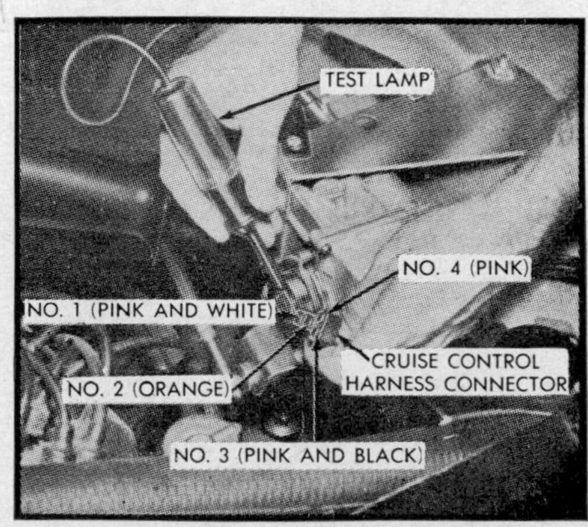

Fig. 12 Electrical connections on Slide Switch type Speedostat

Engine Section

ENGINE, REPLACE

1968-69

NOTE: Disregard optional equipment items mentioned in the following if the car being serviced is not so equipped.

1. Disconnect battery ground cable.
2. Remove hood, air cleaner and automatic level control hoses.
3. Disconnect carburetor linkage at pedal lever.
4. Disconnect Cruise Control linkage.
5. Remove radiator shroud and clamp securing radiator upper hoses to cradle.
6. Disconnect and/or remove all necessary wiring, pipes, hoses, linkage, etc.
7. Remove fan. On Eldorado, remove studs from water pump shaft hub.
8. Remove Cruise Control power head.
9. Remove A/C compressor.
10. Partially remove power steering pump, laying it aside so that pressure and return hoses are above the fluid level in pump reservoir.
11. Position power steering cooler out of the way.
12. Loosen A.I.R. pump and remove belt.
13. Remove water pump pulley and alternator.
14. Remove two upper transmission-to-engine screws. Right screw secures transmission dipstick and modulator line to engine.
15. Remove A/C power servo from heater air selector. On cars other than Eldorado, remove blower relay and master switch from heater air selector.
16. Remove dust shield-to-cowl tie struts.
17. Position a lifting bracket to rear intake manifold attaching screws on Cruise Control cars. Bracket is in place on all others.
18. Raise car and place on jack stands.
19. Remove front engine mount nuts.
20. Remove oil filter.
21. On Eldorado, remove right output shaft.
22. Unfasten starter and allow it to hang by its cables.
23. Remove converter inspection pan.
24. Disconnect exhaust pipes from manifolds.
25. Place a jack under exhaust pipes to support system while engine is removed.
26. Support transmission with a jack.
27. Remove four lower transmission-to-engine screws.
28. Remove three screws securing converter to flex plate.
29. With lifting rig attached, pry engine forward while raising it as far as possible.
30. Lower transmission and again raise engine.
31. Remove flex plate and lift engine free of car.
32. Reverse procedure to install.

1967 Except Eldorado

NOTE: Engine must be removed with transmission attached as follows:

1. Lower radio antenna.
2. Remove hood.
3. Raise and support car (front and rear).
4. Disconnect negative battery cable.
5. Remove carburetor air cleaner.
6. Disconnect and/or remove all necessary wiring, pipes, hoses, linkage, etc.
7. If equipped with A/C, remove compressor.
8. Disconnect transmission fluid cooler lines at radiator, plug lines to prevent loss of fluid and remove radiator.
9. Remove fan blade assembly.

NOTE: Fan clutches used on A/C cars are always to be in an "in car position." When removed from car, support assembly to keep clutch disc in a vertical plane to prevent leaks of silicone fluid from clutch mechanism.

10. Disconnect exhaust pipe components as required.
11. Disconnect speedometer cable at transmission.
12. Unfasten and position steering idler arm to one side.
13. Disconnect propeller shaft, transmission shift linkage and electrical wires from transmission.
14. With hoisting equipment secured, tilt rear of engine down at a 45° angle and lift engine and transmission straight out.

1967 Eldorado

NOTE: The general procedure for removing the engine is similar to standard models up to a point from where it continues as follows:

1. Remove one screw securing brace to final drive.
2. Unfasten right exhaust pipe clamp at exhaust manifold.
3. Remove four screws securing transmission front cover to transmission. *Upper left screw is accessible with an extension and universal socket.*
4. Remove three converter-to-flex plate attaching screws. *This is done by removing cork in vibration damper and inserting a screw in damper. Rotate the screw to gain access to converter-to-flex plate screws. Do not pry on flex plate ring gear to rotate converter as flex plate may become damaged.*
5. Remove vacuum modulator line at transmission and at engine.
6. Working through center crossmember, loosen (do not remove) two transmission mounting nuts.
7. Remove two nuts securing engine mounting studs to front frame crossmember.

CAUTION: There is one bolt left securing the final drive housing to the engine support bracket and two screws securing the transmission to the spacer to the engine. Do not proceed further until chain hoist cable is connected to the engine as engine may shift.

8. Attach chain hoist cable to engine and take up slack.
9. Remove lower right and left transmission-to-adapter-to cylinder block screws.
10. Place small jack under final drive housing to support final drive and transmission.
11. Remove bolt securing final drive housing to engine support bracket.
12. Remove engine by pulling it slightly forward to disengage from transmission and up from engine compartment. Turn engine slightly clockwise while removing to clear engine compartment.
13. Secure a holding strap to transmission to prevent converter from falling out.

1965-66

NOTE: Engine must be removed with transmission attached.

1. Lower radio antenna.
2. Place car on jack stands (front and rear).
3. Disconnect positive battery cable.
4. Remove carburetor air cleaner.
5. Drain cooling system.
6. Disconnect wires, tubing, hoses and linkage attached to engine and transmission.
7. Unfasten and move power steering pump to one side without disconnecting hoses.
8. Remove fan blade, spacer and pulley.
9. On air conditioned cars, remove compressor.
10. Remove crossover pipe.
11. Unfasten and move steering idler arm to one side.
12. Unfasten engine front supports from frame.
13. Disconnect propeller shaft.
14. Remove hood.
15. Place jack with wood block cushion under transmission and take load from rear engine crossmember.
16. Remove two rear engine support mount-to-transmission extension housing screws.
17. Remove rear engine support crossmember.
18. Support engine with a hoist and remove jack from under transmission.
19. With all wires, tubing, straps, etc. disconnected, tilt rear of engine down at a 45-degree angle and lift engine and transmission straight out.
20. Reverse procedure to install.

1963-64

The engine is removed without the transmission. In addition to the usual items to be removed or disconnected, perform the following:

1. Remove hood and radiator.
2. Remove air conditioning compressor.

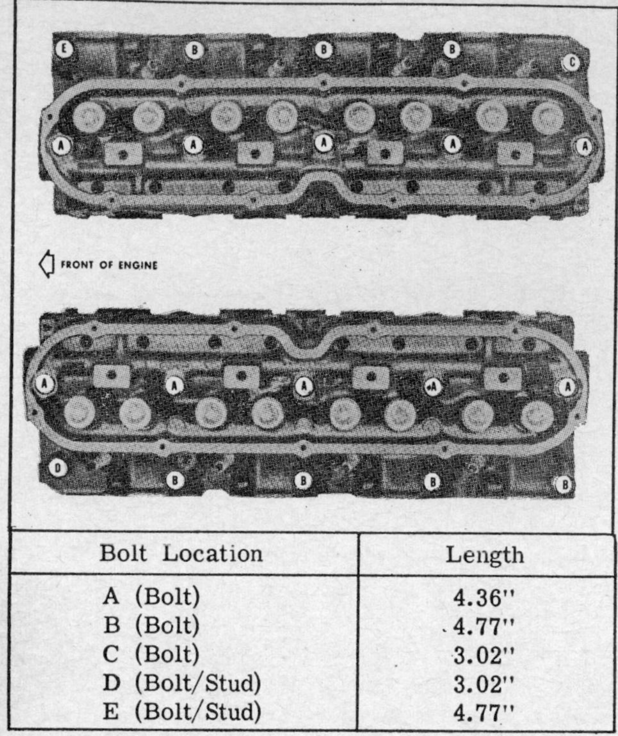

Bolt Location	Length
A (Bolt)	4.36"
B (Bolt)	4.77"
C (Bolt)	3.02"
D (Bolt/Stud)	3.02"
E (Bolt/Stud)	4.77"

Fig. 2 Location and length of cylinder head screws. 1968-69

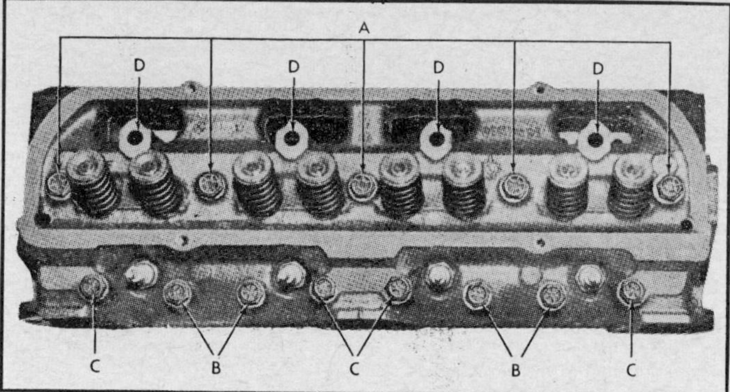

Fig. 3 Cylinder head bolt locations on 1964-67 engines (see Service Bulletin)

3. Remove fan, pulley and all belts.
4. Remove power steering pump with bracket and position bracket and pump to one side. Do not disconnect hoses.
5. With all other items disconnected or removed, remove two center capscrews on each side from lower row of cylinder head attaching screws.
6. If adapter plates are not available, use large eyebolts in holes from which screws were removed.
7. Attach a chain hoist to eyebolts and remove engine by carefully lifting it slightly upward and forward to disengage locating dowels on cylinder block from dowel holes in flywheel housing and flex plate locating studs on flywheel. Then lift straight up until engine front support studs are free from slots in frame.

CYLINDER HEAD, REPLACE

1968-69

1. Remove intake manifold.
2. Drain coolant from radiator.
3. Disconnect ground strap at rear of cylinder heads from cowl.
4. Disconnect wiring connector for high engine temperature warning system from sending unit at rear of left cylinder head.
5. Remove alternator if working on right cylinder head, or partially remove power steering pump if working on left cylinder head.
6. Remove A.I.R. manifold from both cylinder heads.
7. Unfasten wiring harness from cylinder head and position out of the way.
8. Unfasten exhaust manifold from cylinder head.
9. Remove rocker arm cover.
10. Remove rocker arm assemblies and lift out push rods.
11. Unfasten and lift off cylinder head.
12. After carefully removing all gasket material from mating surfaces of head and block, position new gasket over dowels and install cylinder head in reverse order of removal, being sure to install the screws as indicated in Fig. 2.

1963-67

NOTE: On cars equipped with A.I.R. System, release hose clamps and disconnect air delivery hose at check valve fitting. If working on left cylinder head, remove bolt that holds air pump to rear air pump mounting bracket. Remove pump filter from left rocker arm cover and set aside with hoses attached. If working on right cylinder head, release hose clamp and disconnect intake air bleed valve hose at check valve fitting.

If left cylinder head on the Eldorado with Cruise Control is to be removed, the control power unit and bracket must be removed from back of cylinder head.

On cars equipped with A.I.R. System, lift intake manifold with carburetor and air bleed valve attached.

1. Disconnect battery positive cable, remove carburetor air cleaner and drain cooling system. On air conditioned cars, remove compressor.
2. If the right-hand head is to be removed, disconnect vacuum hose and both heater inlet hoses from water control valve. Also remove the capscrew that holds the transmission filler tube bracket to the exhaust manifold.
3. If left-hand head is to be removed, remove power steering pump and bracket and position to one side (do not disconnect hoses).
4. If both heads are to be removed, first disconnect all necessary wiring, carburetor linkage, vacuum lines, fuel lines, etc.
5. Remove rocker arm covers, secondary ignition wiring and distributor cap as a unit.
6. Unfasten and lift intake manifold off locating dowels on cylinder heads and remove manifold with carburetor attached.
7. Disconnect exhaust pipe from exhaust manifolds and remove heat control valve from left manifold.

---

8. Remove rocker arm assembly. *If equipped with air conditioning, the right bank rocker arm assembly must be removed with cylinder head because of interference between rear rocker arm mounting screw and blower motor.*

---

9. Remove push rods and remaining cylinder head bolts.
10. Remove No. 1 and 5 spark plugs from left bank head (2 and 6 for right head) and install lifting hooks in spark plug holes. Lift head off dowels.
11. Reverse removal procedure to install cylinder heads, being sure to use all new gaskets.
12. On cars with air conditioning, the right rocker arm assembly must be installed with cylinder head because of interference between rear rocker arm screw and blower motor.
13. Be sure face of manifold heat valve stamped "TOP" is next to left manifold.

Service Bulletin

Care should be taken when installing cylinder head bolts on 1964-67 engines to make certain they are installed in the proper holes, otherwise the threads can be stripped when the bolts are tightened. Information pertaining to head bolt loca-

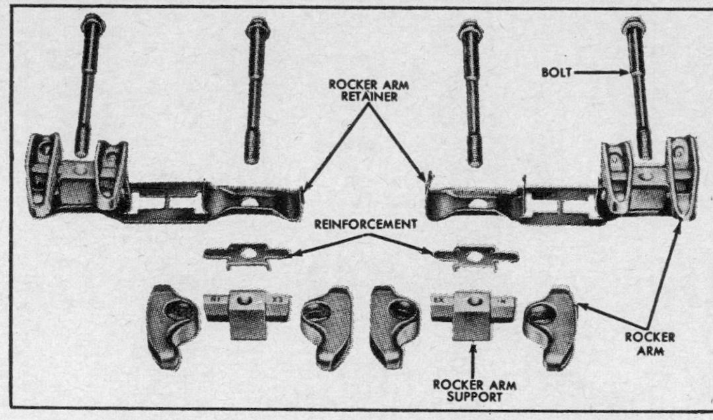

Fig. 4 Rocker arm components disassembled. 1967-69

tions and bolt lengths is given below and in conjunction with Fig. 3 when installing head bolts.

Location	Length
A	4.06″
B	2.75″
C	3.69″
D	5.94″

VALVE ARRANGEMENT

Front to Rear

All Models ....E-I-I-E-E-I-I-E

VALVE LIFT SPECS.

Engine	Year	Intake	Exhaust
V8-390	1963	.451	.451
V8-429	1964-66	.427	.466
V8-429	1967	.440	.440
V8-472	1968-69	.440	.454

VALVE TIMING

Intake Opens Before TDC

Engine	Year	Degrees
V8-390	1963	39
V8-429	1964-66	34
V8-429	1967	39
V8-472	1968-69	18

ROCKER ARMS

1967-69

When disassembling the rocker arm assembly, be sure to keep the supports and rocker arms in order so they can be installed in the exact same position.

Install rocker arms on supports and place supports in retainers as shown in Fig. 2. *Be sure that the "EX" on support is positioned toward the exhaust valve and "IN" toward the intake valve.*

Place capscrews through the reinforcements, supports and retainers and position assemblies on cylinder head. Make sure that push rods are properly seated in the lifter seats and in the rocker arms. Lubricate rocker arm bearing surfaces before assembling in order to prevent wear.

1963-66

1. If a new rocker shaft is necessary, install new cotter pin on end of shaft (end without chamfered edge).
2. Assemble as shown in Fig. 6.

Oil grooves in rocker shaft should face toward cylinder head and notches in end of shafts should face engine when assembly is installed on head.

Line up mounting holes in rocker shaft with holes in brackets and install mounting bolts. *On 1963 engines, thinner end of rocker shaft brackets should be against head of screws.*

VALVE GUIDES

Removable valve guides are used. If a special tool is not available to control the position of the guides when they are installed, carefully measure that portion of the guide that protrudes from the cylinder head and install the new guides accordingly.

VALVE LIFTERS

The valve lifters may be lifted out of their bores after removing the rocker arms and push rods. Adjustable pliers with taped jaws may be used to remove lifters that are stuck due to varnish, carbon, etc. Fig. 7 illustrates the type of lifter used.

ENGINE FRONT COVER

1968-69

1. Disconnect battery ground cable. On 1969 Eldorado, remove engine from chassis.
2. Remove carburetor air cleaner.
3. Drain cooling system.
4. Remove oil pan.
5. Remove upper radiator hose.
6. Remove fan. *On A/C cars, keep fan clutch in "on car" position when removed to prevent leaks of silicone fluid from clutch mechanism.*
7. Remove all drive belts.
8. Remove lower radiator hose.
9. Remove four capscrews that hold crankshaft pulley to vibration damper. *Place scribe marks on pulley and damper for proper installation.*
10. Remove plug from end of crankshaft.
11. Use a suitable puller to remove vibration damper.

NOTE: Use of shop air pressure through a spark plug port to hold one piston within its compression stroke will make it possible to remove vibration damper without turning the crankshaft.

12. Unfasten and remove front cover.
13. Reverse procedure to install, being careful to install the attaching screws as shown in Fig. 8.

1967

1. Disconnect negative battery cable.
2. Remove carburetor air cleaner.
3. Remove two oil pan-to-front cover nuts and studs.
4. Remove fan hub spacer and fan. On A/C cars remove fan.

NOTE: Fan clutches used on air conditioned cars are always to be in an "in car position". When removed from car, support assembly to keep clutch disc in a vertical plane to

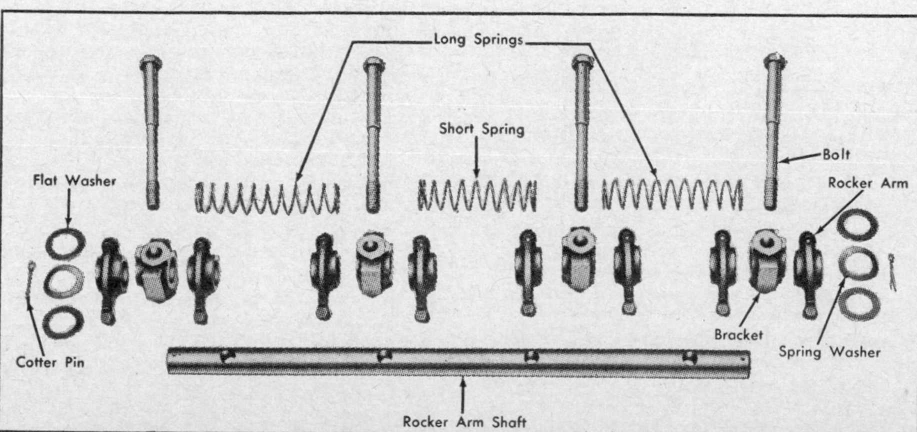

Fig. 6 Rocker arm assembly disassembled. 1963-66

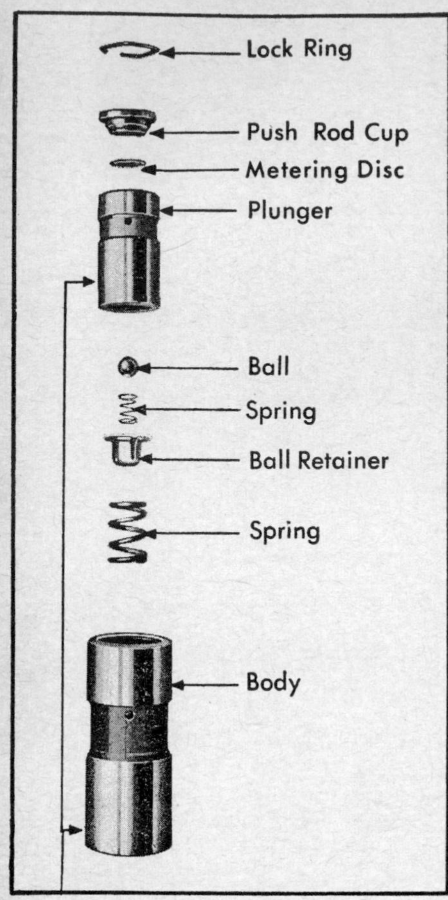

Fig. 7 Hydraulic valve lifter

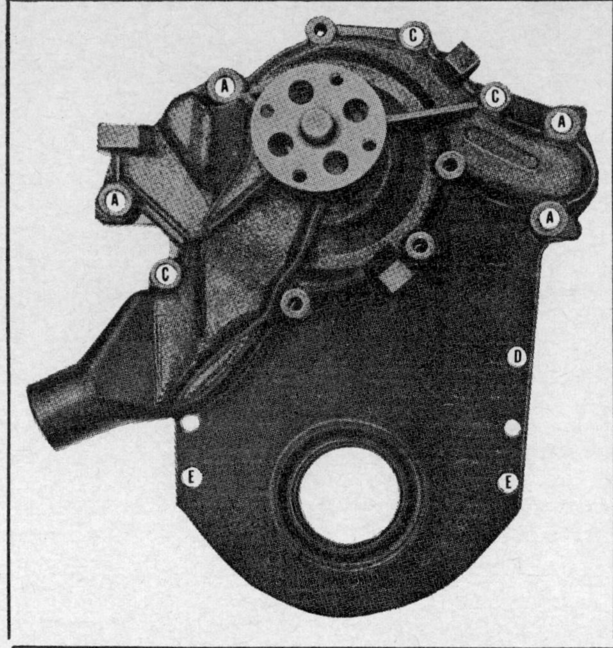

Key	(No.)	Size	Torque
A	(4)	3/8-16 x 1-3/8	25 Foot-Pounds
C	(3)	5/16-18 x 1-1/4	15 Foot-Pounds
D	(1)	5/16-18 x 5/8	15 Foot-Pounds
E	(2)	3/8-16 x 5/8	25 Foot-Pounds

Fig. 8 Engine front cover attaching screws. 1968-69

prevent leaks of silicone fluid from clutch mechanism.

5. Remove power steering drive belt, alternator belt and pulley.
6. Without disconnecting hoses, detach power steering pump and bracket and position to one side.
7. Detach alternator and bracket and position to one side.
8. On Eldorado with air conditioning, partially remove compressor. Also remove compressor lower mounting bracket from engine front cover.
9. Remove ignition distributor.
10. Remove fuel pump.
11. Remove vibration damper.
12. If equipped with A.I.R. System, detach air pump and bracket and swing to one side.
13. Remove oil filter, Fig. 9.
14. Unfasten and remove engine front cover, using care to protect front oil pan seal and gaskets from damage during cover removal.
15. Reverse procedure to install. Tighten cover screws as indicated in Fig. 10.

FRONT COVER OIL SEAL

1968-69

1. Disconnect battery ground cable.
2. Remove carburetor air cleaner.
3. Raise front of car.
4. Remove alternator drive belt.
5. Remove air pump drive belt.
6. Remove power steering pump belt.
7. Working under car, remove four screws that hold crankshaft pulley to vibration damper. Place scribe marks on pulley and damper for proper installation.
8. Remove plug from end of crankshaft.
9. Use a suitable puller to remove vibration damper.
10. Pry out seal.
11. Lubricate new oil seal by filling cavity between lips with wheel bearing grease. Position seal on end of crankshaft with garter spring side toward engine.
12. Using a suitable seal installer, drive seal into front cover until it bottoms against cover.

1963-67

The seal may be replaced without removing the front cover as follows:

1. Remove carburetor air cleaner and all drive belts.
2. Raise front of car and place jack stands under frame near cowl.
3. Working under car, scribe a locating mark shim spacer, crankshaft pulley and vibration damper so that damper may be reinstalled in same position on crankshaft.
4. Remove shim and pulley from vibration damper (6 screws).
5. Remove cork from end of crankshaft.
6. Pull vibration damper off crankshaft.
7. With screwdriver, pry out oil seal.
8. Lubricate new seal with wheel bearing grease and install on crankshaft with garter spring side toward engine.
9. Using a seal driver, drive seal into front cover until it bottoms against shoulder in bore.
10. Lubricate bore of vibration damper with E.P. lube to prevent seizure to crankshaft. Then reassemble parts removed.

1965-66

1. Referring to Figs. 11 and 12, remove carburetor air cleaner. Drain cooling system and remove radiator and oil pan. On 1965 models, remove fan shroud.
2. Remove fan blade. If equipped with air conditioning, remove compressor.
3. Remove power steering and alternator belts and pulley.
4. Unfasten power steering pump and bracket and position to one side (do not disconnect hoses).
5. Unfasten and position alternator and support bracket away from engine.
6. Remove distributor and fuel pump.
7. Unfasten and lower stabilizer bar.
8. Remove four screws from crankshaft pulley.
9. Remove cork plug from end of crankshaft. Then pull off vibration damper with puller.
10. Disconnect heater inlet hose at cylinder head water outlet pipe and heater outlet hose at water pump.

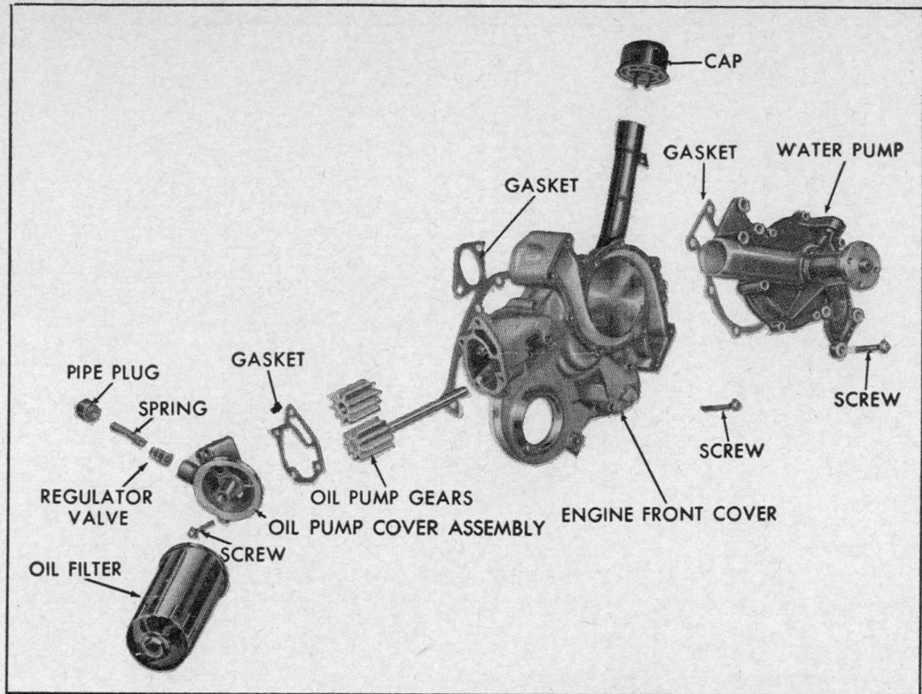

Fig. 9 Engine front cover disassembled. 1967

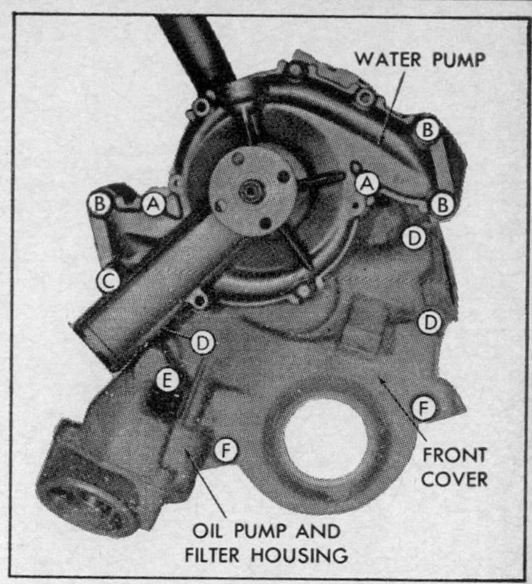

Key	(No.)	Size	Torque
A	(2)	5/16-18 x 3-1/4	10 Foot-Pounds
B	(3)	3/8-16 x 3-5/8	20 Foot-Pounds
C	(1)	3/8-16 x 5	20 Foot-Pounds
D	(3)	5/16-18 x 2-1/8	10 Foot-Pounds
E	(1)	5/16-18 x 2-1/2	10 Foot-Pounds
F	(2)	5/16-18 x 1	10 Foot-Pounds

Fig. 10 Front cover attaching screws. 1967

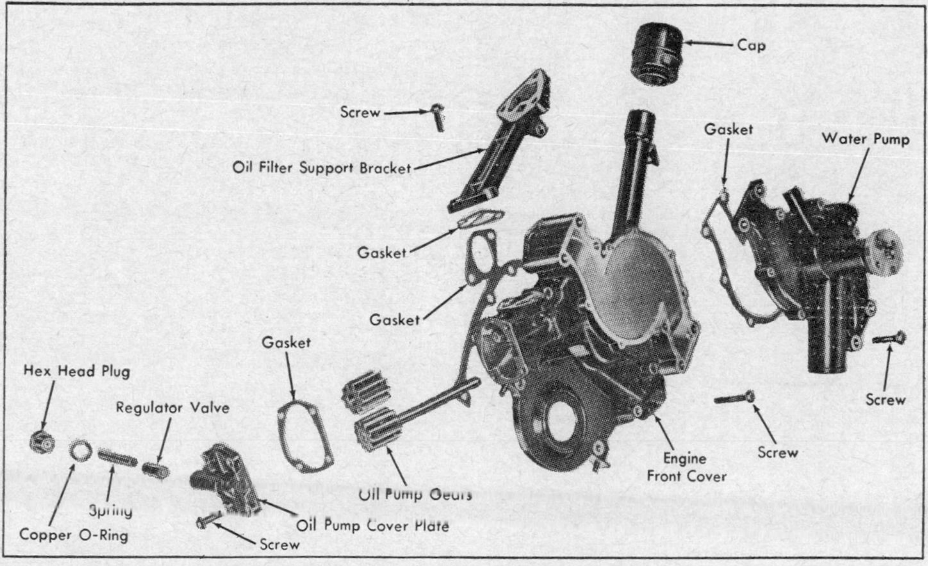

Fig. 11 Engine front cover disassembled. 1963-64

11. Remove oil filter.
12. Remove water outlet pipe from cylinder heads.
13. Remove capscrew holding fuel filter to bracket on oil filler tube.
14. Remove 12 screws that hold front cover to block and take off cover with water pump attached.
15. Reverse removal procedure to install the assembly, referring to Figs. 13 and 14 for attaching screw locations and torque specifications. Also Fig. 14 for vibration damper installation.

Service Bulletin

1963-66: When it is necessary to replace a single lip front cover oil seal due to oil leakage, it has been the practice also to replace the vibration damper if the damper has been scored or grooved by the seal.

It is no longer necessary to replace the grooved vibration damper now that the new dual lip seal is available. The dual lip seal straddles any groove that may have been worn in the damper and thus provides a good seal.

TIMING CHAIN

1. Remove engine front cover as outlined above.
2. Remove two capscrews and washers that hold sprocket to camshaft.
3. Remove camshaft sprocket with chain.
4. Remove crankshaft sprocket.
5. To install, reverse removal procedure, being sure to line up the timing marks as shown in Fig. 15.

CAMSHAFT

1968-69

In order to replace the camshaft, it is necessary to remove the engine on all 1968 and 1969 Eldorado. Then follow the procedure outlined for 1967 models.

1963-67

1. To remove camshaft, take off engine front cover, timing chain and sprockets.
2. If equipped with air conditioner, remove condenser.
3. Remove hood lock plate support.
4. Remove valve lifters.
5. Slide camshaft out of engine carefully. *Use extreme care to keep cam lobes from scratching camshaft bearings.*
6. When installing camshaft, apply a coating of rear axle lubricant to camshaft bearing journals and camshaft lobes.

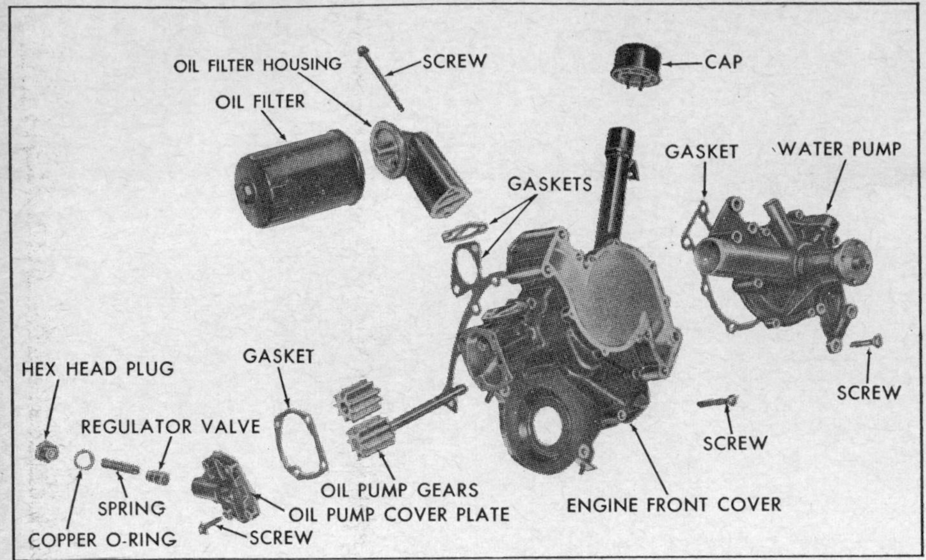

Fig. 12 Engine front cover disassembled. 1965-66

Key	Size	Torque
A	5/16-18x3-1/4	10 foot-pounds
B	3/8-16x3-5/8	15 foot-pounds
C	3/8-16x3-7/8	15 foot-pounds
D	5/16-18x2-1/8	10 foot-pounds
E	5/16-18x2-1/2	10 foot-pounds
F	5/16-18x1	10 foot-pounds

Fig. 13 Engine front cover attaching screws. 1963-64

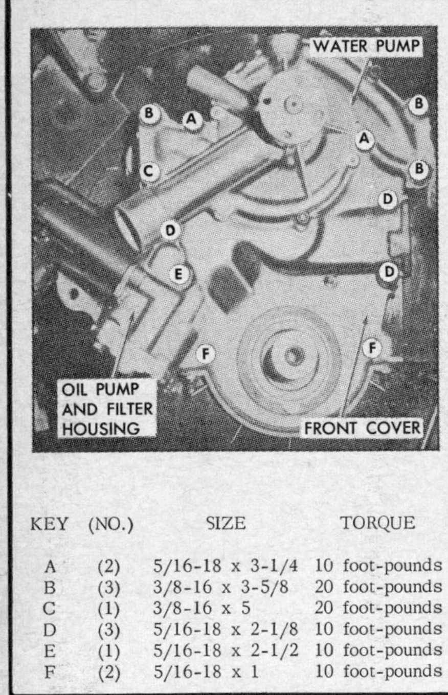

KEY	(NO.)	SIZE	TORQUE
A	(2)	5/16-18 x 3-1/4	10 foot-pounds
B	(3)	3/8-16 x 3-5/8	20 foot-pounds
C	(1)	3/8-16 x 5	20 foot-pounds
D	(3)	5/16-18 x 2-1/8	10 foot-pounds
E	(1)	5/16-18 x 2-1/2	10 foot-pounds
F	(2)	5/16-18 x 1	10 foot-pounds

Fig. 14 Engine front cover attaching screws. 1965-66

Fig. 15 Timing gear locating marks. 1963-69

PISTONS & RODS, ASSEMBLE

On all engines, assemble and install the piston and rod assemblies as shown in Fig. 17.

PISTONS

Service Bulletin

In 1966 engines on cars after approximate V.I. No. 202250, (also 1967) the piston diameters are slightly larger for a better piston to cylinder bore fit.

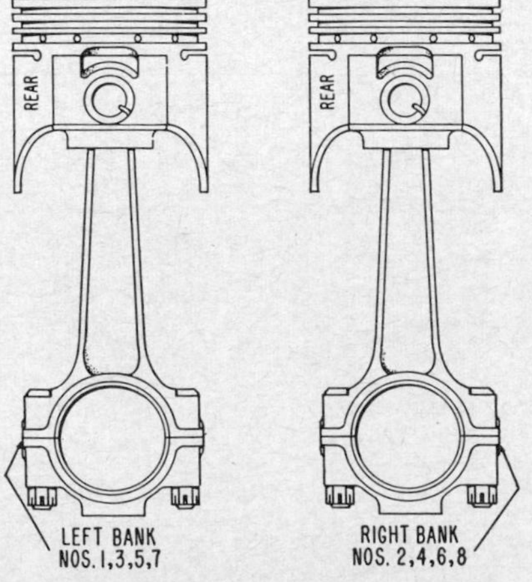

Fig. 17 Piston and rod assembly 1963-67. For 1968-69 odd numbers on right bank

In determining the piston size to order, the diameters of the cylinder bores must be known. Identification of cylinder bore diameters can be made on any Cadillac engine by noting the letter stamped on the valve lifter compartment cover rail, next to the lower inside edge of the cylinder head.

The identification of the letters are grouped in twos, such as "AB", for two adjacent cylinders to which they refer. The letter denotes the diameter size, as shown in the table in Fig. 21, and applies to the letters in the piston size chart shown below.

New Piston Sizes

Letter	Piston Size
A	4.1282-4.1284
B	4.1284-4.1286
C	4.1286-4.1288
D	4.1288-4.1290
E	4.1290-4.1292
H	4.1292-4.1294
J	4.1294-4.1296
K	4.1296-4.1298
L	4.1298-4.1300
M	4.1300-4.1302
AA	4.1382-4.1384
BB	4.1384-4.1386
CC	4.1386-4.1388
DD	4.1388-4.1390
EE	4.1390-4.1392
HH	4.1392-4.1394
JJ	4.1394-4.1396
KK	4.1396-4.1398
LL	4.1398-4.1400
MM	4.1400-4.1402

1963-67

Pistons should be measured for size as

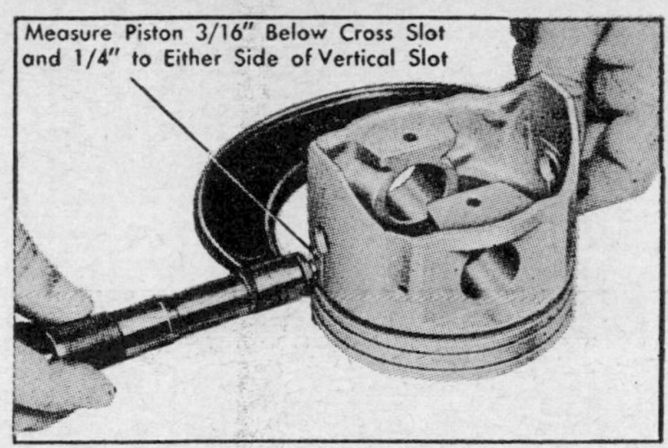

Fig.18 Measuring piston diameter. 1963-69

Cylinder and piston sizes (as indicated by letters stamped on the cylinder head gasket surface). The letters are in groups of two for adjacent cylinders (such as "H" and "B") midway between the two cylinders. The letters denote the cylinder piston sizes as shown below).

Letter	Cylinder Size (Diameter in Inches)	Piston Size (Diameter in Inches)
A	4.3000 - 4.3002	4.2992 - 4.2994
B	4.3002 - 4.3004	4.2994 - 4.2996
C	4.3004 - 4.3006	4.2996 - 4.2998
D	4.3006 - 4.3008	4.2998 - 4.3000
E	4.3008 - 4.3010	4.3000 - 4.3002
H	4.3010 - 4.3012	4.3002 - 4.3004
J	4.3012 - 4.3014	4.3004 - 4.3006
K	4.3014 - 4.3016	4.3006 - 4.3008
L	4.3016 - 4.3018	4.3008 - 4.3010
M	4.3018 - 4.3020	4.3010 - 4.3012
AA	4.3100 - 4.3102	4.3092 - 4.3094
BB	4.3102 - 4.3104	4.3094 - 4.3096
CC	4.3104 - 4.3106	4.3096 - 4.3098
DD	4.3106 - 4.3108	4.3098 - 4.3100
EE	4.3108 - 4.3110	4.3100 - 4.3102
HH	4.3110 - 4.3112	4.3102 - 4.3104
JJ	4.3112 - 4.3114	4.3104 - 4.3106
KK	4.3114 - 4.3116	4.3106 - 4.3108
LL	4.3116 - 4.3118	4.3108 - 4.3110
MM	4.3118 - 4.3120	4.3110 - 4.3112

Fig. 19 Cylinder and piston sizes. 1968-69

shown in Fig. 18. Cylinders should be measured 1⅛" from the top, crosswise to the cylinder block. The clearance should be .0003 to .0007" in this position at room temperature (70°F). Subtract .0001" from measurement for every 6° above 70°.

An identification letter is stamped on the valve lifter compartment cover next to lower inside edge of cylinder head. The letters are in groups of two for adjacent cylinders (such as "A" "B") midway between the two cylinders. This letter denotes the cylinder size as shown in Figs. 20, 21. The table indicates ten piston sizes to match ten bore sizes. This makes it possible to maintain the proper clearance between block and piston.

If double letters (such as "AA" "BB") appear, it indicates that the cylinder has been bored .010" over the diameter indicated by the single letter in the chart.

Oversize Pistons

For 1963 engines, pistons are available from Cadillac in oversizes of .010, .020 and .030 inch. For 1964-65 engines, only .010 inch oversize pistons are supplied by Cadillac.

Letter	Cylinder Size (Diameter in inches)	Piston Size (Diameter in inches)
A	4.0000-4.0002	3.9995-3.9997
B	4.0002-4.0004	3.9997-3.9999
C	4.0004-4.0006	3.9999-4.0001
D	4.0006-4.0008	4.0001-4.0003
E	4.0008-4.0010	4.0003-4.0005
H	4.0010-4.0012	4.0005-4.0007
J	4.0012-4.0014	4.0007-4.0009
K	4.0014-4.0016	4.0009-4.0011
L	4.0016-4.0018	4.0011-4.0013
M	4.0018-4.0020	4.0013-4.0015

Fig. 20 Cylinder and piston sizes. 1963

Letter	Cylinder Sizes (In Inches)	Piston Sizes (In Inches)
A	4.1290 - 4.1292	4.1280 - 4.1282
B	4.1292 - 4.1294	4.1282 - 4.1284
C	4.1294 - 4.1296	4.1284 - 4.1286
D	4.1296 - 4.1298	4.1286 - 4.1288
E	4.1298 - 4.1300	4.1288 - 4.1290
H	4.1300 - 4.1302	4.1290 - 4.1292
J	4.1302 - 4.1304	4.1292 - 4.1294
K	4.1304 - 4.1306	4.1294 - 4.1296
L	4.1306 - 4.1308	4.1296 - 4.1298
M	4.1308 - 4.1310	4.1298 - 4.1300
AA	4.1390 - 4.1392	4.1380 - 4.1382
BB	4.1392 - 4.1394	4.1382 - 4.1384
CC	4.1394 - 4.1396	4.1384 - 4.1386
DD	4.1396 - 4.1398	4.1386 - 4.1388
EE	4.1398 - 4.1400	4.1388 - 4.1390
HH	4.1400 - 4.1402	4.1390 - 4.1392
JJ	4.1402 - 4.1404	4.1392 - 4.1394
KK	4.1404 - 4.1406	4.1394 - 4.1396
LL	4.1406 - 4.1408	4.1396 - 4.1398
MM	4.1408 - 4.1410	4.1398 - 4.1400

Fig. 21 Cylinder and piston sizes. 1964-66. See Service Bulletin for late 1966 and 1967 pistons

PISTON RINGS

For 1963 engines, rings are supplied by Cadillac in oversizes of .020 and .030 inch only. For 1964-66 only .010 inch oversize rings are available.

Service Bulletin

INSTALLS OIL-RING EXPANDER.

When oil rings are installed on a 1964 Cadillac, the expander must be positioned properly in the piston. The ends of the expander should be butted against each other, and aligned with the end of the piston pin.

If the ends of the expander are permitted to overlap, tension on the oil-ring rails will be reduced. This can cause excessive oil consumption. In addition, the ends may score the cylinder wall, necessitating expensive repairs.

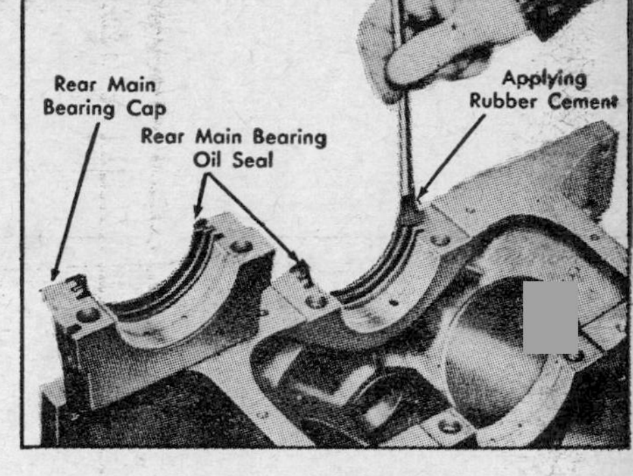

Fig. 24 Rear main bearing cap and seal. 1963-69

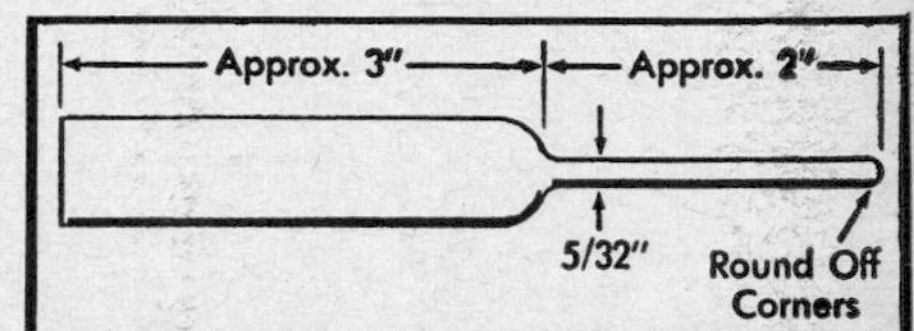

Fig. 25 Rear main bearing oil seal "shoehorn" installer. 1963-66

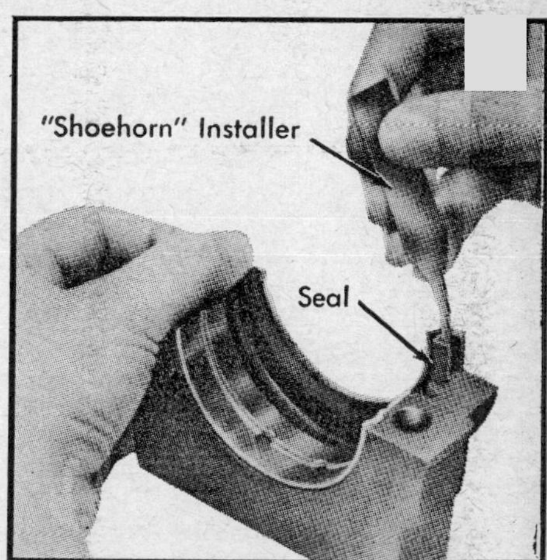

Fig. 26 Installing rear main bearing oil seal. 1963-69

PISTON PINS

Piston pins are a matched fit with the piston and are not available separately. Piston pins are pressed in the connecting rods and will not become loose enough to cause a knock or tapping until after very high mileages. In such cases a new piston and pin assembly should be installed.

MAIN & ROD BEARINGS

Main and rod bearings are supplied by Cadillac in standard sizes only.

CRANKSHAFT OIL SEAL

1963-69

The two seal halves are identical and can be used in either the lower or upper location. However, both seal halves are

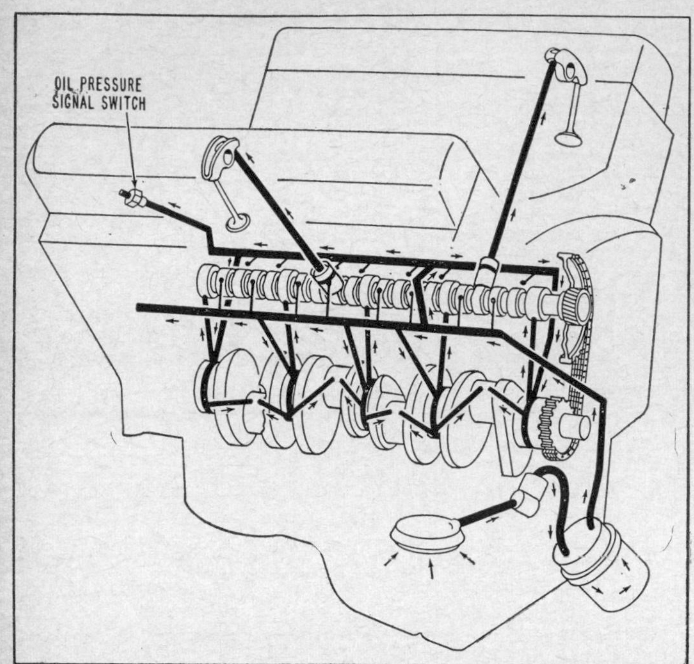

Engine oiling system. 1968-69

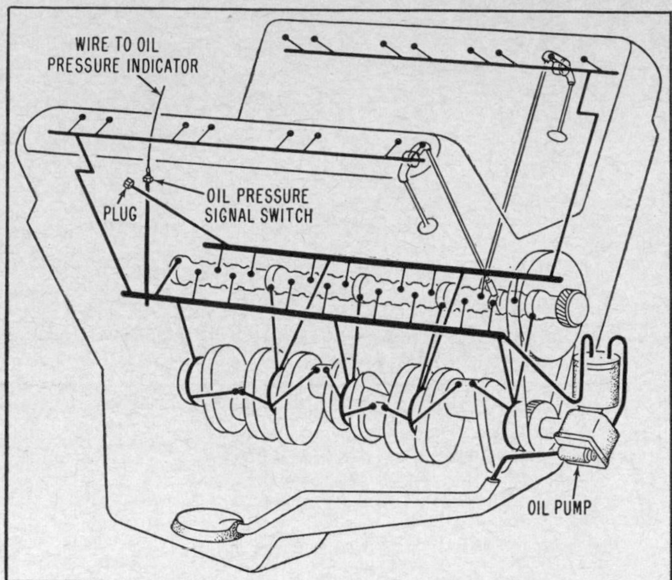

Engine oiling system. 1963-67 (typical)

pre-lubricated with a film of wax for break-in. Do not remove or damage this film. Fig. 24 shows the construction of the main bearing cap and seal.

NOTE: The seal installation cannot properly be made without the use of the "shoehorn" tool shown in Fig. 25. This tool can be made out of metal banding strap or similar shim stock of .020" thickness.

To install the lower half of the seal into the bearing cap, slide either end of seal into position at one end of bearing cap and place tool on seal land at other end of bearing, Fig. 26. Make sure seal is positioned over bearing ridge and lip of seal is facing forward (car position).

Hold thumb over end of seal that is flush with split line to prevent it from slipping upward, and push seal into seated position by applying pressure to the other end. Make sure seal is pressed down firmly and is flush on each side to avoid possibility of a leak at seal split line. Avoid pressing on lip as damage to sealing edge could result.

To install upper half of seal in cylinder block (with crankshaft in car), position "shoehorn" tool on land of block. Start seal into groove in block with lip facing forward and rotate seal into position. Do not press on lip or sealing edge may be damaged. Both ends of seal must be flush at seal split line to avoid leaks. If necessary, Lubriplate or its equivalent may be used to facilitate installation of both upper and lower seal halves. Do not use silicone or a leak may result.

OIL PAN, REPLACE

1968-69 Except Eldorado

NOTE: For easier removal of the oil pan past the stabilizer bar, first remove the two *front* dowel studs from the block by running a jam nut on each stud to lock the pan nut on the stud. Working over the front frame crossmember, use a socket to remove the stud with the two nuts attached. On engines prior to 1968 with studs further rearward, this procedure is not necessary.

1. Disconnect battery ground cable.
2. Drain engine oil.
3. Remove "Y" exhaust pipe at exhaust manifold.
4. Remove starter.
5. Unfasten and lower idler arm support.
6. Disconnect pitman arm at center link and lower steering linkage.
7. Remove transmission lower cover.
8. Unfasten and lower oil pan.

NOTE: To align the oil pan at the rear and prevent damage from the flywheel teeth during installation, first locate the oil pan on the crankcase with two screws at mid-point. Then install two screws at the rear while checking gasket alignment.

1967-69 Eldorado

To remove the oil pan it is necessary to remove the engine as described previously.

1965-67 Except Eldorado

1. Disconnect battery positive cable.
2. Drain engine oil.
3. Disconnect exhaust crossover pipe at exhaust manifold.
4. Disconnect exhaust support bracket at transmission extension housing and position exhaust system to one side.
5. Remove starting motor.
6. Unfasten and lower steering idler arm support.
7. Disconnect pitman arm at drag link and lower steering linkage.
8. Remove transmission lower cover.
9. Unfasten and remove oil pan from cylinder block and engine front cover.
10. Reverse procedure to install pan.

NOTE: Install new oil pan front and rear seals by pulling locating tangs on seals through locating holes in seal flange. Make sure seals are firmly positioned on flange surfaces with ends of each seal properly located in cut-out notches in side gaskets. Seal all four corner notch openings with a coating of rubber cement. Clean out notches in block where ends of oil pan rear seal fit. Fill this rectangular cavity with Transmission Cooler Hose Cement.

1964

1. Disconnect positive battery cable.
2. Drain engine oil.
3. Disconnect exhaust pipe from exhaust manifold, remove heat control valve from left manifold and move exhaust pipe out of the way.
4. Unfasten and lower idler arm support.
5. On cars with Hydra-Matic, remove cap screw that holds transmission rear cooler pipe clamp to upper flywheel cover plate.
6. On cars with Turbo Hydra-Matic, remove bolt that secures rear cooler pipe clamp to adapter ring plate.
7. Remove nut that holds front transmission oil cooler pipe clamp to right front oil pan locating stud, and remove clamp from stud.
8. Disconnect wires from starter solenoid and remove starter.
9. On cars with Hydra-Matic, remove four cap screws and two nuts that hold upper flywheel cover plate to flywheel housing and engine oil pan.
10. On cars with Turbo Hydra-Matic remove three remaining bolts, two nuts

Key	No.	Size	Torque
A	(4)	3/8 - 16 x 1-3/8	25 foot-pounds
B	(4)	1/4 - 20 x 1-1/8	70 inch-pounds
C	(3)	5/16 - 18 x 1-1/4	15 foot-pounds

Fig. 27 Water pump attaching screws. 1968-69

and cap screw that hold front cover plate to adapter ring and engine oil pan, and remove front cover plate.
11. Remove oil pan.
12. Install oil pan by reversing removal procedure. Be sure to use new side gaskets and rubber end seals.

Service Bulletin

CURE FOR OIL LEAK. On 1964 models, beginning with engine No. 028370, the top rear corners of the engine oil pan were redesigned to assure against oil leakage. If a rear oil-pan seal leak develops on any 1964 model with an engine number below 028370, the pan gasket should be replaced. In addition, a $\frac{1}{16}$ to $\frac{1}{8}$ in. coating of suitable cement should be applied to the original pan at the top rear corners under the rear oil seal.

1963

1. Disconnect battery positive cable.
2. Drain oil pan.
3. Remove starter.
4. Remove exhaust pipe from exhaust manifolds, remove heat control valve from left manifold and swing exhaust pipe out of the way.
5. Unfasten and lower steering idler arm support.
6. Unfasten and remove upper flywheel cover plate from flywheel housing and oil pan.
7. Unfasten and remove oil pan.
8. When installing, use new gaskets and rubber end seals.

OIL PUMP

1968-69

1. Raise car and remove oil filter.
2. Remove five screws securing pump to engine. *The screw nearest the pressure regulator should be removed last, allowing the pump to come down with screw.*
3. Remove pump drive shaft.
4. Reverse procedure to install, being sure to pack the pump with petrolatum.

1963-67

The oil pump housing is an integral part of the engine front cover, Figs. 8, 9, and 10. Whenever the oil pump housing components require service, the front cover must be removed from the engine. Refer to "Engine Front Cover" for procedure.

Inspect strainer screen for dirt and float for leaks. Look for nicks or burrs or nicks on pressure regulator valve which might cause leaks or binding in pump body. Inspect pump gears for nicks and burrs. Inspect bottom cover for wear and dress down on a surface plate if necessary. Place bottom cover on pump and check drive shaft end play. If end play exceeds .006 in., replace drive and idler gears. Assemble and install oil

Key	Size	Torque
A	1/4-20x1-1/4	5 foot-pounds
B	5/16-18x3-1/4	10 foot-pounds
C	3/8-16x3-5/8	15 foot-pounds
D	3/8-16x3-7/8	15 foot-pounds

Fig. 28 Water pump screws. 1963-67

pump in the reverse order of its removal and disassembly.

Before installing the oil filter, fill oil passages in filter support bracket with engine oil. This will allow oil pump to prime itself when engine is started.

WATER PUMP, REPLACE

1968-69

1. Disconnect battery ground cable.
2. Drain radiator and remove fan shroud.
3. Remove fan assembly. *On A/C cars, be sure to keep the fan clutch in the "on car" position when removed to prevent leakage of silicone fluid into clutch mechanism.*
4. Remove all drive belts.
5. Pull pump pulley off shaft.
6. Disconnect water inlet from pump.
7. Unfasten and remove pump from front cover.
8. Reverse procedure to install, being sure to install bolts as shown in Fig. 27.

1963-67

1. Disconnect battery positive cable.
2. Drain radiator. On air conditioned cars, partially remove compressor. On 1965 models, remove fan shroud.
3. Remove fan blades, spacer, and drive belts.
4. Unfasten and move generator and support bracket away from engine.
5. Remove oil filter and support bracket.
6. Remove water hose and water outlet pipe.
7. Unfasten water pump from engine.
8. Reverse removal procedure to install pump, tightening mounting bolts to the torque indicated in Fig. 28.

Note: On 1963-64 models, if the oil pump gears were removed for service, fill the oil passages in the oil filter support bracket with engine oil before installing the oil filter. This will enable the pump to prime itself when engine is started.

FUEL PUMP, REPLACE

1968-69

1. Raise car and disconnect fuel line at pump and plug line.
2. Disconnect fuel pipe to fuel filter at pump.
3. Remove mounting screw on upper pump flange.
4. Remove nut from mounting stud at lower pump flange.
5. Tipping pump upward, pull pump straight out from engine and remove.
6. Reverse procedure to install.

1967

NOTE: On cars equipped with A.I.R. system except Eldorado, it is necessary to remove the air pump and the bolt that holds the strut to the pump front mounting bracket. Swing front of strut out of the way to gain access to the fuel pump.

1. Connect a jumper wire from coil primary negative terminal (on distributor side) to a good ground to prevent engine from starting.
2. Loosen two capscrews holding fuel pump to engine front cover.
3. Crank engine until camshaft eccentric is at its low point of contact with fuel pump arm, and pump has minimum pressure on mounting screws.
4. Release clamp securing rubber hose to fuel pump inlet and plug hose opening to prevent fuel drainage. *On Eldorado equipped with A.I.R. System, remove corded rubber baffle from front crossmember and rubber hose from connector located on crossmember instead of at fuel pump inlet.*
5. Remove mounting screws and pump. *On Eldorado equipped with A.I.R. System, remove power steering pump belt to make pump removal easier.*

1963-66

NOTE: On cars equipped with A.I.R. System, it is necessary to remove the air pump and the bolt that holds strut to pump front mounting bracket. Swing front of strut out of the way to gain access to the fuel pump.

1. Disconnect fuel line between fuel filter and pump. Release clamp securing hose to pump. Plug end of hose to prevent drainage.
2. Unfasten and remove pump from engine.
3. To install, crank engine until camshaft eccentric is at its highest point.
4. Place gasket on engine and install pump. Loosely install screws. Then lift pump and tighten screws.
5. Remove plug from hose and install hose and fuel line. Then operate engine and check for leaks.

Automatic Transmission

NOTE: 1969 linkage adjustment information is in this section. Repair procedures on both automatic and manual shift transmissions are covered elsewhere in this manual. Procedures for removing automatic transmissions as well as linkage adjustments on 1963-68 models are included in the automatic transmission chapters. See Chapter Index.

1969 AUTO. TRANS. LINKAGE ADJUSTMENTS

Linkage adjustment procedures for 1969 models are the same as those for 1968 models as outlined in the front of this manual.

Rear Axle, Propeller Shaft & Brakes

REAR AXLE

1967-69 Eldorado

The rear axle used on these models is a welded assembly of the beam type with a drop center. The rear wheel spindles are a press fit and bolted to the rear axle assembly, Fig. 1. As shown, tapered roller bearings are used in the rear wheels. These bearings do not require regularly scheduled repacking. When major brake service work is to be performed, however, it is recommended that the bearings be cleaned and repacked.

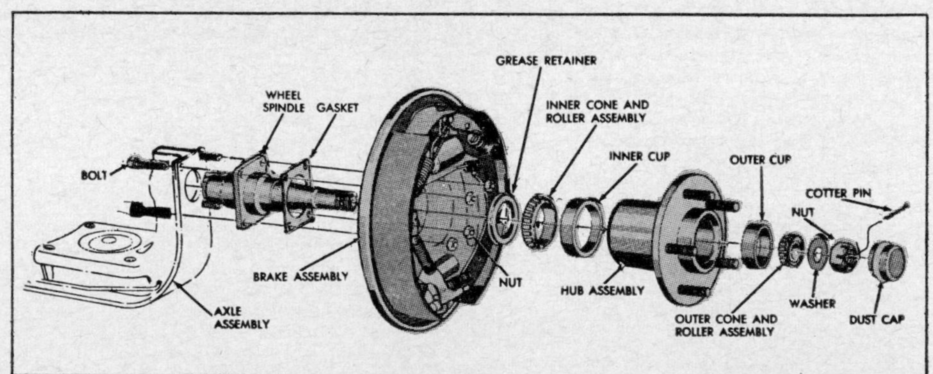

Fig. 1 Rear wheel spindle disassembled. 1967-69 Eldorado

Wheel Bearing Adjustment

Adjustment of the rear wheel bearings should be made while revolving the wheel at least three times the speed of the nut rotation when taking torque readings.

1. Check to make sure that hub is completely seated on wheel spindle.
2. While rotating wheel, tighten spindle nut to 30 ft-lbs. Make certain all parts are properly seated and that threads are free.
3. Back off spindle nut ¼ turn and install cotter pin. *If cotter pin cannot be installed in either the available holes in the spindle with nut in the above position, loosen spindle nut until cotter pin can be installed.*
4. Peen end of cotter pin snug against side of nut. If it can be moved with a finger, vibration may cause it to wear and break.

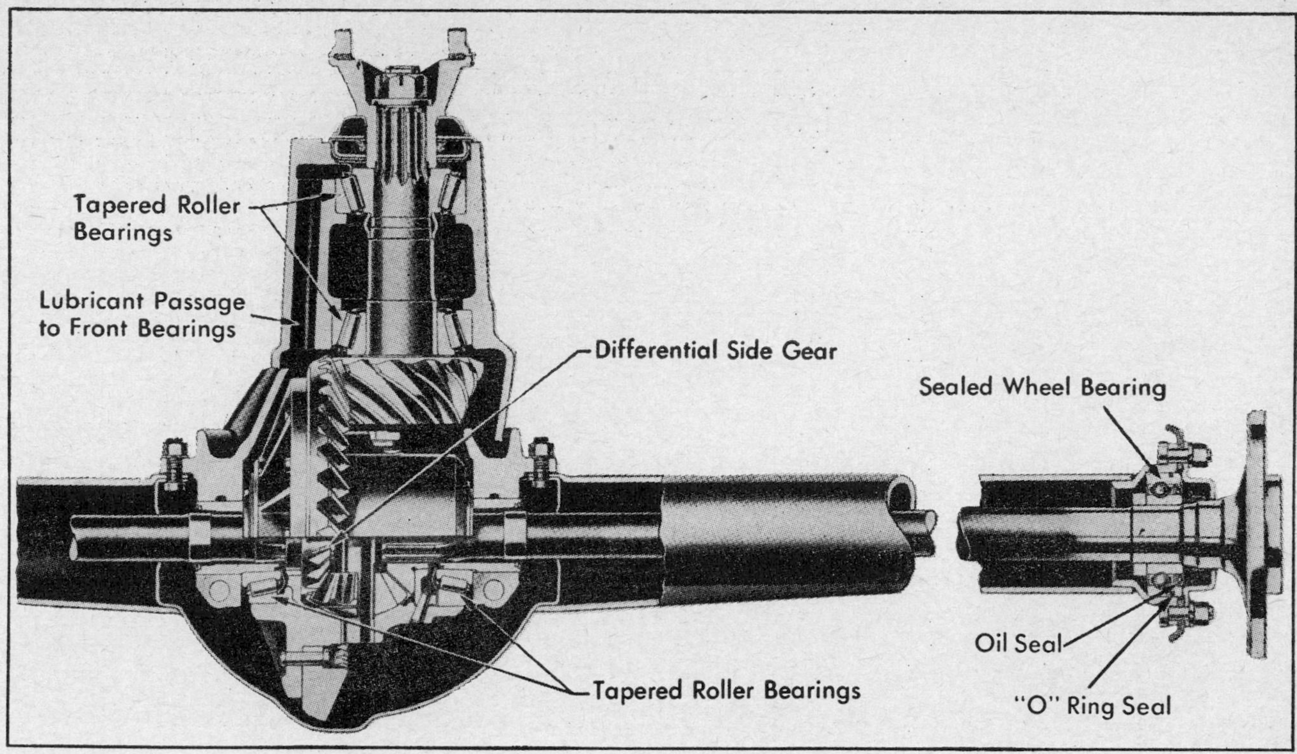

Fig. 2 Rear axle assembly. 1963-69 standard cars

Wheel Spindle, Replace

1. Raise and support rear of car and remove hub.
2. Disconnect brake line at wheel cylinder.
3. Unfasten and remove brake backing plate and position out of the way.
4. Place jack under rear axle.
5. Remove four nuts from center spring clamp and lower rear axle until spindle is accessible.
6. Remove lower spring insulator from rear axle.
7. Drive spindle out of rear axle.

Installation

1. Start new spindle, with keyway up, into axle and install four backing plate to spindle nuts.
2. Progressively tighten nuts until spindle is fully seated and then remove attaching nuts and bolts.
3. Position lower spring insulator to rear axle.
4. Position rear axle to center spring clamp, making sure that spring aligning pin locates into axle. See that lower insulator is properly positioned and that center spring clamp bolts engage rear axle mounting holes.
5. Install four nuts securing center spring clamp to rear axle, tightening to 30 ft-lbs.
6. Install new gasket on wheel spindle.
7. Install brake backing plate and tighten nuts to 40 ft-lbs.
8. Connect brake line to wheel cylinder, tightening fitting to 14 ft-lbs.
9. Install rear hub.

Rear Axle, Replace

NOTE: Any service on the differential carrier assembly should be handled by replacement of the complete assembly. No disassembly or adjustment of these units should be attempted in the field as special equipment is needed for selection of mating parts and setting side bearing preload.

1. Raise and support rear of car with jack stands at rear frame pads ahead of rear wheel opening.
2. Remove rear wheels and hubs.
3. Disconnect brake lines at wheel cylinders.
4. Disconnect parking brake cable at equalizer.
5. Disconnect rubber brake hose at underbody connector.
6. Disconnect overtravel lever link from bracket on rear axle.
7. Remove spring guides retaining parking brake cable to center spring clamp.
8. If rear axle is being replaced, remove brake backing plates.
9. Supporting rear axle at center with a jack, remove eight nuts (4 each side) from center spring clamp assemblies.
10. Lower rear axle with jack and remove from car.
11. Remove lower spring insulators from rear axle.
12. If rear axle is being replaced, remove bolt securing brake line junction fitting to axle. Remove brake line, overtravel lever link bracket, and drive spindles from axle.
13. Reverse procedure to install.

1963-69 Standard Cars

The design of the rear axle carrier assembly is shown in Fig. 2. The axle shafts are supported at the outer ends by ball bearings which are lubricated from the differential carrier. The axle shaft oil seals are an integral part of the bearings and they are not serviceable separately from the bearing. An "O" ring seal is located in the grooved outer surface of the bearing.

Any service on the differential carrier assembly, except drive pinion oil seal or yoke replacement, should be handled by replacement of the complete assembly. No disassembly or adjustment of this unit should be attempted because special equipment is used at the factory for selection of mating parts and setting side bearing preload.

Whenever a carrier is removed because of scored gears, worn bearings, or any failure which causes dirt or metal chips, it will be necessary to remove the housing from the car for thorough cleaning before the new carrier is installed. Also check axle shaft bearings for metal chips and clean if necessary.

In case of lubricant leakage between differential carrier and axle housing, check first to make sure that the nuts are tightened to the recommended torque of 37 ft. lbs. If tightening the nuts does not stop the leak, an extra gasket should be installed, using a non-hardening sealer. The additional sealing effect of the extra gasket should prevent further leakage. If a replacement differential is installed, the special lubricant shipped with the new differential must be used.

Removal

1. Disconnect rear universal joint at pinion yoke. Use suction gun to remove grease from differential

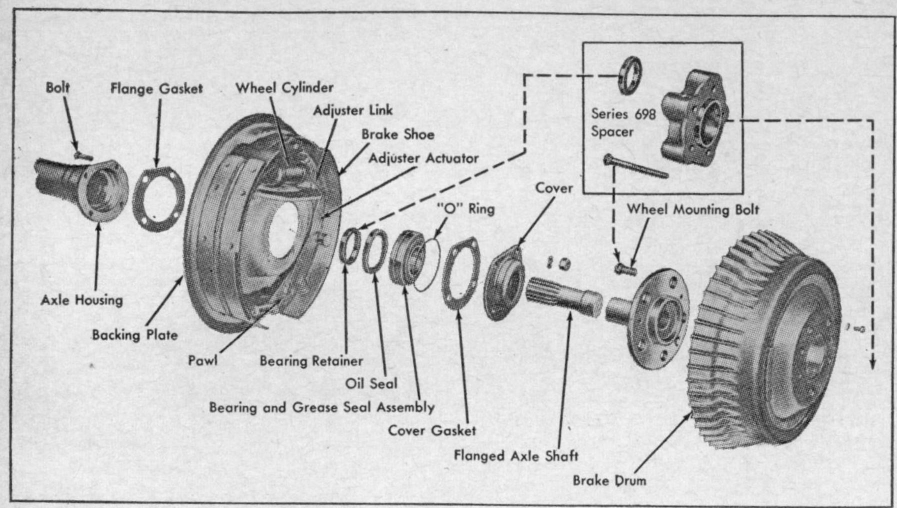

Fig. 3 Rear wheel disassembled. 1963-69

carrier.
2. Remove axle shafts as outlined below.
3. Remove nuts and washers that hold carrier to axle housing and remove entire assembly with gasket.

Installation

Note: Use a new carrier-to-housing gasket and new "O" ring seals on axle shaft bearings.

1. Place gasket on housing, install carrier, nuts and washers, and torque nuts to 37 ft. lbs.
2. Install axle shafts as explained below.
3. Install lubricant in differential to filler plug level.
4. Connect rear universal joint at pinion yoke.

Axle Shaft, Replace

1. Raise car and remove wheel.
2. Remove brake drum.
3. Unfasten and remove brake backing plate from axle housing.
4. Remove axle shaft.

Removing Bearings

1. Using a chisel and hammer, groove spacer next to bearing. The spacer need not be split. Drive chisel into spacer only enough to allow spacer to be slipped from shaft.
2. Press shaft through bearing. *If bearing has been removed because of failure, inspect axle housing and differential carrier for metal chips and, if necessary, clean thoroughly.*

Installing Bearing

1. Install new bearing on shaft so that bearing seal is toward flange end of shaft.
2. Press bearing on shaft so that it is located 3.180" from outer surface of axle shaft flange to inner end of bearing inner race.
3. Install oil ring seal on bearing.

Install Axle Shaft

1. Apply film of differential lube to wheel bearing bore in axle housing after checking for burrs and nicks.
2. Use a new "O" ring seal on wheel bearing and install axle shaft (shorter one on left side), being careful not to damage "O" ring seal.
3. Install brake backing plate and bearing retainer.
4. Install nuts and lockwashers on housing bolts and tighten by inserting socket wrench through rear axle flange.
5. Install brake drum and wheel.

PROPELLER SHAFT

Two Piece Type

Removal

1. With car raised, remove two center bearing support-to-frame bolts, Fig. 4.
2. Remove U-bolts and locks at rear axle pinion.
3. Slide propeller shaft and front yoke

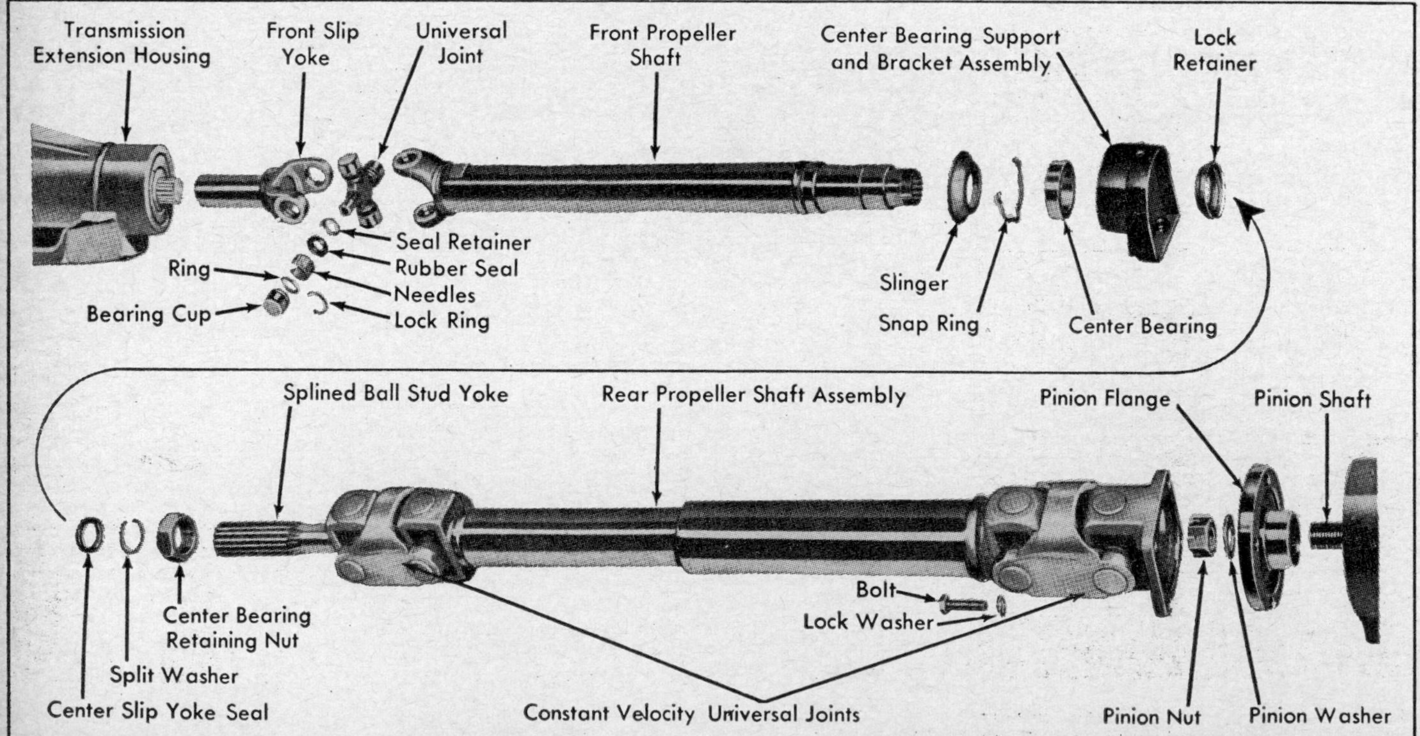

Fig. 4 Propeller shaft disassembled. 1963-64 Series 60, 62

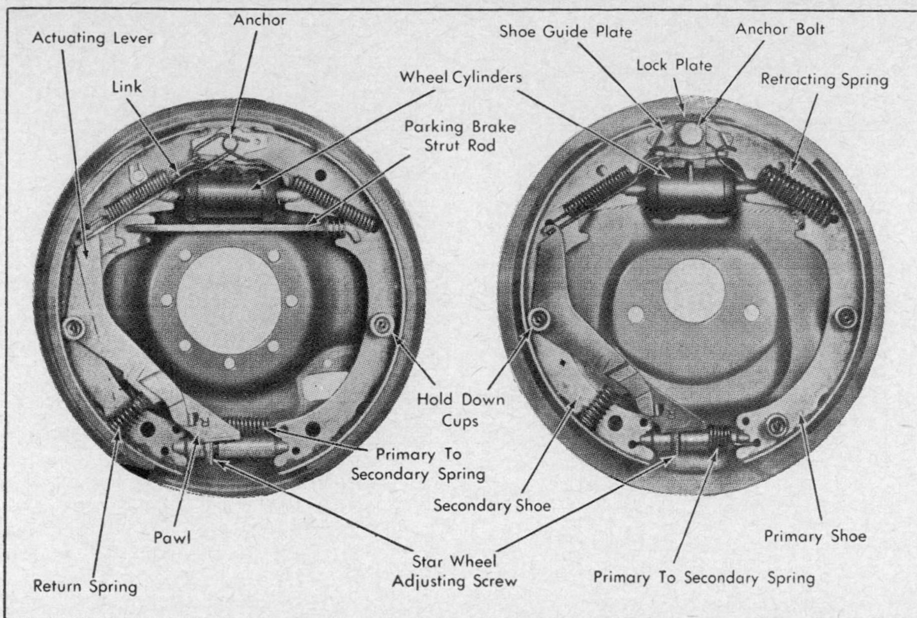

Fig. 5 Right front and rear brake mechanism, 1963-69. Rear only 1969

off transmission output shaft and through frame tunnel section, removing it at the rear. *Slide spare yoke into transmission extension housing to prevent oil from leaking out.*

Installation

1. Lubricate front propeller shaft yoke with automatic transmission oil and remove spare yoke from transmission extension housing that had been installed to prevent oil leaking out.
2. Slide propeller shaft and front yoke into transmission output shaft through frame tunnel section, being careful not to nick yoke. *Be sure to reinstall any shims that may have been removed from between propeller shaft center support and frame tunnel.*
3. Install two center bearing support-to-frame bolts. Install U-bolts and locks at rear axle pinion and torque U-bolt nuts to 15 ft. lbs.

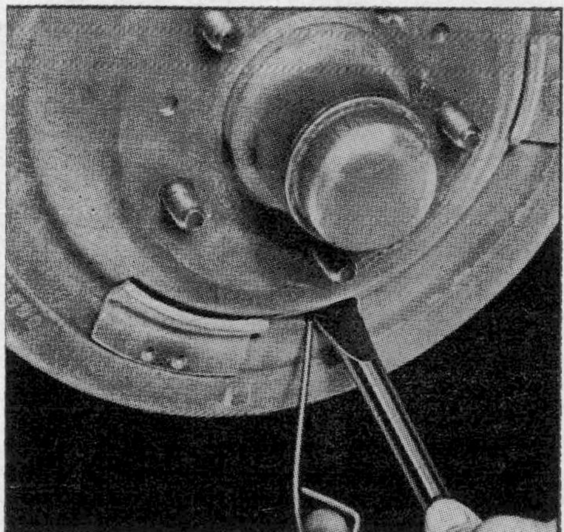

Fig. 7 Adjusting front brakes through holes in brake drums. Hooked tool shown is used to hold pawl free of star wheel while adjusting front brakes on 1963-68 models

IMPORTANT

If drive line shudder, roughness, vibration or rumble is experienced, it may be due to misalignment of the propeller shaft assembly. To make this check, however, a special Propeller Shaft Alignment Gauge Set. No. J-8905 must be used. Inasmuch as this equipment is not likely to be found in general repair shops, it is recommended that a Cadillac dealer having this equipment do the work.

One Piece Type

Removal

1. Raise car on hoist.
2. Remove flange attaching bolts and lower propeller shaft.

NOTE: Do not allow shaft to hang on front constant velocity joint.

3. Push shaft forward so rear universal joint flange clears pinion shaft, then remove shaft by pulling rearward to disengage slip yoke. Install spare yoke into transmission extension housing to prevent loss of oil.

Installation

1. Remove spare yoke and insert front yoke of propeller shaft into extension housing, engaging transmission shaft splines.
2. Install rear flange attaching bolts and torque to 65 ft. lbs.
3. Check transmission oil.

BRAKE ADJUSTMENTS

1963-69 Self-Adjusting Brakes

These brakes, Fig. 5, have self-adjusting shoe mechanisms that assure correct lining-to-drum clearances at all times. The automatic adjusters operate only when the brakes are applied as the car is moving rearward or when the car comes to an uphill stop.

Although the brakes are self-adjusting, an initial adjustment is necessary after the brake shoes have been relined or replaced, or when the length of the star wheel adjuster has been changed during some other service operation.

Frequent usage of an automatic transmission forward range to halt reverse vehicle motion may prevent the automatic adjusters from functioning, thereby inducing low pedal heights. Should low pedal heights be encountered, it is recommended that numerous forward and reverse stops be made with a moderate pedal effort until satisfactory pedal height is obtained.

NOTE

If a low pedal height condition cannot be corrected by making numerous reverse stops (provided the hydraulic system is free of air) it indicates that the self-adjusting mechanism is not functioning. Therefore, it will be necessary to remove the brake drum, clean, free up and lubricate the adjusting mechanism. Then adjust the brakes, being sure the parking brake is fully released.

Manual Shoe Adjustment

1. Check fluid level in master cylinder and add fluid as necessary to a level ¼" below top of reservoir.
2. Check front wheel bearing adjustment.
3. Check to make certain that parking brake cable and linkage, including levers on rear secondary shoes, are free.
4. Tighten star wheel until brake drums can just be rotated forward with a two-foot bar placed between wheel studs.
5. Disengage adjusting pawl from star wheel with a hooked tool and back off star wheel until drum turns freely, Fig. 7.
6. Install wheels and drive car alternately forward and backward, ap-

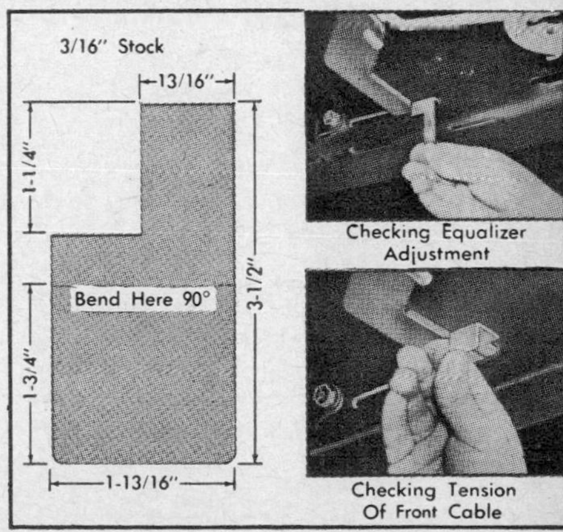

Fig. 8 Parking brake adjustment, 1963-64

plying brakes moderately in each direction until pedal travel is normal and brakes are adjusted satisfactorily.

PARKING BRAKE, ADJUST

1965-69

1. With service brakes properly adjusted, lubricate parking brake linkage at equalizer and cable stud with heat-resistant lubricant, and check for free movement of cables.
2. Depress parking brake pedal about 1¾" from fully released position.
3. Raise rear wheels off floor.
4. Hold brake cable and stud from turning and tighten equalizer nut until a slight drag is felt on either wheel (going forward). After each turn of equalizer nut, check to see if either wheel begins to drag.
5. Release parking brake. No brake drag should be felt at either rear wheel. Operate several times to check adjustment. After adjustment is completed, parking brake pedal should travel 1¾" to 2¾".

1963-64

In order to adjust parking brakes, it will be necessary to make a gauge according to the pattern shown in Fig. 8. Then proceed as follows:

1. First make sure service brakes are properly adjusted as outlined above.
2. Check complete parking brake linkage for free movement of cables in conduit and in equalizer.
3. Check relay lever return spring and replace if weak or broken.
4. With mechanism in released position, check for proper tension of front cable by inserting $\frac{13}{16}''$ portion of gauge between relay lever and end of slot in frame, Fig. 8. Gauge must fit in slot with clearance of less than $\frac{5}{16}''$. If necessary, adjust front cable by aligning one of three clevis holes with one of two relay holes to provide proper gauge fit.
5. Back off parking brake equalizer nut until relay lever can be moved forward enough to slip the $1\frac{13}{16}''$ wide end of gauge between relay lever and end of slot in frame. *NOTE: Be certain that equalizer nut has been backed off enough to leave cable slack when $1\frac{13}{16}''$ wide end of gauge is in place.*
6. Tighten equalizer nut until a near lock-up drag is obtained at rear wheels when they are turned by hand in a forward direction.
7. Remove gauge. *NOTE: After adjustment is performed, parking brake pedal should travel 1¾" to 2¾" with a moderate force on pedal.*

VACUUM RELEASE PARKING BRAKE

1963-69

The foot-operated parking brake is mounted on the cowl to the left of the steering column. It incorporates a vacuum release, Fig. 9, operated by a vacuum diaphragm that is connected to the parking brake mechanism. When the transmission selector is moved into any Drive position, a vacuum valve in the neutral safety switch opens, allowing diaphragm to be actuated by engine vacuum.

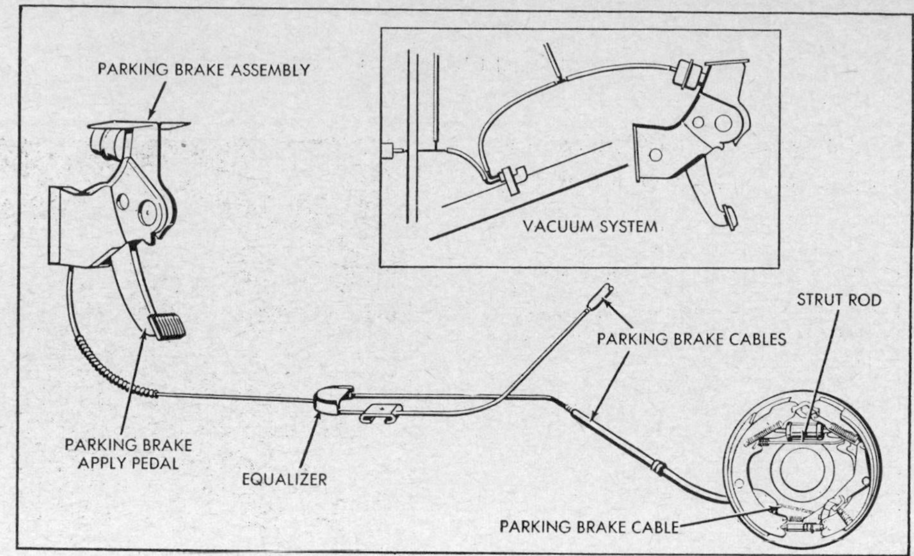

Fig. 9 Parking brake linkage. 1965-69

The diaphragm is connected by a link to a release mechanism on the parking brake. Vacuum acting on the diaphragm unlocks the parking brake pedal, permitting it to return to the released position by spring action. Any abnormal leaks in the vacuum release system will prevent proper brake release. A manual release is provided and may be used if the automatic release is inoperative or if manual release is desired at any time.

Testing Vacuum Release

1. If the mechanism is inoperative, first check for damaged or kinked vacuum hoses and for loose hose connections at the diaphragm, vacuum release valve at neutral safety switch, and at engine manifold connection.
2. Check adjustment of neutral safety switch and operation of vacuum release valve.
3. Check diaphragm piston travel by running engine and moving transmission selector lever from drive to neutral. The manual release lever should move up and down as vacuum is applied and released. If no movement is observed, or if movement is slow (more than 1 or 2 seconds to complete the full stroke) diaphragm is leaking and should be replaced.
4. Check brake release with vacuum applied. If diaphragm piston completes full stroke but does not release brake, a malfunction of the pedal assembly is indicated, and the complete parking brake assembly should be replaced.
5. Check operation of parking brake with engine off. Parking brake should remain engaged regardless of transmission selector lever position. If not, replace parking brake assembly.

POWER BRAKE, REPLACE

Service Bulletin

A sign of brake fluid dampness below the master cylinder at the power brake unit or on wheel cylinders at the bottom of the boot, does not necessarily indicate that these cylinders are leaking.

A small amount of fluid leakage at these areas can occur due to the creeping action of a very light film of fluid on the cylinder bores around the seals. This action provides proper seal lubrication. In addition, normal brake heat will produce a slight escape of lubricant from the impregnated, porous-metal wheel cylinder pistons.

Normal dampness at the master cylinder or wheel cylinders is not easily distinguishable from a definite leak. Therefore, this condition must be checked carefully.

If there is sufficient dampness to form a "teardrop" of fluid at the bottom of the master cylinder or on the bottom of the wheel cylinders at the boot area, the rate of fluid seepage is too high and the cause should be determined and corrected.

1963-69

1. Disconnect hydraulic lines from master cylinder on power unit. Cap line fittings to prevent dirt entering system.
2. Disconnect vacuum hose from vacuum check valve on power unit. On 1967-69, remove steering column lower cover.
3. Remove cotter pin and spring spacer that attach power unit push rod to brake pedal relay lever.
4. Unfasten and remove power unit from cowl.
5. Reinstall in reverse order of removal. *When installed, start engine and allow vacuum to build up before applying brakes.*

Front End and Steering Section

FRONT SUSPENSION 1963-69 STANDARD CARS

The front suspension system consists of two upper and lower control arm assemblies, steel coil springs, shock absorbers, front diagonal tie struts, and a stabilizer bar. Rubber bushings are used at all frame attaching points.

Ball joints are used at the outer ends of the upper and lower control arms. The upper ball joint is pressed into the upper control arm and tack-welded to the arm at two points. It connects the upper control arm to the steering knuckle through a camber adjustment eccentric. The lower ball joint, a tension type joint, is pressed into the lower control arm. It connects the lower control arm to the steering knuckle.

The upper control arms pivot at their inner ends on two flanged rubber bushings, one at each end of the one-piece control arm shaft which is bolted to the top surface of the spring tower on the front frame crossmember. The lower control arms pivot on a single rubber bushing that is bolted to the front suspension frame crossmember.

Diagonal tie struts are used to control the fore and aft movement of the wheels. The struts are bolted to the outer ends of the lower control arms and extend through the frame crossmember. Rubber bushings and a steel spacer are used at the frame mount.

Lubrication

The ball joints are packed with lubricant and sealed at assembly and should not require further lubrication throughout their service life under normal driving conditions. The only maintenance they normally require is an inspection of the seals for physical damage each time the engine oil is changed.

Service plugs are provided in the ball joint covers so that the joints may be packed in the event a seal should become damaged and require replacement. Both the seals and plugs are serviceable.

Fig. 2 Adjusting camber. 1963-69

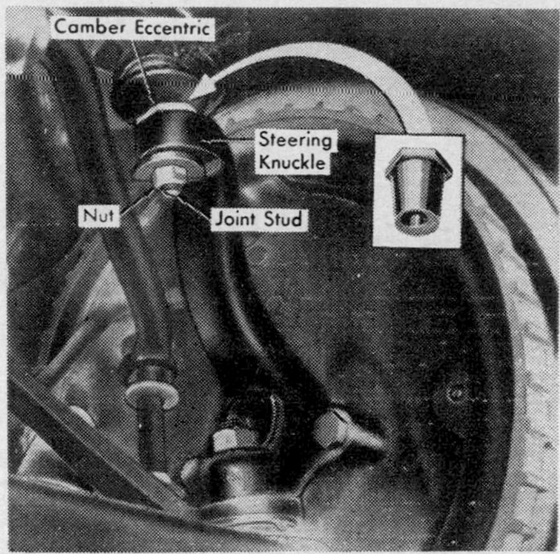

Fig. 1 Camber adjustment eccentric. 1963-69

Wheel Alignment, 1963-69 Standard Cars

Camber, Adjust

Adjustment is made at the camber eccentric located in the steering knuckle upper support, Fig. 1. The upper ball joint stud fits through the camber eccentric and knuckle support. Turning the eccentric repositions the upper ball joint stud.

To adjust camber, loosen the ball joint stud nut one turn and tap bottom of stud with soft mallet to loosen eccentric. Using a suitable wrench, Fig. 2, turn the eccentric as required to obtain the camber specifications listed in the *Wheel Alignment* chart. The final position of the stud should be in the rear portion of the camber eccentric in order to keep steering angle correct. After proper adjustment has been established, torque stud nut to 60 ft. lbs.

NOTE

If the camber eccentric is too tight to be adjusted a tool can easily be made by cutting a piece of 7/16" diameter steel rod about 20" long, chamfering it on one end and rounding it off on the other end.

If the eccentric must be freed for a camber adjustment, position the car on a wheel alignment machine, backing off the self-locking nut on the ball joint stud one turn, and thread a standard nut halfway on the stud. Insert the rounded end of the tool inside the nut and against the bottom of the stud. Then pound on the end of the tool with a heavy hammer to break the camber eccentric loose.

In cases where the eccentric is to be removed but comes loose from the stud instead of the knuckle, place a washer against the bottom of the eccentric and drive the eccentric out from below, using the same tool as described above. When the eccentric must be removed in this manner, inspect it for damage and replace if necessary.

Caster, Adjust

Adjustment is made by turning the retaining nuts on the forward ends of the tie-struts at the frame front crossmember, Fig. 3. To gain access to the retaining nuts, it is necessary to remove the splash shield.

Proper caster adjustment is obtained by shortening or lengthening the struts between the lower suspension arms and the frame front crossmember. To provide more negative caster, lengthen the struts by loosening the front bushing retaining nuts and tightening the rear bushing retaining nuts. One turn of the nuts results in approximately ½° change in caster.

To provide more positive caster, shorten the struts by loosening the rear bushing retaining nuts and tightening the front bushing retaining nuts.

After proper adjustment has been made, tighten front retaining nuts to 60 ft. lbs., being sure to hold the rear nut with a wrench so as not to disturb the adjustment.

Toe-In, Adjust

Toe-in is adjusted by turning the tie rod adjusters at the outer ends of each tie rod after loosening the clamp bolts. (Both right and left pivot ends have right-hand threads.) Be sure to turn both adjusters an equal amount so that the relation of the steering gear high spot to the straight ahead position of the front wheels will not be changed.

When adjustment has been completed according to the specification listed in the *Wheel Alignment* chart, tighten nuts on clamp bolts to 20 ft. lbs. torque.

NOTE

Make certain that both inner and outer tie rod ball pivots are centered in their respective housings prior to tightening the tie rod adjusting clamps.

If the tie rods are not properly positioned, a binding condition may occur, resulting in poor return of wheels to the straight ahead position.

Each tie rod should be checked after

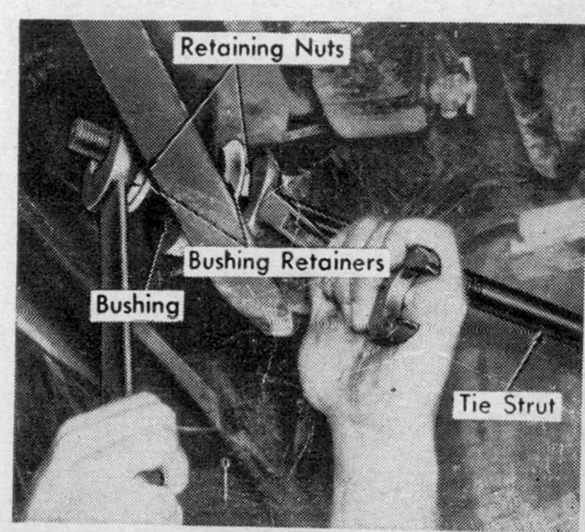

Fig. 3 Adjusting caster. 1963-69

adjustment by grasping the center of the tie rod and rotating it fore and aft. The movement should be equal in both directions. If not, it indicates that the pivot studs are not properly positioned.

Wheel Bearings, Adjust

Service Bulletin

Looseness at a front wheel does not necessarily indicate worn bearings or a loose spindle nut, since the tapered roller bearings used on front wheels of all 1963-69 standard Cadillacs should not be pre-loaded and normally can have up to .004" end play.

When adjusting the front wheel bearings, raise the front of the car and make sure that the wheel is completely seated on the spindle. Tighten the adjusting nut to 30 ft. lbs. torque and rotate the drum to be sure all parts are properly seated and the threads are free. Then back off the nut ¼ turn. If the cotter pin cannot be installed in either of the two available holes in the spindle with the nut in this position, loosen the adjusting nut until the cotter pin can be installed. The wheel should spin freely.

Wheel Bearings, Replace (Disc Brakes)

1968-69

1. Remove two thirds of the total fluid capacity in the front master cylinder reservoir to prevent fluid overflow when the piston is pushed back in its bore.
2. Raise car and remove front wheels.
3. Position 7 inch "C" clamp on the caliper so that solid side rests against the back of the caliper. The screw end rests against the back of the outboard shoe.
4. Tighten "C" clamp until caliper moves out far enough to bottom the piston in its bore. This will release the pressure on the shoe and lining assemblies.
5. Remove "C" clamp.
6. Remove two bolts which hold caliper to support plate.

NOTE: It is not necessary to remove brake hose from caliper during this operation.

7. Slide caliper off of disc. Do not allow caliper to hang from brake hose.
8. Remove spindle nut and hub and disc assembly. Grease retainer and inner bearing can now be removed.

1967

1. Raise car and remove front wheels.
2. Remove two bolts securing caliper to steering knuckle and remove caliper.

NOTE: Disconnect brake line only where necessary.

3. Remove spindle nut and hub and disc assembly. Grease retainer and inner bearing can now be removed.

Fig. 6 Coil Spring installation. 1963-69

Checking Ball Joints For Wear 1963-69 Std. Cars

Upper Ball Joint

Using the regular ball joint stud nut and a second nut as a lock nut, turn joint in its socket with a torque wrench. If the torque is not within the limits of 2 to 4 ft-lbs, the joint should be replaced.

Lower Ball Joint

The lower ball joint is designed to turn freely in its socket and cannot be checked with a torque wrench. It should be checked by noting the amount of free play as the joint is worked vertically in its socket. Free play should not exceed $\frac{1}{16}$". Replace joint if it exceeds this limit.

Ball Joints, Replace

The upper ball joints are pressed into the upper control arm and tack-welded to the arm. Therefore, the upper ball joints are supplied only with the upper control arm. The lower ball joints are pressed into the lower control arms but they are replaceable.

Shock Absorber, Replace

The shock absorbers are removed through the bottom of the lower control arm after unfastening it at the top and bottom.

To install, place the retainer and rubber grommet on the upper stem and fully extend the shock absorber rod. Insert the shock absorber up into the coil spring and guide the stem through the tower in the crossmember. Then place the lower end in position on the lower control arm. Install bolt, washer and nut and torque nut to 90-110 ft. lbs. Fasten shock absorber at top.

Tie-Strut & Bushings 1963-69 Std. Cars

Raise car and jack up under frame side rails. Remove splash shield and disconnect stabilizer link from lower control arm on side tie-strut is to be removed. Remove strut and bushings. Then replace as follows:

1. Insert spacer in rear bushing and install bushing and spacer in frame through rear side of crossmember.
2. Install nut on tie-strut and run nut to bottom of thread.
3. Install rear bushing retainer on strut with concave side toward nut.
4. With strut held in horizontal position, install threaded end of strut through rear bushing in frame crossmember.
5. Install front bushing on end of strut and slide bushing into position in frame crossmember. Front bushing should lock in rear bushing.
6. Install front bushing retainer on threaded end of strut with flat side against bushing. Start front nut on end of strut but do not tighten.
7. Secure opposite end of strut to lower control arm and torque bolts to 55 ft. lbs.
8. Connect stabilizer link.
9. Lower car and with car weight on all four wheels, tighten front nut to 55-70 ft. lbs.
10. Tighten rear nut, compressing bushing until retainer bottoms on metal spacer in bushing.
11. Adjust caster as outlined previously.
12. Install splash shield.

Coil Spring, Replace

1. Disconnect shock absorber at upper end.
2. Raise front of car and place jack stands under frame side rails.
3. Disconnect stabilizer link from side from which spring is to be removed.
4. Disconnect tie strut at lower arm.
5. Remove shock absorber.
6. Remove wheel and brake drum.
7. Place a floor jack under outer end of lower control arm, then separate lower ball joint from steering knuckle.
8. Lower floor jack and remove spring, Fig. 6.
9. Reverse procedure to install.

ELDORADO FRONT SUSPENSION

The front suspension consists of two upper and two lower control arms, a stabilizer bar, shock absorbers and a right and left torsion bar, Fig. 7. Torsion bars are used instead of the conventional coil springs. The front end of the torsion bar is attached to the lower control arm. The rear of the torsion bar is mounted into an adjustable arm in the torsion bar crossmember. The standing height of the car is controlled by this adjustment.

Standing Height, Adjust

The standing height must be checked and

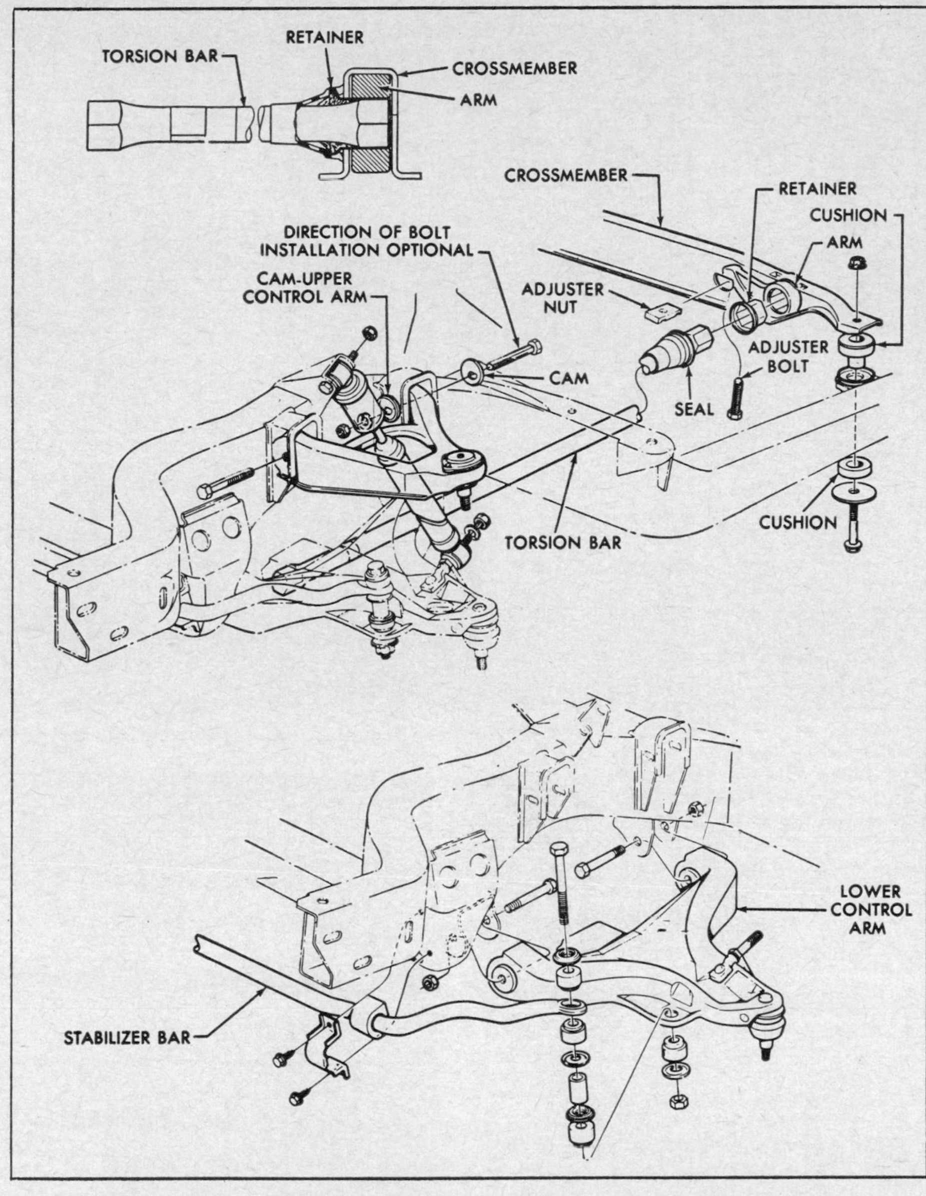

Fig. 7 Front suspension disassembled. 1967-69 Eldorado

adjusted if necessary before checking and adjusting front wheel alignment. The standing height is controlled by the adjustment setting of the torsion bar adjusting bolt, Fig. 7. Clockwise rotation of the bolt increases standing height: counterclockwise rotation decrease standing height.

To check, measure from top of the upper shock absorber mounting bolt to the top of the lower shock mount bolt. As shown in Fig. 8, this dimension should be 14.6". If dimensions are not correct, adjust as required.

Wheel Alignment, Adjust

After checking and, if necessary, adjusting standing height, check camber and caster as follows:

Camber is adjusted by turning the upper control arm rear cam bolt, Fig. 9. Caster is adjusted by turning the upper control arm front and rear cam bolts. Wheels must be in straight ahead position. Use camber reading scale for making this adjustment.

1. Turn rear cam bolt so camber reading is ¼° more than original setting for every 1° of caster change required for a correct reading. Turn to plus side of camber if caster is negative and to the negative side of camber if caster is positive.
2. Turn front cam bolt so camber will return to original setting.
3. Recheck caster reading.

NOTE: If a problem arises where there is not enough cam adjustment remaining to obtain correct reading:

1. Turn front cam bolt so high part of cam is pointing up.
2. Turn rear cam bolt so high part of cam is pointing down. This is a location to start from and a correct reading can be obtained with the above procedure.
3. Tighten upper control arm cam nuts to 75 ft-lbs.. Hold bolt head securely as any movement of the cam will affect the final setting and will require a recheck of camber and caster adjustments.

Toe-In, Adjust

Toe-in is adjusted by turning the tie rod adjusting tubes at outer ends of each tie rod after loosening clamp bolts. Readings should be taken only when front wheels are straight ahead and steering gear is on its high spot.

1. Center steering wheel, raise car and check wheel run-out.
2. Loosen tie rod adjuster nuts and adjust tie rods to obtain the specified toe-in.
3. Tighten tie rod adjuster nuts to 20 ft-lbs.
4. Position adjuster clamps so that opening of clamps are facing up. Interference with front suspension components could occur while turning if clamps are facing down.

Wheel Bearings, Replace

1. Raise car and remove front wheels.
2. Remove drum.

NOTE: For disc brakes remove two bolts securing caliper to steering knuckle and remove caliper.

3. Remove drive axle pin, nut and washer.
4. Position access slot in hub so that each of the attaching bolts can be removed.

NOTE: On disc brakes the attaching bolts are removed from behind the splash shield.

5. Using slide hammer puller, remove hub. Fig. 12.
6. Remove bearing from hub with puller. Fig. 13.
7. Press new bearing into hub.

Ball Joints

Vertical Check for Wear

1. Raise car and position jack stands under lower control arms as near as possible to each ball joint.
2. Clamp vise grips on end of drive axle and position a dial indicator so that dial indicator ball rests on vise grip.
3. Place a pry bar between lower control arm and outer race and pry down on bar. Reading must not exceed ⅛".

Horizontal Check for Wear

1. With car raised as above, position dial indicator as shown in Fig. 10.
2. Grasp front wheel and push in on bottom of tire while pulling out at top. Read dial gauge, then reverse push-pull procedure.
3. Horizontal deflection on gauge should not exceed ⅛" at wheel rim. This procedure checks both the upper and lower ball joints.

Upper Ball Joint, Replace

1. Remove upper control arm and grind

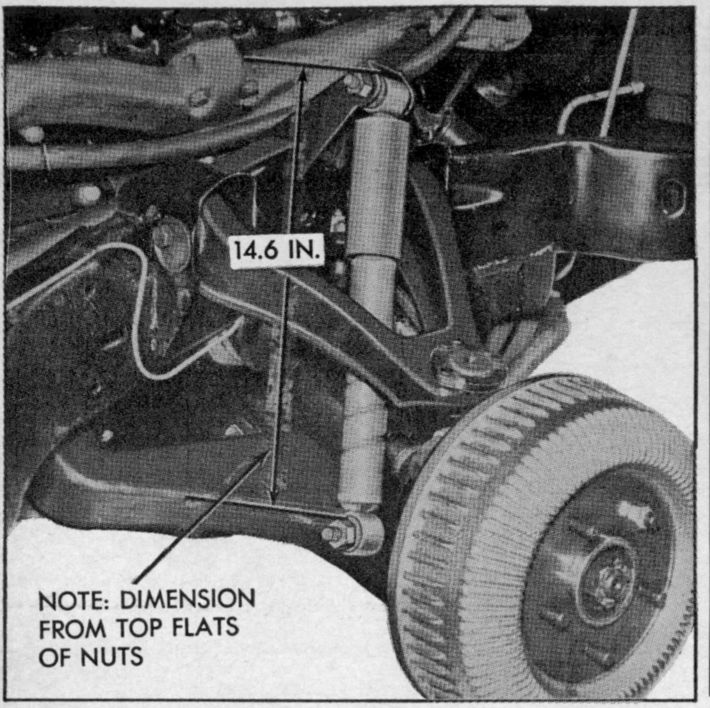

Fig. 8 Checking standing height. 1967-69 Eldorado

Fig. 9 Caster-camber cam locations. 1967-69 Eldorado

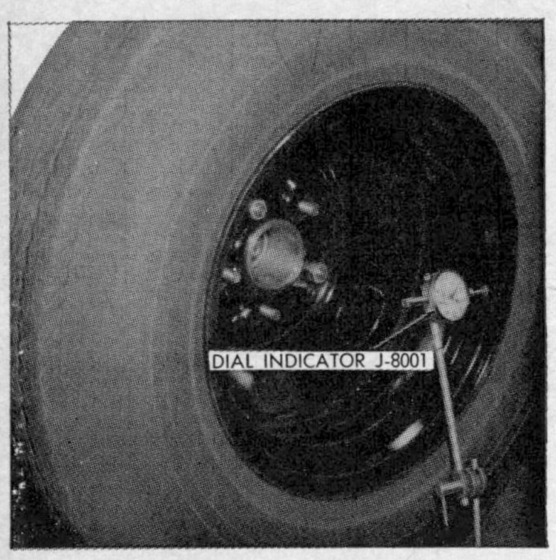

Fig. 10 Horizontal check for ball joint wear. 1967-69 Eldorado

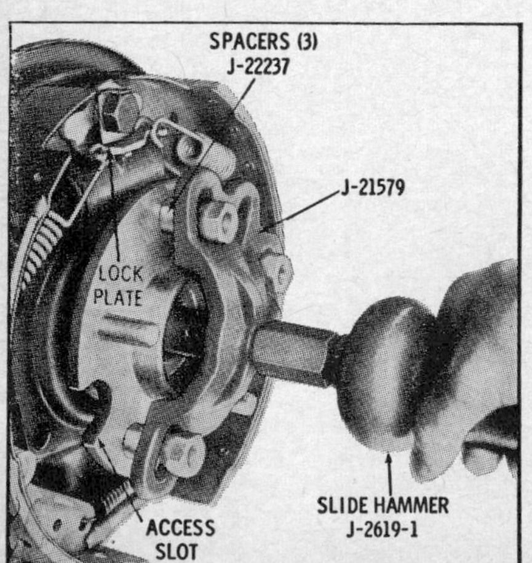

Fig. 12 Removing hub assembly. Eldorado

head off three rivets. Using a hammer and punch, drive out rivets.

2. Install new ball joint, securing it in place with three bolts and nuts contained in the kit.
3. Install upper control arm and lubricate ball joint fitting until grease escapes between seal and steering knuckle, Fig. 11.

Lower Ball Joint, Replace

1. Remove lower control arm and cut off two rivet heads from sides of control arm. Grind off head of rivet at bottom of control arm, then drive rivet out of arm.
2. Install service ball joint, securing it to control arm with bolts and nuts contained in kit.

Torsion Bar, Replace

1. Raise and place car on jack stands.
2. Remove wheel, then install one or two nuts to prevent drum from falling off car.
3. Remove hub cotter pin, nut and washer, and brake line clip attached to frame.
4. Place jack under lower control arm on side torsion bar is to be removed.
5. Disconnect upper ball joint and remove nut and brake line clip.
6. Disconnect shock absorber at lower end.
7. Pull tie rod from steering knuckle.
8. Disconnect stabilizer bar.
9. Disconnect lower ball joint.
10. Disengage brake backing plate from drive axle and wire it to upper control arm.
11. Remove lower control arm-to-frame attaching nuts. *Do not remove bolts yet.*
12. Lower jack from under lower control arm. The torsion bar is now un-

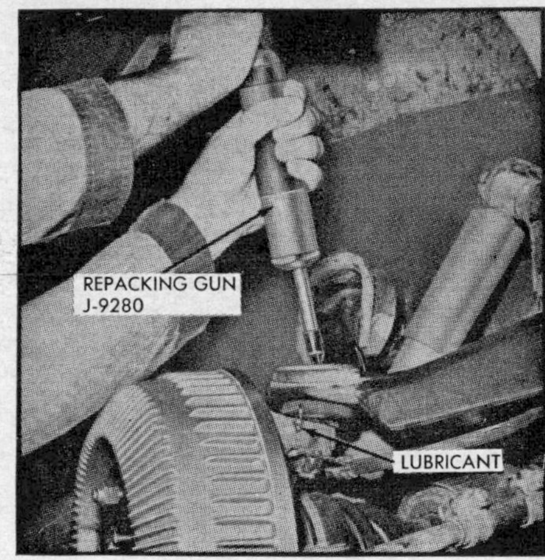

Fig. 11 Repacking upper ball joint. 1967-69 Eldorado

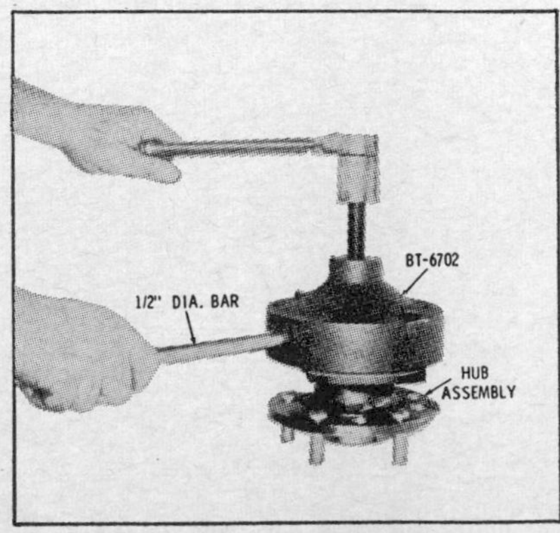

Fig. 13 Removing front wheel bearing. Eldorado

loaded and lower control arm is hanging free.

13. Remove torsion bar adjusting bolt.
14. Pull down on outer end of lower control arm with one hand, while reaching back with the other hand to remove torsion bar adjusting nut from frame crossmember.
15. Remove lower control arm-to-frame attaching bolts and disengage arm from frame mounts.
16. Slide lower control arm off torsion bar and slide bar out of frame crossmember retainer and remove from car.

Inspection

1. Check rubber seal for damage and replace if necessary.
2. A new retainer must be used when torsion bar is replaced.
3. Check torsion bar for nicks, scratches or dents. If any of these conditions exist the torsion bar must be replaced.

Installation

1. Lubricate both ends of bar for about 3" with lubriplate.
2. Lubricate bar retainer in crossmember.
3. Place torsion bar in retainer. *Torsion bar ends are marked and must be installed as indicated as it is possible to reverse bar when installing.*
4. Lubricate lower control arm torsion bar connector and position control arm on bar. *When installing control arm, make sure that arm is installed in the "on car position" and is level. Also check torsion bar, making certain that it is fully seated in crossmember.*
5. With a jack, raise lower control arm and install in chassis mounts. Do not tighten nuts yet.
6. Pull down on lower control arm with one hand, and with the other hand, install torsion bar lock nut through chassis crossmember and under arm.
7. Lubricate adjusting bolt with E.P. chassis lube and install bolt. Do not tighten bolt yet.
8. Install brake backing plate.
9. Install lower ball joint, tighten nut to 40 ft-lbs and install cotter pin.
10. Install upper ball joint to steering knuckle.
11. Complete the installation and lower car. Tighten nuts that were left loose. Finally, check standing height and wheel alignment as outlined previously.

POWER STEERING, REPLACE

Service Bulletin

Whenever steering or front end work is being performed on a 1965-1968 car, it is good practice to check the three steering gear mounting screws, and retorque them to 45 ft-lbs. Any mounting screw that is found below 5 ft-lbs or over-torqued above 60 ft-lbs should be replaced.

1968-69 Standard Cars

1. Disconnect pressure and return line hoses at steering gear. Have container ready to catch dripping oil. Secure hoses in raised position to prevent loss of fluid.
2. Raise car and use a puller to disconnect pitman arm from steering linkage.
3. Remove screw that holds flexible coupling to steering shaft.
4. Unfasten gear from frame side rail, lower gear down and out of car with pitman arm attached.
5. Reverse procedure to install.

1967-69 Eldorado

1. Disconnect hydraulic hoses at rear of pump reservoir. Cap pump fittings to prevent drainage of fluid from pump. Also, cap or tape hose fittings. If equipped with steering pump cooler, disconnect return hose at cooler.
2. Pull pitman arm from drag link.
3. Remove two bolts holding flexible coupling together.
4. Unfasten gear from frame and move gear forward and down out of car.
5. Reverse procedure to install. Check fluid level and bleed hydraulic system as outlined for standard cars.

1963-67 Standard Cars

1. Disconnect pressure and return line hoses at rear of pump reservoir. Cap pump fittings to prevent drainage of fluid from pump.
2. Jack up car and place jack stands near outer ends of lower suspension arms.
3. Disconnect pitman arm from steering gear.
4. Remove screw that holds flexible coupling to upper steering shaft.
5. Remove three screws that hold gear housing to frame and remove gear.
6. Reverse foregoing procedure to install the steering gear. Fill reservoir to level mark. Replace filler cap, start engine and idle for three minutes, then check for leaks in reservoir shell.
7. Any air trapped in the system should be bled out by running engine at a fast idle for about two minutes. Turn wheels occasionally from right to left without hitting the stops. Recheck fluid level after bleeding system.

CAMARO • CHEVELLE • CHEVROLET
CHEVY II • CORVETTE

OLD CAR SPECIFICATIONS: For 1946-62 Tune Up and Wheel Alignment Specifications see back of book.

INDEX OF SERVICE OPERATIONS

PAGE NO.

ACCESSORIES

Automatic Level Controls 1-41
Clock Troubles 1-11
Heater Core, Replace 2-109
Power Top Troubles 1-18
Power Window Troubles 1-18
Radio, Replace 2-109
Speed Controls, Adjust 2-109

BRAKES

Brake Troubles, Mechanical 1-17
Disc Brake Service 1-430
Hydraulic System Service 1-422
Master Cylinder, Replace 2-129
Parking Brake, Adjust 2-129
Power Brake Unit, Replace 2-130
Power Brake Service 1-440
Power Brake Troubles 1-440
Service Brakes, Adjust 2-128

CLUTCH

Clutch Pedal, Adjust 2-119
Clutch, Replace 2-119
Clutch Troubles 1-12

COOLING SYSTEM

Cooling System Troubles 1-6
Variable Speed Fans 1-39
Water Pump, Replace 2-118

ELECTRICAL

Alternator Service 1-63
Dash Gauge Service 1-117
Distributor, Replace 2-100
Distributor Service:
- Standard 1-53
- Transistorized 1-47

Electrical Troubles 1-8
Flasher Location Chart Back of Book
Generator Service 1-91
Headlamps, Concealed Type 1-40
Ignition Coils and Resistors 1-24
Ignition Switch, Replace 2-101
Ignition Timing 2-100
Instrument Cluster Removal 2-105
Light Switch, Replace 2-101
Neutral Safety Switch, Replace 2-102
Spark Plug Condition Chart 2-647
Starter Service 1-101
Starter, Replace 2-100
Starter Switch Service 1-114
Stop Light Switch, Replace 2-102
Turn Signal Switch, Replace 2-102
Turn Signal Troubles 1-11
Windshield Wiper Motor, Replace 2-107
Windshield Wiper Troubles 1-20

PAGE NO.

ENGINE

Camshaft, Replace 2-115
Crankshaft Rear Oil Seal 2-116
Cylinder Head, Replace 2-111
Engine Identification 2-75
Engine, Replace 2-111
Engine Troubles 1-1
Main Bearings 2-116
Piston Rings 2-115
Piston and Rod, Assemble 2-115
Pistons 2-115
Push Rods 2-113
Rocker Arm Studs 2-112
Rod Bearings 2-116
Timing Case Cover, Replace 2-114
Timing Chain or Gears, Replace 2-114
Valves, Adjust 2-111
Valve Arrangement 2-112
Valve Guide 2-113
Valve Lifters 2-114

ENGINE LUBRICATION

Crankcase Ventilation (PCV) 1-29
Exhaust Emission Controls 1-30
Oil Pan, Replace 2-117
Oil Pump 2-118

FUEL SYSTEM

Carburetor Adjustments and Specs. 1-124
Crankcase Ventilation (PCV) 1-29
Exhaust Emission Controls 1-30
Fuel Pump, Replace 2-118
Fuel Pump Service 1-120
Fuel System Troubles 1-2

PROPELLER SHAFT & U JOINTS

Propeller Shaft 2-126
Universal Joint Service 1-418

REAR AXLE

Axle Shaft, Bearing and Seal 2-125
Corvette Rear Wheel Alignment 2-130
Rear Axle Description 2-124
Rear Axle Specifications 2-87
Rear Axle Troubles 1-17

SPECIFICATIONS

Alternator 2-90
Brakes 2-99
Capacities 2-96
Carburetors 1-124
Cooling System 2-96
Crankshaft and Bearings 2-95
Distributors 2-88

PAGE NO.

Engine Tightening Torque 2-94
General Engine Specs. 2-79
Ignition Coils and Resistors 1-24
Pistons, Rings and Pins 2-95
Rear Axle 2-87
Starting Motors 2-91
Tune Up 2-81
Valve Lift Specs. 2-112
Valve Timing 2-113
Valves 2-92
Wheel Alignment 2-96

STEERING GEAR

Horn Sounder Removal 2-104
Mechanical Gear, Replace 2-134
Mechanical Gear Service 1-451
Mechanical Gear Troubles 1-18
Power Gear, Replace 2-134
Steering Wheel, Replace 2-104

SUSPENSION, FRONT

Ball Joints, Replace 2-132
Ball Joints, Check for Wear 2-131
Coil Spring, Replace 2-133
Lubrication 2-130
Shock Absorber, Replace 2-133
Suspension, Description of 2-130
Tire Wear Chart 2-648
Toe-In, Adjust 2-131
Wheel Alignment, Adjust 2-130
Wheel Bearings, Adjust 2-131
Wheel Bearings, Replace 2-131

TRANSMISSIONS

Three Speed Manual:
- Replace 2-120
- Repairs 1-261
- Linkage, Adjust 2-122

Four Speed Manual:
- Replace 2-121
- Repairs 1-298
- Linkage, Adjust 2-123

Automatic Units 1-321
- Linkage, 1969 2-123

Overdrive Service 1-259

TUNE UP

Service 1-21
Specifications 2-81

WINDSHIELD WIPER

Wiper Motor, Replace 2-107
Wiper Linkage, Replace 2-108
Wiper Switch, Replace 2-108
Wiper Troubles 1-20

CAMARO • CHEVELLE • CHEVROLET • CHEVY II • CORVETTE

SERIAL NUMBER LOCATION: Plate on left front door pillar or top of left side instrument panel

ENGINE NUMBER LOCATION:

4 & 6 CYL.: Pad at front right-hand side of cylinder block at rear of distributor

V8 ENGINES: Pad at front right-hand side of cylinder block

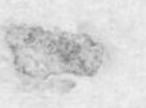

ENGINE IDENTIFICATION CODE

Engines are identified in the following table by the code letter or letters immediately following the engine serial number.

CAMARO

CODE	Engine	Year
AM	6-230 with M/T	1969
AN	6-230 with P/G, T/D	1969
AO	6-230 with T/S	1969
AP	6-230 with A/C	1969
AQ	6-230 with P/G, T/D, A/C	1969
AR	6-230 with A/C, T/S	1969
BA	6-230 with M/T	1968
BB	6-230 with M/T, A/C	1968
BB	6-250 with P/G, T/D	1969
BC	6-230 with HDC	1968
BC	6-250 with P/G, T/D, A/C	1969
BD	6-230 with A/C	1968
BD	6-250 with T/S	1969
BE	6-250 with M/T	1969
BF	6-230 with P/G	1968
BF	6-250 with A/C	1969
BH	6-230 with P/G, A/C	1968
BH	6-250 with T/S, A/C	1969
CM	6-250 with M/T	1968
CN	6-250 with A/C	1968
CQ	6-250 with P/G	1968
CR	6-250 with P/G, A/C	1968
DZ	8-302 with 4 BC	1969
EI	8-396 Hi Perf.	1967
EQ	8-396 with T/H	1967
EY	8-396 with Hi Perf., Air	1967
FA	8-327 with M/T	1969
FB	8-327 with P/G	1969
FC	8-327 with T/S	1969
FH	8-327 with T/S	1969
HA	8-350 with M/T	1969
HB	8-350 with T/S	1969
HC	8-350 with 2 BC	1969
HD	8-350 with 2 BC, T/S	1969
HE	8-350 with P/G	1969
HF	8-350 with 2 BC, P/G	1969
JB	8-396 with P/G	1969
JF	8-396 with HPE	1969
JG	8-396 with T/S	1969
JH	8-396 with SHPE	1969
JI	8-396 with HPE, T/S	1969
JJ	8-396 with A/H	1969
JL	8-396 with SHPE, T/S	1969
JM	8-396 with A/H, T/S	1969
LA	6-230 with M/T	1967
LB	6-230 with M/T, A/C	1967
LC	6-230 with AIR	1967
LD	6-230 with AIR, A/C	1967
LE	6-230 with P/G	1967
LF	6-230 with P/G, A/C	1967
LG	6-230 with P/G, AIR	1967
LH	6-230 with AIR, A/C, P/G	1967
LN	6-250 with M/T	1967
LO	6-250 with M/T, A/C	1967
LP	6-250 with AIR	1967
LQ	6-250 with AIR, A/C	1967
LR	6-250 with M/T, A/C	1967
LS	6-250 with AIR	1967
LT	6-250 with AIR, A/C	1967
LU	6-250 with P/G	1967
MA	8-327 with 2 BC, M/T	1967-68
MB	8-327 with 2 BC, AIR	1967
MD	8-283 with 2 BC, 4 sp. tr.	1967
ME	8-327 with 2 BC, P/G	1967-68
MF	8-327 with 2 BC, P/G, AIR	1967
MJ	8-283 with 2 BC, P/G	1967
MK	8-327 with M/T	1967
ML	8-327 with AIR	1967
MM	8-327 with P/G	1967
MN	8-327 with P/G, AIR	1967
MO	8-302 with 4 BC	1967-68
MP	8-302 with 4 BC, AIR	1967
MQ	8-396 HPE	1967-68
MR	8-396 with AIR, HPE	1967-68
MS	8-350 with M/T	1967-68
MT	8-350 with AIR	1967
MT	8-396 with SHPE, A/H	1968
MU	8-350 with P/G	1967-68
MV	8-350 with P/G, AIR	1967
MW	8-396 with M/T, A/T	1967-68
MX	8-396 with HPE	1967-68
MY	8-396 with T/H	1967-68
MZ	8-396 with T/H, AIR	1967

CHEVROLET

CODE	Engine	Year
A	6 cyl. with 3 sp. tr.	1963-64
AE	6 cyl. with HDC	1963-64
AF	6 cyl. with 3 sp. tr., A/C	1963-64
AG	6 cyl. with HDC, A/C	1963-64
B	6 cyl. with P/G	1963-64
BA	6-250 with M/T	1969
BG	6-250 with M/T, A/C	1969
BQ	6 cyl. with P/G, A/C	1964
C	8-283 with 3 sp. tr.	1963-64
CA	6-250 with M/T	1968
CB	8-283 police	1963-64
CC	6-250 with A/C	1968
CD	8-283 with O/D	1963
CJ	6-250 with HDC	1968
CK	6-250 with HDC, A/C	1968
CL	8-283 with A/C	1963
CM	6-250 with M/T	1968
CN	6-250 with A/C	1968
CQ	6-250 with P/G	1968
CR	6-250 with P/G, A/C	1968
D	8-283 with P/G	1963-64
DK	8-283 with P/G, A/C	1963
DO	8-307 with M/T	1968
DP	8-307 with 4 sp. tr. S.S.	1968
DQ	8-307 with HDC	1968
DR	8-307 with P/G	1968
DS	8-307 with T.H.	1968
FA	6 cyl. with 3 sp. tr.	1965-67
FA	8-327 with M/T	1969
FB	8-327 with P/G	1969
FC	8-327 with T/S	1969
FE	6 cyl. with HDC	1965-67
FF	6 cyl. with HDC, A/C	1965-67
FH	8-327 with T/S	1969
FK	6 cyl. taxi	1965-67
FL	6 cyl. with 3 sp. tr., A/C	1965-67
FM	6 cyl. with P/G	1965-67
FP	6 cyl. taxi	1965-67
FR	6 cyl. with P/G, A/C	1965-67
FV	6 cyl. with AIR	1966-67
FW	6 cyl. with AIR, HDC	1966
FX	6 cyl. with AIR, HDC, A/C	1966
FY	6 cyl. with AIR, A/C	1966-67
FZ	6 cyl. taxi with AIR	1966-67
GA	8-283 with 3 sp. tr.	1965-67
GC	8-283 with 4 sp. tr.	1965-67
GF	8-283 with P/G	1965-67
GK	8-283 with AIR	1966-67
GP	6 cyl. with P/G, AIR	1966-67
GQ	6 cyl. with P/G, A/C, AIR	1966-67
GR	6 cyl. taxi with P/G, AIR	1966-67
GS	8-283 with 4 sp. tr., AIR	1966-67
GT	8-283 with P/G, AIR	1966-67
GU	8-283 with HDC	1967
HA	8-327 with 3 sp. tr.	1965-68
HB	8-327 with 3 sp. tr., HPE	1965-66
HB	8-327 with AIR	1967
HB	8-327 with HDC	1968
HC	8-327 with P/G	1965-68
HD	8-327 with P/G, HPE	1965
HF	8-327 with P/G, AIR	1966-67
HF	8-327 with T/H	1968
HG	8-350 with M/T	1969
HH	8-350 with T/S	1969
HI	8-327 with 4 BC	1968
HI	8-350 with 2 BC	1969
HJ	8-327 with 4 BC, P/G	1968
HJ	8-350 with 2 BC, T/S	1969
HK	8-350 with P/G	1969
HL	8-327 with 4 BC, HDC	1968
HL	8-350 with 2 BC, P/G	1969
HM	8-327 with 4 BC, T/H	1968
HM	8-350 with 2 BC, T/S	1969
HN	8-350 with T/S	1969
IA	8-396 with M/T	1965-68
IB	8-396 with AIR	1965-67
IC	8-396 with M/T, T/I	1965
IC	8-396 with P/G, AIR	1966-67
ID	8-327 with SHPE	1966-68
IE	8-396 with M/T, SHPE	1965
IG	8-396 with P/G	1965-68
IH	8-427 with M/T	1966-68
II	8-396 with P/G, T/I	1965
II	8-427 with AIR	1966-67

Continued

ENGINE IDENTIFICATION CODE—Continued

CHEVROLET—Continued

CODE		
IJ	8-427 with T/H	1966-67
IJ	8-427 with T/H	1968
IN	8-396 with T/H, AIR	1967
IO	8-427 with T/H, AIR	1967
IV	8-396 with T/H	1965-68
IW	8-396 with T/H, T/I	1965
JA	8-409 with M/T, HPE	1965
JB	8-409 with M/T	1965
JC	8-409 with T/I	1965
JD	8-409 with T/I, HPE	1965
JE	8-409 with P/G	1965
JF	8-409 with P/G, T/I	1965

CODE		
JN	8-396 with 2 BC	1969
JQ	8-396 with 2 BC, T/S	1969
KE	8-327 with 4 sp. tr.	1967
LA	8-427 with HPE	1969
LB	8-427 with 4 BC	1969
LC	8-427 with HPE, T/S	1969
LD	8-427 with SHPE	1969
LE	8-427 with 4 BC, T/S	1969
LH	8-427 with HPE	1969
LI	8-427 with T/S	1969
LS	8-427 with SHPE, T/S	1969
QA	8-409 with 4 BC	1963

CODE		
QB	8-409 with 2 carbs.	1963
QC	8-409 with M/T	1963
QG	8-409 with P/G	1963
QM	8-409 with SHPE	1963
R	8-327 with M/T	1963
RA	8-327 with M/T, A/C	1963
RB	8-327 with M/T, HPE	1963
RK	8-327 with M/T, HPE, A/C	1963
S	8-327 with P/G	1963
SA	8-327 with P/G, A/C	1963
SB	8-327 with P/G, HPE	1963
SG	8-327 with P/G, A/C, HPE	1963

CHEVY II

CODE		
AA	4-153 with M/T	1969
AB	4-153 with T/D	1969
AM	6-230 with M/T	1969
AN	6-230 with P/G, T/D	1969
AO	6-230 with T/S	1969
AP	6-230 with A/C	1969
AR	6-230 with T/S, A/C	1969
BA	6-230 with M/T	1968
BB	6-230 with A/C, HDC	1968
BB	6-250 with P/G, T/D	1969
BC	6-230 with HDC	1968
BC	6-250 with P/G, T/D, A/C	1969
BD	6-230 with A/C	1968
BD	6-250 with T/S	1969
BE	6-250 with M/T	1969
BF	6-230 with P/G	1968
BF	6-250 with A/C	1969
BH	6-230 with P/G, A/C	1968
BH	6-250 with T/S, A/C	1969
BT	6-230 with P/G	1963-64
BU	6-230 with P/G, P/V	1963-64
CF	8-283 with 4 sp. tr.	1963-64
CG	8-283 with 4 sp. tr., A/C	1963-64
CH	8-283 with 3 sp. tr.	1963-64
CJ	8-283 with 3 sp. tr., A/C	1963-64
CM	6-250 with M/T	1968
CN	6-250 with A/C	1968
CQ	6-250 with P/G	1968
CR	6-250 with P/G, A/C	1968
DA	8-307 with M/T	1968-69
DB	8-307 with 4 sp. tr.	1968
DC	8-307 with P/G	1969
DD	8-307 with T/S	1969
DE	8-307 with P/G	1968
DE	8-307 with 4 sp. tr.	1969
DE	8-283 with P/G	1963-64
DF	8-283 with P/G, A/C	1963-64
E	4 cyl. with M/T	1963-64
EA	8-327 with M/T	1968
EB	4 cyl. with M/T, HDC	1963-64
EE	8-327 with P/G	1968
EG	4 cyl. with P/G	1963-64

CODE		
EK	4 cyl. taxi with M/T	1963-64
EL	4 cyl. taxi with P/G	1963-64
EP	4 cyl. with M/T, P/V	1963-64
EP	8-327 with SHPE	1968
EQ	4 cyl. with P/G, P/V	1963-64
ER	4 cyl. with M/T, HDC, P/V	1963-64
ES	4 cyl. with M/T, P/V	1963-64
ET	4 cyl. with P/G, P/V	1963-64
H	6-194 with M/T	1963-64
HA	8-350 with M/T	1969
HB	6-194 with M/T, HDC	1963-64
HB	8-350 with T/S	1969
HC	8-350 with 2 BC	1969
HD	8-350 with 2 BC, T/S	1969
HE	8-350 with P/G	1969
HF	8-350 with 2 BC, P/G	1969
HF	6-194 with P/G	1963-64
HL	6-194 taxi with M/T	1963-64
HM	6-194 taxi with P/G	1963-64
HQ	6-230 with P/G, T/D, A/C	1969
HT	6-194 taxi with M/T, P/V	1963-64
HU	6-194 taxi with P/G, P/V	1963-64
JF	8-396 with HPE	1969
JH	8-396 with SHPE	1969
JI	8-396 with HPE, T/S	1969
JL	8-396 with SHPE, T/S	1969
LP	6-230 with M/T	1963-64
LR	6-230 with M/T, P/V	1963-64
MK	8-327 with M/T	1968
ML	8-327 with SHPE	1968
MM	8-327 with P/G	1968
OA	4-153 with M/T	1965-68
OC	4-153 with HDC	1965-68
OG	4-153 taxi	1965-66
OH	4-153 with P/G	1965-68
OJ	4-153 taxi with P/G	1965-66
OK	6-194 with M/T	1965-67
OM	6-194 with HDC	1965-67
OQ	6-194 taxi	1965-66
OR	6-194 with P/G	1965-67
OS	6-194 with P/G, AIR	1966
OT	6-194 taxi with P/G	1965-66

CODE		
PC	6-230 with AIR	1966-67
PD	8-283 with M/T	1965-67
PE	8-283 with 4BC	1965-66
PE	8-283 with AIR	1967
PF	8-283 with A/C	1965-67
PG	8-283 with AIR, A/C	1966
PG	8-283 with 4BC, A/C	1965
PI	6-230 with P/G, AIR	1965-67
PL	8-283 with 4 sp. tr.	1965-67
PM	8-283 with 4 sp. tr., A/C	1965-67
PN	8-283 with P/G	1965-67
PO	8-283 with P/G, 4BC	1965-66
PP	8-283 with P/G, A/C	1965-67
PQ	8-283 with P/G, 4BC, A/C	1965
PQ	8-283 with 4 sp. tr., AIR	1966-67
PS	8-283 with 4 sp. tr., AIR, A/C	1966
PU	8-283 with P/G, AIR	1966-67
PV	6-230 with M/T	1965-67
PX	6-230 with P/G	1965-67
ZA	8-327 with M/T	1965-66
ZA	8-327 with 4BC	1967
ZB	8-327 with AIR	1967
ZB	8-327 with M/T, HPE	1965-66
ZC	8-327 with A/C, AIR	1966
ZD	8-327 with P/G, AIR	1966
ZE	8-327 with M/T, A/C	1965-66
ZE	8-327 with A/C	1967
ZF	8-327 with M/T, A/C, HPE	1965-66
ZG	8-327 with SHPE, AIR	1966-67
ZH	8-327 with SHPE, A/C, AIR	1966
ZI	8-327 with SHPE	1966-67
ZJ	8-327 with SHPE, A/C	1966-67
ZK	8-327 with P/G	1965-67
ZL	8-327 with P/G, HPE	1965-66
ZM	8-327 with P/G, A/C	1965-67
ZN	8-327 with P/G, HPE, A/C	1965-66
ZV	6-194 with HDC, AIR	1966
ZW	6-194 taxi with AIR	1966
ZX	6-194 with P/G, AIR	1966-67
ZY	6-194 with HDC, AIR	1966
ZY	6-194 with AIR	1967

CHEVELLE

CODE		
AA	6-194 with M/T	1965-66
AC	6-194 with HDC	1965-66
AD	6-230 with T/S	1969
AG	6-194 with A/C	1965-66
AH	6-194 with HDC, A/C	1965-66
AK	6-194 taxi	1965-66
AL	6-194 with P/G	1965-66
AM	6-230 with M/T	1969
AN	6-230 with P/G, T/D	1969

CODE		
AN	6-194 taxi with P/G	1965-66
AP	6-230 with A/C	1969
AQ	6-230 with P/G, T/D, A/C	1969
AR	6-230 with T/S, A/C	1969
AR	6-194 with P/G, A/C	1965-66
AS	6-194 with AIR	1966
AT	6-194 with A/C, AIR	1966
AU	6-194 with HDC, A/C, AIR	1966
AV	6-194 taxi with AIR	1966

CODE		
AW	6-194 with HDC, AIR	1966
AX	6-194 with P/G, AIR	1966
AY	6-194 with P/G, AIR, A/C	1966
AZ	6-194 taxi with P/G, AIR	1966
BA	6-230 with M/T	1968
BB	6-230 with HDC, A/C	1967-68
BB	6-250 with P/G, T/D	1969
BC	6-250 with P/G, T/D, A/C	1969
BC	6-230 with HDC	1967-68

Continued

ENGINE IDENTIFICATION CODE—Continued

CHEVELLE—Continued

CODE		
BD	6-230 with A/C	1968
BD	6-250 with T/S	1969
BE	6-250 with M/T	1969
BF	6-250 with A/C	1969
BF	6-230 with P/G	1968
BH	6-230 with P/G, A/C	1968
BH	6-250 with T/S, A/C	1969
BL	6-230 with P/G	1964
BL	6-230 with P/G, AIR	1966-67
BM	6-230 with P/G, A/C	1964
BM	6-230 with P/G, A/C, AIR	1966-67
BN	6-230 with P/G, P/V	1964-66
BN	6-230 with AIR	1967
BO	6-230 with A/C, AIR	1966-67
BP	6-230 with P/G, P/V, A/C	1964
CA	6-230 with M/T	1965-67
CB	6-230 with M/T, A/C	1965-66
CB	6-230 with A/C	1967
CC	6-230 with P/G	1965-67
CD	6-230 with P/G, A/C	1965-67
CM	6-250 with 3 sp. tr.	1967-68
CN	6-250 with A/C	1967-68
CO	6-250 with AIR	1967
CP	6-250 with AIR, A/C	1967
CQ	6-250 with P/G	1967-68
CR	6-250 with P/G, A/C	1967-68
CS	6-250 with P/G, AIR	1967
CT	6-250 with P/G, AIR, A/C	1967
DA	8-283 with 3 sp. tr.	1965-67
DA	8-307 with M/T	1968
DA	8-307 with M/T	1969
DB	8-283 with 4 sp. tr.	1965-67
DB	8-307 with 4 sp. tr.	1968
DC	8-307 with P/G	1969
DD	8-307 with T/S	1969
DE	8-307 with 4 sp. tr.	1969
DE	8-283 with P/G	1967
DE	8-307 with P/G	1968
DF	8-283 with P/G	1965-66
DI	8-283 with AIR	1966-67
DJ	8-283 with P/G, AIR	1966-67
DK	8-283 with 4 sp. tr., AIR	1966-67
DN	8-283 with HDC	1967
DN	8-307 with HDC	1968
EA	8-327 with M/T	1966-68
EA	8-327 with 4 BC	1967
EB	8-327 with AIR	1967
EB	8-327 with HPE	1966
EC	8-327 with SHPE	1966
EC	8-327 with P/G, AIR	1967
ED	8-396 with M/T, P/G	1967
ED	8-396 with T/I	1966
ED	8-396 with M/T	1968
EE	8-327 with P/G	1966-68
EF	8-396 with P/G, HPE	1966
EF	8-396 HPE	1968
EG	8-396 Special HPE	1968
EH	8-327 with 4 BC	1968
EH	8-396 with AIR	1966-67
EI	8-327 with 4 BC, P/G	1968
EJ	8-327 with 4 BC, HDC	1968
EJ	8-396 with HPE, AIR	1966
EK	8-396 with P/G	1966-68
EL	8-396 with P/G, HPE	1966-68
EM	8-396 with P/G, AIR	1966-67
EN	8-396 with P/G, HPE, AIR	1966
EO	8-327 with HDC	1968
EP	8-327 with SHPE	1967-68
EQ	8-327 with HDC	1967
ER	8-327 with SHPE, AIR	1967
ES	8-327 with SHPE, HDC	1967-68
ET	8-396 with T/H	1968
EU	8-396 with T/H, HPE	1968
G	6-194 with M/T	1964
GB	6-194 with HDC	1964
GF	6-194 with M/T, P/V	1964
GG	6-194 with HDC, P/V	1964
GH	6-194 with M/T	1964
GJ	6-194 with M/T, P/V	1964
GK	6-194 with M/T, A/C	1964
GL	6-194 with HDC, A/C	1964
GM	6-194 with M/T, A/C, P/V	1964
GN	6-194 with HDC, A/C	1964
HA	8-350 with M/T	1969
HB	8-350 with T/S	1969
HC	8-350 with 2 BC	1969
HD	8-350 with 2 BC, T/S	1969
HE	8-350 with P/G	1969
HF	8-350 with 2 BC, P/G	1969
J	8-283 with 3 sp. tr.	1964
JA	8-283 with 4 sp. tr.	1964
JA	8-396 with M/T	1969
JC	8-396 with HPE	1969
JD	8-396 with SHPE	1969
JD	8-283 with P/G	1964
JE	8-396 with HPE, T/S	1969
JG	8-283 with P/G, 4BC	1964
JH	8-283 with 4BC	1964
JK	8-396 with T/S	1969
JQ	8-327 with M/T	1964
JR	8-327 with M/T, HPE	1964
JS	8-327 with M/T, SHPE	1964
JT	8-327 with M/T, T/I	1964
K	6-194 with P/G	1964
KB	6-194 with P/G, P/V	1964
KC	6-194 with P/G	1964
KD	6-194 with P/G, P/V	1964
KH	6-194 with P/G, A/C	1964
KJ	6-194 with P/G, A/C, P/V	1964
LL	6-230 with 3 sp. tr., A/C	1964
LM	6-230 with 3 sp. tr., P/V	1964
SR	8-327 with P/G	1964
SS	8-327 with P/G, HPE	1964

CORVETTE

CODE		
HD	8-327 with SHPE, AIR	1966-67
HE	8-327 with M/T	1965-68
HF	8-327 with HPE	1965
HG	8-327 with F/I	1965
HH	8-327 with SHPE	1965
HH	8-327 with AIR	1966-67
HI	8-327 with A/C	1965
HJ	8-327 with A/C, HPE	1965
HK	8-327 with A/C, SHPE	1965
HL	8 327 with T/I	1965
HM	8-327 with A/C, T/I	1965
HN	8-327 with F/I, T/I	1965
HO	8-327 with P/G	1965-67
HO	8-327 with T/H	1968
HP	8-327 with P/G, HPE	1965
HP	8-327 with P/S, SHPE, A/C	1967-68
HQ	8-327 with P/G, A/C	1965
HR	8-327 with P/G, A/C, HPE	1965
HR	8-327 with P/G, AIR	1966-67
HT	8-327 with SHPE, H/L	1965-68
HU	8-327 with SHPE, H/L, A/C	1965
HV	8-327 with SHPE, H/L, T/I	1965
HW	8-327 with SHPE, H/L, T/I, A/C	1965
HW	8-350 with HPE	1969
HX	8-350 with HPE, A/C	1969
HY	8-350 with M/T	1969
HZ	8-350 with T/S	1969
IF	8-396 with SHPE	1965
IK	8-427 with SHPE, H/L	1966
IL	8-427 with HPE	1966-68
IL	8-427 with 4 sp. tr., P/G	1967
IM	8-427 with AIR	1966-67
IM	8-427 HPE, 3 Carbs.	1968
IO	8-427 HPE, T/H, 3 Carbs.	1968
IQ	8-427 with H/T	1967-68
IR	8 427 with P/G, AIR	1967
IR	8-427 HPE, 3 Carbs.	1968
IT	8-427 Heavy Duty	1967-68
IU	8-427 with Alum. Heads	1967-68
JA	8-427 with SHPE, AIR, Tri-Carbs.	1967
JC	8-427 with Tri-Carbs.	1967
JD	8-427 with P/G, Tri-Carbs.	1967
JE	8-427 SHPE, Tri-Carbs.	1967
JF	8-427 Tri-Carbs., AIR	1967
JG	8-427 Tri-Carbs.	1967
JH	8-427 Alum. Heads, AIR	1967
KH	8-327 with SHPE, A/C, AIR	1967
LL	8-427 with HPE, T/S	1969
LM	8-427 with HPE	1969
LN	8-427 with HPE, T/S, 3 Carbs.	1969
LO	8-427 with HD	1969
LP	8-427 with A/H	1969
LQ	8-427 with HPE, 3 Carbs.	1969
LR	8-427 with SHPE, 3 Carbs.	1969
LT	8-427 with SHPE, 3 Carbs., HDC	1969
LU	8-427 with A/H, HDC	1969
LV	8-427 with T/S	1969
LW	8-427 with A/H, T/S	1969
LX	8-427 with SHPE, 3 Carbs., T/S	1969
RC	8-327 with M/T	1963-64
RD	8-327 with M/T, HPE	1963-64
RE	8-327 with M/T, SHPE	1963-64
RF	8-327 with M/T, F/I	1963-64
RP	8-327 with M/T, A/C	1964
RQ	8-327 with M/T, A/C, HPE	1964
RR	8-327 with M/T, A/C, SHPE	1964
RT	8-327 with M/T, T/I	1964
RU	8-327 with M/T, T/I, A/C	1964
RX	8-327 with F/I, T/I	1964
SC	8-327 with P/G	1963-64
SD	8-327 with P/G, HPE	1963-64
SK	8-327 with P/G, A/C	1964
SL	8-327 with P/G, A/C, HPE	1964

A/C: Air conditioned
A/H: Aluminum Heads
A/S: Air suspension
AIR: Air injection reactor
A/T: Automatic transmission
4BC: Four barrel carburetor
F/I: Fuel injection
H/D: Heavy Duty
HDC: Heavy duty clutch
HPE: High performance engine
H/L: Hydraulic lifters
M/T: Manual transmission
O/D: Overdrive
P/G: Powerglide
P/S: Power steering
P/V: Positive crankcase ventilation
SHPE: Special high perf. engine
S.S.: Super Sport
T/D: Torque Drive
T/H: Turbo Hydramatic
T/I: Transistor ignition

GRILLE IDENTIFICATION

1963 Chevy II

1963 Chevrolet

1963-65 Corvette

1964 Chevelle

1964 Chevrolet

1964 Chevy II

1965 Chevelle

1965 Chevrolet

1965 Chevy II

1966 Chevelle

1966 Chevrolet

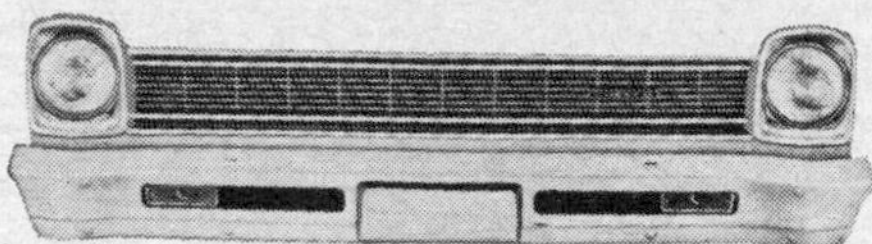
1966 Chevy II

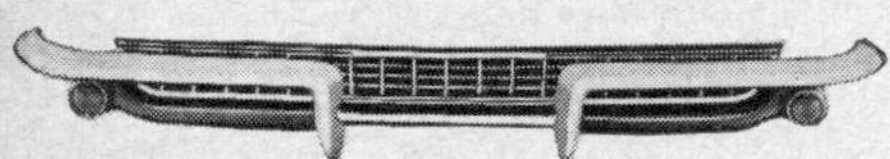
1966-67 Corvette

1967 Camaro

1967 Camaro Super Sport

1967 Chevelle

1967 Chevrolet

1967 Chevy II

1968 Camaro

1968 Camaro Rally Sport

1968 Chevelle

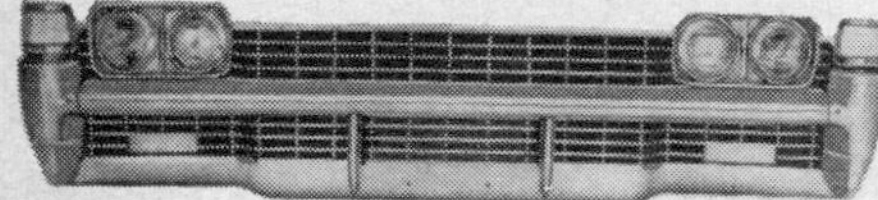
1968 Chevrolet

1968 Chevy II

1968 Corvette

1969 Camaro

1969 Chevelle

1969 Chevelle S. S.

GRILLE IDENTIFICATION—Continued

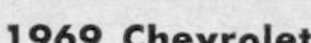
1969 Chevrolet

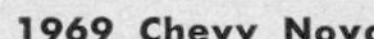
1969 Chevy Nova

1969 Corvette

GENERAL ENGINE SPECIFICATIONS

Year	Engine	Carburetor	Bore and Stroke	Piston Displacement, Cubic Inches	Compression Ratio	Maximum Brake H.P. @ R.P.M.	Maximum Torque Lbs. Ft. @ R.P.M.	Normal Oil Pressure Pounds
1963	90 Horsepower....4-153	1 Barrel	3.875 x 3.25	153	8.5	90 @ 4000	152 @ 2400	30–45
	120 Horsepower....6-194	1 Barrel	3.5635 x 3.25	194	8.5	120 @ 4400	177 @ 2400	30–45
	140 Horsepower....6-230	1 Barrel	3.875 x 3.25	230	8.5	140 @ 4400	220 @ 1600	30–45
	195 Horsepower....V8-283	2 Barrel	3.875 x 3.00	283	9.25	195 @ 4800	285 @ 2400	30–45
	250 Horsepower....V8-327	4 Barrel	4.001 x 3.25	327	10.5	250 @ 4400	350 @ 2800	30–45
	300 Horsepower....V8-327	4 Barrel	4.001 x 3.25	327	10.5	300 @ 5000	360 @ 3200	30–45
	360 Horsepower....V8-327	Fuel Inj.	4.001 x 3.25	327	11.25	360 @ 6000	352 @ 4000	30–45
	340 Horsepower....V8-409	4 Barrel	4.3125 x 3.50	409	10.0	340 @ 5000	420 @ 3200	50
	400 Horsepower....V8-409	4 Barrel	4.3125 x 3.50	409	11.0	400 @ 5800	425 @ 3600	50
	425 Horsepower....V8-409	Two Carbs.	4.3125 x 3.50	409	11.0	425 @ 6000	425 @ 4200	50
1964	90 Horsepower....4-153	1 Barrel	3.875 x 3.25	153	8.5	90 @ 4000	152 @ 2400	30–45
	120 Horsepower....6-194	1 Barrel	3.5635 x 3.25	194	8.5	120 @ 4400	177 @ 2400	30–45
	140 Horsepower....6-230	1 Barrel	3.875 x 3.25	230	8.5	140 @ 4400	220 @ 1600	30–45
	155 Horsepower....6-230	1 Barrel	3.875 x 3.25	230	8.5	155 @ 4400	215 @ 2000	30–45
	195 Horsepower....V8-283	2 Barrel	3.875 x 3.00	283	9.25	195 @ 4800	285 @ 2400	30–45
	220 Horsepower....V8-283	4 Barrel	3.875 x 3.00	283	9.25	220 @ 4800	295 @ 3200	30–45
	250 Horsepower....V8-327	4 Barrel	4.001 x 3.25	327	10.5	250 @ 4400	350 @ 2800	30–45
	300 Horsepower....V8-327	4 Barrel	4.001 x 3.25	327	10.5	300 @ 5000	360 @ 3200	30–45
	365 Horsepower....V8-327	4 Barrel	4.001 x 3.25	327	11.0	365 @ 6200	350 @ 4000	30–45
	375 Horsepower....V8-327	Fuel Inj.	4.001 x 3.25	327	11.0	375 @ 6200	350 @ 4600	30–45
	340 Horsepower....V8-409	4 Barrel	4.3125 x 3.50	409	10.0	340 @ 5000	420 @ 3200	50
	400 Horsepower....V8-409	4 Barrel	4.3125 x 3.50	409	11.0	400 @ 5800	425 @ 3600	50
	425 Horsepower....V8-409	Two Carbs.	4.3125 x 3.50	409	11.0	425 @ 6000	425 @ 4200	30–45
1965	90 Horsepower....4-153	1 Barrel	3.875 x 3.25	153	8 5	90 @ 4000	152 @ 2400	30–45
	120 Horsepower....6-194	1 Barrel	3.5635 x 3.25	194	8.5	120 @ 4400	177 @ 2400	30–45
	140 Horsepower....6-230	1 Barrel	3.875 x 3.25	230	8.5	140 @ 4400	220 @ 1600	30–45
	195 Horsepower....V8-283	2 Barrel	3.875 x 3.00	283	9.25	195 @ 4800	285 @ 2400	30–45
	220 Horsepower....V8-283	4 Barrel	3.875 x 3.00	283	9.25	220 @ 4800	295 @ 3200	30–45
	250 Horsepower....V8-327	4 Barrel	4.001 x 3.25	327	10.5	250 @ 4400	350 @ 2800	30–45
	300 Horsepower....V8-327	4 Barrel	4.001 x 3.25	327	10.5	300 @ 5000	360 @ 3200	30–45
	350 Horsepower....V8-327	4 Barrel	4.001 x 3.25	327	11.0	350 @ 5800	360 @ 3600	30–45
	365 Horsepower....V8-327	4 Barrel	4.001 x 3.25	327	11.0	365 @ 6200	350 @ 4000	30–45
	375 Horsepower....V8-327	Fuel Inj.	4.001 x 3.25	327	11.0	375 @ 6200	350 @ 4600	30–45
	325 Horsepower....V8-396	4 Barrel	4.094 x 3.76	396	10.25	325 @ 4800	410 @ 3200	50–75
	425 Horsepower....V8-396	4 Barrel	4.094 x 3.76	396	11.0	425 @ 6400	415 @ 4000	50–75
	340 Horsepower....V8-409	4 Barrel	4.3125 x 3.50	409	10.0	340 @ 5000	420 @ 3200	50
	400 Horsepower....V8-409	4 Barrel	4.3125 x 3.50	409	11.0	400 @ 5800	425 @ 3600	50
1966	90 Horsepower....4-153	1 Barrel	3.875 x 3.25	153	8.5	90 @ 4000	152 @ 2400	30–45
	120 Horsepower....6-194	2 Barrel	3.5635 x 3.25	194	8.5	120 @ 4400	177 @ 2400	30–45
	140 Horsepower....6-230	1 Barrel	3.875 x 3.25	230	8.5	140 @ 4400	220 @ 1600	30–45
	155 Horsepower....6-250	2 Barrel	3.875 x 3.53	250	8.5	155 @ 4200	235 @ 1600	30–45
	195 Horsepower....V8-283	2 Barrel	3.875 x 3.00	283	9.25	195 @ 4800	285 @ 2400	30–45
	220 Horsepower....V8-283	4 Barrel	3.875 x 3.00	283	9.25	220 @ 4800	295 @ 3200	30–45
	275 Horsepower....V8-327	4 Barrel	4.001 x 3.25	327	10.5	275 @ 4800	355 @ 4200	30–45

Continued

GENERAL ENGINE SPECIFICATIONS—Continued

Year	Engine	Carburetor	Bore and Stroke	Piston Displacement, Cubic Inches	Compression Ratio	Maximum Brake H.P. @ R.P.M.	Maximum Torque Lbs. Ft. @ R.P.M.	Normal Oil Pressure Pounds
1966	300 Horsepower.............V8-327	4 Barrel	4.001 x 3.25	327	10.5	300 @ 5000	360 @ 3400	30-45
	325 Horsepower.............V8-396	4 Barrel	4.094 x 3.76	396	10.25	325 @ 4800	410 @ 3200	50-75
	350 Horsepower.............V8-327	4 Barrel	4.001 x 3.25	327	11.0	350 @ 5800	360 @ 3600	30-45
	360 Horsepower.............V8-396	4 Barrel	4.094 x 3.76	396	10.25	360 @ 5200	420 @ 3600	50-75
	390 Horsepower.............V8-427	4 Barrel	4.251 x 3.76	427	10.25	390 @ 5200	470 @ 3600	50-75
	425 Horsepower.............V8-427	4 Barrel	4.251 x 3.76	427	11.0	425 @ 5600	460 @ 4000	50-75
1967	90 Horsepower.............4-153	1 Barrel	3.875 x 3.25	153	8.50	90 @ 4000	152 @ 2400	30-45
	120 Horsepower.............6-194	1 Barrel	3.563 x 3.25	194	8.50	120 @ 4400	177 @ 2400	30-45
	140 Horsepower.............6-230	1 Barrel	3.875 x 3.25	230	8.50	140 @ 4400	220 @ 1600	30-45
	155 Horsepower.............6-250	1 Barrel	3.875 x 3.53	250	8.50	155 @ 4200	235 @ 1600	30-45
	195 Horsepower.............V8-283	2 Barrel	3.875 x 3.00	283	9.25	195 @ 4800	285 @ 2400	30-45
	290 Horsepower.............V8-302	4 Barrel	4.000 x 3.00	302	11.00	290 @ 5800	290 @ 4200	30-45
	210 Horsepower.............V8-327	2 Barrel	4.001 x 3.25	327	8.75	210 @ 4600	320 @ 2400	30-45
	275 Horsepower.............V8-327	4 Barrel	4.001 x 3.25	327	10.00	275 @ 4800	355 @ 3200	30-45
	295 Horsepower.............V8-350	4 Barrel	4.001 x 3.48	350	10.25	295 @ 4800	380 @ 3200	30-45
	300 Horsepower.............V8-327	4 Barrel	4.001 x 3.25	327	10.00	300 @ 5000	360 @ 3400	30-45
	325 Horsepower.............V8-327	4 Barrel	4.001 x 3.25	327	11.00	325 @ 5600	355 @ 3600	30-45
	325 Horsepower.............V8-396	4 Barrel	4.094 x 3.76	396	10.25	325 @ 4800	410 @ 3200	30-35
	350 Horsepower.............V8-327	4 Barrel	4.001 x 3.25	327	11.00	350 @ 5800	360 @ 3600	30-45
	350 Horsepower.............V8-396	4 Barrel	4.094 x 3.76	396	10.25	350 @ 5200	415 @ 3400	30-35
	375 Horsepower.............V8-396	4 Barrel	4.094 x 3.76	396	11.00	375 @ 5600	415 @ 3600	30-35
	385 Horsepower.............V8-427	4 Barrel	4.251 x 3.76	427	10.25	385 @ 5200	460 @ 3400	30-35
	390 Horsepower.............V8-427	4 Barrel	4.251 x 3.76	427	10.25	390 @ 5400	460 @ 3600	30-35
	400 Horsepower.............V8-427	3 Carbs.	4.251 x 3.76	427	10.25	400 @ 5400	460 @ 3600	30-35
	425 Horsepower.............V8-427	4 Barrel	4.251 x 3.76	427	N.A.	N.A.	N.A.	30-35
	435 Horsepower.............V8-427	3 Carbs.	4.251 x 3.76	427	11.00	435 @ 5800	460 @ 4000	30-35
1968	90 Horsepower.............4-153	1 Barrel	3.875 x 3.25	153	8.50	90 @ 4000	152 @ 2400	30-45
	140 Horsepower.............6-230	1 Barrel	3.875 x 3.25	230	8.50	140 @ 4400	220 @ 1600	30-45
	155 Horsepower.............6-250	1 Barrel	3.875 x 3.53	250	8.50	155 @ 4200	235 @ 1600	30-45
	290 Horsepower.............V8-302	4 Barrel	4.000 x 3.00	302	11.00	290 @ 5800	290 @ 4200	30-45
	200 Horsepower.............V8-307	2 Barrel	3.875 x 3.25	307	9.00	200 @ 4600	300 @ 2400	30-45
	210 Horsepower.............V8-327	2 Barrel	4.001 x 3.25	327	8.75	210 @ 4600	320 @ 2400	30-45
	250 Horsepower.............V8-327	4 Barrel	4.001 x 3.25	327	8.75	250 @ 4800	325 @ 3200	30-45
	275 Horsepower.............V8-327	4 Barrel	4.001 x 3.25	327	10.00	275 @ 4800	355 @ 3200	30-45
	300 Horsepower.............V8-327	4 Barrel	4.001 x 3.25	327	10.00	300 @ 5000	360 @ 3400	30-45
	325 Horsepower.............V8-327	4 Barrel	4.001 x 3.25	327	11.00	325 @ 5600	355 @ 3600	30-45
	350 Horsepower.............V8-327	4 Barrel	4.001 x 3.25	327	11.00	350 @ 5800	360 @ 3600	30-45
	295 Horsepower.............V8-350	4 Barrel	4.001 x 3.48	350	10.25	295 @ 4800	380 @ 3200	30-45
	325 Horsepower.............V8-396	4 Barrel	4.094 x 3.76	396	10.25	325 @ 4800	410 @ 3200	30-35
	350 Horsepower.............V8-396	4 Barrel	4.094 x 3.76	396	10.25	350 @ 5200	415 @ 3400	30-35
	375 Horsepower.............V8-396	4 Barrel	4.094 x 3.76	396	11.00	375 @ 5600	415 @ 3600	30-35
	385 Horsepower.............V8-427	4 Barrel	4.251 x 3.76	427	10.25	385 @ 5200	460 @ 3400	30-35
	390 Horsepower.............V8-427	4 Barrel	4.251 x 3.76	427	10.25	390 @ 5400	460 @ 3600	30-35
	400 Horsepower.............V8-427	3 Carbs.	4.251 x 3.76	427	10.25	400 @ 5400	460 @ 3600	30-35
	425 Horsepower.............V8-427	4 Barrel	4.251 x 3.76	427	11.00	425 @ 5600	460 @ 4000	30-35
	430 Horsepower.............V8-427	4 Barrel	4.251 x 3.76	427	12.50	430 @ 5200	450 @ 4400	30-35
	435 Horsepower.............V8-427	3 Carbs.	4.251 x 3.76	427	11.00	435 @ 5800	460 @ 4900	30-35
1969	90 Horsepower.............4-153	1 Barrel	3.875 x 3.25	153	8.50	90 @ 4000	152 @ 2400	30-45
	140 Horsepower.............6-230	1 Barrel	3.875 x 3.25	230	8.50	140 @ 4400	220 @ 1600	30-45
	155 Horsepower.............6-250	1 Barrel	3.875 x 3.53	250	8.50	155 @ 4200	235 @ 1600	30-45
	290 Horsepower.............V8-302	4 Barrel	4.000 x 3.00	302	11.00	290 @ 5800	290 @ 4200	30-45
	200 Horsepower.............V8-307	2 Barrel	3.875 x 3.25	307	9.00	200 @ 4600	300 @ 2400	30-45
	210 Horsepower.............V8-327	2 Barrel	4.001 x 3.25	327	9.00	210 @ 4600	320 @ 2400	30-45
	235 Horsepower.............V8-327	2 Barrel	4.001 x 3.25	327	9.00	235 @ 4800	325 @ 2800	30-45
	255 Horsepower.............V8-350	4 Barrel	4.001 x 3.48	350	9.00	255 @ 4800	365 @ 3200	30-45
	300 Horsepower.............V8-350	4 Barrel	4.001 x 3.48	350	10.25	300 @ 4800	380 @ 3200	30-45

Continued

GENERAL ENGINE SPECIFICATIONS—Continued

Year	Engine	Carburetor	Bore and Stroke	Piston Displacement, Cubic Inches	Compression Ratio	Maximum Brake H.P. @ R.P.M.	Maximum Torque Lbs. Ft. @ R.P.M.	Normal Oil Pressure Pounds
1969	350 Horsepower.............. V8-350	4 Barrel	4.001 x 3.48	350	11.00	350 @ 5600	380 @ 3600	30–45
	370 Horsepower.............. V8-350	4 Barrel	4.001 x 3.48	350	11.00	370 @ 5800	N.A.	30–45
	265 Horsepower.............. V8-396	2 Barrel	4.094 x 3.76	396	9.00	265 @ 4800	400 @ 2800	30-35
	325 Horsepower.............. V8-396	4 Barrel	4.094 x 3.76	396	10.25	325 @ 4800	410 @ 3200	30–35
	350 Horsepower.............. V8-396	4 Barrel	4.094 x 3.76	396	10.25	350 @ 5200	415 @ 3400	30–35
	375 Horsepower.............. V8-396	4 Barrel	4.094 x 3.76	396	11.00	375 @ 5600	415 @ 3600	30–35
	335 Horsepower.............. V8-427	4 Barrel	4.251 x 3.76	427	10.25	335 @ 4800	470 @ 3200	30–35
	390 Horsepower.............. V8-427	4 Barrel	4.251 x 3.76	427	10.25	390 @ 5400	460 @ 3600	30–35
	400 Horsepower.............. V8-427	4 Barrel	4.251 x 3.76	427	10.25	400 @ 5400	460 @ 3600	30–35
	425 Horsepower.............. V8-427	4 Barrel	4.251 x 3.76	427	11.00	425 @ 5600	460 @ 4000	30–35
	430 Horsepower.............. V8-427	4 Barrel	4.251 x 3.76	427	12.00	430 @ 5200	450 @ 4400	30–35
	435 Horsepower.............. V8-427	3 Carbs.	4.251 x 3.76	427	11.00	435 @ 5800	460@ 4000	30–35

TUNE UP SPECIFICATIONS

OLD CAR SPECIFICATIONS: For 1946-62 Tune Up Specifications see back of book.

★When using a timing light, disconnect vacuum hose or tube at distributor and plug opening in hose or tube so idle speed will not be affected.

Year	Engine Model	Spark Plugs		Distributor		Firing Order	Ignition Timing★		Hot Idle Speed(11)		Comp. Press. Lbs. (3)	Fuel Pump Press. Lbs.
		Type AC	Gap Inch	Point Gap Inch	Dwell Angle Deg.		BTDC (1)	Mark	Std. Trans.	Auto. Trans. (2)		
CAMARO												
1967	6-230	46N	.035	.019	31–34	Fig. G	4°	Fig. A	500(11)	500D(11)	130	3-4½
	6-230(12)	46N	.035	.019	31–34	Fig. G	4°	Fig. A	700(16)	500D(16)	130	3-4½
	6-250	46N	.035	.019	31–34	Fig. G	4°	Fig. A	500(11)	500D(11)	130	3-4½
	6-250(12)	46N	.035	.019	31–34	Fig. G	4°	Fig. A	700(16)	500D(16)	130	3-4½
	8-302	43	.035	.019	28–32	Fig. E	6°	Fig. A	800(11)	—	190	5-6½
	8-327, 210 H.P.	44	.035	.019	28–32	Fig. E	2°	Fig. A	500(11)	600D(11)	160	5-6½
	8-327, 210 H.P.(12)	44	.035	.019	28–32	Fig. E	2°	Fig. A	700(16)	600D(16)	160	5-6½
	8-327, 275 H.P.	44	.035	.019	28–32	Fig. E	8°	Fig. A	500(11)	500D(11)	160	5-6½
	8-327, 275 H.P.(12)	44	.035	.019	28–32	Fig. E	6°	Fig. A	700(16)	600D(16)	160	5-6½
	8-327, 350 H.P.	44	.035	.019	28–32	Fig. E	10°	Fig. A	700(11)	—	150	5-6½
	8-327, 350 H.P.(12)	44	.035	.019	28–32	Fig. E	10°	Fig. A	750(11)	—	150	5-6½
	8-396, 375 H.P.	43N	.035	.019	28–32	Fig. E	6°	Fig. A	750(11)	—	160	5-6½
	8-350	44	.035	.019	28–32	Fig. E	4°	Fig. A	500(11)	500D(11)	160	5-6½
	8-350(12)	44	.035	.019	28–32	Fig. E	4°	Fig. A	700(11)	500D(11)	160	5-6½
1968	6-230, 250 Std. Tr.	46N	.035	.019	31–34	Fig. G	TDC	Fig. A	700(16)	—	130	3-4½
	6-230, 250 Auto. Tr.	46N	.035	.019	31–34	Fig. G	4°	Fig. A	—	600D(11)	130	3-4½
	8-302	43	.035	.019	28–32	Fig. E	4°	Fig. A	900(16)	—	190	5-6½
	8-327, 210 H.P.(18)	44	.035	.019	28–32	Fig. E	2 ATC	Fig. A	700(16)	—	160	5-6½
	8-327, 210 H.P.(19)	44	.035	.019	28–32	Fig. E	2°	Fig. A	—	600D(16)	160	5-6½
	8-327, 275 H.P.(18)	44	.035	.019	28–32	Fig. E	TDC	Fig. A	700(11)	—	160	5-6½
	8-327, 275 H.P.(19)	44	.035	.019	28–32	Fig. E	4°	Fig. A	—	600D(16)	160	5-6½
	8-350, 295 H.P.(18)	44	.035	.019	28–32	Fig. E	TDC	Fig. A	700(16)	—	160	5-6½
	8-350, 295 H.P.(19)	44	.035	.019	28–32	Fig. E	4°	Fig. A	—	600D(16)	160	5-6½
	8-396, 325 H.P.	43N	.035	.019	28–32	Fig. E	4°	Fig. A	700(16)	600D(16)	160	5-8½
	8-396, 375 H.P.	43N	.035	.019	28–32	Fig. E	10°	Fig. A	750(11)	—	160	5-8½
1969	6-230, 250(18)	R46N	.035	.019	31–34	Fig. G	TDC	Fig. A	700(16)	—	130	3-4½
	6-230, 250(19)	R46N	.035	.019	31–34	Fig. G	4°	Fig. A	—	550D(16)	130	3-4½
	8-302	R43	.035	.019	28–32	Fig. E	4°	Fig. A	900(16)	—	190	5-6½
	8-327, 210 H.P.(18)	R45S	.035	.019	28–32	Fig. E	2° ATC	Fig. A	700(16)	—	160	5-6½
	8-327, 210 H.P(19).	R45S	.035	.019	28–32	Fig. E	2°	Fig. A	—	600D(16)	160	5-6½

Continued

TUNE UP SPECIFICATIONS—Continued

OLD CAR SPECIFICATIONS: For 1946-62 Tune Up Specifications see back of book.

★When using a timing light disconnect vacuum tube or hose at distributor and plug opening in hose or tube so idle speed will not be affected.

Year	Engine Model	Spark Plugs		Distributor		Firing Order	Ignition Timing★		Hot Idle Speed(11)		Comp. Press. Lbs. (3)	Fuel Pump Press. Lbs.
		Type AC	Gap Inch	Point Gap Inch	Dwell Angle Deg.		BTDC (1)	Mark	Std. Trans.	Auto. Trans. (2)		
1969	8-350, 255 H.P.(18)	R44	.035	.019	28–32	Fig. E	TDC	Fig. A	700(16)	—	160	5–6½
	8-350, 255 H.P.(19)	R44	.035	.019	28–32	Fig. E	4°	Fig. A	—	600D(16)	160	5–6½
	8-350, 300 H.P.(18)	R44	.035	.019	28–32	Fig. E	TDC	Fig. A	700(16)	—	160	5–6½
	8-350, 300 H.P.(19)	R44	.035	.019	28–32	Fig. E	4°	Fig. A	—	600D(16)	160	5–6½
	8-396, 325 H.P.	R44N	.035	.019	28–32	Fig. E	4°	Fig. A	800(16)	600D(16)	160	5–8½
	8-396, 350 H.P.(18)	R43N	.035	.019	28–32	Fig. E	TDC	Fig. A	800(16)	—	160	5–8½
	8-396, 350 H.P.(19)	R43N	.035	.019	28–32	Fig. E	4°	Fig. A	—	600D(16)	160	5–8½
	8-396, 375 H.P.	R43N	.035	.019	28–32	Fig. E	4°	Fig. A	750(16)	700D(16)	160	5–8½

CHEVELLE

Year	Engine Model	Type AC	Gap Inch	Point Gap Inch	Dwell Angle Deg.	Firing Order	BTDC (1)	Mark	Std. Trans.	Auto. Trans. (2)	Comp. Press. Lbs. (3)	Fuel Pump Press. Lbs.
1964	6-194	46N	.035	(4)	31–34	Fig. G	8°	Fig. A	500(11)	500D(11)	130	3½–4½
	6-230	46N	.035	(4)	31–34	Fig. G	4°	Fig. A	500(11)	500D(11)	130	3½–4½
	V8-283, 195 H. P.	45	.035	(4)	28–32	Fig. E	4°	Fig. A	475(11)	450D(11)	150	5¼–6½
	V8-283, 220 H. P.	44	.035	(4)	28–32	Fig. E	4°	Fig. A	475(11)	450D(11)	150	5¼–6½
	V8-327, 250 H. P.	44	.035	(4)	28–32	Fig. E	4°	Fig. A	475(11)	450D(11)	160	5¼–6½
	V8-327, 300 H. P.	44	.035	(4)	28–32	Fig. E	8°	Fig. A	475(11)	450D(11)	160	5¼–6½
1965	6-194	44N	.035	(4)	31–34	Fig. G	8°	Fig. A	500(11)	500D(11)	130	3¼–4½
	6-230	44N	.035	(4)	31–34	Fig. G	4°	Fig. A	500(11)	500D(11)	130	3¼–4½
	V8-283, 195 H. P.	45	.035	(4)	28–32	Fig. E	4°	Fig. A	500(11)	475D(11)	150	5¼–6½
	V8-283, 220 H. P.	45	.035	(4)	28–32	Fig. E	6°	Fig. A	500(11)	475D(11)	150	5¼–6½
	V8-327, 250 H. P.	44	.035	(4)	28–32	Firing E	4°	Fig. A	475(11)	450D(11)	160	5¼–6½
	V8-327, 300 H. P.	44	.035	(4)	28–32	Fig. E	8°	Fig. A	475(11)	450D(11)	160	5¼–6½
	V8-327, 350 H. P.	44	.035	(4)	28–32	Fig. E	8°	Fig. A	550(11)	...	160	6–7½
1966	6-194 Std. Eng.	46N	.035	(4)	31–34	Fig. G	8°	Fig. A	500(11)	500D(11)	130	3–4½
	6-194 Man. Tr.(12)	46N	.035	(4)	31–34	Fig. G	3°	Fig. A	700(11)	...	130	3–4½
	6-194 Auto. Tr.(12)	46N	.035	(4)	31–34	Fig. G	8°	Fig. A	...	600D(11)	130	3–4½
	6-230 Std. Eng.	46N	.035	(4)	31–34	Fig. G	4°	Fig. A	500(11)	500D(11)	130	3–4½
	6-230(12)	46N	.035	(4)	31–34	Fig. G	4°	Fig. A	700(11)	600D(11)	130	3–4½
	8-283 Std. Eng.	45	.035	(4)	28–32	Fig. E	4°	Fig. A	500(11)	500D(11)	150	5–6½
	8-283(12)	45	.035	(4)	28–32	Fig. E	4°	Fig. A	700(11)	600D(11)	150	5–6½
	8-327, 275 H.P.	44	.035	(4)	28–32	Fig. E	8°	Fig. A	500(11)	500D(11)	160	5–6½
	8-327, 275 H.P.(13)	44	.035	(4)	28–32	Fig. E	8°	Fig. A	700(11)	...	160	5–6½
	8-327, 275 H.P.(14)	44	.035	(4)	28–32	Fig. E	2°(15)	Fig. A	...	600D(11)	160	5–6½
	8-396, 325 H.P.	43N	.035	(4)	28–32	Fig. E	4°	Fig. A	500(11)	500D(11)	160	5–6½
	8-396, 325 H.P.(12)	43N	.035	(4)	28–32	Fig. E	4°	Fig. A	500(11)	500D(11)	160	5–6½
	8-396, 360 H.P.	43N	.035	(4)	28–32	Fig. E	4°	Fig. A	550(11)	600D(11)	160	5–6½
	8-396, 360 H.P.(12)	43N	.035	(4)	28–32	Fig. E	4°	Fig. A	550(11)	550D(11)	160	5–6½
1967	6-230	46N	.035	.019	31–34	Fig. G	4°	Fig. A	500(11)	500D(11)	130	3–4½
	6-230(12)	46N	.035	.019	31–34	Fig. G	4°	Fig. A	700(16)	500D(16)	130	3–4½
	6-250	46N	.035	.019	31–34	Fig. G	4°	Fig. A	500(11)	500D(11)	130	3–4½
	6-250(12)	46N	.035	.019	31–34	Fig. G	4°	Fig. A	700(16)	500D(16)	130	3–4½
	8-283	45	.035	.019	28–32	Fig. E	4°	Fig. A	500(11)	500D(11)	150	5–6½
	8-283 Std. Tr.(12)	45	.035	.019	28–32	Fig. E	TDC	Fig. A	700(16)	600D(16)	150	5–6½
	8-283 Auto. Tr.(12)	45	.035	.019	28–32	Fig. E	4°	Fig. A	700(16)	600D(16)	150	5–6½
	8-327, 275 H.P.	44	.035	.019	28–32	Fig. E	8°	Fig. A	500	500	160	5–6½
	8-327, 275 H.P.(12)	44	.035	.019	28–32	Fig. E	6°	Fig. A	700	600	160	5–6½
	8-327, 325 H.P.	44	.035	.019	28–32	Fig. E	10°	Fig. A	700(11)	—	150	5–6½
	8-327, 325 H.P.(12)	44	.035	.019	28–32	Fig. E	10°	Fig. A	750(11)	—	150	5–6½
	8-396, 325 H.P.	43N	.035	.019	28–32	Fig. E	4°	Fig. A	500(11)	500D(11)	160	5–6½
	8-396, 325 H.P.(12)	43N	.035	.019	28–32	Fig. E	4°	Fig. A	700(11)	500D(11)	160	5–6½
	8-396, 350 H.P.	43N	.035	.019	28–32	Fig. E	4°	Fig. A	550(11)	550D(11)	160	5–6½
	8-396, 350 H.P.(12)	43N	.035	.019	28–32	Fig. E	4°	Fig. A	700(11)	500D(11)	160	5–6½
1968	6-230, 250 Std. Tr.	46N	.035	.019	31–34	Fig. G	TDC	Fig. A	700(16)	—	130	3–4½
	6-230, 250 Auto. Tr.	46N	.035	.019	31–34	Fig. G	4°	Fig. A	—	600D(11)	130	3–4½

Continued

TUNE UP SPECIFICATIONS—Continued

OLD CAR SPECIFICATIONS: For 1946-62 Tune Up Specifications see back of book.

★When using a timing light, disconnect vacuum tube or hose at distributor and plug opening in hose or tube so idle speed will not be affected.

Year	Engine Model	Spark Plugs		Distributor		Firing Order	Ignition Timing★		Hot Idle Speed(11)		Comp. Press. Lbs. (3)	Fuel Pump Press. Lbs.
		Type AC	Gap Inch	Point Gap Inch	Dwell Angle Deg.		BTDC (1)	Mark	Std. Trans.	Auto. Trans. (2)		
1968	8-307	45S	.035	.019	28-32	Fig. E	2°	Fig. A	700(16)	600D(16)	150	5-6½
	8-327, 275 H.P.(18)	44	.035	.019	28-32	Fig. E	TDC	Fig. A	700(11)	—	160	5-6½
	8-327, 275 H.P.(19)	44	.035	.019	28-32	Fig. E	4°	Fig. A	—	600D(16)	160	5-6½
	8-327, 325 H.P.	44	.035	.019	28-32	Fig. E	4°	Fig. A	750(11)	—	150	5-6½
	8-396, 350 H.P.	43N	.035	.019	28-32	Fig. E	TDC	Fig. A	700(16)	—	160	5-8½
	8-396, 350 H.P.	43N	.035	.019	28-32	Fig. E	4°	Fig. A	—	600D(16)	160	5-8½
1969	6-230, 250(18)	R46N	.035	.019	31-34	Fig. G	TDC	Fig. A	700(16)	—	130	3-4½
	6-230, 250(19)	R46N	.035	.019	31-34	Fig. G	4°	Fig. A	—	550D(16)	130	3-4½
	8-307	R45S	.035	.019	28-32	Fig. E	2°	Fig. A	700(16)	600D(16)	160	5-6½
	8-350, 255 H.P.(18)	R44	.035	.019	28-32	Fig. E	TDC	Fig. A	700(16)	—	160	5-6½
	8-350, 255 H.P.(19)	R44	.035	.019	28-32	Fig. E	4°	Fig. A	—	600D(16)	160	5-6½
	8-350, 300 H.P.(18)	R44	.035	.019	28-32	Fig. E	TDC	Fig. A	700(16)	—	160	5-6½
	8-350, 300 H.P.(19)	R44	.035	.019	28-32	Fig. E	4°	Fig. A	—	600D(16)	160	5-6½
	8-396, 325 H.P.	R44N	.035	.019	28-32	Fig. E	4°	Fig. A	800(16)	600D(16)	160	5-8½
	8-396, 350 H.P.(18)	R43N	.035	.019	28-32	Fig. E	TDC	Fig. A	800(16)	—	160	5-8½
	8-396, 350 H.P.(19)	R43N	.035	.019	28-32	Fig. E	4°	Fig. A	—	600D(16)	160	5-8½
	8-396, 375 H.P.	R43N	.035	.019	28-32	Fig. E	4°	Fig. A	750(16)	750D(16)	160	5-8½
CHEVY II												
1963	4-153	46N	.035	(4)	31-34	Fig. H	4°	Fig. A	500(11)	500D(11)	130	3½-4½
	6-194	46N	.035	(4)	31-34	Fig. G	8°	Fig. A	500(11)	500D(11)	130	3½-4½
1964	4-153	46N	.035	(4)	31-34	Fig. H	4°	Fig. A	500(11)	500D(11)	130	3½-4½
	6-194	46N	.035	(4)	31-34	Fig. G	8°	Fig. A	500(11)	500D(11)	130	3½-4½
	6-230	46N	.035	(4)	31-34	Fig. G	4°	Fig. A	500(11)	500D(11)	130	3½-4½
	V8-283, 195 H. P.	45	.035	(4)	28-32	Fig. E	4°	Fig. A	475(11)	450D(11)	150	5¼-6½
	V8-283, 220 H. P.	45	.035	(4)	28-32	Fig. E	8°	Fig. A	475(11)	450D(11)	150	5¼-6½
1965	4-153	46N	.035	(4)	31-34	Fig. H	4°	Fig. A	500(11)	500D(11)	130	3¼-4½
	6-194	46N	.035	(4)	31-34	Fig. G	8°	Fig. A	500(11)	500D(11)	130	3¼-4½
	6-230	46N	.035	(4)	31-34	Fig. G	4°	Fig. A	500(11)	500D(11)	130	3¼-4½
	V8-283, 195 H. P.	45	.035	(4)	28-32	Fig. E	4°	Fig. A	500(11)	475D(11)	150	5¼-6½
	V8-283, 220 H. P.	45	.035	(4)	28-32	Fig. E	6°	Fig. A	500(11)	475D(11)	150	5¼-6½
	V8-327, 250 H. P.	44	.035	(4)	28-32	Fig. E	4°	Fig. A	475(11)	450D(11)	160	5¼-6½
	V8-327, 300 H. P.	44	.035	(4)	28-32	Fig. E	8°	Fig. A	475(11)	450D(11)	160	5¼-6½
1966	4-153	46N	.035	(4)	31-34	Fig. H	4°	Fig. A	500(11)	500D(11)	130	3-4½
	6-194 Std. Eng.	46N	.035	(4)	31-34	Fig. G	8°	Fig. A	500(11)	500D(11)	130	3-4½
	6-194 Std. Tr.(12)	46N	.035	(4)	31-34	Fig. G	3°	Fig. A	700(11)	...	130	3-4½
	6-194 Auto. Tr.(12)	46N	.035	(4)	31-34	Fig. G	8°	Fig. A		600D(11)	130	3-4½
	6-230 Std. Eng.	46N	.035	(4)	31-34	Fig. G	4°	Fig. A	500(11)	500D(11)	130	3-4½
	6-230(12)	46N	.035	(4)	31-34	Fig. G	4°	Fig. A	700(11)	600D(11)	130	3-4½
	8-283 Std. Eng.	45	.035	(4)	28-32	Fig. E	4°	Fig. A	500(11)	500D(11)	150	5-6½
	8-283(12)	45	.035	(4)	28-32	Fig. E	4°	Fig. A	700(11)	600D(11)	150	5-6½
	8-327, 275 H.P.	44	.035	(4)	28-32	Fig. E	8°	Fig. A	500(11)	500D(11)	160	5-6½
	8-327, 275 H.P.(13)	44	.035	(4)	28-32	Fig. E	8°	Fig. A	700(11)	...	160	5-6½
	8-327, 275 H.P.(14)	44	.035	(4)	28-32	Fig. E	2°(15)	Fig. A	...	600D(11)	160	5-6½
	8-327, 350 H.P.	44	.035	(4)	28-32	Fig. E	10°	Fig. A	700(11)	...	150	5-6½
	8-327, 350 H.P.(12)	44	.035	(4)	28-32	Fig. E	10°	Fig. A	750(11)	...	150	5-6½
	8-396, 325 H.P.	43N	.035	(4)	28-32	Fig. E	4°	Fig. A	500(11)	500D(11)	160	5-6½
	8-396, 325 H.P.(12)	43N	.035	(4)	28-32	Fig. E	4°	Fig. A	500(11)	500D(11)	160	5-6½
1967	4-153	46N	.035	.019	31-34	Fig. H	4°	Fig. A	500(11)	500D(11)	130	3-4½
	6-194	46N	.035	.019	31-34	Fig. G	4°	Fig. A	500(11)	500D(11)	130	3-4½
	6-194 Std. Tr.(12)	46N	.035	.019	31-34	Fig. G	2°	Fig. A	700(16)	—	130	3-4½
	6-194 Auto. Tr.(12)	46N	.035	.019	31-34	Fig. G	4°	Fig. A	—	600D(16)	130	3-4½
	6-250	46N	.035	.019	31-34	Fig. G	4°	Fig. A	500(11)	500D(11)	130	3-4½
	6-250(12)	46N	.035	.019	31-34	Fig. G	4°	Fig. A	700(16)	500D(16)	130	3-4½

Continued

TUNE UP SPECIFICATIONS—Continued

OLD CAR SPECIFICATIONS: For 1946-62 Tune Up Specifications see back of book.

★ When using a timing light, disconnect vacuum tube or hose at distributor and plug opening in hose or tube so idle speed will not be affected.

Year	Engine Model	Spark Plugs		Distributor		Firing Order	Ignition Timing★		Hot Idle Speed(11)		Comp. Press. Lbs. (3)	Fuel Pump Press. Lbs.
		Type AC	Gap Inch	Point Gap Inch	Dwell Angle Deg.		BTDC (1)	Mark	Std. Trans.	Auto. Trans. (2)		
1967	8-283	45	.035	.019	28-32	Fig. E	4°	Fig. A	500(11)	500D(11)	150	5-6½
	8-283 Std. Tr.(12)	45	.035	.019	28-32	Fig. E	TDC	Fig. A	700(16)	—	150	5-6½
	8-283 Auto. Tr.(12)	45	.035	.019	28-32	Fig. E	4°	Fig. A	—	600D(16)	150	5-6½
	8-327, 275 H.P.	44	.035	.019	28-32	Fig. E	8°	Fig. A	500(11)	500D(11)	160	5-6½
	8-327, 275 H.P.(12)	44	.035	.019	28-32	Fig. E	6°	Fig. A	700(16)	600D(16)	160	5-6½
1968	4-153 Std. Tr.	46N	.035	.019	31-34	Fig. H	TDC	Fig. A	750(16)	—	130	3-4½
	4-153 Auto. Tr.	46N	.035	.019	31-34	Fig. H	4°	Fig. A	—	600D(16)	130	3-4½
	6-230, 250 Std. Tr.	46N	.035	.019	31-34	Fig. G	TDC	Fig. A	700(16)	—	130	3-4½
	6-230, 250 Auto. Tr.	46N	.035	.019	31-34	Fig. G	4°	Fig. A	—	600D(11)	130	3-4½
	8-307	45S	.035	.019	28-32	Fig. E	2°	Fig. A	700(16)	600D(16)	150	5-6½
	8-327, 275 H.P.(18)	44	.035	.019	28-32	Fig. E	TDC	Fig. A	700(11)	—	160	5-6½
	8-327, 275 H.P.(19)	44	.035	.019	28-32	Fig. E	4°	Fig. A	—	600(16)	160	5-6½
	8-350 Std. Tr.	44	.035	.019	28-32	Fig. E	TDC	Fig. A	700(16)	—	160	5-6½
	8-350 Auto. Tr.	44	.035	.019	28-32	Fig. E	4°	Fig. A	—	600(16)	160	5-6½
1969	4-153(18)	R46N	.035	.019	31-34	Fig. G	TDC	Fig. A	750(16)	—	130	3-4½
	4-153(19)	R46N	.035	.019	31-34	Fig. G	4°	Fig. A	—	600D(16)	130	3-4½
	6-230, 250(18)	R46N	.035	.019	31-34	Fig. G	TDC	Fig. A	700(16)	—	130	3-4½
	6-230, 250(19)	R46N	.035	.019	31-34	Fig. G	4°	Fig. A	—	550D(16)	130	3-4½
	8-307	R45S	.035	.019	28-32	Fig. E	2°	Fig. A	700(16)	600D(16)	160	5-6½
	8-327, 210 H.P.(18)	R45S	.035	.019	28-32	Fig. E	2° ATC	Fig. A	700(16)	—	160	5-6½
	8-350, 255 H.P.(18)	R44	.035	.019	28-32	Fig. E	TDC	Fig. A	700(16)	—	160	5-6½
	8-350, 255 H.P.(19)	R44	.035	.019	28-32	Fig. E	4°	Fig. A	—	600D(16)	160	5-6½
	8-350, 300 H.P.(18)	R44	.035	.019	28-32	Fig. E	TDC	Fig. A	700(16)	—	160	5-6½
	8-350, 300 H.P.(19)	R44	.035	.019	28-32	Fig. E	4°	Fig. A	—	600D(16)	160	5-6½
	8-396, 350 H.P.(18)	R43N	.035	.019	28-32	Fig. E	TDC	Fig. A	800(16)	—	160	5-8½
	8-396, 350 H.P.(19)	R43N	.035	.019	28-32	Fig. E	4°	Fig. A	—	600D(16)	160	5-8½
	8-396, 375 H.P.	R43N	.035	.019	28-32	Fig. E	4°	Fig. A	750(16)	750D(16)	160	5-8½

CHEVROLET

Year	Engine Model	Type AC	Gap Inch	Point Gap Inch	Dwell Angle Deg.	Firing Order	BTDC (1)	Mark	Std. Trans.	Auto. Trans. (2)	Comp. Press. Lbs. (3)	Fuel Pump Press. Lbs.
1963	6-230	46N	.035	(4)	31-34	Fig. G	4°	Fig. A	500(11)	500D(11)	130	3½-4½
	V8-283	45	.035	(4)	30	Fig. E	4°	Fig. A	475(11)	450D(11)	140	5¼-6½
	V8-327-250 H. P.	44	.035	(4)	30	Fig. E	4°	Fig. A	475(11)	450D(11)	160	5¼-6½
	V8-327-300 H. P.	44	.035	(4)	30	Fig. E	8°	Fig. A	475(11)	450D(11)	160	5¼-6½
	V8-409-340 H. P.	43N	.035	(4)	30	Fig. F	6°	Fig. A	500(11)	475D(11)	150	5¼-6½
	V8-409-400 H. P.	43N	.035	(4)	30	Fig. F	12°	Fig. A	750(11)	—	150	7¼-8½
	V8-409-425 H. P.	43N	.035	(4)	30	Fig. F	12°	Fig. A	750(11)	—	150	7¼-8½
1964	6-230	46N	.035	(4)	31-34	Fig. G	4°	Fig. A	500(11)	500D(11)	130	3½-4½
	V8-283	45	.035	(4)	30	Fig. E	4°	Fig. A	475(11)	450D(11)	150	5¼-6½
	V8-327-250 H. P.	44	.035	(4)	30	Fig. E	4°	Fig. A	475(11)	450D(11)	160	5¼-6½
	V8-327-300 H. P.	44	.035	(4)	30	Fig. E	8°	Fig. A	475(11)	450D(11)	160	5¼-6½
	V8-409-340 H. P.	43N	.035	(4)	30	Fig. F	6°	Fig. A	500(11)	475D(11)	150	7¼-8½
	V8-409-400 H. P.	43N	.035	(4)	30	Fig. F	12°	Fig. A	(9)	—	150	7¼-8½
	V8-409-425 H. P.	43N	.035	(4)	30	Fig. F	12°	Fig. A	(9)	—	150	7¼-8½
1965	6-230	44N	.035	(4)	31-34	Fig. G	4°	Fig. A	500(11)	475D(11)	130	3¼-4½
	V8-283, 195 H. P.	45	.035	(4)	28-32	Fig. E	4°	Fig. A	500(11)	475D(11)	150	5¼-6½
	V8-283 Four Bar Carb.	45	.035	(4)	28-32	Fig. E	4°	Fig. A	500(11)	475D(11)	150	5¼-6½
	V8-327, 250 H. P.	44	.035	(4)	28-32	Fig. E	4°	Fig. A	475(11)	450D(11)	160	5¼-6½
	V8-327, 300 H. P.	44	.035	(4)	28-32	Fig. E	8°	Fig. A	475(11)	450D(11)	160	5¼-6½
	V8-396, 325 H. P.	43N	.035	(4)	28-32	Fig. E	4°(10)	Fig. A	500(11)	475D(11)	160	5½-7½
	V8-396, 425 H. P.	43N	.035	(4)	28-32	Fig. E	10°	Fig. A	800(11)	—	160	5½-7½
	V8-409, 340 H. P.	C42N	.035	(4)	28-32	Fig. F	6°	Fig. A	475(11)	450D(11)	150	7¼-8½
	V8-409, 400 H. P.	C42N	.035	(4)	28-32	Fig. F	12°	Fig. A	975(11)	—	150	7¼-8½
1966	6-250 Std. Eng.	46N	.035	(4)	31-34	Fig. G	6°	Fig. A	500(11)	500D(11)	130	3-4½
	6-250(12)	46N	.035	(4)	31-34	Fig. G	6°	Fig. A	700(11)	600D(11)	130	3-4½
	8-283 Std. Eng.	45	.035	(4)	28-32	Fig. E	4°	Fig. A	500(11)	500D(11)	150	5-6½
	8-283(12)	45	.035	(4)	28-32	Fig. E	4°	Fig. A	700(11)	600D(11)	150	5-6½

Continued

TUNE UP SPECIFICATIONS—Continued

OLD CAR SPECIFICATIONS: For 1946-62 Tune Up Specifications see back of book.

★When using a timing light, disconnect vacuum hose or tube at distributor and plug opening in hose or tube so idle speed will not be affected.

Year	Engine Model	Spark Plugs		Distributor		Firing Order	Ignition Timing★		Hot Idle Speed(11)		Comp. Press. Lbs. (3)	Fuel Pump Press. Lbs.
		Type AC	Gap Inch	Point Gap Inch	Dwell Angle Deg.		BTDC (1)	Mark	Std. Trans.	Auto. Trans. (2)		
1966	8-327, 275 H.P.	44	.035	(4)	28-32	Fig. E	8°	Fig. A	500(11)	500D(11)	160	5-6½
	8-327, 275 H.P.(13)	44	.035	(4)	28-32	Fig. E	8°	Fig. A	700(11)	—	160	5-6½
	8-327, 275 H.P.(14)	44	.035	(4)	28-32	Fig. E	2°(15)	Fig. A	—	600D(11)	160	5-6½
	8-396, 325 H.P.	43N	.035	(4)	28-32	Fig. E	4°	Fig. A	550(11)	500D(11)	160	5-6½
	8-396, 325 H.P.(12)	43N	.035	(4)	28-32	Fig. E	4°	Fig. A	500(11)	500D(11)	160	5-6½
	8-427, 390 H.P.	43N	.035	—	—	Fig. E	4°	Fig. A	550(11)	550D(11)	160	5-6½
	8-427, 390 H.P.(12)	43N	.035	—	—	Fig. E	4°	Fig. A	550(11)	550D(11)	160	5-6½
	8-427, 425 H.P.	43N	.035	—	—	Fig. E	10°	Fig. A	800(11)	—	150	5-6½
1967	6-250	46N	.035	.019	31-34	Fig. G	4°	Fig. A	500(11)	500D(11)	130	3-4½
	6-250(12)	46N	.035	.019	31-34	Fig. G	4°	Fig. A	700(16)	500D(16)	130	3-4½
	8-283	45	.035	.019	28-32	Fig. E	4°	Fig. A	500(11)	500D(11)	150	5-6½
	8-283 Std. Tr.(12)	45	.035	.019	28-32	Fig. E	TDC	Fig. A	700(16)	600D(16)	150	5-6½
	8-283 Auto. Tr.(12)	45	.035	.019	28-32	Fig. E	4°	Fig. A	700(16)	600D(16)	150	5-6½
	8-327, 275 H.P.	44	.035	.019	28-32	Fig. E	8°	Fig. A	500(11)	500D(11)	160	5-6½
	8-327, 275 H.P.(12)	44	.035	.019	28-32	Fig. E	6°	Fig. A	700(16)	600D(16)	160	5-6½
	8-396, 325 H.P.	43N	.035	.019	28-32	Fig. E	4°	Fig. A	500(11)	500D(11)	160	5-6½
	8-396, 325 H.P.(12)	43N	.035	.019	28-32	Fig. E	4°	Fig. A	500(11)	500D(11)	160	5-6½
	8-427, 385 H.P.	43N	.035	.019	28-32	Fig. E	4°	Fig. A	700(11)	500D(11)	160	5-6½
	8-427, 385 H.P.(12)	43N	.035	.019	28-32	Fig. E	4°	Fig. A	550(11)	550D(11)	160	5-6½
		43N	.035	.019	28-32	Fig. E	4°	Fig. A	700(11)	550D(11)	160	5-6½
1968	6-250 Std. Tr.	46N	.035	.019	31-34	Fig. G	TDC	Fig. A	700(16)	—	130	3-4½
	6-250 Auto. Tr.	46N	.035	.019	31-34	Fig. G	4°	Fig. A	—	600D(11)	130	3-4½
	8-307	45S	.035	.019	28-32	Fig. E	2°	Fig. A	700(16)	600D(16)	150	5-6½
	8-327, 250 H.P.	44S	.035	.019	28-32	Fig. E	4°	Fig. A	700(11)	600D(16)	160	5-6½
	8-327, 275 H.P.(18)	44	.035	.019	28-32	Fig. E	TDC	Fig. A	700(11)	—	160	5-6½
	8-327, 275 H.P.(19)	44	.035	.019	28-32	Fig. E	4°	Fig. A	—	600D(16)	160	5-6½
	8-396, 325 H.P.	43N	.035	.019	28-32	Fig. E	4°	Fig. A	700(16)	600D(16)	160	5-8½
	8-396, 375 H.P.	43N	.035	.019	28-32	Fig. E	4°	Fig. A	750(16)	—	160	5-8½
	8-427, 385 H.P.	43N	.035	.019	28-32	Fig. E	4°	Fig. A	700(16)	600D(16)	160	5-8½
1969	6-250(18)	R46N	.035	.019	31-34	Fig. G	TDC	Fig. A	700(16)	—	130	3-4½
	6-250(19)	R46N	.035	.019	31-34	Fig. G	4°	Fig. A	—	550D(16)	130	3-4½
	8-327, 235 H.P.(18)	45S	.035	.019	28-32	Fig. E	2° ATC	Fig. A	700(16)	—	160	5-6½
	8-327, 235 H.P.(19)	45S	.035	.019	28-32	Fig. E	2°	Fig. A	—	600D(16)	160	5-6½
	8-350, 255 H.P.(18)	R44	.035	.019	28-32	Fig. E	TDC	Fig. A	700(16)	—	160	5-6½
	8-350, 255 H.P.(19)	R44	.035	.019	28-32	Fig. E	4°	Fig. A	—	600D(16)	160	5-6½
	8-350, 300 H.P.(18)	R44	.035	.019	28-32	Fig. E	TDC	Fig. A	700(16)	—	160	5-6½
	8-350, 300 H.P.(19)	R44	.035	.019	28-32	Fig. E	4°	Fig. A	—	600D(16)	160	5-6½
	8-396, 265 H.P.(18)	R44N	.035	.019	28-32	Fig. E	TDC	Fig. A	700(16)	—	160	5-6½
	8-396, 265 H.P.(19)	R44N	.035	.019	28-32	Fig. E	4°	Fig. A	—	600D(16)	160	5-6½
	8-427, 425 H.P.	R43N	.035	.019	28-32	Fig. E	4°	Fig. A	750(16)	750D(16)	150	5-8½
	8-427, 335 H.P.	R44N	.035	.019	28-32	Fig. E	4°	Fig. A	800(16)	600D(16)	160	5-8½
	8-427, 390 H.P.	R43N	.035	.019	28-32	Fig. E	4°	Fig. A	800(11)	600D(11)	160	5-8½
	8-427, 425 H.P.	R43N	.035	.019	28-32	Fig. E	4°	Fig. A	750(16)	750D(16)	150	5-8½

CORVETTE

Year	Engine Model	Type AC	Gap Inch	Point Gap Inch	Dwell Angle Deg.	Firing Order	BTDC	Mark	Std. Trans.	Auto. Trans.	Comp. Press. Lbs.	Fuel Pump Press. Lbs.
1963	V8-327-250 H. P.	44	.035	(4)	30	Fig. E	4°	Fig. A	475	450D	160	5¼-6½
	V8-327-300 H. P.	44	.035	(4)	30	Fig. E	8°	Fig. A	475	450D	160	5¼-6½
	V8-327-340 H. P.	44	.035	(4)	30	Fig. E	10°	Fig. A	750	—	150	5¼-6½
	V8-327-360 H. P.	44	.035	(4)	30	Fig. E	10°	Fig. A	850	—	150	5¼-6½
1964	V8-327-250 H. P.	44	.035	(4)	30	Fig. E	4°	Fig. A	475	450D	160	5¼-6½
	V8-327-300 H. P.	44	.035	(4)	30	Fig. E	8°	Fig. A	475	450D	160	5¼-6½
	V8-327-365 H. P.	44	.035	(4)	30	Fig. E	10°	Fig. A	800	—	150	5¼-6½
	V8-327-375 H. P.	44	.035	(4)	30	Fig. E	10°	Fig. A	850	—	150	5¼-6½
1965	V8-327, 250 H. P.	44	.035	(4)	28-32	Fig. E	4°	Fig. A	475	475D	160	5¼-6½
	V8-327, 300 H. P.	44	.035	(4)	28-32	Fig. E	8°	Fig. A	475	475D	160	5¼-6½
	V8-327, 350 H. P.	44	.035	(4)	28-32	Fig. E	8°	Fig. A	665	—	150	5¼-6½

Continued

TUNE UP SPECIFICATIONS—Continued

OLD CAR SPECIFICATIONS: For 1946-62 Tune Up Specifications see back of book.

★When using a timing light, disconnect vacuum hose or tube at distributor and plug opening in hose or tube so idle speed will not be affected.

Year	Engine Model	Spark Plugs		Distributor		Firing Order	Ignition Timing★		Hot Idle Speed(11)		Comp. Press. Lbs. (3)	Fuel Pump Press. Lbs.
		Type AC	Gap Inch	Point Gap Inch	Dwell Angle Deg.		BTDC (1)	Mark	Std. Trans.	Auto. Trans. (2)		
1965	V8-327, 365 H. P.	44	.035	(4)	28–32	Fig. E	12°	Fig. A	765	—	150	6½–7½
	V8-327, 375 H. P.	44	.035	(4)	28–32	Fig. E	12°	Fig. A	850	—	150	6½–7½
	V8-396, 425 H. P.	43N	.035	(4)	28–32	Fig. E	10°	Fig. A	800	—	160	5½–7½
1966	8-327, 300 H.P.	44	.035	(4)	28–32	Fig. E	6°	Fig. A	500	500D	160	5–6½
	8-327, 300 H.P.(13)	44	.035	(4)	28–32	Fig. E	4 ATC	Fig. A	700	—	160	5–6½
	8-327, 300 H.P.(14)	44	.035	(4)	28–32	Fig. E	4 ATC	Fig. A	—	600D	160	5–6½
	8-327, 350 H.P.	44	.035	(4)	28–32	Fig. E	10°	Fig. A	700	—	150	5–6½
	8-327, 350 H.P.(12)	44	.035	(4)	28–32	Fig. E	10°	Fig. A	700	—	150	5–6½
	8-427, 390 H.P.	43N	.035	—	—	Fig. E	4°	Fig. A	550	550D	160	5–6½
	8-427, 390 H.P.(12)	43N	.035	—	—	Fig. E	4°	Fig. A	600	550D	160	5–6½
	8-427, 425 H.P.	43N	.035	—	—	Fig. E	8°	Fig. A	800	—	150	5–6½
1967	8-327, 300 H.P.	44	.035	.019	28–32	Fig. E	6°	Fig. A	500(11)	500D(11)	160	5–6½
	8-327, 300 H.P.(13)	44	.035	.019	28–32	Fig. E	4 ATC	Fig. A	700(16)	600D(16)	160	5–6½
	8-327, 300 H.P.(14)	44	.035	.019	28–32	Fig. E	4 ATC	Fig. A	700(16)	600D(16)	160	5–6½
	8-427, 390 H.P.	43N	.035	.019	28–32	Fig. E	4°	Fig. A	550(11)	550D(11)	160	5–6½
	8-427, 390 H.P.(12)	43N	.035	.019	28–32	Fig. E	4°	Fig. A	700(11)	550D(11)	160	5–6½
	8-427, 400 H.P.	43N	.035	.019	28–32	Fig. E	4°	Fig. A	550(11)	550D(11)	160	5–6½
	8-427, 400 H.P.(12)	43N	.035	.019	28–32	Fig. E	4°	Fig. A	750(11)	600D(11)	160	5–6½
	8-427, 425 H.P.	43N	.035	.019	28–32	Fig. E	12°(17)	Fig. A	1000(11)	—	150	5–6½
	8-427, 435 H.P.	43N	.035	.019	28–32	Fig. E	5°	Fig. A	750(11)	—	150	5–6½
	8-427, 435 H.P.(12)	43N	.035	.019	28–32	Fig. E	5°	Fig. A	750(11)	—	150	5–6½
1968	8-327, 300 H.P.	44	.035	.019	28–32	Fig. C	4°	Fig. A	700(11)	600D(16)	160	5–6½
	8-327, 350 H.P.	44	.035	.019	28–32	Fig. C	4°	Fig. A	750(11)	—	150	5–6½
	8-427, 390 H.P.	43N	.035	.019	28–32	Fig. E	4°	Fig. A	1000(11)	600D(16)	160	5–8½
	8-427, 400 H.P.	43N	.035	.019	28–32	Fig. E	4°	Fig. A	1000(11)	600D(16)	160	5–8½
	8-427, 425 H.P.	43N	.035	.019	28–32	Fig. E	4°	Fig. A	750(16)	—	150	5–8½
	8-427, 430 H.P.	43XL	.035	.019	28–32	Fig. E	12°	Fig. A	1000(16)	—	150	5–8½
	8-427, 435 H.P.	43N	.035	.019	28–32	Fig. E	4°	Fig. A	750(16)	—	150	5–8½
1969	8-350, 300 H.P.(18)	R44	.035	.019	28–32	Fig. E	4°	Fig. A	700(16)	—	160	5–6½
	8-350, 300 H.P.(19)	R44	.035	.019	28–32	Fig. E	4°	Fig. A	—	600D(16)	160	5–6½
	8-350, 350 H.P.	R44	.035	.019	28–32	Fig. E	4°	Fig. A	750(16)	—	160	5–6½
	8-350, 370 H.P.	R43	.035	.019	28–32	Fig. E	4°	Fig. A	750(16)	—	190	5–6½
	8-427, 390 H.P.	R43N	.035	.019	28–32	Fig. E	4°	Fig. A	800(11)	600D(11)	160	5–8½
	8-427, 400 H.P.	R43N	.035	.019	28–32	Fig. E	4°	Fig. A	800(11)	600D(11)	160	5–8½
	8-427, 425 H.P.	R43N	.035	.019	28–32	Fig. E	4°	Fig. A	750(16)	750D(16)	150	5–8½
	8-427, 430 H.P.	R43XL	.035	.019	28–32	Fig. E	12°(5)	Fig. A	1000(16)	—	150	5–8½
	8-427, 435 H.P.	R43N	.035	.019	28–32	Fig. E	4°	Fig. A	750(16)	750D(16)	150	5–8½

(1)—BTDC: Before top dead center.

(2)—D: Drive. N: Neutral.

(3)—Plus or minus 20 lbs.

(4)—New points .019″, used .016″. On V8s, turn adjusting screw in (clockwise) until engine misfires; then back off ½ turn.

(5)—Adjust timing at 800 R.P.M.

(9)—Early production 750 R.P.M. Engine date stamped to 1118 QA or QB, 950–1000 R.P.M.

(10)—Transistorized ignition 6° BTDC.

(11)—With A/C "ON".

(12)—With Air Injection Reactor System.

(13)—Manual transmission and Air Injection Reactor System.

(14)—Automatic transmission and Air Injection Reactor System.

(15)—After top dead center.

(16)—With A/C "OFF".

(17)—At 800 R.P.M.

(18)—With standard transmission.

(19)—With automatic transmission.

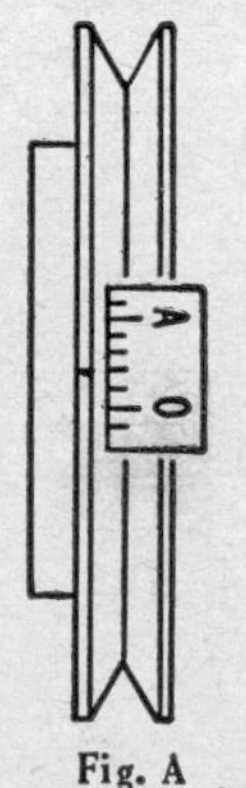

Fig. A

"O" is TDC
Marks 2° Increments

Continued

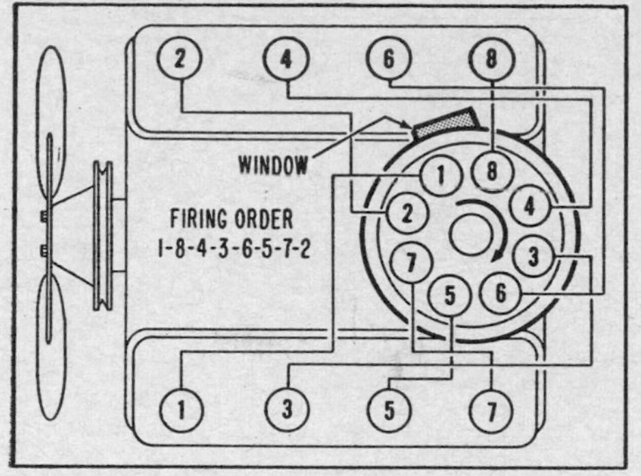

Fig. C

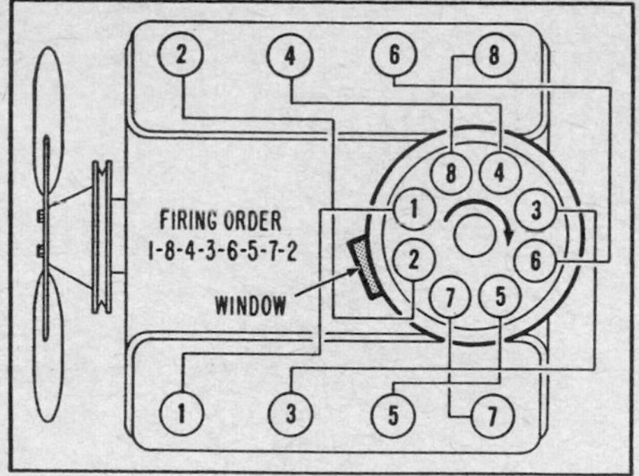

Fig. E

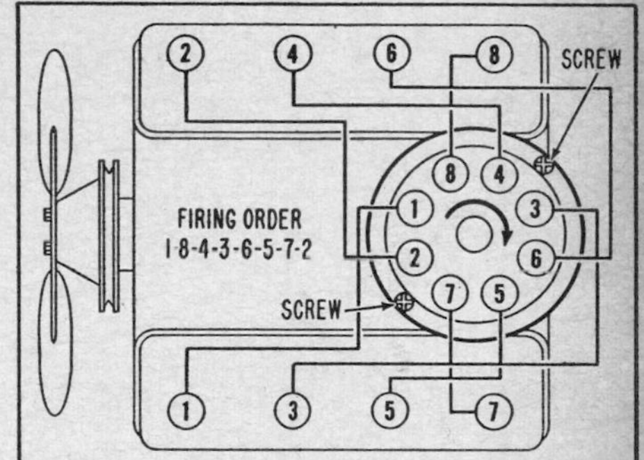

Fig. F

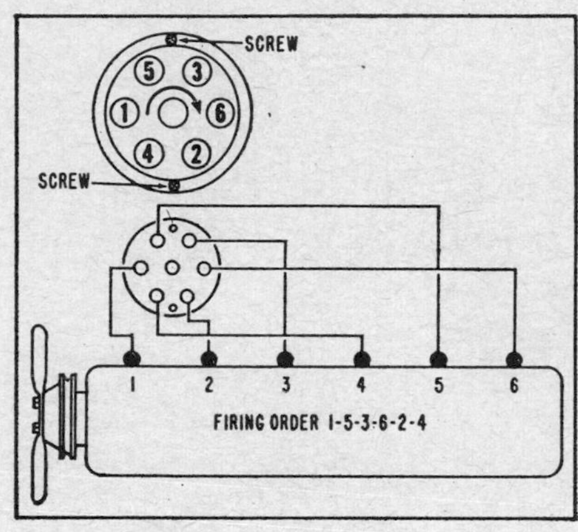

Fig. G

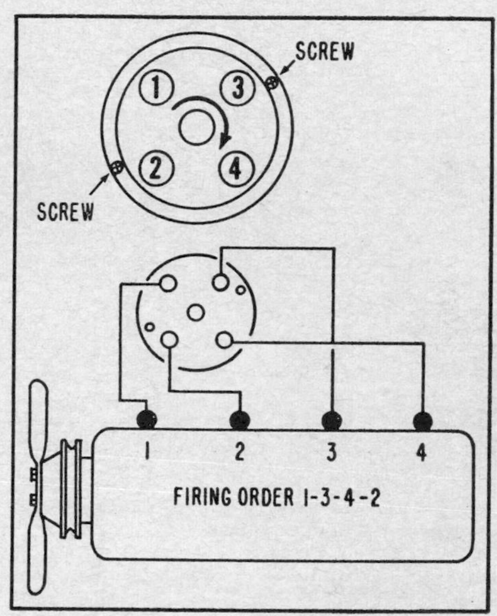

Fig. H

REAR AXLE SPECIFICATIONS

Year	Model	Carrier Type	Ring Gear & Pinion Backlash		Pinion Bearing Preload			Differential Bearing Preload		
			Method	Adjustment	Method	New Bearings Inch-Lbs.	Used Bearings Inch-Lbs.	Method	New Bearings Inch-Lbs.	Used Bearings Inch-Lbs.
1963	All	Removable	①	.005–.008	Spacer	15–25②	5–15②	③	③	③
1964	Chevrolet	Removable	①	.005–.008	Spacer	15–25②	5–15②	③	③	③
	Others	Integral	④	.005–.008	Spacer	20–25②	—	Shims	.010	.010
1965–69	All	Integral	④	.005–.008	Spacer	20–25②	—	Shims	.010	.010

①—Rock ring gear back and forth with box wrench on ring gear bolt.

②—Use inch-pound torque wrench on pinion shaft nut.

③—Threaded sleeves. Tighten right-hand sleeve 2 to 3 notches tight (from zero end play) to locking position.

④—Check with dial gauge.

DISTRIBUTOR SPECIFICATIONS

★NOTE: If advance is checked on vehicle, double the R.P.M. and degrees advance to get crankshaft figures.

Year	Model	Distributor Part No.②	Rotation ①	Breaker Gap	Dwell Angle Deg.	Breaker Arm Spring Tension	Centrifugal Advance Degrees @ R.P.M. of Distributor★		Vacuum Advance	
							Advance Starts	Full Advance	Inches of Vacuum To Start Plunger	Max. Adv. Dist. Deg. @ Vacuum
CAMARO, CHEVROLET, CHEVELLE, CHEVY II										
1963–64	4-153	1110292	C	③	31-34	19-23	1 @ 400	14 @ 1850	5 to 7	11 @ 13
	6-194, 6-230	1110293	C	③	31-34	19-23	1 @ 375	13 @ 1150	5 to 7	11 @ 13
	6-230	1110280	C	③	31-34	19-23	1 @ 450	15 @ 1500	6	11 @ 13
	V8-283 2 Bar. Carb.	1111015	C	③	28-32	19-23	1 @ 450	15 @ 2000	8	8 @ 16
	V8-283 4 Bar. Carb.	1111051	C	③	28-32	19-23	2 @ 400	14 @ 1850	7 to 9	8 @ 16
	V8-327	1111016	C	③	28-32	19-23	1 @ 425	12 @ 2300	8	8 @ 16
	V8-409	1111023	C	③	29	19-23	1 @ 425	12 @ 2300	8	8 @ 16
1965	4-153	1110292	C	③	31-34	19-23	1 @ 400	14 @ 1850	5 to 7	11 @ 13
	6-194	1110293	C	③	31-34	19-23	1 @ 375	13 @ 1150	5 to 7	11 @ 13
	6-230	1110280	C	③	31-34	19-23	1 @ 450	15 @ 1500	5 to 7	11 @ 13
	6-230	1110321	C	③	31-34	19-23	1 @ 400	16 @ 2200	5 to 7	10 @ 14
	V8-283 2 Bar. Carb.	1111015	C	③	28-32	19-23	1 @ 450	15 @ 2000	7 to 9	8 @ 16
	283, 327 4 Bar. Carb.	1111075	C	③	28-32	19-23	2 @ 450	13 @ 2050	5 to 7	12 @ 14
	V8-327	1111071	C	③	27-31	19-23	1 @ 425	15 @ 2550	6 to 8	8 @ 8
	V8-327	1111072	C	...	...	...	1 @ 425	14 @ 2300	6 to 8	8 @ 8
	V8-396 325 H.P.	1111073	C	③	28-32	19-23	1 @ 300	13 @ 2050	6	12 @ 13
	V8-396 425 H.P.	1111074	C	③	28-32	19-23	1 @ 500	14 @ 2200	8	7 @ 15
	V8-409	1111023	C	③	27-31	19-23	1 @ 425	12 @ 2300	7 to 9	8 @ 16
	V8-409	1111059	C	...	...	...	1 @ 453	13 @ 3000	7 to 9	8 @ 16
	V8-409	1111085	C	③	27-31	19-23	1 @ 425	12 @ 2300	6 to 8	8 @ 8
	V8-409	1111086	C	...	...	...	1 @ 435	13 @ 3000	6 to 8	8 @ 8
1966	4-153	1110292	C	③	31-34	19-23	0 @ 300	14 @ 1850	6	11 @ 12
	6-250	1110351	C	③	31-34	19-23	0 @ 450	14 @ 1400	6	10 @ 14
	6-194	1110360	C	③	31-34	19-23	0 @ 450	13 @ 1150	6	10 @ 14
	6-230	1110362	C	③	31-34	19-23	0 @ 450	15 @ 1600	6	10 @ 14
	8-396, 325 H.P.	1111109	C	③	28-32	19-23	0 @ 450	15 @ 2500	8	10 @ 17
	8-427, 390 H.P.	1111112	C	③	28-32	19-23	0 @ 450	15 @ 2500	6	7 @ 12
	8-427, 425 H.P.	1111113	C	...	...	...	...	...	...	...
	8-396, 325 H.P.	1111137	C	③	28-32	19-23	0 @ 450	15 @ 2500	8	10 @ 17
	8-396, 360 H.P.	1111138	C	③	28-32	19-23	0 @ 450	15 @ 2500	7	6 @ 12
	8-396, 360 H.P.	1111139	C	③	28-32	19-23	0 @ 450	15 @ 2500	7	6 @ 12
	8-427, 390 H.P.	1111140	C	...	...	...	0 @ 450	15 @ 2500	6	7 @ 12
	8-427, 425 H.P.	1111143	C	...	...	...	...	...	...	...
	8-283	1111150	C	③	28-32	19-23	0 @ 450	14 @ 2200	8	7 @ 15
	8-327, 275 H.P.	1111152	C	③	28-32	19-23	0 @ 450	13 @ 2050	8	7 @ 15
	8-327, 350 H.P.	1111154	C	③	28-32	19-23	0 @ 450	15 @ 2550	6	7 @ 12
	8-327, 350 H.P.	1111155	C	③	28-32	19-23	0 @ 450	15 @ 2550	6	7 @ 12
1967	4-153	1110292	C	.019	31-34	19-23	0 @ 300	14 @ 1850	6	12 @ 12
	6-194	1110388	C	.019	31-34	19-23	0 @ 450	14 @ 1900	6	11 @ 14
	6-230	1110362	C	.019	31-34	19-23	0 @ 450	15 @ 1600	6	11 @ 14
	6-230 With A.I.R.	1110387	C	.019	31-34	19-23	0 @ 475	13 @ 2000	6	11 @ 14
	6-250	1110351	C	.019	31-34	19-23	0 @ 450	14 @ 1400	6	11 @ 14
	8-283	1111150	C	.019	28-32	19-23	0 @ 450	14 @ 2100	8	8 @ 15
	8-283 With A.I.R.	1111256	C	.019	28-32	19-23	0 @ 450	15 @ 2050	8	8 @ 15
	8-302, 290 H.P.	1111266	C	.019	28-32	19-23	0 @ 500	16 @ 2075	10	7½ @ 17
	8-302, 290 H.P.	1111467	C	.019	28-32	19-23	0 @ 625	12 @ 1100	10	7½ @ 17
	8-327, 210 H.P.	1111101	C	.019	28-32	19-23	0 @ 450	16 @ 1975	8	8 @ 15
	8-327, 275 H.P.	1111249	C	.019	28-32	19-23	0 @ 450	13 @ 2050	8	8 @ 15
	8-327, 275 H.P.④	1111150	C	.019	28-32	19-23	0 @ 450	14 @ 2100	8	8 @ 15
	8-327, 325 H.P.	1111195	C	.019	28-32	19-23	0 @ 450	15 @ 2550	6	8 @ 12
	8-350	1111168	C	.019	28-32	19-23	0 @ 450	13 @ 2350	10	8 @ 17
	8-396, 325 H.P.	1111169	C	.019	28-32	19-23	0 @ 450	16 @ 2500	8	8 @ 15
	8-396, 350 H.P.	1111170	C	.019	28-32	19-23	0 @ 450	16 @ 2500	7	6 @ 12

Continued

DISTRIBUTOR SPECIFICATIONS—Continued

★NOTE: If advance is checked on the vehicle, double the R.P.M. and degrees advance to get crankshaft figures.

Year	Model	Distributor Part No.②	Rotation ①	Breaker Gap	Dwell Angle Deg.	Breaker Arm Spring Tension	Centrifugal Advance Degrees @ R.P.M. of Distributor★		Vacuum Advance	
							Advance Starts	Full Advance	Inches of Vacuum To Start Plunger	Max. Adv. Dist. Deg. @ Vacuum
CAMARO, CHEVROLET, CHEVELLE, CHEVY II—Continued										
1967	8-427, 385 H.P.	1111170	C	.019	28-32	19-23	0 @ 450	16 @ 2500	7	6 @ 12
1968	4-153	1110447	C	.019	31-34	19-23	0 @ 450	14 @ 1850	7	12 @ 15
	4-153	1110246	C	.019	31-34	19-23	0 @ 450	12 @ 1800	7	12 @ 15
	6-230	1110436	C	.019	31-34	19-23	0 @ 500	18 @ 2300	7	11½ @ 16
	6-230	1110433	C	.019	31-34	19-23	0 @ 500	16 @ 2300	7	11½ @ 16
	6-250	1110439	C	.019	31-34	19-23	0 @ 450	16 @ 2100	7	11½ @ 16
	6-250	1110399	C	.019	31-34	19-23	0 @ 450	14 @ 2100	7	11½ @ 16
	8-302	1111467	C	.019	28-32	19-23	0 @ 625	16 @ 2200	10	7½ @ 17
	8-307	1111257	C	.019	28-32	19-23	0 @ 500	14 @ 2150	6	7½ @ 12
	8-327, 210 H.P.	1111440	C	.019	28-32	19-23	0 @ 500	18 @ 1975	6	7½ @ 12
	8-327, 210 H.P.	1111443	C	.019	28-32	19-23	0 @ 450	16 @ 1975	6	7½ @ 12
	8-327, 275 H.P.	1111298	C	.019	28-32	19-23	0 @ 450	17 @ 2050	8	7½ @ 15½
	8-327, 275 H.P.	1111297	C	.019	28-32	19-23	0 @ 450	15 @ 2050	10	7½ @ 17
	8-327, 250 H.P.	1111150	C	.019	28-32	19-23	0 @ 450	14 @ 2100	8	7½ @ 15½
	8-327, 325 H.P.	1111444	C	.019	28-32	19-23	0 @ 475	15 @ 2350	8	7½ @ 15½
	8-350, 295 H.P.	1111264	C	.019	28-32	19-23	0 @ 475	15 @ 2350	10	7½ @ 17
	8-350, 295 H.P.	1111168	C	.019	28-32	19-23	0 @ 450	13 @ 2350	10	7½ @ 17
	8-396, 325, 350 H.P.	1111169	C	.019	28-32	19-23	0 @ 450	16 @ 2500	8	7½ @ 15½
	8-396, 325, 350 H.P.	1111445	C	.019	28-32	19-23	0 @ 450	18 @ 2500	8	7½ @ 15½
	8-427, 385 H.P.	1111169	C	.019	28-32	19-23	0 @ 450	16 @ 2500	8	7½ @ 15½
	8-396, 375 H.P.	1111170	C	.019	28-32	19-23	0 @ 450	16 @ 2500	7	6 @ 12
	8-427, 425 H.P.	1111170	C	.019	28-32	19-23	0 @ 450	16 @ 2500	7	6 @ 12
1969	4-153	1110457	C	.019	31-34	19-23	0 @ 450	14 @ 1850	7	12 @ 15
	4-153	1110458	C	.019	31-34	19-23	0 @ 450	12 @ 1800	7	12 @ 15
	6-230	1110459	C	.019	31-34	19-23	0 @ 500	18 @ 2300	7	11½ @ 16
	6-230	1110460	C	.019	31-34	19-23	0 @ 500	16 @ 2300	7	11½ @ 16
	6-250	1110463	C	.019	31-34	19-23	0 @ 450	16 @ 2100	7	11½ @ 16
	6-250	1110464	C	.019	31-34	19-23	0 @ 450	14 @ 2100	7	11½ @ 16
	8-302	1111480	C	.019	28-32	19-23	0 @ 625	16 @ 2200	8	7½ @ 15½
	8-307	1111481	C	.019	28-32	19-23	0 @ 500	14 @ 2100	6	7½ @ 12
	8-327	1111482	C	.019	28-32	19-23	0 @ 500	16 @ 2100	6	7½ @ 12
	8-327	1111483	C	.019	28-32	19-23	0 @ 450	14 @ 2100	6	7½ @ 12
	8-350	1111486	C	.019	28-32	19-23	0 @ 400	18 @ 2050	7	6½ @ 17
	8-350	1111487	C	.019	28-32	19-23	0 @ 450	16 @ 2200	7	6½ @ 17
	8-350, 255 H.P.	1111955	C	.019	28-32	19-23	0 @ 450	16 @ 2200	7	6½ @ 17
	8-350, 255 H.P.	1111956	C	.019	28-32	19-23	0 @ 450	16 @ 2200	7	12 @ 13
	8-350, 300 H.P.	1111488	C	.019	28-32	19-23	0 @ 475	15 @ 2360	10	5 @ 17
	8-350, 300 H.P.	1111489	C	.019	28-32	19-23	0 @ 450	13 @ 2360	10	5 @ 17
	8-396, 265 H.P.	1111949	C	.019	28-32	19-23	0 @ 450	19 @ 2100	8	7½ @ 15½
	8-396, 265 H.P.	1111950	C	.019	28-32	19-23	0 @ 450	17 @ 2150	8	7½ @ 15½
	8-396, 325 H.P.	1111497	C	.019	28-32	19-23	0 @ 450	16 @ 2500	8	7½ @ 15½
	8-427, 335 H.P.	1111497	C	.019	28-32	19-23	0 @ 450	16 @ 2500	8	7½ @ 15½
	8-396, 350 H.P.	1111498	C	.019	28-32	19-23	0 @ 450	18 @ 2500	8	7½ @ 15½
	8-396, 350, 375 H.P.	1111499	C	.019	28-32	19-23	0 @ 450	16 @ 2500	6	7½ @ 12
	8-396, 390 H.P.	1111925	C	.019	28-32	19-23	0 @ 400	13 @ 1900	8	7½ @ 15½
CORVETTE										
1963-64	V8-327 Std. Eng.	1111022	C	③	28-32	19-23	1 @ 425	12 @ 2300	7-9	8 @ 16
	V8-327 Hi Perf.	1111024	C	③	21-31	19-23	1 @ 425	12 @ 2300	7-9	8 @ 16
1965	Mag. Pulse Dist.	1111060	C	...	...	...	1 @ 435	13 @ 3000	3 to 5	8 @ 8
	Mag. Pulse Dist.	1111064	C	...	...	...	2 @ 500	14 @ 3000	3 to 5	8 @ 8
	V8-327 365 H.P.	1111069	C	③	27-31	19-23	1 @ 460	12 @ 1175	3 to 5	8 @ 8

Continued

DISTRIBUTOR SPECIFICATIONS—Continued

★NOTE: If advance is checked on the vehicle, double the R.P.M. and degrees advance to get crankshaft figures.

Year	Model	Distributor Part No.②	Rotation ①	Breaker Gap	Dwell Angle Deg.	Breaker Arm Spring Tension	Centrifugal Advance Degrees @ R.P.M. of Distributor★ Advance Starts	Centrifugal Advance Full Advance	Vacuum Advance Inches of Vacuum To Start Plunger	Vacuum Advance Max. Adv. Dist. Deg. @ Vacuum
CORVETTE—Continued										
1965	V8-327 375 H.P.	1111070	C	③	27-31	19-23	1 @ 460	12 @ 1175	3 to 5	8 @ 8
	V8-327 250, 300 H.P.	1111076	C	③	27-31	19-23	2 @ 450	13 @ 2050	5 to 7	12 @ 14
	V8-327 350 H.P.	1111087	C	③	27-31	19-23	2 @ 450	13 @ 2050	3 to 5	8 @ 8
	V8-396 425 H.P.	1111093	C	③	28-32	19-23	1 @ 500	14 @ 2200	8	7 @ 15
1966	8-427, 390 H.P.	1111141	C	③	28-32	19-23	0 @ 450	15 @ 2500	6	7 @ 12
	8-427, 390 H.P.	1111142	C	...	...	...	0 @ 450	15 @ 2500	6	7 @ 12
	8-427, 425 H.P.	1111145	C	...	...	...	...	...	...	...
	8-327, 300 H.P.	1111153	C	③	28-32	19-23	0 @ 450	13 @ 2050	6	7 @ 12
	8-327, 350 H.P.	1111156	C	③	28-32	19-23	0 @ 450	15 @ 2550	4	8 @ 8
	8-327, 350 H.P.	1111157	C	③	28-32	19-23	0 @ 450	15 @ 2550	4	8 @ 8
1967	8-327, 300 H.P.⑥	1111117	C	.019	28-32	19-23	0 @ 450	20 @ 2550	6	[illegible] @ 12
	8-327, 350 H.P.	1111157	C	—	—	—	0 @ 450	14 @ 2300	4	8 @ 7
	8-327, 300 H.P.	1111194	C	.019	28-32	19-23	0 @ 450	15 @ 2550	6	8 @ 12
	8-237, 350 H.P.	1111196	C	.019	28-32	19-23	0 @ 450	15 @ 2550	4	8 @ 7
	8-427, 390, 400 H.P.	1111247	C	.019	28-32	19-23	0 @ 450	16 @ 2500	7	6 @ 12
	8-427, Tri-Carb.	1111248	C	.019	28-32	19-23	0 @ 450	16 @ 2500	7	6 @ 12
	8-427, 435 H.P.	1111258	C	—	—	—	0 @ 450	15 @ 1900	8	8 @ 15
1968	8-327, 300 H.P.	1111194	C	.019	28-32	19-23	0 @ 450	15 @ 2550	6	7½ @ 12
	8-327, 350 H.P.	1111438	C	.019	28-32	19-23	0 @ 450	15 @ 2550	6	7½ @ 12
	8-327, 350 H.P.	1111441	C	.019	28-32	19-23	0 @ 450	15 @ 2200	8	7½ @ 15½
	8-427, 390, 400 H.P.	1111293	C	.019	28-32	19-23	0 @ 450	16 @ 2500	7	6 @ 12
	8-427, 435 H.P.	1111296	C	.019	28-32	19-23	0 @ 450	15 @ 1900	8	7½ @ 15½
	8-427, 430 H.P.	1111295	C	.019	28-32	19-23	0 @ 600	15 @ 2500	—	—
	8-427, 390, 400 H.P.	1111294	C	.019	28-32	19-23	0 @ 450	16 @ 2500	7	6 @ 12
1969	8-350, 300 H.P.	1111490	C	.019	28-32	19-23	0 @ 450	16 @ 2550	8	5 @ 17
	8-350, 350 H.P.	1111493	C	.019	28-32	19-23	N.A.	N.A.	7	7½ @ 12
	8-427, 390, 400 H.P.	1111926	C	.019	28-32	19-23	0 @ 400	13 @ 1900	7	6 @ 12
	8-427, 430 H.P.	1111927	C	—	—	—	0 @ 600	14½ @ 2500	—	—
	8-427, 435 H.P.	1111928	C	—	—	—	0 @ 450	15 @ 1900	8	7½ @ 15½

①—As viewed from above.
②—Stamped on distributor housing plate.
③—New points .019″, used points .016″.
④—With A.I.R. System.

ALTERNATOR & REGULATOR SPECIFICATIONS

Year	Alternator Model	Rated Hot Output Amps.	Field Current 12 Volts @ 80°F.	Output @ 14 Volts 2000 R.P.M. Amps.	Output @ 14 Volts 5000 R.P.M. Amps.	Regulator Model	Field Relay Air Gap In.	Field Relay Point Gap In.	Field Relay Closing Voltage	Voltage Regulator Air Gap In.	Voltage Regulator Point Gap In.	Voltage Regulator Voltage @ 125°F.
1963	1100628	37	1.9-2.3	25	35	1119512	.015	.030	1.5-2.7	.057	.014	13.5-14.4
	1100629	42	1.9-2.3	28	40	1119512	.015	.030	1.5-2.7	.057	.014	13.5-14.4
	1100630	32	1.9-2.3	21	30	1119512	.015	.030	1.5-2.7	.057	.014	13.5-14.4
	1100633	55	1.9-2.3	32	50	1119512	.015	.030	1.5-2.7	.057	.014	13.5-14.4
1964	1100665	55	2.2-2.6	32	50	1119515	.015	.030	1.5-2.7	.067	.014	13.5-14.4

Continued

ALTERNATOR & REGULATOR SPECIFICATIONS—Continued

Year	Alternator					Regulator							
	Model	Rated Hot Output Amps.	Field Current 12 Volts @ 80°F.	Output @ 14 Volts		Model	Field Relay			Voltage Regulator		
				2000 R.P.M. Amps.	5000 R.P.M. Amps.		Air Gap In.	Point Gap In.	Closing Voltage	Air Gap In.	Point Gap In.	Voltage @ 125°F.
1964	1100668	37	1.9–2.3	25	35	1119515	.015	.030	1.5–2.7	.067	.014	13.5–14.4
	1100669	42	1.9–2.3	28	40	1119515	.015	.030	1.5–2.7	.067	.014	13.5–14.4
	1100670	32	1.9–2.3	21	30	1119515	.015	.030	1.5–2.7	.067	.014	13.5–14.4
1965–68	1100693	37	2.2–2.6	25	35	1119515	.015	.030	1.5–3.2	.067	.014	13.5–14.4
	1100694	55	2.2–2.6	32	50	1119515	.015	.030	1.5–3.2	.067	.014	13.5–14.4
1965–67	1100695	32	2.2–2.6	21	30	1119515	.015	.030	1.5–3.2	.067	.014	13.5–14.4
1965–68	1100696	42	2.2–2.6	28	40	1119515	.015	.030	1.5–3.2	.067	.014	13.5–14.4
1966	1100697	60	2.8–3.2	36	58	1116368	.015	.025	2.5–3.5	—	—	13.4–14.3
1966–67	1100742	63	2.85–3.15	35	59	1119519	.015	.030	1.5–3.2	.067	.014	13.5–14.4
1966–68	1100750	61	2.2–2.6	33	58	1119515	.015	.030	1.5–3.2	.067	.014	13.5–14.4
1966–67	1117754	62	3.7–4.4	20	55	1116378	.015	.025	2.5–3.5	—	—	13.4–14.3
1967	1117777	62	4.14–4.62	20	55	1116378	.015	.025	2.5–3.5	—	—	13.4–14.3
1968	1100794	37	2.2–2.6	25	35	1119515	.015	.030	1.5–3.2	.067	.014	13.4–14.3
	1100795	42	2.2–2.6	28	40	1119515	.015	.030	1.5–3.2	.067	.014	13.4–14.3
	1100796	61	2.2–2.6	33	58	1119515	.015	.030	1.5–3.2	.067	.014	13.4–14.3
	1100810	63	2.2–2.6	35	59	1119515	.015	.030	1.5–3.2	.067	.014	13.4–14.3
	1100813	37	2.2–2.6	25	35	1119515	.015	.030	1.5–3.2	.067	.014	13.4–14.3
	1100814	37	2.2–2.6	25	35	1119515	.015	.030	1.5–3.2	.067	.014	13.4–14.3
	1100815	42	2.2–2.6	28	40	1119515	.015	.030	1.5–3.2	.067	.014	13.4–14.3
	1100817	61	2.2–2.6	33	58	1119515	.015	.030	1.5–3.2	.067	.014	13.4–14.3
	1100818	63	2.2–2.6	35	59	1119515	.015	.030	1.5–3.2	.067	.014	13.4–14.3
1969	1100825(1)	61	2.2–2.6	—	—	—	—	—	—	—	—	—
	1100833(1)	42	2.2–2.6	—	—	—	—	—	—	—	—	—
	1100834	37	2.2–2.6	—	—	1119515	.015	.030	1.5–3.2	.067	.014	13.4–14.3
	1100836	37	2.2–2.6	—	—	1119515	.015	.030	1.5–3.2	.067	.014	13.4–14.3
	1100837	37	2.2–2.6	—	—	1119515	.015	.030	1.5–3.2	.067	.014	13.4–14.3
	1100839	42	2.2–2.6	—	—	1119515	.015	.030	1.5–3.2	.067	.014	13.4–14.3
	1100841	42	2.2–2.6	—	—	1119515	.015	.030	1.5–3.2	.067	.014	13.4–14.3
	1100843	61	2.2–2.6	—	—	1119515	.015	.030	1.5–3.2	.067	.014	13.4–14.3
	1100845	61	2.2–2.6	—	—	1119515	.015	.030	1.5–3.2	.067	.014	13.4–14.3
	1100846	63	2.2–2.6	—	—	1119515	.015	.030	1.5–3.2	.067	.014	13.4–14.3
	1100847	61	2.2–2.6	—	—	1119515	.015	.030	1.5–3.2	.067	.014	13.4–14.3
	1100859(1)	42	2.2–2.6	—	—	—	—	—	—	—	—	—

(1)—Integral System.

STARTING MOTOR SPECIFICATIONS

Year	Model	Starter Number	Brush Spring Tension Oz(1)	Free Speed Test			Resistance Test(3)	
				Amps.	Volts	R.P.M.(1)	Amps.	Volts
1963	Chevy II	1107259	35	49–76(2)	10.6	6200	270–310(2)	4.3
	Chevy II	1107260	35	49–76(2)	10.6	6200	270–310(2)	4.3
	6-230	1107259	35	49(2)	10.6	6200	270–310(2)	4.3
	V8-283	1107237	35	49(2)	10.6	6200	270–310(2)	4.3
	V8-327, 409	1107242	35	65(2)	10.6	3600	300–360(2)	3.5
	V8-327, 409	1107711	40	65(2)	10.6	3600	300–360(2)	3.5
	V8-327, 409	1107233	40	65(2)	10.6	3600	300–360(2)	3.5
	V8-327, 409	1107286	40	65(2)	10.6	3600	300–360(2)	3.5
1964	V8-283	1107247	35	49–76(2)	10.6	6200	270–310	4.3

Continued

STARTING MOTOR SPECIFICATIONS—Continued

Year	Model	Starter Number	Brush Spring Tension, Oz①	Free Speed Test			Resistance Test③	
				Amps.	Volts	R.P.M.①	Amps.	Volts
1964	6 Cyl.	1107259	35	49–76②	10.6	6200	270–310②	4.3
	V8-409	1107274	35	65–100②	10.6	3600	300–360	3.5
	V8-409	1107286	35	70–105②	10.6	3800	480–540②	3.0
	V8-283	1107303	35	49–76②	10.6	6200–9400	270–310②	4.3
1965–66	V8-283	1107247	35	49–76②	10.6	6200–9400	270–310②	4.3
	4 & 6 Cyl.	1107259	40	49–76②	10.6	6200–9400	270–310②	4.3
	4 & 6 Cyl.	1107260	35	49–76②	10.6	6200–9400	270–310②	4.3
1965-67	V8-327	1107320	35	65–100②	10.6	3600–5100	300–360②	3.5
1965-66	V8-409	1107342	35	70–105②	10.6	3800–6200	480–540②	3.0
1965-66	V8-327	1107320	35	65–100②	10.6	3600	300–360	3.5
1965-66	V8-396,427	1107352	35	65–100②	10.6	3600–5100	300–360②	3.5
1965-68	V8-396,427	1107365	35	65–100②	10.6	3600–5100	300–360②	3.5
1966-68	6-230, 250	1107372	35	55–95②	10.6	3800–6000	300–360	3.5
1966	6-250	1107374	35	65–100②	10.6	3600–5100	300–360	3.5
1967	4 & 6 Cyl.	1107399	35	49–87②	10.6	6200–10700	290–425②	4.2
	4 & 6 Cyl. P.G.	1107400	35	49–87②	10.6	6200–10700	290–425②	4.2
	V8-283	1107496	35	49–87②	10.6	6200–10700	290–425②	4.2
	V8-283, 327, 350	1107388	35	65–100②	10.6	3600–5100	300–360	3.5
1968-69	8-307, 327, 350	1107368	35	65–100②	10.6	3600–5100	300–360	3.5
	8-327, 427	1108351	35	70–99②	10.6	7800–12000	300–360	3.5
	8-327, 350	1108361	35	65–100②	10.6	3600–5100	300–360②	3.5
	4-153, 6-230, 250	1108365	35	49–87②	10.6	6200–10700	290–425②	4.2
	4-153	1108366	35	49–87②	10.6	6200–10700	290–425②	4.2
	8-307, 302, 327	1108367	35	49–87②	10.6	6200–10700	290–425②	4.2
	8-350	1108338	35	55–85②	9	3100–4900	—	—
	8-396, 427	1108418	35	54–80②	9	6800–9400	—	—
	8-327	1108382	35	53–69②	9	6400–8600	—	—
	6-250	1107372	35	55–95②	9	3000–4800	—	—
	8-427	1108400	35	54–80②	9	6800–9400	—	—

①—Minimum. ②—Includes solenoid.

③—Check capacity of motor by using a 500 ampere meter and a carbon pile rheostat to control voltage. Apply the volts listed across motor with armature locked. Current should be as listed.

VALVE SPECIFICATIONS

★Adjust hydraulic lifters by tightening rocker arm stud nut just to the point where all lash is eliminated. Then turn nut the additional turns listed. See Valves Adjust text for details.

Year	Engine Model	Valve Lash★		Valve Angles		Valve Spring Installed Height	Valve Spring Pressure Lbs. @ In.	Stem Clearance		Stem Diameter	
		Int.	Exh.	Seat	Face			Intake	Exhaust	Intake	Exhaust
1963	4-153	1 Turn⑤		46	45	$1\frac{23}{32}$	165 @ $1\frac{23}{64}$	.001–.0027	.0015–.0032	.3410–.3417	③
	6-194	1 Turn⑤		46	45	$1\frac{23}{32}$	165 @ $1\frac{23}{64}$	.001–.0027	.0015–.0032	.3410–.3417	③
	6-230	1 Turn⑤		46	45	1.66	170 @ 1.33	.001–.0033	.001–.0027	.3404–.3417	.3410–.3417
	8-283	1 Turn⑤		46	45	1.66	175 @ 1.26	.001–.0033	.001–.0027	.3404–.3417	.3410–.3417
	8-327 250 H.P.	1 Turn⑤		46	45	1.66	175 @ 1.26	.001–.0033	.001–.0027	.3404–.3417	.3410–.3417
	8-327 300 H.P.	1 Turn⑤		46	45	1.66	175 @ 1.26	.001–.0033	.001–.0027	.3404–.3417	.3410–.3417
	8-327 340 H.P.	.008H	.018H	46	45	$1\frac{11}{16}$	164 @ $1\frac{19}{64}$	.001–.0027	.0016–.0033	③	.3410–.3417
	8-327 360 H.P.	.008H	.018H	46	45	$1\frac{11}{16}$	164 @ $1\frac{19}{64}$	.001–.0027	.0016–.0033	③	.3410–.3417
	8-409 340 H.P.	1 Turn⑤		46	45	1.66	170 @ 1.33	.001–.0027	.001–.0027	.3715–.3722	.3710–.3717
	8-409 400 H.P.	②		46	45	1.68	330 @ 1.20	.001–.0027	.0015–.0032	.3715–.3722	.3710–.3717
	8-409 425 H.P.	②		46	45	1.68	330 @ 1.20	.001–.0027	.0015–.0032	.3715–.3722	.3710–.3717

Continued

VALVE SPECIFICATIONS—Continued

★Adjust hydraulic lifters by tightening rocker arm stud nut just to the point where all lash is eliminated. Then turn nut the additional turns listed. See Valves Adjust text for details.

Year	Engine Model	Valve Lash★		Valve Angles		Valve Spring Installed Height	Valve Spring Pressure Lbs. @ In.	Stem Clearance		Stem Diameter	
		Int.	Exh.	Seat	Face			Intake	Exhaust	Intake	Exhaust
1964	4-153	1 Turn⑤		46	45	1.66	175 @ 1.26	.001-.0033	.001-.0027	.3404-.3417	.3410-.3417
	6-194	1 Turn⑤		46	45	1.66	170 @ 1.33	.001-.0033	.001-.0027	.3404-.3417	.3410-.3417
	6-230	1 Turn⑤		46	45	1.66	175 @ 1.26	.001-.0033	.001-.0027	.3404-.3417	.3410-.3417
	8-283	1 Turn⑤		46	45	1.66	175 @ 1.26	.001-.0033	.001-.0027	.3404-.3417	.3410-.3417
	8-327 250 H.P.	1 Turn⑤		46	45	1.66	175 @ 1.26	.001-.0033	.001-.0027	.3404-.3417	.3410-.3417
	8-327 300 H.P.	1 Turn⑤		46	45	1.66	175 @ 1.26	.001-.0033	.001-.0027	.3404-.3417	.3410-.3417
	8-327 365 H.P.	.030H	.030H	46	45	1.66	175 @ 1.26	.001-.0027	.001-.0027	.3410-.3417	.3410-.3417
	8-327 375 H.P.	.030H	.030H	46	45	1.66	175 @ 1.26	.001-.0027	.001-.0027	.3410-.3417	.3410-.3417
	8-409 340 H.P.	1 Turn⑤		46	45	1.66	170 @ 1.33	.001-.0027	.001-.0027	.3715-.3722	.3710-.3717
	8-409 400 H.P.	②		46	45	1.68	330 @ 1.20	.001-.0027	.0015-.0032	.3715-.3722	.3710-.3717
	8-409 425 H.P.	②		46	45	1.68	330 @ 1.20	.001-.0027	.0015-.0032	.3715-.3722	.3710-.3717
1965	4-153	1 Turn⑤		46	45	1.66	175 @ 1.26	.001-.0033	.001-.0027	.3404-.3417	.3410-.3417
	6-194	1 Turn⑤		46	45	1.66	170 @ 1.33	.001-.0033	.001-.0027	.3404-.3417	.3410-.3417
	6-230	1 Turn⑤		46	45	1.66	175 @ 1.26	.001-.0033	.001-.0027	.3404-.3417	.3410-.3417
	8-283	1 Turn⑤		46	45	1.66	175 @ 1.26	.001-.0033	.001-.0027	.3404-.3417	.3410-.3417
	8-327 250 H.P.	1 Turn⑤		46	45	1.66	175 @ 1.26	.001-.0033	.001-.0027	.3404-.3417	.3410-.3417
	8-327 300 H.P.	1 Turn⑤		46	45	1.66	175 @ 1.26	.001-.0033	.001-.0027	.3404-.3417	.3410-.3417
	8-327 350 H.P.	1 Turn⑤		46	45	1.66	175 @ 1.26	.001-.0033	.001-.0027	.3404-.3417	.3410-.3417
	8-327 365 H.P.	.030H	.030H	46	45	1.66	175 @ 1.26	.001-.0027	.001-.0027	.3410-.3417	.3410-.3417
	8-327 375 H.P.	.030H	.030H	46	45	1.66	175 @ 1.26	.001-.0027	.001-.0027	.3410-.3417	.3410-.3417
	8-396 325 H.P.	1 Turn⑤		46	45	1 7/8	220 @ 1.46	.0005-.0024	.0012-.0029	.3715-.3722	.3713-.3720
	8-396 425 H.P.	.020H	.024H	46	45	1 7/8	315 @ 1.38	.0005-.0024	.0012-.0029	.3715-.3722	.3713-.3720
	8-409 340 H.P.	1 Turn⑤		46	45	1.66	170 @ 1.33	.001-.0027	.001-.0027	.3715-.3722	.3710-.3717
	8-409 400 H.P.	.018H	.030H	46	45	1.68	330 @ 1.20	.001-.0027	.0015-.0032	.3715-.3722	.3710-.3717
1966	4-153	1 Turn⑤		46	45	1.66	175 @ 1.26	.001-.0027	.0015-.0032	.3410-.3417	.3410-.3417
	6-194	1 Turn⑤		46	45	1.66	175 @ 1.33	.001-.0027	.0015-.0032	.3410-.3417	.3410-.3417
	6-230	1 Turn⑤		46	45	1.66	175 @ 1.33	.001-.0027	.0015-.0032	.3410-.3417	.3410-.3417
	6-250	1 Turn⑤		46	45	1.66	185 @ 1.27	.001-.0027	.0015-.0032	.3410-.3417	.3410-.3417
	8-283	1 Turn⑤		46	45	1.66	175 @ 1.26	.001-.0027	.001-.0027	.3410-.3417	.3410-.3417
	8-327, 275, 300 H.P.	1 Turn⑤		46	45	1.66	175 @ 1.26	.001-.0027	.001-.0027	.3410-.3417	.3410-.3417
	8-327, 350 H.P.	1 Turn⑤		46	45	1.66	182 @ 1.21	.001-.0027	.001-.0027	.3410-.3417	.3410-.3417
	8-396, 325 H.P.	1 Turn⑤		46	45	1.88	220 @ 1.46	.001-.0025	.0012-.0027	.3715-.3722	.3713-.3720
	8-396, 360 H.P.	1 Turn⑤		46	45	1.88	315 @ 1.38	.001-.0025	.0012-.0027	.3715-.3722	.3713-.3720
	8-427, 390 H.P.	1 Turn⑤		46	45	1.88	315 @ 1.38	.001-.0025	.0012-.0027	.3715-.3722	.3713-.3720
	8-427, 425 H.P.	.020H	.024H	46	45	1.88	315 @ 1.38	.001-.0025	.0012-.0027	.3715-.3722	.3713-.3720
1967	4-153	1 Turn⑤		46	45	1 21/32	175 @ 1.26	.001-.0027	.0015-.0032	.3410-.3417	.3410-.3417
	6-194, 230	1 Turn⑤		46	45	1 21/32	177 @ 1.33	.001-.0027	.0015-.0032	.3410-.3417	.3410-.3417
	6-250	1 Turn⑤		46	45	1 21/32	186 @ 1.27	.001-.0027	.0015-.0032	.3410-.3417	.3410-.3417
	8-283, 327, 350	1 Turn⑤		46	45	1 5/32	200 @ 1.25	.001-.0027	.0012-.0027	.3410-.3417	.3410-.3417
	8-302	.030H	.030H	46	45	1 5/32	200 @ 1.25	.001-.0027	.0012-.0027	.3410-.3417	.3410-.3417
	8-396, 325 H.P.	1 Turn⑤		46	45	1 7/8	220 @ 1.46	.001-.0025	.0012-.0027	.3715-.3722	.3713-.3720
	8-396, 350 H.P.	1 Turn⑤		46	45	1 7/8	315 @ 1.38	.001-.0025	.0012-.0027	.3715-.3722	.3713-.3720
	8-396, 375 H.P.	.020H	.024H	46	45	1 7/8	315 @ 1.38	.001-.0025	.0012-.0027	.3715-.3722	.3713-.3720
	8-427⑥	1 Turn⑤		46	45	1 7/8	315 @ 1.38	.001-.0025	.0012-.0027	.3715-.3722	.3713-.3720
	8-427, 425 H.P.	.022H	.024H	46④	45	1 7/8	193 @ 1.32	.001-.0025	.0012-.0027	.3715-.3722	.3713-.3720
	8-427, 435 H.P.	.024H	.028H	46④	45	1 7/8	315 @ 1.38	.001-.0025	.0012-.0027	.3715-.3722	.3713-.3720
1968	4-153	1 Turn⑤		46	45	1.66	175 @ 1.26	.001-.0027	.0017-.0027	.3410-.3417	.3410-.3417
	6-230, 250	1 Turn⑤		46	45	1.66	186 @ 1.27	.001-.0027	.0017-.0027	.3410-.3417	.3410-.3417
	8-302	.030H	.030H	46	45	1.56	200 @ 1.25	.001-.0027	.0012-.0027	.3410-.3417	.3410-.3417
	8-307, 327, 350	1 Turn⑤		46	45	1.70	198 @ 1.25	.001-.0027	.0017-.0027	.3410-.3417	.3410-.3417
	8-396, 325 H.P.	1 Turn⑤		46	45	1.88	215 @ 1.48	.001-.0027	.0015-.0032	.3715-.3722	.3713-.3722
	8-396, 350 H.P.	1 Turn⑤		46	45	1.88	315 @ 1.38	.001-.0027	.0015-.0032	.3715-.3722	.3713-.3722
	8-396, 375 H.P.	.024H	.028H	46④	45	1 7/8	315 @ 1.38	.001-.0025	.0012-.0027	.3715-.3722	.3713-.3720
	8-427⑥	1 Turn⑤		46	45	1.88	315 @ 1.38	.001-.0027	.0015-.0032	.3715-.3722	.3713-.3722
	8-427, 435 H.P.	.024H	.028H	46	45	1.88	315 @ 1.38	.001-.0027	.0015-.0032	.3715-.3722	.3713-.3722

Continued

VALVE SPECIFICATIONS—Continued

★Adjust hydaulic lifters by tightening rocker arm stud nut just to the point where all lash is eliminated. Then turn nut the additional turns listed. See Valves Adjust text for details.

Year	Engine Model	Valve Lash★		Valve Angles		Valve Spring Installed Height	Valve Spring Pressure Lbs. @ In.	Stem Clearance		Stem Diameter	
		Int.	Exh.	Seat	Face			Intake	Exhaust	Intake	Exhaust
1969	4-153	1 Turn⑤		46	45	1.66	175 @ 1.26	.001–.0027	.0015–.0032	.3410–.3417	.3410–.3417
	6-230	1 Turn⑤		46	45	1.66	175 @ 1.33	.001–.0027	.0015–.0032	.3410–.3417	.3410–.3417
	6-250	1 Turn⑤		46	45	1.66	186 @ 1.27	.001–.0027	.0015–.0032	.3410–.3417	.3410–.3417
	8-302	.030H	.030H	46	45	1.56	200 @ 1.25	.001–.0027	.001 –.0027	.3410–.3417	.3410–.3417
	8-307, 327, 350①	1 Turn⑤		46	45	1.56	200 @ 1.25	.001–.0027	.001 –.0027	.3410–.3417	.3410–.3417
	8-350, 370 H.P.	.030H	.030H	46	45	1.56	200 @ 1.25	.001–.0027	.001 –.0027	.3410–.3417	.3410–.3417
	8-396, 265, 325 H.P.	1 Turn⑤		46	45	1.88	220 @ 1.46	.001–.0025	.0012–.0027	.3715–.3722	.3713–.3722
	8-396, 350	1 Turn⑤		46	45	1.88	312 @ 1.38	.001–.0025	.0012–.0027	.3715–.3722	.3713–.3722
	8-396, 375	.024H	.028H	46	45	1.88	312 @ 1.38	.001–.0025	.0012–.0027	.3715–.3722	.3713–.3722
	8-427⑥	1 Turn		46	45	1.88	312 @ 1.38	.001–.0025	.0012–.0027	.3715–.3722	.3713–.3722
	8-427, 425 H.P.	.024H	.028H	46	45	1.88	312 @ 1.38	.001–.0025	.0012–.0027	.3715–.3722	.3713–.3722
	8-427, 430 H.P.	.022H	.024H	46④	45	1.88	198 @ 1.32	.001–.0025	.0012–.0027	.3715–.3722	.3713–.3722
	8-427, 435 H.P.	.024H	.028H	46④	45	1.88	312 @ 1.38	.001–.0025	.0012–.0027	.3715–.3722	.3713–.3722

①—255, 300, 350 H.P.

②—Early production: intake .012H, exhaust .020H. Engines date stamped TO-1118 QA or QB: intake .018H, exhaust .030H.

③—Tapers .3414″ at top to .3404″ at bottom.

④—Aluminum heads 45°.

⑤—Turn rocker arm stud nut until all lash is eliminated, then tighten nut the additional turn listed.

⑥—385, 390, 400 H.P.

ENGINE TIGHTENING SPECIFICATIONS★

★Torque specifications are for clean and lightly lubricated threads only. Dry or dirty threads produce increased friction which prevents accurate measurement of tightness.

Year	Engine Model	Spark Plugs Ft. Lbs.	Cylinder Head Bolts Ft. Lbs.	Intake Manifold Ft. Lbs.	Exhaust Manifold Ft. Lbs.	Rocker Arm Stud Ft. Lbs.	Rocker Arm Cover Ft. Lbs.	Connecting Rod Cap Bolts Ft. Lbs.	Main Bearing Cap Bolts Ft. Lbs.	Flywheel to Crankshaft Ft. Lbs.	Vibration Damper or Pulley Ft. Lbs.
1963–68	4-153	25	95	③	③	—	55④	35	65	60	②
1963–67	6-194	25	95	③	③	—	55④	35	65	60	②
1963–68	6-230	25	95	③	③	—	55④	35	65	60	②
1966–68	6-250	25	95	③	③	—	55④	35	65	60	②
1963–67	8-283	25	65	30	20	—	55④	35	80	60	②
1967	8-302	25	65	30	20	—	55④	⑩	80	60	60
1968–69	8-302	25	65	30	20	—	55④	45	80	60	60
1968–69	8-307	25	65	30	20	—	55④	45	80	60	60
1963–67	8-327	25	65	30	20	—	55④	35	80	60	60
1968–69	8-327	25	65	30	20	—	55④	⑩	80	60	60
1967	8-350	25	65	30	20	—	55④	35	80	60	②
1968–69	8-350	25	65	30	20	—	55④	45	80	60	②
1965–67	8-396	25	80	30	20	50	50④	50	⑤	60	85
1968–69	8-396	25	80	30	20	50	50④	45	⑤	60	85
1963–65	8-409	25	65	30	③	—	25④	40	100	60	②
1966	8-427	25	80	30	20	50	50④	50	⑤	60	85
1967	8-427	25	80⑧	30	20	50⑨	50④	50	⑤	60	85
1968–69	8-427	25	80⑧	30	20	50⑨	50④	45	⑤	60	85

①—Clamp bolts 15–20, stud nuts 25–30.

②—Pressed on.

③—End clamp bolts 20, center bolts 30.

④—Inch lbs.

⑤—2 bolt caps 95 ft.-lbs., 4 bolt caps 105 ft.-lbs.

⑧—Aluminum Head–Short bolts 65 ft. lbs Long bolts 75 ft. lbs.

⑨—Aluminum Head–60 ft. lbs.

⑩—For 3/8″ bolts 45 ft.-lbs.; for 11/32″ bolts 35 ft.-lbs.

PISTONS, PINS, RINGS, CRANKSHAFT & BEARINGS

Year	Engine Model	Piston Clearance	Ring End Gap ①		Wrist-pin Diam-eter	Rod Bearings		Main Bearings			
			Comp.	Oil		Shaft Diameter	Bearing Clearance	Shaft Diameter	Bearing Clearance	Thrust on Bear. No.	Shaft End Play
1963–67	4-153	.0005–.0011	.010	.015	.927	1.999–2.000	.0007–.0027	2.2983–2.2993	.0003–.0029	5	.002–.006
1968	4-153	.0005–.0011	.010	.015	.927	1.999–2.000	.0007–.0027	2.3004	.0003–.0029	5	.002–.006
1969	4-153	.0005–.0015	.010	.015	.927	1.999–2.000	.0007–.0027	2.983 –2.993	.0003–.0029	5	.002–.006
1963–67	6-194	.0005–.0011	.010	.015	.927	1.999–2.000	.0007–.0027	2.2983–2.2993	.0003–.0029	7	.002–.006
1963–67	6-230	.0005–.0011	.010	.015	.927	1.999–2.000	.0007–.0027	2.2983–2.2993	.0003–.0029	7	.002–.006
1968	6-230	.0005–.0011	.010	.015	.927	1.999–2.000	.0007–.0027	2.3004	.0003–.0029	7	.002–.006
1966–67	6-250	.0005–.0011	.010	.015	.927	1.999–2.000	.0007–.0027	2.2983–2.2993	.0003–.0029	7	.002–.006
1968	6-250	.0005–.0011	.010	.015	.927	1.999–2.000	.0007–.0027	2.3004	.0003–.0029	7	.002–.006
1969	6-230, 250	.0005–.0015	.010	.015	.927	1.999–2.000	.0007–.0027	2.983 –2.993	.0003–.0029	7	.002–.006
1963–67	8-283	.0005–.0011	.010	.015	.927	1.999–2.000	.0007–.0027	⑨	.0003–.0029	5	.003–.011
1967	8-302	.0024–.0030	.013	.015	.927	1.999–2.000	.0007–.0028	2.2984–2.2993	.0008–.0030	5	.003–.011
1969	8-302	.0024–.0030	.013	.015	.927	1.999–2.000	.0007–.0028	2.4479–2.4488	.0008–.0030	5	.003–.011
1968	8-307	.0005–.0011	.010	.015	.927	2.099–2.100	.0007–.0027	⑫	.004 Max.	5	.002–.006
1969	8-307	.0005–.0011	.010	.015	.927	2.099–2.100	.0007–.0027	2.4479–2.4488	.0008–.0020	5	.003–.011
1963–67	8-327⑤	.0005–.0011	.013	.015	.927	1.999–2.000	.0007–.0027	⑨	.004 Max.	5	.003–.011
1965–67	8-327⑥	.0024–.0030	.010	.015	.927	1.999–2.000	.0007–.0027	⑨	.004 Max.	5	.003–.011
1968	8-327⑬	.0005–.0011	.013	.015	.927	2.099–2.100	.0007–.0028	⑫	.004 Max.	5	.003–.011
1968	8-327⑭	.0024–.0030	.010	.015	.927	2.099–2.100	.0007–.0028	⑫	.004 Max.	5	.002–.006
1969	8-327	.0005–.0011	.013	.015	.927	2.099–2.100	.0007–.0028	2.4479–2.4488	.0008–.0020	5	.003–.011
1967	8-350	.0005–.0011	.010	.015	.927	2.099–2.100	.0007–.0028	⑮	.004 Max.	5	.003–.011
1968	8-350	.0007–.0013	.010	.015	.927	2.099–2.100	.0007–.0028	⑫	.004 Max.	5	.002–.006
1965	8-396⑧	.0027–.0033	.010	.010	.989	2.199–2.200	.0009–.0029	⑩	.004 Max.	5	.006–.010
1965–67	8-396⑦	.0007–.0013	.010	.010	.989	2.199–2.200	.0009–.0029	⑩	.004 Max.	5	.006–.010
1968	8-396	.0010–.0016	.010	.015	.989	2.199–2.200	.0009–.0029	③	.004 Max.	5	.006–.010
1969	8-396⑰	.001–.0018	.010	.010	.989	2.199–2.200	.0009–.0025	⑲	.004 Max.	5	.006–.010
	8-396⑱	.0036–.0044	.010	.010	.989	2.198–2.199	.0014–.003	④	.004 Max.	5	.006–.010
1966	8-427⑦	.0009–.0015	.010	.010	.989	2.199–2.200	.0009–.0029	⑩	.004 Max.	5	.006–.010
	8-427⑧	.0037–.0043	.010	.010	.989	2.199–2.200	.0009–.0029	⑩	.004 Max.	5	.006–.010
1967	8-427⑧	.0054–.0053	.010	.010	.989	2.199–2.200	.0009–.0029	⑩	.004 Max.	5	.006–.010
	8-427⑪	.0037–.0043	.010	.010	.989	2.199–2.200	.0009–.0029	⑩	.004 Max.	5	.006–.010
1968	8-427⑯	.0012–.0018	.010	.010	.989	2.199–2.200	.0009–.0029	③	.004 Max.	5	.006–.010
	8-427⑪	.0040–.0046	.010	.010	.989	2.199–2.200	.0014–.0034	③	.004 Max.	5	.006–.010
1969	8-427⑳	.0012–.002	.010	.010	.989	2.199–2.200	.0009–.0025	㉑	.004 Max.	5	.006–.010
	8-427㉒	.0037–.0043	.010	.010	.989	2.1985–2.1995	.0014–.003	㉑	.004 Max.	5	.006–.010
	8-427㉓	.0058–.0066	.010	.010	.989	2.1985–2.1995	.0014–.003	㉑	.004 Max.	5	.006–.010
	8-427㉔	.004–.0048	.010	.010	.989	2.1985 2.1995	.0014–.003	㉑	.004 Max.	5	.006–.010

①—Fit rings in tapered bores to the clearance listed in tightest portion of ring travel.

③—No. 1–2: 2.7507
No. 3–4: 2.7505
No. 5: 2.7506

④—1: 2.7484–2.7493
2, 3 & 4: 2.7481–2.7490
5: 2.7478–2.7488

⑤—With 2 bar. carb.

⑥—With 4 bar. carb.

⑦—Except 425 H.P.

⑧—425 H.P.

⑨—Front: 2.2984–2.2993
Rear: 2.2978–2.2988
Others: 2.2983–2.2993

⑩—1 & 2: 2.7487–2.7497
3 & 4: 2.7482–2.7492
5: 2.7478–2.7488

⑪—435 H.P.

⑫—Front: 2.4502
Rear: 2.4507
Others: 2.4505

⑬—Except 325 H.P.

⑭—325 H.P.

⑮—Rear: 2.4478–2.4488
Others: 2.4483–2.4493

⑯—385, 390, 400 H.P.

⑰—Except 375 H.P.

⑱—375 H.P.

⑲—1 & 2: 2.7484–2.7493
3 & 4: 2.7481–2.7490
5: 2.7478–2.7488

⑳—335, 390, 400 H.P.

㉑—1, 2, 3 & 4: 2.7481–2.7490
5: 2.7478–2.7488

㉒—425 H.P.

㉓—430 H.P.

㉔—435 H.P.

WHEEL ALIGNMENT SPECIFICATIONS

OLD CAR SPECIFICATIONS: For 1946-62 Wheel Alignment Specifications see back of book.

Year	Model	Caster Angle, Degrees		Camber Angle, Degrees				Toe-In. Inch	Toe-Out on Turns, Deg.①	
		Limits	Desired	Limits Left	Limits Right	Desired Left	Desired Right		Outer Wheel	Inner Wheel
CAMARO										
1967	All	0 to +1	+½	—¼ to +½	—¼ to +½	+¼	+¼	⅛ to ¼	—	—
1968-69	All	0 to +1	+½	—¼ to +¾	—¼ to +¾	+½	+½	⅛ to ¼	—	20
CHEVELLE										
1964	All	—½ to —1½	—1	+¼ to +1¼	+¼ to +1¼	+¾	+¾	1/16 to 3/16	18¾	20
1965-66	Super Sport	0 to —½	—½	0 to +1	0 to +1	+½	+½	⅛ to ¼	18.4	20
	Others	—½ to —1½	—1	0 to +1	0 to +1	+½	+½	⅛ to ¼	18.4	20
1967-69	Super Sport	—1 to 0	—½	0 to +1	0 to +1	+½	+½	⅛ to ¼	18.4	20
	Others	—1½ to —½	—1	0 to +1	0 to +1	+½	+½	⅛ to ¼	18.4	20
CHEVY II										
1963-64	All	+½ to +1½	+1	0 to +1	0 to +1	+½	+½	3/16 to 5/16	18½	20
1965-67	All	+½ to +1½	+1	0 to +1	0 to +1	+½	+½	¼ to ⅜	18.7	20
1968-69	All	0 to +1	+½	—¼ to +¾	—¼ to +¾	+½	+½	⅛ to ¼	—	20
CHEVROLET										
1963	All	—½ to +½	0	0 to +1	0 to +1	+½	+½	1/16 to 3/16	18	20
1964	All	—½ to +½	0	0 to +1	0 to +1	+½	+½	1/32 to 3/32	18	20
1965-69	All	+¼ to +1¼	+¾	—¼ to +¾	—¼ to +¾	+¼	+¼	⅛ to ¼	20	20½
CORVETTE										
1963-64	All	0 to +1	+½	+2 to +3	+2 to +3	+2½	+2½	3/16 to 5/16	18	20
1965	All	+1 to +2	+1½	+¼ to +1¼	+¼ to +1¼	+¾	+¾	7/32 to 11/32	18½	20
1966-67	All	+½ to +1½	+1	+¼ to +1¼	+¼ to +1¼	+¾	+¾	3/16 to 5/16	18½	20
1968	Manual Steer.	+½ to +1½	+1	+¼ to +1¼	+¼ to +1¼	+¾	+¾	3/16 to 5/16	—	20
	Power Steer.	+1¾ to +2¾	+2¼	+¼ to +1¼	+¼ to +1¼	+¾	+¾	3/16 to 5/16	—	20
	Rear Wheel Align.	—	—	—⅜ to —1⅜	—⅜ to —1⅜	—¾	—¾	1/32 to 3/32	—	—
1969	Manual Steer.	+½ to +1½	+1	+¼ to +1¼	+¼ to +1¼	+¾	+¾	3/16 to 5/16	—	20
	Power Steer.	+1¾ to +2¾	+2¼	+¼ to +1¼	+¼ to +1¼	+¾	+¾	3/16 to 5/16	—	20
	Rear Wheel Align.	—	—	—⅜ to —1⅜	—⅜ to —1⅜	—⅞	—⅞	1/32 to 3/32	—	—

①—Incorrect toe-out, when other adjustments are correct, indicates bent steering arms.

COOLING SYSTEM & CAPACITY DATA

Year	Model or Engine	Cooling Capacity, Qts.			Radiator Cap Relief Pressure, Lbs.		Thermo. Opening Temp. ①	Fuel Tank Gals.	Engine Oil Refill Qts. ②	Transmission Oil			Rear Axle Oil Pints
		No Heater	With Heater	With A/C	With A/C	No A/C				3 Speed Pints	4 Speed Pints	Auto. Trans. Qts. ⑮	
CAMARO													
1967	6-230, 250	10	11	11	15	15	195	18	4	3	3	⑥	3½
	V8-327	14	16	16	15	15	180	18	4	3	3	⑫	4
	V8-350	15	16	16	15	15	180	18	4	3½	3	⑫	4
1968	6-230, 250	11	12	12	15	15	195	18	4	3	3	⑥	3½
	8-327	15	16	16	15	15	195	18	4	3	3	⑥	3½
	8-350	14	15	16	15	15	195	18	4	3⑧	3	⑥	3½
	8-396	22	23	23	15	15	195	18	4	3⑧	3	⑭	3½

Continued

COOLING SYSTEM & CAPACITY DATA—Continued

Year	Model or Engine	Cooling Capacity, Qts.			Radiator Cap Relief Pressure, Lbs.		Thermo. Opening Temp. (1)	Fuel Tank Gals.	Engine Oil Refill Qts. (2)	Transmission Oil			Rear Axle Oil Pints
		No Heater	With Heater	With A/C	With A/C	No A/C				3 Speed Pints	4 Speed Pints	Auto. Trans. Qts. (15)	
CAMARO—Continued													
1969	6-230, 250	11	13	13	15	15	195	18	4	3(8)	3	(19)	3½
	8-327	16	17	17	15	15	195	18	4	3(8)	3	(19)	3½
	8-350	15	16	17	15	15	195	18	4	3(8)	3	(19)	3½
	8-396	22	23	23	15	15	195	18	4	3(8)	3	(19)	4
CHEVELLE													
1964	6-194	10½	12	12	15	13	180	20	4	2	...	(4)	3½
	6-230	10½	12	12	15	13	180	20	4	2	...	(4)	3½
	V8-283	16	17	17	15	13	180	20	4	2	2½	(5)	3½
	V8-327, 250 H.P.	15	16	16	15	13	180	20	4	2	2½	(5)	3½
	V8-327, 300 H.P.	17	18	18	15	13	180	20	4	2	2½	(5)	3½
1965	6-194	10	11	11	15	13	180	20	4	2	2½	(4)	3½
	6-230	11	12	12	15	13	180	20	4	2	2½	(4)	3½
	V8-283	16	17	17	15	13	180	20	4	2	2½	(5)	3½
	V8-327, 250 H.P.	15	16	16	15	13	180	20	4	2	2½	(5)	4
	V8-327, 300 H.P.	15	16	16	15	13	180	20	4	2	2½	(5)	4
	V8-327, 350 H.P.	17	18	18	15	13	180	20	4	2	2½	(5)	4
1966	6-194	11	12	12	15	15	180	20	4	2	2½	(4)	3½
	6-230	11	12	12	15	15	180	20	4	2	2½	(4)	3½
	8-283	15	16	17	15	15	180	20	4	2	2½	(5)	3½
	8-327	14	15	16	15	15	180	20	4	2	2½	(5)	4
	8-396	22	23	24	15	15	180	20	4	2	2½	(13)	4
1967	6-230, 250	10	11	11	15	15	195	20	4	3	3	(6)	3½
	V8-283	15	16	16	15	15	180	20	4	3	3	(6)	4
	V8-327	15	16	16	15	15	180	20	4	3	3	(12)	4
	V8-396	21	23	23	15	15	180	20	4	3	3	(13)	4
1968	6-230, 250	11	12	12	15	15	195	20	4	3	3	(6)	3½
	8-307	16	17	18	15	15	195	20	4	3(8)	3	(6)	3½
	8-327, 275 H.P.	15	16	17	15	15	195	20	4	3(8)	3	(13)	4
	8-327, 325 H.P.	16	17	17	15	15	195	20	4	3(8)	3	(13)	4
	8-396	23	24	24	15	15	195	20	4	3(8)	3	(13)	4
1969	6-230, 250	11	13	13	15	15	195	20(20)	4	3(8)	3	(19)	3½
	8-307	16	17	18	15	15	195	20(20)	4	3(8)	3	(19)	3½
	8 350	15	16	17	15	15	195	20(20)	4	3(8)	3	(19)	4
	8-396	22	23	23	15	15	195	21(20)	4	3(8)	3	(19)	4
CHEVY II													
1963	4-153	(8)	9	9	15	13	180	16	3½(11)	2	...	(4)	4
	6-194	(11)	12	12	15	13	180	16	4	2	...	(4)	4
1964	4-153	8	9	9	15	13	180	16	3½(11)	2	...	(4)	3½
	6-194	10½	12	12	15	13	180	16	4	2	...	(4)	3½
	6-230	10½	12	12	15	13	180	16	4	2	...	(4)	3½
	V8-283	16	17	17	15	13	180	16	4	2	...	(4)	3½
1965	4-153	8	9	9	15	13	180	16	3½(11)	2	2½	(5)	3½
	6-194	10	11	11	15	13	180	16	4	2	2½	(4)	3½
	6-230	11	12	12	15	13	180	16	4	2	2½	(4)	3½
	V8-283	16	17	17	15	13	180	16	4	2	2½	(4)	3½
	V8-327	16	17	17	15	13	180	16	4	2	2½	(5)	3½
1966	4-153	8	9	9	15	15	180	16	3½(11)	2	2½	(5)	4
	6-194	11	12	12	15	15	180	16	4	2	...	(4)	3½
	6-230	11	12	12	15	15	180	16	4	2	...	(4)	3½
	8-283	15	16	17	15	15	180	16	4	2	...	(4)	3½
	8-327, 275 H.P.	14	15	16	15	15	180	16	4	2	2½	(5)	3½
	8-327, 350 H.P.	15	16	17	15	15	180	16	4	2	2½	(5)	3½

Continued

COOLING SYSTEM & CAPACITY DATA—Continued

Year	Model or Engine	Cooling Capacity, Qts.			Radiator Cap Relief Pressure, Lbs.		Thermo. Opening Temp. ①	Fuel Tank Gals.	Engine Oil Refill Qts. ②	Transmission Oil			Rear Axle Oil Pints
		No Heater	With Heater	With A/C	With A/C	No A/C				3 Speed Pints	4 Speed Pints	Auto. Trans. Qts. ⑮	
CHEVY II—Continued													
1967	4-153	8	9	9	15	15	195	16	3½⑪	3	3	⑥	3½
	6-194, 250	10	11	11	15	15	195	16	4	3	3	⑥	3½
	V8–283	15	16	16	15	15	180	16	4	3	3	⑥	4
	V8-327	15	16	16	15	15	180	16	4	3	3	⑫	4
1968	4-153	8	9	9	15	15	195	18	4	3	—	⑥	3½
	6-230, 250	11	12	12	15	15	195	18	4	3	—	⑥	3½
	8-307	16	17	17	15	15	195	18	4	3	3	⑥	3½
	8-327, 350	15	16	16	15	15	195	18	4	3⑧	4	⑥	3½
1969	4-153	8	9	9	15	15	195	18	4	3⑧	—	⑲	3½
	6-230, 250	11	13	13	15	15	195	18	4	3⑧	—	⑲	3½
	8-307	16	17	17	15	15	195	18	4	3⑧	3	⑲	3½
	8-350	15	16	16	15	15	195	18	4	3½	3	⑲	4
	8-396	22	23	23	15	15	195	18	4	3½	3	⑲	4
CHEVROLET													
1963	6-230	11	12	12	15	13	180	20⑩	4	2⑭	...	⑯	4
	V8-283	17½	18½	18½	15	13	180	20⑩	4	2⑭	2½	⑰	4
	V8-327	17½	18½	18½	15	13	180	20⑩	4	2⑭	2½	⑰	4
	V8-409	21	18½	18½	15	13	180	20⑩	5	2⑭	2½	⑰	4
1964	6-230	11	12	12	15	13	180	20⑩	4	2⑭	...	⑯	4
	V8-283	17½	18½	18½	15	13	180	20⑩	4	2⑭	2½	⑰	4
	V8-327	17½	18½	18½	15	13	180	20⑩	4	2	2½	⑰	4
	V8-409	21	22	22	15	13	180	20⑩	5	2	2½	⑰	4
1965	6-230	11	12	12	15	13	180	20⑦	4	2	2½	④	4
	V8-283	16	17	17	15	13	180	20⑦	4	2	2½	⑤	4
	V8-327, 250 H.P.	15	16	16	15	13	180	20⑦	4	2	2½	⑤	4
	V8-327, 300 H.P.	17	18	18	15	13	180	20⑦	4	2	2½	⑤	4
	V8-396, 325 H.P.	22	23	23	15	15	180	20⑦	4	2½	2½	...	4
	V8-396, 425 H.P.	23	24	24	15	15	180	20⑦	4	2½	2½	...	4
	V8-409	21	22	22	15	13	180	20⑦	5	2½	2½	⑤	4
1966	6-250	12	13	14	15	15	180	20⑦	4	2	...	⑯	3½
	8-283	16	17	18	15	15	180	20⑦	4	2	2½	⑯	3½
	8-327	14	15	16	15	15	180	20⑦	4	2	2½	⑤	4
	8-396, 325 H.P.	22	23	23	15	15	180	20⑦	4	2	2½	⑬	4
	8-396, 390 H.P.	21	22	22	15	15	180	20⑦	4	2	2½	⑬	4
	8-427, 425 H.P.	22	23	23	15	15	180	20⑦	4	2	2½	⑭	4
1967	6-250	11	12	12	15	15	195	24	4	3	—	⑯	3½
	V8-283	16	17	17	15	15	180	24	4	3	3	⑯	4
	V8-327	14	15	15	15	15	180	24	4	3	3	⑫	4
	V8-396	21	22	22	15	15	180	24	4	3½	3	⑬	4
	V8-427	21	22	22	15	15	180	24	4	3½	3	⑭	4
1968	6-250	11	12	13	15	15	195	24	4	3	—	⑥	3½
	8-307	16	17	18	15	15	195	24	4	3	3	⑬	3½
	8-327	14	15	16	15	15	195	24	4	3	3	⑬	3½
	8-396, 427	21	22	22	15	15	195	24	4	3⑧	3	⑬	3½
1969	6–250	11	12	13	15	15	195	24	4	3⑧	—	⑲	3½
	8–327	16	17	18	15	15	195	24	4	3⑧	3	⑲	3½
	8–350	14	15	16	15	15	195	24	4	3½	3	⑲	4
	8-396	22	23	23	15	15	195	24	4	3½	3	⑲	4
	8-427	21	22	22	15	15	195	24	4	3½	3	⑲	4

Continued

COOLING SYSTEM & CAPACITY DATA—Continued

Year	Model or Engine	Cooling Capacity, Qts.			Radiator Cap Relief Pressure, Lbs.		Thermo. Opening Temp. ①	Fuel Tank Gals.	Engine Oil Refill Qts. ②	Transmission Oil			Rear Axle Oil Pints
		No Heater	With Heater	With A/C	With A/C	No A/C				3 Speed Pints	4 Speed Pints	Auto. Trans Qts. ⑮	
CORVETTE													
1963	250, 300 H.P.	15½	16½	16½	15	13	180	20⑱	4	2	2½	③	4
	340, 360 H.P.	15½	16½	16½	15	13	180	20⑱	5	2	2½	③	4
1964	Standard Engine	18	19	19	15	13	180	20⑱	4	2	2½	③	4
	Hi. Perf. Engine	18	19	19	15	13	180	20⑱	5	2	2½	③	4
1965	8-327, 250, 300 H.P.	18	19	19	15	15	180	20⑱	4	2	2½	⑤	3.7
	8-327, 350, 365 H.P.	18	19	19	15	15	180	20⑱	5	2	2½	⑤	3.7
	8-327, 375 H.P.	18	19	19	15	15	180	20⑱	5	2	2½	⑤	3.7
	8-396, 425 H.P.	21	22	22	15	15	180	20⑱	5	..	2½	..	3.7
1966	8-327, 300 H.P.	15	16	16	15	15	180	20⑱	4	2	2½	⑤	3.7
	8-327, 350 H.P.	15	16	16	15	15	180	20⑱	5	...	2½	...	3.7
	8-427, 425 H.P.	22	23	23	15	15	180	20⑱	5	...	2½	...	3.7
1967	V8-327—300 H.P.	15	16	16	15	15	180	20⑱	4	2		⑫	4
	V8-327—350 H.P.	15	16	16	15	15	180	20⑱	5	2	3	⑫	4
	V8-427	22	23	23	15	15	180	20⑱	5	2	3	⑫	4
1968	8-327	14	15	15	15	15	195	20	4	3	3	⑭	3.7
	8-427	21	22	22	15	15	195	20	5	3	3	⑭	3.7
1969	8-350	14	15	15	15	15	195	20	4	3	3	㉑	4
	8-427	21	22	22	15	15	195	20	5	3	3	㉑	4

①—For permanent type anti-freeze.
②—Add one quart with filter change.
③—Refill 1¾ qts. Total capacity 10½ qts.
④—Refill 1½ qts. Total capacity 7½ qts.
⑤—Refill 1½ qts. Total capacity 9 qts.
⑥—Refill 1½ qts. Total capacity 8½ qts.
⑦—Wagons 24 gallons.
⑧—Heavy duty unit 3½.
⑩—Wagons 19 gallons.
⑪—Add one pint with filter change.
⑫—Refill 1½ qts. Total capacity 9½ qts.
⑬—Powerglide see ⑫. Turbo Hydramatic see ⑭.
⑭—Refill 2 qts. Total capacity 13 qts.
⑮—Approximate. Make final check with dipstick.
⑯—Refill 1½ qts. Total capacity 8¾ qts.
⑰—Refill 1½ qts. Total capacity 10 qts.
⑱—36 gallon tank also available.
⑲—Powerglide & Torque Drive: Refill 3 qts. Total capacity 8½ qts. Turbo-Hydramatic 350: Refill 2½ qts. Total capacity 10 qts. Turbo-Hydramatic 400: Refill 4 qts. Total capacity 11 qts.
⑳—Wagons 22 gallons.
㉑—Refill 4 qts. Total capacity 11 qts.

BRAKE SPECIFICATIONS

Year	Model	Brake Drum Inside Diameter	Wheel Cylinder Bore Diameter			Master Cylinder Bore Diameter		
			Disc Brake	Front Drum Brake	Rear Drum Brake	Disc Brakes	Drum Brakes	Power Brakes
1963	Chevrolet, Corvette	11	—	1³⁄₁₆	1	—	1	1
	Chevy II	9	—	1	⅞	—	1①	1
1964	Chevy II	9½	—	1¹⁄₁₆	⅞	—	1①	1
	Chevelle	9½	—	1⅛	¹⁵⁄₁₆	—	1①	1
	Chevrolet, Corvette	11	—	1³⁄₁₆	1	—	1①	1
1965–67	Chevy II	9½	—	1¹⁄₁₆	⅞	—	1①	1
	Chevelle	9½	—	1⅛	¹⁵⁄₁₆	—	1①	1
	Chevrolet	11	—	1³⁄₁₆	1	—	1①	1
	Corvette	11¾	1⅞	—	1⅜	1	1	1
	Camaro	9½	—	1⅛	¹⁵⁄₁₆	—	1	1

Continued

BRAKE SPECIFICATIONS—Continued

Year	Model	Brake Drum Inside Diameter	Wheel Cylinder Bore Diameter			Master Cylinder Bore Diameter		
			Disc Brake	Front Drum Brake	Rear Drum Brake	Disc Brakes	Drum Brakes	Power Brakes
1968–69	Camaro	9½	2 1/16④	1⅛	⅞	—	1	1
	Chevelle	9½	2 1/16	1⅛	②	1⅛	1⑤	1
	Chevy II	9½	2 1/16	1⅛	⅞	—	1⑤	1
	Chevrolet	11	2 1/16	1 3/16	1	1	1⑤	1
	Corvette	—	③	—	—	1	—	1

①—⅞" with metallic linings.
②—1968 15/16; 1969 ⅞.
③—Front 1⅞; Rear 1⅜.
④—Front discs only. For 4 wheel disc option, see Corvette.
⑤—1968, ⅞ with metallic linings.

Electrical Section

IGNITION TIMING

If a timing light is to be used to set ignition timing, disconnect the vacuum advance pipe to the carburetor and place a piece of tape over open end of pipe. *This is important as carburetor trouble can affect timing adjustments.*

Lacking a power timing light, an accurate method of setting ignition timing with the engine stopped is with the aid of a jumper light. Be sure to use a light bulb that corresponds with the system voltage of the vehicle.

1. Remove distributor cap and rotor and see that the breaker gap is set according to specifications.
2. Rotate engine until No. 1 cylinder is at the ignition timing point as indicated by the timing pointer and timing mark being lined up with each other.
3. Connect the jumper light between distributor ignition terminal and ground.
4. Turn on ignition switch.
5. Loosen distributor and turn it in the direction of normal rotation until the points just close (light out). Then slowly turn distributor in the opposite direction just to the exact point that the light goes on. Tighten distributor in this position.

DISTRIBUTOR

Removal

1. Disconnect distributor primary wire from coil terminal.
2. Remove distributor cap and rotor. *Mark position of rotor arm on distributor housing so distributor can be installed in same position.*
3. Remove vacuum line and distributor hold-down clamp.
4. Note relative position of distributor in block, then work it out of the engine.

Installation

1. Turn rotor about ⅛ of a turn counterclockwise past the mark previously placed on the distributor housing.
2. Push the distributor down into the block with the housing in the normal "installed" position. *It may be necessary to move the rotor slightly to start gear into mesh with camshaft gear, but rotor should line up with mark when distributor is down in place.*
3. Tighten distributor clamp screw snugly and connect vacuum line, primary wire to coil, and install cap.

NOTE

If the engine was disturbed while the distributor was removed from the engine, first crank the engine to bring No. 1 piston up on its compression stroke and continue cranking until the timing mark is adjacent to the timing indicator. Then rotate the distributor cam until the rotor is in position to fire No. 1 cylinder. Install the distributor and set the ignition timing.

STARTER, REPLACE

1965-69 All Models

1. Disconnect ground cable at battery.
2. Raise vehicle to working height.
3. Disconnect all wires at solenoid.

NOTE: Reinstall terminal nuts as each wire is disconnected as thread size is different but may be mixed and stripped.

4. Loosen starter front bracket (nut on V8 and bolt on Sixes) then remove two mounting bolts. *On 1968 Chevelle V8 with single exhaust, it is necessary to disconnect and lower the exhaust crossover pipe.*
5. Remove front bracket bolt or nut and rotate bracket clear of work area. Then lower starter from vehicle by lowering front end first (hold starter against bell housing and sort of roll end-over end.
6. Reverse removal procedure to install and torque mount bolts to 25-35 ft-lbs.

1964 Chevelle

1. Disconnect ground cable at battery.
2. Observe and record color coding of solenoid wiring connections for installation purposes, then disconnect all wires at solenoid terminals.

NOTE: It is a good idea to reinstall the nuts as each wire is disconnected as thread size is different but may be mixed and stripped.

3. Loosen starter front bracket (nut on V8, bolt on 6-cyl.), then remove two mount bolts.
4. Remove front bracket bolt or nut and rotate bracket clear of work area, then lower starter from vehicle by lowering front end first. Hold starter against flywheel housing and sort of roll it end-over-end.
5. Reverse removal procedure to install.

1964 Chevy II

1. Disconnect ground cable at battery.
2. Disconnect all wiring at solenoid.

NOTE: It is a good idea to reinstall terminal nuts as each lead is disconnected. They are different thread size but could get mixed up.

3. Remove starter front hanger bracket nut and loosen bolt at block end of bracket (leave bracket in place over stud).
4. Remove two mount bolts while supporting starter, then slide front bracket from starter stud and remove starter from vehicle.

NOTE: When installing starter, hang starter on front bracket first which will ease supporting and aligning starter while installing mounting bolts.

1963 Chevy II & Chevrolet 6

1. Disconnect lead wires from S, R, and battery terminals. Observe and record color coding of lead wires to insure proper reinstallation.
2. Remove starter pad mounting bolts. Remove stud nut at front of motor and rotate bracket out of the way.
3. Pull starter forward to clear housing and remove from engine.

Chevrolet 1963-64 V8's

1. Disconnect battery ground strap and remove cable from fender clip.
2. Unplug starter motor harness dash connector.
3. Unfasten starter from its mounting.
4. Pull starter forward to clear housing and carefully lower it.

IGNITION SWITCH, REPLACE

1969

The ignition switch is mounted on top of the mast jacket inside the brake pedal support and is actuated by a rod and rack assembly.

1. Disconnect battery cable.
2. Disconnect and lower steering column.
3. The switch should be in the "Lock" position before removal. If lock cylinder has been removed, the actuating rod is pulled up to the stop then back one detent, to place it in the "Lock" position. Remove retaining screws and switch.
4. Reverse procedure to install being sure that the switch is in the "Lock" position before installing.

1968 Except Corvette

1. Disconnect battery ground cable.
2. On Chevelle and Chevy II, remove ash tray and retainer. Remove radio knobs, nuts, connectors, bracket and radio.

NOTE: On Chevy II, the radio does not have to be removed. Access can be gained by removing the ash tray only.

3. On all models, remove lock cylinder by positioning in "ACC" position and inserting a wire in small hole in cylinder face. Push in on wire to depress plunger and continue turning key counter-clockwise until lock cylinder can be removed.
4. Remove switch bezel nut and pull switch out from under dash.
5. Using a screwdriver, unsnap the "theft resistant" locking tangs on the connector from the position on the switch shown in Fig. 1. Unplug the connector.
6. Reverse procedure to install.

1968 Corvette

With Air Conditioning

1. Disconnect battery ground cable.
2. Remove screws securing mast jacket trim covers and remove covers.

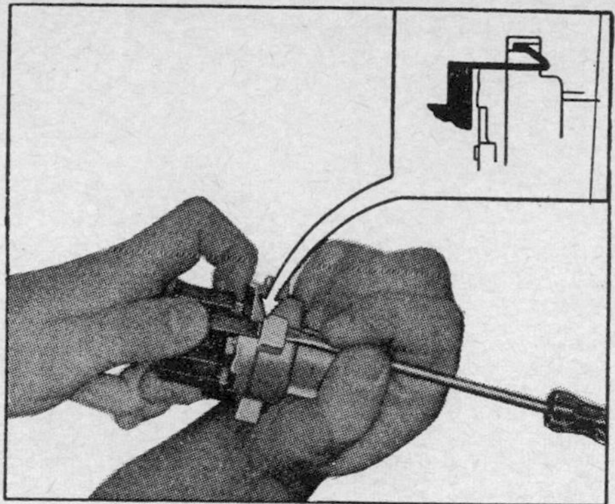

Fig. 1 Unlocking ignition switch connector. 1964-68

3. Remove left side console forward trim panel.
4. Lower steering column.
5. Remove screws securing left instrument panel to door opening, top of dash and left side of center instrument panel.
6. Pull cluster assembly down and tip forward for access to switch.
7. Remove switch as outlined above for other 1968 models.

Less Air Conditioning

1. Disconnect battery cable.
2. Remove screws securing "Corvette" cover plate in top center of cluster.
3. Remove switch as outlined above for other 1968 models.

1966-67 Chevelle

1. Disconnect battery ground cable.
2. Remove ash tray and retainer
3. Remove A/C distributor duct.
4. Unfasten and push A/C and/or heater control panel from console. *If interference between control panel and radio is encountered, loosen radio retaining nuts.*
5. Remove radio knobs, bezels and nuts.
6. Disconnect wiring harness and antenna lead-in.
7. Remove radio rear brace attaching screw and remove radio from vehicle.
8. Remove ignition switch bezel nut and push switch rearward from panel opening. Disconnect wiring connector from rear of switch

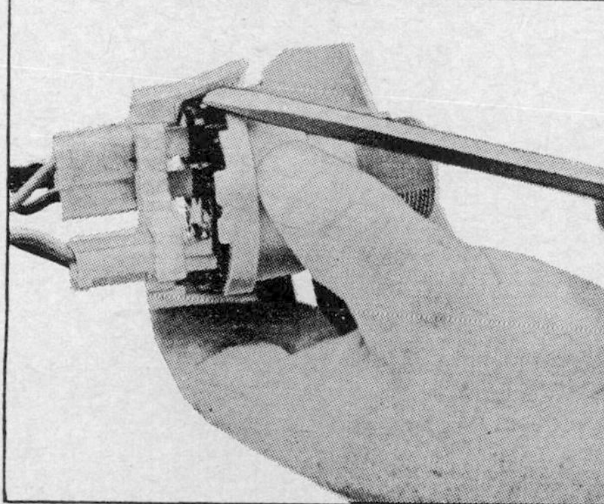

Fig. 2 Unlocking ignition switch connector. 1963 All cars

9. Reverse removal procedure to install.

1963-67 Except '66 Chevelle

1. Disconnect battery ground cable.
2. Remove lock cylinder by positioning switch in "off" position and inserting a paper clip in small hole in cylinder face.
3. Push in on wire to depress plunger and continue to turn ignition key counter-clockwise until lock cylinder can be removed.
4. Remove switch nut from passenger side of dash.
5. Pull switch out from under dash and remove wiring connectors.

NOTE: To remove "theft resistant" connector, use a screwdriver to unsnap the locking tangs on the connector from their position on the switch, Figs. 1 and 2. Then unplug the connector.

6. Reverse above procedure to install.

LIGHT SWITCH, REPLACE

1968-69 Corvette

1. Disconnect battery cable.
2. Remove screws securing mast jacket trim covers and remove covers.
3. Remove left side console forward trim panel.
4. Lower steering column.
5. Remove screws securing left instrument panel to door opening, top of dash and left side of center instrument panel.
6. Pull cluster down and tip forward for access.
7. Depress switch shaft retainer and remove the knob and shaft assembly. Remove switch retaining bezel.
8. Disconnect vacuum hoses from switch, tagging them for assembly. Pry the connector from the switch and remove the switch.

1968-69 Except Corvette

1. Disconnect battery ground cable.

NOTE: On Chevy II remove the parking brake bracket and lower assembly to the floor. Heater or air conditioning control head must also be removed.

2. Pull switch knob to "ON" position.
3. Reach up under instrument panel and depress switch shaft retainer, then remove knob and shaft assembly.
4. Remove ferrule nut and switch from panel.

NOTE: Remove vacuum hoses from Camaro and Chevrolet optional headlight switches. Tag location of hoses for assembly.

5. Disconnect multi-contact connector from light switch.
6. Reverse procedure to install.

1963-67 All Cars

1. Disconnect battery ground cable.

2. Pull control knob to headlight "ON" position.
3. Reach under instrument panel and depress switch shaft retainer and remove knob and shaft assembly.
4. Remove retaining ferrule and bezel.
5. Remove switch from panel.
6. Disconnect multi-plug connector from lighting switch.
7. Reverse above procedure to install.

STOP LIGHT SWITCH, REPLACE

1968-69

1. Disconnect wiring harness connector from switch.
2. Remove retaining nut (if equipped) and unscrew switch from bracket.

NOTE: On Corvettes, remove screw holding switch bracket to brake pedal housing.

3. On Chevelles, depress brake pedal and push new switch into clip until shoulder bottoms out.
4. On Corvettes, align switch bracket on brake pedal housing and install screw.
5. On all other models, install inboard adjusting nut, install switch through bracket and install retaining nut.
6. Plug connector onto switch.

1963-66 Chevrolet, Chevy II & Corvette

1. From under instrument panel adjacent to brake pedal, disconnect two connectors from switch.
2. Remove lock nut from plunger end of switch and remove switch.
3. Locate new switch in same position on mounting bracket or brace and install connectors to switch.
4. Adjust switch position. Electrical contact should be made when brake pedal is depressed ⅜" to ½" from fully released position.

1964-66 Chevelle & All 1967

1. Disengage retaining fingers, disconnect wiring harness connector from switch and unscrew switch from its mounting clip.
2. Depress brake pedal and push new switch into clip until shoulder bottoms out against clip.
3. Check switch for proper position. Electrical contact should be made when brake pedal is depressed ⅜" to ⅝" from fully released position.

NEUTRAL SAFETY SWITCH, REPLACE

1969 Clutch Operated Switch

1. Unplug connector from switch.
2. Remove retainer from pins or link on clutch pedal arm.
3. Remove retaining screw and switch.

1964-69 Column Shift

1. Disconnect wiring connectors at switch terminals.
2. Unfasten and remove switch from mast jacket.
3. To install, locate shift lever in "Drive" and locate lever tang against transmission selector plate.
4. If provided for, align slot in contact support with hole in switch and insert a $\frac{3}{32}$" rod to hold support in place. Switch is now in drive position.
5. Place contact support drive slot over shifter tube drive tang and tighten screws. Remove clamp and $\frac{3}{32}$" rod.
6. Connect wiring harness and check operation of switch.

1966-68 Floor Shift Except Corvette

1. Position shift lever in "Drive" position. Remove ash tray, trim plate, and indicator lens and housing from console.
2. Disconnect bulbs from housing. Disconnect multiple connector at switch terminals (on Camaro models from wiring harness at the in-line connector).
3. Remove retaining nuts and switch.
4. To install new switch, clamp pawl rod against contact point of detent and align slot in contact support with drive hole in switch. Insert a $\frac{3}{32}$" rod to hold in place. Switch is now in drive position.
5. Position switch to lever and bracket assembly with lever engaged in contact support and install retaining nuts.
6. Remove clamp and $\frac{3}{32}$" rod, connect wiring and check switch operation.
7. Install bulbs, housing, lens, ash tray and trim plate.

1966-68 Corvette, 1969 All Floor Shift

1. Disconnect shift control lever arm from transmission control rod.
2. Remove shift control knob.
3. Remove trim plate.
4. Remove control assembly from seal and cut switch wiring.
5. Remove switch from control assembly.
6. To install, position gearshift in Drive position, align hole in contact support with hole in switch and insert a pin ($\frac{3}{32}$") to hold support in place.
7. Place contact support drive slot over drive tang and tighten switch mounting screws.
8. Connect wiring harness to switch wiring.
9. Install trim plate control knob and connect shift lever arm to transmission control rod.

1964-65 Floor Shift

1. Remove bezel dial indicator and seal from seat separator console.
2. Disconnect switch wiring from harness at in-line connector.
3. Unfasten and remove switch.
4. To install new switch, clamp pawl rod against contact point of detent and align slot in contact support with drive hole in switch and insert pin to hold in place.
5. Position switch to lever and bracket with lever engaged in contact support and install retaining nuts.
6. Remove clamp and pin and check switch operation.

1963 Chevrolet & 1963-64 Chevy II

1. To adjust the switch, place shift lever in Neutral.
2. Loosen screws securing switch retainer. Then, while holding ignition switch in "Start" position, adjust position of switch until engine turns over.
3. Hold switch in this position and tighten retainer screws.
4. Check adjustment by testing for cranking in both Neutral and Park.

1965-66 Corvette

Service Note

The neutral safety switch on these models is serviced with 95 inches of wire attached to the switch. The following procedure for replacing the switch permits cutting and splicing the wire approximately 4 inches from the switch rather than replace the entire assembly.

1. Disconnect battery ground cable.
2. Raise rear of vehicle and place on stands.
3. Disconnect shifter arm at clevis.
4. Remove center console trim plate.
5. Disconnect shifter boot and retainer.
6. Disconnect switch from shifter and cut electrical leads approximately 4" from switch.
7. Splice wires from new switch to existing harness. Solder spliced connections and wrap with electrician's tape.
8. Install and adjust switch as outlined below.

1963-64 Corvette

The neutral safety switch adjustment is made by varying the length of the bell crank-to-switch control rod. A swivel is provided at one end of this rod to permit adjustment.

TURN SIGNAL SWITCH, REPLACE

1969

1. Disconnect battery cable and remove steering wheel.
2. Remove cover from shaft. *The cover retaining screws need not be completely removed from the cover.*
3. Using a suitable tool, compress lock plate and remove snap ring.
4. Remove cancelling cam, spring, thrust washer and signal lever.
5. Push hazard warning knob in and unscrew knob.
6. Pull connector from bracket and wrap upper part of connector with tape to prevent snagging the wires during removal. On Tilt models, position shifter housing in "Low" position. Remove harness cover.
7. Remove retaining screws and remove switch.

1968

1. Disconnect steering column harness at connector.

2. Disconnect neutral safety switch and back-up lamp switch connectors.
3. Remove steering wheel.
4. Slide upper bearing preload spring and cancelling cam off end of shaft.
5. Remove turn signal lever retaining screw and remove lever.
6. Push hazard warning switch in, unscrew and remove knob.
7. Drive out shift lever retaining pin and remove shift lever.
8. Remove "C" retaining ring from upper steering shaft.
9. Slide thrust washer and wave washer off upper steering shaft.
10. Loosen three turn signal mounting screws until switch cover can be rotated counter-clockwise. It may be necessary to push on top of screws to loosen cover.
11. Rotate turn signal switch cover counter-clockwise and pull cover off top of jacket.
12. Remove shift lever bowl from top of jacket.
13. If necessary, pry upper shift lever spring from bowl and discard spring. Remove bowl washer.
14. If necessary to service components within signal switch cover, remove three signal switch mounting screws completely from engagement with the lock plate. Use care to control the three springs as screws are removed.
15. Remove turn signal switch and upper bearing housing from cover.
16. Reverse procedure to install.

1967 Except Corvette

All Columns Except Tilt & Telescoping

1. Disconnect battery ground cable.
2. Disconnect signal switch wiring from chassis harness at multiple connector under instrument panel.
3. Remove steering wheel.
4. Remove shift lever roll pin and lever from column (if applicable).
5. Push in hazard warning switch knob and unscrew knob.
6. Remove switch lever arm.
7. On Chevy II and Camaro with automatic transmission, remove column-mounted dial indicator housing and lamp assembly (if applicable).
8. Remove mast jacket lower trim cover(s).
9. On Chevrolet and Chevelle with automatic transmission, remove quadrant dial pointer (if applicable).
10. Remove retaining "C" ring from upper steering shaft and slide thrust and wave washers from steering shaft.
11. Loosen signal switch screws until assembly can be rotated counter-clockwise. *Do not completely remove screws until unit is on work bench.*
12. Rotate switch counterclockwise and pull unit from top of mast jacket. Allow unit to hang from top of column.
13. Remove upper support bracket. *Do not suspend column by lower reinforcement only.*
14. Reinforce column and remove wire harness protector and clip, then position bracket and reinstall bolts finger tight.

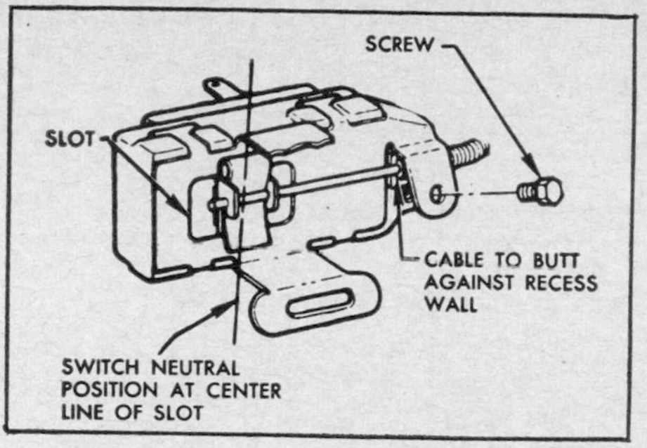

Fig. 5 Turn signal switch. 1963 Corvette

15. Remove shift lever bowl from mast jacket and disengage from wire harness.
16. Remove three screws from engagement with lock plate, using care not to lose three springs as screws are removed.
17. Disassemble switch and upper bearing housing from switch cover.
18. Reverse procedure to install, using a new switch as it is not repairable.

Tilt Column

1. Disconnect battery ground cable.
2. Disconnect signal wire harness from body harness at multiple connector under instrument panel.
3. Remove steering wheel.
4. Remove preload spring and cancelling cam from end of shaft.
5. Remove shift lever pin and lever from steering column (except floor shift).
6. Remove turn signal lever.
7. Push in and remove hazard warning knob.
8. On Camaro with automatic transmission, remove quadrant dial and lamp assembly from column.
9. Remove mast jacket trim cover(s).
10. On Chevrolet and Chevelle with automatic transmission, remove quadrant dial pointer.
11. Assemble a suitable slide hammer to turn signal cover, place a cover remover over turn signal cover, tighten clamp and pull cover from end of column with slide hammer.
12. Remove three switch mounting screws, *noting short length of top screw.*
13. Cut multiple connector from switch wiring and slide switch from end of column.

Installation

1. Feed wiring through bearing housing, around support and through shift bowl and shroud.
2. Feed through wiring protector. If clearance is not sufficient, loosen mast jacket bracket retaining bolts.
3. Insert switch wiring terminals in multiple connector. *Use old connector and wiring for color guide.*
4. Position switch and install three mounting screws with short screw in top position.
5. Complete the installation in reverse order of removal.

1967 Corvette

Standard & Telescoping Column

1. Disconnect battery ground cable.
2. Disconnect signal switch harness wiring from chassis wire harness at multiple connector under instrument panel.
3. Remove steering wheel.
4. Remove preload spring and cancelling cam.
5. Remove turn signal lever.
6. Push in and unscrew hazard warning knob.
7. Remove lower trim cover.
8. Remove retaining ring, thrust and wave washers from upper end of shaft.
9. Cut wiring above connector.
10. Remove three switch mounting screws and slide switch, cover and upper bearing housing from column, pulling wire through protector and escutcheon.
11. Reverse procedure to install.

1965-66 Chevrolet

1. Remove steering wheel.
2. Remove lever from cancelling mechanism.
3. Remove shift lever retaining pin and lever.
4. Disconnect turn signal wiring from harness quick disconnect.
5. Remove lower trim cover plate and mast jacket upper clamp.
6. With Powerglide, remove dial indicator retaining screws.
7. Separate turn signal control from signal housing (3 screws).
8. Remove wiring clamps (slide components upward on column to expose upper clamp).
9. Remove turn signal assembly and housing, shift lever housing and mast jacket cover extension from steering column.
10. Remove turn signal from housings and mast jacket.

CAUTION: Turn signal control assembly must be in neutral position when assembling steering wheel to prevent damage to cancelling cam and control assembly.

1964-66 Chevelle

1. Remove steering wheel.
2. Remove cancelling cam, spring, turn signal lever screw and lever.
3. Remove shift lever pin and lever from shift bowl.
4. Disconnect signal wiring from instrument panel harness at multiple connector.
5. Disconnect mast jacket upper clamp and bend away from column. Remove wiring harness retainer and cover.
6. Remove three screws and take off switch, housing and shift bowl from steering column. Disengage switch and wiring harness from other units. On cars with Powerglide, the dial quadrant lamp and socket must be detached from signal housing first.
7. Reverse above procedure to install.

CAUTION: Turn signal control assembly must be in neutral position when assembling steering wheel to prevent damage to cancelling cam and control assembly.

1964-66 Chevy II

1. Remove steering wheel.

2. Remove lever from cancelling mechanism.
3. Remove control lever retaining pin and lever.
4. Remove mast jacket upper support clamp.
5. Disconnect turn signal, horn and shift indicator light (Powerglide) wiring at chassis harness quick disconnect and disconnect plastic harness cover attaching harness to mast jacket.
6. Separate turn signal control from switch housing (3 screws).
7. Remove turn signal, housing and shift bowl from steering column.
8. Disconnect shift indicator light (Powerglide only) and horn wires from multiple connector. Disengage turn signal from signal and shift lever housings.
9. On 1964-65 remove upper shaft bearing and horn wire from turn signal control assembly.
10. Reverse above procedure to install.

CAUTION: Turn signal control assembly must be in neutral position when assembling steering wheel to prevent damage to cancelling cam and control assembly.

1964 Chevrolet

1. Remove steering wheel.
2. Remove lever from cancelling mechanism.
3. Remove shift lever pin and lever.
4. Disconnect turn signal, horn and shift indicator light (Powerglide only) wiring at harness quick disconnect.
5. Remove instrument panel trim cover plate and mast jacket upper clamp bolt. Bend clamp from steering column.
6. Separate signal control from housing (3 screws).
7. Remove wiring clamps (slide components upward on steering column to expose upper clamp).
8. Remove turn signal and housing, shift lever housing and mast jacket cover extension from steering column.
9. Disconnect shift indicator light and horn wires from multiple connector.
10. Remove turn signal from signal and shift lever housings and mast jacket.
11. Remove upper shaft bearing and horn contact assembly from turn signal control.
12. Reverse above procedure to install.

1963 Chevrolet & Chevy II

1. Remove steering wheel.
2. Remove lever from cancelling mechanism.
3. Detach switch from its housing (3 screws).
4. Disconnect switch wiring connector from chassis wiring harness connector and two clips.
5. Remove turn signal assembly and upper horn bearing from housing.
6. Reverse above procedure to install.

1963 Corvette

The turn signal lever and cancelling mechanism are located in the turn signal housing adjacent to the steering wheel. The switch mechanism, Fig. 5, operated by means of a cable from the housing, is attached to the lower portion of the mast jacket. The switch adjusts itself automatically, eliminating any need for further adjustment. However, if any malfunction of the mechanism should occur, the steering wheel may be removed and the mechanism checked for defective parts.

1964-66 Corvette

Standard Steering

1. Remove steering wheel.
2. Remove terminal leads from multiple connector and disconnect harness cover from mast jacket.
3. Remove control lever, three screws retaining control unit to housing retainer plate and slide control unit from steering shaft.
4. Remove retainer plate, housing and control unit from mast jacket.

CAUTION: Wiring terminals must be individually pulled through slot in mast jacket escutcheon to prevent damage to harness assembly.

5. Transfer wiring harness cover to new control unit and reverse above procedure to install new unit.

Telescoping Steering

1. Disconnect battery ground cable.
2. Remove steering wheel and hub.
3. Remove spring and cancelling cam from steering shaft.
4. Remove signal lever.
5. Remove signal control from retaining plate.
6. Remove clamp and cover from signal wire harness.
7. Remove terminals from plastic connectors.
8. Guiding wiring, pull signal switch out of housing.
9. Reverse above procedure to install.

HORN SOUNDER & STEERING WHEEL

1968-69 Deluxe Wheel

1. Disconnect battery ground cable.
2. Disconnect steering column wiring harness from chassis harness at connector.
3. Remove three screws from underside of steering wheel.
4. Remove four screws securing both horn blowing buttons. This will permit wires to hang loose.
5. Remove steering wheel shroud.
6. Remove wheel nut and washer.
7. Use a puller to remove wheel.
8. Reverse procedure to install.

1967-69 Standard Wheel

1. Disconnect battery ground cable and steering column harness from chassis wiring harness.
2. Pull out horn button cap or center ornament and retainer.
3. Remove three screws from receiving cup.
4. Remove receiving cup, belleville spring, bushing and pivot ring.
5. Remove wheel nut and washer and use a suitable puller to remove wheel.
6. Remove turn signal switch.

CAUTION: Turn signal control assembly must be in neutral position when assembling steering wheel to prevent damage to cancelling cam and control assembly.

1967-69 Simulated Wood Wheel

1. Disconnect steering column harness from chassis wiring harness at connector.
2. Disconnect battery ground cable.
3. Remove horn cap by pulling up.
4. Remove screws and contact assembly.

NOTE: If steering wheel only is to be replaced, perform Step 4. If turn signal cancelling cam is to be replaced, omit Step 4 and proceed with Steps 5 and 6.

5. Remove retaining screws and remove wheel from hub assembly.
6. Remove wheel nut and washer.
7. Use a suitable puller to remove wheel.

NOTE: Turn signal control assembly must be in neutral position when assembling the hub to prevent damage to cancelling cam and control assembly.

8. Reverse procedure to install.

1967-69 Corvette Telescoping Wheel

1. Disconnect steering column harness at wiring connector.
2. Pry off horn button cap.
3. Remove three screws securing horn contact to spacer and hub.
4. Remove two screws securing lock screw to lock knob and remove screw, knob and spacer.

NOTE: If wheel only is to be replaced, perform Step 5. If turn signal cancelling cam is to be replaced, omit Step 5 and proceed with Steps 6 and 7.

5. Remove wheel from hub (6 screws).
6. Remove nut and washer from shaft and use a suitable puller to remove wheel and hub.
7. Slide cancelling cam and spring off shaft.

1967-68 Tilt Type

On vehicles with tilt steering columns, it will be necessary to install steering column upper bearing preload spring prior to the cancelling cam. This differs from all other steering upper bearing preload springs as they are installed after the cancelling cam.

1967 Deluxe Wheel

1. Disconnect battery ground cable.
2. Pull out horn button center ornament.
3. Remove receiving cup (3 screws).
4. Remove wheel nut and washer.
5. Remove three screws securing spoke ornament with horn tabs. Remove ornament with belleville spring and insulator still installed inside.
6. Remove steering wheel with a puller.

1964-66 (Except Corvette)

1. Disconnect turn signal switch har-

ness from chassis wiring harness at connector.
2. On standard models, pull out horn button. On other models pull out center ornament from horn ring.
3. Remove receiving cup or horn ring (3 screws), spring, and bushing; on deluxe wheels also remove pivot ring.
4. Remove steering wheel nut and use a puller to remove wheel.

CAUTION: Turn signal control assembly must be in neutral position when assembling steering wheel to prevent damage to cancelling cam and control assembly.

Chevelle Note

Before installing steering wheel, make certain steering shaft stop clamp at bottom of mast jacket is secured and that steering shaft is 1¾" above top of turn signal housing.

Corvette 1963-66

1. Pry off horn cap.
2. Remove washer and nut from steering shaft.
3. Use a suitable puller to remove wheel.

1963 Chevy II

1. To remove, pry out horn button.
2. Remove three screws attaching receiver cup (or horn ring) and bushing spacer to steering wheel. Then remove flat belleville spring.
3. Remove nut and washer from steering shaft. Then use a suitable puller to remove steering wheel. *Do not lose the spring or seal located on the shaft under the steering wheel.*
4. Replace all components in the reverse order of removal. Make sure that the mark on the steering shaft lines up with the mark on the steering wheel hub. Torque wheel retaining nut to 35-40 ft. lbs.

1963 Chevrolet

Remove two screws from back of steering wheel and remove ornamental cap and horn sounding mechanism.

After removing horn sounding mechanism as outlined above, remove steering wheel nut and use a puller to remove steering wheel.

INSTRUMENT CLUSTER

1969 Chevrolet

1. Disconnect battery ground cable.
2. Remove glove box for access to pad fasteners.
3. Remove A/C center outlet.
4. Remove retaining screws and gently pry panel pad loose from clips.
5. Remove A/C lap cooler and three hex screws from under dash. Disconnect shift indicator wire.
6. Disconnect radio connections. Lower steering column.
7. Remove screws at top of panel and lift and tilt panel forward.
8. Disconnect speedometer cable, and all electrical connections.
9. Remove screws retaining top illumination can.
10. To remove indicator bulb bezel, push in on right side of each cover to expose a screw. Remove four retaining screws and bezel.
11. Remove eight screws from rear of carrier and remove cluster.

1968 Chevrolet

1. Disconnect battery ground cable.
2. Unplug forward wiring harness connector from fuse panel under hood.
3. Remove fuse panel from firewall.
4. Unfasten instrument cluster from instrument panel (8 screws).
5. Remove screw retaining column mounted automatic transmission pointer cable from mast jacket.
6. Reaching behind cluster, disconnect speedometer cable, chassis harness connector, clock, speed warning device connections, defogger, convertible top or tail gate switches and vacuum hose connections (if so equipped). *On models with gauge pack, disconnect oil pressure line also.*
7. After all disconnects are made, tip cluster forward and remove.
8. Reverse procedure to install.

1968-69 Chevelle

1. Disconnect battery ground cable.
2. Remove ash tray and retainer.
3. Remove radio knobs, nuts, electrical connections, aerial plug and radio rear support, then lift out radio.
4. Remove heater control screws, then push control head out of instrument panel.
5. Lower steering column. If equipped, remove automatic transmission indicator cable on steering column.
6. Remove instrument panel retaining screws at top, sides and bottom of panel. Also remove any attachments to underside of panel such as speedometer stem, defogger or tail gate control switch.
7. Lift loosened instrument panel up and back slightly, reach behind cluster and remove speedometer cable housing retaining nut, then support instrument panel on protected steering column.
8. Remove clips on top of instrument cluster rear cover and remove all connectors at back of cover and oil pressure pipe fitting from rear of oil pressure gauge (if so equipped).
9. Remove five screws securing twin window cluster to back of instrument panel and remove cluster.
10. Reverse procedure to install.

1968-69 Corvette

Left Hand Side

1. Disconnect battery ground cable.
2. Lower steering column.
3. Remove screws and washers securing left instrument panel to door opening, top of dash and left side of center instrument panel.
4. Unclip and remove floor console trim panel.
5. Pull cluster slightly forward to obtain clearance for removal of speedometer cable housing nut, tachometer cable housing nut, headlamp and ignition switch connectors and panel illuminating lamps.
6. Reverse procedure to install.

Center Cluster

1. Disconnect battery positive cable at battery.
2. Remove wiper switch trim plate screws and tip plate forward for access to switch connector. Lift trim plate out from cluster.
3. Unclip and remove right and left console forward trim pads to gain access to studs at lower edge of cluster.
4. Remove nuts from studs at lower edge of cluster.
5. Remove remaining screws retaining cluster to instrument panel.
6. Remove right instrument panel pad.
7. Remove radio knobs, bezel retaining nuts and one radio support bolt (from behind cluster).
8. Slide radio back towards firewall and pull cluster forward. Reach behind cluster, disconnect oil pressure line, wiring harness and bulbs.

CAUTION: The center cluster trim plate is designed to collapse under impact. Consequently, do not try to deflect the cluster plate forward to gain access to back of gauges.

9. Lift cluster assembly up and forward to remove.
10. Reverse procedure to install cluster.

1968-69 Camaro

1. Disconnect battery ground cable.
2. On 1969, remove instrument panel pad, A/C attachments and radio brace attachments.
3. Remove mast jacket supports at toe pan and dash, and lower column. *Both supports must be detached to prevent distortion of mast jacket.*
4. Remove cluster retaining screws from face of panel and partially remove assembly from console opening.
5. Reaching behind cluster assembly, disconnect speedometer cable, speed warning device (if equipped) and chassis harness connector at rear of panel.
6. Remove assembly from console.
7. Reverse procedure to install.

1968-69 Chevy II

1. Disconnect battery.
2. Unfasten heater control from cluster (2 screws).
3. Remove radio knobs, bezel nuts and front support at lower edge of cluster. This will allow radio to remain in instrument panel during cluster removal.
4. On 1968, remove mast jacket from trim cover. Disengage Powerglide range indicator cable (if equipped). On 1969, disconnect and lower column.
5. Remove toe pan trim cover.
6. Remove bolts securing steering column retainer to toe pan. Loosen bolts securing retainer halves.
7. Remove bolts at top, bottom and sides of cluster securing it to instrument panel.
8. Remove steering column-to-dash panel bracket nuts and carefully lower column. Be careful not to jar or apply any load on column during this operation.

9. Remove ignition switch tumbler and bezel through cluster and leave hanging.
10. Tilt cluster forward and disconnect speedometer cable and necessary electrical connectors. Then remove cluster.
11. Reverse procedure to install and align steering column.

1967 Chevrolet

1. Disconnect battery ground strap.
2. Remove four screws retaining instrument bezel to top edge of instrument console. Disengage tabs on bezel lower section from clips on instrument console and remove bezel.
3. Remove eight screws retaining leading edges of instrument cluster to console and pull cluster forward from console opening.
4. Reaching behind cluster, disconnect speedometer cable, chassis harness connector, clock and speed warning device connections (if equipped) at rear of cluster. *On models with gauge pack, disconnect oil pressure line also.*
5. When all disconnections are made, remove cluster.
6. Reverse above procedure to install. Make sure ground strap between cluster case and center right lower attachment is properly installed.

1967 Camaro

1. Disconnect battery ground cable.
2. Remove mast jacket lower support screws at toe pan.
3. Remove mast jacket upper support bolts and allow steering wheel to rest on seat cushion. *Both supports must be detached to prevent distortion of mast jacket.*
4. Remove cluster attaching screws from face of panel and partially remove assembly from console opening.
5. Reaching behind cluster assembly, disconnect speedometer cable, speed warning device (if equipped) and chassis harness connector at rear of panel.
6. Remove cluster from console opening.
7. Reverse procedure to install.

1966 Chevrolet

1. Disconnect battery ground cable.
2. Remove A/C hose connecting left outlet to distributor duct (if equipped).
3. Disconnect speedometer cable at cluster.
4. Disconnect panel wiring harness connector and clock or tachometer wiring lead connections at rear of cluster housing.
5. Remove radio knobs, bezels and retaining nuts. Push radio in to disengage shafts from panel openings. *On rear seat speaker models, make sure speaker fader control wiring is disconnected from radio harness wiring.*
6. Remove instrument panel compartment door and compartment retaining screws.
7. Remove upper and lower instrument panel console screws.
8. Protect mast jacket and outer edges of console.
9. Open right front door, roll console forward and slide to right to remove assembly from vehicle.
10. Reverse procedure to install.

1966-67 Chevelle

1. Disconnect battery ground cable.
2. Separate steering shaft from coupling.
3. Loosen mast jacket lower clamp.
4. Remove A/C center distributor duct (if equipped).
5. Remove radio rear support bracket screw.
6. On 1966 models, remove mast jacket trim cover and upper support clamp. On 1967 models, remove mast jacket upper support clamp and retaining bolts from lower support.
7. On 1966 models, loosen set screw and remove Powerglide dial indicator (if equipped).
8. Disconnect speedometer cable.
9. Remove instrument panel retaining screws (9 upper and 5 lower).
10. Working underneath console, remove four lower screws from instrument cluster housing.
11. Pull instrument panel from console and lay it forward on protected mast jacket.
12. Disconnect wiring harness, cluster lamps and wiring terminals from rear of cluster.
13. Remove four screws retaining upper section of cluster housing to panel and remove cluster from instrument panel.
14. Reverse procedure to install.

1966-67 Chevy II

1. Disconnect battery ground cable.
2. On 1966 models, remove Powerglide dial indicator (if equipped) and mast jacket upper support clamp. On 1967 models, remove mast jacket upper support clamp.
3. Disconnect retaining collar securing speedometer cable to speedometer head.
4. Separate cluster from console.
5. Pull cluster forward of console opening and disconnect all wiring and lamp connections.
6. Remove cluster from vehicle.

CAUTION: Do not pull cluster outward further than slack in wiring will permit, otherwise wiring and lamp connections may be damaged.

1966-67 Corvette

1. Remove mast jacket assembly.
2. Disconnect tachometer drive cable at distributor.
3. Disconnect cowl vent control cable brackets and headlamp panel control switch from instrument cluster.
4. Remove light switch.
5. Remove ignition switch. Disconnect ignition switch lamp support at instrument panel.
6. On 1966 models, disconnect parking brake lever support at cowl crossmember.
7. Disconnect pressure line at oil gauge, then remove lead wires from ammeter, wiper switch and cigar lighter. Disconnect trip odometer at mast jacket support.
8. Remove cluster-to-dash screws and pull cluster slightly forward to obtain clearance for removal of speedometer cable, tachometer cable, cluster ground wire, fuel gauge lead wires and remaining lamps.
9. Reverse procedure to install.

1965 Chevrolet

1. Disconnect battery ground cable.
2. Remove steering wheel.
3. Disconnect speedometer cable.
4. Disconnect cluster wiring harness from panel wiring harness at multiple connector.
5. Remove left ash tray and retainer.
6. Remove radio.
7. Remove screws attaching upper lip of cluster to console.
8. Unfasten rear of cluster from panel (4 nuts).

NOTE: As cluster is removed from panel opening observe position of mounting clips for the four lower studs.

9. Slide cluster to right side of vehicle, pulling it gently forward out of console. Tip cluster forward slightly to clear console edge.

NOTE: Cluster must be pulled forward enough so speedometer neck will clear console reinforcing stud.

10. With cluster removed from vehicle all gauges and instruments may be quickly removed for service.
11. Reverse above procedure to install. When installing cluster be sure J-nuts are in position. Pull down gently on upper lip of cluster to prevent dislodging these clips.

NOTE: On air conditioned vehicles it is necessary to remove the entire panel console and cluster unit as an assembly.

1965 Chevelle

1. Disconnect battery ground cable.
2. Remove upper mast jacket clamp bolt and bend clamp away from steering column.
3. Unscrew retaining collar securing speedometer cable to speedometer.
4. Disconnect oil pressure line at gauge on Super Sports model.
5. Detach console from instrument panel (9 screws) and lean console forward onto mast jacket. Remove radio control knobs before attempting to remove console from panel.
6. Disconnect all cluster indicator and illumination lamps, other instrument cluster harness wiring connections and two harness retaining clips back of cluster panel.
7. Lift cluster forward and upward to remove from vehicle completely.
8. Remove cluster housing attaching screws and cluster from console.
9. Reverse above procedure to install.

NOTE: Be sure to reinstall ground straps held on by cluster to console attaching screws otherwise cluster function will be impaired.

1965 Chevy II

1. Loosen and lower mast jacket from dash panel.
2. Unscrew retaining collar securing speedometer cable to speedometer.

3. Separate cluster from dash panel (4 screws). Cluster may now be pulled clear of dash.

CAUTION: Do not pull cluster outward further than slack in wiring harness will allow, otherwise harness retaining clips may be damaged.

4. Remove two harness retaining clips from rear of cluster. Cluster may now be positioned face down on mast jacket for removal of fuel gauge.
5. Disconnect all indicator and illuminating bulb sockets, carefully noting their location for proper reinstallation.
6. Remove cluster from vehicle.
7. Reverse above procedure to install.

1964 Chevelle

It is not necessary to remove the instrument console from the vehicle to service the instruments and gauges in the regular model instrument cluster. These units may be removed with the cluster and console in the vehicle.

On Super Sports models, however, the console and cluster must be loosened to service the fuel, ammeter, temperature and oil pressure gauges. With the console loosened, these units may then be easily removed from the rear of the cluster housing for servicing.

1963-64 Chevy II

1. Loosen and lower mast jacket from dash panel.
2. Unscrew retaining collar securing speedometer cable to speedometer head.
3. Unfasten cluster from dash panel (4 screws). Cluster may now be pulled clear of dash. *Do not pull cluster outward further than slack in wiring harness will allow, otherwise harness retaining clips may be damaged.*
4. Remove two harness retaining clips from rear of cluster. Cluster may now be positioned face down on mast jacket for removal of fuel gauge.
5. Disconnect all bulb sockets, carefully noting their location for proper installation. Remove cluster from car.

1963-64 Chevrolet

1. Detach speedometer cable.
2. Unfasten console from instrument panel (9 screws) and lean console forward onto mast jacket.
3. Reach behind console on driver's side and disconnect the two multiple lead wire harness connectors.
4. Lift console forward and upward to remove from vehicle. *Be sure to attach the single ground washer on one of the console attaching screws. The clock and fuel gauge may be removed with the console in the vehicle.*

W/S WIPER MOTOR

1968-69

1. Make sure wiper motor is in park position.
2. Disconnect washer hoses and electrical connectors from assembly.
3. Remove the air intake grille on Chevy II, Camaro and Corvette models. On Chevrolet models, remove plastic access cover.
4. Loosen nuts which retain the drive link to the crank arm ball stud on Chevrolet models. On all other models, remove the nut which retains the crank arm to the motor.
5. On Corvette, it is necessary to remove the ignition shield and distributor cap to gain access to the motor retaining screws or nuts. *Note: Remove left bank spark plug wires from the cap and mark both cap and wires for aid in reinstallation.*
6. Remove three motor retaining screws or nuts and remove motor.

CAUTION: Wiper motor must be in the park position prior to installation on the cowl. Do not install a motor that was dropped or hung by the drive link.

1967 Camaro & Chevrolet

1. Make certain motor is in Park position.
2. Disconnect washer hoses and electrical connectors from assembly.
3. On Chevrolet models, remove plenum chamber side cover and loosen nuts retaining drive rod ball stud to crank arm.
4. Remove three mounting bolts and motor. On Camaro models, pull motor from cowl opening and loosen nuts retaining drive rod ball stud to crank arm.
5. Reverse procedure to install.

CAUTION: Motor must be in Park position prior to installation to cowl. Do not install a motor that has dropped or hung from drive link.

1967 Chevelle

1. Make certain motor is in Park position.
2. Disconnect washer hoses and all electrical connectors.
3. Remove three motor mounting bolts, carefully remove motor from firewall and detach clip retaining drive arm to motor crank arm.

CAUTION: Motor must be in Park position prior to installation to cowl. Do not install motor that has dropped or hung from drive link.

1967 Chevy II

1. Make certain motor is in Park position.
2. Working under instrument panel, remove special retainer clip securing transmission linkage to motor crank arm.
3. Disconnect linkage, electrical connectors and washer hoses.
4. Unfasten (3 bolts) and remove motor from cowl opening.

CAUTION: Motor must be in Park position prior to installation to cowl. Do not install motor that has dropped or hung from drive link.

1965-66 Chevrolet

1. To remove motor, first make certain it is in park position, then remove wiper arm and blade assemblies.
2. Remove plenum chamber side cover.
3. Loosen nuts retaining drive rod to crank arm.
4. Disconnect battery ground cable, then remove washer hoses, if present, and all electrical connectors.
5. Unfasten and remove motor (3 bolts).

1963-66 Chevy II

1. Make certain wiper motor is in park position.
2. Remove special clip retaining transmission linkage to motor crank arm. Then remove linkage, electrical connectors and washer hoses (if equipped).
3. Unfasten and remove motor (3 screws).
4. Install in reverse order of removal. Check and replace motor gasket if necessary. Use sealing compound in screw holes.

1963-67 Corvette

1. Disconnect ground lead at battery.
2. Remove engine distributor shield and left-bank spark plug wiring vertical shield.
3. Disconnect left-bank spark plug wire bracket-to-manifold and position to one side.
4. Disconnect ignition resistor at firewall, then remove washer pump inlet and outlet hose at pump valve.
5. Remove ignition distributor cap and position to one side, then disconnect washer pump and motor lead wires.
6. Remove glove box door and compartment.
7. Make sure wiper arms and blades are in parked position, then remove transmission clip and disconnect both transmission and spacer from crank arm.

1963 Chevrolet

1. Make certain motor is in parked position.
2. Remove plenum chamber ventilator grille. Remove windshield washer nozzles (if used).
3. Remove ground strap retainer screw, washer hoses if present, all electrical connectors and wiper transmission drive arm to motor crank arm retainer clip. *Mark washer hoses for correct installation.*
4. Unfasten and remove motor.
5. When installed, check wiper operation before installing chamber ventilating grille. Make sure motor is properly grounded.

1964 Chevrolet

1. Make certain motor is in parked position.
2. Remove plenum chamber ventilating grille.
3. Remove washer hoses (if equipped) and all electrical connections.
4. Remove motor (3 bolts) and detach clip retaining wiper transmission drive arm to motor crank arm.
5. To install, check sealing gaskets at

motor and retaining bolts. Then reverse removal procedure to install motor.
6. Check wiper operation before installing chamber ventilating grille. Make sure motor is properly grounded.

1964-66 Chevelle

1. Make certain motor is in parked position.
2. Disconnect electrical connections and washer hoses (if equipped).
3. Remove motor retaining bolts. Carefully pull motor from firewall and detach clip retaining wiper transmission drive rod to crank arm.
4. To install, check sealing gaskets at motor and retaining bolts and replace if necessary. Then reverse removal procedure to install.

W/S WIPER TRANSMISSION

1968-69

1. Make sure wiper motor is in park position.
2. On Corvette only, remove rubber plug from front of wiper motor actuator, then insert a screwdriver, pushing internal piston rearward to actuate wiper door open.
3. On all models, remove wiper arm and blade assembly from one transmission. On articulated left-hand arm assemblies, remove clip retaining pinned arm to blade arm.
4. Remove air intake grille or screen (if equipped).
5. Loosen nuts retaining drive rod ball stud-to-crank arm and detach rod from arm.
6. Remove transmission retaining screws, or nuts, then lower drive rod assemblies into plenum chamber.
7. Remove transmission and linkage through cowl opening.
8. Reverse procedure to install. Make sure wiper blades are installed in the park position (plus or minus ⅜″ from top of reveal molding on recessed wiper arms).

1967 Chevy II

1. Make certain wiper motor is in park position. Remove wiper arm and blade assembly from transmission shaft.
2. From under left side of dash, remove special retainer clip securing transmission linkage to wiper crank arm and remove linkage from crank.
3. Remove glove box door and interior. Remove screws securing defroster duct to fire wall and lower duct. Remove retainer clip securing crank link to right transmission and remove linkage from right transmission.
4. Remove retaining capscrews securing transmission to cowl (2 each side). Remove right and left transmission with connector link still attached through glove box opening. Disconnect connecting link from the transmission being replaced.
5. Reverse procedure to install. Check and replace gasket if necessary. Use waterproof cement to seal screw holes.

1965-67 Chevrolet & 1967 Camaro

1. Make certain motor is in park position, then remove wiper arm and blade assemblies.
2. Remove plenum chamber ventilator grille.
3. Loosen nuts retaining drive rod to crank arm and detach rod from arm.
4. Remove transmission retaining screws and lower transmission and drive rod assemblies into plenum chamber.
5. Remove transmission and linkage from plenum chamber through cowl opening.

1965-67 Chevelle

1. Make certain motor is in park position, then remove wiper arm and blade assemblies.
2. Remove plenum chamber grille.
3. Remove clip retaining transmission drive rod to crank arm and detach rod from arm.
4. Remove transmission retaining screws, lower assembly into plenum chamber and remove unit from chamber.

1965-66 Chevy II

1. Make certain motor is in park position, then remove wiper arm and blade.
2. Remove special retainer clip securing transmission linkage to wiper crank arm and remove linkage from crank.
3. Remove retainer clip securing left transmission link to right transmission and remove link from right transmission.
4. Remove two retaining screws securing transmission to cowl (one side) and remove transmission from under dash.

1963-64 Chevrolet

1. Make certain motor is in park position. Then remove wiper arms and blades.
2. Remove plenum chamber ventilator grille.
3. Remove wiper motor and unclip transmission drive arm from motor crank arm.
4. Unclip left transmission drive link from right transmission.
5. Unfasten transmission and lower it into plenum chamber.
6. Remove transmission and linkage through cowl opening.
7. To install reverse removal procedure.

1963-66 Corvette

1. Remove wiper block and arm from transmission.
2. Remove glove box.
3. Remove three transmission-to-cowl screws.
4. Unclip and remove transmission from crank arm.
5. Remove transmission through glove box opening.
6. To install reverse removal procedure.

1964 Chevelle

1. Make certain motor is in park position. Then remove wiper arms and blades.
2. Remove plenum chamber grille.
3. Unclip right transmission drive rod from motor crank arm.
4. Unclip left transmission rod from base of right transmission.
5. Unfasten and lower transmission into plenum chamber and remove.
6. To install reverse removal procedure.

1963-64 Chevy II

1. Make certain motor is in park position. Then remove wiper arms and blades.
2. Unclip transmission linkage from wiper crank arm and remove linkage from crank.
3. Unclip left transmission link from right transmission and remove link from right transmission.
4. Unfasten transmission from cowl and remove from under dash.
5. To install reverse removal procedure. Check and replace gasket if necessary. Use waterproof cement to seal screw holes.

W/S WIPER SWITCH

1968 Except Chevelle, 1969 Chevrolet

1. Disconnect battery ground cable.
2. On 1968 Chevy II, remove parking brake and heater control assemblies.
3. On 1968, remove left A/C outlet duct. On 1969, remove trim plate and lap cooler outlet.
4. On 1968, loosen set screw and remove knob.
5. Disconnect and remove switch from rear of panel.
6. Reverse procedure to install.

1969 Camaro, Chevelle, Nova

1. Disconnect battery ground cable.
2. On Chevelle, remove left air outlet and headlight switch.
3. Disconnect and remove switch from rear of panel.
4. Reverse procedure to install.

1969 Corvette

1. Disconnect battery ground cable.
2. Remove screws from upper part of center console marked "Corvette".
3. Disconnect and remove switch and plate.
4. Carefully pry knob from switch then remove switch from plate.
5. To install, insert a small rod in the switch arm before pushing the knob on the arm outside of the trim plate then reverse the above procedure.

1967-68 Chevelle

1. Disconnect battery ground cable.
2. Remove wiper knob.
3. Slip a section of wiper hose about 3 feet long, over the end of the stem of the switch. Make sure it fits tightly on the shaft.
4. Remove bezel nut and push switch down and out of instrument panel, guiding it through the wiring.

5. Bring switch down far enough to remove electrical connector.
6. Then remove hose from switch and remove switch.
7. Reverse foregoing to install the switch.

1967 Except Chevelle

1. Disconnect battery ground cable.
2. Remove connectors from rear of switch.
3. On A/C models it is necessary to remove the left A/C outlet duct to gain access to rear of switch.
4. Loosen set screw and pull knob from switch.
5. Withdraw switch from behind console.
6. Reverse procedure to install.

1964-66 Chevrolet, Chevy II & Chevelle

1. Disconnect battery ground cable.
2. Remove connector(s) from rear of switch.
3. Remove small set screw from bottom of wiper knob and remove knob.
4. Remove retaining nut and withdraw switch from under dash panel.
5. Reverse above procedure to install.

1963

To remove the switch, disconnect wire leads, unfasten switch from its mounting and remove from dash panel.

RADIO, REPLACE

NOTE: When installing radio, be sure to adjust antenna trimmer for peak performance.

1968-69 Except Corvette

1. Disconnect battery ground cable.
2. On Chevelle and Chevrolet, remove ash tray and retainer.
3. Remove radio knobs, nuts, electrical connections, rear support and lift radio out.

1968-69 Corvette

Coupe

1. Disconnect battery ground cable.
2. Remove left and right door sill plates and kick pads. Disconnect radio to speaker connectors (left and right side).
3. Remove right side dash pad.
4. Remove right and left console forward trim pads.
5. Remove one bolt securing heater floor outlet duct to center distributor assembly.
6. Remove floor outlet duct by pulling it through left hand opening.
7. From front of console, tape radio push buttons in depressed position. From rear of console, disconnect electrical connector, brace and antenna.
8. Remove radio knobs and bezel retaining nuts. Push radio forward (towards front of car). From rear of console, tip back of radio up and remove from right side opening.
9. Reverse procedure to install.

Convertible

1. Disconnect battery cable.
2. Remove right instrument panel pad.
3. Disconnect speaker connectors.

NOTE: On some vehicles it may be necessary to remove kick panels to gain access to speaker connectors.

4. Remove wiper switch trim plate screws and tip plate for access to switch connector. Remove switch connector and trim plate from cluster assembly.
5. Unclip and remove right and left console forward trim pads. Remove forwardmost screw on each side of console.
6. Insert a flexible drive socket between the console and metal horseshoe brace, remove the nuts from the two studs on the lower edge of the console cluster.
7. Remove remaining screws retaining cluster to instrument panel.
8. From rear of console, disconnect radio connector, brace and antenna lead.
9. Remove radio knobs and bezel retaining nuts.
10. Pull top of console forward. Separate radio from console and remove it from the right side opening.

NOTE: The center instrument cluster trim plate is designed to collapse under impact. Consequently, do not try to deflect the cluster plate forward to gain more access to remove the radio. Also use care so as not to damage the plastic oil pressure line when pulling console forward.

1966 Chevy II

1. Disconnect battery ground cable.
2. Remove radio knobs and retaining nuts, including trim plate.
3. Remove glove box door (including one upper left screw retaining compartment interior box) for access to radio brace retaining screw.
4. Remove two instrument panel radio braces and retaining screws and nuts, including one radio rear brace retaining screw.
5. Disconnect electrical connections and remove radio through front of dash panel.
6. Reverse procedure to install.

1966 Chevelle with 4 Season A/C

1. Disconnect battery cable.
2. Remove ash tray and retainer.
3. Remove center air distributor duct.
4. Remove heater and A/C control panel.
5. Remove radio knobs, retaining nuts and support bolt.
6. Remove radio electrical connectors and antenna lead.
7. Remove radio from under dash.
8. Reverse procedure to install.

1965 Chevrolet

1. Disconnect battery ground cable.
2. Remove ash tray and retainer (both trays on A/C models).
3. On A/C models, disconnect hoses and remove air distributor duct. Lower A/C control assembly from panel opening. Remove A/C center outlet nozzle and duct assembly.
4. Remove radio control knobs, bezels and retaining nuts.
5. Disconnect all wiring and antenna lead, remove support bracket attaching nut and remove radio from console.
6. Reverse above procedure to install.

HEATER CORE REMOVAL

1965-69 Chevrolet, Chevelle, Camaro

1. Remove all cables except defroster cable on Chevrolet, and all electrical connectors from heater and defroster assembly.
2. From engine side of dash, remove two screws and stud nuts attaching air inlet assembly to dash.
3. From inside of car, pull entire heater and defroster assembly from firewall, removing defroster cable on Chevrolet at this time.
4. On 1967-68 models, three case-to-firewall mounting screws must be removed before assembly can be removed from firewall.
5. With heater on bench, remove heater core springs and lift out core.

1965-69 Chevy 11

1. Remove three nuts from blower motor that attach heater to dash.
2. From inside of car, remove glove box and its door.
3. Remove screw attaching distributor bracket to dash.
4. Remove screw attaching heater case bracket to adapter bracket, pull heater from dash and lower it to the floor.
5. Cables, wiring connector and defroster hoses may now be removed.
6. With heater removed, take out screws attaching core cover to heater.
7. Remove core mounting screws and lift it out.

1963-64 Chevrolet & Chevelle

1. Remove blower and air inlet case assembly from its mount on engine side of cowl.
2. Remove heater and defroster from inside of car.
3. Separate heater case from core shroud, then remove two screws at each core mounting yoke and take out core.

1963-64 Chevy 11

1. Remove three nuts around blower motor that attach heater to cowl.
2. Remove glove box.
3. Remove screws attaching heater case bracket to dash.
4. Detach heater carefully and disconnect all cables, wiring and defroster hoses.
5. Heater core is now accessible through cover plate on heater assembly.

SPEED CONTROLS

1967-69 Cruise Master

Servo Unit Adjustment

Adjust the bead chain so that it is as tight as possible without holding the

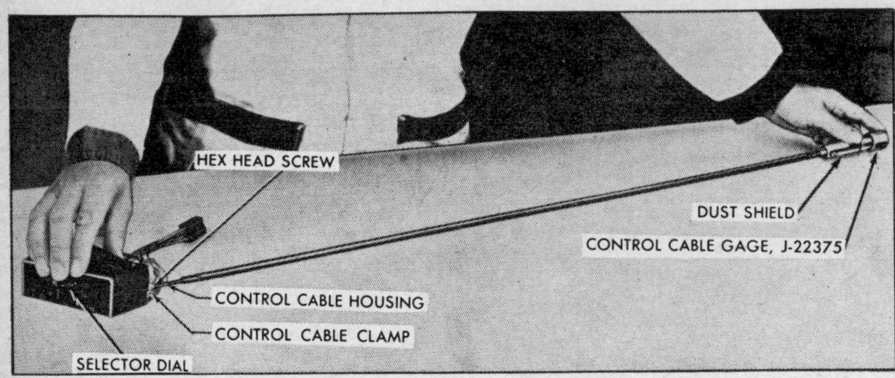

Fig. 6 Control cable adjustment for Slide Switch Speedostat

throttle open when the carburetor is set at its lowest idle throttle position.

When connecing the bead chain (engine stopped) manually set the fast idle cam at its lowest step and connect the chain so that it does not hold the idle screw off the cam. If the chain needs to be cut, cut it three beads beyond the bead that pulls the linkage.

Regulator Unit Adjustment

To remove any difference between engagement and cruising speed, one adjustment is possible. However, no adjustment should be made until the following items have been checked or serviced.

1. Bead chain properly adjusted.
2. All hoses in good condition, properly attached, not leaking, pinched or cracked.
3. Regulator air filter cleaned and properly oiled.
4. Electric and vacuum switches properly adjusted.

Engagement - Cruising Speed Zeroing

If the cruising speed is lower than the engagement speed, loosen the orifice tube locknut and turn the tube outward; if higher turn the tube inward. Each 1/8 turn will alter the engagement-cruising speed difference one mph. Tighten locknut after adjustment and check the system operation at 50 mph.

Fig. 7 Accelerator linkage adjustment for Slide Switch type Speedostat

Accelerator Linkage

1. Adjust throttle rod.
2. Start engine and operate at slow idle with transmission lever in "Park".
3. Separate linkage from exterior arm.
4. Adjust trunnion so that when it is installed through exterior arm, the stop stud will be aligned with locating notch and throttle valves will be closed.
5. Install washer on trunnion and secure with cotter pin.

NOTE: Due to the angle at which the trunnion enters hole in exterior arm, it is necessary to rotate the exterior arm slightly forward when inserting the trunnion. Repeat this operation until proper alignment is obtained. Be careful not to turn trunnion too far back or throttle valves will unseat and cause an incorrect adjustment. Insert the gauge shown in Fig. 7 (or small diameter pipe) over stop stud to check alignment.

Brake Release Switch

1. Turn on ignition but do not start engine.
2. Momentarily move slide switch to AUTO position until red indicator light glows.
3. Using a test lamp, ground one lead and touch the other lead to terminal No. 4, Fig. 8.
4. Loosen mounting screw securing release switch to brake pedal mounting bracket.
5. Adjust release switch so that lamp will light when brake pedal is fully released, and will go out when brake pedal is depressed about 1/4 inch. Tighten switch mounting screw. If switch cannot be adjusted, it is defective and should be replaced.

1963-66 Speedostat

Control Cable Adjustment, Prior to 1966

1. Rotate selector dial rearward as far as it will turn without forcing.
2. Loosen set screw on cable dust shield.
3. Again try to rotate selector dial rearward only in order to make certain it is against the stop.
4. Push in lightly on control cable at dust shield, making certain cable is against stop (do not force cable beyond stop).
5. Hold cable against stop and tighten set screw on dust shield securely.

Control Cable Adjustment, 1966-67

The cable is preset at the factory and should not require adjustment unless a new cable is installed. This adjustment must be performed off the car as follows:

1. Remove the selector assembly.
2. Rotate selector dial to low speed position until it is positioned against its stop but do not force beyond its stop.
3. Position assembly flat on workbench and make certain there are no kinks in cable.
4. Loosen hex head set screw at cable clamp on selector control.
5. Pull cable housing until it is approximately half-way out of cable clamp. Position control cable gauge shown in Fig. 6 in end of dust shield. Hold dust shield and gauge and push toward selector control assembly until gauge bottoms. While holding in this position, tighten set screw at cable clamp.

NOTE: The gauge shown in Fig. 6 is used on Chevrolet and Chevelle. The .090" end of the tool is used for Chevrolet adjustment; the .125" end for Chevelle.

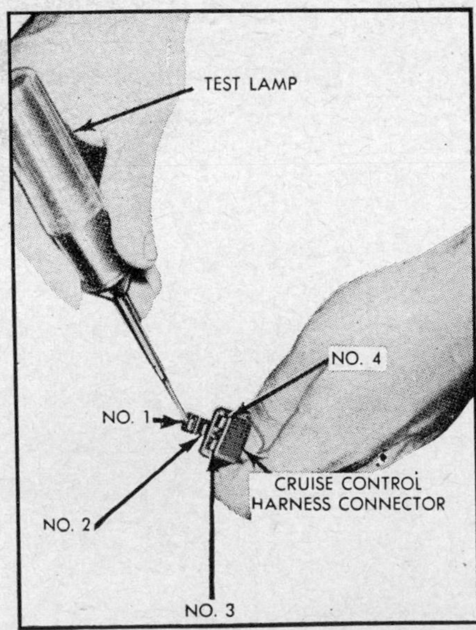

Fig. 8 Electrical connection on Slide Switch type Speedostat

Engine Section

ENGINE, REPLACE

1963-69 Except Corvette

NOTE: The engine and transmission are removed as a unit. First disconnect and/or remove as required wires, tubes, hoses and linkage attached to engine and transmission. Then do the following:

1. Remove hood, radiator and fan. Also power steering pump and A/C compressor (if equipped).
2. On V8-409, detach power brake unit and move it aside.
3. Remove drive shaft.
4. Unfasten and lower exhaust pipes. On 1963-64 Chevrolet V8, remove exhaust crossover pipe and manifold heat valve.
5. Remove rocker arm cover(s) and attach lifting device.
6. Remove front mount through bolts.
7. Raise engine to take weight off mounts, then remove rear mount bolts and crossmember. On Chevrolet models it will be necessary to remove mount from transmission before crossmember can be removed. On Camaro it will be necessary to remove mount from transmission and loosen rear frame cushion bolts before crossmember can be removed. On 1968 Camaro, it is not necessary to remove the crossmember completely; after removing the bolts, slide it back.
8. Remove engine and transmission assembly.

1963-64 Corvette

NOTE: Engine is removed separately, leaving transmission in chassis. First disconnect and/or remove as required wires, tubes, hoses and linkage attached to engine. Then do the following:

1. Remove rocker arm covers and distributor cap.
2. Disconnect exhaust pipe.
3. Remove oil filter.
4. Block clutch pedal in up position, remove clutch cross shaft (frame bracket end first) then slide it off engine ball stud.
5. Remove starter and flywheel or converter cover plate or underpan.
6. Remove engine mount front bolts.
7. Support transmission with jack, then remove all but top two bell housing-to-engine bolts.
8. Install engine lifting rig, then remove two remaining bell housing bolts.
9. On Powerglide models, remove flywheel-to-converter bolts and install a strap or bracket across housing to prevent converter from falling out.
10. Remove engine from vehicle.

1965-69 Corvette

When necessary to remove the engine, it is recommended that the engine and transmission assembly be lifted from the vehicle as a unit. It takes considerably less time to remove the engine and transmission as a unit than it would to "split" the engine from the transmission in the vehicle and remove the engine alone.

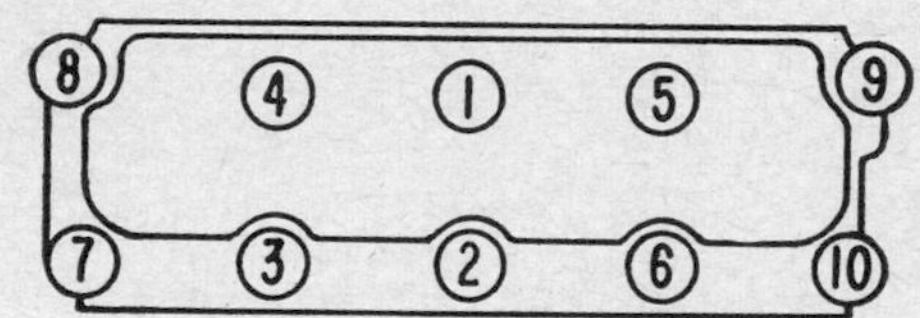

Fig. 1 Cylinder head tightening sequence. 4-153 engine

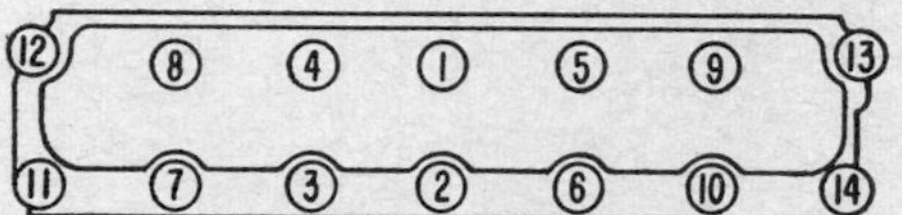

Fig. 2 Cylinder head tightening sequence. 6-194, 230, 250

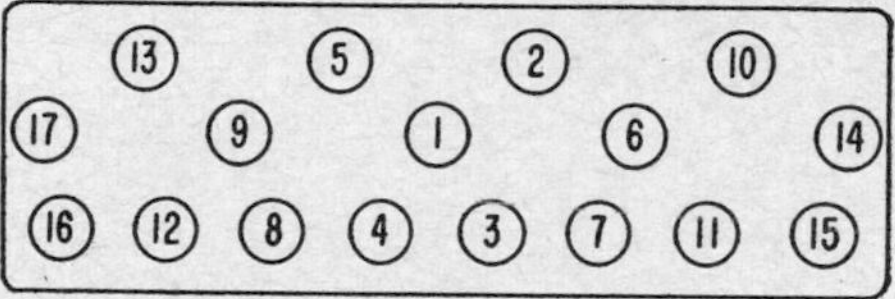

Fig. 3 Cylinder head tightening sequence. 8-283, 302, 307, 327, 350

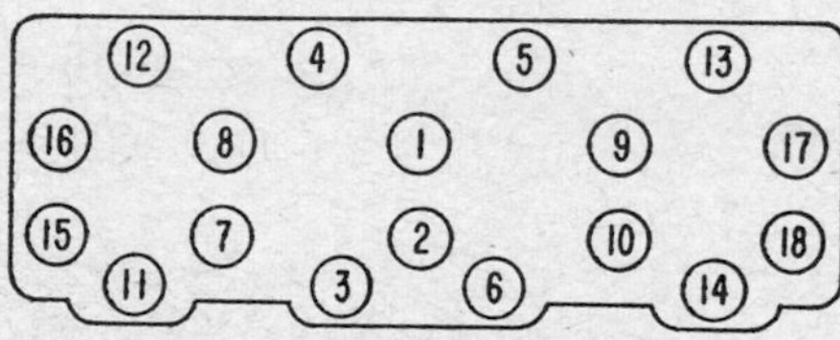

Fig. 4 Cylinder head tightening sequence. V8-409 engines

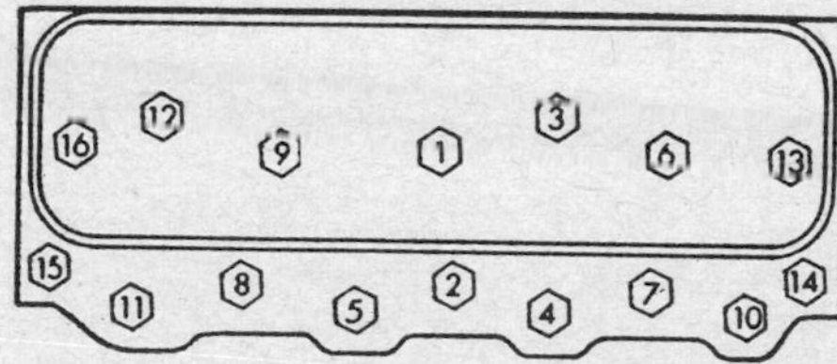

Fig. 5 Cylinder head tightening sequence. V8-396 and 427 engines

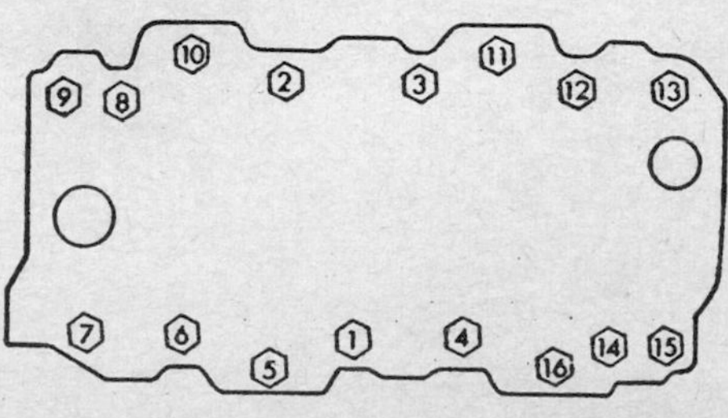

Fig. 6 Intake manifold tightening sequence. V8-396 and 427 engines

CYLINDER HEAD

1963-69 Four & Six Cylinder

1. Drain cooling system and remove air cleaner.
2. Disconnect choke rod or choke cable, accelerator pedal rod at bellcrank on manifold, and fuel and vacuum lines at carburetor.
3. Disconnect exhaust pipe at manifold flange, then unfasten and remove manifolds and carburetor as an assembly.
4. Remove fuel and vacuum line retaining clip from water outlet and disconnect wire harness from temperature sending unit and coil, leaving harness clear of clips on rocker arm cover.
5. Disconnect radiator hose at water outlet housing and battery ground strap at cylinder head.
6. Remove spark plugs and coil.
7. Remove rocker arm cover. Back off rocker arm nuts, pivot rocker arms to clear push rods and lift out push rods.
8. Unfasten and remove cylinder head.
9. Reverse procedure to install and tighten head bolts in the sequence shown in Figs. 1 and 2.

1963-69 V8s

NOTE: On Camaro and Chevy II with V8-396 and air conditioning it is necessary to remove the battery, A/C compressor, radiator shroud, air injector pump and starter. As the engine must be raised 2½" to remove the exhaust manifold it will be necessary to remove the engine mount through bolts and the transmission mount bolts.
On 1963-64 V8-409, when removing the right head on air conditioned cars, A/C compressor must be removed. When removing left head, power steering pump or air suspension compressor must be removed if so equipped.

On all other models, proceed as follows:

1. Remove intake and exhaust manifolds.
2. Remove rocker arm covers.
3. Back off rocker arm nuts, pivot rocker arms to clear push rods and remove push rods.
4. Unfasten and remove cylinder heads.
5. Reverse procedure to install and tighten head bolts in the sequence shown in Figs. 3 to 6.

VALVES, ADJUST

Hydraulic Lifters

NOTE—After the engine has been thoroughly warmed up the valves may be adjusted with the engine shut off as follows: With engine in position to fire No. 1 cylinder the following valves may be adjusted: Exhaust 1-3-4-8, intake 1-2-5-7.

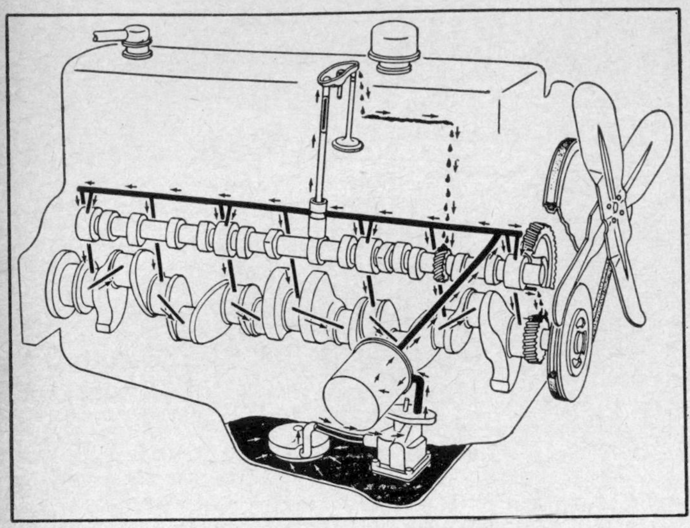

Engine oiling system. 6-194, 230, 250. Four cylinder is similar

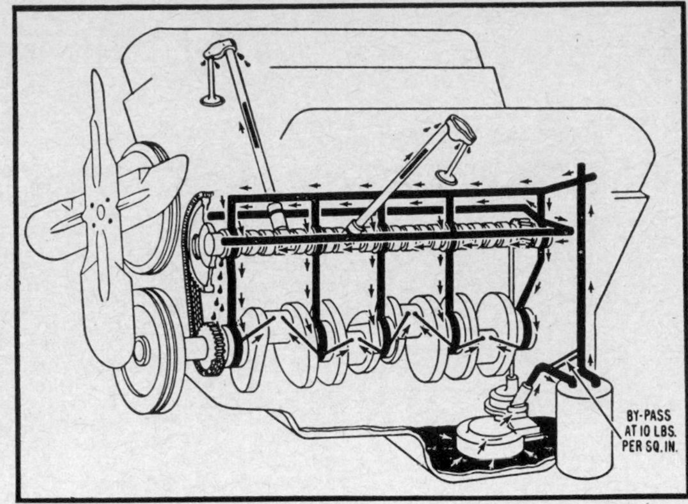

Engine oiling system. V8-283, 302, 307, 327, 350

Then crank the engine one more complete revolution which will bring No. 6 cylinder to the firing position at which time the following valves may be adjusted: Exhaust 2-5-6-7, intake 3-4-6-8.

The following procedure, performed with the engine running should be done only in case readjustment is required.

1. After engine has been warmed up to operating temperature, remove valve cover and install a new valve cover gasket on cylinder head to prevent oil from running out.
2. With engine running at idle speed, back off valve rocker arm nut until rocker arm starts to clatter.
3. Turn rocker arm nut down slowly until the clatter just stops. This is the zero lash position.
4. Turn nut down ¼ additional turn and pause 10 seconds until engine runs smoothly. Repeat additional ¼ turns, pausing 10 seconds each time, until nut has been turned down the number of turns listed in the *Valve Specifications Chart* from the zero lash position.

NOTE

This preload adjustment must be done slowly to allow the lifter to adjust itself to prevent the possibility of interference between the intake valve head and top of piston, which might result in internal damage and/or bent push rods. Noisy lifters should be replaced.

Mechanical Lifters

With the engine warmed to operating temperature as described above, turn rocker arm stud nut (V8's) or adjusting screw (6's) as required to obtain the clearances given in the *Valve Specifications* table.

NOTE

To be sure that the valves and lifters function perfectly, it is strongly recommended that a vacuum gauge be used when making the adjustment on hydraulic lifter jobs. With vacuum gauge connected and engine idling, tighten each rocker arm nut until the *highest and steadiest vacuum is indicated on the gauge.*

VALVE ARRANGEMENT

Front to Rear

4 Cylinder	E-I-I-E-E-I-I-E
6 Cylinder	E-I-I-E-E-I-I-E-E-I-I-E
8-283, 302, 307, 327, 350	E-I-I-E-E-I-I-E
V8-396, 427	I-E-I-E-I-E-I-E

ROCKER ARM STUDS

Rocker arm studs that have damaged threads may be replaced with standard studs. If studs are loose in the head, oversize studs (.003″ or .013″) may be installed after reaming the holes with a proper size reamer.

1. Remove the old stud by placing a suitable spacer, Fig. 8, over stud. Install nut and flat washer and remove stud by turning nut.
2. Ream hole for oversize stud.
3. Coat press-fit area of stud with rear axle lube. Then install new stud, Fig. 9. If tool shown is used, it should bottom on the head.

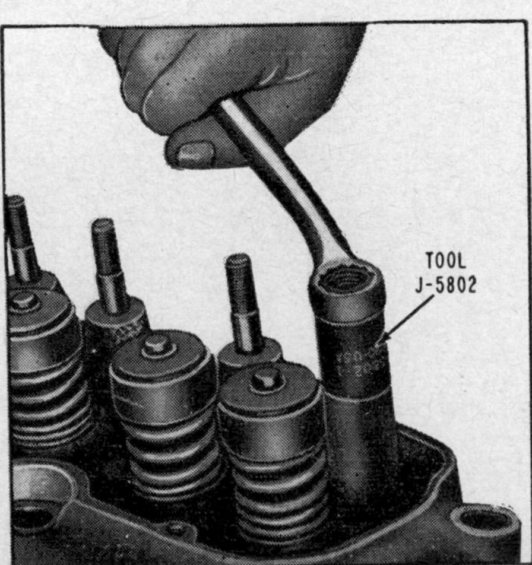

Fig. 8 Removing valve rocker arm stud

VALVE LIFT SPECS

Engine	Year	Intake	Exhaust
4-153	1963-64	.335	.335
	1965-69	.3973	.3973
6-194	1963-64	.335	.335
	1965-67	.3318	.3318
6-230	1963-66	.3349①	.3349①
	1967	.388	.388
	1968-69	.3317	.3317
6-250	1967-69	.388	.388
8-283	1963-66	.3987	.3987
	1967	.390	.410
8-302	1968-69	.4851	.4851
8-307	1968	.390	.410
	1969③⑯	.3945	.3945
8-327	1963-66②	.3987	.3987
	1963-66③	.3987	.3987
	1965-68④	.4472	.4472
	1965⑤	.4471	.4850
	1966⑥	.3987	.3987
	1967-68⑦	.390	.410
	1967-68⑥	.390	.410
	1967-68⑧	.390	.410
	1967-68③	.390	.410
	1967-68⑨	.4472	.4471
	1969	.3945	.3945
8-350	1967-68	.390	.410
	1969③⑯	.3945	.3945
	1969④	.4500	.4600
	1969⑰	.4851	.4851
8-396	1965-69⑨⑱	.398	.398
	1965⑩	.500	.496
	1967-69④	.4614	.4800
	1969⑲	.5197	.5197
8-409	1963-65⑪	.400	.4119
	1963-64⑫	.5068	.5185
	1963-64⑩	.5068	.5185
	1965⑫	.5567	.5567
8-427	1966-68⑬	.4614	.4800
	1966-69⑭	.4614	.4800
	1967-69⑫	.4614	.4800
	1966-69⑮	.5917	.5917
	1966-69⑮	.5197	.5197
	1969⑳	.398	.398
	1969㉑	.5586	.580

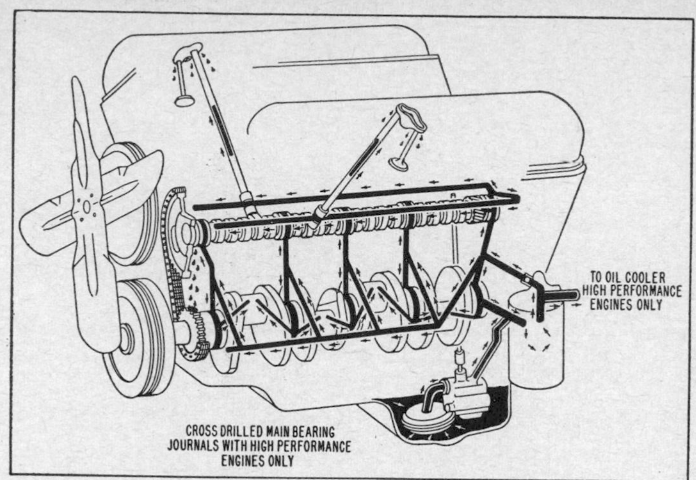

Engine lubrication. V8-396 and 427 engines

Engine oiling system. V8-409

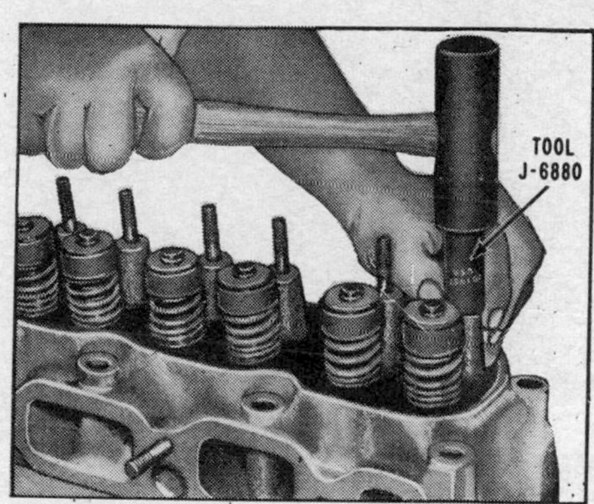

Fig. 9 Installing valve rocker arm stud

①—1964 Chevelle .407.
②—250 H.P. ⑫—400 H.P.
③—300 H.P. ⑬—385 H.P.
④—350 H.P. ⑭—390 H.P.
⑤—365 H.P. ⑮—435 H.P.
⑥—275 H.P. ⑯—255 H.P.
⑦—210 H.P. ⑰—370 H.P.
⑧—295 H.P. ⑱—265 H.P.
⑨—325 H.P. ⑲—375 H.P.
⑩—425 H.P. ⑳—335 H.P.
⑪—340 H.P. ㉑—430 H.P.

VALVE TIMING

Intake Opens Before TDC
All Except Corvette

Engine	Year	Degrees
4-153	1963-67	33½
	1968-69	17½
6-194	1963-64	34
	1965-67	62
6-230	1963-64 Chevrolet	34
	1963-64 Chevelle	34
	1963-64 Chevy II	49
	1965-67	62
	1968-69	16
6-250	1966-67	62
	1968-69	16
8-283	1963-66	32½
	1967 Chevrolet	38
	1967 Chevelle	38
	1967 Chevy II	36
8-307	1968-69	28
8-327	1963-66	32½
	1965 350 H.P.	54
	1966 350 H.P.	50
	1967 Chevrolet	38
	1967 Chevelle	38
	1967 Camaro	36
	1967-68 325 H.P.	54
	1968-69	28
8-350	1968	28
	1969 255, 300 H.P.	28
	1969 350 H.P.	52
8-396	1969 265, 325 H.P.	28
	1969 350 H.P.	56
	1968	28
	1965-68 325, 350 H.P.	40
	1965 425 H.P.	54
	1966-67 360 H.P.	56
8-409	1963-64 340 H.P.	38½
	1963 400, 425 H.P.	110
	1964 400, 425 H.P.	19¼
8-427	1966-67 385, 390 H.P.	56
	1966 425 H.P.	54
	1969 390, 400 H.P.	56
	1969 435 H.P.	44

Corvette

Engine	Year	Degrees
8-327	1963-66 250, 300 H.P.	32½
	1963 340, 360 H.P.	35
	1964-65 365, 375 H.P.	61
	1965-67 350 H.P.	54
	1967 300 H.P.	38
	1967-68 435 H.P.	44
	1968 300 H.P.	28
	1968 350 H.P.	40
8-427	1966-67 390, 400 H.P.	56
	1966 425 H.P.	54
	1967-69 435 H.P.	44
	1968 390, 400 H.P.	40
	1969 390, 400 H.P.	56
	1969 435 H.P.	44

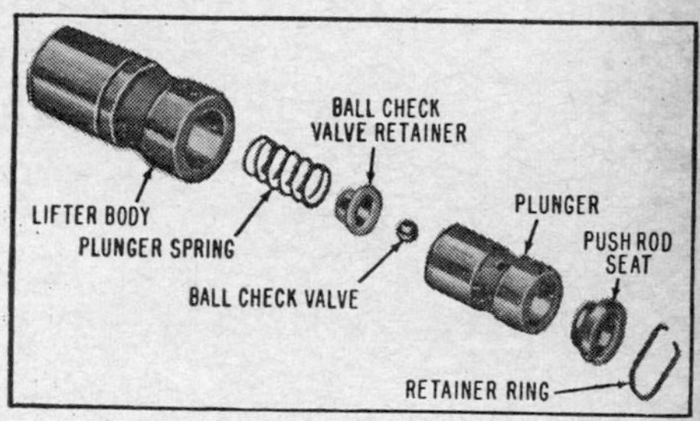

Fig. 11 Hydraulic valve lifter

PUSH RODS

On engines that use push rods with a hardened insert at one end, the hardened end is identified by a color stripe and should always be installed toward the rocker arm during assembly. The V8-409 engine exhaust push rods are longer than the intake and carry different color stripe for further identification.

Service Bulletin

On 6-cylinder engines with air conditioning, it is not necessary to remove the distributor wires, etc. to replace the valve push rod cover and/or gasket.

1. Remove coil and bracket from block.
2. Remove distributor hold-down clamp.
3. Lift distributor up for clearance (do not disengage from cam gear), then remove push rod cover.
4. Use new gasket and reverse procedure to install.

VALVE GUIDES

On all engines valves operate in guide holes bored in the head. If clearance becomes excessive, use the next oversize valve and ream the bore to fit. Valves with oversize stems are available in .003, .015 and .030".

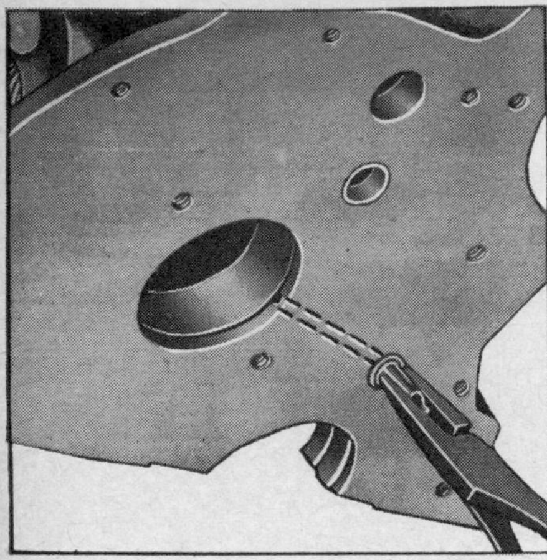

Fig. 12 Timing gear oil nozzle removal. 4-153, 6-194, 230, 250

HYDRAULIC LIFTERS

Valve lifters may be lifted from their bores after removing rocker arms and push rods. Adjustable pliers with taped jaws may be used to remove lifters that are stuck due to varnish, carbon, etc. Fig. 11 illustrates the type of lifter used.

TIMING CASE COVER

NOTE: On all engines the cover oil seal may be replaced without taking off the timing gear cover. After removing the vibration damper, pry out the old seal with a screwdriver. Install the new seal with the lip or open end toward inside of cover and drive it into position.

Fig. 14 Removing camshaft gear from camshaft. 4-153 and all 6 cylinder engines

1963-69 Four & Six Cylinder

1. To remove cover, remove radiator.
2. Remove vibration damper (6-cyl.) or pulley (4-cyl.).
3. Remove oil pan.
4. Unfasten and remove cover.
5. Pry oil seal out of cover with a large screwdriver. Install new seal with open side of seal inside of cover and drive or press seal into place.
6. If oil nozzle is to be replaced, remove it with pliers as shown in Fig. 12. Drive new nozzle in place, using a suitable light plastic or rubber hammer.
7. Clean gasket surfaces.
8. Install a suitable centering tool over end of crankshaft.
9. Coat gasket with light grease and stick it in position on block.
10. Install cover over centering tool, Fig. 13, and install cover screws, tightening them to 6 to 8 ft. lbs. *It is important that the centering tool be used to align the cover so the vibration damper installation will not damage the seal and position seal evenly around damper hub surface.*

1963-69 V8s

Remove vibration damper, oil pan, heater hose from water pump, and water pump from cylinder block. Unfasten and remove cover and gaskets.

Pry old seal out of cover from the front with a large screwdriver. Install the new seal so the open end of the seal is toward the inside of the cover and drive it into position with a suitable driver, being sure to support cover at sealing area.

1. Make certain that the mating faces of cover and block are clean and flat.
2. Make certain oil slinger is in place against crankshaft sprocket.
3. Coat oil seal with light grease and, using a new cover gasket, install cover and gasket over dowel pins in cylinder block.
4. Install and tighten cover screws to 6-8 lb. ft. torque.
5. Install oil pan, harmonic balancer and water pump.
6. Start engine and check for leaks.

TIMING GEARS

4-153 & All 6 Cyl. Engines

When necessary to install a new camshaft gear, the camshaft will have to be removed as the gear is a pressed fit on the shaft. The camshaft is held in position by a thrust plate which is fastened to the crankcase by two capscrews which are accessible through two holes in the gear web.

Use an arbor press to remove the gear and when doing so, a suitable sleeve, Fig. 14, should be employed to support the gear properly on its steel hub.

Before installing a new gear, assemble a new thrust plate on the shaft and press the gear on just far enough so that the thrust plate has practically no clearance, yet is free to turn. The correct clearance is from .001" to .005", Fig. 15.

The crankshaft gear can be removed by utilizing the two tapped holes in conjunction with a gear puller.

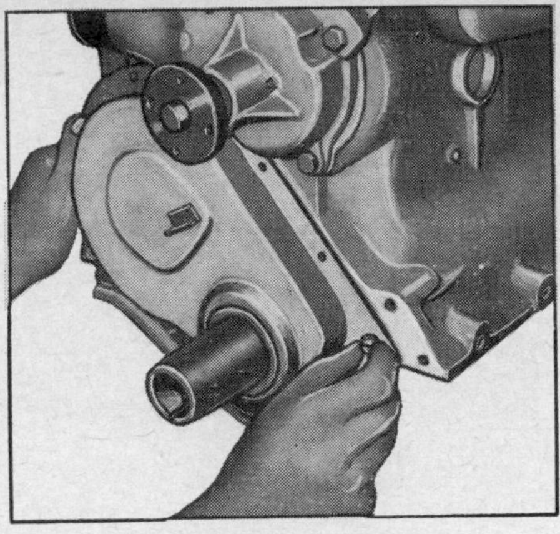

Fig. 13 Installing timing case cover. 4-153, 6-194, 230, 250

When the timing gears are installed, be sure the punch-marks on both gears are in mesh, Fig. 16. Backlash between the gears should be from .004" to .006", Fig. 17. Check the run-out of the gears, and if the camshaft gear run-out exceeds .004" or the crank gear run-out is in excess of .003", remove the gear (or gears) and examine for burrs, dirt or some other fault which may cause the run-out. If these conditions are not the cause, replace the gear (or gears).

TIMING CHAIN

V8 Engines

1. Remove timing chain cover as outlined previously.
2. Remove crankshaft oil slinger.
3. Crank engine until "O" marks on sprockets are in alignment, Fig. 18.
4. Remove three camshaft-to-sprocket bolts.
5. Remove camshaft sprocket and timing chain together. Sprocket is a light press fit on camshaft for approximately ⅛". If sprocket does not come off easily, a light blow with a plastic hammer on the lower edge of the sprocket should dislodge it.
6. If crankshaft sprocket is to be replaced, remove it with a suitable gear puller. Install new sprocket,

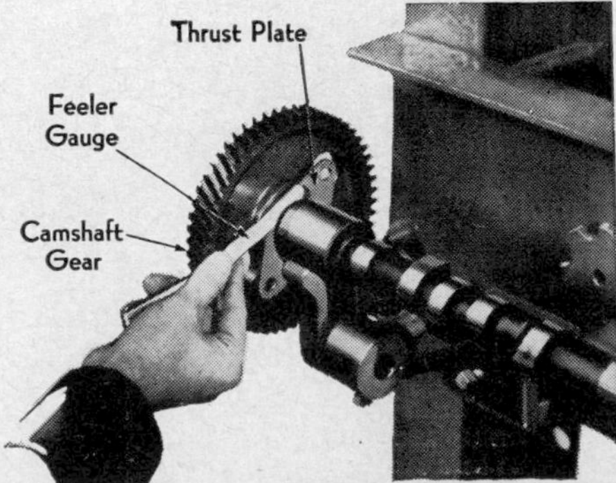

Fig. 15 Checking camshaft end play which should be .001 to .005". 4-153 and all 6 cylinder engines

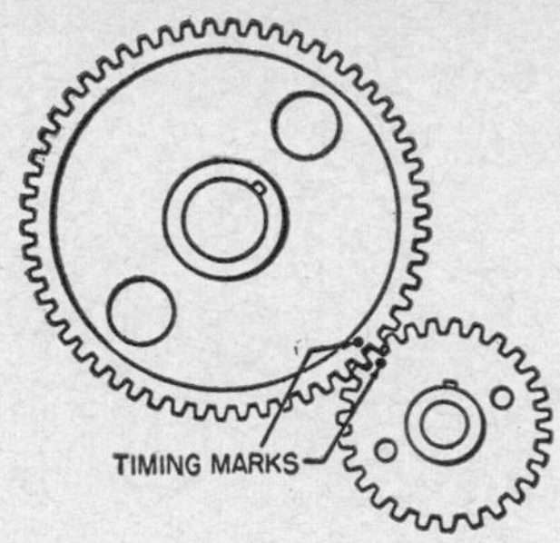

Fig. 16 Timing gear locating marks. 4-153 and all 6 cylinder engines

aligning key and keyway.

7. Install chain on camshaft sprocket. Hold sprocket vertical with chain hanging below and shift around to align the "O" marks on sprockets.
8. Align dowel in camshaft with dowel hole in sprocket and install sprocket on camshaft. *Do not attempt to drive sprocket on camshaft as welch plug at rear of engine can be dislodged.*
9. Draw sprocket onto camshaft, using the three mounting bolts. Tighten to 15-20 lb. ft. torque.
10. Lubricate timing chain and install cover.

CAMSHAFT

Service Bulletin

Camaro Camshaft Removal: On 6-cylinder jobs, it has been found that it is much easier to remove the engine from the chassis rather than performing the operation with the engine in the car. Once the engine is removed, take out the camshaft as outlined below.

4-153, 6-194, 6-230, 6-250

To remove the camshaft, remove radiator, grille, push rods, valve lifters, oil pan, vibration damper (6 cyl) or pulley (4 cyl), and timing case cover. Then pull out camshaft and gear assembly.

If necessary to replace bearings, the engine will have to be removed from the chassis. Then remove camshaft, flywheel and crankshaft. Drive out the expansion plug at the rear of the rear camshaft bearing and use suitable equipment to remove and replace the bearings.

Fig. 17 Checking timing gear backlash with feeler gauge. Lash should be .004 to .006". 4-153 and all 6 cylinder engines

V8 Engines

To remove the camshaft, remove valve lifters, fuel pump and its push rod, radiator, timing chain and camshaft sprocket. Install two $\frac{5}{16}$"-18 x 4" bolts in two camshaft bolt holes. Using these bolts as a puller, remove camshaft.

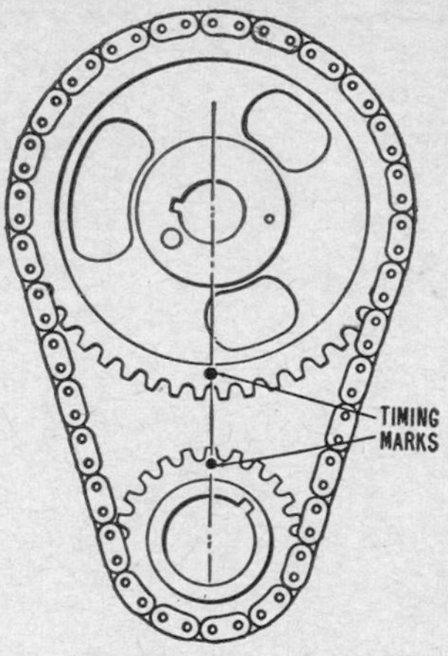

Fig. 18 Timing gear locating marks. V8 engines

PISTONS & RODS, ASSEMBLE

1963-69

Assemble pistons to connecting rods as shown in Figs. 21 to 29.

PISTON OVERSIZES

4-153	.001, .020, .030, .040"
6 Cyl.	.001, .020, .030, .040"
V8-283	.001, .020, .030, .040"
V8-302, 307, 327	.001, .020, .030"
V8-348, 409	.001, .030"
V8-396	.001, .020, .030"
V8-427 390 H.P.	.001, .020, .030"
V8-427, 425, 435 H.P.	.001, .030, .060"

RING OVERSIZES

4-153, 6-230, 6-250	.020, .030, .040"
V8-327	.020, .030"
6-194	.020, .040"
V8-283, 409	.020, .030, .040"
V8-396	.020, .030"
V8-427 390 H.P.	.020, .030"
V8-427, 425, 435 H.P.	.030, .060"

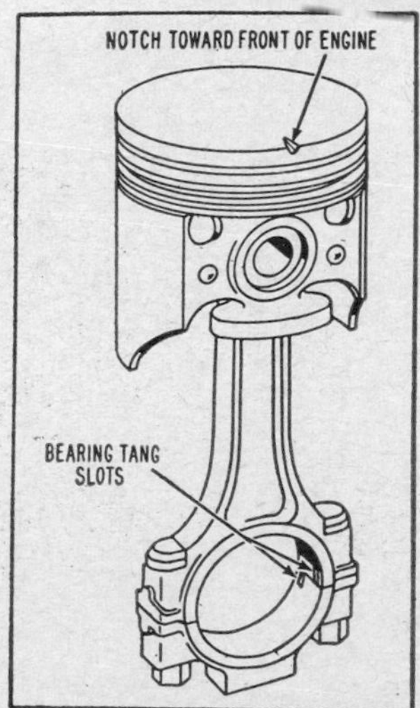

Fig. 21 Piston and rod assembly. 6-194 engine

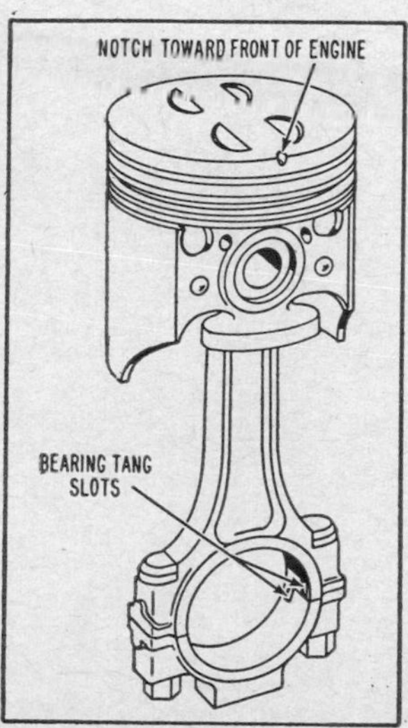

Fig. 22 Piston and rod assembly. 4-153 and 6-230 engines

Fig. 23 Piston and rod assembly. 6-250 engine

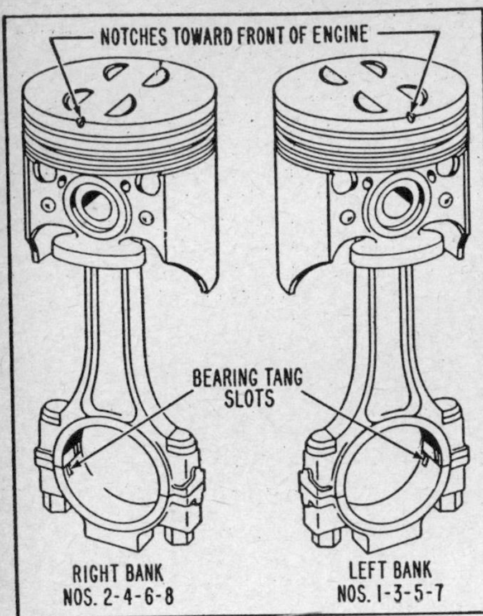

Fig. 24 V8-283, 307, 350 and 327 (except 325 and 350 H.P.)

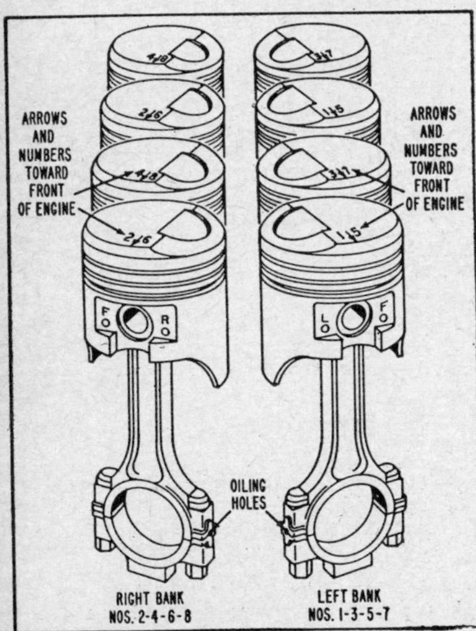

Fig. 25 V8-409 standard engine

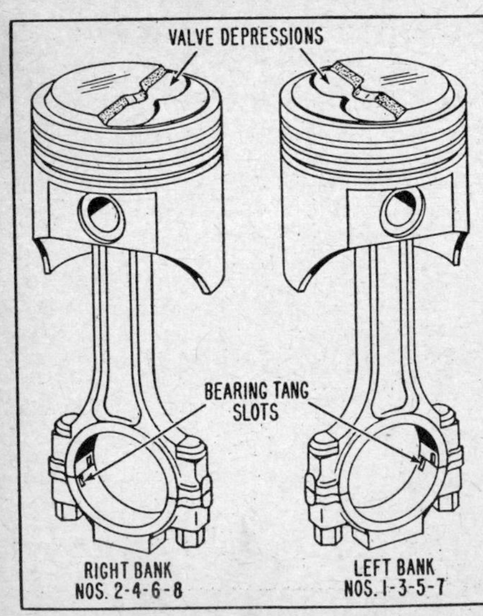

Fig. 26 V8-302, 327 (325 and 350 H.P.)

MAIN & ROD BEARINGS

Undersizes

On all engines main and rod bearings are available in undersizes of .001, .002, .010 and .020".

SERVICE BULLETIN

Connecting rod type noise correction on 6-194 and 6-230 engines may be made as follows:

Remove connecting rod cap and Plastigage the bearings. If clearance is within .001 to .002", reinstall cap and retaining nuts. Then tighten nuts to the proper torque as listed in the *Engine Tightening Specifications* table.

NOTE 4-153 & All 6 Cyl.

The rear main bearing journal has no oil hole drilling. To remove the upper bearing half (bearing half with oil hole) proceed as follows after cap is removed:

1. Use a small drift punch and hammer to start the bearing rotating out of the block.
2. Use a pair of pliers (tape jaws) to hold the bearing thrust surface to the oil slinger and rotate the crankshaft to pull the bearing out.
3. To install, start the bearing (side not notched) into side of block by hand, then use pliers as before to turn bearing half into place.
4. The last ¼" movement may be done by holding just the slinger with the pliers or tap in place with a drift punch.

CRANKSHAFT REAR OIL SEAL

4-153, 6-194, 230, 250

Both halves of the seal Fig. 30 can be removed without removal of the crankshaft. Always replace upper and lower seal as a unit.

1. Remove oil pan and rear main bearing cap.
2. Remove seal from groove, prying from bottom with a small screwdriver.
3. Clean crankshaft surface. Then insert a new seal, well lubricated with engine oil, in bearing cap groove. *Keep oil off parting line surface as this surface is treated with glue.*
4. Gradually push with a hammer handle until seal is rolled into place.
5. To replace upper half of seal, use a small hammer and brass pin punch to tap one end of seal until it protrudes far enough to be removed with pliers. Install the new seal.
6. Install bearing cap and oil pan.

1963-69 V8

When necessary to correct an oil leak due to a defective seal, always replace the upper and lower seal halves as a unit. *When installing either half, lubricate the lip portion only with engine oil, keeping oil off the parting line surface as this is*

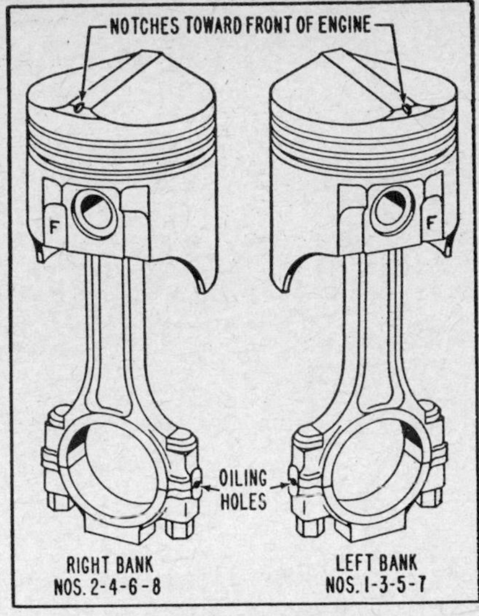

Fig. 27 V8-409 High performance engine

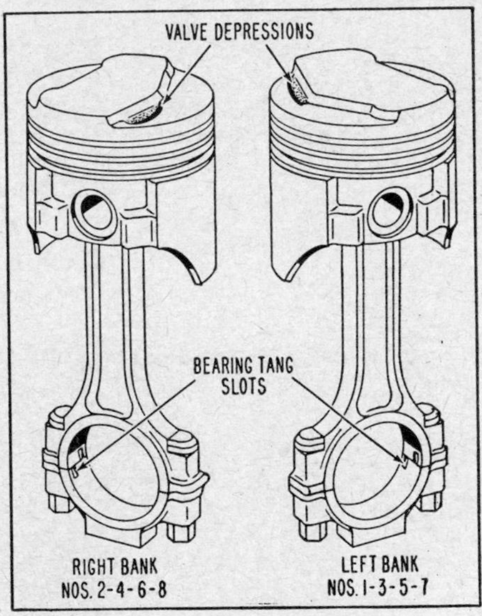

Fig. 28 V8-396 engine

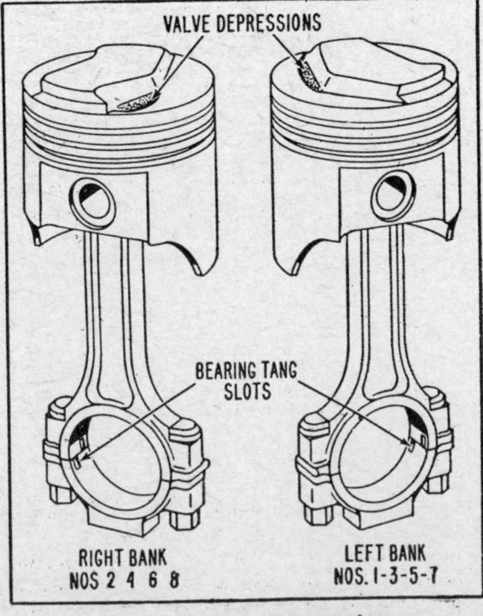

Fig. 29 V8-427 engine

treated with glue. Always clean crankshaft surface before installing a new seal. Be careful of seal retainer tang while inserting a new seal so that it doesn't cut the seal.

1. To replace the lower seal, remove seal from groove in bearing cap, using a small screwdriver to pry it out.
2. Insert new seal and roll it in place with finger and thumb.
3. To replace the upper seal (with engine in car) use a small hammer and tap a brass pin punch on one end of the seal until it protrudes far enough to be removed with pliers.
4. Insert the new seal, gradually pushing with a hammer handle until seal is rolled into place.
5. Install bearing cap with new seal and tighten bearing cap bolts.

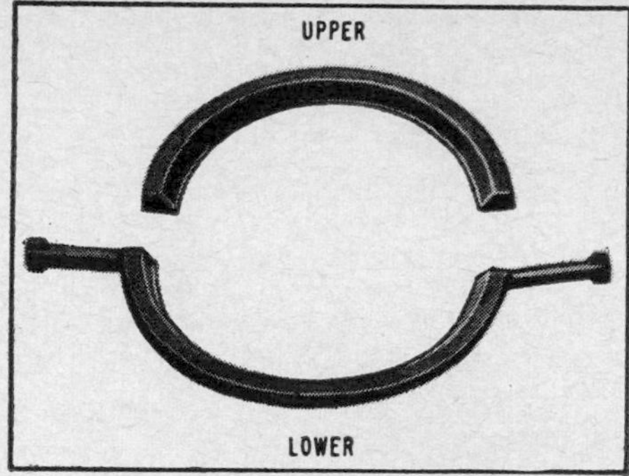
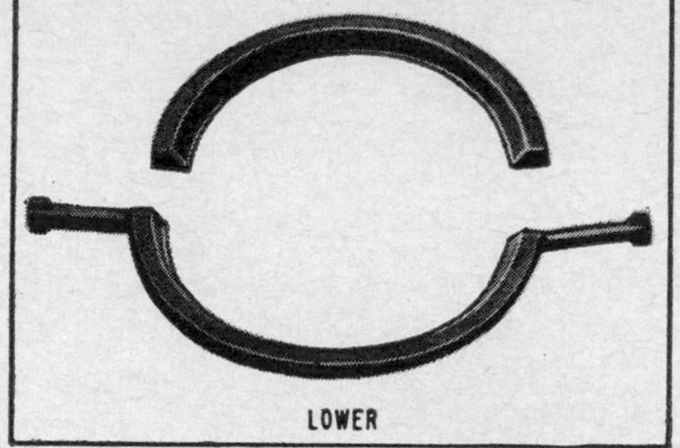

Fig. 30 Crankshaft rear oil seal. 4-153, 6-194, 230, 250

OIL PAN

1965-69 Chevrolet, Camaro, 1968-69 Chevelle with Auto. Trans. Exc. V8-396 1968-69 Chevy II

1. Disconnect battery ground cable.
2. On V8s, lift cap off distributor to prevent damaging cap when engine is raised.
3. Remove through bolts from engine front mounts.
4. Remove fan blade and starter.
5. Disconnect cooler lines (if equipped) at transmission and remove converter housing underpan.
6. Disconnect steering linkage at idler lever and swing linkage for pan clearance.
7. Rotate crankshaft until timing mark on vibration damper is at 6 o'clock position.
8. Use a suitable jack and a block of wood to prevent damage to oil pan and raise engine enough to insert 2" x 4" wood blocks under engine mounts; then lower engine to blocks.

On 1968-69 Chevy II, attach a cantilever hoist or chain-fall to engine. If chain-fall is used, disconnect and move hood out of the way.

NOTE: If 2" x 4" wood blocks are cut 5½" long they can be used on all Chevrolet engines. The 5½" length up for 4 and 6 cylinder engines and the 4" side for V8 engines.

9. On Camaro six-cylinder models, after oil pan bolts are removed and oil pan lowered, remove the oil pump, then remove the pan. On all other models, remove the pan without removing the pump.

NOTE: On 396 and 427 engines the oil pan has three ¼"-20 attaching bolts at the crankcase front cover—one at each corner and one at lower center.

1969 Chevelle V8 with Std. Trans. & V8-396 with Auto. Trans.

The engine must be completely disconnected from its mounts, front and rear, and the crossmember disconnected and moved rearward to allow the engine to be raised high enough to provide clearance for the oil pan to be removed. The engine therefore, must be supported by a fabricated hook and a suitable chain, hung over the cowl, Fig. 31, or by removing the hood and attaching a chain hoist to raise the engine. *Because the engine is free and the crossmember removed, use caution.*

Fig. 31 Install strap over cowl

Once the engine has been raised and secured, proceed as outlined for Chevelle V8 with auto. trans.

1965-67 Chevelle All & 1968-69 Chevelle Six with Std. Trans.

1. Remove engine from vehicle.
2. Remove flywheel or converter housing underpan.
3. Remove starter and oil pan.

1965-67 Chevy II

1. Disconnect battery ground cable.
2. Remove starter.
3. Disconnect steering idler arm bracket at right frame side rail and swing linkage down for pan clearance.
4. On 6-cylinder engines, remove front crossmember. On Station Wagons, let stabilizer bar hang down while removing crossmember.
5. On V8s, disconnect exhaust pipes from manifolds and allow pipes to hang.
6. Remove oil pan.

1965-69 Corvette

1. Disconnect battery and remove oil dipstick and tube.
2. Remove starter and flywheel underpan.
3. Disconnect steering linkage idler arm at frame and lower linkage.
4. Remove oil pan.
5. On high performance engines, the oil baffle must be removed before additional operations can be performed.

NOTE: On 427 engines the oil pan has three ¼"-20 bolts at the crankcase front cover—one at each corner and one at lower center.

1964 V8-283, 327 Engines

1. Raise front of car and place on jack stands or raise on hoist.
2. Drain cooling system and crankcase.
3. Disconnect radiator hoses from engine.

NOTE: Remove water outlet from engine instead of removing hose clamps from upper hose.

4. Disconnect battery ground cable.
5. Remove fuel lines from pump.

SERVICE NOTE: Before removing fuel pump, remove upper bolts from engine front mount boss, located to right of timing chain cover on front of engine. This threaded hole enters fuel pump push rod bore with a production installed bolt acting as a plug. Next install a ⅜-16x1¾" bolt into the hole, turning it by hand until it stops, which indicates it is contacting push rod. A wrench should never be used to draw up on the bolt as this would result in push rod damage.

6. Remove fuel pump.
NOTE: After the pump has been reinstalled, the original (shorter) bolt must be reinstalled in the front of the engine block.

7. Remove accelerator control rod from both control rod lever and carburetor.
8. If equipped with power steering, disconnect power cylinder at relay rod.
9. Unfasten exhaust pipe flange from manifold and lower exhaust pipe and muffler assembly.
10. Loosen but do not remove transmission mounting bolts.
11. Remove radiator fan.
12. Remove thru-bolt from engine front mounts.
13. Rotate crankshaft so that keyway in vibration damper or crankshaft hub is at bottom of engine. This will index crankshaft counterweights so baffle in oil pan will clear.
14. Remove carburetor air cleaner.
15. Remove distributor cap with wires.
16. Remove starter motor.
17. Raise front of engine slightly more than 3" to clear frame crossmember for oil pan removal.
    NOTE: Engine may be raised from below by placing a suitable wood block under vibration damper or crankshaft hub.
18. Lower engine on to wood blocks to support engine at front mount locations. These blocks should be about 3" in thickness.
19. Unfasten and remove oil pan.

1963-64 V8-409

When necessary to remove the oil pan, the engine and transmission should be removed as a unit.

NOTE: To gain clearance for removal of the engine and transmission on 425 H.P. engine, it will be necessary first to remove the right-hand exhaust manifold.

1963-64 Chevrolet Six

The oil pan can be removed by either of two methods: (1) After removing the engine from the vehicle or (2) with the engine in the vehicle. However, inasmuch as it takes less time to remove and replace the engine than it does for the oil pan, and since the pan removal operation is so complex, it is recommended that the engine be removed.

1964 Chevelle 6 & V8

1. Remove engine from vehicle as outlined previously.
2. Remove starting motor.
3. Remove oil pan.
   NOTE: On 6-cylinder engines, the oil pan front seal curvature should straddle front main bearing cap and rear of oil pan will then just clear flywheel.

1963-64 Chevy II 4 & 6 Cyl.

1. Disconnect battery ground strap.
2. Remove starter.
3. Disconnect steering idler arm bracket at right frame side rail and swing steering linkage down for pan clearance.
4. On 6 cylinder only, remove front crossmember. On station wagon, let stabilizer bar hang while removing crossmember.
5. Unfasten and remove pan.
6. Install seal in rear main bearing cap. Install front seal in timing gear cover, pressing tips into holes provided in cover.
7. Install side gaskets in cylinder block, using grease as a retainer. Side gasket tabs index into notches of front seal.
8. Install oil pan. *Screws into timing gear cover should be installed last. They are installed at an angle and holes line up after rest of pan bolts are snugged up.*

1964 Chevy II V8

1. Disconnect battery ground strap.
2. Remove starting motor.
3. Disconnect dipstick tube bracket at manifold, then disconnect steering idler arm bracket at right hand frame side rail and swing steering linkage down for pan clearance.
4. Disconnect exhaust cover at manifolds and allow crossover to hang free.
5. Drain oil, remove pan bolts and pan.

1963 V8-283, 327

1. Drain crankcase and cooling system.
2. Disconnect hoses at radiator.
3. Disconnect ground strap at engine.
4. If equipped with synchromesh transmission, disconnect clutch pedal push rod at clutch pedal control, intermediate lever and shaft. Remove clutch pedal control, intermediate lever and shaft assembly at frame mounting bracket, leaving shaft assembly attached to engine.
5. Remove fuel pump.
6. If equipped with Air Suspension, disconnect hose to alcohol vaporizer bottle and hose assembly from air compressor to accumulator tank.
7. Remove accelerator control rod from its lever.
8. If equipped with power brake, remove vacuum hose at check valve at engine manifold.
9. If equipped with power steering, remove power pump from generator in order to clear power brake master cylinder.
10. Remove transmission lower control rods at transmission levers.
11. Disconnect and lower exhaust pipe and muffler assembly from exhaust manifold. Then remove starter.
12. Remove oil filter.
13. Loosen transmission mounting bolts.
14. Remove long bolt from each front mounting.
15. Turn crankshaft so that vibration damper keyway slot is at bottom of engine. This will position crankshaft counterweights so baffle in oil pan will clear.
16. Engine will have to be raised approximately 3" to clear frame crossmember for oil pan removal. Raise engine until transmission housing comes in contact with underbody toe pan. Note clearance at fan blade and shroud while lifting engine and adjust for clearance as required.
17. Remove pan bolts and tilt oil pan while removing.

Note—Removal of the oil pan with Turboglide transmission installed is identical to the foregoing procedure except that the transmission control lever cross shaft at the transmission shifter lever and shaft assembly must be removed.

1963-64 Corvette

1. Disconnect battery ground cable.
2. Raise and support vehicle.
3. Drain oil pan.
4. Remove starter and flywheel (or converter) underpan.
5. On 340 and 360 H.P. engines, disconnect steering linkage idler arm at frame and lower linkage for clearance of pan-to-bearing cap mounted oil baffle plate.
6. Unfasten and remove oil pan.

OIL PUMP

4-153, 6-194, 6-230, 6-250

The pumps used in these engines are of the positive gear type. After disassembling the pump, examine the shaft and gears for excessive wear and replace where necessary, or better still, install a new pump. When assembling the pump, be sure the ground side of the idler gear is toward the cover.

The gasket used between the pump cover and the body is special in that it controls the clearance in the pump. If the relief valve parts show wear, install new parts. Be sure that the tapered set screw which holds the pump in place is fully seated and locked with its lock nut.

V8 Engines

After removing the oil pan, unfasten pump from rear main bearing cap. Disconnect pump shaft from extension by removing clip from collar. Remove pump cover and take out idler gear, drive gear and shaft.

Should any of the following conditions be found it is advisable to replace the pump assembly.

1. Inspect pump body for cracks or wear.
2. Inspect gears for wear or damage.
3. Check shaft for looseness in housing.
4. Check inside of cover for wear that would permit oil to leak past the ends of gear.
5. Check oil pick-up screen for damage to screen, by-pass valve or body.
6. Check for oil in air chamber.

WATER PUMP, REPLACE

All Models

1. Drain radiator and break loose fan pulley bolts.
2. Disconnect heater hose at water pump.
3. Loosen Delcotron and remove fan belt, then unfasten and remove pump. On 6-cylinder engines, pull pump straight out of block first to prevent damage to impeller.
4. Reverse procedure to install.

FUEL PUMP, REPLACE

1963-69

1. Disconnect fuel lines at pump.
2. Unfasten and remove pump.
3. If push rod is to be removed on 396 and 427 engines, remove pipe plug, then remove push rod. On 8-283, 302, 307, 327 and 350 engines, remove

fuel pump adapter and gasket, then remove push rod.

4. Reverse procedure to install. *On V8 engines, a pair of mechanical fingers may be used to hold fuel pump push rod up while installing pump.*

NOTE

Installation of the pump on V8-283 and 327 engines can be performed faster by using the following means of retaining the fuel pump push rod in the engine during pump replacement.

1. Before removing the pump, remove upper bolt from engine front mount boss located to the right of the timing chain cover on the front of the engine. This bolt enters the push rod bore acting as a plug.
2. Remove the original bolt and install one that is 1¾" long. Turn it down by hand until it is stopped by the push rod. *Do not use a wrench to turn in this bolt as it may damage the push rod, necessitating its replacement.*
3. The fuel pump can then be removed without the push rod slipping from its installed position. After installing the pump, the original shorter bolt must be reinstalled to avoid oil leakage.

Service Bulletin

On 396 and 427 engines the access hole for removal of the fuel pump push rod is located below the fuel pump mounting bolts. This access hole, which permits removal of the push rod after the pump has been removed, has a threaded plug with a square recessed hole. The plug may be removed by using a hand-made tool. A $\frac{5}{16}$" square end for inserting and turning the plug for removal is required. A piece of bar stock, approximately 1½" long is suggested.

Clutch and Transmission Section

NOTE: 1969 linkage adjustment information is in this section. Repair procedures on both automatic and manual shift transmissions are covered elsewhere in this manual. Procedures for removing automatic transmissions as well as linkage adjustments on 1963-68 models are included in the automatic transmission chapters. See Chapter Index.

CLUTCH PEDAL, ADJUST

1968-69 Chevrolet & Corvette

1. Disconnect spring between clutch push rod and cross shaft lever.
2. With clutch pedal against stop, loosen jam nuts just enough to allow adjusting rod to move against the clutch fork until the release bearing contacts the pressure plate fingers lightly.
3. Rotate upper nut against swivel and back off 4½ turns. Tighten lower nut to lock swivel against nut.
4. Install return spring and check clutch pedal free travel:
   Chevrolet 1 to 1½".
   Corvette standard clutch 1¼ to 2".
   Corvette heavy duty clutch 2 to 2½".

1968-69 Chevelle, Camaro, Chevy II

1. Disconnect return spring at clutch fork.
2. With clutch pedal against stop, loosen lock nut just enough to allow the adjusting rod to be turned out off swivel and against clutch fork until release bearing contacts pressure plate fingers lightly.
3. Rotate push rod into swivel three turns and tighten lock nut.

NOTE: Chevy II and Camaro V8 models use a two-piece push rod. Turn adjusting rod portion of push rod three turns into rod end and tighten lock nut.

4. Reinstall return spring and check clutch pedal free travel:
   Chevelle 1⅛ to 1¾".
   Chevy II and Camaro 1 to 1⅛".

1966-67 Models

There is one linkage adjustment (clutch fork push rod or pedal push rod) to compensate for all normal clutch wear.

The clutch pedal should have 1 to 1¼" free travel (measured at clutch pedal pad) before the clutch release bearing engages the clutch diaphragm levers. Lash is required to prevent clutch slippage that would occur if the bearing was held against the diaphragm levers and to prevent the bearing from running continually until failure occurs.

1965 Models

There is one linkage adjustment (clutch fork push rod or pedal push rod) to compensate for all normal clutch wear. The clutch pedal should have ¾" to 1⅛" travel on Chevrolet, Chevelle and Chevy II models and 1¼" on Corvette.

1963-64 Chevrolet & Corvette

Adjustment is made on the lower end of the pedal push rod. Adjust the push rod so there is free pedal travel of ⅞" to 1⅛" on Chevrolet and ¾" to 1" on Corvette.

1963-64 Chevy II

Adjust clutch pedal free travel by turning the adjusting rod portion of the push rod to obtain about ⅛" clearance between clutch fork and end of rod, then tighten locknut. Free pedal travel should be ¾" to 1⅛".

1964 Chevelle

1. Disconnect spring between cross shaft lever and clutch fork.
2. Loosen push rod locknut about three turns.
3. If there is no free travel, shorten rod by turning at square wrench area until it is free of clutch fork.
4. Hold clutch fork rearward to move release bearing lightly against clutch release fingers. Then adjust rod length until rod just touches its seat in fork.
5. Adjust locknut to obtain about $\frac{3}{16}$" clearance between nut and rod sleeve end.
6. Turn rod with wrench until nut just comes in contact with rod sleeve end, then hold rod with wrench and tighten locknut.
7. Free travel at pedal should be ¾ to 1⅛". Readjust if necessary.

CLUTCH, REPLACE

Clutch Disc Installation

On all 4 and 6-cylinder engines the clutch disc is installed with the damper springs to the flywheel side. On V8's install clutch disc with damper springs and grease slinger to transmission side.

1964-69

1. Support engine and remove transmission as outlined in Transmission Section.
2. Disconnect clutch fork push rod and spring.
3. Remove flywheel housing.
4. Slide clutch fork from ball stud and remove fork from dust boot.

NOTE: Look for "X" mark on flywheel and on clutch cover. If "X" mark is not evident, prick punch marks on flywheel and clutch cover for indexing purposes during installation.

5. Loosen clutch-to-flywheel attaching bolts evenly one turn at a time until spring pressure is released. Then remove bolts and clutch assembly.
6. Reverse procedure to install.

1964 Chevelle

1. Remove transmission.
2. Disconnect clutch fork push rod and spring.
3. Remove flywheel housing.

NOTE: Look for "X" marks on flywheel and on clutch cover. If "X" mark is not evident, prick punch marks on flywheel and clutch cover for indexing purposes during installation.

4. Loosen clutch-to-flywheel attaching bolts evenly one turn at a time until spring pressure is released, then remove bolts and clutch assembly.
5. Reverse removal procedure to install the clutch, then adjust pedal free travel as outlined above.

1963 Chevy II

1. Remove transmission as outlined further on.
2. Disconnect clutch linkage return spring from clutch fork and let push rod hang free of fork.
3. Remove release bearing from fork.
4. Remove attaching screws and remove clutch housing.
5. Slide clutch fork from ball stud and remove fork from dust boot.
6. Loosen clutch attaching bolts a little at a time until clutch diaphragm spring tension is relieved. Then remove clutch.
7. Replace in the reverse order of removal and adjust clutch linkage.

1963 Chevrolet & 1963-65 Corvette

1. Remove transmission.
2. Remove clutch release bearing from fork.
3. Remove clutch fork tension spring.
4. Disconnect clutch fork push rod.
5. To remove fork, force it forward and toward center of vehicle.
6. Loosen clutch attaching bolts one turn at a time until diaphragm spring tension is released. Then remove bolts and take clutch from vehicle.

THREE SPEED TRANSMISSION, REPLACE

1968-69 Corvette

1. Disconnect battery ground cable.
2. Remove shift ball.
3. Remove console trim plate.
4. Raise vehicle on a hoist.
5. Remove right and left exhaust pipes. *In order to remove the exhaust pipes on 8-396 and 427 engines, it will be necessary to remove the forward stud on each manifold.*
6. Disconnect and lower front of propeller shaft. Remove slip yoke from transmission.
7. Remove bolts retaining rear mounts to bracket. Raise engine, lifting transmission off mount bracket.
8. Unfasten transmission linkage mounting bracket from frame.
9. Detach gearshift from mounting bracket and remove bracket. Remove shifter mechanism with rods attached.
10. Disconnect shifter levers at transmission. Disconnect speedometer cable.
11. Unfasten and remove transmission mount bracket. Unfasten rear mount cushion and exhaust pipe yoke.
12. Unfasten transmission from clutch housing.
13. Pull transmission rearward and rotate clockwise until it is clear of clutch housing. *To allow room for transmission removal, slowly lower rear of engine until tachometer drive cable at the distributor just clears horizontal ledge across front of dash.*

CAUTION: The tachometer cable can be easily damaged by heavy contact with the dash. Slide transmission rearward out of the clutch, then tip front end of transmission downward and lower assembly from vehicle.

14. Reverse procedure to install.

1968-69 Except Corvette

1. Support vehicle on a hoist.
2. Disconnect speedometer cable at transmission and, on floor shift models, disconnect back-up lamp switch.
3. Remove propeller shaft.
4. On Camaro models, disconnect exhaust pipe at manifold.
5. Remove crossmember-to-frame attaching bolts. On floor shift models, remove crossmember-to-control lever support attaching bolts. On Chevelle, also remove control lever brace-to-crossmember attaching bolt.
6. Remove bolts retaining transmission mount to crossmember.
7. Support engine and raise slightly until crossmember may be slid rearward or removed.
8. Remove shift levers at transmission side cover. On floor shift models, remove stabilizer-to-control lever retaining nut. Push bolt toward transmission until stabilizer rod may be disconnected.
9. Remove transmission-to-clutch housing upper retaining bolts and install guide pins in holes, then remove lower bolts.
10. Slide transmission rearward and remove from vehicle.
11. Reverse procedure to install.

1963-67 Corvette

1. Disconnect battery ground cable.
2. Disassemble shift lever.
3. Raise front and rear of vehicle.
4. Insert a block of wood between top of differential carrier housing and underbody to prevent upward travel of carrier when carrier front support is disconnected.
5. Disconnect differential carrier front support from its frame bracket by removing nut on underside of biscuit mount.
6. Pry carrier downward to relieve load while removing two center mounting bolts from carrier front support.

NOTE: To pry carrier downward, insert crowfoot end of a pry bar through opening in carrier front support, hooking end of bar over top of center mounting bolt pad cast in underside of carrier.

7. Pivot carrier support downward for access to propeller shaft U-joint.
8. Disconnect propeller shaft front and then rear U-bolts.
9. Disconnect parking brake cable from ball socket at idler lever, located near center of underbody.
10. Move propeller shaft forward to remove from car.
11. Remove heat deflectors from right and left exhaust pipes.
12. Remove left bank exhaust pipe.
13. Remove right bank exhaust pipe and heat riser.
14. Disassemble transmission mount, supporting engine with a jack and wood block under oil pan. Raise engine to remove load from rear mount cushion.
15. Remove transmission-to-mount bracket bolts. Remove two bolts from mount pad-to-transmission case and remove rubber mount cushion and exhaust pipe "yoke".
16. Disconnect shift levers from transmission side cover.
17. Disconnect speedometer cable.
18. Remove transmission output shaft slip yoke. *Yoke is removed to prevent tearing deflecting pad on underbody when transmission is being removed.*
19. Disconnect transmission shift control lever and bracket assembly from adapter plate on side of transmission.
20. Lower transmission, letting shift lever slide down and through dust boot in console.
21. Remove transmission-to-clutch housing bolts.
22. Slide transmission rearward from clutch and rotate it for access to three flat head machine screws in control lever bracket adapter plate. Then rotate transmission back to upright position.
23. To allow room for transmission removal, slowly lower rear of engine until tachometer drive cable at distributor just clears horizontal ledge across front of dash.

CAUTION: The tachometer cable can easily be damaged by heavy contact with dash. Slide transmission rearward out of clutch, then tip front end of transmission downward and lower assembly from vehicle.

24. Reverse procedure to install.

1965-67 Except Corvette

1. Remove propeller shaft.
2. Disconnect speedometer cable at transmission.
3. Disconnect shift rods at transmission levers.
4. Support engine.
5. Remove transmission-to-flywheel housing bolts.
6. Remove transmission crossmember-to-mount bolts.
7. Loosen transmission crossmember and move it rearward to allow ample room to remove the transmission.

NOTE: On Camaro models moving the crossmember rearward is not

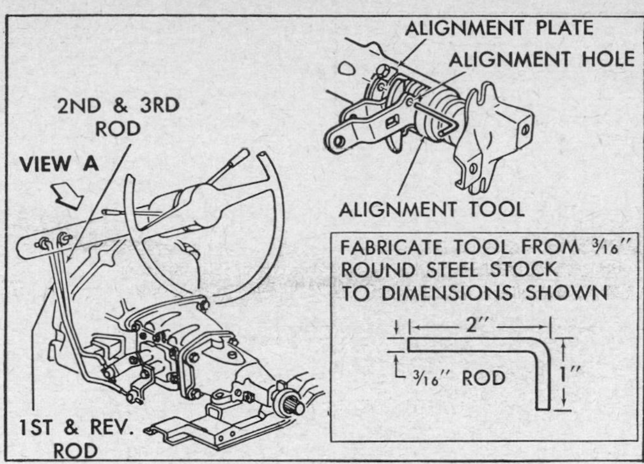

Fig. 1 Three-speed column shift linkage adjustment. Late 1967 and 1968 Chevrolet, Chevy II, Chevelle and Camaro

possible because the crossmember is mounted in a recess in the frame which is enclosed by the underbody of the car. Consequently, rather than moving the crossmember rearward, it must be completely removed during transmission assembly removal.

8. Slide transmission rearward and remove.
9. Reverse procedure to install.

1964 Chevelle

1. Remove propeller shaft.
2. Disconnect speedometer cable and shifter rods at transmission.
3. Support engine at rear.
4. Remove transmission-to-flywheel housing bolts.
5. Remove transmission mount.
6. Loosen transmission crossmember and move it rearward.
7. Slide transmission rearward and remove.
8. Reverse removal procedure to install, then check shift linkage adjustment.

1963-64 Chevy II

1. Disconnect speedometer cable and shift control rods at transmission.
2. Remove propeller shaft.
3. Support rear of engine and remove transmission mounting block-to-support (crossmember) bolts. Remove support-to-frame bolts and support.
4. Remove two top transmission-to-clutch housing capscrews and insert guide pins in these holes.
5. Remove the two lower attaching capscrews and slide transmission back and out of car.
6. Reverse removal procedure to install the transmission.

1963-64 Chevrolet

1. Disconnect speedometer cable.
2. Disconnect shift control rods from shift levers at transmission.
3. Remove propeller shaft.
4. Support rear of engine and remove transmission mounting block-to-support bolts and washers.
5. Remove support from frame, noting number of shims present (if any) so the same amount may be installed.
6. Remove two top transmission attaching cap screws and insert guide pins in these holes. Remove two lower attaching screws.
7. Slide transmission straight back on the guide pins until the clutch gear is free of the clutch disc splines.
8. Remove transmission from under body.
9. Reverse above procedure to install.

NOTE

If high gear hop-out is experienced on Corvette V8-283 engine, it is probably due to the transmission-to-clutch housing bolts being too short.

To insure proper attachment of the manual transmission to the aluminum clutch housing on these engines, it is necessary that 1¾" bolts be used. It is possible for shorter bolts to loosen, resulting in transmission misalignment and high gear hop-out.

The 1¾" bolt specified for this usage is available under Part No. 427565. An installation torque of 40-50 ft. lbs. is recommended when these bolts are used in the aluminum housing.

FOUR SPEED TRANSMISSION, REPLACE

1968-69 All Models

The procedure for removing this transmission is similar to that described for the 1968 3-speed units.

1963-67 Corvette

The procedure for removing these transmissions is similar to that described for the 3-speed units of the corresponding year.

1965-67 Except Corvette

1. Remove shift lever trim plate and dust boot.
2. Remove shift lever assembly.
3. Raise vehicle to working height.
4. Disconnect speedometer cable from driven gear fitting.
5. Remove propeller shaft.
6. Support engine at oil pan rail with a suitable jack or other device capable of supporting engine when transmission is removed.
7. Disconnect shift lever bracket from extension housing and remove all three shift levers from shifter shafts and remove bracket, levers and linkage.
8. Remove extension mount-to-crossmember bolts.
9. Loosen transmission crossmember and move it rearward or remove it entirely.
10. Remove transmission-to-clutch housing bolts and install guide pins in the two top holes.
11. Slide transmission rearward enough to allow sufficient clearance of input shaft and clutch housing. Then tilt input shaft end of transmission downward and withdraw transmission from vehicle.
12. Reverse procedure to install.

1964 Models

1. Remove shift lever trim plate and dust boot.
2. Remove shift lever assembly.
3. Raise vehicle to working height.
4. Disconnect speedometer cable.
5. Remove propeller shaft.
6. Support engine at oil pan rail with a jack or other suitable support capable of supporting engine when transmission is removed.
7. Disconnect shift lever bracket assembly from extension housing and remove all three transmission shift levers to shift shafts (leave linkage connected to levers) and remove bracket, levers and linkage.
8. Remove extension-to-crossmember bolts. Remove shims and note quantity so same amount may be reinstalled.
9. Loosen transmission crossmember frame side rail bracket bolts, removing one bolt completely allowing support crossmember to swing downward. On Chevelle, loosen transmission and move rearward.
10. Remove transmission-to-clutch housing bolts and install two guide pins in top holes.
11. Slide transmission straight back until input shaft is free of splines in clutch disc, and remove transmission from vehicle.
12. Reverse removal procedure to install, and adjust linkage as outlined further on.

1963 Models

1. Drain lubricant from transmission.
2. Disconnect speedometer cable and control rods from shift levers at transmission.
3. Remove drive shaft.
4. Support rear of engine and remove transmission mounting plate bolts.
5. Remove crossmember.
6. Unfasten transmission from clutch housing and install guide pins in two of the mounting holes.
7. Slide transmission back on guide pins and out of car.
8. Reverse procedure to install.

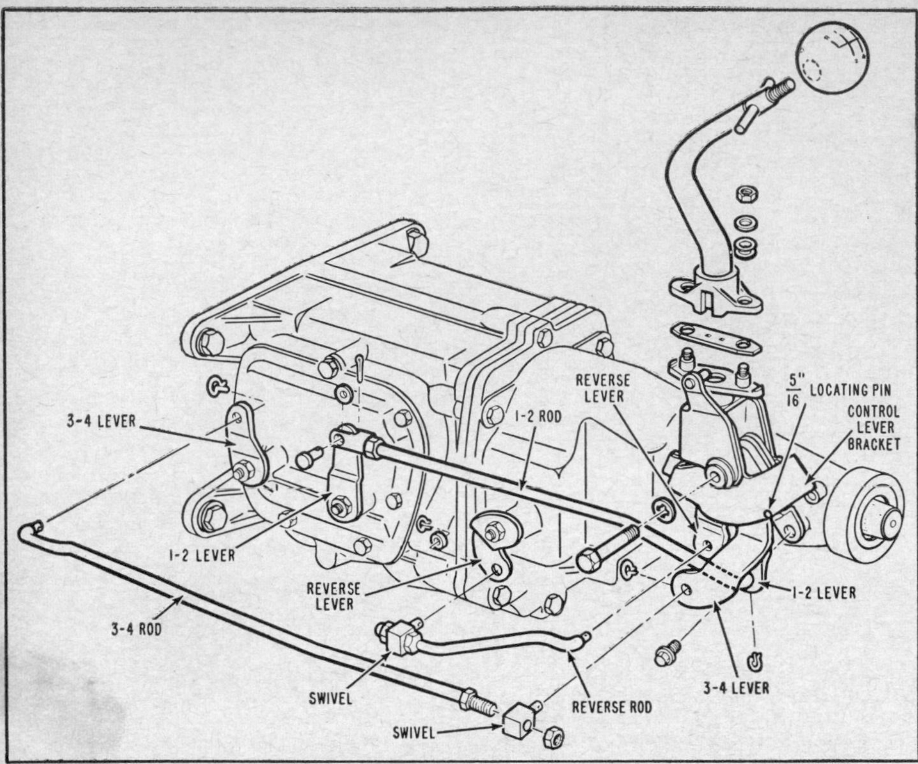

Fig. 2 Four speed transmission linkage. 1964-67 (typical)

THREE SPEED SHIFT LINKAGE, ADJUST

1968-69 (Also Late 1967) Chevrolet, Camaro, Chevelle, Chevy II

Column Shift

1. On 1969, place ignition switch in "Off" position. Loosen swivel locking clamps on both shift rods. Shift rods must pass freely through swivels.
2. Place shift lever handle in neutral. Insert fabricated L-shaped tool, Fig. 1, through 1/R lever, the relay lever and the 2/3 lever and then into the hole in the alignment plate bolted to the mast jacket.
3. Place transmission shift levers in neutral position.
4. Tighten both swivel clamp nuts on the rods, supporting swivels with one hand while tightening to insure against any movement of the swivels or rods.
5. Remove alignment tool from levers. Shift transmission through all ranges, then return to neutral. Reinsert tool; if it does not pass freely through alignment holes and bracket, loosen clamps and readjust linkage.
6. On 1969, turn key to "Lock" position and check ignition interlock control. If binding, leave control in "Lock" and readjust 1st/Rev. rod at the swivel.

1965-66 & Early 1967 Chevrolet, Camaro, Chevelle, Chevy II

Column Shift

1. Move both transmission shift levers until transmission is in neutral. Neutral detents in transmission cover must both be engaged to make this adjustment correctly. To check, start engine with clutch disengaged, and release clutch slowly.
2. Move selector lever to neutral position. Also align low-reverse tube lever with 2-3 shifter tube lever on mast jacket.
3. Align shift control rods and levers in neutral position.
4. Move selector levers through all positions to check adjustment and to insure over-travel in all positions.

1968-69 Chevelle, Camaro, Chevy II

Floor Shift

1. On 1969, place ignition switch in "Off" position. Loosen swivel locking clamps on both shift rods. Shift rods must pass freely through swivel.
2. Set shift lever in neutral and install a suitable locating gauge into the control lever bracket.
3. Manually place transmission shift levers in neutral.
4. Run 1/R shift rod nut against swivel and tighten lock nut against swivel.
5. Run 2/3 shift rod nut against swivel, then tighten lock nut against swivel.
6. Remove locating gauge and check operation.
7. On 1969, turn key to "Lock" position and check ignition interlock control. If binding, leave control in "Lock" and readjust back drive control rod.

1968-69 Corvette

1. On 1969, place ignition switch in "Off" position. Loosen swivel locking clamps on both shift rods. Shift rods must pass freely through swivels.
2. Place shift lever in neutral. Insert a $\frac{41}{64}$" locating gauge in notch of lever and bracket assembly.
3. Manually place transmission levers in neutral position.
4. With 1/R rod and lever against locating gauge, tighten lock nut against swivel.
5. With 2/3 rod and lever against locating gauge, run forward nut against swivel and then tighten other nut against swivel.
6. Remove gauge and check shifts. Return to neutral position and re-insert locating gauge. If gauge does not freely enter bracket, readjust linkage.
7. On 1969, move ignition key through "Off" and "Lock" position. If binding occurs, readjust interlock linkage.

1965-67 Corvette

1. Set transmission levers in neutral.
2. Move transmission control lever to neutral detent and insert a locating pin into notch of lever and bracket assembly.
3. Install nut and clevis on rod loosely.
4. With lever against locating pin, adjust clevis at lever until clevis pin passes freely through holes and secure with washer and cotter pin.
5. Install nuts and swivel loosely on rod, attach rod to lever and secure with retainer.
6. With lever against locating pin, attach swivel to lever and secure with retainer. Tighten nuts against swivel.
7. Remove locating pin and check shifts to insure proper operation.

1963-64

1. Move both control rods until transmission is in neutral. Neutral detents in transmission cover must both be engaged to make this adjustment correctly. To check, start engine with clutch disengaged, and release clutch slowly.
2. Move selector lever to neutral position. Engage second and third shifter lever on tube with relay lever.
3. Center levers in mast jacket by measuring from edge of slot in jacket to edge of slot in spacer at each side of lever.
4. Adjust swivel on end of second and third shifter control rod until swivel enters hole in lever. Install swivel and insert retaining clip.
5. Move first and reverse lever on tube until lug on lever lines up with slot in relay lever. Pull relay lever to make sure lug will mate with slot.
6. Adjust swivel on end of first and reverse shifter control rod until swivel enters hole in lever. Install swivel and insert retaining clip.

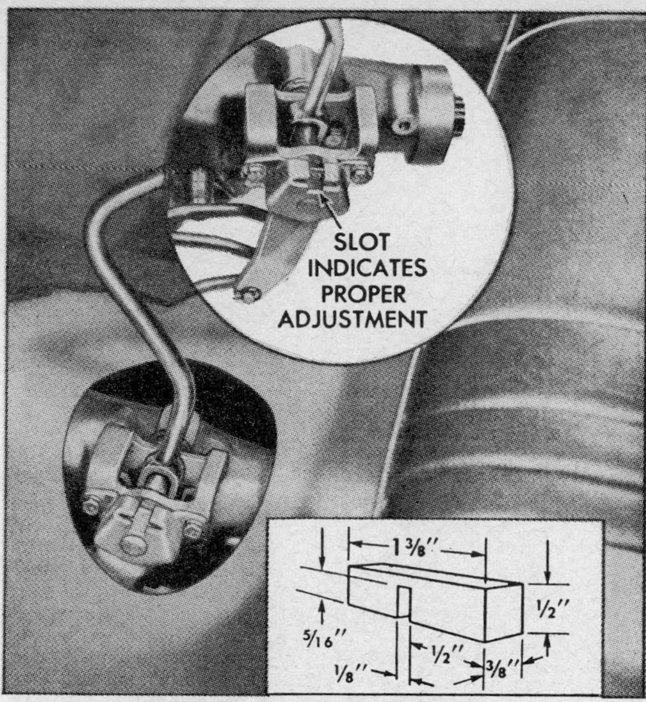

Fig. 3 Four speed manual shift transmission gearshift linkage adjustments. 1963

7. Move selector lever through all positions to check adjustment and to insure over-travel in all positions.

FOUR SPEED SHIFT LINKAGE, ADJUST

1967-69

1. On 1969, place ignition key in "Off" position. Loosen swivel locking clamps on both shift rods. Shift rods must pass freely through swivels.
2. Set transmission shift levers in neutral detent position.
3. Move shift control lever to neutral detent position and insert a suitable locating gauge into control lever bracket.
4. Tighten reverse lever swivel lock nuts.
5. Repeat step 4 for the ½ shift rod and the ¾ rod.
6. Remove locating gauge. After removing locating gauge on Camaro with Muncie transmission, readjust rod by shortening the rod three turns by use of jam nuts. Check shift for proper operation and readjust if necessary.
7. On 1969, check interlock. Ignition key should move freely to the "Lock" position. If necessary, readjust interlock linkage.

1963

As shown in Fig. 1, a simple gauge block, locally made to the specifications indicated, will aid in making the proper adjustments. The adjustments can be made without the gauge block by having an assistant hold the manual shift lever in neutral position.

1. Referring to Fig. 3, remove gearshift from floor pan.
2. Place transmission in neutral and, if gauge block is used, position in slot.
3. Remove clevis pin at each shift lever.
4. On each shift rod, adjust threaded clevis to permit free entry of pin into hole in transmission shift lever.
5. Connect clevises to levers.
6. Remove gauge block and check shifts. If any roughness exists, one of the clevises may require adjustment of about ½ turn. Determine the rod and clevis requiring adjustment by sighting along the slot where the gauge block was used.

If transmission is removed from car, shift linkage should be adjusted before transmission is reinstalled.

1966

Two makes of transmissions are used in 1966, the Muncie and the Saginaw. Linkage adjustments are similar to the 1965 procedure except that a locating gauge (1/8" thick to 41/64" wide and 3" long) is placed in the slot of the control lever bracket. Use Fig. 2 as a guide only.

1964-65

1. Referring to Fig. 2, set transmission levers in neutral detent position.
2. Move shift lever to neutral position and insert a 5/16" locating pin into control lever bracket.
3. Install 1-2 shift rod into 1-2 shift control lever. Holding lever against locating pin, adjust clevis at lever until clevis pin freely passes through holes in clevis and lever. Tighten jam nut.
4. Install reverse rod into reverse shift control lever. With jam nuts and swivel loose on rod, attach swivel to lever. Maintaining reverse lever against locating pin and while holding swivel, run jam nut against swivel until it contacts swivel. Then tighten jam nut against swivel.
5. Install 3-4 rod to 3-4 transmission lever. With jam nuts and swivel loose on 3-4 rod, attach swivel to lever. Holding 3-4 control lever against locating pin and while holding swivel, tighten jam nut against swivel.
6. Remove locating pin and check shifts to insure proper operation. Readjust clevis and swivel if necessary.

1969 AUTO. TRANS. LINKAGE, ADJUST

The 1969 linkages are basically the same as the 1968 models with the exception that in 1969, an anti-theft lock is incorporated into the transmission linkage. After adjusting linkages, be sure that, with shift lever in "Park" ignition key moves freely to "Lock" position.

Rear Axle, Propeller Shaft & Brakes

REAR AXLE

Figs. 1, 2, 3 and 5 illustrate the various rear axle assemblies used. When necessary to overhaul any of these units, refer to the *Rear Axle Specifications* table in this chapter.

1963-64 Chevrolet, 1963 Chevy II, 1963-69 Corvette

In these axles, Figs. 1 and 2, the drive pinion is mounted in two tapered roller bearings that are preloaded by a spacer. The pinion is positioned by a shim located between the head of the drive pinion and the rear pinion bearing. The front bearing is held in place by a large washer and a locking pinion nut.

The differential is supported in the carrier by two tapered roller side bearings.

On Chevy II to 1963 and 1963-64 Chevrolet, these bearings are preloaded by two threaded adjusting sleeves or ring nuts between the bearings and the pedestals, Fig. 1. The differential assembly is positioned for proper ring gear and pinion backlash by varying the adjustment of these ring nuts.

On Corvette, the differential side bearings are preloaded by shims between the bearings and carrier housing, Fig. 2. The differential assembly is positioned for proper ring gear and pinion backlash by varying the position of these shims.

On both axles, the ring gear is bolted to the case. The case houses two side gears in mesh with two pinions mounted on a pinion shaft which is held in place by a lock screw. The side gears are backed by thrust washers.

In the Corvette axle, Fig. 2, the differential side gears drive two splined yokes which are retained by snap rings located on the yoke splined end. The yokes are supported on caged needle bearings pressed into the carrier, adjacent to the differential bearings. A lip seal, pressed in the outboard of the bearings, prevents oil leakage and dirt entry.

SERVICE BULLETIN

A groan or vibration noise, which may occur on a 1964 model with Powerglide when backing up slowly, can mistakenly be attributed to the transmission. The noise is heard only in reverse, when the axle lubricant is warm. It occurs only on models with 327 or 409 cu. in. V-8 engines and Powerglide transmissions with standard rear axles.

The source of the noise is in the rear axle. It can easily be eliminated by draining the original lubricant from the rear axle, and replacing it with the type lubricant recommended for limited-slip differentials.

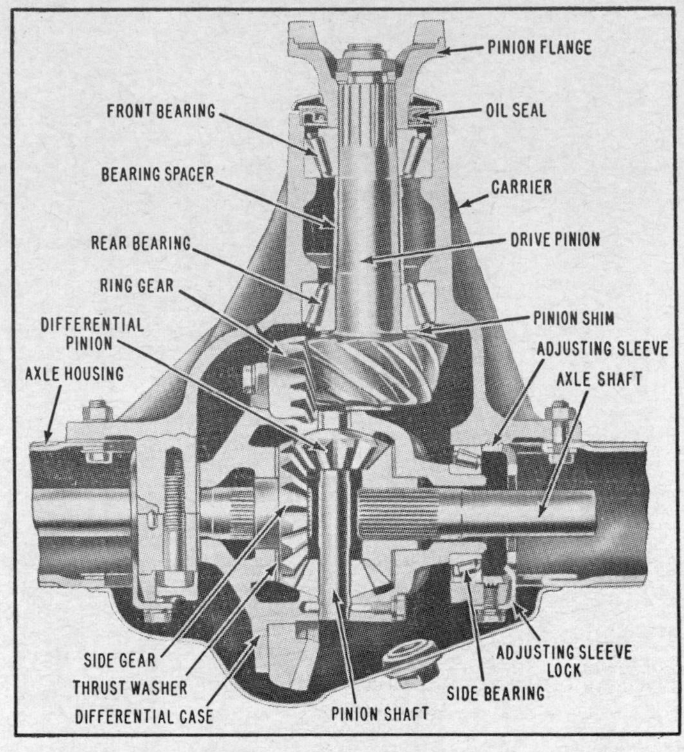

Fig. 1 Rear axle. Chevrolet 1963-64, Chevy II 1963

Remove & Replace

It is not necessary to remove the rear axle assembly for any normal repairs. The axle shafts and carrier assembly can easily be removed from the vehicle, leaving the rear axle housing in place.

Corvette 1963-69

1. Disconnect spring and spring links.
2. Disconnect axle drive shafts at carrier by removing U-bolts securing trunnion to side gear yoke, Fig. 4.
3. Disconnect carrier front support bracket at frame crossmember. Remove bolts and bracket.
4. Disconnect propeller shaft at transmission and at companion flange. Slide transmission yoke forward into transmission. Drop propeller shaft down and out toward the rear.
5. Mark camber cam and bolt relative location on strut rod bracket and loosen cam bolts, Fig. 4.
6. Remove four bolts securing bracket to carrier lower surface and drop bracket. Remove camber cam bolts and swing strut rods up and out of the way.
7. Loosen carrier-to-cover bolts gradually to allow grease to drain out.
8. With mounting bolts removed, pull carrier partially out of cover, drop nose to clear crossmember and gradually work carrier down and out.

CAUTION: When removing carrier, use care so as not to scrape or gouge gasket mounting surface on cover with ring gear. A deep scratch or gouge at this point may cause a lubricant leak after assembly.

9. Reverse removal procedure to install carrier, *being sure to move the camber cams to marked location before tightening nuts.*

Chevrolet & Chevy II, 1963

1. Remove axle shafts as explained further on.
2. Remove two trunnion bearing "U" bolts from rear universal joint and split joint. Lower propeller shaft to floor. Tape bearings to trunnion.
3. Drain lubricant.
4. Remove sealing lock nuts that attach carrier to housing and remove carrier assembly.
5. Reverse foregoing procedure to install the differential carrier assembly and fill with lubricant to the filler plug hole.

SERVICE BULLETIN

An oil leak from the area of the rear-axle pinion on a late 1964 car may not be caused by leakage past the seal on the companion flange. In some cases, the oil may pass the splines on the pinion shaft, and come out past the nut on the companion flange.

If an examination shows the leak to be past the splines, rather than the seal, remove the nut and washer used to retain the companion flange. Apply a non-hardening type sealer to the end of the spline and the area on the flange con-

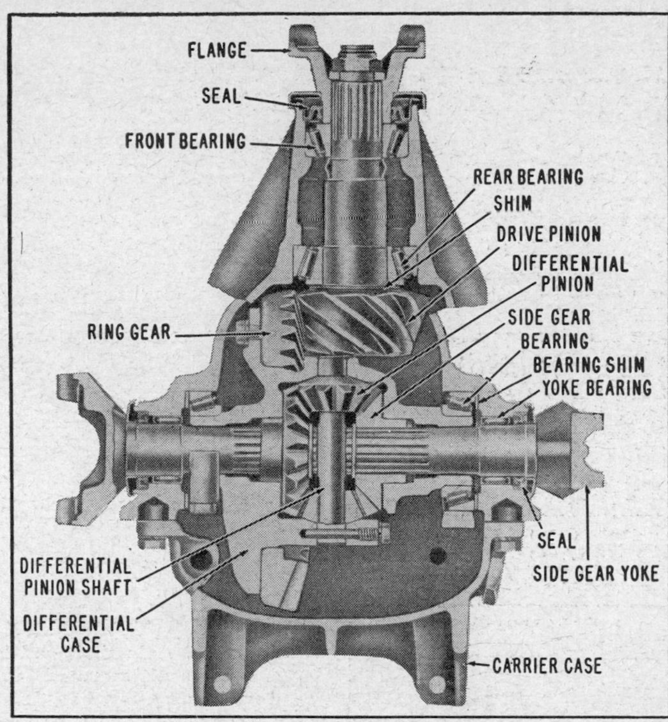

Fig. 2 Rear axle. 1963-69 Corvette

tacted by the washer. Then reinstall the washer and nut.

Sealer is applied to this area in production, and should be reapplied if the flange is removed for any type service operation.

REAR AXLE

1967-69 Camaro, 1965-69 Chevrolet, 1964-69 Chevelle & Chevy II

In these rear axles, Fig. 5, the rear axle housing and differential carrier are cast into an integral assembly. The drive pinion assembly is mounted in two opposed tapered roller bearings. The pinion bearings are preloaded by a spacer behind the front bearing. The pinion is positioned by a washer between the head of the pinion and the rear bearing.

The differential is supported in the carrier by two tapered roller side bearings. These bearings are preloaded by spacers located between the bearings and carrier housing. The differential assembly is positioned for proper ring gear and pinion backlash by varying these spacers. The differential case houses two side gears in mesh with two pinions mounted on a pinion shaft which is held in place by a lock pin. The side gears and pinions are backed by thrust washers.

Remove & Replace

Construction of the axle assembly is such that service operations may be performed with the housing installed in the vehicle or with the housing removed and installed in a holding fixture. The following procedure is necessary only when the housing requires replacement.

1. Raise vehicle and place stand jacks under frame side rails.
2. Remove rear wheels.
3. Support rear axle assembly with a suitable jack so that tension is relieved in springs and tie rod.
4. Disconnect tie rod at axle housing bracket.
5. Remove trunnion bearing "U" bolts from rear yoke, split universal joint, position propeller shaft to one side and tie it to frame side rail.
6. Remove axle "U" bolt nuts and allow control arm and shock absorbers to hang freely so that they do not interfere with axle.
7. Disconnect hydraulic brake hose at connector on axle housing.
8. Remove brake drum and disconnect parking brake cable at lever and at flange plate.
9. Lower axle and remove from vehicle.
10. Reverse foregoing procedure to install axle assembly.

AXLE SHAFT

NOTE

Several types of axle shaft bearings have been used. Some bearings have the seal mounted outboard as shown in Fig. 6 while others have the seal mounted inboard as shown in Fig. 7. These various installations cannot accurately be applied to specific car models. Therefore, when necessary to replace a bearing, examine the installation carefully and, if the new bearing is identical with the old, install it in the same way. However, should a roller bearing be installed where the original bearing was a ball type (or vice versa) follow the installation instructions contained in the bearing package.

1967-69 Camaro, 1965-69 Chevrolet, 1964-69 Chevelle & Chevy II

1. Raise vehicle and remove wheel and brake drum.
2. Drain lube from carrier and remove cover.
3. Remove differential pinion shaft lock screw and remove differential pinion shaft.
4. Pull flanged end of axle shaft toward center of vehicle and remove "C" lock from button end of shaft.
5. Remove axle shaft from housing, being careful not to damage seal.
6. Reverse foregoing procedure to install the axle shaft.

Corvette 1963-69

1. Disconnect inboard drive shaft trunnion from side gear yoke, Fig. 4.
2. Remove four bolts securing shaft flange to spindle drive flange.
3. Pry drive shaft out of outboard drive flange pilot and remove by withdrawing outboard end first.
4. If necessary, overhaul universal joints as described in the *Universal Joint* chapter.
5. Install axle shaft in reverse order of removal, *being certain to rotate yokes so that trunnion seats are phased 90 degrees apart.* Torque drive flange bolts to 70-90 ft-lbs and U-bolt nuts to 14-18 ft-lbs.

Chevrolet 1963-64, Chevy II 1963

1. Raise car and place jack stands under rear axle housing.
2. Remove wheels and brake drums.
3. Remove four nuts and lockwashers from bearing retainer bolts (on inside of axle flange).
4. If bearing is a tight fit in axle housing, attach a slide hammer type axle shaft puller to hub bolts and remove axle shaft and bearing, Fig. 8. Be careful not to disturb brake backing plate and inner gasket. *If bearing retainer and parking brake strut interfere raise strut slightly with screwdriver to obtain clearance.*
5. Install bolt and nut to hold backing plate and inner gasket to axle housing.

Installation

1. Replace "O" ring seal in groove in bearing outer race. *When installing axle shaft with heavy duty bearing, spacer ring must be installed between bearing and axle housing bearing bore. Be certain chamfer on ring is installed toward center of vehicle.*
2. Install new retainer gasket.
3. Install axle shaft. Rotate shaft to align splines of shaft and differential side gear. Outer race of bearing must seat against shoulder in axle housing.
4. Secure bearing retainer with nuts and lockwashers, install brake drum gasket, drum, wheel and hub.
5. Lower vehicle to floor and road test for leaks and noise.

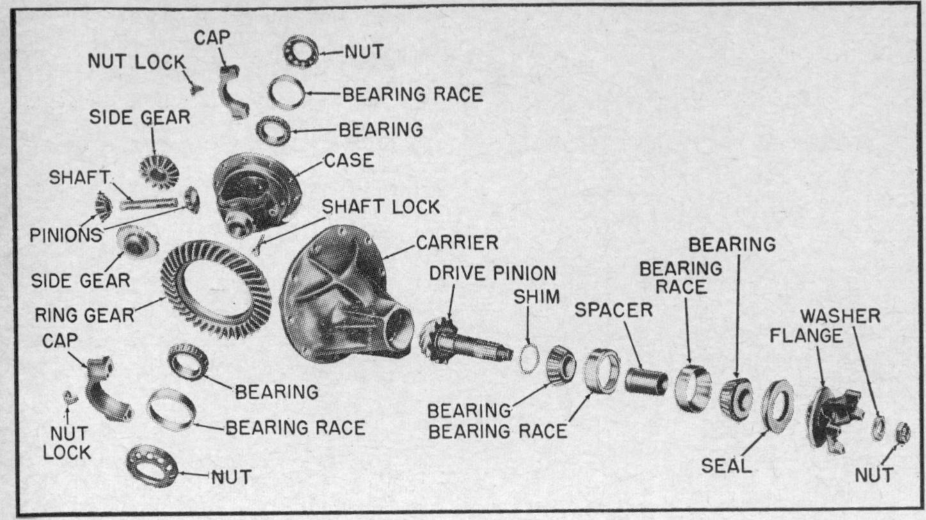

Fig. 3 Rear axle. 1963-64 Chevrolet, 1963 Chevy II

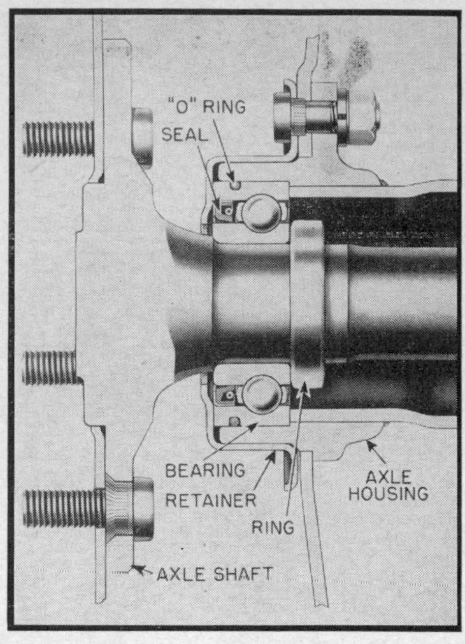

Fig. 6 Axle shaft and bearing with seal mounted outboard

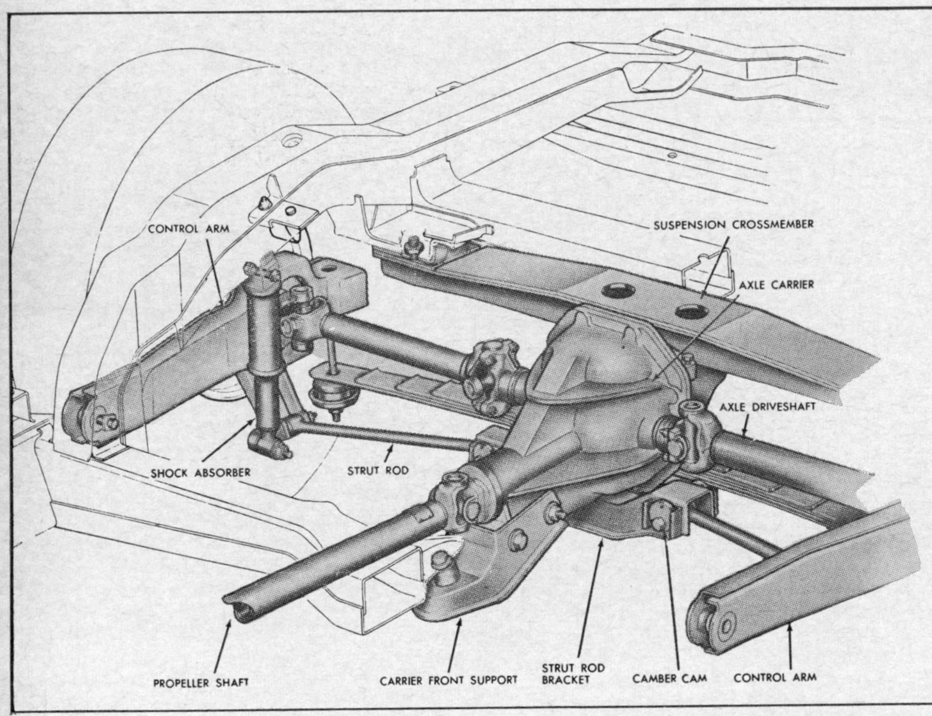

Fig. 4 Rear suspension. 1963-69 Corvette

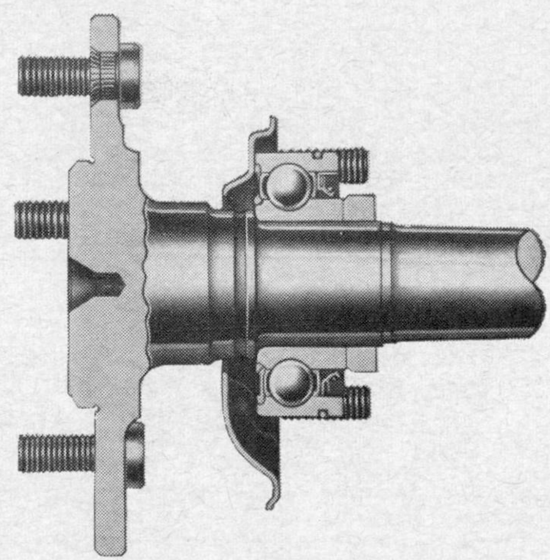

Fig. 7 Axle shaft and bearing with inboard mounted seal

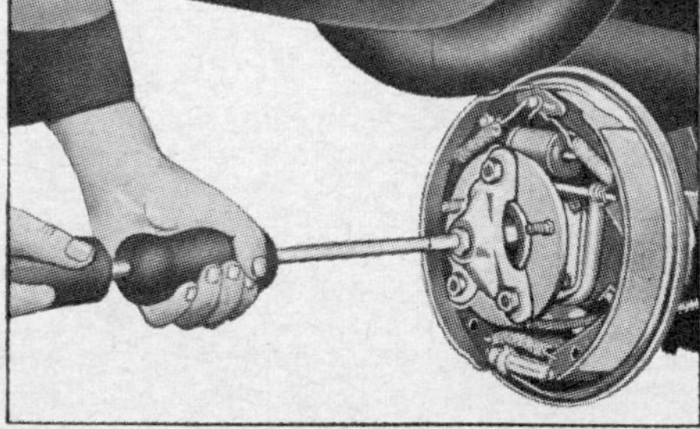

Fig. 8 Removing axle shaft with sliding hammer type puller

PROPELLER SHAFT

1965-69

These models use a one-piece propeller shaft instead of the two-piece type used previously. Powerglide models use a propeller shaft tube which incorporates rubber insulators for quieter operation. These insulators, which are bonded to the smaller tube, press fit to the larger tube.

1963-64 Chevrolet

Due to the design of the drive line, Fig. 9, the relative angles formed by the propeller shafts and transmission output shaft and pinion gear are very critical. Consequently these angles must be checked whenever a drive line shudder, roughness, vibration or rumble is experienced.

In many cases it has been found to be more practical to shim at the center bearing support instead of trying to compensate for adjustment at "Angle A" and "Angle C", Fig. 10. The center bearing support, which controls "Angle B", is shimmed by loosening the two attaching bolts under the frame center section and placing shims between frame section and support (inside drive shaft tunnel). However, if this is done, angles "A" and "C" must be rechecked to see if they are still within specifications, as listed below.

1. If a driveline shudder appears at 20-30 mph with four or more passengers, it is probably due to the center angle being too large under the heavier load conditions.

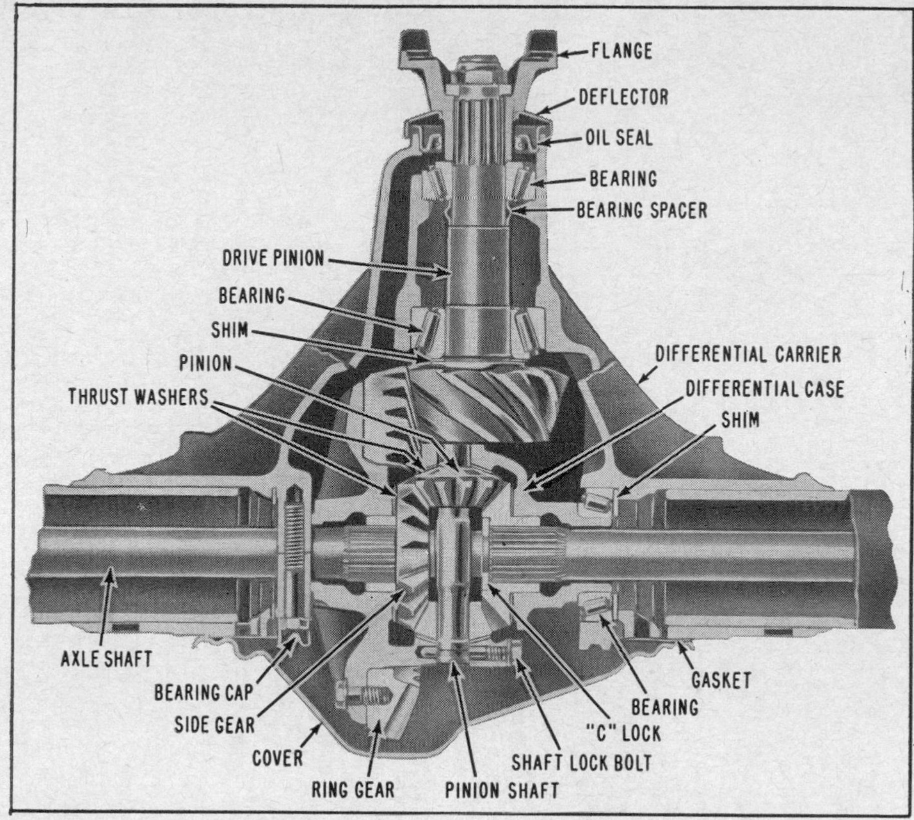

Fig. 5 Rear axle. 1967-69 Camaro, 1965-69 Chevrolet, 1964-69 Chevelle and Chevy II

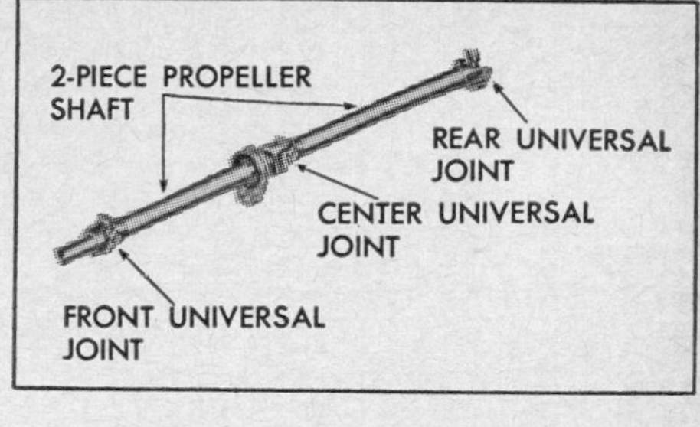

Fig. 9 Propeller shaft components. 1963-64 Chevrolet

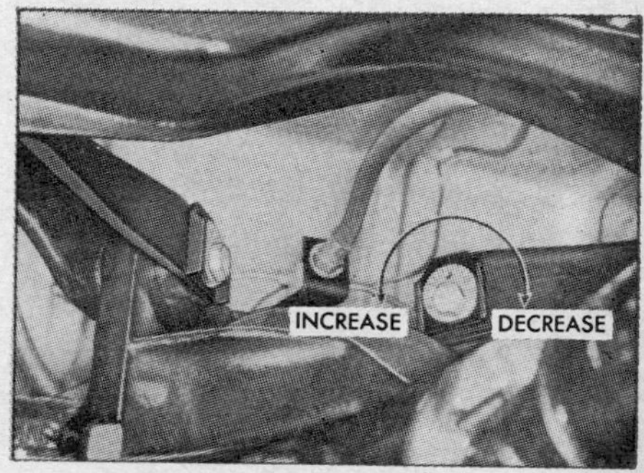

Fig. 11 Rear universal joint angle adjusting cams. Chevelle

2. Check the axle-to-frame height dimension. This should be at least 6¼″ on 1963-64. If less, corrective steps should be taken to raise rear vehicle height before attempting any propeller shaft shudder correction.
3. Install two 3750050 shims under the center bearing mounting and add one 3758116 spacer to the existing shim pack at the rear upper control arm attachment. Road test with five or six passengers and then with one or two passengers.
4. The above action may bring in a lower frequency shudder at about 10 mph with only one or two passengers. If this occurs, it can usually be corrected by installing one 3750050 shim at the transmission support. Again road test vehicle with one or two passenger load and with five or six passenger load.
5. If the 20 to 30 mile shudder with five or six passengers has returned, add one more 3750050 shim at the center bearing and road test.

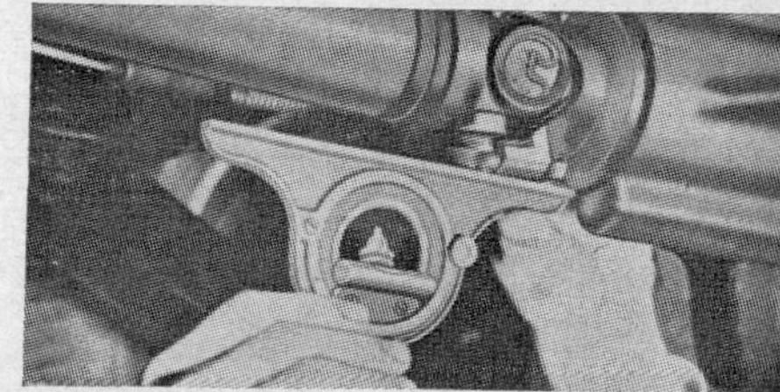

Fig. 12 Measuring pinion angle with bubble protractor

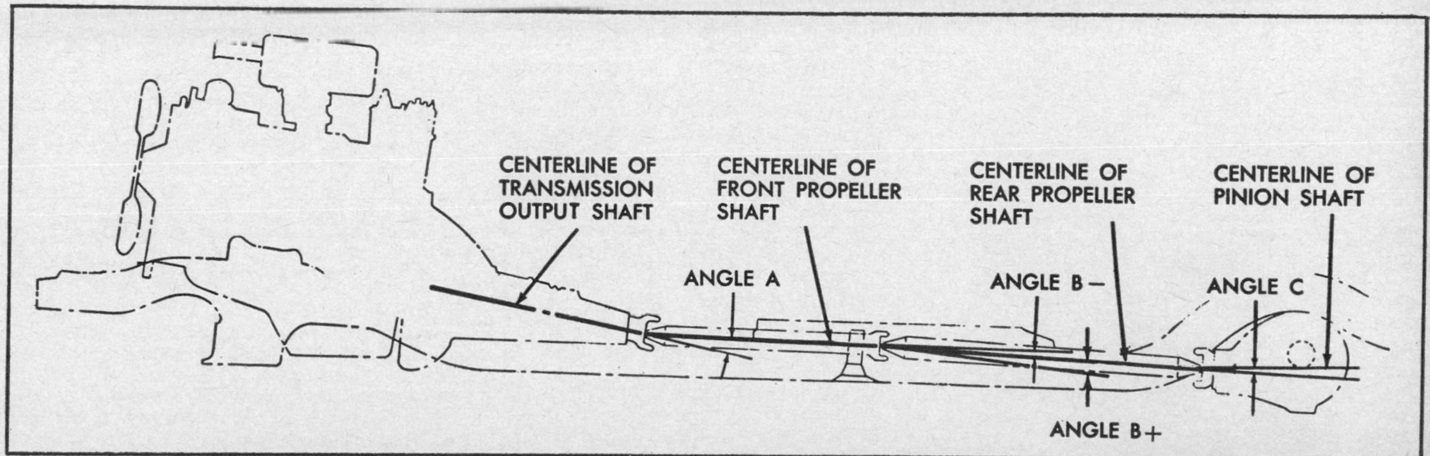

Fig. 10 Schematic diagram of drive line angles. 1963-64 Chevrolet. Angles pointing down are positive; those pointing up are negative. Angles are measured with a bubble protractor shown in Fig. 12

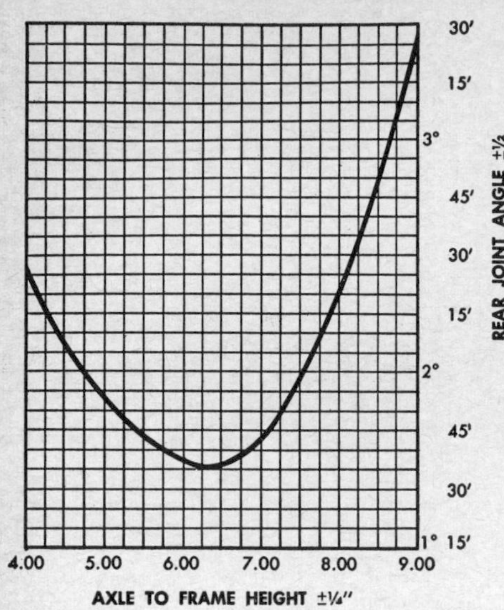

Fig. 13 Rear universal joint angle curve. Chevelle

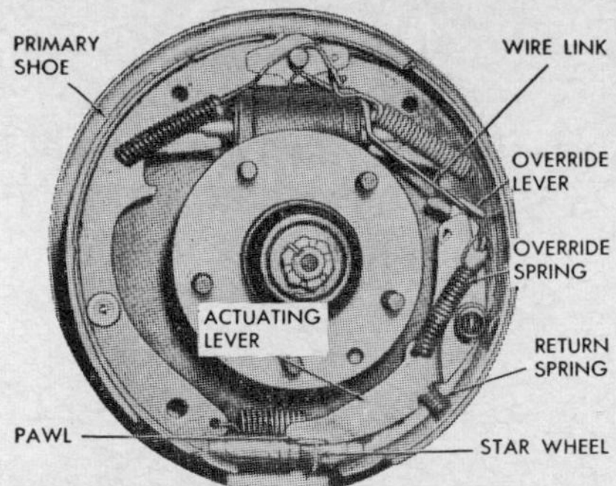

Fig. 14 Left front brake. 1963-69

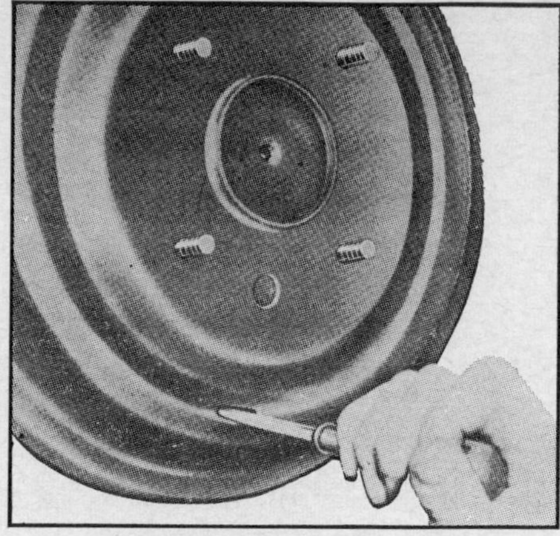

Fig. 15 Brake drum access hole

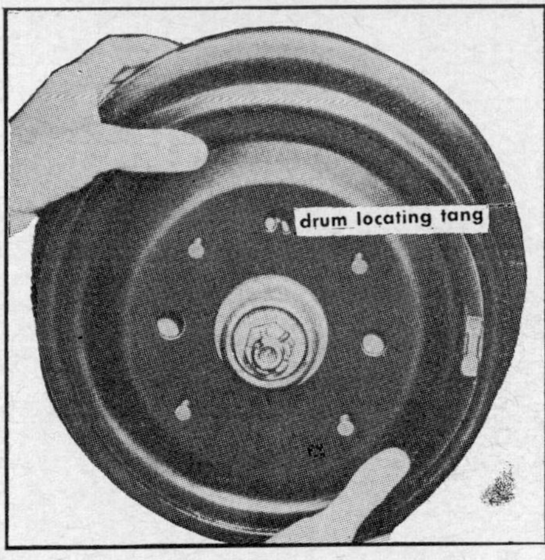

Fig. 16 Aligning drum tang with wheel hub. 1963-69

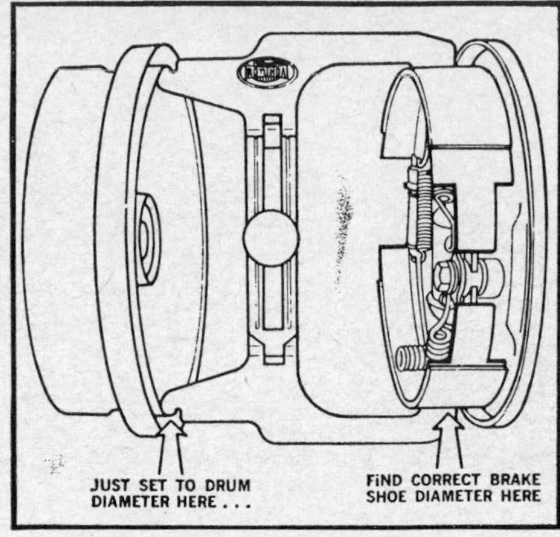

Fig. 17 Use of Drum-to-Brake Shoe Clearance Gauge (J-21177)

6. If the complaint is driveline vibration starting at higher vehicle speeds, either the front or rear propeller shaft may be bent or out of balance. Check for undercoat material on the shafts or evidence of a missing balance weight that may have been knocked off the ends of either shaft.
7. Check for a bent shaft by using a dial indicator at the ends and middle of each shaft. Runout limits are .010″ at the ends of the shafts, and .015″ at the center of either shaft. Propeller shaft assembly may have to be removed from the vehicle and placed in "V" blocks.
8. If there is a shudder or heavy vibration over 30 mph, stop vehicle and run engine at approximately 2400 rpm. If the vibration comes under this condition, the trouble is engine vibration.
9. If the foregoing procedure still fails to correct the shudder, the only solution is to use a bubble protractor and correct angle settings as necessary, using the following specifications and referring to Fig. 10.

Drive Line Angles, Fig. 10

Angle A—1963	+2¾°
1964 Standard Models	+2⅔°
1964 Wagons	+1⅔°
1964 Super Sport	+3°
Angle B—	
1963	—1¼°
1964 Standard Models	—1½°
1964 Wagons	—2⅓°
1964 Super Sport	— ¼°
Angle C—	
1963	+3°
1964	+3¼°
Axle-to-Frame Height	
1963	6¼″
1964 Standard Models	$6\frac{17}{32}$″
1964 Wagons	$7\frac{21}{32}$″
1964 Super Sport	$5\frac{41}{64}$″

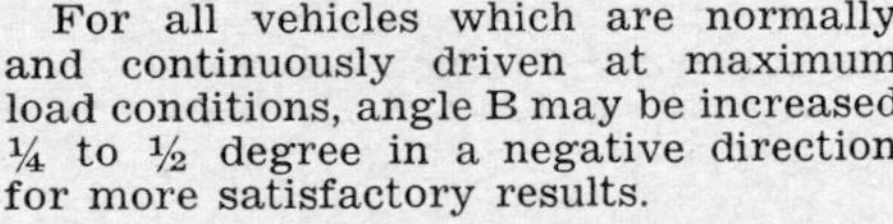

For all vehicles which are normally and continuously driven at maximum load conditions, angle B may be increased ¼ to ½ degree in a negative direction for more satisfactory results.

1964-65 Chevelle

The rear universal joint angle is adjusted by means of the cam-type adjuster provided at each rear upper control arm-to-differential carrier attaching point, Fig. 11. This cam-type adjuster controls the pinion angle, that is, it rotates the axle assembly, thereby changing the pinion shaft centerline in relation to the propeller shaft centerline. (No method is provided for adjusting the front universal joint angle.)

1. Raise vehicle so weight is supported on axle.
2. Check engine angle, propeller shaft and spring condition to make sure riding height is satisfactory.
3. Measure distance from top of axle housing to frame kick-up. Record this measurement for future reference.
4. By use of a bubble protractor, Fig. 12, measure propeller shaft angle. Record this reading for future reference.
5. Rotate propeller shaft until one of the four machined surfaces of the pinion shaft drive flange is parallel to floor. Measure this angle as shown in Fig. 12.
6. Referring to Fig. 13, select angle applicable to the axle-to-frame dimension recorded in Step 3.
7. If the result obtained in Step 6 is not the same (plus or minus ½°) adjust pinion shaft as follows:
8. Loosen cam nut, Fig. 11, and rotate cams as required. Rotate each cam an equal amount to maintain correct suspension-to-frame relationship. *NOTE: Each index mark on cam represents about 5/6 degree change in joint angle. If proper angle cannot be obtained, inspect engine mounts, transmission support and drive line to determine faulty parts.*

BRAKE ADJUSTMENTS

1963-69 Self-Adjusting Brakes

These brakes, Fig. 14, have self-adjusting shoe mechanisms that assure correct lining-to-drum clearances at all times. The automatic adjusters operate only when the brakes are applied as the car is moving rearward or when the car comes to an uphill stop.

Although the brakes are self-adjusting, an initial adjustment is necessary after the brake shoes have been relined or re-

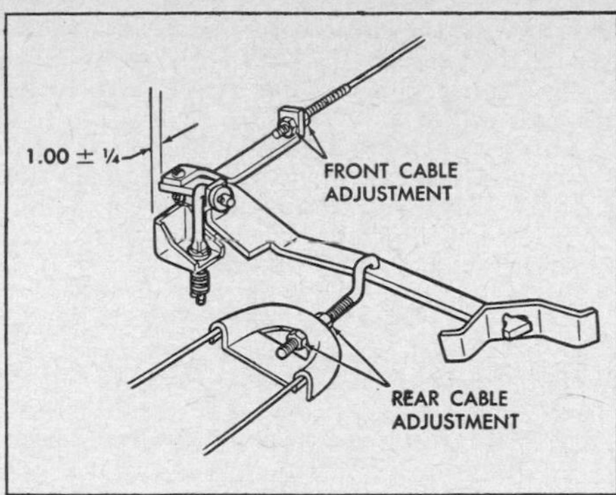

Fig. 19 Parking brake linkage adjustment. 1963-64 Chevrolet

placed, or when the length of the adjusting screw has been changed during some other service operation.

Frequent usage of an automatic transmission forward range to halt reverse vehicle motion may prevent the automatic adjusters from functioning, thereby inducing low pedal heights. Should low pedal heights be encountered, it is recommended that numerous forward and reverse stops be made until satisfactory pedal height is obtained.

NOTE

If a low pedal condition cannot be corrected by making numerous reverse stops (provided the hydraulic system is free of air) it indicates that the self-adjusting mechanism is not functioning. Therefore it will be necessary to remove the brake drum, clean, free up and lubricate the adjusting mechanism. Then adjust the brakes, being sure the parking brake is fully released.

Adjustment

A lanced "knock out" area, Fig. 15, is provided in the web of the brake drum for servicing purposes in the event retracting of the brake shoes is required in order to remove the drum.

1. With brake drum off, disengage the actuator from the star wheel and rotate the star wheel by spinning or turning with a screwdriver.
2. Using the brake drum as an adjustment fixture, turn the star wheel until the drum slides over the brake shoes with a slide drag.
3. Turn the star wheel 1¼ turns to retract the brake shoes. This will allow sufficient lining-to-drum clearance so final adjustment may be made.
4. Install drum and wheel. *NOTE: If lanced area in brake drum was knocked out, be sure all metal has been removed from brake compartment. Install new hole cover in drum to prevent contamination of brakes. Make certain that drums are installed in the same position as when removed with the drum locating tang in line with the locating hole in the wheel hub, Fig. 16.*
5. Make final adjustment by driving and stopping in forward and reverse until satisfactory pedal height is obtained.

NOTE: The recommended method of adjusting the brakes is by using the Drum-to-Brake Shoe Clearance Gauge shown in Fig. 17 to check the diameter of the brake drum inner surface. Turn the tool to the opposite side and fit over the brake shoes by turning the star wheel until the gauge just slides over the linings. Rotate the gauge around the brake shoe lining surface to assure proper clearance.

PARKING BRAKE, ADJUST

1965-69 Except Corvette

1. Jack up both rear wheels.
2. Apply parking brake two notches from fully released position.
3. Loosen equalizer forward check nut and tighten rear nut until a light to moderate drag is felt when rear wheels are rotated.
4. Tighten check nuts securely.
5. Fully release parking brake and rotate rear wheels; no drag should be present.

1963-64 Chevrolet

1. Raise rear of vehicle.
2. Depress parking brake pedal to first notch.
3. Adjust front cable to position parking brake idler lever 1" forward of rear edge of bracket, Fig. 19.
4. Adjust rear cable to obtain a moderate brake drag on rear wheels.
5. When parking brake pedal is released, there should be no brake drag.

1964 Chevelle & 1963-64 Chevy II

1. Jack up rear wheels.
2. Pull parking brake lever up one notch (Chevy II) or push pedal two notches (Chevelle) from fully released position.
3. Loosen equalizer forward check nut and tighten rear nut until a moderate drag is felt when rear wheels are rotated.
4. Tighten check nuts securely.
5. Fully release parking brake and rotate rear wheels; no drag should be present.

1963 Corvette

1. Raise rear wheels.
2. Loosen equalizer front nut.
3. Set parking brake hand cable at 4 notches.
4. Tighten rear equalizer nut up against equalizer until a light uniform drag is felt when both rear wheels are rotated.
5. Tighten front check nut.
6. Release hand brake lever and check rear wheels for free movement without drag.

1964 Corvette

1. Raise rear of car.
2. Pull parking brake handle up 4 notches from fully released position.
3. Loosen forward check nut on equalizer and tighten rear check nut until a moderate drag is felt when wheels are rotated.
4. Tighten forward check nut.
5. Fully release brake handle. There should be no drag when wheels are rotated.

Fig. 20 Adjusting parking brake shoes. 1965-69 Corvette

1965-69 Corvette

1. With car on lift or jack stands, remove wheel. (On optional knock-off wheels, the adapter bracket must be removed to gain access to the hole in the hat section of the disc.)
2. Turn disc until the adjusting screw can be seen through hole in disc.
3. Insert a screwdriver through hole in disc and tighten adjusting screw by moving your hand away from the floor on both the left and right sides, Fig. 20.
4. Tighten until disc will not move, then back off ten notches.
5. Apply emergency brake four notches from inside of car.
6. Tighten brake cables at equalizer to produce a light drag with wheels mounted.
7. Fully release parking brake handle and rotate rear wheels. No drag should be evident with handle released.

MASTER CYLINDER, REPLACE

1965-69

Disconnect hydraulic line from master cylinder. Unfasten and remove cylinder from its mounting.

1963-64

To remove the master cylinder, disconnect the hydraulic line from the end of the cylinder. Remove clevis pin from brake pedal arm. Unfasten master cylinder from dash panel and remove from vehicle.

Reverse the above procedure to install the cylinder, fill the reservoir with brake fluid and bleed the system as outlined in the *Hydraulic Brake System Chapter.*

POWER BRAKE UNIT

Repairs on the power brake unit are contained in the *Power Brake Chapter*. To remove and install the unit, proceed as follows:

1965-69

1. Remove vacuum hose from vacuum check valve.
2. Disconnect hydraulic line at main cylinder.
3. On 1968-69 Chevelle with standard transmission, remove main cylinder from power unit and from inside vehicle remove nuts holding unit to firewall. Push brake pedal to floor. There is now enough clearance to remove the pivot pin.
4. On all other models, disconnect push rod at brake pedal and unfasten and remove power unit.

1963-64

1. Disconnect clevis at brake pedal.
2. Remove hoses from power unit.
3. Disconnect hydraulic line from master cylinder.
4. Unfasten and remove power unit from dash.
5. Installation is made in the reverse order of removal.

1963-69 CORVETTE REAR WHEEL ALIGNMENT

Rear wheel camber and toe-out should be inspected and corrected if rear tires show unusual wear.

Camber, Adjust

Wheel camber is obtained by adjusting the eccentric cam and bolt assembly located at the inboard mounting of the strut rod (see Fig. 4). Place rear wheels on alignment machine and determine camber angle.

To adjust, loosen cam bolt nut and rotate cam and bolt assembly until the camber angle is minus ⅓ degree (plus or minus ½ degree). Tighten nut securely and torque to 55-70 ft-lbs.

Toe-Out, Adjust

Rear wheel toe-out is adjusted by inserting slotted shims of varying thickness inside the frame side member on both sides of the torque control arm pivot bushing. Shims are available in thicknesses of $\frac{1}{32}$", ⅛" and ¼".

To adjust, loosen torque arm pivot bolts until shims are free enough to remove. Position torque arm assembly to obtain toe-out of $\frac{1}{32}$" to $\frac{3}{32}$" per wheel. Shim gap toward vehicle centerline between end of control arm bushing and frame side inner wall.

Front End and Steering Section

FRONT SUSPENSION

All front suspension systems are basically similar, being of the S.L.A. (short-long arm) type with independent coil springs. In Camaro, Chevrolet, Chevelle, Chevy II (1968-69) and Corvette the springs ride on the lower control arms. In the Chevy II (to 1967) the springs ride on the upper control arms. Ball joints connect the upper and lower control arms to the steering knuckles. See Figs. 1, 2 and 3.

LUBRICATION

IMPORTANT

On 1963-69 models that have a recommended chassis lubrication period of 6000 miles, the car should be warmed up before lubricating the front suspension ball joints. If the car has been outdoors in extreme cold weather it should be allowed to warm up to at least 10°F. above zero before this job is started. Inadequate ball joint lubrication or seal damage can result should the job be done while the parts are at lower temperatures.

WHEEL ALIGNMENT

NOTE: Before adjusting caster and camber angles after complaint of excessive tire wear or poor handling, the front bumper should be raised and quickly released to allow car to return to its normal height.

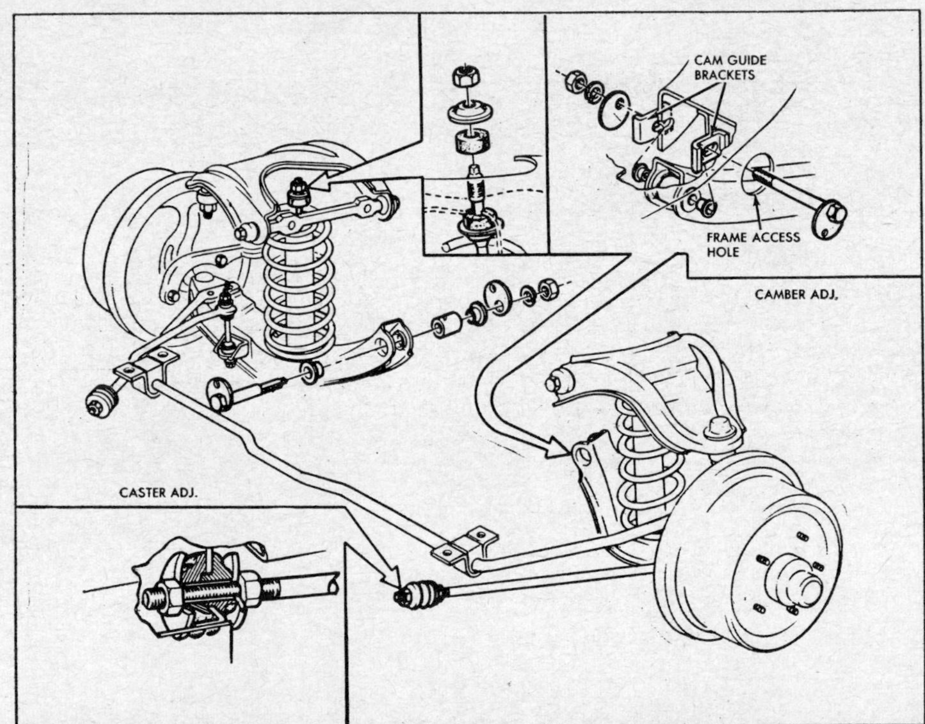

Fig. 1 Front suspension. 1965-69 Chevrolet

1965-69 Chevrolet & 1963-67 Chevy II

The caster angle is adjusted by turning the two nuts at the front of the lower control arm strut rod, Fig. 1. Shortening this rod will increase caster, lengthening it will decrease caster.

Camber angle is adjusted by loosening the lower control arm pivot bolt and rotating the cam located on this pivot, Fig. 1. This eccentric cam action will move the lower control arm in or out, thereby varying camber.

1968-69 Chevy II
1967-69 Camaro
1963-64 Chevrolet
1964-69 Chevelle
1963-69 Corvette

Caster and camber adjustments are made by means of shims between the upper control arm inner support shaft and the support bracket attached to the frame. Shims may be added, subtracted or transferred to change the readings as follows:

Caster, Adjust

Transfer shims from front to rear or rear to front. The transfer of one shim to the front bolt from the rear bolt will decrease positive caster. One shim ($\frac{1}{32}$") transferred from the rear bolt to the front bolt will change caster about ½ degree.

Fig. 2 Front suspension. 1963-67 Chevy II

Camber, Adjust

Change shims at both the front and rear of the shaft. Adding an equal number of shims at both front and rear of the support shaft will decrease positive camber. One shim ($\frac{1}{32}$") at each location will move camber approximately 1/5 degree on Camaro, Chevelle and Chevy II; on Chevrolet and Corvette the change will be about 1/6 degree.

TOE-IN, ADJUST

Toe-in can be adjusted by loosening the clamp bolts at each end of each tie rod and turning each tie rod to increase or decrease its length as necessary until proper toe-in is secured and the steering gear is on the high point for straight-ahead driving.

WHEEL BEARINGS, ADJUST

1963-69

1. While rotating wheel, tighten spindle nut to 12 ft-lbs torque.
2. Back off adjusting nut one flat and insert cotter pin. If slot and pin hole do not line up, back off adjusting nut an additional ½ flat or less as required to insert cotter pin.
3. Spin wheel to see that it turns freely, then spread cotter pin.
4. Bearings should have zero preload and .001 to .008" end movement when properly adjusted.

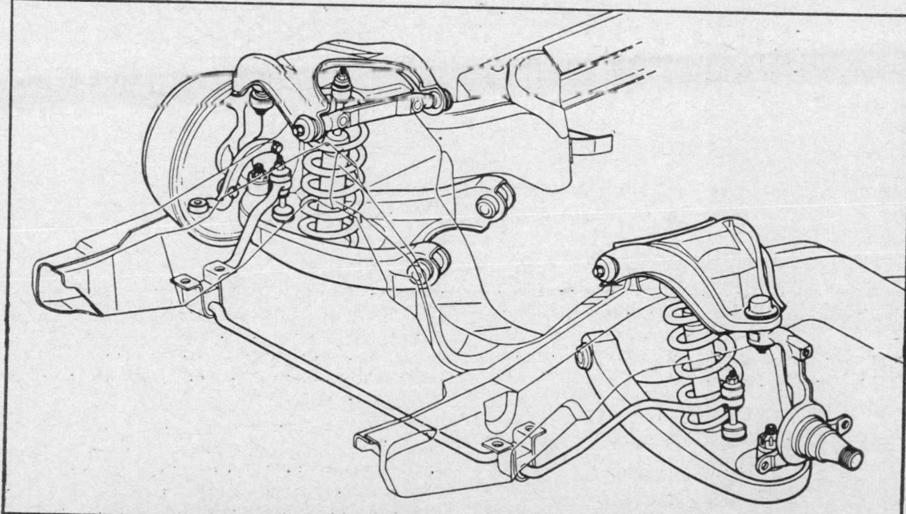

Fig. 3 Front suspension. 1968-69 Chevy II, 1967-69 Camaro, 1964-69 Chevelle. Typical of 1963-64 Chevrolet and 1963-69 Corvette

WHEEL BEARINGS, REPLACE

Disc Brakes

1. Raise car and remove front wheels.
2. Remove bolts holding brake caliper to its mounting and insert a fabricated block ($1\frac{1}{16}$ x $1\frac{1}{16}$ x 2 inches in length) between the brake pads as the caliper is being removed. Once removed, the caliper can be wired or secured in some manner away from the disc.
3. Remove spindle nut and hub and disc assembly. Grease retainer and inner wheel bearing can now be removed.

CHECKING BALL JOINTS FOR WEAR

1963-69 Except 1963-67 Chevy II

Upper Ball Joint

The upper ball joint is checked for wear by checking the torque required to rotate the ball stud in the assembly. To make this type of check it will be necessary to remove the stud from the steering knuckle.

Install a nut on the ball stud and measure the torque required to turn the stud in the assembly with a torque wrench. Specified torque for a new ball joint is 3 to 10 ft-lbs. If torque readings are excessively high or low, replace the ball joint. If excessive wear is indicated in the upper ball joint, both upper and lower ball joints should be replaced.

Lower Ball Joint

Raise car and support lower control arm so spring is compressed in the same manner as if the wheels were on the ground and check axial (up and down) play at ball joint. If play exceeds $\frac{1}{16}$", replace the joint.

Another indication of lower ball joint excessive wear is when difficulty is experienced when lubricating the joint. If the liner has worn to the point where the lubrication grooves in the liner have been worn away, then abnormal pressure is required to force lubricant through the joint. Should this condition be evident, replace both lower ball joints.

Chevy II, 1963-67

With front wheel bearings properly adjusted and control arms tight, refer to Fig. 4 and raise wheel with a jack under the frame as shown. Then test by moving the wheel up and down to check axial play, and rocking the wheel at the top and bottom to measure radial play.

1. Lower ball joint should be replaced if there is any noticeable looseness at this joint.
2. Upper ball joint should be replaced if radial play exceeds .250".
3. Upper ball joint should be replaced if axial play between upper control arm and spindle exceeds the following:

1963	.093"
1964-67	.0625"

UPPER BALL JOINT, REPLACE

1963-69 Except 1963-67 Chevy II

1. Support weight of vehicle at outer end of lower control arm.
2. Remove wheel assembly.
3. Remove nut from upper ball joint stud.
4. Remove stud from knuckle.
5. Cut off ball rivets with a chisel.
6. Enlarge ball stud attaching holes in control arm (if necessary) to accept the bolts included in the ball joint replacement kit.
7. Install and tighten new ball joint.
8. Reassemble ball joint to steering knuckle.

1963-67 Chevy II

1. With wheels on floor, install spacer support as shown in Fig. 5 between upper control arm and frame side rail. Then raise vehicle.
2. Remove wheel and tire.
3. Disconnect stabilizer link (if so equipped) and strut rod at lower control arm.
4. Remove nut from upper ball stud.
5. Strike upper part of steering knuckle with a hammer (backing up with another hammer). Drop lower control arm, steering knuckle and brake assembly with an adjustable jack until upper ball joint is easily accessible.
6. Chisel off three ball joint retaining rivet heads.
7. Attach replacement ball joint to control arm, using special bolts furnished with the replacement kit. Torque to 20-25 ft. lbs. *Do not attempt to use any bolts other than those in the kit as they are special hardened bolts.*
8. Raise lower control arm and steering knuckle in position. Insert upper ball stud into knuckle and torque stud nut to 42-47 ft. lbs.
9. Lubricate ball stud and complete the installation. Then check caster and camber.

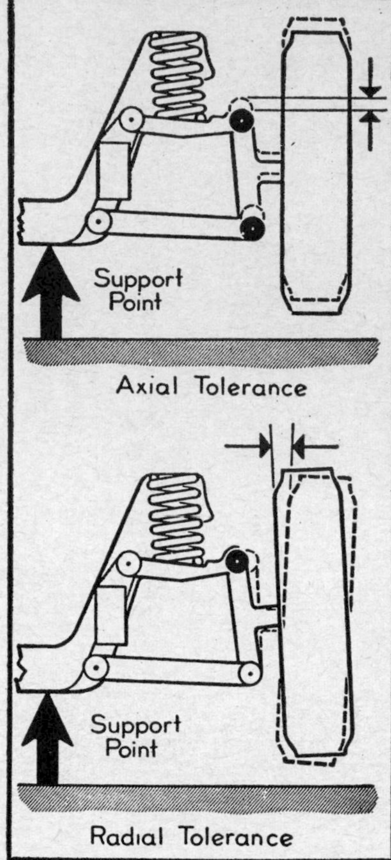

Fig. 4 Checking ball joints for wear. 1963-67 Chevy II

LOWER BALL JOINT, REPLACE

1963-69 Chevrolet & Corvette

1. Support lower control arm at outer end on floor jack with hoist or jack pad clear of lower ball stud nut and seal.
2. If equipped with disc brakes, remove caliper assembly.
3. Remove upper and lower ball stud nuts, free ball studs from steering knuckle and wire knuckle and brake drum or disc assembly out of the way.
4. Being careful not to enlarge holes in control arm, cut off rivets.
5. Install new joint against underside of control arm and retain in place with special bolts supplied with replacement ball joint kit. Use only the alloy bolts supplied for this operation. The special thick headed bolt must be installed in the forward side of the control arm.
6. Tighten bolts and nut on ball stud and lubricate joint.

1963-69 Chevelle, Camaro & 1968-69 Chevy II

1. Support lower control arm at outer end on floor jack with hoist or jack pad clear of lower ball stud and remove wheel. If equipped with disc brakes, remove caliper assembly.
2. Remove upper and lower ball stud nuts, free ball studs from steering knuckle and wire knuckle and brake drum or disc assembly out of the way.
3. Use a screwdriver to pry out seal and retainer. Use a suitable extractor to push out ball joint.
4. Start replacement ball joint into control arm and use a suitable puller tool to pull the ball joint into position. Be sure to position air vent in rubber boot inboard.
5. Install stud into steering knuckle and secure in place.

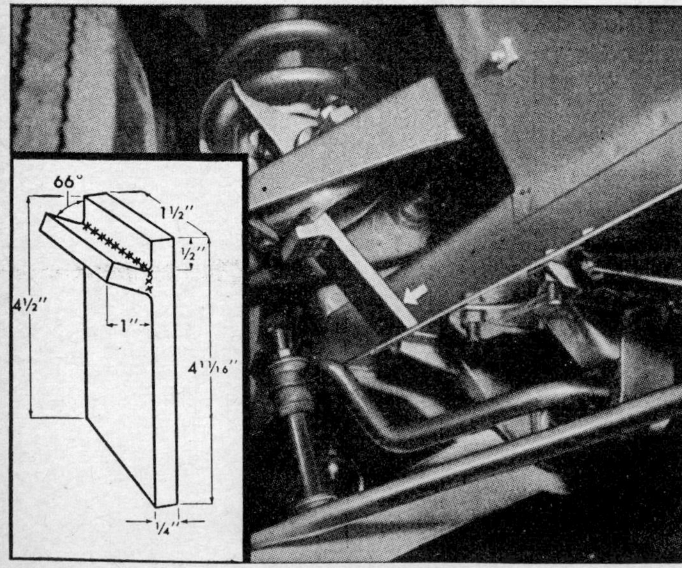

Fig. 5 Chevy II (to 1967 only) upper control arm support installed. Right side control arm support bracket is shown. For left side, angled support should be welded to reverse side of plate

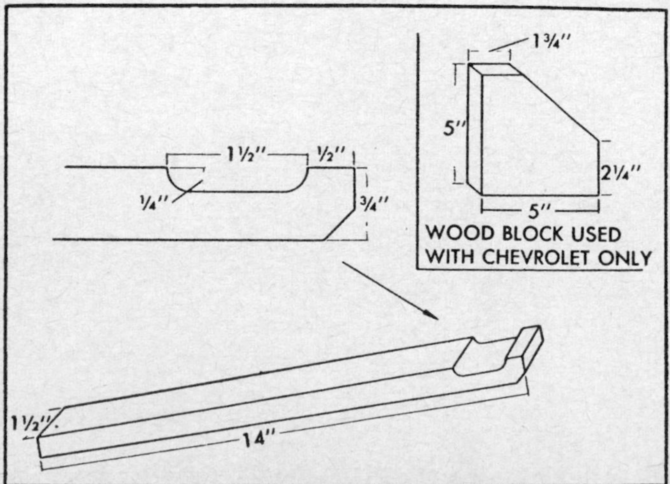

Fig. 6 Spring removal tools. 1965-69 Chevrolet

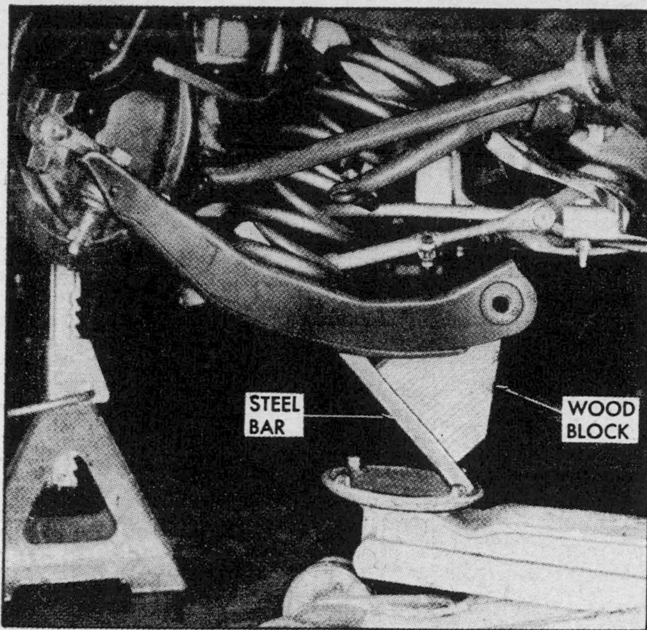

Fig. 7 Removing front spring. 1965-69 Chevrolet

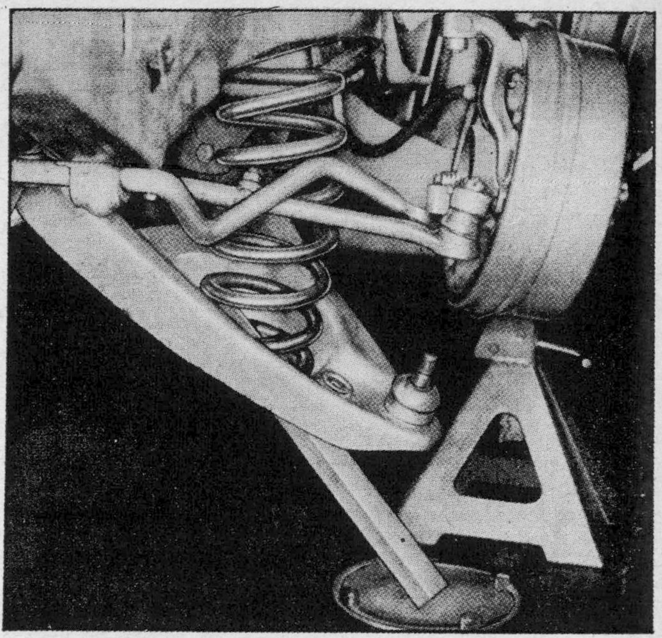

Fig. 8 Removing front spring. 1968-69 Chevy II, 1967-69 Camaro, 1964-69 Chevelle

1963-67 Chevy II

1. With car weight on front wheels, position support between upper control arm and frame side rail, Fig. 5.
2. Raise vehicle and remove nut from ball stud.
3. Disconnect stabilizer at upper link. Break loose lower ball stud and drop lower control arm until lower ball joint is accessible.
4. Cut off rivets from retaining plate.
5. Remove ball joint from arm.
6. Install new ball joint in arm, using special bolts furnished with repair kit.
7. Raise lower control arm and insert ball stud into knuckle. Secure with nut and cotter pin and connect stabilizer.

SHOCK ABSORBER, REPLACE

1963-67 Chevy II

1. With car weight on floor, place support as shown in Fig. 5.
2. Raise car and remove wheel.
3. Disconnect shock absorber lower mounting nuts.
4. Remove shock absorber upper mounting bracket bolts.
5. Lift bracket and shock from car.
6. Reverse above procedure to install.

1963-69 Except 1963-67 Chevy II

1. Hold shock upper stem from turning with a suitable wrench and remove nut and grommet.
2. Unfasten lower shock pivot from lower control arm and pull shock and mounting out through bottom of spring housing.
3. Reverse removal procedure to install. Tighten upper retaining nut until it bottoms on shoulder of stem.

COIL SPRING, REPLACE

1963-67 Chevy II

1. Remove wheel and tire.
2. Support lower control arm with an adjustable jack and raise slightly from full rebound position.
3. Remove shock absorber.
4. With a suitable spring compressor, compress spring.
5. Remove lower spring seat retaining nuts and lift spring and seat from control arm and guide it down and out through fender skirt.
6. When installing new spring, *see that the spring coil ends are against spring stops in upper and lower seats. Locating tab on upper spring seat may be flattened before installing spring.*

1965-69 Chevrolet

1. With suitable wrench, hold shock absorber upper stem from turning, then remove retaining nut, retainer and upper grommet.
2. With car supported by the frame so that control arms hang free, remove wheel assembly. Replace one wheel nut to hold brake drum.
3. Remove shock absorber, stabilizer bar-to-lower control arm link, strut rod-to-lower control arm attaching nuts and tie rod end.
4. Install a steel bar (made to the dimensions shown in Fig. 6) through shock absorber mounting hole in lower control arm so that notch seats over bottom spring coil and bar extends inboard and under inner bushing.
5. Fit a 5" wood block, Fig. 7, between bar and bushing.
6. With suitable jack or hoist, lift up slightly on end of bar to remove tension from inner pivot cam bolt, which can then be removed.
7. Lower inner end of lower control arm. Tension on spring will be removed before spring can be removed from vehicle.
8. Reverse procedure to install and check wheel alignment.

1964-69 Chevelle, Camaro, 1969 Chevy II

1. Perform Steps 1, 2 and 3 as outlined for 1965 Chevrolet. However, place the bar, Fig. 8, in the shock absorber mounting hole in the lower control arm so that the notch seats over the bottom spring coil and the bar extends outboard beyond the end of the control arm and slightly toward the front of the car.
2. Remove ball stud from knuckle, using extreme care not to damage the seal.
3. Reverse above procedure to install.

1963-64 Chevrolet, 1963-69 Corvette

Remove and install the front spring in the conventional manner and as suggested by Fig. 9. It may be necessary to assist the spring out of its tower with a pry bar.

Disconnect the lower ball joint from the steering knuckle and lower the control arm with the compressed spring. *Immediately* release compression on the spring by backing off the long screw. Release spring and tool and withdraw spring.

CAUTION

The spring force under compression is very great. Exercise every safety precaution when performing this operation to see that individuals and materials subject to damage are removed from the path of the spring when the control arm is being lowered. Also, the compressed spring should be relaxed immediately after lowering the control arm to reduce

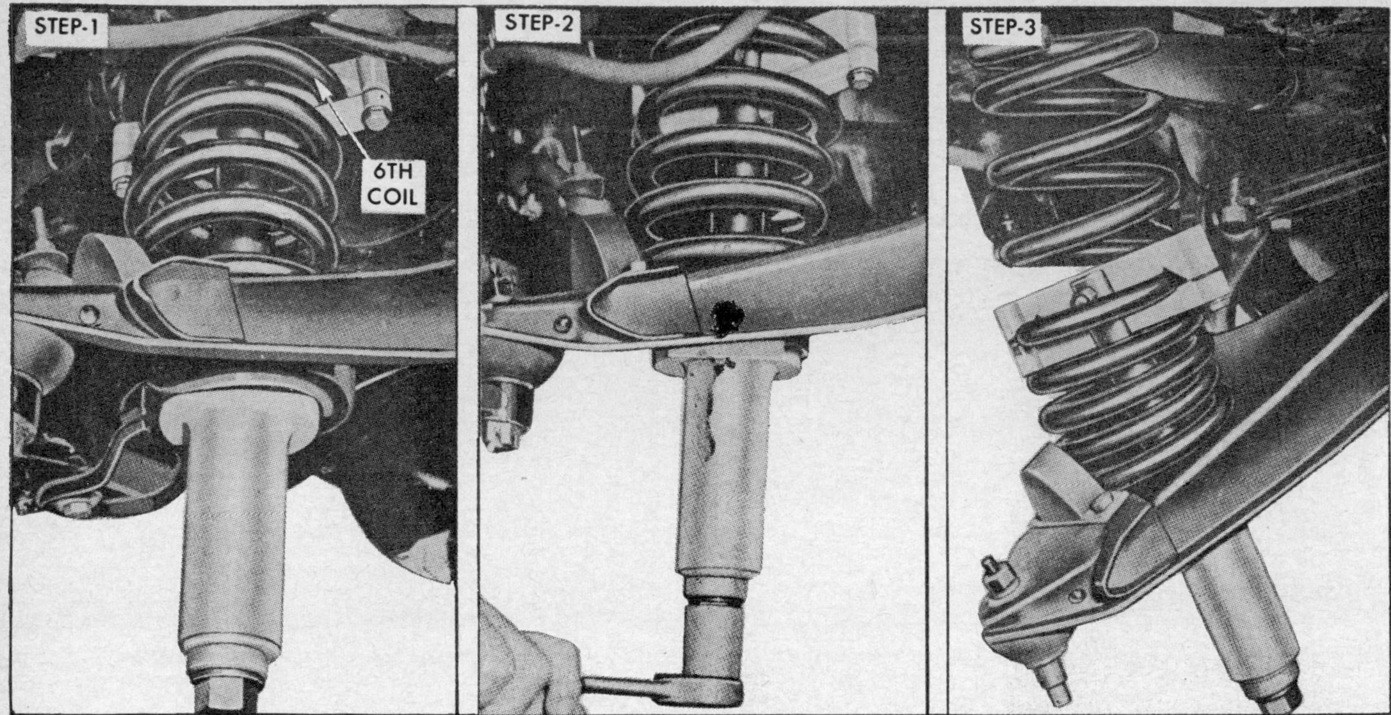

Fig. 9 Removing front spring. 1963-64 Chevrolet and 1963-69 Corvette

the time of exposure to the great compressive force.

STEERING GEAR, REPLACE

1968-69 All Models

1. Remove nuts, washers and bolts at steering coupling.
2. Remove pitman arm nut and washer from sector shaft and mark relation of arm position to shaft.
3. Use a suitable puller to remove pitman arm. On Camaro models, use care not to bend or fracture brake pipe when removing steering gear.
4. Unfasten gear from frame and remove assembly.
5. Reverse procedure to install.

1965-67 Camaro, Chevrolet, Chevelle & Corvette

1. Remove steering coupling lower clamp bolt and spread clamp slightly.
2. Remove pitman arm nut. Scribe mark on arm and shaft for assembly and then use a suitable puller to remove arm.
3. On Chevelle only, remove stabilizer bar-to-frame mounting brackets. Remove left front bumper arm-to-frame rear attaching bolt. Mark eccentric washer-to-frame location and loosen front attaching bolt enough to release eccentric washer from notches in arm.
4. While supporting steering gear, remove three gear-to-frame bolts and washers. Then lower assembly down and out of vehicle.

1965-67 Chevy II

1. Remove steering wheel and mast jacket.
2. Remove remaining gear-to-frame mounting bolt and pull gear assembly out of vehicle through engine compartment. **NOTE:** It will be necessary to move steering gear towards engine in order to allow the steering shaft to clear front seat cushion.

1963-64 Chevy II

1. If car is equipped with power brake cylinder and/or clutch push rod, these must be removed.
2. Remove pitman arm retaining nut. Mark position of pitman arm on sector shaft with a punch.
3. Remove pitman arm from sector shaft.
4. Remove mast jacket.
5. Unfasten steering gear from its mounting and remove from car.

1963-64 Chevrolet

Removal of the steering gear is essentially the same as for previous models. However, the lower coupling shaft now has the coupling parts riveted together. When service of the coupling parts is required, the rivets may be removed by drilling or cutting, the faulty parts replaced, and the coupling reassembled using special hardware furnished as a repair unit through Chevrolet part outlets.

1964 Chevelle

1. Remove steering shaft coupling attaching bolts.
2. Remove pitman arm retaining nut. Scribe mark on arm and shaft and use a suitable puller to remove arm.
3. Remove stabilizer bar-to-frame brackets.
4. Remove left front bumper arm-to-frame rear attaching bolt. Mark eccentric washer-to-frame location and loosen front attaching bolt enough to release eccentric washer from notches in arm.
5. While supporting steering gear, remove gear-to-frame mounting bolts, then lower assembly down and out of vehicle.

INTEGRAL POWER STEERING

1968-69 Chevrolet, Camaro, Chevelle, Chevy II

To remove gear assembly, disconnect pressure and return hoses from gear housing and cap both hoses and steering gear outlets to prevent foreign material from entering system, then follow procedure as outlined under *Steering Gear, Replace*.

1967 Camaro, 1965-67 Chevrolet, 1964-67 Chevelle

1. To remove the gear assembly, disconnect pressure and return hoses from gear housing and cap both hoses and steering gear outlets to prevent foreign material from entering system.
2. Remove steering shaft coupling clamp bolt.
3. Remove pitman arm nut. Scribe a mark on arm and shaft for assembly and use a suitable puller to remove pitman arm.
4. On Chevelle only, remove stabilizer bar-to-frame mounting brackets. Remove left front bumper arm-to-

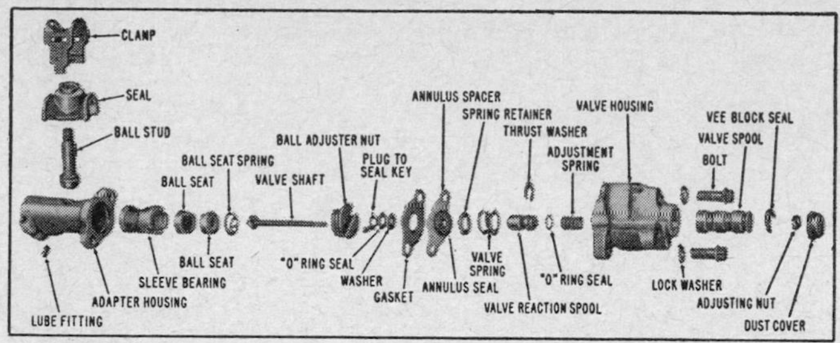

Fig. 10 Power steering control valve and adapter assembly. 1963-67

frame rear attaching bolt. Mark eccentric washer-to-frame location and loosen front attaching bolt enough to release eccentric washer from notches in arms.

5. While supporting steering gear, remove gear housing-to-frame bolts, then lower assembly down and out of vehicle.

LINKAGE TYPE POWER STEERING

1963-67

Power steering equipment consists of a recirculating ball type steering gear and linkage to which a hydraulic power mechanism has been added as part of the steering linkage. The hydraulic mechanism furnishes additional power to *assist* the manual operation so that the turning effort at the steering wheel is greatly reduced. The hydraulic mechanism consists of three basic units: a hydraulic pump and reservoir, a control valve, and a power cylinder.

Control Valve, Adjust

1. Disconnect cylinder rod from frame bracket.
2. With car on a hoist, start the engine. One of the following two conditions will exist:
   a. If piston rod remains retracted, turn the adjusting nut clockwise until the rod begins to move out. Then turn the nut counterclockwise until the rod just begins to move in. Now turn the nut clockwise to exactly one half the rotation needed to change the direction of shaft movement.
   b. If the rod extends upon starting the pump, move the nut counterclockwise until the rod begins to retract, then clockwise until the rod begins to move out again. Now turn the rod to exactly one half the rotation needed to change the direction of shaft movement.

Do not turn the nut back and forth more than is absolutely necessary to balance the valve.

3. Restart engine. Front wheels should not turn from center if valve has been properly balanced.

Power Cylinder Repairs

Removal

1. Disconnect two hydraulic lines at power cylinder.
2. Unfasten power cylinder rod from brace at frame.
3. Unfasten power cylinder from relay rod bracket.
4. Remove power cylinder from car.

Inspection

1. Inspect seals for leaks around cylinder rod and if leaks are present, replace seals as follows:
2. Use a hook tool to remove retaining ring. Remove wiper ring, back-up washer, back-up ring and seal. *Piston rod seal should not be removed unless there are signs of leakage along the piston shaft at shaft seal.*
3. Examine brass fitting hose connection seats for cracks or damage and replace if necessary.
4. For service other than seat or seal replacement, replace the power cylinder.

Installation

1. Install power cylinder on car by reversing removal procedure.
2. Reconnect two hoses, fill system with fluid and bleed system as outlined below.

Filling & Bleeding System

1. Fill reservoir to proper level with Automatic Transmission Fluid and let fluid remain undisturbed for about two minutes.
2. Raise front wheels off floor.
3. Run engine at idle for two minutes.
4. Increase engine speed to about 1500 rpm.

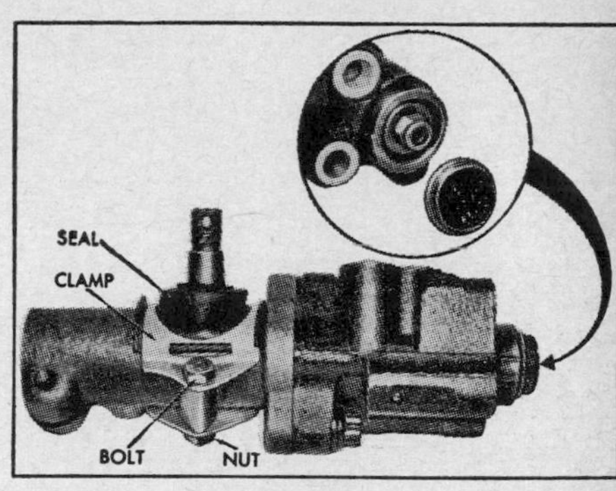

Fig. 11 Power steering control valve ball stud seal replacement. Chevy II 1964-67

5. Turn wheels from one extreme to the other, lightly contacting stops.
6. Lower wheels to floor and turn wheels right and left.
7. Recheck for leaks.
8. Check oil level and refill as required.

Pump pressures that should obtain are as follows:

1964-69	870 lbs.
1963	850 lbs.

Control Valve Repairs

Removal, Fig. 10

1. Loosen relay rod-to-control valve clamp.
2. Disconnect hose connections at control valve.
3. Disconnect control valve from pitman arm.
4. Unscrew control valve from relay rod.
5. Remove control valve from car.

Ball Stud Seal, Replace

In servicing the control valve, refer to Fig. 10. To replace the ball stud seal, refer to Fig. 11 and proceed as follows:

1. Remove pitman arm with a suitable puller.
2. Remove clamp by removing nut, bolt and spacer. If crimped type clamp is used, straighten clamp end and pull clamp and seal off end of stud.
3. Install new seal and clamp over stud so lips on seal mate with clamp. (A nut and bolt attachment type clamp replaces the crimped type for service, Fig. 11).
4. Center the ball stud, seal and clamp in opening in adapter housing, then install spacer, bolt and nut.

CHRYSLER • DODGE IMPERIAL • PLYMOUTH

OLD CAR SPECIFICATIONS: For 1946-62 Tune Up and Wheel Alignment Specifications see back of book.

INDEX OF SERVICE OPERATIONS

PAGE NO.

ACCESSORIES

Automatic Level Controls 1-41
Clock Troubles 1-11
Heater Core, Replace 2-180
Power Top Troubles 1-18
Power Window Troubles 1-18
Radio, Replace 2-177
Speed Controls, Adjust 2-181

BRAKES

Brake Troubles, Mechanical 1-17
Disc Brake Service 1-430
Hydraulic System Service 1-422
Master Cylinder, Replace 2-204
Parking Brake, Adjust 2-204
Power Brake Unit, Replace 2-204
Power Brake Service 1-440
Power Brake Troubles 1-440
Service Brakes, Adjust 2-203
Vacuum Release Parking Brake 2-204

CLUTCH

Clutch Pedal, Adjust 2-194
Clutch, Replace 2-194
Clutch Troubles 1-12

COOLING SYSTEM

Cooling System Troubles 1-6
Variable Speed Fans 1-39
Water Pump, Replace 2-193

ELECTRICAL

Alternator Service 1-63
Dash Gauge Service 1-117
Distributor, Replace 2-164
Distributor Service:
  Standard 1-53
  Transistorized 1-47
Electrical Troubles 1-8
Flasher Location Chart .... Back of Book
Generator Service 1-91
Headlamps, Concealed Type 1-40
Horn Sounder, Remove 2-167
Ignition Coils and Resistors 1-24
Ignition Switch, Replace 2-165
Ignition Timing 2-164
Instrument Cluster Removal 2-168
Light Switch, Replace 2-165
Neutral Safety Switch, Replace 2-166
Radio, Replace 2-177
Spark Plug Condition Chart 2-647
Starter Service 1-101
Starter, Replace 2-165
Starter Switch Service 1-114
Stop Light Switch, Replace 2-166
Turn Signal Switch, Replace 2-167
Turn Signal Troubles 1-11
Windshield Wiper Motor, Replace 2-172
Windshield Wiper Troubles 1-20

PAGE NO.

ENGINE

Camshaft, Replace 2-190
Crankshaft Rear Oil Seal 2-191
Cylinder Head, Replace 2-184
Engine, Replace 2-184
Engine Troubles 1-1
Main Bearings 2-190
Piston Pins 2-190
Piston Rings 2-190
Piston and Rod, Assemble 2-190
Pistons 2-190
Rocker Arm Service 2-187
Rod Bearings 2-190
Timing Case Cover, Replace 2-189
Timing Chain, Replace 2-190
Valve Arrangement 2-186
Valve Guide Service 2-188
Valve Lifters 2-188
Valves, Adjust 2-186

ENGINE LUBRICATION

Crankcase Ventilation (PCV) 1-29
Exhaust Emission Controls 1-30
Oil Pan, Replace 2-191
Oil Pump, Service 2-192

FUEL SYSTEM

Carburetor Adjustments and Specs. 1-124
Crankcase Ventilation (PCV) 1-29
Exhaust Emission Controls 1-30
Fuel Pump, Replace 2-193
Fuel Pump Service 1-120
Fuel System Troubles 1-2

PROPELLER SHAFT & U JOINTS

Propeller Shaft 2-202
Universal Joint Service 1-418

REAR AXLE

Axle Shaft, Bearing and Seal 2-198
Rear Axle Description 2-197
Rear Axle Specifications 2-159
Rear Axle Troubles 1-17

SPECIFICATIONS

Alternator 2-155
Brakes 2-160
Capacities 2-161
Carburetors 1-124
Cooling System 2-161
Crankshaft and Bearings 2-157
Distributors 2-151

PAGE NO.

Engine Tightening Torque 2-159
General Engine Specs. 2-141
Ignition Coils and Resistors 1-24
Pistons, Rings and Pins 2-157
Rear Axle 2-159
Starting Motors 2-155
Tune Up 2-145
Valve Lift 2-186
Valve Timing 2-187
Valves 2-155
Wheel Alignment 2-158

STEERING GEAR

Horn Sounder Removal 2-167
Mechanical Gear, Replace 2-208
Mechanical Gear Service 1-451
Mechanical Gear Troubles 1-18
Power Gear, Replace 2-208
Steering Wheel, Replace 2-167

SUSPENSION, FRONT

Ball Joints, Check for Wear 2-206
Ball Joints, Replace 2-206
Lubrication 2-205
Riding Height, Adjust 2-207
Suspension, Description of 2-205
Tire Wear Chart 2-648
Toe-In, Adjust 2-206
Torsion Bar, Replace 2-207
Wheel Alignment, Adjust 2-206
Wheel Bearings, Adjust 2-206
Wheel Bearings, Replace 2-206

TRANSMISSIONS

Three Speed Manual:
  Replace 2-194
  Repairs 1-261
  Linkage, Adjust 2-195
Four Speed Manual:
  Replace 2-194
  Repairs 1-298
  Linkage, Adjust 2-196
Automatic Units 1-321
  1969 Linkage 2-197

TUNE UP

Service 1-21
Specifications 2-145

WINDSHIELD WIPER

Wiper Motor, Replace 2-172
Wiper Linkage, Replace 2-174
Wiper Switch, Replace 2-177
Wiper Troubles 1-20

VEHICLE NUMBER LOCATION

1963-67: ON LEFT FRONT DOOR PILLAR.

1968-69: ON PLATE ATTACHED TO DASH PANEL PAD AND VISIBLE THROUGH WINDSHIELD.

ENGINE NUMBER LOCATION

1963-69 Six: Right front of block below cylinder head.

1963-69 V8-273, 318, 340: Left front of block below cylinder head.

1963-67 V8-361, 383: Right front of block below distributor.

1963-65 V8-413: Top of block behind water pump.

1963-67 V8-426: Left front of block left of water pump.

1966-67 V8-440: Left front of block below thermostat housing.

1968-69 V8-383, 426, 440: Left side rear of block near oil pan flange.

ENGINE IDENTIFICATION CODE

YEAR	MODEL	ENGINE PREFIX
1963	6-170	T17
	6-225	T22
	V8-318	V318
	V8-361	T36
	V8-383	T38
	V8-413	T41
	V8-413 "300J"	C-300J
	V8-426 (11:1 C.R.)	TMP-426
	V8-426 (13.5:1 C.R.)	TMP-HC-426
1964	6-170	V17
	6-225	V22
	V8-273	V273
	V8-318	V318
	V8-361	V36
	V8-383	V38
	V8-413	V41
	V8-413 "300K"	C-300K
	V8-426 (Same as 1963)	
1965	6-170	A170
	6-225	A225
	V8-273	A273
	V8-318	A318
	V8-361	A361
	V8-383	A383
	V8-413	A413
	V8-426 (Same as 1963)	
1966	6-170	B170
	6-225	B225
	V8-273	B273
	V8-318	B318
	V8-361	B361
	V8-383	B383
	V8-426	BH426
	V8-440	B440
1967	6-170	C170
	6-225	C225
	V8-273	C273
	V8-318 U.S. Built	C318
	V8-318 Canadian Built	CC318
	V8-383	C383
	V8-426	CH426
	V8-440	C440

1968-69 engines are identified by the cubic inch displacement and prefixed by either the letters PM or PT. These engines are 6-170, 6-225, V8-273, 318, 340, 383, 426 and 440.

IMPERIAL GRILLE IDENTIFICATON

1963

1964

1965

1966

1967

1968

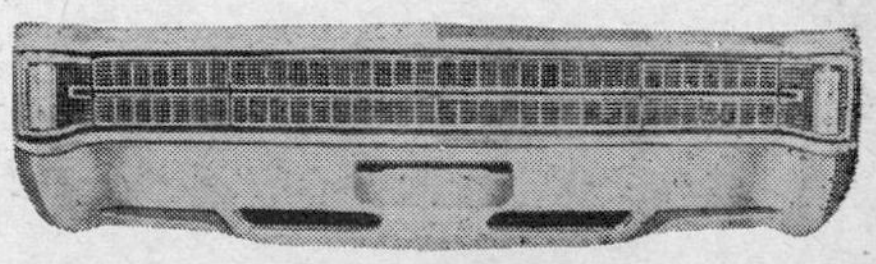

1969

CHRYSLER GRILLE IDENTIFICATION

1963 Newport

1963 "300"

1963 New Yorker

1964 Newport

1964 "300"

1964 New Yorker

1965 Newport

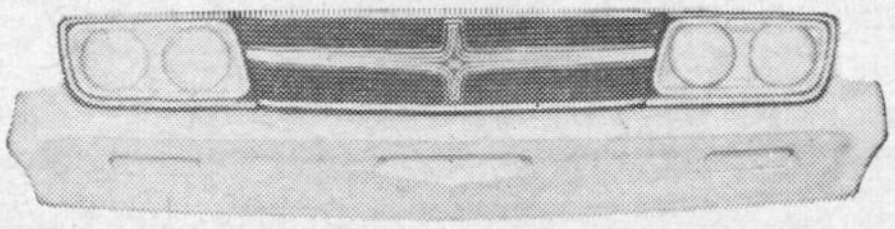

1965 "300"

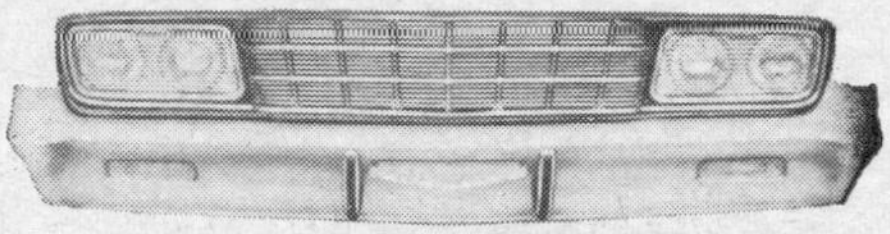

1965 New Yorker

1966 Newport

1966 "300"

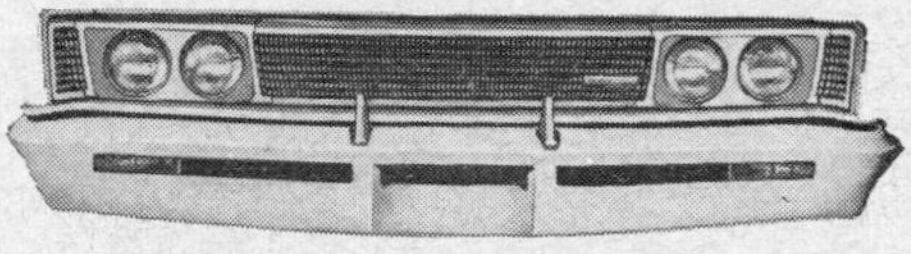

1966 New Yorker

1967 Newport

1967 "300"

1967 New Yorker

1968 Newport

1968 "300"

1968 New Yorker

1969 Newport

1969 "300"

1969 New Yorker

DODGE GRILLE IDENTIFICATION

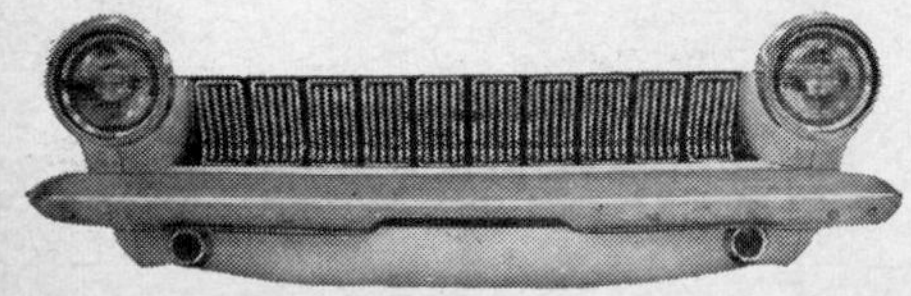

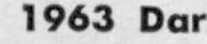

1963 Dart

1963 Dodge (Except 880)

1963 Dodge 880

DODGE GRILLE IDENTIFICATION—Continued

1964 Dart

1964 Dodge (Except 880)

1964 Dodge 880

1965 Dart

1965 Coronet

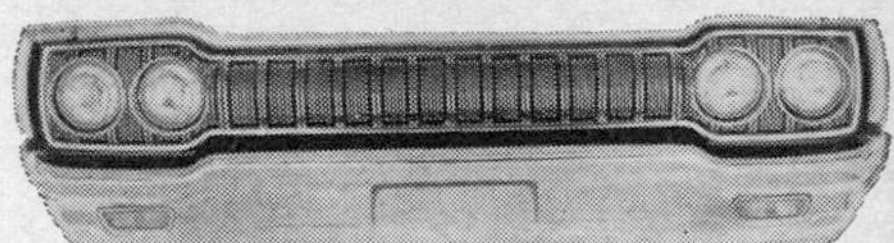
1965 Polara, Monaco, 880

1966 Dart

1966 Coronet

1966 Coronet 500

1966 Polara & Monaco

1966-67 Charger

1967 Polara

1967 Dart

1967 Coronet

1967 Coronet 500

1967 Monaco

1968 Dart

1968 Charger

1968 Coronet

1968 Coronet "500"

1968 Coronet R/T

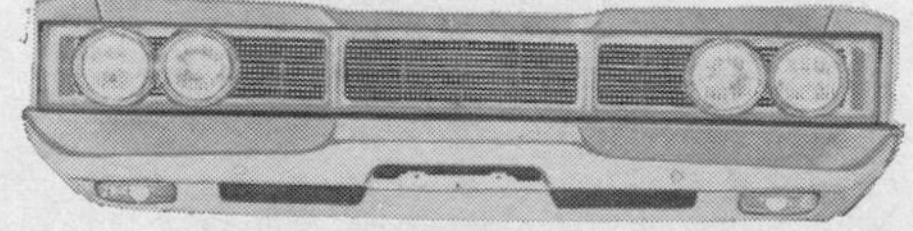
1968 Polara

1968 Monaco

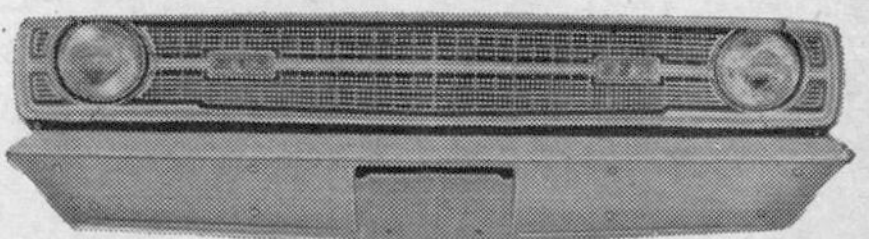
1969 Dart

DODGE GRILLE IDENTIFICATION—Continued

1969 Coronet

1969 Coronet "500"

1969 Charger

1969 Polara

1969 Monaco

PLYMOUTH GRILLE IDENTIFICATION

1963 Valiant

1963 Plymouth

1964 Valiant

1964 Plymouth

1964-65 Barracuda

1965 Valiant

1965 Belvedere

1965 Fury

1966 Valiant

1966 Fury

1966 Belvedere & Satellite

1966 Barracuda

1967 Barracuda

1967 Valiant

1967 Fury

PLYMOUTH GRILLE IDENTIFICATION—Continued

1967 Belvedere

1967 Satellite

1968 Valiant

1968 Barracuda

1968 Belvedere & Road Runner

1968 Satellite

1968 "GTX"

1968 Fury

1968 Sport Fury

1969 Valiant

1969 Barracuda

1969 Belvedere, Road Runner & Satellite

1969 "GTX"

1969 Sport Satellite

1969 Fury

1969 Sport Fury & VIP

GENERAL ENGINE SPECIFICATIONS

Year	Engine	Carburetor	Bore and Stroke	Piston Displacement, Cubic Inches	Compression Ratio (Standard)	Maximum Brake H.P. @ R.P.M.	Maximum Torque Lbs. Ft. @ R.P.M.	Normal Oil Pressure Pounds
CHRYSLER AND IMPERIAL								
1963	265 Horsepower V8-361	2 Barrel	4.1250 x 3.375	361	9.00	265 @ 4400	380 @ 2400	40–65
	305 Horsepower V8-383	2 Barrel	4.2500 x 3.375	383	10.00	305 @ 4600	410 @ 2400	40–65
	360 Horsepower V8-413	4 Barrel	4.1875 x 3.750	413	10.10	360 @ 4800	470 @ 3200	40–65

Continued

GENERAL ENGINE SPECIFICATIONS—Continued

Year	Engine	Carburetor	Bore and Stroke	Piston Displacement, Cubic Inches	Compression Ratio	Maximum Brake H.P. @ R.P.M.	Maximum Torque Lbs. Ft. @ R.P.M.	Normal Oil Pressure Pounds
CHRYSLER AND IMPERIAL—Continued								
1963	340 Horsepower.............V8-413	4 Barrel	4.1875 x 3.750	413	10.10	340 @ 4600	470 @ 2800	40–65
	390 Horsepower.............V8-413	Two 4 Bar.	4.1875 x 3.750	413	9.60	390 @ 4800	485 @ 3600	40–65
1964	265 Horsepower.............V8-361	2 Barrel	4.1250 x 3.375	361	9.00	265 @ 4400	380 @ 2400	40–65
	305 Horsepower.............V8-383	2 Barrel	4.2500 x 3.375	383	10.00	305 @ 4600	410 @ 2400	40–65
	340 Horsepower.............V8-413	4 Barrel	4.1875 x 3.750	413	10.10	340 @ 4600	470 @ 2800	40–65
	360 Horsepower.............V8-413	4 Barrel	4.1875 x 3.750	413	10.10	360 @ 4800	470 @ 3200	40–65
	390 Horsepower.............V8-413	Two 4 Bar.	4.1875 x 3.750	413	9.60	390 @ 4800	485 @ 3600	40–65
1965	270 Horsepower.............V8-383	2 Barrel	4.2500 x 3.375	383	9.20	270 @ 4400	390 @ 2800	40–65
	315 Horsepower.............V8-383	4 Barrel	4.2500 x 3.375	383	10.00	315 @ 4400	420 @ 2800	40–65
	340 Horsepower.............V8-413	4 Barrel	4.1875 x 3.750	413	10.10	340 @ 4600	470 @ 2800	40–65
	360 Horsepower.............V8-413	4 Barrel	4.1875 x 3.750	413	10.10	360 @ 4800	470 @ 3200	40–65
1966	270 Horsepower.............V8-383	2 Barrel	4.2500 x 3.375	383	9.2	270 @ 4400	390 @ 2800	45–65
	325 Horsepower.............V8-383	4 Barrel	4.2500 x 3.375	383	10.0	325 @ 4800	425 @ 2900	45–65
	350 Horsepower.............V8-440	4 Barrel	4.3200 x 3.75	440	10.10	350 @ 4400	480 @ 2800	45–65
1967	270 Horsepower.............V8-383	2 Barrel	4.25 x 3.375	383	9.20	270 @ 4400	390 @ 2800	45–65
	325 Horsepower.............V8-383	4 Barrel	4.25 x 3.375	383	10.00	325 @ 4800	425 @ 2800	45–65
	350 Horsepower.............V8-440	4 Barrel	4.32 x 3.75	440	10.10	350 @ 4400	480 @ 2800	45–65
	375 Horsepower.............V8-440	4 Barrel	4.32 x 3.75	440	10.10	375 @ 4600	480 @ 3200	45–65
1968	290 Horsepower.............V8-383	2 Barrel	4.25 x 3.375	383	9.2	290 @ 4400	390 @ 2800	45–65
	330 Horsepower.............V8-383	4 Barrel	4.25 x 3.375	383	10.0	330 @ 5000	425 @ 3200	45–65
	350 Horsepower.............V8-440	4 Barrel	4.32 x 3.75	440	10.1	350 @ 4400	480 @ 2800	45–65
	375 Horsepower.............V8-440	4 Barrel	4.32 x 3.75	440	10.1	375 @ 4600	480 @ 3200	45–65
1969	290 Horsepower.............V8-383	2 Barrel	4.25 x 3.375	383	9.2	290 @ 4400	380 @ 2400	45–65
	330 Horsepower.............V8-383	4 Barrel	4.25 x 3.375	383	10.0	330 @ 5000	425 @ 3200	45–65
	350 Horsepower.............V8-440	4 Barrel	4.32 x 3.75	440	10.1	350 @ 4400	480 @ 2800	45–65
	375 Horsepower.............V8-440	4 Barrel	4.32 x 3.75	440	10.1	375 @ 4600	480 @ 3200	45–65
DODGE								
1963	101 Horsepower..............6-170	1 Barrel	3.4000 x 3.125	170	8.20	101 @ 4400	155 @ 2400	45–65
	145 Horsepower..............6-225	1 Barrel	3.4000 x 4.125	225	8.20	145 @ 4000	215 @ 2800	45–65
	230 Horsepower.............V8-318	2 Barrel	3.91 x 3.31	318	9.00	230 @ 4400	340 @ 2400	45–65
	265 Horsepower.............V8-361	2 Barrel	4.1250 x 3.375	361	9.00	265 @ 4400	380 @ 2400	45–65
	305 Horsepower.............V8-383	2 Barrel	4.25 x 3.375	383	10.00	305 @ 4600	410 @ 2400	45–65
	320 Horsepower.............V8-383	4 Barrel	4.25 x 3.375	383	11.00	320 @ 4600	430 @ 2800	45–65
	325 Horsepower.............V8-383	Two 4 Bar.	4.25 x 3.375	383	11.00	325 @ 5200	420 @ 3600	45–65
	370 Horsepower.............V8-426	4 Barrel	4.25 x 3.75	426	11.00	370 @ 4600	460 @ 2800	40–60
	375 Horsepower.............V8-426	4 Barrel	4.25 x 3.75	426	13.50	375 @ 4600	465 @ 2800	40–60
	415 Horsepower.............V8-426	Two 4 Bar.	4.25 x 3.75	426	11.00	415 @ 5600	470 @ 4400	40–60
	425 Horsepower.............V8-426	Two 4 Bar.	4.25 x 3.75	426	13.50	425 @ 5600	480 @ 4400	40–60
1964	101 Horsepower..............6-170	1 Barrel	3.40 x 3.125	170	8.50	101 @ 4400	155 @ 2400	45–65
	145 Horsepower..............6-225	1 Barrel	3.40 x 4.125	225	8.40	145 @ 4000	215 @ 2400	45–65
	180 Horsepower.............V8-273	2 Barrel	3.625 x 3.31	273	8.80	180 @ 4200	260 @ 1600	40–65
	230 Horsepower.............V8-318	2 Barrel	3.91 x 3.31	318	9.00	230 @ 4400	340 @ 2400	45–65
	265 Horsepower.............V8-361	2 Barrel	4.125 x 3.375	361	9.00	265 @ 4400	380 @ 2400	45–65
	330 Horsepower.............V8-383	4 Barrel	4.25 x 3.375	383	10.00	330 @ 4600	425 @ 2800	45–65
	305 Horsepower.............V8-383	2 Barrel	4.25 x 3.375	383	10.00	305 @ 4600	410 @ 2400	45–65
	340 Horsepower.............V8-413	4 Barrel	4.1875 x 3.75	413	10.10	340 @ 4600	470 @ 2800	45–65
	375 Horsepower.............V8-426	4 Barrel	4.25 x 3.75	426	10.30	375 @ 4600	465 @ 2800	40–60
	425 H.P. Hemi-Charger.......V8-426	Two 4 Bar.	4.25 x 3.75	426	12.50	425 @ 6000	480 @ 4600	40–60
1965	101 Horsepower..............6-170	1 Barrel	3.4000 x 3.125	170	8.50	101 @ 4400	155 @ 2400	45–65
	145 Horsepower..............6-225	1 Barrel	3.4000 x 4.125	225	8.40	145 @ 4000	215 @ 2400	45–65
	180 Horsepower.............V8-273	2 Barrel	3.625 x 3.31	273	8.80	180 @ 4200	260 @ 1600	40–65
	230 Horsepower.............V8-318	2 Barrel	3.91 x 3.31	318	9.00	230 @ 4400	340 @ 2400	45–65
	235 Horsepower.............V8-273	4 Barrel	3.625 x 3.31	273	10.50	235 @ 5200	280 @ 4000	40–65

Continued

GENERAL ENGINE SPECIFICATIONS—Continued

Year	Engine	Carburetor	Bore and Stroke	Piston Displacement, Cubic Inches	Compression Ratio	Maximum Brake H.P. @ R.P.M.	Maximum Torque Lbs. Ft. @ R.P.M.	Normal Oil Pressure Pounds
DODGE—Continued								
1965	265 Horsepower..............V8-361	2 Barrel	4.125 x 3.375	361	9.00	265 @ 4400	380 @ 2400	45-65
	270 Horsepower..............V8-383	2 Barrel	4.25 x 3.375	383	9.20	270 @ 4400	390 @ 2800	45-65
	315 Horsepower..............V8-383	4 Barrel	4.25 x 3.375	383	10.00	315 @ 4400	420 @ 2800	45-65
	330 Horsepower..............V8-383	4 Barrel	4.25 x 3.375	383	10.00	330 @ 4600	425 @ 2800	45-65
	340 Horsepower..............V8-413	4 Barrel	4.1875 x 3.75	413	10.10	340 @ 4600	470 @ 2800	45-65
	365 Horsepower..............V8-426	4 Barrel	4.25 x 3.75	426	10.30	365 @ 4800	470 @ 3200	40-60
1966	101 Horsepower..............6-170	1 Barrel	3.4000 x 3.125	170	8.50	101 @ 4400	155 @ 2400	45-65
	145 Horsepower..............6-225	1 Barrel	3.4000 x 4.125	225	8.40	145 @ 4000	215 @ 2400	45-65
	180 Horsepower..............V8-273	2 Barrel	3.6250 x 3.31	273	8.80	180 @ 4200	260 @ 1600	40-65
	235 Horsepower..............V8-273	4 Barrel	3.6250 x 3.31	273	10.50	235 @ 5200	280 @ 4000	40-65
	230 Horsepower..............V8-318	2 Barrel	3.91 x 3.31	318	9.00	230 @ 4400	340 @ 2400	45-65
	265 Horsepower..............V8-361	2 Barrel	4.125 x 3.375	361	9.00	265 @ 4400	380 @ 2400	45-65
	270 Horsepower..............V8-383	2 Barrel	4.25 x 3.375	383	9.20	270 @ 4400	390 @ 2800	45-65
	325 Horsepower..............V8-383	4 Barrel	4.25 x 3.375	383	10.00	325 @ 4800	425 @ 2800	45-65
	365 Horsepower..............V8-426	4 Barrel	4.25 x 3.75	426	10.30	365 @ 4800	470 @ 3200	40-60
	350 Horsepower..............V8-440	4 Barrel	4.32 x 3.75	440	10.10	350 @ 4400	480 @ 2800	45-65
1967	115 Horsepower..............6-170	1 Barrel	3.40 x 3.125	170	8.50	115 @ 4400	155 @ 2400	45-65
	145 Horsepower..............6-225	1 Barrel	3.40 x 4.125	225	8.40	145 @ 4000	215 @ 2400	45-65
	180 Horsepower..............V8-273	2 Barrel	3.625 x 3.31	273	8.80	180 @ 4200	260 @ 1600	40-65
	235 Horsepower..............V8-273	4 Barrel	3.625 x 3.31	273	10.50	235 @ 5200	280 @ 4000	40-65
	230 Horsepower..............V8-318	2 Barrel	3.91 x 3.31	318	9.20	230 @ 4400	340 @ 2400	45-65
	270 Horsepower..............V8-383	2 Barrel	4.25 x 3.375	383	9.20	270 @ 4400	390 @ 2800	45-65
	325 Horsepower..............V8-383	4 Barrel	4.25 x 3.375	383	10.00	325 @ 4800	425 @ 2800	45-65
	350 Horsepower..............V8-440	4 Barrel	4.32 x 3.75	440	10.10	350 @ 4400	480 @ 2800	45-65
	375 Horsepower..............V8-440	4 Barrel	4.32 x 3.75	440	10.10	375 @ 4600	480 @ 3200	45-65
	425 H.P. Hemi..............V8-426	Two 4 Bar.	4.25 x 3.75	426	10.25	425 @ 5000	490 @ 4000	40-60
1968	115 Horsepower..............6-170	1 Barrel	3.40 x 3.125	170	8.5	115 @ 4400	155 @ 2400	45-65
	145 Horsepower..............6-225	1 Barrel	3.40 x 4.125	225	8.4	145 @ 4000	215 @ 2400	45-65
	190 Horsepower..............V8-273	2 Barrel	3.625 x 3.31	273	9.0	190 @ 4400	260 @ 2000	45-65
	230 Horsepower..............V8-318	2 Barrel	3.91 x 3.31	318	9.2	230 @ 4400	340 @ 2400	45-65
	275 Horsepower..............V8-340	4 Barrel	4.04 x 3.31	340	10.5	275 @ 5000	340 @ 3200	45-65
	290 Horsepower..............V8-383	2 Barrel	4.25 x 3.375	383	9.2	290 @ 4400	390 @ 2800	45-65
	300 Horsepower..............V8-383	4 Barrel	4.25 x 3.375	383	10.0	300 @ 4400	400 @ 2400	45-65
	330 Horsepower..............V8-383	4 Barrel	4.25 x 3.375	383	10.0	330 @ 5000	425 @ 3200	45-65
	350 Horsepower..............V8-440	4 Barrel	4.32 x 3.75	440	10.1	350 @ 4400	480 @ 2800	45-65
	375 Horsepower..............V8-440	4 Barrel	4.32 x 3.75	440	10.1	375 @ 4600	480 @ 3200	45-65
	425 Horsepower..............V8-426	Two 4 Bar.	4.25 x 3.75	426	10.25	425 @ 5000	490 @ 4000	40-60
1969	115 Horsepower..............6-170	1 Barrel	3.40 x 3.125	170	8.5	115 @ 4400	155 @ 2400	45-65
	145 Horsepower..............6-225	1 Barrel	3.40 x 4.125	225	8.4	145 @ 4000	215 @ 2400	45-65
	190 Horsepower..............V8-273	2 Barrel	3.63 x 3.31	273	9.0	190 @ 4400	260 @ 2000	45-65
	230 Horsepower..............V8-318	2 Barrel	3.91 x 3.31	318	9.2	230 @ 4400	340 @ 2400	45-65
	275 Horsepower..............V8-340	4 Barrel	4.04 x 3.31	340	10.5	275 @ 5000	340 @ 3200	45-65
	290 Horsepower..............V8-383	2 Barrel	4.25 x 3.38	383	9.2	290 @ 4400	390 @ 2800	45-65
	330 Horsepower..............V8-383	4 Barrel	4.25 x 3.38	383	10.0	330 @ 5000	425 @ 3200	45-65
	335 Horsepower..............V8-383	4 Barrel	4.25 x 3.38	383	10.0	335 @ 5000	425 @ 3400	45-65
	350 Horsepower..............V8-440	4 Barrel	4.32 x 3.75	440	10.1	350 @ 4400	480 @ 2800	45-65
	375 Horsepower..............V8-440	4 Barrel	4.32 x 3.75	440	10.1	375 @ 4600	480 @ 3200	45-65
	425 Horsepower..............V8-426	Two 4 Bar.	4.25 x 3.75	426	10.25	425 @ 5000	490 @ 4000	45-65
PLYMOUTH								
1963	101 Horsepower..............6-170	1 Barrel	3.40 x 3.125	170	8.20	101 @ 4400	155 @ 2400	45-65
	145 Horsepower..............6-225	1 Barrel	3.4000 x 4.125	225	8.20	145 @ 4000	215 @ 2800	45-65

Continued

GENERAL ENGINE SPECIFICATIONS—Continued

	Engine	Carburetor	Bore and Stroke	Piston Displacement, Cubic Inches	Compression Ratio	Maximum Brake H.P. @ R.P.M.	Maximum Torque Lbs. Ft. @ R.P.M.	Normal Oil Pressure Pounds
PLYMOUTH—Continued								
1963	230 Horsepower.............V8-318	2 Barrel	3.91 x 3.31	318	9.00	230 @ 4400	340 @ 2400	45–65
	265 Horsepower.............V8-361	2 Barrel	4.1250 x 3.375	361	9.00	265 @ 4400	380 @ 2400	45–65
	330 Horsepower.............V8-383	4 Barrel	4.2500 x 3.375	383	10.00	330 @ 4600	425 @ 2800	45–65
	370 Horsepower.............V8-426	4 Barrel	4.25 x 3.75	426	11.00	370 @ 4600	460 @ 2800	40–60
	375 Horsepower.............V8-426	4 Barrel	4.25 x 3.75	426	13.50	375 @ 4600	465 @ 2800	40–60
	415 Horsepower.............V8-426	Two 4 Bar.	4.25 x 3.75	426	11.00	415 @ 5600	470 @ 4400	40–60
	425 Horsepower.............V8-426	Two 4 Bar.	4.25 x 3.75	426	13.50	425 @ 5600	480 @ 4400	40–60
1964	101 Horsepower.............6-170	1 Barrel	3.40 x 3.125	170	8.50	101 @ 4400	155 @ 2400	45–65
	145 Horsepower.............6-225	1 Barrel	3.40 x 4.125	225	8.40	145 @ 4000	215 @ 2400	45–65
	180 Horsepower.............V8-273	2 Barrel	3.625 x 3.31	273	8.80	180 @ 4200	260 @ 1600	40–65
	230 Horsepower.............V8-318	2 Barrel	3.91 x 3.31	318	9.00	230 @ 4400	340 @ 2400	45–65
	265 Horsepower.............V8-361	2 Barrel	4.125 x 3.38	361	9.00	265 @ 4400	380 @ 2400	45–65
	330 Horsepower.............V8-383	4 Barrel	4.25 x 3.38	383	10.00	330 @ 4600	425 @ 2800	45–65
	375 Horsepower.............V8-426	4 Barrel	4.25 x 3.75	426	10.30	375 @ 4600	465 @ 2800	40–60
	425 Horsepower....... V8-426 Hemi.	Two 4 Bar.	4.25 x 3.75	426	12.50	425 @ 6000	480 @ 4600	40–60
1965	101 Horsepower.............6-170	1 Barrel	3.40 x 3.125	170	8.50	101 @ 4400	155 @ 2400	45–65
	145 Horsepower.............6-225	1 Barrel	3.40 x 4.125	225	8.40	145 @ 4000	215 @ 2400	45–65
	180 Horsepower.............V8-273	2 Barrel	3.625 x 3.31	273	8.80	180 @ 4200	260 @ 1600	40–65
	230 Horsepower.............V8-318	2 Barrel	3.91 x 3.31	318	9.00	230 @ 4400	340 @ 2400	45–65
	235 Horsepower.............V8-273	4 Barrel	3.625 x 3.31	273	10.50	235 @ 5200	280 @ 4000	40–65
	265 Horsepower.............V8-361	2 Barrel	4.125 x 3.38	361	9.00	265 @ 4400	380 @ 2400	45–65
	270 Horsepower.............V8-383	2 Barrel	4.25 x 3.38	383	9.20	270 @ 4400	390 @ 2800	45–65
	330 Horsepower.............V8-383	4 Barrel	4.25 x 3.38	383	10.00	330 @ 4600	425 @ 2800	45–65
	365 Horsepower.............V8-426	4 Barrel	4.25 x 3.75	426	10.30	365 @ 4800	470 @ 3200	45–65
1966	101 Horsepower.............6-170	1 Barrel	3.40 x 3.125	170	8.50	101 @ 4400	155 @ 2400	45–65
	145 Horsepower.............6-225	1 Barrel	3.40 x 4.125	225	8.40	145 @ 4000	215 @ 2400	45–65
	180 Horsepower.............V8-273	2 Barrel	3.625 x 3.31	273	8.80	180 @ 4200	260 @ 1600	40–65
	235 Horsepower.............V8-273	4 Barrel	3.625 x 3.31	273	10.50	235 @ 5200	280 @ 4000	40–65
	230 Horsepower.............V8-318	2 Barrel	3.91 x 3.31	318	9.00	230 @ 4400	340 @ 2400	45–65
	265 Horsepower.............V8-361	2 Barrel	4.125 x 3.38	361	9.00	265 @ 4400	380 @ 2400	45–65
	270 Horsepower.............V8-383	2 Barrel	4.25 x 3.38	383	9.20	270 @ 4400	390 @ 2800	45–65
	325 Horsepower.............V8-383	4 Barrel	4.25 x 3.38	383	10.00	325 @ 4800	425 @ 2800	45–65
	365 Horsepower.............V8-426	4 Barrel	4.25 x 3.75	426	10.30	365 @ 4800	470 @ 3200	40–60
	365 Horsepower.............V8-440	4 Barrel	4.32 x 3.75	440	10.10	365 @ 4600	480 @ 3200	45–65
	425 H.P. Hemi HP2.........V8-426	Two 4 Bar.	4.25 x 3.75	426	10.25	425 @ 5000	490 @ 4000	45–65
1967	115 Horsepower.............6-170	1 Barrel	3.40 x 3.125	170	8.50	115 @ 4400	155 @ 2400	45–65
	145 Horsepower.............6-225	1 Barrel	3.40 x 4.125	225	8.40	145 @ 4000	215 @ 2400	45–65
	180 Horsepower.............V8-273	2 Barrel	3.625 x 3.31	273	8.80	180 @ 4200	260 @ 1600	40–65
	235 Horsepower.............V8-273	4 Barrel	3.625 x 3.31	273	10.50	235 @ 5200	280 @ 4000	40–65
	230 Horsepower.............V8-318	2 Barrel	3.91 x 3.31	318	9.20	230 @ 4400	340 @ 2400	45–65
	270 Horsepower.............V8-383	2 Barrel	4.25 x 3.38	383	9.20	270 @ 4400	390 @ 2800	45–65
	325 Horsepower.............V8-383	4 Barrel	4.25 x 3.38	383	10.00	325 @ 4800	425 @ 2800	45–65
	350 Horsepower.............V8-440	4 Barrel	4.32 x 3.75	440	10.10	350 @ 4400	480 @ 2800	45–65
	375 Horsepower.............V8-440	4 Barrel	4.32 x 3.75	440	10.10	375 @ 4600	480 @ 3200	45–65
	425 H.P. Hemi.............V8-426	Two 4 Bar.	4.25 x 3.75	426	10.25	425 @ 5000	490 @ 4000	40–60
1968	115 Horsepower.............6-170	1 Barrel	3.40 x 3.125	170	8.5	115 @ 4400	155 @ 2400	45–65
	145 Horsepower.............6-225	1 Barrel	3.40 x 4.125	225	8.4	145 @ 4000	215 @ 2400	45–65
	190 Horsepower.............V8-273	2 Barrel	3.625 x 3.31	273	9.0	190 @ 4400	260 @ 2000	45–65
	230 Horsepower.............V8-318	2 Barrel	3.91 x 3.31	318	9.2	230 @ 4400	340 @ 2400	45–65
	275 Horsepower.............V8-340	4 Barrel	4.04 x 3.31	340	10.5	275 @ 5000	340 @ 3200	45–65
	290 Horsepower.............V8-383	2 Barrel	4.25 x 3.375	383	9.2	290 @ 4400	390 @ 2800	45–65
	300 Horsepower.............V8-383	4 Barrel	4.25 x 3.375	383	10.0	300 @ 4400	400 @ 2400	45–65
	330 Horsepower.............V8-383	4 Barrel	4.25 x 3.375	383	10.0	330 @ 5000	425 @ 3200	45–65
	350 Horsepower.............V8-440	4 Barrel	4.32 x 3.75	440	10.1	350 @ 4400	480 @ 2800	45–65

Continued

GENERAL ENGINE SPECIFICATIONS—Continued

Year	Engine	Carburetor	Bore and Stroke	Piston Displacement, Cubic Inches	Compression Ratio	Maximum Brake H.P. @ R.P.M.	Maximum Torque H.P. @ R.P.M.	Normal Oil Pressure Pounds
PLYMOUTH—Continued								
1968	375 Horsepower............V8-440	4 Barrel	4.32 x 3.75	440	10.1	375 @ 4600	480 @ 3200	45–65
	425 Horsepower............V8-426	Two 4 Bar.	4.25 x 3.75	426	10.25	425 @ 5000	490 @ 4000	40–60
1969	115 Horsepower............6-170	1 Barrel	3.40 x 3.125	170	8.5	115 @ 4400	155 @ 2400	45–65
	145 Horsepower............6-225	1 Barrel	3.40 x 4.125	225	8.4	145 @ 4000	215 @ 2400	45–65
	190 Horsepower............V8-273	2 Barrel	3.63 x 3.31	273	9.0	190 @ 4400	260 @ 2000	45–65
	230 Horsepower............V8-318	2 Barrel	3.91 x 3.31	318	9.2	239 @ 4400	340 @ 2400	45–65
	275 Horsepower............V8-340	4 Barrel	4.04 x 3.31	340	10.5	275 @ 5000	340 @ 3200	45–65
	290 Horsepower............V8-383	2 Barrel	4.25 x 3.38	383	9.2	290 @ 4400	390 @ 2800	45–65
	330 Horsepower............V8-383	4 Barrel	4.25 x 3.38	383	10.0	330 @ 5000	425 @ 3200	45–65
	335 Horsepower............V8-383	4 Barrel	4.25 x 3.38	383	10.0	335 @ 5000	425 @ 3400	45–65
	350 Horsepower............V8-440	4 Barrel	4.32 x 3.75	440	10.1	350 @ 4400	480 @ 2800	45–65
	375 Horsepower............V8-440	4 Barrel	4.32 x 3.75	440	10.1	375 @ 4600	480 @ 3200	45–65
	425 Horsepower............V8-426	Two 4 Bar.	4.25 x 3.75	426	10.25	425 @ 5000	490 @ 4000	45–65

TUNE UP SPECIFICATIONS

OLD CAR SPECIFICATIONS: For 1946-62 Tune Up Specifications see back of book.

★ When using a timing light, disconnect vacuum tube or hose at distributor and plug opening in hose or tube so idle speed will not be affected.

Year	Engine	Spark Plug		Distributor		Firing Order	Ignition Timing★		Hot Idle Speed		Comp. Press. Lbs. ③	Fuel Pump Press. Lbs.
		Type ⑦	Gap Inch	Point Gap Inch	Dwell Angle Deg.		BTDC ①	Mark	Std. Trans.	Auto. Trans. ②		
CHRYSLER AND IMPERIAL												
1963	V8-361 Newport	J12Y	.035	.017	27-32	Fig. J	10°	Fig. A	500⑥	500N⑥	150	3½–5
	V8-383 Series 300	J12Y	.035	.017	27-32	Fig. J	10°	Fig. A	500⑥	500N⑥	150	3½–5
	V8-413 Series 300	J9Y	.035	.017	⑨	Fig. J	10°	Fig. A	500⑥	500N⑥	165	3½–5
	V8-413 New Yorker	J12Y	.035	.017	28-33	Fig. J	10°	Fig. A	...	500N⑥	165	3½–5
	V8-413 "300J"	J9Y	.035	.017	⑨	Fig. J	12½°	Fig. A	750⑥	750N⑥	165	3½–5
	V8-413 Imperial	J12Y	.035	.017	27-32	Fig. J	10°⑪	Fig. A	...	500N⑥	165	3½–5
1964	V8-361 Newport	J12Y	.035	.017	28-33	Fig. J	10°	Fig. A	500⑥	500N⑥	150	3½–5
	V8-383 Series 300	J12Y	.035	.017	28-33	Fig. J	10°	Fig. A	500⑥	500N⑥	165	3½–5
	V8-413 Series 300	J10Y	.035	.017	⑨	Fig. J	10°	Fig. A	500⑥	500N⑥	165	3½–5
	V8-413 New Yorker	J12Y	.035	.017	28-33	Fig. J	10°	Fig. A	500⑥	500N⑥	165	3½–5
	300K, 1 Carb.	J10Y	.035	.017	⑨	Fig. J	10°	Fig. A	700⑥	700N⑥	150	3½–5
	300K, 2 Carbs.	J10Y	.035	.017	⑨	Fig. J	12½°	Fig. A	700⑥	700N⑥	150	3½–5
	V8-413 Imperial	J12Y	.035	.017	28-33	Fig. J	10°⑪	Fig. A	...	500N⑥	165	3½–5
1965	V8-383, 270 H.P.	J14Y	.035	.017	28-32	Fig. J	10°	Fig. A	500⑥	500N⑥	140	3½–5
	V8-383, 315 H.P.	J14Y	.035	.017	28-32	Fig. J	10°	Fig. A	500⑥	500N⑥	150	3½–5
	V8-413, 340 H.P.	J14Y	.035	.017	28-32	Fig. J	12½°	Fig. A	500⑥	500N⑥	150	3½–5
	V8-413, 360 H.P.	J10Y	.035	.017	⑩	Fig. J	12½°	Fig. A	550⑥	550N⑥	150	3½–5
	V8-413 Imperial	J14Y	.035	.017	28-32	Fig. J	10°⑪	Fig. A	...	500N⑥	150	3½–5
1966	8-383 2 Bar. Carb.⑫	J14Y	.035	.017	28-32	Fig. J	12½°	Fig. F	500⑥	500N⑥	140	4–5½
	8-383 2 Bar. Carb.⑬	J14Y	.035	.017	28-32	Fig. J	5° ATC	Fig. F	600⑥	600N⑥	140	4–5½
	8-383 4 Bar. Carb.⑫	J13Y	.035	.017	28-32	Fig. J	12½°	Fig. F	500⑥	500N⑥	150	4–5½
	8-383 4 Bar. Carb.⑬	J13Y	.035	.017	28-32	Fig. J	5° ATC	Fig. F	650⑥	600N⑥	150	4–5½
	8-440 Chrysler⑫	J13Y	.035	.017	28-32	Fig. J	12½°	Fig. F	500⑥	500N⑥	150	4–5½
	8-440 Chrysler⑬	J13Y	.035	.017	28-32	Fig. J	5° ATC	Fig. F	650⑥	600N⑥	150	4–5½
	8-440 Imperial⑫	J13Y	.035	.017	28-32	Fig. J	12½°⑪	Fig. F	...	500N⑥	150	4–5½
	8-440 Imperial⑬	J13Y	.035	.017	28-32	Fig. J	5° ATC⑪	Fig. F	...	600N⑥	150	4–5½

Continued

TUNE UP SPECIFICATIONS—Continued

OLD CAR SPECIFICATIONS: For 1946-62 Tune Up Specifications see back of book.

★When using a timing light, disconnect vacuum hose or tube at distributor and plug opening in hose or tube so idle speed will not be affected.

Year	Engine	Spark Plug		Distributor		Firing Order	Ignition Timing★		Hot Idle Speed		Comp. Press. Lbs. ③	Fuel Pump Press. Lbs.
		Type ⑦	Gap Inch	Point Gap Inch	Dwell Angle Deg.		BTDC ①	Mark	Std. Trans.	Auto. Trans. ②		
CHRYSLER AND IMPERIAL—Continued												
1967	V8-383 2 Bar. Carb.⑫	J14Y	.035	.017	28–32	Fig. J	12½°	Fig. F	550⑥	550N⑥	140	3½–5
	V8-383 2 Bar. Carb.⑱	J14Y	.035	.017	28–32	Fig. J	5°	Fig. F	. . .	650N⑥	140	3½–5
	V8-383 2 Bar. Carb.⑲	J14Y	.035	.017	28–32	Fig. J	TDC	Fig. F	600⑥	. . .	140	3½–5
	V8-383 4 Bar. Carb.⑫	J13Y	.035	.017	28–32	Fig. J	12½°	Fig. F	500⑥	500N⑥	150	3½–5
	V8-383 4 Bar. Carb.⑱	J13Y	.035	.017	28–32	Fig. J	5°	Fig. F	650⑥	. . .	150	3½–5
	V8-383 4 Bar. Carb.⑲	J13Y	.035	.017	28–32	Fig. J	TDC	Fig. F	. . .	650N⑥	150	3½–5
	V8-440 Chrysler⑫	J13Y	.035	.017	28–32	Fig. J	12½°	Fig. F	650⑥	650N⑥	150	3½–5
	V8-440 Chrysler⑱	J13Y	.035	.017	28–32	Fig. J	5°	Fig. F	. . .	650N⑥	150	3½–5
	V8-440 Chrysler⑲	J13Y	.035	.017	28–32	Fig. J	TDC	Fig. F	650⑥	. . .	150	3½–5
	V8-440 Imperial⑫	J11Y	.035	.017	28–32	Fig. J	12½°⑪	Fig. F	. . .	650N⑥	150	3½–5
	V8-440 Imperial⑬	J11Y	.035	.017	28–32	Fig. J	5°⑪	Fig. F	. . .	650N⑥	150	3½–5
1968	V8-383 Std. Tr.㉑	J14Y	.035	.017	28–33	Fig. J	TDC	Fig. F	650⑥	—	140	3½–5
	V8-383 Auto. Tr.㉑	J14Y	.035	.017	28–33	Fig. J	7½°	Fig. F	—	600N⑥	140	3½–5
	V8-383 Std. Tr.④	J11Y	.035	.017	28–33	Fig. J	TDC	Fig. F	650⑥	—	150	3½–5
	V8-383 Auto. Tr.④	J11Y	.035	.017	28–33	Fig. J	5°	Fig. F	—	650N⑥	150	3½–5
	V8-440 Std. Tr.	J13Y	.035	.017	28–33	Fig. J	7½°	Fig. F	650⑥	—	150	3½–5
	V8-440 Auto. Tr.	J13Y	.035	.017	28–33	Fig. J	TDC	Fig. F	—	550N⑥	150	3½–5
	V8-440 Std. Tr.㉒	J11Y	.035	.017	28–33	Fig. J	5°	Fig. F	650N⑥	—	150	3½–5
	V8-440 Auto. Tr.㉒	J11Y	.035	.017	28–33	Fig. J	TDC	Fig. F	—	650N⑥	150	3½–5
1969	V8-383 Std. Tr.㉑	J14Y	.035	.017	30–35	Fig. J	TDC	Fig. F	700⑥	—	140	3½–5
	V8-383 Auto. Tr.㉑	J14Y	.035	.017	30–35	Fig. J	7½°	Fig. F	—	600⑥	140	3½–5
	V8-383 Auto. Tr.④	J11Y	.035	.017	30–35	Fig. J	5°	Fig. F	700⑥	650⑥	150	3½–5
	V8-440 Auto. Tr.	J13Y	.035	.017	30–35	Fig. J	7½°	Fig. F	—	650⑥	150	3½–5
	V8-440 Auto. Tr.㉒	J11Y	.035	.017	30–35	Fig. J	5°	Fig. F	—	650⑥	150	3½–5
	V8-440 Std. Tr.㉒	J11Y	.035	.017	⑨	Fig. J	TDC	Fig. F	700⑥	—	150	3½–5
DODGE												
1963	6-225	N14Y	.035	.020	40–45	Fig. G	2½°	Fig. B	550⑭	500D⑭	140	3½–5
	8-318 Std. Trans.	J12Y	.035	.017	28–33	Fig. H	5°	Fig. A	500⑥	. . .	150	5–7
	8-318 Auto. Trans.	J12Y	.035	.017	28–33	Fig. H	10°	Fig. A	. . .	500N⑥	150	5–7
	8-361, 383 2 Bar. Carb.	J12Y	.035	.017	28–33	Fig. J	10°	Fig. A	500⑥	500N⑥	160	3½–5
	8-383 4 Bar. Carb.	J9Y	.035	.017	⑨	Fig. J	10°	Fig. A	750⑥	750N⑥	200	3½–5
	8-426, 426A	J10Y	.035	.017	⑨	Fig. J	10°	Fig. A	800⑥	800N⑥	200	6–8
1964	6-170, 225	N14Y	.035	.020	40–45	Fig. G	2½°	Fig. B	550⑭	550N⑭	140	3½–5
	8-273 Std. Trans.	N14Y	.035	.017	28–33	Fig. H	5°	Fig. A	500⑭	. . .	135	6–7½
	8-273 Auto. Trans.	N14Y	.035	.017	28–33	Fig. H	10°	Fig. A	. . .	500N⑭	135	6–7½
	8-318 Std. Trans.	J12Y	.035	.017	28–33	Fig. H	5°	Fig. A	500⑭	. . .	150	5–7
	8-318 Auto. Trans.	J12Y	.035	.017	28–33	Fig. H	10°	Fig. A	. . .	500N⑭	150	5–7
	8-361, 383 2 Bar. Carb.	J12Y	.035	.017	28–33	Fig. J	10°	Fig. A	500⑭	500N⑭	160	3½–5
	8-413	J12Y	.035	.017	28–33	Fig. J	10°	Fig. A	500⑭	500N⑭	165	3½–5
	8-383, 426 4 Bar. Carb.	J10Y	.035	.017	⑨	Fig. J	10°	Fig. A	500⑭	500N⑭	160	3½–5
	8-426 Hemi-Charger	⑧	.020	.017	⑮	Fig. J	⑤	. . .	1400⑭	1400	160	6–8
1965	6-170, 225	N14Y	.035	.020	40–45	Fig. G	2½°	Fig. B	550⑭	550N⑭	125	3½–5
	8-273 Std. Trans.	N14Y	.035	.017	28–33	Fig. H	5°	Fig. A	600⑭	. . .	135	5–7
	8-273 Auto. Trans.	N14Y	.035	.017	28–33	Fig. H	10°	Fig. A	. . .	600N⑭	135	5–7
	8-273 4 Bar. Carb.	N10Y	.035	.017	28–33	Fig. H	10°	Fig. A	600⑭	600N⑭	135	5–7
	8-318 Std. Trans.	J14Y	.035	.017	28–33	Fig. H	5°	Fig. A	500⑭	. . .	140	5–7
	8-318 Auto. Trans.	J14Y	.035	.017	28–33	Fig. H	10°	Fig. A	. . .	500N⑭	140	5–7
	8-361, 383 2 Bar. Carb.	J14Y	.035	.017	28–32	Fig. J	10°	Fig. A	500⑭	500N⑭	140	3½–5
	8-383 4 Bar. Carb.	J10Y	.035	.017	⑩	Fig. J	10°	Fig. A	550⑭	550N⑭	145	3½–5
	8-413	J14Y	.035	.017	⑩	Fig. J	12½°	Fig. A	550⑭	550N⑭	145	3½–5
	8-426	J10Y	.035	.017	⑩	Fig. J	10°	Fig. A	550⑭	550N⑭	145	3½–5

Continued

TUNE UP SPECIFICATIONS—Continued

OLD CAR SPECIFICATIONS: For 1946-62 Tune Up Specifications see back of book.

★When using a timing light, disconnect vacuum hose or tube at distributor and plug opening in hose or tube so idle speed will not be affected.

Year	Engine	Spark Plug		Distributor		Firing Order	Ignition Timing★		Hot Idle Speed		Comp. Press. Lbs. (3)	Fuel Pump Press. Lbs.
		Type (7)	Gap Inch	Point Gap Inch	Dwell Angle Deg.		BTDC (1)	Mark	Std. Trans.	Auto. Trans. (2)		
DODGE—Continued												
1966	6-170(12)	N14Y	.035	.020	40-45	Fig. G	5°	Fig. E	550(14)	550N(14)	125	3½-5
	6-170(13)	N14Y	.035	.020	40-45	Fig. G	5° ATC	Fig. E	650(14)	650N(14)	125	3½-5
	6-225(12)	N14Y	.035	.020	40-45	Fig. G	2½°	Fig. E	550(14)	550N(14)	125	3½-5
	6-225(13)	N14Y	.035	.020	40-45	Fig. G	5° ATC	Fig. E	650(14)	650N(14)	125	3½-5
	8-273 Std. Trans.(12)	N14Y	.035	.017	28-32	Fig. H	5°	Fig. F	500(6)	...	135	5-7
	8-273 Auto. Trans.(12)	N14Y	.035	.017	28-32	Fig. H	10°	Fig. F	...	500N(6)	135	5-7
	8-273 2 Bar. Carb.(13)	N14Y	.035	.017	28-32	Fig. H	5° ATC	Fig. F	700(16)	650N(16)	135	5-7
	8-273 4 Bar. Carb.(12)	N10Y	.035	.017	(20)	Fig. H	10°	Fig. F	500(6)	500N(6)	135	5-7
	8-273 4 Bar. Carb.(13)	N10Y	.035	.017	(20)	Fig. H	5° ATC	Fig. F	600(6)	600N(6)	135	5-7
	8-318 Std. Trans.(12)	(10)a	.035	.017	28-32	Fig. H	5°	Fig. F	500(6)	...	140	5-7
	8-318 Auto. Trans.(12)	(10)a	.035	.017	28-32	Fig. H	10°	Fig. F	...	500N(6)	140	5-7
	8-318 2 Bar. Carb.(13)	(10)a	.035	.017	28-32	Fig. H	4° ATC	Fig. F	650(16)	600N(16)	140	5-7
	8-361, 383 2 B.C.(12)	J14Y	.035	.017	28-32	Fig. J	12½°	Fig. F	500(6)	500N(6)	140	3½-5
	8-361, 383 2 B.C.(13)	J14Y	.035	.017	28-32	Fig. J	5° ATC	Fig. F	650(6)	600N(6)	140	3½-5
	8-383, 426, 440 4 B.C.(12)	J13Y	.035	.017	28-32	Fig. J	12½°	Fig. F	500(6)	500N(6)	145	3½-5
	8-383, 426, 440 4 B.C.(13)	J13Y	.035	.017	28-32	Fig. J	5° ATC	Fig. F	600(6)	600N(6)	145	3½-5
1967	6-170(12)	N14Y	.035	.020	40-45	Fig. G	5°	Fig. E	550(14)	550N(14)	125	3½-5
	6-170(13)	N14Y	.035	.020	40-45	Fig. G	5° ATC	Fig. E	700(14)	650N(14)	125	3½-5
	6-225(12)	N14Y	.035	.020	40-45	Fig. G	5°	Fig. E	550(14)	550N(14)	125	3½-5
	6-225(13)	N14Y	.035	.020	40-45	Fig. G	TDC	Fig. E	650(14)	650N(14)	125	3½-5
	8-273 Std. Trans.(12)	N14Y	.035	.017	28-32	Fig. H	5°	Fig. F	500(6)	...	135	5-7
	8-273 Auto. Trans.(12)	N14Y	.035	.017	28-32	Fig. H	10°	Fig. F	...	500N(6)	135	5-7
	8-273 Std. Trans.(13)	N14Y	.035	.017	28-32	Fig. H	5° ATC	Fig. F	700(6)	...	135	5-7
	8-273 Auto. Trans.(13)	N14Y	.035	.017	28-32	Fig. H	5° ATC	Fig. F	...	650N(6)	135	5-7
	8-273 4 Bar. Carb.(12)	N10Y	.035	.017	(20)	Fig. H	10°	Fig. F	600(6)	600N(6)	135	5-7
	8-273 4 Bar. Carb.(13)	N10Y	.035	.017	(20)	Fig. H	5° ATC	Fig. F	700(6)	650N(6)	135	5-7
	8-318 Std. Trans.(12)	(10)a	.035	.017	28-32	Fig. H	5°	Fig. F	500(6)	...	140	5-7
	8-318 Auto. Trans.(12)	(10)a	.035	.017	28-32	Fig. H	10°	Fig. F	...	500N(6)	140	5-7
	8-318(13)	(10)a	.035	.017	28-32	Fig. H	5° ATC	Fig. F	650(6)	650N(6)	140	5-7
	8-383 2 Bar. Carb.(12)	J14Y	.035	.017	28-32	Fig. J	12½°	Fig. F	550(6)	550N(6)	140	3½-5
	8-383 2 Bar. Carb.(18)	J14Y	.035	.017	28-32	Fig. J	5°	Fig. F	...	600N(6)	140	3½-5
	8-383 2 Bar. Carb.(19)	J14Y	.035	.017	28-32	Fig. J	TDC	Fig. F	650(6)	...	140	3½-5
	8-383 4 Bar. Carb.(12)	J13Y	.035	.017	28-32	Fig. J	12½°	Fig. F	500(6)	500N(6)	150	3½-5
	8-383 4 Bar. Carb.(18)	J13Y	.035	.017	28-32	Fig. J	5°	Fig. F	...	600N(6)	150	3½-5
	8-383 4 Bar. Carb.(19)	J13Y	.035	.017	28-32	Fig. J	TDC	Fig. F	650(6)	...	150	3½-5
	8-440(12)	J13Y	.035	.017	28-32	Fig. J	12½°	Fig. F	650(6)	650N(6)	150	3½-5
	8-440(18)	J13Y	.035	.017	28-32	Fig. J	5°	Fig. F	...	650N(6)	150	3½-5
	8-440(19)	J13Y	.035	.017	28-32	Fig. J	TDC	Fig. F	650(6)	...	150	3½-5
	8-440 Hi Perf.(12)	J11Y	.035	.017	28-32	Fig. J	12½°	Fig. F	650(6)	650N(6)	150	3½-5
	8-440 Hi Perf.(18)	J11Y	.035	.017	28-32	Fig. J	5°	Fig. F	...	650N(6)	150	3½-5
	8-440 Hi Perf.(19)	J11Y	.035	.017	28-32	Fig. J	TDC	Fig. F	650(6)	...	150	3½-5
	8-426 Hemi(12)	N10Y	.035	.017	(17)	Fig. J	12½°	Fig. F	750(6)	750N(6)	175	3½-5
	8-426 Hemi(13)	N10Y	.035	.017	(17)	Fig. J	TDC	Fig. F	750(6)	750N(6)	175	3½-5
1968	6-170 Std. Trans.	N14Y	.035	.020	40-45	Fig. G	5° ATC	Fig. E	700(14)	—	125	3½-5
	6-170 Auto. Tr.	N14Y	.035	.020	40-45	Fig. G	2½° ATC	Fig. E	—	650N(14)	125	3½-5
	6-225	N14Y	.035	.020	40-45	Fig. G	TDC	Fig. E	650(14)	650N(14)	125	3½-5
	V8-273 Std. Trans.	N14Y	.035	.017	28-33	Fig. H	5° ATC	Fig. F	700(6)	—	135	5-7
	V8-273 Auto. Tr.	N14Y	.035	.017	28-33	Fig. H	2½° ATC	Fig. F	—	650N(6)	135	5-7
	V8-318 Std. Trans.	N14Y	.035	.017	28-33	Fig. H	5° ATC	Fig. F	650(6)	—	140	5-7
	V8-318 Auto. Tr.	N14Y	.035	.017	28-33	Fig. H	2½° ATC	Fig. F	—	600N(6)	140	5-7
	V8-340 Std. Trans.	N9Y	.035	.017	(17)	Fig. H	TDC	Fig. F	700(6)	—	180	5-7
	V8-340 Auto. Tr.	N9Y	.035	.017	(17)	Fig. H	5°	Fig. F	—	650N(6)	180	5-7

Continued

TUNE UP SPECIFICATIONS—Continued

OLD CAR SPECIFICATIONS: For 1946-62 Tune Up Specifications see back of book.

★When using a timing light, disconnect vacuum hose or tube at distributor and plug opening in hose or tube so idle speed will not be affected.

Year	Engine	Spark Plug		Distributor		Firing Order	Ignition Timing★		Hot Idle Speed		Comp. Press. Lbs. ③	Fuel Pump Press. Lbs.
		Type ⑦	Gap Inch	Point Gap Inch	Dwell Angle Deg.		BTDC ①	Mark	Std. Trans.	Auto. Trans. ②		
DODGE—Continued												
1968	V8-383 Std. Tr.④	J11Y	.035	.017	28–33	Fig. J	TDC	Fig. F	650⑥	—	150	3½–5
	V8-383 Auto. Tr.④	J11Y	.035	.017	28–33	Fig. J	5°	Fig. F	—	650N⑥	150	3½–5
	V8-383 Std. Tr.㉑	J14Y	.035	.017	28–33	Fig. J	TDC	Fig. F	650⑥	—	140	3½–5
	V8-383 Auto. Tr.㉑	J14Y	.035	.017	28–33	Fig. J	7½°	Fig. F	—	600N⑥	140	3½–5
	V8-440 Std. Tr.㉒	J11Y	.035	.017	⑰	Fig. J	TDC	Fig. F	650⑥	—	150	6–7½
	V8-440 Auto. Tr.㉒	J11Y	.035	.017	28–33	Fig. J	5°	Fig. F	—	650N⑥	150	6–7½
	V8-440, 350 H.P.	J13Y	.035	.017	28–33	Fig. J	7½°	Fig. F	—	600N⑥	150	3½–5
	V8-426	N10Y	.035	.017	⑰	Fig. J	TDC	Fig. F	750⑥	750N⑥	175	7–8½
1969	6-170 Std. Tr.	N14Y	.035	.020	42–47	Fig. G	5° ATC	Fig. E	750⑭	—	125	3½–5
	6-170 Auto. Tr.	N14Y	.035	.020	42–47	Fig. G	TDC	Fig. E	—	750N⑭	125	3½–5
	6-225	N14Y	.035	.020	42–47	Fig. G	TDC	Fig. E	650⑭	650N⑭	125	3½–5
	V8-273	N14Y	.035	.017	30–35	Fig. H	2½° ATC	Fig. F	700⑭	650N⑭	135	5–7
	V8-318	N14Y	.035	.017	30–35	Fig. H	TDC	Fig. F	700⑭	650N⑭	140	5–7
	V8-340 Std. Tr.	N9Y	.035	.017	⑰	Fig. H	TDC	Fig. F	750⑭	—	155	5–7
	V8-340 Auto. Tr.	N9Y	.035	.017	⑰	Fig. H	5°	Fig. F	—	700N⑭	155	5–7
	V8-383 Std. Tr.㉑	J14Y	.035	.017	30–35	Fig. J	TDC	Fig. F	700⑭	—	140	3½–5
	V8-383 Auto. Tr.㉑	J14Y	.035	.017	30–35	Fig. J	7½°	Fig. F	—	600N⑭	140	3½–5
	V8-383 Std. Tr.④	J11Y	.035	.017	30–35	Fig. J	TDC	Fig. F	700	—	140	3½–5
	V8-383 Auto. Tr.④	J11Y	.035	.017	30–35	Fig. J	5°	Fig. F	—	650N⑭	140	3½–5
	V8-383 Std. Tr.㉓	J11Y	.035	.017	⑰	Fig. J	TDC	Fig. F	700	—	140	3½–5
	V8-383 Auto. Tr.㉓	J11Y	.035	.017	⑰	Fig. J	5°	Fig. F	—	650N⑭	140	3½–5
	V8-440, 350 H.P.	J13Y	.035	.017	30–35	Fig. J	7½°	Fig. F	—	600N⑭	150	3½–5
	V8-440 Std. Tr.㉒	J11Y	.035	.017	⑰	Fig. J	TDC	Fig. F	700	—	150	6–7½
	V8-440 Auto. Tr.㉒	J11Y	.035	.017	30–35	Fig. J	5°	Fig. F	—	650N⑭	150	6–7½
	V8-426 Hemi.	N10Y	.035	.017	⑰	Fig. J	TDC	Fig. F	750	750N⑭	175	7–8½

PLYMOUTH

Year	Engine	Spark Plug Type ⑦	Gap Inch	Point Gap Inch	Dwell Angle Deg.	Firing Order	BTDC ①	Mark	Std. Trans.	Auto. Trans. ②	Comp. Press. Lbs. ③	Fuel Pump Press. Lbs.
1963	6-170, 225	N14Y	.035	.020	40–45	Fig. G	2½°	Fig. B	550⑭	550N⑭	145	3½–5
	8-318 Std. Trans.	J12Y	.035	.017	28–33	Fig. H	5°	Fig. A	500⑥	. . .	160	5–7
	8-318 Auto. Trans.	J12Y	.035	.017	28–33	Fig. H	10°	Fig. A	. . .	500N⑥	160	5–7
	8-361, 383	J12Y	.035	.017	28–33	Fig. J	10°	Fig. A	500⑥	500N⑥	160	3½–5
	8-383, 426 Hi-Perf.	J9Y	.035	.017	⑨	Fig. J	10°	Fig. A	750⑥	750N⑥	200	3½–5
1964	6-170, 225	N14Y	.035	.020	40–45	Fig. G	2½°	Fig. B	550⑭	550N⑭	140	3½–5
	8-273 Std. Trans.	N14Y	.035	.017	28–33	Fig. H	5°	Fig. A	500⑥	. . .	135	6–7½
	8-273 Auto. Trans.	N14Y	.035	.017	28–33	Fig. H	10°	Fig. A	. . .	500N⑥	135	6–7½
	8-318 Std. Trans.	J12Y	.035	.017	28–33	Fig. H	5°	Fig. A	500⑥	. . .	150	5–7
	8-318 Auto. Trans.	J12Y	.035	.017	28–33	Fig. H	10°	Fig. A	. . .	500N⑥	150	5–7
	8-361	J12Y	.035	.017	28–33	Fig. J	10°	Fig. A	500⑥	500N⑥	160	5–7
	8-383, 426	J10Y	.035	.017	⑨	Fig. J	10°	Fig. A	500⑥	500N⑥	160	5–7
	8-426 Hemi-Charger	⑧	.020	.017	⑮	Fig. J	⑤	. . .	1400	1400	160	6–8
1965	6-170, 225	N14Y	.035	.020	40–45	Fig. G	2½°	Fig. B	550⑭	550N⑭	125	3½–5
	8-273 Std. Trans.	N9Y	.035	.017	28–33	Fig. H	5°	Fig. A	500⑥	. . .	135	5–7
	8-273 Auto. Trans.	N9Y	.035	.017	28–33	Fig. H	10°	Fig. A	. . .	500N⑥	135	5–7
	8-273 4 Bar. Carb.	N10Y	.035	.017	⑩	Fig. H	10°	Fig. A	600⑥	600N⑥	135	5–7
	8-318 Std. Trans.	J14Y	.035	.017	28–33	Fig. H	5°	Fig. A	500⑥	. . .	140	5–7
	8-318 Auto. Trans.	J14Y	.035	.017	28–33	Fig. H	10°	Fig. A	. . .	500N⑥	140	5–7
	8-361, 383	J14Y	.035	.017	28–32	Fig. J	10°	Fig. A	500⑥	500N⑥	140	3½–5
	8-426	J14Y	.035	.017	⑩	Fig. J	10°	Fig. A	550⑥	550N⑥	150	3½–5
1966	6-170⑫	N14Y	.035	.020	40–45	Fig. G	5°	Fig. E	550⑭	550N⑭	125	3½–5
	6-170⑬	N14Y	.035	.020	40–45	Fig. G	5° ATC	Fig. E	650⑭	650N⑭	125	3½–5

Continued

TUNE UP SPECIFICATIONS—Continued

OLD CAR SPECIFICATIONS: For 1946-62 Tune Up Specifications see back of book.

★When using a timing light, disconnect vacuum hose or tube at distributor and plug opening in hose or tube so idle speed will not be affected.

Year	Engine	Spark Plug		Distributor		Firing Order	Ignition Timing★		Hot Idle Speed		Comp. Press. Lbs. (3)	Fuel Pump Press. Lbs.
		Type (7)	Gap Inch	Point Gap Inch	Dwell Angle Deg.		BTDC (1)	Mark	Std. Trans.	Auto. Trans. (2)		
PLYMOUTH—Continued												
1966	6-225(12)	N14Y	.035	.020	40-45	Fig. G	2½°	Fig. E	550(14)	550N(14)	125	3½-5
	6-225(13)	N14Y	.035	.020	40-45	Fig. G	5° ATC	Fig. E	650(14)	650N(14)	125	3½-5
	8-273 Std. Trans.(12)	N14Y	.035	.017	28-32	Fig. H	5°	Fig. F	500(6)	...	135	5-7
	8-273 Auto. Trans.(12)	N14Y	.035	.017	28-32	Fig. H	10°	Fig. F	...	500N(6)	135	5-7
	8-273 2 Bar. Carb.(13)	N14Y	.035	.017	28-32	Fig. H	5° ATC	Fig. F	700(16)	650N(16)	135	5-7
	8-273 4 Bar. Carb.(12)	N10Y	.035	.017	28-32	Fig. H	10°	Fig. F	500(6)	500N(6)	135	5-7
	8-273 4 Bar. Carb.(13)	N10Y	.035	.017	28-32	Fig. H	5° ATC	Fig. F	600(6)	600N(6)	135	5-7
	8-318 Std. Trans.(12)	(10)a	.035	.017	28-32	Fig. H	5°	Fig. F	500(6)	...	140	5-7
	8-318 Auto. Trans.(12)	(10)a	.035	.017	28-32	Fig. H	10°	Fig. F	...	500N(6)	140	5-7
	8-318 2 Bar. Carb.(13)	(10)a	.035	.017	28-32	Fig. H	4° ATC	Fig. F	650(16)	600N(16)	140	5-7
	8-361, 383 2 B.C.(12)	J14Y	.035	.017	28-32	Fig. J	12½°	Fig. F	500(6)	500N(6)	140	3½-5
	8-361, 383 2 B.C.(13)	J14Y	.035	.017	28-32	Fig. J	5° ATC	Fig. F	650(6)	600N(6)	140	3½-5
	8-383, 440 4 B.C.(12)	J13Y	.035	.017	28-32	Fig. J	12½°	Fig. F	500(6)	500N(6)	145	3½-5
	8-383, 440 4 B.C.(13)	J13Y	.035	.017	28-32	Fig. J	5° ATC	Fig. F	600(6)	600N(6)	145	3½-5
	426 Hemi	N10Y	.035	.017	(17)	Fig. J	12½°	Fig. F	750(6)	750N(6)	175	6½-8
1967	6-170(12)	N14Y	.035	.020	40-45	Fig. G	5°	Fig. E	550(14)	550N(14)	125	3½-5
	6-170(13)	N14Y	.035	.020	40-45	Fig. G	5° ATC	Fig. E	700(14)	650N(14)	125	3½-5
	6-225(12)	N14Y	.035	.020	40-45	Fig. G	5°	Fig. E	550(14)	550N(14)	125	3½-5
	6-225(13)	N14Y	.035	.020	40-45	Fig. G	TDC	Fig. E	650(14)	650N(14)	125	3½-5
	8-273 Std. Trans.(12)	N14Y	.035	.017	28-32	Fig. H	5°	Fig. F	500(6)	...	135	5-7
	8-273 Auto. Trans.(12)	N14Y	.035	.017	28-32	Fig. H	10°	Fig. F	...	500N(6)	135	5-7
	8-273 Std. Trans.(13)	N14Y	.035	.017	28-32	Fig. H	5° ATC	Fig. F	700(6)	...	135	5-7
	8-273 Auto. Trans.(13)	N14Y	.035	.017	28-32	Fig. H	5° ATC	Fig. F	...	650N(6)	135	5-7
	8-273 4 Bar. Carb.(12)	N10Y	.035	.017	(20)	Fig. H	10°	Fig. F	600(6)	600N(6)	135	5-7
	8-273 4 Bar. Carb.(13)	N10Y	.035	.017	(20)	Fig. H	5° ATC	Fig. F	700(6)	650N(6)	135	5-7
	8-318 Std. Trans.(12)	N14Y	.035	.017	28-32	Fig. H	5°	Fig. F	500(6)	...	140	5-7
	8-318 Auto. Trans.(12)	N14Y	.035	.017	28-32	Fig. H	10°	Fig. F	...	500N(6)	140	5-7
	8-318(13)	N14Y	.035	.017	28-32	Fig. H	5° ATC	Fig. F	650(6)	650N(6)	140	5-7
	8-383 2 Bar. Carb.(12)	J14Y	.035	.017	28-32	Fig. J	12½°	Fig. F	550(6)	550N(6)	140	3½-5
	8-383 2 Bar. Carb.(18)	J14Y	.035	.017	28-32	Fig. J	5°	Fig. F	...	600N(6)	140	3½-5
	8-383 2 Bar. Carb.(19)	J14Y	.035	.017	28-32	Fig. J	TDC	Fig. F	650(6)	...	140	3½-5
	8-383 4 Bar. Carb.(12)	J13Y	.035	.017	28-32	Fig. J	12½°	Fig. F	500(6)	500N(6)	150	3½-5
	8-383 4 Bar. Carb.(18)	J13Y	.035	.017	28-32	Fig. J	5°	Fig. F	...	600N(6)	150	3½-5
	8-383 4 Bar. Carb.(19)	J13Y	.035	.017	28-32	Fig. J	TDC	Fig. F	650(6)	...	150	3½-5
	8-440(12)	J13Y	.035	.017	28-32	Fig. J	12½°	Fig. F	650(6)	650N(6)	150	3½-5
	8-440(18)	J13Y	.035	.017	28-32	Fig. J	5°	Fig. F	...	650N(6)	150	3½-5
	8-440(19)	J13Y	.035	.017	28-32	Fig. J	TDC	Fig. F	650(6)	...	150	3½-5
	8-440 Hi Perf.(12)	J11Y	.035	.017	28-32	Fig. J	12½°	Fig. F	650(6)	650N(6)	150	3½-5
	8-440 Hi Perf.(18)	J11Y	.035	.017	28-32	Fig. J	5°	Fig. F	...	650N(6)	150	3½-5
	8-440 Hi Perf.(19)	J11Y	.035	.017	28-32	Fig. J	TDC	Fig. F	650(6)	...	150	3½-5
	8-426 Hemi(12)	N10Y	.035	.017	(17)	Fig. J	12½°	Fig. F	750(6)	750N(6)	175	3½-5
	8-426 Hemi(13)	N10Y	.035	.017	(17)	Fig. J	TDC	Fig. F	750(6)	750N(6)	175	3½-5
1968	6-170 Std. Trans.	N14Y	.035	.020	40-45	Fig. G	5° ATC	Fig. E	700(14)	—	125	3½-5
	6-170 Auto. Tr.	N14Y	.035	.020	40-45	Fig. G	2½° ATC	Fig. E	—	650N(14)	125	3½-5
	6-225	N14Y	.035	.020	40-45	Fig. G	TDC	Fig. E	650(14)	650N(14)	125	3½-5
	V8-273 Std. Trans.	N14Y	.035	.017	28-33	Fig. H	5° ATC	Fig. F	700(6)	—	135	5-7
	V8-273 Auto. Tr.	N14Y	.035	.017	28-33	Fig. H	2½° ATC	Fig. F	—	650N(6)	135	5-7
	V8-318 Std. Trans.	N14Y	.035	.017	28-33	Fig. H	5° ATC	Fig. F	650(6)	—	140	5-7
	V8-318 Auto. Tr.	N14Y	.035	.017	28-33	Fig. H	2½° ATC	Fig. F	—	600N(6)	140	5-7
	V8-340 Std. Trans.	N9Y	.035	.017	(17)	Fig. H	TDC	Fig. F	700(6)	—	180	5-7
	V8-340 Auto. Tr.	N9Y	.035	.017	(17)	Fig. H	5°	Fig. F	—	650N(6)	180	5-7
	V8-383 Std. Tr.(4)	J11Y	.035	.017	28-33	Fig. J	TDC	Fig. F	650(6)	—	150	3½-5
	V8-383 Auto. Tr.(4)	J11Y	.035	.017	28-33	Fig. J	5°	Fig. F	—	650N(6)	150	3½-5

Continued

TUNE UP SPECIFICATIONS—Continued

OLD CAR SPECIFICATIONS: For 1946-62 Tune Up Specifications see back of book.

★When using a timing light, disconnect vacuum hose or tube at distributor and plug opening in hose or tube so idle speed will not be affected.

Year	Engine	Spark Plug		Distributor		Firing Order	Ignition Timing★		Hot Idle Speed		Comp. Press. Lbs. (3)	Fuel Pump Press. Lbs.
		Type (7)	Gap Inch	Point Gap Inch	Dwell Angle Deg.		BTDC (1)	Mark	Std. Trans.	Auto. Trans. (2)		
PLYMOUTH—Continued												
1968	V8-383 Std. Tr.(21)	J14Y	.035	.017	28–33	Fig. J	TDC	Fig. F	650(6)	—	140	3½–5
	V8-383 Auto. Tr.(21)	J14Y	.035	.017	28–33	Fig. J	7½°	Fig. F	—	600N(6)	140	3½–5
	V8-440 Std. Tr.(22)	J11Y	.035	.017	(17)	Fig. J	TDC	Fig. F	650(6)	—	150	6–7½
	V8-440 Auto. Tr.(22)	J11Y	.035	.017	28–33	Fig. J	5°	Fig. F	—	650N(6)	150	6–7½
	V8-440, 350 H.P.	J13Y	.035	.017	28–33	Fig. J	7½°	Fig. F	—	600N(6)	150	3½–5
	V8-426 Hemi	N10Y	.035	.017	(17)	Fig. J	TDC	Fig. F	750(6)	750N(6)	175	7–8½
1969	6-170 Std. Tr.	N14Y	.035	.020	42–47	Fig. G	5° ATC	Fig. E	750(14)	—	125	3½–5
	6-170 Auto. Tr.	N14Y	.035	.020	42–47	Fig. G	TDC	Fig. E	—	750N(14)	125	3½–5
	6-225	N14Y	.035	.020	42–47	Fig. G	TDC	Fig. E	650(14)	650N(14)	125	3½–5
	V8-273	N14Y	.035	.017	30–35	Fig. H	2½° ATC	Fig. F	700(14)	650N(14)	135	5–7
	V8-318	N14Y	.035	.017	30–35	Fig. H	TDC	Fig. F	700(14)	650N(14)	140	5–7
	V8-340 Std. Tr.	N9Y	.035	.017	(17)	Fig. H	TDC	Fig. F	750(14)	—	155	5–7
	V8-340 Auto. Tr.	N9Y	.035	.017	(17)	Fig. H	5°	Fig. F	—	700N(14)	155	5–7
	V8-383 Std. Tr.(21)	J14Y	.035	.017	30–35	Fig. J	TDC	Fig. F	700(14)	—	140	3½–5
	V8-383 Auto. Tr.(21)	J14Y	.035	.017	30–35	Fig. J	7½°	Fig. F	—	600N(14)	140	3½–5
	V8-383 Std. Tr.(4)	J11Y	.035	.017	30–35	Fig. J	TDC	Fig. F	700	—	140	3½–5
	V8-383 Auto. Tr.(4)	J11Y	.035	.017	30–35	Fig. J	5°	Fig. F	—	650N(14)	140	3½–5
	V8-383 Std. Tr.(23)	J11Y	.035	.017	(17)	Fig. J	TDC	Fig. F	700	—	140	3½–5
	V8-383 Auto. Tr.(23)	J11Y	.035	.017	(17)	Fig. J	5°	Fig. F	—	650N(14)	140	3½–5
	V8-440, 350 H.P.	J13Y	.035	.017	30–35	Fig. J	7½°	Fig. F	—	600N(14)	150	3½–5
	V8-440 Std. Tr.(22)	J11Y	.035	.017	(17)	Fig. J	TDC	Fig. F	700	—	150	6–7½
	V8-440 Auto. Tr.(22)	J11Y	.035	.017	30–35	Fig. J	5°	Fig. F	—	650N(14)	150	6–7½
	V8-426 Hemi.	N10Y	.035	.017	(17)	Fig. J	TDC	Fig. F	750	750N(14)	175	7–8½

(1)—BTDC: Before top dead center.

(2)—D: Drive. N: Neutral.

(3)—Plus or minus 20 lbs.

(4)—Four barrel carburetor.

(5)—With N61Y plugs, 31° at 3000 R.P.M.; with N58R plugs, 34° at 3000 R.P.M.

(6)—Set idle speed with air conditioning compressor operating.

(7)—Champion.

(8)—Champion N61Y or N58R.

(9)—Each set of points 27–32°; total dwell both sets 34–40°.

(10)—Each set of points 27–31°; total dwell both sets 36–40°.

(10)a—Some Canadian built 318 engines are being used in some American passenger cars. These engines are equipped with J14Y (3/8″ reach) spark plugs. The Canadian engine has wide scallop cylinder head covers the U. S. built engines have narrow oblong covers these engines use N14Y plugs (3/4″ reach).

(11)—Whenever idle speed or ignition timing is adjusted, vacuum line to break release mechanism must be disconnected and plugged to prevent parking brake from releasing when selector lever is moved to Drive. Set idle speed with A/C compressor operating.

(12)—Without CAP (cleaner air package).

(13)—With CAP (cleaner air package). ATC: After top center.

(14)—Adjust idle speed with headlights on. If air conditioned turn A/C switch to "Full On" position.

(15)—Each set 27-31°. Total dwell both sets 34–38°.

(16)—With A/C switch off.

(17)—Each set of points 27–32°; total dwell both sets 37–42°.

(18)—With CAP (cleaner air package) and Torqueflite.

(19)—With CAP (cleaner air package) and manual transmission.

(20)—Each set of points 27–31°; total dwell both sets 36–40°.

(21)—Two barrel carburetor.

(22)—375 H.P. engine.

(23)—Formula "S" and Super Bee only.

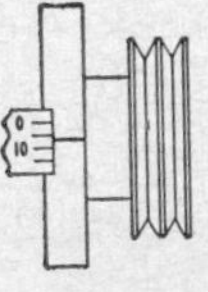

Fig. A

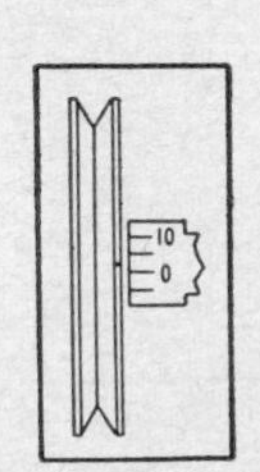

Fig. B

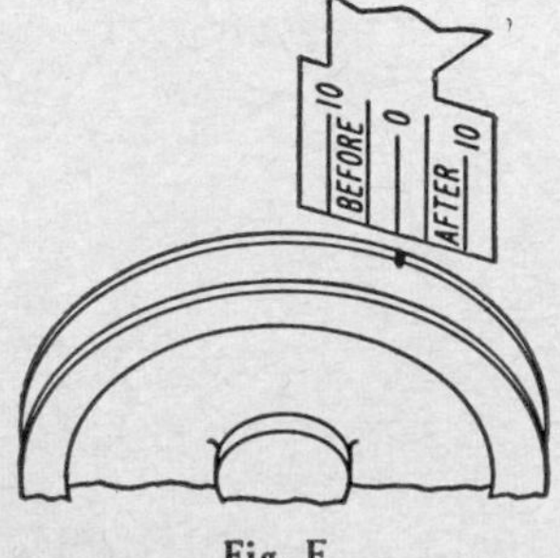

Fig. E

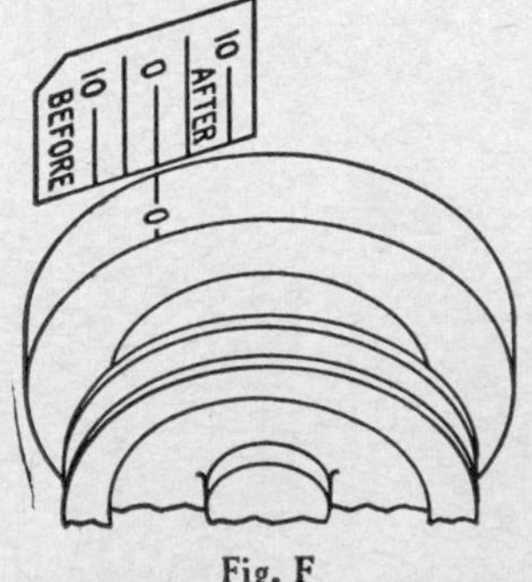

Fig. F

Continued

TUNE UP DATA—Continued

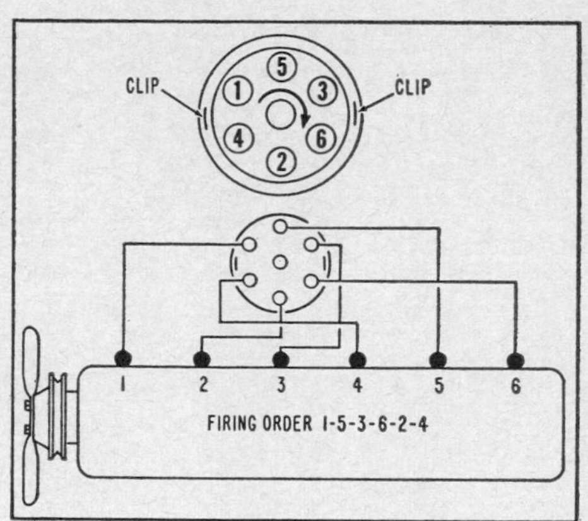

Fig. G

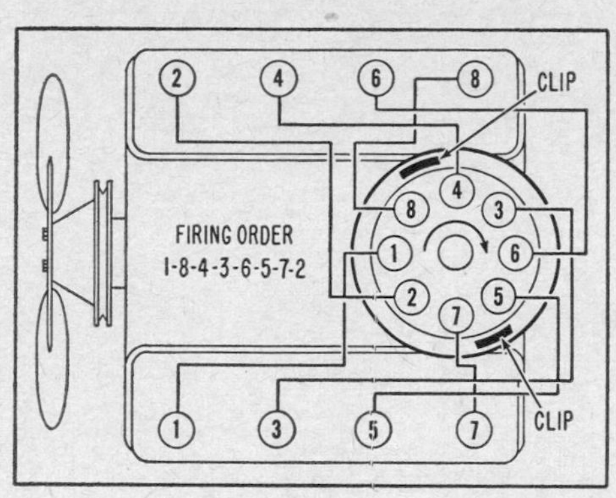

Fig. H

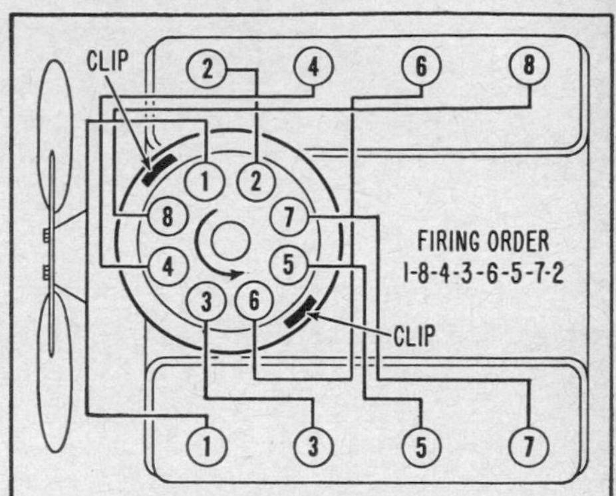

Fig. J

DISTRIBUTOR SPECIFICATIONS

★NOTE: If advance is checked on the vehicle, double the R.P.M. and degrees advance to get crankshaft figures.

Year	Model	Distributor Part No.(1)	Rotation (2)	Breaker Gap	Dwell Angle Deg.	Breaker Arm Spring Tension	Centrifugal Advance Degrees @ R.P.M. of Distributor★		Vacuum Advance	
							Advance Starts	Full Advance	Inches of Vacuum To Start Plunger	Max. Adv. Dist. Deg. @ Vacuum
CHRYSLER & IMPERIAL										
1963	Newport & 300	2095836	CC	.017	27-32	17-20	1 @ 450	12 @ 2150	4½-8	14 @ 16
"	Newport & 300	IBS-4011A	CC	.017	(5)	17-21	2 @ 475	11 @ 2400	7.2-8.9	10 @ 14
"	New Yorker & Imp.	2098690	CC	.017	28-33	17-20	2 @ 490	10 @ 2300	6-9	8 @ 13
	300J	2098620	CC	.017	(5)	17-21	2 @ 675	6 @ 910	6-9	10 @ 14
1964	Newport & 300	2444261	CC	.017	28-33	17-20	1 @ 450	12 @ 2150	4.5-8	14 @ 16
	Newport & 300	IBS-4011C	CC	.017	(5)	17-21	2 @ 475	11 @ 2400	7.2-8.9	10 @ 14
	New York. & Imp.	2444623	CC	.017	(5)	17-21	2 @ 675	6 @ 910	6-9	10 @ 14
	300K	IBS-4011D	CC	.017	28-33	17-20	1 @ 490	10 @ 2300	6-9	8 @ 13
1965	V8-383	2444676	CC	.017	28-32	17-20	1 @ 450	12 @ 2150	4.5-8	12 @ 14
	V8-413	2444867	CC	.017	28-32	17-20	1 @ 490	10 @ 2300	6-9	11 @ 15
	V8-413 Power Pack	2444683	CC	.017	(6)	17-21	2 @ 475	11 @ 2400	7.2-8.9	10 @ 14
	V8-413 Power Pack	IBS-4006K	CC	.017	(6)	17-21	2 @ 475	11 @ 2400	7.2-8.9	10 @ 14
1966	V8-383 2 Bar. Carb.(3)	2642244	CC	.017	28-32	17-20	1 @ 450	11 @ 2150	4.5-8.0	11 @ 13
	V8-383 2 Bar. Carb.(8)	2642289	CC	.017	28-32	17-20	4 @ 500	19 @ 2200	4.5-8.0	13 @ 16
	V8-383 2 Bar. Carb.(9)	2642373	CC	.017	28-32	17-20	4 @ 500	19 @ 2200	4.5-6.9	13 @ 14
	V8-383 4 Bar. Carb.(3)	2642248	CC	.017	28-32	17-20	1 @ 490	8 @ 2100	6.0-9.0	11 @ 15
	V8-383 4 Bar. Carb.(9)	2642367	CC	.017	28-32	17-20	4 @ 500	16 @ 2400	4.5-8.0	14 @ 16
	V8-383 4 Bar. Carb.(8)	2642363	CC	.017	28-32	17-20	2 @ 500	16 @ 2400	4.5-8.0	14 @ 16
	V8-440(3)	2642252	CC	.017	28-32	17-20	1 @ 490	8 @ 2400	6.0-9.0	11 @ 15
	V8-440(8)	2642365	CC	.017	28-32	17-20	2 @ 500	16 @ 2400	4.5-8.0	14 @ 16
	V8-440(9)	2642369	CC	.017	28-32	17-20	3 @ 500	16 @ 2400	4.5-8.0	14 @ 16
1967	8-383 2 Bar. Carb.(3)	2642727	CC	.017	28-32	17-20	1 @ 450	12 @ 2150	5-8	8 @ 10
	8-383 2 Bar. Carb.(8)	2642810	CC	.017	28-32	17-20	2 @ 550	16 @ 2200	4.5-8	9 @ 12
	8-383 2 Bar. Carb.(9)	2642949	CC	.017	28-32	17-20	3 @ 525	16 @ 2300	4.5-8	9 @ 12
	8-383 4 Bar. Carb.(3)	2642248	CC	.017	28-32	17-20	1 @ 490	9 @ 2400	6-9	11 @ 15
	8-383 4 Bar. Carb.(9)	2642949	CC	.017	28-32	17-20	3 @ 525	16 @ 2300	4.5-8	14 @ 16
	8-383 4 Bar. Carb.(8)	2642745	CC	.017	28-32	17-20	3 @ 575	12 @ 2450	4.5-8	14 @ 16
	8-440(3)	2642730	CC	.017	28-32	17-20	1 @ 490	10 @ 2300	8-10	12 @ 16
	8-440(8)	2642816	CC	.017	28-32	17-20	3 @ 575	14 @ 2400	8-10	14 @ 17
	8-440(9)	2642813	CC	.017	28-32	17-20	3 @ 500	16 @ 2300	8-10	14 @ 17
	8-440 Hi Perf.(3)	2642748	CC	.017	28-32	17-20	2 @ 475	10 @ 2200	8-10	12 @ 16
	8-440 Hi Perf.(8)	2642822	CC	.017	28-32	17-20	3 @ 475	14 @ 2400	8-10	12 @ 16

Continued

DISTRIBUTOR SPECIFICATIONS—Continued

★NOTE: If advance is checked on the car, double the R.P.M. and degrees advance to get crankshaft figures.

CHRYSLER & IMPERIAL—Continued

Year	Model	Distributor Part No.①	Rotation ②	Breaker Gap	Dwell Angle Deg.	Breaker Arm Spring Tension	Centrifugal Advance Degrees @ R.P.M. of Distributor★ Advance Starts	Full Advance	Vacuum Advance Inches of Vacuum To Start Plunger	Max. Adv. Dist. Deg. @ Vacuum
1968	V8-383 Std. Tr.⑫	2857358	CC	.017	28–33	17–20	3 @ 525	16 @ 2500	5–7.6	12 @ 14¾
	V8-383 Auto. Tr.⑫	2857356	CC	.017	28–33	17–20	3 @ 525	18 @ 2500	5–7.6	12 @ 14¾
	V8-383 Std. Tr.⑬	2875354	CC	.017	28–33	17–20	0 @ 325	16 @ 2250	5–8	13½ @ 13½
	V8-383 Auto. Tr.⑬	2875352	CC	.017	28–33	17–20	3 @ 525	20 @ 2250	5–8	13½ @ 13½
	V8-440 Std. Tr.⑮	2875360	CC	.017	28–33	17–20	5 @ 500	16 @ 2500	9–10	12 @ 15.8
	V8-440 Auto. Tr.⑮	2875362	CC	.017	28–33	17–20	3 @ 475	12 @ 2450	9–10	12 @ 15.8
	V8-440 Std. Tr.⑭	2875102	CC	.017	⑦	17–21	7 @ 500	16 @ 2300	8–9.8	10¾ @ 15
	V8-440 Auto. Tr.⑭	2875209	CC	.017	28–33	17–20	5 @ 500	13 @ 2100	8–9.8	10¾ @ 15
1969	V8-383 Std. Tr.⑬	2875742	CC	.017	30–35	17–20	1 @ 550	23 @ 2350	8.5	13.5 @ 13.5
	V8-383 Auto. Tr.⑬	2875747	CC	.017	30–35	17–20	1 @ 500	19 @ 2300	8.5	13.5 @ 13.5
	V8-383 Auto. Tr.⑫	2875731	CC	.017	30–35	17–20	1 @ 550	17 @ 2500	8	12 @ 15
	V8-440 Auto. Tr.⑮	2875764	CC	.017	30–35	17–20	1 @ 500	14 @ 2250	11.5	13.5 @ 16
	V8-440 Std. Tr.⑭	2875772	CC	.017	⑦	17–20	1 @ 550	19 @ 2500	10.5	12 @ 16
	V8-440 Auto. Tr.⑭	2875758	CC	.017	30–35	17–20	2 @ 550	16 @ 2400	10.5	12 @ 16

DODGE AND PLYMOUTH

Year	Model	Distributor Part No.①	Rotation ②	Breaker Gap	Dwell Angle Deg.	Breaker Arm Spring Tension	Advance Starts	Full Advance	Inches of Vacuum To Start Plunger	Max. Adv. Dist. Deg. @ Vacuum
1963	6-170 Auto. Trans.	2098675	C	.020	40–45	17–20	1 @ 325	14 @ 2200	4–6	8 @ 10
	6-170 Std. Trans.	2098665	C	.020	40–45	17–20	1 @ 375	14 @ 2200	4–6	8 @ 10
	6-225	2098670	C	.020	40–45	17–20	1 @ 390	12 @ 2500	4–6	7 @ 13
	8-318 Auto. Trans.	2098685	C	.017	28–33	17–20	1 @ 330	9 @ 2600	7–9	11 @ 15
	8-318 Auto. Trans.	IBP-4003-2	C	.017	26–32	17–22	1 @ 570	9 @ 2600	8–10	12 @ 15
	8-318 Std. Trans.	2098680	C	.017	28–33	17–20	1 @ 325	10 @ 2000	7–9	11 @ 15
	8-361, 383	2095836	CC	.017	28–33	17–21	1 @ 250	12 @ 2150	4–6	14 @ 16
	8-383, 426 Hi-Perf.	IBS-4006G	CC	.017	⑤	17–21	1 @ 275	13 @ 2050	7–9	12 @ 16
	8-426	IBB-4202	CC	.017	⑤	30 Max.	1 @ 500	13 @ 1030	None	None
1964	6-170 Std. Trans.	2444255	C	.020	40–45	17–20	2 @ 525	14 @ 2200	5–7	11 @ 12
	6-170 Auto. Trans.	2444256	C	.020	40–45	17–20	2 @ 475	14 @ 2200	5–7	8 @ 10
	6-225	2444254	C	.020	40–45	17–20	1 @ 560	12 @ 2500	5–7	7 @ 13
	8-273 Std. Trans.	2444448	C	.017	28–33	17–20	2 @ 450	11 @ 2300	7–9	12 @ 15
	8-273 Auto. Trans.	2444449	C	.017	28–33	17–20	2 @ 475	10 @ 2300	7–9	12 @ 15
	8-318 Std. Trans.	2444258	C	.017	28–33	17–20	1 @ 480	12 @ 2300	8–10	12 @ 16
	8-318 Auto. Trans.	2444259	C	.017	28–33	17–20	1 @ 570	10 @ 2300	8–10	12 @ 16
	8-361, 383 2 Bar. Carb.	2444261	CC	.017	28–33	17–20	1 @ 450	12 @ 2150	5–8	14 @ 16
	8-383 4 Bar. Carb.	IBS-4006J	CC	.017	⑤	17–21	2 @ 475	11 @ 2400	7–9	10 @ 14
	8-426 Std. Trans.	IBS-4011E	CC	.017	⑤	17–21	1 @ 540	9 @ 2400	6–9	10 @ 14
	8-426 Hemi-Charger	2444814	CC	.012	⑥	24–30	1 @ 550	24 @ 880	None	None
1965	6-170 Std. Trans.	2444255	C	.020	40–45	17–20	1 @ 525	14 @ 2200	5–7	11 @ 12
	6-170 Auto. Trans.	2444256	C	.020	40–45	17–20	2 @ 475	14 @ 2200	5–7	8 @ 10
	6-225 Std. Trans.	2444907	C	.020	40–45	17–20	1 @ 475	12 @ 2200	7–9	7 @ 15
	6-225 Auto. Trans.	2444648	C	.020	40–45	17–20	1 @ 475	12 @ 2200	5–7	7 @ 13
	8-273 Std. Trans.	2444794	C	.017	28–33	17–20	1 @ 450	12 @ 1750	7–9	13 @ 15
	8-273 Auto. Trans.	2444795	C	.017	28–33	17–20	1 @ 475	10 @ 1750	7–9	13 @ 15
	8-273 4 Bar. Carb.	2444853	C	.017	⑥	17–21	1 @ 475	10 @ 2300	7–9	11 @ 13
	8-273 Dodge (4 B.C.)	IBS-4013	C	.017	⑥	17–21	1 @ 475	10 @ 2300	7–9	11 @ 13
	8-318 Std. Trans.	2444258	C	.017	28–33	17–20	1 @ 480	12 @ 2300	8–10	12 @ 16
	8-318 Auto. Trans.	2444259	C	.017	28–33	17–20	1 @ 570	10 @ 2300	8–10	12 @ 16
	8-361	2444676	CC	.017	28–32	17–20	1 @ 450	12 @ 2150	5–8	12 @ 14
	8-383 Dodge Only	2444358	CC	.017	⑥	17–21	2 @ 475	11 @ 2400	7–9	10 @ 14
	8-383 Dodge Only	IBS-4006J	CC	.017	⑥	17–21	2 @ 475	11 @ 2400	7–9	10 @ 14
	8-413 Dodge Only	2444683	CC	.017	⑥	17–21	2 @ 475	11 @ 2400	7–9	10 @ 14
	8-413 Dodge Only	IBS-4006K	CC	.017	⑥	17–21	2 @ 475	11 @ 2400	7–9	10 @ 14

Continued

DISTRIBUTOR SPECIFICATIONS—Continued

★NOTE: If advance is checked on the car, double the R.P.M. and degrees advance to get crankshaft figures.

Year	Model	Distributor Part No.(1)	Rotation (2)	Breaker Gap	Dwell Angle Deg.	Breaker Arm Spring Tension	Centrifugal Advance Degrees @ R.P.M. of Distributor		Vacuum Advance	
							Advance Starts	Full Advance	Inches of Vacuum To Start Plunger	Max. Adv. Dist. Deg. @ Vacuum
DODGE AND PLYMOUTH—Continued										
1965	8-426	2444684	CC	.017	(6)	17-21	1 @ 540	9 @ 2400	6-9	10 @ 14
	8-426	IBS-4006L	CC	.017	(6)	17-21	1 @ 540	9 @ 2400	6-9	10 @ 14
1966	6-170 Std. Trans.(3)	2444255	C	.020	40-45	17-20	1 @ 525	14 @ 2200	5-7	11 @ 12
	6-170 Auto. Trans.(3)	2444256	C	.020	40-45	17-20	4 @ 475	14 @ 2200	5-7	8 @ 10
	6-170 Std. Trans.(4)	2642349	C	.020	40-45	17-20	2 @ 500	19 @ 2500	5-7	11 @ 12
	6-170 Auto. Trans.(4)	2642352	C	.020	40-45	17-20	3 @ 475	19 @ 2500	5-7	8 @ 10
	6-225 Std. Trans.(3)	2444907	C	.020	40-45	17-20	2 @ 475	12 @ 2200	7-9	7 @ 15
	6-225 Auto. Trans.(3)	2444648	C	.020	40-45	17-20	2 @ 475	12 @ 2200	5-7	7 @ 13
	6-225 Std. Trans.(4)	2642354	C	.020	40-45	17-20	2 @ 500	17 @ 2200	5-7	7 @ 13
	6-225 Auto. Trans.(4)	2642329	C	.020	40-45	17-20	4 @ 475	17 @ 2200	5-7	8 @ 10
	8-273 Std. Trans.(3)	2642234	C	.017	28-32	17-20	1 @ 450	12 @ 1750	5-8	13 @ 13
	8-273 Auto. Trans.(3)	2642238	C	.017	28-32	17-20	1 @ 475	10 @ 1750	5-8	13 @ 13
	8-273 Std. Trans.(4)	2642356	C	.017	28-32	17-20	4 @ 500	17 @ 1500	5-8	13 @ 13
	8-273 Auto. Trans.(4)	2642346	C	.017	28-32	17-20	4 @ 500	17 @ 1900	7-9	13 @ 15
	8-273 4 Bar. Carb.(3)	2642242	C	.017	(6)	17-21	2 @ 475	9 @ 1800	5-8	11 @ 12
	8-273 4 Bar. Carb.(4)	2642358	C	.017	(6)	17-21	3 @ 500	16 @ 2000	5-8	11 @ 12
	8-318 Std. Trans.(3)	2444258	C	.017	28-32	17-20	1 @ 480	12 @ 2300	8-10	12 @ 16
	8-318 Auto. Trans.(3)	2444259	C	.017	28-32	17-20	1 @ 570	10 @ 2300	8-10	12 @ 16
	8-318 Std. Trans.(4)	2642360	C	.017	28-32	17-20	3 @ 475	17 @ 2350	8-10	12 @ 16
	8-318 Std. Trans.(4)	2642343	C	.017	28-32	17-20	2 @ 475	17 @ 2350	8-10	12 @ 16
	8-361, 383 2 Bar. Carb.(3)	2642244	CC	.017	28-32	17-20	1 @ 450	12 @ 2150	5-8	11 @ 13
	8-361, 383 2 Bar. Carb.(4)	2642289	CC	.017	28-32	17-20	4 @ 500	20 @ 2200	5-8	14 @ 16
	8-361, 383 2 Bar. Carb.(4)	2642373	CC	.017	28-32	17-20	4 @ 500	20 @ 2200	5-7	14 @ 14
	8-383 4 Bar. Carb.(3)	2642248	CC	.017	28-32	17-20	1 @ 490	8 @ 2400	6-9	11 @ 15
	8-383 4 Bar. Carb.(4)	2642367	CC	.017	28-32	17-20	4 @ 500	16 @ 2400	4.5-8.0	14 @ 16
	8-383 4 Bar. Carb.(4)	2642363	CC	.017	28-32	17-20	2 @ 500	16 @ 2400	4.5-8.0	14 @ 16
	8-426, 440(10)	2642252	CC	.017	28-32	17-20	1 @ 490	8 @ 2400	6.0-9.0	11 @ 15
	8-426, 440(11)	2642365	CC	.017	28-32	17-20	2 @ 500	16 @ 2400	4.5-8.0	14 @ 16
	8-426, 440(11)	2642369	CC	.017	28-32	17-20	3 @ 500	16 @ 2400	4.5-8.0	14 @ 16
	8-426 Hemi	IBS-4006P	CC	.017	(7)	17-21	2 @ 575	9 @ 1400	6-9	11 @ 15
1967	6-170 Std. Trans.(3)	2642758	C	.020	40-45	17-20	2 @ 525	14 @ 2200	4.5-7.5	10 @ 10
	6-170 Auto. Trans.(3)	2642755	C	.020	40-45	17-20	3 @ 475	14 @ 2200	5-7.1	8 @ 10
	6-170 Std. Trans.(4)	2642786	C	.020	40-45	17-20	2 @ 500	18 @ 2200	5-7.1	11 @ 12
	6-170 Auto. Trans.(4)	2642789	C	.020	40-45	17-20	3 @ 475	18 @ 2200	5-7.1	8 @ 10
	6-225 Std. Trans.(3)	2444907	C	.020	40-45	17-20	2 @ 475	12 @ 2200	6.9-9.1	7 @ 15
	6-225 Auto. Trans.(3)	2444648	C	.020	40-45	17-20	2 @ 475	12 @ 2200	4.9-7.1	7 @ 13
	6-225 Std. Trans.(4)	2642702	C	.020	40-45	17-20	2 @ 500	14 @ 2400	6.9-9.1	8 @ 16
	6-225 Auto. Trans.(4)	2642795	C	.020	40-45	17-20	3 @ 475	14 @ 2400	5-7.1	8 @ 10
	8-273 Std. Trans.(10)	2642234	C	.017	28-32	17-20	2 @ 450	12 @ 1750	5-8	13 @ 13
	8-273 Auto. Trans.(10)	2642238	C	.017	28-32	17-20	1 @ 475	10 @ 1750	5-8	13 @ 13
	8-273 2 Bar. Carb.(4)	2642805	C	.017	28-32	17-20	4 @ 500	17 @ 1900	5-8	13 @ 13
	8-273 4 Bar. Carb.(3)	2642242	C	.017	(6)	17-21	2 @ 475	9 @ 1800	5-8	11 @ 12
	8-273 4 Bar. Carb.(4)	2642358	C	.017	(6)	17-21	3 @ 500	16 @ 2000	5-8	11 @ 12
	8-318 Std. Trans.(3)	2642721	C	.017	28-32	17-20	1 @ 475	13 @ 2250	7-9	13 @ 15
	8-318 Auto. Trans.(3)	2642718	C	.017	28-32	17-20	1 @ 480	12 @ 2350	7-9	13 @ 15
	8-318(4)	2642724	C	.017	28-32	17-20	3 @ 475	19 @ 2350	7.5-10.5	13 @ 16
	8-383 2 Bar. Carb.(3)	2642727	CC	.017	28-32	17-20	1 @ 450	12 @ 2150	5-8	13 @ 13
	8-383 Auto. Trans.(11)	2642810	CC	.017	28-32	17-20	2 @ 550	15 @ 2200	4.5-8	14 @ 16
	8-383 Std. Trans.(11)	2642949	CC	.017	28-32	17-20	4 @ 525	15 @ 2300	4.5-8	14 @ 16
	8-383 4 Bar. Carb.(3)	2642248	CC	.017	28-32	17-20	1 @ 490	8 @ 2400	6-9	11 @ 15
	8-383 4 Bar. Carb.(9)	2642949	CC	.017	28-32	17-20	3 @ 525	15 @ 2300	4.5-8	14 @ 16
	8-383 4 Bar. Carb.(8)	2642745	CC	.017	28-32	17-20	3 @ 575	12 @ 2450	4.5-8	14 @ 16

Continued

DISTRIBUTOR SPECIFICATIONS—Continued

★NOTE: If advance is checked on the car, double the R.P.M. and degrees advance to get crankshaft figures.

Year	Model	Distributor Part No.(1)	Rotation (2)	Breaker Gap	Dwell Angle Deg.	Breaker Arm Spring Tension	Centrifugal Advance Degrees @ R.P.M. of Distributor		Vacuum Advance	
							Advance Starts	Full Advance	Inches of Vacuum To Start Plunger	Max. Adv. Dist. Deg. @ Vacuum
DODGE AND PLYMOUTH—Continued										
1967	8-440(3)	2642730	CC	.017	28-32	17-20	1 @ 490	10 @ 2300	8-10	12 @ 16
	8-440 Auto. Trans.(4)	2642816	CC	.017	28-32	17-20	2 @ 575	14 @ 2400	8-10	14 @ 17
	8-440 Std. Trans.(4)	2642813	CC	.017	28-32	17-20	3 @ 500	16 @ 2300	8-10	14 @ 17
	8-440 Hi Perf.(3)	2642748	CC	.017	28-32	17-20	2 @ 475	10 @ 2200	8-10	12 @ 16
	8-440 Hi Perf.(8)	2642822	CC	.017	28-32	17-20	3 @ 475	14 @ 2400	8-10	12 @ 16
	8-440 Hi Perf.(9)	2642819	CC	.017	28-32	17-20	4 @ 475	16 @ 2250	8-10	12 @ 16
	8-440 Hi Perf.(3)	2642899	CC	.017	(7)	17-21	2 @ 475	10 @ 2200	8-10	12 @ 16
	8-440 Hi Perf.(4)	2642911	CC	.017	(7)	17-21	3 @ 475	16 @ 2250	8-10	12 @ 16
	8-426 Hemi.(3)	IBS-4006P	CC	.017	(7)	17-21	2 @ 575	9 @ 1400	6-9	11 @ 15
	8-426 Hemi(4)	IBS-4006W	CC	.017	(7)	17-21	4 @ 600	16 @ 1550	6-9	11 @ 15
1968	6-170 Std. Trans.	2875199	C	.020	40-45	17-20	3 @ 500	18 @ 2200	5-7.1	8 @ 10
	6-170 Auto. Tr.	2875202	C	.020	40-45	17-20	6 @ 500	15 @ 2200	5-7.1	8 @ 10
	6-225 Std. Trans.	2875364	C	.020	40-45	17-20	3 @ 500	14 @ 2000	6.2-9.7	6 @ 13
	6-225 Auto. Tr.	2875366	C	.020	40-45	17-20	3 @ 500	14 @ 2000	5-7	6 @ 8
	V8-273	2875334	C	.017	28-33	17-21	7 @ 500	16 @ 1900	5-8	13 @ 13
	V8-318	2875342	C	.017	28-33	17-21	5 @ 450	19 @ 2350	8.1-9.8	10 @ 15
	V8-340 Std. Trans.	2875086	C	.017	(7)	17-21	5 @ 500	14 @ 2000	4.5-7.5	10 @ 10
	V8-340 Auto. Tr.	2875105	C	.017	(7)	17-21	3 @ 475	12 @ 2000	4.5-7.5	10 @ 10
	V8-383 Std. Tr.(12)	2857356	CC	.017	28-33	17-20	6 @ 525	18 @ 2500	5-7.6	12 @ 14
	V8-383 Auto. Tr.(12)	2857358	CC	.017	28-33	17-20	6 @ 525	16 @ 2500	5-7.6	12 @ 14
	V8-383 Std. Tr.(13)	2875352	CC	.017	28-33	17-20	6 @ 525	11 @ 760	5-8	13 @ 13
	V8-383 Auto. Tr.(13)	2875354	CC	.017	28-33	17-20	0 @ 325	16 @ 2250	5-8	13.5 @ 13.5
	V8-440 Std. Tr.(14)	2875102	CC	.017	(7)	17-20	7 @ 500	16 @ 2300	8-9.8	10 @ 15
	V8-440 Auto. Tr.(14)	2875209	CC	.017	28-33	17-20	5 @ 500	13 @ 2100	8-9.8	10 @ 15
	V8-440, 350 H.P.	2875362	CC	.017	28-33	17-20	3 @ 475	12 @ 2450	9.2-10.7	12 @ 15
	V8-426	2875140	CC	.017	(7)	17-21	7 @ 600	16 @ 1550	6-9	11 @ 15
1969	6-170 Std. Trans.	2875813	C	.020	42-47	17-20	2 @ 600	19 @ 2200	7.5	8.5 @ 10
	6-170 Auto. Trans.	2875855	C	.020	42-47	17-20	1 @ 550	16 @ 2200	7.5	8 @ 10
	6-225 Std. Trans.	2875822	C	.020	42-47	17-20	1 @ 550	14 @ 2000	10	8 @ 16
	6-225 Auto. Trans.	2875826	C	.020	42-47	17-20	1 @ 550	14 @ 2000	7	8 @ 10
	V8-273	2875790	C	.017	30-35	17-20	2 @ 550	16 @ 1900	8.5	13.5 @ 13.5
	V8-318	2875796	C	.017	30-35	17-20	1.5 @ 550	19 @ 2400	10.5	10.75 @ 15
	V8-340 Std. Trans.	2875782	C	.017	(7)	17-20	1 @ 550	14 @ 1800	8	10 @ 10.5
	V8-340 Auto. Trans.	2875779	C	.017	(7)	17-20	2 @ 600	12 @ 2000	8	10 @ 10.5
	V8-383 Std. Trans.(12)	2875750	CC	.017	30-35	17-20	1 @ 550	19 @ 2500	8	12 @ 15
	V8-383 Auto. Trans.(12)	2875731	CC	.017	30-35	17-20	1 @ 550	17 @ 2500	8	12 @ 15
	V8-383 Std. Trans.(13)	2875742	CC	.017	30-35	17-20	1 @ 550	23 @ 2350	8.5	13.5 @ 13.5
	V8-383 Auto. Trans.(13)	2875747	CC	.017	30-35	17-20	1 @ 500	19 @ 2300	8.5	13.5 @ 13.5
	V8-440 Std. Trans.	2875772	CC	.017	(7)	17-20	1 @ 550	19 @ 2500	10.5	12 @ 16
	V8-440 Auto. Trans.	2875758	CC	.017	(7)	17-20	2 @ 550	16 @ 2400	10.5	12 @ 16
	V8-426	2875140	CC	.017	(7)	17-21	2.5 @ 650	16 @ 1550	10	11 @ 15
	V8-426	IBS-4014A	CC	.017	(7)	17-21	2.5 @ 650	16 @ 1550	10	11 @ 15

(1)—Stamped on distributor housing.
(2)—As viewed from above.
(3)—Without CAP (cleaner air package).
(4)—With CAP (cleaner air package).
(5)—Each set 27–32°; total both sets 34–40°.
(6)—Each set 27–31°; total both sets 36–40°.
(7)—Each set 27–32°; total both sets 37–42°.
(8)—With CAP and Torqueflite.
(9)—With CAP and manual transmission.
(10)—With 2 bar. carb. without CAP.
(11)—With 2 bar. carb. with CAP.
(12)—With 4 bar. carb.
(13)—With 2 bar. carb.
(14)—375 H.P. engine.
(15)—350 H.P. engine.

ALTERNATOR & REGULATOR SPECIFICATIONS

Year	Unit Number	Ground Polarity	Field Coil Draw Amperes	Current Output			Operating Voltage			Voltage Regulator Point Gap	Regulator Armature Air Gap
				Engine R.P.M.	Amperes	Volts	Engine R.P.M.	Volts	Voltage @ 120° ①		
1963–65	2098835	Negative	2.38–2.75②	1250	26③	15	1250	15	13.5–14.3④	.015	.048–.052
	2098830	Negative	2.38–2.75②	1250	35③	15	1250	15	13.5–14.3④	.012–.016	.048–.052
	2098850	Negative	2.38–2.75②	1250	39③	15	1250	15	13.5–14.3④	.012–.016	.048–.052
1966–68	⑥	Negative	2.38–2.75②	1250	26③	15	1250	15	13.3–14.3④	.012–.016	.048–.052⑤
	⑦	Negative	2.38–2.75②	1250	35③	15	1250	15	13.3–14.3④	.012–.016	.048–.052⑤
	⑧	Negative	2.38–2.75②	1250	44③	15	1250	15	13.3–14.3④	.012–.016	.048–.052⑤
	⑨	Negative	2.38–2.75②	1250	51③	15	1250	15	13.3–14.3④	.012–.016	.048–.052⑤
1969	⑥	Negative	2.38–2.75②	1250	26③	15	1250	15	13.3–14.3	.012–.016	.048–.052
	⑦	Negative	2.38–2.75②	1250	34.5③	15	1250	15	13.3–14.3	.012–.016	.048–.052
	⑧	Negative	2.38–2.75②	1250	41③	15	1250	15	13.3–14.3	.012–.016	.048–.052
	⑨	Negative	2.38–2.75②	1250	51③	15	1250	15	13.3–14.3	.012–.016	.048–.052

①—For each 10 degree rise in temperature subtract .04 volt. Temperature is checked with thermometer two inches from installed voltage regulator cover.

②—Current draw at 12 volts while turning rotor shaft by hand.

③—Plus or minus three amperes. If output is low, stator or rectifier is shorted.

④—At 117 degrees F.

⑤—Essex Wire built .032–.042″.

⑥—Standard with 6-cyl. engines.

⑦—Standard with V8 engines.

⑧—Heavy duty and/or air conditioning.

⑨—Special equipment.

STARTING MOTOR SPECIFICATIONS

Year	Part No.	Rotation ①	Brush Spring Tension, Ounces	No Load Test			Torque Test		
				Amperes	Volts	R.P.M.	Amperes	Volts	Torque, Lbs. Ft.
1963–69	2095150	Clockwise	32–48	85	11	1950	475	4	24.0
	2098500	Clockwise	32–48	90	11	2950	340–420	4	. . .
	1889100	Clockwise	32–48	78	11	3800	350	4	8.5
	2642930	Clockwise	32–36	78	11	3800	310–445	4	. . .

①—Viewed from drive end. C: Clockwise.

VALVE SPECIFICATIONS

Year	Model	Valve Lash		Valve Angles		Valve Spring Installed Height	Valve Spring Pressure Lbs. @ In.	Stem Clearance		Stem Diameter	
		Int.	Exh.	Seat	Face			Intake	Exhaust	Intake	Exhaust
CHRYSLER & IMPERIAL											
1963	300H, 300J	Hydraulic①		45	45	1⅞	195 @ 1 15/32	.001–.003	.002–.004	.372–.373	.371–.372
	300H, 300J	.015H	.024H	45	45	1⅞	225 @ 1.43	.001–.003	.002–.004	.372–.373	.371–.372
	Others	Hydraulic①		45	45	1⅞	195 @ 1 15/32	.001–.003	.002–.004	.372–.373	.371–.372
1964	360 H.P.	.017H	.028H	45	45	1⅞	195 @ 1 15/32	.001–.003	.002–.004	.372–.373	.371–.372
	390 H.P.	.017H	.028H	45	45	1⅞	225 @ 1.43	.001–.003	.002–.004	.372–.373	.371–.372
	Others	Hydraulic①		45	45	1⅞	195 @ 1 15/32	.001–.003	.002–.004	.372–.373	.371–.372
1965	360 H.P.	Hydraulic①		45	45	1⅞	195 @ 1 15/32	.001–.003	.002–.004	.372–.373	.371–.372
	Others	Hydraulic①		45	45	1⅞	195 @ 1 15/32	.001–.003	.002–.004	.372–.373	.371–.372
1966	2 Bar. Carb.	Hydraulic①		45	45	1 55/64	190 @ 1 15/32	.001–.003	.002–.004	.372–.373	.371–.372
	4 Bar. Carb.	Hydraulic①		45	45	1 55/64	200 @ 1 7/16	.001–.003	.002–.004	.372–.373	.371–.372
1967	8-383, 440 Std.	Hydraulic①		45	45	1 55/64	200 @ 1 7/16	.001–.003	.002–.004	.372–.373	.371–.372
	8-440 Hi Perf.	Hydraulic①		45	45	1 55/64	246 @ 1 23/64	.001–.003	.002–.004	.372–.373	.371–.372

Continued

VALVE SPECIFICATIONS—Continued

CHRYSLER & IMPERIAL—Continued

Year	Model	Valve Lash		Valve Angles		Valve Spring Installed Height	Valve Spring Pressure Lbs. @ In.	Stem Clearance		Stem Diameter	
		Int.	Exh.	Seat	Face			Intake	Exhaust	Intake	Exhaust
1968–69	8-383, 290 H.P.	Hydraulic①		45	45	1.86	200 @ 1.43	.001–.003	.002–.004	.372–.373	.371–.372
	8-383, 330 H.P.	Hydraulic①		45	45	1.86	225 @ 1.43	.001–.003	.002–.004	.372–.373	.371–.372
	8-440, 350 H.P.	Hydraulic①		45	45	1.86	200 @ 1.43	.001–.003	.002–.004	.372–.373	.371–.372
	8-440, 375 H.P.	Hydraulic①		45	45	1.86	230 @ 1.41	.001–.003	.002–.004	.372–.373	.371–.372

DODGE & PLYMOUTH

Year	Model	Int.	Exh.	Seat	Face	Valve Spring Installed Height	Valve Spring Pressure Lbs. @ In.	Stem Clearance Intake	Stem Clearance Exhaust	Stem Diameter Intake	Stem Diameter Exhaust
1963–64	6-170, 225	.010H	.020H	45	②	1 11/16	177 @ 1 5/16	.001–.003	.002–.004	.372–.373	.371–.372
	8-273	.013H	.021H	45	45	1 11/16	145 @ 1 5/16	.001–.003	.002–.004	.372–.373	.371–.372
	8-318	.013H	.021H	45	45	1 11/16	177 @ 1 5/16	.001–.003	.002–.004	.372–.373	.371–.372
	8-361, 383, 426	Hydraulic①		45	45	1 55/64	195 @ 1 15/32	.001–.003	.002–.004	.372–.373	.371–.372
	8-426 Hemi-Char.	.028C	.032C	45	45	1 55/64	266 @ 1.36	.002–.004	.003–.005	.309	.308
1965–66	6-170, 225	.010H	.020H	45	②	1 11/16	145 @ 1 5/16	.001–.003	.002–.004	.372–.373	.371–.372
	8-273 2 Bar. Carb.	.013H	.021H	45	45	1 11/16	145 @ 1 5/16	.001–.003	.002–.004	.372–.373	.371–.372
	8-273 4 Bar. Carb.	.013H	.021H	45	45	1 11/16	177 @ 1 5/16	.001–.003	.002–.004	.372–.373	.371–.372
	8-318	.013H	.021H	45	45	1 11/16	145 @ 1 5/16	.001–.003	.002–.004	.372–.373	.371–.372
	8-361, 383	Hydraulic①		45	45	1 55/64	195 @ 1 15/32	.001–.003	.002–.004	.372–.373	.371–.372
	8-413, 426	Hydraulic①		45	45	1 55/64	195 @ 1 15/32	.001–.003	.002–.004	.372–.373	.371–.372
	8-426 Hemi-Char.	.028C	.032C	45	45	1 55/64	266 @ 1.36	.002–.004	.003–.005	.3085–.3095	.3075–.3085
	8-426 Hemi	Hydraulic①		45	45	1 55/64	184 @ 1 13/32	.002–.004	.003–.005	.3085–.3095	.3075–.3085
	8-440	Hydraulic①		45	45	1 55/64	200 @ 1 7/16	.001–.003	.002–.004	.372–.373	.371–.372
1967	6-170, 225	.010H	.020H	45	③	1 11/16	145 @ 1 5/16	.001–.003	.002–.004	.372–.373	.371–.372
	8-273 2 Bar. Carb.	.013H	.021H	45	45	1 11/16	145 @ 1 5/16	.001–.003	.002–.004	.372–.373	.371–.372
	8-273 4 Bar. Carb.	.013H	.021H	45	45	1 11/16	177 @ 1 5/16	.001–.003	.002–.004	.372–.373	.371–.372
	8-318	Hydraulic①		45	45	1 11/16	148 @ 1 5/16	.001–.003	.002–.004	.372–.373	.371–.372
	8-383	Hydraulic①		45	45	1 55/64	200 @ 1 7/16	.001–.003	.002–.004	.372–.373	.371–.372
	8-440	Hydraulic①		45	45	1 55/64	246 @ 1 23/64	.001–.003	.002–.004	.372–.373	.371–.372
	8-426 Hemi	.028C	.032C	45	45	1 55/64	184 @ 1 13/32	.002–.004	.003–.005	.3085–.3095	.3075–.3085
1968	6-170, 225	.010H	.020H	45	②	1.65	145 @ 1 5/16	.001–.003	.002–.004	.372–.373	.371–.372
	8-273, 318	Hydraulic①		45	45	1.65	177 @ 1 5/16	.001–.003	.002–.004	.372–.373	.371–.372
	8-340	Hydraulic①		45	45	1.65	242 @ 1.21	.001–.003	.002–.004	.372–.373	.371–.372
	8-383, 300 H.P.	Hydraulic①		45	45	1.86	225 @ 1.43	.001–.003	.002–.004	.372–.373	.371–.372
	8-383, 290 H.P.	Hydraulic①		45	45	1.86	200 @ 1.43	.001–.003	.002–.004	.372–.373	.371–.372
	8-383, 330 H.P.	Hydraulic①		45	45	1.86	225 @ 1.43	.001–.003	.002–.004	.372–.373	.371–.372
	8-440, 375 H.P.	Hydraulic①		45	45	1.86	230 @ 1.41	.001–.003	.002–.004	.372–.373	.371–.372
	8-440, 350 H.P.	Hydraulic①		45	45	1.86	200 @ 1.43	.001–.003	.002–.004	.372–.373	.371–.372
	8-426	.028C	.032C	45	45	1.86	280 @ 1.37	.001–.003	.002–.004	.372–.373	.371–.372
1969	6-170, 225	.010H	.020H	45	②	1 11/16	145 @ 1 5/16	.001–.003	.002–.004	.372–.373	.371–.372
	8-273, 318	Hydraulic①		45	②	1 11/16	177 @ 1 5/16	.001–.003	.002–.004	.372–.373	.371–.372
	8-340	Hydraulic①		45	②	1 11/16	242 @ 1 7/32	.001–.003	.002–.004	.372–.373	.371–.372
	8-383, 290 H.P.	Hydraulic①		45	45	1 57/64	200 @ 1 7/16	.001–.003	.002–.004	.372–.373	.371–.372
	8-383, 330 H.P.	Hydraulic①		45	45	1 57/64	246 @ 1 23/64	.001–.003	.002–.004	.372–.373	.371–.372
	8-383, 335 H.P.	Hydraulic①		45	45	1 57/64	246 @ 1 23/64	.001–.003	.002–.004	.372–.373	.371–.372
	8-440, 350 H.P.	Hydraulic①		45	45	1 57/64	200 @ 1 7/16	.001–.003	.002–.004	.372–.373	.371–.372
	8-440, 375 H.P.	Hydraulic①		45	45	1 57/64	246 @ 1 23/64	.001–.003	.002–.004	.372–.373	.371–.372
	8-426	.028C	.032C	45	45	1 57/64	280 @ 1 3/8	.001–.003	.002–.004	.372–.373	.371–.372

①—No adjustment. ②—Intake 45°, exhaust 43°. ③—Intake 45°, exhaust 47°.

PISTONS, PINS, RINGS, CRANKSHAFT & BEARINGS

Year	Model	Piston Clearance Top of Skirt	Ring End Gap ① Comp.	Ring End Gap ① Oil	Wrist-pin Diameter	Rod Bearings Shaft Diameter	Rod Bearings Bearing Clearance	Main Bearings Shaft Diameter	Main Bearings Bearing Clearance	Main Bearings Thrust on Bear. No.	Main Bearings Shaft End Play
CHRYSLER & IMPERIAL											
1963–64	V8-361, 383	.0003–.0013	.013	.013	1.0936	2.374–2.375	.0005–.0015	2.6245–2.6255	.0005–.0015	3	.002–.007
	V8-413	.0003–.0013	.013	.013	1.0936	2.374–2.375	.0005–.0015	2.7495–2.7505	.0005–.0015	3	.002–.007
1965	V8-383	.0003–.0013	.013	.013	1.0936	2.374–2.375	.0005–.0015	2.6245–2.6255	.0005–.0015	3	.002–.007
	V8-413	.0003–.0013	.013	.013	1.0936	2.374–2.375	.0005–.0015	2.7495–2.7505	.0005–.0015	3	.002–.007
1966–67	V8-383	.0005–.0015	.013	.015	1.0936	2.374–2.375	.0005–.0015	2.6245–2.6255	.0005–.0015	3	.002–.007
	V8-440	.0005–.0015	.013	.015	1.0936	2.374–2.375	.0005–.0015	2.7495–2.7505	.0005–.0015	3	.002–.007
1968	8-383	.0002–.0012	.013	.015	1.0936	2.374–2.375	.0005–.003	2.6245–2.6255	.0005–.0015	3	.002–.007
	8-440	.0002–.0012	.013	.015	1.094	2.374–2.375	.0005–.003	2.7495–2.7505	.0005–.0015	3	.002–.007
1969	8-383	.0003–.0013	.013	.015	1.0936	2.374–2.375	.001–.002	2.7495–2.7505	.0005–.0015	3	.002–.007
	8-440	.0003–.0013	.013	.015	1.0936	2.374–2.375	.001–.002	2.7495–2.7505	.0005–.0015	3	.002–.007
DODGE & PLYMOUTH											
1963–64	6-170, 6-225	.0005–.0015	.010	.015	.9008	2.1865–2.1875	.0005–.0015	2.7495–2.7505	.0005–.0015	3	.002–.007
	V8-273	.0005–.0015	.010	.015	.9842	2.124–2.125	.0005–.0015	2.4995–2.5005	.0005–.0015	3	.002–.007
	V8-318	.0005–.0015	.015	.015	.9842	2.124–2.125	.0005–.0015	2.4995–2.5005	.0005–.0015	3	.002–.007
	V8-361, 383	.0005–.0015	.013	.013	1.0936	2.374–2.375	.0005–.0015	2.6245–2.6255	.0005–.0015	3	.002–.007
	V8-426③	.0005–.0015	.013	.013	1.0936	2.374–2.375	.0005–.0015	2.7495–2.7505	.0005–.0015	3	.002–.007
	V8-426④	.004 . . .	.013	.013	1.0936	2.374–2.375	.002–.0045	2.7495–2.7505	.0015–.004	3	.002–.007
	V8-426⑤	.0095 . . .	.023	.023	1.0936	2.374–2.375	.002–.0045	2.7495–2.7505	.0015–.004	3	.002–.007
	V8-426Hemi-C	.0125 . . .	.013	.015	1.0936	2.373–2.374	.0025–.0035	2.7495–2.7505	.002–.004	3	.002–.0085
1965–66	6-170, 225	.0005–.0015	.010	.015	.9008	2.1865–2.1875	.0005–.0015	2.7495–2.7505	.0005–.0015	3	.002–.007
	V8-273, 318	.0005–.0015	.010	.015	.9842	2.124–2.125	.0005–.0015	2.4995–2.5005	.0005–.0015	3	.002–.007
	V8-361, 383	.0005–.0015	.013	.013	1.0936	2.374–2.375	.0005–.0015	2.6245–2.6255	.0005–.0015	3	.002–.007
	V8-413, 426, 440	.0005–.0015	.013	.013	1.0936	2.374–2.375	.0005–.0015	2.7495–2.7505	.0005–.0015	3	.002–.007
	8-426 HP2	.0025–.0035	.013	.015	1.0311	2.374–2.375	.0015–.0025	2.7495–2.7505	.0015–.0025	3	.002–.007
1967	6-170, 225	.0005–.0015	.010	.015	.9008	2.1865–2.1875	.0005–.0015	2.7495–2.7505	.0005–.0025	3	.002–.007
	8-273, 318	.0005–.0015	.010	.015	.9842	2.124–2.125	.0005–.0015	2.4995–2.5005	.0005–.0015	3	.002–.007
	8-383	.0003–.0013	.013	.015	1.0936	2.374–2.375	.0005–.0015	2.6245–2.6255	.0005–.0015	3	.002–.007
	8-440	.0003–.0013	.013	.015	1.0936	2.374–2.375	.0005–.0015	2.7495–2.7505	.0005–.0015	3	.002–.007
	8-426 Hemi	.0025–.0035	.013	.015	1.0311	2.374–2.375	.0015–.0025	2.7495–2.7505	.0015–.0025	3	.002–.007
1968	6-170, 225	.0005–.0015	.010	.015	.9008	2.1865–2.1875	.0002–.0022	2.7495–2.7505	.0005–.0015	3	.002–.007
	8-273, 318	.0005–.0015	.010	.015	.9842	2.124–2.125	.0002–.0022	2.4995–2.5005	.0005–.0015	3	.002–.007
	8-340	.0005–.0015	.013	.015	.9842	2.124–2.125	.0002–.0027	2.4995–2.5005	.0005–.0015	3	.002–.007
	8-383	.0002–.0012	.013	.015	1.0936	2.374–2.375	.0005–.003	2.6245–2.6255	.0005–.0015	3	.002–.007
	8-440	.0002–.0012	.013	.015	1.094	2.374–2.375	.0005–.003	2.7495–2.7505	.0005–.0015	3	.002–.007
	8-426	.0025–.0035	.013	.015	1.0311	2.374–2.375	.001–.0035	2.7495–2.7505	.0005–.0015	3	.002–.007
1969	6-170	.0005–.0015	.010	.010	.9008	2.1865–2.1875	.0005–.0015	2.7495–2.7505	.0005–.0015	3	.002–.007
	6-225	.0005–.0015	.010	.015	.9008	2.1865–2.1875	.0005–.0015	2.7495–2.7505	.0005–.0015	3	.002–.007
	8-273, 318	.0005–.0015	.010	.015	.9842	2.124–2.125	.0005–.0015	2.4995–2.5005	.0005–.0015	3	.002–.007
	8-340	.0005–.0015	.010	.015	.9842	2.124–2.125	.0005–.0020	2.4995–2.5005	.0005–.0015	3	.002–.007
	8-383, 290 H.P.	.0003–.0013	.013	.015	1.0936	2.374–2.375	.0005–.0015	2.6245–2.6255	.0005–.0015	3	.002–.007
	8-383, 330 H.P.	.0003–.0013	.013	.015	1.0936	2.374–2.375	.001–.002	2.6245–2.6255	.0005–.0015	3	.002–.007
	8-383, 335 H.P.	.0003–.0013	.013	.015	1.0936	2.374–2.375	.001–.002	2.6245–2.6255	.0005–.0015	3	.002–.007
	8-440	.0003–.0013	.013	.015	1.0936	2.374–2.375	.001–.002	2.7495–2.7505	.0005–.0015	3	.002–.007
	8-426	.0025–.0035	.013	.015	1.0311	2.374–2.375	.0015–.0025	2.7495–2.7505	.0015–.0025	3	.002–.007

①—Fit rings in tapered bores for clearance listed in tightest portion of ring travel.
③—With 10.5 to 1 compression ratio.
④—With 11 to 1 compression ratio.
⑤—With 13.5 to 1 compression ratio.

WHEEL ALIGNMENT SPECIFICATIONS

NOTE: See that riding height is correct before checking wheel alignment.

OLD CAR SPECIFICATIONS: For 1946-62 Wheel Alignment Specifications see back of book.

Year	Model	Caster Angle, Degrees		Camber Angle, Degrees				Toe-In. Inch	Toe-Out on Turns, Deg.	
		Limits	Desired	Limits		Desired			Outer Wheel	Inner Wheel
				Left	Right	Left	Right			
CHRYSLER & IMPERIAL										
1963–68	Manual Steer.	0 to —1	—½	+¼ to +¾	0 to +½	+½	+¼	⅛	18.8①	20
	Power Steer.	+¼ to +1¼	+¾	+¼ to +¾	0 to +½	+½	+¼	⅛	18.8①	20
1969	Manual Steer.	+1/16 to —1 1/16	—½	+¼ to +¾	0 to +½	+½	+¼	⅛	18.8①	20
	Power Steer.	+1/16 to —1 1/16②	—½	+¼ to +¾	0 to +½	+½	+¼	⅛	18.8①	20

①—1967–69 Imperial 17.9°, 1963–66 18.5°. ②—Imperial +3/16 to +1 5/16 with +¾ preferred.

Year	Model	Caster Limits	Caster Desired	Camber Limits Left	Camber Limits Right	Camber Desired Left	Camber Desired Right	Toe-In. Inch	Toe-Out Outer Wheel	Toe-Out Inner Wheel
DODGE										
1963–64	Man. Steer.	0 to —1	—½	+½	+¼	+½	+¼	⅛	18	20
	Power Steer.	+¼ to +1¼	+¾	+½	+¼	+½	+¼	⅛	18	20
1965–66	Man. Steer.①	0 to —1	—½	+½	+¼	+½	+¼	⅛	17.6	20
	Power Steer.①	+¼ to +1¼	+¾	+½	+¼	+½	+¼	⅛	17.6	20
	Man. Steer.②	0 to —1	—½	+½	+¼	+½	+¼	⅛	17.8	20
	Power Steer.②	+¼ to +1¼	+¾	+½	+¼	+½	+¼	⅛	17.8	20
	Man. Steer.③	—0 to —1	—½	+½	+¼	+½	+¼	⅛	18.8	20
	Power Steer.③	+¼ to +1¼	+¾	+½	+¼	+½	+¼	⅛	18.8	20
1967	Man. Steer.①	0 to —1	—½	+½	+¼	+½	+¼	⅛	17.6	20
	Power Steer.①	+¼ to +1¼	+¾	+½	+¼	+½	+¼	⅛	17.6	20
	Man. Steer.②	0 to —1	—½	+½	+¼	+½	+¼	⅛	17.8	20
	Power Steer.②	+¼ to +1¼	+¾	+½	+¼	+½	+¼	⅛	17.8	20
	Man. Steer.③	0 to —1	—½	+½	+¼	+½	+¼	⅛	18.8	20
	Power Steer.③	+¼ to +1¼	+¾	+½	+¼	+½	+¼	⅛	18.8	20
1968	Man. Steer.①	0 to —1	—½	+½	+¼	+½	+¼	⅛	18	20
	Power Steer.①	+¼ to +1¼	+¾	+½	+¼	+½	+¼	⅛	18	20
	Man. Steer.②	0 to —1	—½	+½	+¼	+½	+¼	⅛	18.1	20
	Power Steer.②	+¼ to +1¼	+¾	+½	+¼	+½	+¼	⅛	18.1	20
	Man. Steer.③	0 to —1	—½	+½	+¼	+½	+¼	⅛	17.7	20
	Power Steer.③	+¼ to +1¼	+¾	+½	+¼	+½	+¼	⅛	17.7	20
1969	Man. Steer.①	0 to —1	—½	+¼ to +¾	0 to +½	+½	+¼	⅛	17.6	20
	Power Steer.①	+¼ to +1¼	+¾	+¼ to +¾	0 to +½	+½	+¼	⅛	17.6	20
	Man. Steer.②	0 to —1	—½	+¼ to +¾	0 to +½	+½	+¼	⅛	17.8	20
	Power Steer.②	+¼ to +1¼	+¾	+¼ to +¾	0 to +½	+½	+¼	⅛	17.8	20
	Man. Steer.③	0 to —1	—½	+¼ to +¾	0 to +½	+½	+¼	⅛	18.8	20
	Power Steer.③	0 to —1	—½	+¼ to +¾	0 to +½	+½	+¼	⅛	18.8	20

①—Dart. ②—Coronet and Charger. ③—Monaco, Polara, 880.

Year	Model	Caster Limits	Caster Desired	Camber Limits Left	Camber Limits Right	Camber Desired Left	Camber Desired Right	Toe-In. Inch	Toe-Out Outer Wheel	Toe-Out Inner Wheel
PLYMOUTH										
1963–64	Man. Steer.	0 to —1	—½	+½	+¼	+½	+¼	⅛	17½	20
	Power Steer.	+¼ to +1¼	+¾	+½	+¼	+½	+¼	⅛	17½	20
1965–67	Man. Steer.	0 to —1	—½	+½	+¼	+½	+¼	⅛	①	20
	Power Steer.	+¼ to +1¼	+¾	+½	+¼	+½	+¼	⅛	①	20
1968-69	Man. Steer.	+1/16 to —1 1/16	—½	+¼ to +¾	0 to +½	+½	+¼	⅛	②	20
	Power Steer.	+3/16 to +1 5/16	+¾	+0¼ to +¾	0 to +½	+½	+¼	⅛	②	20

①—Fury 18.8°, others 17.8°. ②—Fury 17.7°, others 18°.

ENGINE TIGHTENING SPECIFICATIONS★

★Torque specifications are for clean and lightly lubricated threads only. Dry or dirty threads produce increased friction which prevents accurate measurement of tightness. On aluminum 1963 6-225 engines, none of these bolts, including cylinder head bolts, should be re-tightened with the engine at normal operating temperature.

Year	Engine	Spark Plugs Ft. Lbs.	Cylinder Head Bolts Ft. Lbs.	Intake Manifold Ft. Lbs.	Exhaust Manifold Ft. Lbs.	Rocker Arm Shaft Bracket Ft. Lbs.	Rocker Arm Cover Ft. Lbs.	Connecting Rod Cap Bolts Ft. Lbs.	Main Bearing Cap Bolts Ft. Lbs.	Flywheel to Crank-shaft Ft. Lbs.	Vibration Damper or Pulley Ft. Lbs.
1963–65	6-170	30	65	200①	10	30	40①	45	85	60	②
1966–69	6-170	30	65	200①	10	25	40①	45	85	55	②
1963	6-225	30	65	200①	10	30	40①	45	④	60	②
1964–65	6-225	30	65	200①	10	30	40①	45	85	60	②
1966–69	6-225	30	65	200①	10	25	40①	45	85	55	②
1964–65	8-273	30	85	270①	1[illegible]	15	40①	45	8[illegible]	60	135
1966–68	8-273	30	85	35	30	15	36①	45	85	55	200①
1969	8-273	30	85	35	30	30	36①	45	85	55	200①
1963–65	8-318	30	85	40	15	25	36①	45	85	60	135
1966–68	8-318	30	85	35	30	15	36①	45	85	55	200①
1969	8-318	30	85	35	30	30	36①	45	85	55	200①
1968	8-340	30	95	35	30	15	36①	45	85	55	200①
1969	8-340	30	95	35	30	30	36①	45	85	55	200①
1963–65	8-361	30	70	45	30	25	40①	45	85	70	135
1966	8-361	30	70	50	30	25	40①	45	85	55	135
1963–65	8-383	30	70	45	30	25	40①	45	85	70	135
1966–68	8-383	30	70	50	30	25	40①	45	85	55	135
1969	8-383	30	70	40	30	25	40①	45	85	55	200①
1963–65	8-413	30	70	50	30	30	40①	45	85	70	135
1963–65	8-426	30	70	50	30	25	40①	45	85	70	135
1966	8-426 Std.	30	70	50	30	25	40①	45	85	70	135
1966–69	8-426 Hemi	30	75	③	35	30	40①	75	100	70	135
1966–68	8-440	30	70	50	30	25	40①	45	85	55	135
1969	8-440	30	70	40	30	25	40①	45	85	55	200①

①—Inch pounds.
②—Press fit.
③—Tighten 8 (4 each side) center screws to 72 inch-lbs; all others 48 inch-lbs.
④—Aluminum block 50 Ft-lbs.; Cast iron block 85 Ft-lbs.

REAR AXLE SPECIFICATIONS

Year	Model	Carrier Type	Ring Gear & Pinion Backlash		Pinion Bearing Preload			Differential Bearing Preload		
			Method	Adjustment	Method	New Bearings Inch-Lbs.	Used Bearings Inch-Lbs.	Method	New Bearings Inch-Lbs.	Used Bearings Inch-Lbs.
1963–69	All	Removable①	②	.006–.008	Shims	20-30④	10-15④	②	③	③
1963–69	All	Integral	Washer	.004–.007	Shims	15-25④	8-12④	②	③	③
1967–69	8-426	Integral	Shims	.004–.009	Shims	10-20④	10-20④	Shims	③	③

①—Adjust axle shaft end play to .008–.018″.

②—Threaded adjusters.

③—Preload is correct when ring gear and pinion backlash is properly adjusted.

④—Adjust by turning pinion shaft nut with an inch-pound torque wrench and seal removed.

BRAKE SPECIFICATIONS

Year	Model	Brake Drum Inside Diameter	Wheel Cylinder Bore Diameter			Master Cylinder Bore Diameter		
			Disc Brake	Front Drum Brake	Rear Drum Brake	Disc Brakes	Drum Brakes	Power Brakes
CHRYSLER & IMPERIAL								
1963–65	All	11	—	1⅛	15/16	—	1	1
1966	All	11	1.638	1⅛	15/16	1	1	1
1967–68	All	11	2.375	1⅛	15/16	1⅛	1	1
1969	Chrysler	11	2.757	1⅛	15/16	1⅛	1	1
	Imperial	11	2.375	—	15/16	1⅛	—	—
DODGE								
1963–64	Dart	9	—	1	13/16	—	1	1
	Dodge	10	—	1⅛	15/16	—	1	1
1965	Dart	9	—	1	13/16	—	1	1
	Coronet	10	—	1⅛	15/16	—	1	1
	Others	11	—	1⅛	15/16	—	1	1
1966–67	Polara, Monaco	11	1.638	1⅛	15/16	1	1	1
	Coronet, Charger	10①	2.00	1⅛	15/16	1⅛	1	1
	Dart 6	9	1.638	1	13/16	—	1	1
	Dart V8	10	1.638	1⅛	15/16	1	1	1
1968–69	Dart 6	9	1.638	1	13/16	1	1	1
	Dart V8	10	1.638	1⅛	15/16	1	1	1
	Coronet DeLuxe, 440	10	2.00	1⅛	15/16	1⅛	1	1
	Coronet R/T, 500	11	2.00	1⅛	15/16	1⅛	1	1
	Charger	10	2.00	1⅛	15/16	1⅛	1	1
	Polara, Monaco	11	②	1⅛	15/16	1⅛	1	1
PLYMOUTH								
1963–67	Valiant	9	—	1	13/16	—	1	1
1963–64	Plymouth	10	—	1⅛	13/16	—	1	1
1965	Plymouth	10	—	1⅛	15/16	—	1	1
1966	Fury, VIP	11	1.638	1⅛	15/16	1	1	1
	Valiant, Barracuda 6	9	1⅛	1	13/16	1	1	1
	Valiant, Barracuda V8	10	1⅛	1	13/16	1	1	1
	Belvedere, Satellite	10①	—	1⅛	15/16	1	1	1
1967–69	Valiant, Barracuda 6	9	1.638	1	13/16	1	1	1
	Valiant, Barracuda V8	10	1.638	1⅛	15/16	1	1	1
	Belvedere, Satellite	10①	2.00	1⅛	15/16	1⅛	1	1
	Fury, VIP	11	②	1⅛	15/16	1⅛	1	1

①—With 383, 426 or 440 engine, 11″ drums. ②—For 1968, 2.375 For 1969, 2.757.

COOLING SYSTEM & CAPACITY DATA

Year	Model or Engine	Cooling Capacity, Qts.			Radiator Cap Relief Pressure, Lbs.		Thermo. Opening Temp. (1)	Fuel Tank Gals.	Engine Oil Refill Qts. (2)	Transmission Oil			Rear Axle Oil Pints
		No Heater	With Heater	With A/C	With A/C	No A/C				3 Speed Pints	4 Speed Pints	Auto. Trans. Qts. (12)	
CHRYSLER													
1963	All	16	17	17	16	14	180	23	5	4½	7½	9½	4
1964	All	16	17	17	16	14	180	23(5)	5	5	7½	10	4
1965	All	16	17	17	16	14	180	23(5)	5	5	7½	9½	4
1966	All	—	17	18	16	14	180	25(3)	5	6	—	9½	4
1967	All	—	17(9)	18(9)	16	16	180	25(3)	4	6½	9	9¼	4
1968	With 8-383	—	17(9)	18(9)	16	16	180	24(3)	4	6	—	9¼	4
	With 8-440	—	18(9)	19(9)	16	16	180	24(3)	4	6	—	9¼	4
1969	8-383	—	16(9)	17	16	16	190	24(3)	4	6	—	9¼	4
	8-440	—	17(9)	18	16	16	190	24(3)	4	6	—	9¼	4
IMPERIAL													
1963	All	16	17	17	16	14	180	23	5	—	—	9½	4
1964	All	16	17	17	16	14	180	23	5	—	—	10	4
1965	All	16	17	17	16	14	180	23	5	—	—	9¼	4
1966	All	—	18	18	16	14	180	23	5	—	—	9½	4
1967	All	—	18(9)	19(9)	16	16	180	25	4	—	—	9¼	4
1968	All	—	17(9)	18(9)	16	16	180	24	4	—	—	9¼	4
1969	All	—	19(9)	19	16	16	190	24(3)	4	—	—	9¼	4
DODGE													
1963	6-170	11	12	12	16	14	180	18(5)	4	5	—	7½	2
	6-225	12	13	13	16	14	180	18(5)	4	5	—	7½	2
	V8-318	20	21	21	16	14	180	19(5)	4	5	3⅛	9½	4
	V8-361, 383, 426	16	17	17	16	14	180	19(5)	5	5	3⅛	9½	4
1964	6-170	11	12	12	16	14	180	19(5)	4	6	7	9	2
	6-225	12	13	13	16	14	180	19(5)	4	6	7	9	2
	V8-273	16	17	17	16	14	180	19(5)	4	4½	7½	10	4
	V8-318	20	21	21	16	14	180	19(5)	4	4½	7½	10	4
	V8-361, 383, 426	16	17	17	16	14	180	19(5)	5	4½	7½	10	4
1965	6-170	11	12	12	16	14	180	(6)	4	6	7½	8½	4
	6-225	12	13	13	16	14	180	(6)	4	6	7½	8½	4
	V8-273	17	18	18	16	14	180	(6)	4	6	7½	8½	4
	V8-318	20	21	21	16	14	180	(6)	4	6	7½	9¾	4
	Other V8s	16	17	17	16	14	180	(6)	4	5	7½	9¾	4
1966	Dart 6-170	—	12	—	16	14	180	18	4	6½	—	8	2
	Dart 6-225	—	13	13	16	14	180	18	4	6½	—	8	2
	Dart 8-273	—	18	18	16	14	180	18	4	6	8½	8	2
	Cor. & Charg. 6-225	—	13	13	16	14	180	19	4	6½	—	8	2
	Cor. & Charg. 8-273	—	19	19	16	14	180	19	4	6	—	8	4
	Cor. & Charg. 8-318	—	21	22	16	14	180	19	4	6	—	9¼	4
	Cor. & Charg. 8-361	—	17	18	16	14	180	19	4	—	8½	9¼	4
	Cor. & Charg. 8-383	—	17	18	16	14	180	19	4	—	8½	9¼	4
	Cor. & Charg. 8-426	—	17	18	16	14	180	19	5	—	8½	9¼	4
	Polara, Monaco 8-318	—	21	22	16	14	180	25(3)	4	6	—	9¼	4
	Polara, Monaco 8-383	—	17	18	16	14	180	25(3)	4	6	8½	9¼	4
	Polara, Monaco 8-440	—	17	18	16	14	180	25(3)	4	—	8½	9¼	4
1967	Dart 6-170	—	12	13	16	16	180	18	4	6½	—	8	2
	Dart 6-225	—	13	14	16	16	180	18	4	6½	—	8	2
	Dart 8-273 (2 B.C.)	—	19	20	16	16	180	18	4	6½	8	8	2
	Dart 8-273 (4 B.C.)	—	19	20	16	16	180	18	4	6½	8	8	4

Continued

COOLING SYSTEM & CAPACITY DATA—Continued

Year	Model or Engine	Cooling Capacity, Qts.			Radiator Cap Relief Pressure, Lbs.		Thermo. Opening Temp. (1)	Fuel Tank Gals.	Engine Oil Refill Qts. (2)	Transmission Oil			Rear Axle Oil Pints
		No Heater	With Heater	With A/C	With A/C	No A/C				3 Speed Pints	4 Speed Pints	Auto. Trans. Qts. (12)	
DODGE—Continued													
1967	Cor. & Charg. 6-225	—	13	14	16	16	180	19	4	6½	—	8	2
	Cor. & Charg. 8-273	—	19	20	16	16	180	19	4	6½	—	8	4
	Cor. & Charg. 8-318	—	18	19	16	16	180	19	4	6½	—	9¼	4
	Cor. & Charg. 8-383	—	17	18	16	16	180	19	4	—	8½	9¼	4
	Cor. & Charg. 8-426	—	18	19	16	16	180	19	5	—	8½	9¼	4
	Cor. & Charg. 8-440	—	18	19	16	16	180	19	4	—	8½	9¼	4
	Polara, Monaco 8-318	—	18	19	16	16	180	25(3)	4	6½	—	9¼	4
	Polara, Monaco 8-383	—	17	18	16	16	180	25(3)	4	6½	9	9¼	4
	Polara, Monaco 8-440	—	17	18	16	16	180	25(3)	4	—	9	9¼	4
	8-440 Hi Perf.	—	18	19	16	16	180	25(3)	4	—	9	9¼	4
1968	Dart 6-170	—	12	13	16	16	180	18	4	6½	—	7¾	2
	Dart 6-225	—	13	14	16	16	180	18	4	6½	—	7¾	2
	Dart 8-273	—	19	20	16	16	180	18	4	6	8	7¾	2
	Dart 8-318	—	18	19	16	16	180	18	4	—	8	9¼	2(10)
	Dart 8-340	—	18	19	16	16	180	18	4	—	8	9¼	4
	Dart 8-383	—	17	18	16	16	180	18	4	—	8	7¾	4
	Coro. Charger 6-225	—	13	14	16	16	180	19	4	6½	—	7¾	2(7)
	Coro. Charger 8-273	—	19	20	16	16	180	19	4	6	—	7¾	4
	Coro. Charger 8-318	—	18	19	16	16	180	19	4	6	—	9¼	4
	Coro. Charger 8-383	—	17	18	16	16	180	19	4	—	9	7¾	4
	Coro. Charger 8-440	—	17(11)	18(11)	16	16	180	19	4	—	9	7¾	4(13)
	Coro. Charger 8-426	—	18	19	16	16	180	19	6	—	9	7¾	4(13)
	Polara, Monaco 8-318	—	18	19	16	16	180	24(3)	4	6	—	9¼	4
	Polara, Monaco 8-383	—	17	18	16	16	180	24(3)	4	6	9	7¾	4
	Polara, Monaco 8-440	—	17	18	16	16	180	24(3)	4	—	9	7¾	4(14)
1969	Dart 6-170	—	12(15)	—	—	16	200	18	4	6½	—	7¾	2
	Dart 6-225	—	13	15	16	16	190	18	4	6½	—	7¾	2
	Dart 8-273	—	17	19	16	16	190	18	4	6	7	7¾	2
	Dart 318	—	16	18	16	16	190	18	4	6	7	7¾	2(10)
	Dart 8-340	—	16	16	16	16	190	18	4	—	7	7¾	4
	Dart 8-383	—	16	16	16	16	190	18	4	—	7	7¾(16)	4
	Coro. Charger 6-225	—	13	15	16	16	190	19	4	6½	—	7¾	2(7)
	Coro. Charger 8-318	—	16	19	16	16	190	19	4	6	—	7¾	4
	Coro. Charger 8-383	—	16	17	16	16	190	19	4	—	7½	7¾(16)	4
	Coro. Charger 8-440	—	17	18	16	16	190	19	4	—	7½	9¼	4(13)
	Coro. Charger 8-426	—	18	—	16	16	190	19	6	—	7½	8	4(13)
	Polara, Monaco 8-318	—	16	19	16	16	190	24(3)	4	6	—	7¾	4
	Polara, Monaco 8-383	—	16	17	16	16	190	24(3)	4	6	—	7¾(16)	4
	Polara, Monaco 8-440	—	17	18	16	16	190	24(3)	4	—	—	9¼	4(14)
PLYMOUTH													
1963	6 Cylinder	12	13	13	16	14	180	20(5)	4	5	—	7½	4
	V8-318	20	21	21	16	14	180	20(5)	4	5	3⅛	9½	4
	V8-361, 383	16	17	17	16	14	180	20(5)	4	5	3⅛	9½	4
1964	6 Cylinder	12	13	13	16	14	180	18	4	6	7	9	2
	V8-318	20	21	21	16	14	180	19(5)	4	4½	7½	10	4
	V8-361, 383, 426	16	17	17	16	14	180	19(5)	4	4½	7½	10	4
1965	6 Cylinder	12	13	13	16	14	180	19(5)	4	6	7½	8½	4
	V8-273	17	18	18	16	14	180	19(5)	4	6	7½	8½	4
	V8-318	20	21	21	16	14	180	19(5)	4	6	7½	9¾	4
	V8-361, 383, 426	16	17	17	16	14	180	19(5)	4	6	7½	9¾	4

Continued

COOLING SYSTEM & CAPACITY DATA—Continued

Year	Model or Engine	Cooling Capacity, Qts.			Radiator Cap Relief Pressure, Lbs.		Thermo. Opening Temp. ①	Fuel Tank Gals.	Engine Oil Refill Qts. ②	Transmission Oil			Rear Axle Oil Pints
		No Heater	With Heater	With A/C	With A/C	No A/C				3 Speed Pints	4 Speed Pints	Auto. Trans. Qts. ⑫	
PLYMOUTH—Continued													
1966	Belvedere 6-225	—	13	14	16	14	180	19	4	6½	—	8	2⑦
	8-273⑧	—	18	19	16	14	180	19	4	6	—	8	4
	8-318⑧	—	21	22	16	14	180	19	4	6	—	9¼	4
	8-361, 383⑧	—	17	18	16	14	180	19	4	—	8½	9¼	4
	8-426⑧	—	17	17	16	14	180	19	5	—	8½	9¼	4
	Fury 6-225	—	13	14	16	14	180	25③	4	6½	—	8	4
	Fury 8-318	—	21	22	16	14	180	25③	4	6	—	9¼	4
	Fury 8-383, 440	—	17	18	16	14	180	25③	4	6	8½	9¼	4
1967	Belvedere 6-225	—	13	14	16	16	180	19	4	6½	—	8	2⑦
	8-273⑧	—	18	19	16	16	180	19	4	6½	—	8	4
	8-318⑧	—	21	22	16	16	180	19	4	6½	—	9¼	4
	8-383⑧	—	17	18	16	16	180	19	4	—	8½	9¼	4
	8-426⑧	—	18	19	16	16	180	19	4	—	8½	9¼	4
	Fury 6-225	—	13	14	16	16	180	25③	4	6½	—	8	4
	Fury 8-318	—	18	19	16	16	180	25③	4	6½	—	9¼	4
	Fury 8-383	—	17	18	16	16	180	25③	4	6½	8½	9¼	4
	8-440 Hi Perf.	—	18	19	16	16	180	25③	4	6½	9	9¼	4
1968	Fury, VIP 6-225	—	13	14	16	16	180	24③	4	6½	—	7¾	4
	Others 6-225	—	13	14	16	16	180	19	4	6½	—	7¾	2⑦
	8-273	—	19	20	16	16	180	19	4	6	—	7¾	4
	Fury, VIP 8-318	—	18	19	16	16	180	24③	4	6	—	9¼	4
	Others 8-318	—	18	19	16	16	180	19	4	6	—	9¼	4
	Fury, VIP 8-383	—	17	18	16	16	180	24③	4	—	9	7¾	4
	Others 8-383 2 B.C.	—	17	18	16	16	180	19	4	—	9	7¾	4
	8-383 4 Bar. Carb.	—	17	18	16	16	180	19	4	—	9	7¾	4
	8-426 Hemi.	—	18	19	16	16	180	19	6	—	9	7¾	4⑬
	Fury, VIP 8-440 Std.	—	17	18	16	16	180	24③	4	—	9	7¾	4¼
	Fury,VIP 8-440 Hi Perf.	—	18	19	16	16	180	24③	4	—	9	7¾	4¼
	Others 8-440 Hi Perf.	—	17⑪	18⑪	16	16	180	19	4	—	9	7¾	4⑬
1969	Fury, VIP 6-225	—	13	—	16	—	190	24③	4	6½	—	7¾	4
	Others 6-225	—	13	15	16	16	190	19	4	6½	—	7¾	2⑦
	Fury, VIP 8-318	—	16	19	16	16	190	24③	4	6½	—	7¾	4
	Others 8-318	—	16	19	16	16	190	19	4	6½	—	7¾	4
	Fury, VIP 8-383 2 B.C.	—	16	17	16	16	190	24③	4	—	7¾	9¼	4
	Others 8-383 2 B.C.	—	16	17	16	16	190	19	4	—	7½	9¼	4
	Fury, VIP 8-383 4 B.C.	—	16	17	16	16	190	24③	4	—	7¾	7¾	4
	Others 8-383 4 B.C.	—	16	17	16	16	190	19	4		7½	7¾	4
	8-426 Hemi.	—	18	—	16	—	190	19	6	—	7½	8	4⑬
	Fury, VIP 8-440	—	17	18	16	16	190	24③	4	—	7¾	9¼	4
	Others 8-440	—	17	18	16	16	190	19	4	—	7½	9¼	4⑬

VALIANT AND BARRACUDA

Year	Model or Engine	No Heater	With Heater	With A/C	With A/C	No A/C	Thermo. Opening Temp.	Fuel Tank Gals.	Engine Oil Refill Qts.	3 Speed Pints	4 Speed Pints	Auto. Trans. Qts.	Rear Axle Oil Pints
1963	6-170	11	12	12	16	14	180	11	4	5	—	7½	2
	6-225	12	13	13	16	14	180	11	4	5	—	7½	2
1964	6-170	11	12	12	16	14	180	18	4	6	7	9	2
	6-225	12	13	13	16	14	180	18	4	6	7	9	2
	V8-273	16	17	17	16	14	180	18	4	4½	7½	10	2
1965	6-170	11	12	12	16	14	180	18	4	6	—	8½	2
	6-225	12	13	13	16	14	180	18	4	6	—	8½	2
	V8-273	17	18	18	16	14	180	18	4	6	7½	8½	2
1966	6-170	—	12	—	16	14	180	18	4	6½	—	8	2
	6-225	—	13	14	16	14	180	18	4	6½	—	8	2

Continued

COOLING SYSTEM & CAPACITY DATA—Continued

Year	Model or Engine	Cooling Capacity, Qts.			Radiator Cap Relief Pressure, Lbs.		Thermo. Opening Temp. (1)	Fuel Tank Gals.	Engine Oil Refill Qts. (2)	Transmission Oil			Rear Axle Oil Pints
		No Heater	With Heater	With A/C	With A/C	No A/C				3 Speed Pints	4 Speed Pints	Auto. Trans. Qts. (12)	
VALIANT AND BARRACUDA—Continued													
1966	8-273	—	18	18	16	14	180	18	4	6	8½	8	2
1967	6-170	—	12	—	16	16	180	18	4	6½	—	8	2
	6-225	—	13	14	16	16	180	18	4	6½	—	8	2
	8-273 2 Bar. Carb.	—	19	20	16	16	180	18	4	6½	8	8	2
	8-273 4 Bar. Carb.	—	19	20	16	16	180	18	4	6½	8	8	4
1968	6-170	—	12	13	16	16	180	18	4	6½	—	7¾	2
	6-225	—	13	14	16	16	180	18	4	6½	—	7¾	2
	8-273	—	19	20	16	16	180	18	4	6	8	7¾	2
	8-318	—	17	18	16	16	180	18	4	—	8	9¼	4
	8-340	—	18	19	16	16	180	18	4	—	8	9¼	4
	8-383	—	17	18	16	16	180	18	4	—	8	7¾	4
1969	6-170	—	12	14	16	16	200	18	4	6½	—	7¾	2
	6-225	—	13	15	16	16	190	18	4	6½	—	7¾	2
	8-273	—	17	19	16	16	190	18	4	6½	7	7¾	4
	8-318	—	16	18	16	16	190	18	4	6½	7	9¼	4
	8-340	—	16	—	16	—	190	18	4	6½	7	9¼	4
	8-383 2 Bar. Carb.	—	16	—	16	—	190	18	4	6½	7	9¼	4
	8-383 4 Bar. Carb.	—	16	—	16	—	190	18	4	6½	7	7¾	4

(1)—With alcohol type anti-freeze use a 160° unit.

(2)—Add one qt. with filter change.

(3)—Wagons 22 gals.

(5)—Wagons 21 gals.

(6)—Polara, Monaco, 880: Cars, 25, Wagons 21. Dart and Coronet: 111″ W.B. 18, 106″ W.B. 16, 119″ W.B. 19, 116″ W.B. 21.

(7)—Station Wagon 4 pints.

(8)—Belvedere and Satellite.

(9)—Add 1½ qts. for rear seat heater.

(10)—With manual transmission 4 pints.

(11)—With 4 speed trans., 18 (19 with A/C).

(12)—Approximate. Make final check with dipstick.

(13)—With manual trans. 5½ pints.

(14)—5½ pints for High Perf. engine.

(15)—Add 2 qts. for 22″ radiator.

(16)—9¼ qts. for High Perf.

Electrical Section

IGNITION TIMING

If a timing light is to be used to set ignition timing, disconnect the vacuum advance pipe to the carburetor and place a piece of tape over open end of pipe. *This is important as carburetor trouble can affect timing adjustments.*

Lacking a power timing light, an accurate method of setting ignition timing with the engine stopped is with the aid of a jumper light. Be sure to use a light bulb that corresponds with the system voltage of the vehicle.

1. Remove distributor cap and rotor and see that the breaker gap is set according to specifications.
2. Rotate engine until No. 1 cylinder is at the ignition timing point as indicated by the timing pointer and timing mark being lined up with each other.
3. Connect the jumper light between distributor ignition terminal and ground.
4. Turn on ignition switch.
5. Loosen distributor and turn it in the direction of normal rotation until the points just close (light out). Then slowly turn distributor in the opposite direction just to the exact point that the light goes on. Tighten distributor in this position.

DISTRIBUTOR, REPLACE

6-170, 225

The distributor rotates clockwise. To remove, take off cap, disconnect primary wire and vacuum line. Remove hold-down bolt and lift out distributor. Install in the following manner.

1. Rotate crankshaft until mark on inner edge of crankshaft pulley is in line with the "O" (TDC) mark on timing chain cover.
2. With distributor gasket in position, hold distributor over mounting pad.
3. Turn rotor to point forward, corresponding to 4 o'clock position.
4. Install distributor so that when fully seated on engine, the gear has spiraled to bring rotor to 5 o'clock position.
5. Turn housing until ignition points are separating and rotor is under No. 1 cap tower.
6. Install hold-down bolt.
7. Adjust timing with timing light.

1963-69 V8s

To remove the distributor, disconnect the vacuum control line and low tension wire and remove the cap and lock plate hold-down screw.

When installing the distributor, make sure that No. 1 piston is on top dead center on compression stroke and that the distributor rotor is in No. 1 firing position.

SERVICE BULLETIN

FUSIBLE LINK REPAIR: Alternator-equipped 1965-69 cars have charging circuits protected by a fuse-type wire. This fusible link is installed on the starter relay battery terminal.

If the charging circuit becomes overloaded, the inner fuse wire of this link burns out and the insulation heats up and breaks apart. This cuts off the battery from the charging system.

In the event one of these cars has none of its electrical parts functioning, check for a burned out fusible link. After locating and correcting the short, a new fusible link should be installed. Do not allow the insulation to contact any other wiring.

In situations like this, never use an uninsulated wire as a jumper if a fusible link replacement is not available. This can cause a fire in the electrical system.

STARTER, REPLACE

Reduction Gear Type

1. To remove starter, disconnect ground cable at battery.
2. Remove cable at starter.
3. Disconnect wires at solenoid.
4. Remove one stud nut and one bolt attaching starter motor to flywheel housing.
5. Slide transmission oil cooler bracket off stud (if so equipped).
6. Remove starter motor and removable seal.
7. Reverse above procedure to install.

NOTE: When tightening attaching bolt and nut be sure to hold starter away from engine to insure proper alignment.

Direct Drive Type

1. Disconnect battery ground cable.
2. Remove cable at starter.
3. Disconnect lead wire from solenoid.
4. Unfasten and remove starter and removable seal.

NOTE: On 1965 Valiant and Dart with V8-273 engine, before the starter can be removed, it will be necessary to remove the pitman arm, exhaust crossover pipe and torque converter housing-to-oil pan brace.

NOTE

Noisy or erratic starter operation may be caused by lack of lubrication or deposits of foreign material on the Bendix driveshaft.

To correct this condition, remove the inspection plate at the bottom of the torque converter or clutch housing. Then apply a suitable upper-cylinder rust inhibitor or SAE 5W or SAE 10W oil to the shaft by means of a 7" piece of tubing attached to the spout of a pressure oil can. In extreme cases, it may be necessary to remove, disassemble and clean the starter.

IGNITION SWITCH, REPLACE

1969 Polara & Monaco

1. Remove center air conditioning duct and left cooler duct.
2. Remove ignition switch bezel nut.
3. Remove ignition switch from under side of panel and disconnect main harness.

1967-69 Chrysler & Imperial

1. Remove switch bezel nut from front of panel.
2. Push switch into and down below panel.
3. Disconnect wiring harness multiple connector and remove switch.
4. To install, connect multiple connector to switch terminal and insert switch in panel opening, indexing key in switch with slot in panel. Install bezel nut and tighten securely.

1968-69 Charger

1. Remove lower center A/C duct and left A/C duct (if equipped).
2. Remove steering column for visual assist, and remove ignition switch spanner.
3. Disconnect wiring connector and remove switch.

1968-69 Coronet & Dart

1. Remove A/C duct (if equipped).
2. Remove switch bezel.
3. On Coronet, loosen harness from clip for access.
4. Disconnect wiring connector and pull switch out from under panel.

1963 Imperial

1. Disconnect battery ground cable.
2. Remove switch bezel nut.
3. Remove dial plate and back dial.
4. Remove dial lamp and switch retaining nut.
5. Remove switch from rear of instrument panel.
6. Disconnect connector plug and remove switch.
7. Reverse above procedure to install.

1963-66 Chrysler

All switches in the instrument panel or in the instrument cluster can be serviced from under the instrument panel by removing the switch knob, mounting nut or bezel and disconnecting wiring to switch.

1964-66 Imperial

1. Remove lower steering column cover plate.
2. Remove accessory switch knobs.
3. Remove screw that attaches left end of switch bezel to instrument panel. This screw can be reached from inside steering column opening.
4. Remove screw in ignition switch well.
5. Lift off switch bezel.
6. Remove mounting nut from ignition switch.
7. From under instrument panel pull switch down, disconnect wiring and remove switch.
8. Reverse above procedure to install.

1967-69 Plymouth & Valiant

1. Where necessary, remove air conditioning elbow. Remove bezel nut and lower switch behind panel far enough to remove multiple connector.
2. Before installing switch, connect multiple connector and position switch in panel.
3. Install and tighten bezel nut.

1966 Plymouth

Valiant, Barracuda and Fury switches are removed from under the panel after disconnecting the multiple connector from the back and removing the bezel on the panel.

In Belvedere and Satellite models, it is necessary to remove the turn signal flasher before disconnecting the multiple connector. The bezel is then removed and the switch is dropped from under the panel.

1966-67 Dart, Charger, Coronet

On all models remove bezel. On Coronet models, loosen the harness from the retaining clip before lowering the switch and disconnecting the multiple connector.

1967-68 Polara & Monaco

1. Remove bezel nut, disconnect multiple connector from switch and remove switch from under panel.
2. Before installing switch, connect multiple connector and insert switch in opening. Install and tighten bezel nut.

1966 Polara & Monaco

The ignition switch is serviced through the instrument cluster opening (see Instrument Cluster Removal). Remove the multiple connector from the back of the switch. The knob is retained by a set screw and is removed before removing the bezel nut.

1963-65 Dodge & Plymouth

1. Disconnect battery ground cable.
2. Remove switch bezel nut.
3. Remove switch from rear of instrument panel.
4. Reverse above procedure to install.

LIGHT SWITCH, REPLACE

1969 Coronet, Belvedere & Satellite

1. Disconnect battery ground cable at battery.
2. Disconnect all wiring connectors from back of switches.
3. Remove switch bezel mounting screws.
4. Remove switches and bezel assembly and remove headlight switch.

NOTE: Carefully pull trim bezel straight to avoid damaging trim pad.

5. Reverse procedure to install.

1969 Monaco & Polara

1. Remove switch bezel.
2. Remove two mounting screws and remove switch.

1969 Chrysler & Imperial

1. Remove lamp panel.
2. Remove instrument cluster to gain access to switch.
3. Remove switch mounting screws and switch.

1967-68 Chrysler & Imperial

The Safeguard Sentinel, headlight, panel dimmer light, windshield washer-wiper switches and rear heater switch (Imperial only) are mounted to the back of the instrument cluster bezels. To service any of these switches, remove the appropriate bezel as outlined under *Instrument Cluster Removal.*

To remove the headlight switch, windshield wiper or washer switch, remove eight adapter plate mounting screws and two rear seat heater switch bezel nuts (Imperial only).

To install, insert threaded shank of switch through respective hole in mounting bracket and fasten with nut.

1968 Monaco & Polara

1. Remove dimmer switch.
2. Remove two light switch mounting screws, disconnect electrical connectors from switch and remove switch from panel.

1968-69 Charger

1. Remove instrument cluster as described further on.
2. Disconnect wiring connector.
3. Disconnect heater vacuum hoses for accessibility.
4. Remove two switch mounting screws.
5. Reverse procedure to install.

1963 Chrysler

The headlight and panel light switches are combined into one unit but are operated by separate controls.

On all models, switch (or switches) is held in instrument panel by a threaded sleeve and hex nut. The panel light switch control encircles inner headlight switch and is indexed on its shaft by lugs in tab plate and slots in shaft. The headlight switch knob is held on its shaft by a recessed hex screw.

If a switch is inoperative or defective, replace complete unit.

1963 Imperial

1. Disconnect battery ground cable.
2. Remove switch knob by releasing retainer on body of switch. Knob must be in full "out" position before knob stem can be released.
3. Remove bezel nut and chrome plate.
4. Remove switch back dial plate and dial bulb.

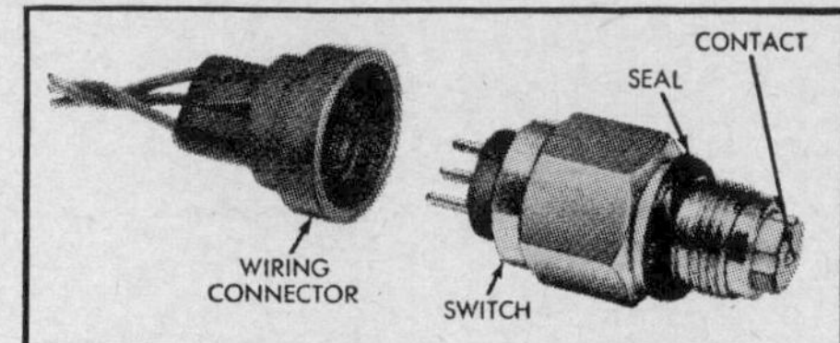

Fig. 1 Neutral safety switch

5. Remove switch retaining nut and take switch from panel. Disconnect connector plug.
6. Reverse above procedure to install.

1964-66 Chrysler

All switches in the instrument panel or in the instrument cluster can be serviced from under the instrument panel by removing the switch knob, mounting nut or bezel and disconnecting wire to switch.

1964-66 Imperial

1. Remove lower steering column cover plate.
2. Remove headlight switch knob and stem and windshield wiper switch knob.
3. Remove screw that attaches right end of switch bezel to instrument panel. This screw can be reached from inside steering column opening.
4. Remove headlamp switch retaining nut and lift off switch bezel.
5. Remove headlamp switch and windshield wiper stem seals.
6. Remove mounting nut from headlamp switch and, from under instrument panel, pull switch down and disconnect wiring.
7. Reverse above procedure to install.

1963-65 Dodge & Plymouth

The light switch can be serviced from under the instrument panel by removing the switch knob, mounting nut or bezel and disconnecting the wiring at the switch.

1967-69 Valiant, Barracuda, 1967-68 Belvedere & Satellite

1. From under instrument panel, remove screw retaining fuse block to panel and move fuse block out of the way.
2. Reaching under panel, depress release button on right side of switch and pull knob out of switch.
3. Remove bezel nut and lower switch under panel to disconnect multiple connector and remove switch.
4. Reverse procedure to install. Insert switch knob into switch until a "click" is heard.

1967-69 Fury & V.I.P.

1. On models with air conditioning, remove left spot cooler hose from duct and move out of the way.
2. Remove fuse block retaining screw and move fuse block out of the way to gain access to switch.
3. From under panel, use a magnetic screwdriver to remove two screws retaining switch to rear of panel sheet metal.
4. Move switch down from panel reinforcement far enough to disconnect multiple connector and remove switch.
5. Reverse procedure to install.

1966 Plymouth

The switches on Valiant, Barracuda, Belvedere and Satellite models are serviced from under the instrument panel by disconnecting the multiple connector, removing the knob and bezel.

On Fury models it is necessary to remove the instrument cluster (see Instrument Cluster Removal) far enough from the panel to gain access to the multiple connector and the knob release button on the switch.

1966-69 Dart & 1966-68 Coronet, 1967 Charger

The switch is serviced from under the instrument panel after removing the fuse block mounting screw. Move the fuse block out of the way. If air conditioned, remove the left spot cooler hose from the outlet.

Remove knob by depressing release button on switch and pull out knob. After removing bezel, lower switch and disconnect multiple connector.

1967 Polara & Monaco

The headlight and panel dimmer switch are serviced from under the panel after removal of the fuse block. Remove two screws and take out switch.

1966 Polara & Monaco

The switch is removed through the speedometer cluster opening (see Speedometer Cluster Removal). After removing the cluster and multiple connector, the switch knob is removed by depressing the release button on the terminal side of the switch. Then remove the bezel nut on the front of the panel and withdraw the switch through the cluster opening.

STOP LIGHT SWITCH, REPLACE

1963-69 All Cars

To remove the switch, disconnect wires from switch and remove switch from its mounting. Install the new switch and connect the wires.

NEUTRAL SAFETY SWITCH

1963-69 All Cars

1. Unscrew switch from transmission case, allowing fluid to drain onto a container, Fig. 1.
2. Move shift lever to "Park" and then to "Neutral" positions and inspect to see that switch operating lever is centered in switch opening in case.
3. Screw switch into transmission case and torque to 25-35 ft-lbs.
4. Add fluid to proper level.
5. Check to see that switch operates only in "Park" and "Neutral".

HORN SOUNDER & STEERING WHEEL

1967-69 All Cars

1. Disconnect ground cable at battery.
2. Remove horn ring ornament by turning counterclockwise.
3. Disconnect wires at horn switch.
4. Remove three screws attaching horn ring and switch to steering wheel, then remove horn ring and switch.
5. Remove wheel nut and use a suitable puller to remove steering wheel.

CAUTION: Do not bump or hammer on steering shaft to remove wheel as damage to shaft may result. See *Steering Gear, Replace* for other precautions.

1965-66 Chrysler

1. Disconnect battery ground cable.
2. Compress and turn horn button ¼ turn counter-clockwise to remove button.
3. Disconnect horn wire at switch.
4. Remove horn switch-to-steering wheel retaining screws and insulators, then remove horn ring and switch.
5. Remove steering shaft nut and use a puller to remove steering wheel.

1965-66 Imperial

1. Disconnect battery ground cable.
2. Remove two screws from underside of steering wheel. Lift up wheel cover and disconnect ground wire and two horn switch wires.
3. Remove steering wheel retaining nut and use a puller to remove wheel.

1963-64 Chrysler

1. Disconnect ground cable at battery.
2. Compress and turn horn button ¼ turn counterclockwise to release button from retainer.
3. Disconnect horn wire at horn switch.
4. Remove three screws and insulators attaching horn ring and switch to steering column. Remove horn ring and switch.
5. Loosen steering column nut several turns and remove wheel with a puller.

1963-64 Imperial

1. Remove two screws from underside of steering wheel and remove horn blowing actuator and wheel cover.
2. Disconnect horn blowing wire at switch.
3. Remove four screws and insulators and remove switch.
4. Loosen wheel nut several turns and pull wheel off with a puller.

1966 Dart, Charger, Coronet

1. Disconnect battery ground cable.
2. Remove horn ring on Coronet models by placing steering wheel in straight-ahead position. Lift horn ring at seven o'clock position and turn counterclockwise ¼ turn.
3. For Dart models, pry cap off horn button with a screwdriver, using care to avoid damaging cap.
4. Disconnect wire at horn switch.
5. Remove three screws and insulators attaching horn ring retainer and switch to steering column. Remove retainer and switch.
6. Loosen steering wheel nut several turns and, with a suitable puller, loosen steering wheel. Then remove nut and steering wheel.

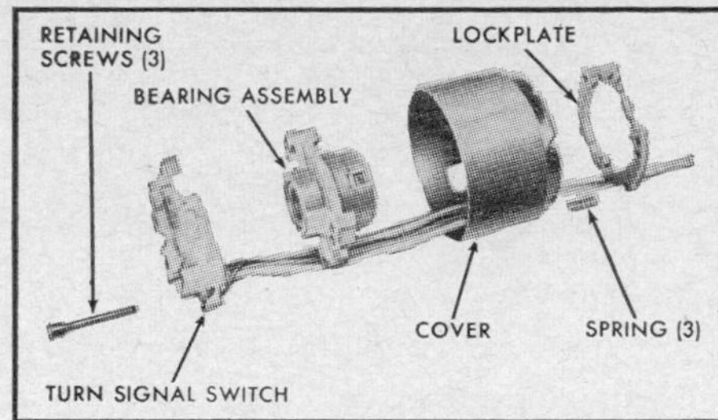

Fig. 2 Turn signal switch. 1969

1966 Polara & Monaco

1. Disconnect battery ground cable.
2. Compress and turn horn button ¼ turn counterclockwise to release button from retainer.
3. Disconnect wire at horn switch.
4. Remove three screws and insulators attaching horn ring and switch to steering column. Remove horn ring and switch.
5. Loosen steering wheel nut several turns and, with a suitable puller, loosen wheel. Then remove nut and steering wheel.

1963-65 Dart, 1962 Lancer

Remove the horn button by inserting a small screwdriver into slot in steering wheel at edge of horn button and pry button and retaining "O" ring out of wheel. Then use a suitable puller to remove steering wheel after steering shaft nut is removed.

1963-65 Dodge

1. Disconnect battery ground cable.
2. On standard models, remove horn button by turning it ¼ turn counterclockwise and lift it out.
3. On 1965 Coronet models, place steering wheel with cross bars in horizontal position. Disconnect horn wire. Slightly raise horn ring at the seven o'clock position, which will release retaining tabs. Hold horn ring up and turn counter-clockwise ¼ turn and lift ring from wheel. On other models with horn ring, remove two screws from underside of steering wheel and lift off horn ring.
4. Remove steering wheel nut.
5. Use a suitable puller to remove wheel.

1966 Plymouth

1. Disconnect battery ground cable.
2. Remove horn ring on Belvedere, Satellite and Fury models by placing steering wheel in straight-ahead position. Lift horn ring at 7 o'clock position and turn counterclockwise ¼ turn.
3. On Valiant models, pry cap off horn button with a screwdriver.
4. Disconnect wire at horn switch.
5. Remove three screws and insulators attaching horn ring retainer and switch to steering column. Remove retainer and switch.
6. Loosen steering wheel nut several turns and, with a suitable puller, loosen wheel. Then remove nut and steering wheel.

1963-65 Valiant

Remove horn button by inserting a screwdriver into slot in steering wheel at edge of horn button, and pry horn button and retaining "O" ring out of steering wheel. Then use a suitable puller to remove the steering wheel after steering shaft nut is removed.

1963-65 Plymouth

1. Disconnect battery ground cable.
2. On standard models, remove horn button by turning it ¼ turn counterclockwise and lift it out.
3. To remove horn ring (if equipped), remove two screws from underside of steering wheel and lift off horn ring.
4. Remove steering wheel nut.
5. Use a suitable puller to remove wheel.

TURN SIGNAL SWITCH

1969 All Cars

1. Disconnect battery ground cable.
2. Remove steering wheel as outlined above.
3. Disconnect switch wiring multiple connector at steering column jacket. Remove each terminal from connector, tying them together with a piece of string or fine wire, Fig. 2.
4. Remove screws attaching turn signal switch to steering column and remove switch and wires from column. Leave string or wire in column to aid installation.
5. Reverse procedure to install, using wire or string to pull wires through column. Tighten switch lever to 30 inch pounds, steering wheel nut to 24 foot pounds.

1967-68 All Cars

1. Remove steering wheel as outlined previously.
2. Remove snap ring from upper end of steering shaft.
3. Remove turn signal switch and upper bearing retainer screws.
4. Remove retainer and lift out switch.

1963 Imperial

1. Disconnect battery ground cable.
2. Remove two screws from underside of steering wheel and remove horn blowing actuator and steering wheel cover.
3. Disconnect horn wire at horn sounding switch.
4. Remove horn sounding switch (4 screws).

5. Remove horn sounding switch mounting plate (4 screws).
6. Loosen steering wheel nut several turns and, using a suitable puller, remove steering wheel.
7. Remove turn signal lever.
8. Remove steering column lower cover.
9. Remove two screws and disconnect switch wires and remove signal switch and wires.
10. Reverse above procedure to install.

1963-66 Chrysler

1. Disconnect battery ground cable.
2. Compress and turn horn button ¼ turn counter-clockwise to release button from its retainer.
3. Disconnect horn wire at horn sounding switch.
4. Remove horn ring and switch from steering column (3 screws).
5. Remove steering wheel.
6. Remove turn signal lever.
7. Disconnect turn signal wiring at steering column jacket tube below instrument panel.

NOTE: Attach a piece of string or fine wire to switch wiring before removing switch from steering column. When switch is removed leave string or wire in steering column jacket tube as an aid in replacement of wiring.

8. Remove attaching screws and lift switch off top of steering column.
9. Reverse above procedure to install.

1964-66 Imperial

1. Disconnect battery ground cable.
2. Remove two screws from underside of steering wheel and remove horn sounding actuator and steering wheel cover.
3. Remove steering wheel.
4. Remove turn signal lever.
5. Remove column lower cover.
6. Remove signal switch and wires (2 screws).
7. Reverse above procedure to install.

1966 Dart & Coronet

1. Remove steering wheel and horn switch as outlined above.
2. Disconnect turn signal switch multiple connector at steering column jacket. Remove each terminal from connector, tying them together with a piece of string.
3. Remove screws from steering column and remove switch and switch wires from column. Leave string in column as an aid in installation.
4. Reverse procedure to install.

1966 Polara & Monaco

1. Remove steering wheel and horn switch as outlined above.
2. Remove turn signal operating lever.
3. Disconnect turn signal wiring at steering column jacket tube below instrument panel.

NOTE: Attach a piece of string to turn signal switch wiring before removing switch from steering column. When switch is removed leave string in column jacket tube as an aid to replacement of wire.

4. Unfasten turn signal switch from steering column and remove switch from top of column.
5. Reverse procedure to install.

1966 Plymouth

1. Remove steering wheel and horn switch as outlined above.
2. Disconnect switch multiple connector at steering column jacket. Remove each terminal from connector, tying them together with a piece of string.
3. Unfasten turn signal switch from steering column and remove switch and switch wires from column. Leave string in column as an aid to installation.

1963-65 Dodge

1. Disconnect battery ground cable.
2. On Dart models, pry cap from horn button with a screwdriver. On 1965 Coronet, place steering wheel with cross bars in horizontal position. Disconnect horn wire. Slightly raise horn ring at the seven o'clock position, which will release the retaining tabs. Hold horn ring up and turn counter-clockwise ¼ turn and lift ring from wheel.
3. On all other models with horn ring, remove two screws from underside of steering wheel.
4. Disconnect horn wire from horn switch.
5. Remove horn ring and switch from steering column (3 screws).
6. Remove steering wheel.
7. Remove turn signal lever.
8. Disconnect switch wiring at steering column jacket tube below instrument panel.

NOTE: Attach a piece of string or fine wire to signal switch wiring before removing switch from column. When switch is removed, leave string or wire in column tube as an aid to replacement of wiring.

9. Remove switch from top of steering column.
10. Reverse above procedure to install.

1963-65 Plymouth

1. Disconnect battery ground cable.
2. On Valiant models, pry cap from horn button with a screwdriver. On all other models compress and turn horn button ¼ turn counter-clockwise to release button from retainer. If equipped with horn ring, remove two screws from underside of steering wheel.
3. Disconnect horn wire at horn switch.
4. Remove horn ring and switch from steering column (3 screws).
5. Remove steering wheel.
6. Remove turn signal lever.
7. Disconnect switch wiring at steering column jacket tube below instrument panel.

NOTE: Attach a piece of string or fine wire to signal switch wiring before removing switch from column. When switch is removed, leave string or wire in column tube as an aid to replacement of wiring.

8. Remove switch from top of steering column.
9. Reverse above procedure to install.

INSTRUMENT CLUSTER REMOVAL

1968 Chrysler

1. Disconnect battery ground cable.
2. Remove steering column cover (4 screws).
3. Disconnect one gear shift indicator mounting nut and disassemble gear shift indicator link from indicator shaft.
4. Remove warning light bezel (8 screws).
5. Pull bezel out slightly to disconnect main wiring harness from bezel, then remove light bezel from panel.
6. Remove cluster bezel (8 screws) and pull bezel out slightly to reach and disconnect wire connectors from headlamp, panel dimmer, washer and wiper switches.
7. Remove cluster bezel from panel.
8. Disconnect odometer reset cable.
9. Disconnect speedometer cable.
10. Remove eight cluster mounting screws.
11. Pull cluster out slightly to reach and disconnect ammeter (2 nuts), gasoline gauge, clock and cluster lighting lamps from main harness.
12. Remove cluster from panel.
13. Reverse procedure to install.

1968-69 Dart

1. Disconnect battery ground cable.
2. Remove column opening cover (4 screws).
3. Remove lower column plate (3 bolts) and upper mounting clamp.
4. Remove six cluster mounting screws.
5. Disconnect speedometer cable.
6. Remove fuse block (1 screw).
7. Rock cluster out and release wiring harness from spring clip at back of cluster, then continue to rock cluster out while using a screwdriver to hold harness clear of speedometer.
8. Disconnect left printed circuit board connector and brake system warning light.
9. From front of panel, disconnect right printed circuit board connector and ammeter leads, then complete cluster roll-out.

1968-69 Belvedere & Satellite, 1968 Coronet 440, 500 & 1969 Coronet

1. Disconnect battery ground cable.
2. Remove steering column cover (4 screws).
3. Roll carpeting down and remove steering column cover plate (4 bolts).
4. Remove column clamp at instrument panel (2 nuts).
5. Remove upper trim molding (6 screws if equipped).
6. Remove left side trim molding (1 screw if equipped).
7. Remove left side trim plate (1 screw and 1 T-bolt, if equipped).
8. Remove radio trim plate (2 screws).
9. Remove switch bezel (4 screws).
10. Remove ignition switch.
11. Remove A/C center opening cover (if equipped).
12. Remove lower left trim pad (6

screws from under panel and 4 screws from front of instrument panel).
13. Disconnect speedometer cable.
14. Remove six screws attaching cluster to panel, rock cluster out far enough to reach and disconnect wiring harness and connectors and remove cluster.
15. Reverse procedure to install.

1968-69 Charger & 1968 Coronet R/T

1. Disconnect battery ground cable.
2. Remove steering column opening cover (4 screws).
3. Remove steering column lower support plate (3 bolts).
4. Remove upper mounting bracket support bolts.
5. Disconnect speedometer cable.
6. Remove five screws mounting cluster to panel. A small screwdriver may be used in removing the medallion from the cluster bezel.
7. Release wire harness from retainer clips and roll cluster out of panel far enough to disconnect wiring from ammeter, switches, tachometer, clock, light bulbs and printed circuit board connectors, then complete cluster roll-out.

1969 Monaco & Polara

1. Disconnect battery ground cable.
2. Remove steering column cover.
3. Remove gear shift indicator from the column.
4. Remove lower column floor plate.
5. Remove upper column mounting nuts and lower steering column down to seat.
6. Remove switch and radio bezels, cluster trim pad and trim bezel.
7. Disconnect clock reset cable at the instrument panel lower reinforcement.
8. Disconnect clock lead and remove five cluster mounting screws.
9. Roll cluster out slightly and disconnect the speedometer cable.
10. Disconnect gear shift indicator lamp, main harness and alternator gauge leads and remove cluster.

1969 Chrysler

1. Disconnect battery ground cable.
2. Remove lower steering column cover and shift indicator pointer.
3. Disconnect turn signal wiring connector.
4. Remove outside floor plate mounting bolts, steering column clamp and ground strap and lower column.
5. Remove ash tray, radio and heater controls.
6. Remove vent control mounting screws and allow vent to hang free.
7. Remove map lamp and lamp panel and lay it on top of instrument panel.
8. From under panel, remove four mounting screws from right and accessory switch cover.
9. Disconnect speedometer cable, remove wiring harness from clip on column and remove cluster mounting screws.
10. Move cluster to right, rotating right end to front of car and down.
11. Roll top of cluster down and rock panel slightly left to gain access to wiring. Disconnect wiring and roll cluster out of panel.

1969 Imperial

1. Disconnect battery ground cable.
2. Remove ash tray, radio and heater controls.
3. Disconnect vent control cables at fresh air doors. Remove vent control mounting screws and move control to allow for lamp panel removal.
4. Remove map lamp, lamp panel, cluster bezel, steering column cover, steering column clamp at instrument panel and cover screws at floor panel. Lower column.
5. Disconnect speedometer cable.
6. Remove cluster mounting screws.
7. Move cluster to right, pushing right end of cluster to front of car while turning top of cluster down, then pull left end of cluster out of panel.
8. Disconnect wiring and remove cluster.

1969 Fury & V.I.P.

1. Disconnect battery ground cable.
2. Remove lamp panel, steering column cover and radio trim bezel.
3. Remove left trim bezel and/or spot cooler if so equipped.
4. Remove left and center A/C duct if so equipped.
5. From under panel, disconnect leads to switches, clock and lamp assemblies and disconnect speedometer cable.
6. Remove shift indicator pointer.
7. Remove steering column upper clamp nuts, three bolts at lower support at floor and lower column.
8. Remove cluster mounting screws, roll cluster out, disconnect leads to high beam indicator, fuel gauge, ammeter and temperature gauge and remove cluster.

1968 Monaco & Polara

1. Disconnect battery ground cable.
2. Remove steering column trim plate (4 screws).
3. Remove gear selector indicator link nut and bolt and slip link off indicator arm.
4. Raise floor carpet and remove three steering column support plate bolts at bulkhead. Remove steering column upper clamp nuts and lower column down to seat cushion.
5. Disconnect left spot cooler hose (if equipped) from A/C and heater housing and move hose out from behind cluster.
6. Disconnect speedometer cable.
7. Disconnect clock reset cable (if equipped).
8. Disconnect main harness connector from printed circuit.
9. Remove eight bezel mounting screws (3 in upper center bezel, 3 in upper right trim bezel and 2 in lower center trim bezel).
10. Pull center bezel out slightly and disconnect fader control harness (if equipped).
11. Remove two screws from rear of fader control housing.
12. Slide center trim bezel out of upper molding toward cluster.
13. Remove left trim bezel from panel (4 screws).
14. Remove four screws and pull cluster out slightly and disconnect alternator indicator leads from rear of cluster housing and remove cluster from panel.
15. Reverse procedure to install.

1968-69 Barracuda

1. Disconnect battery ground cable.
2. Disconnect speedometer cable and multiple connector from left printed circuit board.
3. Remove four cluster screws from underside of crash pad and four screws from lower front face of cluster.
4. Remove clock reset cable.
5. Pull cluster out far enough to reach behind and disconnect right printed circuit board multiple connector, ammeter wires, vacuum gauge hose or tachometer wire and emergency switch flaser connector.
6. Loosen A/C or heater knobs and remove from slide control. Remove A/C or heater mounting screws and move control out of the way.
7. Depress headlight switch knob release button on bottom side of switch and pull knob and shaft out of switch. Remove switch bezel and allow switch to remain connected to wire harness.
8. Pull w/s wiper knob from shaft. Remove wiper switch bezel nut and allow switch to remain connected to wire harness.
9. Roll cluster out from panel opening, face down and to the right.

1968 Fury & V.I.P.

Bezel Removal

1. Remove instrument cluster light panel (8 screws) and rest panel on top of trim pad. It is not necessary to disconnect feed wire.
2. Remove heater or A/C control knobs.
3. Remove clock reset knob.
4. Remove bezel (6 screws).

Cluster Removal

1. Disconnect battery ground cable.
2. Remove instrument cluster bezel.
3. Remove four screws in steering column cover and drop cover down with vent controls attached.
4. With automatic transmission and column mounted gear selector, remove gear selector link nut, spring washer and bolt from right side of shift tube.
5. Disconnect speedometer cable.
6. Remove four stereo speaker grille mounting screws and place speaker on top of instrument panel (left side only).
7. Remove five cluster mounting screws, raise up on cluster slightly, roll upper edge out, and disconnect leads at ammeter.
8. With cluster face down, disconnect fuel and temperature gauge wires. Remove high beam, oil pressure and turn signal light sockets.
9. Remove cluster.

1967 Chrysler

1. Disconnect ground cable at battery.

2. Remove steering column cover (4 screws).
3. With automatic transmission and column shift, unfasten and slide shift indicator link off end of indicator quadrant arm.
4. Raise carpet and remove three steering column lower support plate and two column upper clamp bolts.
5. Lower steering column to front seat cushion.
6. Remove seven indicator bezel screws and pull bezel out far enough to disconnect printed circuit board multiple connector and remove bezel.
7. Remove four upper and four lower screws retaining instrument cluster bezel.
8. Pull bezel out far enough to disconnect headlight, panel dimmer, windshield wiper and washer connectors and remove bezel.
9. Remove four upper and four lower cluster mounting screws.
10. Pull cluster out of opening far enough to reach behind cluster to disconnect speedometer cable, ammeter and fuel gauge wires and unplug five cluster bulb sockets.
11. Disconnect speedometer cable by depressing locking tab on flange and pulling straight out of speedometer drive.
12. Remove cluster.

1967-68 Imperial

1. Disconnect ground cable at battery.
2. Tape top of steering column to protect painted finish.
3. Remove steering column trim plate (4 screws).
4. Loosen Allen screw on right underside of column and push gear selector indicator forward and rotate clockwise to remove.
5. Remove steering column upper clamp and allow column to rest in lowered position.
6. If equipped with air conditioning, remove left spot cooler hose at "T" connection under panel by releasing alligator clamp.
7. Remove four upper and lower bezel screws. The four lower screws are located on lower left corner of bezel, each side of column opening and one inside ash receiver.
8. Raise lower edge of bezel and disconnect multiple connectors. Remove vacuum hose from rear air switch (if equipped) by reaching through column opening in panel.
9. Carefully remove bezel with spot cooler hose attached (if A/C equipped).
10. Remove odometer reset cable bezel nut at lower edge of instrument panel and push cable up into panel.
11. Remove eight cluster mounting screws and roll cluster (bottom edge first) out of panel far enough to disconnect multiple connector at printed circuit board. Disconnect speedometer cable by depressing locking tab on ferrule and pulling straight out.
12. Disconnect ammeter wires and remove cluster.

1963 Imperial

1. Disconnect battery ground cable. *If equipped with heater and/or air conditioning, it will be necessary to remove defroster and spot cooler hoses.*
2. Disconnect speedometer cable.
3. Disconnect odometer reset cable at instrument panel cluster.
4. Unfasten (5 screws) and remove instrument cluster by tilting lower edge of cluster outward.
5. For speedometer or complete cluster removal, disconnect all electrical connections, and disengage wire harness loom from clips.

1963-64 Chrysler

1. Disconnect battery ground cable.
2. Remove screws attaching upper and lower mouldings at center of instrument panel. Remove heater bezel and disconnect Bowden cable, vacuum lines, and wiring to heater control switch.
3. Remove instrument panel lower hood.
4. Remove wiper switch knob, retaining bezel and push wiper switch out of instrument cluster.
5. Remove six screws and pull instrument cluster forward to expose speedometer cable. Disconnect speedometer cable.
6. Roll instrument cluster down onto steering column jacket tube and disconnect two printed circuit multi-connectors, heater switch connectors, etc.
7. Remove instrument cluster.

1964-66 Imperial

NOTE: The instrument cluster contains three separate main groups, speedometer, printed circuit and clock. When servicing the cluster it is necessary to remove only the group containing the desired instrument or gauge.

1. Remove instrument cluster chrome bezel.
2. Remove trip odometer (1964) and clock reset knobs and temperature control level knob.
3. Remove lens from cluster. *On 1964, the lens is removed, take note of the small circular spacer around the trip odometer reset knob. This spacer must be installed before the lens is installed.*
4. Remove cluster face plate. Then remove desired cluster as follows:

Speedometer

Disconnect speedometer cable from under instrument panel. Unfasten and remove speedometer.

Printed Circuit

Remove screws attaching printed circuit to cluster. Pull assembly forward slightly and disconnect multi-connector. Remove assembly for service of fuel, oil, temperature or ammeter gauges.

Clock

Remove screws attaching clock to cluster. Pull clock forward and disconnect feed wire. Remove clock.

1965 Chrysler

1. Disconnect battery ground cable.
2. Remove steering column lower access panel. Disconnect wiring to accessory switches (if so equipped).
3. Disconnect gearshift indicator link from steering column and disconnect back-up lamp switch wiring on cars with automatic transmission.
4. Remove two steering column clamp bolts and lower column.
5. Remove steering column upper filler.
6. Remove ignition switch (and accessory switch if equipped) from panel by removing retaining bezel and pushing switch clear of panel.
7. Remove lower, then upper, cluster trim panel.
8. Remove four screws that mount cluster to panel.
9. Lower cluster and disconnect ammeter wires.
10. Remove cluster from under instrument panel.

1966 Chrysler

1. Disconnect battery ground cable.
2. Remove steering column cover.
3. Disconnect gear selector indicator link, remove column clamp and loosen steering column lower support plate to partially lower steering column.
4. Disconnect speedometer, odometer cables and multiple connector at printed circuit board.
5. Remove ignition switch bezel and allow switch to hang under panel.
6. From under cluster, remove two lower trim moulding screws and moulding.
7. Loosen three screws retaining cluster upper trim bezel, two screws (under panel) from steering column filler and instrument bezel. Remove filler assembly.
8. Remove four cluster retaining screws and rotate cluster clockwise around steering column 180 degrees.
9. Disconnect two wires at ammeter gauge terminals and remove cluster.

NOTE: Speedometer head and gauges are removed from front of cluster after separating lens from cluster housing.

1967 Dart

1. Disconnect ground cable at battery.
2. Disconnect speedometer cable and left printed circuit board multiple connector.
3. Remove steering column lower support plate and upper column clamp. Lower column out of the way.
4. Remove four screws from underside of upper lip and two screws from lower lip of cluster.
5. Under instrument panel, remove main wire harness from clip on back of cluster housing just above speedometer head drive. Hold wire harness away from speedometer drive while rolling cluster out of panel (top edge first).
6. With cluster face down in panel opening, disconnect ammeter leads and right printed circuit board multiple connector. Remove cluster from vehicle.

1967 Polara & Monaco

1. Disconnect ground cable at battery.
2. Remove steering column trim plate (4 screws).
3. Remove gear selector indicator link nut and bolt and slip link off indicator arm.
4. Remove retaining screw and move

fuse block down as an aid in disconnecting speedometer cable. Then remove clock reset cable ferrule nut from bottom of instrument panel.
5. Loosen three steering column support plate bolts at bulkhead.
6. Remove column upper clamp bolts and lower column down to seat cushion.
7. Remove four left bezel retaining screws (two in lower face and two in underside of upper lip) and remove bezel.
8. Remove heater or A/C control knobs and three center retaining screws from underside of upper bezel lip. Remove two center bezel lower retaining screws from front face and pull bezel out far enough to disconnect auto pilot light (if equipped) and remove bezel.
9. Remove four cluster retaining screws and pull cluster out of panel opening far enough to reach behind and disconnect two printed circuit board multiple connectors, ammeter wires and clock feed wire (if equipped).
10. Remove cluster from vehicle.

1966 Dart

1. Disconnect battery ground cable.
2. If air conditioned, remove left spot cooler, duct, hose and fuse block.
3. Disconnect speedometer cable.
4. Remove steering column support bracket and lower column support plate at bulkhead.
5. Remove radio control knobs, mounting nuts, ash receiver and housing assembly, and cigar lighter.
6. From under instrument panel, remove nut next to heater blower switch.
7. Remove light switch knob and bezel by depressing release button on switch and pulling out switch knob. Do not remove switch from panel.
8. Remove wiper switch knob and bezel. Do not remove switch from panel.
9. Remove four instrument cluster retaining screws and pull cluster out far enough to disconnect printed circuit board and ignition switch multiple connectors. Disconnect two ammeter wires and remove cluster.

1966-67 Coronet & Charger

1. Disconnect battery ground cable.
2. Remove heater control knobs.
3. Remove radio control knobs and nuts.
4. Open glove box door.
5. Disconnect speedometer cable.
6. Remove wire harness from two clips at steering column bracket.
7. Remove eight cross recessed screws from upper and lower lips of cluster bezel.
8. Carefully pull cluster out to the right, far enough to reach around left end of cluster and disconnect printed circuit board multiple connector.
9. Remove two ammeter wires from terminals, and clock light socket.
10. Roll top of cluster down while working it from the right over open glove box door. Then remove cluster.

1965-66 Polara, Monaco, 880

Instrument Cluster

1. Disconnect battery ground cable.
2. Remove three screws that mount cluster to housing.
3. Roll cluster out and disconnect printed circuit plug and ammeter wires.
4. Remove cluster.

Speedometer Cluster

1. Disconnect battery ground cable.
2. Disconnect speedometer cable.
3. Unfasten cluster from housing (3 screws).
4. Roll cluster out and disconnect printed circuit plug.
5. Remove cluster.

1965 Coronet

1. Disconnect battery ground cable.
2. Remove heater control knob.
3. Remove heater control bezel (2 screws).
4. Remove steering column opening cover from instrument panel.
5. Remove steering column-to-instrument panel support strap.
6. Remove steering column-to-instrument panel lower reinforcement support bracket and drop column slightly.
7. Disconnect speedometer cable.
8. Unfasten cluster from panel (4 screws).
9. Roll cluster out slightly and disconnect heater control cable, printed circuit plug, ammeter wires, heater switch vacuum hoses and two wires to heater switch.
10. Remove instrument cluster.

1965 Dart

1. Disconnect battery ground cable.
2. Loosen steering column clamp screws and lower column slightly.
3. Disconnect speedometer cable.
4. Remove light and wiper switches.
5. Remove four screws on face of cluster and pull cluster forward. Tilt cluster downward and to the right and disconnect lead wires to ammeter, ignition switch, cigar lighter and printed circuit board.

1964 Dodge Except 880

1. Disconnect battery.
2. Remove transmission parking sprag and heater temperature control knobs.
3. Remove heater control bezel.
4. Remove transmission push button bezel.
5. Remove steering column opening cover.
6. Remove steering column-to-instrument panel support strap.
7. Remove steering column lower reinforcement support bracket and drop steering column slightly.
8. Disconnect speedometer cable.
9. Remove four instrument panel attaching screws. Roll cluster out slightly and disconnect heater cable, printed circuit plug, ammeter wires, heater vacuum switch hoses and two wires to heater switch.
10. Remove instrument cluster.

1964 Dodge 880

1. Disconnect battery.
2. Remove six screws attaching cluster housing lower access plate.
3. Working through lower access opening, unfasten cluster bezel from cluster housing (4 screws).
4. Remove parking sprag, temperature control lever and clock reset knobs.
5. Remove cluster bezel.
6. Disconnect wiring terminals at cluster gauges and clock.
7. Unfasten cluster from cluster housing (4 screws).
8. Remove cluster through housing lower access opening.

1963 Dodge

To service any of the instruments, including the speedometer, it is necessary to remove the instrument cluster from the panel. Cover the battery at the ground terminal before removing the cluster.

1. Remove wiper switch knob.
2. Remove wiper switch retaining bezel.
3. Pull headlamp knob to full out position and reach underneath instrument panel and depress spring release button and headlamp switch. With spring release button held down pull out headlamp knob and stem assembly.
4. Remove heater or air-conditioning control knob.
5. Remove sleeve on heater or air-conditioning control lever.
6. Remove four screws attaching instrument cluster trim plate and remove trim plate to expose two lower instrument cluster mounting screws.
7. Unfasten cluster from panel housing (4 screws) and carefully pull cluster forward out of panel housing.
8. Reach over top of cluster and disconnect speedometer cable. Then disconnect wires and remove cluster from vehicle.

1963-64 Dart

1. Loosen steering column clamp screws several turns to lower steering column slightly.
2. Reach up under instrument panel and disconnect speedometer cable.
3. Remove four screws visible on face of cluster and pull cluster forward.
4. Tilt cluster downward and to the right and disconnect wires as required to remove cluster.

1967-69 Valiant

1. Disconnect ground cable at battery.
2. Disconnect speedometer cable and printed circuit board multiple connector.
3. Loosen steering column floor plate attaching screws, remove column upper clamp and allow column to rest in lowered position.
4. Remove six mounting screws from cluster (three in underside of cluster bezel and three in lower edge).
5. Before rolling cluster out of instrument panel, reach behind and above cluster and bend three wire harness clips out of the way. Roll upper edge of cluster out far enough to disconnect ammeter wires, emergency flasher, windshield wiper and headlight switch connectors.

1967 Fury & V.I.P.

Bezel Removal

1. Remove eight cluster light panel screws, remove panel and rest it on top of trim pad. It is not necessary to disconnect feed wire.
2. Remove heater or A/C control knobs.
3. Remove bezel (6 screws).

Cluster Removal

1. Disconnect ground cable at battery.
2. Remove steering column cover (4 screws).
3. With automatic transmission and column shift, remove gear selector link nut and bolt from right side of shift tube.
4. Disconnect speedometer cable.
5. Remove seven cluster mounting screws, raise up on cluster slightly and roll upper edge out.
6. With cluster face down, disconnect ammeter, fuel and temperature gauge wires.
7. Remove high beam, oil pressure and turn signal light sockets.
8. Remove cluster from vehicle.

1966 Valiant

1. Disconnect battery ground cable.
2. Disconnect speedometer cable.
3. Remove steering column clamp and lower column support plate at bulkhead to lower column.
4. Remove four screws and pull cluster out far enough to disconnect printed circuit board and ignition switch multiple connectors.
5. Disconnect ammeter wires and remove cluster.

1966 Barracuda

1. Disconnect battery ground cable.
2. Disconnect speedometer cable.
3. Remove heater control knobs.
4. Remove three screws in heater control bezel and remove bezel.
5. Remove ignition switch bezel.
6. Remove steering column clamp and loosen screws in steering column support plate at bulkhead.
7. Remove four screws and pull cluster out far enough to disconnect the two printed circuit multiple connectors, and ammeter gauge wires.
8. Roll cluster out and remove.

1966-67 Belvedere & Satellite

1. Disconnect battery ground cable.
2. Disconnect speedometer cable.
3. Remove steering column cover and clamp.
4. Remove six screws in upper and lower face of cluster bezel. Pull cluster out far enough to remove multiple connectors from headlight and wiper switches and printed circuit board. Next remove two ammeter gauge wires, heater switch wires and control cables.
5. Remove cluster from car.

1966 Fury

Instrument Cluster

1. Disconnect battery ground cable.
2. Remove five screws from bezel and pull cluster out far enough to provide access to multiple connector and ammeter gauge wires.
3. Disconnect printed circuit multiple connector and two ammeter leads.
4. Remove cluster.

Speedometer Cluster

1. Disconnect battery ground cable.
2. Remove instrument cluster.
3. Disconnect speedometer cable, remove steering column cover plate and gear selector indicator. Then remove steering column bracket.
4. Remove four screws and pull cluster out far enough to disconnect multiple connector and turn signal bulbs from printed circuit board.
5. Remove cluster from car.

1965 Belvedere & Satellite

1. Disconnect battery ground cable.
2. Disconnect speedometer cable.
3. Remove four screws from steering column opening cover to instrument panel.
4. Remove screw on steering column strap and two screws on steering column brace to allow column to drop.
5. Remove heater temperature control knob.
6. Remove heater control bezel (2 screws).
7. Remove four cluster screws.
8. Roll cluster out to allow removal of wires and cables from cluster.
9. Disconnect cable from heater control.
10. Remove two printed circuit board plugs and ammeter wires.
11. Disconnect heater switch vacuum hoses and two wires from heater control.
12. Remove instrument cluster.

1965 Fury

NOTE: For cars with automatic transmission do not drop steering column before disconnecting gear indicator link. The instruments and gauges are contained in two clusters, instruments and speedometer.

Speedometer Cluster

1. Disconnect battery ground cable.
2. Remove steering column cover plate.
3. Disconnect gearshift indicator link at shift tube bracket and disconnect back-up lamp switch wiring (if equipped with automatic transmission).
4. Remove steering column clamp and lower column, taking care to avoid damaging back-up lamp switch.
5. Remove mounting screws. Pull cluster out and disconnect speedometer cable and printed circuit board plug.
6. Remove cluster.

Instrument Cluster

1. Disconnect battery ground cable.
2. Remove four screws, pull cluster out and disconnect wiring to cluster.
3. Remove cluster.

1964 Plymouth

1. Disconnect battery ground cable.
2. Disconnect speedometer cable.
3. Remove four screws from steering column opening cover in panel.
4. Remove screw on steering column strap and two screws on brace to allow column to drop.
5. Remove transmission control sprag arm knob.
6. Remove transmission control bezel (3 screws).
7. Remove heater control knob.
8. Remove heater control bezel (2 screws).
9. Remove four instrument cluster screws.
10. Roll cluster out to allow removal of wires and cables to cluster.
11. Disconnect cable from heater control.
12. Remove two printed circuit plugs and ammeter wires.
13. Disconnect heater switch vacuum hoses and two wires from heater control.
14. Remove instrument cluster.

1963-65 Valiant

1. Loosen steering column clamp screws several turns to lower steering column slightly.
2. Reach under instrument panel and disconnect speedometer cable.
3. Remove four screws visible on face of cluster and pull cluster forward.
4. Tilt cluster downward and to the right and disconnect wires as required to remove cluster.

1963 Plymouth

To service any of the instruments, including the speedometer, it is necessary to remove the instrument cluster from the panel.

1. Disconnect battery cable.
2. Remove heater blower switch knob.
3. Remove temperature control knob.
4. Disconnect speedometer cable.
5. Remove four screws visible on the face of the cluster bezel.
6. Pull cluster assembly forward and tilt it downward to expose wiring harness, connectors and printed circuit.
7. Disconnect wire connectors, snap out lamp sockets and lead wires to clock and ammeter.
8. The instrument cluster can then be removed.

W/S WIPER MOTOR, REPLACE

1963 Imperial

1. Remove glove compartment door.
2. Remove glove compartment.
3. Remove bolts attaching wiper motor bracket to the cowl panel to the instrument panel brace.
4. Disconnect wires at wiper motor.
5. Disconnect links at the pivot cranks. Clips are removed by lifting the top tab and sliding it sideways out of engagement with the groove in the pivot crank pin.
6. Remove the spacing washer and remove the link from the pivot crank.
7. Slide the complete wiper with the links far enough towards the left so the right hand link will clear the glove compartment opening in instrument panel and remove assembly using care so as not to bend the links.

1963-64 Chrysler

1. Disconnect battery negative cable.

2. Remove screws attaching upper and lower mouldings to center of instrument panel. Slip mouldings out from behind passenger assist handle.
3. Loosen screws attaching heater bezel to instrument panel. Do not remove bezel.
4. Remove speaker grille.
5. Remove radio speaker and mounting plate as a unit.
6. Remove glove box.
7. Disconnect wiper links at pivots.
8. Remove panel support bracket from wiper motor mounting bracket to instrument panel lower reinforcement.
9. Disconnect lead wires at wiper motor.
10. Remove three nuts attaching wiper motor bracket to cowl panel.
11. Remove wiper motor with both links attached out through glove box opening and out of right side of vehicle.

1964 Imperial

1. Disconnect battery negative cable.
2. On air conditioned cars remove left spot cooler hose from under instrument panel.
3. Remove right defroster hose.
4. From under instrument panel remove right instrument panel lower reinforcement-to-wiper motor mounting bracket pencil brace.
5. Remove remote trunk lock switch from inside glove box. Unfasten and remove glove box out through its opening (air conditioned cars only).
6. Remove two nuts that attach defroster heat vacuum actuator to mounting bracket and move actuator down out of the way.
7. Disconnect wire leads at wiper motor, and right and left wiper links at wiper pivots.
8. Unfasten and remove motor, mounting bracket and wiper links as an assembly.

1966-69 Chrysler & 1967-69 Imperial

1. Remove wiper arms and blades.
2. Remove windshield lower moulding.
3. Remove cowl grille panel.
4. Remove drive crank from motor (one nut) and disconnect wiring to motor.
5. Unfasten motor from dash panel (3 nuts) and remove motor out through cowl grille panel opening.

1965 Imperial

1. Disconnect battery ground cable.
2. From under instrument panel, remove left spot cooler hose (A/C only).
3. Remove right defroster hose.
4. From under instrument panel, remove right instrument panel lower reinforcement to windshield wiper mounting bracket pencil brace.
5. Remove remote trunk lock switch from inside glove box. Remove glove box (8 screws) through glove box opening (A/C only).
6. From under instrument panel, remove two nuts that attach defroster control vacuum actuator to mounting bracket and pivot actuator down out of the way.
7. Disconnect wiring at wiper motor.
8. Disconnect wiper links at pivots.
9. Unfasten wiper motor mounting bracket from cowl panel.
10. Remove motor, bracket and links as an assembly from under instrument panel.

1966 Imperial

1. Disconnect battery ground cable.
2. If air conditioned, remove right spot cooler hose and distributor duct.
3. From under instrument panel, remove panel lower reinforcement-to-windshield wiper motor mounting bracket pencil brace.
4. Disconnect wiring at motor.
5. From under panel, remove both left and right link-to-pivot retainers.
6. Remove three motor bracket mounting nuts.
7. Carefully work motor and link assembly out from under panel towards right side of car.
8. Remove links and motor mounting bracket.

1967-69 Dart, Charger, Coronet, Valiant, Belvedere & Satellite

Without Air Conditioning

1. Disconnect ground cable at battery.
2. Disconnect wiper motor wire harness at bulkhead multiple connector.
3. From under instrument panel, remove crank arm nut and arm from motor shaft.
4. Remove mounting nuts and work motor off studs.

With Air Conditioning

1. Disconnect ground cable at battery.
2. Disconnect wiper motor wire harness at bulkhead multiple connector.
3. Remove motor mounting nuts.
4. On 1967-68 Coronet, Charger, Belvedere and Satellite, remove instrument cluster to provide access to left pivot.
5. Disconnect linkage.
6. Work motor off mounting studs far enough to gain access to crank arm mounting nut. *Do not force or pry motor from studs as drive link may be distorted.*
7. Remove motor crank arm nut, pry arm off shaft and remove motor.

1966 Coronet & Charger

1. Disconnect battery ground cable.
2. Disconnect motor multiple connector from engine side of bulkhead.
3. Remove three nuts and pull motor out far enough to gain access to drive crank.
4. Rotate crank until drive link retainer is accessible.
5. Using a short screwdriver, carefully pry lip of retainer over drive link pivot pin and remove retainer and spring washer and drive link.
6. Remove motor from car.

1965-69 Polara, Monaco, 880

1. Remove wiper arms and blades.
2. Remove windshield lower moulding.
3. Remove cowl grille panel.
4. Remove nut that mounts drive crank to motor. Remove drive crank and disconnect wiring at motor.
5. Unfasten motor from dash panel (3 nuts) and take motor out through cowl grille panel opening.

1965 Coronet, 1964 Dodge Except 880

NOTE: With air conditioning, wiper motor must be serviced through glove box opening in instrument panel.

1. Remove clips that retain wiper drive links to left and right wiper pivots. Lift drive links off pivot pins.
2. Disconnect wiring at motor.
3. Remove support brace from motor mounting bracket-to-instrument panel reinforcement.
4. Unfasten motor from cowl panel.
5. Remove motor, mounting bracket and drive links as an assembly by carefully pulling assembly down and to the right and out through right door opening.

1964 Dodge 880

1. Remove glove box door and box.
2. Unfasten motor bracket from cowl panel brace.
3. Disconnect wires at motor.
4. Disconnect links at pivot cranks. Clips are removed by lifting the top and sliding it sideways out of engagement with groove in pivot crank pin.
5. Remove spacing washer and link from pivot crank.
6. Slide motor out (with links) far enough to left so that right hand link will clear glove box opening in instrument panel and remove assembly.

1963 Dodge

1. Remove radio speaker grille and speaker. If equipped with padded dash, remove padding to gain access to speaker grille.
2. Remove radio.
3. Remove bolts attaching wiper motor to cowl panel to instrument panel brace.
4. Disconnect wires at wiper motor.
5. Disconnect links at pivot cranks. Clips are removed by lifting top tab and sliding it sideways out of engagement with groove in pivot crank pin. The right pivot may be reached through glove box opening.
6. Tip wiper motor and bracket on its side and remove left link.
7. Remove right defroster tube, and the pencil brace between panel reinforcement and wiper motor mounting.
8. Remove motor and bracket through speaker opening.

1963-66 Dart

1. Disconnect wiper link at motor.
2. Disconnect motor lead wires at motor.
3. Unfasten motor from cowl panel and pull motor out from underneath instrument panel.

1966 Belvedere & Satellite

Without Air Conditioning

1. Disconnect battery ground cable.
2. Disconnect motor multiple connector from engine side of bulkhead.
3. Remove three mounting nuts and pull motor out far enough to gain access to drive crank.
4. Rotate crank until drive link retainer is accessible.
5. Using a short screwdriver, pry lip of retainer over drive link pivot pin and remove retainer and spring washer.
6. Remove motor from car.

With Air Conditioning

1. Disconnect battery ground cable.
2. Disconnect wiper motor harness at bulkhead multiple connector.
3. Remove three wiper motor mounting nuts.
4. Remove instrument cluster.
5. Reaching through instrument cluster opening, remove the drive link retaining clip from left pivot arm. Remove felt washer and drive link from pivot arm pin.
6. Work motor off mounting studs far enough to gain access to crank arm mounting nut. *Do not force or pry motor from studs as drive link might be distorted.*
7. Remove motor crank arm nut and carefully pry arm off shaft and remove motor.
8. Reverse procedure to install.

1965-69 Fury & V.I.P.

1. Remove wiper arms and blades.
2. Remove windshield lower moulding.
3. Remove cowl grille panel.
4. Remove nut that mounts drive crank to motor. Then remove drive crank and disconnect wiring at motor.
5. Unfasten motor from dash panel (3 nuts) and take motor out through cowl grille panel opening.

1965 Belvedere & Satellite, 1964 Plymouth

NOTE: On air conditioned cars wiper motor must be serviced through the glove box opening in the instrument panel.

1. From under instrument panel remove clips that retain wiper drive links to left and right wiper pivots. Lift drive links off pivot pins.
2. Disconnect wiring terminals at motor.
3. Remove support brace from motor mounting bracket-to-instrument panel lower reinforcement.
4. Remove four nuts attaching motor bracket to studs on cowl panel.
5. Remove motor, bracket and drive links as an assembly from under panel by carefully pulling assembly down and to the right and out through right door opening.

1963-66 Barracuda & Valiant

1. Disconnect wiper link at motor. For variable speed motors, note position of follower cam or spring trip.
2. Disconnect motor lead wires at motor.
3. Remove three nuts attaching motor and bracket to cowl panel and pull motor and bracket down from bracket mounting studs and out from underneath instrument panel.

1963 Plymouth

1. Remove radio, speaker grille and speaker. If equipped with padded dash it is necessary to remove padding to allow removal of speaker grille.
2. Remove bolts attaching wiper motor bracket-to-cowl panel-to-instrument panel brace.
3. Disconnect wires at wiper motor.
4. Disconnect links at pivot cranks. Clips are removed by lifting top tab and sliding it sideways out of engagement with groove in pivot crank pin. The right pivot may be reached through glove box opening.
5. Tip wiper motor and bracket on its side and remove left link.
6. Remove right defroster tube, the pencil brace between instrument panel reinforcement and wiper motor mounting.
7. Remove motor and mounting through speaker opening.

W/S WIPER TRANSMISSION

1969 Chrysler, Imperial, Polara & Monaco

To service either the drive link or the connecting link, it is necessary to remove the wiper arms and blades, windshield lower moulding and cowl grille panel to gain access to the wiper system. Before starting the installation procedure, make certain the wiper system is in the "Park" position and the battery ground cable disconnected.

1. With connecting and drive links assembled as a unit, insert links through cowl top opening and bolt pivots in position.
2. Position motor crank arm on motor shaft and tighten to 140 inch-pounds. Reconnect battery ground cable.
3. Test wiper system operation and then replace cowl screen and windshield lower moulding.
4. Using a pin or drill, install and adjust wiper arm and blade assemblies.

1969 Belvedere, Satellite, Barracuda, Valiant, Coronet, Charger, Dart

NOTE: On air conditioned models, after disconnecting the battery ground cable, remove left spot cooler duct and carefully pry the link and bushing from the pivot pin. Remove motor mounting nuts, pull motor away from bulkhead and remove motor crank arm retaining nut and crank arm. Remove drive link assembly from under panel.

On models without air conditioning, remove crank arm from motor, remove drive link from left pivot pin and withdraw assembly from under panel. Remove crank arm from drive link after assembly is removed from vehicle. Connecting link can be removed from pivots by removing glove box and reaching through the opening to pry bushing and link from pivot pin. Withdraw from under left side of panel.

1. Install bushing on motor crank arm pin, position drive link on bushing so large side of pivot bushing faces away from drive crank arm. Large side of bushing will be on same side of link as crank arm retainer.
2. Install spring washer with convex side towards link and install retainer. *If retainer was distorted in removal, it should be replaced.*
3. In heater equipped vehicles, insert drive link assembly under left side of panel, position crank arm on motor shaft, indexing flats on shaft with flats on arm and install retaining nut.

On air conditioned models, install drive link from under instrument panel. Install crank arm on motor shaft from engine side of bulkhead. Secure motor with three nuts. Press plastic bushing over pin on left pivot.

4. Insert connecting link into place with "R" (right side) and "L" (left side) facing instrument panel side. Press link bushings onto pivot crank pins.
5. Reconnect battery cable and test operation. Install glove box if necessary.

1967-68 Chrysler, Imperial, Polara & Monaco

To service either the drive link or the connecting link it is necessary to remove the wiper arms and blades, windshield lower moulding and cowl grille panel to gain access to the wiper system. Before starting the installation procedure, make certain the wiper system is in the "Park" position.

1. With connecting and drive links assembled as a unit, insert links through cowl grille panel opening and install felt washer on pin of right pivot and install one felt washer, link, second felt washer, brass washer and retainer clip. Make certain retainer clip is completely seated on pivot pin.
2. Install left pivot.
3. Position motor end of drive link on motor crank pin and install spring washer with convex side towards link and clip retainer in place on pin. *If retainer clip was distorted in removal, it should be replaced.*

1965-66 Chrysler

To service the drive link or connecting link it is necessary to remove wiper arm and blade assemblies, windshield lower moulding and cowl grille panel to gain access to wiper system. Before starting the installation procedure, make certain the wiper system is in the Park position.

1. With connecting and drive links assembled as a unit, insert links in through cowl grille panel opening and position bushing of connecting link on pin of right pivot and install retainer clip.
2. Install left pivot.
3. Position motor end of drive link on drive crank pin of motor. Make

certain "O" ring, release spring, retainer and cam are in proper positions for variable speed wiper systems.
4. Install cover on mechanism on variable speed systems.
5. Install cowl grille panel, windshield lower moulding and wiper arms and blades.

Variable Speed Wiper 1963-66 Chrysler & Imperial

1. To assemble the linkage, install spring washer with concave surface toward crank arm. Install crank pivot coil spring on pivot, and install spring release.
2. Install parking cam to index with spring release and engage spring ends between release and parking cam in openings at point of index, Fig. 1.
3. When assembling to the left link, the "L" on the left crank and on the parking cam should be seen. The cam marked "R" is installed in the same manner. If the intermediate crank is held so that the letter "L" can be seen from this position, the opposite side will show three letters "R".
4. Install link with stop projection on link arm toward cam assembly. Install spring washer with convex surface toward cam assembly.
5. Install retaining nut and bolt, Fig. 2.
6. Assemble left link and cam assembly in the same manner, locking in place with a clip.

Single Speed Wiper 1963-64

1. Install a felt washer over intermediate crank arm stud.
2. Install right-hand link and another felt washer.
3. Install intermediate crank arm stud (with link installed) on motor crank and secure with nut.
4. Install a felt washer, left-hand link, another felt washer and a shim washer over remaining pin of intermediate crank and secure with clip.

1967-68 Barracuda, Dart, Charger, Coronet, Belvedere, Satellite, Valiant

NOTE: On models with air conditioning, the instrument cluster must be removed to gain access to the wiper system. When installing the links, first make certain that all pins and bushings are lubricated with Multi Purpose lubricant.

1. Install bushing on motor crank arm pin, position drive link on bushing so large side of pivot bushing faces away from drive crank arm. Large side of pivot bushing will be on same side of link as crank arm retainer.
2. Install spring washer with convex side towards link and install retainer. *If retainer was distorted in removal, it should be replaced.*
3. In heater equipped vehicles, insert

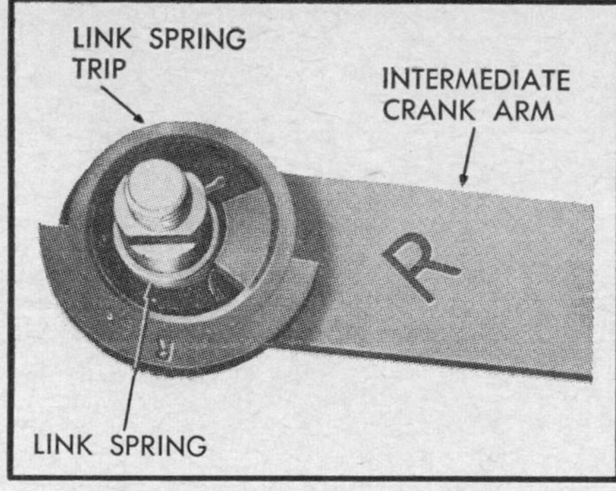

Fig. 1 Variable speed wiper link spring trip installed

drive link assembly under left side of instrument panel, position crank arm on motor shaft, indexing flats on motor shaft with flats on crank arm and install crank arm retaining nut.
4. In Coronet, Charger, Belvedere and Satellite models with air conditioning, install drive link through instrument cluster opening. In Dart and Valiant models, install drive link from under instrument panel.
5. Install motor crank arm on motor shaft from engine side of bulkhead. Position motor on studs and secure with nuts. Install drive link, felt washer and retaining clip on left pivot crank arm.
6. Insert connecting link into place with "R" (right side) and "L" (left side) stamped in link facing instrument panel side.
7. Position felt washers on crank arm pins, install connecting link and felt washers and secure with retainers.

1967-68 Fury & V.I.P.

NOTE: To service either the drive link or the connecting link, it is necessary to remove the wiper arm and blade assemblies, the windshield lower moulding and the cowl grille panel to gain access to the wiper system. The installation is made as follows:

1. Make sure the wiper system is in "Park" position. Then with connecting and drive links assembled as a unit, insert links through cowl grille panel opening.
2. Install one felt washer on pivot pin

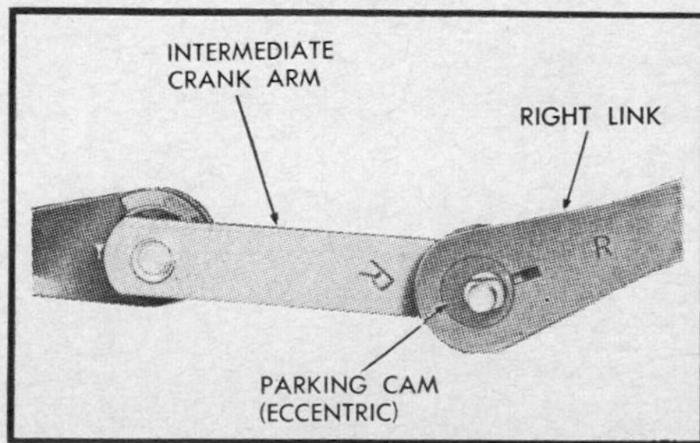

Fig. 2 Variable speed wiper link arm installed

and position bushing of connecting link on pin of right pivot. Install second felt washer, brass washer and retainer clip, making sure clip is completely seated on pivot pin.
3. Install left pivot.
4. Position motor end of drive link on motor crank pin and install spring washer with convex side toward link and clip retainer in place on pin. *If retainer clip was distorted in removal, it should be replaced.*

1965-66 Polara, Monaco, 880 & Fury

NOTE: To service either the drive link or the connecting link it is necessary to remove wiper arm and blade assemblies, windshield lower moulding and cowl grille panel to provide access to wiper system. To make the installation, proceed as follows:

1. With wiper system in "Park" position, insert assembled drive and connecting links through cowl grille panel opening. Position bushing of connecting link on pin of right pivot and install retainer clip.
2. Install left pivot.
3. Position motor end of drive link on drive crank pin of motor. Make certain O-ring, release, spring, retainer and cam are in proper positions for variable speed wiper systems, Fig. 3.
4. Install cover on mechanism on variable speed wiper systems.
5. Install cowl grille panel, windshield lower moulding and install and adjust wiper arm and blade assemblies.

1966 Coronet, Charger, Belvedere & Satellite

REMOVAL: If air conditioned, remove glove box for access to right pivot retainer.
1. Disconnect battery ground cable.
2. Unfasten and move fuse block out of the way.
3. Unfasten motor and pull it out far enough to remove drive link retainer, spring washer and link from drive crank arm. *If retainer lip is distorted in removal it should be replaced.*
4. From under panel, remove left pivot mounting nuts and right pivot retainer.
5. Remove two links and left pivot as an assembly from under panel or through glove box if air conditioned.

INSTALLATION: The connecting link is marked "R" and "L" (right and left) on side facing bulkhead.
1. Install felt washer on pivot farthest from pivot shaft.
2. Install connecting link with "L" facing away from pivot crank.
3. Install outside felt washer and retainer.
4. Install felt washer on pivot pin closest to pivot shaft.
5. Install drive link (small end) outside felt washer and retainer.
6. Install links and left pivot as an assembly under instrument panel.
7. Install left pivot and mounting nuts,

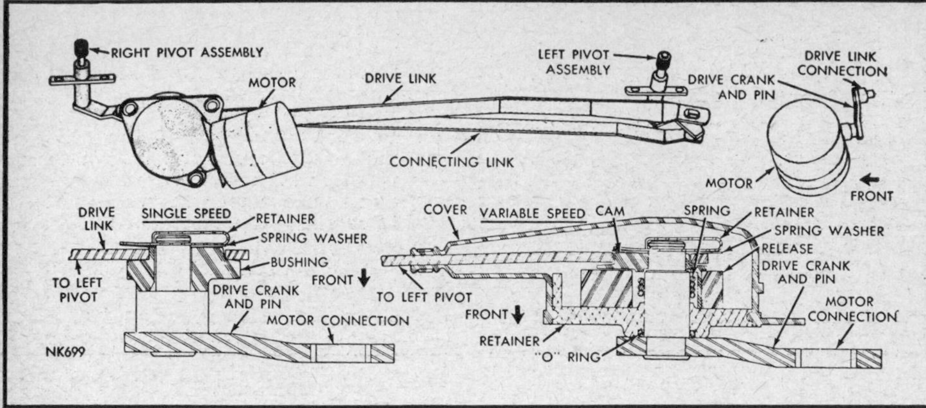

Fig. 3 Windshield wiper system. 1965-68 Chrysler, Imperial, Polara, Monaco, 880, Fury & V.I.P.

connecting link on right pivot and pivot retainer.
8. Through wiper motor opening in bulkhead, install drive link to crank arm and retainer. Lip of retainer must be tight on pivot shaft.
9. Install motor.

1965 Coronet, Belvedere & Satellite

Variable Speed Wiper

1. Install spring washer with concave side toward crank arm.
2. Install spring on pin of crank arm.
3. Install spring trip.
4. Install parking cam to index with spring release and engage spring ends between release and parking cam in openings at point of index, Fig. 1.

NOTE: If intermediate crank is held so that letter "L" is visible, install spring trip so that letter "L" can be seen from that position. The opposite side will show three letters "R", Fig. 2.

5. Install left link with spring trip on link arm toward cam assembly.

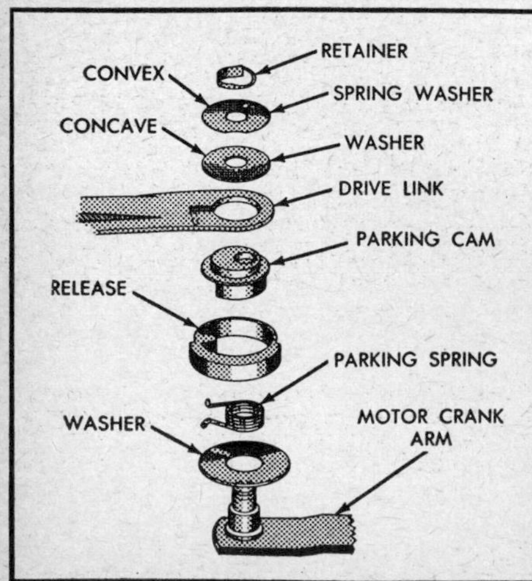

Fig. 4 Variable speed wiper parking mechanism. Dart and Valiant 1965-66

6. Install spring washer with convex side toward cam.
7. Install retaining washer and motor crank arm.
8. Assemble right link and cam in same manner, locking in place with a clip.

Single Speed Wiper

1. Install bushing over intermediate crank arm stud. Follow with left-hand link and retaining washer.
2. Install intermediate crank stud (with link installed) on wiper motor crank and install washer and attaching nut.
3. Install bushing, left-hand link, another felt washer and a shim washer over remaining pin of intermediate crank and install retaining clip.

1965-66 Dart & Valiant

Variable Speed Wiper

1. Install flat washer on motor crank arm pin.
2. Assemble release parking cam and pin of crank arm and install on motor crank arm pin, Fig. 4.
3. Install drive link on motor crank arm pin, making sure parking cam is seated correctly in opening in drive link.
4. Install convex washer and concave spring washer.

Single Speed Wiper

1. Place bushing in end of wiper drive link with spring trip of drive link into keying slot.
2. Install link and bushing on motor crank pin.
3. Install cone washer and retaining clip.

1963-64 Dodge & Plymouth 1963 Dart & Valiant

Variable Speed Wiper

1. To assemble linkage, install spring washer with concave surface toward crank arm. Install crank pivot coil spring on pivot, and install spring release.
2. Install parking cam to index with spring release and engage spring ends between release and parking cam in openings at point of index, Fig. 1.

NOTE: When assembling left link, the "L" on left crank and on parking cam should be visible. Cam marked "R" is installed in same manner. If intermediate crank is held so that letter "L" can be seen from this position, opposite side will show three letters "R".

3. Install link arm with stop projection in link arm toward cam. Install spring washer with convex surface toward cam.
4. Install retaining nut and bolt, Fig. 2.
5. Assemble left link and cam in same manner, locking in place with a clip.

1964 Dart & Valiant

Variable Speed Wiper

1. Referring to Fig. 5, install flat washer on motor crank arm pin.
2. Assemble release, parking cam, parking spring, and install motor on crank arm pin.
3. Install drive link on motor crank arm pin, making sure parking cam is seated correctly in opening in drive link.
4. Install convex washer and concave spring washer as shown.
5. Install retainer on end of motor crank arm pin.

1963-64 Dodge & Plymouth,

Single Speed Wiper

1. Install felt washer over intermediate crank arm stud.
2. Install right-hand link and another felt washer.

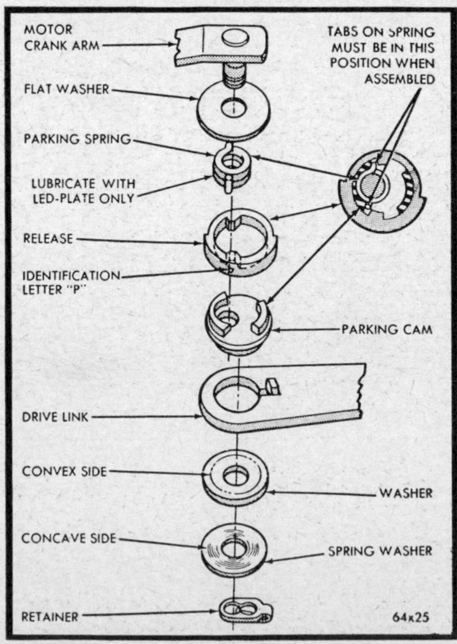

Fig. 5 Variable speed wiper parking mechanism. Dart and Valiant 1964

3. Install intermediate crank arm stud (with link installed) on motor crank and secure with nut.
4. Install a felt washer, left-hand link, another felt washer and a shim washer over remaining pin of intermediate crank and secure with clip.

1963-64 Dart & Valiant

Single Speed Wiper

1. Place nylon insert in end of wiper drive link with metal ear into keying slot.
2. Install link and bushing.
3. Install cone washer and clip.

W/S WIPER SWITCH

1969 Coronet, Belvedere & Satellite

The wiper switch is serviced in the same manner as the headlight switch.

1969 Dart, Barracuda & Valiant

1. Remove air conditioning duct (if so equipped).
2. Loosen set screw and remove switch knob.
3. Remove spanner nut.
4. Remove wiring harness from clip. Disconnect wiring and remove switch.

1969 Polara & Monaco

The wiper switch is serviced in the same manner as the headlight switch.

1969 Fury & V.I.P.

1. Remove all A/C ducts from underside of panel if so equipped.
2. From under panel, disconnect electrical leads.
3. Remove two mounting screws and remove switch.

1969 Chrysler & Imperial

1. Remove lamp panel.
2. Remove instrument panel to gain access to switch.
3. Remove two switch mounting screws and remove switch.

1967-68 Chrysler & Imperial

To service the wiper and washer switches it is necessary to remove the instrument cluster bezel as outlined previously. After bezel is removed, the switches are serviced as follows:

1. Remove eight adapter plate mounting screws, and two rear seat heater switch bezel nuts (Imperial only).
2. Separate adapter plate from bezel and remove switch mounting nut from front side of plate and lift switch from plate.

1968-69 Charger

The wiper switch is serviced in the same manner as the headlight switch.

1968 Coronet & Dart

1. Remove A/C duct (if equipped).
2. Loosen set screw and remove switch knob.
3. Remove switch spanner nut.
4. Remove wiring harness from clip to gain access.
5. Disconnect wiring connector at switch and remove switch.

1968 Fury & V.I.P.

1. Remove steering column cover and drop cover down with vent controls attached.
2. Remove ash tray and housing.
3. Remove left spot cooler hose (if equipped).
4. Using a magnetic screwdriver under instrument panel, remove two switch retaining screws.
5. Move switch out of panel reinforcement and down far enough to disconnect multiple connector. When removing washer switch, the button will remain in the panel behind the bezel.
6. To install the washer switch, it will be necessary to locate switch shaft in button before securing switch to rear of panel.

1967 Dart, Coronet & Charger

The wiper switch is serviced in the same manner as the headlight switch except that the knob is retained on the switch by a set screw.

1967-68 Polara & Monaco

To service either the wiper or washer switch the ash receiver and housing assembly must be removed. On air conditioned cars the distribution duct and push button control bracket must be removed before the ash receiver housing. Remove switch retaining screws by reaching up through ash receiver housing.

1967-68 Barracuda, Valiant, Belvedere & Satellite

On Valiant models with air conditioning, it will be necessary to remove the outlet duct from the lower edge of the instrument panel. Unfasten the duct (2 nuts) and pull duct straight down.

To replace the wiper switch, loosen Allen screw in knob and remove knob. Remove bezel nut, lower switch below panel and disconnect multiple connector.

Connect multiple connector to replacement switch and position in panel opening. Install bezel nut and tighten securely.

1967 Fury & V.I.P.

From under instrument panel, use a magnetic screwdriver to remove two retaining screws. Move switch out of panel reinforcement and down far enough to disconnect multiple connector.

1963-66 Chrysler, Dodge & Plymouth

To remove switch, disconnect lead wires at switch, unfasten switch from its mounting and remove it. Be sure to note color code of wires to be sure they are connected to proper terminals when switch is installed.

1963 Imperial

1. Disconnect battery ground cable.
2. Loosen set screw and remove control knob and windshield washer control stem.
3. Remove bezel nut and dial plate.
4. Remove back dial plate and dial lamp to uncover switch retaining nut.
5. Remove switch from rear of instrument panel. Disconnect wires and connections and remove switch.
6. Remove washer switch from wiper switch.
7. Reverse above procedure to install.

1964-66 Imperial

1. Remove lower steering column cover plate.
2. Remove headlamp switch knob and stem and windshield wiper switch knob.
3. Remove screw that attaches right end of switch bezel to instrument panel. This screw can be reached from inside steering column opening.
4. Remove headlamp switch retaining nut.
5. Lift off switch bezel.
6. Remove headlamp and windshield wiper stem seals.
7. Remove mounting nut from windshield wiper switch, pull switch down and disconnect wiring.
8. Remove switch from under panel.

RADIO REPLACE

NOTE: When installing radio, be sure to adjust antenna trimmer for peak performance.

1969 Polara & Monaco

1. Disconnect battery ground cable.
2. Remove Auto-Temp. control (if so equipped).
3. Remove radio bezel and two radio mounting bolts at front of instrument panel.
4. Remove air conditioning duct (if so equipped).
5. Disconnect electrical leads, loosen radio mounting bracket stud nut and slide radio and stud towards front of car from mounting bracket. Carefully remove radio from under panel.

1969 Dart, Barracuda & Valiant

1. Disconnect battery ground cable.
2. Disconnect electrical leads.
3. From under panel, remove two radio mounting nuts and remove radio mounting bracket. Remove radio down and out from under panel.

1969 Chrysler & Imperial

1. Disconnect battery ground cable.
2. Remove left ash receiver and steering column cover.
3. Unscrew stereo tape reset knob if so equipped.
4. Disconnect all electrical leads.
5. Loosen defroster vacuum actuator and move it to facilitate radio removal.
6. Remove two radio mounting screws through access openings in lower

panel. On search-tune radios, remove knobs bezels and nuts.
7. Remove support bracket screw from lower reinforcement. *Support radio.*
8. Working through ash tray opening, remove support bracket from radio.
9. Remove radio from under panel.

1968 Chrysler

Without Air Conditioning

1. Disconnect battery ground cable.
2. Remove ash receiver from housing.
3. Remove ash receiver housing (6 screws). Lower housing slightly and disconnect the two lamps, then remove housing.
4. Remove knob from heater temperature control arm.
5. Remove blower switch connector.
6. Remove heater control plate attaching nuts and pull controls out of bezel and drop controls down to ash receiver opening.
7. Disconnect all electrical connections, vacuum switch connector and Bowden cable.
8. Remove heater controls through ash receiver opening.
9. Remove fader cover plate (2 screws).
10. Remove reverberator cover plate (2 screws).
11. Remove center bezel (2 screws upper and 1 screw lower). Open glove box and remove center bezel from panel.
12. Remove two mounting nuts from front of panel (attaching radio).
13. Remove radio mounting bracket (1 screw).
14. Reach up through ash receiver opening and disconnect electrical leads and antenna plug.
15. Remove radio by tilting it towards dash panel and slightly towards the right to disconnect stereo plug at radio (if equipped) and remove radio through ash receiver opening.

With Auto-Temp Air Conditioning

1. Remove ash receiver.
2. Remove A/C controls.
3. Remove Auto-Temp lamp.
4. Remove radio knobs and nuts.
5. If equipped, remove stereo switch, upper left, and cover plate upper right.
6. Remove center bezel. Open glove box door to allow clearance and remove center bezel far enough to disconnect center air outlet hose and remove bezel from panel.
7. Remove two screws from front of panel (attaching radio to panel).
8. Disconnect radio mounting bracket from back of radio and swing bracket toward glove box.
9. Reach up through ash receiver opening and disconnect all electrical leads and antenna plug.
10. Remove radio by tilting it toward dash panel and slightly toward right to disconnect stereo plug at radio, and remove radio through ash receiver opening.

1967-68 Imperial

1. Disconnect battery ground cable.
2. Remove screws from bottom of A/C distribution duct and hoses from duct (if equipped).
3. Disconnect heater blower motor wire connectors from resistor.
4. From under instrument panel, disconnect radio feed wires and antenna lead from radio.
5. Remove radio support bracket (right side of radio) from radio and instrument panel.
6. Remove radio knobs and mounting nuts and slide radio down and to the right under panel. Rotate front of radio up and remove from under panel.

1968 Polara & Monaco

1. Disconnect battery ground cable.
2. Disconnect cigar lighter lead and remove ash receiver and housing.
3. Remove automatic temperature control.
4. Remove center air outlets (if equipped).
5. Remove radio mounting bracket (loosen one nut at radio, remove one screw in lower reinforcement and swing bracket toward glove box to clear area for radio removal).
6. Remove eight bezel mounting screws. Pull bezel out slightly and disconnect fader control harness and remove two fader control mounting screws from rear of fader and reverberator housing (if equipped).
7. Remove reverberator knob (if equipped).
8. Slide center trim bezel out of upper molding toward cluster.
9. Remove two radio mounting screws.
10. Reach through ash receiver opening and disconnect antenna lead and electrical leads.
11. Remove radio panel by tipping radio down and lowering through ash receiver opening.

1968 Dart

1. Disconnect battery ground cable.
2. Remove instrument cluster.
3. Unfasten and collapse glove box and remove box from panel.
4. Remove temperature control knobs.
5. Working through cluster and glove box openings, remove two heater or A/C mounting stud nuts and move controls out of the way.
6. Remove center bezel (7 screws).
7. Remove radio mounting bracket.
8. Disconnect speaker and antenna leads.
9. Remove ash receiver (4 screws).
10. Remove two radio mounting screws and remove radio.

1968-69 Charger

1. Disconnect battery ground cable.
2. Remove radio finish plate.
3. On A/C models, remove lower center air duct, left air duct and upper center duct.
4. Remove radio mounting bracket.
5. Unfasten radio from instrument panel (2 screws).
6. Disconnect antenna and speaker leads and remove radio.

1969 Fury & V.I.P.

1. Disconnect battery ground cable.
2. Remove lamp panel and steering column cover.
3. Remove radio trim bezel.
4. Remove center lower A/C duct if so equipped.
5. Disconnect electrical leads.
6. Remove radio support bracket and mounting bolts.
7. Remove radio down through bottom of panel carefully to avoid damage to vacuum and electrical connections.

1969 Belvedere & Satellite, 1968-69 Coronet

1. Disconnect battery ground cable.
2. Remove radio upper trim panel.
3. Remove radio finish plate.
4. Remove radio rear mounting nut from bracket.
5. Disconnect electrical wiring and antenna lead.
6. Remove two screws from front of instrument panel and remove radio.

1968 Fury & V.I.P.

1. Remove lighting hood and instrument cluster bezel.
2. From under bezel, loosen radio support bracket nut at upper end.
3. If so equipped, remove center A/C spot cooler and disconnect left defroster hose.
4. Disconnect feed wires, speaker wires and antenna cable at radio.
5. From front of instrument panel, remove three radio mounting screws and lift radio out of panel.

1967 Chrysler

Thumbwheel Radio

1. Disconnect ground cable at battery.
2. Remove ash receiver and housing.
3. If air conditioned, pry out on lower edge of outlet hose duct adapter and snap out of distribution duct. Remove hose from adapter and pull hose through ash receiver opening without removing hose from center outlet duct. Remove duct (3 screws).
4. Remove screws in each bezel next to map light and remove bezels.
5. Remove two upper radio bezel screws now exposed and remove screw in lower center of bezel.
6. Disconnect antenna cable.
7. Remove radio mounting screws from instrument panel sheet metal.
8. Remove support bracket screw at lower lip of instrument panel and loosen nut on mounting stud at back of radio.
9. Rotate edge of radio out and down far enough to disconnect speaker and feed wires before removing from under panel.

Search Tune Radio

The removal procedure on these units is the same as above except that it is not necessary to remove the radio bezel.

1967 Dart

1. Disconnect ground cable at battery.
2. Remove radio control knobs and mounting nuts.
3. On air conditioned models, remove center outlet duct hose and duct. Also remove right defroster hose and hose bracket in back of radio.
4. From under instrument panel, remove radio support bracket lower screw and upper stud nut. Remove bracket.
5. Lower radio and disconnect feed and speaker wires and antenna cable. Remove radio from vehicle.

1967 Polara & Monaco

1. Disconnect ground cable at battery.
2. Remove heater or A/C control knobs.
3. Remove five center bezel screws (3 in underside of upper lip and 2 in face of bezel) and remove bezel.
4. Remove ash receiver and housing.
5. Disconnect right defroster hose at heater outlet and move hose out of the way.
6. Reaching through ash receiver opening, remove two heater or A/C control mounting nuts and move control assembly out of the way. It is not necessary to disconnect control cables.
7. Disconnect radio feed wires and antenna cable from radio.
8. Remove support bracket upper retaining nut and lower retaining screw and remove bracket.
9. Remove two mounting screws from front of panel and remove radio from under panel.

NOTE: If equipped with air conditioning, it is necessary to remove distribution duct and center outlet assembly from instrument panel.

1967 Fury & V.I.P.

1. Remove instrument cluster bezel as outlined previously.
2. From under panel, loosen radio support bracket nut at upper end.
3. Disconnect feed wires, speaker wires and antenna cable at radio.
4. From front of instrument panel, remove three mounting screws and lift radio out of panel.

1963 Imperial

1. Disconnect battery.
2. Remove radio-to-dash support bracket.
3. Remove two screws attaching fuse block to instrument panel and lower the fuse block.
4. Disconnect "A" lead, light lead, speaker leads, antenna leads and foot selector switch connector.
5. Remove radio assembly from bottom of instrument panel.

1963-64 Chrysler

1. Disconnect battery ground cable.
2. Remove upper and lower instrument panel mouldings.
3. Remove speaker grille.
4. Remove speaker and mounting plate attaching screws.
5. Remove speaker.
6. Disconnect the "A" lead, light lead, antenna lead, and foot selector switch lead (if equipped).
7. Remove control knobs and shaft mounting nuts.
8. Remove radio-to-dash support brackets and remove radio through opening at instrument panel.

1964-66 Imperial

1. Disconnect battery ground cable.
2. Unfasten and lower ash receiver and disconnect turn signal flasher and ash receiver lamp wiring.
3. Remove ash receiver.
4. Remove radio-to-instrument panel lower reinforcement mounting bracket and remove bracket.
5. Disconnect antenna lead, speaker leads and radio feed wire.
6. Remove pencil brace from instrument panel lower reinforcement to dash panel. This brace is located just to the left of radio.
7. Remove radio control knobs and mounting nuts.
8. Pull radio out of panel opening and rotate it 90 degrees so its face is to the right of vehicle, then carefully remove radio from under instrument panel.

CAUTION: Do not operate radio with speaker detached, since damage to transistors may result. If rear seat speaker is disconnected from the radio, insert a jumper wire in rear speaker socket to allow receiver to operate.

1965-66 Chrysler

NOTE: On cars with air conditioning, it is necessary to remove the center air conditioning outlet hose.

1. Disconnect battery ground cable.
2. Remove ash receiver and housing.
3. Remove radio control knobs.
4. Remove radio mounting nuts.
5. Working through ash receiver opening, disconnect speaker leads, radio feed wire and antenna lead cable.
6. Remove radio-to-instrument panel mounting bracket.
7. Remove radio through ash receiver opening.

1966 Dart

1. Disconnect battery ground cable.
2. If air conditioned, remove spot cooler and tubes.
3. Disconnect antenna, speaker and power supply leads.
4. Remove radio control knobs and nuts.
5. Remove radio support bracket.
6. Rotate front edge of radio down and remove from under panel.

1966-67 Charger & Coronet

1. On air conditioned models it is necessary to remove the instrument cluster. Then, after disconnecting the antenna leads and feed wires, loosen radio bracket upper support nut and remove radio through cluster opening. On models without A/C, proceed as follows:
2. Disconnect battery ground cable.
3. Remove upper half of glove box and disconnect speaker leads from speaker terminals.
4. Remove radio control knobs and two mounting nuts.
5. Disconnect both defroster hoses at heater.
6. Disconnect antenna cable and radio feed wires at connector.
7. Loosen radio support bracket retaining nut at radio and remove support bracket mounting screw from lower edge of instrument panel.
8. Remove radio from under instrument panel.

1966 Monaco & Polara

1. Disconnect battery cable.
2. Remove radio control knobs.
3. Remove radio mounting nuts.
4. If air conditioned, remove distributor duct and three spot cooler hoses.
5. From under instrument panel, disconnect speaker leads, radio feed wire and antenna lead cable at radio.
6. Remove radio-to-instrument panel mounting bracket and remove radio.

1965 Dart

1. Disconnect battery ground cable.
2. Remove radio control knobs.
3. Disconnect radio feed wire at connector.
4. Remove bottom screw from radio mounting bracket.
5. Remove left defogger tube.
6. Loosen top screw on radio mounting bracket and remove bracket.
7. Disconnect antenna and speaker leads.
8. Remove mounting nuts from front of radio and remove radio bezel.
9. Remove radio from below panel.

1965 Polara, Monaco, 880

NOTE: If equipped with air conditioning, remove center air conditioning outlet hose.

1. Disconnect battery ground cable.
2. Remove radio control knobs.
3. Remove radio mounting nuts.
4. Disconnect speaker leads, radio feed wire and antenna lead cable at radio.
5. Remove radio-to-instrument panel bracket and remove radio.

1965 Coronet, 1964 Dodge Except 880

NOTE: If equipped with air conditioning, radio is serviced through glove box opening in instrument panel.

1. Disconnect battery ground cable.
2. Remove radio control knobs.
3. Disconnect radio feed wire at fuse block.
4. Disconnect radio and speaker leads.
5. Remove screw attaching radio mounting bracket to instrument panel lower reinforcement.
6. Remove top screw on mounting bracket and take out bracket.
7. Remove two nuts from front of radio and remove radio from under instrument panel.

1964 Dodge 880

1. Disconnect battery ground cable.
2. Disconnect antenna lead, radio feed wire, radio light wire and speaker leads.
3. Remove ash tray.
4. Remove radio mounting screws through ash tray opening.
5. Remove radio-to-instrument panel lower reinforcement mounting bracket.
6. Remove radio from under instrument panel.

1964 Dart

1. Disconnect battery ground cable.
2. Remove radio control knobs.
3. Disconnect radio feed wire at fuse block.
4. Remove bottom screw from radio mounting bracket.

5. Remove left defogger tube.
6. Loosen top screw and remove radio mounting bracket.
7. Disconnect antenna and speaker leads.
8. Remove radio bezel.
9. Remove radio from below instrument panel.

1963 Dodge

1. Disconnect battery ground cable.
2. Remove radio speaker grille. On units equipped with padded dash, remove padded dash to gain access to speaker grille.
3. Remove radio speaker.
4. Remove control knobs from radio.
5. Remove mounting nuts from front of radio.
6. Remove radio mounting bracket lower screw.
7. Loosen radio mounting bracket top screw and remove bracket.
8. Remove right defroster tube.
9. Disconnect antenna lead.
10. Lift radio through speaker opening and disconnect radio wires at fuse block.
11. Remove radio assembly.

1963 Dart

1. Disconnect battery ground cable.
2. Remove radio control knobs.
3. Remove two screws mounting heater control bezel to panel and remove bezel.
4. Remove bottom screw from radio mounting bracket.
5. Remove left defroster tube.
6. Loosen top screw on radio mounting bracket and remove bracket.
7. Disconnect speaker and antenna leads.
8. Remove mounting nuts from front of radio.
9. Remove radio bezel.
10. Lower radio and disconnect radio power feed cable.
11. Remove radio from under panel.

1966-68 Valiant & Barracuda

NOTE: On air conditioned models it is necessary to remove the two outlet duct retaining nuts and remove duct. Also remove the right defroster hose and hose bracket in back of radio.

1. Disconnect battery ground cable.
2. Remove radio control knobs.
3. Remove bottom screw from radio mounting bracket.
4. Remove left defroster tube.
5. Loosen top screw on radio mounting bracket and remove bracket.
6. Disconnect speaker and antenna leads.
7. Remove mounting nuts from front of radio.
8. Remove radio bezel.
9. Lower radio and disconnect radio power feed cable.
10. Remove radio from under panel.

1966-68 Belvedere & Satellite

1. Disconnect battery ground cable.
2. If air conditioned, remove spot cooler hoses and distribution duct.
3. Remove control knobs, two mounting nuts and bezel.
4. From under instrument panel, disconnect speaker, power and antenna leads.
5. Remove support bracket and radio.

1966 Fury

1. Disconnect battery ground cable.
2. Remove control knobs and two mounting nuts.
3. If air conditioned, remove transition duct and two spot cooler hoses before disconnecting speaker, power supply and antenna leads.
4. Remove radio support bracket.
5. Rotate front end of radio down and remove it from under panel.

1965 Fury

NOTE: If equipped with air conditioning, radio is serviced through glove box opening in instrument panel. **CAUTION:** Do not operate radio with speaker detached since damage to transistors may result.

1. Disconnect battery ground cable.
2. Remove radio control knobs.
3. Remove radio mounting nuts.
4. From under instrument panel, disconnect speaker leads, radio feed wire and antenna lead cable at radio.
5. Remove radio-to-instrument panel bracket and take out radio.

1965 Belvedere & Satellite

NOTE: If equipped with air conditioning, radio is serviced through glove box opening in instrument panel.

1. Disconnect battery ground cable.
2. Remove radio control knobs.
3. From under instrument panel, disconnect radio feed and alumination wires at fuse block.
4. Disconnect antenna and speaker leads.
5. Remove screws attaching radio mounting bracket to instrument panel lower reinforcement.
6. Loosen top screw on radio mounting bracket and remove bracket.
7. From front of radio, remove two nuts attaching radio to instrument panel and remove radio.

1965 Valiant

1. Disconnect battery ground cable.
2. Remove radio control knobs.
3. Remove bottom screw from radio mounting bracket.
4. Remove left defroster tube.
5. Loosen top screw and remove radio mounting bracket.
6. Disconnect speaker and antenna leads.
7. Remove radio front mounting nuts.
8. Remove radio bezel.
9. Lower radio and disconnect power feed cable.
10. Remove radio from under instrument panel.

1964 Plymouth

NOTE: For air conditioned cars the radio is serviced through glove box opening in instrument panel.

1. Disconnect battery ground cable.
2. Remove radio control knobs.
3. Disconnect radio feed and radio light wires at fuse block.
4. Disconnect antenna and speaker leads.
5. Remove screw attaching radio mounting bracket to instrument panel lower reinforcement.
6. Loosen top screw and remove mounting bracket.
7. From front of radio remove two nuts attaching radio to panel and remove radio from under panel.

1963-64 Valiant

1. Disconnect battery ground cable.
2. Remove radio control knobs.
3. Remove heater control bezel from panel (2 screws).
4. Remove bottom screw from radio mounting bracket.
5. Remove left defroster tube.
6. Loosen top screw on radio mounting bracket and remove bracket.
7. Disconnect speaker and antenna leads.
8. Remove mounting nuts from front of radio.
9. Remove radio bezel.
10. Lower radio and disconnect power feed cable.
11. Remove radio from under panel.

1963 Plymouth

1. Disconnect battery ground cable.
2. Remove radio speaker grille. If equipped with padded dash, remove padding to gain access to speaker grille.
3. Remove radio speaker.
4. Remove radio control knobs and mounting nuts from front of radio.
5. Loosen radio mounting bracket top screw and remove bracket.
6. Remove right defroster tube.
7. Disconnect antenna lead.
8. Lift radio to speaker opening and disconnect radio wires at fuse block.
9. Remove radio assembly.

HEATER CORE REMOVAL

Before attempting to remove a heater core, disconnect one of the battery cables, drain the radiator and remove inlet and outlet hoses from heater assembly in engine compartment.

1963-64 Chrysler & Imperial

Separate heater housing and core from engine side of dash by removing attaching screws. Core is retained in housing with plastic rivets covered over with mastic (1963), steel screws (1964). Use care when pressing out rivets to avoid damaging housing or rivets.

1963-64 Dodge & Plymouth

Remove fresh air intake duct from blower and remove screw at blower bracket. Disconnect lines, cable and ground wire, then remove defroster tubes. From engine side of cowl, remove nuts that attach heater to cowl, then take out heater. Next, remove temperature control valve from housing. This permits separating core from heater housing.

1963-64 Dart & Valiant

Remove seal and retainer plate of blower motor. Inside car, disconnect wiring and cables at heater, then remove defroster

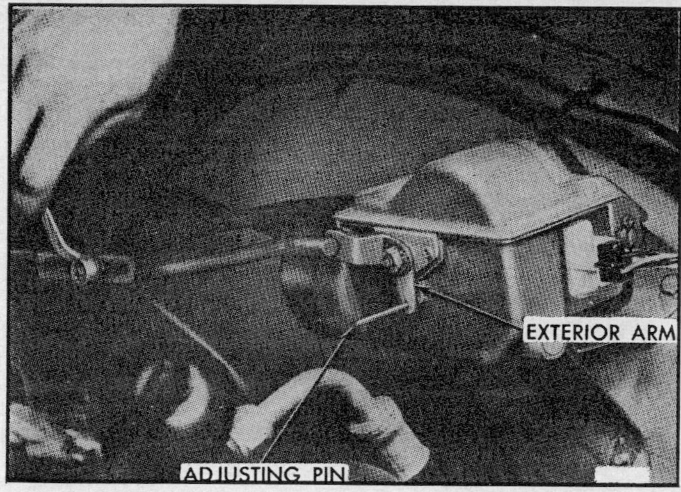

Fig. 6 Auto Pilot accelerator linkage adjustment. 1967

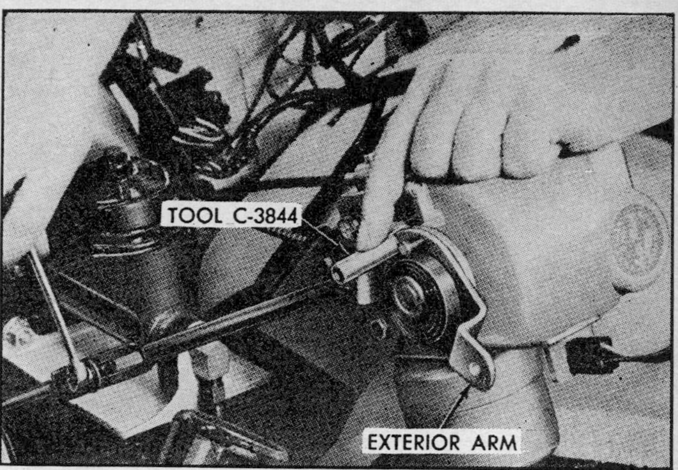

Fig. 7 Auto Pilot accelerator linkage adjustment. 1964-66

tubes. To take off heater housing, disconnect two support rods at right-hand fresh air duct. When this is done, take out heater motor and fan from housing, then remove seal of fresh air duct from either inner or outer half of housing only. Separate halves to gain access to core.

1965-66 Imperial

Remove screws attaching heater core housing to dash panel and remove housing and core as a unit. Then remove mastic material covering core mounting screws. Remove screws and lift out heater core.

1969 Chrysler, Imperial, Polara, Monaco, Fury & V.I.P.

From under dash, remove antenna lead, vacuum hoses from trunk lock and electrical connectors from blower motor resistor block. Remove vacuum hoses from defroster actuator and heater shutoff door actuator. Remove bottom retaining nut from support bracket and swing bracket up out of the way.

In engine compartment, remove retaining nuts from housing. Remove locating bolt from under bottom center of passenger side housing. Roll or tip housing out from under panel and remove temperature control cable from door crank. Remove retaining screws and nuts and remove core.

1965-68 Chrysler, Imperial, Polara, Monaco Fury & V.I.P.

From under dash remove bracket from top of heater to dash panel, defroster hoses at heater end, actuator vacuum hoses, and wiring at blower motor resistor. Next, remove glove box and then disconnect control cables at heater end. Unclamp flexible connector at right end of heater but do not remove connector from side cowl.

From engine side of dash, remove three nuts that secure heater to dash. Then from inside car, pull heater toward rear of vehicle until studs are clear. Rotate assembly until studs are down and remove heater from car. Take off heater cover plate, remove heater core mounting screws and lift out core.

Chrysler & Imperial Rear Seat Heater

To remove core from rear seat heater on 1966-69 models, from under car, remove heater hose and tubing support clamps at rear of floor pan and drain system. Then remove rear seat cushion and seat back. From inside car remove hoses from heater, and spare tire from trunk. Disconnect motor feed wire, fresh air intake hose and floor air duct hoses from heater. Take out three metal screws from heater mounting brackets and remove heater assembly. With heater on bench, remove 11 screws from end plate and take off plate. Then remove four screws retaining heater core to heater body and lift out core.

1965-69 Dart & Valiant

Remove heater motor seal and retainer plate from right side of dash in engine compartment. Then disconnect all control cables from heater assembly, along with heater motor resistor wire and defroster tubes. Remove heater housing support rod from fresh air duct and take out heater assembly.

To get at the core, remove retaining clips from two halves of heater housing and separate halves. Then remove screw attaching seal retainer and seal around the heater core tubes. Take off heater core support clamp, remove screws attaching heater core to heater and lift out core.

1965 Belvedere & Coronet

Remove air intake duct from blower-to-plenum bracket screw. Then disconnect actuator lines and heater wire receptacle from left side of heater. Take off heater ground wire, control cable from heater control valve and defroster tubes from heater housing.

From the engine compartment, remove three nuts and screws attaching heater to dash and lift out heater assembly. Next, remove retaining screws and heater control valve by pulling valve straight out from housing. Valve is held in place by an O-ring only. Take out screws attaching heater core to heater housing and remove core.

1966-69 Belvedere, Satellite, Charger & Coronet

On models equipped with console shift, it is necessary to move console rearward before removing heater. After doing this, remove upper half of glove box and then take off heater-to-cowl support bracket. Next, disconnect defroster hoses, wiring from heater motor resistor, fresh air vent control, and cables for shut-off door at heater end.

Now, reach through glove box door and disconnect cable from temperature control door. From engine compartment, remove three nuts that retain heater assembly to firewall. Then rotate heater assembly until mounting studs are up and lift heater assembly from under dash. To remove core, take off heater cover from front of heater and take out core mounting screws.

SPEED CONTROLS

1963-67 Auto Pilot Accelerator Linkage

Before attempting to adjust the accelerator linkage, the carburetor must be at curb idle position with the choke completely open. Then operate the linkage by moving the Auto Pilot exterior arm several times, allowing linkage to ease into normal position. *Do not force linkage to close throttle.*

1967 Adjustment, Fig. 6

1. Loosen locknut on Auto Pilot linkage rod and insert a ⅛" diameter rod through hole in exterior arm and into hole in Auto Pilot housing.
2. Hold exterior arm and tighten locknut on linkage.

1964-66 Adjustment, Fig. 7

1. Loosen locknut on Auto Pilot linkage rod and insert locking arm gauge Tool C-3844 or equivalent over stop stud on Auto Pilot.
2. Hold exterior arm against gauge pin and tighten locknut on linkage. This will provide proper clearance between stop stud and exterior arm with carburetor in idle position.

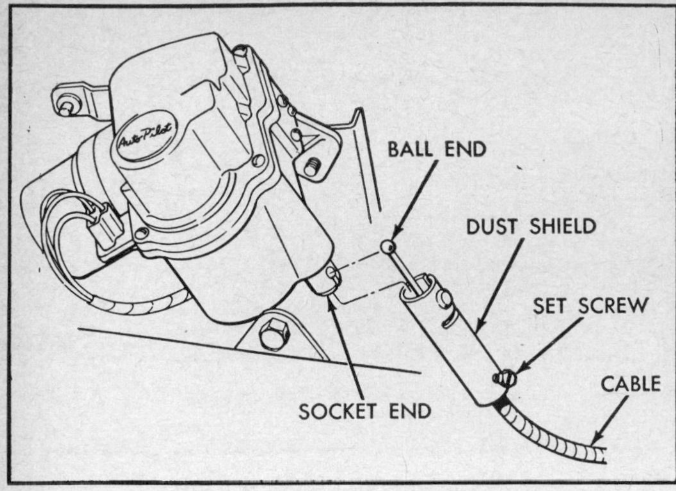

Fig. 8 Auto Pilot control cable and dust shield. 1964-66

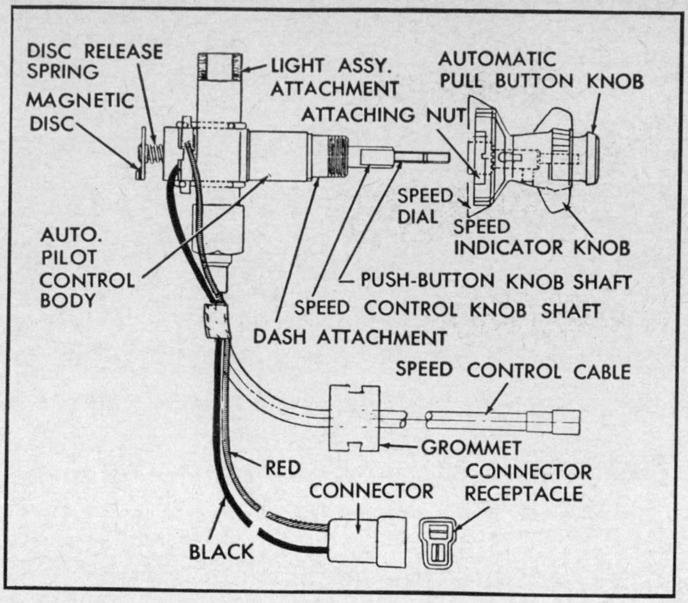

Fig. 9 Auto Pilot selector control assembly. 1963

1963 Adjustment

1. Adjust throttle control rod.
2. Start engine and operate at slow idle.
3. Remove cotter pin securing trunnion on exterior arm plate, remove washers and separate linkage from exterior arm.
4. Insert locking arm gauge tool (see Fig. 7) or equivalent over stop stud and hold exterior arm securely against gauge.
5. Turn trunnion until it aligns with and enters hole in exterior arm freely, making certain arm is still against gauge when trunnion is inserted.
6. Install washers on trunnion and secure with cotter pin.
7. Remove gauge and shut off engine.

Control Cable

1964-66 Adjustment, Fig. 8

1. Loosen but do not remove set screw on dust shield.
2. Rotate instrument panel control dial counterclockwise until it contacts internal stop.
3. Push in lightly on control cable at dust shield. This will position control rod, to which inner cable attaches, against its upper stop. *Do not force cable beyond this position.*
4. Make certain control dial is still in its extreme counterclockwise stop.
5. Tighten screw on dust shield securely. *A correctly adjusted control cable will not spring back on full rotation in either direction.*

1963 Adjustment, Fig. 9

1. Loosen set screw on end of dust shield and work control cable back and forth, making certain the ferrule on end of cable is free to move when dial is rotated.
2. Rotate selector dial backward to "low" position, or as far as it will go without forcing.
3. Carefully insert ferrule back into dust shield without forcing until ball socket just bottoms in housing. After positioning ferrule in dust shield, test selector dial to be sure it is still in the extreme low speed position.
4. Tighten set screw securely on end of dust shield, being careful not to change cable position when tightening set screw.

Brake Switch Adjustment

It is important that the brake switch adjustment be carefully performed to insure proper Auto Pilot operation. With a test lamp connected to the blue wire side of switch, Fig. 10, test lamp should go out with approximately ¼ to ½ inch of brake pedal movement. To replace the brake switch, brake pedal and bracket assembly will have to be removed.

1968-69 Speed Control

Servo Adjustments

There are three adjustment set screws in the servo housing, Figs. 11, 12 and 13. The adjustment of these set screws have been factory set and under normal conditions there should be no need for altering the factory setting during the life of the vehicle.

Need for adjustment can be determined only after accurate diagnosis of the system operation. If adjustment is found to be necessary, perform the appropriate adjustment outlined below; if screw is loose stake side of servo housing adjacent to screw to insure a snug fit.

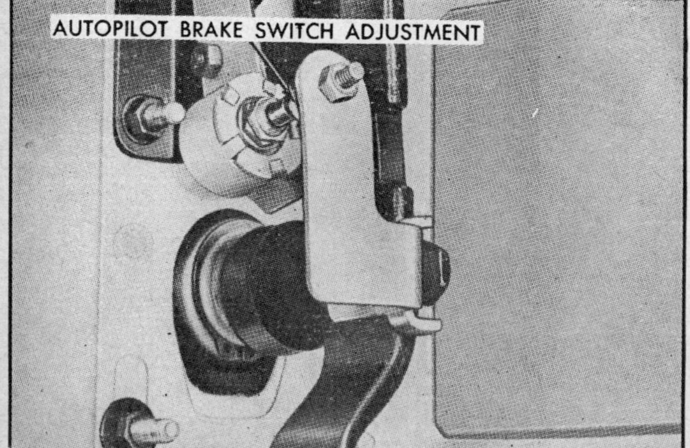

Fig. 10 Auto Pilot brake switch

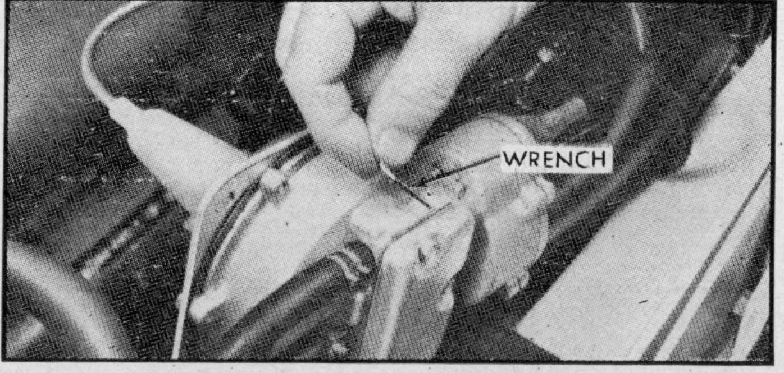

Fig. 11 Speed Control lock-in screw adjustment. 1968-69

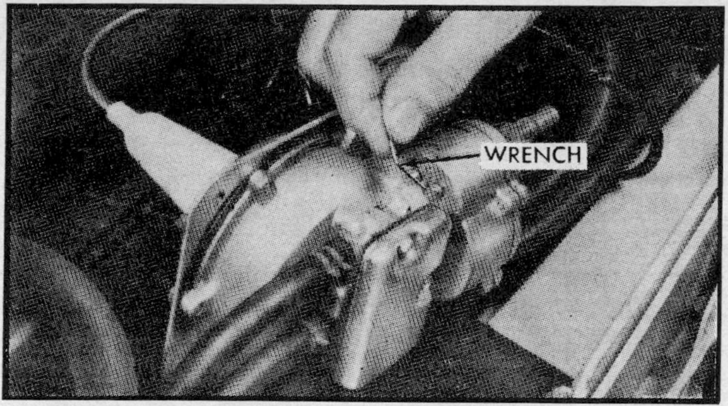

Fig. 12 Speed Control cut-in screw adjustment. 1968-69

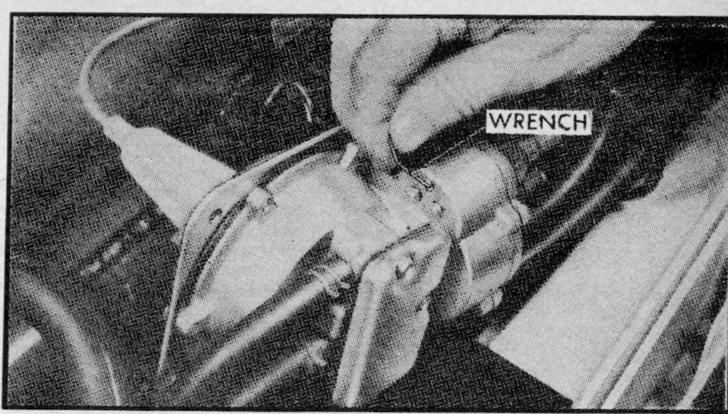

Fig. 13 Speed Control cut-out screw adjustment. 1968-69

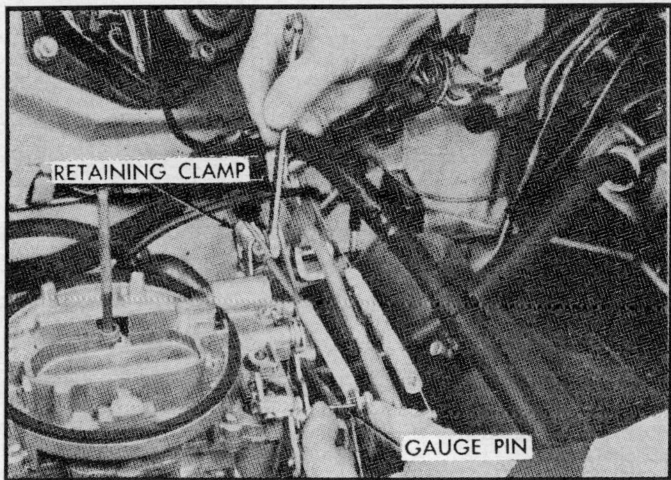

Fig. 14 Speed Control servo cable throttle adjustment. 1968-69

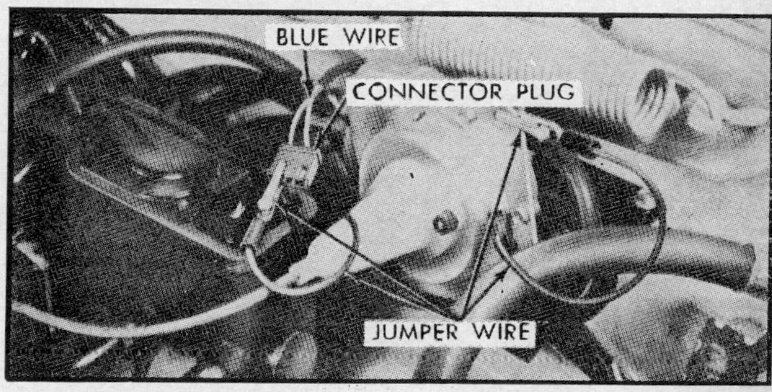

Fig. 15 Speed Control brake switch adjustment. 1968-69

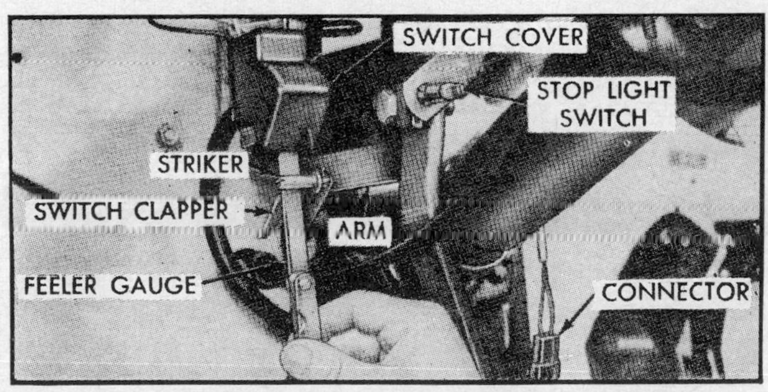

Fig. 16 Checking clapper and striker pin clearance on intermediate size cars. 1968-69 Speed Control

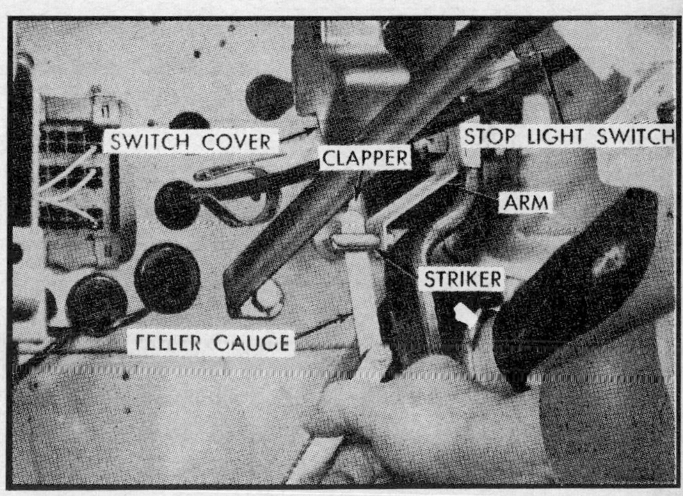

Fig. 17 Checking clapper and striker pin clearance on full size cars. 1968-69 Speed Control

Lock-In Screw Adjustment, Fig. 11

Lock-in accuracy will be affected by poor engine performance (need for tune-up), loaded gross weight of car (trailering), improper slack in control cable. After the foregoing items have been considered and the speed sags or drops more than 2 to 3 mph when the speed control is activated, the lock-in adjusting screw should be turned counter-clockwise approximately ¼ turn per one mph correction required.

If a speed increase of more than 2 to 3 mph occurs, the lock-in adjusting screw should be turned clockwise ¼ turn per one mph correction required.

CAUTION: This adjustment must not exceed two turns in either direction or damage to the unit may occur.

Cut-In Speed Adjustment, Fig. 12

This adjustment regulates the minimum road speed at which the low speed inhibit switch allows the speed control to be activated. This should range from 25 to 33 mph. If cut-in speed is too low, turn set screw counter-clockwise. If too high, turn set screw clockwise. Make adjustments in ⅛ turn increments; total adjustment must not exceed two turns.

Cut-Out Adjustment, Fig. 13

This adjustment affects the road speed at which the system is deactivated during deceleration. Turning the screw clockwise increases road speed at which the system deactivates (cuts out). A counter-clockwise adjustment decreases the cut-out speed. The desired cut-out speed should occur approximately 5 mph below the cut-in setting. Make adjustments in 1/8 turn increments; total adjustment must not exceed two turns.

Throttle Cable Adjustment, Fig. 14

Optimum servo performance is obtained with a given amount of free play in the throttle control cable. To obtain proper free play, insert a 1/16" diameter pin between forward end of slot in cable end of carburetor linkage pin (hair pin clip removed from linkage pin). With choke in full open position and carburetor at curb idle, pull cable back toward dash panel without moving carburetor linkage until all free play is removed. Tighten cable clamp bolt to 45 inch-pounds, remove 1/16" pin and install hair pin clip.

Brake Switch Adjustment

1. Disconnect harness connector at speed control servo and run a jumper wire from the blue wire terminal of connector to a good ground, Fig. 15.
2. Turn ignition key to accessory position, depress and release turn signal lever push button and check clearance between engaged actuator arm and striker pin on brake pedal, Figs. 16 and 17. Clearance should be .070" to .100".
3. If clearance is not correct, loosen striker pin attaching nut and move pin to obtain this clearance. Then tighten nut securely, insuring that the adjusted clearance is maintained.

NOTE: Before making the low speed inhibit switch adjustment, check speedometer cables to assure proper core length so that both cable drive ends are properly engaged in servo shaft keyways without binding. Also be sure that cable ferrule nuts are properly positioned on servo pilot diameters and nuts properly tightened.

Engine Section

ENGINE, REPLACE

1963-69 Chrysler & Imperial

In addition to the usual items such as fuel lines, linkage, propeller shaft, etc., perform the following:

1. Scribe a line on hinge brackets on hood to assure proper adjustments when installing. Then remove hood.
2. Remove battery, drain cooling system, remove all hoses, fan shroud, disconnect oil cooler lines and remove radiator.
3. Attach lifting fixture to carburetor flange studs on intake manifold.
4. Raise vehicle on hoist and install an engine support fixture on frame to support rear of engine.
5. Drain transmission and torque converter.
6. Remove engine rear support crossmember and transmission.
7. Lower vehicle and attach chain hoist to fixture eyebolt.
8. Remove engine front mounting bolts. Then raise and work engine out of chassis.

Dodge & Plymouth 1963-69 V8s

1. Scribe hood hinge outlines on hood and remove hood.
2. Drain cooling system and remove battery.
3. Remove fan shroud (if equipped) and radiator.
4. Disconnect fuel lines and wiring to engine.
5. Remove carburetor. Attach engine lifting fixture to carburetor flange studs on intake manifold.
6. Remove engine front mounting nuts.
7. Disconnect propeller shaft and tie out of the way.
8. Disconnect wires and linkage at transmission.
9. Disconnect exhaust pipes at manifold.
10. Attach engine support fixture and remove engine rear crossmember.
11. Remove transmission.
12. Lift engine out of chassis.

6-170, 225

1. Scribe hood hinge outlines on hood and remove hood.

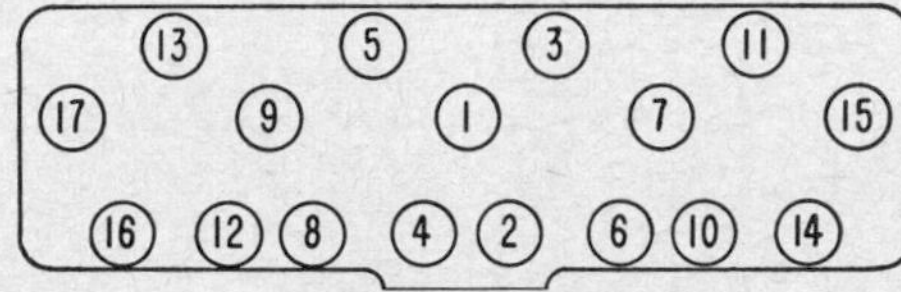

Fig. 1 Cylinder head tightening sequence. V8s with distributor at front of engine

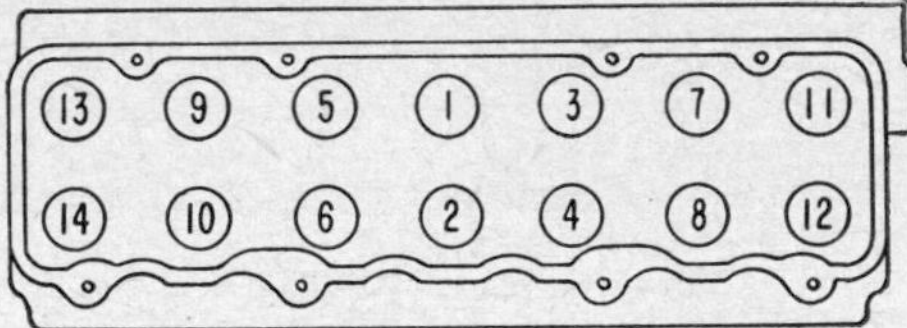

Fig. 2 Cylinder head tightening sequence. 6-170, 225

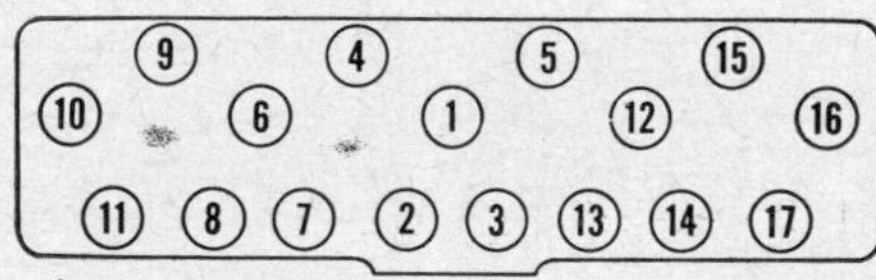

Fig. 3 Cylinder head tightening sequence. V8-426 HP2 engine

2. Drain cooling system and remove battery and carburetor air cleaner.
3. Disconnect transmission cooler lines at radiator (if equipped).
4. Remove radiator and hoses.
5. Remove outlet vent pipe or closed vent system and rocker arm cover.
6. Disconnect fuel lines, carburetor linkage and wiring to engine.
7. Disconnect exhaust pipe at manifold.
8. Disconnect propeller shaft and tie out of the way.
9. Remove speedometer cable and gearshift rods.
10. Remove clutch torque shaft, brake cables and rods.
11. Remove converter cover plate.
12. Drain converter and transmission. Remove oil cooler lines, filler tube and push button cable (if equipped).
13. Support rear of engine.
14. Remove engine rear support crossmember.
15. Disconnect converter from flexible mounting plate.
16. Remove transmission bolts from clutch housing.
17. Remove transmission and converter as an assembly. *Do not remove converter from transmission.*
18. Attach lifting fixture to cylinder head and attach chain hoist.
19. Remove engine support and front engine mounting bolts and lift engine from chassis.

CYLINDER HEAD

1963-69 Chrysler & Imperial

Some cylinder head gaskets are coated with a special lacquer to provide a good seal once the parts have warmed up. Do not use any additional sealer on such gaskets. If the gasket does not have this lacquer coating, apply suitable sealer to both sides.

1. Drain cooling system and disconnect battery ground cable.
2. Remove alternator or generator, carburetor air cleaner and fuel line.
3. Disconnect accelerator linkage.
4. Remove vacuum control tube at carburetor and distributor.
5. Disconnect heat indicator sending unit wire.
6. Remove spark plugs.
7. Remove intake manifold, ignition coil and carburetor as a unit.
8. Remove valve lifter chamber cover.
9. Remove rocker arm covers. *On Imperial air conditioned cars prior to 1967 the No. 8 cylinder exhaust valve must be open to allow clearance between rightbank cylinder head cover and heater housing.*
10. Remove exhaust manifolds.
11. Remove rocker arm assemblies.
12. Remove push rods.
13. Remove head attaching bolts and take off heads.
14. Installing the heads is a matter of reversing the removal procedure. Tighten attaching bolts in the sequence shown in Fig. 1.

1963-69 Dodge & Dart Six

1. Drain cooling system.
2. Remove carburetor air cleaner and fuel line.

3. Disconnect accelerator linkage.
4. Remove vacuum control tube at carburetor and distributor.
5. Disconnect spark plug wires, heater hose and clamp holding by-pass hose.
6. Disconnect heat indicator sending unit wire.
7. Disconnect exhaust pipe at manifold.
8. Remove intake and exhaust manifold and carburetor as a unit.
9. Remove closed vent system and rocker arm cover.
10. Remove rocker arms and push rods.
11. Remove head bolts and lift off head.
12. Install the head in the reverse order of removal, and tighten the bolts in the sequence shown in Fig. 2.
13. *When installing the manifolds, loosen the three bolts holding the intake and exhaust manifolds together. This is required to maintain proper alignment.* Install intake and exhaust manifolds with cup side of the conical washers against the manifolds.

Dodge V8-273, 318, 340

NOTE: The intake manifold attaching bolts on some engines are tilted upward about 30 degrees at an angle to the manifold-to-cylinder head gasket face. The purpose of this design is to provide more effective sealing at the cylinder block end gaskets. If the intake manifold is removed the installation should be such that the bolt tightening is done evenly and in the sequence shown in Fig. 4.

With gaskets in place start all bolts, leaving them loose. Run bolts 1 through 4 down so the heads just touch manifold. Then tighten these four bolts to 25 foot-pounds torque. After checking to see that gaskets are properly seated at all surfaces, tighten remaining bolts to 25 foot-pounds. Finally tighten all bolts in the sequence shown to 35 foot-pounds.

1. Drain cooling system and disconnect battery ground cable.
2. Remove alternator, carburetor air cleaner and fuel line. Disconnect accelerator linkage.
3. Remove vacuum advance hose and distributor cap and wires.
4. Disconnect coil wires, heat indicator wire, heater and by-pass hoses.
5. Remove closed ventilation system and rocker arm covers.
6. Remove intake manifold, coil and carburetor as an assembly.
7. Remove exhaust manifolds.
8. Remove rocker arm and shaft assemblies. Remove push rods.
9. Remove head bolts and lift off cylinder heads.
10. Reverse procedure to install heads and tighten bolts in sequence shown in Fig. 5.

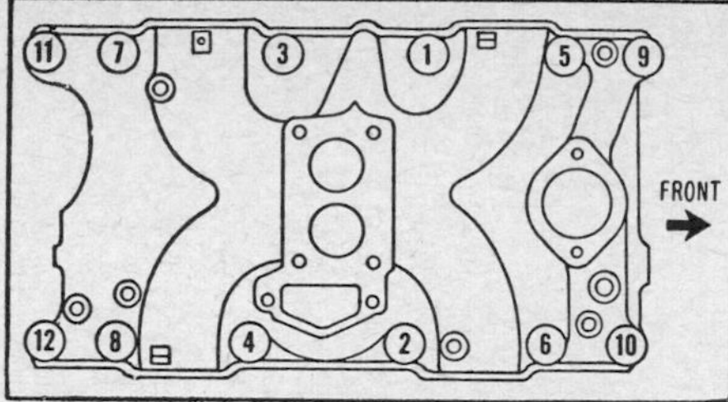

Fig. 4 Intake manifold tightening sequence. V8-273, late 318 & 340

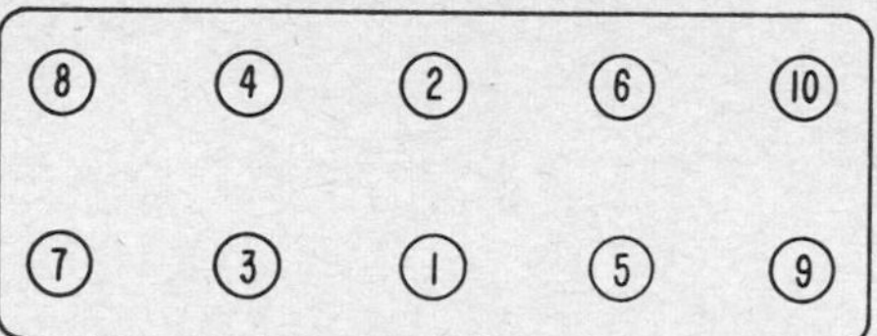

Fig. 5 Cylinder head tightening sequence. V8s with distributor at rear of engine

V8-361, 383, 413, 426, 440

Rocker arm assemblies can be removed without disturbing the cylinder heads or cooling system. To remove the heads, proceed as follows:

1. Drain cooling system, remove air cleaner, fuel line from pump and carburetor, distributor vacuum tube and generator.
2. Disconnect throttle linkage at carburetor, distributor cap, coil wires, heat indicator sending unit wire and heater hoses at engine.
3. Remove spark plugs and cables, and engine vent pipe or closed vent system.
4. Remove intake manifold, carburetor and coil as an assembly.
5. Remove exhaust manifolds.
6. Remove cylinder head covers and spark plug cable support brackets.
7. Remove rocker shaft assemblies. *Do not remove bolts from end brackets.*
8. Remove push rods and valve lifter chamber cover.
9. Remove attaching bolts and lift off heads.

NOTE: V8-426 Hemi-Charger engines, in addition to the regular cylinder head bolts, have four stud nuts holding the heads in place. These stud nuts must be removed from inside the tappet chamber before any attempt is made to remove the head.

10. Reverse the foregoing procedure to install the heads and tighten bolts in the sequence shown in Figs. 1 and 3.

V8-426 Hemi-Charger Engine

Cylinder head bolt torque is critical on this engine and in order to obtain proper cylinder head gasket compression, Lubriplate should be applied to the bolt threads and between the bolt head and hardened washer.

NOTE: Care must be taken so as not to get any of the Lubriplate between the hardened washer and bolt boss as this can cause excessive bolt tension and may result in head bolt breakage.

Plymouth 6-170, 225

1. To remove head, drain cooling system.
2. Remove carburetor air cleaner and fuel line.
3. Disconnect accelerator linkage.
4. Remove vacuum control tube at carburetor and distributor.
5. Disconnect spark plug wires, heater hose and clamp holding by-pass hose.
6. Disconnect heat indicator sending unit wire.
7. Disconnect exhaust pipe at manifold.
8. Remove intake and exhaust manifold and carburetor as a unit.
9. Remove vent system and rocker arm cover.
10. Remove thermostat housing and thermostat.
11. Remove rocker arms and push rods.
12. Remove head bolts and lift off head.
13. Check all surfaces of head with a straightedge if there is any reason to suspect leakage. *Cylinder head warpage should not exceed .005" lengthwise or .003" crosswise.* If there is any reason to suspect restricted water passages, the large recessed screw plug in the rear of the head can be removed.
14. Clean the oil return passages in the head and block.
15. Install the head in the reverse order of removal and tighten the bolts in the sequence shown in Fig. 1 and to the torque listed in the *Engine Torque* table.
16. *When installing the manifolds, loosen the three bolts holding the intake manifold to the exhaust manifold. This is required to maintain proper alignment.* Install intake and exhaust manifold with carburetor with the cup side of the conical washers against the manifolds.

Plymouth 1963-69 V8s

NOTE, V8-273: The intake manifold attaching bolts on this engine are tilted upward about 30 degrees at an angle to the manifold-to-cylinder head gasket face. The purpose of this design is to provide more effective sealing at the cylinder block end gaskets. If the manifold is removed the installation should be such that the bolt tightening is done evenly and in the sequence shown in Fig. 4.

With gaskets in place start all bolts, leaving them loose. Run bolts 1 through 4 down so heads just touch manifold. Then tighten these four bolts to 60 inch-pounds torque. After checking to see that gaskets are properly seated at all surfaces, tighten remaining bolts to 60 inch-pounds. Finally, tighten all bolts to 270 inch-pounds.

1. Drain cooling system. Remove air cleaner, fuel line, alternator and distributor vacuum line.
2. Disconnect throttle linkage, coil wires, heat indicator sending unit wire, and heater hoses at engine.
3. Remove distributor cap and spark plug cables.
4. Remove intake manifold, coil and carburetor as an assembly.
5. On 361, 383, 413, 440, 426 engines, remove valve lifter chamber cover and spark plugs located under exhaust manifolds.
6. On all engines, remove rocker arm covers, closed vent system and exhaust manifolds.

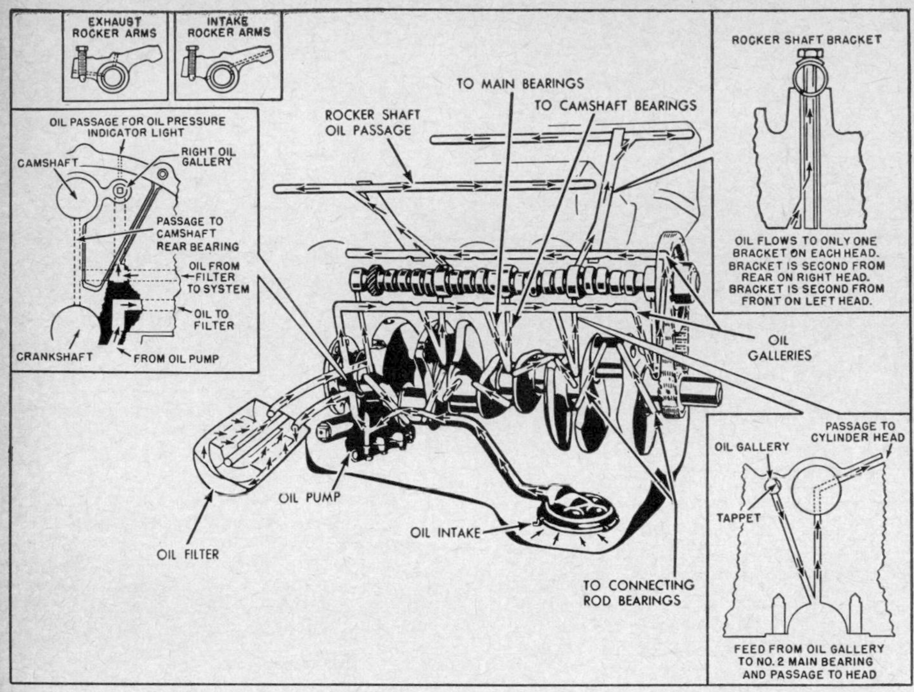

Engine oiling system. V8-273, 318, 340

7. On 361, 383, 413, 440, 426 engines, remove rocker arms and shaft assemblies. Lift out push rods and place them in a suitable holder in their respective slots. *On 318 engines, push rods and rocker arms are removed with cylinder head.*
8. Remove head bolts from each head and lift off heads.
9. Reverse the removal procedure to install the heads and tighten head bolts in the sequence shown in the diagrams and to the torque listed in the *Engine Tightening Specifications* table.

V8-426 HEMI-CHARGER: Cylinder head bolt torque is critical on this engine and in order to obtain proper cylinder head gasket compression, Lubriplate should be applied to the bolt threads and between bolt head and hardened washer.

NOTE: Care must be taken so as not to get any Lubriplate between hardened washer and bolt boss as this can cause excessive bolt tension and may result in head bolt breakage.

VALVES, ADJUST

6-170, 225

Before the final valve lash adjustment is made, operate the engine for 30 minutes at a fast idle to stabilize engine temperatures.

Before starting the adjustment procedure, make two chalk marks on the vibration damper. Space the marks approximately 120° apart (⅓ of circumference) so that with the timing mark the damper is divided into three equal parts. Adjust the valves for No. 1 cylinder. Repeat the procedure for the remaining valves, turning the crankshaft ⅓ turn in the direction of normal rotation while adjusting the valves in the firing order sequence of 153624.

NOTE

To adjust valves on aluminum engines, first run the engine until normal operating temperature is reached. Then remove the rocker arm cover. After the rocker arm cover has been removed, run the engine an additional five minutes at idle speed. Then adjust the valves in the usual manner. It is necessary that the foregoing procedure be followed because of the different expansion characteristics of the metals involved.

V8s With Mechanical Lifters

Engines with mechanical lifters can be identified by the rocker arm adjusting screws. These screws are self-locking and when turning them during the process of adjustment they should indicate some resistance to turning (a minimum of 3 lb. ft. tension). If any screw turns too easily it should be replaced and, if necessary, the rocker arm as well.

Valve clearances should be set up after the engine is warmed up to operating temperature and to the clearances listed in the *Valve Specifications* table.

VALVE ARRANGEMENT

Front to Rear

8-318:
Right Bank ....I-E-I-E-I-E-I-E
Left Bank ....E-I-E-I-E-I-E-I
8-273, 340 ....E-I-I-E-E-I-I-E
8-361, 383, 413, 426, 440..E-I-I-E-E-I-I-E
6-170, 225 ......E-I-E-I-E-I-I-E-I-E-I-E

VALVE LIFT SPECS.

Engine	Year	Intake	Exhaust
6–170	1963–65	.375	.360
	1966	.375	.365
	1967	.395	.395
	1968	.394	.390
	1969	.395	.395
6–225	1963–65	.375	.360
	1966–67	.395	.395
	1968	.394	.390
	1969	.395	.395
8–273	1964–67①	.395	.405
	1965–67②	.415	.425
	1968	.372	.400
	1969	.373	.399
8–318	1963–66	.397	.403
	1967	.390	.390
	1968	.372	.400
	1969	.373	.399

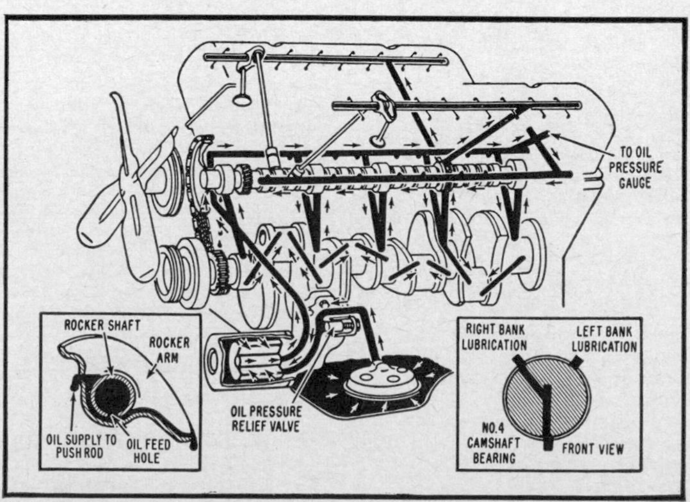

Engine oiling system. V8-361, 383, 413, 426, 440 engines

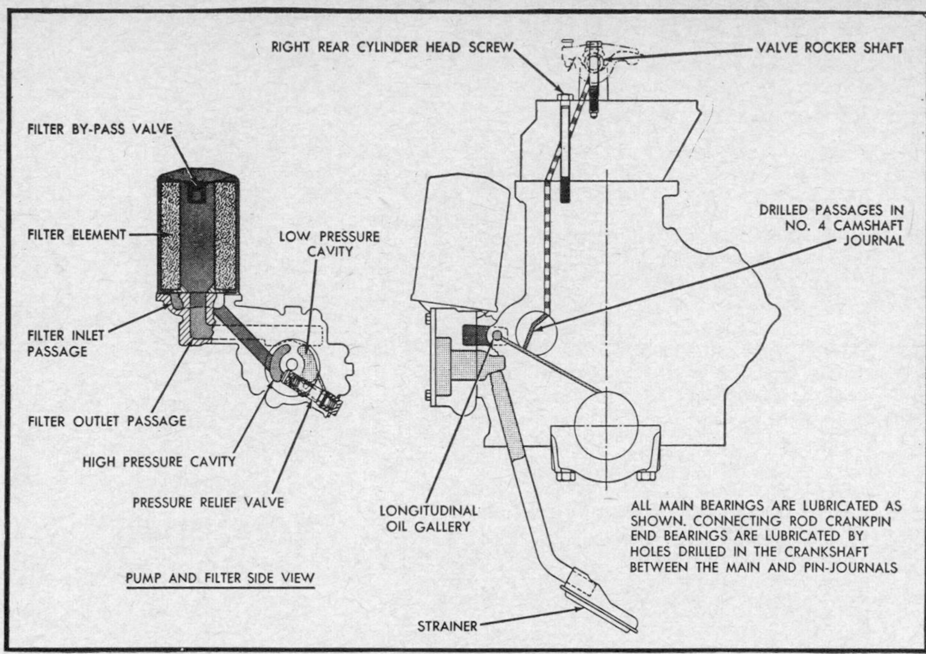

Engine oiling system. 6-170, 225

8-340	1968⑪	.445	.455
	1968⑫	.430	.445
	1969	.429	.444
8-361	1963-64	.389	.389
	1965①	.392	.390
	1965②	.430	.430
	1966	.392	.390
8-383	1963	.389	.389
	1964–65①	.392	.390
	1964–65②	.430	.430
	1966①	.392	.390
	1966–67②	.425	.437
	1968②	.425	.437
	1969①	.425	.435
	1969②	.450	.458
8-413	1963⑨	.430	.430
	1963⑩	.444	.450
	1964⑥	.430	.430
	1964-65③	.389	.389
	1964-65⑦	.430	.430
	1964⑧	.444	.450
8-426	1964-65	.430	.430
	1966	.425	.435
	1967	.467	.473
	1968	.490	.480
	1969	.467	.473
8-440	1966	.425	.435
	1967④	.425	.435
	1967⑤	.450	.465
	1968④	.425	.437
	1968⑤	.450	.465
	1969①	.425	.435
	1969②	.450	.458

①—2 bar. carb. ②—4 bar. carb.
③—340 H.P.
④—350 H.P. ⑤—375 H.P.
⑥—330 H.P. ⑦—360 H.P.
⑧—390 H.P. ⑨—Exc. 300J
⑩—300J ⑪—Man. Trans.
⑫—Auto. Trans.

VALVE TIMING SPECS.

Intake Opens Before TDC

Engine	Year	Degrees
6-170	1963-66	8
	1967-69	10
6-225	1963-69	10
8-273	1964-67	14
	1968-69	10
8-318	1963-66	19
	1967	14
	1968-69	10
8-340	1968 Man. Tr.	26
	1968 Auto. Tr.	22
	1969	22
8-361	1963-66	13
8-383	1963	13
	1964–65 2 B.C.	13
	1964–65 4 B.C.	24
	1966 2 B.C.	13
	1966 4 B.C.	14
	1967	16
	1968	18
	1969 2 B.C.	18
	1969 4 B.C.	21
8-413	1963 300J	18
	1963 Imperial	13
	1963 Others	24
	1964 330 H.P.	24
	1964–65 340 H.P.	14
	1964–65 360 H.P.	24
	1964 390 H.P.	18
8-426	1964-65	24
	1966-67	30
	1968-69	36
8-440	1966	14
	1967–68 350 H.P.	18
	1967 375 H.P.	19
	1968 375 H.P.	21
	1969 L/Power Pack	18
	1969 W/Power Pack	21

ROCKER ARMS

6-170, 225

1. To remove rocker arms, take off head cover outlet tube.
2. Remove rocker arm cover.
3. Remove rocker shaft bolts and retainers.
4. Lift off rocker arms and shaft.

Inspection

Clean all parts with a suitable solvent. Be sure the inside of the shaft is clean and the oil holes are open. The drilled oil hole in the bore of the rocker arm must be open to the trough and valve end of the arms. The trough also feeds oil to the adjusting screw and push rod.

The shaft should be free from excessive wear in arm contact areas. The shaft should be smooth in retainer contact areas. The adjusting screws in the rocker arms should have a uniform round end. The drag torque should be smooth and uniform. The retainers should be smooth and undamaged in the shaft contact area.

Assemble and Install

1. Referring to Fig. 6, note flat on forward end of rocker shaft which denotes the upper side of the shaft. Rocker arms must be put on the shaft with the adjusting screw to the right side of the engine. Place one of the small retainers on the one long bolt and install the bolt in the rear hole in the shaft from the top side.
2. Install one rocker arm and one spacer; then two rocker arms and a spacer. Continue in same sequence until all rocker arms and spacers are on the shaft.
3. Place a bolt and small retainer in front hole in shaft.
4. Place a bolt and the one *wide* retainer through the center hole in the shaft with six rocker arms on each side of center.
5. Install remaining bolts and retainers, separating the four pairs of rocker arms.
6. Locate the assembly on the cylinder head and position rocker arm adjusting screws in push rods.
7. Tighten bolts finger tight, bringing retainers in contact with the shaft *between rocker arms.*
8. Tighten bolts to specified torque.
9. After running engine to normal operating temperature, adjust valve lash to specifications.
10. Complete the job by installing the remaining parts removed.

V8-273 & 1967-69 V8-318, 340

To provide correct lubrication for the rocker arms on these engines, the rocker shafts have a small notch machined at one end, Fig. 7, and these notches must always face inward toward the center of the engine when installed. In other words, the notched end must be toward the rear of the engine on the right bank, and to the front of the engine on the left bank.

Rocker arms must be correctly positioned on the shaft prior to installation

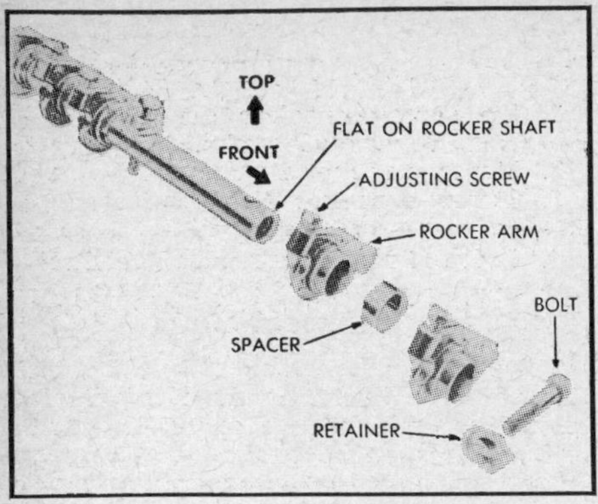

Fig. 6 Rocker arm and shaft assembly. 6-170, 225

on cylinder head. A good way to do this is to place each rocker arm on the shaft so the adjusting screw is on the same side as the notch of the shaft when the rocker arm is right side up.

It is also important when installing the rocker shaft assembly on the cylinder head to position the short retainers at each end and in the center, and to place long retainers in the two remaining positions.

1963-66 V8-318 U.S. & 1967 Canadian Built

1. Referring to Fig. 8, slide rocker shaft into bore of strut and at the same time engage intake rocker arm.
2. Install spring and engage exhaust rocker arm.
3. Install remainder of rocker arms in same sequence.
4. Make sure that head bolt holes in rocker shaft line up with head bolt holes in rocker arm shaft strut. In addition, plug hole in strut must also line up with hole in rocker shaft.
5. Install plugs in both ends of rocker arm shaft.

V8-361, 383, 413, 426, 440

1. Install rocker shafts so that the $\frac{3}{16}$" diameter rocker arm lubrication holes point downward into rocker arm, and so that the 15 degree angle of these holes point outward toward valve end of rocker arm, Figs. 9 and 9A. The 15 degree angle is determined from the center line of the bolt holes through the shaft which are used to attach the shaft assembly to the cylinder head.
2. On all engines, install rocker arms and shaft assembly, making sure to install long stamped steel retainers in No. 2 and 4 positions.

NOTE: Use extreme care in tightening the bolts so that valve lifters have time to bleed down to their operating length. Bulged lifter bodies, bent push rods and permanent noisy operation may result if lifters are forced down too rapidly.

3. Installation should be as shown in Fig. 10.

426 Hemi-Charger Service Note

This engine has three different rocker shaft brackets and it is very important that they are positioned as shown in Fig. 11. Because the oil feed holes in the cylinder block are the number 2 and 4 positions, and the number 1 and 3 positions do not have cylinder head gasket beads, mis-location of the brackets can cause either of the following conditions:

1. No. 1 and 3 brackets installed in No. 2 and 4 positions will cause a dry cylinder head.
2. No. 2 and 4 brackets installed in No. 1 and 3 positions will cause a cylinder head gasket leak.

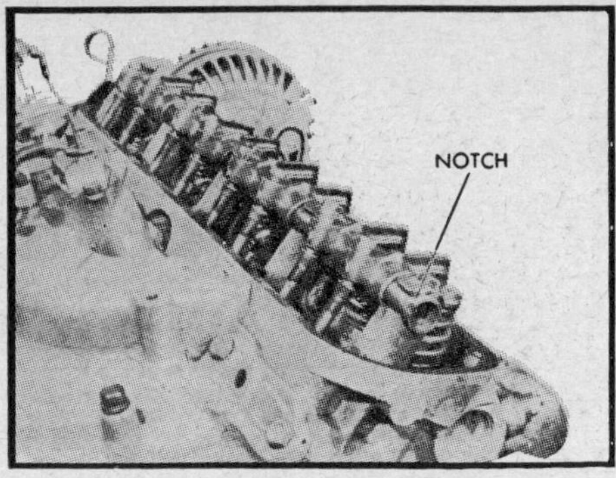

Fig. 7 Notches at end of both rocker arm shafts must face toward center of engine. V8-273 and 1967-69 V8-318, 340

VALVE GUIDES

Non-Removable Type

Valves operate in guide holes bored directly in the cylinder head. When valve stem-to-guide clearance becomes excessive, valves with oversize stems of .005" .015" and .030" are available for service replacement. When necessary to install valves with oversize stems the valve bores should be reamed to provide the proper operating clearance.

V8s With Removable Guides

Remove the old guides by driving them out through the top of the cylinder head. Drive the new guides in place by driving them up through the valve port opening.

When installing exhaust valve guides, make certain that the oil holes in the top of the guides are facing up.

After valve guides are properly installed, ream each guide to the clearances listed in the Valve Specification Table.

VALVE LIFTERS

6-170, 225

After taking off rocker arm and shaft assembly, lift out push rods. The valve lifters may then be removed with a suitably long magnet rod. If the lifters cannot be removed with the magnet rod, a

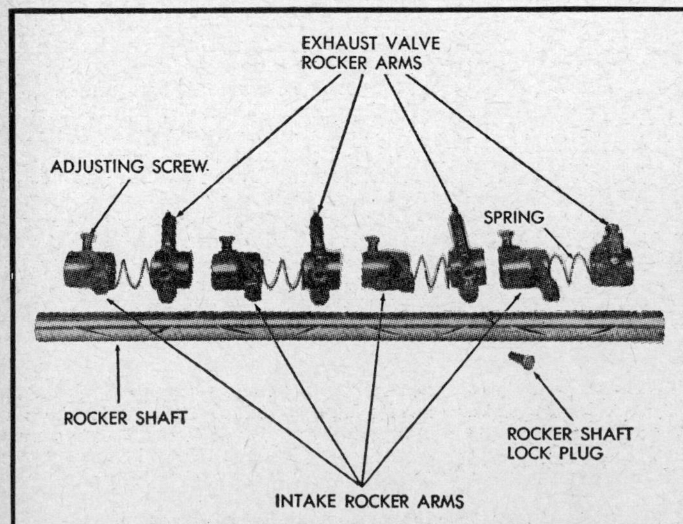

Fig. 8 Rocker arm and shaft assembly. V8-318 through 1966 U.S. and 1967 Canadian built. The 1967 U.S. built 318 and 340 engine is similar to the V8-273 engine

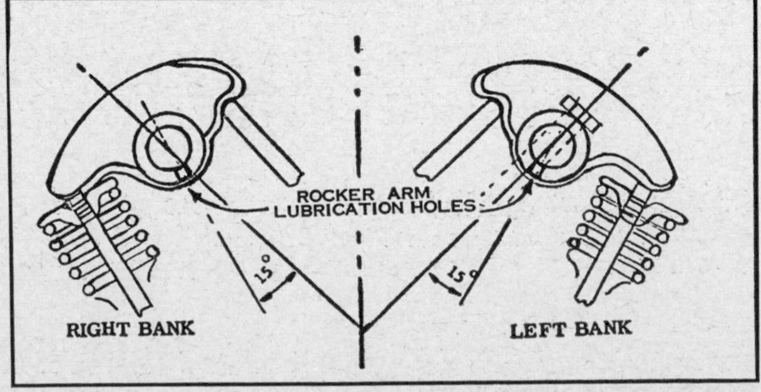

Fig. 9 Rocker arm shaft installation. V8-361, 383, 413, 426, 440

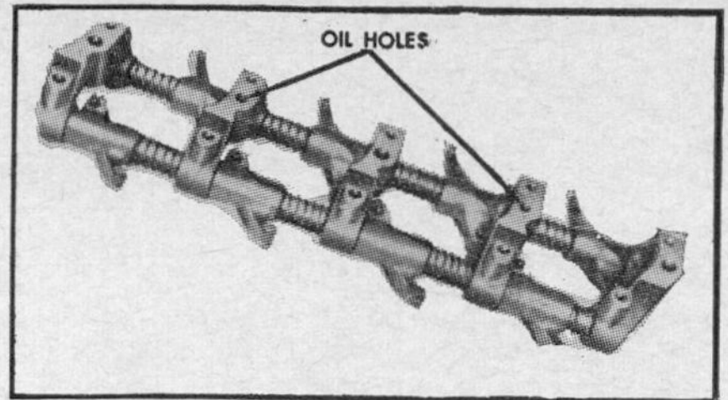

Fig. 9A Rocker arm shaft assembly. V8-426 HP2 engine

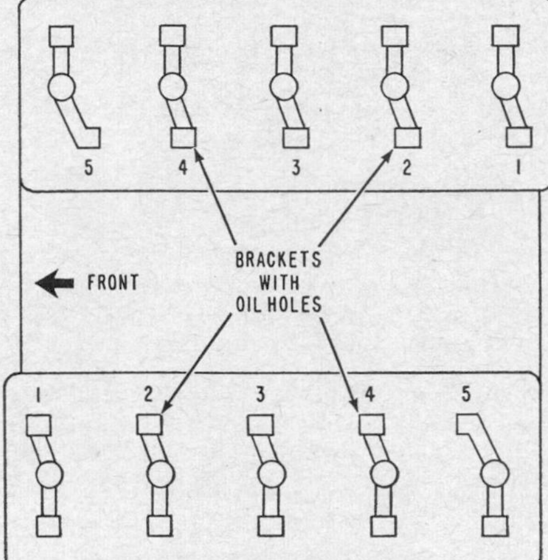

Fig. 11 Valve rocker shaft bracket locations. V8-426 Hemi-Charger engine

special tool (C-3661) may be used, Fig. 13. Insert the tool through the push rod opening in the cylinder head and into lifter. Turn the handle to expand the tool in the lifter, then with a twisting motion remove the lifter from its bore.

NOTE

In the aluminum engine, the valve lifters operate in machined bores in the engine and may be rebored to accommodate oversize lifters of .001", .008" and .030".

HYDRAULIC LIFTERS

Lifter, Replace

Chrysler Tool is available for this operation. To remove the lifter, insert the tool in the lifter body. (This portion of the tool can be used to remove lifters without a varnish build-up around the bottom of the body.) Lift the lifter out of the bore, Fig. 12. If they are stuck proceed as follows:

Slide the puller portion of the tool through the cylinder head push rod holes and seat it firmly in the top of the lifter. Insert the puller pin through the body and tool shaft in the holes provided, Fig. 13. Grasp the tool handle and pull the lifter out of the bore as shown.

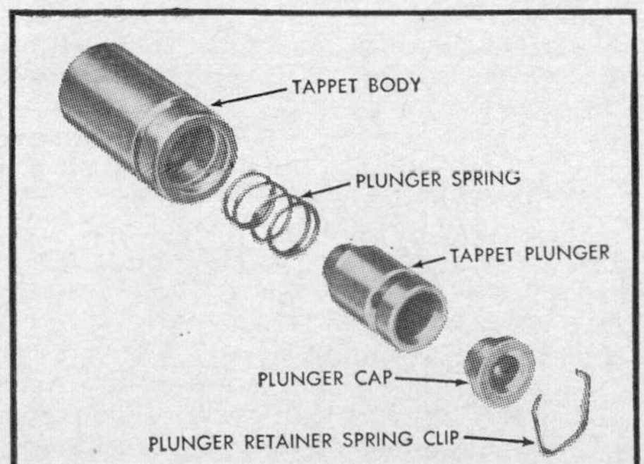

Fig. 12 Hydraulic valve lifter

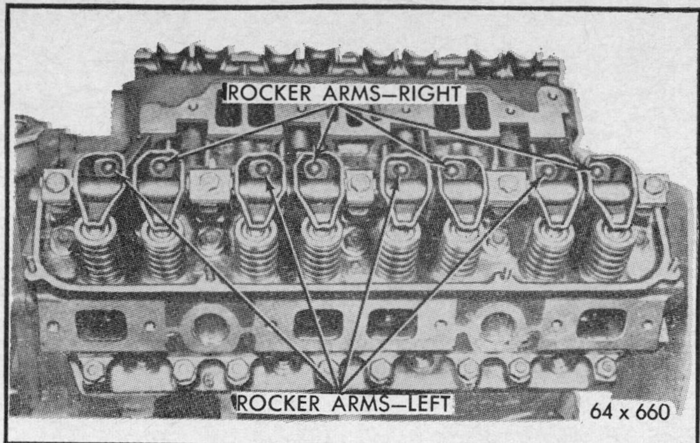

Fig. 10 Rocker arm and shaft assembly installed. 8-273, 361, 383, 413, 426, 440

Checking Hydraulic Lifter Static Clearance

After performing a valve grind job or replacing a cylinder head the hydraulic lifters should be collapsed and the valve stem-to-rocker arm clearance checked. Each lifter should be checked individually to guard against differences in machining or wear variables.

Valve stem-to-rocker arm clearance should check within the limits given in the *Valve Specifications* chart. If the actual measured clearance is less than the minimum specified, very likely the valve has been ground down too much and a new valve should be installed.

When the actual measured clearance is more than the maximum specified, the valve face should be ground down further to bring it at or below the maximum static clearance specified.

To check the clearance a special spanner-type tool is commercially available to apply pressure on the rocker arm to bleed down the hydraulic lifter until the plunger is completely bottomed. Of course, checking must be done with the lifter on the heel of the cam. If the special tool is not available, a stiff rod, such as a socket extension, and a length of wire can be used to collapse the lifter. Wire one end of the rod to the rocker arm as close to the valve stem as possible and apply pressure to the other end until the lifter is collapsed.

TIMING CHAIN COVER

NOTE: In order to replace the cover oil seal the cover must be removed from the engine.

6-170, 225

1. To remove cover, drain cooling system and remove radiator and fan.
2. Remove vibration damper with a puller.
3. Loosen oil pan bolts to allow clearance and remove chain case cover.
4. Reverse above procedure to install cover.

V8-361, 383, 413, 426, 440

1. Drain cooling system.
2. Remove radiator, fan and belt.
3. Remove water pump and housing as an assembly.
4. Remove crankshaft bolt and pulley from vibration damper and remove damper with a puller.
5. Remove key from crankshaft. On V8-426 Hemi-Charger, remove two front pan bolts.
6. Remove chain case cover and gasket. *Use extreme caution to avoid damaging the oil pan gasket; if damaged it will be necessary to remove the oil pan in order to install a new pan gasket.*

V8-273, 318, 340

1. Remove radiator, fan and belt.

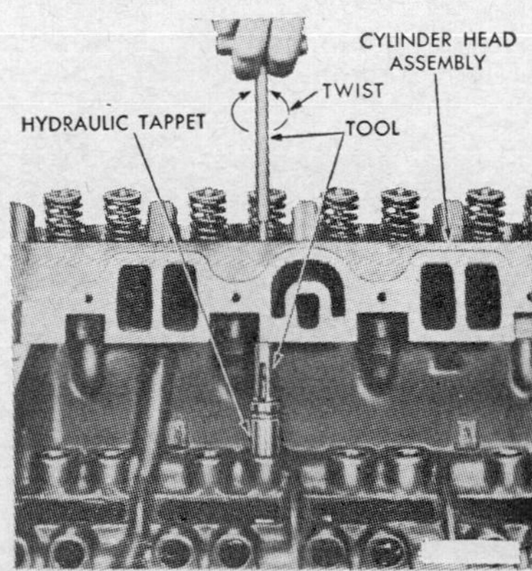

Fig. 13 Removing stuck valve lifter

2. Remove water pump and housing as a unit.
3. Remove crankshaft pulley.
4. Remove key from crankshaft.
5. Remove fuel pump.
6. Remove chain case cover and gasket, *using extreme caution to avoid damaging oil pan gasket otherwise oil pan will have to be removed. It is normal to find particles of neoprene collected between crankshaft seal retainer and oil slinger.*

TIMING CHAIN

6-170, 225

1. After removing chain case cover as outlined above, take off camshaft sprocket attaching bolt.
2. Remove chain with camshaft sprocket.
3. Clean all parts and dry with compressed air.
4. Inspect timing chain for broken or damaged links. Inspect sprockets for cracks and chipped, worn or damaged teeth.

Installation

1. Turn crankshaft so sprocket timing mark is toward and directly in line with centerline of camshaft.
2. Temporarily install camshaft sprocket. Rotate camshaft to position sprocket timing mark toward and directly in line with centerline of crankshaft; then remove camshaft sprocket.
3. Place chain on crankshaft sprocket and position camshaft sprocket in chain so sprocket can be installed with timing marks aligned without moving camshaft, Fig. 15.
4. Install parts removed in reverse order of removal.

V8 Engines

To install chain and sprockets, lay both the camshaft and crankshaft sprockets on the bench. Position the sprockets so that the timing marks are next to each other. Place the chain on both sprockets, then push the gears apart as far as the chain will permit. Use a straightedge to form a line through the exact centers of both gears. The timing marks must be on this line, Fig. 16.

This is the same procedure as in previous models, except that now the alignment is done on the bench rather than on the engine.

Slide the chain with both sprockets on the camshaft and crankshaft at the same time; then recheck the alignment.

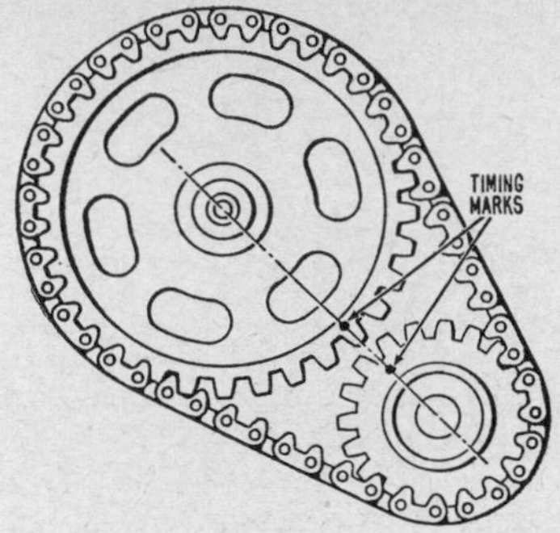

Fig. 15 Valve timing marks aligned for correct valve timing. All Sixes

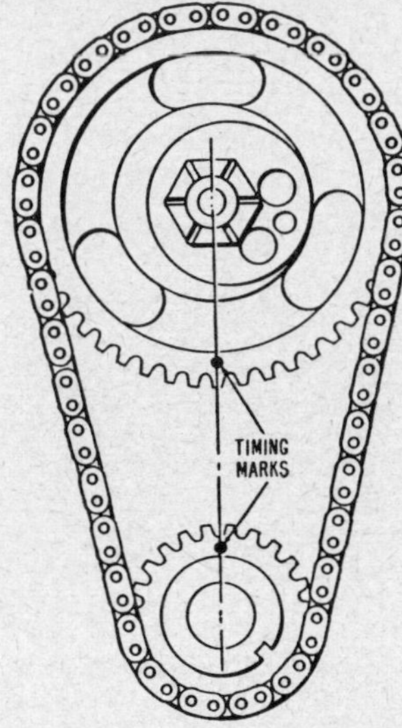

Fig. 16 Valve timing marks aligned for correct valve timing. All V8s

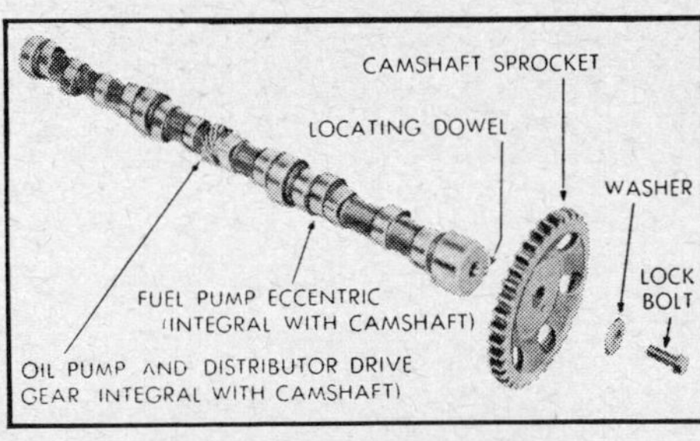

Fig. 17 Camshaft and related parts. 6-170, 225

CAMSHAFT & BEARINGS

6-170, 225

In the aluminum engine the camshaft bearings are an integral part of the cylinder block casting and are not replaceable.

In the cast iron engine, the camshaft is supported by four precision type, steel-backed, babbitt-lined bearings. Rearward thrust is taken by the rear face of the sprocket hub, contacting the front of the engine block.

The camshaft, Fig. 17, can be removed after removing the grille, radiator and timing chain. To remove the camshaft bearings, the torque converter (or flywheel) must also be removed.

1. Remove valve lifters, oil pump and distributor.
2. Slide camshaft out of engine.
3. Remove welch plug back of rear camshaft bearing.
4. Remove bearings with suitable puller equipment.
5. Install new bearings, being sure the oil holes in bearings line up with the corresponding oil holes in the crankcase.

V8 Engines

To remove the camshaft, remove all valve lifters, timing chain and sprockets. Remove distributor and oil pump-distributor drive gear. Remove fuel pump and see that push rod has moved away from eccentric drive cam. Withdraw the camshaft from the engine, using care to see that the cam lobes do not damage the camshaft bearings.

If camshaft bearings are to be replaced, it is recommended that the engine be removed from the chassis and the crankshaft taken out in order that any chips or foreign material may be removed from the oil passages.

PISTON & ROD, ASSEMBLE

6-170, 225

Piston and rod assemblies must be installed as shown in Fig. 19.

V8 Engines

When installing piston and rod assemblies in the cylinders, the compression ring gaps should be diametrically opposite one another and not in line with the oil ring gap. The oil ring expander gap should be toward the outside of the "V" of the engine. The oil ring gap should be turned toward the inside of the engine "V".

Immerse the piston head and rings in clean engine oil and, with a suitable piston ring compressor, insert the piston and rod assembly into the bore. Tap the piston down into the bore, using the handle of a hammer.

Assemble the pistons to the rods as shown in Fig. 20.

PISTONS, PINS & RINGS

Pistons are available in standard sizes and the following oversizes: V8-413 and 440: .005, .020". All others: .005, .020, .040".

Pins are available in the following oversizes: V8-273, 318, 326, .003, .008". Not furnished on all other engines.

Rings are available in the following oversizes: 1963-69 Six and all V8s, std. to .009, .020-.029, .040-.049".

NOTE

The cylinder block for the aluminum engine is die-cast aluminum with cast-in-place iron cylinder bore liners .100" thick. The liners are not replaceable. When conditions require reboring, the cylinder can be rebored up to a maximum of .040" oversize. After reboring, do not re-chamfer the liner top so that the sealing surface at the top of the liner is maintained.

MAIN & ROD BEARINGS

Main bearings are furnished in standard sizes and the following undersizes: 1963-69 Six, .001, .002, .010". 1963-67 V8s, .001, .002, .003, .010, .012".
Hemi-Head, standard only.

Rod bearings are furnished in standard sizes and the following undersizes: 1963-69 Six, .001, .002, .010". V8s, .001, .002, .003, .010, .012". Hemihead, standard only.

Fig. 19 Piston and rod assembly. 6-170, 225 engines with cast iron block. On aluminum block engines assemble rod to piston with oil hole toward left side of engine

NOTE

Servicing of main bearings in aluminum engines is identical to the cast iron engine. However, make certain that any new bearings installed are applicable to the aluminum engine. The oil hole location in the aluminum engine upper main bearings differs from the cast iron engine location. Upper main bearings with two oil holes will fit in both engines, but upper main bearings with one oil hole fit only in the cast iron block.

CRANKSHAFT REAR OIL SEAL

SERVICE BULLETIN

V8-273, 318 SEAL: When oil seal replacement is necessary on these engines, thoroughly clean the bearing cap and block to assure proper seating of the cap. Install a new rope seal in the conventional manner. Then apply an All Purpose cement (Mopar 1316241) on the joint face on the ends of the rope and ¼" to each side of the rubber side gaskets. Do not use sealer on the rope where it contacts the crankshaft or near the bearing shell.

This new procedure using sealer at the rear main bearing rope seal and side gasket area entered production (effective November 17, 1964) and all 273 and 318 engines.

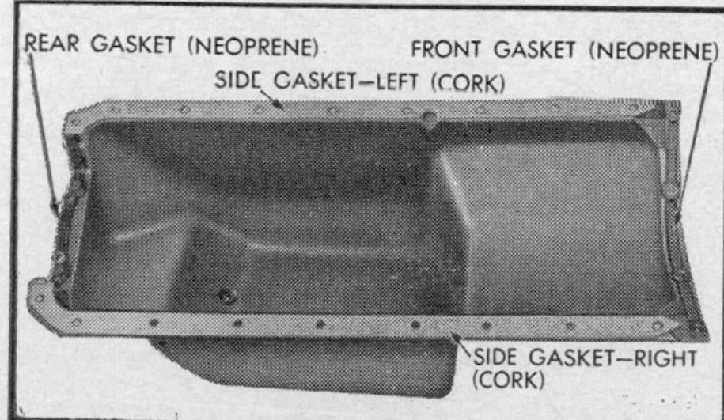

Fig. 21 Location of oil pan gaskets. 6-170, 225

SERVICE BULLETIN

V8-361, 383 SIDE SEALS: The side seals used with the crankshaft rear bearing retainer on these engines should be installed in the retainer as rapidly as possible as they are made from a material that expands rapidly when oiled. Apply mineral spirits or kerosene to the seals and install them in the grooves immediately. Install seal retainer and torque to 30 ft-lbs. Failure to pre-oil seals will result in an oil leak.

OIL PAN

CAUTION: Engine oil pan bolts on all V8-361, 383, 413, 426, 440 engines are $\frac{13}{16}$" long with the exception of two bolts at the rear center of the oil pan. The two rear center bolts are $\frac{9}{16}$" long and thread into the aluminum seal retainer. Do not use longer bolts than $\frac{9}{16}$" at this location as they will bottom in the aluminum seal retainer and, if forced in may strip the threads and damage the seal retainer, causing an oil leak.

1963-69 Chrysler & Imperial, 1965-69 Dodge & Plymouth V8-361, 383, 413, 426, 440

1. Disconnect battery cable and drain crankcase.
2. Raise car on hoist and disconnect steering linkage from idler arm and pitman arm.
3. Remove outlet vent pipe and disconnect exhaust pipe branches from manifolds.
4. Remove clamp attaching exhaust pipe to extension and remove exhaust pipe.
5. Remove converter dust shield.
6. Remove oil pan bolts and turn flywheel until counterweight and connecting rods at the front end of crankshaft are at their highest position to provide clearance, and lower the pan. Turn the pan to clear oil screen and suction pipe.

1965-69 Dart & Valiant Six

1. Raise car and drain oil pan.
2. Use a puller to remove steering and idler arm ball joints from steering linkage center link.
3. Remove dust shield and engine mount stud nuts.
4. Lower vehicle and remove horns and mounting brackets, then disconnect battery ground cable.
5. Raise engine from 1½ to 2 inches, using a lifting rig.
6. Again raise vehicle, then remove oil pan.
7. When installing pan, refer to Figs. 21 and 22.

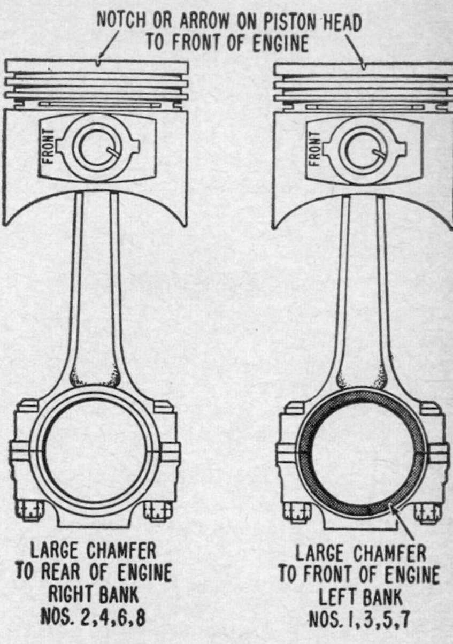

Fig. 20 Piston and rod assembly, V8. On V8-426 Hemi, bearing tangs must face outboard

1965-69 Dodge & Plymouth Six

1. Remove oil dipstick, disconnect battery ground cable. Raise vehicle and drain oil.
2. Use a puller to remove steering and idler arm ball joints from steering center link. Remove dust shield.
3. Remove oil pan bolts, rotate engine crankshaft to clear counterweights, then remove oil pan.
4. When installing pan, refer to Figs. 21 and 22.

1965-69 V8-273, 318, 340

1. Disconnect battery ground cable.
2. Remove oil level dipstick.
3. Raise vehicle and drain oil.

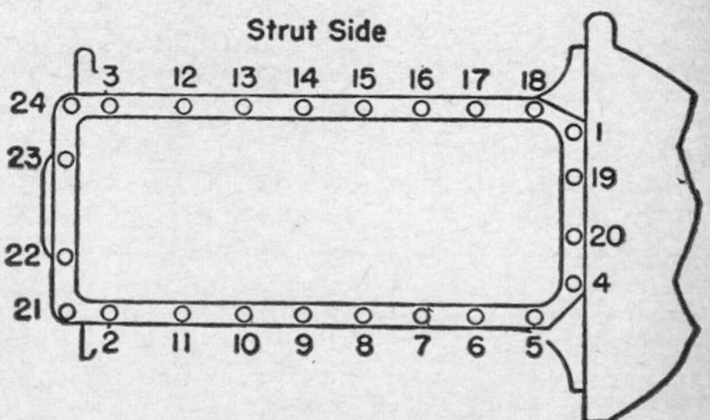

Fig. 22 Tighten oil pan screws to 200 inch pounds in the sequence shown. 6-170, 225

4. On 273, 318, 340 engines, remove engine-to-torque converter left housing brace.
5. Remove steering and idler arm ball joints from steering center link.
6. Remove exhaust crossover pipe from exhaust manifolds and leave it hang without disconnecting it from muffler.
7. On some models it will be necessary to remove crossover pipe.
8. Unfasten and remove oil pan.

1963-64 Dart Six

1. Raise car and drain oil.
2. Pull steering and idler arm ball joints from steering linkage center link.
3. Remove dust shield and motor mount nuts.
4. Lower car and remove horns and mounting brackets. Then disconnect battery ground cable.
5. Raise engine about 2 inches.
6. Again raise car on hoist and remove oil pan.
7. When installing pan, refer to Figs. 21 and 22.

1963-64 Dodge & Plymouth Six

1. Raise car and drain oil pan.
2. Remove steering and idler arm ball joints from steering linkage center link.
3. Remove dust shield.
4. Remove oil pan bolts, rotate engine crankshaft to clear counterweights and remove oil pan.
5. When installing pan, refer to Figs. 21 and 22.

1963-64 V8 Dodge & Plymouth (Except 8-273)

1. Disconnect ground cable from battery and remove oil dipstick.
2. Raise car, drain oil, and remove engine-to-torque converter housing brace.
3. On V8-318, remove exhaust crossover pipe from exhaust manifolds and leave it hang without disconnecting it from muffler.
4. Remove steering and idler arm ball joints from steering linkage center link.
5. Unfasten and remove oil pan.

1964 Dodge & Plymouth V8-273

1. Disconnect steering linkage from steering gear arm and idler arm.
2. Loosen front engine mount lower studs.
3. Raise engine ½" and install a spacer between frame bracket and engine mount.

CAUTION: Do not raise engine too far to prevent damage to radiator.

4. Loosen entire exhaust system.
5. Disconnect exhaust pipe at "Y" connection and remove "Y" pipe.
6. Unfasten and remove oil pan.

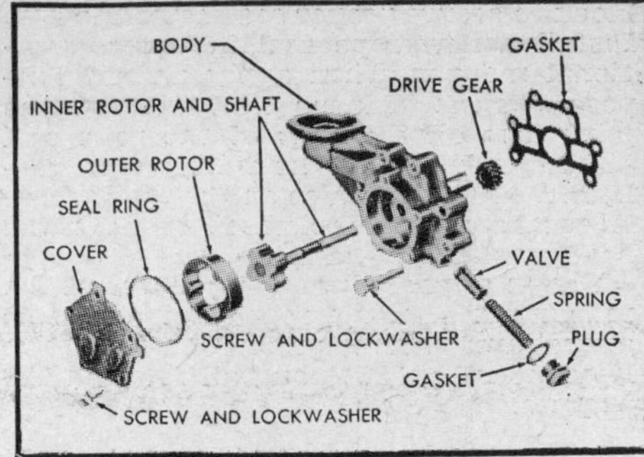

Fig. 23 Oil pump. 6-170, 6-225

1963-64 Valiant Six

1. Raise car and drain oil.
2. Remove steering and idler arm ball joints from steering linkage center link with a puller.
3. Lower vehicle and remove horns and mounting brackets.
4. Disconnect battery ground cable.
5. Raise engine about 1½ to 2 inches.
6. Again raise vehicle and remove oil pan.
7. When installing pan, refer to Figs. 21 and 22.

OIL PUMP, REPLACE

1967-69 Six Cylinder

1. Drain radiator and disconnect upper and lower hoses.
2. Remove fan shroud (if equipped).
3. Raise vehicle on a hoist, support front of engine with a jack stand placed under right front corner of engine oil pan. *Do not support engine at crankshaft pulley or vibration damper.*
4. Remove front engine mounts.
5. Raise engine 1½ to 2 inches.
6. Remove oil filter, pump attaching bolts and remove pump assembly.

V8 Engines

On 273, 318, 340 engines, remove oil pump from rear main bearing cap.

On 361, 383, 413, 426, 440 engines, unfasten oil pump from engine and remove pump and filter assembly from bottom of engine.

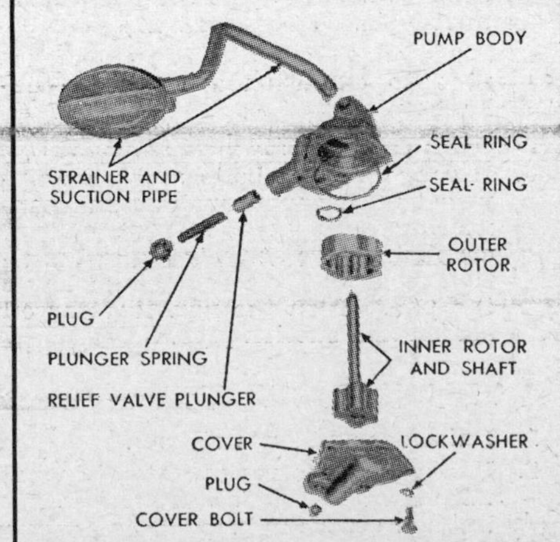

Fig. 24 Oil pump. V8-361, 383, 413, 426, 440

1963-66 Dart 6, 1965-66 Coronet 6, 1963-66 Valiant 6, 1963-66 Plymouth 6

1. Drain radiator and disconnect hoses.
2. Disconnect fuel line at pump inlet, and throttle linkage at carburetor.
3. With car on a hoist, support front of engine with a jack stand placed under right front corner of oil pan (not crankshaft pulley).
4. Cut a piece of 2x4 eight inches long.
5. Raise front of engine just high enough to insert the wood block between front rail and "K" member and right front lower portion of oil pan. Position wood block so one end is against edge of right front engine mount support where it is welded to the "K" member.
6. Lower front of engine so it rests on wood block near right front corner of oil pan.
7. Exert light pressure with a pry bar against right side of engine. This will cause wood block and front of engine to slide to the left about 1½", and will also cause engine to tip slightly toward the left.
8. Remove oil filter, oil pump cover and outer pump rotor. *The outer rotor will drop out when pump cover is removed, so be sure to catch it so it will not be damaged by falling.*
9. There should now be enough clearance between engine and "K" member to allow removal of oil pump.
10. After repairing, install pump, without outer rotor and cover, using a new gasket.
11. Center engine in its original position and, using a jack stand to support it at the front end, install front engine mounts.
12. Connect fuel line, throttle linkage, radiator hoses and refill radiator.

OIL PUMP REPAIRS

6-170, 225

To disassemble, remove the pump cover seal ring, Fig. 23. Press off the drive gear, supporting the gear to keep load off aluminum body. Remove rotor and shaft and lift out outer pump rotor. Remove oil pressure relief valve plug and lift out spring and plunger. Remove oil pressure sending unit.

Inspection

1. The rotor contact area and the bores for the shaft and valve in the pump body should be smooth, free from scratches, scoring or excessive wear.
2. The pump cover should be smooth, flat and free from scoring or ridges. Lay a straightedge across the cover. If a .0015" feeler gauge can be inserted under the straightedge, the cover should be replaced.
3. All surfaces of the outer rotor should be smooth and uniform, free from ridges, scratches or uneven wear. Discard a rotor less than .649" thick and/or less than 2.469" in diameter.

4. The inner rotor and shaft assembly should be smooth, free from scoring and uneven wear. Discard rotors less than .649" thick.
5. Place outer rotor in pump body and measure clearance between rotor and body. Discard pump body if clearance is more than .012".
6. Install inner rotor and shaft in pump body. Shaft should turn freely but without side play. If clearance between rotor teeth is more than .010", replace both rotors.
7. Measure rotor end clearance. If feeler gauge of more than .004" can be inserted between straightedge and rotors, install a new pump body.
8. The oil pressure relief valve should be smooth, free from scratches or scoring, and should be a free fit in its bore.
9. Relief valve springs are painted either gray, red or brown to denote free lengths of 2.19, 2.29 and 2.39 inches Rather than change the length, replace a spring with one of the same color.

Assemble and Install

1. With pump rotors in body, press drive gear on shaft, flush with end of shaft.
2. Install seal ring in groove in body and install cover. Tighten bolts to 10 ft. lbs. Test pump for free turning.
3. Install oil pressure relief valve spring. Use new washer (gasket) and tighten plug securely.
4. If pump shaft turns freely, remove pump cover and outer rotor before installation of pump on engine.
5. Install oil pressure sending unit and tighten to 60 inch lbs. (5 ft. lbs.)
6. Using a new gasket, install pump on engine and tighten bolts to 200 inch lbs. (16 ft. lbs.)
7. Install oil filter reservoir on pump. Install filter element and tighten cover nuts to 25 ft. lbs.
8. Connect oil pressure sending unit wire.
9. Complete the installation by reversing steps as given under Oil Pump, Replace.

V8-361, 383, 413, 426, 440

After removing the pump from the engine it should be disassembled, cleaned and inspected for wear, Fig. 24.

1. Remove the cotter pin holding the oil strainer to the oil suction pipe. Then remove the pipe from the pump body.
2. Remove the pump cover and discard the oil seal ring.
3. Remove pump rotor and shaft and lift out rotor body.
4. Remove oil pressure relief valve plug and lift out the spring and plunger.
5. Wash all parts in cleaning solvent and inspect carefully for damage or wear.
6. The mating face of the oil pump cover should be smooth. If it is scratched or grooved, the cover should be replaced with a new one.
7. Check for excessive cover-to-rotor wear by laying a straight edge across the cover surface. If a .0015" feeler gauge can be inserted between cover and straight edge, the cover should be discarded and a new one installed.
8. Slide rotor body and rotor into pump body and then place a straight edge across the face of the pump body between the bolt holes. If a feeler gauge of less than .003" or more than .006" can be inserted between the rotors and straight edge, install a new pump body.
9. Remove the pump rotor and shaft, leaving rotor body in pump cavity. Press rotor body to one side with the fingers and measure the clearance between rotor and pump bodies. If it is more than .012", install a new pump body.
10. Check the clearance between the pump rotor and rotor body. If the measurement is more than .012", install a new pump rotor and rotor body.
11. Check the oil pump relief valve plunger for scoring and free operation in its bore. If the plunger is scored, install a new one.

WATER PUMP, REPLACE

Chrysler & Imperial

Drain cooling system, and on air conditioned cars only remove upper half of fan shroud. Loosen power steering pump or idler pulley, and generator. Remove all belts, fan, space and pulley.

On air conditioned cars, remove pulley from water pump fan hub, loosen all nuts from fan and remove the fan drive.

On all models, remove bolts holding water pump body to housing and remove water pump.

Dodge & Plymouth

To remove the water pump, drain cooling system and loosen the fan belt. Remove the fan, spacer, pulley and belt. Remove the pump inlet hose and the heater hose. Remove clamp from by-pass hose. Remove water pump bolts and push pump body down and off the by-pass hose.

Service Bulletin

CORE HOLE PLUG SIZES: When replacing a cup-type core hole plug in an engine, the size of the hole in the cylinder head, water jacket or rear bearing bore for the camshaft should be checked. At these locations a $\frac{1}{16}$" oversize hole is sometimes bored in production and an oversize core plug installed.

Core plugs $\frac{1}{16}$" oversize are available for replacement should they be required at these locations.

Service Bulletin

On late 1966 and early 1967 273 and 318 engines, two water pump chain case cover gaskets are used. When necessary to remove and install the water pump on either of these engines, be sure to install two service gaskets for proper sealing.

FUEL PUMP, REPLACE

SERVICE NOTE: Before installing the pump, it is good practice to crank the engine so that the nose of the camshaft eccentric is out of the way of the fuel pump rocker arm when the pump is installed. In this way there will be the least amount of tension on the rocker arm, thereby easing the installation of the pump.

1. Remove all gasket material from the pump and block gasket surfaces. Apply sealer to both sides of new gasket.
2. Position gasket on pump flange and hold pump in position against its mounting surface. Make sure rocker arm is riding on camshaft eccentric.
3. Press pump tight against its mounting. Install retaining screws and tighten them alternately.
4. Connect fuel lines. Then operate engine and check for leaks.

Clutch and Transmission Section

NOTE: 1969 linkage adjustment information is in this section. Repair procedures on both automatic and manual shift transmissions are covered elsewhere in this manual. Procedures for removing automatic transmissions as well as linkage adjustments on 1963-68 models are included in the automatic transmission chapters. See Chapter Index.

CLUTCH PEDAL, ADJUST

1966-69 All Cars

1. Inspect condition of clutch pedal rubber stop, if stop is damaged install a new one.
2. On models using the A-745 transmission, first disconnect interlock clutch rod at transmission end.
3. Adjust linkage by turning self-locking adjusting nut to provide $\frac{5}{32}$" free movement at outer end of fork. This movement will provide the prescribed one-inch free play at pedal.
4. Assemble interlock clutch rod (if used) to transmission pawl.

1963-65 Chrysler & Imperial

Shorten or lengthen the clutch release fork rod by turning the adjusting nut until there is $\frac{5}{32}$" free movement of the clutch fork outer end. This will give one inch free play at pedal.

1963-65 Dodge & Plymouth

Shorten or lengthen the clutch release fork rod by turning the adjusting nut until there is $\frac{5}{32}$" free movement of the clutch fork outer end. This adjustment, if correctly set, will give the necessary one inch free play at the pedal.

CLUTCH, REPLACE

Unless special clutch rebuilding equipment is available, it is recommended that the clutch assembly be exchanged for a rebuilt unit should the clutch require rebuilding. The driven disc, however, may be replaced without special equipment. If clutch rebuilding equipment is available, follow the equipment manufacturer's instructions.

Removal

1. Remove transmission and clutch pan.
2. Pull out release bearing and sleeve.
3. Mark clutch cover and flywheel so they may be assembled in the same relative position and thus maintain original balance.
4. Remove cap screws which retain clutch cover to flywheel. Loosen each screw a few turns in succession until cover is free.
5. Clutch assembly and driven disc may now be removed from the housing.

Installation

1. Coat the pilot bearing in crankshaft with wheel bearing grease.
2. Clean surfaces of flywheel and pressure plate, making certain no oil or grease remains on these parts.
3. Hold cover plate and disc in place and insert a special clutch aligning tool or a spare clutch shaft through the hub of the disc and into the crankshaft pilot bearing.
4. Bolt clutch cover loosely to flywheel, being sure marks previously made are lined up.
5. To avoid distortion of clutch cover, tighten cover bolts a few turns each in progression until all are tight. The final tightening should be 15-20 lb. ft. torque.
6. Install transmission by guiding it into place with guide studs inserted in the two top holes of the housing.
7. Adjust clutch pedal free travel.

THREE SPEED TRANSMISSION, REPLACE

NOTE: On 1965 Chrysler, Polara, Monaco, 880 as well as Plymouth Station Wagons the torsion bar rear anchor and rubber isolators must first be removed before the transmission can be removed from the vehicle.

1965-69 Chrysler, 1963-69 Dodge & Plymouth

1. Drain lubricant from transmission.
2. Disconnect propeller shaft, speedometer cable and housing and gearshift control rods.
3. Remove speedometer cable with hand so that housing is not crushed.
4. Remove back-up light switch leads (if so equipped).
5. Support engine with a jack or suitable fixture against underside of oil pan flange.
6. Raise engine slightly and disconnect extension housing from removable center crossmember.
7. Support transmission with a suitable jack. Then tap out four long bolts and remove center crossmember. Remove bolts that attach transmission to clutch housing.
8. Slide transmission rearward until clutch shaft clears clutch disc before lowering transmission. Lower and remove transmission.
9. Reverse removal procedure to install.

1963-64 Chrysler

1. Disconnect propeller shaft, speedometer cable and housing and gearshift control rods.
2. Remove back-up light switch leads.
3. Support engine with a jack stand or suitable fixture. Raise engine slightly and remove rear support crossmember attaching bolts.
4. Support transmission, using a suitable jack, and remove bolts that secure transmission to clutch housing.
5. Slide transmission rearward until clutch shaft clears clutch disc before lowering transmission.

NOTE: It is necessary to support engine and remove crossmember.

FOUR SPEED TRANSMISSION, REPLACE

NOTE: On 1965 Chrysler, Polara, Monaco, 880 as well as Plymouth Station Wagons the torsion bar rear anchor and rubber isolators must first be removed before the transmission can be removed from the vehicle.

1967-69 Dodge & Plymouth

1. Remove console and shift components.
2. Drain fluid from transmission.
3. Disconnect propeller shaft at rear universal joint and carefully pull yoke out of extension housing. *Be careful not to scratch or nick ground surface on sliding spline yoke during removal and installation of shaft.*
4. Disconnect speedometer cable and stop light switch leads.
5. Disconnect left-hand exhaust pipe (dual exhaust) from manifold.
6. Disconnect parking cable where necessary.
7. Support rear of engine with a jack.
8. Raise engine slightly and disconnect extension housing from removable center crossmember.
9. Support transmission with a suitable jack and remove center crossmember.
10. Remove transmission-to-clutch housing bolts.
11. Slide transmission rearward and out of vehicle.
12. Reverse procedure to install.

1965 Chrysler

1. Remove console trim plate.
2. Remove shift lever boot screws and slide boot up on lever.
3. Shift transmission into reverse. Lubricate lever opening in lower boot and push boot down over bolt heads. Then unscrew two bolts and remove shift lever.
4. Drain lubricant from transmission.
5. Disconnect propeller shaft, speedometer cable and pinion. Remove cable by hand to avoid crushing cable housing.
6. Disconnect left-hand exhaust pipe

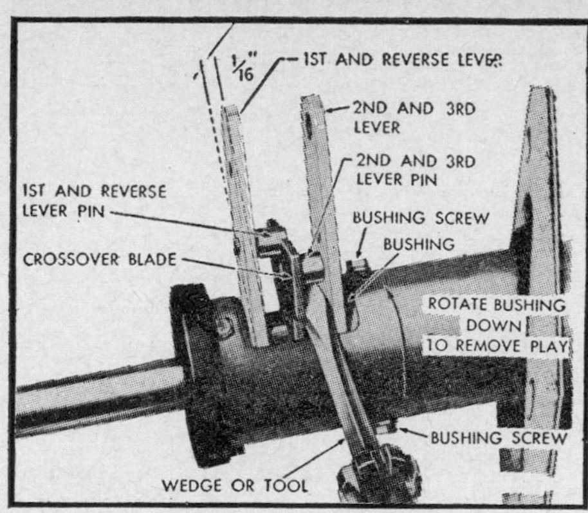

Fig. 1 Gearshift lever adjustment. 1965-69 Three Speed Transmission

(dual exhaust) from exhaust manifold.

7. Disconnect parking brake control cable.
8. Disconnect back-up light switch leads (if equipped).
9. Support engine with a jack or fixture against underside of oil pan flange.
10. Raise engine slightly.
11. Disconnect transmission extension housing from the removable center crossmember.
12. Support transmission with a jack.
13. Tap out four long bolts and remove center crossmember.
14. Remove bolts that attach transmission to clutch housing.
15. Rotate transmission until shift housing and stub lever clear, then slide transmission toward rear and out.
16. Reverse procedure to install.

1964 Chrysler

1. To remove transmission, unfasten and slide boot up on shift lever. Remove attaching bolts and take shift lever and boot from stub lever of shift housing.
2. Disconnect propeller shaft, speedometer cable and driven gear.
3. Disconnect left-hand exhaust pipe (dual exhaust) from exhaust manifold.
4. Disconnect parking brake control cable.
5. Support engine with a jack.
6. Raise engine slightly and remove rear crossmember.
7. Use another jack to support transmission. Then remove transmission attaching bolts.
8. Rotate transmission until shift housing and stub lever clear, then slide transmission rearward and out of vehicle.
9. Reverse removal procedure to install.

1963-66 Dodge & Plymouth

1. Remove console trim plate (1965).
2. Remove shift lever boot screws and slide boot up on lever.
3. Shift transmission into reverse, lubricate lever opening in lower boot and push boot down over bolt heads. Unscrew two bolts and remove shift lever.
4. On Non-Console type floor shifts, disconnect transmission shift rods.
5. Drain transmission lubricant.
6. Disconnect propeller shaft, speedometer cable and pinion. Remove cable by hand to avoid crushing housing.
7. Disconnect left-hand exhaust pipe (dual exhaust) from exhaust manifold.
8. Disconnect parking brake control cable, and back-up light switch at connector (if equipped).
9. Support engine against underside of oil pan flange.
10. Raise engine slightly and remove rear crossmember.
11. Support transmission, then remove attaching bolts.
12. Rotate transmission until shift housing and stub lever clear, then slide transmission to the rear and downward out of vehicle.

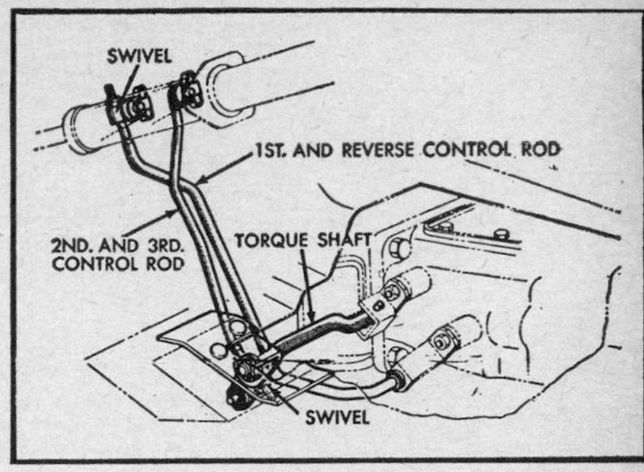

Fig. 2 Gearshift controls. 1965-69 Three Speed Transmission

13. Reverse procedure to install.

SHIFT LINKAGE, ADJUST THREE SPEED TRANS.

1965-69

1. With 2-3 control rod disconnected from lever on steering column and 1st-reverse rod disconnected from transmission lever, position both transmission levers in neutral.

NOTE: The neutral detent balls must be engaged to make this adjustment. To check this, start engine (clutch disengaged) then release clutch slowly.

2. Inspect fore and aft movement of shift levers in steering column. If movement at outer end of levers exceeds $\frac{1}{16}$", loosen two upper bushing screws, Fig. 1, and rotate bushing downward until all free play of levers has been removed. Then retighten bushing screws.
3. Wedge a screwdriver between crossover blade and the 2-3 lever so that crossover blade is engaged with both lever crossover pins.
4. Adjust length of 2-3 control rod until stub shaft of control rod or swivel enters hole in column lever, Fig. 2. Install washer and clip and tighten swivel lock nut. During the above setting the 2-3 control rod should be adjusted also to position selector lever on column 5°-10° above horizontal.
5. Slide clamp and swivel (on end of 1st-reverse control rod) either in or out until swivel stub shaft enters hole in transmission lever, Fig. 2. Install washers and clip. Determine middle backlash position in linkage, then tighten control rod lock nut.
6. Remove screwdriver from crossover blade and lever. Then move selector lever through all positions to check adjustments and to insure crossover smoothness.

1963-64 Chrysler

1. Remove screws that hold upper boot and retaining ring to floor pan. Remove retaining ring and slide boot up on gearshift lever far enough to expose gearshift mechanism.

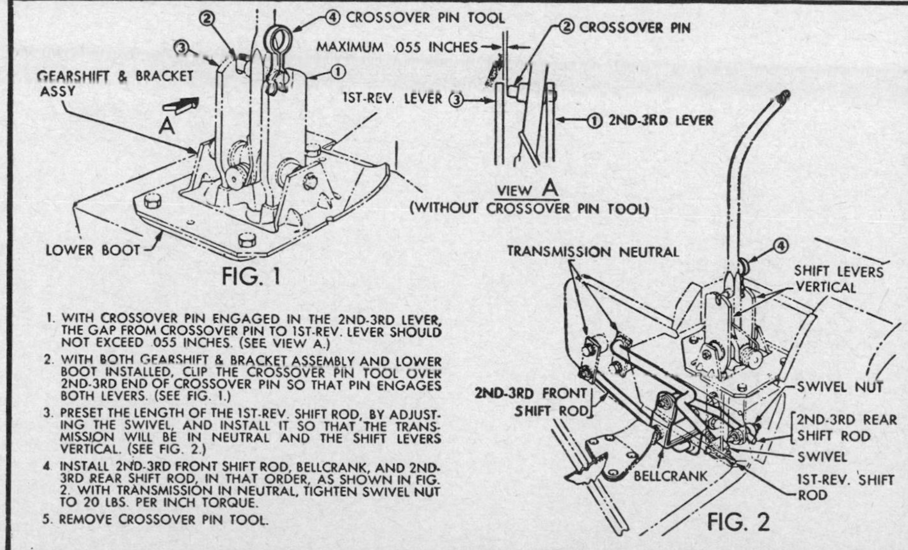

② ③ ④ CROSSOVER PIN TOOL
①
GEARSHIFT & BRACKET ASSY
A
MAXIMUM .055 INCHES
② CROSSOVER PIN
1ST-REV. LEVER ③
① 2ND-3RD LEVER
VIEW A
(WITHOUT CROSSOVER PIN TOOL)
LOWER BOOT
FIG. 1
1. WITH CROSSOVER PIN ENGAGED IN THE 2ND-3RD LEVER, THE GAP FROM CROSSOVER PIN TO 1ST-REV. LEVER SHOULD NOT EXCEED .055 INCHES. (SEE VIEW A.)
2. WITH BOTH GEARSHIFT & BRACKET ASSEMBLY AND LOWER BOOT INSTALLED, CLIP THE CROSSOVER PIN TOOL OVER 2ND-3RD END OF CROSSOVER PIN SO THAT PIN ENGAGES BOTH LEVERS. (SEE FIG. 1.)
3. PRESET THE LENGTH OF THE 1ST-REV. SHIFT ROD, BY ADJUSTING THE SWIVEL, AND INSTALL IT SO THAT THE TRANSMISSION WILL BE IN NEUTRAL AND THE SHIFT LEVERS VERTICAL. (SEE FIG. 2.)
4. INSTALL 2ND-3RD FRONT SHIFT ROD, BELLCRANK, AND 2ND-3RD REAR SHIFT ROD, IN THAT ORDER, AS SHOWN IN FIG. 2. WITH TRANSMISSION IN NEUTRAL, TIGHTEN SWIVEL NUT TO 20 LBS. PER INCH TORQUE.
5. REMOVE CROSSOVER PIN TOOL.
TRANSMISSION NEUTRAL
④
SHIFT LEVERS VERTICAL
2ND-3RD FRONT SHIFT ROD
SWIVEL NUT
2ND-3RD REAR SHIFT ROD
SWIVEL
BELLCRANK
1ST-REV. SHIFT ROD
FIG. 2

Fig. 3 Gearshift linkage adjustment. 1963-64 Three Speed Trans.

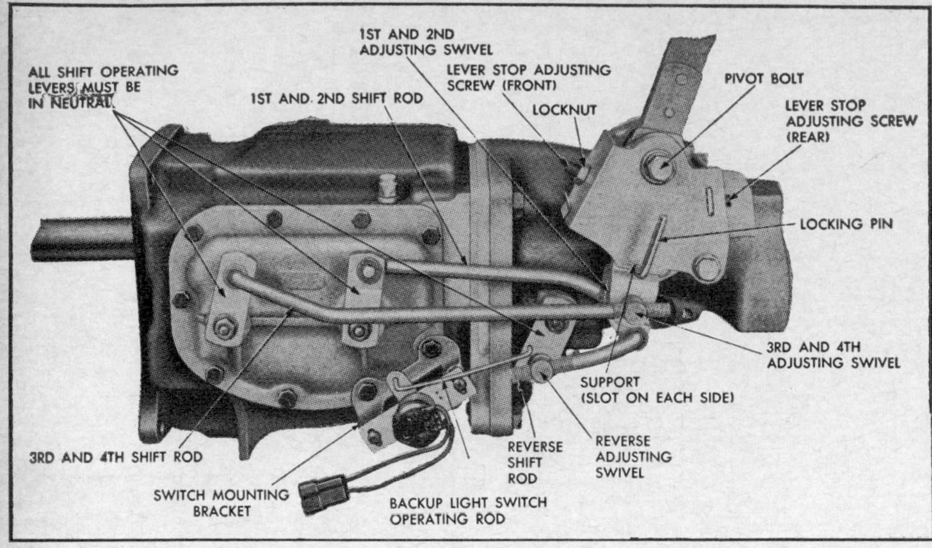

Fig. 8 Four speed transmission shift linkage adjustments. 1963

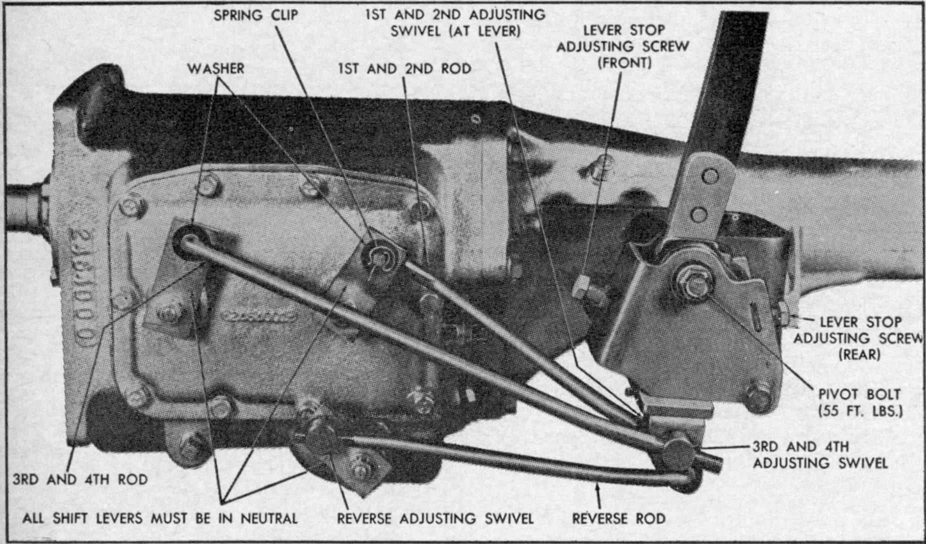

Fig. 9 Four speed transmission shift linkage adjustments. 1964-65

2. Disconnect 1st-reverse shift rod and 2-3 shift rod from their respective levers.
3. Place transmission shift levers in neutral position and adjust linkage as directed in Fig. 3.

1963-66 Dodge & Plymouth

1. With 2-3 control rod disconnected from its lever on the steering column and the 1st-reverse control rod disconnected from transmission lever, position both levers in neutral.
2. Check the axial freedom of shift levers in steering column. If outer end of levers move more than 1/16″ as shown in Fig. 1, loosen two upper bushing screws and rotate plastic bushing until all free play of levers has been removed.
3. Tighten bushing screws securely.
4. Install a wedge or screwdriver between cross-over blade and 2-3 lever, Fig. 1, so that cross-over blade is engaged with both lever cross-over pins.
5. Adjust swivel on end of 2-3 control rod until stub shaft of swivel enters hole in column lever. Tighten swivel nut.
6. Slide clamp and swivel on end of 1st-reverse control rod either in or out until swivel stub shaft enters hole in transmission lever.

SHIFT LINKAGE, ADJUST FOUR SPEED TRANS.

1963 Four Speed Trans.

1. Referring to Fig. 8, detach and slide boot up on shift lever.
2. Check to be sure pivot bolt is tightened securely.
3. Disconnect all shift rods at adjusting swivels.

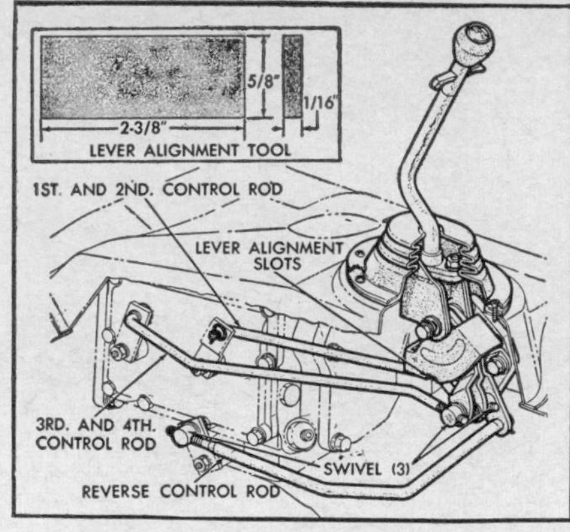

Fig. 10 Gearshift linkage adjustment. 1966-69 four speed transmission

4. Bend a ¼″ diameter rod to a right angle and insert it through aligning holes in control rod levers and slots provided in gear shift support. This holds the three levers in neutral position.
5. Adjust length of the three shift rods by turning swivels in or out as required until swivel stub shafts match control rod lever holes.
6. Install swivel stub shafts and secure with washers and spring clip retainers.
7. Remove the ¼″ aligning rod.

1964-65 Four Speed Trans.

1. Referring to Fig. 9, remove shift boot attaching screws and slide boot up on shift lever. Check to be sure that pivot bolt is torqued to 55 ft-lbs, and see that the shift lever bolts are torqued to 30 ft-lbs.
2. Disconnect shift rods from levers at adjusting swivels.
3. A special tool (C-3591) is available for aligning all three levers in the shift control assembly. Lacking this tool, the levers must be held in the exact neutral detent position while adjusting the length of the shift rods.
4. Adjust the rods by turning the swivels in or out until the swivel stub shafts match the control rod lever holes. Install the stub shafts and secure with washers and clip retainers.
5. Remove aligning tool (if used). Then with hand shift lever in the 3rd or 4th speed detent position, adjust lever stop screws (front and rear) to provide .020-.040″ clearance between lever and stops. Tighten screw lock nuts securely.

1966-69 Four Speed Trans.

1. Fabricate a lever alignment tool from $\frac{1}{16}$″ thick metal to the dimensions shown in Fig. 10.
2. Shift transmission into neutral, then disconnect all control rods from transmission levers.
3. Insert lever alignment tool through slots in levers, making sure it is through all levers and against the back plate.

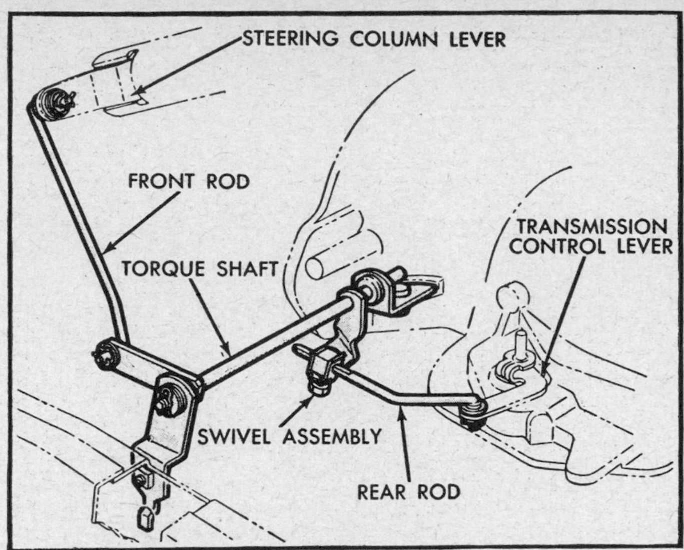

Fig. 11 Shift linkage. Column shift

Fig. 12 Shift linkage. Console shift

4. Adjust length of control rods so they enter transmission levers freely without any rearward or forward movement.
5. Secure adjustment and remove tool.
6. Check linkage for ease of shifting into all gears and for crossover smoothness.

1969 AUTO. TRANS. LINKAGE ADJUST

Column Shift

1. Place selector lever in "Park" position and loosen control rod swivel clamp screw, Fig. 11.
2. Move transmission control lever all the way to rear to place it in "Park".
3. Tighten swivel clamp screw to 100 in. lbs.

Console Shift

1. Place selector lever in "Park" position and loosen lower rod swivel clamp screw, Fig. 12.
2. Move transmission control lever all the way to rear to place it in "Park" position.
3. Tighten swivel clamp screw to 100 in. lbs.

Rear Axle, Propeller Shaft & Brakes

REAR AXLES

Figs. 1, 2 and 3 illustrate the various rear axle assemblies used on these cars. When necessary to overhaul any of these units, refer to the *Rear Axle Specifications* table in this chapter.

Integral Carrier Type

In these rear axles, Fig. 1, the rear axle housing and differential carrier are cast into an integral assembly. The drive pinion assembly is mounted in two opposed tapered roller bearings. The pinion bearings are preloaded by a spacer behind the front bearing. The pinion is positioned by a washer between the head of the pinion and the rear bearing.

The differential is supported in the carrier by two tapered roller side bearings. These bearings are preloaded by spacers located between the bearings and carrier housing. The differential assembly is positioned for proper ring gear and pinion backlash by varying these spacers. The differential case houses two side gears in mesh with two pinions mounted on a pinion shaft which is held in place by a lock pin. The side gears and pinions are backed by thrust washers.

Remove & Replace

Since the axle tubes are pressed into the carrier to form a one-piece housing, major service work requires the removal of the rear axle assembly.

1. Raise rear of vehicle until rear wheels clear floor, and support body at front of rear springs.
2. Block brake pedal up.
3. Remove rear wheels.
4. Disconnect hydraulic flex line.
5. Disconnect parking brake cable.
6. Disconnect propeller shaft at drive pinion yoke.
7. Remove rear spring U-clips and shock absorbers.
8. Remove rear axle from vehicle.
9. Reverse removal procedure to install. Torque U-clips to exactly 45 ft. lbs., and wheel nuts to 55 ft. lbs. Remove brake pedal block and bleed brake system.

Removable Carrier Type

In these rear axles, Figs. 2 and 3, the drive pinion is mounted in two tapered roller bearings. The bearings are preloaded by a spacer and shims behind the front bearing. The drive pinion is positioned by an adjusting washer between the head of the drive pinion and the rear pinion bearing. The front bearing is held in place by a large washer and nut.

The differential is supported in the carrier by two tapered roller side bearings. These bearings are preloaded by two threaded ring nuts between the bearings and the pedestals. The differential assembly is positioned for proper ring gear and pinion backlash by varying the adjustment of these ring nuts. The differential case houses two side gears in mesh with two pinions mounted on a pinion shaft which is held in place by a lock pin. The side gears and pinions are backed up by thrust washers. Side thrust of the wheels is transferred from one axle shaft to the other by means of a thrust block in the center of the differential case.

Remove & Replace

It is not necessary to remove the rear axle assembly for any normal repairs. The axle shafts and carrier assembly can easily be moved from the vehicle, leaving the rear axle housing in place.

1. Remove axle shafts as outlined below.
2. Disconnect rear universal joint and move propeller shaft out of the way.

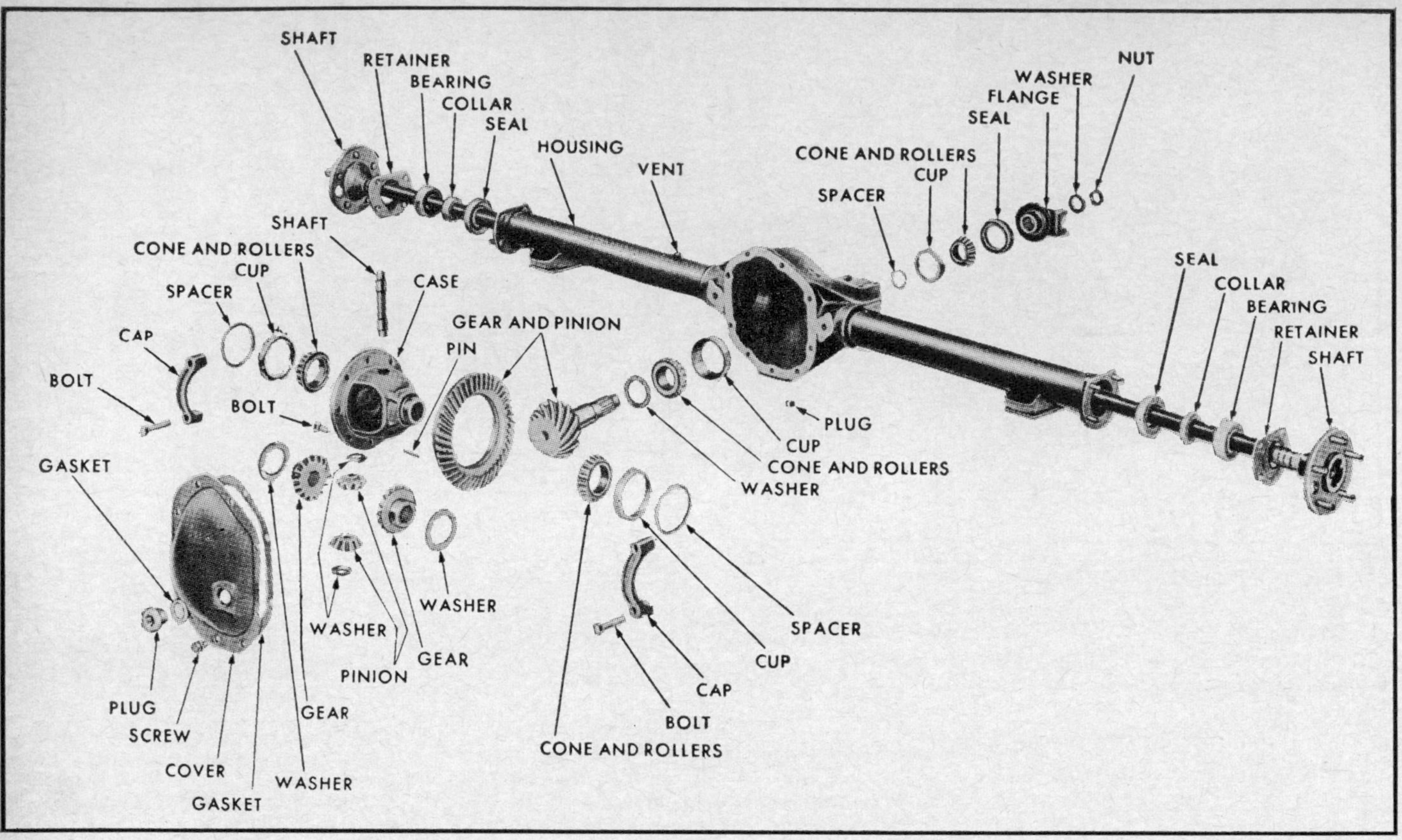

Fig. 1 Rear axle assembly. Integral type with 7¼" ring gear

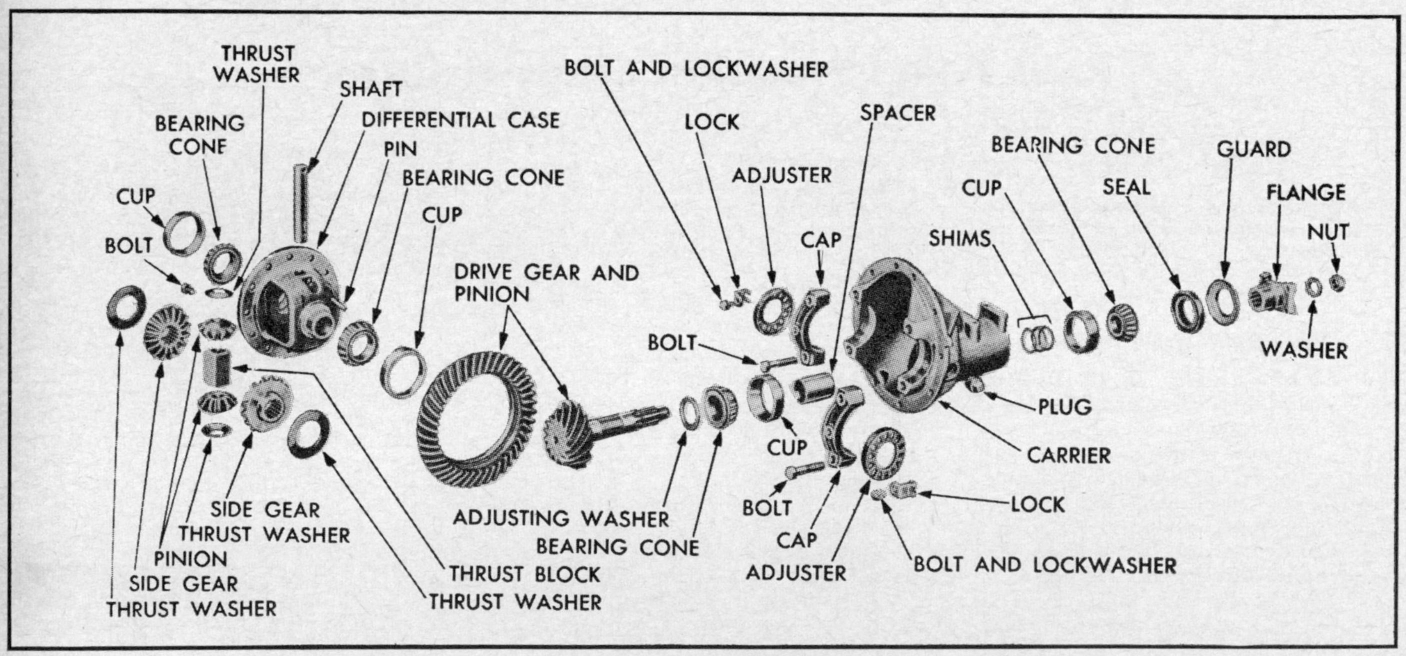

Fig. 2 Removable type rear axle assembly with large pinion

Support shaft to relieve strain on the front universal joint.

3. Remove lubricant from axle housing with a suction gun.
4. Remove attaching nuts and lift carrier assembly out of axle housing.
5. Reverse removal procedure to install.

AXLE SHAFTS, REPLACE

1963-69

With Rear Axles Figs. 2 and 3

Removal

1. With wheels removed, remove clips holding brake drum on axle shaft studs and remove brake drum.
2. Using access hole in axle shaft flange, remove retainer nuts. The right shaft with threaded adjuster in retainer plate will have a lock under one of the studs that should be removed at this time, Fig. 4.

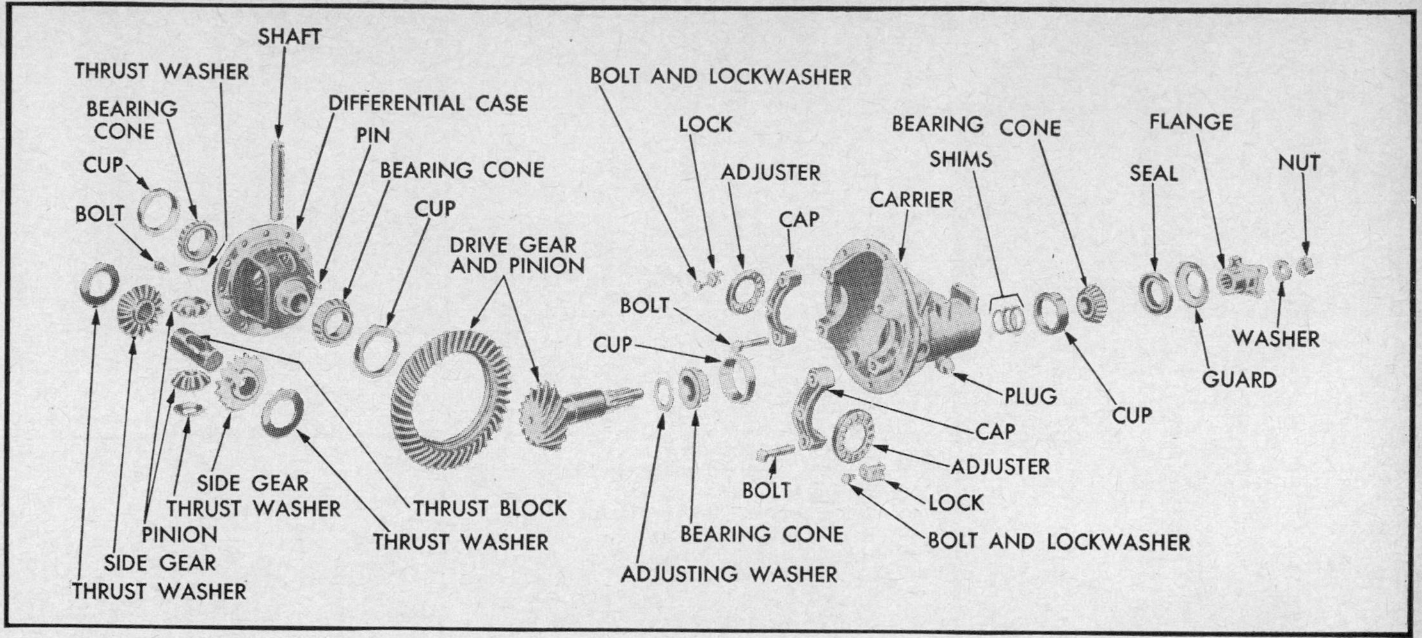

Fig. 3 Removable type rear axle assembly with small pinion

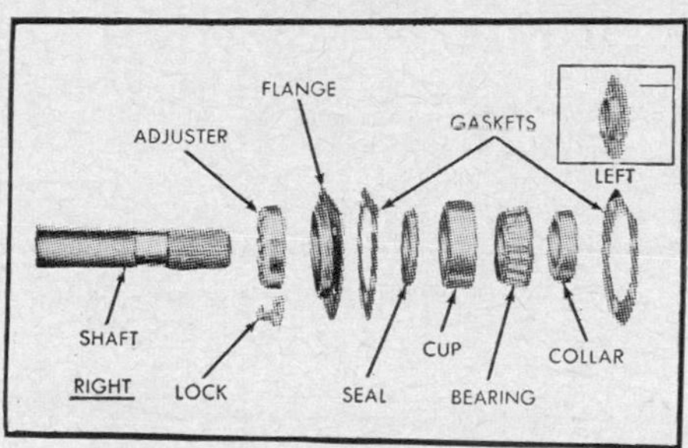

Fig. 4 Axle shaft disassembled

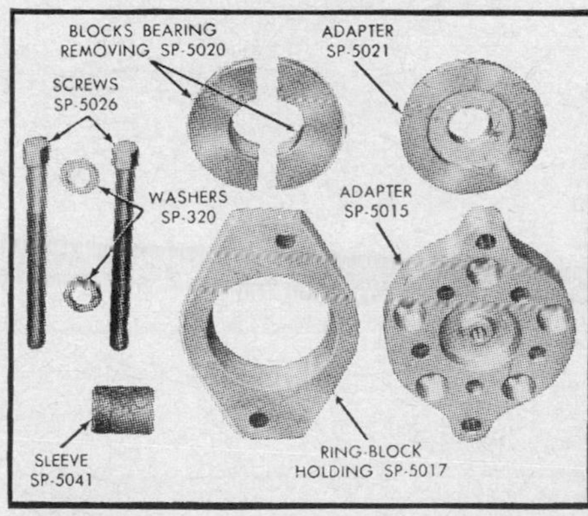

Fig. 5 Tool set for removing axle shaft

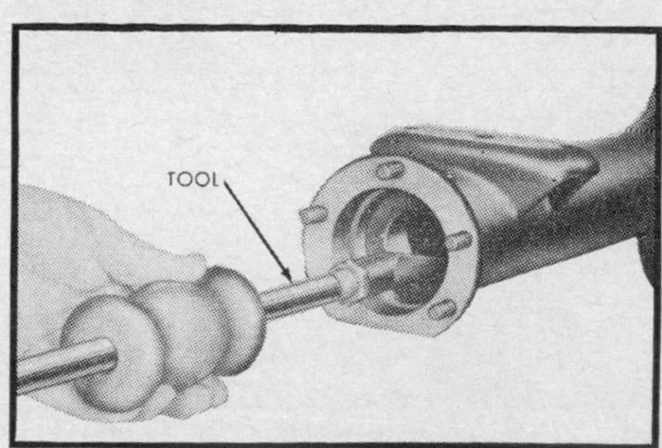

Fig. 6 Removing inner oil seal

3. Remove parking brake strut.
4. Attach axle shaft remover tool, Fig. 5, to axle shaft flange and remove axle shaft. Remove brake assembly and foam gaskets.
5. Remove oil seal, Fig. 6.
6. Wipe axle shaft housing seal bore clean and install a new seal, Fig. 7.

Disassembly

To prevent the possibility of damaging axle shaft scal surface, slide a protective sleeve over seal surface next to bearing collar, Fig. 8.

1. Position axle shaft bearing collar on a heavy vise and, using a chisel, cut deep grooves into retaining collar at 90-degree intervals, as shown in Fig. 8. This will enlarge bore of collar and permit it to be driven off axle shaft.
2. Remove bearing roller retainer flange by cutting off lower edge with a chisel, Fig. 9.
3. Grind a section off flange of inner bearing cone, Fig. 10, and remove bearing rollers, Fig. 11.
4. Pull bearing roller retainer down as far as possible and cut with side cutters and remove, Fig. 12.
5. Remove roller bearing cup and protective sleeve from axle shaft.

CAUTION: Sleeve should not be used as a protector for the seal journal when pressing off bearing cone as it was not designed for this purpose.

6. To avoid scuffing seal journal when bearing cone is being removed, it should be protected by a single wrap of .002" shim stock held in place by a rubber band, Fig. 13.
7. Remove bearing cone with tool set shown in Fig. 5. Tighten bolts of tool alternately until cone is removed, Fig. 14.
8. Remove seal in bearing retainer plate and replace with a new seal.

Fig. 7 Installing inner oil seal

Fig. 8 Notching bearing retainer collar

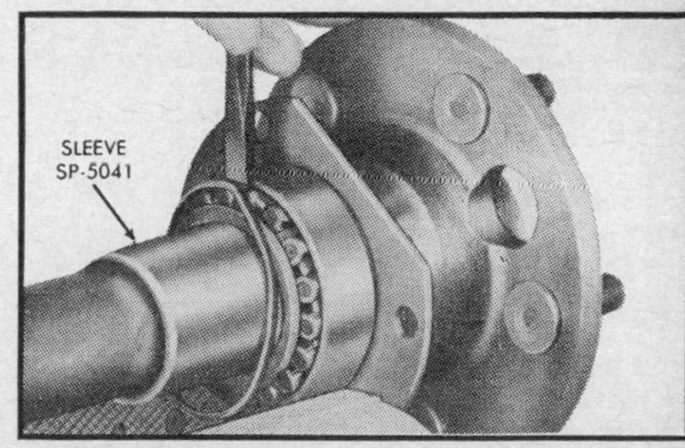

Fig. 9 Removing roller retainer

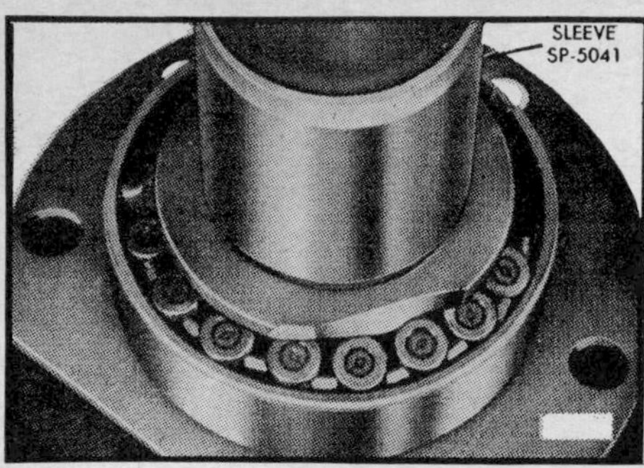

Fig. 10 Flange ground off inner bearing cone

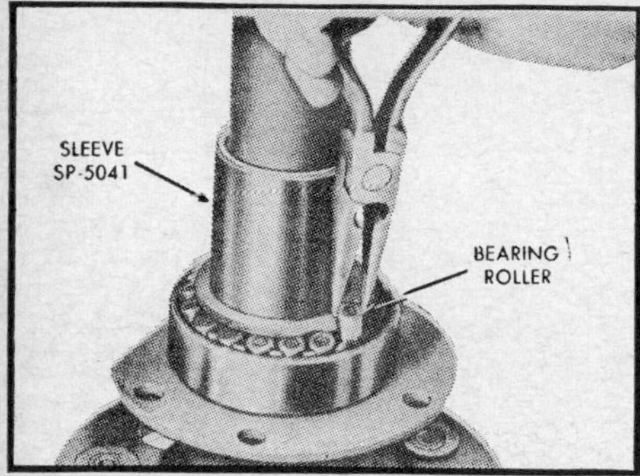

Fig. 11 Removing bearing rollers

Fig. 12 Cutting out bearing retainer

Fig. 13 Seal journal protection

Assembly

1. Install retainer plate and seal on axle shaft.
2. Install new axle shaft bearing cup, cone and collar on shaft, using tool shown in Fig. 15. Tighten bolts of tool alternately until bearing and collar are seated properly.
3. Inspect axle shaft seal journal for scratches and polish with #600 crocus cloth if necessary.
4. Lubricate wheel bearings with approved grease.

Installation

1. Clean axle shaft flange face and install new gasket followed by brake support plate on left side of axle housing.
2. Install foam gasket on studs of axle housing and slide shaft through oil seal and engage splines in differential side gear.
3. Tap end of axle shaft lightly with a plastic mallet to position axle shaft bearing in housing bearing bore. Position retainer plate over axle housing studs. Install retainer nuts and torque to 30-35 ft-lbs. Start by tightening bottom nut.
4. Repeat Step 1 on right side of axle housing.
5. Back off threaded adjuster on right axle shaft until inner face of adjuster is flush with inner face of retainer plate. Carefully slide axle shaft through oil seal and engage splines in differential side gears.
6. Repeat Step 3.

Axle Shaft End Play

When setting end play both rear wheels must be off the ground, otherwise a false end play setting will occur.

1. Using a dial indicator mounted as shown in Fig. 16, turn the adjuster clockwise until both wheel bearings are seated and there is zero end play in axle shafts. Back off adjuster counterclockwise four notches to establish an axle shaft end play of .013-.023".
2. Tap end of axle shaft lightly with a plastic mallet to seat right wheel bearing cup against adjuster, and rotate axle shaft several revolutions so that a true end play reading is indicated.
3. Remove one retainer plate nut and install adjuster lock. If tab on lock does not mate with notch in adjuster, turn adjuster slightly until it does. Install nut and torque to 30-35 ft-lbs.
4. Recheck axle shaft end play. If not within prescribed limits, repeat adjustment procedure.
5. Remove dial indicator and install brake drum, drum retaining clips and wheel.

For Figs. 2 & 3 Rear Axles

SERVICE BULLETIN

Should the shim pack on each end of the rear axle housing on a 1963-64 model have to be separated for any reason, such as replacing axle shaft bearings or adjusting axle shaft end play, two gaskets should be used at each end on reassembly.

When installing the gaskets, place one on each side of the shim pack. Where the proper end play is achieved with all shims removed, use one gasket. Always use new gaskets when assembling the rear axle since used gaskets will not give adequate sealing.

Fig. 14 Removing bearing cone

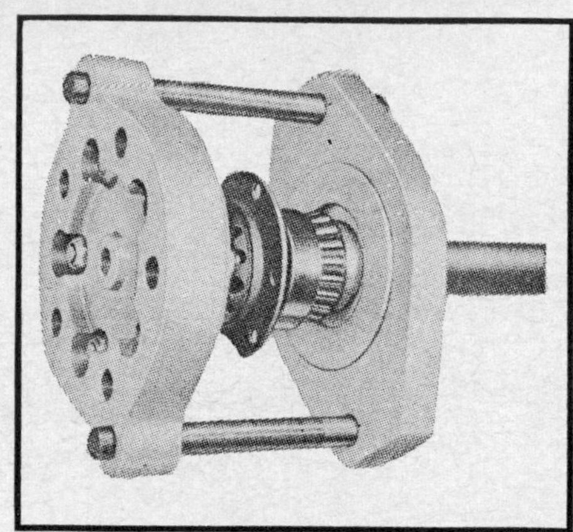

Fig. 15 Installing bearing and collar

Fig. 16 Measuring axle shaft end play

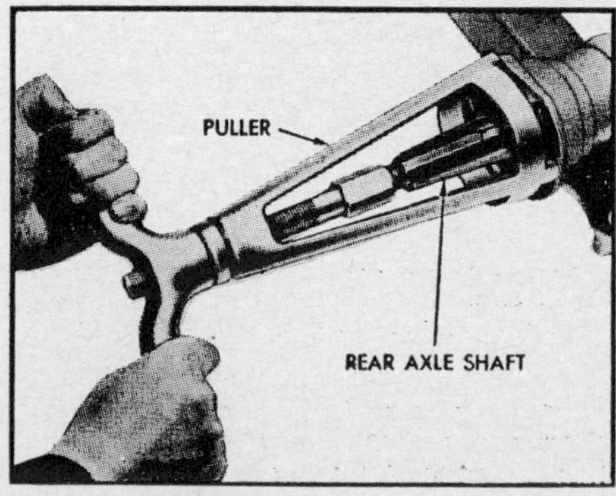

Fig. 17 Removing axle shaft. 1963-64 with Figs. 2 and 3 rear axles

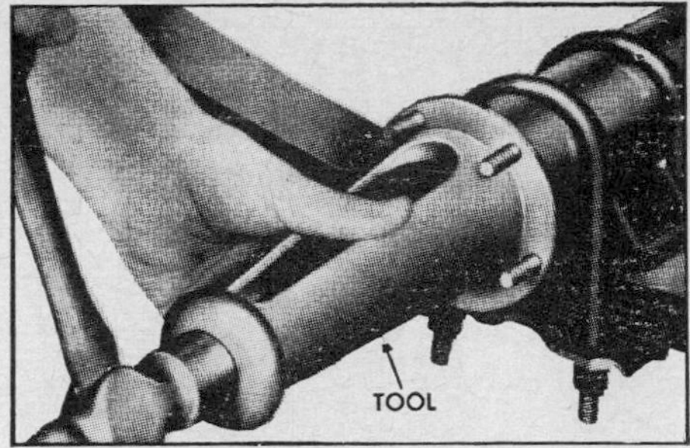

Fig. 18 Installing axle shaft bearing cup. 1963-64 with Figs. 2 and 3 rear axles

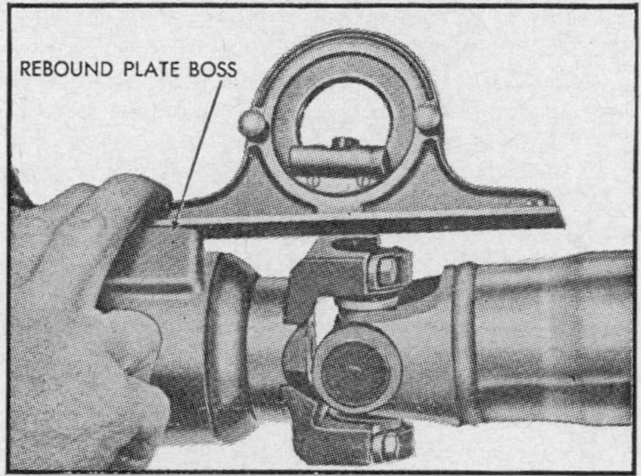

Fig. 19 Checking rear axle angle

Fig. 20 Installing tapered wedge between spring and axle housing spring plates

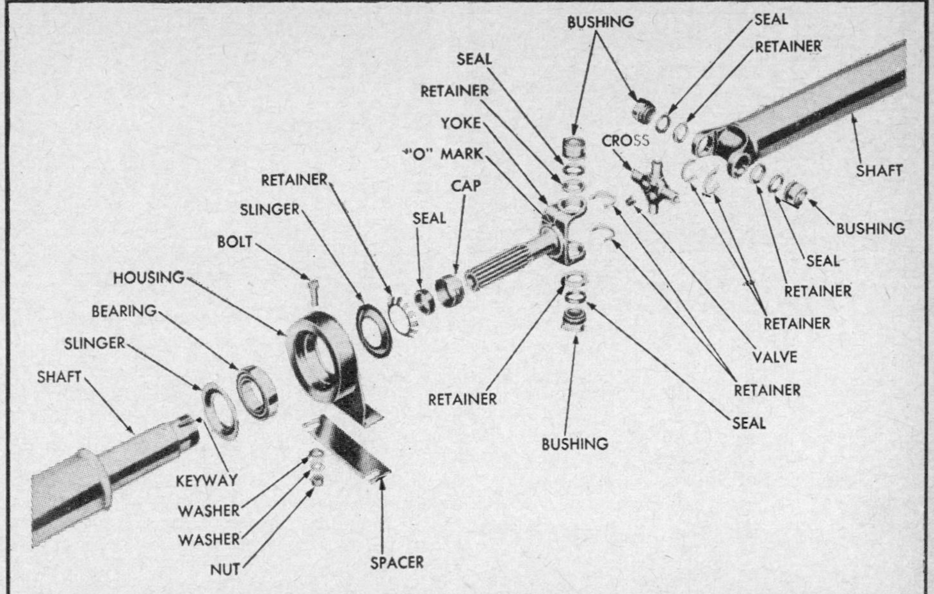

Fig. 21 Two-piece propeller shaft and center bearing assembly. 1963-64 Imperial

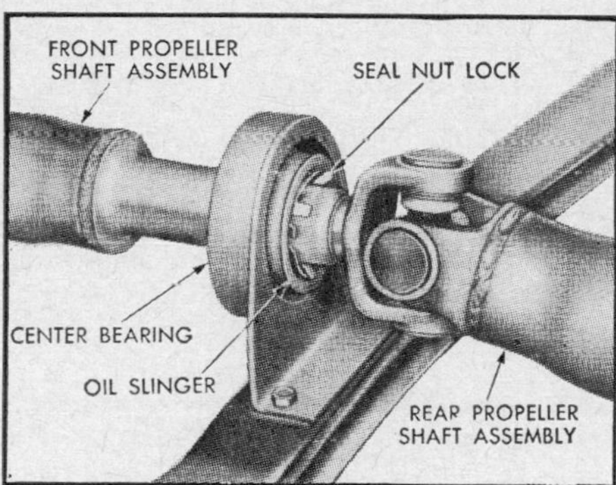

Fig. 22 Center bearing installed. 1963-64 Imperial

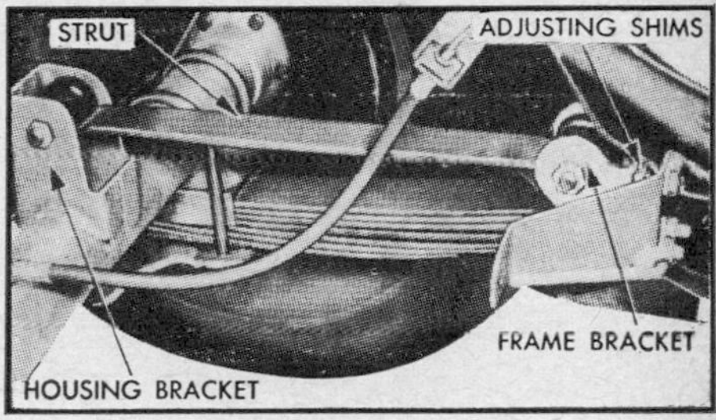

Fig. 23 Rear axle control strut. 1963-64 Imperial

Removal

1. Raise car and remove wheels, hub and drum, using a suitable puller. *Do not strike end of axle shaft or use a knock-off type puller as damage to bearings and thrust block may result.*
2. Block brake pedal to prevent its being depressed and disconnect brake lines at wheel cylinders.
3. Remove key from axle shaft keyway and remove brake support and dust shield.
4. Carefully remove shim pack from each end of axle housing. Identify each shim pack as to location to aid in reassembly.
5. Remove axle shaft and bearing assembly, using a puller of the type shown in Fig. 17. If necessary, the bearings may be removed from the shafts with a suitable puller.
6. Remove axle shaft inner seals with a hook-type puller.

Installation

1. Where original axle shafts and/or bearings are used, start measurement of end play with original shim packs, after recording thickness of each. Where either or both the axle shaft and bearing is replaced, use shim packs totaling .040″ per side. Shims are available in thicknesses of .005.″, .0125″, .015″ and .030″.
2. Install inner oil seals in axle housing.
3. Starting at one end of axle housing, install a .040″ shim pack on flange studs.
4. Working from same side of axle housing, lubricate axle shaft bearing with wheel bearing grease and install axle shaft.
5. Install bearing cup with tool shown in Fig. 18 or equivalent. Make certain cup is driven into axle housing until face of installing tool bottoms against shims, not the housing flange. Remove tool and install brake support, lockwashers and nuts, tightening nuts to 30-35 ft. lbs.
6. Working from opposite side of axle housing, lubricate bearing and install other axle shaft until it contacts axle thrust block.
7. With a fiber mallet, tap end of axle shaft against thrust block. This will force opposite axle shaft bearing into its cup to its fullest extent.
8. Install bearing cup, Fig. 18. The cup must be tapped into position until the axle shaft end play just disappears. The bearing cup will protrude slightly beyond the face of the axle shaft flange.
9. While the tool is held firmly against bearing cup, insert a feeler gauge between the housing flange and face of tool to measure the clearance.
10. To obtain the required axle shaft end play, add a minimum of .013″ of shimming to whatever the feeler gauge reading is. Compare the thickness of the shim pack with the thickness of the opposite pack. If the difference between the packs exceeds .020″, divide the difference to center the axle shafts and thrust block.
11. Position shim packs on flange studs and drive bearing cups in until tool, Fig. 18, bottoms on shim pack.
12. Install new outer oil seal in brake support plate with lip of seal toward center of car.
13. Insert a suitable sleeve in outer seal to protect seal when brake support is installed.

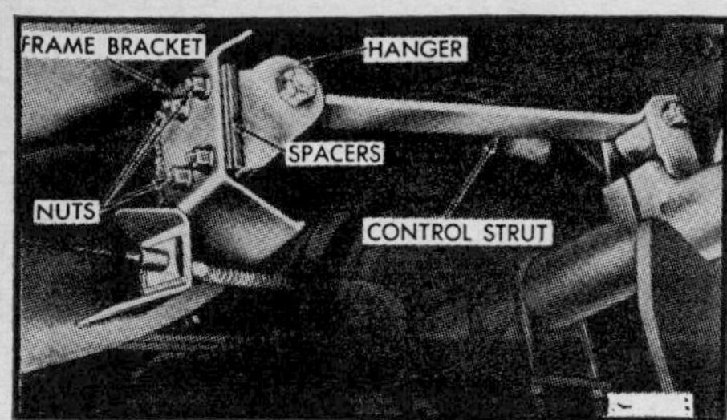

Fig. 24 Rear axle control strut. 1965 Imperial

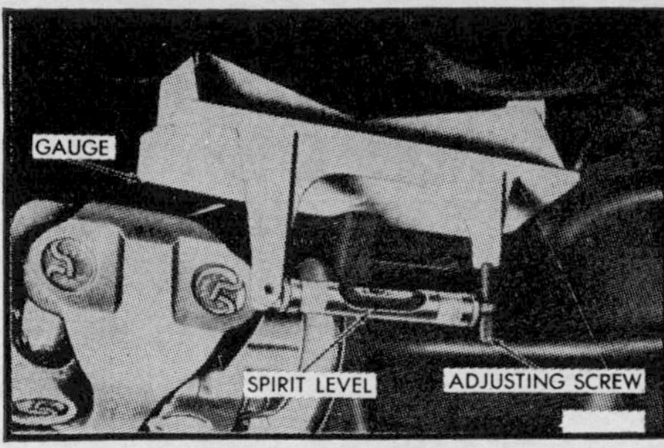

Fig. 25 Measuring rear axle angle. 1965-69 Imperial

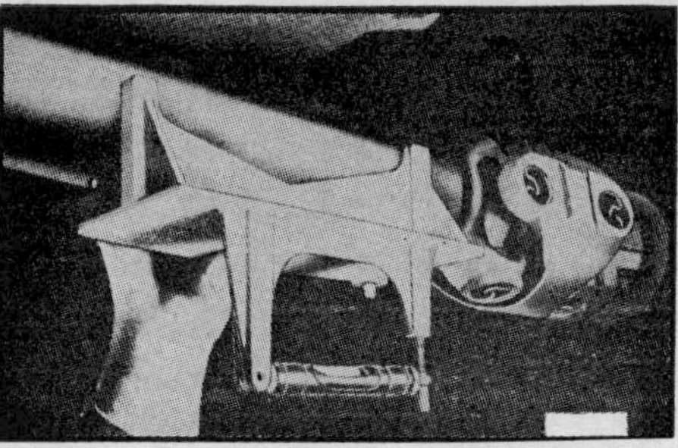

Fig. 26 Measuring propeller shaft angle. 1965-69 Imperial

14. Install dust shield and brake support. Tighten attaching nuts to 30-35 ft. lbs.
15. Install wheels, hub and drum. *Axle shaft key should be flush with outboard end of hub.*

1963-69 with Fig. 1 Rear Axle

1. With wheel removed, remove clips holding brake drum on wheel studs and remove drum.
2. Disconnect brake lines at wheel cylinders.
3. Using access hole in axle flange, remove retainer nuts from end of housing.
4. Remove axle shaft and brake assembly, using a slide hammer-type puller.
5. Remove brake assembly from axle shaft with care to avoid damaging shaft in seal contact area.
6. Remove oil seal from axle housing.
7. *Remove axle shaft bearings only when necessary. Removal of bearings makes them unfit for further use.*
8. *Axle shaft end play is pre-set and not adjustable. End play is accomplished by the amount of end play built into the bearings. The two axle housing brake support plate gaskets on each side are used for sealing purposes only. Always replace the gaskets once they have been removed.*
9. Press bearing and collar on shaft firmly against shoulders on shaft.
10. Install new oil seal in housing.
11. Install brake assembly on axle housing and carefully slide axle shaft through oil seal and into side gear splines.
12. Tap end of axle shaft lightly to position axle shaft bearing into bearing bore and attach retainer plate to housing.
13. Install brake drums and wheels.

PROPELLER SHAFT

One Piece Shaft, 1963-69

1. Remove both rear universal joint roller and bushing assembly clamps from pinion yoke. Do not disturb retaining strap holding roller assemblies on cross.
2. If equipped with sliding yoke front joint, lower front of vehicle slightly to prevent loss of transmission oil and pull drive shaft out as an assembly. If equipped with ball and trunnion front joint, disconnect joint from transmission.
3. To install sliding yoke type, carefully slide yoke into splines on transmission output shaft. For ball and trunnion type, connect front universal to transmission flange and torque retaining nuts to 35 ft. lbs.
4. Align rear of propeller shaft with pinion yoke and position roller and bushing assemblies into seats of pinion yoke.
5. Install bushing clamps and tighten clamp bolts to 170 inch lbs.

Two Piece Shaft, 1963-64

1. Disconnect front joint adapter flange from brake drum.
2. Remove rear joint clamps from pinion yoke. If bushing retainer is holding bushings on cross, it is not necessary to remove bushings.
3. Remove center bearing housing bolts and remove shims from under housing.
4. Remove propeller shaft as an assembly toward rear of vehicle.
5. To install, insert forward section of shaft assembly over body crossmember, and connect front joint. Tighten nuts to 35 ft. lbs.
6. Connect rear joint and tighten clamp bolts to 170 inch lbs.
7. Position shims under center bearing housing, install and tighten bolts to 35 ft. lbs.

Two Piece Shaft, 1965-66

1. Referring to Fig. 27, remove cross and roller bushing clamps from transmission yoke.
2. Disengage front U-joint cross and roller bushings from yoke. NOTE: Tie up or otherwise support front end of propeller shaft to prevent damaging center joint.
3. Unfasten rear U-joint from rear axle pinion yoke. Support rear end of shaft.
4. Unfasten center bearing bracket from frame crossmember.
5. Reverse procedure to install.

PROP. SHAFT ANGLES

One Piece Shaft, 1963-64

The smooth quiet operation of the propeller shaft and universal joints depends upon proper alignment together with lubrication of universal joints at regular intervals. Therefore, if drive line shudder, roughness, vibration or rumble is experienced, the propeller shaft and rear axle housing angles may be measured with a spirit level protractor with the vehicle in level position and no additional weight in the car.

1. Level vehicle. Check level at underside of body sill at center of front door.
2. Remove rebound plate and bumper from top of differential carrier housing.
3. Place protractor on machined surfaces of rebound plate bosses, Fig. 19.
4. Level bubble and record reading of angularity. The differential carrier housing should incline slightly. If the housing is level or elevated, add tapered shims between rear springs and differential housing spring plates to obtain a slight downward angle, Fig. 20. Recheck angularity.
5. Place protractor on underside of propeller shaft near rear universal joint and record the angle.
6. Add the readings of the carrier housing and propeller shaft. This should total approximately 2 degrees. Adjust to this total by adding or subtracting various thickness shims, Fig. 20.
7. Install rebound plate and bumper assembly on carrier. Tighten to 200 inch lbs.
8. Tighten spring U-clips to 70 ft. lbs.

One Piece Shaft 1965-69

Front Joint Angle

1. Position spirit level gauge and adapter at left side of engine so that adapter pins contact flat surface of engine oil pan flange adjacent to vertical wall of oil pan.
2. Set position of bubble in spirit level.
3. Remove adapter and position gauge firmly along underside of propeller shaft, Fig. 26.
4. Observe position of bubble. Reading should not exceed 2 degrees. If bubble is slightly forward of tolerance, the angle is smaller than specified and need not be corrected. If bubble is rearward of tolerance, angle must be corrected. To reduce angle by one graduation, install a ⅛" shim between transmission extension housing and rear engine mount.

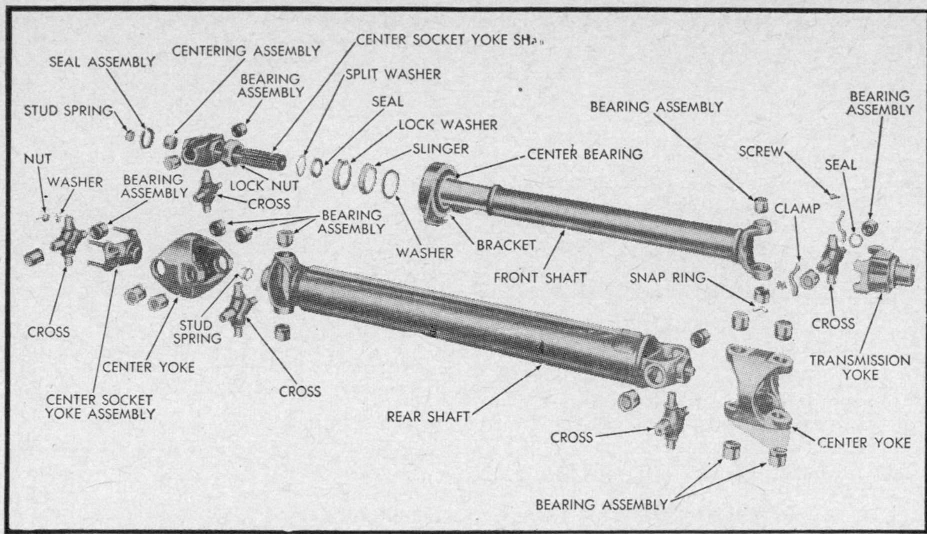

Fig. 27 Two-piece propeller shaft details. 1965-66 Imperial

Rear Joint Angle

1. Remove pinion bumper plate and position gauge on machined pads with locating pin in rear bolt hole, Fig. 25.
2. Set bubble in spirit level.
3. Remove gauge from carrier and position it firmly along underside of propeller shaft, Fig. 26.
4. Observe position of the bubble. Reading should not exceed 2 degrees. Rear joint angle is corrected by installing wedge type shims between both rear springs and axle housing pads. If bubble is too far forward, insert shim with thick end toward front of car. If bubble is too far rearward, thick end of shim goes to rear of car.

Two Piece Shaft, 1963-64

The two-piece propeller shaft, Fig. 21, has three universal joints. The shaft is supported by a ball bearing located ahead of the center universal joint. When the vehicle is in motion the middle universal joint is free to slide fore and aft inside the splines of the front section of the shaft.

Conditions may arise under certain passenger loads which may create a propeller shaft shudder or vibration at low speeds. In order to control shudder or vibration, a rear axle control strut is incorporated. To correct a shudder condition, make sure engine has been tuned and is operating smoothly with no hesitation or stumble on acceleration.

Before checking propeller shaft angles, the vehicle should have the weight of a full tank of fuel. Check the indexing of the universal joints and propeller shafts. The letter "O" on the front face of the spline should be lined up with the key slot at the rear of the front shaft, Fig. 21. The seal retainer must be removed in order to see the key slot in shaft, Fig. 22.

1. With a spirit level protractor of the type shown in Fig. 19, measure rear universal joint angle. This angle should be three degrees with no passenger load. If angle is not three degrees, add or remove shims between control strut brackets and rear axle brackets. Adding a $\frac{1}{16}$" shim will reduce the angle about one degree, and vice versa, Fig. 23.
2. After rear universal joint angle has been adjusted as near to three degrees as possible, measure middle universal joint angle. This angle should be 2½ degrees when rear universal angle is three degrees. Adjust middle universal angle by adding or removing shims between center bearing insulator and crossmember. Adding a ⅛" shim will increase angle about ½ degree, and vice versa.
3. If a large number of shims must be removed or added at center bearing, rear joint angle should be rechecked to be sure that it has not appreciably altered from three degrees.

These adjustments provide the least amount of shudder on a two-passenger load. If it is desirable to have the least amount of shudder on a full-passenger load, center bearing must be raised slightly by adding shims.

Two Piece Shaft, 1965-66

When measuring propeller shaft angularity, the vehicle should be in a level position and have no extra weight except that of a full tank of fuel. **CAUTION:** The vehicle must be supported by the wheels or front suspension lower control arms and rear axle housing. Do not use a frame contact hoist.

1. Remove differential carrier rebound bumper and bracket assembly. Also remove spacers from both rear axle control strut hangers, Fig. 24.
2. Hold alignment gauge, Fig. 25, on machined bosses of differential carrier.
3. Adjust the gauge spirit level to center the bubble. The axle pinion housing should be pointing downward at a slight angle. Each time the gauge is used the level must be on the same side of the propeller shaft.
4. Hold gauge on underside of propeller shaft near rear U-joint and note location of bubble in spirit level, Fig. 26. The entire bubble should be within one and three graduations forward from center.
5. If it is necessary to adjust rear joint angle, loosen all U-bolt nuts and install two-degree tapered wedges between both rear springs and axle housing spring pads (see Fig. 20). If the bubble is forward of the third graduation, install wedges with the thick edge of wedge toward front of vehicle.
6. If the bubble is centered or behind the center graduation, install the wedges with the thick edge toward the rear of the vehicle. Tighten U-bolt nuts to 55 ft-lbs.
7. Temporarily place two passengers in the front seat and one in the rear to load the rear springs. Install sufficient spacers to fill the space between the strut hanger and frame brackets on both sides, Fig. 24. Install bracket bolts and tighten nuts to 35 ft-lbs.
8. Remeasure rear U-joint angle, then install rebound bumper and plate. Torque attaching screws 200 in-lbs.

BRAKE ADJUSTMENTS

Service Bulletin

BRAKE GRAB CORRECTION: The cause of brake grab with light pedal pressure on 1964 model equipped with a Midland-Ross power brake can lie either in the brake booster or in the wheel components of the brake.

To check the cause, first be sure the brakes are properly adjusted. Then disconnect the vacuum hose from the brake booster and plug the hose to prevent vacuum loss. Now road-test. If the brakes operate normally without power assist, the trouble is in the brake booster. Should the grabbing persist, the trouble must be in the wheel brake components. Possible causes are contaminants on the lining, incorrect lining, or an uneven finish on the brake drum.

When severe grabbing is found to be caused by the booster, a correction can be made by installing a new reaction-lever retaining ring and reaction ring.

Service Bulletin

BRAKE SQUEAKS: A mid-frequency brake noise (squeak) may be encountered on some 1963-65 cars. A wave-type washer inserted between the adjuster socket and the adjacent face of the adjuster screw star wheel (in place of the existing flat washer) has been found to be effective in controlling mid-range brake noise and squeaks. The wave-type washer is available under Part Number 2534914.

1963-69 Self Adjusting Brakes

These brakes, Fig. 28, have self-adjusting shoe mechanisms that assure correct lining-to-drum clearances at all times. The automatic adjusters operate only when the brakes are applied as the car is moving rearward or when the car comes to an uphill stop.

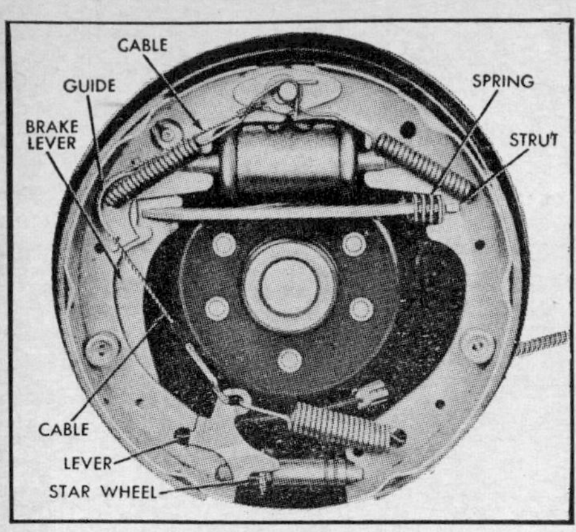

Fig. 28 Right rear brake (10-11 inch). 1963-69

Although the brakes are self-adjusting, an initial adjustment is necessary when the brake shoes have been relined or replaced, or when the length of the star wheel adjuster has been changed during some other service operation.

Frequent usage of an automatic transmission forward range to halt reverse vehicle motion may prevent the automatic adjusters from functioning, thereby inducing low pedal heights. Should low pedal heights be encountered, it is recommended that numerous forward and reverse stops be made until satisfactory pedal height is obtained.

Service Note

If a low pedal height condition cannot be corrected by making numerous reverse stops (provided the hydraulic system is free of air) it indicates that the self-adjusting mechanism is not functioning. Therefore, it will be necessary to remove the drum, clean, free up and lubricate the adjusting mechanism. Then adjust the brakes, being sure the parking brake is fully released.

Adjustment

1. Each backing plate has two adjusting hole covers; remove the rear cover and turn the adjusting screw upward with a screwdriver or other suitable tool to expand the shoes until a slight drag is felt when the drum is rotated.
2. Remove the drum.
3. While holding the adjusting lever out of engagement with the adjusting screw, Fig. 29, back off the adjusting screw about one turn with the fingers. *NOTE—If finger movement will not turn the screw, free it up. If this is not done, the adjusting lever will not turn the screw during subsequent vehicle operation. Lubricate the screw with oil and coat with wheel bearing grease.*
4. Install wheel and drum, and adjusting hole cover. Adjust brakes on remaining wheels in the same manner.
5. If pedal height is not satisfactory, drive the vehicle and make sufficient reverse stops until proper pedal height is obtained.

PARKING BRAKE, ADJUST

1963-69

1. Release parking brake lever and loosen cable adjusting nut to be sure cable is slack.
2. With rear wheel brakes properly adjusted, tighten cable adjusting nut until a slight drag is felt when the rear wheels are rotated. Then loosen the cable adjusting nut until both rear wheels can be rotated freely.
3. To complete the operation, back off an additional two turns of the cable adjusting nut.
4. Apply and release parking brake several times to be sure rear wheels are not dragging when cable is in released position.

Service Bulletin

REPLACES BRAKE CABLE: When replacing a parking brake cable that has broken at the brake lever on a 1963-64 model, a new, larger bumper should be installed in the lever bracket.

To install the new bumper, simply pull the old bumper out of its retaining slot in the lever bracket. Then use hand pressure to press the larger bumper into the retaining slot.

VACUUM RELEASE PARKING BRAKE

1963-69 Imperial

The parking brake is pedal applied and released by a vacuum chamber. When the engine is started and vacuum is developed, energy is then available to release the parking brake. This is controlled by the transmission push buttons or shift linkage. When the transmission is in "Neutral", vacuum is cut off from the release chamber and there is no action of the parking brake pedal.

When the transmission is shifted into a drive gear (forward or reverse), the vacuum control valve is opened, actuating the vacuum release chamber mounted on the parking brake assembly.

NOTE: In the event of engine failure and no vacuum, the brake may be released by a manual release lever mounted on the left side of the parking brake pedal assembly. This assembly prevents the vehicle from being driven with the parking brake in the applied position.

Testing Vacuum Release

1. If the mechanism is inoperative, first check for damaged or kinked vacuum hoses and for loose hose connections at the vacuum chamber, vacuum release valve at neutral safety switch, and at engine manifold connection.
2. Check adjustment of neutral safety switch and operation of vacuum release valve.
3. Check vacuum chamber piston travel by running engine and shifting transmission selector from drive to neutral. The manual release lever should move up and down as vacuum is applied and released. If no movement is observed or if movement is slow (more than 1 or 2 seconds to complete full stroke), the vacuum chamber is leaking and should be replaced.
4. Check brake release with vacuum applied. If vacuum chamber piston completes full stroke but does not release brake, a malfunction of the pedal assembly is indicated.
5. Check operation of parking brake with engine off. Parking brake should remain engaged regardless of transmission selector position.

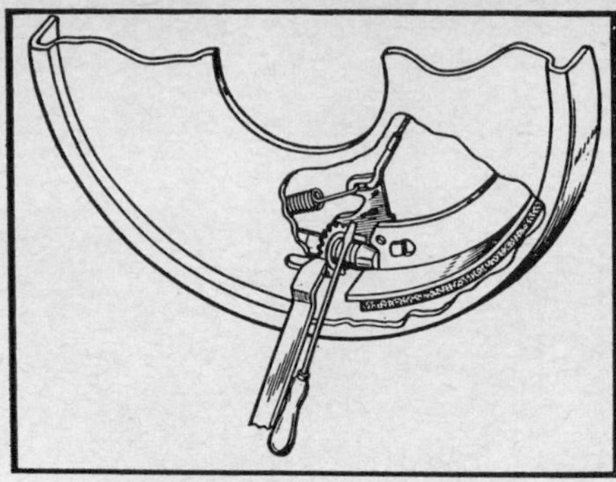

Fig. 29 Releasing brake lever with screwdriver while adjusting star wheel

BRAKE MASTER CYLINDER, REPLACE

1967-69 All Cars

1. Disconnect front and rear brake tubes from master cylinder (residual pressure valves will keep cylinder from draining).
2. Remove nuts that attach master cylinder to cowl panel and/or power brake unit.
3. Disconnect pedal push rod (manual brakes) from brake pedal.
4. Slide master cylinder straight out from cowl panel and/or power brake unit.
5. Reverse procedure to install.

1963-66 All Cars

To remove the master cylinder, disconnect the master cylinder push rod from brake pedal. Disconnect brake line and stop light wires from cylinder. Remove attaching nuts and remove cylinder from car.

POWER BRAKE

1963-69 Bendix Booster

1. Disconnect brake line(s) from master cylinder.
2. Remove vacuum hose from booster.
3. From under dash, remove brake pedal and push rod attaching bolt.
4. Remove four booster attaching nuts and lift booster from vehicle.
5. Installation is made in the reverse order of removal. Bleed system and check booster operation.

1963-69 Midland-Ross Booster

1. With engine shut off, apply brake several times to balance the internal pressure of the booster.
2. Disconnect hydraulic line at master cylinder and vacuum hose from booster.
3. From underneath dash, remove bolt from plunger and brake pedal linkage.
4. Remove four attaching bolts and lift off booster and master cylinder.

1963-64 Remote Booster, 300J-K

1. Remove hose clamps that secure air hose and vacuum hose to control valve housing and to booster.
2. Disconnect master cylinder line and wheel cylinder line at tubing connectors on slave cylinder housing.
3. Unfasten and remove slave booster.

1965-66 Kelsey Hayes Booster

1. With engine shut off, apply brakes several times to balance internal pressure of brake.
2. Disconnect hydraulic brake line from master cylinder.
3. Disconnect vacuum hose from booster check valve.
4. Unfasten booster push rod from pedal linkage (under instrument panel).
5. Unfasten booster unit from dash panel.
6. Remove booster and master cylinder assembly.

Front End and Steering Section

FRONT SUSPENSION

All Cars Except 1967-69 Imperial

This suspension, Fig. 1, consists of two torsion bar springs (right and left), two sets of upper and lower control arms, four ball joints and two struts.

The front ends of the torsion bar springs engage the lower control arms at the inner pivot points. The rear end of the torsion bars engage adjustable anchor and cam assemblies that are supported by brackets welded to the frame side rails and a removable crossmember.

The upper control arms are mounted on removable brackets that are bolted to the frame side rails. The lower control arms are attached to the frame front crossmember by a pivot shaft and bushing assembly. The pivot shafts are mounted in replaceable rubber bushings.

The steering knuckles are connected to the upper and lower control arms by means of ball joints. To prevent the possibility of fore and aft movement of the lower control arms, a strut is attached to the front crossmember and to the lower control arm.

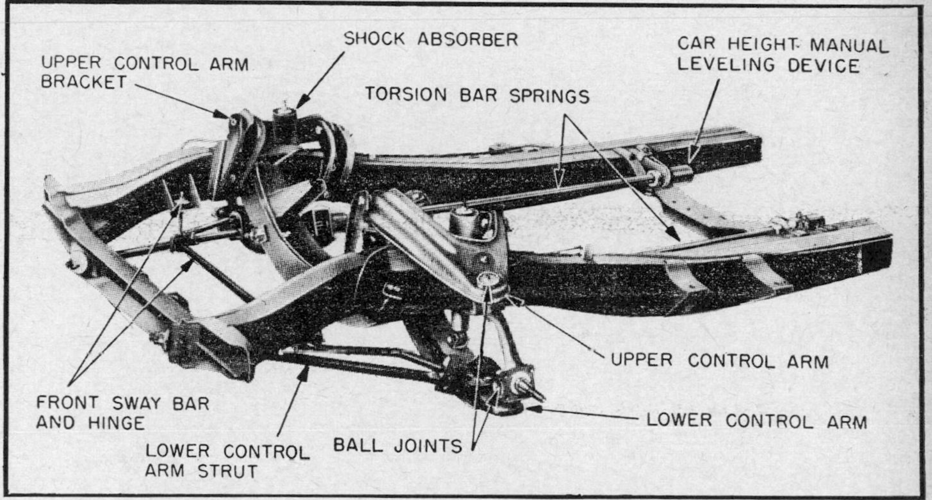

Fig. 1 Torsion bar front suspension. All models except 1967-69 Imperial

1967-69 Imperial

The front suspension has a front "K" crossmember that is isolated from the stub frame by four rubber bushing type isolators. The torsion bar rear anchor crossmember is isolated from the stub frame crossmember by two sandwich type rubber insulators. The front anchors are part of the lower control arms and provide the means of adjusting the vehicle front height. The upper control arm is mounted on a pivot bar and the *front wheel alignment is set by the adjustment of two vertically mounted cam bolts.*

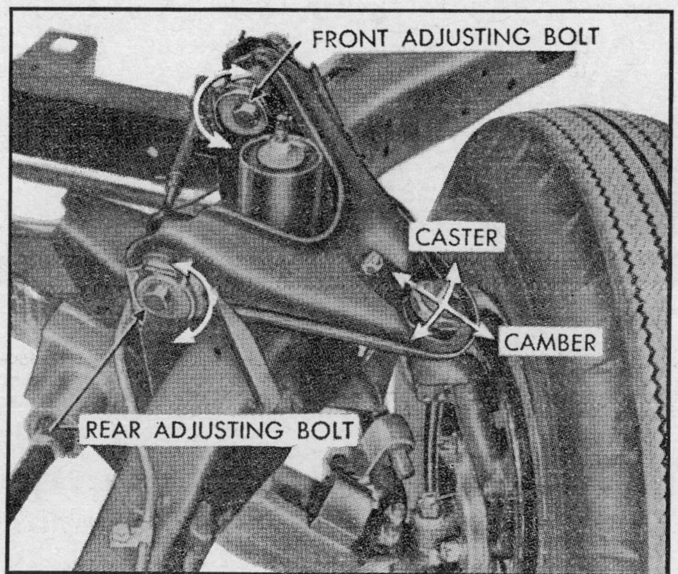

Fig. 2 Camber and caster adjusting bolts. All models except 1967-69 Imperial

LUBRICATION

1963-69

All ball joints and torsion bars are effectively sealed against road splash by tightly fitted balloon type flexible type seals. The ball joints are semi-permanently lubricated with special lubricant, and should not under normal conditions require lubrication before 32,000 miles.

All ball joints, tie rod end seals and protectors should be inspected at all oil change periods. Damaged seals must be replaced to prevent lubricant leakage or contamination and subsequent component failure.

WARNING

Do not use pressure type lubrication equipment as the pressure may damage the balloon type seals. Use a hand type lubrication gun filled only with the special lubricant specified for the job. Fill each unit slowly to avoid rupturing the seal.

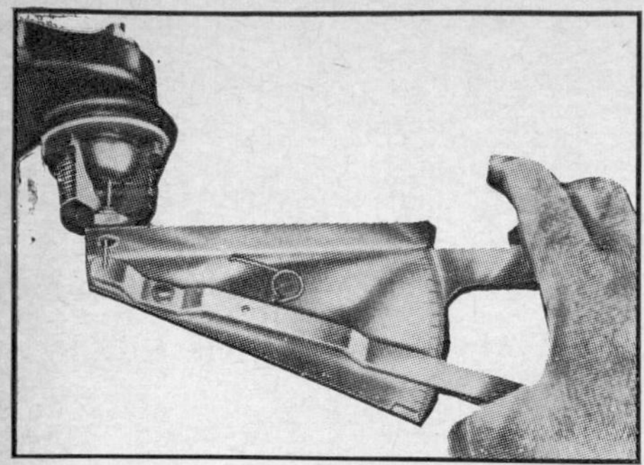

Fig. 3 Scale used to check lower ball joint for wear (tool C-3911)

Every 32,000 miles remove the plug from the ball joint and install a grease fitting. Using a hand gun, pump the grease into the unit until the seal balloons—indicating fullness. Remove the grease fitting and reinstall the plug.

WHEEL ALIGNMENT

Front suspension height must be correct before measuring caster and camber. After using a suitable solvent to loosen any rust, carefully loosen the upper control arm attaching nuts while holding the bolts from turning. Once caster and camber have been adjusted, Fig. 2, a very small turn of the bolts will affect the gauge readings.

Turning one bolt affects caster more than camber. By bringing caster to approximate specifications, then turning both bolts an equal amount in the same direction to bring camber to the preferred specification, will usually bring caster to the preferred setting.

NOTE: Turning both cams in the same direction an equal amount will change camber with little or no caster change. Turning both cams an equal amount in opposite directions will change caster with little or no change of camber.

TOE-IN, ADJUST

1963-69

With the front wheels in straight ahead position, loosen the clamps at each end of both adjusting tubes. Adjust toe-in by turning the tie rod sleeve which will "center" the steering wheel spokes. If the steering wheel was centered, make the toe-in adjustment by turning both sleeves an equal amount. Position the clamps so they are on the bottom and tighten bolts to 15 ft. lbs.

WHEEL BEARINGS, ADJUST

1. Tighten wheel bearing adjusting nuts to 90 inch pounds on Dodge models (70 on Dart and Valiant) while rotating wheels.
2. Position nut lock on adjusting nut so one pair of cotter pin slots align with pin hole in spindle.

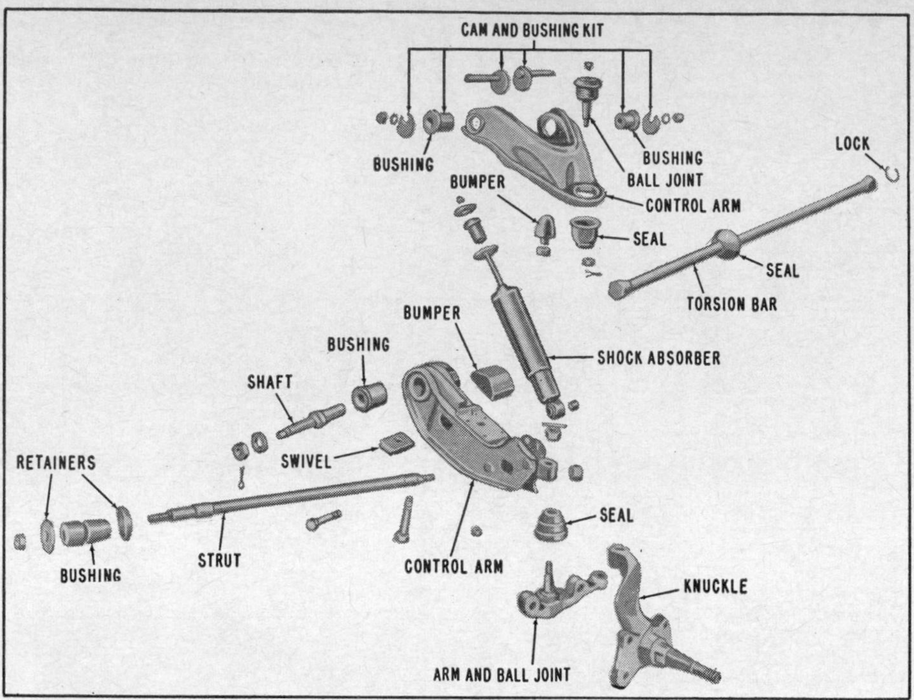

Fig. 5 Front suspension. 1965-69 Chrysler, 1963-69 Dodge (except '63-'64 880), 1963-69 Plymouth

3. Back off adjusting nut and nut lock one slot and install cotter pin. The resulting adjustment should be zero (no preload) to .003" end play.
4. Clean grease cap, coat inside with wheel bearing grease (do not fill) and install cap.

WHEEL BEARINGS, REPLACE

(Disc Brakes)

1. Raise car and remove front wheels.
2. Remove grease cap, cotter pin, lock nut and bearing adjusting nut.
3. Remove bolts that attach caliper to steering knuckle.
4. Slowly slide caliper up and away from disc and support caliper on steering knuckle arm.

NOTE: Do not allow caliper to hang by brake hose.

5. Remove thrust washer and outer bearing cone. Remove hub and disc assembly. Grease retainer and inner bearing can now be removed.

CHECKING BALL JOINTS FOR WEAR

If loose ball joints are suspected, first make sure the front wheel bearings are properly adjusted and that the control arms are tight.

Fig. 3 illustrates tool No. C-3911 which has been developed to measure accurately lower ball joint wear and to eliminate needless replacement of ball joints not excessively worn. Checking procedure is as follows:

1. Raise front of vehicle at lower control arms to bring wheels clear of floor. *CAUTION — Lower control arms must be supported sufficiently outboard so that the rebound bumper is not compressed in order to unload lower ball joint.*
2. Remove ball joint plug and screw threaded fitting of tool into ball joint hole until it is firmly seated as shown.
3. Raise and lower wheel either by hand or with a pry bar and note free play indicated on scale of tool. The scale is graduated to indicate free play in minor increments of .010" with the major increments indicating .050" (.070" on 1968-69).
4. Replacement for excessive wear is necessary only when movement of the gauge arm exceeds the above.

NOTE: On 1967-69 Imperial, the lower ball joints are pre-loaded (zero axial end play). Therefore, if any up and down movement is observed the ball joint and lower control arm should be replaced. This is due to the fact that the lower ball joint is a press fit and requires very high removing and installing forces.

BALL JOINTS, REPLACE

On 1963-64 Dodge 880 and Chrysler and 1963-66 Imperial, both upper and lower ball joints are threaded into their respective control arms. On 1967-69 Imperial, the upper ball joint is threaded into the control arm and the lower ball joint is serviced as an assembly with the lower control arm. On all other models, the upper ball joint is threaded into the control arm whereas the lower ball joint is furnished as an assembly with the steering arm.

Use a suitable tool to press the ball

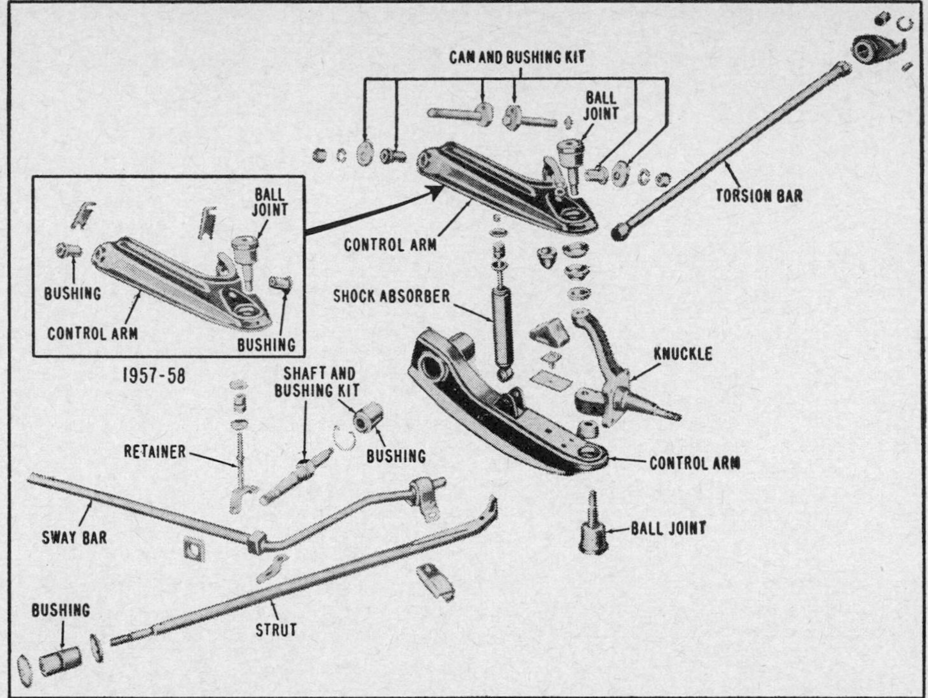

Fig. 6 Front suspension. 1963-64 Dodge 880, 1963-64 Chrysler and 1963-66 Imperial

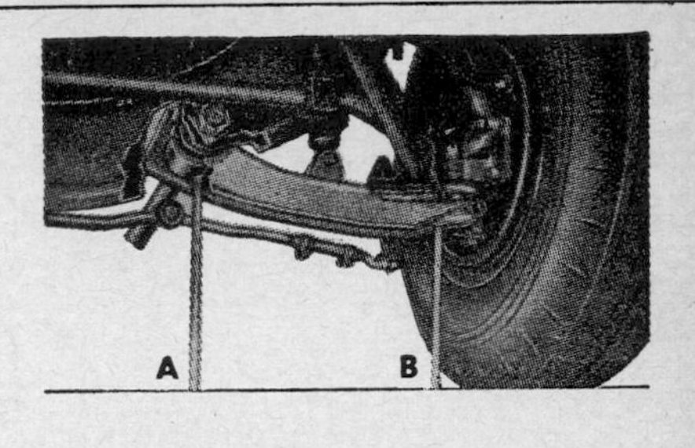

Fig. 7 Measuring front suspension height (typical)

joints from the steering knuckles, and when installing a ball joint, be sure to start it squarely into the control arm threads.

TORSION BAR, REPLACE

The torsion bars are not interchangeable side for side. The bars are marked either right or left by an "R" or an "L" stamped on one end of the bar. The general procedure for replacing a torsion bar is as follows:

Removal

1. Remove upper control arm rebound bumper.
2. If vehicle is to be raised on a hoist, make sure it is lifted on the body only so suspension is in full rebound position (no load).
3. Release all load from torsion bar by turning anchor adjusting bolt counterclockwise.

NOTE: On 1967-69 Imperial models, load on *both* torsion bars will have to be released by turning the anchor adjusting bolts counterclockwise. This is necessary because the rubber isolator rear crossmember would be under load and could possibly cause severe damage or personal injury.

4. Slide rear anchor balloon seal off of rear anchor and remove lock ring from anchor.
5. Remove torsion bar, by sliding bar out through rear of rear anchor. Use care not to damage balloon seal when it is removed from torsion bar.

Inspection

1. Inspect balloon seal for damage and replace if necessary.
2. Inspect torsion bar for scores or nicks. Dress down all scratches and nicks to remove sharp edges, then paint repaired areas with a rust preventive.
3. Remove all foreign material from hex openings in anchors and from hex ends of torsion bars.
4. Inspect adjusting bolt and swivel and replace if there is any sign of corrosion or other damage. Lubricate for easy operation.

Installation

1. Insert torsion bar through rear anchor.
2. Slide balloon seal over torsion bar with cupped end toward rear of bar.
3. Coat both ends of torsion bar with a long mileage lubricant.
4. Slide torsion bar in hex opening of lower control arm.
5. Install lock ring, making sure it is seated in groove.
6. Pack annular opening in rear anchor completely full of a long mileage lubricant.
7. Position lip of balloon seal in groove of anchor. *On 1967-69 Imperial models, install balloon seal clamp.*
8. On all models except 1967-69 Imperial, turn adjusting bolt clockwise to place a load on torsion bar. *On 1967-69 Imperial, turn both adjusting bolts clockwise to place a load on both torsion bars.*
9. Lower vehicle to floor and adjust front suspension height.
10. Install upper control arm rebound bumper.

RIDING HEIGHT, ADJUST

Before taking measurements, grasp the bumpers at the center (rear bumper first) and jounce the car up and down several times. Jounce the car at the front bumper the same number of times and release the bumper at the same point in the cycle each time.

1. Measure from the ball joint to the floor (measurement "A"), and from the control arm torsion bar spring anchor housing to the floor (measurement "B"), Fig. 7.
2. Subtract "A" from "B". The distance should be as listed below (plus or minus 1/8").
3. Measure the other side in the same manner.
4. Adjust by turning the torsion bar anchor adjusting nut *clockwise to increase* the height and *counterclockwise to decrease* the height. The difference from side-to-side should not exceed 1/8".
5. After adjusting, jounce the car and recheck the measurements on both sides, even if only one side may have been adjusted.

Dodge & Dart

1963 Dart (standard) .... 2 1/8"
Dart (heavy duty) .... 2 3/8"
Dodge (standard) .... 1 3/4"
Dodge (heavy duty) .... 2 1/8"
880 Cars .... 2"
880 Suburbans .... 2 3/8"
1964 Dart (standard) .... 2"
Dart (heavy duty) .... 2 3/8"
Dodge (standard) .... 1 3/4"
Dodge (heavy duty) .... 2 1/8"
880 all models .... 2"
1965 Coronet (standard) .... 1 3/4"
Dart (standard) .... 2"
Dart & Coronet (H.D.) .... 2 3/8"
Polara, Monaco, 880, ... 1 1/8"
1966 Dart (standard) .... 1 7/8"
Coronet (standard) .... 1 7/8"
Polara, Monaco .... 1 1/2"
Dart & Coronet (H.D.) .... 2 3/8"
1967-69 Dart .... 2 1/8"
Coronet, Charger .... 1 7/8"
Polara, Monaco .... 1 1/8"

Valiant

1963 (standard) .... 2 1/8"
1963 (heavy duty) .... 2 3/8"
1964-66 (standard) .... 2"
1964-66 (heavy duty) .... 2 3/8"
1967 .... 2 1/8"
1968-69 Barracuda .... 1 3/8"
Valiant .... 2 1/8"

Plymouth

1963 (standard) .... 1 3/4"
(heavy duty) .... 2 1/8"

1964 (standard) ....1¾"
(heavy duty) ....2⅛"
1965 Fury (standard) ....1⅜"
Others (standard) ....1¾"
(heavy duty) ....2⅛"
1966 Fury ....1⅜"
Others (standard) ....1⅞"
(heavy duty) ....2⅜"
1967-69 Belvedere, Satellite,
Roadrunner ....1⅞"
Fury, V.I.P. ....1⅜"

Chrysler & Imperial

1963 Cars ....2"
Suburbans ....2⅜"
1964 All Models ....2"
1965-66 Chrysler ....1⅛"
Imperial ....2"
(heavy duty) ....2⅜"
1967-69 Chrysler ....1⅛"
Imperial ....1¾"

MANUAL STEERING GEAR, REPLACE

1968-69 Chrysler, Monaco, Polara

1. Use a suitable puller to remove steering arm.
2. Disconnect transmission gear selector linkage (if column mounted).
3. Remove pin from coupling clamp at upper end of steering gear worm shaft.
4. To provide sufficient clearance at coupling, loosen column jacket-to-instrument panel clamp bolts enough to disengage tab on clamp from slot in column jacket. Slide column up far enough to disengage coupling from worm shaft.
5. Raise carpet and remove column lower support plate-to-floor pan bolts.
6. Remove three gear housing mounting bolts and remove gear from under vehicle.

1968-69 Dodge & Plymouth (Except Monaco & Polara)

1. Perform Steps 1 through 4 as described above for other 1968-69 models.
2. Then on Dart and Valiant with 273 engines, from under vehicle remove left front engine mount stud nut and washer. Using a suitable jack, raise engine about 1½ inches. Remove starter. After removing the three steering gear mounting bolts, lower gear through opening.
3. On models with 426 engine, remove battery and battery tray. Remove left front engine mount stud nut and washer. Using a suitable jack, raise engine about 1½ inches. After removing the three gear mounting bolts, rotate gear forward between cylinder head and shock absorber tower, and up through opening left by battery tray removal.
4. On models with 273, 318, 340, 383 and 440 engines (except Dart and Valiant), remove the three steering gear mounting bolts and lower gear from under vehicle.
5. On all 6-cylinder models, remove steering gear mounting bolts and remove gear through engine compartment.

1963-64 Chrysler & Imperial

1. Disconnect battery ground cable.
2. Use puller to remove steering arm from steering gear.
3. Remove bolt attaching lower coupling to steering gear worm shaft.
4. Loosen steering column jacket clamp screw at instrument panel (do not remove).
5. Tap coupling upward and carefully lift steering column and jacket up and off end of worm shaft.
6. Unfasten steering gear from frame (3 bolts).
7. Remove gear through engine compartment by lowering upper end of gear towards driver's compartment, then raise rear end of gear up and remove from vehicle.
8. Install the gear in the reverse order of removal.

1965-67 Chrysler & 1965-67 Dodge & Plymouth (Except Dart & Valiant With V8-273 Engine)

1. Remove nut and use a puller to take off steering arm.
2. Remove bolt or pin from coupling clamp at upper end of steering worm shaft.
3. To provide sufficient clearance at coupling, loosen column jacket-to-instrument panel clamp bolts enough to disengage tab on clamp from slot in column jacket. Slide column up away from steering gear to disengage coupling from worm shaft.

NOTE: It is not necessary to disconnect shift linkage on models equipped with manual transmission or to remove the floor plate-to-toe board bolts when removing steering gear. If floor plate bolts are loosened, it will be necessary to realign the steering column when reinstalling gear.

4. Unfasten and remove gear.

NOTE: On six-cylinder models, gear can be removed through engine compartment. On cars with V8 engines, remove gear from underneath vehicle.

1965-67 Valiant & Dart With V8-273 Engine

1. Disconnect battery ground cable.
2. Loosen worm shaft coupling clamp.
3. Loosen column jacket-to-instrument panel clamp bolts and slide column up far enough to disengage coupling from worm shaft.
4. Raise vehicle and remove left front engine mount stud nut. Jack up engine slightly to provide clearance between left exhaust manifold and body sheet metal to allow removal of gear.
5. Remove starting motor.
6. Remove nut and use a puller to take off steering arm.
7. Unfasten and remove gear from under vehicle.

1963-64 Dodge, Dart & Plymouth

1. Remove steering gear arm with a suitable puller.
2. Remove bolt from coupling clamp at upper end of steering gear worm-shaft.
3. To provide sufficient clearance at coupling, loosen column jacket to instrument panel clamp bolts enough to disengage tab on clamp from slot in column jacket. Slide column up far enough to disengage coupling from wormshaft.
4. Remove three steering gear mounting bolts and remove gear from vehicle.
5. On six-cylinder models remove gear through engine compartment. On V8 models remove gear from underneath car. It is also necessary to remove the starter on cars with V8-318 engine.

POWER STEERING, REPLACE

1968-69 Imperial

1. Disconnect battery ground cable.
2. Disconnect pressure and return hoses at steering gear and fasten ends of hoses above oil level in pump reservoir.
3. Remove rubber coupling heat shield.
4. Remove two capscrews attaching rubber coupling to upper flange of steering column shaft.
5. Remove roll pin from pot coupling.
6. Move upper end of intermediate shaft until rubber coupling clears upper flange and carefully tap lower coupling up and off steering gear worm shaft.
7. Using a suitable puller, remove steering gear arm.
8. Disconnect exhaust pipe at ball coupling and exhaust manifold flanges and remove pipe.
9. Disconnect transmission cooler lines from transmission and clamp at starter flange bolt.
10. Remove two steering gear mounting bolts and stud nut. Then remove gear from under vehicle.

1967 Imperial

1. Disconnect battery ground cable.
2. Disconnect pressure and return hoses at steering gear. Fasten hose ends above fluid level in pump.
3. Use a suitable puller to remove steering arm.
4. Remove frame-to-gear mounting bolts and remove gear from under vehicle.

1967-69 Chrysler, Plymouth & Dodge

1. Disconnect battery ground cable.
2. Remove column coupling-to-worm shaft roll pin.
3. Loosen column jacket clamp nuts enough to allow column to be pulled up two inches. On some models it will be necessary to remove column

finish plate to get at the clamp.
4. Remove three bolts in lower column support plate at floor pan.
5. Tap coupling and column upward and lift off end of worm shaft.
6. Disconnect pressure and return hoses at gear. Fasten hose ends above fluid level in pump.
7. Use a suitable puller to remove steering arm.
8. Remove gear-to-frame bolts and remove gear from vehicle as follows:
9. On six-cylinder models, remove gear from top of engine compartment.
10. Dart and Valiant with 8-273 engine, remove left front engine mount stud nut. Using suitable jack, raise engine slightly to provide clearance between left exhaust manifold and body sheet metal. Remove starter and then take steering gear out from under vehicle.
11. Dodge and Plymouth with 8-426 engine, remove battery and battery tray. From top side of engine compartment, remove left engine mount insulator stud nut, through bolt and bracket upper bolt. Jack up left side of engine about 1½". Separate engine from engine mount and allow insulator to rest on frame. Rotate steering gear (worm shaft end) up between cylinder head and shock absorber tower and out through battery tray opening.
12. On all other models remove gear from under vehicle.

1966 Imperial

1. Disconnect battery ground cable.
2. Disconnect center link from steering gear.
3. Use puller to remove steering arm.
4. Disconnect pressure and return hoses from gear. Fasten hose ends above fluid level in pump.
5. Drive out roll pin in flexible coupling.
6. Unfasten master cylinder from power brake unit and move master cylinder toward engine.
7. If equipped, unfasten auto pilot from its bracket and lay to one side.
8. Remove steering column cover plate (inside vehicle).
9. Remove three capscrews in lower support plate.
10. Disconnect transmission indicator linkage.
11. Remove column-to-instrument panel clamp while supporting weight of column. Pull up on steering wheel far enough to disengage flexible coupling from worm shaft. Allow steering gear to rest on front seat.
12. Remove gear-to-frame mounting bolts and alignment wedge.
13. Remove gear through engine compartment.

1966 Chrysler, Polara, Monaco, Fury

1. Disconnect battery ground cable.
2. Disconnect pressure and return hoses from gear. Fasten hose ends above fluid level in pump.
3. Remove rubber coupling heat shield.
4. Disconnect rubber coupling from flange of intermediate shaft.
5. Remove roll pin that attaches rubber coupling upper flange to column shaft.
6. Tap rubber coupling as far as it will go upward onto column shaft splines.
7. Remove roll pin that attaches pot coupling to steering worm shaft.
8. Move intermediate shaft until upper flange clears rubber coupling and withdraw from worm shaft splines.
9. Use a suitable puller to remove steering arm.
10. Unfasten gear from crossmember and remove gear from under vehicle.

1963-64 Chrysler & Imperial

1. Disconnect battery ground cable.
2. Remove steering wheel.
3. Remove turn signal lever.
4. Remove steering column lower cover.
5. Remove turn switch and wires.
6. Remove snap ring from groove in steering tube at top of bearing.
7. Remove jacket tube shield and clamp.
8. Raise carpet to expose floor panel. Move rubber grommet up on jacket column.
9. Remove screws attaching rubber dust boot at firewall. On Imperial models, remove floor inspection panel.
10. Loosen jacket tube clamp at steering gear housing.
11. Disconnect cover link from arm.
12. Use puller to remove steering arm from gear shaft.
13. Disconnect brake line at master cylinder and brake tee (not necessary on Imperial models).
14. Disconnect hydraulic lines at gear.
15. Slide jacket tube up and off steering gear through driver's compartment. Remove jacket tube upper spring and retainer, rubber insulator boot and horn ground strap.
16. Remove steering tube coupling pin, two plastic inserts, horn ground strap, rubber insulator and upper steering tube.
17. Remove gear housing-to-frame bolts, washers and alignment wedge.
18. Unfasten and slide off master cylinder.
19. Slide steering gear toward rear of car and at the same time, raise lower end of gear to remove it at engine compartment.
20. Reverse removal procedure to install.

1965 Chrysler & Imperial

1. Disconnect battery ground cable.
2. Disconnect hoses at gear control valve and fasten end of hoses above oil level in reservoir.
3. Loosen worm shaft-to-steering shaft coupling clamp bolt.
4. From inside of vehicle loosen steering column-to-instrument panel bracket and pull up on column assembly until coupling is clear of worm shaft (about 2 inches).
5. Raise vehicle. Remove center link from steering arm with a puller.
6. Remove three gear mounting bolts from crossmember and take gear out from under vehicle.

1965 Polara, Monaco, Fury V8s

1. Disconnect battery ground cable.
2. Disconnect hoses at gear control valve and fasten ends of hoses above oil level in reservoir.
3. Loosen worm shaft-to-steering shaft coupling clamp.
4. From inside of vehicle, loosen steering column-to-instrument panel bracket and pull up on column until coupling is clear of worm shaft.
5. Raise vehicle. Remove nut from steering arm at center link and use a puller to remove center link.
6. Unfasten and remove steering gear from crossmember and take it out from under vehicle.

1965-66 V8 Valiant, Dart, Coronet, Charger

1. Disconnect battery ground cable.
2. Loosen bolt at worm shaft coupling clamp. Loosen column jacket-to-instrument panel clamp bolts and slide column up far enough to disengage coupling from worm shaft.
3. Disconnect hoses at control valve.
4. On Dart models, raise vehicle and remove left front engine mount stud nut. Jack up engine slightly to provide clearance between left exhaust manifold and body sheet metal to allow removal of gear.
5. Remove starting motor.
6. Remove nut and use a puller to take off steering arm.
7. Unfasten and remove gear.

1965-66 Six Except Fury

1. Disconnect battery ground cable.
2. Remove worm shaft coupling clamp bolt or roll pin.
3. Loosen column jacket clamp at instrument panel and pull jacket up two inches.
4. Tap coupling upward and lift it off end of worm shaft.
5. Disconnect hoses from gear and fasten ends above oil level in reservoir.
6. Raise vehicle. Remove nut and use a puller to take off steering arm.
7. Unfasten and remove gear through engine compartment.

1963-64 Dodge, Plymouth, Valiant

1. Unscrew gear shaft arm retaining nut and remove arm with a puller.
2. Disconnect hydraulic lines from steering gear valve.
3. Remove bolts attaching gear to frame.
4. Remove bolt from coupling clamp at shaft.
5. While supporting gear, tap coupling assembly upward with a mallet until it is free from worm shaft splines. Then lift gear out of car.
6. Lift steering gear through engine compartment on six-cylinder models. On V8s remove steering gear from underneath the car. It is also necessary to remove the starter on cars with V8-318 engine.

CORVAIR

OLD CAR SPECIFICATIONS: For 1946-62 Tune Up and Wheel Alignment Specifications see back of book.

INDEX OF SERVICE OPERATIONS

PAGE NO.

ACCESSORIES

Automatic Level Controls 1-41
Clock Troubles 1-11
Power Top Troubles 1-18
Power Window Troubles 1-18
Radio, Remove 2-220

BRAKES

Brake Troubles, Mechanical 1-17
Disc Brake Service 1-430
Hydraulic System Service 1-422
Master Cylinder, Replace 2-243
Parking Brake, Adjust 2-243
Power Brake Service 1-440
Power Brake Troubles 1-440
Service Brakes, Adjust 2-242

CLUTCH

Clutch Linkage, Adjust 2-235
Clutch, Replace 2-236
Clutch Troubles 1-12

COOLING SYSTEM

Blower Bearing, Replace 2-225
Blower, Replace 2-226
Crankcase Cover, Replace 2-226

ELECTRICAL

Alternator Service 1-63
Dash Gauge Service 1-117
Distributor, Replace 2-217
Distributor Service:
  Standard 1-53
  Transistorized 1-47
Electrical Troubles 1-8
Flasher Location Chart .... Back of Book
Generator, Replace 2-217
Generator Service 1-91
Horn Sounder, Remove 2-219
Ignition Coils and Resistors 1-24
Ignition Switch, Replace 2-217
Ignition Timing 2-217
Instrument Cluster Removal 2-219
Light Switch, Replace 2-218
Neutral Safety Switch, Replace 2-218
Spark Plug Condition Chart 2-647
Starter Service 1-101
Starter, Replace 2-217
Starter Switch Service 1-114
Stop Light Switch, Replace 2-218
Turn Signal Switch, Replace 2-218
Turn Signal Troubles 1-11
Windshield Wiper Motor, Replace 2-220
Windshield Wiper Troubles 1-20

ENGINE "IN CAR" OPERATIONS

Engine Seal & Shields 2-222
Engine Cooling Components 2-223

PAGE NO.

Crankcase Cover & Blower Bearing 2-226
Oil Filter & Generator Adaptor 2-226
Oil Cooler 2-226
Oil Pump 2-226
Crankshaft Pulley 2-227
Vibration Damper 2-227
Engine Rear Housing Seal 2-227
Engine Rear Housing 2-227
Distributor Drive Gear 2-227
Fuel Pump Eccentric 2-227
Cylinder Head Service 2-227
Valve Service 2-227
Piston Rings, Replace 2-230
Rod Bearings, Replace 2-230

ENGINE OPERATIONS (Removed)

Engine (Power Train) Replace 2-231
Engine Disassemble 2-231
Engine Reassemble 2-231
Camshaft 2-231
Crankshaft 2-231
Timing Gear Marks 2-232
Pistons, Cylinders & Rods 2-232
Crankcase Cover & Blower Bearing 2-232
Push Rod Oil Drain Tubes 2-232
Crankcase 2-233
Main Bearings 2-233
Oil Pump Repairs 2-234
Oil Cooler & By-Pass Valves 2-234
Engine Rear Housing 2-234
Flywheel Housing Seal 2-234

ENGINE LUBRICATION

Crankcase Ventilation (PCV) 1-29
Exhaust Emission Controls 1-30
Oil Pump, Replace 2-226

FUEL SYSTEM

Accelerator Linkage 2-221
Carburetor Adjustments and Specs. 1-124
Crankcase Ventilation (PCV) 1-29
Exhaust Emission Controls 1-30
Fuel Pump, Replace 2-220
Fuel Pump Service 1-120
Fuel System Troubles 1-2
Turbocharger Service 2-220

REAR AXLE

Axle Shaft, Replace 2-238
Description 2-237
Rear Axle Repairs 2-240
Rear Axle Specifications 2-216
Side Bearing Sleeve Seal, Replace 2-239
Rear Axle U-Joint, Replace 2-238
Rear Wheel Alignment 2-244
Rear Wheel Bearing, Adjust 2-238

PAGE NO.

SPECIFICATIONS

Alternator 2-214
Brakes 2-216
Capacities 2-216
Carburetors 1-124
Crankshaft and Bearings 2-215
Distributors 2-212
Engine Tightening Torque 2-216
General Engine Specs. 2-212
Generators 2-214
Ignition Coils and Resistors 1-24
Pistons, Rings and Pins 2-215
Rear Axle 2-216
Starting Motors 2-215
Tune Up 2-213
Valve Lift 2-230
Valves 2-215
Valve Timing 2-230
Wheel Alignment 2-216

STEERING GEAR

Horn Sounder Removal 2-219
Mechanical Gear Service 1-451
Mechanical Gear Troubles 1-18
Steering Gear, Replace 2-245
Steering Wheel, Replace 2-219

SUSPENSION, FRONT

Ball Joints, Replace 2-245
Ball Joints, Check for Wear 2-244
Coil Spring, Replace 2-245
Shock Absorber, Replace 2-245
Tire Wear Chart 2-648
Toe-In, Adjust 2-244
Wheel Alignment, Adjust 2-243
Wheel Bearings, Adjust 2-243

TRANSMISSIONS

Three Speed Manual:
  Replace 2-236
  Repairs 1-261
  Linkage, Adjust 2-236
Four Speed Manual:
  Replace 2-236
  Repairs 1-298
  Linkage, Adjust 2-236
Automatic Units 1-321
Power Train, Replace 2-231

TUNE UP

Service 1-21
Specifications 2-213

WINDSHIELD WIPER

Wiper Motor, Replace 2-220
Wiper Linkage, Replace 2-220
Wiper Switch, Replace 2-220
Wiper Troubles 1-20

SERIAL NUMBER LOCATION

1963-64: Left front door pillar. 1965-67: Left-hand top of frame side rail rearward of battery bolts.
1968-69: Top of instrument panel on left front side.

ENGINE NUMBER LOCATION

1963-64: Top of engine block forward of generator-oil filter adapter.
1965-68: Top of engine block behind oil pressure sending unit.
1969: Top of engine block forward of oil filter adapter.

ENGINE IDENTIFICATION

Engines are identified in the following table by the code letter or letters immediately following the engine serial number.

CODE		
YC	6 cyl. with M/T	1963-64
YL	6 cyl. with M/T, A/C	1963-64
YM	6 cyl. with A/C, HPE	1963
YM	6 cyl. with T/C, 4 sp. tr.	1964
YN	6 cyl. with M/T, HPE	1963-64
Z	6 cyl. with A/T	1963-64
ZD	6 cyl. with A/T, A/C	1963-64
ZF	6 cyl. with A/T, HPE	1963-64
ZG	6 cyl. with A/T, A/C, HPE	1963-64
ZH	6 cyl. with A/T	1963-64
Y	6 cyl. with M/T, HPE	1963
RL	6-164 with T/C	1966
RM	6-164 with M/T, SHPE	1965-67
RN	6-164 with SHPE, P/G	1965-67
RQ	6-164 with SHPE, A.I.R.	1966-67
RR	6-164 with A/C	1966
RS	6-164 with M/T, A.I.R.	1965-68
RS	6-164 with A.I.R.	1966
RU	6-164 with M/T, HPE, A.I.R.	1965-68
RV	6-164 with P/G, A.I.R.	1965-68
RW	6-164 with HPE, A.I.R., P/G	1966-68
RX	6-164 with P/G, HPE, A.I.R.	1965-67
RY	6-164 with P/G, A/C, SHPE	1966-67
RZ	6-164 with SHPE, A/C	1966-67
RA	6-164 with M/T and A/T	1965-67
RB	6-164	1965-66
RD	6-164 with HPE	1965-67
RE	6-164 with A/C	1965-68
RF	6-164 with HPE, A/C	1965-68
RG	6-164 with P/G	1965-67
RH	6-164 with P/G, HPE	1965-67
RJ	6-164 with P/G, A/C	1965-68
RK	6-164 with P/G, HPE, A/C	1965-68
QO	6-164 with P/G, A.I.R., A/C	1967
QP	6-164 with HPE, P/G, A.I.R., A/C	1967
QQ	6-164 with SPHE, A.I.R., A/C	1967
QR	6-164 with SPHE, A.I.R., A/C, P/G	1967
QS	6-164 with HPE, A.I.R., A/C	1967
AC	6-164 with M/T	1969
AD	6-164 with HPE	1969
AE	6-164 with P/G	1969
AF	6-164 with P/G, HPE	1969
AG	6-164 with SHPE	1969
AH	6-164 with P/G, HPE	1969

A/C: Air conditioned
A.I.R.: Air injection reactor
A/T: Automatic transmission
HPE: High performance engine
M/T: Manual transmission
P/G: Powerglide
SHPE: Special Hi Perf. engine
T/C: Turbocharged

FRONT VIEW IDENTIFICATION

1963

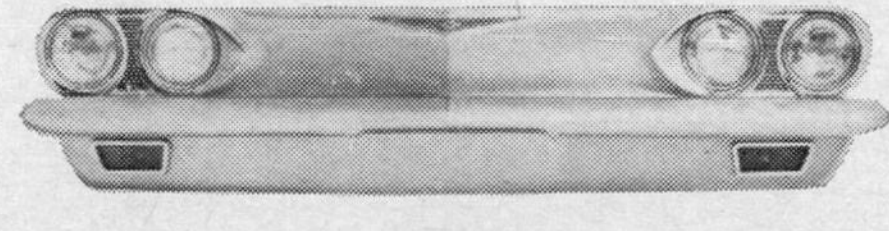

1965

1964

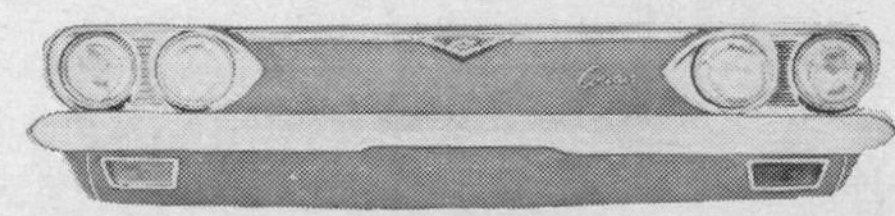

1966-69

GENERAL SPECIFICATIONS

Year	Engine		Car-buretor	Bore and Stroke	Piston Dis-place-ment, Cubic Inches	Com-pres-sion Ratio	Maximum Brake H.P. @ R.P.M.	Maximum Torque Lbs. Ft. @ R.P.M.	Normal Oil Pressure Pounds
1963	Turbo-Air 80 H.P.	6-145	2 One Bar.	3.4375 x 2.60	145	8.0	80 @ 4400	128 @ 2300	40
	Monza 84 H.P.	6-145	2 One Bar.	3.4375 x 2.60	145	9.0	84 @ 4400	130 @ 2300	40
	Super Turbo-Air 102 H.P.	6-145	2 One Bar.	3.4375 x 2.60	145	9.0	102 @ 4400	134 @ 2800	40
	Turbocharged 150 H.P.	6-145	1 One Bar.	3.4375 x 2.60	145	8.0	150 @ 4400	210 @ 3200	40
1964	95 Horsepower	6-164	2 One Bar.	3.4375 x 2.94	164	8.25	95 @ 3600	154 @ 2400	40
	110 Horsepower	6-164	2 One Bar.	3.4375 x 2.94	164	9.25	110 @ 4400	160 @ 2600	40
	Turbocharged 150 H.P.	6-164	1 One Bar.	3.4375 x 2.94	164	8.25	150 @ 4000	232 @ 3200	40
1965-66	95 Horsepower	6-164	2 One Bar.	3.4375 x 2.94	164	8.25	95 @ 3600	154 @ 2400	40
	110 Horsepower	6-164	2 One Bar.	3.4375 x 2.94	164	9.25	110 @ 4400	160 @ 2800	40
	140 Horsepower	6-164	4 One Bar.	3.4375 x 2.94	164	9.25	140 @ 5200	160 @ 3600	40
	Turbocharged 180 H.P.	6-164	1 One Bar.	3.4375 x 2.94	164	8.25	180 @ 4000	265 @ 3200	40
1967-69	95 Horsepower	6-164	2 One Bar.	3.4375 x 2.94	164	8.25	95 @ 3600	154 @ 2400	40
	110 Horsepower	6-164	2 One Bar.	3.4375 x 2.94	164	9.25	110 @ 4400	160 @ 2800	40
	140 Horsepower	6-164	4 One Bar.	3.4375 x 2.94	164	9.25	140 @ 5200	160 @ 3600	40

DISTRIBUTOR SPECIFICATIONS

★NOTE: If advance is checked on vehicle, double the R.P.M. and degrees advance to get crankshaft figures.

Year	Model	Distributor Part No.①	Rotation ②	Breaker Gap	Dwell Angle Deg.	Breaker Arm Spring Tension	Centrifugal Advance Degrees @ R.P.M. of Distributor★		Vacuum Advance	
							Advance Starts	Full Advance	Inches of Vacuum To Start Plunger	Max. Adv. Dist. Deg. @ Vacuum
1963	Std. Trans.	1110294	C	③	31-34	19-23	1 @ 400	17 @ 1800	6	12 @ 16
	Powerglide	1110295	C	③	31-34	19-23	1 @ 800	13 @ 1850	7	12 @ 17
	Super Turbo-Air	1110296	C	③	31-34	19-23	1 @ 425	13 @ 2400	6	12 @ 16
	Monza Powerglide	1110297	C	③	31-34	19-23	1 @ 925	11 @ 2050	7	12 @ 17
	Turbocharged	1110298	C	③	31-34	19-23	1 @ 2000	16 @ 2250	④	④
1964	95 H. P. -Std. Tr.	1110310	C	③	31-34	19-23	1 @ 450	14 @ 2100	5 to 7	12 @ 14
	95 H. P.-Auto. Tr.	1110311	C	③	31-34	19-23	1 @ 975	10 @ 2100	6 to 8	12 @ 15
	110 Horsepower	1110319	C	③	31-34	19-23	1 @ 500	10 @ 2400	6 to 8	12 @ 15
	150 Horsepower	1110314	C	③	31-34	19-23	1 @ 2000	6 @ 2250	④	④
1965-67	95 H.P.-Std. Tr.	1110310	C	③	31-34	19-23	1 @ 450	14 @ 2100	5 to 7	12 @ 15
	95 H.P.-Auto. Tr.	1110311	C	③	31-34	19-23	1 @ 975	10 @ 2100	6 to 8	12 @ 15
	110 Horsepower	1110319	C	③	31-34	19-23	1 @ 500	10 @ 2400	6 to 8	12 @ 15
1965-66	Turbo-Charged	1110329	C	③	31-34	19-23	1 @ 2050	9 @ 2450	None	None
	4 Carb. Eng.	1110330	C	③	31-34	19-23	1 @ 500	9 @ 1400	None	None
1967	95 H.P. With A.I.R.	1110369	C	③	31-34	19-23	0 @ 450	20 @ 2200	7	12 @ 15
	110 H.P. With A.I.R.	1110389	C	③	31-34	19-23	0 @ 450	20 @ 2200	7	12 @ 15
1968	95 H.P.-Std. Tr.	1110434	C	③	31-34	19-23	0 @ 450	14 @ 2100	7	12 @ 15
	95 H.P.-Auto. Tr.	1110311	C	③	31-34	19-23	0 @ 850	10 @ 2100	7	12 @ 15
	110 H.P.-Std. Tr.	1110389	C	③	31-34	19-23	0 @ 450	13 @ 2200	7	12 @ 15
	110 H.P.-Auto. Tr.	1110319	C	③	31-34	19-23	0 @ 400	10 @ 2400	7	12 @ 15
	140 H.P.	1110371	C	③	31-34	19-23	0 @ 450	16 @ 1500	6	11 @ 14
1969	95 H.P.-Std. Tr.	1110452	C	③	31-34	19-23	0 @ 450	14 @ 2100	7	12 @ 16
	95 H.P.-Auto. Tr.	1110453	C	③	31-34	19-23	0 @ 850	10 @ 2100	7	12 @ 16
	110 H.P.-Std. Tr.	1110454	C	③	31-34	19-23	0 @ 450	13 @ 2200	7	12 @ 16
	110 H.P.-Auto. Tr.	1110455	C	③	31-34	19-23	0 @ 400	10 @ 2400	7	12 @ 16
	140 H.P.	1110454	C	③	31-34	19-23	0 @ 450	13 @ 2200	7	12 @ 16

①—Stamped on distributor housing plate. ②—As viewed from above. ③—New points .019″, used .016″.
④—No vacuum advance — unit operates on positive pressure.

TUNE UP SPECIFICATIONS

★Because of the difference in rate of expansion between aluminum head and steel spark plug it is advisable to allow engine to cool before removing plugs.

• When using a timing light, disconnect vacuum hose at distributor and plug opening in hose so idle speed will not be affected.

Year	Model	Spark Plug★ Type AC	Spark Plug★ Gap Inch	Distributor Point Gap Inch	Distributor Dwell Angle Deg.	Firing Order	Ignition Timing• BTDC ①	Ignition Timing• Mark	Hot Idle Speed Std. Trans.	Hot Idle Speed Auto. Trans. ②	Comp. Press. Lbs. ③	Fuel Pump Press. Lbs.
1963	Turbo-Air, Std. Tr.	46FF	.035	④	31-34	Fig. D	4°	Fig. B	500	—	140	5¼-6½
	Turbo-Air, Auto. Tr.	46FF	.035	④	31-34	Fig. D	13°	Fig. B	—	500D	140	5¼-6½
	Monza with P.G.	44FF	.035	④	31-34	Fig. D	13°	Fig. B	—	500D	160	¼-6½
	Super Turbo-Air	44FF	.035	④	31-34	Fig. D	13°	Fig. B	600	500D	160	5¼-6½
	Turbocharged Eng.	44FF	.035	④	31-34	Fig. D	24°	Fig. A	850	—	140	5¼-6½
1964	95 H.P.-Std. Tr.	46FF	.035	④	31-34	Fig. D	6°	Fig. B	500⑥	—	130	4-5
	95 H.P.-Auto. Tr.	46FF	.035	④	31-34	Fig. D	14°	Fig. B	—	500D⑥	130	4-5
	110 Horsepower	44FF	.030	④	31-34	Fig. D	14°	Fig. B	600⑥	500D⑥	130	4-5
	150 Horsepower	44FF	.030	④	31-34	Fig. D	24°	Fig. A	850⑥	—	130	4-5
1965	95 H.P.-Std. Trans.	46FF	.035	④	31-34	Fig. D	6°	Fig. B	475⑥	—	130	4-5
	95 H.P.-Auto. Tr.	46FF	.035	④	31-34	Fig. D	14°	Fig. B	—	450D⑥	130	4-5
	110 Horsepower	44FF	.030	④	31-34	Fig. D	24°	Fig. B	625⑥	600D⑥	130	4-5
	4 Carb. Engine	44FF	.030	④	31-34	Fig. D	18°⑧	Fig. B	625⑥	—	130	4-5
	Turbocharged Eng.	44FF	.030	④	31-34	Fig. D	24°	Fig. A	850⑥	—	130	4-5
1966	95 H.P. Std. Trans.	46FF	.035	④	31-34	Fig. D	6°	Fig. B	475⑥	—	130	4-5
	95 H.P. Std. Trans.⑨	46FF	.035	④	31-34	Fig. D	6°	Fig. B	700⑥	—	130	4-5
	95 H.P. Auto. Tr.	46FF	.035	④	31-34	Fig. D	14°	Fig. B	—	475D⑥	130	4-5
	95 H.P. Auto. Tr.⑨	46FF	.035	④	31-34	Fig. D	14°	Fig. B	—	600D⑥	130	4-5
	110 H.P. Std. Tr.	44FF	.030	④	31-34	Fig. D	14°⑦	Fig. B	625⑥	—	130	4-5
	110 H.P. Std. Tr.⑨	44FF	.030	④	31-34	Fig. D	14°⑦	Fig. B	700⑥	—	130	4-5
	110 H.P. Auto. Tr.	44FF	.030	④	31-34	Fig. D	14°⑦	Fig. B	—	475D⑥	130	4-5
	110 H.P. Auto. Tr.⑨	44FF	.030	④	31-34	Fig. D	14°⑦	Fig. B	—	600D⑥	130	4-5
	140 H.P. Std. Tr.	44FF	.030	④	31-34	Fig. D	18°⑧	Fig. B	625⑥	—	130	4-5
	140 H.P. Std. Tr.⑨	44FF	.030	④	31-34	Fig. D	18°⑧	Fig. B	700⑥	—	130	4-5
	140 H.P. Auto. Tr.	44FF	.030	④	31-34	Fig. D	18°⑧	Fig. B	—	475D⑥	130	4-5
	140 H.P. Auto. Tr.⑨	44FF	.030	④	31-34	Fig. D	18°⑧	Fig. B	—	600D⑥	130	4-5
	Turbocharged Eng.	44FF	.030	④	31-34	Fig. D	24°	Fig. A	825⑥	—	130	4-5
1967	95 H.P. Std. Tr.	46FF	.035	④	31-34	Fig. D	6°	Fig. B	500⑥	—	130	3½-5
	95 H.P. Auto. Tr.	46FF	.035	④	31-34	Fig. D	14°	Fig. B	—	500D⑥	130	3½-5
	95 H.P.⑨	44FF	.035	④	31-34	Fig. D	TDC	Fig. B	700⑥	500D⑥	130	3½-5
	110 H.P.	44FF	.030	④	31-34	Fig. D	14°	Fig. B	650⑥	500D⑥	130	3½-5
	110 H.P. with P/G, A/C	44FF	.030	④	31-34	Fig. D	24°	Fig. B	—	500D⑥	130	3½-5
	110 H.P.⓪	44FF	.030	④	31-34	Fig. D	4°	Fig. B	700⑥	600D⑥	130	3½-5
1968	95 H.P.	46FF	.035	④	31-34	Fig. D	⑩	Fig. B	700⑥	600D⑥	130	5½-6¾
	110 H.P.	44FF	.030	④	31-34	Fig. D	⑪	Fig. B	700⑥	600D⑥	130	5½-6¾
	140 H.P.	44FF	.030	④	31-34	Fig. D	4°	Fig. B	650⑥	550D⑥	130	5½-6¾
1969	95 H.P.-Std. Tr.	R44FF	.035	④	31-34	Fig. D	6°	Fig. B	700	—	130	5½-6¾
	95 H.P.-Auto. Tr.	R44FF	.035	④	31-34	Fig. D	14°	Fig. B	—	600D	130	5½-6¾
	110 H.P.-Std. Tr.	R44FF	.035	④	31-34	Fig. D	4°	Fig. B	700	—	130	5½-6¾
	110 H.P.-Auto. Tr.	R44FF	.035	④	31-34	Fig. D	12°	Fig. B	—	600D	130	5½-6¾
	140 H.P.	R44FF	.035	④	31-34	Fig. D	4°	Fig. B	650	550D	130	5½-6¾

①—BTDC-Before top dead center.
②—D-Drive
③—Plus or minus 20 lbs.
④—New points .019″, used .016″.
⑥—If air conditioned, turn A/C switch to "Full On" position and add 50 R.P.M. to idle speed listed.
⑦—1966 with A/C 24°.
⑧—With head gasket (Part No. 3891552) set at 14°.
⑨—With A.I.R. system.
⑩—Manual trans. 6°; automatic trans. 14°.
⑪—Manual trans. 4°; automatic trans. 12°.

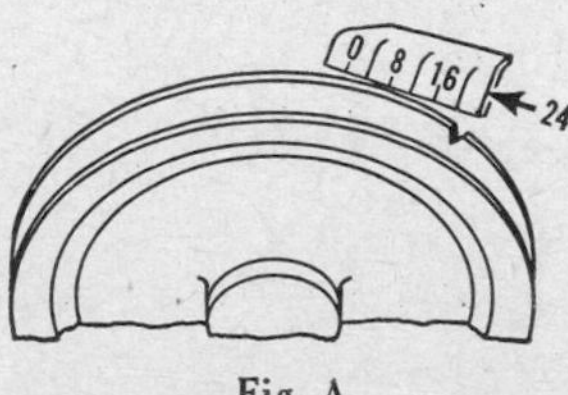

Fig. A

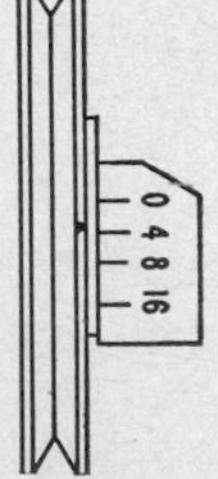

Fig. B

Continued

TUNE UP SPECIFICATIONS—Continued

★Because of the difference in rate of expansion between aluminum head and steel spark plug it is advisable to allow engine to cool before removing plugs.

•When using a timing light, disconnect vacuum hose at distributor and plug opening in hose so idle speed will not be affected.

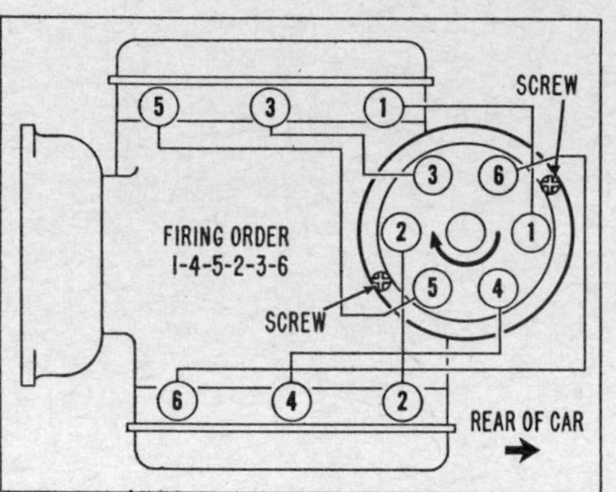

Fig. D

ALTERNATOR & REGULATOR SPECIFICATIONS

Year	Alternator					Regulator						
				Output @ 14 Volts			Field Relay			Voltage Regulator		
	Model	Rated Hot Output Amps.	Field Current 12 Volts @ 80° F.	2000 R.P.M. Amps.	5000 R.P.M. Amps.	Model	Air Gap In.	Point Gap In.	Closing Voltage	Air Gap In.	Point Gap In.	Voltage @ 125° F.
1965–69	1100639	37	2.2–2.6	25	35	1119515	.015	.030	1.5–3.2	.067	.014	13.5–14.4
	1100698	47	2.8–3.2	31	45	1119515	.015	.030	1.5–3.2	.067	.014	13.5–14.4

GENERATOR AND REGULATOR SPECIFICATIONS

★To polarize generator, reconnect the leads to the regulator; then momentarily connect a jumper wire from the "Gen" to the "Bat" terminals of the regulator.

Car & Model	Generator				Brush Spring Tension, Ounces	Field Current Amperes	Regulator Number	Regulator				
								Cutout Relay				
	Gen-erator Number	Ground Polarity	Rated Cap. Amps.	Gen. Field Ground Loca-tion★				Vol-tage to Close Points	Arma-ture Air Gap, Inch	Voltage Regu-lator Setting Volts	Current Regu-lator Setting Amperes	Current and Voltage Arma-ture Air Gap, Inch
1963	1102226	Negative	30	External	28	1.69–1.79	1119001	12.7	.020	14.3	30	①
	1102227	Negative	30	External	28	1.69–1.79	1119001	12.7	.020	14.3	30	①
	1105135	Negative	35	External	28	2.73–3.00	1119635	12.4	.023	14.3	35	②
	1105139	Negative	40	External	28	2.73–3.00	1119654	12.4	.023	14.3	40	②
1964	1102336	Negative	35	External	28	1.69–1.79	1119002	12.7	.020	14.3	35	75

①—Voltage regulator .060″, current regulator .075″.

②—Voltage regulator .067″, current regulator .075″.

STARTING MOTOR SPECIFICATIONS

Year	Model	Part No.	Brush Spring, Tension, Ounces	No Load Test			Resistance Test③	
				Amperes	Volts	R.P.M.	Amperes	Volts
1963–66	Standard Trans.	1108306	35①	58–80②	10.6	6750–10500	280–320	4
	Automatic Trans.	1108307	35①	58–80②	10.6	6750–10500	280–320	4
1967–69	Standard Trans.	1108317	35	58–80②	10.6	6750–10500	280–320	4
	Automatic Trans.	1108318	35	58–80②	10.6	6750–10500	280–320	4

①—Minimum.

②—Includes solenoid.

③—Check capacity of motor by using a 500 ampere meter and a carbon pile rheostat to control voltage. Apply volts listed across motor with armature locked. Current should be as listed.

VALVE SPECIFICATIONS

Year	Engine Model	Valve Lash	Valve Seat Angle	Valve Face Angle	Valve Spring Installed Height	Valve Spring Pressure Lbs. @ In.	Valve Stem Clearance		Valve Stem Diameter	
							Intake	Exhaust	Intake	Exhaust
1963	Turbo-Air	1 Turn①	45	44	$1\frac{1}{2}$	60 @ $1\frac{1}{2}$	.001–.0027	.0015–.0032	.3415–.3422	.3410–.3417
	Monza	1 Turn①	45	44	$1\frac{1}{2}$	60 @ $1\frac{1}{2}$	.001–.0027	.0015–.0032	.3415–.3422	.3410–.3417
	Super Turbo-Air	1 Turn①	45	45	$1\frac{11}{16}$	77 @ $1\frac{11}{16}$	.001–.0027	.0015–.0032	.3415–.3422	.3410–.3417
	Turbo Charged	1 Turn①	45	45	$1\frac{11}{16}$	77 @ $1\frac{11}{16}$	.001–.0027	.0015–.0032	.3415–.3422	.3410–.3417
1964	All	1 Turn①	45	44	$1\frac{21}{32}$②	175 @ 1.26②	.001–.0027	.0014–.0029	.3414–.3422	.3413–.3418
1965–67	Turbo-Charged	1 Turn①	44	44	$1\frac{21}{32}$②	175 @ 1.26②	.001–.0027	.0014–.0029	.3414–.3422	.3407–.3418
	All Others	1 Turn①	44	44	$1\frac{21}{32}$②	175 @ 1.26②	.001–.0027	.0014–.0029	.3414–.3422	.3707–.3418
1968	All	1 Turn①	45	44	1.66②	175 @ 1.26②	.001–.0027	.0014–.0035	.3414–.3422	.3407–.3418
1969	All	1 Turn①	46	45	$1\frac{21}{32}$②	175 @ 1.26②	.001–.0028	.0014–.0029	.3414–.3422	.3407–.3418

①—Tighten adjusting screw until all clearance between valve stem and rocker arm has been eliminated. Then tighten screw the additional number of turns listed to center the lifter plunger. See details under "Valves, Adjust" in text.

②—Outer spring.

PISTONS, PINS, RINGS, CRANKSHAFT & BEARINGS

Year	Model	Piston Clearance	Ring End Gap① Minimum		Wrist-pin Diameter	Rod Bearings		Main Bearings			
			Comp.	Oil		Shaft Diameter	Bearing Clearance	Shaft Diameter	Bearing Clearance	Thrust on Bearing No.	Shaft End Play
1963	All	.0011–.0017②	.010	.010	.8001	1.799–1.800	.003 Max.	③	.003 Max.	1	.002–.006
1964–67	All	.0011–.0017②	.013	.015	.8001	1.799–1.800	.003 Max.	③	.003 Max.	1	.002–.006
1968	All	.0011–.0017②	.010	.015	.8001	1.799–1.800	.0007–.0028	④	.003 Max.	1	.002–.007
1969	All	.0011–.0017②	.013	.015	.8001	1.799–1.800	.0004–.0025	③	.003 Max.	1	.002–.006

①—Oversize rings not furnished. New rings should be fitted to tightest part of cylinder if cylinder is tapered.

②—Cylinder and piston must be replaced as a unit if bore is worn or tapered in excess of .005".

③—No. 1 and 2: 2.0978–2.0988. No. 3 and 4: 2.0983–2.0993.

④—No. 2: 2.0991, all others 2.0996.

CAPACITY DATA

Year	Model	Fuel Tank Gallons	Engine Oil			3 Speed Trans. Pints	4 Speed Trans. Pints	Powerglide, Quarts③	Differential, Pints
			Refill, Qts. ①	Summer Grade	Winter Grade				
1963	All	14	4	30	10W	2	3¾	②	4½
1964-66	All	14	4	30	10W	3.1	3.6	②	4
1967	All	14	4	30	10W	3.7	3.7	②	4
1968	All	14	4	30	10W	3.1	3.5	②	4
1969	All	14	4	30	10W	3.7	3.7	②	2.7

①—Add ½ quart for filter change. ②—Oil pan 3 qts. Total capacity 6½ qts. ③—Approximate. Make final check with dipstick.

WHEEL ALIGNMENT SPECIFICATIONS

Year	Model	Front Wheel Alignment			Rear Wheel Alignment			Toe-Out on Turns, Deg.	
		Caster Degrees	Camber Degrees	Toe-In Inch	Caster Degrees	Camber Degrees	Toe-In Inch	Outer Wheel	Inner Wheel
1963	All	+1½ to +2	0 to +1	¼ to ⅜	—	+½ to +1½	⅛ to ⅜	18	20
1964	All	+1½ to +2	−½ to +½	¼ to ⅜	—	—	⅛ to ⅜	18	20
1965-66	All	+3	+1	¼	—	+1	—	18.4	20
1967-69	All	+1½ to +2¼	+½ to +1½	3/16 to 5/16	—	+½ to +1½	3/16 to 5/16	18.4	20

REAR AXLE & BRAKE SPECIFICATIONS

Year	Model	Carrier Type	Diff. Bear. Preload		Ring Gear & Pinion Backlash		Pinion Bear. Preload		Brake Drum Dia.	Brake Cyl. Bore Diameter		
										Wheel Cylinders		Master Cylinder
			Method	Adjust.	Method	Adjust.	Method	Adjust.		Front	Rear	
1963-64	All	Integral	①	②	①	.005-.008	①	③	9	⅞	15/16	1
1965-69	All	Integral	①	②	①	.005-.008	①	④	9½	⅞	15/16	1

①—Threaded adjuster.
②—2 to 3 notches tight.
③—New bearings 14-16 inch-lbs. used bearings 9-11 inch-lbs.
④—New bearings 5-10 inch-lbs.

ENGINE TIGHTENING SPECIFICATIONS★

★Torque specifications are for clean and lightly lubricated threads only. Dry or dirty threads produce increased friction which prevents accurate measurement of tightness.

Year	Spark Plugs Ft. Lbs.	Cylinder Head Bolts Ft. Lbs.	Exhaust Manifold Ft. Lbs.	Rocker Arm Stud Nut Ft. Lbs.	Rocker Arm Stud Ft. Lbs.	Rocker Arm Cover Ft. Lbs.	Connecting Rod Cap Bolts Ft. Lbs.	Crankcase Bolts Ft. Lbs.	Flywheel to Crankshaft Ft. Lbs.	Vibration Damper or Pulley Ft. Lbs.
1963-64	20-25	27-33	22-27	55-125①	27-33	30-50①	20-26	55	40-50	50-60
1965-69	20	40	25	100①	40	50①	25	55	45	45

①—Inch lbs.

Electrical Section

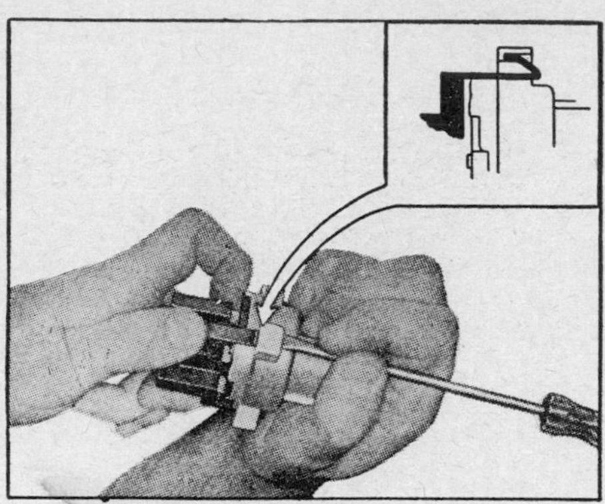

Fig. 1 Unlocking ignition switch connector. 1965-69

IGNITION TIMING

If a timing light is to be used to set ignition timing, disconnect the vacuum advance pipe to the carburetor and place a piece of tape over open end of pipe. *This is important as carburetor trouble can affect timing adjustments.*

Lacking a power timing light, an accurate method of setting ignition timing with the engine stopped is with the aid of a jumper light. Be sure to use a light bulb that corresponds with the system voltage of the vehicle.

1. Remove distributor cap and rotor and see that the breaker gap is set according to specifications.
2. Rotate engine until No. 1 cylinder is at the ignition timing point as indicated by the timing pointer and timing mark being lined up with each other.
3. Connect the jumper light between distributor ignition terminal and ground.
4. Turn on ignition switch.
5. Loosen distributor and turn it in the direction of normal rotation until the points just close (light out). Then slowly turn distributor in the opposite direction just to the exact point that the light goes on. Tighten distributor in this position.

DISTRIBUTOR REPLACE

To remove distributor, disconnect primary wire from coil. Remove distributor cap and vacuum line from distributor. Mark position of rotor arm on housing so that distributor may be reinstalled in same position. Unfasten and remove distributor from engine.

If necessary to remove secondary leads from distributor cap, mark position on cap tower for lead to No. 1 cylinder.

When installing distributor, turn rotor about ⅛ turn counterclockwise past the mark previously placed on distributor housing. Push distributor down into position in block with housing in normal installed position. It may be necessary to move the rotor slightly to start gear into mesh with camshaft gear but rotor should line up with mark when distributor is down in place. Fasten distributor in place and check ignition timing.

GENERATOR REPLACE

1965-69 Delcotron

1. Disconnect battery ground cable.
2. Disconnect wiring leads at Delcotron.
3. Remove blower belt.
4. Unfasten and remove Delcotron.

1964

1. Disconnect ground cable at battery.
2. Disconnect armature and field wires from generator.
3. Loosen idler pulley bracket to permit removal of belt from generator pulley.
4. Disconnect fuel inlet line at fuel pump.
5. Remove oil pressure sending unit from top of oil filter bracket.
6. Remove generator pulley (nut has left-hand thread).
7. Unfasten and remove generator.
8. Reverse procedure to install.

1963

1. Disconnect ground cable at battery.
2. Disconnect armature and field wires at generator.
3. Loosen idler pulley on belt to permit removal of belt from pulley.
4. Unfasten and remove generator.

STARTER REPLACE

1965-69

1. Disconnect battery ground cable.
2. Raise and support car.
3. Observe and record color coding at solenoid connections, then disconnect all wires from solenoid.

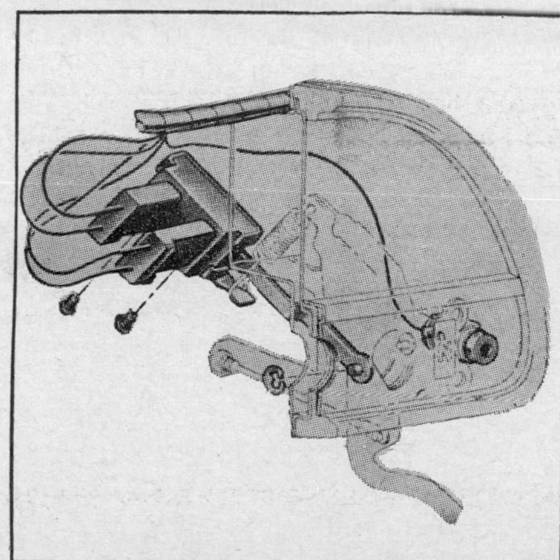

Fig. 3 Neutral safety switch installation. 1963-64

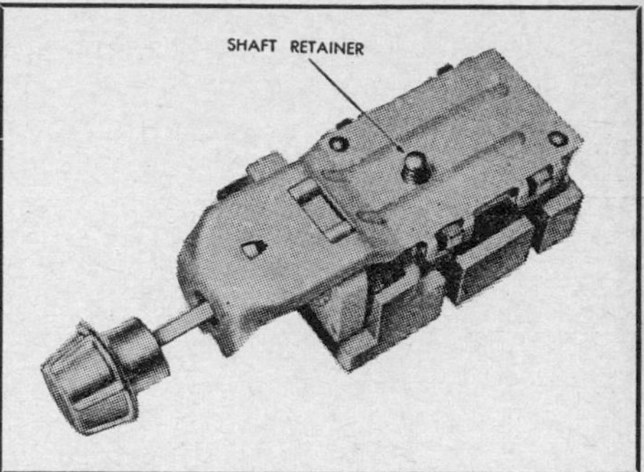

Fig. 2 Light switch shaft retainer

NOTE: Reinstall nut as each wire is disconnected as thread size is different and may be mixed and stripped.

4. Unfasten and pull starter forward to clear housing and remove starter.
5. Reverse procedure to install.

1963-64

1. Disconnect battery ground cable at battery to avoid a short circuit.
2. Raise rear of car.
3. Disconnect rear throttle control rod from bellcrank at transmission and from cross shaft in engine compartment. This allows rod to be moved out of the way when removing starter.
4. Disconnect 3 wires at starter solenoid. It helps to have a ¼" drive midget socket for removing the nuts from the terminal posts of the two smaller gauge wires.
5. With a ⅜" drive $\frac{9}{16}$" shallow socket on a 9" extension with ratchet, remove the two starter mounting bolts. *Be sure to remove the upper bolt first as this makes the job easier.*
6. Pull starter forward and out of engine.

IGNITION SWITCH, REPLACE

1963-64

1. Disconnect battery ground cable.
2. Remove lock cylinder by positioning switch in "Lock" position. Insert a paper clip in small hole in cylinder face. Push in on wire to depress plunger and continue to turn key counter-clockwise until lock cylinder can be removed.
3. Using a suitable spanner wrench, remove front attaching nut.
4. Withdraw switch and remove three wire connectors from rear of switch.
5. To remove the "theft resistant" connector, fashion a suitable tool out of heavy wire stock and press tool on lock clip within slot in connector. Holding wire tool firmly in place, gently work connector away from

switch until connector is released.
6. Reverse above procedure to install.

1965-69

1. Disconnect battery ground cable.
2. Remove lock cylinder by positioning switch in "Off" position.
3. Insert a paper clip in small hole in cylinder face.
4. Push in on wire to depress plunger and continue to turn ignition key counter-clockwise until lock cylinder can be removed.
5. Using a suitable spanner wrench, remove front attaching nut.
6. Pull switch out from under dash and remove wiring connectors.
7. To remove "theft resistant" connector, use a screwdriver to unsnap locking tangs on connector, Fig. 1. Unplug connector.
8. Reverse above procedure to install.

LIGHT SWITCH, REPLACE

1963-64

1. Disconnect battery ground cable.
2. Pull knob to "On" position.
3. Reach under instrument panel and depress switch shaft retainer and remove knob and shaft assembly, Fig. 2.
4. Remove retaining ferrule, using a wide-blade screwdriver, and bezel, then lower switch.
5. Disconnect multi-plug connector from switch. A screwdriver may be inserted in side of switch to pry plug from switch.
6. Reverse above procedure to install.

1965-69

1. Disconnect battery ground cable.
2. Pull switch knob out to "On" position.
3. Reach under instrument console and depress switch shaft retainer, Fig. 2.
4. With retainer depressed, pull knob and shaft from switch.
5. Disconnect multi-plug connector from switch. A screwdriver may be inserted in side of switch to pry plug from switch.
6. Reverse above procedure to install.

STOP LIGHT SWITCH, REPLACE

1963-69

1. Disconnect two connectors from switch terminals, located under instrument panel adjacent to brake pedal.
2. Remove lock nut from plunger end of switch and remove switch from bracket or brace.
3. Remove second lock nut from switch and install on new switch.
4. Position switch on bracket or brace and install remaining lock nut.
5. Install two electrical connectors.
6. Check operation of switch and adjust as required. Electrical contact should be made when brake pedal is depressed ⅜″ to ½″ (½″ to ¾″ on 1963-64) from fully released position.

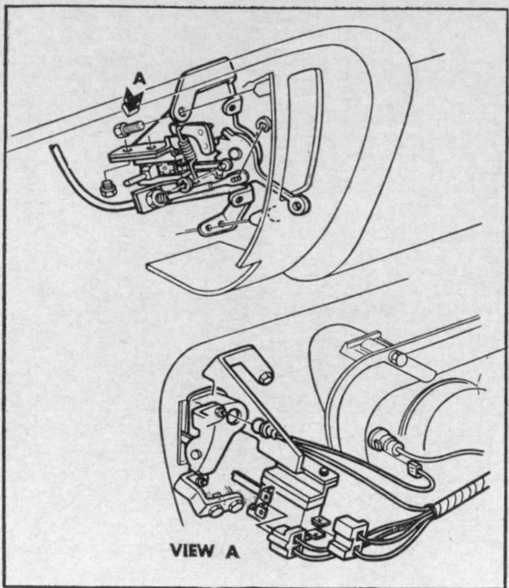

Fig. 4 Neutral safety switch installation. 1965-69

NEUTRAL SAFETY SWITCH, REPLACE

1963-64, Fig. 3

1. Remove retainer from pin on transmission range selector.
2. Remove two switch attaching screws.
3. Lower switch and remove starter circuit connector and back-up lamp circuit connector (if used).
4. Install connector(s) on new switch.
5. Place switch plunger onto pin on range selector and loosely install switch attaching screws.
6. Install retainer onto pin on range selector.
7. Place transmission range selector in "N" position.
8. Push switch in direction toward front of vehicle as far as possible to extend plunger. Insert gauge (.680-.685″) between end of plunger and switch. Then move switch tightly against gauge and plunger and tighten screws while holding in this position.

NOTE: This gauging dimension is extremely critical. A gauge of 1″ x 13/32″ x .680/.685″ can be made from steel stock.

---

9. Test operation of switch. Engine must only start in "N". Check operation of back-up lamps (if used).

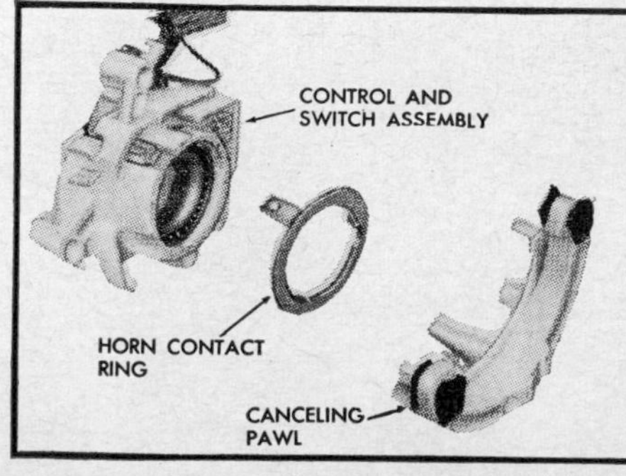

Fig. 5 Turn signal control. 1964-66

1965-69, Fig. 4

1. Disconnect battery ground cable.
2. Remove instrument cluster.
3. Remove retaining ring securing switch lever arm to range selector.
4. Unfasten switch from range selector (2 screws).
5. Lower switch and disconnect wiring harness connectors from switch terminals.
6. Install wiring harness connectors onto new switch.
7. Extend switch plunger to its outer most position and insert gauge block (.68″) in switch case.
8. Position switch plunger pin to range selector and loosely install attaching screws.
9. Install retainer securing plunger pin to range selector.
10. Place transmission range selector in "N".
11. Push forward on switch case until contact carrier is against gauge block.
12. Tighten switch screws and remove gauge block.
13. Test operation of switch. Engine must start in "N" position only. Check operation of back-up lamps (if used).

TURN SIGNAL SWITCH, REPLACE

1963

The switch is fastened to the steering gear mast jacket with two screws. Pull connector plug from switch, remove attaching screws and switch cable and remove switch.

Install new switch, being sure cable is adjusted to switch to provide proper operation of turn signal lever.

1964-66, Fig. 5

STANDARD MODELS

1. Disconnect battery ground cable.
2. Remove steering wheel.
3. Disconnect signal wiring at harness connector.
4. Remove steering column mast jacket upper support clamp.
5. Remove signal lever and three screws attaching control to retaining plate.
6. Remove retaining plate and signal housing from steering column, and disengage wiring from housing.
7. Reverse above procedure to install.

CAUTION: Turn signal control assembly must be in neutral position when assembling steering wheel to prevent damage to cancelling cam and control assembly.

TELESCOPING WHEEL

1. Disconnect battery ground cable.
2. Remove steering wheel and hub.
3. Remove spring and cancelling cam from steering shaft.
4. Remove turn signal lever.
5. Unfasten signal control from retaining plate (3 screws).
6. Remove wiring clamp and cover from signal wiring harness.

7. Remove wire terminals from plastic connectors, using a screwdriver. *To facilitate reassembly, record color code of wires.*
8. Guiding wiring, carefully pull signal switch out of housing.
9. Reverse above procedure to install.

CAUTION: Turn signal control assembly must be in neutral position when assembling steering wheel to prevent damage to cancelling cam and control assembly.

1967-69

1. Disconnect battery ground cable.
2. Disconnect turn signal multiple connector from chassis harness connector under instrument panel.
3. Remove steering wheel.
4. Slide upper bearing preload spring and turn signal cancelling cam from upper steering shaft.
5. Remove turn signal lever.
6. Push in hazard warning switch knob, unscrew and remove knob.
7. Remove mast jacket trim cover.
8. Remove retaining ring and steering shaft upper wave and thrust washers.
9. Cut harness near connector.
10. Loosen mast jacket upper support bolts.
11. Remove three switch mounting screws and slide assembly from mast jacket and steering shaft.
12. Remove wire connector, clip and/or cover.
13. Reverse procedure to install. Turn signal should be in neutral position before installing steering wheel. Install connector to wiring and connect turn signal wire harness to chassis harness connector.

HORN SOUNDER & STEERING WHEEL

1967-69

Standard Wheel

1. Disconnect steering column wire harness from chassis wire harness at connector.
2. Pull horn button cap or center ornament and retainer.
3. Remove receiving cup or horn ring, Belleville spring, bushing and pivot ring (3 screws).
4. Remove wheel nut and washer and use a suitable puller to remove wheel.
5. Reverse procedure to install. *Turn signal control assembly must be in neutral position when assembling steering wheel to prevent damage to cancelling cam and control assembly.*

Simulated Wood Wheel

1. Disconnect steering column harness from chassis wire harness at connector.
2. Pull up to remove horn cap.

NOTE: If steering wheel only is to be removed perform Step 4. If turn placed, skip Step 4 and proceed with Step 5.

3. Remove horn contact assembly.
4. Remove steering wheel.
5. Pull off wheel hub.
6. Remove turn signal cancelling cam.
7. Reverse procedure to install. *Turn signal control assembly must be in neutral position when assembling wheel hub to prevent damage to cancelling cam and control assembly.*

Telescoping Wheel

1. Disconnect column harness at wiring connector.
2. Pry off horn button cap and remove retainer.
3. Remove control lever.
4. Remove spacer, cup, spring and insulator from center of wheel (3 screws).
5. Pull off steering wheel.
6. If necessary, remove spring and cancelling cam.
7. Reverse procedure to install.

1965-66

1. Disconnect horn wire at chassis wiring harness.
2. Pull out horn button on standard models. On other models pull out center ornament from horn ring.
3. Remove contact assembly (3 screws).
4. Use a suitable puller to remove steering wheel.

1963-64

1. To remove, first pry out horn button. Remove three screws attaching receiver cup and bushing spacer to steering wheel. Remove flat spring.
2. Remove nut from steering shaft and use a puller to remove wheel, being careful not to lose spring or seat located under wheel.
3. Reverse above procedure to install, making sure that mark on steering shaft lines up with mark on steering wheel hub.

INSTRUMENT CLUSTER

1967-69

1. Disconnect battery ground cable.
2. Remove light and wiper switch bezel nuts.
3. On Powerglide models, remove shift lever knob.
4. Remove heater or A/C control retaining screws and allow control to hang below instrument console. On A/C models remove air outlet from panel.
5. Disconnect speedometer cable. If equipped, disconnect trip odometer and speed warning unit.
6. On Powerglide models, remove upper mast jacket support clamp and lower support bolts.

NOTE: On 1968-69 models the instrument panel center pad must be removed. This pad overlaps the edge of the instrument cluster bezel, preventing direct removal of the cluster. To remove the center pad, proceed as follows:

1. Remove radio bezel or radio hole plate to gain access to the center pad retaining rivets.
2. Using a #25 or #26 drill, drill out rivets (one at each upper corner of opening).
3. Remove two screws securing pad at lower edge of instrument panel and remove center pad.

When installing, use suitable tapping screws in place of the rivets. An oval Phillips head screw is best for this application because the height of the screw head must be kept at a minimum to prevent interference with the radio bezel or hole cover.

7. *Allow steering wheel to rest on seat cushion to prevent distortion to the mast jacket.*
8. Unfasten cluster from console.
9. Pull instrument cluster forward from console and disconnect cluster wiring harness from panel wiring harness at multiple connector.
10. On Powerglide models, remove shift lever mechanism from rear of cluster housing.
11. Remove cluster from console.
12. Reverse procedure to install.

1965-66

SERVICE BULLETIN

A revised method of removing the instrument cluster assembly on 1965 Corvairs eliminates the need to take out the steering column when performing this operation. An application of masking tape to the steering mast jacket on the area between the instrument panel and the steering wheel will protect that section from any paint damage while removing the cluster.

The support clamp for the upper mast jacket must be removed on models that have Powerglide transmissions to free the steering column.

1. Disconnect battery ground cable.
2. Remove steering wheel.
3. Remove light and wiper switch bezel nuts.
4. On Powerglide models, remove shift lever knob.
5. Remove heater or air conditioning control retaining screws and allow control to hang below instrument console.
6. Disconnect speedometer cable.
7. Remove screws retaining instrument cluster to console.
8. Pull instrument cluster forward from console and disconnect cluster wiring from panel wiring harness at multiple disconnect.
9. On Powerglide models, remove shift lever mechanism from rear of cluster housing.
10. Remove cluster from console completely.

1963-64

1. Disconnect battery ground cable from battery.
2. Remove the connectors from back of instrument cluster and pull harness out of retaining clips on back of cluster.
3. Disconnect speedometer cable.
4. Remove light switch and from beneath dash remove nut attaching lighter (if equipped) and withdraw lighter.
5. Lower mast jacket and steering wheel assembly from instrument panel or remove steering wheel on 3-speed models or steering wheel and turn signal housing on automatic transmission models to give clearance for cluster removal.
6. Remove cluster attaching screws and remove the cluster, instrument

center panel and seal by pulling straight out, turning slightly to clear transmission range selector.
7. Remove two harness clips from back of cluster.
8. Remove screws attaching the cluster back to the cluster.
9. Remove instruments and speedometer as required.

W/S WIPER MOTOR

1968-69

1. If possible, place motor in park position and disconnect battery ground cable.
2. Remove wiper blades and arms.
3. Remove plenum chamber grille.
4. Loosen nuts retaining drive link to crank arm ball stud.
5. Disconnect all wiring and washer hose connections at motor and pump.
6. Unfasten and remove motor from firewall.
7. Reverse procedure to install.

1963-67

1. Remove retainer securing drive link to wiper motor drive arm.
2. If equipped with a washer, note location of washer hoses to wiper motor, then remove hoses from motor from inside front compartment. Also remove electrical connectors from motor.
3. Remove screws securing motor to the body and remove motor.
4. To install, reverse above procedure. *It is important that the three screws attaching motor be fully tightened so that the sleeves surrounding the screws bottoms to prevent "floating" of the motor.*

W/S WIPER TRANSMISSION

1968-69

1. Make certain motor is in park position, then remove wiper arm and blades.
2. Remove plenum chamber grille.
3. Loosen nuts retaining drive link to crank arm ball joint and disconnect drive link from crank arm.
4. Remove transmission retaining screws, lower assembly into plenum chamber and remove complete unit from chamber.
5. Reverse procedure to install.

1963-67

1. Position wiper in park position. Then remove wiper arms and blades.
2. Remove retainer securing drive link to wiper motor drive arm.
3. Remove retainers securing ends of link to each wiper transmission and remove link.
4. Unfasten and remove transmission (3 screws each side).
5. To install reverse removel procedure. Apply sealer to weld nuts before tightening transmission retaining screws. Tips of wiper blades should be 1½" above lower windshield opening with motor in park position. Arms and blades should be parallel. Operate wipers and check linkage for running clearance.

W/S WIPER SWITCH

1963-69

1 Disconnect battery ground cable.
2. Loosen small set screw at bottom of wiper arm and remove knob.
3. Remove bezel, lock nut and washer.
4. Withdraw wiper switch from instrument panel and remove connector from rear of switch. A single connector is used on units without a windshield washer. Two connectors are used with windshield washer.
5. Reverse above procedure to install.

RADIO REMOVAL

NOTE: When installing radio, be sure to adjust antenna trimmer for peak performance.

1967-69 With A/C

1. Disconnect battery ground cable.
2. Remove ash tray and bracket.
3. Remove radio attaching bracket and light from radio. Disconnect radio electrical connector and antenna lead.
4. Disconnect center air conditioning flexible hose at evaporator case.
5. Remove cigar lighter and ignition switch.
6. Remove radio knobs, bezel and retaining nuts.
7. Lower and remove radio.

Fuel Pump, Accelerator Linkage & Turbocharger

FUEL PUMP, REPLACE

1. Disconnect fuel lines at pump. Leave "T" connector and pipe in pump.
2. Loosen lock nut and remove set screw holding pump in place.
3. Remove fuel pump and push rod.

INSTALLATION

1. If removed, install "T" connector and pipe in outlet connection.
2. Install pump into housing with outlet connection to front. Carefully feel pump position with set screw, being sure set screw pilots in locking hole.
3. Tighten set screw and then lock nut.
4. Install fuel lines. Then operate engine and check for leaks.

TURBOCHARGER

The turbocharger is an exhaust driven unit that forces air-fuel mixture into the intake manifold at higher than atmospheric pressure, thereby improving engine breathing and power output. It consists of a precision-balanced rotating group with a turbine wheel at one end and a centrifugal impeller at the other, each wheel enclosed in a contoured housing.

The hot exhaust gases are directed against the turbine wheel blades, spinning the wheel, shaft and impeller wheel at a high rate of speed. The impeller, in the compressor housing, draws air-fuel mixture from the carburetor and passes it to the intake manifold under a higher than atmospheric pressure. This increases the amount of air-fuel mixture available to the cylinder, resulting in a greater horsepower output.

Under heavy load, the turbocharger speed automatically increases due to increase in exhaust gases, providing more fuel-air mixture to meet the engine's demand.

The turbocharger is provided with a semi-floating sleeve bearing which is lubricated with engine oil taken from the oil filter adapter and drained through a larger tube into the rocker arm area of the right cylinder head.

Inspection

If trouble is suspected in the turbocharger, it should be inspected and serviced as follows:

1. Disconnect oil drain line at elbow. Connect a hose from the elbow to a container placed at side of engine. Start engine and run at idle speed for one minute to determine oil flow (should be about one quart per minute at idle).
2. Remove turbocharger and carburetor from engine and separate the two units.
3. Inspect the turbine wheel for damage, carbon build-up on blades, and carbon accumulation on back face of turbine wheel. Check for free rotation by depressing the shield against the spring ring, then rotating the wheel. If the wheel does not rotate freely, disassemble the unit and inspect for damaged parts or foreign material causing the interference.

Service, Fig. 1

1. Remove compressor housing. Inspect it for signs of damage on the inner contour.
2. Inspect impeller wheel for damaged blades or evidence of rubbing in the housing.
3. Note any oil accumulation in housing or on impeller, indicating a defective oil seal.

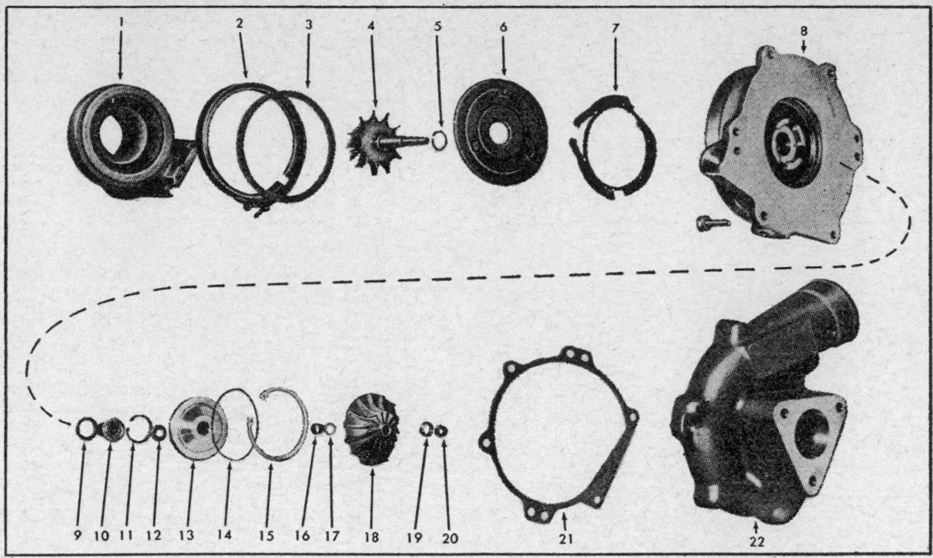

Fig. 1 Disassembled view of turbocharger

1. Turbine housing
2. Charger housing clamp
3. Gasket
4. Turbine wheel and shaft
5. Oil seal ring
6. Shield plate
7. Spring ring
8. Bearing housing
9. Bearing shim
10. Bearing
11. Bearing retaining ring
12. Mating ring (washer)
13. Oil seal
14. "O" ring seal
15. Seal retaining ring
16. Shaft sleeve
17. Impeller shim
18. Impeller
19. Impeller special washer
20. Nut
21. Gasket
22. Compressor housing

4. If impeller requires cleaning, use a nylon bristle brush and a solvent such as diesel fuel or kerosene to remove accumulated dirt. Thoroughly clean impeller and compressor housing. *Failure to remove all dirt may result in a more severe unbalance than existed prior to cleaning.*
5. Measure turbine shaft end play with a dial indicator attached to the bearing housing so that indicator point is resting on impeller nut.
6. Rest assembly squarely on hub of turbine wheel, then push down on housing and record indicator reading. Release pressure on housing and check measurement again. Allowable end play is .005" to .008". If end play is excessive, the unit should be rebuilt.
7. Check turbine shaft radial play, the maximum allowable being .022". If excessive, unit should be rebuilt.
8. If unit is in satisfactory condition, install compressor housing, using a new gasket, and torque the bolts to 80 in-lb.
9. Install carburetor to turbocharger, then install assembly on vehicle.

ACCELERATOR LINKAGE

1966-69

NOTE: Accelerator linkage should be adjusted to get simultaneous full throttle position at the accelerator pedal, the linkage idler lever and the carburetor throttle lever. The pedal downward travel stop (at idler lever at transmission) is adjustable to furnish a pedal angle comfortable to the driver.

1. To adjust, disconnect accelerator pull rod swivel from rear idler lever, Fig. 2.
2. Disconnect carburetor pull-back spring. Remove carburetor cross shaft actuating rod swivel from cross shaft.

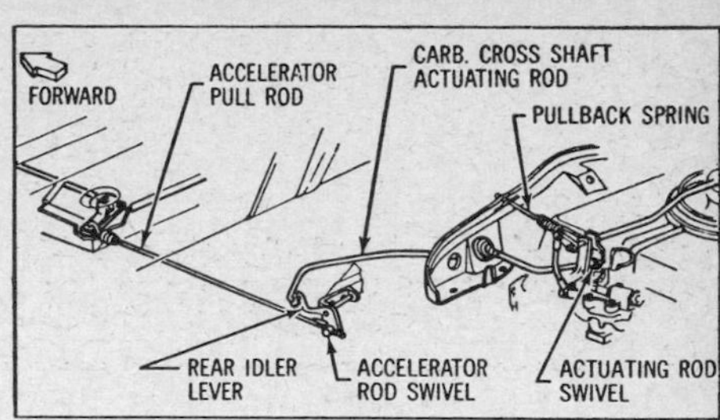

Fig. 2 Accelerator linkage adjustment. 1966-69

3. Pull carburetor cross shaft actuating rod rearward until rear idler lever hits stop on its bracket. Rotate carburetor cross shaft to move L.H. primary carburetor into wide open throttle position (thru detent on Powerglide).
4. With carburetor cross shaft and its actuating rod held in the foregoing positions, align actuating rod swivel until it freely engages its mating hole in cross shaft lever. Remove swivel and back it off five full turns and replace it in lever hole.
5. Connect pull-back spring.
6. Depress pedal to within 1⅛" of floor carpet and block pedal in this position. *This pedal setting is measured from the underside of the rubber flange at the top of the pedal.*
7. Rotate rear idler lever into wide open throttle position and reconnect accelerator pull rod after adjusting rod swivel so it freely engages its mating hole in idler lever.
8. Remove pedal block and check complete accelerator control linkage adjustment by depressing pedal and inspecting carburetor throttle valve to be sure it is at wide open position.

1963-65

1. Using Fig. 2 as a guide, disconnect accelerator rod swivel.
2. Disconnect actuating rod swivel at L.H. carburetor lever.
3. Pull cross shaft actuating rod to wide open position and turn cross shaft lever to wide open throttle position (carburetor throttle lever against stop). Adjust actuating rod swivel to align with hole in cross shaft lever, then lengthen accelerator rod by backing off swivel five full turns.
4. Position accelerator pedal one inch from the floor mat (1¼" on Powerglide) by placing a block of wood between pedal and floor mat.
5. Hold rear idler lever in wide open throttle position and turn swivel to align with hole in lever.

Engine Section

"In Car" Operations

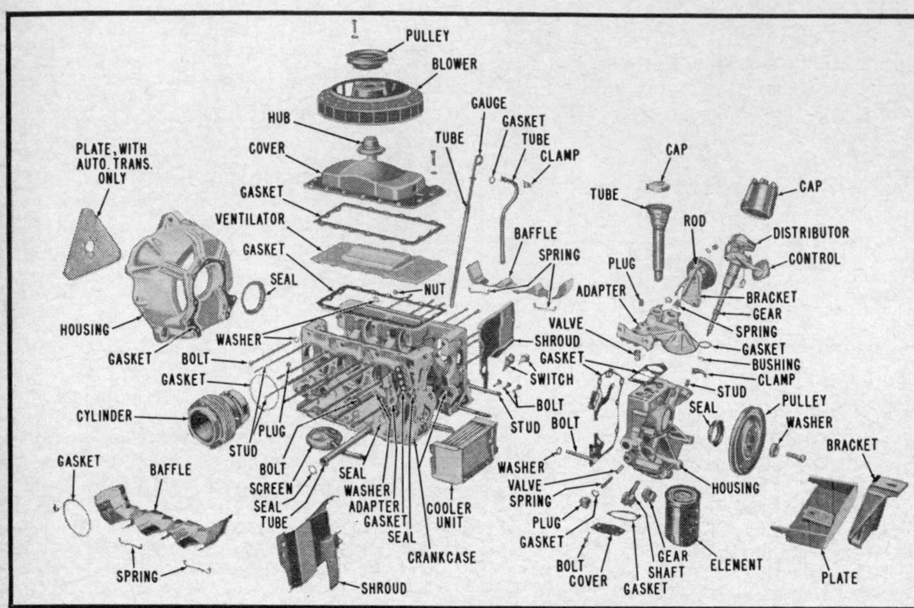

Engine block and attaching parts

ENGINE SEAL & SHIELDS

Seal & Retainer

REMOVAL, Fig. 1

1. Remove spare tire and air cleaner.
2. Remove retainer-to-body screws.
3. Disconnect seal from engine shields by pushing groove of seal off shield flange.
4. Remove seal and retainer.

INSTALLATION

1. Lubricate groove of seal with liquid soap or silicone and place seal and retainer in position over shields.
2. While guiding groove of seal on shield flange (with one hand) press seal in place, using a block of wood or hammer handle.
3. Install all screws finger tight, then tighten them securely.

Front Shield

REMOVAL, Fig. 2

1. Disconnect battery positive cable.
2. Remove spare tire and air cleaner.
3. Remove vacuum balance tube.
4. Disconnect heater hose at upper shroud.
5. Remove grommet for Powerglide dipstick tube (if equipped).
6. Disconnect seal from flange of front shield.
7. Remove grommet (for starter wiring and fuel line) from front shield.
8. Disconnect starter wiring (engine side).
9. From underside of vehicle disconnect accelerator rod at transmission bellcrank and fuel line at flex hose (plug fuel line from tank), then disconnect axle dipstick tube at differential carrier.
10. Disconnect accelerator rod at carburetor cross shaft, then remove rod and bellows from front shield.
11. Disconnect grommet from front shield and remove axle dipstick tube.
12. Disconnect fuel line at fuel pump, then remove fuel line from front shield.
13. Remove attaching bolts and front shield.

INSTALLATION

1. Install front shield by guiding it over starter wiring and Powerglide dipstick tube (if equipped).
2. Install front shield bolts finger tight, then tighten them securely.
3. Install fuel line through front shield, then connect fuel line at fuel pump.
4. Install accelerator rod through front shield, then connect bellows to front shield and connect accelerator rod at carburetor cross shaft.
5. Install axle dipstick tube through front shield and connect grommet in front shield.
6. Connect starter wiring.
7. Install grommet (for starter wiring and fuel line) in front shield.
8. Lubricate groove of seal with liquid soap or silicone. Then, while guiding groove of seal onto flange (with one hand), press seal in place with a block of wood or hammer handle.
9. Install grommet for Powerglide dipstick tube (if equipped).
10. Connect heater hose at upper shroud.
11. Install vacuum balance tube.
12. From underside of vehicle connect fuel line at flex hose, accelerator rod at transmission bellcrank and axle dipstick tube at differential carrier.

Left Shield

REMOVAL, Fig. 2

1. Remove bolts attaching left side of upper shroud and left shield to cylinder head.
2. Remove bolts attaching left shield to left exhaust duct.
3. Remove bolt attaching left shield and oil cooler to cylinder head.
4. Remove bolts attaching left shield to front shield and (if equipped) remove screw from ground strap.
5. Disconnect seal from flange of left shield.
6. Remove left shield by pulling from under upper shroud, front shield and oil cooler flange.

INSTALLATION

1. Place left shield in position under upper shroud, front shield and oil cooler flange.
2. Install all bolts attaching left shield finger tight, then tighten them securely.
3. Lubricate groove of seal with liquid soap or silicone. Then, while guiding groove of seal onto shield flange (with one hand), press seal in place with a block of wood or hammer handle.
4. Connect ground strap (if equipped).

Right Shield

REMOVAL, Fig. 2

1. Remove spare tire, then remove bolts attaching right side of upper shroud and right shield to cylinder head.
2. Remove bolts attaching right shield to right exhaust duct.
3. Remove ignition coil and bracket.
4. Remove bolts attaching right shield to front shield and (if equipped) remove screw from ground strap.
5. Disconnect seal from flange of right shield.
6. Remove bolt attaching muffler bracket to right shield.
7. Remove muffler.
8. Remove right shield by pulling from under upper shroud and front shield.

INSTALLATION

1. Place right shield in position under

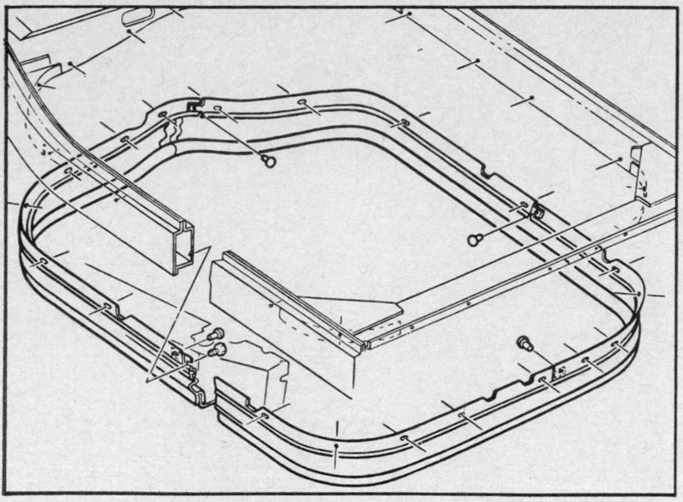

Fig. 1 Engine seal and retainer

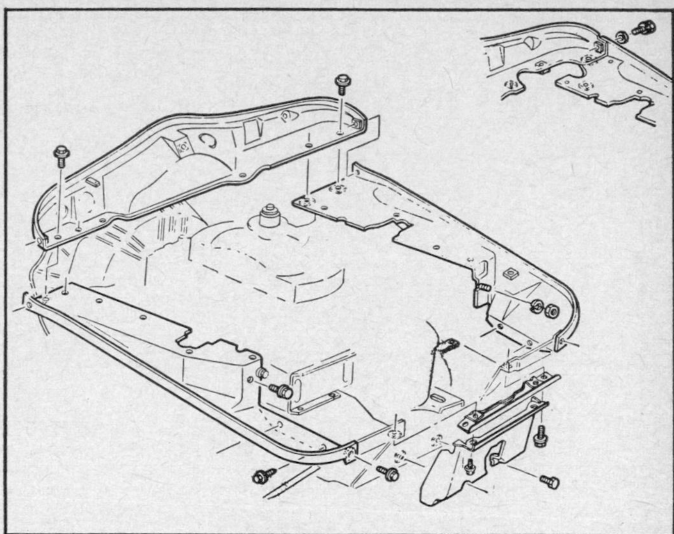

Fig. 2 Engine shields

upper shroud and front shield.

2. Install all bolts attaching right shield finger tight, then tighten them securely.
3. Lubricate groove of seal with liquid soap or silicone. Then, while guiding groove of seal onto shield flange (with one hand), press seal in place with a block of wood or hammer handle.
4. Connect ground strap (if equipped).
5. Install ignition coil and bracket, then spare tire.

Rear Center Shield

NOTE: The rear center shield is two pieces. The engine seal is connected to the upper half, which need not be removed under normal conditions.

LOWER HALF, Fig. 2

1. Remove bolts attaching rear center shield to skid plate and exhaust ducts.
2. Remove rear center shield.
3. Place rear center shield in position with attaching bolts finger tight, then tighten bolts securely.

UPPER HALF

1. Remove lower half of center shield.
2. Disconnect seal from flange of rear center shield.
3. Remove bolts and upper half.
4. Install upper half and tighten securely.
5. Install lower half (see above).
6. Lubricate groove of seal with liquid soap or silicone. Then, while guiding groove of seal onto shield flange (with one hand), press seal in place with a block of wood or hammer handle.

Muffler Heat Shield

REMOVAL, Fig. 3

1. Remove two bolts attaching heat shield to muffler hanger.
2. Loosen two bolts attaching rear of heat shield and right rear shroud to cylinder head.
3. Remove heat shield.

INSTALLATION

1. Install heat shield in position under head of two bolts in rear of cylinder head.
2. Install bolts attaching heat shield to muffler hanger and tighten securely.
3. Tighten two bolts attaching rear of heat shield and right rear shroud to cylinder head.

ENGINE COOLING COMPONENTS

Upper Shroud

REMOVAL, FIG. 4

1. Remove spare tire and air cleaner.
2. Disconnect fuel lines at fuel pump and carburetors, then remove fuel lines to carburetors.
3. Disconnect vacuum advance hose at right carburetor.
4. Disconnect accelerator rod at carburetor cross shaft, and choke control rods at choke levers. Then

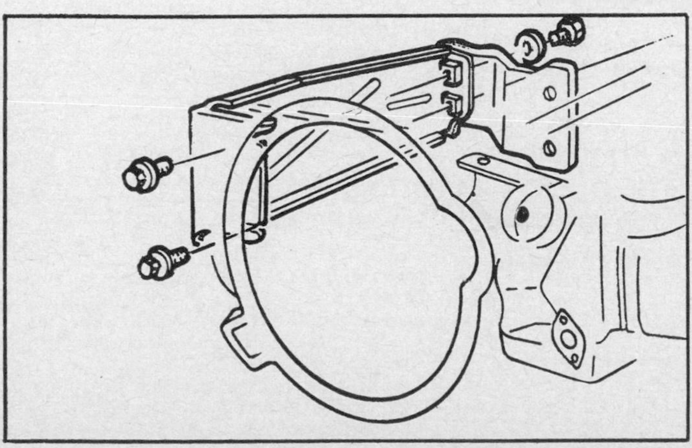

Fig. 3 Muffler heat shield

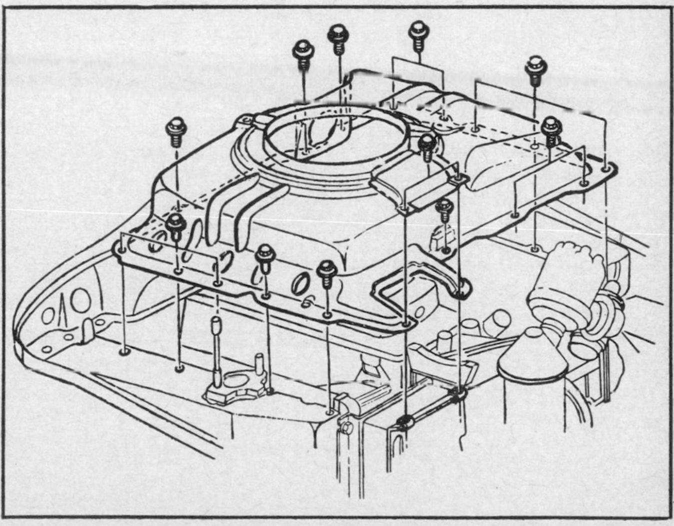

Fig. 4 Upper shroud

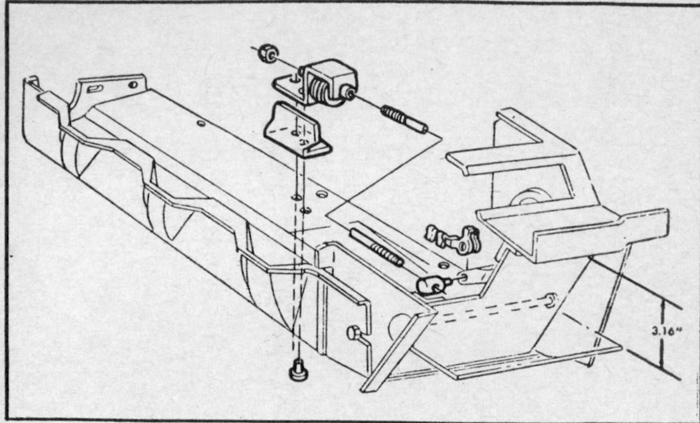

Fig. 5 Lower shroud and thermostat

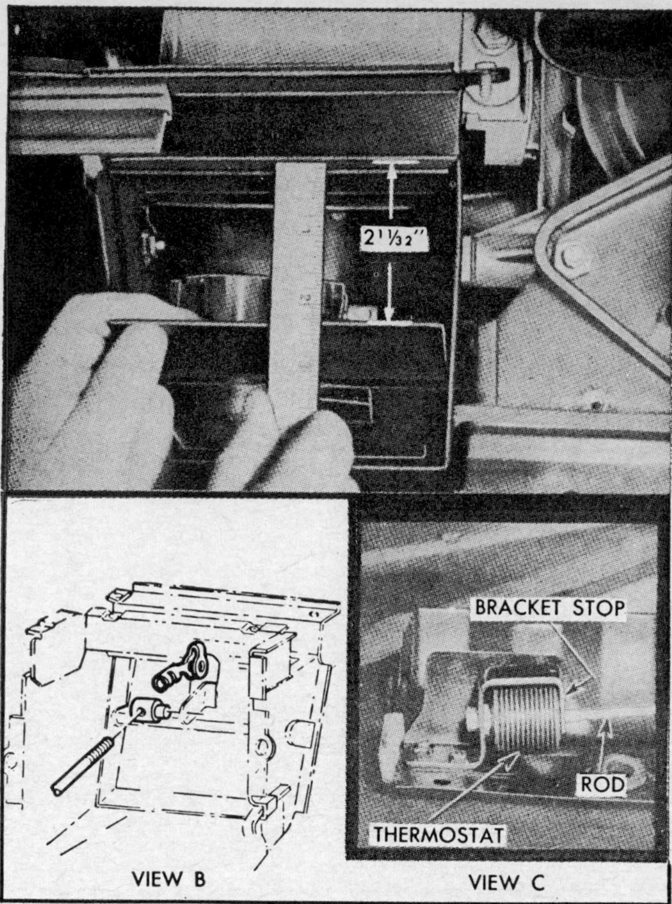

Fig. 5A Adjusting cooling air damper door opening

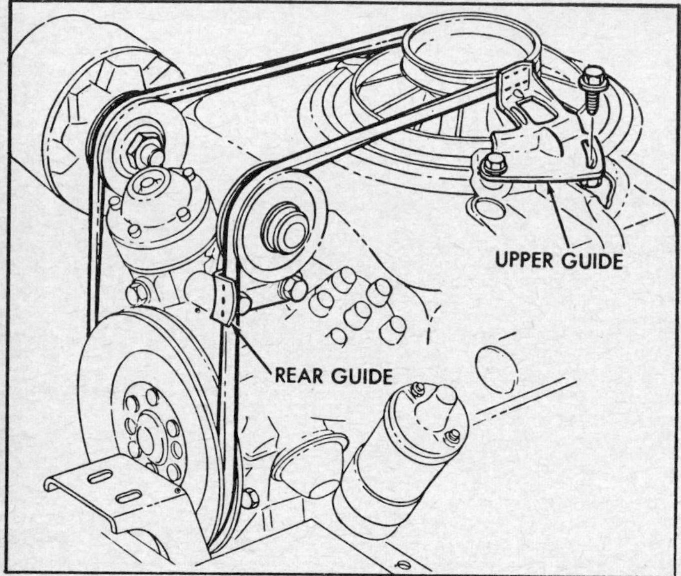

Fig. 6 Blower belt and guides. Guides are standard equipment on 1964 and later engines but they can be installed on earlier engines

remove upper choke control rods.

5. Remove carburetors with cross shaft and linkage attached.
6. Remove blower belt.
7. Disconnect crankcase ventilation tube at upper shroud. Then disconnect vacuum balance tube at bracket and cylinder heads.
8. Remove vacuum balance tube and crankcase ventilation tube and hoses as an assembly.
9. Remove generator with bracket attached.
10. Disconnect heater hose at upper shroud.
11. Remove oil cooler access hole cover and oil dipstick.
12. Remove distributor cap. Then remove spark plug wires and cap as an assembly.
13. Remove bolts attaching upper shroud. Then remove shroud by raising front of shroud and rotating clockwise to clear oil filter and generator adapter.

INSTALLATION

1. Install upper shroud in position and install attaching bolts finger tight. Then rotate blower, checking clearance while tightening bolts securely.
2. Install oil cooler access hole cover and oil dipstick. Then install spark plug wires and distributor cap.
3. Connect heater hose to upper shroud.
4. Install generator and bracket.
5. Install vacuum balance tube and crankcase ventilation tube and hoses.
6. Install blower belt and adjust.
7. Install carburetors and cross shaft. Then connect vacuum advance hose at right carburetor.
8. Install, adjust and connect upper choke control rods. Then adjust and connect accelerator rod.
9. Install and connect fuel lines.
10. Install air cleaner and spare tire.

Lower Shrouds & Thermostats

REMOVAL, FIG. 5

1. Remove bolts attaching lower shroud to crankcase, cylinder head, front shroud and exhaust duct.
2. Drop lower shroud until swivel on thermostat rod can be disconnected from exhaust duct damper.
3. Disconnect swivel and remove lower shroud and thermostat assembly.

THERMOSTAT, REPLACE

NOTE: In the event of a failed thermostat bellows, the exhaust duct damper will remain in the open position, allowing a maximum air flow over engine to prevent overheating.

1. Remove lower shroud (see above).
2. Using an open end wrench on the flat provided, hold thermostat and remove its actuating rod and swivel assembly.
3. Remove nut attaching thermostat to bracket, then remove thermostat.
4. Install new thermostat and tighten securely.
5. Install thermostat actuating rod and swivel and tighten securely.

CAUTION: To prevent damage to thermostat bellows while tightening actuating rod, hold flat on thermostat with an open end wrench.

COOLING AIR DAMPER

The rate of engine cooling is regulated by a bellows type thermostat mounted in the lower part of each engine lower shroud and exhaust duct, Fig. 5A. The exhaust duct damper doors in the duct are controlled by the thermostat to start opening at 195° and are fully open at 210° F. In normal operation, the damper door angles will vary between full open and closed to maintain engine temperature in operating range.

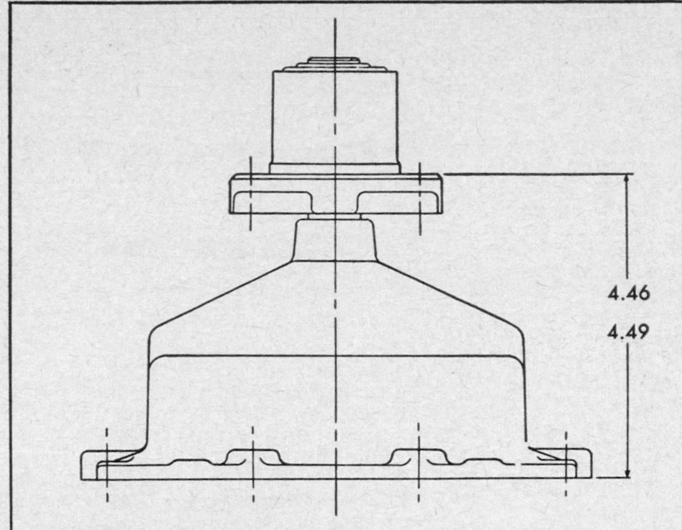

Fig. 7 Blower bearing replacement, 1965-68. For 1963-64 dimension is $4\frac{15}{32}''$ to $4\frac{31}{64}''$

Fig. 8 Oil cooler and exhaust ducts

To check the operation of the damper doors, have the engine at operating temperature. Open the damper door until the bellows is stopped within its mounting bracket. Measure the opening of the damper door from its upper edge as shown and, if necessary, adjust the swivel to obtain approximately $2\frac{11}{32}''$.

THERMOSTAT, ADJUST

1. Install lower shroud with two bolts (one to crankcase and one to cylinder head).
2. Hold exhaust duct damper in fully open position and pull thermostat actuating rod out to maximum travel (thermostat against bracket stop).
3. Adjust swivel until it just enters hole provided in exhaust duct damper.
4. Remove lower shroud and connect retaining clip, then install lower shroud.

INSTALLATION

1. Connect swivel to exhaust duct damper. Then install all lower shroud attaching bolts and tighten securely.
2. Check adjustment, verifying that thermostat bottoms at bracket before damper hits stop.

Front Shrouds

REMOVAL

1. Remove lower shroud (see above).
2. Remove exhaust manifold.
3. Disconnect heater hose at elbow on front shroud.
4. Remove bolts attaching front shroud to cylinder head and upper shroud. Then remove front shroud and heater elbow as a unit.

NOTE: On left front shroud, one attaching bolt (to cylinder head) is reached through heater elbow.

INSTALLATION

1. Install and tighten front shroud.
2. Connect heater hose.
3. Install exhaust manifold.
4. Install lower shroud.

Exhaust Ducts

REMOVAL

1. Disconnect seal from flange of exhaust duct and rear center shield.
2. Remove ignition coil and bracket (for right exhaust duct).
3. Remove grille, then remove rear center shield.
4. Remove lower shroud.
5. Unfasten and remove exhaust duct.

INSTALLATION

1. Install exhaust duct with all bolts finger tight, then tighten bolts securely.
2. Install lower shroud.
3. Install rear center shield and grille.
4. Lubricate groove of seal with liquid soap or silicone. Then, while guiding groove of seal onto rear center shield and exhaust duct flange (with one hand), press seal in place with a block of wood or hammer handle.
5. Install ignition coil and bracket (if removed).

Rear Shrouds

REMOVAL

1. Remove oil cooler (for left rear shroud) or remove ignition coil and bracket (for right rear shroud).
2. Remove lower shroud.
3. Remove exhaust duct.

NOTE: For right rear shroud it is necessary to disconnect wiring at cylinder head temperature and oil pressure sending units. Then disconnect at harness quick-disconnect so harness may be removed with shroud.

INSTALLATION

1. Install rear shroud. Then install exhaust duct and lower shroud.
2. Install oil cooler and/or ignition coil and bracket.

Blower Belt, Idler Pulley & Belt Guides

REMOVAL, FIG. 6

1. Loosen bolt and nut at idler pulley and remove blower belt.
2. If necessary, remove bolt and idler pulley and rear belt guide as a unit.
3. If necessary, remove bolts attaching upper belt guide and remove guide.

INSTALL & ADJUST

1. If removed, install upper guide, leaving bolts finger tight.
2. If removed, install rear guide and idler pulley as a unit and leave bolt and nut finger tight.
3. Install blower belt over pulleys (generator pulley last).
4. Adjust blower belt as follows: Place a $\frac{1}{16}''$ shim between belt and rear guide. Then, using a bar and a strand tension gauge, adjust blower belt to 55 lbs for a used belt, or 75 lbs for a new belt (plus or minus 5 lbs). Tighten bolt and nut securely. Remove shim from between blower belt and rear guide. Then, using shim as a gauge, adjust upper guide and tighten securely.

Blower

1. Remove upper shroud.
2. Remove bolts from blower pulley. Then remove pulley and blower from blower bearing hub.
3. Reverse procedure to install.

Exhaust Manifolds

REMOVAL

1. Remove lower shroud.
2. Remove nuts at exhaust manifold flange (retaining exhaust pipe).
3. Remove nuts, locks and clamps.
4. Using a soft hammer, tap exhaust manifold off exhaust port sleeves and remove and discard all packings.

INSTALLATION

1. Using new packings, install manifold

Fig. 9 Adjusting valves

over exhaust port sleeves, then install clamps, locks and nuts.
2. Tighten manifold clamp nuts a little at a time until specified torque is reached. Tap manifold in place over exhaust port sleeves with a soft hammer while tightening nuts.
3. Install lower shrouds.
4. Using a new packing, connect exhaust pipe to manifold.

CRANKCASE COVER & BLOWER BEARING

REMOVAL

1. Remove upper shroud.
2. Remove retaining bolts from blower pulley and remove pulley and blower from bearing hub.
3. Remove crankcase vent tube retainer, vent tube and O-ring seal.
4. Remove attaching bolts and take off crankcase cover and blower bearing assembly.
5. Remove crankcase vent and crankcase cover gaskets.

BLOWER BEARING, REPLACE

1969

1. Remove center four crankcase cover bolts and install tool, J-22894.
2. Measure distance from lower edge of tool bridge to bearing flange. Record this dimension.
3. Place puller fingers under bearing flange and remove bearing.

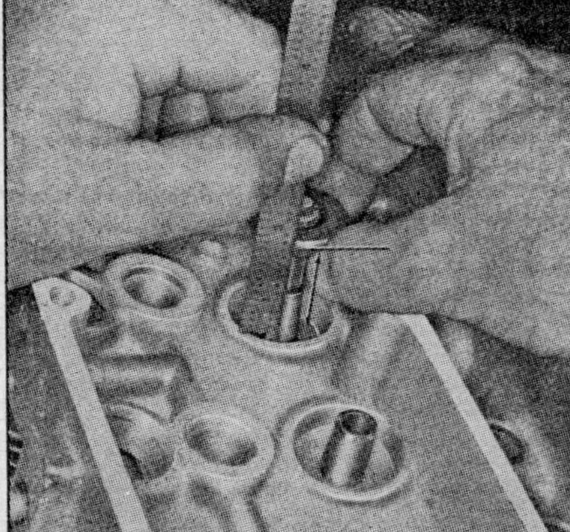

Fig. 11 Measuring valve spring installed height

1963-68

1. While supporting crankcase cover, press blower bearing shaft out of cover.
2. Coat new bearing shaft with hypoid lube. Then, while supporting crankcase cover, press bearing hub into cover to specified height, Fig. 7.

CAUTION: Press on shaft of blower bearing. Do not press on bearing outer race or bearing seal.

INSTALLATION

1. Clean all gasket surfaces.
2. Install crankcase cover gasket and vent, then second crankcase cover gasket.
3. Install crankcase cover.
4. Install crankcase vent tube, using a new O-ring seal.
5. Install blower and pulley.
6. Install upper shroud.

OIL FILTER & GENERATOR ADAPTER

REMOVAL

1. Remove blower belt.
2. Disconnect and remove generator.
3. Disconnect fuel lines at fuel pump.
4. Remove bolts from around oil filler tube, then remove all remaining bolts from adapter.
5. Remove adapter from fuel pump, oil filter, idler pulley and belt guide as a unit.

INSTALLATION

1. Check surface of engine rear housing and adapter for nicks or cracks.
2. Install a new adapter gasket.
3. Place bolts and flat washers (3) in adapter around oil filler tube.
4. Start fuel pump push rod and return spring into push rod guide.
5. Hold adapter cover in place and tighten bolts around oil filler tube finger tight.
6. Install remaining bolts and washers, then tighten all bolts securely.
7. Install and connect generator and fuel lines.
8. Start engine and check for leaks.

OIL COOLER

REMOVAL

1. Remove cooler access hole cover, Fig. 8.
2. Unfasten and remove cooler from shroud, shield and cylinder head.
3. Remove mounting bolt and take off cooler and seals.

INSTALLATION

1. Install new seals on cooler adapter.
2. Install cooler, tightening bolt securely.
3. Install all screws and bolts to shroud, shield and cylinder head, then tighten securely.
4. Install cooler access hole cover.
5. Start engine and check for leaks.

OIL PUMP

GEAR REMOVAL

1. Drain engine oil.

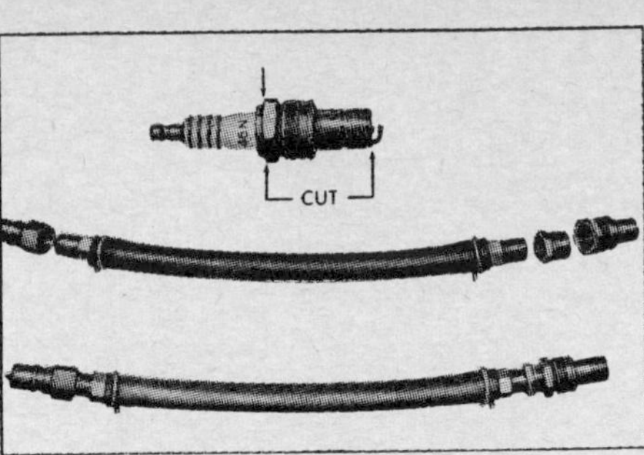

Fig. 10 Air adapter tool

2. Support engine with a jack with a piece of hardwood positioned between oil pan rails adjacent to engine skid plate.
3. Remove grille and rear center shield and disconnect rear mount. Then lower engine about one inch (to clear rear mount bracket).
4. Remove rear mount bracket and engine skid plate.
5. Remove oil pump cover and gasket.

GEAR INSTALLATION

1. Install pump gears. Then, using a new gasket, install pump cover.
2. Install skid plate and rear mount bracket.
3. Raise engine and connect rear mount.
4. Install rear center shield and grille.
5. Remove jack and wood block.
6. Fill with oil, start engine and check for leaks.

Oil Pressure Regulator

1. Drain engine oil.
2. Remove left lower shroud and left exhaust duct.
3. Remove pressure regulator plug, gasket, spring and valve.
4. Reverse procedure to install.
5. Start engine and check for leaks.

NOTE: To check oil pressure regulator, remove oil pressure sending unit and connect oil pressure gauge. Accelerate engine until pressure gauge stops increasing. The regulator should regulate at 35 psi.

Oil Pan

1. Drain engine oil and remove pan.
2. Clean gasket surfaces and install pan with new gasket.
3. Fill with oil, start engine and check for leaks.

Fig. 12 Rocker arm studs and push rod guides

CRANKSHAFT PULLEY OR VIBRATION DAMPER

REMOVAL

1. Disconnect engine seal from rear center shield and remove rear half of left and right side shield flanges.
2. Remove blower belt and oil filter.
3. Drain oil, then place engine jack under engine.
4. Remove grille and rear center shield.
5. Disconnect engine rear mount, then lower engine far enough to remove engine rear mount bracket.
6. Remove attaching bolt and use a suitable puller to remove crankshaft pulley or vibration damper.

INSTALLATION

1. Position pulley or vibration damper on end of crankshaft with key lined up.
2. Using retaining bolt and flat washer, pull pulley or damper in place, then back bolt out ½ turn and torque to specifications.

CAUTION: Do not drive pulley or damper onto crankshaft. To do so may damage crankshaft thrust bearing and crankcase.

3. Install engine rear mount bracket.
4. Raise engine and connect rear mount.
5. Remove engine jack.
6. Install rear center shield and grille.
7. Install new oil filter.
8. Install blower belt.
9. Lubricate groove of oil seal with liquid soap or silicone. Then, while guiding groove of seal onto shield flange (with one hand) press seal into place with a block of wood or a hammer handle.
10. Fill with oil, start engine and check for leaks.

ENGINE REAR HOUSING SEAL

1. Remove crankshaft pulley or vibration damper.
2. Remove seal by prying on outer edge of seal with two screwdrivers.
3. Install new seal over crankshaft and tap in place with a block of hardwood.
4. Install pulley or vibration damper.

ENGINE REAR HOUSING

1. Remove distributor cap and note position of rotor, then disconnect and remove distributor.
2. Remove oil filter and generator adapter.
3. Drain engine oil.
4. Install a suitable engine lift under engine with a piece of hardwood positioned between oil pan rails adjacent to engine skid plate. (Installation of wood block will allow removal of engine skid plate.)
5. Remove rear center shield and disconnect rear mount, then lower engine about 1" to clear rear mount bracket.
6. Remove rear mount bracket and engine skid plate.
7. Remove crankshaft pulley or vibration damper.
8. Remove engine rear housing.
9. Reverse procedure to install.

DISTRIBUTOR DRIVE GEAR & FUEL PUMP ECCENTRIC

1. Remove engine rear housing.
2. Remove distributor drive gear, then remove spacer and fuel pump eccentric.
3. When installing, first be sure woodruff keys are in place in crankshaft, then position fuel pump eccentric and spacer on crankshaft.
4. Lubricate crankshaft and distributor drive gear with engine oil and install gear until it bottoms.
5. Install engine rear housing.

CYLINDER HEAD & VALVE SERVICE

Valves, Adjust

NOTE: In order to adjust valves, the lower shrouds and muffler heat shield must be removed. Then remove rocker arm covers and adjust valves as follows:

1. Remove distributor cap and rotate crankshaft to bring No. 1 piston up on top dead center of its compression stroke. Rotor should be pointing to No. 1 position and timing mark at "O" on timing tab.
2. In this position, valves that can be adjusted are:
   No. 1 intake and exhaust.
   No. 3 intake, No. 5 exhaust.
   No. 4 exhaust, No. 6 intake.
3. To make the adjustment, turn adjusting nut out until there is end play in the push rod. Then turn adjusting nut in until push rod end play is eliminated. Finally, turn adjusting nut in one additional turn to center the plunger in the hydraulic lifter, Fig. 9.
4. Turn crankshaft one revolution to bring No. 2 piston to top dead center on its compression stroke. Then adjust the following valves in the same manner.
   No. 2 intake and exhaust.
   No. 3 exhaust, No. 5 intake.
   No. 4 intake, No. 6 exhaust.

Valve Seals

NOTE: Intake valves are provided with valve stem oil seals. These seals can be replaced with cylinder head installed as follows:

1. Remove spark plug, rocker arm and push rod on cylinder to be serviced.
2. Apply compressed air to spark plug hole to hold valve in place. (A tool to apply air to cylinder is available through local jobbers or it may be manufactured from parts shown in Fig. 10.)
3. Use a suitable compressor to compress valve spring. Then remove valve locks, valve cap, valve spring and damper assembly.
4. Remove seal from valve guide.
5. Install new seal, using a special plastic sleeve to prevent seal damage as seal passes over valve lock grooves. Push seal on guide until it bottoms on guide end.
6. Install valve parts, using grease to hold valve locks in place while releasing valve spring compressor.
7. Adjust valve as outlined previously and complete the installation.

Checking Valve Spring Installed Height

NOTE: Follow procedure for installing valve stem seals. Then check valve spring height as follows:

1. Install spring cap and valve locks without spring.
2. Hold spring cap and pull valve against seat. Then measure distance between spring cap and spring seat, Fig. 11. This locates spring cap in installed position.
3. Remove valve locks and spring cap and, if necessary, shim spring.

NOTE: Spring shims are available in .030" thickness. Do not use shim if it will bring spring height below specification listed in *Valve Specifications* table.

4. Reassemble and adjust valve.

Valve Lifters, Replace

REMOVAL

1. Drain engine oil.
2. Remove lower shrouds (1964-68).
3. For right bank, remove muffler heat shield.
4. Remove valve rocker arm covers.
5. Remove rocker arms and push rods.
6. Remove rocker arm studs and push rod guides, then remove rocker arm stud O-ring seals, Fig. 12.
7. Pull push rod tubes from crankcase bore and remove inner O-ring seal, Fig. 13. Then remove push rod tube from cylinder head and remove O-ring seal.
8. Remove valve lifters with a magnet or a wire hook.
9. Place valve lifters, rocker arm parts and push rods in racks so they may be installed in original locations.

INSTALLATION

1. Lubricate valve lifters and install in crankcase bores.
2. Install new O-ring seals (lightly coated with oil) on long end of push rod tubes, then install tubes through bore in cylinder head. Install new O-ring seals on inner end of tubes.
3. Start push rod tubes into bores in cylinder head and crankcase, then seat tubes with a $\frac{9}{16}$" deep socket placed against cylinder head end of tube and tap lightly with a hammer.
4. Install new O-ring seals into rocker arm stud bore in cylinder head.
5. Install push rod guides, then rocker

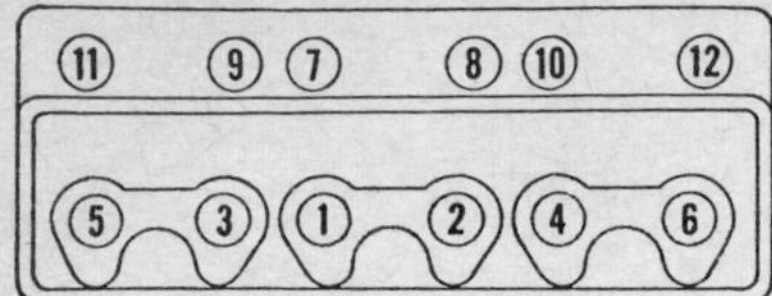

Fig. 14 Cylinder head tightening sequence

arm studs.

6. Torque rocker arm studs to 10 ft-lbs below specifications. Then tighten cylinder head nuts and rocker arm studs a little at a time in the sequence shown in Fig. 14 until specified torque is reached.
7. Install push rods with side hole out, Fig. 15. Then install rocker arms, balls and nuts.
8. Adjust valves as outlined.
9. Install rocker arm covers with new gaskets. Torque to specifications.
10. Install lower shrouds and muffler heat shield as outlined.
11. Fill with oil, start engine and check for leaks.

Cylinder Heads, Replace

SERVICE BULLETIN

New Head Gasket and Timing: On 1966 Corvair 500 and Monzas with 4 x 1 (140 H.P.) engines, air conditioning and Powerglide, use new cylinder head gaskets No. 3891552, which are copper flashed for identification, on these engines.

The thicker gasket has been designed to obtain the desired compression ratio of 8.75:1. In conjunction with the cylinder head and latest gasket design, the distributor timing has been changed from 18° BTDC to 14° BTDC for the above models only.

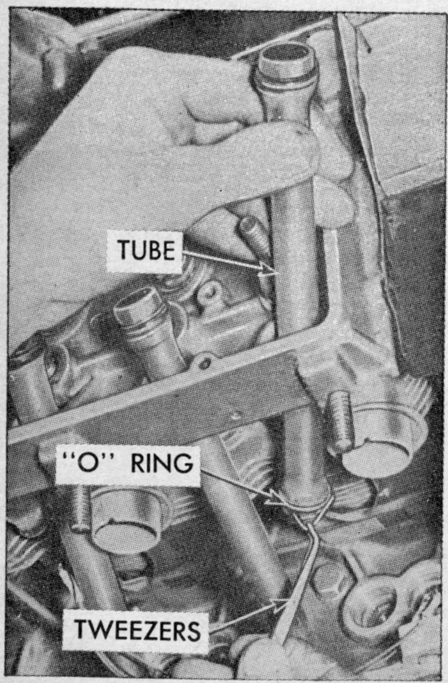

Fig. 13 Removing push rod tubes

1965-69

1. Drain engine oil.
2. Disconnect battery cable.
3. Remove spare tire and air cleaner.
4. Remove from cylinder head:
   a. Carburetor, carburetor mounting studs and upper choke control rods.
   b. Ignition coil and bracket (right head). Air Injector pump, tubes and hoses.
   c. Side shield, lower shroud and exhaust duct.
   d. Oil cooler (left head).
   e. Muffler, muffler shield and muffler hanger (right head).
   f. Spark plugs and vacuum advance tube hose at cylinder head.
   g. Bolts attaching upper shroud to front and rear shrouds and bolts attaching front and rear shrouds to cylinder head.
   h. Exhaust manifolds. *On front shroud for 1966-68, it will be necessary to disconnect heater hose to gain access to one bolt.*

NOTE: On left rear shroud it will be necessary to disconnect heater hose at elbow to gain access to one bolt.

5. On right head, disconnect wire to cylinder head temperature sending unit.
6. Remove rear center shield.
7. On 1966-69, disconnect engine at rear mount and lower engine several inches.
8. Remove rocker arms and push rods as outlined under *Valve Lifters, Replace,* then unfasten and remove cylinder head.
9. Reverse procedure to install.

1963-64

1. Drain engine oil and disconnect battery positive cable.
2. Remove spare tire and air cleaner.
3. Remove following items from head to be removed: Carburetor, carburetor mounting studs, upper choke control rods, ignition coil and bracket, lower shroud and exhaust duct, oil cooler, muffler, muffler shield and hanger (right head), spark plugs and vacuum balance tube hose at head, bolts attaching upper shroud to front and rear shrouds and bolts attaching front and rear shrouds to cylinder head, exhaust manifolds.
4. On right cylinder head, disconnect wire to temperature sending unit.
5. Remove rocker arms and push rods as outlined under *Valve Lifters, Replace,* then unfasten and remove cylinder head.
6. Reverse procedure to install.

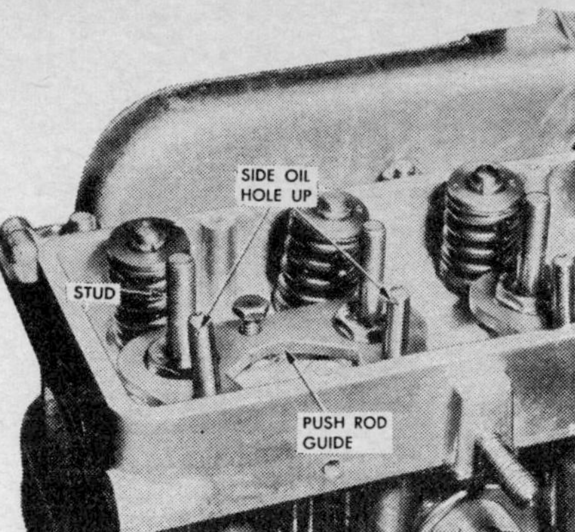

Fig. 15 Push rod installation

Cylinder Head, Disassemble

1. Compress valve springs and remove valve locks, Fig. 16. It may be necessary to tap valve spring caps lightly to loosen valve locks.
2. Release compressor and remove valve spring cap, spring (and damper if used), valve and spring shims.
3. Remove remaining valves.
4. Remove valve stem oil seals from intake valve guides.

NOTE: Under ordinary circumstances no further disassembly of

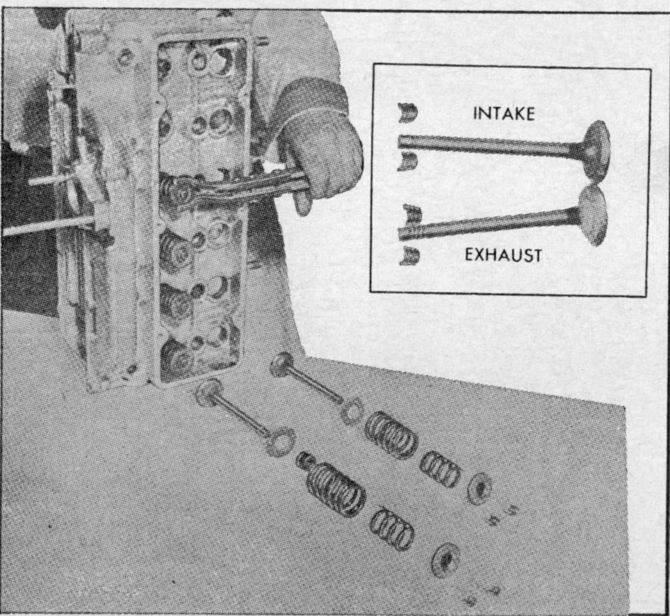

Fig. 16 Compressing valve springs

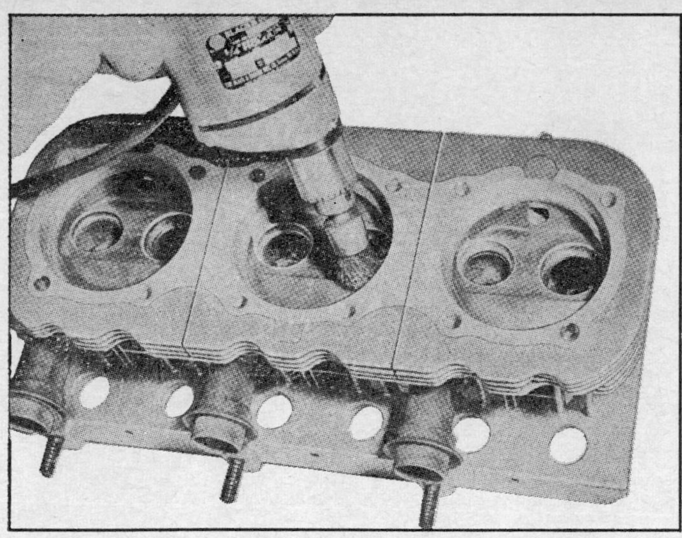

Fig. 17 Removing carbon from combustion chambers

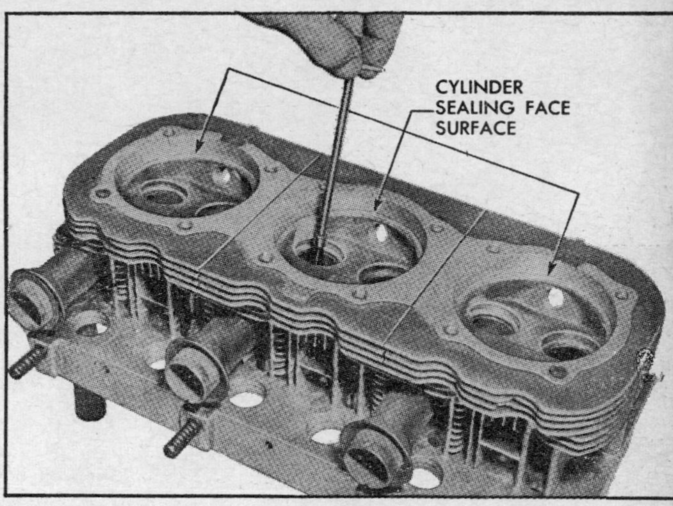

Fig. 18 Cleaning valve guides

the head is necessary. If cylinder head is to be replaced, transfer or install carburetor studs, exhaust manifold studs, choke coil and control rod assembly, vacuum balance tube, carburetor mounting pad plug and cylinder head temperature sending unit.

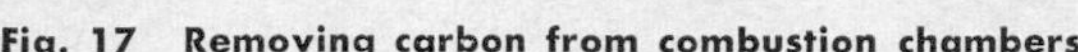

5. Clean carbon from combustion chambers, Fig. 17, and clean valve guides, Fig. 18.

INSPECTION

1. Check cylinder heads for damage. Check fit of exhaust manifold sleeves; if loose or cracked, replace as outlined.
2. Inspect valves for burned faces, excessive seat pound in, cracked faces or badly scuffed or worn valve stems.
3. Inspect valve seats for cracks or burnt seats, and valve guides for cracks or excessive wear.

NOTE: If valve seats are beyond repair, cylinder head replacement is necessary. Excessive valve-to-bore clearance may cause oil consumption. Insufficient clearance will result in noisy and sticky functioning of valve and disturb smoothness of operation.

Fig. 19 Measuring valve stem clearance

4. Measure valve stem clearance with a dial indicator as shown in Fig. 19. With valve head dropped about $\frac{1}{16}$″ off its seat, move stem of valve from side to side, using light pressure to obtain a clearance reading. If clearance exceeds specifications, it will be necessary to ream valve guides for oversize valve or replace valve guides.
5. Check valve spring tension; if not within 5 lbs of specifications, replace spring or springs.
6. Clean air circulating passages formed by cooling fins, Fig. 20.

Reconditioning Valve Seats

Regardless of the methods used for valve seat reconditioning, the final seat width in cylinder head should be $\frac{1}{32}$″ to $\frac{1}{16}$″ on the intake and $\frac{1}{16}$″ to $\frac{3}{32}$″ on exhaust valves. Valve seat angle on all seats should be as specified and should be concentric within .002″ dial indicator reading.

Reconditioning Valve Faces

Valve facing machine should be set as specified for grinding valves. After grinding, if the edge of the valve head is less than $\frac{1}{32}$″ thick, replace the valve, Fig. 21.

Exhaust Manifold Sleeves

NOTE: Do not remove exhaust manifold sleeves unless absolutely necessary. If sleeves are removed they should be replaced with the next largest diameter sleeve.

1. Warm cylinder head to 200°F. Then remove exhaust manifold sleeves with a pipe wrench by turning gradually, Fig. 22. *Do not tap or pry sleeves from cylinder head.*
2. Check sleeve installation holes in head for nicks or damage.
3. Coat new sleeves with anti-freeze compound and locate flat side parallel to exhaust push rod tube hole.

NOTE: Sleeves are installed in cylinder head with a press fit and must be started into place square with the exhaust bore in head. Sleeves are available in standard, .002″ and .010″ oversize for service.

4. Place sleeve in container of dry ice for about 10 minutes.
5. Warm cylinder head to about 200°F. *Do not use an open flame.*
6. Remove sleeves one at a time from the dry ice and tap into place with a soft-faced hammer.

Reaming Valve Guides

Oversize valves can be utilized to obtain proper valve-to-guide clearance in all cases except when guide is either cracked or is worn to the extent that reaming will not clean up the guide bore to permit use of the largest oversize valve available. Valves are available in standard, .003″, .010″ and .020″ oversize stems.

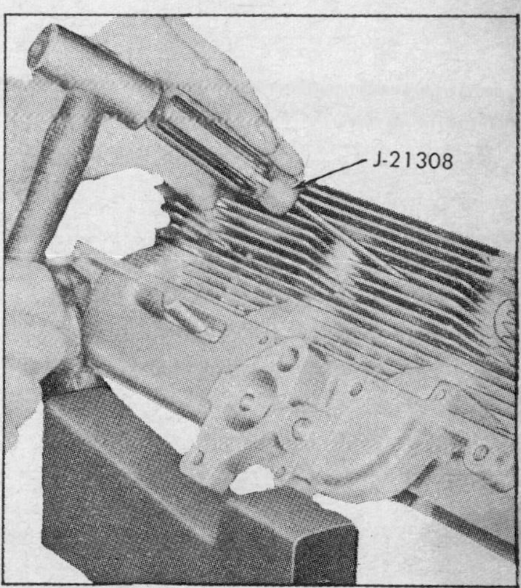

Fig. 20 Cleaning cooling fins

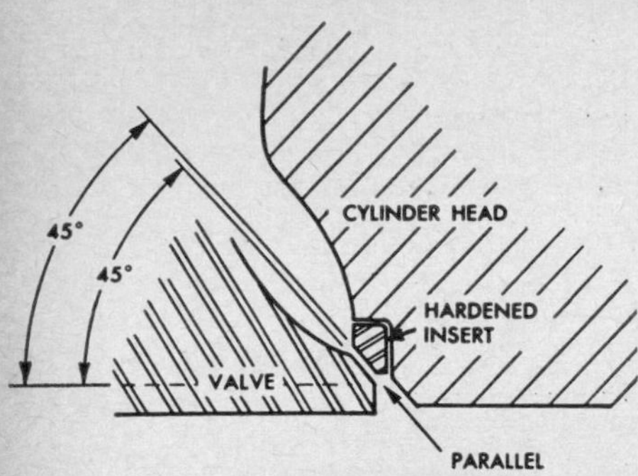

Fig. 21 Relation of valve and seat angles

Valve Guides, Replace

Replacement valve guides on all engines except turbocharged engine are available in oversizes of .002″ (standard replacement), .010″ and .020″. Service guides are bored to permit use of valves with standard diameter stems.

Remove valve guide as shown in Fig. 23 and install as shown in Fig. 24.

VALVE LIFT SPECS.

Year and Model	Intake	Exhaust
1963 80 H.P.	.314	.344
1963 Others	.378	.378
1964-67 95 H.P.	.385	.385
1964 110, 150 H.P.	.390	.390
1965-67 110, 140 H.P.	.390	.390
1965-67 180 H.P.	.390	.390
1968 95 H.P.	.403	.403
1968 110, 140 H.P.	.409	.409
1969 95 H.P.	.385	.385
1969 110, 140 H.P.	.390	.390

VALVE TIMING

Intake Opens Before TDC

Year and Model		Degrees
1963	80 H.P.	43
	102 H.P.	54
	150 H.P.	70
1964	95 H.P.	44
	110, 150 H.P.	55
1965	95 H.P.	44
	110, 140 H.P.	55
	180 H.P.	82
1966	95 H.P.	44
	110, 140 H.P.	55
	180 H.P.	82
1967	95 H.P.	44
	110 H.P.	55
1968	95 H.P.	26
	110 H.P.	37
	140 H.P.	70
1969	95 H.P.	26
	110 H.P.	37
	140 H.P.	26

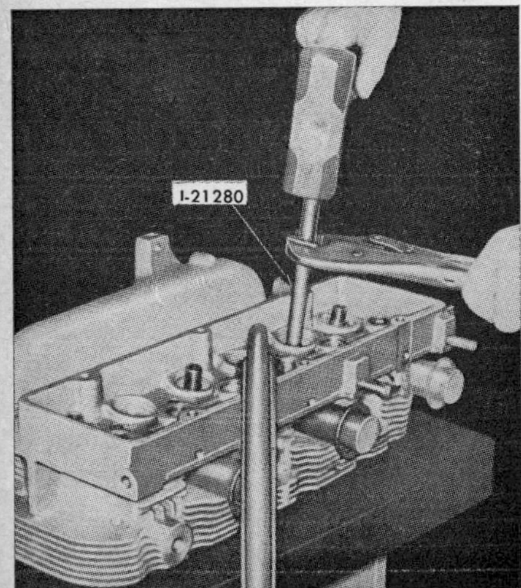

Fig. 23 Removing valve guide

Fig. 25 Installing piston rings with aid of ring compressor (J-8356)

PISTON RINGS REPLACE

Bear in mind that cylinders and pistons are serviced as a unit and the operation outlined below is for replacing one or more pistons in one bank requiring ring replacement. It is not intended for complete piston and ring replacement.

1. Drain crankcase oil and remove cylinder head.
2. Remove cylinder from piston requiring new rings.
3. Remove old and install new rings. *Position oil control ring gap towards top of engine and compression rings with gap 45° from oil ring gap location. Rings must be installed with markings and inside bevel toward top of piston. Lubricate piston rings with engine oil and slide ring compressing tool, Fig. 25, over rings just enough to compress rings into piston.*
4. Reverse above procedure to install parts removed. Add engine oil, start engine and check for oil leaks.

ROD BEARINGS REPLACE

1. Remove air cleaner element and carburetor intake hose.
2. Remove choke heat tube, choke fresh air hose and carburetor linkage.
3. Disconnect fuel lines at carburetor.

Fig. 22 Removing exhaust manifold sleeve

4. Remove left bank carburetor.
5. Disconnect choke link to choke assembly. Remove choke and air horn by removing nuts at legs of air horn support.
6. Disconnect spark plug wires.
7. Remove blower drive belt.
8. Disconnect fuel lines at fuel pump.
9. Remove carburetor cross shaft and vacuum balance tube.
10. Remove all engine upper shroud bolts and screws.
11. Remove screws on each side of front engine shield.
12. Disconnect cooling air throttle valve thermostat rod and remove cooling air throttle valve.
13. Remove all fuel lines.
14. Remove engine upper shroud, tipping front lip up so it clears front engine shield.
15. Remove blower pulley and blower.
16. Remove crankcase cover, gaskets and crankcase vent.
17. Remove spark plug from cylinder requiring new rod bearing and remove rod cap and bearing insert. Use a piece of $\frac{5}{16}''$ plastic hose on each rod bolt to protect crankshaft journals from being scratched.
18. Reverse above procedure to install parts removed. While tightening upper shroud bolts, rotate blower and check for interference at blow-

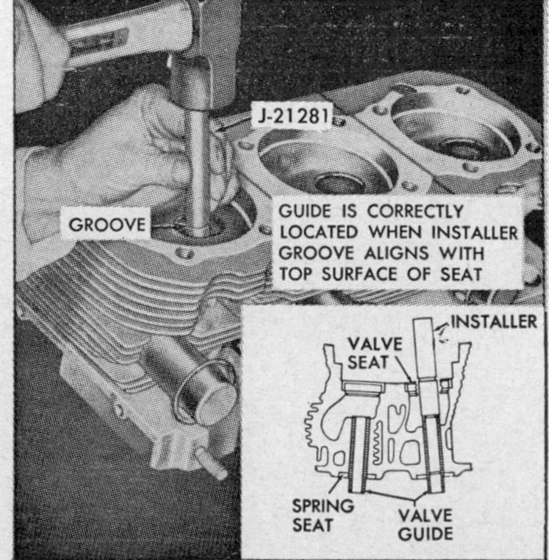

Fig. 24 Installing new valve guide

er to upper shroud. Add engine oil, start engine and check for oil leaks.

Rod bearing inserts are available in standard sizes and undersizes of .001", .002", .010" and .020". These bearings are not shimmed and when clearance becomes excessive the next undersize bearing insert should be used. *Do not file rod or caps in an attempt to fit bearings.*

Rod bearing clearance is checked with Plastigage in the same manner outlined for main bearings. If flattened Plastigage measurement is not over .003" (worn) or .002" (new) or not less than .001" the fit is satisfactory.

Repairs Requiring Engine Removal

ENGINE, REPLACE

Power Train

1. Remove shrouds and shields as required and as outlined previously.
2. Back car into place so that rear bumper is under a chain hoist.
3. Use holes provided to attach a chain to bumper.
4. Raise car with hoist and install jack stands.
5. Disconnect all necessary wires, hoses, pipes, linkage, etc.
6. Loosen (do not remove) bolts attaching engine to mounts.
7. Lower car so that engine rests absolutely flat on two 6 x 6 inch blocks.
8. Reach under car and remove loosened bolts from mounts.
9. Raise car body to clear engine.
10. Slide power train out from under car.
11. Reverse procedure to install.

SERVICE BULLETIN

DIFFICULTY INSTALLING STRUT RODS: On 1965-69 models, some difficulty has been experienced connecting the rear strut rod brackets to the differential carrier during engine installation. The procedure is as follows:

1. With spring compressed to curb height, position strut bracket to differential carrier. To prevent distortion to strut bracket it is recommended that the retaining bolts be installed in the following manner.
2. Using a long drift, align bracket with differential carrier and install forward bolt on side of carrier. Do not tighten bolt. Remaining bolts will require further alignment.
3. Align bracket with rear bolt on underside of carrier, using drift to align bracket during bolt installation.
4. Install rear bolt on side of carrier, then install remaining bolt to underside of carrier.
5. Alternately tighten all bolts a little at a time to permit an even draw against bracket. Then tighten bolts snugly and check bracket for proper seating against carrier. *It is recommended that the strut rods be installed before installing the axle drive shafts.*

ENGINE DISASSEMBLY

1. Remove transmission from power train.
2. Remove differential carrier from engine.

Fig. 27 Installing camshaft in crankcase

3. Remove clutch from engine (if equipped).
4. Remove carburetor linkage and related parts.
5. Remove blower belt.
6. Remove fuel pump.
7. Remove generator.
8. Remove engine front shield.
9. Remove vacuum balance tube.
10. Remove both carburetors.
11. Remove fuel lines and oil level gauge.
12. Remove distributor and spark plugs.
13. Remove coil and generator brace from cylinder head.
14. Remove engine upper shroud and side shields.
15. Remove oil filter and generator adapter.
16. Remove blower and pulley.
17. Remove crankcase vent tube.
18. Remove crankcase cover and blower bearing.
19. Remove engine front and lower shrouds and exhaust ducts.
20. Remove oil pan.
21. Remove exhaust manifold.
22. Remove choke heat tube at right cylinder head.
23. Remove engine rear mounting bracket and skid plate at engine rear housing.
24. Remove cylinder heads. *When crankshaft is turned for further disassembly cylinders will need a holding fixture which can readily be made. Six ½" x 4¼" long steel tubes to be used on long cylinder studs (one on each cylinder) and six ½" x 3½" long tubes for each short stud. Slip the tubes on the studs and keep them in place by means of the stud nuts.*
25. Remove valve lifters with a magnet or wire hook.
26. Remove connecting rod caps, being sure they are marked so that they will be returned to the correct connecting rod.
27. Remove spring retainers and take off cylinder air baffle.
28. Remove each cylinder with piston and connecting rod as a unit.
29. Push piston out of cylinder with a hammer handle. *Ridges and/or deposits on upper end of cylinder can be removed after piston has been removed from cylinder with a cylinder mounted ridge reamer.*
30. Remove crankshaft pulley.
31. Remove engine rear housing.

ENGINE, REASSEMBLE

Crankshaft

1. To install crankshaft gear, mount shaft in an arbor press and support it between front crankshaft throw and front journal.
2. Press on crankshaft gear and install two woodruff keys.
3. Position fuel pump eccentric and spacer on shaft.
4. Lubricate crankshaft and distributor drive gear and install distributor drive gear.
5. Install oil slinger with concave side away from distributor drive gear.
6. Install crankshaft and main bearings.

Camshaft

Camshaft bearing journal clearance should be .0015" to .0035" new and .002" to .004" used. If clearance is not within limits either the crankcase or camshaft should be replaced.

1. To assemble camshaft gear and thrust washer to camshaft, firmly support shaft at back of front journal in an arbor press.
2. Place thrust washer over end of shaft and install woodruff key in keyway.
3. Lubricate camshaft with hypoid lubricant.
4. Install camshaft gear and press into place until it bottoms against thrust washer.

Fig. 29 Installing cylinder and piston. Tubes "A" and "B" are holding cylinders in place

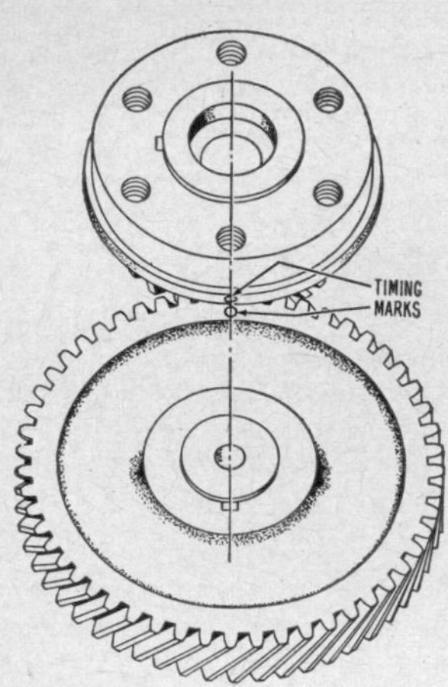

Fig. 28 Valve timing

Timing Gear Marks

1. Install camshaft, guiding camshaft thrust washer into groove in crankcase, Fig. 27, while indexing camshaft gear to crankshaft gear so that valve timing marks line up as shown in Fig. 28.
2. Install other half of crankcase onto crankshaft and camshaft and fasten both halves together. Tighten bolts to the proper torque and in proper sequence.
3. Check camshaft end play, which should be .003″ to .007″.
4. Check timing gear backlash which should be .002″ to .004″.
5. Install front crankshaft oil slinger on crankshaft gear with flange side toward crankcase. Install slinger retaining snap ring, using care to avoid scratching sealing surface.
6. Install main oil gallery plugs with Permatex 404 anti-freeze compound or its equivalent.
7. Install flywheel housing with new gasket and torque bolts to 20-30 ft. lbs.

Pistons, Cylinders and Rods

NOTE: When installing the 1964-69 type (notched) engine cylinder over piston and rings, position the oil control ring gap toward the top of the engine. Place the compression rings with the gap 45° from the oil ring gap, and on the opposite side of the piston from the notch in the cylinder. Installing the cylinder with the ring gaps in line with the cylinder notch could result in broken rings.

Fig. 31 Installing cylinder head

1. Push piston into cylinder with hammer handle while holding cylinder in one hand until it is slightly below top of cylinder bore. *Notch on piston top must be installed towards front of engine (flywheel end) on both banks.*
2. With pistons and cylinders installed, install rod bearings.
3. Position crankcase pins by turning crankshaft with pulley so that crankshaft journal is in line with piston and rod to be installed.
4. Place a piece of plastic hose with at least a $\frac{5}{16}$″ diameter over each rod bolt to protect shaft journal.
5. Install a new copper cylinder gasket over cylinder pilot, Fig. 29.
6. Push piston with hammer handle while guiding cylinder bore pilot into crankcase. Remove plastic hose from rod bolts and install rod bearing and cap. Torque rod nuts to 20-26 ft. lbs.
7. Install cylinder holding tubes (used previously on disassembly) on cylinder studs to hold cylinder in place. Continue procedure until all cylinders and pistons are installed.
8. Install cylinder air baffles with retaining springs. Fig. 29. *Air baffles are not interchangeable.*

Crankcase Cover and Blower Bearing

1. Install new gasket on crankcase.
2. Install crankcase vent and another crankcase gasket.
3. Install crankcase cover and blower bearing and torque bolts to 7-13 ft. lbs.
4. Install crankcase vent tube and gasket.

Oil Pump Screen and Tube

If the original or a new oil pump screen and tube assembly is to be installed in the original crankcase, the outside diameter of the end of the tube will have to be tinned with solder before installing in crankcase.

1. Install oil pump screen and pick-up tube into cylinder case with pick-up screen positioned parallel to oil pan rails. Secure tube with clamp.
2. Coat threads on engine temperature and oil pressure sending units with anti-seize compound (Permatex 404) or its equivalent. Torque oil pressure unit to 45-65 ft. lbs. and temperature unit 35-45 ft. lbs.

Cylinder Head

Be sure all cylinder head gaskets are in cylinder head combustion chambers as shown in Fig. 30. Remove all cylinder retaining tubes from cylinder bank to which cylinder head is to be installed.

1. Install cylinder head, Fig. 31.
2. Install six flat washers and nuts on long studs, adjacent to intake manifold.
3. Install six new "O" rings, lubricated with lubriplate, in counterbore of cylinder head (location for rocker arm studs) and coat rocker stud bore with anti-seize compound.
4. Install rocker arm studs, Fig. 32, with threads coated with anti-seize compound.
5. Tighten nuts and rocker studs in sequence shown in Fig. 14. Torque nuts and rocker studs to 27-33 ft. lbs.

Fig. 30 Installing cylinder head gaskets

Push Rod Oil Drain Tubes

1. Lightly oil hydraulic lifters and install in their proper bores.
2. Install push rod oil drain tubes through cylinder head, Fig. 34. Place "O" rings, one on each end of drain tube as shown. Oil "O" rings and push in place at lifter bore in crankcase and cylinder head.
3. Install push rods with side oil hole up into valve rocker socket.
4. On early production engines, install push rod guides in place over rocker studs and push rods and tighten bolts. *On late production engines, push rod guides are installed under valve rocker studs.*
5. Install rocker arms, balls and nuts loosely in place. Adjust valve lash as outlined elsewhere in this section, after installing distributor.

Final Assembly

1. Install engine rear housing.
2. Install crankshaft pulley. After pulley bottoms in place, back off retaining bolt one turn and then torque it to 60-80 ft. lbs. *Do not drive pulley*

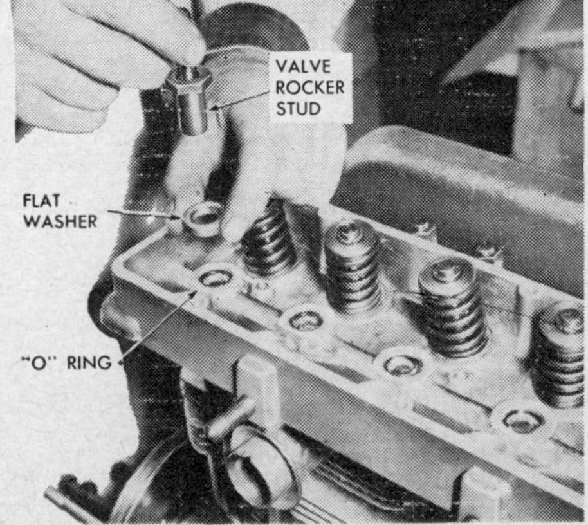

Fig. 32 Installing rocker arm studs

Fig. 34 Installing push rod drain tubes

shaft thrust bearing and crankcase.

3. Install oil cooler.
4. Install exhaust manifolds.
5. Install oil filter and generator adapter.
6. Install sheet metal removed.
7. Install wires, fuel lines, etc.
8. Install spark plugs.
9. Install oil pan. Check parting line to see if flywheel housing gasket is far enough up for good sealing.
10. Install fuel pump and add engine oil.

CRANKCASE

Engine Disassembled

1. Remove two oil gallery plugs located at flywheel housing end of crankcase. These passages should be cleaned with solvent.
2. Check cylinder pilot bores and bearing surfaces in each half of crankcase for nicks, cracks or other damage that would interfere with the proper fit of component parts.
3. Do not use scrapers or other sharp tools to clean gasket surfaces. A good cleaning solvent should be used to dissolve gasket material or varnish that may adhere to the surfaces.

Stud and Thread Repairs

Always use anti-seize compound (Permatex 404 or equivalent) on all threads entering aluminum.

To replace crankcase studs, install long and short studs as indicated in Fig. 35. Studs are available in oversizes of .003″, .006″ and .009″.

It should require a torque of 10 to 30 ft. lbs. to install studs. If torque is less than 10, another selected stud should be used.

Heli-coils for thread repairs are available at local auto parts jobbers and should be installed to Heli-Coil prescribed methods.

All cylinder studs installed in crankcase adjacent to the main bearing webs have blind holes while the others do not.

MAIN BEARINGS

Engine Disassembled

Whenever the crankcase is parted, the bearings and crankshaft journals should be inspected. If upon inspection one half shows evidence of fatigue, distress, abrasion, erosion, scoring or the like, both crankcase halves should be replaced. *Never should one half be replaced without replacing the other half.*

If the running clearance of a bearing is too great with used bearing inserts, it will be necessary to replace both bearing halves. Should this become necessary, the crankshaft journal should be checked with a micrometer for out-of-round, taper or undersize dimensions.

Service Note

To prevent the possibility of mismatch of the thrust flanges of rear main bearings, with the resulting reduction of crankshaft end play, engines produced after April 16, 1962 (date stamped T 0146) will have a flanged rear bearing in the left half of the case only. An unflanged bearing will be installed in the right half of the crankcase.

Main Bearing Clearance

Main bearing clearance is checked with Plastigage, a wax-like material, available at auto parts jobbers.

Fig. 35 Installed length of crankcase and rear housing studs

To assure proper seating of the bearings, all crankcase bolts must be at their specified torque. Eight long $\frac{7}{16}$″ bolts 42-48 ft. lbs., and three $\frac{5}{16}$″ bolts 7-13 ft. lbs. Hold bolt head on $\frac{7}{16}$″ bolts while tightening the nut. Do not tighten at bolt head. Fig. 36 shows tightening sequence. To check main bearing clearance, proceed as follows:

1. Starting with rear main bearing, remove one half of the crankcase while the other is supported on its side. Wipe oil from bearings and journal.
2. Place a strip of Plastigage the full width of the bearing (parallel to crankshaft on journal). *Crankcase split line surfaces must be free of nicks and foreign matter.*
3. Install other half of crankcase with bearings and evenly tighten crankcase bolts to proper torque. *Do not rotate crankshaft while Plastigage is between bearing and journal.*
4. Remove one half of crankcase. Then measure the width of the flattened Plastigage with the graduated scale on the edge of the Plastigage envelope.
5. If the flattened Plastigage is not over .004″ (worn) or .003″ (new) or less than .001″ the bearing insert is satisfactory. If not within these limits replace bearing insert.

Fig. 36 Crankcase tightening sequence

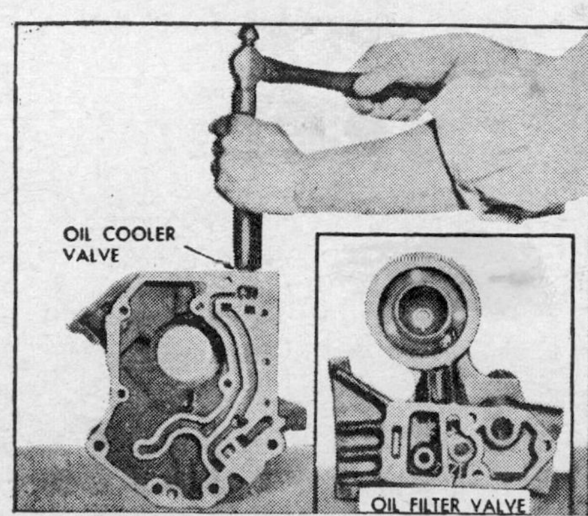

Fig. 37 Oil filter and oil cooler by-pass valve installation

Fig. 38 Installing oil pressure regulator stop groove pin

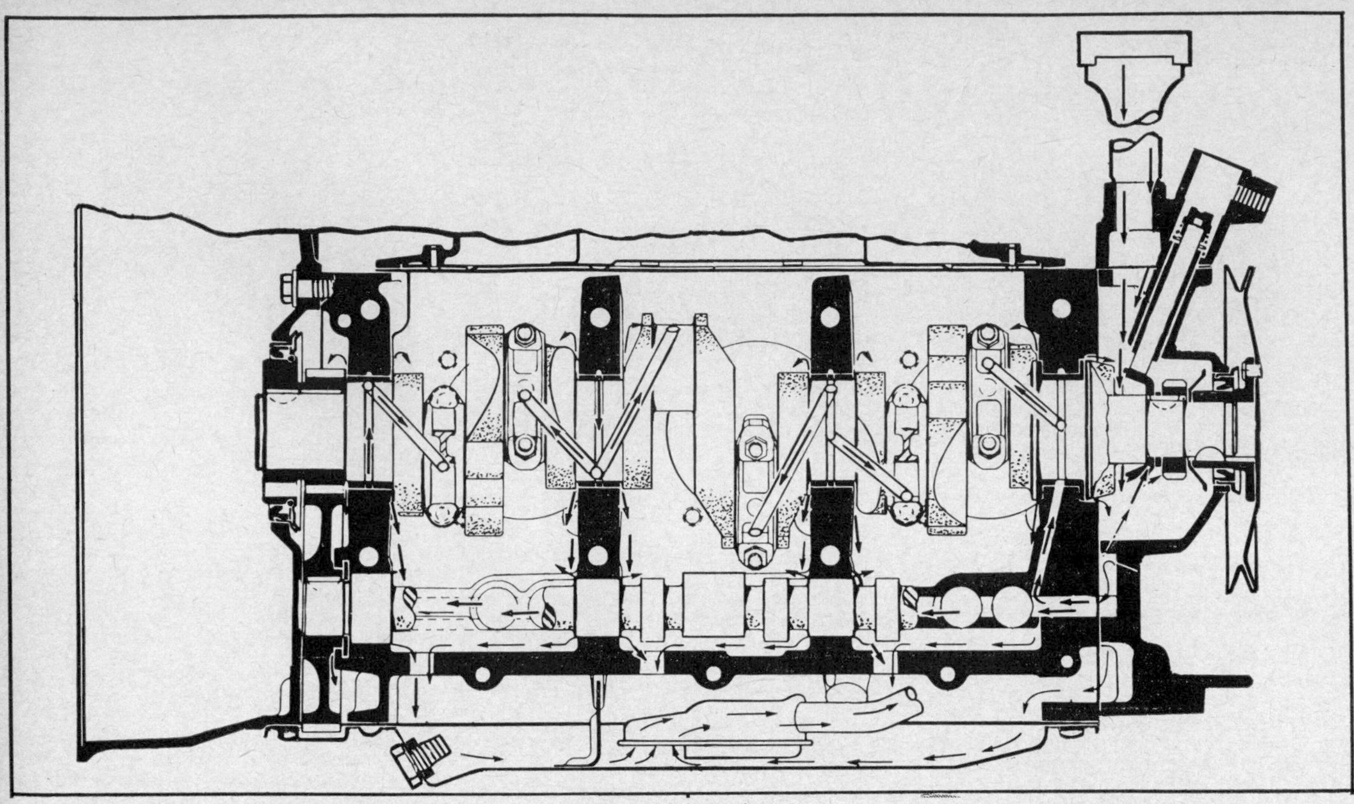

Engine lubrication

6. A .002″ undersize bearing may produce the proper clearance. If not, it will be necessary to regrind the crankshaft journal for use with the next undersize bearing. Bearings are available in undersizes of .001″, .002″, .010″ and .020″.
7. Proceed to the next bearing. After all bearings have been checked and installed, rotate the crankshaft to see that there is no excessive drag.
8. Check the end play by forcing the crankshaft to the extreme forward position. End play should be .002″ to .006″.

OIL PUMP REPAIRS

Engine Disassembled

1. When assembling the oil pump to the engine rear housing, install the idler gear on the shaft. Idler gear shaft should be .010″ to .020″ below gasket surface.
2. Place drive gear and shaft in pump housing.
3. Check projection of oil pump gears above gasket surface; this should be .0045″ maximum and .0025″ minimum. Clearance between gears and housing should be .005″.
4. Lubricate pump gears before installation. Install pump cover and tighten bolts.
5. Install a long screwdriver down the distributor mounting hole in the engine rear housing and turn oil pump drive shaft to see that pump turns freely.
6. Install pressure regulator valve, spring, gasket and plug.

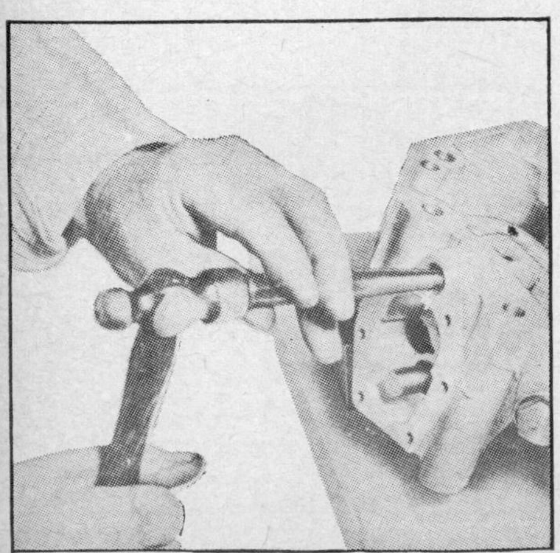

Fig. 39 Installing oil gallery plug

OIL COOLER & BY-PASS VALVES

Engine Disassembled

1. Referring to Fig. 37, remove oil filter by-pass valve by catching the inner edge of the valve with a suitable hook or small screwdriver.
2. Install the new filter valve with the spring *up* in the adapter housing.
3. Remove the oil cooler valve in the same manner as the filter valve. However, the valve spring should be installed *down.*

ENGINE REAR HOUSING

Engine Disassembled

When replacing the engine rear housing as a new unit, the following operations are required.

1. Install groove pin, Fig. 38, which holds oil pump pressure regulator valve in place.
2. Install oil pump gallery plug flush with counterbore, using sealing compound, Fig. 39.
3. Install new rear housing seal.
4. Install distributor holding stud 1⅛″ measured from distributor pad on engine rear housing.

FLYWHEEL HOUSING SEAL

Engine Disassembled

1. Tap seal out of housing with a wood or fibre drift.
2. Clean flywheel housing seal surface with solvent and check surface for nicks or damage.
3. Lubricate outer seal surface (beaded area) with lubriplate or petrolatum and install with suitable driver. *If seal is removed and still usable, pack sealing lips with a good grade of cup grease with a high melting point (350°). New seals are packed with this type grease to last the life of the seal.*

Clutch and Manual Transmission Section

NOTE: Transmission repair procedures are covered in separate sections.

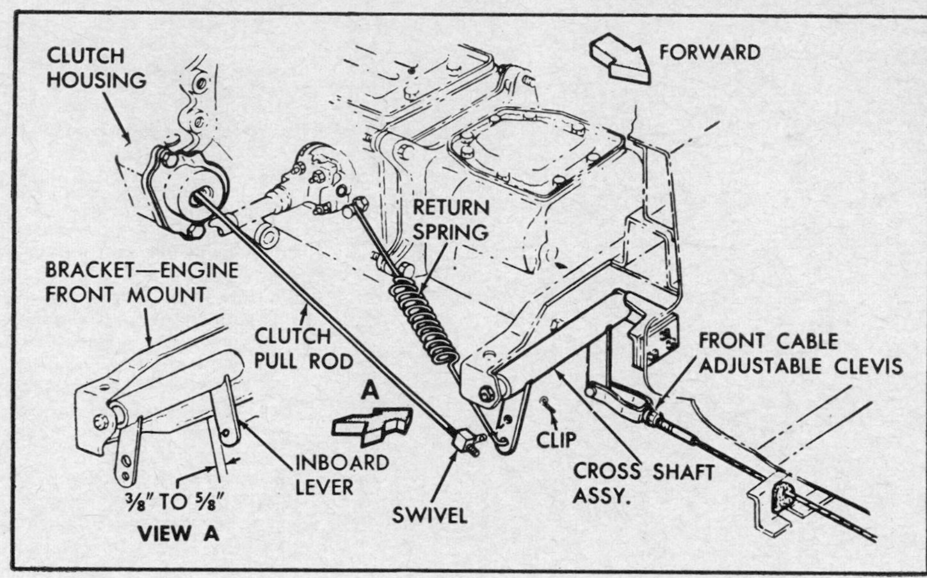

Fig. 1 Clutch linkage adjustment. 1963-64

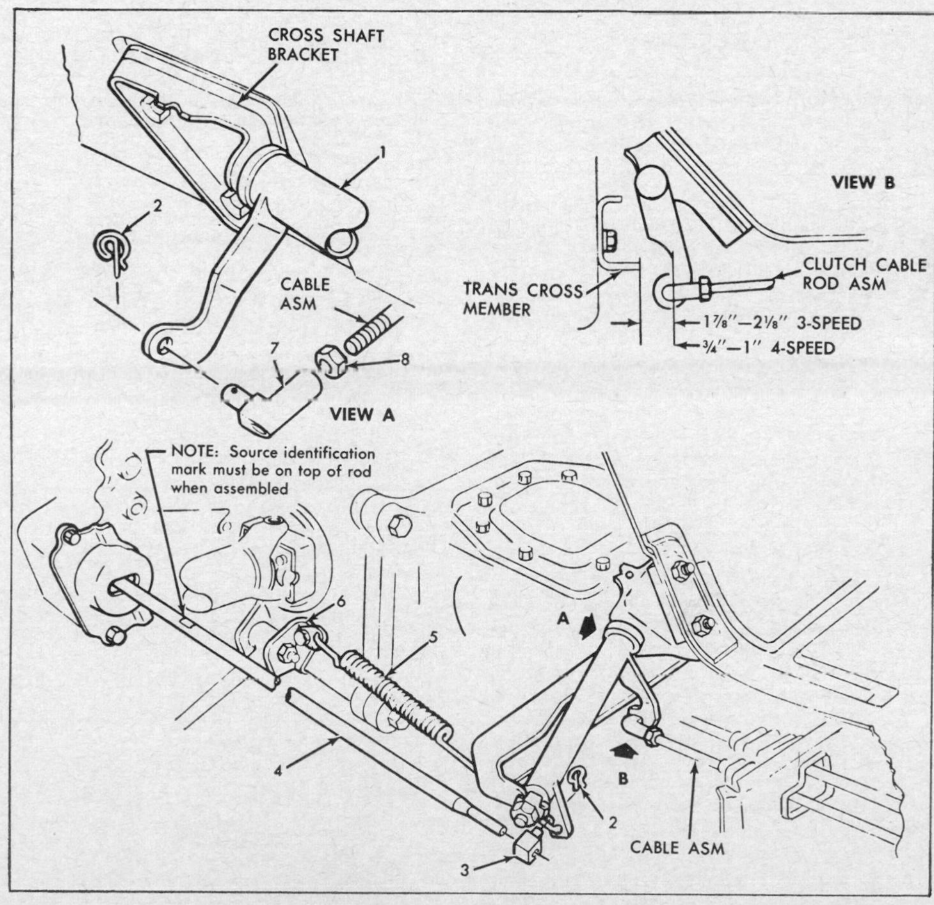

Fig. 2 Clutch linkage adjustment. 1965-68. Dimension shown is 3/8" for 1969

CLUTCH LINKAGE, ADJUST

1963

With either a 3 or 4 speed manual shift transmission, the clutch linkage should be adjusted to permit 3/4" to 1 1/8" free travel of the clutch pedal before the clutch release bearing makes contact with the clutch diaphragm spring. If the pedal free travel is not correct, adjust as follows, referring to Fig. 1.

1. Disengage clutch pull rod from cross shaft.
2. Adjust length of front control cable at the cross shaft clevis to obtain 3/8" to 5/8" spacing between the rear edge of the cross shaft inboard lever and the lower edge of the engine front mounting bracket (View A), Fig. 1. *NOTE: While performing the foregoing adjustment, exert approximately 5 lbs. tension on the cable (using a spring scale) to assure that cable seats in its pulleys.*
3. With the clutch pull rod held forward to remove slack at clutch fork, align rod swivel with upper hole in cross shaft lever, then back off swivel three complete turns and install pull rod in upper hole in lever.

NOTE: On some early 1963 models, if a pull rod lever having a total of three holes is encountered, the pull rod should be installed in the center hole. The upper hole in the 3-hole lever is never used.

1964

Clutch pedal free travel should be 3/4 to 1 1/4" measured at the pedal before the clutch release bearing engages the diaphragm spring.

1. Disconnect clutch fork pull rod swivel from cross shaft lever.
2. Clearance between clutch fork pull rod and transmission mount bracket should be 1/2" to 5/8". If necessary, disconnect return spring and adjust cable clevis as required.
3. Pull clutch fork pull rod until slack is taken up at clutch fork and turn swivel to align with hole in cross shaft lever.
4. Back off swivel three complete turns, then connect swivel to cross shaft lever.

1965-69

1. Referring to Fig. 2, drive nut (8) to within 1/8" of threads on clutch cable rod assembly.
2. Tension clutch cable rod to 15 lbs and thread swivel (7) to line up with shaft (1) inboard lever with lever located to dimension shown from transmission crossmember. Assemble swivel (7) to lever with clip (2).
3. Torque nut (8) to swivel (7) to 7-12 ft-lbs.
4. Install spring (5) to bracket (6) and to shaft (1).
5. Manually pull clutch pull rod (4)

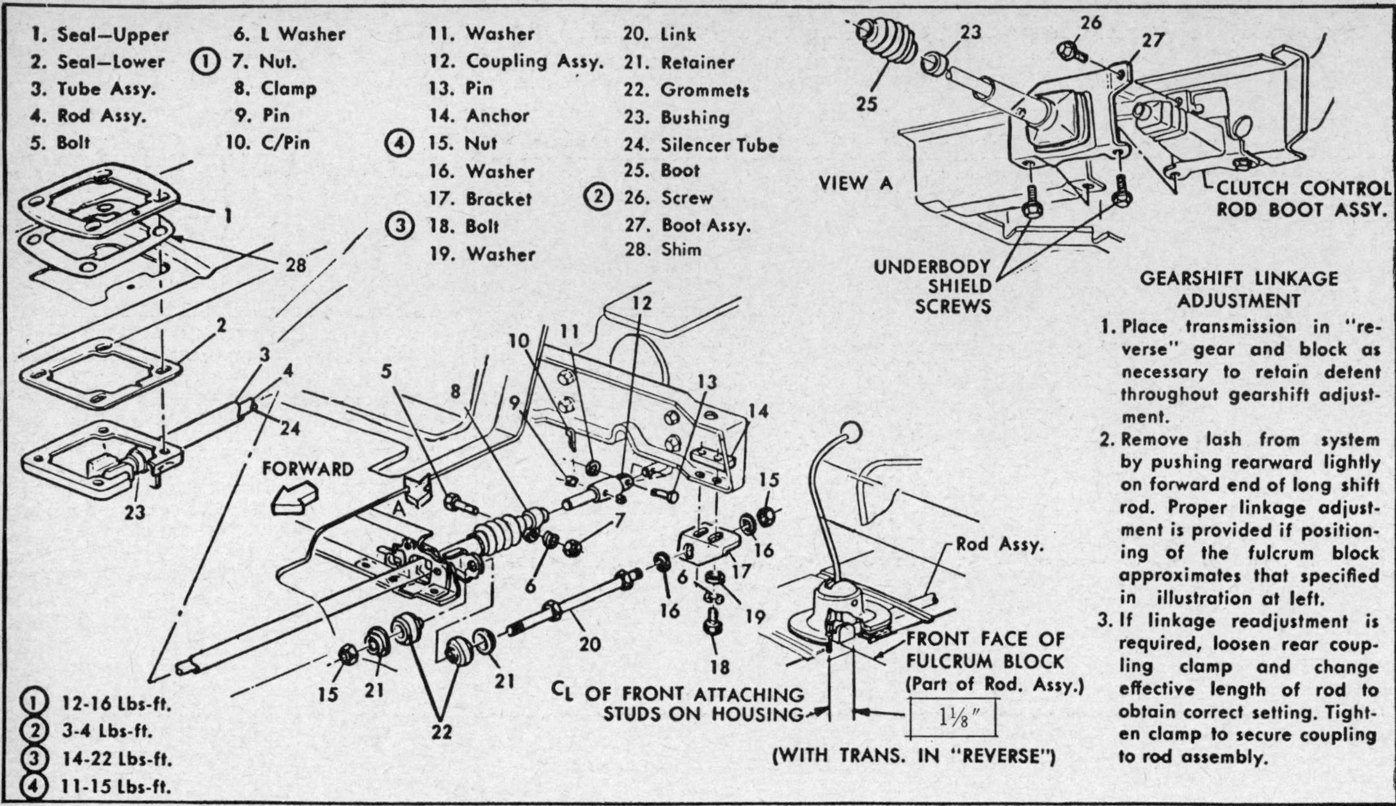

Fig. 4 Three and four-speed transmission shift linkage installation and adjustment. 1966-69

forward until slack is taken up at clutch fork. With clutch pull rod in this position, align swivel (3) with hole in outboard to shaft lever. Back off swivel two turns and assemble to lever with clip (2).

CLUTCH REPLACE

1. Remove engine, axle and transmission from the car and separate the axle and transmission from the engine as outlined in the *Power Train Section.*
2. The clutch fork, ball stud and clutch release bearing are removed with the axle housing.
3. Disconnect clutch fork from ball stud and remove clutch release bearing from shaft.
4. Remove 6 clutch attaching bolts, one turn at a time, until clutch spring pressure is released. Then remove clutch from engine.
5. Reverse above procedure to install the clutch, being sure the cushion springs of the clutch disc are located on the flywheel side of the driven plate hub.

3 & 4 SPEED TRANS., REPLACE

1963-64

Either transmission is removed together with the engine. The transmission is then removed from the engine. Repair procedures on both transmissions are covered in separate chapters.

1965-69

NOTE: Either transmission can be removed from the vehicle, leaving the engine in the chassis as follows:

1. Disconnect engine seal (both sides) at front shield. *This is done by grasping at lower edge and pulling groove of seal off shield flanges.*
2. Disconnect starter motor wires at quick disconnect. Disconnect both battery cables at battery to avoid battery post damage when engine is lowered.
3. Disconnect radio ground straps (if equipped) at left and right shields.
4. Raise vehicle and support on jack stands, then remove rear-center shield.
5. Support weight of engine with a suitable lift.
6. Loosen two engine rear mount nuts until they are flush with end of stud.
7. Disconnect fuel line from body clip so that line can swing away from floor pan.
8. To allow clearance for transaxle to swing down, loosen front upper bolt from each rear strut rod bracket at differential a few turns to relieve tension on lockwasher. Remove the three others on each side.
9. Disconnect accelerator rods at transmission bellcrank.
10. Disconnect left and right front strut rod brackets at engine front mount bracket.
11. Disconnect clutch fork pull rod and spring at clutch cross shaft. Loosen nut attaching cross shaft to engine front mount. Cross shaft can be rotated and pushed up out of the way.
12. Disconnect shift rod coupling at transmission shift rod.
13. Disconnect emergency brake return spring at front mount bracket.
14. Remove back-up lamp switch wiring (if equipped).
15. Lower front of engine enough for transmission to clear underbody on removal. Remove bolts retaining transmission to differential, allowing transaxle to partially drain; then remove transmission from differential.

NOTE: Transmission input shaft remains engaged in clutch and will protrude out through differential. Transmission is removed with front mount bracket attached. To install transmission, reverse removal procedure. If the replacement transmission is being installed in a vehicle without back-up lights, be sure an expansion plug is installed in the lamp switch hole.

SHIFT LINKAGE, ADJUST

1966-69

To adjust the linkage, see Figs. 3 and 4 for details on the installation and for adjustment procedure.

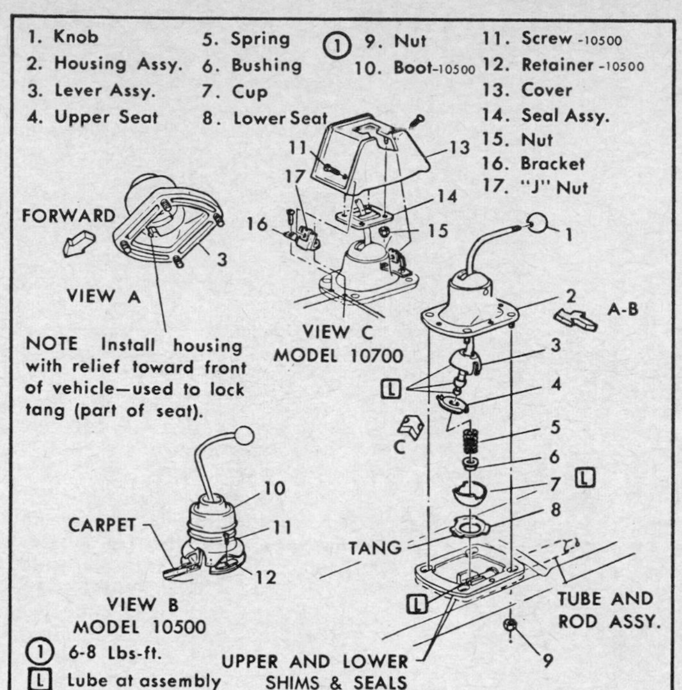

Fig. 3 Three and four-speed transmission gearshift control. 1966-69

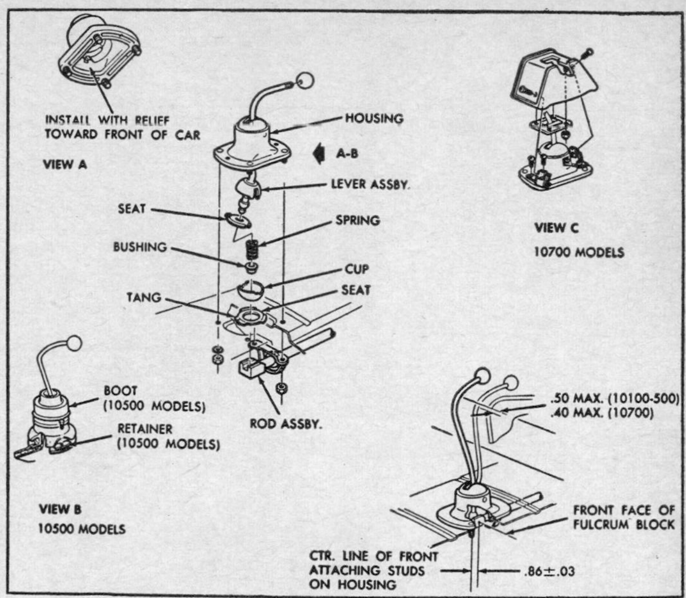

Fig. 6 Three-and four-speed gearshift control. 1965

1963-65 3 & 4 Speed Units

1. Move front seat to its full forward position.
2. Shift transmission into gear range used for checking control lever positioning, Fig. 5 and 6.
3. To remove any lash from system, push rearward lightly on the long shifter tube located in the tunnel.
4. Using a scale, check positioning of gearshift control lever relative to front edge of seat or centerline of lever housing (refer to illustration).

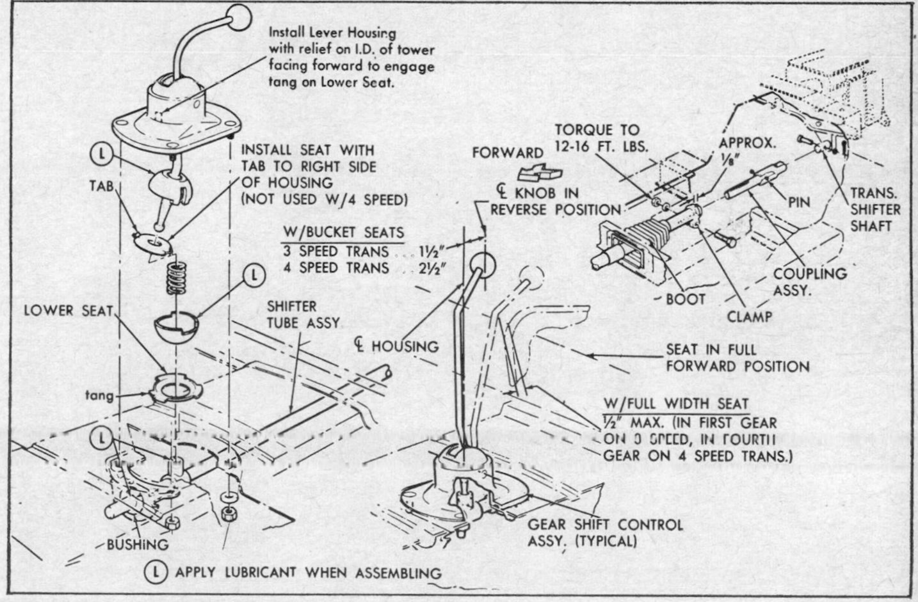

Fig. 5 Assembly and adjustment of 1963-64 manual transmission shift linkage

Rear Axle and Brake Section

AXLE DESCRIPTION

The Corvair rear axle is of the straddle-mounted hypoid type which embodies a differential carrier mounted rigidly to the engine; no rear axle housing is used, Figs. 1 and 2. Independently suspended axle shafts are attached to universal joints which, in turn, are splined into the differential side gears.

A hollow shaft is used with the drive pinion to permit passage of the engine output shaft forward to the transmission. To permit the axial hole in the pinion shaft, the drive pinion and gear are two pieces coupled together. The drive pinion shaft is directly connected to the transmission output member. Preloaded tapered roller bearings support the drive pinion at fore and aft locations in the differential carrier. The ring gear is bolted to the differential case which is mounted on preloaded tapered roller bearings on each side of the differential carrier.

Components of the differential assembly are conventional with the exception of the side gears which have integral elongated splined hubs which project to the outboard extremity of the differential case and cover to receive the axle shaft universal joints.

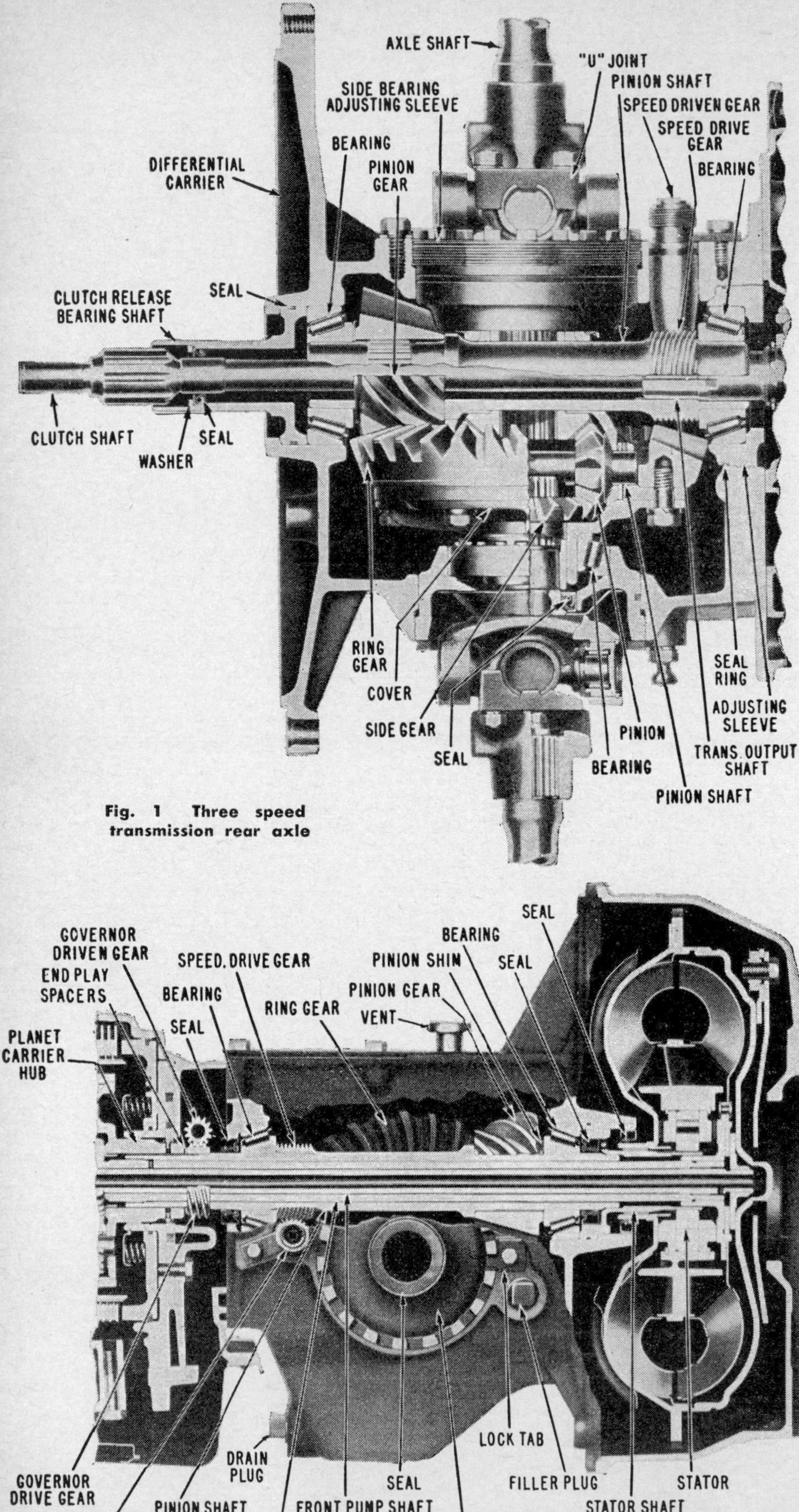

Fig. 1 Three speed transmission rear axle

Fig. 2 Powerglide transmission rear axle

WHEEL BEARINGS, ADJUST

1965-69

NOTE: The wheel spindle, spindle support, spindle bearings and spacer are the various items that affect wheel bearing end play. Therefore, when replacing any of these items, it will be necessary to ascertain proper adjusting shim thickness to maintain specified end play. Tool J-21836 is available to ascertain the shim thickness required. To use the tool, proceed as follows:

1. Remove knurled nut from each end of the gauge tool.
2. Position spindle inner bearing on small end of gauge (small end of bearing toward pin on gauge). Then finger tighten knurled nut against bearing, Fig. 3.
3. Position gauge and bearing assembly through inboard side of spindle support.
4. Install bearing spacer over large end of gauge, then position spindle outer bearing on gauge and against spacer, Fig. 4. Install undercut end of knurled nut against bearing and hand tighten nut so that there is no play in gauge body.
5. Install dial indicator as shown in Fig. 4 with gauge finger against movable shaft of tool J-21836.
6. Move shaft of tool so that it travels the maximum permissible distance limited by spacer and inner bearing. Record reading obtained and recheck to ensure accuracy.
7. To the reading obtained, add .097". The total obtained is the required shim thickness necessary to maintain specified end play.

EXAMPLE: If the dial indicator reading is .026" and we add .097", the total shim thickness is .123". The shim to be installed would be .124" thick since this is the shim with a thickness nearer to the value as computed above. The gauge is constructed to represent the smallest shim, which is .097".

8. Disassemble gauge and install spindle outer bearing. Pack both wheel bearings with the recommended grease prior to installation.
9. Position support outer seal on a suitable tool and install seal in support. Connect brake line.
10. Reassemble spindle to support.
11. Reassemble axle shaft, brake drum and wheel.

AXLE SHAFT, BEARING & U-JOINT

1965-69

1. Raise vehicle and support with jack stands at jacking pads on underbody.
2. Position hydraulic jack under torque arm bracket and raise jack until drive shaft is at or near curb position.

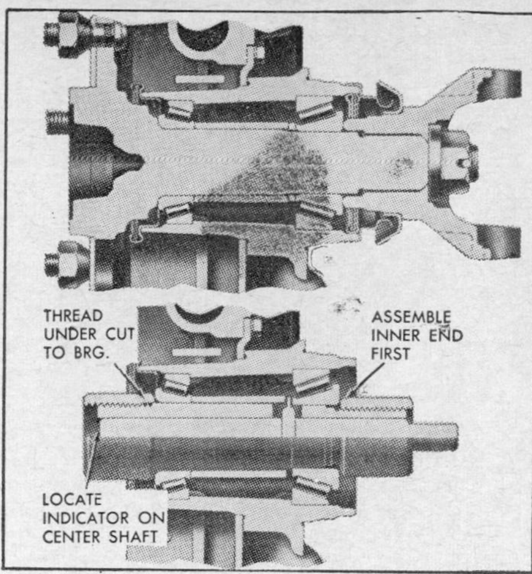

Fig. 3 Spindle bearing gauge installation. 1965-69

Fig. 4 Gauging rear wheel bearing shim requirements. 1965-69

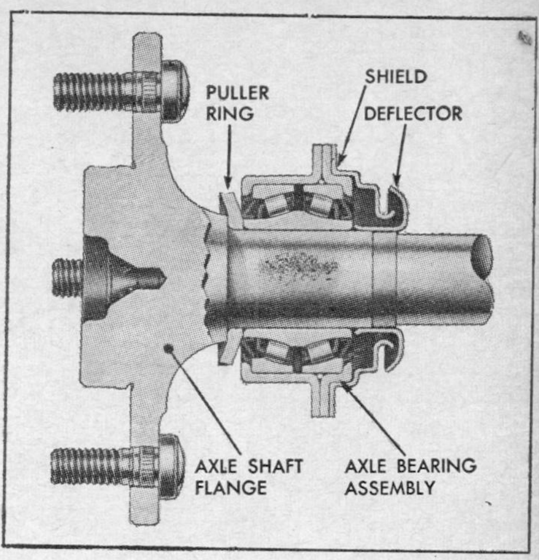

Fig. 6 Axle shaft bearing. 1963-64

3. Bend lock tabs downward from their position against trunnion retaining bolts.
4. Disconnect inboard drive shaft trunnion from side gear yoke by removing the four bolts, retaining straps and bolt locks.
5. Remove four bolts, retaining straps and bolt locks securing outboard drive shaft trunnion to drive spindle flange.
6. Pry drive shaft out of flange or yoke and remove shaft.
7. Reverse procedure to install, Rotate drive shaft so that loose ends of trunnion are in a horizontal position, then tighten retaining bolts alternately until both ends of drive shaft are seated in trunnion seats.

1963-64

AXLE SHAFT

1. Remove wheel and brake drum.
2. Unfasten bearing retainer from backing plate (four nuts accessible through hole in axle shaft flange).
3. Pull backing plate outward slightly then push it back onto the control arm studs to break away from the bearing retainer. The axle shaft can now be pulled outward sufficiently to free the U-joint splines from the differential side gears.
4. Remove U-joint from axle shaft (4 nuts from U-bolts).
5. Remove yoke from axle shaft.
6. Reverse procedure to install.

AXLE SHAFT BEARINGS

1. Place axle shaft in a press with puller plate below the puller ring, Fig. 6.
2. Remove oil deflector, bearing and puller ring.
3. To install, place a new puller ring, bearing and oil deflector on axle shaft. *To prevent damaging bearing during installation of the new parts, place the old puller ring with its flat side against the bearing inner race and then press the puller ring and bearing onto the axle shaft.*
4. Remove old puller ring and install oil deflector.

INSTALLATION

1. Insert axle shaft through lower control arm and install U-joint yoke on splines of axle shaft. It may be necessary to lightly tap yoke onto splines if original pieces are being installed. *When assembling new pieces for the first time, it is good practice to assemble and disassemble the yoke to the axle shaft with a press to ease the assembly of the pieces in the vehicle.*
2. Secure U-joint flange to axle shaft.
3. Attach U-joint to yoke on shaft with U-bolts.
4. With bearing retainer holes lined up with control arm studs, insert U-joint splines through seals in side bearing adjusting sleeves and index with side gear splines.
5. Secure bearing retainer to brake backing (4 nuts) via access hole in axle shaft flange.
6. Position brake drum control arm studs and secure wheel and drum.

SIDE BEARING SLEEVE SEAL

1965-69

1. Raise vehicle and remove axle drive shaft and differential side bearing yoke.
2. Mark relationship of side bearing adjusting sleeve to differential carrier, making sure that these marks are easily identified as they are to be used to re-align sleeve to maintain differential side bearing preload.
3. Remove adjusting sleeve lock tab

Fig. 7 Removing side bearing adjusting sleeve

Fig. 8 Removing pinion adjusting sleeve

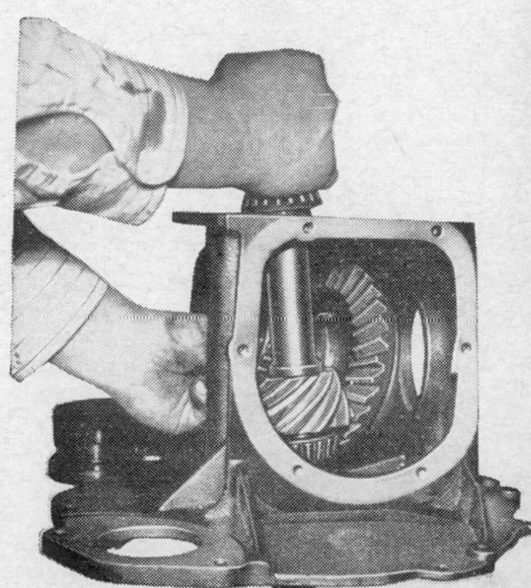

Fig. 9 Removing pinion from carrier

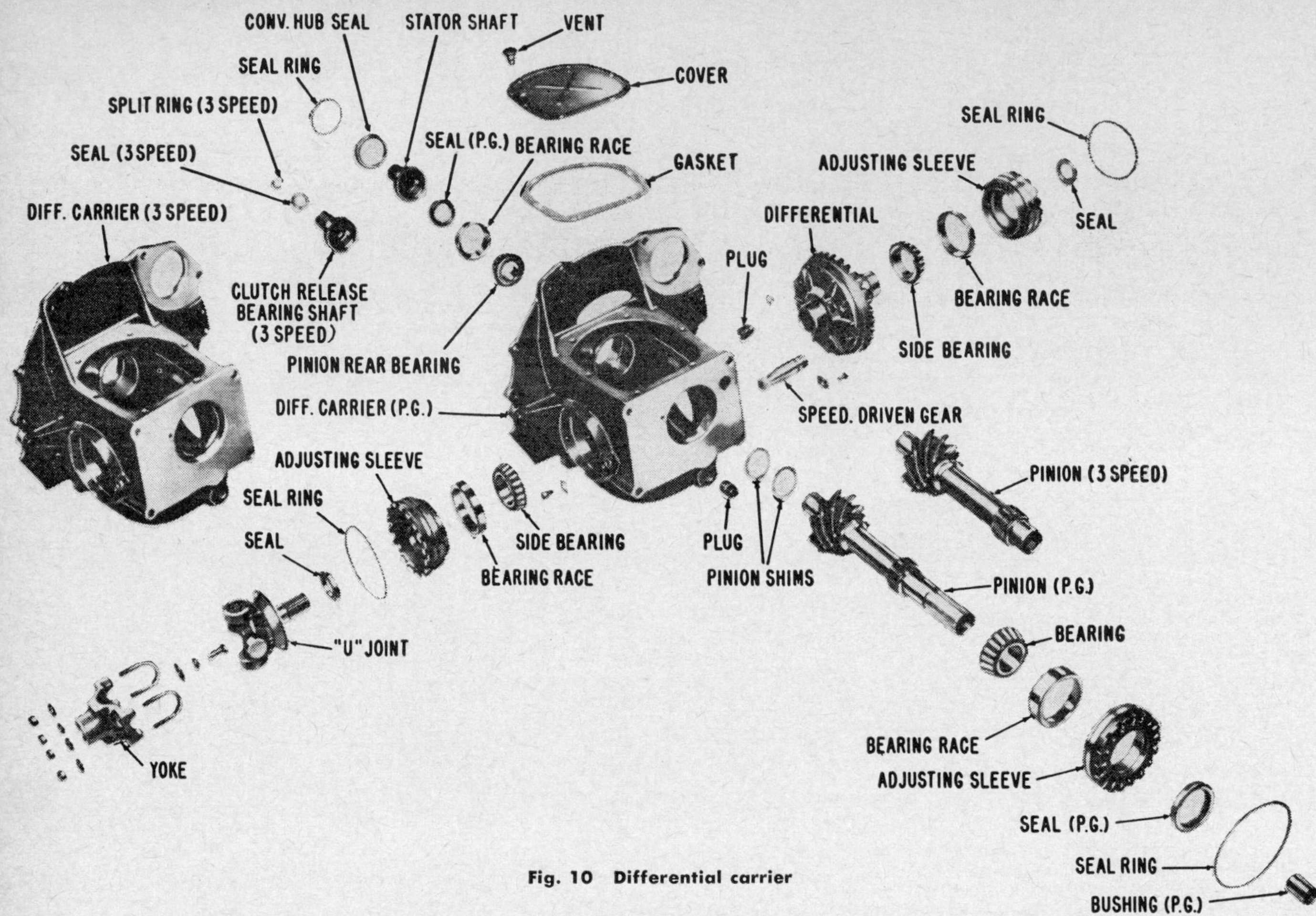

Fig. 10 Differential carrier

and sleeve. Record the number of turns necessary to remove sleeve from carrier, using marks scribed in Step 2 as a reference.

4. Remove damaged seal ring and install a new one in the groove. Apply a thin coating of vaseline to seal after installation in groove.
5. Install sleeve in carrier, making sure that sleeve is turned to correspond with the number of turns recorded in Step 3.
6. Back off the number of turns to relieve seal windup, then reposition to original setting and install lock tab.
7. Install side bearing yoke and axle drive shaft.

DIFFERENTIAL CARRIER

1963-64

1. After removing the engine from the car, the differential is then removed from the engine. Disassemble differential carrier by first removing speedometer driven gear.
2. Remove differential carrier cover.
3. Remove side gear adjusting sleeves, Fig. 7.
4. Remove pinion adjusting sleeve, Fig. 8.
5. Remove pinion drive gear with bearings attached, Fig. 9.
6. Remove differential from carrier by shifting differential to one side of carrier and then turning 90 degrees in order to remove via the cover hole in carrier.

Inspection

1. Inspect all bearing cups, races and rollers for damage and wear, especially large end of rollers as this is where wear is most evident on taper roller bearings. *The rear axle pinion bearings are of the preloaded type, and the natural wear pattern is a slightly frosted condition with occasional slight scratches on races and rollers. This does not indicate a defective bearing.*
2. On Powerglide axles, inspect oil seal in stator support and at converter hub for evidence of wear or damage.
3. Inspect pinion splines for evidence of excessive wear.
4. Inspect ring gear and pinion teeth for scoring, chipping or cracking.
5. Check fit of differential side gears in case.
6. Check fit of side gear and U-joint shaft splines.
7. Inspect differential pinion shaft for scoring or evidence of excessive wear.
8. Inspect differential carrier for cracks or crossed threads.

AXLE REPAIRS

For Three Speed and Powerglide Axles

Note—Repairs required on three speed axles only, and those for Powerglide axles only are outlined further on. Refer to Fig. 10 for relationship of parts.

Pinon and Bearing, Replace

When it becomes necessary to replace pinion bearings and/or ring gear and drive pinion, it is necessary to re-establish the pinion mounting distance.

Pinion bearings may be removed with the aid of a press. It will be noted that a shim or shims are used between the pinion rear bearing and pinion. To determine the shim thickness to be used when installing new parts special gauges are required. Fig. 11. Lacking this equipment, check the ring gear contact pattern as shown in Fig. 12. To do this the differential carrier must be assembled. If a change is indicated, disassemble the parts and change the shimming as required to obtain the proper tooth contact pattern. Shims are available in thicknesses of .006, .009, .012, .015 and .018".

Fig. 11 Pinion depth shim selection gauges

Pinion Front Bearing Race

1. Thread adjusting sleeve and race assembly into carrier until finger tight and remove old race with a punch or other suitable tool. On Powerglide models it is necessary to remove the seal.

CAUTION: Adjusting sleeve should engage sufficient threads in carrier to prevent possible thread damage when driving out race.

2. Install new race in pinion adjusting sleeve.

Side Bearing Adjusting Sleeve Bearing Race

1. Thread side bearing adjusting sleeve and race assembly into carrier until finger tight and drive out old race with a punch or other suitable tool.

CAUTION: Adjusting sleeve should engage sufficient threads in carrier to prevent possible thread damage when driving out race.

2. Install new bearing race in adjusting sleeve, using a suitable flat plate as a driver. Drive bearing race until it is flush with sleeve face.

Differential Overhaul

Disassemble the differential as suggested by Fig. 13. To remove the differential pinions after the case has been separated, drive out the roll pin securing the differential pinion shaft to the case. *Before separating the differential case halves, punch mark the rim of both halves so that they may be attached in the original position. Fig. 16.* When securing the ring gear to the case, tighten all bolts to a torque of 40-60 ft. lbs. in a criss-cross pattern.

REPAIRS ON 3 SPEED TRANS. AXLES ONLY

Clutch Release Bearing Shaft Seal

Remove split ring and old seal from clutch release bearing shaft by prying out with a punch. Install the new seal, open side inward, using a suitable socket (¾") and socket extension. Drive seal until it bottoms, then install split ring in clutch release bearing shaft.

Clutch Release Bearing Shaft and/or Pinion Bearing Rear Race

1. Place differential carrier in arbor press and press out shaft and race.
2. If a new shaft is being installed, first install the inner seal. Install a new seal ring in groove on outer diameter of bearing shaft and lubricate with vaseline.
3. Support differential carrier only on boss at clutch release bearing location with a suitable cylinder; then place bearing race on shaft and press both into differential carrier. Press until cup is flush with adjacent surface inside carrier.

REPAIRS ON POWERGLIDE AXLES ONLY

Pinion Shaft Front Oil Seal and/or Converter Hub Oil Seal

The pinion shaft front oil seal and the converter hub oil seal are located diametrically opposite fore and aft respectively, in the differential carrier.

Remove the oil seal by prying out with a punch or similar tool. Coat outer diameter of new seal with a non-hardening sealer and install seal. The converter hub seal is mounted flush. A special driver is available to install the pinion seal. A stop is provided on this driver which insures the seal being installed to the proper depth. This same driver (J-8340) is also used to drive the converter hub seal.

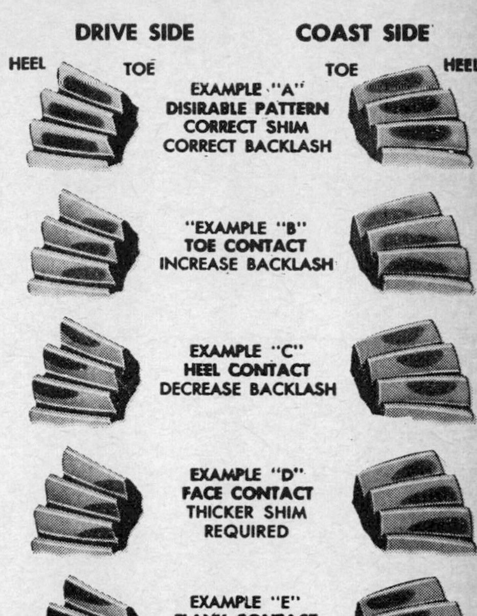

Fig. 12 Ring gear contact patterns

Pinion Shaft Rear Oil Seal

Drive out the old seal with a pin punch inserted through access hole in stator shaft. Install new seal as shown in Fig. 15 until it bottoms.

Pinion Shaft Bushing

Remove old bushing from inside diameter of pinion shaft using a chisel or other suitable tool. Use care not to damage the bushing mating surfaces in pinion shaft during removal.

Install new bushing with a suitable driver. Special tool J-8333 is available for this operation; it has a stop provided thereon to press the bushing to the proper depth.

Stator Shaft and/or Pinion Rear Bearing Race

1. Remove stator shaft and pinion bearing cup from carrier by placing carrier in a press and pressing downward on end of stator shaft. Replace parts removed.
2. Install seal ring in groove on outside diameter of stator shaft and lubricate with vaseline. *Outer diameter seal is not used on later production stator shafts.*
3. If a new stator shaft is being installed, it will be necessary to install a new pinion rear oil seal as previously described.
4. Align notch in stator shaft, Fig. 15, with drain back passage boss in differential carrier. Place bearing race on stator shaft and press race and shaft into housing, Fig. 16. *Carrier must be supported only at stator shaft boss for this operation.*

THRUST WASHER
COVER
SIDE GEAR
THRUST WASHER
PINION
CASE
RING GEAR
PINION
SIDE GEAR
THRUST WASHER
THRUST WASHER
SHAFT PIN
PINION SHAFT

Fig. 13 Differential assembly

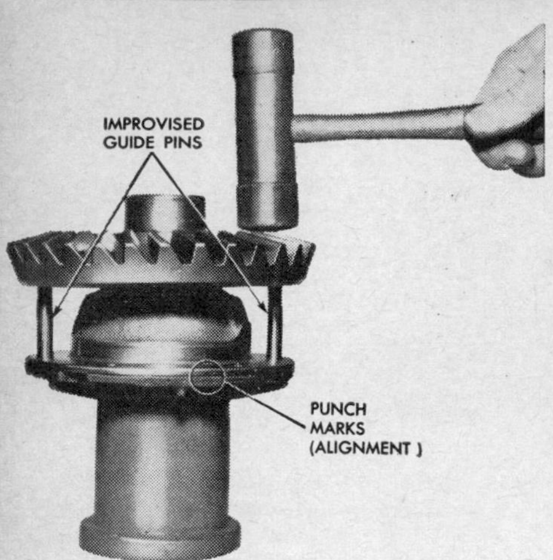

Fig. 14 Installing ring gear on differential case and cover, using improvised guide pins

Fig. 15 Installing pinion rear oil seal in stator shaft

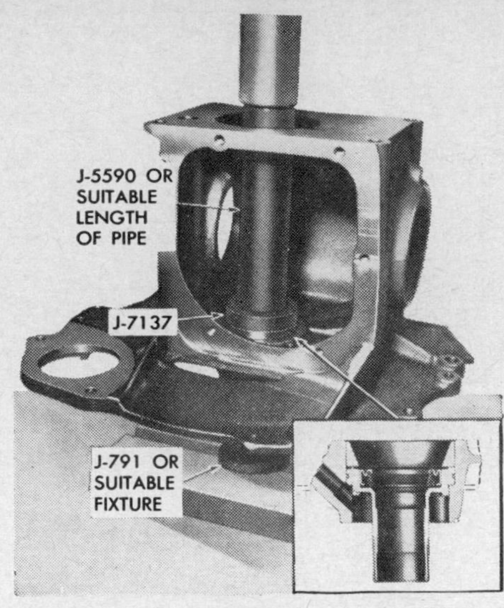

Fig. 16 Installing stator shaft and pinion rear bearing race

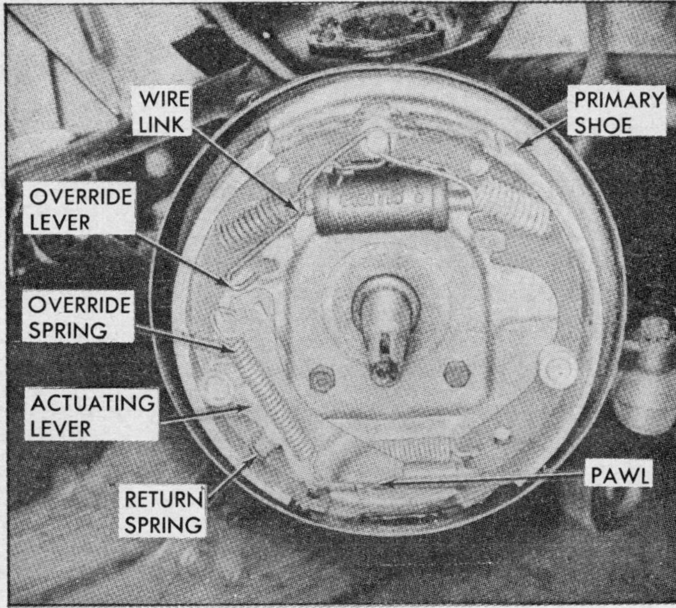

Fig. 17 Right front brake. 1963-69

Fig. 18 Brake drum access hole. 1963-69

Fig. 19 Aligning drum tong with wheel hub. 1963-69

ASSEMBLE DIFFERENTIAL CARRIER

1. Referring to Fig. 10, insert differential into carrier with side bearing cones installed on differential hubs.
2. While differential is loose in carrier, insert pinion into carrier through cover hole. Then engage pinion with ring gear and carefully position pinion rear bearing in race. On Powerglide models, care must be used not to damage seal at this location when pinion is installed.
3. Install new O-ring seals in side bearing adjusting sleeves. Coat adjusting sleeve threads with a non-hardening pipe thread compound. Loosely install sleeves in carrier with side bearings positioned in sleeves.
4. On Powerglide models, install a new O-ring seal in pinion adjusting sleeve. Position pinion so that its front bearing will pick up the bearing race in sleeve and loosely install sleeve in carrier. Use care not to damage seal lips when inserting pinion shaft over adjusting sleeve.
5. Tighten both side bearing adjusting sleeves and pinion adjusting sleeve to the point of contact between bearings and races. At this point, there should be no preload on any of the bearings and ring gear and pinion backlash should be just enough so that the pinion and differential can be rotated easily and smoothly. The assembly is now ready for ring gear and pinion adjustment.

BRAKE ADJUSTMENTS

1963-69 Self-Adjusting Brakes

These brakes, Fig. 17, have self-adjusting shoe mechanisms that assure correct lining-to-drum clearances at all times. The automatic adjusters operate only when the brakes are applied as the car is moving rearward or when the car comes to an uphill stop.

Although the brakes are self-adjusting, an initial adjustment is necessary after the brake shoes have been relined or replaced, or when the length of the star wheel adjuster has been changed during some other service operation.

Frequent usage of an automatic transmission forward range to halt reverse vehicle motion may prevent the automatic adjusters from functioning, thereby inducing low pedal heights. Should low pedal heights be encountered, it is recommended that numerous forward and reverse stops be made until satisfactory pedal height is obtained.

NOTE

If a low pedal height condition cannot be corrected by making numerous reverse stops (provided the hydraulic system is free of air) it indicates that the self-adjusting mechanism is not functioning. Therefore, it will be necessary to remove the brake drum, clean, free up and lubricate the adjusting mechanism. Then adjust the brake, being sure the parking brake is fully released.

Adjustment

A lanced "knock out" area, Fig. 18, is provided in the web of the brake drum for servicing purposes in the event retracting of the brake shoes is required in order to remove the drum.

1. With brake drum off, disengage the actuator from the star wheel and rotate the star wheel by spinning or turning with a screwdriver.
2. Using the brake drum as an adjustment fixture, turn the star wheel until the drum slides over the brake shoes with a slide drag.
3. Turn the star wheel 1¼ turns to retract the brake shoes. This will allow sufficient lining-to-drum clearance so final adjustment may be made.
4. Install drum and wheel. *NOTE: If lanced area in brake drum was knocked out, be sure all metal has been removed from brake compartment. Install new hole cover in drum to prevent contamination of brakes. Make certain that drums are installed in the same position as when removed with the drum locating tang in line with the locating hole in the wheel hub, Fig. 19.*
5. Make final adjustment by driving and stopping vehicle forward and reverse until satisfactory pedal height is obtained.

PARKING BRAKE, ADJUST

1. With service brakes properly adjusted and rear wheels raised, pull parking brake lever up one notch on 1965-69 (4 on earlier models) from fully released position.
2. Loosen forward check nut on equalizer and tighten rear nut until a heavy drag is felt when rear wheels are rotated.
3. Tighten check nuts securely.
4. Fully release parking brake and rotate rear wheels; no drag should be present.

MASTER CYLINDER, REPLACE

1. Disconnect hydraulic lines from outlet end of cylinder.
2. Remove pedal return spring.
3. Unfasten mounting nuts from dash wall and remove cylinder.

Suspension and Steering Section

FRONT WHEEL BEARINGS

1965-69

1. With spindle nut loosened slightly, rotate wheel while applying 12 ft-lbs torque to spindle nut.
2. To align cotter pin hole, back off spindle nut more than one nut flat but less than 1½ flats. Then insert cotter pin. Spindle nut back-off must exceed one flat in order to achieve the .001 to .008" bearing end play required.

1963-64

1. Raise car and remove cotter pin from spindle.
2. Tighten spindle nut to 100 inch lbs. while rotating wheel.
3. Back off nut one flat (1/6 turn).
4. Insert cotter pin if slot in nut and hole in spindle align. If not, back off an additional ½ flat or less and insert cotter pin.
5. Spin wheel to make certain it rolls freely. *Wheel bearings should have .000" to .004" end play when properly adjusted.*

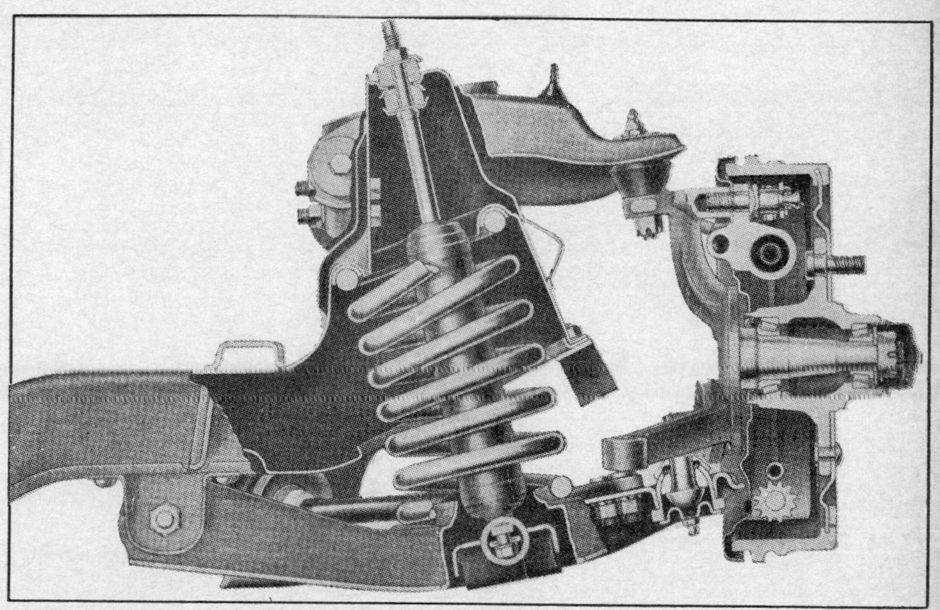

Front suspension

FRONT WHEEL ALIGNMENT

1966-69

CAMBER ADJUST

Camber angle is adjusted by loosening the lower control arm pivot bolt and rotating the cams located on this pivot, Fig. 1. The eccentric cam action will move the lower control arm in or out, thereby varying camber.

CASTER ADJUST

Caster is adjusted by turning the two nuts at the rear of the strut rod, Fig. 2. Lengthening this rod by turning the nuts increases caster. Shortening the rod by turning the nuts decreases caster.

1963-64

CAMBER ADJUST

This is the first adjustment to be performed on the front suspension. The adjustment is made by means of shims between the upper control arm inner shaft and the front crossmember, Fig. 3. Although shims can be changed at either the front or rear attachment, it is important that the shimming be done equally so as to have no effect on caster. Adding shims at both front and rear of support shaft will decrease positive camber.

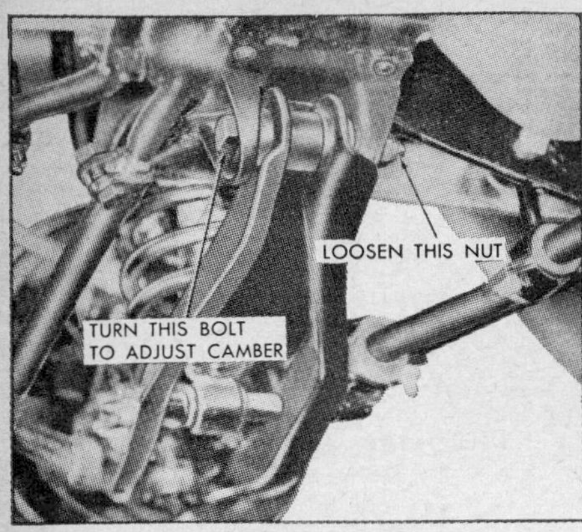

Fig. 1 Front wheel camber adjustment. 1965-69

The procedure for adjustment is to loosen the upper support shaft-to-crossmember bolts and add or remove shims equally as required and retighten bolts. *It may be necessary to remove the wheel to secure these bolts.*

CASTER ADJUST
Caster is adjusted by turning the two nuts at the rear of the strut rod, Fig. 4. Lengthening this rod by turning the nuts increases caster while shortening the rod decreases caster.

NOTE

Due to manufacturing tolerances, it is possible to "run out" of threads on the strut rod or cause the front coil spring to be cocked in its seat and rub the spring tower. Only when this happens is it permissible to shim unevenly at the upper control arm. However, if this is the case, camber must be rechecked.

TOE-IN ADJUST

1. Set steering gear on high point, with "saw cut" in steering shaft coupling at 6 o'clock position and steering wheel positioned for straight ahead driving.
2. Loosen clamp bolt at each end of each tie rod individually and adjust toe-in to specifications. Tighten clamp bolts and remove equipment.

REAR WHEEL ALIGNMENT

1965-69

CAMBER, ADJUST

1. Camber angle of rear wheels should be $+\frac{1}{2}^\circ$ to $+1\frac{1}{2}^\circ$. Adjustment is made by rotating the eccentric cam and bolt assembly, located at the outboard mounting of rear strut rod, Fig. 5
2. Place rear wheels on an alignment machine and determine camber angle.
3. Loosen cam bolt and rotate cam and bolt assembly to obtain the specified camber. Tighten nut on bolt securely.

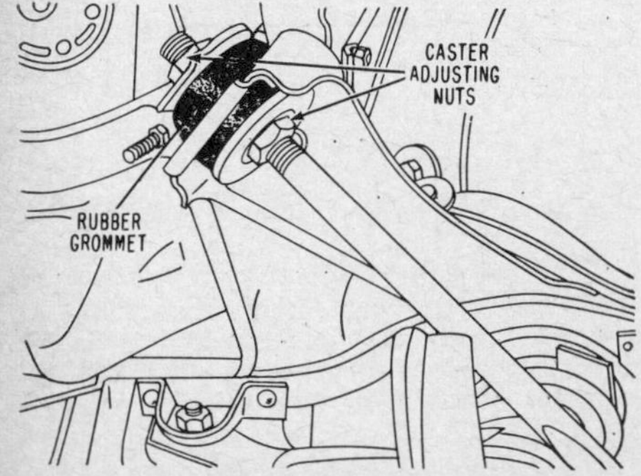

Fig. 4 Caster adjustment. 1963-64

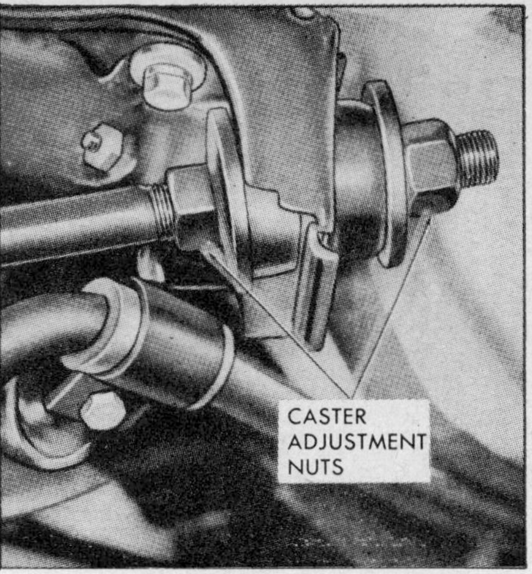

Fig. 2 Front wheel caster adjustment. 1965-69

TOE-IN, ADJUST

1. Total toe-in of rear wheels is $\frac{1}{8}''$ to $\frac{3}{8}''$. It is adjusted by moving the torque arm-to-underbody bracket horizontally as required, Fig. 6.
2. To adjust, loosen front strut rod inner bracket-to-transmission support bolts so that bracket is loose on slots. Then loosen bracket-to-underbody attaching bolts until bracket is free enough to be moved.
3. Position torque arm to obtain specified toe-in and tighten bolts securely.

1963-64

TOE-IN, ADJUST
Due to the design of this independently sprung rear axle and suspension, it will be necessary to check and adjust rear wheel toe-in. *If drive on type equipment is used, reverse the vehicle and back it into position. Toe-in will be read as toe-out when vehicle is backwards because readings will be taken from the rear of the tires rather than the front. A tram may also be used in a similar procedure as that used on the front wheels except both sides will be adjusted at the same time. It must be pointed out, however, that since the wheels are adjusted by adding or removing shims at the front edge of the transmission, both wheels are adjusted at the same time.*

A $\frac{1}{16}''$ shim added to each side will increase toe-in. Removal of a $\frac{1}{16}''$ shim from each side will decrease toe-in. Shims must be added or removed in pairs so that there is always the same number at each point.

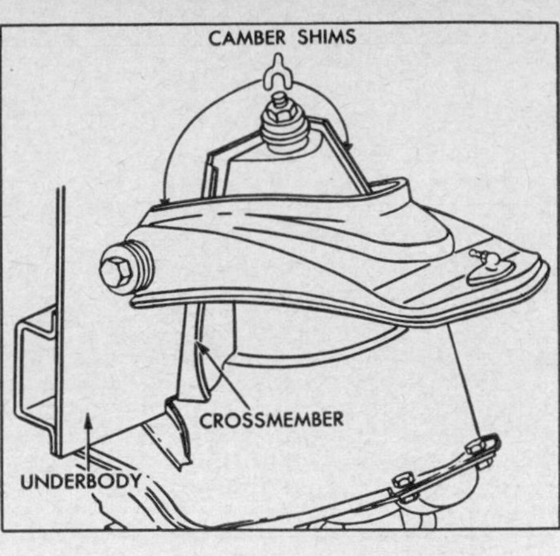

Fig. 3 Camber shim. 1963-64

Due to manufacturing tolerances and parts "stack-up" it is possible to have toe-out on one wheel and toe-in on the opposite wheel. In this case, adjust the suspension to bring the wheel with the toe-out as close to specifications as possible but not letting the opposite wheel go out of specifications. For example, if one wheel toes-out by $\frac{1}{4}''$, then the opposite wheel must toe in enough to give 0" to $\frac{1}{4}''$ overall toe-in.

CAMBER
There is no provision for adjustment of this item and it is provided as a checking specification only.

If camber is not within limits, either the crossmember is out of alignment with the body or has become distorted due to collision, etc., or else the control arm has become distorted, bent, etc.

CHECKING BALL JOINTS FOR WEAR

Before checking, make sure front wheel bearings are properly adjusted and that control arms are tight.

Referring to Fig. 7, raise wheel with a jack placed under the lower control at the point shown. Then test by moving the wheel up and down to check axial play, and rocking it at the top and bottom to measure radial play.

1. Upper ball joint should be replaced if there is any noticeable looseness

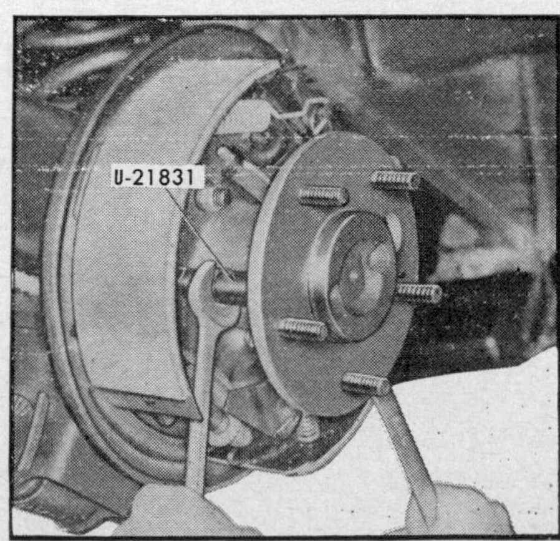

Fig. 5 Rear wheel camber adjustment. 1965-69

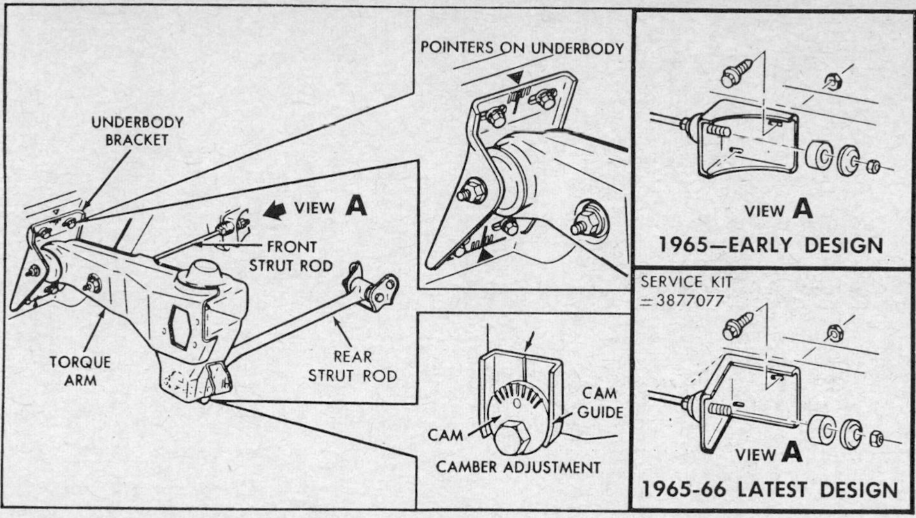

Fig. 6 Rear wheel toe-in adjusting bracket. 1965-69

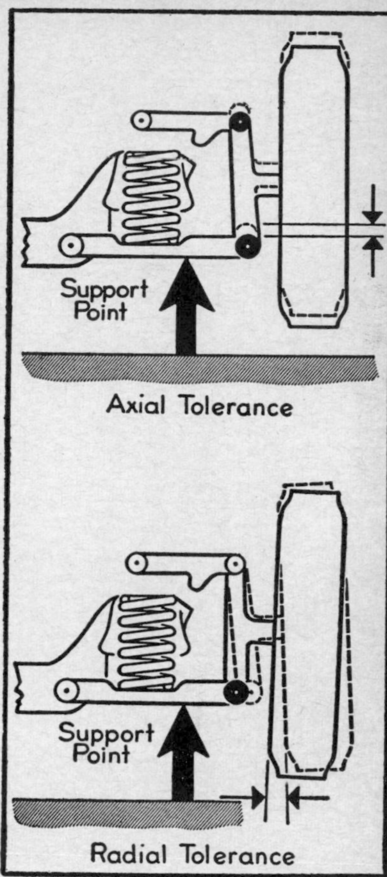

Fig. 7 Checking ball joints for wear

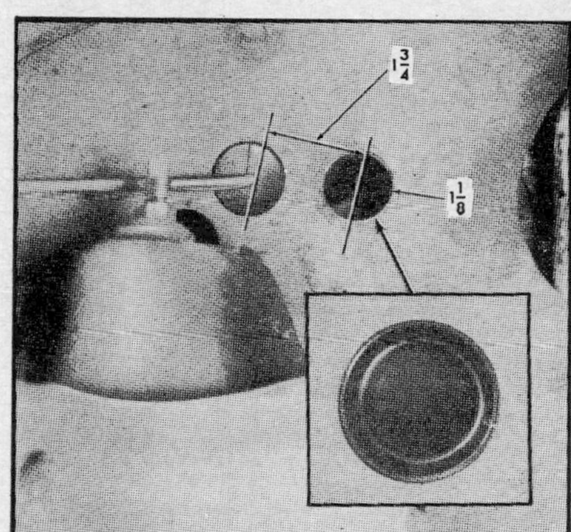

Fig. 8 Drill hole in location shown to provide an access hole for removal of steering gear, 1966 only. Insert shows plug used to close hole after gear is installed

at the joint.
2. Lower ball joint should be replaced if radial play exceeds .250".
3. Lower ball joint should be replaced if the axial play between lower control arm and spindle exceeds the following:

1963	.093"
1964-69	.060"

BALL JOINTS, REPLACE

On all models the upper ball joints are riveted to the upper control arm. All service ball joints, however, are provided with bolt, nut and washer assemblies for replacement purposes.

On all models, the lower ball joints are pressed into the lower control arms.

In servicing the front suspension, it will be desirable to raise the car on a hoist and the suspension allowed to swing free. If a twin post hoist or similar equipment is used, support the front of the vehicle at the forward end of the body side rail extension (each side) with jackstands and lower front of hoist.

SHOCK ABSORBER, REPLACE

1. With vehicle supported and front end hanging free, remove upper attaching nut, cup washer and grommet.
2. Remove two lower attaching bolts.
3. Withdraw shock absorber through lower control arm.
4. Reverse above procedure to install, extending shock absorber shaft to its full length to facilitate installation.

COIL SPRING, REPLACE

1. Raise vehicle and allow front control arms to swing free.
2. Remove shock absorber.
3. Remove strut rod nuts (pressed in).
4. *Loosen but do not remove* lower control arm inner pivot nut.
5. Place jackstand under inner end of control arm under bushing.
6. Remove control arm pivot nut and tap out pivot pin.
7. Lower hoist or jackstand until spring is free and take it out. *A bar placed through control arm and into spring tower will retain spring and keep it from slipping until free. Otherwise, keep clear of suspension until all compression is removed from spring.*

Reverse above procedure to replace the spring. When installing, place rubber spacer in place on top of spring and secure it with friction tape. Step in spacer must contact end of spring.

STEERING GEAR

1966-69

1. To remove steering gear, raise front of vehicle and (1966 only) drill a 1⅛" diameter hole in left front splash shield, Fig. 8.
2. Remove steering coupling clamp bolt.
3. Use a puller to remove pitman arm.
4. Unfasten and remove steering gear from below vehicle.
5. Reverse procedure to install. From below vehicle, guide steering gear and shaft into position carefully to align coupling with notch in steering shaft. Insert plug in access hole drilled in splash shield.

1965

1. Remove steering wheel.
2. Use a suitable puller to remove pitman arm.
3. Support gear and remove three mounting bolts.
4. Remove steering gear from below vehicle.
5. Reverse procedure to install.

1963-64

1. Disconnect pitman arm from pitman shaft. On 1964, remove left horn.
2. Unfasten steering gear from frame (3 bolts).
3. Unfasten steering shaft coupling (3 bolts) and slide steering gear forward, down and out.
4. Reverse procedure to install.

FORD & MERCURY

Full Size Models

OLD CAR SPECIFICATIONS: For 1946-62 Tune Up and Wheel Alignment Specifications see back of book.

INDEX OF SERVICE OPERATIONS

PAGE NO.

ACCESSORIES

Automatic Level Controls 1-41
Clock Troubles 1-11
Heater Core, Replace 2-268
Power Top Troubles 1-18
Power Window Troubles 1-18
Radio, Replace 2-267
Speed Controls, Adjust 2-268

BRAKES

Brake Troubles, Mechanical 1-17
Disc Brake Service 1-430
Hydraulic System Service 1-422
Master Cylinder, Replace 2-288
Parking Brake, Adjust 2-288
Power Brake Service 1-440
Power Brake Troubles 1-440
Power Brake Unit, Replace 2-289
Service Brakes, Adjust 2-287
Vacuum Release Parking Brake Unit 2-288

CLUTCH

Clutch Pedal, Adjust 2-283
Clutch, Replace 2-283
Clutch Troubles 1-12

COOLING SYSTEM

Cooling System Troubles 1-6
Variable Speed Fans 1-39
Water Pump, Replace 2-282

ELECTRICAL

Alternator Service 1-63
Dash Gauge Service 1-117
Distributor, Replace 2-259
Distributor Service:
  Standard 1-53
  Transistorized 1-47
Electrical Troubles 1-8
Flasher Location Chart .... Back of Book
Generator Service 1-91
Headlamps, Concealed Type 1-40
Ignition Coils and Resistors 1-24
Ignition Switch, Replace 2-260
Ignition Timing 2-259
Instrument Cluster Removal 2-264
Light Switch, Replace 2-261
Neutral Safety Switch, Replace 2-262
Spark Plug Condition Chart 2-647
Starter Service 1-101
Starter, Replace 2-260
Starter Switch Service 1-114
Stop Light Switch, Replace 2-262
Turn Signal Switch, Replace 2-262
Turn Signal Troubles 1-11
Windshield Wiper Motor, Replace 2-266
Windshield Wiper Troubles 1-20

PAGE NO.

ENGINE

Camshaft, Replace 2-277
Camshaft Bearings 2-278
Crankshaft Rear Oil Seal 2-279
Cylinder Head, Replace 2-270
Engine, Replace 2-269
Engine Troubles 1-1
Main Bearings 2-279
Piston Pins 2-278
Piston Rings 2-278
Piston and Rod, Assemble 2-278
Pistons 2-278
Rocker Arm Service 2-275
Rocker Arm Stud 2-275
Rod Bearings 2-279
Timing Case Cover, Replace 2-276
Timing Chain, Replace 2-277
Timing Gears, Replace 2-277
Valves, Adjust 2-272
Valve Arrangement 2-271
Valve Guides 2-275
Valve Lifters 2-275

ENGINE LUBRICATION

Crankcase Ventilation (PCV) 1-29
Exhaust Emission Controls 1-30
Oil Pan, Replace 2-280
Oil Pump Repairs 2-281

FUEL SYSTEM

Carburetor Adjustments and Specs 1-124
Crankcase Ventilation (PCV) 1-29
Exhaust Emission Controls 1-30
Fuel Pump, Replace 2-282
Fuel Pump Service 1-120
Fuel System Troubles 1-2

PROPELLER SHAFT & U JOINTS

Propeller Shaft 2-286
Universal Joint Service 1-418

REAR AXLE

Axle Shaft, Bearing and Seal 2-285
Rear Axle Description 2-284
Rear Axle Troubles 1-17

SPECIFICATIONS

Alternator 2-252
Brakes 2-258
Capacities 2-257
Carburetors 1-124
Cooling System 2-257
Crankshaft and Bearings 2-256
Distributors 2-253
Engine Tightening Torque 2-256

PAGE NO.

General Engine Specs. 2-248
Generators 2-258
Ignition Coils and Resistors 1-24
Pistons, Rings and Pins 2-256
Rear Axle 2-258
Starting Motors 2-249
Tune Up 2-250
Valve Lift 2-271
Valve Timing 2-272
Valves 2-255
Wheel Alignment 2-259

STEERING GEAR

Horn Sounder Removal 2-264
Linkage Type Power Steering 2-292
Mechanical Gear, Replace 2-292
Mechanical Gear Service 1-451
Mechanical Gear Troubles 1-18
Power Gear, Replace 2-292

SUSPENSION, FRONT

Ball Joints, Replace 2-292
Ball Joints, Check for Wear 2-291
Coil Spring, Replace 2-292
Lubrication 2-289
Shock Absorber, Replace 2-291
Suspension, Description of 2-289
Tire Wear Chart 2-648
Toe-In, Adjust 2-291
Wheel Alignment, Adjust 2-290
Wheel Bearings, Adjust 2-291
Wheel Bearings, Replace 2-291

TRANSMISSIONS

Three Speed Manual:
  Replace 2-283
  Repairs 1-261
  Linkage, Adjust 2-284
Four Speed Manual:
  Replace 2-283
  Repairs 1-298
  Linkage, Adjust 2-284
Automatic Units 1-321
  1969 Linkage 2-284

TUNE UP

Service 1-21
Specifications 2-250

WINDSHIELD WIPER

Wiper Motor, Replace 2-266
Wiper Linkage, Replace 2-267
Wiper Switch, Replace 2-266
Wiper Troubles 1-20

ENGINE & SERIAL NUMBER LOCATION

Plate On Left Front Door Pillar

ENGINE IDENTIFICATION

★Serial number on Vehicle Warranty Plate.
Engine code for 1963-69 is the last letter in the serial number.

Year	Engine	Engine Code★
1963	6-223	V
	V8-260	F
	V8-289①	C
	V8-289②	K
	V8-352①	X
	V8-390①	Y
	V8-390②	Z
	V8-406②	B
	V8-406④	G
	V8-427③	R
	V8-427②	Q
1964	6-223	V
	V8-289①	C
	V8-289②	K
	V8-352②	X
1964	V8-390②	Z
	V8-427③	R
	V8-427②	Q
1965	6-240	V
	V8-289	C
	V8-352	X
	V8-390⑥	H
	V8-390⑦	P
	V8-390①	Y
	V8-399②	Z
	V8-427③	R
1966–67	6-240	B
	6-240	V
	V8-289	C
1966–67	V8-352	X
	V8-390①	H
	V8-390①	Y
	V8-390②	Z
	V8-410	M
	V8-427③	R
	V8-427②	W
	V8-428	P
	V8-428	Q
1968	6-240	V
	V8-302①	F
	V8-390①	Y
	V8-390①	H
	V8-390②	Z
	V8-428②	Q
	V8-427③	R
1969	6-240	V
	V8-302①	F
	V8-390①	Y
	V8-390①⑤	X
	V8-429①	K
	V8-429②	N

①—Two barrel carburetor.
②—Four barrel carburetor.
③—Two 4 barrel carburetors.
④—Three carburetors.
⑤—Premium fuel.
⑥—Two barrel special.
⑦—Four barrel special.

1963 Ford

1963 Mercury

1964 Ford

1964 Mercury

1965 Ford

1965 Mercury

1966 Ford

1966 Mercury

1967 Ford

1967 Mercury

1968 Ford Custom, Galaxie

1968 Ford "LTD", XL, Squire

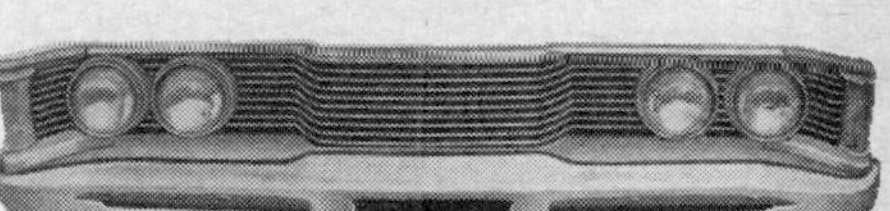
1968 Mercury

1969 Ford Custom, Galaxie

1969 Ford "LTD", XL, Squire

1969 Mercury Monterey

1969 Mercury Marauder, Marquis

FORD & MERCURY — Full Size Models

GENERAL ENGINE SPECIFICATIONS

Year	Engine	Carburetor	Bore and Stroke	Piston Displacement, Cubic Inches	Compression Ratio	Maximum Brake H.P. @ R.P.M.	Maximum Torque Lbs. Ft. @ R.P.M.	Normal Oil Pressure Pounds
FORD								
1963	138 Horsepower.............. 6-223	1 Barrel	3.6250 x 3.600	223	8.40	138 @ 4200	203 @ 2200	35–55
	164 Horsepower.............. V8-260	2 Barrel	3.8000 x 2.87	260	8.70	164 @ 4400	258 @ 2200	35–55
	195 Horsepower.............. V8-289	2 Barrel	4.0000 x 2.87	289	8.70	195 @ 4400	282 @ 2400	50–60
	220 Horsepower.............. V8-352	2 Barrel	4.0000 x 3.500	352	8.90	220 @ 4300	336 @ 2600	35–55
	300 Horsepower.............. V8-390	4 Barrel	4.0468 x 3.781	390	9.6	300 @ 4600	427 @ 2800	35–55
	330 Horsepower.............. V8-390	4 Barrel	4.0468 x 3.781	390	10.50	330 @ 5000	427 @ 3200	35–55
	385 Horsepower.............. V8-406	4 Barrel	4.1300 x 3.78	406	11.40	385 @ 5800	444 @ 3400	40–55
	405 Horsepower.............. V8-406	3 Two Bar.	4.1300 x 3.78	406	12.10	405 @ 5800	448 @ 3500	40–55
	410 Horsepower.............. V8-427	4 Barrel	4.2328 x 3.784	427	11.60	410 @ 5600	476 @ 3400	40–55
	425 Horsepower.............. V8-427	Two 4 Bar.	4.2328 x 3.784	427	12.00	425 @ 6000	480 @ 3700	40–55
1964	138 Horsepower.............. 6-223	1 Barrel	3.6250 x 3.600	223	8.50	138 @ 4200	203 @ 2200	52–62
	195 Horsepower.............. V8-289	2 Barrel	4.0000 x 2.87	289	9.00	195 @ 4400	282 @ 2400	50–60
	250 Horsepower.............. V8-352	2 Barrel	4.0000 x 3.50	352	9.30	250 @ 4400	352 @ 2600	52–62
	300 Horsepower.............. V8-390	4 Barrel	4.0468 x 3.781	390	10.10	300 @ 4600	427 @ 2800	52–62
	410 Horsepower.............. V8-427	4 Barrel	4.2328 x 3.784	427	11.60	410 @ 5600	476 @ 3400	40–55
	425 Horsepower.............. V8-427	Two 4 Bar.	4.2328 x 3.784	427	12.00	425 @ 6000	480 @ 3700	40–55
1965	150 Horsepower.............. 6-240	1 Barrel	4.0000 x 3.18	240	9.20	150 @ 4000	234 @ 2200	35–60
	200 Horsepower.............. V8-289	2 Barrel	4.0000 x 2.87	289	9.30	200 @ 4400	282 @ 2400	35–55
	250 Horsepower.............. V8-352	4 Barrel	4.0000 x 3.50	352	9.30	250 @ 4400	352 @ 2800	35–55
	300 Horsepower.............. V8-390	4 Barrel	4.0468 x 3.781	390	10.10	300 @ 4600	427 @ 2800	35–55
	330 Horsepower.............. V8-390	4 Barrel	4.0468 x 3.781	390	10.10	330 @ 5000	427 @ 3200	45–70
	425 Horsepower.............. V8-427	Two 4 Bar.	4.2328 x 3.784	427	11.10	425 @ 6000	480 @ 3700	40–55
1966	155 Horsepower.............. 6-240	1 Barrel	4.00 x 3.18	240	9.2	155 @ 4200	239 @ 2200	35–60
	200 Horsepower.............. V8-289	2 Barrel	4.00 x 2.87	289	9.3	200 @ 4400	282 @ 2400	35–55
	250 Horsepower.............. V8-352	4 Barrel	4.00 x 3.50	352	9.3	250 @ 4400	352 @ 2800	35–55
	265 Horsepower.............. V8-390	2 Barrel	4.05 x 3.78	390	9.5	265 @ 4400	401 @ 2600	35–55
	315 Horsepower.............. V8-390	4 Barrel	4.05 x 3.78	390	10.5	315 @ 4600	427 @ 2800	35–55
	345 Horsepower.............. V8-428	4 Barrel	4.13 x 3.98	428	10.5	345 @ 4600	462 @ 2800	35–55
	425 Horsepower.............. V8-427	Two 4 Bar.	4.23 x 3.78	427	11.1	425 @ 6000	480 @ 3700	40–55
1967	155 Horsepower.............. 6-240	1 Barrel	4.00 x 3.18	240	9.2	155 @ 4200	239 @ 2200	35–60
	200 Horsepower.............. V8-289	2 Barrel	4.00 x 2.87	289	9.3	200 @ 4400	282 @ 2400	35–55
	265 H.P., Std. Tr.............. V8-390	2 Barrel	4.05 x 3.78	390	9.5	265 @ 4400	401 @ 2600	35–55
	275 H.P., Auto. Tr.............. V8-390	2 Barrel	4.05 x 3.78	390	9.5	275 @ 4400	405 @ 2600	35–55
	315 Horsepower.............. V8-390	4 Barrel	4.05 x 3.78	390	10.5	315 @ 4600	427 @ 2800	35–55
	345 Horsepower.............. V8-428	4 Barrel	4.13 x 3.98	428	10.5	345 @ 4600	462 @ 2800	35–55
	360 Horsepower.............. V8-428	4 Barrel	4.13 x 3.98	428	10.5	360 @ 5400	459 @ 3200	35–55
	425 Horsepower.............. V8-427	Two 4 Bar.	4.23 x 3.78	427	11.1	425 @ 6000	480 @ 3700	40–55
1968	150 Horsepower.............. 6-240	1 Barrel	4.00 x 3.18	240	9.2	150 @ 4000	234 @ 2200	35–60
	210 Horsepower.............. V8-302	2 Barrel	4.00 x 3.00	302	9.5	210 @ 4400	295 @ 2400	35–55
	270 Horsepower.............. V8-390	2 Barrel	4.05 x 3.78	390	9.5	270 @ 4400	403 @ 2600	35–55
	315 Horsepower.............. V8-390	4 Barrel	4.05 x 3.78	390	10.5	315 @ 4600	427 @ 2800	35–55
	345 Horsepower.............. V8-428	4 Barrel	4.13 x 3.98	428	10.5	345 @ 4600	462 @ 2800	35–55
	390 Horsepower.............. V8-427	4 Barrel	4.23 x 3.78	427	10.9	390 @ 5600	460 @ 3200	40–55
1969	150 Horsepower.............. 6-240	1 Barrel	4.00 x 3.18	240	9.2	150 @ 4000	234 @ 2200	35–60
	210 Horsepower.............. V8-302	2 Barrel	4.00 x 3.00	302	9.5	210 @ 4400	295 @ 2400	35–60
	270 Horsepower.............. V8-390	2 Barrel	4.05 x 3.78	390	9.5	270 @ 4400	390 @ 2600	35–60
	320 Horsepower.............. V8-429	2 Barrel	4.36 x 3.59	429	10.5	320 @ 4400	460 @ 2200	35–60
	360 Horsepower.............. V8-429	4 Barrel	4.36 x 3.59	429	11.0	360 @ 4600	476 @ 2800	35–60
MERCURY								
1963	300 Horsepower.............. V8-390	2 Barrel	4.0500 x 3.784	390	10.50	300 @ 4600	427 @ 2800	35–55
	330 Horsepower.............. V8-390	4 Barrel	4.0500 x 3.784	390	10.50	330 @ 5000	427 @ 2800	45–70
	385 Horsepower.............. V8-406	4 Barrel	4.1300 x 3.784	406	11.40	385 @ 5800	444 @ 3400	40–55
	405 Horsepower.............. V8-406	3 Two Bar.	4.1300 x 3.784	406	12.10	405 @ 5800	448 @ 3500	40–55

Continued

GENERAL ENGINE SPECIFICATIONS—Continued

Year	Engine	Carburetor	Bore and Stroke	Piston Displacement, Cubic Inches	Compression Ratio	Maximum Brake H.P. @ R.P.M.	Maximum Torque Lbs. Ft. @ R.P.M.	Normal Oil Pressure Pounds
MERCURY—Continued								
1963	410 Horsepower............V8-427	4 Barrel	4.2328 x 3.784	427	11.60	410 @ 5600	476 @ 3400	40–55
	425 Horsepower............V8-427	Two 4 Bar.	4.2328 x 3.784	427	12.00	425 @ 5600	480 @ 3700	40–55
1964–65	250 Horsepower............V8-390	2 Barrel	4.0468 x 3.781	390	9.40	250 @ 4400	378 @ 2400	52–62
	266 Horsepower............V8-390	2 Barrel	4.0468 x 3.781	390	9.40	266 @ 4400	378 @ 2400	52–62
	300 Horsepower............V8-390	4 Barrel	4.0468 x 3.781	390	10.10	300 @ 4600	427 @ 2800	52–62
	410 Horsepower (1964)........V8-427	4 Barrel	4.2328 x 3.784	427	11.60	410 @ 5600	476 @ 3400	40–55
	425 Horsepower............V8-427	Two 4 Bar.	4.2328 x 3.784	427	12.00	425 @ 6000	480 @ 3700	40–55
1966	265 H.P. Std. Tr............V8-390	2 Barrel	4.05 x 3.7800	390	9.5	265 @ 4400	397 @ 2600	35–55
	275 H.P. Auto. Tr............V8-390	2 Barrel	4.05 x 3.7800	390	10.5	275 @ 4400	405 @ 2600	35–55
	330 Horsepower............V8-410	4 Barrel	4.05 x 3.9800	410	10.5	330 @ 4600	444 @ 2800	35–55
	345 Horsepower............V8-428	4 Barrel	4.13 x 3.9800	428	10.5	345 @ 4600	462 @ 2800	35–55
	425 Horsepower............V8-427	Two 4 Bar.	4.23 x 3.7800	427	11.1	425 @ 6000	480 @ 3700	40–55
1967	270 Horsepower............V8-390	2 Barrel	4.05 x 3.78	390	9.5	270 @ 4400	403 @ 2600	35–55
	330 Horsepower............V8-410	4 Barrel	4.05 x 3.98	410	10.5	330 @ 4600	444 @ 2800	35–55
	345 Horsepower............V8-428	4 Barrel	4.13 x 3.98	428	10.5	345 @ 4600	462 @ 2800	35–55
1968	265 Horsepower............V8-390	2 Barrel	4.05 x 3.78	390	9.5	265 @ 4400	390 @ 2600	35–55
	280 Horsepower............V8-390	2 Barrel	4.05 x 3.78	390	10.5	280 @ 4400	403 @ 2600	35–55
	315 Horsepower............V8-390	4 Barrel	4.05 x 3.78	390	10.5	315 @ 4600	427 @ 2800	35–55
	340 Horsepower............V8-428	4 Barrel	4.13 x 3.98	428	10.5	340 @ 4600	462 @ 2800	35–55
1969	270 Horsepower............V8-390	2 Barrel	4.05 x 3.78	390	9.5	270 @ 4400	390 @ 2600	35–60
	280 Horsepower............V8-390	2 Barrel	4.05 x 3.78	390	10.5	280 @ 4400	403 @ 2600	35–60
	320 Horsepower............V8-429	2 Barrel	4.36 x 3.59	429	10.5	320 @ 4400	460 @ 2200	35–60
	360 Horsepower............V8-429	4 Barrel	4.36 x 3.59	429	11.0	360 @ 4600	476 @ 2800	35–60

STARTING MOTOR SPECIFICATIONS

Year	Model	Starter Number	Rotation	Brush Spring Tension Ounces	No Load Test			Torque Test		
					Amperes	Volts	R.P.M.	Amperes	Volts	Torque Ft. Lbs.
1963–64	All	C30F-11001A	C	48–56	80–110	12	5200	580	5.0	14.8
1965	6-240, V8-289 Std. Tr.	C5TF-11001A	C	40	70	12	9500	670	6.0	15.5
	6-240, V8-289 At. Tr.	C40F-11001A	C	40	70	12	9500	670	6.0	15.5
	V8-352, 390, 427 St. Tr.	C5AF-11001A	C	40	70	12	9500	670	6.0	15.5
	V8-352, 390 Auto. Tr.	C40F-11001A	C	40	110	12	5200	580	5.0	14.8
1966–67	4″ Diameter	...	C	40	70	12	...	460	5.0	9.0
	4½″ Diameter	...	C	40	70	12	...	670	5.0	15.5
1968	6-240, 8-302	C7AF-11001-B	C	40	70	12	9500	670	5.0	15.5
	6-240, 8-302	C7AF-11001-D	C	40	70	12	9500	670	5.0	15.5
	6-240, 8-302	C7AF-11001-F	C	40	70	12	9500	670	5.0	15.5
	8-390, 427, 428	C7AF-11001-C	C	40	70	12	9500	670	5.0	15.5
	8-390, 427, 428	C7AF-11001-E	C	40	70	12	11000	700	4.0	15.5
1969	6-240, 8-302	C5TZ-11002-A	C	40	70	12	9500	670	5.0	15.5
	6-240, 8-302	C2OZ-11002-A	C	40	70	12	9500	670	5.0	15.5
	8-390	C3OZ-11002-C	C	40	70	12	9500	670	5.0	15.5
	8-429	C8VY-11002-C	C	40	70	12	10000	700	5.0	15.5

TUNE UP SPECIFICATIONS

OLD CAR SPECIFICATIONS: For 1946-62 Tune Up Specifications see back of book.

★ When using a timing light, disconnect vacuum hose or tube at distributor and plug opening in tube or hose so idle speed will not be affected.

Year	Engine	Spark Plug		Distributor		Firing Order	Ignition Timing★		Hot Idle Speed		Comp. Press. Lbs. (3)	Fuel Pump Press. Lbs.
		Type (5)	Gap Inch	Point Gap Inch	Dwell Angle Deg.		BTDC (1)	Mark	Std. Trans.	Auto. Trans. (2)		
1963	6-223 Std. Trans.	BTF-6	.034	.025	37–42	Fig. G	4°	Fig. E	500(10)	. . .	150	3½–5½
	6-223 Auto. Trans.	BTF-6	.034	.025	37–42	Fig. G	10°	Fig. E	. . .	485D(10)	150	3½–5½
	V8-260 Std. Trans.	BF-42	.034	.017	26–31	Fig. N	6°	Fig. L	500(10)	. . .	150	4½–5½
	V8-260 Auto. Trans.	BF-42	.034	.017	26–31	Fig. N	10°	Fig. L	. . .	485D(10)	150	4½–5½
	V8-289 Std. Trans.	BF-42	.034	.017	26–31	Fig. N	6°	Fig. A	500(10)	. . .	150	4½–5½
	V8-289 Auto. Trans.	BF-42	.034	.017	26–31	Fig. N	10°	Fig. A	. . .	485D(10)	150	4½–5½
	V8-352 Std. Trans.	BF-42	.034	.017	26–31	Fig. N	5°	Fig. A	500(10)	. . .	180	5–6
	V8-352 Auto. Trans.	BF-42	.034	.017	26–31	Fig. N	8°	Fig. A	. . .	485D(10)	180	5–6
	V8-390 Std. Trans.(6)	BF-42	.034	.017	26–31	Fig. N	5°	Fig. A	500(10)	. . .	180	5–6
	V8-390 Auto. Trans.(6)	BF-42	.034	.017	26–31	Fig. N	8°	Fig. A	. . .	485D(10)	180	5–6
	V8-390(7)	BF-42	.034	.017	26–31	Fig. N	6°	Fig. A	500(10)	485D(10)	180	5–6
	V8-390, 330 H.P.	BF-32	.034	.017	26–31	Fig. N	10°	Fig. B	500(10)	485D(10)	180	4½–5½
	V8-406, 427	BF-32	.035	.017	26–31	Fig. N	5°	Fig. A	700(10)	. . .	180	4–6
	V8-406, 427 Two Carbs.	BF-32	.034	.017	26–31	Fig. N	8°	Fig. B	700(10)	. . .	180	4½–5½
1964	6-223 Std. Trans.	BTF-6	.034	.025	37–42	Fig. G	4°	Fig. E	500(10)	. . .	150	3½–5½
	6-223 Auto. Trans.	BTF-6	.034	.025	37–42	Fig. G	10°	Fig. E	. . .	485D(10)	150	3½–5½
	V8-289 Std. Trans.	BF-42	.034	.017	26–31	Fig. N	6°	Fig. K	500(10)	. . .	150	5–6
	V8-289 Auto. Trans.	BF-42	.034	.017	26–31	Fig. N	10°	Fig. K	. . .	485D(10)	150	5–6
	V8-352 Std. Trans.	BF-42	.034	.017	26–31	Fig. N	6°	Fig. A	500(10)	. . .	180	5–6
	V8-352 Auto. Trans.	BF-42	.034	.017	26–31	Fig. N	10°	Fig. A	. . .	485D(10)	180	5–6
	V8-390 Std. Trans.	BF-42	.034	.017	26–31	Fig. N	4°	Fig. A, C	500(10)	. . .	180	5–6
	V8-390 Auto. Trans.	BF-42	.034	.017	26–31	Fig. N	6°	Fig. A, C	. . .	485D(10)	180	5–6
	V8-427	BF-32	.034	.017	26–31	Fig. N	8°	Fig. B	700(10)	. . .	180	4½–5½
1965	6-240 Std. Trans.	BTF-6	.034	.025	37–42	Fig. H	6°	Fig. J	525(10)	. . .	150–200	4–6
	6-240 Auto. Trans.	BTF-6	.034	.025	37–42	Fig. H	8°	Fig. J	. . .	525(10)	150–200	4–6
	V8-289	BF-42	.034	.017	26–31	Fig. N	6°	Fig. K	600(10)	500(10)	130–170	4–6
	V8-352	BF-42	.034	.017	26–31	Fig. N	6°	Fig. C	600(10)	500(10)	160–200	4½–6½
	V8-390(6) Std. Trans.	BF-42	.034	.017	26–31	Fig. N	4°	Fig. C	600(10)	. . .	170–210	4½–6½
	V8-390(6) Auto. Trans.	BF-42	.034	.017	26–31	Fig. N	6°(9)	Fig. C	. . .	500(9)	170–210	4½–6½
	V8-390(7) Std. Trans.	BF-42	.034	.017	26–31	Fig. N	6°	Fig. C	600(10)	. . .	180	4½–6½
	V8-390(7) Auto. Trans.	BF-42	.034	.017	26–31	Fig. N	6°(9)	Fig. C	. . .	500D(9)	180	4½–6½
	V8-427	BF-32	.030	.020	(8)	Fig. N	8°	Fig. C	750(10)	. . .	160–200	4½–6½
1966	6-240(13) Auto. Tr.	BF-42	.034	.025	37–42	Fig. H	12°	Fig. J	. . .	500D(12)	175	4–6
	6-240(13) Std. Tr.	BF-42	.034	.025	37–42	Fig. H	6°	Fig. J	525(12)	. . .	175	4–6
	6-240(11) Auto. Tr.	BF-42	.034	.025	37–42	Fig. H	4°	Fig. J	. . .	500D(12)	175	4–6
	6-240(11) Std. Tr.	BF-42	.034	.025	37–42	Fig. H	TDC	Fig. J	600(12)	. . .	175	4–6
	V8-289(13)	BF-42	.034	.017	26–31	Fig. N	6°	Fig. K	575(12)	475D(12)	150	4–6
	V8-289(11)	BF-42	.034	.017	26–31	Fig. N	TDC	Fig. K	625(12)	550D(12)	150	4–6
	V8-352, 390, 410, 428(13)	BF-42	.034	.017	26–31	Fig. N	10°(9)	Fig. C	575(12)	475D(12)	180	4½–6½
	V8-352, 390, 410, 428(11)	BF-42	.034	.017	26–31	Fig. N	6°(9)	Fig. C	625(12)	550D(12)	180	4½–6½
	V8-427	BF-32	.030	.020	22–24	Fig. N	10°	Fig. C	700(12)	. . .	190	4½–6½
1967	6-240(13) Auto. Tr.	BF-42	.034	.025	37–42	Fig. H	10°	Fig. J	. . .	500D(12)	175	4–6
	6-240(13) Std. Tr.	BF-42	.034	.025	37–42	Fig. H	6°	Fig. J	525(12)	. . .	175	4–6
	6-240(11) Auto. Tr.	BF-42	.034	.025	37–42	Fig. H	4°	Fig. J	. . .	500D(12)	175	4–6
	6-240(11) Std. Tr.	BF-42	.034	.025	37–42	Fig. H	TDC	Fig. J	600(12)	. . .	175	4–6
	V8-289(13)	BF-42	.034	.017	26–31	Fig. N	6°	Fig. K	575(12)	475D(12)	150	4–6
	V8-289(11)	BF-42	.034	.017	26–31	Fig. N	TDC	Fig. K	625(12)	550D(12)	150	4–6
	V8-390, 410, 428(13)	BF-32	.034	.017	26–31	Fig. N	10°(9)	Fig. C	575(12)	475D(12)	180	4½–6½
	V8-390, 410, 428(11)	BF-32	.034	.017	26–31	Fig. N	6°(9)	Fig. C	625(12)	550D(12)	180	4½–6½
	V8-427	BF-32	.034	.020	22–24	Fig. N	8°	Fig. C	750(12)	. . .	180	4½–6½
1968	6-240	BF-42	.034	.027	35–40	Fig. H	6°	Fig. D	600(12)	500D(4)	175	4–6
	V8-302(13)	BF-42	.034	.021	24–29	Fig. N	6°	Fig. F	625(12)	550D(4)	150	4–6

Continued

TUNE UP SPECIFICATIONS—Continued

OLD CAR SPECIFICATIONS: For 1946-62 Tune Up Specifications see back of book.

★When using a timing light, disconnect vacuum hose or tube at distributor and plug opening in tube or hose so idle speed will not be affected.

Year	Engine	Spark Plug		Distributor		Firing Order	Ignition Timing★		Hot Idle Speed		Comp. Press. Lbs. ③	Fuel Pump Press. Lbs.
		Type ⑤	Gap Inch	Point Gap Inch	Dwell Angle Deg.		BTDC ①	Mark	Std. Trans.	Auto. Trans. ②		
1968	V8-390⑬ Std. Tr.	BF-42	.034	.021	24–29	Fig. N	6°	Fig. I	625⑫	...	180	4½–6½
	V8-390⑦ Auto. Tr.	BF-42	.034	.017	26–31	Fig. N	6°	Fig. I	...	550D⑫	180	4½–6½
	V8-428⑬ Std. Tr.	BF-42	.034	.021	24–29	Fig. N	6°	Fig. I	625⑫	...	180	4½–6½
	V8-428⑦ Auto. Tr.	BF-42	.034	.017	26–31	Fig. N	6°	Fig. I	...	550D⑫	180	4½–6½
	V8-427⑬	BF-32	.034	.017	26–31	Fig. N	6°	Fig. I	...	600D⑫	180	4½–6½
1969	6-240	BF-42	.034	.027	35–40	Fig. H	6°	Fig. D	⑭	500D	175	5
	V8-302 Std. Tr.	BF-42	.030	.021	24–29	Fig. N	6°	Fig. F	650	...	150	5
	V8-302 Auto. Tr.	BF-42	.030	.017	26–31	Fig. N	6°	Fig. F	...	550D	150	5
	V8-390	BF-42	.034	.017	26–31	Fig. N	6°	Fig. I	650	550D	180	5
	V8-390⑮	BF-42	.034	.021	24–29	Fig. N	6°	Fig. I	...	550D	180	5
	V8-429	BF-42	.034	.017	26–31	Fig. N	6°	Fig. I	...	550D	180	5

①—BTDC: Before top dead center.
②—D: Drive. N: Neutral
③—Plus or minus 20 lbs.
④—With headlights on and A/C off.
⑤—Autolite.
⑥—Four barrel carburetor.
⑦—With IMCO system.
⑧—Conventional ignition 30-33°, transistor ignition 22-24°.
⑨—Whenever idle speed or ignition timing is adjusted, vacuum line to brake release mechanism (if equipped) must be disconnected and vacuum hole plugged to prevent parking brake from releasing when selector lever is moved to Drive.
⑩—If air conditioned, turn A/C switch to "Full On" position.
⑪—With Thermactor Exhaust Emission Control System.
⑫—With Headlights and A/C On.
⑬—Without Thermactor Exhaust Emission Control.
⑭—Use 775 with throttle modulator energized and 500 when de-energized.
⑮—Premium fuel.

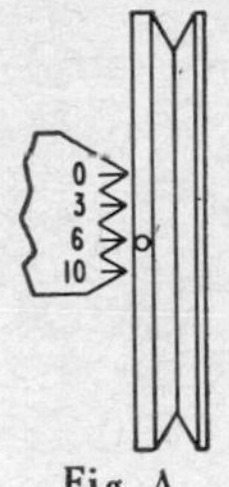

Fig. A

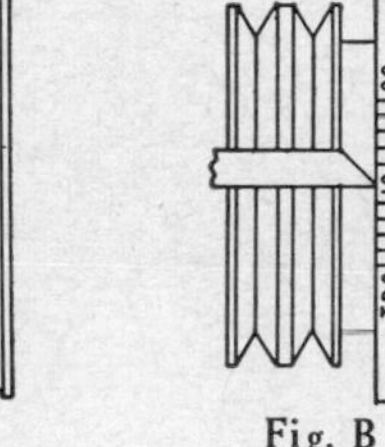

Fig. B

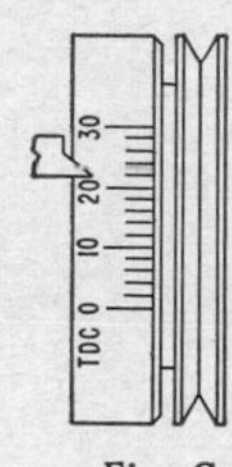

Fig. C

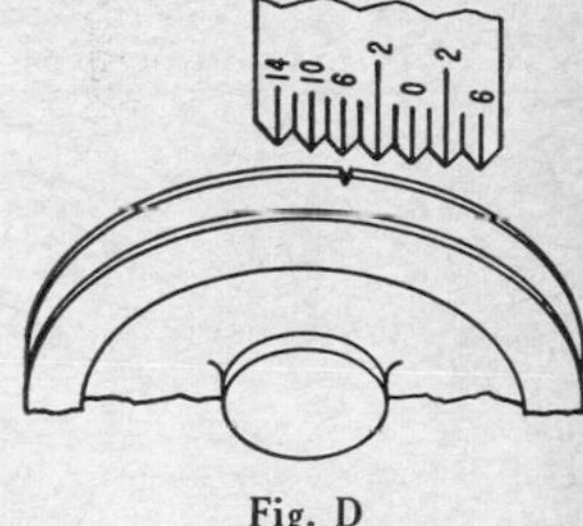
Fig. D

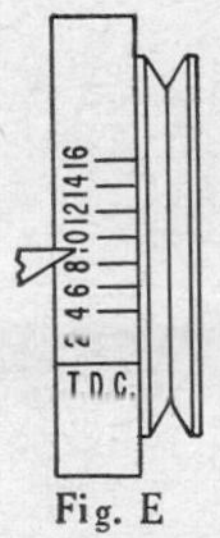

Fig. E

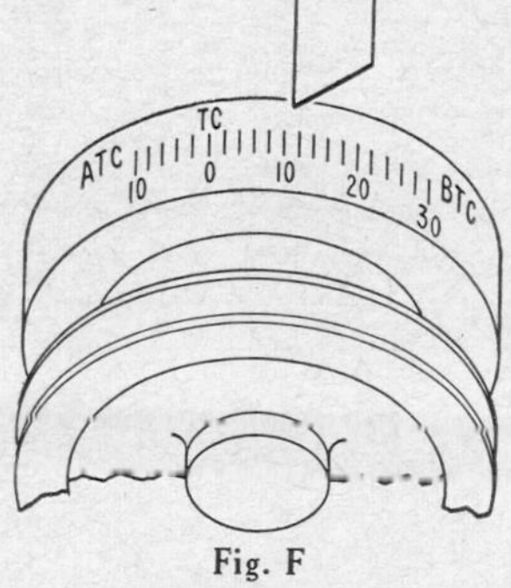

Fig. F

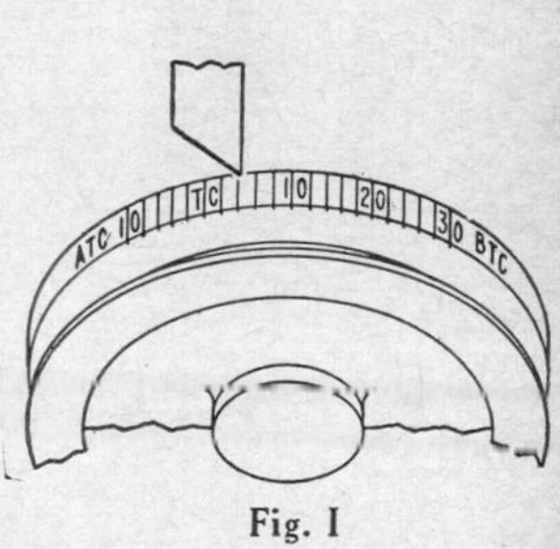

Fig. I

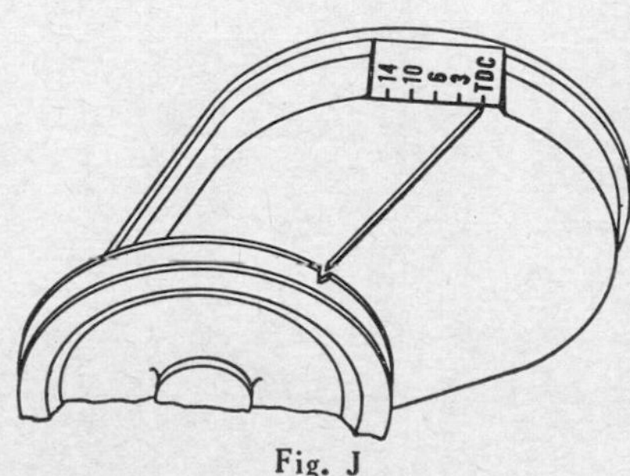

Fig. J

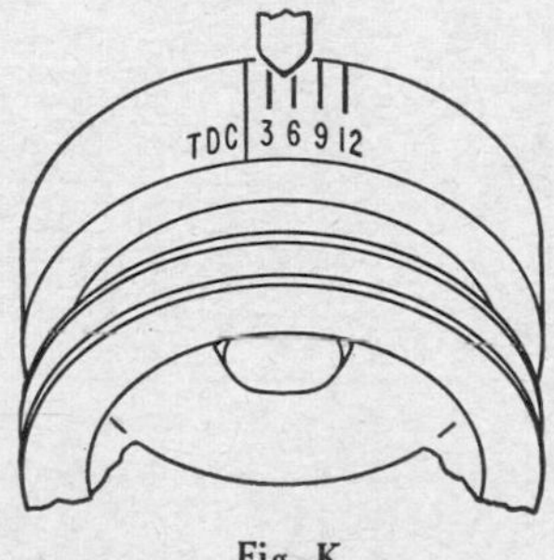

Fig. K

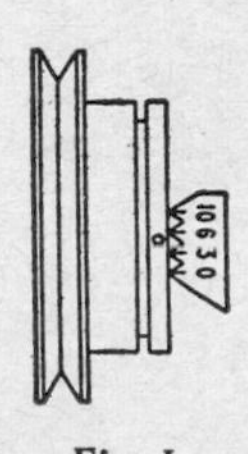
Fig. L

Continued

TUNE UP SPECIFICATIONS—Continued

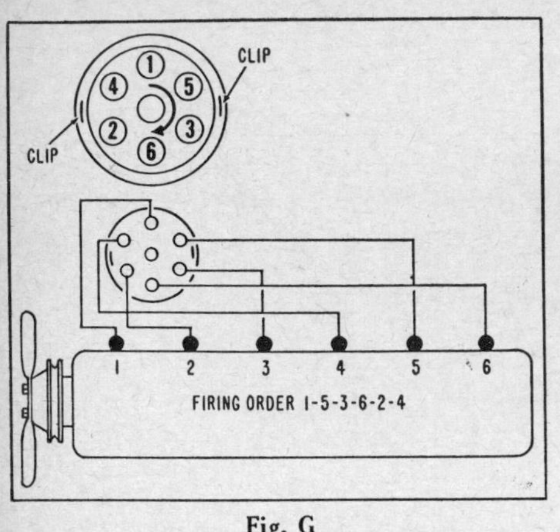

Fig. G

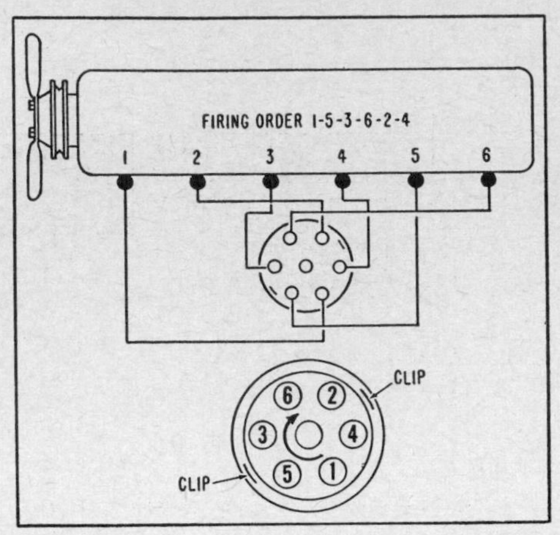

Fig. H

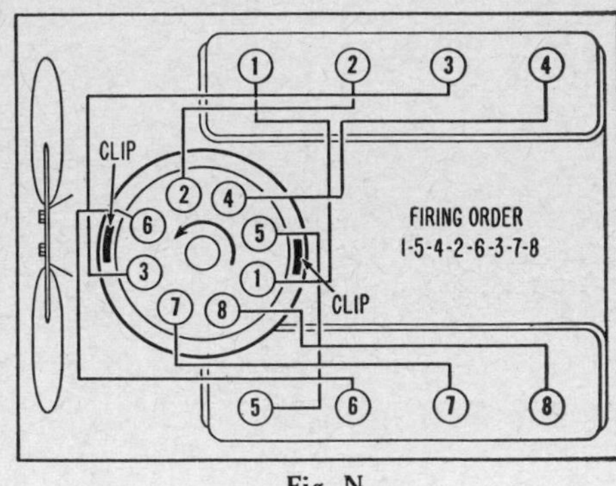

Fig. N

ALTERNATOR & REGULATOR SPECIFICATIONS

Year	Make or Model	Current Rating		Field Current @ 75°F.		Voltage Regulator				Field Relay	
		Amperes	Volts	Amperes	Volts	Make	Voltage @ 75°F.	Contact Gap	Armature Air Gap	Armature Air Gap	Closing Voltage @ 75°F.
1963	Ford	30	15	2.3–2.5	12	Ford	14.1–14.9	.010–.015	.045–.052	.022–.030	3–4
	Ford	40	15	2.9–3.1	12	Ford	14.1–14.9	.010–.015	.045–.052	.022–.030	3–4
1964	Ford	30	15	2.4–2.6	12	Ford	14.1–14.9	.017–.022	.049–.056	.015–.025	2½–4
	Ford	40	15	2.4–2.6	12	Ford	14.1–14.9	.017–.022	.049–.056	.015–.025	2½–4
	Ford	42	15	2.4–2.6	12	Ford	14.1–14.9	.017–.022	.049–.056	.015–.025	2½–4
1965	Ford	42	15	2.8–3.3	12	Ford	14.1–14.9	.017–.022	.049–.056	.015–.022	2½–4
	Ford	30	15	2.8–3.3	12	Ford	14.1–14.9	.017–.022	.049–.056	.015–.022	2½–4
1966–67	Purple①	38	15	2.5	12	Autolite	14.1–14.9	.017–.022	.049–.056	.010–.018	2½–4
	Orange①	42	15	2.9	12	Autolite	14.1–14.9	.017–.022	.049–.056	.010–.018	2½–4
	Black①	45	15	2.9	12	Autolite	14.1–14.9	.017–.022	.049–.056	.010–.018	2½–4
	Red①	55	15	2.9	12	Autolite	14.1–14.9	.017–.022	.049–.046	.010–.018	2½–4
	Green①	60	15	4.6	12	Autolite	14.1–14.9	.017–.022	.049–.056	.010–.018	2½–4
1968	C6AF-10300-A	42	15	2.8–3.3	12	Autolite	13.5–15.3	②	②	②	2.3–4.2
	C6AF-10300-C	42	15	2.8–3.3	12	Autolite	13.5–15.3	②	②	②	2.3–4.2
	C6AF-10300-G	55	15	2.8–3.3	12	Autolite	13.5–15.3	②	②	②	2.3–4.2
	C6TF-10300-E	55	15	2.8–3.3	12	Autolite	13.5–15.3	②	②	②	2.3–4.2
	C6TF-10300-F	55	15	2.8–3.3	12	Autolite	13.5–15.3	②	②	②	2.3–4.2
	C6AF-10300-F	55	15	2.8–3.3	12	Autolite	13.5–15.3	②	②	②	2.3–4.2
	C6AF-10300-D	42	15	2.8–3.3	12	Autolite	13.5–15.3	②	②	②	2.3–4.2
	C6AF-10300-B	42	15	2.8–3.3	12	Autolite	13.5–15.3	②	②	②	2.3–4.2
	C7AF-10300-A	65	15	2.9	12	Autolite	13.5–15.3	②	②	②	2.3–4.2
1969	C6AF-10300-A	55	15	2.8–3.3	12	Autolite	13.5–15.3	②	②	②	2.3–4.2
	C6AF-10300-B	42	15	2.8–3.3	12	Autolite	13.5–15.3	②	②	②	2.3–4.2
	C6AF-10300-F	55	15	2.8–3.3	12	Autolite	13.5–15.3	②	②	②	2.3–4.2
	C6AF-10300-G	55	15	2.8–3.3	12	Autolite	13.5–15.3	②	②	②	2.3–4.2
	C7AF-10300-A	65	15	2.9	12	L-N	14.3–15.1	.045–.052	.010–.015	.015	3.0–4.0
	C9AF-10300-A	42	15	2.8–3.3	12	Autolite	13.5–15.3	②	②	②	2.3–4.2

①—Color stamped. Autolite. ②—Not adjustable.

DISTRIBUTOR SPECIFICATIONS

★If advance is checked on vehicle, double the R.P.M. and degrees advance to get crankshaft figures.

Year	Model	Basic Distributor Part No.(1) 12127	Rotation (2)	Breaker Gap	Cam Angle	Breaker Arm Spring Tension	Centrifugal Advance Degrees @ R.P.M. of Distributor★		Vacuum Advance	
							Advance Starts	Full Advance	Inches of Vacuum To Start Plunger	Max. Adv. Dist. Deg. @ Vacuum
1963	6-223 Std. Trans.	C3AF-G	C	.025	37–42	17–20	None	None	.30	13 @ 10
	6-223 Auto Trans.	C3AF-H	C	.025	37–42	17–20	None	None	.45	10 @ 8½
	V8-260 Std Trans.	C3OF-B	CC	.017	26–31	17–20	2 @ 500	12 @ 2000	8	11 @ 20
	V8-260 Auto. Trans.	C3AF-U	CC	.017	26–31	17–20	1 @ 500	9 @ 2000	10	10 @ 20
	V8-352 Std. Trans.	COAF-E	CC	.017	26–31	17–20	2 @ 775	13 @ 2000	5	12 @ 17
	V8-352 Auto. Trans.	COAF-D	CC	.017	26–31	17–20	1 @ 500	13 @ 2000	5	12 @ 17
	V8-352, 390	C2AF-A	CC	.017	26–31	17–20	1 @ 400	12 @ 2000	6	8 @ 15
	V8-390	C3MF-A	CC	.017	26–31	17–20	2 @ 500	15 @ 2000	7	10 @ 17
	V8-390 Hi. Perf.	C2SF-A	CC	.020	26–31	27–32	1 @ 400	16 @ 2000	5	8 @ 15
	V8-406	COAF-K	CC	.017	26–31	27–32	3 @ 650	13 @ 2000	None	None
1964	6-223 Std. Trans	C4AF-G	C	.025	37–42	17–20	None	None	.30	13 @ 4.30
	6-223 Auto. Trans.	C4AF-H	C	.025	37–42	17–20	None	None	.30	13 @ 4.30
	V8-289 Std. Trans.	C4GF-A	CC	.017	26–31	17–20	2 @ 500	14 @ 2000	8	11 @ 20
	V8-289 Auto. Trans.	C4GF-B	CC	.017	26–31	17–20	1 @ 600	11 @ 2000	8	12 @ 20
	V8-352 Std. Trans.	C4AF-L	CC	.017	26–31	17–20	2 @ 600	11 @ 2000	8	10 @ 20
	V8-352 Auto. Trans.	C4AF-M	CC	.017	26–31	17–20	1 @ 400	9 @ 2000	8	10 @ 20
	V8-390 Two Bar. Carb.	C3MF-A	CC	.017	26–31	17–20	2 @ 500	14 @ 2000	7	10 @ 17
	V8-390 Four Bar. Carb.	C3AF-AH	CC	.017	26–31	17–20	1 @ 400	13 @ 2000	8	7 @ 20
	V8-427	C3AF-AF	CC	.020	(3)	(4)	1 @ 500	15 @ 2000	None	None
1965	6-240 Std. Trans.	C5AF-AD	C	.025	37–42	17–21	None	None	.70	13 @ 4.90
	6-240 Auto. Trans.	C5AF-AE	C	.025	37–42	17–21	None	None	.34	10 @ 4.80
	V8-289 Std. Trans.	C5AF-M	CC	.017	26–31	17–21	2 @ 650	13 @ 2000	8	9 @ 14
	V8-289 Auto. Trans.	C5AF-N	CC	.017	26–31	17–21	2 @ 450	12 @ 2000	8	11 @ 14
	V8-352 Std. Trans.	C5AF-A	CC	.017	26–31	17–21	3 @ 650	11 @ 2000	8	10 @ 18
	V8-352 Auto. Trans.	C5AF-B	CC	.017	26–31	17–21	2 @ 450	12 @ 2000	8	9 @ 14
	V8-390 Two Bar. Carb.	C5MF-A	CC	.017	26–31	17–21	2 @ 500	14 @ 2000	8	10 @ 18
	V8-390 Four Bar. Carb.	C5AF-C	CC	.017	26–31	17–21	2 @ 450	12 @ 2000	8	8 @ 4
	V8-427 Conventional	C5AF-E	CC	.020	30–33	27–30	4 @ 650	13 @ 2000	None	None
	V8-427 Transistor	C5AF-F	CC	.020	22–24	22–24	4 @ 650	13 @ 2000	None	None
	6-240 Std. Tr.(10)	C6TF-AC	C	.025	37–42	17–21	None	None	1.2	11 @ 4.9
	6-240 Std. Tr.(5)	C6AF-AC	C	.025	37–42	17–21	½ @ 400	10 @ 1550	5	11 @ 15
	6-240 Auto. Tr.(10)	C6AF-Y	C	.025	37–42	17–21	None	None	.90	10 @ 4.80
	6-240 Auto. Tr.(5)	C6AF-AD	C	.025	37–42	17–21	½ @ 300	11 @ 2000	4	12 @ 18
	8-289 Std. Tr.(10)	C5AF-M	CC	.017	26–31	17–21	2 @ 650	13 @ 2000	8	9 @ 14
	8-289 Std. Tr.(5)	C6AF-J	CC	.017	26–31	17–21	7 @ 600	15 @ 1800	7	8 @ 16
	8-289 Auto. Tr.(10)	C5AF-N	CC	.017	26–31	17–21	2 @ 450	12 @ 2000	8	11 @ 14
	8-289 Auto. Tr.(5)	C6AF-S	CC	.017	26–31	17–21	3 @ 600	14 @ 1800	5	10 @ 12
	8-352(10)	C5AF-BG	CC	.017	26–31	17–21	1 @ 300	9 @ 2000	10	10 @ 20
	8-390(6)(10)	C6AF-A	CC	.017	26–31	17–21	½ @ 400	8 @ 1800	5	10 @ 15
	8-390(5)(6)	C6AF-K	CC	.017	26–31	17–21	3 @ 500	13 @ 2000	5	11 @ 17
	8-390(7)(10)	C6AF-B	CC	.017	26–31	17–21	2 @ 625	10 @ 2000	5	9 @ 13
	8-390(5)(7)	C6AF-T	CC	.017	26–31	17–21	2 @ 475	11 @ 1800	5	11 @ 18
	8-390(8)(10)	C6AF-C	CC	.017	26–31	17–21	3 @ 600	10 @ 2000	5	10 @ 17
	8-390(5)(8)	C6AF-L	CC	.017	26–31	17–21	3 @ 500	12 @ 2000	6	10 @ 15
	8-390(9)(10)	C6AF-D	CC	.017	26–31	17–21	3 @ 500	10 @ 2000	6	12 @ 18
	8-390(5)(9)	C6AF-L	CC	.017	26–31	17–21	3 @ 500	12 @ 2000	6	10 @ 15
	8-410 Std. Tr.(10)	C6MF-A	CC	.017	26–31	17–21	3 @ 500	10 @ 2000	5	11 @ 18
	8-410(5)	C6AF-L	CC	.017	26–31	17–21	3 @ 500	12 @ 2000	6	10 @ 15
	8-410 Auto. Tr.(10)	C6AF-D	CC	.017	26–31	17–21	3 @ 500	10 @ 2000	6	12 @ 18
	8-427 Transistor(10)	C5AF-F	CC	.020	22–24	22–24	4 @ 650	13 @ 2000	None	None
	8-428(5)	C6AF-L	CC	.017	26–31	17–21	3 @ 500	12 @ 2000	6	10 @ 15
	8-428(10)	C6AF-E	CC	.017	26–31	17–21	2 @ 500	10 @ 2000	6	10 @ 15
1967	6-240 Std. Tr.(10)	C6TF-AC	C	.025	37–42	17–21	None	None	1.2	11 @ 4.9
	6-240 Auto. Tr.(10)	C6AF-Y	C	.025	37–42	17–21	None	None	.90	10 @ 4.8
	6-240 Std. Tr.(5)	C6AF-AC	C	.025	37–42	17–21	½ @ 400	10 @ 1550	5	11 @ 15

Continued

DISTRIBUTOR SPECIFICATIONS—Continued

★If advance is checked on vehicle, double the R.P.M. and degrees advance to get crankshaft figures.

Year	Model	Basic Distributor Part No.(1) 12127	Rotation (2)	Breaker Gap	Dwell Angle Deg.	Breaker Arm Spring Tension	Centrifugal Advance Degrees @ R.P.M. of Distributor★		Vacuum Advance	
							Advance Starts	Full Advance	Inches of Vacuum To Start Plunger	Max. Adv. Dist. Deg. @ Vacuum
1967	6-240 Auto. Tr.(5)	C6AF-AD	C	.025	37–42	17–21	½ @ 300	11 @ 2000	4	12 @ 18
	8-289 Std. Tr.(10)	C7OF-A	CC	.017	26–31	17–21	½ @ 400	11 @ 1500	5	11 @ 20
	8-289 Auto. Tr.(10)	C7OF-B	CC	.017	26–31	17–21	½ @ 300	12 @ 2000	5	12 @ 20
	8-289 Std. Tr.(5)	C7OF-D	CC	.017	26–31	17–21	½ @ 300	14 @ 2000	5	12 @ 20
	8-289 Auto. Tr.(5)	C7OF-E	CC	.017	26–31	17–21	½ @ 300	13 @ 2000	5	11 @ 20
	8-289(5)	C7AF-AH	CC	.017	26–31	17–21	½ @ 300	12 @ 2000	5	10 @ 20
	8-289(10)	C7AF-AE	CC	.017	26–31	17–21	½ @ 300	12 @ 2000	5	12 @ 20
	8-390(10)	C7AF-AB	CC	.017	26–31	17–21	½ @ 300	9 @ 2000	5	11 @ 20
	8-390(10)	C7AF-Y	CC	.017	26–31	17–21	½ @ 300	10 @ 2000	5	12 @ 20
	8-390(5)(6)	C7AF-Z	CC	.017	26–31	17–21	½ @ 300	12 @ 2000	5	12 @ 20
	8-390(5)(7)	C7AF-AA	CC	.017	26–31	17–21	½ @ 300	12 @ 2000	5	11 @ 20
	8-428(5)(8)(9)	C7AF-AC	CC	.017	26–31	17–21	½ @ 300	12 @ 2000	5	12 @ 20
	8-390(6)(10)	C7AF-A	CC	.017	26–31	17–21	½ @ 300	9 @ 2000	5	12 @ 20
	8-390(7)(10)	C7AF-B	CC	.017	26–31	17–21	½ @ 300	10 @ 2000	5	12 @ 20
	8-390(6)(5)	C7AF-C	CC	.017	26–31	17–21	½ @ 300	13 @ 2000	5	12 @ 20
	8-390(7)(5)	C7AF-D	CC	.017	26–31	17–21	½ @ 300	12 @ 2000	5	12 @ 20
	8-390(8)(10)	C7AF-E	CC	.017	26–31	17–21	½ @ 300	10 @ 2000	5	12 @ 20
	8-390, 410(9)(10)	C7SF-A	CC	.017	26–31	17–21	½ @ 300	10 @ 2000	5	12 @ 20
	8-390, 410(8)(9)(5)	C7SF-B	CC	.017	26–31	17–21	½ @ 300	12 @ 2000	5	12 @ 20
	8-410(8)(10)	C7MF-A	CC	.017	26–31	17–21	½ @ 300	10 @ 2000	5	11 @ 20
	8-427	C5AF-F	CC	.020	22–24	22–24	4 @ 650	13 @ 2000	None	None
	8-428(10)	C7AF-J	CC	.017	26–31	17–21	½ @ 300	10 @ 2000	5	12 @ 20
	8-428(5)(8)	C7AF-L	CC	.017	26–31	17–21	½ @ 300	9 @ 1400	5	11 @ 20
	8-428(5)(9)	C7SF-B	CC	.017	26–31	17–21	½ @ 300	12 @ 2000	5	12 @ 20
1968	6-240 Std. Tr.	C8AF-A	C	.027	35–40	17–21	½ @ 350	10 @ 2000	5	8 @ 25
	6-240 Auto. Tr.	C8AF-B	C	.027	37–40	17–21	½ @ 350	11 @ 2000	5	9 @ 25
	8-302(6)	C8AF-E	CC	.021	24–29	17–21	½ @ 350	14 @ 2000	5	11 @ 25
	8-302(7)	C8OF-C	CC	.021	24–29	17–21	½ @ 350	12 @ 2000	5	11½ @ 25
	8-390(6)	C8AF-M	CC	.021	24–29	17–21	½ @ 350	11 @ 2000	5	12½ @ 25
	8-390(7)	C8AF-R	CC	.017	26–31	17–21	½ @ 350	14 @ 2000	5	12½ @ 25
	8-390(7)	C8AF-AA	CC	.017	26–31	17–21	½ @ 350	14 @ 2000	5	11½ @ 20
	8-390(8)	C8AF-S	CC	.021	24–29	17–21	½ @ 350	14 @ 2000	5	12½ @ 25
	8-390(9)	C7AF-AC	CC	.017	26–31	17–21	½ @ 350	14 @ 2000	5	12½ @ 25
	8-427	C7OF-F	CC	.017	26–31	17–21	½ @ 300	14½ @ 2000	5	11 @ 20
	8-428	C8AF-Y	CC	.017	26–31	19–21	½ @ 350	14 @ 2000	5	12½ @ 25
1969	6-240 Std. Tr.	C8AF-A	C	.027	35–40	17–21	½ @ 350	10 @ 2000	5	8 @ 25
	6-240 Auto. Tr.	C8AF-B	C	.027	35–40	17–21	½ @ 350	11 @ 2000	5	9 @ 25
	8-302 Std. Tr.	C8AF-E	CC	.021	24–29	17–21	½ @ 350	14 @ 2000	5	11 @ 25
	8-302 Auto. Tr.	C9AF-N	CC	.017	26–31	17–21	½ @ 350	10¾ @ 2000	5	11½ @ 20
	8-302 A–C(7)	C9AF-R	CC	.021	24–29	17–21	½ @ 350	10¾ @ 2000	5	11½ @ 20
	8-390 Std. Tr.	C9AF-J	CC	.017	26–31	17–21	½ @ 350	10¾ @ 2000	5	12½ @ 20
	8-390 Auto. Tr.	C7AF-AA	CC	.021	24–29	17–21	½ @ 350	12 @ 2000	5	11½ @ 20
	8-390 Premium Fuel	C8AF-R	CC	.021	24–29	17–21	½ @ 350	12¼ @ 2000	5	12½ @ 25
	8-429	C8VF-A	CC	.017	26–31	17–21	½ @ 350	13½ @ 2000	5	9½ @ 25

(1)—Stamped on distributor housing plate.
(2)—As viewed from above.
(3)—Conventional distributor (combined) 33–36°, transistor ignition 22–24°.
(4)—Conventional distributor 27–30°, transistor ignition 21–24°.
(5)—With Thermactor Exhaust Emission Control System.
(6)—Std. trans. and two-barrel carb.
(7)—Auto. trans. and two-barrel carb.
(8)—Std. trans. and four-barrel carb.
(9)—Auto. trans. and four-barrel carb.
(10)—Without Thermactor Exhaust Emission Control.

VALVE SPECIFICATIONS

Year	Engine Model	Valve Lash		Valve Angles		Valve Spring Installed Height	Valve Spring Pressure Lbs. @ In.	Stem Clearance		Stem Diameter	
		Int.	Exh.	Seat	Face			Intake	Exhaust	Intake	Exhaust
1963	6-223(6)	.025H	.025H	45	44	1 3/4	100 @ 1.78	.001-.0024	.0028-.0042	.3416-.3423	.3398-.3405
	V8-260	3/4 Turn(8)		45	44	1 3/4	60 @ 1.77	.0008-.0025	.0018-.0035	.3100-.3107	.3090-.3097
	V8-289	3/4 Turn(8)		45	44	1 3/4	170 @ 1 3/8	.001-.0027	.002-.0037	.3416-.3423	.3398-.3405
	V8-352	.083-.183(7)		45	44	1 13/16	100 @ 1.82	.001-.0024	.0028-.0042	.3711-.3718	.3693-.3700
	V8-390	.083-.183(7)		45	44	1 13/16	200 @ 1.42	.001-.0024	.0028-.0042	.3711-.3718	.3693-.3700
	V8-390(4)	.025H	.025H	45	44	1 13/16	200 @ 1.42	.001-.0024	.0028-.0042	.3711-.3718	.3693-.3700
	V8-406	.025H	.025H	(2)	(3)	1 13/16	200 @ 1.42	.001-.0024	.002-.0034	.3711-.3718	.3701-.3708
	V8-427	.025H	.025H	(2)	(3)	1 13/16	200 @ 1.42	.001-.0024	.002-.0034	.3711-.3718	.3701-.3708
1964	6-223(6)	.025H	.025H	45	44	1 3/4	100 @ 1.78	.001-.0024	.0028-.0042	.3416-.3423	.3398-.3405
	V8-289	3/4 Turn(8)		45	44	1 25/32	170 @ 1.39	.001-.0027	.002-.0037	.3416-.3423	.3398-.3405
	V8-352	(9)		45	44	1 13/16	190 @ 1.42	.001-.0024	(10)	.3711-.3718	(11)
	V8-390	(9)		45	44	1 13/16	200 @ 1.42	.001-.0024	(10)	.3711-.3718	(11)
	V8-390(4)	.025H	.025H	45	44	1 13/16	200 @ 1.42	.001-.0024	.002-.0034	.3711-.3718	.3693-.3700
	V8-427	.025H	.025H	(2)	(3)	1 13/16	200 @ 1.42	.001-.0024	.002-.0034	.3711-.3718	.3701-.3708
1965	6-240	3/4 Turn(8)		45	44	1 11/16	80 @ 1.70	.001-.0027	.001-.0027	.3416-.3423	.3416-.3423
	V8-289	3/4 Turn(8)		45	44	1 3/4	75 @ 1.78	.001-.0027	.002-.0037	.3416-.3423	.3406-.3413
	V8-352	.050-.150(7)		45	44	1 13/16	100 @ 1.82	.001-.0024	.001.-0024	.3711-.3718	.3693-.3700
	V8-390	.050-.150(7)		45	44	1 13/16	80 @ 1.82	.001-.0024	.001-.0024	.3711-.3718	.3693-.3700
	V8 390(1)	.025H	.025H	45	44	1 13/16	85 @ 1.82	.001-.0024	.001-.0024	.3711-.3718	.3693-.3700
	V8-427	.025H	.025H	(2)	(3)	1 13/16	85 @ 1.82	.001-.0024	.002-.0034	.3711-.3718	.3701-.3708
1966	6-240	3/4 Turn(8)		45	44	1 11/16	80 @ 1.70	.001-.0027	.001-.0027	.3416-.3423	.3416-.3423
	8-289	3/4 Turn(8)		45	44	1 3/4	75 @ 1.78	.001-.0027	.002-.0037	.3416-.3423	.3406-.3413
	8-352	.050-.150(7)		45	44	1 13/16	100 @ 1.82	.001-.0024	.001-.0024	.3711-.3718	.3711-.3718
	8-390	.050-.150(7)(12)		45	44	1 13/16	85 @ 1.82	.001-.0024	.001-.0024	.3711-.3818	.3711-.3718
	8-410	.050-.150(7)(12)		45	44	1 13/16	85 @ 1.82	.001-.0024	.001-.0024	.3711-.3718	.3711-.3718
	8-427	.025H	.025H	(2)	(3)	1 13/16	85 @ 1.82	.001-.0024	.002-.0034	.3711-.3718	.3701-.3708
	8-428	.050-.150(7)(12)		45	44	1 13/16	85 @ 1.82	.001-.0024	.001-.0024	.3711-.3718	.3711-.3718
1967	6-240	3/4 Turn(8)		45	44	1 11/16	80 @ 1.70	.001-.0027	.001-.0027	.3416-.3423	.3416-.3423
	8-289	3/4 Turn(8)		45	44	1 21/32	60 @ 1.64	.001-.0027	.001-.0027	.3416-.3423	.3416-.3423
	8-390, 410	.100-.200(7)		45	44	1 13/16	85 @ 1.82	.001-.0024	.001-.0024	.3711-.3718	.3711-.3718
	8-428	.100-.200(7)		45	44	1 13/16	85 @ 1.82	.001-.0024	.001-.0024	.3711-.3718	.3711-.3718
	8-427	.025H	.028H	(2)	(3)	1 13/16	85 @ 1.82	.001-.0024	.002-.0034	.3711-.3718	.3701-.3708
1968	6-240	3/4 Turn(8)		45	44	1 9/16	80 @ 1.70	.001-.0027	.001-.0027	.3416-.3423	.3416-.3423
	8-302	3/4 Turn(8)		45	44	1 5/8	75 @ 1.66	.001-.0027	.0015-.0032	.3416-.3423	.3411-.3418
	8-390	.100-.200(7)		45	44	1 7/8	90 @ 1.82	.001-.0024	.0015-.0032	.3711-.3718	.3706-.3713
	8-427	.100-.200(7)		(2)	(3)	1 13/16	85 @ 1.82	.001-.0024	.002-.0034	.3711-.3718	.3701-.3708
	8-428	.100-.200(7)		45	44	1 13/16	90 @ 1.82	.001-.0024	.0015-.0032	.3711-.3718	.3706-.3713
1969	6-240	1 Turn(8)		45	44	1 9/16	80 @ 1.70	.001-.0027	.001-.0027	.3416-.3423	.3416-.3423
	8-302	1 Turn(8)		45	44	1 5/8	75 @ 1.66	.001-.0027	.0015-.0032	.3416-.3423	.3411-.3418
	8-390	.100-.200(7)		45	44	1 7/8	90 @ 1.82	.001-.0027	.0015-.0032	.3711-.3718	.3706-.3713
	8-429	1 Turn(8)		45	44	1 13/16	80 @ 1.81	.001-.0027	.001-.0027	.3416-.3423	.3416-.3423

(2)—Intake 30°, exhaust 45°. (3)—Intake 29°, exhaust 44°. (4)—High performance engines with mechanical lifters.

(5)—Conventional adjustment.

(6)—"Silent Lash"—Clearance specified is obtained at valve stem tip with eccentric spring compressed. See text for details

(7)—Clearance specified is obtainable at valve stem tip with lifter collapsed. See "Valves, Adjust" text.

(8)—See text under Valves, Adjust for procedure.

(9)—Before 11-18-63 .083-.183", from 11-18-63 .050-.150" (see note (7)).

(10)—Before 11-18-63 .002-.0034", from 11-18-63 .001-.0024".

(11)—Before 11-18-63 .3711-.3718", from 11-18-63 .3721-.3728".

(12)—Engines built after 12-20-65, .050-.200".

FORD & MERCURY — Full Size Models

PISTONS, PINS, RINGS, CRANKSHAFT & BEARINGS

Year	Engine Model	Piston Clearance	Ring End Gap ①		Wrist-pin Diameter	Rod Bearings		Main Bearings			
			Comp.	Oil		Shaft Diameter	Bearing Clearance	Shaft Diameter	Bearing Clearance	Thrust on Bear. No.	Shaft End Play
1963–64	Six	.0008–.0026	.010	.015	.9121	2.2984–2.2988	.0006–.0025	2.4984–2.4988	.0006–.0028	3	.004–.008
	V8-260	.0021–.0039	.010	.015	.912	2.1232–2.1240	.0009–.0025	2.2482–2.2490	.0006–.0026	3	.004–.008
	V8-289	.0021–.0039	.015	.015	.912	2.1228–2.1236	.0009–.0029	2.2482–2.2490	.0006–.0026	3	.004–.008
	V8-352	.0012–.0030	.015	.015	.9752	2.4380–2.4388	.0007–.0028	2.7484–2.7492	.0006–.0031	3	.004–.008
	V8-390	.0017–.0035	.015	.015	.9752	2.4380–2.4388	.0007–.0028	2.7484–2.7492	.0006–.0027	3	.004–.008
	406,427	.0043–.0049	.015	.015	.9752	2.4380–2.4388	.0009–.0029	2.7484–2.7492	.0006–.0031	3	.004–.008
1965	6-240	.0014–.0022	.010	.015	.9121	2.1228–2.1236	.0006–.0022	2.3982–2.3990	.0006–.0024	5	.004–.008
	V8-289	.0014–.0022	.010	.015	.9121	2.1228–2.1236	.0009–.0029	2.2482–2.2490	.0005–.0028	3	.004–.008
	V8-352	.0015–.0023	.010	.015	.9751	2.4380–2.4388	.0007–.0028	2.7484–2.7492	③	3	.004–.010
	V8-390	.0015–.0023	.010	.015	.9751	2.4380–2.4388	.0007–.0028	2.7484–2.7492	③	3	.004–.010
	V8-427	.0042–.0066	.010	.015	.9751	2.4380–2.4388	.0013–.0032	2.7484–2.7492	.0007–.0031	3	.004–.010
1966-67	6-240	.0014–.0022	.010	.015	.9121	2.1228–2.1236	.0008–.0024	2.3982–2.3990	.0005–.0015	5	.004–.008
	8-289	.0018–.0026	.010	.015	.9121	2.1228–2.1236	.0008–.0026	2.2482–2.2490	.0005–.0015	3	.004–.008
	8-352 (1966)	.0015–.0023	.010	.015	.975	2.4380–2.4388	.0008–.0026	2.7484–2.7492	.0005–.0015	3	.004–.010
	8-390	.0015–.0023	.010	.015	.975	2.4380–2.4388	.0008–.0026	2.7484–2.7492	.0005–.0015	3	.004–.010
	8-410	.0015–.0023	.010	.015	.975	2.4380–2.4388	.0008–.0026	2.7484–2.7492	.0005–.0015	3	.004–.010
	8-427	.0042–.0066	.010	.015	.975	2.4380–2.4388	.0013–.0032	2.7484–2.7492	.0007–.0031	3	.004–.010
	8-428	.0015–.0023	.010	.015	.975	2.4380–2.4388	.0008–.0026	2.7484–2.7492	.0005–.0015	3	.004–.010
1968-69	6-240	.0014–.0022	.010	.015	.9121	2.1228–2.1236	.0008–.0015	2.3982–2.3990	.0005–.0015	5	.004–.008
	8-302	.0018–.0026	.010	.015	.9121	2.1228–2.1236	.0008–.0015	2.2482–2.2490	.0005–.0015	3	.004–.008
	8-390	.0015–.0023	.010	.015	.975	2.4380–2.4388	.0008–.0015	2.7484–2.7492	.0005–.0015	3	.004–.010
	8-427 (1968)	.0030–.0038	.018	.015	.975	2.4380–2.4388	.0008–.0015	2.7484–2.7492	.0005–.0015	3	.004–.010
	8-428 (1968)	.0015–.0023	.010	.015	.975	2.4380–2.4388	.0008–.0015	2.7484–2.7492	.0005–.0015	3	.004–.010
	8-429 (1969)	.0014–.0022	.010	.015	1.041	2.4992–2.5000	.0008–.0015	2.994–3.0002	.0005–.0015	3	.004–.008

①—Fit rings in tapered bores for clearance listed in tightest portion of ring travel.

③—No. 1 and 3: .0007–.0031, others .0005–.0028.

ENGINE TIGHTENING SPECIFICATIONS★

★Torque specifications are for clean and lightly lubricated threads only. Dry or dirty threads produce increased friction which prevents accurate measurement of tightness.

Year	Engine Model	Spark Plugs Ft. Lbs.	Cylinder Head Bolts Ft. Lbs.	Intake Manifold Ft. Lbs.	Exhaust Manifold Ft. Lbs.	Rocker Arm Shaft Bracket Ft. Lbs.	Rocker Arm Cover Ft. Lbs.	Connecting Rod Cap Bolts Ft. Lbs.	Main Bearing Cap Bolts Ft. Lbs.	Flywheel to Crankshaft Ft. Lbs.	Vibration Damper or Pulley Ft. Lbs.
1963–64	6-223	15–20	105–115	23–28	23–28	45–55	4–7	40–45	95–105	75–85	70–90
1965–68	6-240	15–20	70–75	20–25	20–25	...	7–9	40–45	60–70	75–85	130–145
1969	6-240	15–20	70–75	23–28	23–28	...	7–9	40–45	60–70	75–85	130–150
1963	V8-260	15–20	75–70	12–15	13–18	...	3–5	19–24	60–70	75–85	70–90
1964–68	V8-289, 302	15–20	65–70	20–22	13–18	...	3–5	19–24	60–70	75–85	70–90
1969	V8-302	15–20	65–72	23–25	12–16	...	3–5	19–24	60–70	75–85	70–90
1963–67	V8-352	15–20	80–90	32–35	12–18	40–45	10–12	40–45	95–105	75–85	70–90
1963–68	V8-390	15–20	80–90	32–35	12–18	40–45	4–7	40–45	95–105	75–85	70–90
1969	V8-390	15–20	80–90	32–35	18–24	40–45	4–7	40–45	95–105	75–85	70–90
1963	V8-406	15–20	100–110	25–28	12–18	40–45	4–7	53–58	95–105	75–85	70–90
1966–67	V8-410	15–20	80–90	32–35	12–18	40–45	4–7	40–45	95–105	75–85	70–90
1963–68	V8-427	15–20	100–110	32–35	12–18	40–45	4–7	53–58	95–105	75–85	70–90
1966–68	V8-428	15–20	80–90	32–35	12–18	45–50	4–7	40–45	95–105	75–85	70–90
1969	V8-429	15–20	130–140	25–30	28–33	65–75①	5–6	40–45	95–105	75–85	70–90

①—Rocker arm stud to cylinder head.

COOLING SYSTEM & CAPACITY DATA

Year	Model or Engine	Cooling Capacity, Qts.			Radiator Cap Relief Pressure, Lbs.		Thermo. Opening Temp. (1)	Fuel Tank Gals.	Engine Oil Refill Qts. (2)	Transmission Oil			Rear Axle Oil Pints
		No Heater	With Heater	With A/C	With A/C	No A/C				3 Speed Pints	4 Speed Pints	Auto. Trans. Qts. (15)	
FORD													
1963	6 Cylinder	15	16	20	12–15	12–15	185	20(4)	4	3	—	9¼	5
	V8-260	14	15	15	12–15	12–15	185	20(4)	4	3	—	9¼	5
	Other V8s	19	20	20	12–15	12–15	185	20(4)	5	3	3	(3)	5
1964	6 Cylinder	15	16	16	12–15	12–15	185	20(4)	4	3½	—	8½	5
	V8-289	13½	14½	14½	12–15	12–15	185	20(4)	4	3½	3	(11)	5
	Other V8s	19½	20½	20½	12–15	12–15	185	20(4)	5	3½	3	10	5
1965	6 Cylinder	15	16	16	12–15	12–15	185	20	4	3½	4	8½	5
	V8-289	15	16	16	12–15	12–15	195	20	4	3½	4	(11)	5
	Other V8s	19½	20½	20½	12–15	12–15	195	20	5	3½	4	10	5
1966-67	6-240	12	13	13	12–15	12–15	195	25(6)	4	3½	4	(12)	5(9)
	8-289	14	15	15	12–15	12–15	195	25(6)	4	3½	4	(12)	5(9)
	8-352 (1966)	19½	20½	20½	12–15	12–15	195	25(6)	5	3½	4	13(8)	5½(10)
	8-390, 410, 428	19½	20½	20½	12–15	12–15	195	25(6)	4	3½	4	13(8)	5½(10)
	8-427	19½	20½	20½	12–15	12–15	195	25(6)	5	3½	4	13(8)	5½(10)
1968	6 240	12	13	13	12–15	12–15	195	24(6)	4	3½	4	(11)	4½
	8-302	14	15	15	12–15	12–15	195	24(6)	4	3½	4	(11)	4½
	8-390	19½	20½	20½	12–15	12–15	195	24(6)	4	3½	4	(13)	5
	8-427	19½	20½	20½	12–15	12–15	195	24(6)	5	3½	4	13	5
	8-428	19½	20½	20½	12–15	12–15	195	24(6)	4	3½	4	13	5
1969	6-240	12	13	13	12–15	12–15	195	24(6)	4	3½	4	(13)	4½
	8-302	14	15	15	12–15	12–15	195	24(6)	4	3½	4	(13)	4½
	8-390	19½	20½	20½	12–15	12–15	195	24(6)	4	3½	4	(14)	5
	8-429	19½	20½	20½	12–15	12–15	195	24(6)	4	3½	4	12¾	5
MERCURY													
1963	V8-390, 406	19	20	20	12–15	12–15	185	20	5	3	4	11½	5
1964	V8-390, 427	19½	20½	20½	12–15	12–15	185	20(4)	5	3½	3	10	5
1965	V8-390, 427	19½	20½	20½	12–15	12–15	195	20	5	3½	4	10	5
1966-67	8-390, 410, 428	19½	20½	20½	12–15	12–15	195	25(6)	4	3½	4	(14)	5½(10)
	8-427	19½	20½	20½	12–15	12–15	195	25(6)	5	3½	4	13(8)	5½(10)
1968	All	19½	20½	22½	12–15	12–15	195	24(6)	4	3½	—	13	5
1969	All	19½	20½	20½	12–15	12–15	195	24(6)	4	3½	—	12¾	5

(1)—For alcohol type anti-freeze use a 160° unit.
(2)—Add one quart with filter change.
(3)—V8-352 11 qts., V8-390 11½ qts.
(4)—Station Wagons 21 gals.
(6)—Station Wagons 20 gals.
(8)—C6 Transmission.
(9)—With limited-slip differential 4½ pints.
(10)—With limited-slip differential 5¼ pints.
(11)—Three spd. 10 qts., C4 8½ qts.
(12)—1966 three spd. 10 qts., 1967 three spd. 11 qts., C4 10¼ qts.
(13)—Three spd. 11 qts., C4 10¼ qts., C6 13 qts.
(14)—Three spd. 11 qts., C6 13 qts.
(15)—Approximate. Make final check with dipstick.

BRAKE SPECIFICATIONS

Year	Model	Brake Drum Inside Diameter	Wheel Cylinder Bore Diameter			Master Cylinder Bore Diameter		
			Front Disc Brake	Front Drum Brake	Rear Brake	With Disc Brakes	With Drum Brakes	With Power Brakes
1963–64	Ford and Mercury	11.03	—	1 3/32	15/16	—	1.00	1.00
1965	All Passenger Cars	11.03	—	1 3/32	31/32	—	1.00	1.00
	All Wagons	11.03	—	1 1/16	31/32	—	1.00	1.00
1966	All Passenger Cars	11.03	1.9375	1.094	.969	.938	1.00	7/8
	All Wagons	11.03	—	1.062	.969	.938	1.00	7/8
1967–68	With 6-240, 8-289, 8-302 Engines	11.03	1.938	1.094	.969	.9375	1.00	.9375
	All Others	11.03	1.938	1.094	.938	.9375	1.00	.9375
1969	All	11.03	2.755	1.094	.938	1.00	1.00	1.00

D.C. GENERATOR AND REGULATOR SPECIFICATIONS

★To Polarize Generator: For internally grounded systems, disconnect field lead from regulator and momentarily flash this lead to the regulator battery terminal. For externally grounded systems, reconnect leads to the regulator; then momentarily connect a jumper wire from the "Gen" or "Arm" to the "Bat" terminals of the regulator.

Year	Generator Rating Amperes ①	Field Current Draw @ 12 Volts	Field Ground Location ★	Brush Spring Tension Ounces	Maximum Charging Rate		Regulator		
					Amperes	Generator R.P.M. ③	Cut-In Voltage (cut-out)	Voltage Regulation @ 75° F. ②	Current Regulation Amperes ②
1964	30	1.0–1.5	Internal	20–26	30	3400	12.2–13.2	14.6–15.4	28–32
1963	30	1.2–1.8	Internal	20–26	30	2525	12.0–12.8	14.6–15.4	28–32
	40	1.2–1.8	External	34–41	40	1800	12.5–13.8	14.3–15.1	32–48

①—Rating stamped on housing
②—Stamped on regulator cover.
③—To find equivalent engine R P.M., divide crankshaft pulley diameter by generator pulley diameter and multiply by generator R.P.M.

REAR AXLE SPECIFICATIONS

Year	Model	Carrier Type	Ring Gear & Pinion Backlash Inch	Nominal Pinion Locating Shim, Inch	Pinion Bearing Preload				Differential Bearing Preload	Pinion Nut Torque Ft.-Lbs.①
					New Bearings With Seal Inch-Lbs.	Used Bearings With Seal Inch-Lbs.	New Bearings Less Seal Inch-Lbs.	Used Bearings Less Seal Inch-Lbs.		
1963–64	All	Removable	.004–.009	.020	17–27	8–12	—	—	2½–3②	175
1965	All	Removable	.004–.009	.020	22–32⑤	10–14⑤	—	—	2½–3②	175
1966	All	Removable	.008–.012	.020	22–32⑤	10–14⑤	—	—	.008–.012③	200
1967–69	④	Integral	.008–.012	.030	15–35	—	12½–32½	—	.008–.012③	175
	Others	Removable	.008–.012	.020	15–35	—	12½—32½	—	.008–.012③	200

①—If torque cannot be obtained, install new spacer.
②—Threaded adjusters — notches tight.
③—Case spread with new bearings; with used bearings .005–.008″.
④—8-289, 302 engines with two-barrel carburetor and 6-240 engine.
⑤—Collapsible spacer. With solid spacer 15-35 inch-lbs. with seal in place; 12½–32½ inch-lbs. without seal.

1963-66 Ford and Mercury

1. Disconnect battery ground cable.
2. Turn ignition key to accessory position. Slightly depress pin with a paper clip, Fig. 4. Turn key counterclockwise and pull key and lock cylinder out of switch. If only lock cylinder is to be replaced, proceed to step 8 below.
3. Press in on rear of switch and rotate it ⅛ turn counter-clockwise (as viewed from terminal end). Remove bezel and switch.
4. Remove insulated plug and wires from rear of switch.
5. If a new switch as well as lock cylinder is to be installed, insert a screwdriver into lock opening of switch and turn slot in switch to full counter-clockwise position.
6. Connect insulated plug and accessory wires to back of switch.
7. Place bezel and switch into switch opening, press switch toward instrument panel and rotate it ⅛ turn to lock in position.
8. If a new lock cylinder is to be installed, insert key in cylinder and turn it to accessory position. Place lock and key in switch, depress pin slightly, Fig. 4, and turn key counter-clockwise. Push lock cylinder into switch, turn key and check lock cylinder operation.
9. Connect battery cable and check operation of switch.

1967 Ford

1. Disconnect ground strap from battery.
2. Remove cigar lighter and radio knobs.
3. Remove instrument cluster trim cover (10 screws).
4. Remove radio rear support nut.
5. Unfasten radio from instrument cluster (2 bolts).
6. Take radio out of cluster and disconnect antenna, speaker and power leads.
7. Remove ignition switch bezel nut.

Fig. 8 Light switch. 1964-69 Ford and Mercury

8. Position ignition switch through radio opening and remove accessory wire retaining nut.
9. Disconnect ignition switch wire connector from switch and remove switch.
10. Reverse procedure to install.

1967 Mercury

1. Disconnect ground cable from battery.
2. On units equipped with Safety Convenience Panel, lower panel to floor.
3. Remove switch lock cylinder.
4. Remove switch bezel nut by turning to left.
5. Pull ignition switch from back of panel and lower switch. Remove multiple connector retaining nut and disengage connector from ignition switch.

1968-69 Ford & Mercury

1. Disconnect battery ground cable.
2. On Mercury only, remove screw retaining washer valve behind ignition switch and position valve to the side.
3. Insert ignition key in switch. Turn key to accessory position and insert a wire pin in hole on ignition switch. Slightly depress pin while turning counterclockwise past the accessory position; this will release lock cylinder from switch. Pull lock cylinder from switch with the key.
4. Remove bezel nut retaining switch to instrument panel and lower switch.
5. Depress tabs securing multiple connector from switch and remove switch.
6. Reverse procedure to install.

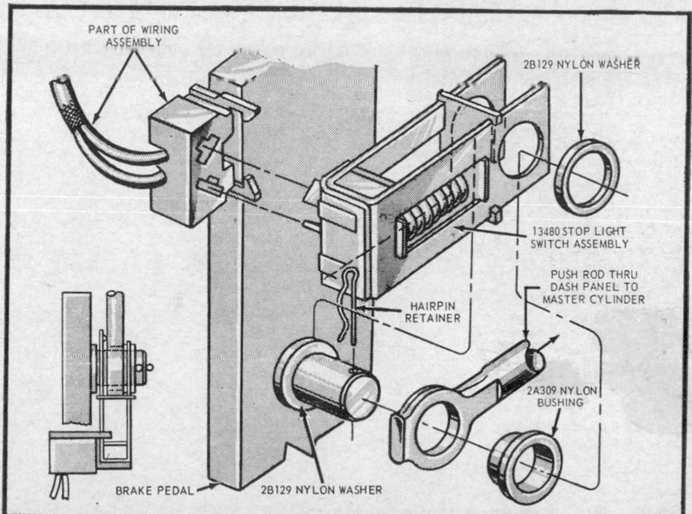

Fig. 9 Mechanical stop light switch. 1965-69 Ford and Mercury

LIGHT SWITCH, REPLACE

1963 Ford

1. Remove control knob and shaft by pressing knob release button on switch housing, with knob in "off" position.
2. Turn knob clockwise as far as possible and pull it out of switch.
3. Remove mounting nut, bezel and switch, and remove fuse panel from switch.
4. To install, connect fuse panel to switch, insert switch into instrument panel and install bezel and mounting nut.
5. Install knob and shaft by inserting it all the way into switch until a distinct click is heard. In some instances it may be necessary to rotate shaft slightly until it engages switch contact carrier.

1963 Mercury

1. Disconnect battery ground cable.
2. Remove junction block clamp and disconnect fuse junction block from base of switch.
3. Remove switch control knob and shaft by pressing spring release button, Fig. 8, with knob in "off" position. Turn shaft slightly and pull it out of switch.
4. Unscrew bezel nut and remove switch.
5. Reverse above procedure to install.

1964-66 Ford & Mercury

1. Remove control knob and shaft by pressing knob release button on switch housing, Fig. 8, with knob in full "on" position. Pull knob out of switch.
2. Unscrew mounting nut, remove switch and disconnect wire connector.
3. To install, attach wire connector, insert switch in instrument panel and secure with mounting nut.
4. Install knob and shaft assembly by inserting it all the way into switch until a distinct click is heard. In some instances it may be necessary to rotate switch slightly until it engages switch contact carrier.

1967 Ford

1. Disconnect ground strap from battery.
2. Remove cigar lighter and radio knobs.
3. Remove instrument cluster trim cover (10 screws).
4. Remove set screw from light switch control knob and remove knob.
5. Remove light switch bezel nut.
6. Lower switch and disconnect wiring connector.
7. Reverse procedure to install.

1967 Mercury

1. Disconnect ground cable from battery.
2. Remove light switch knob.
3. Remove bezel nut and bezel.
4. Reach up behind instrument panel and remove light switch from panel. Lower switch and wiring beneath panel. Disconnect junction block from switch.

1968-69 Ford & Mercury

1. Disconnect battery and ground cable.
2. Remove control knob and shaft by pressing knob release button on switch housing with knob in full on position. Pull knob out of switch.
3. On Mercury only, remove two screws retaining wiring harness bracket at back of switch and remove bracket.
4. Remove bezel nut and lower switch.
5. Disconnect multiple plug to switch. If vehicle has concealed headlamp doors, disconnect the three vacuum hoses and remove switch from vehicle.
6. Reverse procedure to install.

STOP LIGHT SWITCH, REPLACE

1963-64 Master Cylinder Type

Disconnect wires at switch and unscrew switch from master cylinder. Have the new switch ready for installation before removing the old one to avoid undue loss of brake fluid.

1965-68 Mechanical Type

1. Referring to Fig. 9, disconnect wires at connector.
2. Remove hairpin retainer and slide switch, push rod and nylon washers and bushing away from pedal, and remove switch.
3. Position the new switch, push rod, bushing and washers on brake pedal pin and secure with hairpin retainer.
4. Connect wires at connector and install wires in retaining clip.

TURN SIGNAL SWITCH, REPLACE

1968-69 Ford & Mercury

Removal

1. Disconnect battery ground cable.
2. Remove horn button and steering wheel.
3. Remove turn indicator handle.
4. Unscrew and remove turn indicator switch from steering column tube.
5. Disconnect connector blocks at the column. Release tabs one at a time and remove wires from block connectors on 1968 models. It is not necessary to remove wires from connectors on 1969 models.
6. From lower portion of column, remove cover from wiring and tie a cord to the wire ends. Remove switch from top of column, feeding wiring and cord up the column.

Installation

1. Attach the wire ends of a new turn indicator switch to the cord and feed wires down through steering column. Remove cord and install cover.
2. Install connector blocks in column. Plug in electrical leads and secure wiring in retaining clip.
3. Install switch to steering column tube and install indicator handle.
4. Install steering wheel and horn button, and connect battery cable.

SERVICE BULLETIN

1963-67 MODELS: Before judging the turn signal switch to be the cause of malfunction and replacing as defective, first check the following to make certain that they are not causing the problem:

1. The steering shaft should be centered in the column so that the steering wheel hub canceling fingers are in proper relation to the switch canceling mechanism. This can be accomplished by loosening the column attachment to the dash panel and shifting the tube in relation to the shaft.
2. Make sure that the ignition switch is not sticking between the "Start" and the normal engine "On" position, thereby adversely affecting the electrical circuit.
3. Excessive "Locktite" on the threads of the turn signal lever may be contacting the turn signal switch mechanism, causing a binding condition.
4. The fingers on the steering wheel hub canceling cam may be bent so that proper contact with the canceling mechanism cannot be accomplished.

1963-64 Ford & 1964 Mercury

1. Remove steering wheel and horn contact ring.
2. Remove turn signal lever.
3. Remove switch and bracket from steering column.
4. Remove conical tension spring and switch actuating arm.
5. Disconnect switch wires at bullet connectors, remove wire protector from side of steering column, and remove switch and wires.

NOTE: When installing the new switch, make sure the canceling cam on the steering wheel makes contact with the canceling pawls on the switch. The clearance between steering wheel hub and steering shaft housing flange should not be more than 1/16" for proper switch canceling. Reposition steering shaft if necessary.

1963 Mercury

1. Disconnect battery ground cable.
2. Remove transmission selector cover from steering wheel.
3. Remove steering wheel hub cap by pressing and rotating it counterclockwise.
4. Remove steering wheel.
5. Disconnect turn signal and horn wires at connector.
6. Remove lever and horn contact brush from signal switch.
7. Remove shroud attaching screw located on bottom side of steering column.
8. Remove switch retaining plate (3 screws).
9. Remove switch and wires from column.
10. Reverse procedure to install, being sure turn signal wires are routed to prevent them from being pinched and shorted.

1965 Ford & Mercury

1. Disconnect battery ground cable.
2. Remove steering wheel.
3. Disconnect two wire connector blocks at dash panel above steering column.
4. Remove wires and terminals from connector blocks. This can be done by depressing tab on wire terminal with an awl; then pull wire and terminal from connector block.
5. Record color code and location of each wire before removing from block. Tape wires together and attach a piece of heavy cord to wires to help pull them through steering column during installation.
6. Remove turn signal lever.
7. Remove three bearing retainer attaching screws and remove retainer, signal switch and wires from steering column. Disconnect cord from wires.
8. Tape ends of switch wires together and attach cord to wires. Then make the installation in the reverse order of removal.

1966-67 Ford & Mercury

1. Disconnect battery ground cable.
2. Remove horn button.
3. Remove steering wheel.
4. Remove turn signal handle.
5. Remove screws and turn switch from steering column.
6. Remove connector blocks at column. Release tabs one at a time and remove wires from block connectors.
7. From lower portion of column, remove cover from wiring assembly and tie a cord to wire ends. Remove switch from top of column, feeding wire and cord up the column.
8. Attach wire ends of new switch to cord and feed wires down through column. Remove cord and install wiring cover. Then complete the installation in reverse order of removal.

NEUTRAL SAFETY SWITCH

1969 Ford & Mercury

Column Shift

To adjust the switch proceed as follows:

1. Place transmission selector lever against the stop of the neutral detent.
2. Loosen two retaining screws on the steering column.
3. With the selector lever against neutral stop, rotate the switch until a

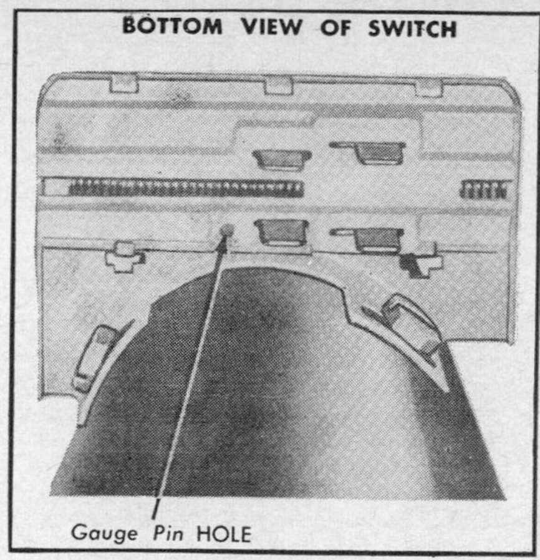

Fig. 10 Neutral safety switch (column shift). All 1967 and 1964-66 with Cruiseomatic

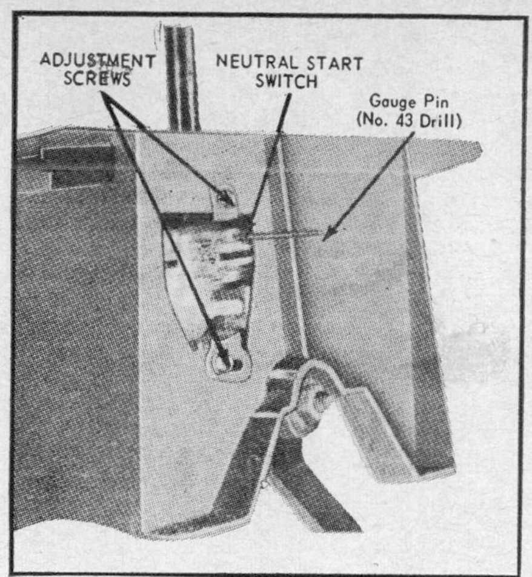

Fig. 11 Neutral safety switch (console shift). 1967-69 with C4 and C6 transmissions

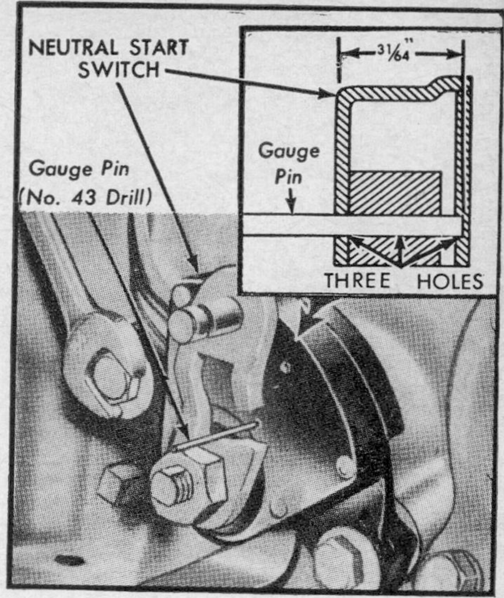

Fig. 12 Neutral safety switch (transmission mounted). 1964-66 with C4 and 1966 with C6 transmissions

start in neutral position is obtained. Then tighten the two screws.

4. With the switch properly adjusted in neutral, place the selector lever in the "1" position and push the park reset button, located on the right side of the switch, to the left until it stops.

NOTE: The park reset must be performed whenever the switch has been adjusted.

1968 Ford & Mercury

Column Shift

The redesigned neutral start switch is mounted on top of the steering column but has been moved closer to the toeboard just below the collapsible section of the jacket.

To adjust the switch, it must be removed from the column. Put the selector lever in neutral and set the parking brake. Then disconnect the electrical and vacuum connections, remove the two fastening screws and lift the switch straight up and out.

After removing the switch body, remove the separate actuator lever. Compress the protruding ends of the lever with pliers and lift the lever out of the column. To adjust the switch, proceed as follows:

1. Hold switch with the wire terminal facing toward you, and with actuator lever in place. Move actuator lever all the way to your left, but don't force it or the switch will be damaged internally.
2. Insert a 3/32" drill or rod ½ inch into the hole in the boss on the top of the switch.
3. Gently but firmly move actuator lever back to the right until it stops. Excessive pressure on the lever will damage the switch. This will move the Park circuit to its position of minimum travel, which must be done if the switch is to function properly upon installation.
4. Remove the 3/32" rod while you align the two gauge pin holes in the switch case. Then reinsert the 3/32" rod.
5. Install the actuator lever to the column by squeezing it slightly and pressing it into position in the shift tube.
6. With the transmission selector lever held against the stop in the neutral detent position, fasten switch to column with the two screws.

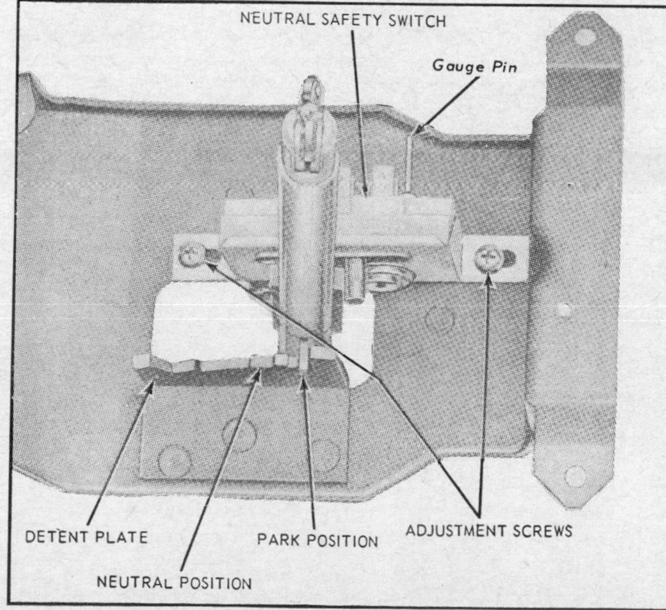

Fig. 13 Neutral safety switch (console shift). 1965-66 Cruiseomatic

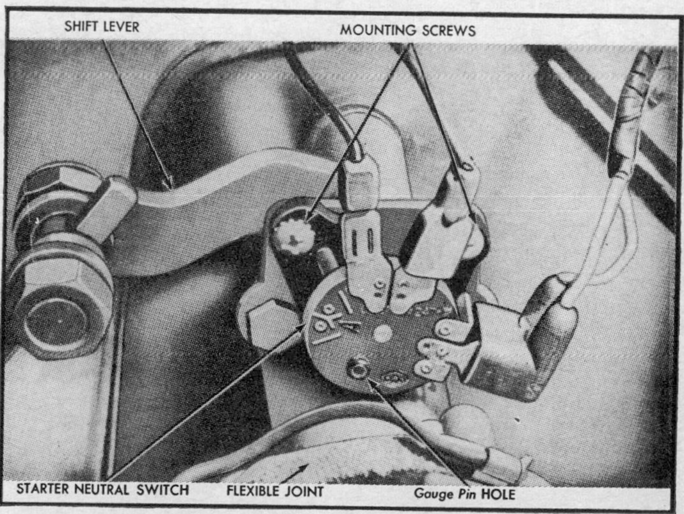

Fig. 14 Neutral safety switch (column shift). 1963

7. After connecting wiring and any vacuum hose, be sure to remove the $\frac{3}{32}$" rod.

All 1967 & 1964-66 Cruiseomatic

Column Shift, Fig. 10

1. With manual linkage properly adjusted, check starter engagement circuit in all transmission selector lever positions. The circuit must be open in all drive positions and closed only in Park and Neutral.
2. To adjust switch, loosen retaining screws that locate switch on steering column.
3. Place transmission selector lever firmly against the stop of the neutral detent position.
4. Rotate switch actuating lever until gauge pin (#43 drill) can be inserted in gauge pin holes.
5. Tighten switch screws and remove gauge pin.

1967-69 C4 & C6 Units

Console Shift, Fig. 11

1. Remove selector lever handle.
2. Unfasten and position console to one side.
3. Loosen adjusting screws.
4. Move selector lever back and forth until gauge pin (#43 drill) can be fully inserted into gauge pin holes.
5. Place transmission selector lever firmly against stop of neutral detent position.
6. Slide combination neutral start and back-up light switch forward or rearward as required until switch actuating lever contacts selector lever.
7. Tighten switch attaching screws, remove gauge pin and check for starting in Park position.

1964-66 With C4 and 1966 With C6

Replace and Adjust, Fig. 12

1. Apply penetrating oil to outer lever attaching nut to prevent breaking inner lever shaft. Remove transmission downshift outer lever attaching nut and lever.
2. Remove two neutral start switch screws.
3. Disconnect two multiple wire connectors and remove switch from transmission.
4. Install new switch.
5. With transmission manual lever in neutral, check location of switch with gauge pin (#43 drill) and adjust switch if necessary.
6. Tighten switch bolts and remove gauge pin.
7. Install outer downshift lever, and downshift linkage rod to lever.
8. Install switch wires and check operation of switch.

1965-66 With Cruiseomatic

Console Shift, Fig. 13

1. Remove handle from selector lever.
2. Remove chrome trim panel from top of console.
3. Place lever in neutral position and remove three quadrant attaching screws. Remove indicator light from quadrant base and lift quadrant from console.
4. Loosen two adjustment screws.
5. Move selector lever back and forth until gauge pin (#43 drill) can be fully inserted in gauge pin holes.
6. Place transmission selector lever firmly against stop of neutral detent position.
7. Slide combination neutral start and back-up light switch forward or rearward as required until switch actuating lever contacts selector lever.
8. Tighten switch attaching screws and check for starting in Park position.
9. Complete operation in reverse order.

1963

Column Shift, Fig. 14

1. Check starter circuit in all selector positions. Engine should start when selector lever is placed in Neutral and Park only.
2. To adjust switch, loosen steering column attaching screws.
3. Shift selector lever to Neutral.
4. Move switch in elongated mounting holes until a .090" gauge pin can be inserted through switch housing and into switch plate, Fig. 14.
5. With gauge pin in place, tighten screws and remove gauge pin.
6. Recheck starter circuit in all selector lever positions.

HORN SOUNDER, REPLACE

1969 Rim-Blow Type

The rubber insert and copper strip assembly is not replaceable. Therefore if a new insert assembly is required the entire steering wheel must be replaced.

1. Remove the pad from the steering wheel (three screws).
2. Remove medallion from the pad.
3. After removing the steering wheel nut the wheel can be removed from the shaft with a wheel puller.

1968-69 Except Rim-Blow Type

1. Disconnect battery ground cable.
2. Remove steering column pad (2 screws).
3. Push down and turn horn ring and remove ring and spring.
4. Reverse procedure to install.

1965-67 Ford

1. Disconnect horn wire connector that has a yellow and yellow-green wire in it, under instrument panel to the left of steering column.
2. Press down evenly on horn ring and turn counterclockwise until it lifts out from steering wheel.
3. Remove horn ring and spring.
4. The horn ring contacts are integral with the turn signal switch and are removed with the switch.
5. Reverse procedure to install.

1966-67 Mercury

1. Disconnect horn wires at connector at lower end of steering column.
2. Remove hub from steering column by pressing it down and rotating it counterclockwise.
3. Remove screws from center retaining the wires.
4. Remove center screws retaining the ring to the column and from end of ring to steering wheel. A spring will fall out from under each button.
5. Position springs under buttons. Place ring to wheel and install center screws. Install ring to steering column, securing it with a screw at each end of the buttons located in steering spokes. Then complete the installation in reverse order of removal.

1965 Mercury

1. Disconnect horn wires at connector under instrument panel.
2. Remove center steering wheel cover by pressing down and rotating it counterclockwise.
3. Remove two screws at center of wheel and one screw securing three horn wires.
4. Remove three screws under steering wheel retaining horn button and remove button.
5. Reverse procedure to install.

1963-64 Ford & Mercury

Remove horn ring emblem by turning counterclockwise. Remove steering shaft nut and, with suitable puller, remove horn ring and steering wheel.

When installing, align mark in steering wheel hub with mark on steering gear shaft.

INSTRUMENT CLUSTER

1969 Ford

Fuel Gauge & Speedometer

1. From passenger side of instrument panel, remove lighter element and all of the control knobs, and then remove the cluster trim cover (10 screws).
2. Remove the attaching screws and the lens.
3. Remove attaching screws and lift the mask from the speedometer and fuel gauge.
4. Remove spring washers and nuts (one at each side) and the attaching screw at the bottom, then remove fuel gauge from the studs.
5. Remove attaching screws and pull speedometer head out of cluster far enough to reach the cable disconnect.
6. To disengage the cable, press on the flat surface of the disconnect and at the same time pull the cable from the head.
7. Remove the speedometer.
8. Reverse the procedure to install.

Instrument Cluster

1. Remove the instrument panel pad (20 screws).
2. From behind cluster disconnect all

electrical connections to cluster.
3. Disconnect heater, air conditioner and speedometer cables.
4. Remove lighter element and all control knobs from passenger side of cluster.
5. Remove cluster trim cover (10 screws).
6. Remove eight mounting screws and withdraw cluster from panel.
7. Reverse procedure to install.

1969 Mercury

Instrument Cluster

1. Remove wiper knob and bezel, cigar lighter element and the finish panel.
2. Remove instrument panel pad.
3. Remove wiper nut and the bracket (3 screws) from left end of pad support.
4. Remove lighter socket and bracket from right end of pad support.
5. Remove five pad support-to-instrument panel screws and three lower left panel-to-instrument panel screws and then remove pad support and lower panel as an assembly.
6. From behind cluster, disconnect all electrical connections to cluster and speedometer cable.
7. Remove the cluster assembly from panel (6 screws).
8. Reverse procedure to install.

Fuel Gauge & Speedometer

After removal of cluster as described above, the speedometer and fuel gauge can be removed from the cluster.

1968 Ford

Fuel Gauge & Speedometer

1. Disconnect battery ground cable.
2. Remove right and left windshield pillar mouldings.
3. Pry moulding from right side of instrument panel pad covering pad screws.
4. Pry off two access covers located above speedometer lens and on underside of pad.
5. Remove instrument panel pad (11 screws).
6. Pull pad off radio control knobs.
7. Remove instrument cluster mask and lens (10 button clips).
8. Disconnect speedometer cable.
9. Remove instrument panel lower pad (5 screws).
10. Remove clock upper retainer (2 screws).
11. Remove two clock screws and position clock forward.
12. Remove plate under speedometer (1 screw).
13. Remove speedometer and black out cover (2 rubber spacers and 5 screws).
14. Remove two fuel gauge screws and position gauge out. Disconnect two wire connectors and remove fuel gauge.
15. Reverse procedure to install.

1968 Mercury

Fuel Gauge

1. Disconnect battery ground cable.
2. Remove control knobs from heater controls, radio, clock, wiper switch (pull off) and headlight switch.
3. Remove speedometer bezel.
4. Remove right and left instrument panel finish panels.
5. Remove speedometer cover lens (4 buttons).
6. Remove fuel gauge cover lens.
7. Remove screws retaining fuel gauge to cluster and position gauge out. Disconnect two push on connectors to gauge and remove gauge.
8. Reverse procedure to install.

Speedometer

1. Disconnect battery ground cable.
2. Remove knobs from heater control, radio and clock.
3. Pull knob from wiper switch.
4. Remove headlight switch knob.
5. Remove speedometer bezell (4 screws).
6. Remove right and left finish panels from cluster.
7. Remove speedometer dial cover (4 buttons).
8. Remove four screws retaining speedometer from cluster and position speedometer out by working speedometer cable out with assembly.
9. Disconnect speedometer cable and also disconnect instrument voltage regulator and remove speedometer and housing.
10. Unfasten speedometer from housing.
11. Reverse procedure to install.

1967 Ford

Fuel Gauge

1. Disconnect ground strap from battery.
2. Remove cigar lighter and radio knobs.
3. Remove instrument trim cover (10 screws).
4. Unfasten warning light housing (4 screws).
5. Disconnect fuel gauge and remove warning light housing.
6. Remove warning light housing lens and mask.
7. Remove fuel gauge from housing.
8. Reverse procedure to install.

Speedometer

1. Disconnect ground strap from battery.
2. Remove instrument panel pad.
3. Remove clock re-set knob.
4. Remove warning light housing.
5. Remove eight friction pins retaining instrument cluster and mask. Remove lens.
6. Remove four rubber spacers.
7. Remove three screws retaining speedometer to its back can. Position speedometer outward, disconnect cable and remove speedometer.

1967 Mercury

Fuel Gauge

1. Disconnect ground strap from battery.
2. Remove radio knobs.
3. Remove cluster housing screws.
4. Remove speedometer mask and lens (4 friction pins).
5. Remove left hand lens and mask (4 friction pins).
6. Unfasten fuel gauge from instrument cluster rear housing (3 screws). Position fuel gauge outward, disconnect two connectors and remove gauge.
7. Reverse procedure to install.

Speedometer

1. Disconnect ground strap from battery
2. Remove radio knobs.
3. Remove instrument cluster housing.
4. Remove speedometer mask and lens (4 friction pins).
5. Unfasten speedometer (4 screws). Position speedometer outward, disconnect cable and remove speedometer.
6. Reverse procedure to install.

1965-66 Ford

Fuel Gauge & Speedometer

1. Disconnect battery ground cable.
2. Remove cluster pad and retainer.
3. Remove upper and lower cluster covers.
4. Remove radio knobs.
5. Remove friction pins retaining cluster lens and mask and remove lens and mask.
6. Disconnect speedometer cable and remove speedometer retaining bracket.
7. Remove left standoffs and speedometer.
8. Remove screws retaining fuel gauge, pull back on left side of speedometer (if not already removed) and ease out fuel gauge. Remove wires and take out fuel gauge.

1965-66 Mercury

1. Disconnect battery ground cable.
2. Remove headlight, radio, w/s wiper, heater and air conditioner control knobs.
3. Remove screws from instrument cluster center finish panel.
4. Pull finish panel out of instrument panel, disconnect wires from heater and air conditioner switches and remove finish panel.
5. With finish panel removed, all instruments are individually accessible.

1964 Ford

1. Disconnect battery cable.
2. Disconnect speedometer cable at instrument.
3. Remove two nuts retaining wiring harness at rear of instrument panel.
4. Remove cluster front cover.
5. Disconnect instrument wiring harness from two clips at rear of panel.
6. Detach instrument cluster from panel (5 screws). Pull out cluster and place it on steering column.
7. Disconnect wires to instruments and remove bulbs from cluster.
8. Remove cluster assembly, and service instruments as required.

1964 Mercury

1. Disconnect battery cable and speedometer cable from instrument.

2. Detach cluster from panel (9 screws). Pull out cluster and place it on steering column.
3. Unclip main wiring loom at back of cluster.
4. Disconnect main wiring loom lead and ammeter lead at junction block in center of cluster. Pull ammeter lead out of ammeter loop.
5. Disconnect wires at instruments and remove instrument bulbs.
6. Remove cluster assembly, and service instruments as required.

1963 Mercury

1. Disconnect battery ground cable.
2. Disconnect speedometer cable.
3. Remove wires from clip at right hand clock retaining nut.
4. Release instrument cluster wire loom from two clips.
5. Protect upper cluster and steering column from damage with cloth.
6. Remove automatic transmission quadrant dial cover moulding.
7. Place transmission selector lever in low gear position.
8. Remove ten upper cluster-to-instrument panel retaining screws. Four long screws at top, four screws at bottom and two screws just above steering column.
9. Turn automatic transmission indicator to one side.
10. Carefully pull upper cluster outward and lay it on protective cloth on steering column.
11. Remove wiring harness and clips. Disconnect gauge wires, remove sockets and lamps and remove cluster.

1963 Ford

1. Disconnect battery cable.
2. Remove steering column cover plate.
3. On cars with automatic transmission, turn indicator needle downward on shifting shaft.
4. Disconnect speedometer cable at instrument.
5. Disconnect cluster wiring harness from clips at rear of panel.
6. Unfasten and pull out cluster and lay it on steering column.
7. Disconnect wires at instruments and remove lamp bulbs.
8. Remove cluster assembly and service instruments as required.

W/S WIPER MOTOR

1969 Ford & Mercury

1. Remove wiper arm and blade assemblies from pivot shafts.
2. Remove cowl top grille (10 screws).
3. Disconnect linkage drive arm from motor output arm crankpin by removing clip.
4. Disconnect wire push-on connectors from motor.
5. From engine side of dash, remove bolts retaining motor to dash and remove motor. If output arm catches on dash during removal, hand turn the arm clockwise so it will clear opening in dash.
6. When installing motor, align output arm with opening in dash and turn the arm clockwise as necessary.

1968 Ford & Mercury

1. Remove cowl intake screen.
2. Disconnect wiper links at motor output arm pin. Disconnect motor harness by removing clip.
3. Disconnect motor harness connector and remove motor.
4. Unfasten motor from bracket.

Installation

1. Assemble new motor to bracket. Correctly position vapor seal gasket or replace if required.
2. Connect harness connector to new motor.
3. Position motor and install retaining bolts. Temporarily connect motor wiring connector to motor and run motor so that it is in park position before connecting linkage to motor.
4. Complete installation in reverse order of removal.

1967 Ford & Mercury

1. Remove cowl intake screen.
2. Disconnect wiper links at motor output arm pin. Disconnect motor harness by removing retension clip.
3. Disconnect motor harness connector and take off motor.
4. Reverse procedure to install, being sure motor is in park position before connecting linkage to motor.

1964-66 Ford & Mercury

1. To remove wiper motor, disconnect wiper links at motor output arm pins.
2. Unfasten and lower motor.
3. Disconnect motor harness connector and remove motor.

1963 Ford

To remove the wiper motor on car with air conditioner, remove the glove box liner, radio, speaker, and right defroster nozzle-to-instrument panel brace (if equipped). Then remove the wiper motor through the speaker opening.

To remove the wiper motor on cars without air conditioning, proceed as follows:

1. Remove two bolts retaining motor and lower the motor.
2. Disconnect wiper motor vacuum line at motor or at bullet connector.
3. Loosen screw retaining wiper control cable at motor and disconnect cable.
4. Reverse above procedure to install motor and adjust control cable.

1963 Mercury Electric Type

1. If equipped with air conditioner, remove glove box liner, radio speaker and radio.
2. Disconnect ground cable from battery.
3. Disconnect black motor feed wire at bullet connector.
4. Remove one screw and disconnect control cable from motor.
5. Remove two bolts attaching motor flange to cowl.
6. Remove 10 screws and remove cowl grille.
7. Remove nut and washer attaching auxiliary drive to motor output shaft and remove wiper motor.

W/S WIPER SWITCH

1969 Ford

1. To allow removal of cluster trim cover, remove the radio, wiper, washer, interval and heater switch knobs and the lighter element.
2. Remove retaining screws and cluster trim cover assembly.
3. Remove screws that retain the switch to the cluster, lower switch and disconnect multiple connector and vacuum hose from switch.

1969 Mercury

1. Remove wiper knob and bezel from switch shaft.
2. Remove nut that retains switch to bracket.
3. Lower switch from behind panel and disconnect multiple connector and vacuum hoses from the switch.

1968 Ford

1. Remove wiper and washer control knobs.
2. Reaching under instrument panel, remove two screws retaining switch to lower portion of instrument panel.
3. Disconnect multiple connector and two single connectors from switch.
4. Separate wiper switch from washer switch.

1968 Mercury

1. Disconnect battery ground cable.
2. Remove screw retaining washer coordinator to lower edge of instrument panel and position co-ordinator to the side.
3. Pull off wiper control knob.
4. Remove nut retaining switch to cluster. Lower switch and disconnect multiple connector and five vacuum hoses, then remove switch.

1967 Ford

1. Disconnect ground strap from battery.
2. Remove cigar lighter and radio knobs.
3. Remove instrument cluster trim cover (10 screws).
4. Unfasten switch and bracket from cluster back plate (4 screws).
5. Position switch outward. Disconnect wiring and remove switch and bracket.
6. Remove control knob.
7. Remove bezel nut and remove switch from bracket.
8. Reverse procedure to install.

1967 Mercury

1. Disconnect ground strap from battery.
2. Loosen set screw and remove control knob.
3. Remove switch bezel.
4. Lower switch and remove three vacuum hoses.
5. Unplug connector and remove switch.

6. Reverse procedure to install.

1964-66 Ford & Mercury

1. Loosen retaining screw and take off switch knob.
2. Remove switch bezel nut.
3. Remove switch from instrument panel.
4. To install reverse removal procedure.

1963 Ford & Mercury

1. Loosen control cable retaining and adjusting screw at wiper motor. Disconnect wiper control cable.
2. Loosen retaining screw and take off control knob.
3. Remove wiper control bezel nut.
4. Remove wiper control from instrument panel.
5. To install reverse removal procedure.

W/S WIPER TRANSMISSION

1969 Ford & Mercury

1. Remove wiper arm and blades from pivot shafts.
2. Remove cowl top grille.
3. The right pivot shaft and link has to be removed before the left assembly or drive arm can be removed. Remove three retaining screws at right pivot shaft and disconnect the right link from the plate on the inner side of the dash panel by removing the clip. Lift the pivot assembly out of cowl opening.
4. Remove three retaining screws at the left pivot shaft and disconnect the left link from the plate and lift out of cowl opening.
5. Reverse the procedure to install.

1968 Ford & Mercury

1. Remove wiper arms and blades.
2. Remove cowl top ventilator grille, hood pad and windshield washer nozzles.
3. Through cowl opening remove clip retaining wiper arms to motor drive arm.
4. Remove pivot shaft screws, then remove pivot and arms as an assembly from right side of cowl openings.
5. Remove arm to pivot retaining clip.

Installation

1. Install new arm or pivot and clip.
2. Position arm assembly through right side of cowl opening and install screws.
3. On Mercury only, position left hand pivot and pump assembly with hoses through cowl top hole and install grommet. Recouple hoses at connectors after mounting screws are attached.
4. Position wiper arm to motor drive arm and install clip.
5. On Mercury only, disconnect vacuum and washer hoses at plastic connectors; remove grommet around hoses on left side for pivot and pump vibra jet. Removal of right hand pivot shaft is same as Ford.
6. Install washer nozzles, position cowl top hood pad and grill and install retaining screws. Install wiper arms and blades.

1965-67 Ford & Mercury

1. Remove wiper arms and blades.
2. Remove cowl top ventilator grille, hood pad and w/s washer nozzles.
3. Through cowl opening, remove clip from wiper arms-to-drive arms.
4. Remove pivot and arms as an assembly from right side of cowl opening.
5. Remove arm-to-pivot retaining clip.
6. Reverse procedure to install.

1964 Ford & Mercury

1. To remove wiper pivot shaft and link first remove arm and blade.
2. Disconnect wiper link at motor output arm pin. *Be sure to note sequence in which link and washers are installed on pin for reassembly.*
3. Remove pivot shaft and link.
4. To install reverse removal procedure.

1963 Ford & Mercury

1. To remove pivot shaft and link, remove hood, cowl panel, windshield washer nozzles and hood ground strap.
2. On cars with radio, swing cowl top panel around and lay it across air cleaner without removing antenna.
3. Remove cowl vent screen and water seal.
4. Remove wiper arm and blade.
5. Disconnect wiper link at motor arm.
6. Remove nut and washer and guide pivot shaft down into air duct and remove pivot and link assembly.
7. To install reverse removal procedure.

RADIO REPLACE

NOTE: When installing radio, be sure to adjust antenna trimmer for peak performance.

1969 Ford

1. Remove the trim cover from instrument panel.
2. Remove three nuts retaining front of radio to cluster.
3. Remove screw retaining the rear support to the bottom of the radio.
4. Pull radio from cluster and disconnect wires from chassis.

1969 Mercury

1. Disconnect battery ground cable.
2. Remove control knobs from radio.
3. Disconnect all wires from radio and remove nut attaching the rear support to the back of the radio.
4. Remove nut attaching the front edge of radio to instrument panel and remove radio.
5. Remove nut from radio control shaft.

1968 Ford

1. Disconnect battery ground cable.
2. Remove side garnish mouldings from windshield pillars.
3. Unsnap moulding from right side of instrument panel pad to reveal pad attaching screws.
4. Remove two pop-off access covers from instrument panel pad in cluster area.
5. Remove four screws attaching right half of pad to instrument panel.
6. Remove two screws attaching left side of pad to instrument panel above cluster.
7. Remove three screws attaching left side of pad below cluster.
8. Remove one screw attaching each end of instrument panel lower pad to upper pad and remove upper pad.
9. Pull off radio control knobs.
10. Remove lens and mask from cluster (10 buttons).
11. Remove black out cover at right of speedometer (2 screws).
12. Unfasten radio front mounting plate from instrument panel (4 screws).
13. Unfasten radio rear bracket from instrument panel (1 screw).
14. Pull radio part way out and disconnect antenna lead-in cable. Then pull radio out and disconnect power and speaker wires from radio.
15. Remove front mounting plate and rear bracket from radio.
16. Reverse procedure to install.

1968 Mercury

1. Disconnect battery ground cable.
2. Pull off radio control knobs.
3. Remove speedometer bezel (4 screws).
4. Pull W/S wiper knob off shaft.
5. Remove clock and heater knobs.
6. Remove cluster right finish panel (4 screws).
7. Remove nut attaching rear support to radio.
8. Unfasten radio and mounting plate from instrument panel (4 screws). Pull radio out from panel and disconnect radio feed wires, speaker wires and antenna lead from radio.
9. Remove mounting plate from radio.
10. Reverse procedure to install.

1967 Ford & Mercury

1. Disconnect ground cable at battery.
2. Remove radio knobs and, on Ford, remove cigar lighter.
3. Remove instrument cluster cover (10 screws on Ford, 13 on Mercury)
4. Remove radio rear support nut.
5. Remove two bolts (Ford) or four screws (Mercury) that retain radio to instrument cluster.
6. Pull radio forward out of cluster and disconnect antenna, speaker and power leads from radio.
7. Reverse procedure to install.

1965-66 Ford & Mercury

1. Disconnect battery ground cable.
2. If air conditioned, disconnect ducts from plenum and remove nozzle adapter plate.
3. On air conditioned Mercury, remove ash tray and slide bracket.
4. Remove radio knobs.
5. Remove nut from radio bracket and position bracket out of the way (if air conditioned, remove bracket).
6. Disconnect antenna, speaker, power and pilot light leads from radio.

7. On Ford, remove two mounting bolts from under instrument panel and remove radio. On Mercury, remove two mounting nuts and remove radio.

1964 Ford & Mercury

Without Air Conditioning

1. Pull off radio control knobs and nuts retaining radio to panel.
2. Disconnect antenna lead at right side of radio.
3. Disconnect speaker lead and pilot light wire at wiring harness.
4. Disconnect radio lead wire at fuse panel.
5. Remove nut retaining radio to back support bracket and lift out radio.

With Air Conditioning

1. Remove glove box liner, radio speaker and right mounting support.
2. Remove radio through speaker opening.

1963 Mercury

1. Disconnect battery ground cable.
2. On air conditioned cars, remove glove box liner.
3. Disconnect antenna lead in cable and speaker plug from radio.
4. On air conditioned cars, remove speaker grille and speaker. If rear speaker is employed, unplug speaker from speaker harness.
5. Disconnect dial lamp lead at bullet connector and power lead at main lighting junction block.
6. Remove control knobs and two nuts and washers from front of radio.
7. Remove bracket retaining nut from back of radio; on air conditioned cars remove bracket.
8. Remove radio from car. On air conditioned cars, remove radio through speaker grille opening with push buttons facing down.

1963 Ford

1. Pull off radio knobs and remove nuts retaining radio to instrument panel.
2. Disconnect antenna lead at right side of radio.
3. Disconnect speaker leads and pilot light wire at wiring harness.
4. Disconnect radio lead wire at fuse panel and wire from retaining clips.
5. Remove radio support bolt and nut.
6. Lift radio out of instrument panel.
7. Reverse removal procedure to install.

1963 Ford Air Conditioned

Remove the glove box liner, radio speaker, right radio mounting support and then lift the radio through the speaker opening.

HEATER CORE REMOVAL

1969 Ford & Mercury less Air Cond.

1. Drain cooling system and disconnect heater hoses from the core.
2. Remove the core cover and gasket and remove the heater core.

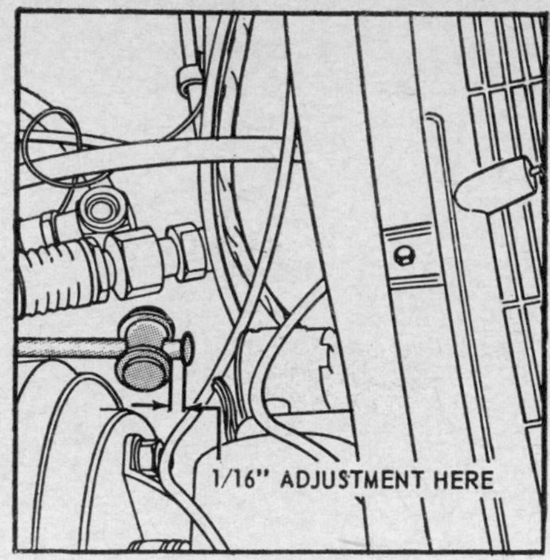

Fig. 15 Bead chain adjustment. 1967-68

1969 Ford & Mercury with Air Cond.

1. Drain cooling system.
2. Remove carburetor air cleaner.
3. Remove vacuum manifold from dash panel.
4. Disconnect heater hoses, remove core cover and remove the core.

1965-68 Ford & Mercury less Air Cond.

1. Drain cooling system and remove heater hoses at core.
2. Remove retaining screws, heater core cover and seal from plenum.
3. Remove heater core from plenum.
4. Before installing new core, apply a thin film of silicone lubricant to pads.

1965-68 Ford & Mercury with Air Cond.

1. Remove the hood, right hinge support bracket and the right hinge and mounting assembly. Do not separate the hinge from the mounting.
2. Loosen the wiring harness from the right fender and move harness to one side.
3. Drain cooling system and disconnect heater hoses from core and move them out of way.
4. Run a strip of masking tape down the leading edge of right front door to protect the edge.
5. Unfasten, at the rear of the right front fender, the bolts holding the fender to the body.
6. Block fender away from body and remove bolts holding heater housing to the dash.
7. Lift the fender and pull out the heater housing and core assembly.
8. Take cover off the housing and remove the core.
9. Reverse the procedure to install.

1963-64 Ford & Mercury

It is necessary to remove the heater assembly from the vehicle to gain access to the core. Make necessary disconnections. Then, with unit on bench, remove core cover plate and temperature control valve as an assembly.

SPEED CONTROLS

1969

Bead Chain, Adjust

With the engine at hot idle, adjust the bead chain to obtain ½ to 1 ball slack in the chain.

1967-68

Bead Chain, Adjust

With the carburetor set at hot idle, adjust the Bowden cable to provide a 1/16" clearance between the Bowden cable end "C" washer and the accelerator linkage sleeve, Fig. 15.

1965-66

Brake Release Switch

1. Remove plug connector from inhibitor switch and install a jumper wire.
2. Remove plug connector from vacuum valve.
3. Ground one lead of a test lamp and touch other lead to red wire from vacuum valve.
4. Turn ignition switch to ACC position. Pull out switch button to ON position.
5. Depress brake pedal; test light should go out within first ¼ inch of travel measured at bottom of brake pedal pad.
6. If test lamp does not go out in ¼ inch of pedal pad travel, loosen brake pedal bracket attaching bolts and position bracket so it just clears plunger of brake release switch.
7. Vehicles equipped with power brakes should have the engine started and brake pedal depressed several times to assure correct operation of brake release switch with vacuum applied to power brake booster.
8. If brake switch cannot be adjusted, it must be replaced.

Accelerator Linkage, Adjust

Improper accelerator linkage adjustment can result in engine not returning to normal idle, the unit not allowing control at high speeds, or a lag in response to speed changes.

1. Disconnect ball chain from accelerator pedal arm attachment.
2. Check throttle linkage adjustment, being sure that linkage is against normal idle adjusting screw with engine stopped.
3. With vacuum bellows in released position, hold ball chain taut to accelerator pedal arm attachment. Hold attachment up in its normal position.
4. Allow one-half to one ball slack in chain. Cut off extra chain and reconnect chain to accelerator pedal arm attachment. If chain is too short a new chain must be installed.

Control Cable, Adjust

1. Remove two vacuum hoses and air filter from metering valve.
2. Loosen jam nut from cam adjusting

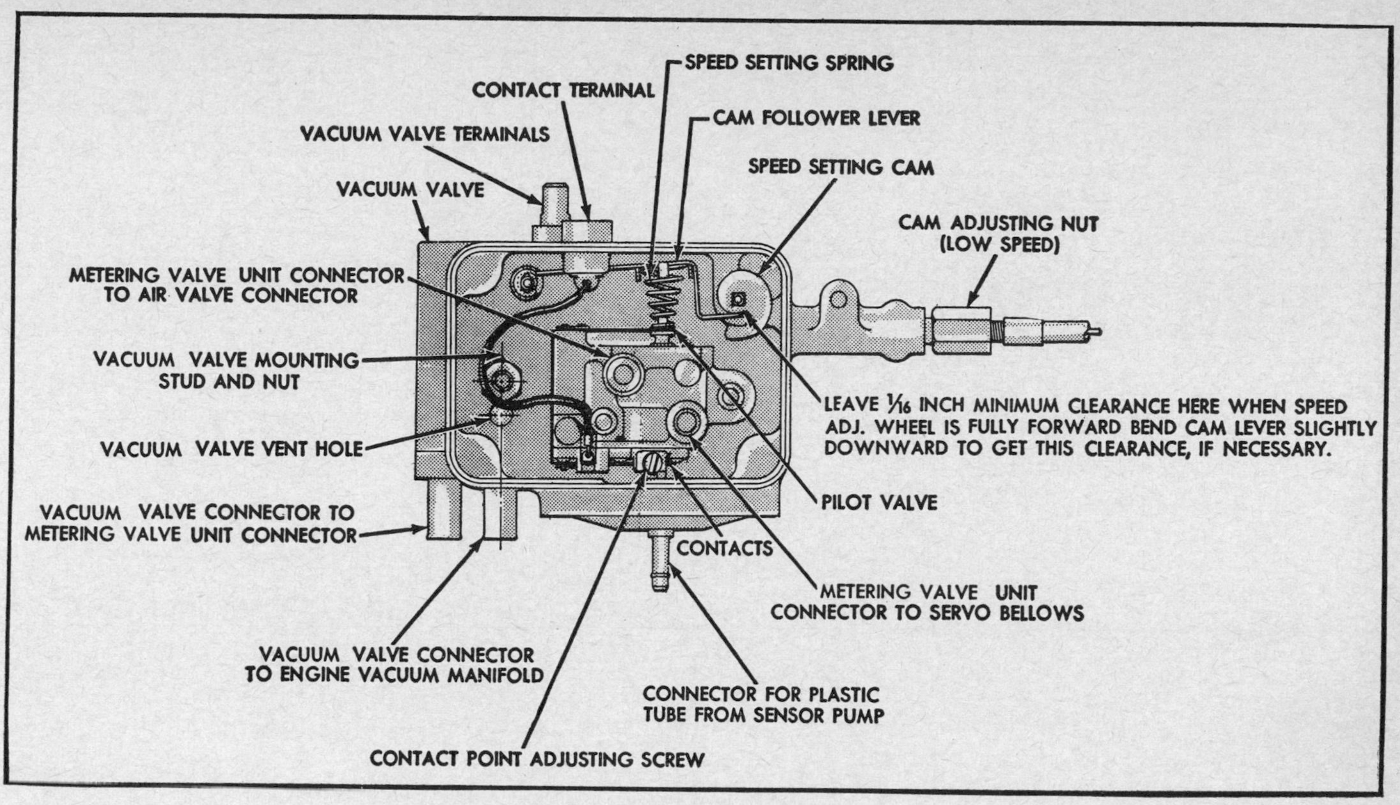

Fig. 16 Metering valve details. The 1/16" setting applies to early 1965 units not having an inhibitor switch; otherwise clearance is 3/16"

nut.

3. Rotate selector dial against low speed stop.
4. Rotate cam adjusting nut until clearance between cam follower lever and speed setting cam is $\frac{3}{16}$ inch. *As shown in Fig. 16, the $\frac{1}{16}$ inch clearance applies to early 1965 units without an inhibitor switch.*
5. Tighten jam nut snugly against cam adjusting nut. The cam adjusting nut is designed to be loose in the metering valve; it cannot be held tight.
6. Install air filter and the two vacuum hoses.

NOTE: When there is insufficient thread for cable adjustment when installing a new metering valve, proceed as follows:

1. Remove two vacuum hoses and air filter from metering valve.
2. Remove first screw from control cable cover plate and loosen other screw.
3. Rotate cover plate so it faces upward.
4. Remove control cable rack from speed setting cam pinion.
5. Replace metering valve if required.
6. Position speed setting cam to provide approximately $\frac{3}{16}$" clearance to cam follower lever ($\frac{1}{16}$ inch on early 1965 units without inhibitor switch).
7. Rotate selector dial against low speed stop.
8. Loosen jam nut. Position jam nut so that there are three threads visible beyond jam nut. Position cam adjusting nut against jam nut.
9. Install control cable rack onto speed setting cam pinion. Try to maintain $\frac{3}{16}$ inch (or $\frac{1}{16}$ inch on early 1965 units) clearance.
10. With jam adjusting nut in its groove, lower control cable cover plate and install and tighten attaching screws.
11. Final control cable adjustment is made as outlined previously.

Engine Section

ENGINE, REPLACE

NOTE: Because of engine compartment tolerances, the engine should not be removed and installed with the transmission attached.

1. Drain cooling system and crankcase.
2. Remove radiator and air cleaner.
3. Remove hood.
4. Remove fuel and vacuum lines and all hoses, wires and linkage attached to engine.
5. Disconnect exhaust pipe from manifolds.
6. Remove starter and automatic transmission filler tube (if equipped).
7. Remove converter or flywheel housing lower cover.
8. Remove clutch release linkage (if equipped).
9. Support transmission with jack.
10. Unfasten converter or flywheel housing from engine.
11. Remove engine mounting bolts and lift engine out of chassis.

Fig. 1 Cylinder head tightening sequence. 6-240 engine

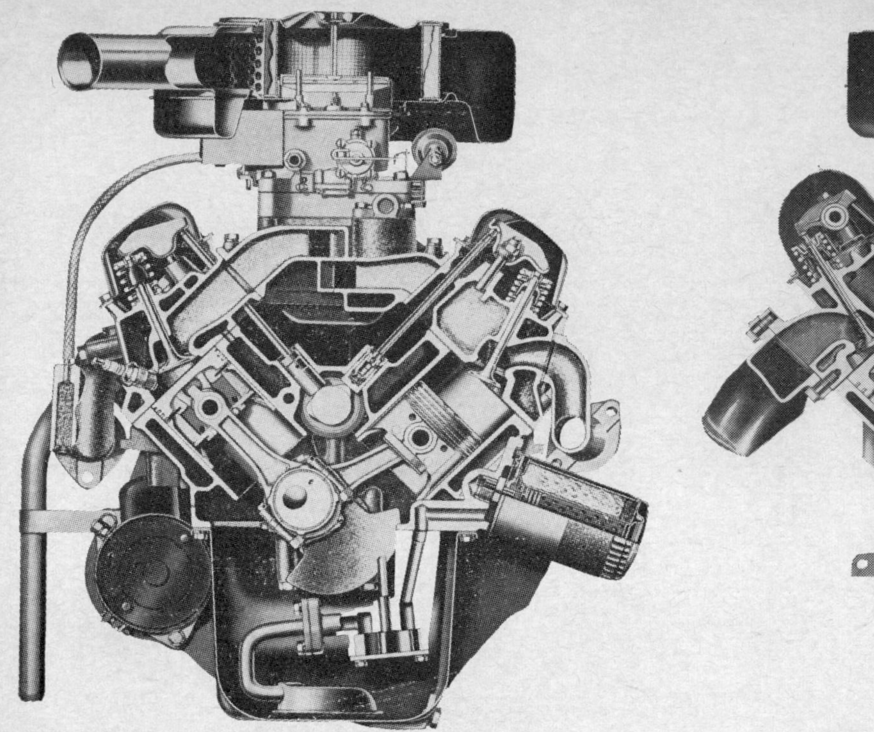

Cross section of V8-260, 289, 302 engines

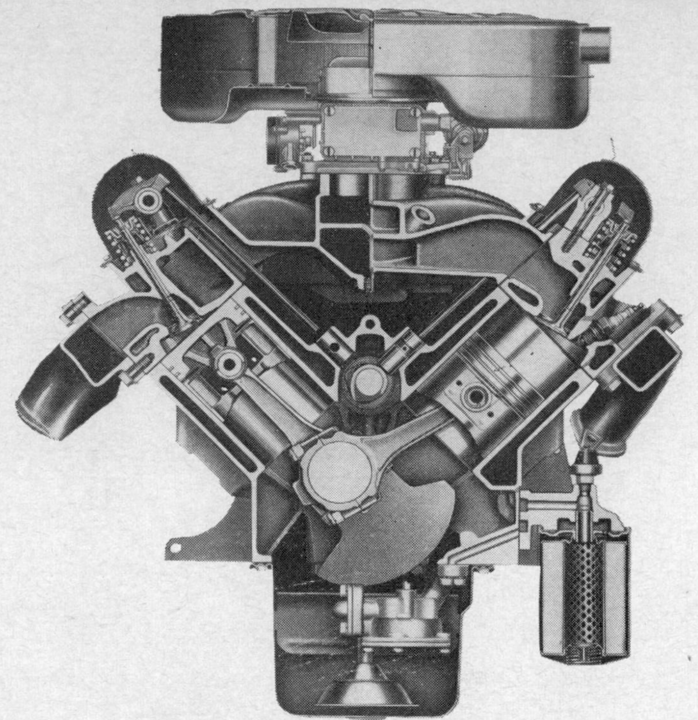

Cross section of V8-352, 390, 410, 428 engines

CYLINDER HEAD REPLACE

SERVICE BULLETIN

REMOVE CYLINDER HEAD: In some cases it is difficult to remove the cylinder head from 1963 223, 260 and 289 cu. in. engines. The problem is due to the adhesion or sticking condition of the cylinder head gasket. The problem does not exist on 1964 engines.

To remove a V-8 head without risk of damaging engine parts, place a wood block in the tappet galley. Then, using the block as a base, place the tip of a pry bar under the exhaust crossover area of the head, and the fulcrum of the bar on the block. A force exerted on the bar will pry the head loose without risk of causing damage. An alternate method is to use a scissors-type power jack, in place of the bar, to supply needed force.

On 6 cyl. 223 cu. in. engines, insert one end of a pry bar in the exhaust port in the center of the head. Then lift the other end of the bar to break the head loose from the block.

Tighten cylinder head bolts a little at a time in three steps in the sequence shown in the illustrations. Final tightening should be to the torque specifications listed in the *Engine Tightening* table. After bolts have been tightened to specifications, *they should not be disturbed.*

In instances where cylinder head gasket leakage is hard to control, aluminum paint can be applied to the gasket as a sealer.

Spray one coat of the aluminum paint on both sides of the gasket and allow the paint to dry. Then spray a second coat on both sides and, while the paint is still wet, install the gasket. Torque the head and manifold bolts to specifications to complete the job.

1965-69 6-240 Engine

1. Drain cooling system and remove air cleaner.
2. Disconnect hoses, tubing, wires and linkage attached to head.
3. Grasp crankcase ventilation regulator valve and pull it from rocker arm cover. Disconnect crankcase vent hose from inlet tube on intake manifold and remove hose and valve.

NOTE: If equipped with Thermactor Exhaust Emission Control System, disconnect air pump outlet hose at air manifold assembly. Remove air manifold. Disconnect anti-backfire valve air and vacuum lines at intake manifold.

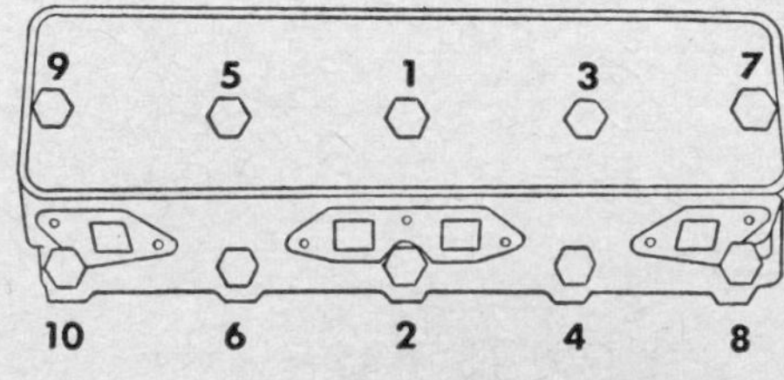

Fig. 2 Cylinder head tightening sequence. V8 engines

4. Remove rocker arm cover. Loosen rocker arm stud nuts so that rocker arms can be rotated to one side.
5. Remove push rods and identify them so they can be installed in their original locations.
6. Disconnect exhaust pipe from engine.
7. Remove head bolts.
8. Install cylinder head lifting eyes in locations shown in Fig. 1.
9. Lift head with intake and exhaust manifolds from engine.
10. Reverse procedure to install and tighten head down in the sequence shown in Fig. 1.

1963-68 V8-260, 289, 302

1. Remove intake manifold and carburetor as an assembly.
2. Disconnect battery ground cable at cylinder head.
3. Remove rocker arm cover.
4. On air conditioned cars, remove compressor.
5. On car with power steering, disconnect pump bracket from left cylinder head and remove drive belt. Wire power steering pump out of the way and in position that will prevent oil from draining out.

NOTE: If left cylinder head is being removed on an engine equipped with Thermactor Exhaust Emission Control System, disconnect hose from air manifold on left head. If a right head is to be removed, remove air pump and bracket and disconnect hose on right head.

---

6. Remove generator or alternator.

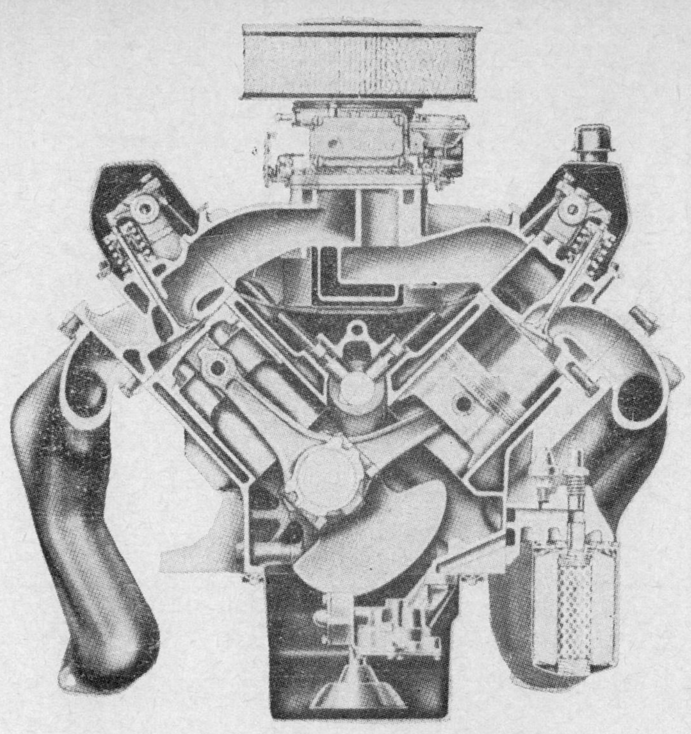

Cross section of V8-427 engine

Engine Oiling System. V8-429

7. Disconnect exhaust manifold at exhaust pipes.
8. Loosen rocker arm stud nuts so that rocker arms can be rotated to the side.
9. Remove push rods, keeping them in sequence so they may be returned to their original locations.
10. Unfasten and remove cylinder head.
11. Reverse removal procedure to install the head. Tighten cylinder head down in the sequence shown in Fig. 2.

1963-69 V8-352, 390, 406, 410, 427, 428, 429

NOTE

When installing intake manifold attaching bolts on these engines, apply a liberal coat of oil resistant sealer to the underside of bolt heads or to the bolt head bosses on the intake manifold. Failure to do so can result in oil leakage.

On V8-427 engines, the exhaust manifolds must be detached from the cylinder heads before the heads are removed.

1. Remove intake manifold, carburetor and radiator supply tank as an assembly.

NOTE: If equipped with Thermactor Exhaust Emission Control System, disconnect air lines and hoses as necessary for accessibility. Then remove intake manifold, positive crankcase vent system components (if applicable), carburetor and thermostat housing (or radiator supply tank) as an assembly.

2. Disconnect exhaust pipes from exhaust manifolds.
3. Remove bolts and lift off head.
4. Install cylinder heads in the reverse order of removal and tighten bolts in the sequence shown in Fig. 2.

1963-64 Six

1. Drain cooling system and remove air cleaner.
2. Disconnect hoses, tubes, wires and linkage attached to head.
3. Remove coil, distributor cap and spark plugs.
4. On engine with positive crankcase ventilation, disconnect exhaust tube at regulator valve and crankcase outlet. Remove exhaust tube.
5. Remove valve rocker arm shaft assembly. Lift out push rods and identify them as to location so they can be installed in their original position.
6. Unfasten and pull manifold away from cylinder head.
7. Remove radiator supply tank (if used).
8. Remove all cylinder head bolts and lift head off engine.
9. Reverse removal procedure to install and tighten head in the sequence shown in Fig. 3.

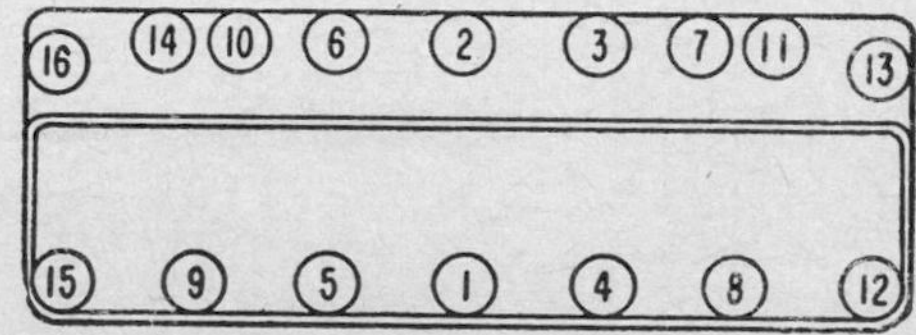

Fig. 3 Cylinder head tightening sequence. 6-223 engine

NOTE

If a noise is encountered after the cylinder head is installed on six-cylinder engines, check for interference between push rod and push rod hole in cylinder head. If interference exists check push rod for straightness. If push rod is straight, then the cylinder head has not been aligned properly during its installation. The use of cylinder head guide pins (one at each end) on cylinder head installation will insure correct head alignment.

VALVE ARRANGEMENT

Front to Rear

6-223 ....E-I-I-E-I-E-E-I-E-I-I-E
6-240 ....E-I-E-I-E-I-E-I-E-I-E I
260, 289 Right Bank ....I-E-I-E-I-E-I-E
260, 289 Left Bank .....E-I-E-I-E-I-E-I
302, 429 Right Bank ...I-E-I-E-I-E-I-E
302, 429 Left Bank ....E-I-E-I-E-I-E-I
352, 361, 390 ....E-I-E-I-I-E-I-E
406, 410, 427, 428........E-I-E-I-I-E-I-E

VALVE LIFT SPECS.

Engine	Year	Intake	Exhaust
6-223	1963-64	.369	.369
6-240	1965-69	.376	.400
8-260	1963	.380	.380
8-289	1963-67	.368	.380
8-302	1968-69	.368	.381
8-352	1963-66	.408	.408
8-390	1963-64	.408	.408
	1965	.439	.439

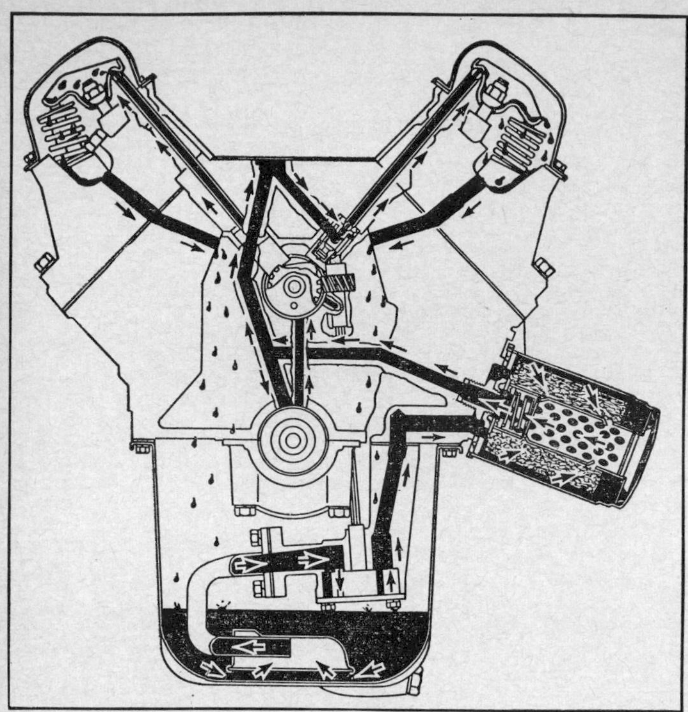

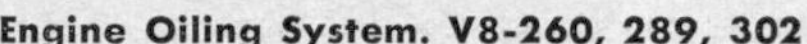
Engine Oiling System. V8-260, 289, 302

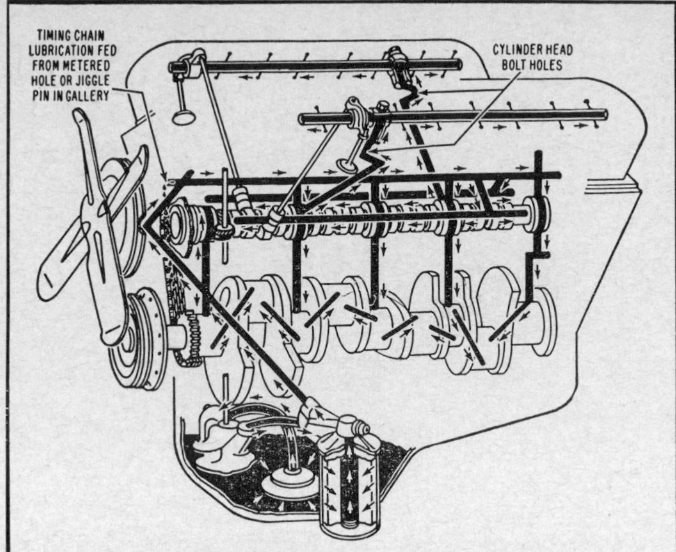

Engine Oiling System. V8-352, 390, 406, 410, 427, 428

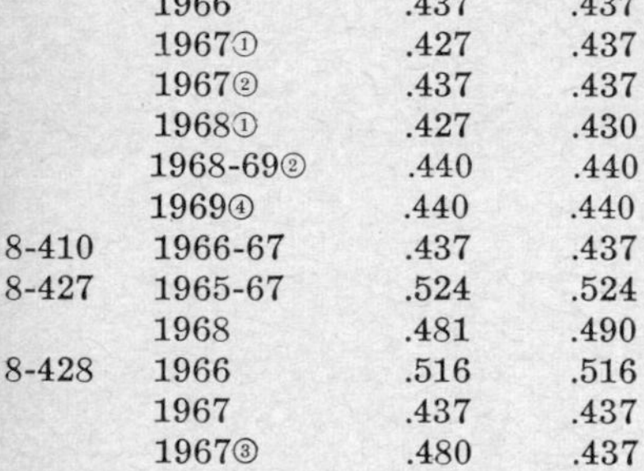

	1966	.437	.437
	1967①	.427	.437
	1967②	.437	.437
	1968①	.427	.430
	1968-69②	.440	.440
	1969④	.440	.440
8-410	1966-67	.437	.437
8-427	1965-67	.524	.524
	1968	.481	.490
8-428	1966	.516	.516
	1967	.437	.437
	1967③	.480	.437
	1968	.440	.440
8-429	1969	.443	.486

①—2 bar. carb. ②—4 bar. carb.
③—Interceptor engine.
④—2 bar. carb.-premium fuel.

VALVE TIMING

Intake Opens Before TDC

Engine	Year	Degrees
6-223	1963-64	23
6-240	1965-69	12
8-260	1963	21
8-289	1963-64	20
	1965-67	16
8-302	1968-69	16
8-352	1963-66	22
8-390	1963-65 4 B.C.	26
	1964 2 B.C.	18
	1964-65 330 H.P.	28½
	1966-67 4 B.C.	16
	1967 2 B.C.	13
	1968	16
	1969 Reg. Fuel	13
	1969 Prem. Fuel	16
8-410	1966-67	16
8-427	1968	18
8-428	1966	40½
	1967-68	16
8-429	1969	16

VALVES, ADJUST

With Mechanical Lifters

If the cylinder head or rocker arm assemblies have been removed and installed, a preliminary (cold) valve lash adjustment should be made before starting the engine. If the adjustment is made in connection with an engine tune-up, the valve lash adjustment should be made with the engine at operating temperature.

To make the "hot" adjustment, operate the engine for a minimum of 30 minutes at a fast idle to stabilize engine temperatures. With the engine idling, check the valve lash with the proper feeler gauge between valve stem and rocker arm. Adjust the lash by means of the adjusting screw to the clearance given in the *Valve Specifications* table.

To make the "cold" adjustment, first turn over the engine to bring No. 1 piston up on its compression stroke, which will be indicated by the TDC mark on the vibration damper. Then proceed as follows:

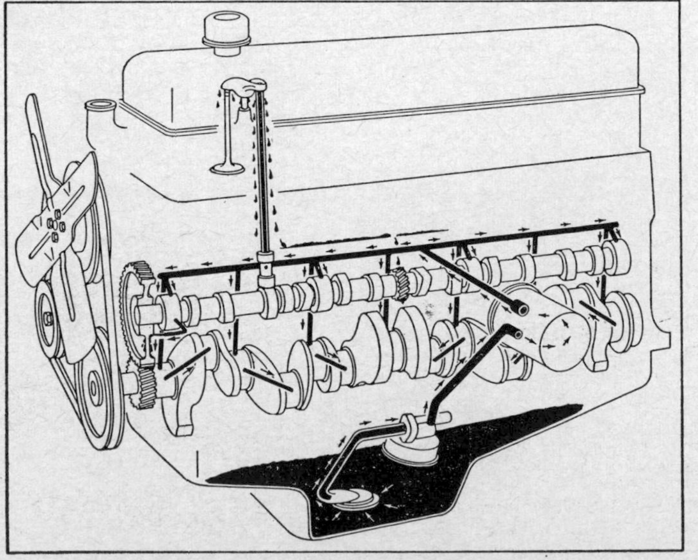
Engine oiling system. 6-240 engine

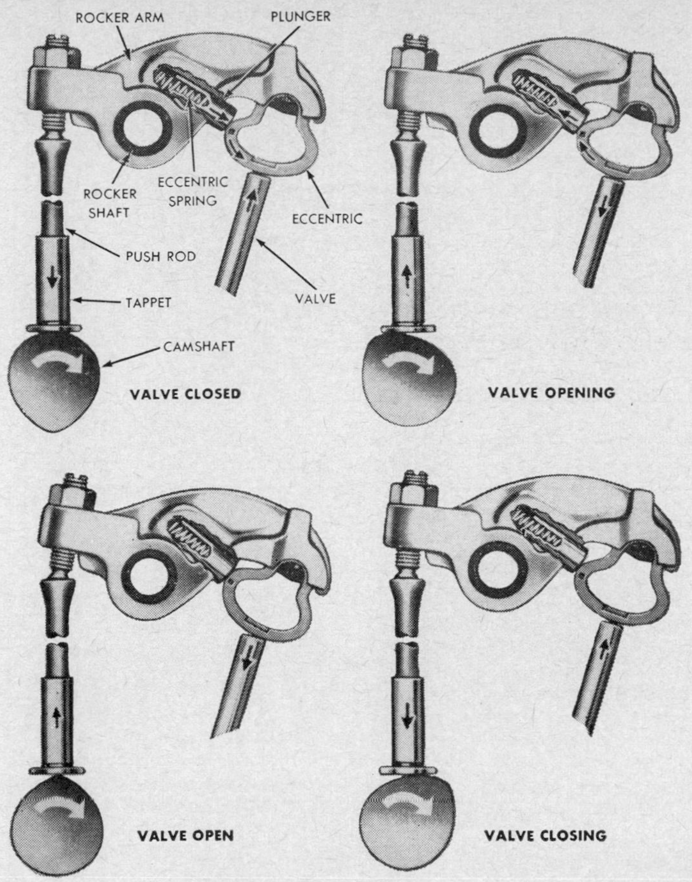

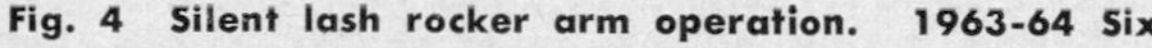

Fig. 4 Silent lash rocker arm operation. 1963-64 Six

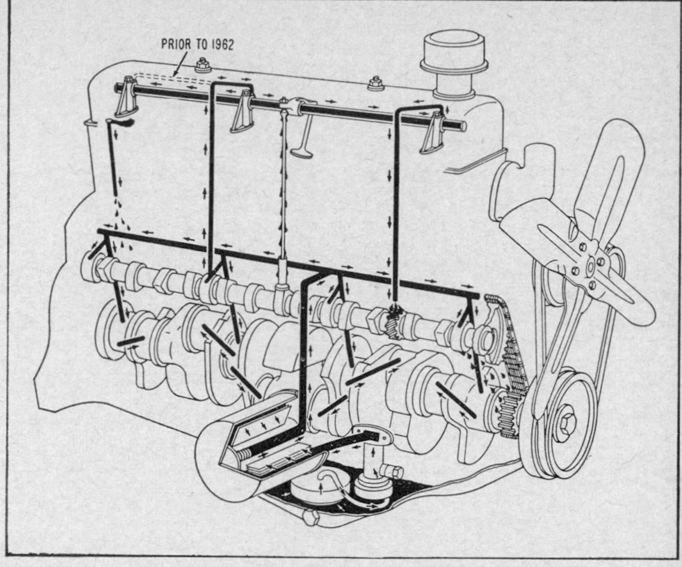

Engine Oiling System. 6-223 engines

Silent Valve Lash Mechanism, 1963-64 Six

As shown in Fig. 4, the rocker arm eccentric functions throughout the rocker arm motion during the valve opening and closing cycle, compensating for expansion or wear of the valve train. Therefore, solid contact, "silent lash" between all parts of the valve train mechanism is maintained.

After removal or replacement of rocker arm or associated parts, the eccentrics are to be adjusted to their operating position in two steps: First to an initial adjustment and, second, to the final position. The initial position is accomplished with the engine shut off; the final adjustment is made with the engine running at normal idle speed. Adjustments for noise complaints and "out-of-position" eccentrics require only the final adjustment procedure.

In making the initial adjustment, position each piston at approximately T.D.C. of compression stroke and adjust the two associated rocker arms as follows:

1. Remove rocker arm cover.
2. Adjust rocker arm by pushing eccentric toward rocker arm until plunger is completely into its rocker arm bore, Fig. 5. Turn adjusting screw in until eccentric and plunger are held in the depressed position.
3. Slowly turn adjusting screw out until adjustment mark on eccentric is centered over valve stem, Fig. 6, and lock jam nut. Correct position of adjustment mark is shown in Fig. 7.
4. Repeat foregoing adjustment on remaining rocker arms, bringing the piston of each cylinder up on its compression stroke so that both valves are closed.
5. After all rocker arms have been adjusted, start engine and operate at normal idle speed. Observe position of adjustment mark on each eccentric.
6. Make minor adjustments as necessary with engine idling by turning adjusting screws as necessary.
7. After adjustments have been completed, torque jam nuts to 35 ft. lbs., stop engine and install rocker cover.

V8-332, 352, 390, 406, 427 With Mechanical Lifters

Make three chalk marks on the vibration damper. Space the marks 90 degrees apart (¼ of circumference) so that with the timing mark the damper is divided

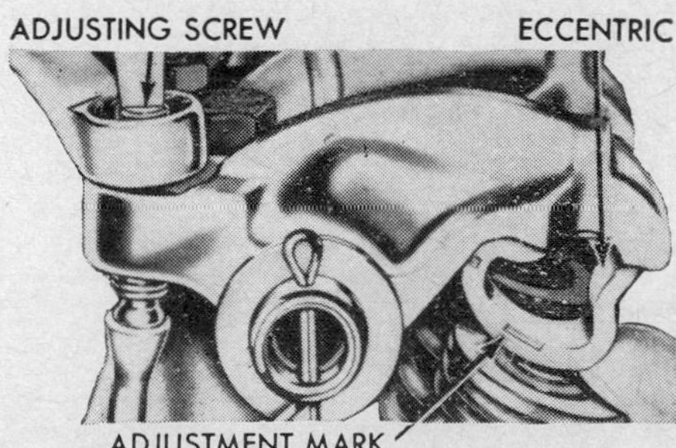

Fig. 5 Depressing valve rocker arm eccentric. 1963-64 Six

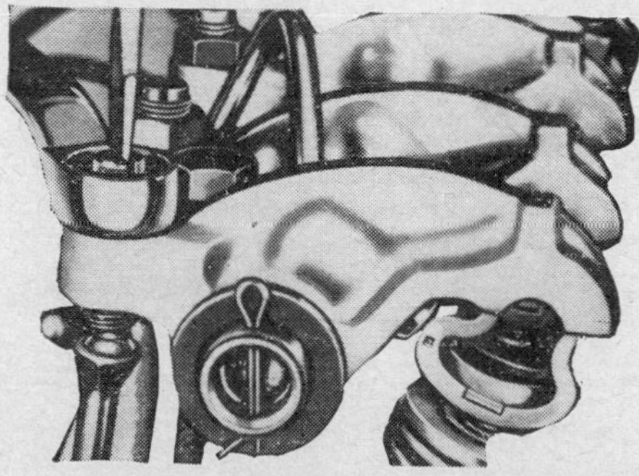

Fig. 6 Aligning eccentric mark with valve stem. 1963-64 Six

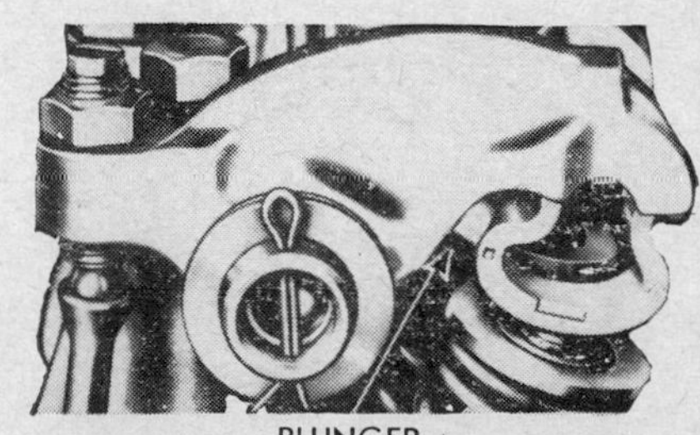

Fig. 7 Correct position of eccentric. 1963-64 Six

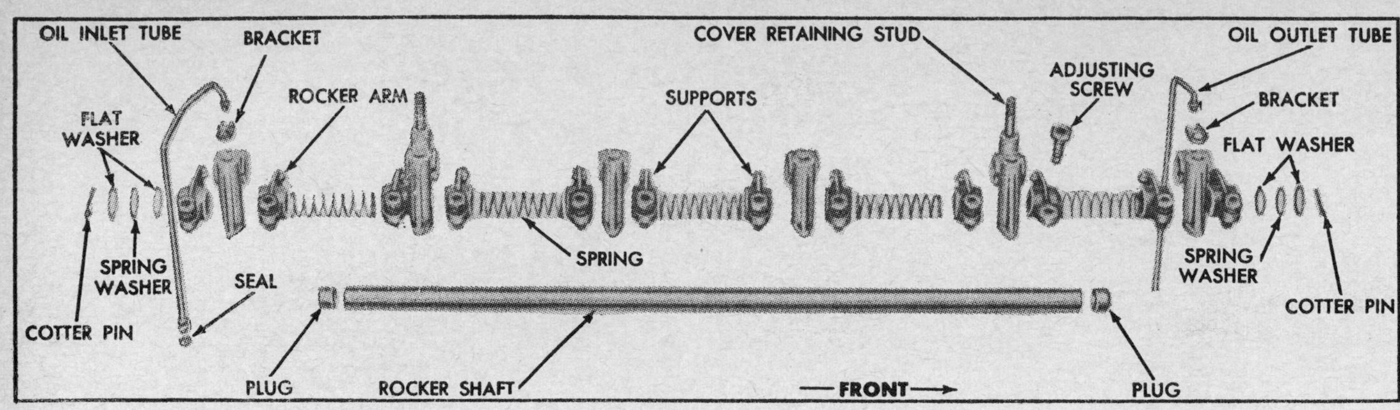

Fig. 8 Rocker arm shaft assembly. 6-223 engine

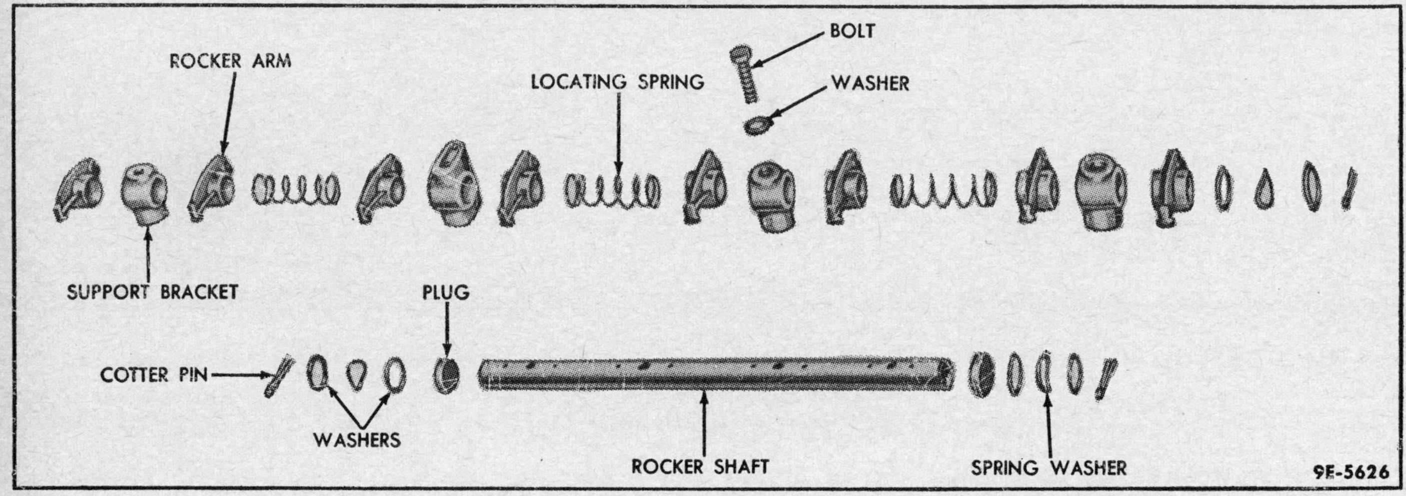

Fig. 9 Rocker arm shaft assembly. V8-352, 390, 406, 410, 427 and 428 engines

into four equal parts. Rotate the crankshaft until No. 1 piston is near TDC at the end of the compression stroke and adjust the following valves:

No. 1 intake and exhaust
No. 4 exhaust
No. 5 exhaust
No. 7 intake
No. 8 intake

Rotate the crankshaft 180 degrees (½ turn) which puts No. 4 piston on TDC. Then adjust the following valves:

No. 2 exhaust
No. 4 intake
No. 5 intake
No. 6 exhaust

Rotate the crankshaft 270 degrees (¾ turn), which puts No. 3 piston on TDC. Then adjust the following valves:

No. 2 intake
No. 3 intake and exhaust
No. 6 intake
No. 7 exhaust
No. 8 exhaust

V8-352 With Rocker Arm Adjusting Screws and Hydraulic Lifters

These engines may be identified by a daub of orange paint on the engine front cover visible from the left side of the engine. In making an adjustment on these valves, follow the procedure outlined above for engines with mechanical lifters insofar as positioning the valves. Then proceed as follows:

1. With lifter being adjusted on base circle of cam on camshaft, turn adjusting screw so that clearance is obtained between push rod and rocker arm adjusting screw.
2. Adjust screw until clearance is just removed.
3. Tighten screw an additional 2½ turns.
4. Apply steady force to the push rod end of the rocker arm, depress the arm until the push rod bottoms in the lifter.
5. Check clearance between end of valve stem and rocker arm. A clearance of at least .060" should exist. If less than .060", back off the adjusting screw until at least .060" clearance is obtained.
6. Repeat adjustment on all other valves in the sequence given for mechanical lifter jobs.

6-240, V8-260, 289, 302

SERVICE BULLETIN

On V8-260 and 289 engines, to minimize the possibility of burned valves the service procedure has been revised as follows: When the push rod to rocker arm clearance has been eliminated, tighten the rocker arm stud nut an additional ¾ of a turn. The previous procedure required an additional 1½ turn.

With the piston at top dead center of its compression stroke, loosen the rocker arm stud nut until there is end clearance in the push rod. Then tighten the nut just to the point where all end clearance is eliminated. This may be determined by moving the push rod with the fingers as the stud nut is tightened. When the end clearance has been eliminated, tighten the stud nut the additional number of turns listed in the *Valve Specifications Table.*

Operate the engine and check for rough engine idle or noisy lifters. Valve clearance set too tight will cause rough engine idle; if set too loose, noisy lifters will result.

If an adjustment is necessary because of the foregoing conditions, apply pressure on the push rod slowly to bleed down the valve lifter until the plunger is completely bottomed. While holding the lifter in the fully collapsed position, check the available clearance between rocker arm and valve stem tip. If clearance is not within specifications, turn the rocker arm stud nut clockwise to decrease the clearance and counterclockwise to increase clearance.

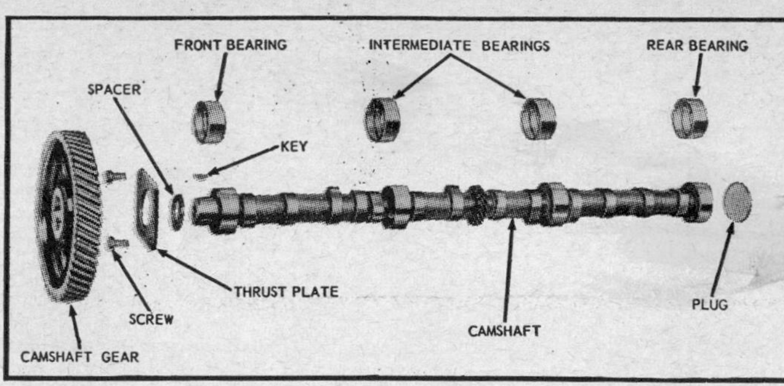

Fig. 15 Camshaft and related parts. 6-240 engine

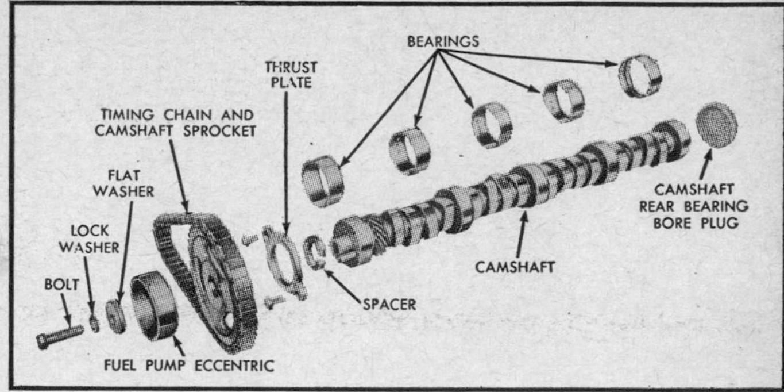

Fig. 16 Camshaft and related parts. V8-260, 289, 302

8. Remove crankshaft pulley and vibration damper.
9. Unfasten and lay fuel pump to one side with flexible fuel line attached.
10. Remove crankshaft sleeve.
11. Unfasten and remove front cover.
12. Reverse procedure to install.

1963-64 V8-260, 289

1. To remove cover, drain cooling system and crankcase. Remove air cleaner and disconnect battery ground cable.
2. Remove water hose as necessary.
3. Remove generator support bolt at water pump, and loosen generator mounting bolts.
4. Remove fan, spacer and pulley.
5. Remove power steering drive belt (if equipped). If air conditioned, remove compressor drive belt.
6. Remove crankshaft pulley vibration damper.
7. Remove fuel pump and lay it to one side with flexible fuel line attached.
8. Remove oil level dipstick tube bracket and oil filler tube bracket.
9. Remove oil pan-to-front cover bolts.
10. Remove cover and water pump as an assembly.
11. Drive out cover seal with a pin punch. Clean out recess in cover.
12. Coat a new seal with grease and drive seal in until it is fully seated in recess. Check seal after installation to be sure spring is properly positioned in seal.
13. Reverse removal procedure to install cover.

1963-64 V8-352, 390, 406, 410, 427

1. Remove radiator and fuel pump.
2. On cars with power steering, disconnect pump bracket from water pump.
3. Remove water pump.
4. Remove vibration damper with puller.
5. Unfasten and remove front cover. *If oil pan gasket is broken or damaged in removing cover, remove oil pan and install new gasket.*
6. Install a new cover oil seal and reinstall the cover in the reverse order of removal.

6-223 Engine

1. To remove cover, drain cooling system and oil pan.
2. Disconnect transmission oil cooler lines (if equipped).
3. Remove radiator, fan, belt and pulley.
4. If equipped, remove power steering pump belt, and pump pulley from crankshaft.
5. Remove vibration damper.
6. Remove oil pan.
7. Remove water pump.
8. Unfasten and remove front cover.
9. Install new seal in cover. Then reverse removal procedure.

TIMING GEARS

1965-69 6-240 Engine

CAUTION

When the camshaft and crankshaft lose their timing relationship through removal of the timing gears, interference may occur between crankshaft and cam lobes. Therefore, to prevent possible damage to the camshaft lobes, do not rotate the camshaft or crankshaft in the engine without the timing gears installed.

1. To remove gears, remove cylinder front cover and camshaft.
2. Remove oil slinger from crankshaft
3. Use a puller to remove crankshaft gear.
4. Press gear off camshaft and remove thrust plate, spacer and key.
5. Reverse procedure to install, being sure timing marks are aligned as shown in Fig. 12.

NOTE: Be sure the camshaft gear and spacer are tight against the shoulder on camshaft and that the thrust plate can be moved freely.

TIMING CHAIN

V8-260, 289, 302

After removing the cover as outlined above, remove the crankshaft front oil slinger. Crank the engine until the timing marks are aligned as shown in Fig. 13. Remove crankshaft sprocket retaining bolt and washer. Slide both sprockets and chain forward and remove them as an assembly.

Reverse the order of the foregoing procedure to install the chain and sprockets, being sure the timing marks are aligned.

V8-352, 390, 406, 410, 427, 428, 429

1. To remove the chain, first take off the front cover as outlined previously.
2. Crank engine until timing mark on camshaft sprocket is adjacent to timing mark on crankshaft sprocket, Fig. 13.
3. Remove camshaft sprocket cap screw and fuel pump eccentric.
4. Slide both sprockets and chain forward and remove as an assembly.
5. Reverse foregoing procedure to install the chain, being sure to align the timing marks as shown.

6-223 Engine

To make the sprocket and chain accessible, remove the radiator, vibration damper and cylinder front cover. Before removing the crankshaft sprocket, align the timing marks as shown in Fig. 14. Remove the camshaft sprocket retaining bolt and washer. Slide the camshaft sprocket, timing chain and crankshaft sprocket forward until the camshaft sprocket comes off the camshaft.

To install, place the chain over the crankshaft sprocket and insert the camshaft sprocket in the chain so the timing marks on both sprockets are aligned as shown. Align the keyway in the camshaft with the camshaft sprocket keyway and slide the assembly into position.

CAMSHAFT, REPLACE

1965-69 6-240 Engine

1. To remove camshaft, remove radiator and grille.
2. Remove rocker arm cover. Loosen rocker arm stud nuts and move rocker arms to one side and take out push rods. Place push rods in a rack so they can be installed in their original location.
3. Remove valve push rod cover and

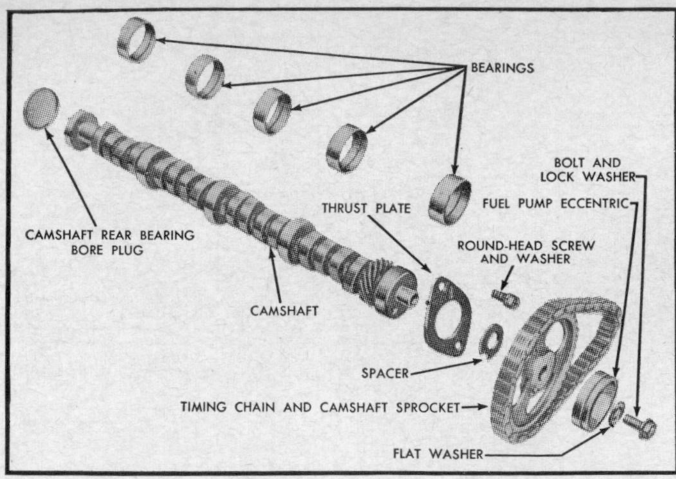

Fig. 17 Camshaft and related parts. V8-352, 390, 410, 427, 428, 429

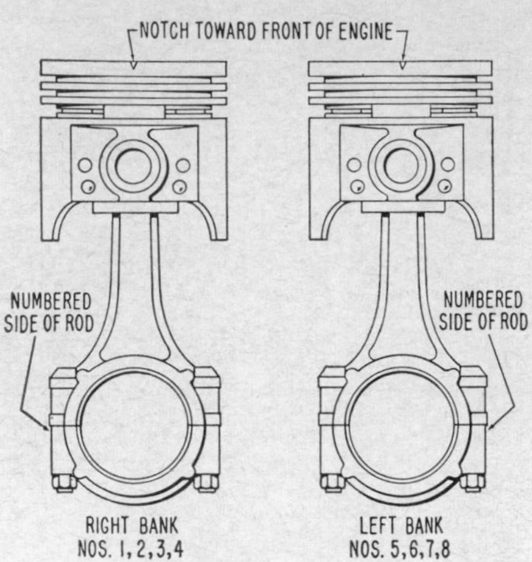

Fig. 18 Piston and rod assembly. All V8 engines

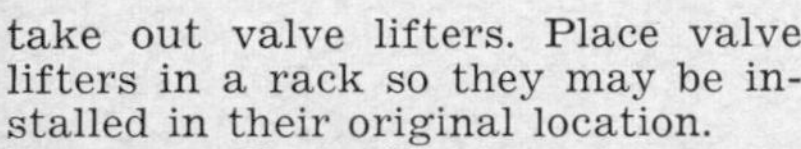
take out valve lifters. Place valve lifters in a rack so they may be installed in their original location.

4. Remove cylinder front cover.
5. Turn crankshaft to align timing marks as shown in Fig. 12.
6. Carefully remove camshaft with gear attached, Fig. 15.
7. Reverse procedure to install.

V8-260, 289, 302

1. To remove camshaft, remove cylinder front cover and timing chain.
2. Remove distributor cap and spark plug wires, then remove distributor.
3. Disconnect automatic transmission oil cooler lines from radiator and remove radiator.
4. Remove intake manifold and carburetor as an assembly.
5. Remove rocker arm covers.
6. Loosen rocker arm stud nuts and rotate rocker arms to one side.
7. Remove push rods, keeping them in sequence in a rack so they may be installed in their original location.
8. Using a magnet, remove valve lifters and place them in a rack in sequence so they may be installed in their original location.
9. Remove camshaft thrust plate, Fig. 16, and carefully pull camshaft from engine, using care to avoid damaging camshaft bearings.
10. Reverse procedure to install.

1963-64 Six

1. Remove timing chain cover and oil pan.
2. Remove grille and its center support.
3. Remove rocker arm assembly.
4. Remove push rods.
5. Remove distributor.
6. Remove push rod cover. Raise valve lifters clear of camshaft lobes and secure them with spring-type clothes pins or window regulator clips.
7. Remove fuel pump.
8. Remove timing chain and sprockets.
9. Remove camshaft thrust plate and spacer.
10. Slide camshaft out of engine.

V8-352, 390, 406, 410, 427, 428, 429

1. Remove timing chain cover, chain, sprockets and intake manifold.
2. Remove grille and distributor.
3. Remove rocker arm assembly.
4. Remove push rods.
5. Position an inspection light through push rod opening and into valve push rod valley. Remove valve lifters with a magnet through push rod openings. *It may be necessary in some cases to transfer the lifter over to an adjoining push rod opening in order to remove it.*
6. Remove oil pan.
7. Slide camshaft out of engine, Fig. 17.

CAMSHAFT BEARINGS

When necessary to replace camshaft bearings, the engine will have to be removed from the vehicle and the plug at the rear of the cylinder block will have to be removed in order to utilize the special camshaft bearing removing and installing tools required to do this job. If properly installed, camshaft bearings require no reaming—nor should this type bearing be reamed or altered in any manner in an attempt to fit bearings.

PISTON & ROD, ASSEMBLE

All V8's

Assemble the pistons to the rods as shown in Fig. 18.

All Sixes

Piston heads are marked for location on the forward side, Figs. 19, 20. Rods and caps are numbered on the same side as the piston they serve.

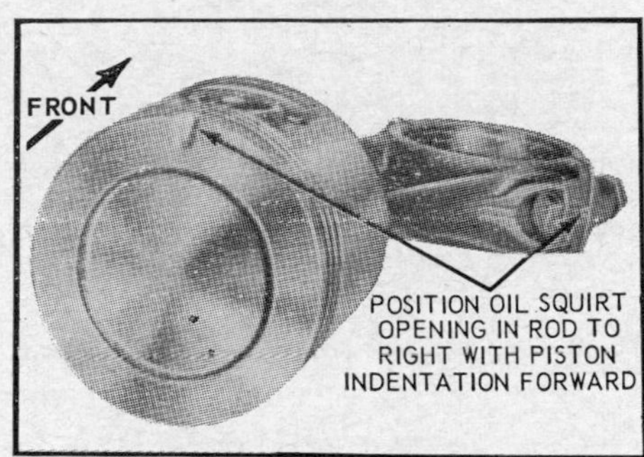

Fig. 19 Piston and rod assembly. 6-223 and 1965 6-240

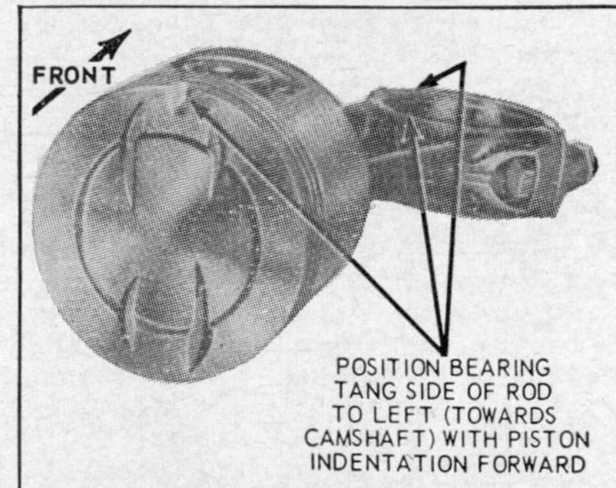

Fig. 20 Piston and rod assembly. 1966-69 6-240 engine

PISTONS, PINS & RINGS

SERVICE BULLETIN

Piston and Pin Replacement: When servicing engines using press fit piston pins, the piston and pin must be replaced as an assembly if either does not meet specifications. These components are not serviced separately for the principle reason that excess clearances are usually caused by piston wear rather than pin wear. Elimination of excessive clearance by using oversize pins may result in fracture of the connecting rod.

Pistons and rings are available in standard sizes and the following oversizes:

6-144, 170, 223, 260, 352, 390,

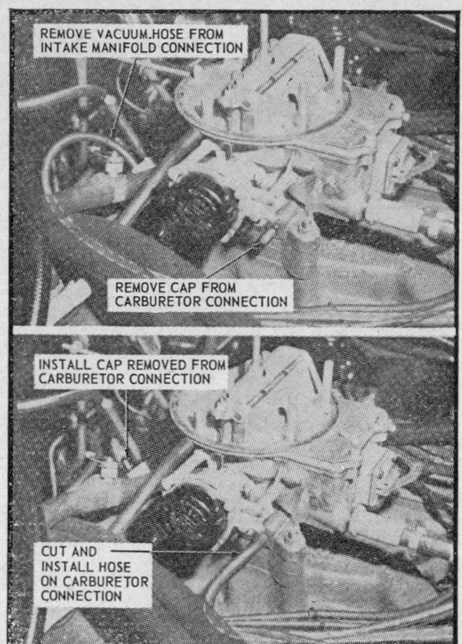

Fig. 21 Procedure for correcting front main bearing knock on 1967 V8-289 engines

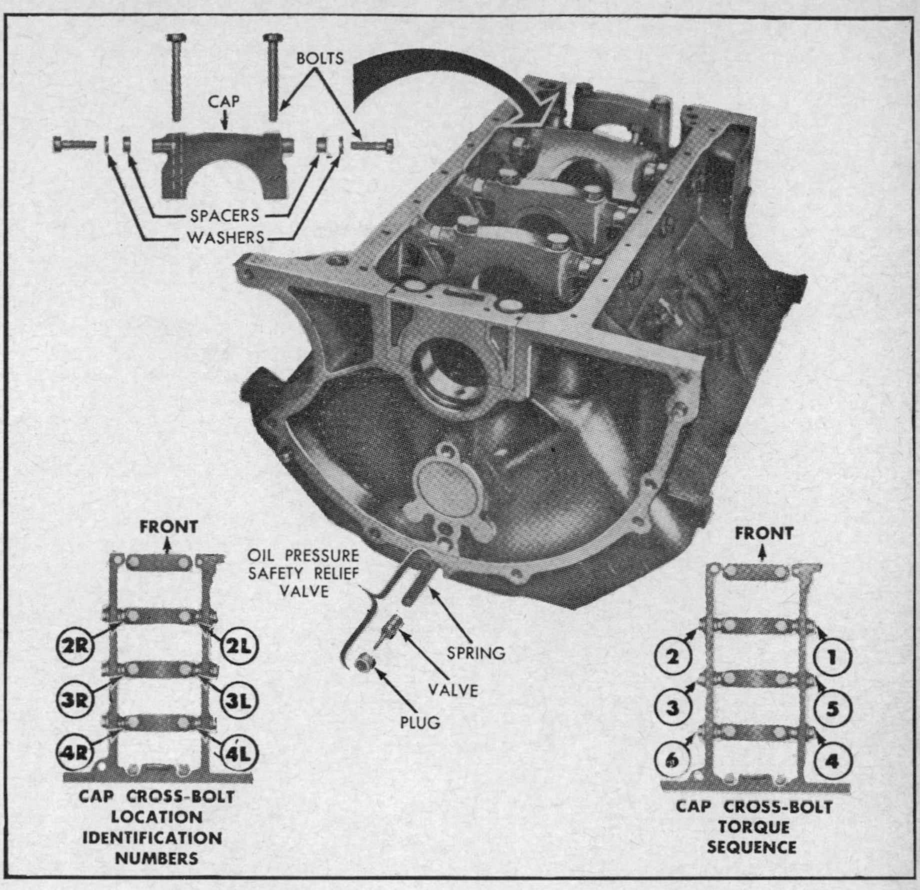

Fig. 22 Cylinder block details. V8-427

410, 428: .020, .030, .040, .060″, 6-200, 240, V8-289: .020, .030, .040″.

V8-406, 427: Standard only.

Oversizes piston pins of .001 and .002″ are available on 6-223-240, V8-352 and 390 only.

MAIN & ROD BEARINGS

Front Main Bearing Knock

1967 V8-289 Engines: This problem occurs at 800-1600 rpm under load, and is caused by a high degree of spark advance at idle provided by attachment of the distributor vacuum line to full manifold vacuum; also excessive front main bearing clearance.

To correct the trouble, it is recommended that the distributor vacuum hose be removed from the intake manifold take-off connection and attached to the connection at the base of the carburetor, Fig. 21. Reduce the length of the vacuum hose to provide direct routing to the carburetor connection, free from sharp bends or kinks. The cap removed from the carburetor fitting should be used to close the vacated connection on the manifold.

If the engine knock is not reduced to an acceptable level, then a new front main bearing must be select fitted, utilizing the available .001″ or .002″ undersize bearing in any combination to provide a desired operating clearance of .0005″ to .0015″.

Service Bulletin

Undersize Crankshafts: Crankshafts with .010″ undersize rod and/or main journals were authorized for use in all 1965-68 engines beginning March 12, 1965. All assemblies containing undersize crankshafts will be identified on the cylinder block date stamp pad with a letter M for undersize main journals and/or a letter P for .010″ undersize crankpin (rod) journals. There crankshafts can appear in both production or service engines and short block assemblies. Bearing clearances will remain the same as for standard crankshafts. All rod and/or main journals will be ground undersize if any one of the rod and/or main journals are undersize. This avoids mixing of standard and undersize bearings in the same engine. Three possible combinations can exist on crankshafts with undersize bearing journals:

1. All rod journals .010″ undersize with standard main bearing journals.
2. All rod journals standard with .010″ undersize main journals.
3. Both rod and main bearing journals .010″ undersize.

Main and rod bearings are available in standard sizes and the following undersizes:

V8-352, 390, 410, 428: .002, .010, .020, .030, .040″.

All other engines: .002, .010, .020, .030″.

NOTE

Main and rod bearings are a selective fit. Do not file or lap bearing caps or use bearing shims to obtain proper bearing clearance. Selective fit bearings are available for service in standard sizes only. Standard bearings are divided into two sizes and are identified by a daub of red or blue paint. Red marked bearings increase the clearance; blue marked bearings decrease clearance. When replacing standard bearings with new bearings, it is good practice first to try to obtain the proper clearance with two blue bearing halves.

V8-427 NOTE

Whenever the main bearings are removed, they should be installed as follows, referring to Fig. 22.

1. Torque main bearing cap bolts to 95-105 ft-lbs.
2. Make sure cross-bolt spacers are installed in their proper locations. Production spacers are marked L-2, R-2, L-3, R-3, L-4, R-4.
3. Install and torque cross-bolts in two steps. First torque all cross-bolts to 20 ft-lbs.; then torque them all to 40 ft-lbs.

CRANKSHAFT OIL SEAL

1965-69 6-240 Engine

NOTE: If crankshaft rear oil seal replacement is the only operation being performed, it can be done in the vehicle. If the oil seal is being replaced in conjunction with a rear main bearing replacement, the engine must be removed from the vehicle. To replace the seal only, proceed as follows:

1. Remove starting motor.
2. Disconnect transmission from engine and slide it back. On manual shift transmission, remove clutch assembly.
3. Remove flywheel and engine rear cover plate.
4. Use an awl to punch two holes in crankshaft rear oil seal. Punch holes on opposite sides of crankshaft and just above bearing cap-to-cylinder block split line. Insert a sheet metal screw in each hole.
5. Use two large screwdrivers or pry bars and pry against both screws at the same time to remove seal. It may be necessary to place small blocks of wood against cylinder block to provide a fulcrum point for pry bars. Use caution to avoid scratching or otherwise damaging crankshaft oil seal surfaces.

Installation

1. Clean oil seal recess in cylinder block and rear main bearing cap.
2. Coat new oil seal and crankshaft with a light film of engine oil.
3. Start seal in recess and install it until it is fully seated in seal recess, Fig. 23.
4. Be sure seal was not damaged during installation and reverse the procedure of removal to complete the operation.

V8-260, 289, 302

A braided oil seal is pressed into the upper and lower grooves behind the rear main bearing. Directly in front of this seal is an oil slinger which deflects the oil back into the oil pan. Should the braided seal require replacement, the installation of the lower half is accomplished as follows:

With the bearing cap and lower bearing half removed, install a new seal so that both ends protrude above the cap. Tap the seal down into position or roll it snugly in its groove with a smooth rounded tool. Then cut off the protruding end of the seal with sharp knife or razor blade.

SERVICE BULLETIN

PROTECT OIL SEAL: When replacing a front or rear crankshaft oil seal on a 1963-66 engine, the surface of the crankshaft contacting the seal must be cleaned with solvent. This will remove any corrosion, sludge or varnish which might be present. In addition, polish the surface with crocus cloth to remove any deposits, burrs or sharp edges that could damage the new seal or cause it to wear prematurely.

Where there is excessive wear on the contact surface, or a satisfactory surface cannot be obtained by polishing, it may be necessary to replace the crankshaft.

Before the new seal is installed, coat it with suitable lubricant along with the contact surface of the shaft. This will prevent damage during installation, and provide lubrication when the engine is first started.

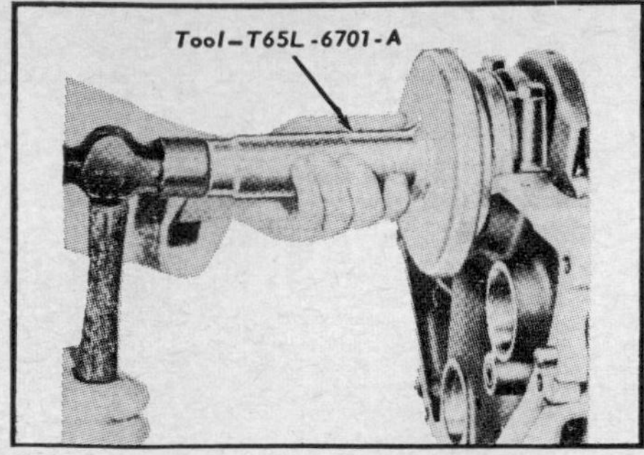

Fig. 23 Crankshaft rear oil seal installation. 6-240 engine

V8-260, 289 NOTE

The crankshaft rear seal is in contact with the outer surface of the flywheel flange rather than on the main bearing journal. In this design, the front face of the flange is exposed to crankcase splash. Therefore, to eliminate the possibility of oil leaks through the threaded holes in the flange, the flywheel attaching capscrews must be coated with an oil resistant sealer.

6-223, V8-352, 406, 427

Oil sealing at the rear of the crankshaft is obtained by seal halves in the cylinder block and rear bearing cap. Side seals are also used in the vertical grooves in the bearing cap. Install and test seals in the same manner outlined for other models above.

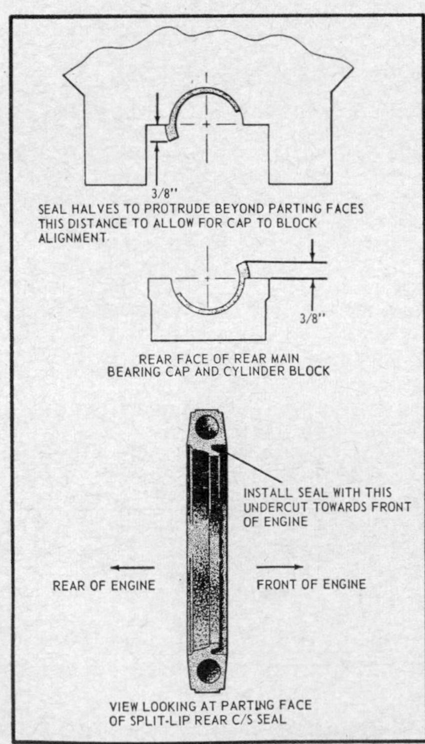

Fig. 23A New split-lip rear crankshaft seal installation on 1964-68 V8-390, 410, 428

New Rear Crankshaft Seal

1964-68 V8-390, 410, 428: A new rubber split-lip rear crankshaft oil seal is released for service. This seal can be installed without removal of the crankshaft and also eliminates the necessity of seal installation tools.

1. Remove oil pan.
2. Remove rear main bearing cap.
3. Loosen remaining bearing caps, allowing crankshaft to drop down about $\frac{1}{32}$".
4. Remove old seals from both cylinder block and rear main bearing cap. Use a brass rod to drift upper half of seal from cylinder block groove. Rotate crankshaft while drifting to facilitate removal.
5. Carefully clean seal groove in block with a brush and solvent. Also clean seal groove in bearing cap.
6. Dip seal halves in clean engine oil.
7. Carefully install upper seal half in its groove with undercut side of seal toward front of engine, Fig. 23A, by rotating it on shaft journal of crankshaft until approximately ⅜" protrudes below the parting surface. *Be sure no rubber has been shaved from outside diameter of seal by bottom edge of groove.*
8. Retighten main bearing caps and torque to specifications.
9. Install lower seal in main bearing cap with undercut side of seal toward front of engine, and allow seal to protrude about ⅜" above parting surface to mate with upper seal upon cap installation.
10. Apply suitable sealer to parting faces of cap and block. Install cap and torque to specifications.

NOTE: If difficulty is encountered in installing the upper half of the seal in position, lightly lap (sandpaper) the side of the seal opposite the lip side using a medium grit paper. After sanding, the seal must be washed in solvent, then dipped in clean engine oil prior to installation.

OIL PAN, REPLACE

1965-69 6-240 Engine

1. Drain crankcase and cooling system.
2. Remove radiator.
3. Disconnect flexible fuel line at fuel pump.
4. With automatic transmission disconnect kickdown rod at bellcrank.
5. With manual shift transmission, disconnect clutch linkage.
6. Raise car and remove starter.
7. Remove engine front support retaining nuts.
8. Raise transmission, remove rear support insulator and lower transmission to crossmember.
9. Raise engine and place 3" thick wood blocks between both front support insulators and intermediate support brackets.
10. Remove oil pan bolts and oil pump retaining bolts.
11. Remove oil pump from block and lay

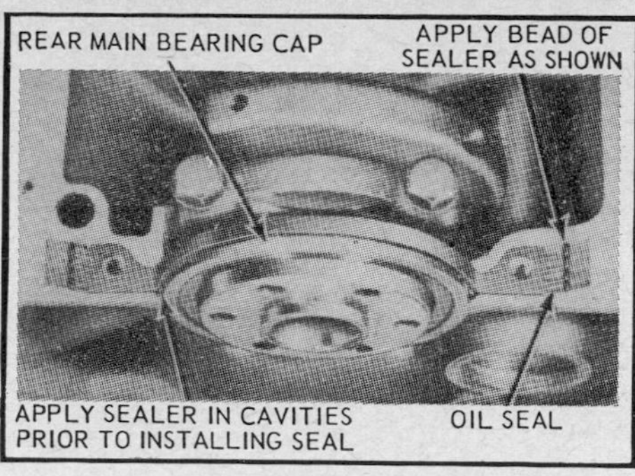

Fig. 24 Oil pan rear seal installation. 6-240 engine

it in bottom of oil pan.

12. Rotate crankshaft as required to remove oil pan.
13. Remove inlet tube and screen from pump.

Installation

1. After cleaning, install inlet tube and screen on oil pump, using a new gasket.
2. Clean gasket surfaces of oil pump, pan and block.
3. Remove rear main bearing cap-to-oil pan seal and cylinder front cover-to-oil pan seal. Clean seal grooves.
4. Apply oil-resistant sealer in cavities between bearing cap and cylinder block, Fig. 24.
5. Install new side gaskets on oil pan with oil-resistant sealer.
6. Position a new cylinder front cover seal on oil pan.
7. Place oil pump assembly in pan. Position pan under engine. Install oil pump with new gasket on cylinder block. Install oil pan and tighten screws securely.
8. Complete the operation by reversing the removal procedure.

1965-69 V8-289, 302

1. Drain crankcase and remove dipstick.
2. Unfasten and position oil pan on No. 2 crossmember.
3. Remove one of the inlet tube retaining bolts and loosen the other. This allows inlet tube to be positioned out of the way when removing oil pan.
4. Crank engine as required to obtain clearance and remove oil pan.
5. Remove oil pump inlet tube and screen.

Installation

1. Position oil inlet tube and loosely install one retaining bolt.
2. Clean gasket surfaces of block and pan.
3. Coat block surface and oil pan gasket with sealer. Position pan gaskets on cylinder block.
4. Position front seal on cylinder front cover, being sure tabs on seal are over oil pan gasket.
5. Position rear oil pan seal on rear main bearing cap, being sure tabs on seal are over oil pan gasket.
6. Place pan on No. 2 crossmember and install other inlet tube retaining bolt.
7. Complete installation in reverse order of removal.

1963-64 V8-260, 289

1. Drain crankcase and remove dipstick.
2. Remove starter and dust seal.
3. Remove oil pan retaining bolts and crank engine as required to obtain clearance for oil pan removal.
4. Reverse procedure to install, following procedure outlined for 1965 engine regarding installation of seals.

Ford 1963-64 Six

1. Drain crankcase.
2. Remove flywheel housing lower cover and oil level dipstick.
3. On Station Wagons, unfasten stabilizer bar from lower control arm and frame and position the bar as far forward as possible.
4. On engines with vent tube type crankcase ventilation system, remove ventilation tube.
5. Remove oil pan bolts and turn crankshaft as required to gain clearance to remove the pan.
6. After removing the pan, remove oil pump inlet tube and screen.

NOTE

A new oil pan gasket incorporating a dovetail design which mates with the flywheel housing cover gasket provides improved sealing in the dust cover area. Whenever the oil pan is removed it will be necessary to remove the flywheel housing cover. Also, when installing the new pan gasket, it may be necessary to install a new flywheel housing cover gasket. A suitable sealer should be applied to the two junction points of the oil pan and flywheel housing cover gasket, Fig. 25.

Ford 1963 V8-352, 390, 406, 427

1. Drain oil from crankcase and remove oil level dipstick.
2. Remove flywheel housing lower cover.

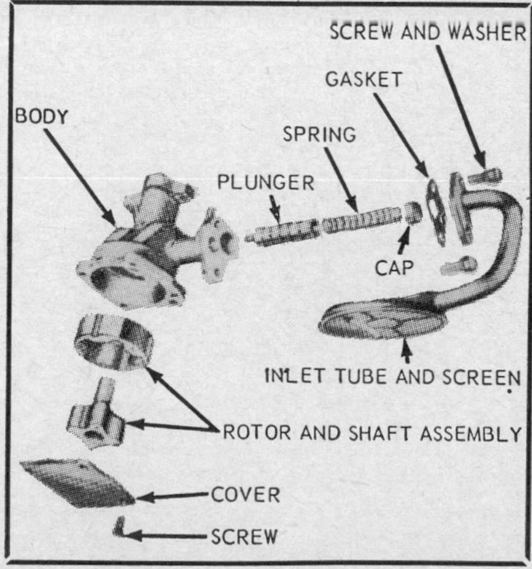

Fig. 26 Oil pump. 6-240 engine

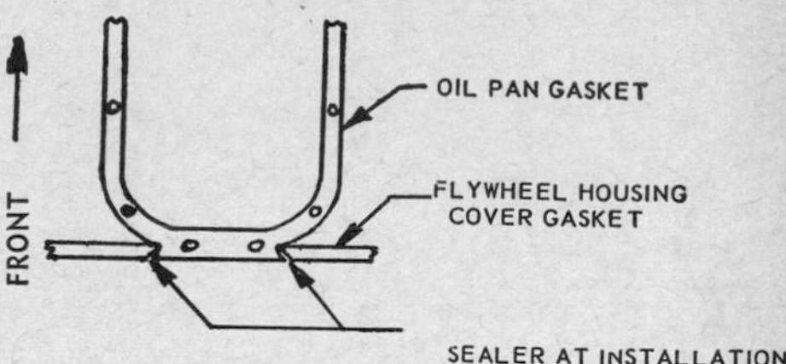

Fig. 25 Oil pan gasket installation. 1963-64 Six

3. Unfasten and lower oil pan to frame crossmember.
4. Crank engine to obtain necessary clearance between crankshaft counterweight and rear of oil pan.
5. If oil pump is to be removed, remove retaining bolts and allow pump to fall into oil pan. If pump is not to be removed, loosen pump inlet tube upper bolt and remove lower bolt; then swing inlet tube clear of pan.
6. Remove oil pan by bringing it forward and tilting it down.

1964-69 V8-352, 390, 410, 427, 428

1. Drain engine oil and disconnect stabilizer bar at connecting links and pull ends down.

NOTE: To allow clearance for removal of oil pan, remove the front engine mount nuts. Then position floor jack under front leading edge of oil pan (use wood block between pan and jack). Raise engine about 1¼" and insert a 1" block of wood between insulators and frame crossmember. Then remove floor jack.

2. Remove oil pan screws and lower pan to crossmember.
3. Crank engine to obtain necessary clearance between crankshaft counterweight and rear of oil pan. Then remove pan.

Mercury 1963 V8's

1. For oil pan and crankshaft clearance purposes, crank engine to place No. 1 piston on top dead center. Remove oil level dipstick.
2. Drain oil pan.
3. Remove ends of stabilizer from mounting studs and pull the ends downward to allow clearance for oil pan removal.
4. On 352, 390 and 406 engines, unfasten and lower oil pan onto frame crossmember. Then reach into crankcase with a socket wrench and unfasten oil pick-up tube from oil pump. Allow screen and tube to drop into pan. Move pan forward and down to remove it from chassis.

OIL PUMP REPAIRS

Figs. 26, 27, 28

1. With all parts clean and dry, check the inside of the pump housing and

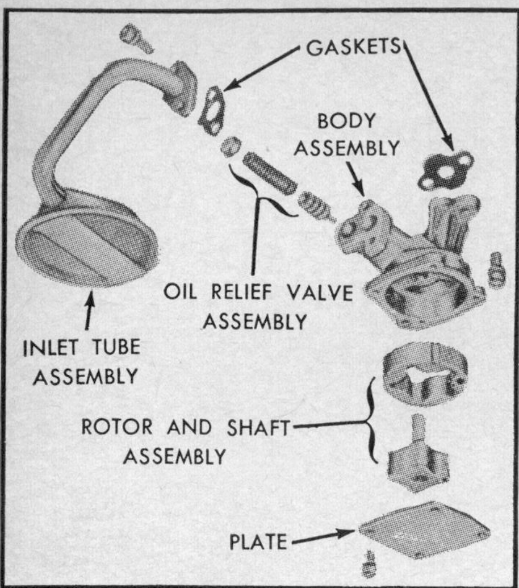

Fig. 27 Oil pump. V8-260, 289, 302

the outer race and rotor for damage or excessive wear.

2. Check the mating surface of the pump cover for wear. If this surface is worn, scored or grooved, replace the cover.
3. Measure the clearance between the outer race and housing. This clearance should be .006-.009″.
4. With the rotor assembly installed in the housing, place a straight edge over the rotor assembly and housing. Measure the clearance between the straight edge and the rotor and outer race. Recommended limits are .001-.0035″. *The outer race, shaft and rotor are furnished only as an assembly.*
5. Check the drive shaft-to-housing bearing clearance by measuring the O.D. of the shaft and the I.D. of the housing bearing. The recommended clearance limits are .0015-.0029″.
6. Inspect the relief valve spring for a collapsed or worn condition.
7. Check the relief valve piston for scores and free operation in the bore. The specified piston clearance is .0015-.0029″.

WATER PUMP, REPLACE

1969 Six

1. Drain cooling system.
2. Loosen and remove alternator, power steering and air conditioning belts.
3. Disconnect radiator lower hose and heater hose at pump.
4. Remove fan, spacer, pulley and belt.
5. Unfasten and remove the water pump.

1969 V8-429

The water pump is a part of the front cover on this engine and the procedure for removal is found under *Timing Case Cover*.

1964-68 Six

1. Drain cooling system.
2. Remove power steering belt (if equipped). If air conditioned, remove compressor belt.
3. Disconnect radiator lower hose and heater hose at water pump. Remove fan, pulley and drive belt.
4. On 1964, remove water pump back plate bolt retaining generator bracket.
5. Remove bolts securing pump to block and remove pump.

1964-69 V8-289, 302

1. Drain cooling system.
2. Remove power steering drive belt (if equipped). If air conditioned, remove compressor belt.
3. Disconnect radiator lower hose and heater hose at water pump.
4. Remove drive belt, fan, spacer or fan drive clutch and pulley.
5. Unfasten and remove water pump from cylinder front cover.

1964-69 V8-352, 390, 410, 427, 428

1. Drain cooling system.
2. Remove power steering drive belt (if equipped). If air conditioned, remove compressor drive belt.
3. Disconnect radiator lower hose and heater hose at water pump.
4. Remove radiator upper support and fan guard.
5. Remove fan belt or belts, fan, spacer or fan drive clutch and pulley.
6. Unfasten and remove water pump.

Ford 1963 Six

1. Drain cooling system and disconnect hoses at pump.
2. Remove fan, pulley and drive belt.
3. Remove water pump back plate bolt which retains radiator supply tank support bracket and generator bracket.
4. Unfasten and remove pump.

1963 V8 Ford

1. Drain cooling system and disconnect hoses from water pump.
2. Remove fan, belt and pulley (also spacer on 260, 289 engines).
3. Remove bolts retaining pump to cylinder front cover (260, 289) or to block.
4. Remove pump from engine.

Mercury 1963 V8's

1. Drain cooling system and disconnect hoses from water pump.
2. Remove fan belt, fan, spacer (if equipped) and pulley.
3. On power steering jobs, remove power steering pump with hoses attached and place it in a position that will prevent fluid from draining out of reservoir.
4. Unfasten and remove water pump from cylinder block (352 and 390).

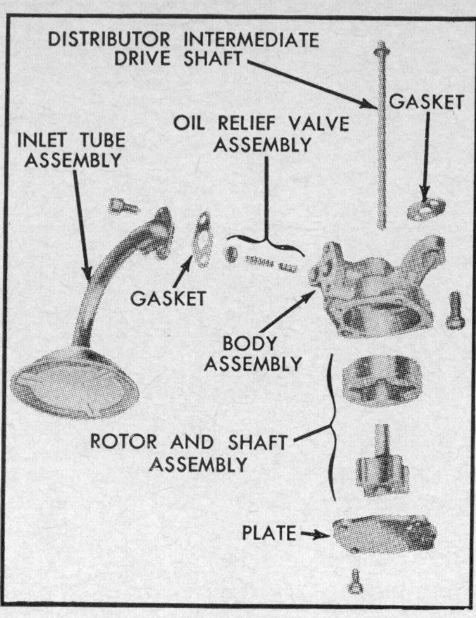

Fig. 28 Oil pump. V8-352, 390, 410, 427, 428, 429

FUEL PUMP, REPLACE

1. Remove all gasket material from the pump and block gasket surfaces. Apply sealer to both sides of new gasket.
2. Position gasket on pump flange and hold pump in position against its mounting surface. Make sure rocker arm is riding on camshaft eccentric.
3. Press pump tight against its mounting. Install retaining screws and tighten them alternately.
4. Connect fuel lines. Then operate engine and check for leaks.

NOTE: Before installing the pump, it is good practice to crank the engine so that the nose of the camshaft eccentric is out of the way of the fuel pump rocker arm when the pump is installed. In this way there will be the least amount of tension on the rocker arm, thereby easing the installation of the pump.

Clutch and Transmission Section

NOTE: 1969 linkage adjustment information is in this section. Repair procedures on both automatic and manual shift transmissions are covered elsewhere in this manual. Procedures for removing automatic transmissions as well as linkage adjustments on 1963-68 models are included in the automatic transmission chapters. See Chapter Index.

CLUTCH PEDAL, ADJUST

1969

1. Disconnect clutch release lever spring from release lever.
2. Loosen release lever rod locknut and adjusting nut.
3. Move clutch release lever rearward until release bearing lightly touches pressure plate release fingers.
4. Adjust adapter length until adapter seats in release lever pocket.
5. Insert a .194" feeler against the back face of rod adapter and tighten the adjusting nut finger tight against the feeler gauge.
6. Tighten locknut against adjusting nut being careful not to disturb adjustment.
7. Remove feeler gauge.
8. Install release lever spring and check pedal free travel. Travel should be ⅞" to 1⅛".

1965-68

Assist Spring

1. With clutch pedal against its bumper (pedal released), measure distance between assist spring bracket and equalizer upper lever. This distance should be ⅛". It may be necessary to depress pedal to insert gauge.
2. To decrease gap, loosen rearward nut and tighten front nut.
3. To increase gap, loosen forward nut and tighten rearward nut.
4. Tighten nuts securely, being careful not to change the adjustment.

Free Travel

1. Disconnect clutch return spring from release lever.
2. Loosen release lever rod lock nut 3 or 4 turns.
3. If there is no free travel, shorten rod (by turning at square wrench area) until it is free of clutch release lever.
4. Move clutch release lever rearward until release bearing lightly contacts clutch release fingers.
5. Adjust rod length until rod just contacts its seat in release lever.
6. Adjust lock nut to obtain approximately $\frac{3}{16}$" clearance between nut and rod sleeve end.
7. Turn rod at the square wrench area until nut just contacts rod sleeve end.
8. Tighten lock nut against sleeve while holding rod with wrench.
9. Install clutch return spring.
10. As a final check, measure free travel with engine idling. Dimension should not be less than ½".

1963-64

A clutch pedal adjustment should be made whenever the clutch does not disengage or engage properly, or when new clutch parts are installed.

If an adjustment is necessary, loosen the lock nut on the clutch pedal release rod and turn the adjusting nut. When the adjusting nut is turned clockwise, free travel is increased, and vice versa. Tighten lock nut after adjustment has been made. Free travel should be at least one inch.

The centrifugal weights in the clutch at high speed will move the release levers closer to the release bearing and reduce the pedal free travel by as much as ¾". Therefore, it is recommended that the pedal free travel be checked while the engine is running at approximately 3000 rpm. This check can be made while the car is standing and transmission is in neutral. The free pedal travel under these conditions must be at least ½". Readjust if necessary to obtain at least ½" free pedal travel with engine running at approximately 3000 rpm.

CLUTCH REPLACE

1964-69

1. Remove transmission as outlined.
2. On cars with aluminum clutch housing, remove starter. Unfasten housing from engine and move housing back just far enough to clear pressure plate, then move it to the right to free the pivot from clutch equalizer bar. Be careful not to lose bushing or disturb linkage or assist spring.
3. Remove flywheel housing cover (cast iron housings only).
4. Remove release lever return spring. Then slide release bearing and hub off release lever (cast iron housings only).
5. Loosen pressure plate attaching bolts gradually and evenly to release spring tension. If same clutch is being installed, first mark clutch cover and flywheel so installation may be made in same position.
6. Remove clutch and driven plate.

1963

1. Remove transmission as outlined further on.
2. Remove flywheel housing cover.
3. Remove release lever retracting spring and slide release bearing and hub off release lever.
4. If same pressure plate and cover assembly is to be reinstalled, mark cover and flywheel so that pressure plate can be installed in the same position.
5. Loosen clutch cover-to-flywheel bolts evenly to release the pressure plate spring tension.
6. Remove clutch and disc through opening in bottom of flywheel housing.
7. Reverse the foregoing procedure to install the clutch. Then adjust the free pedal travel as outlined previously.

MANUAL SHIFT TRANS.

Transmission Replace

Three Speed Units

1. Raise car and drain lube from transmission.
2. Mark drive shaft so that it may be installed in the same relative position.
3. Disconnect drive shaft from U-joint flange and slide it out of extension housing.
4. Disconnect speedometer cable.
5. Disconnect shift rods from levers at transmission.
6. Disconnect parking brake cable at equalizer.
7. Unfasten extension from rear support.
8. Raise engine high enough to remove weight from frame crossmember.
9. Support transmission with a jack and detach it from flywheel housing.
10. Slide transmission back and out of car.
11. Reverse removal procedure to install transmission.

Four Speed Units

1. Remove transmission gearshift lever boot retainer. Working under boot, remove shift lever retaining bolts and remove lever. The remaining shift linkage may be left on the transmission during removal.
2. Raise car and disconnect drive shaft from rear U-joint flange and remove drive shaft.
3. Disconnect speedometer cable.
4. Disconnect parking brake cable at equalizer bar and raise rear of engine.
5. Unfasten extension housing from engine rear support.
6. Raise transmission slightly with a jack. Disconnect and remove crossmember and engine rear support as a unit.
7. Unfasten transmission from clutch housing and install guide pins in the two lower holes.
8. Remove transmission. If necessary,

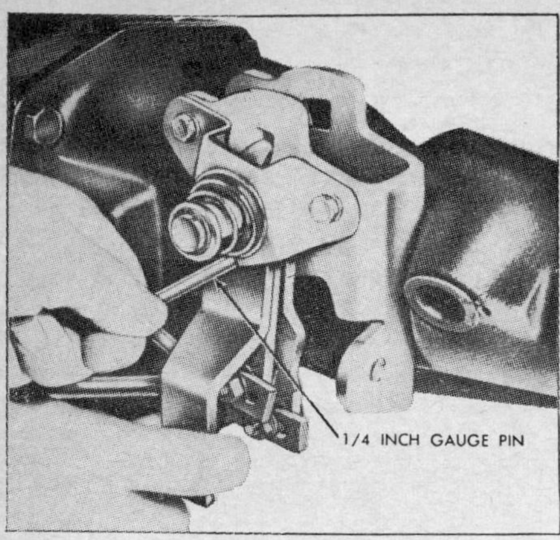

Fig. 1 Four speed transmission linkage adjustment. 1963-64

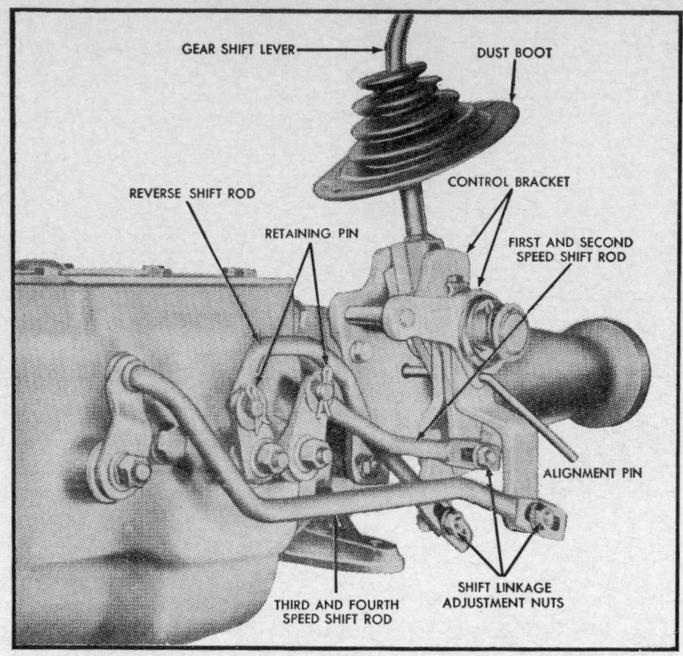

Fig. 2 Shift linkage. 1965-68 four speed transmission

lower engine to gain enough clearance for removal of transmission.

9. Reverse removal procedure to install.

SHIFT LINKAGE, ADJUST

1963-69 3 Speed Units

1. Place selector lever in neutral.
2. Loosen the two shift rod adjusting nuts.
3. Insert a $\frac{3}{16}''$ drill shank through the low-reverse and 2-3 shift levers at steering column. It may be necessary to align levers to insert drill.
4. Tighten adjusting nuts.
5. Remove drill gauge.
6. Start engine and move shift lever to each position to be sure it operates freely.

1963-64 4 Speed Units

1. Place selector lever in neutral and raise car.
2. Insert a ¼" drill shank into alignment hole, Fig. 1. If drill will not enter, check for bent shift rods. If rods are the correct shape, check for loose lever lock nuts at rod ends.
3. Reset linkage by loosening three rod lock nuts and moving levers until the drill gauge will enter alignment holes.

NOTE: Make sure transmission shift levers are in neutral and reverse shift lever is in reverse detent. If there is any doubt about location of neutral position, disconnect shift rods at lock nuts and rotate each forward speed shift lever through its three positions until center (neutral) position is positively located. Move reverse lever forward until positive engagement of detent is felt.

---

4. Install shift rods and tighten lock nuts. Remove drill gauge and operate shift levers to make sure detents are engaging.
5. Lower car and check for smooth cross-over operation.

1965-69 4 Speed Unit

1. Loosen three shift linkage adjustment nuts.
2. Install a ¼" diameter alignment tool through control bracket and levers as shown in Fig. 2.

NOTE: An alignment tool can be made from ¼" diameter drill rod bent to an "L" shape. The extensions should be 1½" and 3¾" from elbow. Short end of tool should be inserted into control bracket and linkage holes until it bottoms.

---

3. Tighten three linkage adjusting nuts and then remove alignment tool.
4. Check shift lever for smooth crossover.

1969 AUTO. TRANS. LINKAGE ADJUST

Although the linkage has been changed for 1969 column shift models, the adjustment procedures remain the same as for 1968 models described in the front section of this manual.

Rear Axle, Propeller Shaft & Brakes

REAR AXLES

Figs. 1 and 3 illustrate the rear axle assemblies used on these cars. When necessary to overhaul either of these units, refer to the *Rear Axle Specifications* table in this chapter.

Integral Carrier Type

The gear set consists of an 8½" diameter ring gear and an overhung drive pinion which is supported by two opposed tapered roller bearings, Fig. 1. The differential case is a one-piece design with openings allowing assembly of the internal parts and lubricant flow. The differential pinion shaft is retained with a threaded bolt (lock) assembled to the case.

The roller type wheel bearings have no inner race, and the rollers directly contact the bearing journals of the axle shafts. The axle shafts do not use an inner and outer bearing retainer. Rather, they are held in the axle by means of C-locks, Fig. 2. These C-locks also fit into a machined recess in the differential side gears within the differential case. There is no retainer bolt access hole in the axle shaft flange.

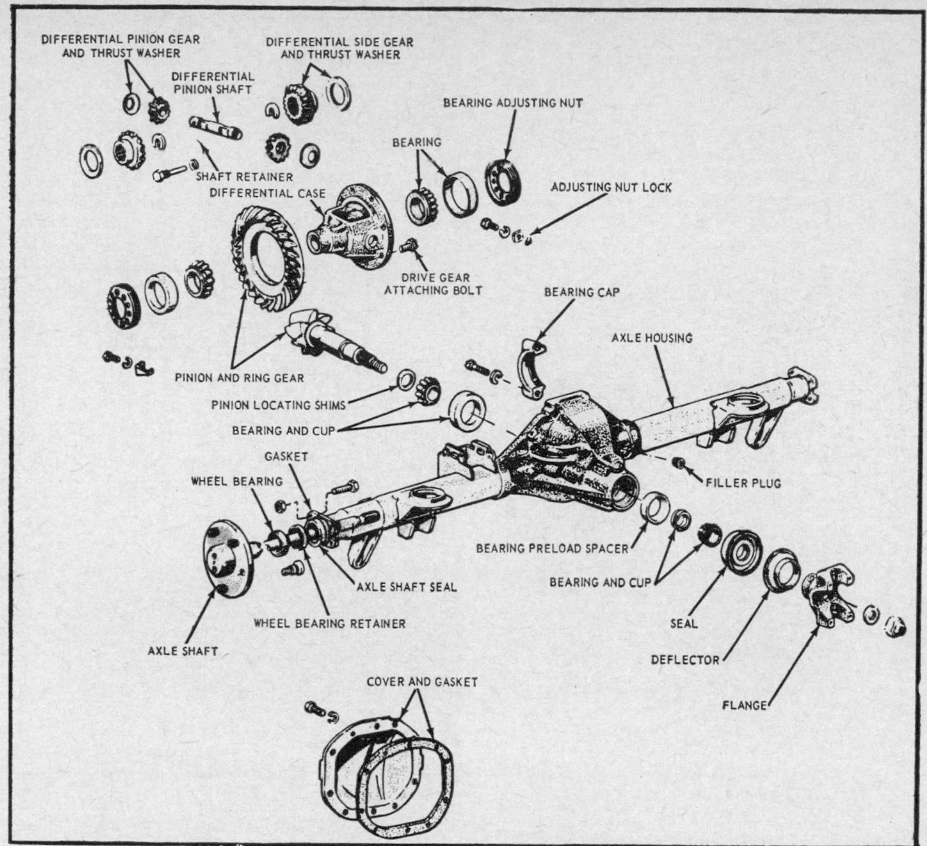

Fig. 1 Integral type rear axle assembly. 1967-69 Ford with 6-240, V8-289 and V8-302 with two barrel carburetor

Axle Shaft, Bearing & Oil Seal

1. Raise car on hoist and remove wheels.
2. Drain differential lubricant.
3. Remove brake drums.
4. Remove differential housing cover.
5. Position safety stands under rear frame member and lower hoist to allow axle to lower as far as possible.
6. Working through differential case opening, remove pinion shaft lock bolt and pinion shaft.
7. Push axle shaft(s) inward toward center of axle housing and remove C-lock(s) from housing, Fig. 2.
8. Remove axle shaft, using extreme care to avoid contact of shaft seal lip with any portion of axle shaft except seal journal.
9. Use a hook-type puller to remove seal and bearing, Fig. 7.
10. Reverse procedure to install, using suitable driving tools, Fig. 8, to install seal and bearing. New seals are pre-packed with lubricant and do not require oil soaking before installation.

Removable Carrier Type

In these axles, Fig. 3, the drive pinion is straddle-mounted by two opposed tapered roller bearings which support the pinion shaft in front of the drive pinion gear, and straight roller bearing that supports the pinion shaft at the rear of the pinion gear. The drive pinion is assembled in a pinion retainer that is bolted to the differential carrier. The tapered roller bearings are preloaded by a collapsible spacer between the bearings. The pinion is positioned by a shim or shims located between the drive pinion retainer and the differential carrier.

The differential is supported in the carrier by two tapered roller side bearings. These bearings are preloaded by two threaded ring nuts or sleeves between the bearings and pedestals. The differential assembly is positioned for proper ring gear and pinion backlash by varying the adjustment of these ring nuts. The differential case houses two side gears in mesh with two pinions mounted on a pinion shaft which is held in place by a pin. The side gears and pinions are backed by thrust washers. With high performance engines, an optional rear axle having a four-pinion differential is also used.

The axle shafts are of unequal length, the left shaft being shorter than the right. The axle shafts are mounted in sealed ball bearings that are pressed on the shafts.

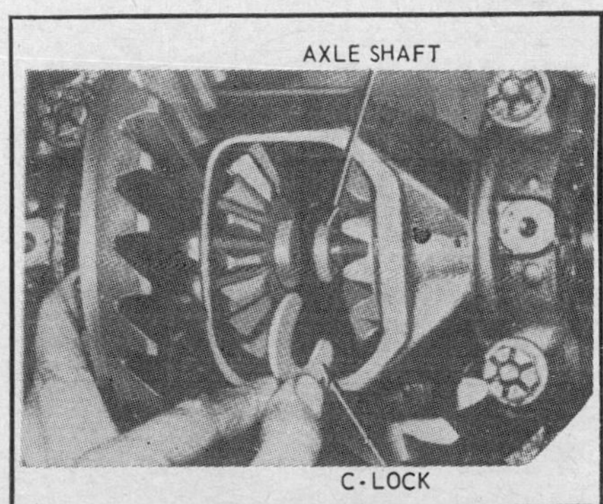

Fig. 2 Axle shaft C-locks. 1967-69 Ford integral type axle

Service Bulletin

All Ford Built Rear Axles: Recent manufacturing changes have eliminated the need for marking rear axle drive pinions for individual variations from nominal shim thicknesses. In the past, these pinion markings, with the aid of a shim selection table, were used as a guide to select correct shim thicknesses when a gear set or carrier assembly replacement was performed.

With the elimination of pinion markings, use of the shim selection table is no longer possible and the methods outlined below must be used.

1. Measure the thickness of the original pinion depth shim removed from the axle. Use the same thickness upon installation of the replacement carrier or drive pinion. If any further shim change is necessary, it will be indicated in the tooth pattern check.
2. If the original shim is lost, substitute a nominal shim for the original and use the tooth pattern check to determine if further shim changes are required.

Axle Shaft, Bearing & Seal

1. Remove wheel assembly.
2. Remove brake drum from flange.
3. Working through hole provided in axle shaft flange, Fig. 4, remove nuts that secure bearing retainer.
4. Pull axle shaft out of housing. If bearing is a tight fit in axle housing, use a slide hammer-type puller, Fig. 5. *Brake carrier plate must not be dislodged. Install one nut to hold plate in place after axle shaft is removed.*
5. If axle shaft bearing is to be replaced, loosen inner retainer by nicking it deeply with a chisel in several places, Fig. 6. The bearing will then slide off easily.

NOTE: On 1969 models a heavier, hardened retainer ring is used and it is therefore necessary to first drill a 1/4" hole not more than 5/16" deep in the retainer ring surface before using a chisel.

6. Press bearing from axle shaft.
7. Inspect machined surfaces of axle shaft and housing for rough spots that would affect the sealing action of the oil seal. Carefully remove any burrs or rough spots.
8. Press new bearing on shaft until it seats firmly against shoulder on shaft.
9. Press inner bearing retainer on shaft until it seats firmly against bearing.
10. If oil seal is to be replaced, use a

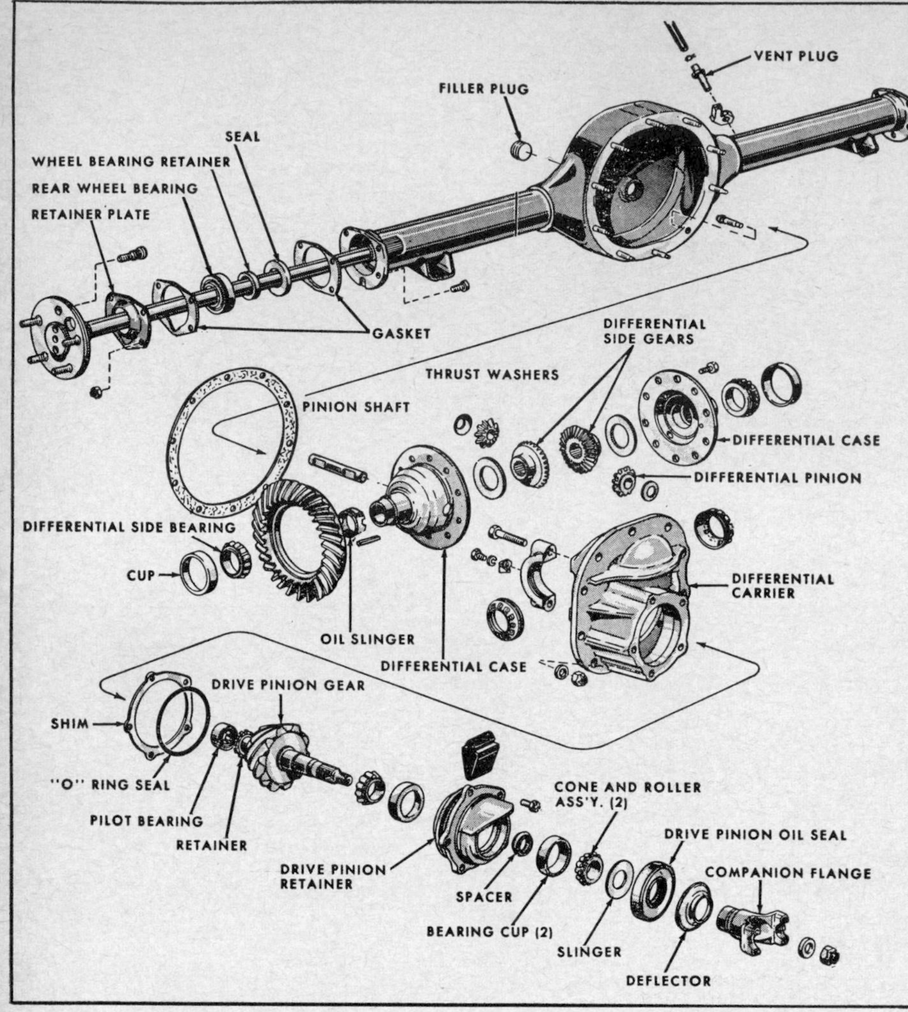

Fig. 3 Removable carrier type of rear axle assembly. On some high performance engines a four-pinion differential is also used

Fig. 4 Removing nuts from rear bearing retainer

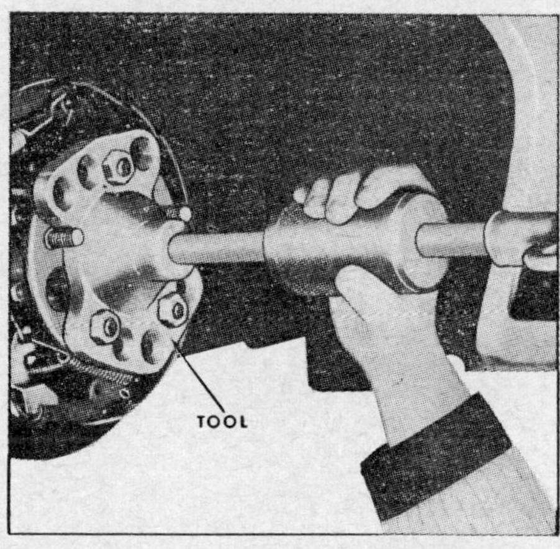

Fig. 5 Removing axle shaft with slide hammer-type puller

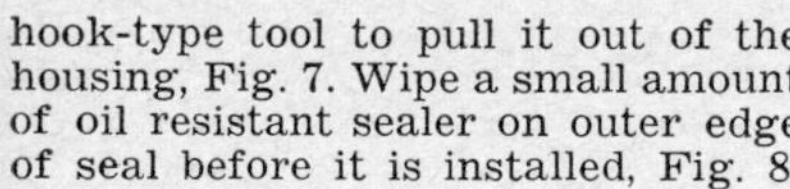

hook-type tool to pull it out of the housing, Fig. 7. Wipe a small amount of oil resistant sealer on outer edge of seal before it is installed, Fig. 8.

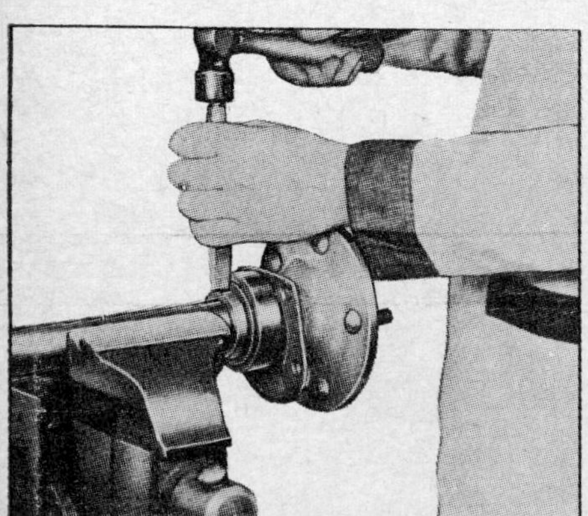

Fig. 6 Splitting bearing inner retainer for bearing removal

Installation

1. Place a new gasket on each side of brake carrier plate and slide axle shaft into housing. Start the splines into the differential side gear and push the shaft in until bearing bottoms in housing.
2. Install retainer and tighten nuts to 30-40 ft. lbs.
3. Install brake drum and wheel.

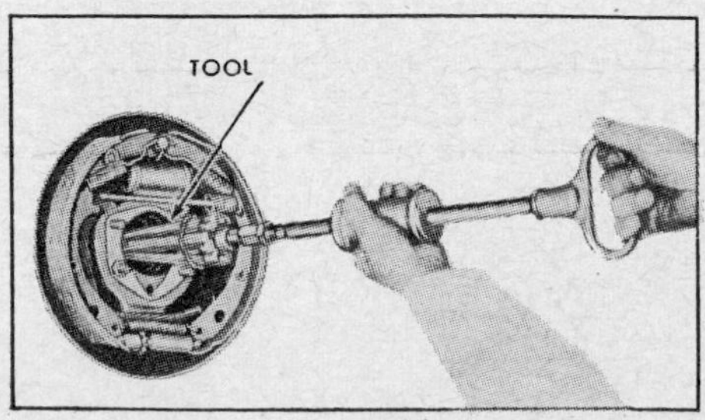

Fig. 7 Using hook-type tool to remove oil seal

PROPELLER SHAFT

Remove & Replace

1. Disconnect rear U-joint from drive

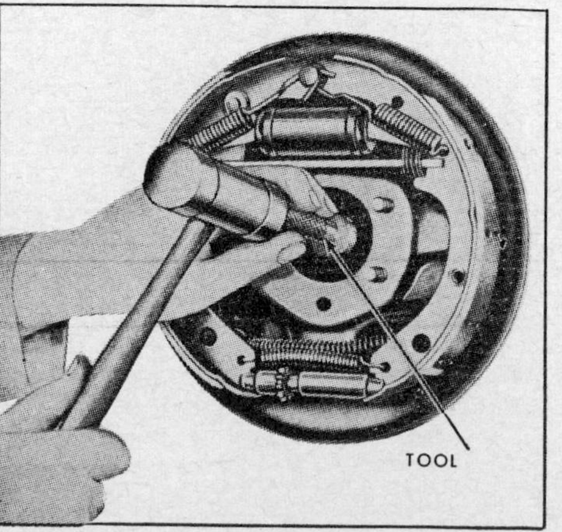

Fig. 8 Using special driver to install oil seal

ment, remove eccentric bolt, bushing and lock nut that secures master cylinder push rod to brake pedal. Remove push rod and bushing from pedal.
2. Remove hydraulic outlet fitting.
3. Remove stop light switch.
4. Unfasten master cylinder from dash panel (2 capscrews).
5. Reverse above procedure to install and bleed hydraulic system.

POWER BRAKE UNIT, REPLACE

1965-69 Ford & Mercury

1. Working from inside of car under instrument panel, disconnect booster push rod link from brake pedal. To do this, proceed as follows:
2. Disconnect stop light switch wires at connector. Remove hairpin retainer. Slide switch off brake pedal pin just far enough for switch outer hole to clear pin. Then lift switch straight upward from pin. Slide master cylinder push rod and nylon washers and bushing off brake pedal pin.
3. Open hood and disconnect brake line at master cylinder outlet fitting.
4. Disconnect vacuum hose from booster unit. If equipped with automatic transmission disconnect transmission vacuum unit hose.
5. Remove four attaching nuts and remove booster and bracket from dash panel, sliding push rod link out from engine side of dash panel. Remove four spacers.
6. Remove push rod link boot from dash panel.
7. Reverse procedure to install.

1963-64 Ford, 1964 Mercury

1. Working inside car below instrument panel, disconnect booster push rod link from brake pedal by removing the horseshoe retaining clip and sliding push rod link off pin that is integral with pedal.
2. Open hood and disconnect wires from stop light switch at master cylinder.
3. Disconnect brake line at master cylinder outlet fitting.
4. Disconnect vacuum hose from booster unit. Also disconnect transmission throttle valve hose (if equipped).
5. Unfasten booster (4 bolts) from dash panel and slide push rod link out from engine side of dash panel.
6. Reverse removal procedure to install the booster. Then bleed the brake system.

1963 Mercury

Remove master cylinder outlet fitting from cylinder. If only the brake booster is to be removed, support the master cylinder with a prop from the underside. This eliminates the necessity of disconnecting the outlet fitting and consequently bleeding is not required during assembly.

Remove vacuum hoses. Unfasten and remove master cylinder. Remove power brake unit from bracket on dash panel (4 capscrews) and remove power brake.

Front End and Steering Section

FRONT SUSPENSION

1963-64

Referring to Fig. 1, each front wheel rotates on a spindle. The upper and lower ends of the spindle are attached to upper and lower ball joints that are mounted to an upper and lower control arm. The upper arm pivots on a bushing and shaft assembly that is bolted to the frame. The lower arm pivots on two studs, one being located in the front crossmember and the other in the No. 2 crossmember. A coil spring seats between the lower control arm and the top of the spring housing. A double-acting shock absorber is bolted to the arm and the top of the spring housing.

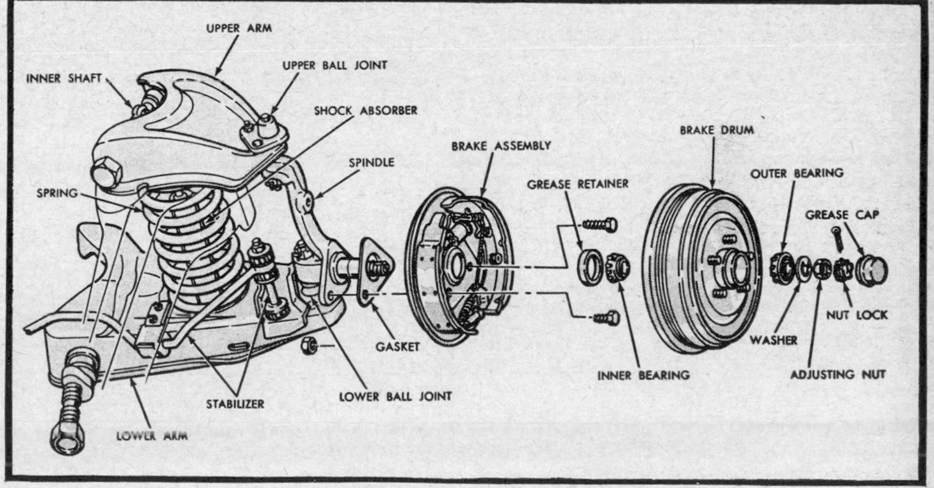

Fig. 1 Front suspension. 1964 Ford and Mercury. Typical of earlier models

1965-69

Referring to Fig. 2, the construction of the front suspension differs from earlier models in that the lower control arm pivots on a bolt in the front crossmember. The struts, which are connected between the lower control arms and frame crossmember, prevent the control arms from moving forward and backward.

LUBRICATION

1963-69

Ball joints are prelubricated with a special lubricant. The lubricating interval is 36,000 miles. At these intervals, remove the plugs, apply the special lubricant, remove the fittings and replace the plugs.

SERVICE BULLETIN

Some uninformed service people recommend that conventional grease fittings be installed and that the car be lubricated every 1000 miles. This is completely unnecessary and, in fact, may cause damage to the special seals used in the lubrication points.

The use of conventional lubricants not only can do damage to the special seals but is incompatible with the special lubricant. Moreover, after the special sealing plugs have been replaced by conventional grease fittings, dirt and water can enter and cause excessive wear, rendering the units unfit for further service.

SERVICE BULLETIN, 1965-69

BALL JOINT LUBE: The ball joint seals on these models have been redesigned to provide improved sealing and longer life. The new seals can be damaged and the sealing characteristics destroyed if excessive lubricant is used. Specifications call for the addition of only 10 grams (level teaspoon) of lubricant to the ball joints at 36,000 mile intervals. The initial application of 10 grams of lubricant insures forcing grease

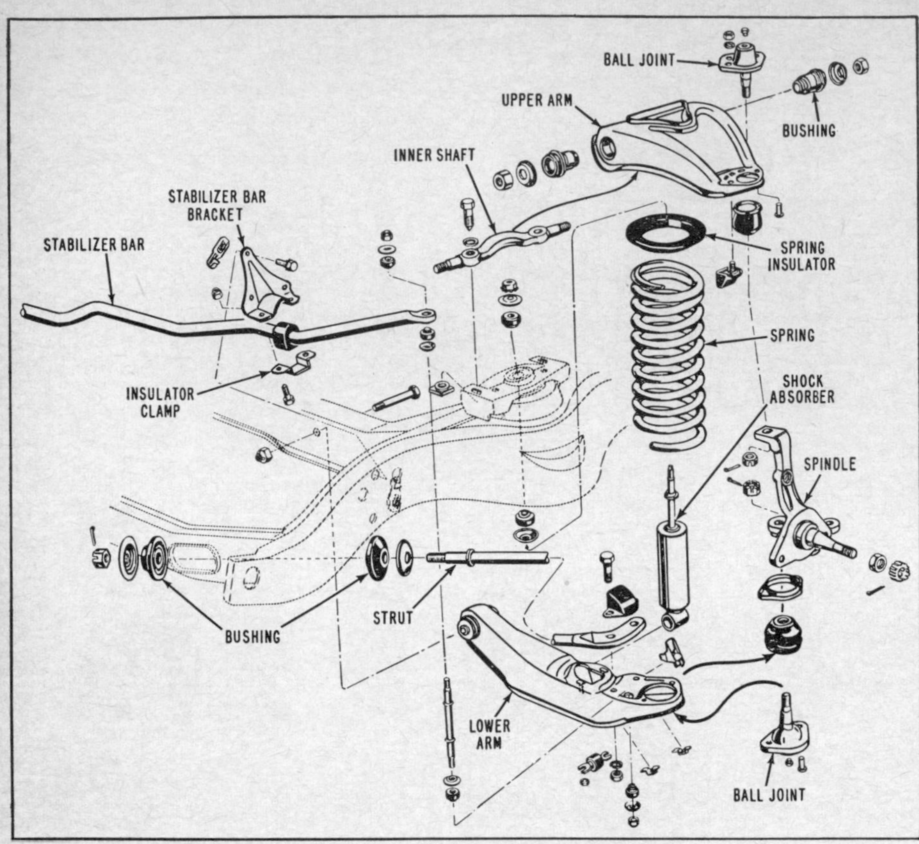

Fig. 2 Front suspension. 1965-69 Ford & Mercury

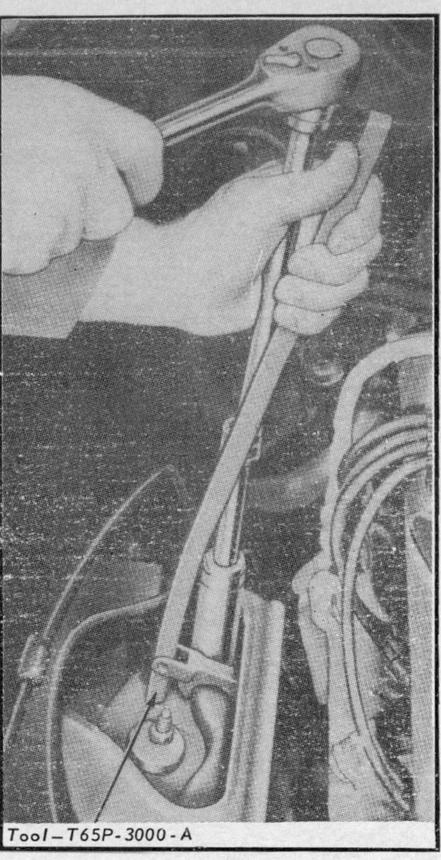

Fig. 3 Adjusting caster and camber. 1965-69 Ford and Mercury

into the bearing area and still allows for three subsequent lubrications of 10 grams each without ballooning the seals and resultant premature failure.

For the above reasons the ball joint seals on new cars might appear to be collapsed and give the mistaken impression that additional lubricant is required. This is not the case and under no circumstances should more than 10 grams of lubricant be added to the ball joints at the 36,000 mile intervals.

SERVICE BULLETIN

1963-69 STEERING LINKAGE LUBE: The steering linkage on these models should be lubricated at intervals of 36,000 miles. Normal breathing of socket joints permits moisture condensation within the joint. Moisture inside the joint assembly will cause no appreciable damage and the joint will function normally. However, if the moisture is concentrated in the bearing grease grooves and is frozen at the time of attempted lubrication, grease cannot flow and pressure greasing may damage the joint.

Do not attempt to lubricate the steering linkage on these vehicles if it has set in temperatures lower than 20 deg. above zero F. The vehicle should be allowed to warm up in a heated garage for 30 minutes or until the joints accept lubrication.

IMPORTANT: A torch must not be used to heat joints because this quantity of heat will melt the nylon bearing within the joint.

WHEEL ALIGNMENT

SERVICE BULLETIN

WHEEL BALANCING DIFFERS: On cars with disc brakes, dynamic balancing of the wheel-and-tire assembly on the car should not be attempted without first pulling back the shoe and lining assemblies from the rotor. If this is not done, brake drag may burn out the motor on the wheel spinner.

The drag can be eliminated by removing the wheel, taking out the two bolts holding the caliper splash shield, and detaching the shield. Then push the pistons into their cylinder bores by applying steady pressure on the shoes on each side of the rotor for at least a minute. If necessary, use waterpump pliers to apply the pressure.

After the pistons have been retracted, reinstall the splash shield and wheel. The wheel-and-tire assembly can then be dynamically balanced in the usual way. After the balancing job has been completed, be sure to pump the brake pedal several times until the shoes are seated and a firm brake pedal is obtained.

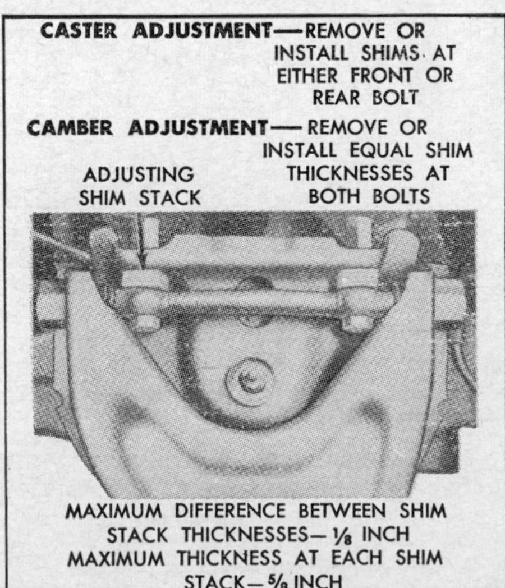

Fig. 4 Caster and camber adjustments. 1964 Ford and Mercury

1965-69 Ford & Mercury

Caster and camber can be adjusted by loosening the bolts that attach the upper suspension arm to the shaft at the frame side rail, and moving the arm assembly in or out in the elongated bolt holes, Fig. 3. Since any movement of the arm affects both caster and camber, both factors should be balanced against one another when making the adjustment.

Caster, Adjust

1. To adjust caster, install the adjusting tool as shown in Fig. 3.
2. Loosen both upper arm inner shaft retaining bolts and move either front or rear of the shaft in or out as

necessary to increase or decrease caster angle. Then tighten bolt to retain adjustment.

Camber, Adjust

1. Loosen both upper arm inner retaining bolts and move both front and rear ends of shaft inward or outward as necessary to increase or decrease camber angle.
2. Tighten bolts and recheck caster and readjust if necessary.

1963-64 Ford & Mercury

Caster—To adjust caster, loosen the two bolts that secure the upper suspension arm shaft to the frame and insert or remove shims as required between shaft and frame, Fig. 4.

A $\frac{1}{16}$" shim added at the front bolt will change caster ½° in the positive direction. A $\frac{1}{16}$" shim removed from the front bolt will change caster ½° in the negative direction. When caster is correct torque bolts to 65-85 ft. lbs.

Camber—To adjust camber, insert or remove an equal number of shims from between the upper suspension arm shaft and frame at both the front and rear bolts. Each $\frac{1}{16}$" of shim will change camber ¼°.

SERVICE BULLETIN

SERVICE ANTI-HARSH SHAFT: When making front alignment checks and adjustments on 1963-64 Mercurys, first inspect the anti-harsh shaft located at the front mounting for the lower control arm. This shaft must be properly lubricated and neutralized.

Inadequate lubrication will cause noise when the front end is jounced up and down. To lubricate, remove the plug from the front end of the front bushing, install a fitting, and use a hand gun. Be careful not to force out the bushing seal.

The crank throw on the shaft must be in a vertical down position to be neutralized. If it is not in this position after the shaft has been lubricated and the front end jounced, loosen the shaft nut at the lower arm end. Again jounce the car and, when the crank is in a vertical down position, torque the nut 40 to 60 ft.-lbs. If required, repeat the operation for the opposite side.

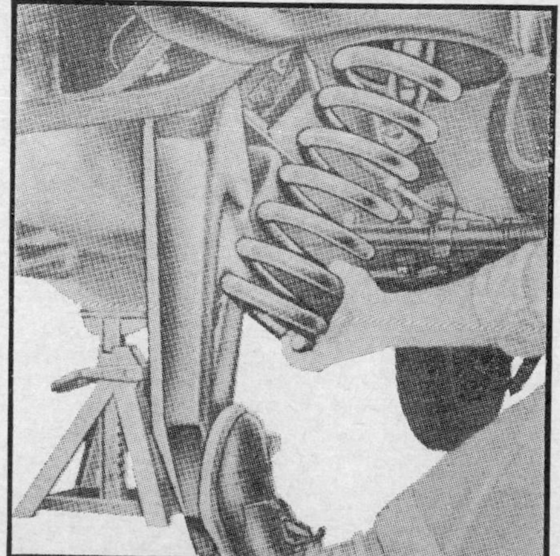

Fig. 6 Removing and installing coil spring. 1963-64

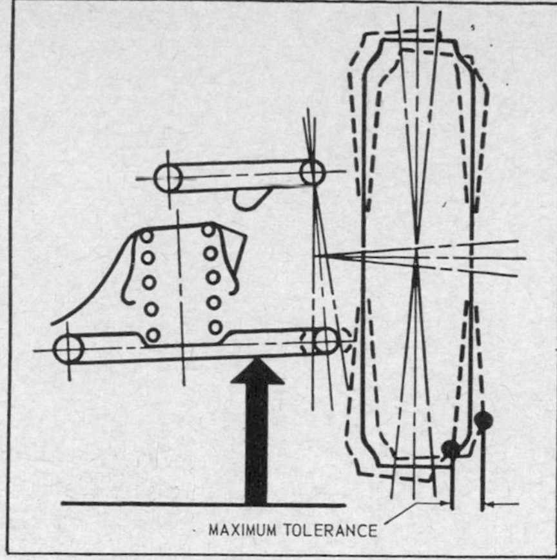

Fig. 5 Measuring lower ball joint radial play, which should not exceed ¼"

TOE-IN, ADJUST

Position the front wheels in their straight-ahead position. Then turn both tie rod adjusting sleeves an equal amount until the desired toe-in setting is obtained.

WHEEL BEARINGS, ADJUST

1. Torque adjusting nut 17 to 25 ft-lbs.
2. Back nut off ½ turn.
3. Retighten it 10 to 15 inch-lbs (finger tight) and install nut lock and cotter pin.

WHEEL BEARINGS, REPLACE

(Disc Brakes)

1. Raise car and remove front wheels.
2. Remove caliper mounting bolts.

NOTE: It is not necessary to disconnect the brake lines for this operation.

3. Slide caliper off of disc, inserting a spacer between the shoes to hold them in their bores after the caliper is removed. Position caliper assembly out of the way.

NOTE: Do not allow caliper to hang by brake hose.

4. Remove hub and disc assembly. Grease retainer and inner bearing can now be removed.

CHECKING BALL JOINTS FOR WEAR

Upper Ball Joint

1. Raise car on floor jacks placed beneath lower control arms.
2. Grasp lower edge of tire and move wheel in and out.
3. As wheel is being moved in and out, observe upper end of spindle and upper arm.
4. Any movement between upper end of spindle and upper arm indicates ball joint wear and loss of preload. If any such movement is observed, replace upper ball joint.

NOTE: During the foregoing check, the lower ball joint will be unloaded and may move. Disregard all such movement of the lower ball joint. Also, do not mistake loose wheel bearings for a worn ball joint.

Lower Ball Joint

1. Raise car on jacks placed under lower control arms as shown in Fig. 6. This will unload ball joints.
2. Adjust wheel bearings.
3. Attach a dial indicator to lower control arm and position so that its plunger rests against the inner side of the wheel rim adjacent to the lower ball joint.
4. Grasp tire at top and bottom and slowly move it in and out as shown in Fig. 5.
5. If reading on dial indicator exceeds ¼", replace lower ball joint.

SHOCK ABSORBER, REPLACE

To remove a shock absorber, unfasten

Fig. 7 Removing and installing coil spring. 1965-69

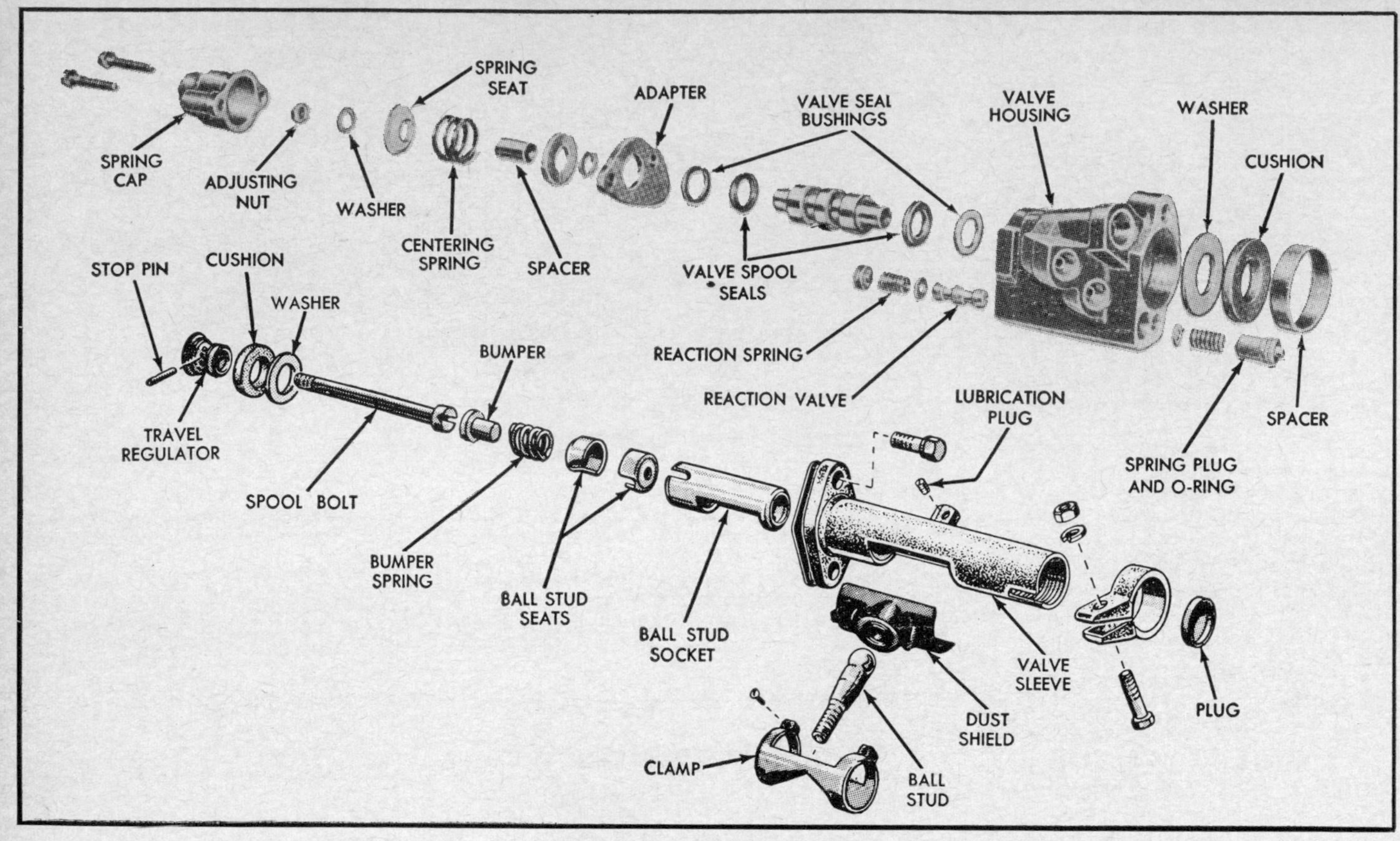

Fig. 8 Control valve disassembled

it at the top and bottom and lower it through the opening in the lower control arm.

COIL SPRING, REPLACE

1. Support the front of the car at the frame side rails.
2. Place a floor jack under the lower arm. Then unfasten the lower ball joint from the knuckle support.
3. Lower the jack under the lower arm and pull out the coil spring as suggested by Figs. 6 and 7.
4. Reverse procedure to install.

BALL JOINTS, REPLACE

The ball joints are riveted to the upper and lower control arms. The ball joints can be replaced on the car by removing the rivets and retaining the new ball joint to the control arm with the attaching bolts, nuts and washers furnished with the ball joint kit.

When removing a ball joint, use a suitable pressing tool to force the ball joint out of the spindle.

STEERING GEAR, REPLACE

1965-69 Ford & Mercury

1. Remove bolt that attaches flex joint to steering gear.
2. Raise front of car and install safety stands.
3. Disconnect pitman arm from sector shaft.
4. If necessary, disconnect muffler inlet pipe.
5. Remove steering gear housing attaching bolts and remove steering gear.

1963-64 Ford & Mercury

1. On a car with a movable steering column, remove pivot bracket-to-steering column bolt nut and washers, then the three bracket-to-steering gear housing bolts. Remove pivot bracket from gear housing and column pivot bolt.
2. On all models, remove clamp bolt that locks the flex joint to steering gear worm shaft.
3. Raise front of car and position safety stands.
4. Disconnect pitman arm from sector shaft, using a suitable puller. On cars equipped with power steering, disconnect power steering cylinder from frame mounting bracket.
5. Remove three steering gear-to-frame retaining bolts and pull steering gear housing out of flex joint.

POWER STEERING GEAR

1965-69 Ford & Mercury

1. Disconnect pressure and return lines from steering gear. Plug lines and ports in gear to prevent entry of dirt.
2. Remove two bolts that secure flex coupling to steering gear and to column.
3. Raise car and remove sector shaft nut.
4. Use a puller to remove pitman arm.
5. If car has a standard transmission, remove clutch release lever retracting spring to provide clearance for gear removal.
6. Support steering gear, then remove attaching bolts.
7. Work steering gear free of flex coupling and remove it from car.
8. Reverse procedure to install.

LINKAGE TYPE POWER STEERING

The power steering system combines a conventional type steering gear with a power-assisted steering linkage. The power-assist mechanism consists of a pump and fluid reservoir, a control valve, a power cylinder, the connecting fluid lines and the steering linkage.

Before performing service operations on the power steering system, make certain that the trouble is not caused by the lack of fluid.

Pump Pressure

Normal oil pressure against either steering stop with engine idling should

be as follows:
Ford
1963-64 6-223, V8-260 ....700- 900
1963-64 V8-289 ....700- 900
1963-64 V8-352, 390 950-1100
Mercury
1963-64 950-1100

Fluid Pressure Test

A fluid pressure test will show whether the pump or some other unit in the power steering system is causing trouble in the system. Disconnect the pressure line hose from the pump outlet and install a pressure testing tool between the hose and pump outlet. *Be sure the pressure gauge is between the pump and shut-off valve on the tool.*

Open the shut-off valve on the testing tool and run the engine at idle speed. If the pump normally operates quietly, ignore the louder pump noise when the tester is connected to the system. Allow at least two minutes for the fluid to warm up before starting the pressure tests.

1. Turn the front wheels all the way to the right, then to the left, and note the fluid pressure reading on the gauge when the wheels are against the stops. Normal fluid pressure at both positions should be as given above. *Do not hold the wheels against the stops for more than 30 seconds at a time as the fluid may overheat.*
2. If the fluid pressure is less than specified with the wheels against the stops, turn the wheels away from the stops. Slowly close the tester shut-off valve and watch the gauge for an increase in pressure. *Do not leave the valve closed for more than 15 seconds.*
3. If the fluid pressure is less than specified with the shut-off valve closed, the pump is causing the trouble. If the pressure increases but does not reach the minimum pressure specified, the pump, control valve and the power cylinder all should be inspected. If the pressure is within limits, the trouble is either in the control valve or the power cylinder.
4. After completing the test, shut off the engine, remove the tester and make the necessary repairs.

Control Valve Removal

1. Remove reservoir cover and, using a suction gun, draw as much fluid as possible from reservoir.
2. Disconnect four hoses at control valve and drain fluid from hoses.
3. Turn front wheels to extreme right and left several times to force all fluid from system.
4. Loosen clamp bolt and nut at right-hand end of sleeve.
5. Pull roll pin out of steering arm-to-idler arm rod through slot in sleeve.
6. Remove control valve ball stud nut.
7. Remove nut from end of ball stud, then raise control valve high enough to remove ball stud from sector shaft arm.
8. Turn wheels fully to left, then turn control valve counterclockwise to remove it.

NOTE: When servicing the control valve, use Fig. 8 as a guide for disassembly and assembly.

Control Valve, Install

1. Thread valve on steering arm-to-idler arm rod until about four threads are still visible on the rod.
2. Position ball stud in sector shaft arm.
3. Measure distance between center of ball stud in sector shaft arm and the center of the stud at the inner end of the left-hand spindle connecting rod. *Be sure that measurement is taken parallel to the centerline of the control valve.* The distance should be $1\frac{15}{16}$".
4. When the correct distance is obtained, install the roll pin in the rod hole to lock the valve on the rod.
5. Tighten the valve sleeve clamp bolt to 30-35 lbs. ft. torque.
6. Install and tighten ball stud nut to a torque of 56-60 lbs. ft.
7. Connect and tighten four hoses on control valve.
8. Fill fluid reservoir to within ½" from top with automatic transmission fluid.
9. Start engine and run at idle speed for about two minutes to warm up fluid.
10. Turn steering wheel to both extremes several times and check for leaks.
11. Increase engine speed to a fast idle and again turn steering wheel several times to both extremes.
12. Stop engine and check system for leaks.
13. Hook a spring scale to steering wheel rim and measure pull required to turn wheel in both directions with engine idling and wheels on dry concrete. The pull should be about equal in both directions with tires inflated at specified pressures.

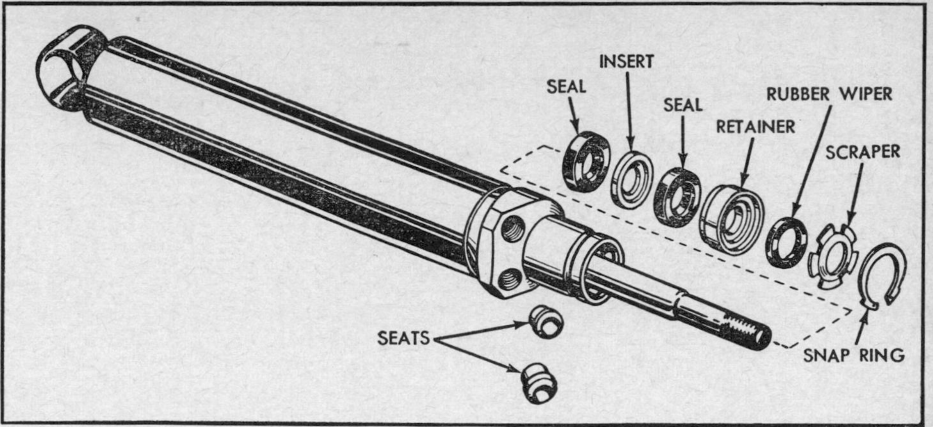

Fig. 9 Power cylinder disassembled

Power Cylinder, Install

NOTE: When servicing the power cylinder, use Fig. 9 as a guide for disassembly and assembly.

1. Install inner washer and bushing on mounting stud in steering arm-to-idler arm rod.
2. Install inner insulator and washer on power cylinder piston rod, then position the cylinder on the mounting stud with the piston rod in the idler arm bracket.
3. Install outer bushing, washer and nut on mounting stud. If a new nut is installed, tighten it to a torque of 60-70 lbs. ft. If a used nut is installed, tighten it to 50-60 lbs. ft.
4. Install the outer insulator, washer and nut on the piston rod, and tighten the nut to a torque of 40-50 lbs. ft.
5. Connect and tighten two hoses to control valve.
6. Fill reservoir to proper level.
7. Start engine and run at idle speed for about two minutes to warm fluid.
8. Turn steering wheel to right and left extremes several times and check system for fluid leaks.
9. Increase engine speed to a fast idle and again turn steering wheel to both extremes several times.
10. Stop engine and check for fluid leaks.

FORD & MERCURY

Compact & Intermediate Models

OLD CAR SPECIFICATIONS: For 1946-62 Tune Up and Wheel Alignment Specifications see back of book.

INDEX OF SERVICE OPERATIONS

PAGE NO.

ACCESSORIES

Automatic Level Controls 1-41
Clock Troubles 1-11
Heater Core, Replace 2-316
Power Top Troubles 1-18
Power Window Troubles 1-18
Radio, Replace 2-316

BRAKES

Brake Troubles, Mechanical 1-17
Disc Brake Service 1-430
Hydraulic System Service 1-422
Master Cylinder, Replace 2-334
Parking Brake, Adjust 2-332
Power Brake Service 1-440
Power Brake Troubles 1-440
Power Brake Unit, Replace 2-334
Service Brakes, Adjust 2-332

CLUTCH

Clutch Pedal, Adjust 2-327
Clutch, Replace 2-327
Clutch Troubles 1-12

COOLING SYSTEM

Cooling System Troubles 1-6
Variable Speed Fans 1-39
Water Pump, Replace 2-326

ELECTRICAL

Alternator Service 1-63
Dash Gauge Service 1-117
Distributor, Replace 2-309
Distributor Service:
Standard 1-53
Transistorized 1-47
Electrical Troubles 1-8
Flasher Location Chart .... Back of Book
Generator Service 1-91
Headlamps, Concealed Type 1-40
Horn Sounder, Remove 2-314
Ignition Coils & Resistors 1-24
Ignition Switch, Replace 2-310
Ignition Timing 2-309
Instrument Cluster Removal 2-314
Light Switch, Replace 2-311
Neutral Safety Switch, Replace 2-311
Spark Plug Condition Chart 2-647
Starter Service 1-101
Starter, Replace 2-309
Starter Switch Service 1-114
Stop Light Switch, Replace 2-311
Turn Signal Switch, Replace 2-313
Turn Signal Troubles 1-11
Windshield Wiper Motor, Replace 2-314
Windshield Wiper Troubles 1-20

PAGE NO.

ENGINE

Camshaft, Replace 2-323
Crankshaft Rear Oil Seal 2-324
Cylinder Head, Replace 2-318
Engine, Replace 2-318
Engine Troubles 1-1
Main Bearings 2-323
Piston Pins 2-323
Piston Rings 2-323
Piston and Rod, Assemble 2-323
Pistons 2-323
Rocker Arm Service 2-321
Rocker Arm Stud 2-321
Rod Bearings 2-323
Timing Case Cover, Replace 2-322
Timing Chain, Replace 2-323
Valve Arrangement 2-319
Valve Guides 2-321
Valve Lifters 2-322
Valves, Adjust 2-320

ENGINE LUBRICATION

Crankcase Ventilation (PCV) 1-29
Exhaust Emission Controls 1-30
Oil Pan, Replace 2-325
Oil Pump, Replace 2-326
Oil Pump Repairs 2-326

FUEL SYSTEM

Carburetor Adjustments and Specs. 1-124
Crankcase Ventilation (PCV) 1-29
Exhaust Emission Controls 1-30
Fuel Pump, Replace 2-326
Fuel Pump Service 1-120
Fuel System Troubles 1-2

PROPELLER SHAFT & U JOINTS

Propeller Shaft 2-331
Universal Joint Service 1-418

REAR AXLE

Axle Shaft, Bearing and Seal 2-330
Rear Axle Description 2-330
Rear Axle Troubles 1-17

SPECIFICATIONS

Alternator 2-303
Brakes 2-308
Capacities 2-307
Carburetors 1-124
Cooling System 2-307
Crankshaft and Bearings 2-305
Distributors 2-300

PAGE NO.

Engine Tightening Torque 2-304
General Engine Specs. 2-296
Generators 2-303
Ignition Coils and Resistors 1-24
Pistons, Rings and Pins 2-305
Rear Axle 2-309
Starting Motors 2-304
Tune Up 2-298
Valve Lift 2-319
Valve Timing 2-320
Valves 2-305
Wheel Alignment 2-306

STEERING GEAR

Horn Sounder Removal 2-314
Mechanical Gear, Replace 2-338
Mechanical Gear Service 1-451
Mechanical Gear Troubles 1-18
Power Steering 2-340
Steering Wheel, Replace 2-314

SUSPENSION, FRONT

Ball Joints, Replace 2-338
Ball Joints, Check for Wear 2-338
Coil Spring, Replace 2-338
Lubrication 2-335
Shock Absorber, Replace 2-338
Suspension, Description of 2-335
Tire Wear Chart 2-648
Toe-In, Adjust 2-337
Wheel Alignment, Adjust 2-335
Wheel Bearings, Adjust 2-337
Wheel Bearings, Replace 2-337

TRANSMISSIONS

Three Speed Manual:
Replace 2-327
Repairs 1-261
Linkage, Adjust 2-329
Four Speed Manual:
Replace 2-328
Repairs 1-298
Linkage, Adjust 2-329
Automatic Units 1-321
1969 Linkage 2-330

TUNE UP

Service 1-21
Specifications 2-298

WINDSHIELD WIPER

Wiper Motor, Replace 2-314
Wiper Linkage, Replace 2-315
Wiper Switch, Replace 2-315
Wiper Troubles 1-20

ENGINE & SERIAL NUMBER LOCATION: Vehicle warranty plate on rear face of left front door.

ENGINE IDENTIFICATION: Engine code is last letter in serial number on vehicle warranty plate.

1963 Comet

1963 Falcon

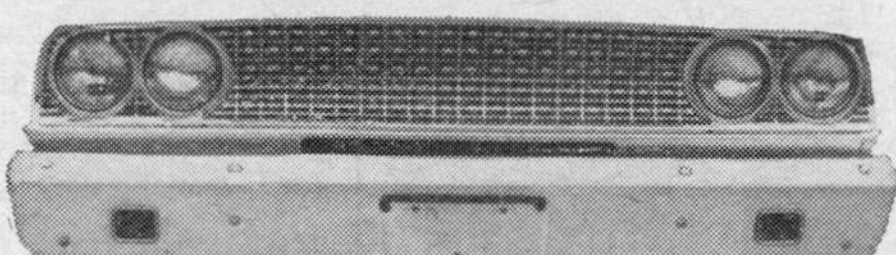
1963 Fairlane

1964 Comet

1964 Falcon

1964 Fairlane

1965 Comet 202, 404, Caliente & Wagons

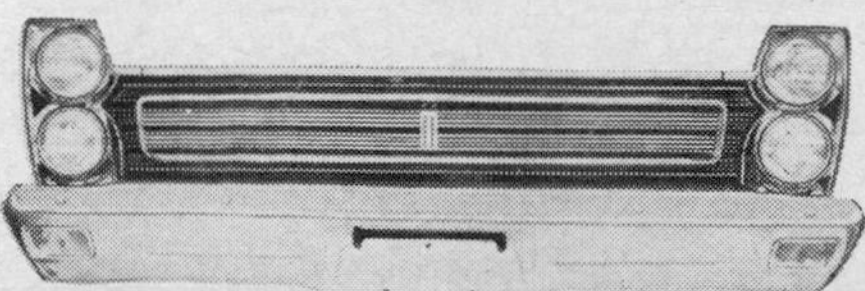
1965 Comet Cyclone

Year	Engine	Engine Code
1963–64	6-144	S
	6-170	U
	6-200	T
	V8-221③	L
	V8-260	F
	V8-289①	C
	V8-289②	K
	V8-289④	D
1965	6-170	U
	6-200	T
	V8-289⑤	A
	V8-289①	C
	V8-289②	K
1966	6-170	U
	6-200	T
	V8-289⑤	A
	V8-289①	C
	V8-289⑥	K
	V8-390①	Y
	V8-390②	Z
	V8-390②	S (GT)
1967	6-170	U
	6-200	T
	V8-289①	C
	V8-289⑤	A
	V8-289⑥	K
	V8-390①	Y
	V8-390①	H
	V8-390②	Z
	V8-390②	S (GT)
1968	6-170	U
	6-200	T
	V8-289①	C
	V8-289⑦	K
	V8-289⑤	A
	V8-302②	J
	V8-302①	F
	V8-390①	Y
	V8-390①⑤	X
	V8-390②	S (GT)
	V8-427②	W
1969	6-170	U
	6-200	T
	6-250	L
	V8-302①	F
	V8-351①	H
	V8-351②	M
	V8-390②	S
	V8-427②	W
	V8-428	Q
	V8-428⑧	R

①—Two barrel carburetor.
②—Four barrel carburetor.
③—1963 only.
④—With transistorized ignition.
⑤—Premium fuel.
⑥—High Performance.
⑦—Special.
⑧—Ram Air.

1965 Falcon

1965 Fairlane

1965 Mustang

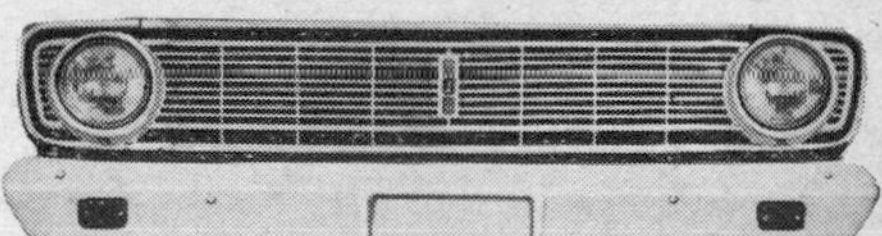
1966 Falcon

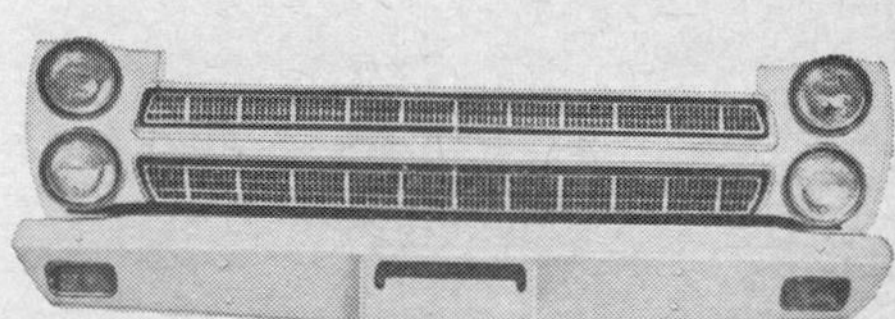
1966 Comet 202, Capri, Caliente & Wagons

1966 Comet Cyclone & GT

1966 Fairlane

1966 Mustang

FORD & MERCURY — Compact & Intermediate Models

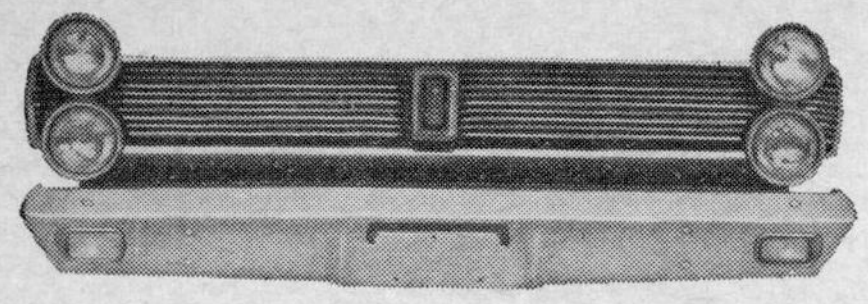
1967 Comet, Capri, Caliente, 202, Wagons

1968 Falcon

1969 Falcon

1967 Cougar

1968 Fairlane

1969 Fairlane, Cobra

1967 Comet Cyclone & GT

1968 Montego and Comet

1969 Torino GT

1967 Fairlane

1968 Cougar

1969 Montego and Cyclone

1967 Falcon

1968 Cougar 7 Litre

1969 Cougar

1967 Mustang

1968 Mustang

1969 Mustang

GENERAL ENGINE SPECIFICATIONS

Year	Engine	Carburetor	Bore and Stroke	Piston Displacement, Cubic Inches	Compression Ratio	Maximum Brake H.P. @ R.P.M.	Maximum Torque Lbs. Ft. @ R.P.M.	Normal Oil Pressure Pounds
1963–64	85 Horsepower.............6-144	1 Barrel	3.500 x 2.50	144	8.7	85 @ 4200	138 @ 2000	35–55
	101 Horsepower.............6-170	1 Barrel	3.500 x 2.94	170	8.7	101 @ 4400	156 @ 2400	35–55
	116 Horsepower.............6-200	1 Barrel	3.680 x 3.12	200	8.7	116 @ 4400	175 @ 2400	35–55
	145 Horsepower (1963).......V8-221	2 Barrel	3.500 x 2.87	221	8.7	145 @ 4400	216 @ 2200	35–55
	164 Horsepower.............V8-260	2 Barrel	3.800 x 2.87	260	8.7	164 @ 4400	258 @ 2200	35–55
	195 Horsepower.............V8-289	2 Barrel	4.000 x 2.87	289	9.0	195 @ 4400	282 @ 2400	35–55

GENERAL ENGINE SPECIFICATIONS—Continued

Year	Engine	Carburetor	Bore and Stroke	Piston Displacement, Cubic Inches	Compression Ratio	Maximum Brake H.P. @ R.P.M.	Maximum Torque Lbs. Ft. @ R.P.M.	Normal Oil Pressure Pounds
1963–64	210 Horsepower.............V8-289	4 Barrel	4.000 x 2.87	289	9.0	210 @ 4400	300 @ 2800	35–55
	271 Horsepower.............V8-289	4 Barrel	4.000 x 2.87	289	10.5	271 @ 6000	312 @ 3400	35–55
1965	105 Horsepower...............6-170	1 Barrel	3.500 x 2.94	170	9.1	105 @ 4400	156 @ 2400	35–55
	120 Horsepower...............6-200	1 Barrel	3.68 x 3.13	200	9.2	120 @ 4400	185 @ 2400	35–55
	200 Horsepower.............V8-289	2 Barrel	4.0000 x 2.87	289	9.3	200 @ 4400	282 @ 2400	35–55
	225 Horsepower.............V8-289	4 Barrel	4.0000 x 2.87	289	10.0	225 @ 4800	305 @ 3200	35–55
	271 Horsepower.............V8-289	4 Barrel	4.0000 x 2.87	289	10.0	271 @ 6000	312 @ 3400	35–55
1966	105 Horsepower...............6-170	1 Barrel	3.50 x 2.94	170	9.1	105 @ 4400	158 @ 2400	35–55
	120 Horsepower...............6-200	1 Barrel	3.68 x 3.126	200	9.2	120 @ 4400	190 @ 2400	35–55
	200 Horsepower.............V8-289	2 Barrel	4.00 x 2.87	289	9.3	200 @ 4400	282 @ 2400	35–55
	225 Horsepower.............V8-289	4 Barrel	4.00 x 2.87	289	10.0	225 @ 4800	305 @ 3200	35–55
	271 H.P. Hi Perf............V8-289	4 Barrel	4.00 x 2.87	289	10.5	271 @ 6000	312 @ 3400	35–55
	265 Horsepower.............V8-390	2 Barrel	4.05 x 3.984	390	9.5	265 @ 4400	401 @ 2600	35–55
	315 Horsepower.............V8-390	4 Barrel	4.05 x 3.984	390	10.5	315 @ 4600	427 @ 2800	35–55
	335 Horsepower "GT".......V8-390	4 Barrel	4.05 x 3.984	390	10.5	335 @ 4800	427 @ 3200	35–55
1967	105 Horsepower...............6-170	1 Barrel	3.50 x 2.94	170	9.1	105 @ 4400	158 @ 2400	35–55
	120 Horsepower...............6-200	1 Barrel	4.00 x 2.87	200	9.2	120 @ 4400	190 @ 2400	35–55
	200 Horsepower.............V8-289	2 Barrel	4.00 x 2.87	289	9.3	200 @ 4400	282 @ 2400	35–55
	225 Horsepower.............V8-289	4 Barrel	4.00 x 2.87	289	10.0	225 @ 4800	305 @ 3200	35–55
	265 Horsepower.............V8-390	2 Barrel	4.05 x 3.984	390	9.5	265 @ 4400	401 @ 2600	35–55
	271 H.P., Hi Perf............V8-289	4 Barrel	4.00 x 2.87	289	10.5	271 @ 6000	312 @ 3400	35–55
	275 Horsepower.............V8-390	2 Barrel	4.05 x 3.9 4	390	9.5	275 @ 4400	405 @ 2600	35–55
	315 Horsepower.............V8-390	4 Barrel	4.05 x 3.984	390	10.5	315 @ 4600	427 @ 2800	35–55
	320 Horsepower.............V8-390	4 Barrel	4.05 x 3.984	390	10.5	320 @ 4800	427 @ 3200	35–55
	335 Horsepower "GT".......V8-390	4 Barrel	4.05 x 3.984	390	10.5	335 @ 4800	427 @ 3200	35–55
1968	105 Horsepower...............6-170	1 Barrel	3.50 x 2.94	170	9.1	105 @ 4400	158 @ 2400	35–55
	120 Horsepower...............6-200	1 Barrel	3.68 x 3.13	200	9.2	120 @ 4400	190 @ 2400	35–55
	200 Horsepower.............V8-289	2 Barrel	4.00 x 2.87	289	9.3	200 @ 4400	282 @ 4400	35–55
	210 Horsepower.............V8-302	2 Barrel	4.00 x 3.00	302	9.5	210 @ 4400	295 @ 2400	35–55
	230 Horsepower.............V8-302	4 Barrel	4.00 x 3.00	302	10.0	230 @ 4800	310 @ 2800	35–55
	235 Horsepower.............V8-302	4 Barrel	4.00 x 3.00	302	10.5	235 @ 4800	318 @ 3200	35–55
	265 Horsepower.............V8-390	2 Barrel	4.05 x 3.78	390	9.5	265 @ 4400	390 @ 2600	35–55
	270 Horsepower.............V8-390	2 Barrel	4.05 x 3.78	390	9.5	270 @ 4400	403 @ 2600	35–55
	271 Horsepower.............V8-289	4 Barrel	4.00 x 2.87	289	10.5	271 @ 6000	312 @ 3400	35–55
	280 Horsepower.............V8-390	2 Barrel	4.05 x 3.78	390	10.5	280 @ 4400	403 @ 2600	35–55
	320 Horsepower "GT".......V8-390	4 Barrel	4.05 x 3.78	390	10.5	320 @ 4800	427 @ 3200	35–55
	325 Horsepower "GT".......V8-390	4 Barrel	4.05 x 3.78	390	10.5	325 @ 4800	427 @ 3200	35–55
	390 Horsepower.............V8-427	4 Barrel	4.23 x 3.78	427	10.9	390 @ 5600	460 @ 3200	35–55
1969	105 Horsepower...............6-170	1 Barrel	3.50 x 2.94	170	9.1	105 @ 4400	158 @ 2400	35–60
	120 Horsepower...............6-200	1 Barrel	3.68 x 3.13	200	8.8	120 @ 4400	190 @ 2400	35–60
	155 Horsepower...............6-250	1 Barrel	3.68 x 3.91	250	9.0	155 @ 4000	240 @ 1600	35–60
	210 Horsepower.............V8-302	2 Barrel	4.00 x 3.00	302	9.5	210 @ 4400	295 @ 2400	35–60
	250 Horsepower.............V8-351	2 Barrel	4.00 x 3.50	351	9.5	250 @ 4600	355 @ 2600	35–60
	290 Horsepower.............V8-351	4 Barrel	4.00 x 3.50	351	10.7	290 @ 4800	385 @ 3200	35–60
	320 Horsepower.............V8-390	4 Barrel	4.05 x 3.78	390	10.5	320 @ 4800	427 @ 3200	35–60
	390 Horsepower.............V8-427	4 Barrel	4.23 x 3.78	427	10.9	390 @ 5600	460 @ 3200	35–60
	335 Horsepower.............V8-428	4 Barrel	4.13 x 3.98	428	10.6	335 @ 5200	440 @ 3400	35–60
	... Ram Air.................V8-428	4 Barrel	4.13 x 3.98	428	10.6	—	—	35–60

TUNE UP SPECIFICATIONS

OLD CAR SPECIFICATIONS: For 1946–62 Tune-Up specifications see back of book.

★ When using a timing light, disconnect vacuum hose or tube at distributor and plug opening in hose or tube so idle speed will not be affected.

Year	Engine	Spark Plug		Distributor		Firing Order	Ignition Timing★		Hot Idle Speed⑫		Comp. Press. Lbs. ③	Fuel Pump Press. Lbs.
		Type	Gap Inch	Point Gap Inch	Dwell Angle Deg.		BTDC ①	Mark	Std. Trans.	Auto. Trans. ②		
1963–64	6-144 Std. Tr.	BF-82	.034	.025	37-42	Fig. H	8°	Fig. A	500⑫	. . .	170	4-5
	6-144 Auto. Tr.	BF-82	.034	.025	37-42	Fig. H	12°	Fig. A	. . .	500D⑫	170	4-5
	6-170 Std. Tr.	BF-82	.034	.025	37-42	Fig. H	6°	Fig. A	500⑫	. . .	170	4-5
	6-170 Auto. Tr.	BF-82	.034	.025	37-42	Fig. H	12°	Fig. A	. . .	500D⑫	170	4-5
	6-200 Std. Tr.	BF-82	.034	.025	37-42	Fig. H	6°	Fig. A	500⑫	. . .	170	4-5
	6-200 Auto. Tr.	BF-82	.034	.025	37-42	Fig. H	12°	Fig. A	. . .	500D⑫	170	4-5
	V8-221 Std. Tr. ⑥	BF-42	.034	.017	26-31	Fig. E	4°	Fig. D	500⑫	. . .	150	4½-5½
	V8-221 Auto. Tr. ⑥	BF-42	.034	.017	26-31	Fig. E	12°	Fig. D	. . .	500D⑫	150	4½-5½
1964	V8-260 Std. Tr.	BF-42	.034	.017	26-31	Fig. E	6°	⑨	525D⑫	. . .	150	4½-5½
	V8-260 Auto. Tr.	BF-42	.034	.017	26-31	Fig. E	10°	⑨	. . .	525D⑫	150	4½-5½
	V8-289 Std. Tr. ⑦	BF-42	.034	.017	26-31	Fig. E	6°	Fig. F	525D⑫	. . .	150	4½-5½
	V8-289 Auto. Tr. ⑦	BF-42	.034	.017	26-31	Fig. E	10°	Fig. F	. . .	525D⑫	150	4½-5½
	V8-289 Std. Tr. ⑧	BF-32	.034	.017	26-31	Fig. E	6°	Fig. F	525D⑫	. . .	150	4½-5½
	V8-289 Auto. Tr. ⑧	BF-32	.034	.017	26-31	Fig. E	10°	Fig. F	. . .	525D⑫	150	4½-5½
	V8-289 Hi Perf.	BF-32	.034	.020	33-36	Fig. E	10°	Fig. F	750D⑫	675D⑫	200	4½-5½
	V8-289⑩	BF-32	.030	.020	22-24	Fig. E	10°⑪	Fig. F	750D⑫	675D⑫	200	4½-5½
1965	6-170 Std. Tr.	BF-82	.034	.025	37-42	Fig. H	6°	Fig. A	585D⑫	. . .	175	4-5
	6-170 Auto. Tr.	BF-82	.034	.025	37-42	Fig. H	12°	Fig. A	. . .	525D⑫	175	4-5
	6-200 Std. Tr.	BF-82	.034	.025	37-42	Fig. H	6°	Fig. A	585D⑫	. . .	175	4-5
	6-200 Auto. Tr.	BF-82	.034	.025	37-42	Fig. H	12°	Fig. A	. . .	525D⑫	175	4-5
	V8-260 Std. Tr.	BF-42	.034	.017	26-31	Fig. E	6°	Fig. F	585D⑫	. . .	150	4½-5½
	V8-260 Auto. Tr.	BF-42	.034	.017	26-31	Fig. E	10°	Fig. F	. . .	525D⑫	150	4½-5½
	V8-289	BF-42	.034	.017	26-31	Fig. E	6°	Fig. F	585D⑫	525D⑫	150	4½-5½
	V8-289 H. Perf.	BF-32	.030	.020	30-33	Fig. E	12°	Fig. F	750D⑫	675D⑫	200	4½-5½
1966	6-170 Std. Tr.⑬	BF-82	.034	.025	37-42	Fig. H	6°	Fig. A	575⑫	. . .	175	4-6
	6-170 Std. Tr.⑭	BF-82	.034	.025	37-42	Fig. H	TDC	Fig. A	625⑫	. . .	175	4-6
	6-170 Auto. Tr.⑬	BF-82	.034	.025	37-42	Fig. H	12°	Fig. A	. . .	500D⑫	175	4-6
	6-170 Auto. Tr.⑭	BF-82	.034	.025	37-42	Fig. H	TDC	Fig. A	. . .	550D⑫	175	4-6
	6-200 Std. Tr.⑬	BF-82	.034	.025	37-42	Fig. H	6°	Fig. A	575⑫	. . .	175	4-6
	6-200 Std. Tr.⑭	BF-82	.034	.025	37-42	Fig. H	TDC	Fig. A	625⑫	. . .	175	4-6
	6-200 Auto. Tr.⑬	BF-82	.034	.025	37-42	Fig. H	12°	Fig. A	. . .	500D⑫	175	4-6
	6-200 Auto. Tr.⑭	BF-82	.034	.025	37-42	Fig. H	TDC	Fig. A	. . .	550D⑫	175	4-6
	8-289 Std. Tr.⑬	BF-42	.034	.017	26-31	Fig. E	6°	Fig. F	575⑫	. . .	150	4-6
	8-289 Std. Tr.⑭	BF-42	.034	.017	26-31	Fig. E	TDC	Fig. F	625⑫	. . .	150	4-6
	8-289 Auto. Tr.⑬	BF-42	.034	.017	26-31	Fig. E	6°	Fig. F	. . .	475D⑫	150	4-6
	8-289 Auto. Tr.⑭	BF-42	.034	.017	26-31	Fig. E	TDC	Fig. F	. . .	625D⑫	150	4-6
	8-289 Hi Perf.	BF-32	.030	.020	30-33	Fig. E	12°	Fig. F	765⑫	765D⑫	180	4-6
	8-390⑬	BF-42	.034	.017	26-31	Fig. E	10°	Fig. K	575⑫	475D⑫	180	4½-5½
	8-390⑭	BF-42	.034	.017	26-31	Fig. E	6°	Fig. K	625⑫	625D⑫	180	4½-6½
1967	6-170 Std. Tr.⑬	BF-82	.034	.025	37-42	Fig. H	6°	Fig. A	575⑫	. . .	175	4-6
	6-170 Std. Tr.⑭	BF-82	.034	.025	37-42	Fig. H	TDC	Fig. A	700⑫	. . .	175	4-6
	6-170 Auto. Tr.⑬	BF-82	.034	.025	37-42	Fig. H	12°	Fig. A	. . .	500D⑫	175	4-6
	6-170 Auto. Tr.⑭	BF-82	.034	.025	37-42	Fig. H	TDC	Fig. A	. . .	550D⑫	175	4-6
	6-200 Std. Tr.⑬	BF-82	.034	.025	37-42	Fig. H	6°	Fig. A	575⑫	. . .	175	4-6
	6-200 Std. Tr.⑭	BF-82	.034	.025	37-42	Fig. H	5°	Fig. A	700⑫	. . .	175	4-6
	6-200 Auto. Tr.⑬	BF-82	.034	.025	37-42	Fig. H	12°	Fig. A	. . .	500D⑫	175	4-6
	6-200 Auto. Tr.⑭	BF-82	.034	.025	37-42	Fig. H	5°	Fig. A	. . .	550D⑫	175	4-6
	8-289 Std. Tr.⑬⑦	BF-42	.034	.017	26-31	Fig. E	6°	Fig. F	575⑫	. . .	150	4-6
	8-289 Std. Tr.⑭⑦	BF-42	.034	.017	26-31	Fig. E	TDC	Fig. F	625⑫	. . .	150	4-6
	8-289 Auto. Tr.⑬⑦	BF-42	.034	.017	26-31	Fig. E	6°	Fig. F	. . .	475D⑫	150	4-6
	8-289 Auto. Tr.⑭⑦	BF-42	.034	.017	26-31	Fig. E	TDC	Fig. F	. . .	550D⑫	150	4-6
	8-289 Std. Tr.⑬⑧	BF-42	.034	.017	26-31	Fig. E	6°	Fig. F	600⑫	. . .	150	4-6
	8-289 Std. Tr.⑭⑧	BF-32	.034	.017	26-31	Fig. E	TDC	Fig. F	625⑫	. . .	150	4-6
	8-289 Auto. Tr.⑬⑧	BF-42	.034	.017	26-31	Fig. E	6°	Fig. F	. . .	475D⑫	150	4-6
	8-289 Auto. Tr.⑭⑧	BF-42	.034	.017	26-31	Fig. E	TDC	Fig. F	. . .	550D⑫	150	4-6

TUNE UP SPECIFICATIONS—Continued

OLD CAR SPECIFICATIONS: For 1946–62 Tune-Up specifications see back of book.

★When using a timing light, disconnect vacuum hose or tube at distributor and plug opening in hose or tube so idle speed will not be affected.

Year	Engine	Spark Plug		Distributor		Firing Order	Ignition Timing★		Hot Idle Speed (12)		Comp. Press. Lbs. (3)	Fuel Pump Press. Lbs.
		Type	Gap Inch	Point Gap Inch	Dwell Angle Deg.		BTDC (1)	Mark	Std. Trans.	Auto. Trans. (2)		
1967	8-289(16)(13)	BF-42	.030	.020	30–33	Fig. E	12°	Fig. F	750(12)	650D(12)	150	4–6
	8-289(16)(14)	BF-32	.030	.020	30–33	Fig. E	6°	Fig. F	750(12)	650D(12)	150	4–6
	8-390(13)	BF-32	.034	.017	26–31	Fig. E	10°	Fig. K	575(12)	475D(12)	180	4½–6½
	8-390(14)	BF-32	.034	.017	26–31	Fig. E	6°	Fig. K	625(12)	550D(12)	180	4½–6½
1968	6-170	BF-82	.034	.027	37–42	Fig. H	6°	Fig. G	700(15)	550D(15)	175	4–6
	6-200	BF-82	.034	.027	37–42	Fig. H	6°	Fig. G	700(15)	550D(5)	175	4–6
	8-289 2 B. Carb.	BF-42	.034	.021	30–33	Fig. E	6°	Fig. B	625(15)	550D(15)	150	4–6
	8-289 4 B. Carb.	BF-32	.034	.020	30–33	Fig. E	6°	Fig. B	750(15)	650D(15)	150	4–6
	8-302 2 B. Carb.	BF-42	.034	.021	30–33	Fig. E	6°	Fig. B	625(15)	550D(5)	150	4–6
	8-302 4 B. Carb.(14)	BF-42	.034	.021	30–33	Fig. E	6°	Fig. B	625(15)	—	150	4–6
	8-302 4 B. Carb.(4)	BF-42	.034	.017	26–31	Fig. E	6°	Fig. B	—	550D(5)	150	4–6
	8-390 2 B. Carb.(14)	BF-42	.034	.021	30–33	Fig. E	6°	Fig. C	625(15)	—	180	4½–6½
	8-390 2 B. Carb.(4)	BF-42	.034	.017	26–31	Fig. E	6°	Fig. C	—	550D(15)	180	4½–6½
	8-390 4 B. Carb.(14)	BF-42	.034	.021	30–33	Fig. E	6°	Fig. C	625(15)	—	180	4½–6½
	8-390 4 B. Carb.(4)	BF-42	.034	.017	26–31	Fig. E	6°	Fig. C	—	550D(15)	180	4½–6½
	8-390 "GT"	BF-32	.034	.016	26–31	Fig. E	6°	Fig. C	700(15)	550D(15)	180	4½–6½
	8-427	BF-32	.034	.017	26–31	Fig. E	6°	Fig. C	—	600D(15)	180	4½–6½
	8-428 Cobra Jet	BF-32	.034	.017	26–31	Fig. E	6°	Fig. C	700(15)	650D(15)	180	5
1969	6-170	BF-82	.034	.027	35–40	Fig. H	6°	Fig. G	750	550D	175	4½
	6-200	BF-82	.034	.027	35–40	Fig. H	6°	Fig. G	750	550D	175	4½
	6-250 Less Air Cond.	BF-82	.034	.025	37–42	Fig. H	6°	Fig. G	700	550D	180	5
	6-250 With Air Cond.	BF-82	.034	.025	37–42	Fig. H	6°	Fig. G	(17)	(18)	180	5
	V8-302 Std. Trans.	BF-42	.030	.021	24–29	Fig. E	6°	Fig. C	650	—	180	5
	V8-302 Auto. Trans.	BF-42	.030	.017	26–31	Fig. E	6°	Fig. C	—	550D	180	5
	V8-351 2 B. Carb.	BF-42	.034	.017	26–31	Fig. J	6°	Fig. C	650	550D	180	5
	V8-351 4 B. Carb.	BF-32	.034	.017	26–31	Fig. J	6°	Fig. C	650	550D	180	5
	V8-390 Std. Trans.	BF-42	.034	.017	26–31	Fig. E	6°	Fig. C	700	—	180	5
	V8-390 Auto. Trans.	BF-32	.034	.017	26–31	Fig. E	6°	Fig. C	—	550D	180	5
	V8-427	BF-32	.034	.017	26–31	Fig. E	6°	Fig. C	—	600D	180	5
	V8-428	BF-32	.034	.017	26–31	Fig. E	6°	Fig. C	700	650D	180	5

(1)—BTDC: Before top dead center.
(2)—D: Drive.
(3)—Plus or minus 20 lbs.
(4)—With IMCO system.
(5)—1963 only.
(7)—With two barrel carburetor.
(8)—With four barrel carburetor.
(9)—1963 Fig. D, 1964 Fig. F.
(10)—With transistorized ignition.
(11)—Do not power time.
(12)—If air conditioned turn A/C switch to "Full On" position.
(13)—Without Thermactor Emission System.
(14)—With Thermactor Emission System.
(15)—On Thermactor equipped engines, adjust idle speed with headlights and with A/C on.
(16)—High performance engine.
(17) 700 with throttle solenoid energized and 500 when de-energized.
(18)—550 with throttle solenoid energized and 450 when de-energized.

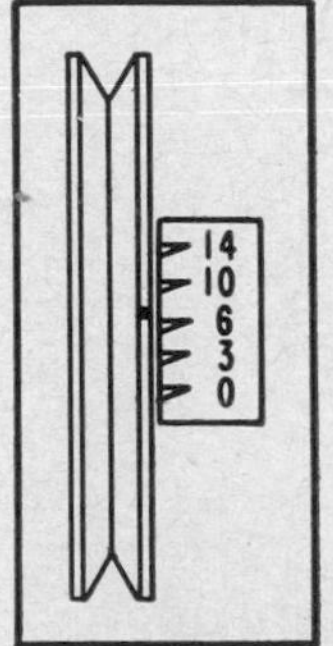

Fig. A

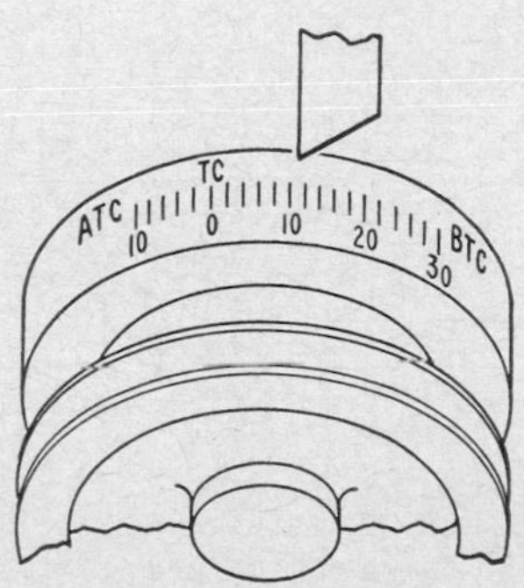

Fig. B

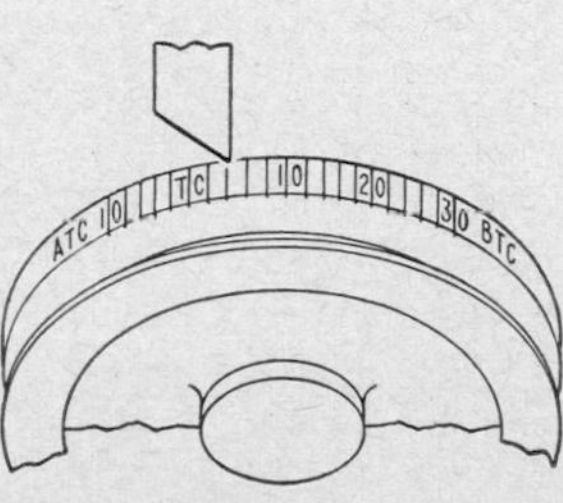

Fig. C

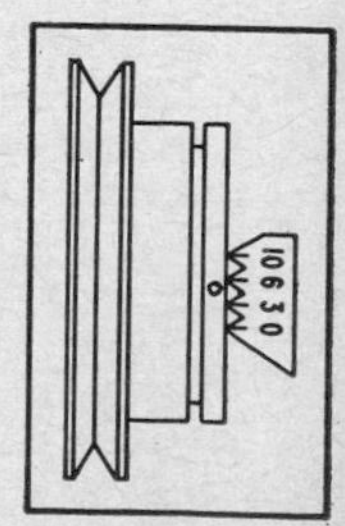
Fig. D

Continued

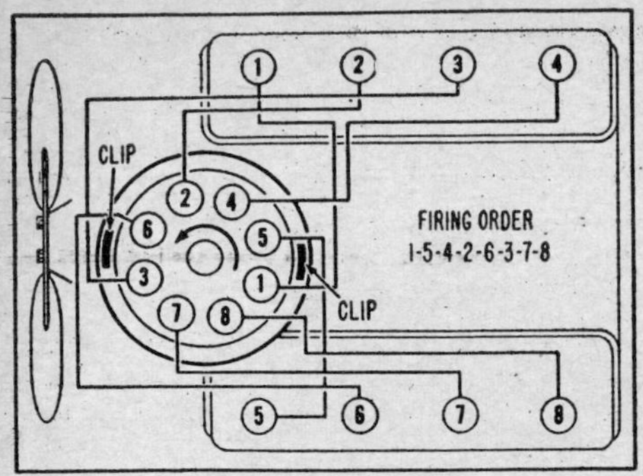

Fig. E

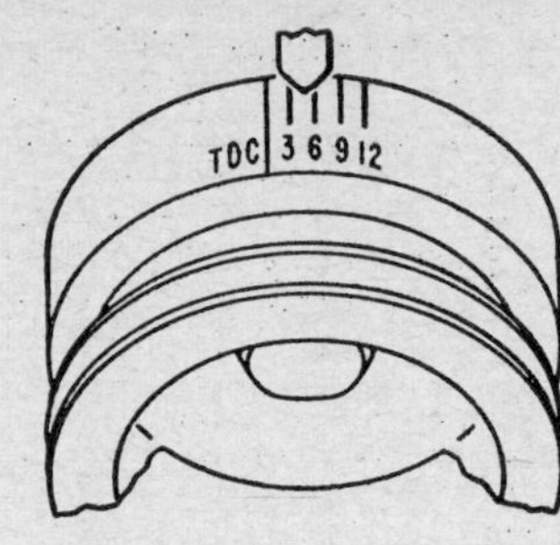

Fig. F

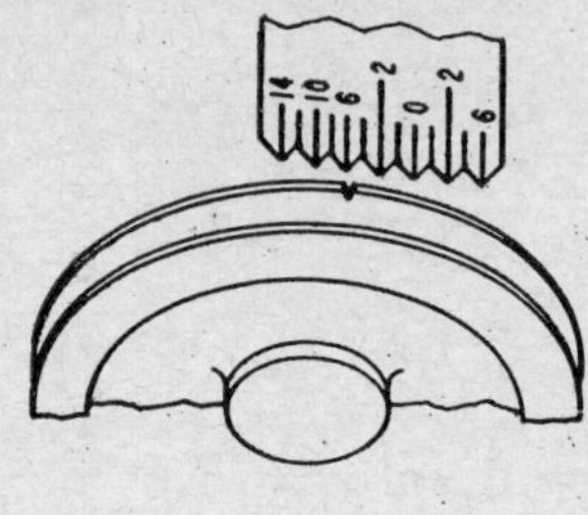
Fig. G

FIRING ORDER 1-5-3-6-2-4

Fig. H

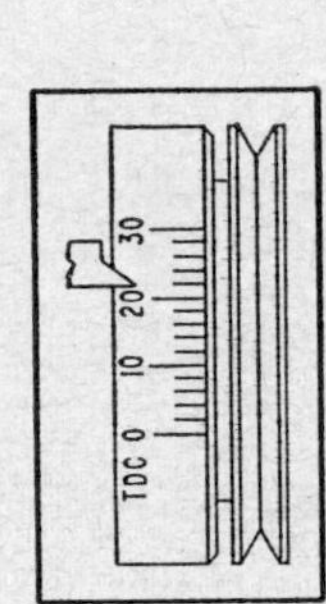

Fig. K

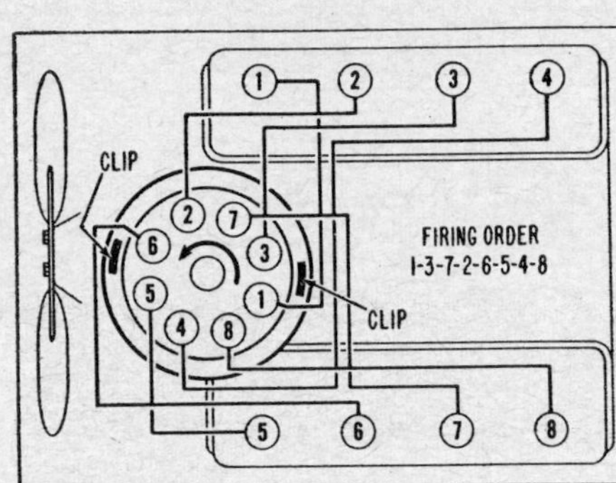

Fig. J

DISTRIBUTOR SPECIFICATIONS

★If advance is checked on vehicle, double R.P.M. and degrees advance to get crankshaft figures.

Year	Engine	Distributor Basic Part No. 12127	Rotation ①	Breaker Gap	Dwell Angle Deg.	Breaker Arm Spring Tension	Centrifugal Advance Degrees @ R.P.M. of Distributor★		Vacuum Advance	
							Advance Starts	Full Advance	Inches of Vacuum To Start Plunger	Max. Adv. Dist. Deg. @ Vacuum
1963	6-144 Std. Tr.	C3DF-E	C	.025	37–42	17–20	None	None	.35	13 @ 10
	6-144 Auto. Tr.	C3DF-F	C	.025	37–42	17–20	None	None	.35	12 @ 10
	6-170 Std. Tr.	C3DF-G	C	.025	37–42	17–20	None	None	.30	16 @ 10
	6-170 Auto. Tr.	C3DF-J	C	.025	37–42	17–20	None	None	.35	14 @ 10
	6-200	C30Z-C	C	.025	37–42	17–20	None	None	.44	12 ½@ 8
	V8-221 Std. Tr.	C20F-J	CC	.017	26–31	17–20	1 @ 525	13 @ 2000	5	10 @ 20
	V8-221 Auto. Tr.	C30F-A	CC	.017	26–31	17–20	1 @ 500	8 @ 2000	8	9 @ 20
	V8-260 Std. Tr.	C30Z-G	CC	.017	26–31	17–20	1 @ 550	11 @ 1950	9	10 @ 17
	V8-260 Auto. Tr.	C3AZ-U	CC	.017	26–31	17–20	1 @ 500	9 @ 2000	10	10 @ 20
	V8-289-4 Bar. Carb.	C30Z-D	CC	.020	33–36	25–28	1 @ 450	10 @ 2500	None	None
1964	6-144 Std. Tr.	C4DF-C	C	.025	37–42	17–20	None	None	.30	14 @ 3.91
	6-144 Auto. Tr.	C4DF-D	C	.025	37–42	17–20	None	None	.35	12 @ 4.1
	6-170 Std. Tr.	C4DF-A	C	.025	37–42	17–20	None	None	.30	15 @ 3.90
	6-170 Auto. Tr.	C4DF-B	C	.025	37–42	17–20	None	None	.35	14 @ 3.90
	6-200 Auto. Tr.	C40F-E	C	.025	37–42	17–20	None	None	.80	12 @ 3.80
	V8-260 Std. Tr.	C40F-A	CC	.017	26–31	17–20	1 @ 500	11 @ 2000	7	12 @ 20
	V8-260 Auto. Tr.	C40F-B	CC	.017	26–31	17–20	1 @ 600	11 @ 2000	8	11 @ 20
	V8-289 Std. Tr.	C4GF-A	CC	.017	26–31	17–20	2 @ 500	14 @ 2000	8	11 @ 20
	V8-289 Auto. Tr.	C4GF-B	CC	.017	26–31	17-20	1 @ 600	11 @ 2000	8	12 @ 20

DISTRIBUTOR SPECIFICATIONS—Continued

★If advance is checked on vehicle, double R.P.M. and degrees advance to get crankshaft figures.

Year	Engine	Distributor Basic Part No. 12127	Rotation ①	Breaker Gap	Dwell Angle Deg.	Breaker Arm Spring Tension	Centrifugal Advance Degrees @ R.P.M. of Distributor★		Vacuum Advance	
							Advance Starts	Full Advance	Inches of Vacuum To Start Plunger	Max. Adv. Dist. Deg. @ Vacuum
1964	V8-289-4 Bar. Carb.	C30F-D	CC	.020	30–33	27–30	1 @ 450	10 @ 2500	None	None
	V8-289②	C4GA-A	CC	.020	22–24	21–24	...	...	...	...
1965	6-170 Auto. Tr.	C4DF-B	C	.025	37–42	17–21	None	None	.30	13 @ 3.90
	6-170 Std. Tr.	C5DF-C	C	.025	37–42	17–21	None	None	.80	11 @ 3.90
	6-170 Auto. Tr.	C5DF-D	C	.025	37–42	17–21	None	None	.80	8 @ 3.90
	6-170 Std. Tr.	C4ZF-A	C	.025	37–42	17–21	None	None	.80	11 @ 3.90
	6-200 Std. Tr.	C5DF-E	C	.025	37–42	17–21	None	None	.44	11 @ 3.80
	6-200 Auto. Tr.	C5DF-F	C	.025	37–42	17–21	None	None	.44	9 @ 3.80
	V8-260 Std. Tr.	C4ZF-B	CC	.017	26–31	17–21	2 @ 700	10 @ 2000	7	12 @ 20
	V8-260 Auto. Tr.	C4ZF-E	CC	.017	26–31	17–21	1 @ 1000	10 @ 2000	7	11 @ 20
	V8-260 Auto. Tr.	C4OF-B	CC	.017	26–31	17–21	1 @ 600	11 @ 2000	8	11 @ 20
	V8-289 Std. Tr.	C5AF-M	CC	.017	26–31	17–21	2 @ 650	13 @ 2000	8	9 @ 14
	V8-289 Auto. Tr.	C5AF-N	CC	.017	26–31	17–21	2 @ 450	12 @ 2000	8	11 @ 14
	V8-289 Std. Tr.	C4ZF-C	CC	.017	26–31	17–21	1 @ 500	10 @ 2000	8	12 @ 20
	V8-289 Auto. Tr.	C4GF-B	CC	.017	26–31	17–21	1 @ 600	11 @ 2000	8	12 @ 20
	V8-289 4 Bar. Carb.	C5GF-A	CC	.017	26–31	17–21	2 @ 550	10 @ 2000	8	11 @ 20
	V8-289 Hi. Perf.	C50F-E	CC	.020	30–33	27–30	3 @ 650	9 @ 2000	None	None
	V8-289 Hi. Perf.	C30F-D	CC	.020	30–33	27–30	1 @ 450	10 @ 2500	None	None
1966	6-170 Std. Tr.	C5DF-C	C	.025	37–42	17–21	None	None	0.8	11 @ 3.9
	6-170 Std. Tr.③	C6DF-A	C	.025	37–42	17–21	½ @ 500	13 @ 1800	5.0	10 @ 15
	6-170 Auto. Tr.	C5DF-K	C	.025	37–42	17–21	None	None	.79	8 @ 3.8
	6-170 Auto. Tr.③	C6DF-D	C	.025	37–42	17–21	½ @ 300	13 @ 1800	5.0	6 @ 15
	6-200 Std. Tr.	C5DF-E	C	.025	37–42	17–21	None	None	.44	11 @ 3.8
	6-200 Std. Tr.③	C6DF-C	C	.025	37–42	17–21	½ @ 300	13 @ 1800	4	12 @ 15
	6-200 Auto. Tr.	C5DF-K	C	.025	37–42	17–21	None	None	.79	8 @ 3.8
	6-200 Auto. Tr.③	C6DF-E	C	.025	37–42	17–21	½ @ 300	12 @ 1800	5	10 @ 15
	8-289 Std. Tr.	C5AF-M	CC	.017	26–31	17–21	2 @ 650	13 @ 2000	8	9 @ 14
	8-289 Std. Tr.③	C6AF-J	CC	.017	26–31	17–21	7 @ 600	15 @ 1800	7	8 @ 16
	8-289 Auto. Tr.	C5AF-N	CC	.017	26–31	17–21	2 @ 450	12 @ 2000	8	11 @ 14
	8-289 Auto. Tr.③	C6AF-S	CC	.017	26–31	17–21	3 @ 600	14 @ 1800	5	10 @ 12
	8-289 Std. Tr.	C5GF-A	CC	.017	26–31	17–21	2 @ 550	10 @ 2000	8	11 @ 20
	8-289 Std. Tr.③	C6ZF-A	CC	.017	26–31	17–21	3 @ 475	13 @ 2000	5	7 @ 14
	8-289 Auto. Tr.③	C6ZF-B	CC	.017	26–31	17–21	4 @ 650	10 @ 2000	5	9 @ 13
	8-289 Hi Perf.	C5OF-E	CC	.020	30–33	27–30	3 @ 650	9 @ 2000	None	None
	8-390 Std. Tr.	C6AF-A	CC	.017	26–31	17–21	½ @ 400	8 @ 1800	8	10 @ 15
	8-390 Std. Tr.③	C6AF-K	CC	.017	26–31	17–21	3 @ 500	13 @ 2000	5	11 @ 17
	8-390 Auto. Tr.	C6AF-D	CC	.017	26–31	17–21	2 @ 625	10 @ 2000	5	9 @ 13
	8-390 Auto. Tr.③	C6AF-T	CC	.017	26–31	17–21	2 @ 475	11 @ 1800	5	11 @ 18
	8-390 Std. Tr.	C6AF-C	CC	.017	26–31	17–21	3 @ 600	10 @ 2000	5	10 @ 17
	8-390 Auto. Tr.③	C6AF-D	CC	.017	26–31	17–21	3 @ 500	10 @ 2000	6	12 @ 18
	8-390③	C6AF-L	CC	.017	26–31	17–21	3 @ 500	12 @ 2000	6	10 @ 15
	8-390 GT	C6OF-J	CC	.017	26–31	17–21	½ @ 300	12 @ 2000	5	12 @ 20
1967	6-170 Std. Tr.	C5DF-C	C	.025	37–42	17–21	None	None	.89	14 @ 3.90
	6-170 Auto. Tr.	C5DF-K	C	.025	37–42	17–21	None	None	.79	12 @ 3.80
	6-170 Std. Tr.③	C7DF-J	C	.025	37–42	17–21	—	—	—	—
	6-170 Auto. Tr.③	C7DF-A	C	.025	37–42	17–21	2 @ 500	14 @ 2000	5	7 @ 20
	6-200 Std. Tr.	C5DF-E	C	.025	37–42	17–21	None	None	.44	15 @ 3.80
	6-200 Auto. Tr.	C5DF-K	C	.025	37–42	17–21	None	None	.79	12 @ 3.80
	6-200 Std. Tr.③	C7DF-C	C	.025	37–42	17–21	1 @ 500	12 @ 2000	5	12 @ 20
	6-200 Auto. Tr.③	C7DF-D	C	.025	37–42	17–21	5 @ 700	13 @ 2000	5	12 @ 20
	8-289 Std. Tr.④	C7OF-A	CC	.017	26–31	17–21	½ @ 400	11 @ 1500	5	11 @ 20
	8-289 Auto. Tr.④	C7OF-B	CC	.017	26–31	17–21	½ @ 300	12 @ 2000	5	12 @ 20
	8-289 Std. Tr.③④	C7OF-D	CC	.017	26–31	17–21	½ @ 300	14 @ 2000	5	12 @ 20
	8-289 Auto. Tr.③④	C7OF-E	CC	.017	26–31	17–21	½ @ 300	13 @ 2000	5	11 @ 20

Continued

DISTRIBUTOR SPECIFICATIONS—Continued

★If advance is checked on vehicle, double R.P.M. and degrees advance to get crankshaft figures.

Year	Engine	Distributor Basic Part No. 12127	Rotation ①	Breaker Gap	Dwell Angle Deg.	Breaker Arm Spring Tension	Centrifugal Advance Degrees @ R.P.M. of Distributor★		Vacuum Advance	
							Advance Starts	Full Advance	Inches of Vacuum To Start Plunger	Max. Adv. Dist. Deg. @ Vacuum
1967	8-289⑤	C7ZF-A	CC	.017	26-31	17-21	½ @ 300	10 @ 2000	5	11 @ 20
	8-289 Std. Tr.③⑤	C7ZF-C	CC	.017	26-31	17-21	½ @ 300	12 @ 2000	5	9 @ 20
	8-289 Auto. Tr.③⑤	C7ZF-D	CC	.017	26-31	17-21	½ @ 300	13 @ 2000	5	7 @ 20
	8-289 Hi Perf. Eng.	C5OF-E	CC	.020	30-33	27-30	3 @ 650	9 @ 2000	None	None
	8-390 Std. Tr.④	C7AF-A	CC	.017	26-31	17-21	1 @ 500	9 @ 2000	5	12 @ 20
	8-390 Auto. Tr.④	C7AF-B	CC	.017	26-31	17-21	½ @ 300	10 @ 2000	5	12 @ 20
	8-390 Std. Tr.③④	C7AF-C	CC	.017	26-31	17-21	½ @ 300	13 @ 2000	5	12 @ 20
	8-390 Auto. Tr.③④	C7AF-D	CC	.017	26-31	17-21	½ @ 300	12 @ 2000	5	12 @ 20
	8-390 Std. Tr.⑤	C7AF-E	CC	.017	26-31	17-21	½ @ 300	10 @ 2000	5	12 @ 20
	8-390 Auto. Tr.⑤	C7SF-A	CC	.017	26-31	17-21	½ @ 300	10 @ 2000	5	12 @ 20
	8-390③⑤	C7SF-B	CC	.017	36-31	17-21	½ @ 300	12 @ 2000	5	12 @ 20
	8-390 "GT"	C7AF-U	CC	.017	26-31	17-21	½ @ 300	11 @ 2000	5	11 @ 20
	8-390 "GT"③	C7OF-F	CC	.017	26-31	17-21	½ @ 300	14 @ 2000	5	11 @ 20
1968	6-170 Std. Trans.	C8DF-A	C	.027	35-40	17-21	½ @ 350	14 @ 2000	5	8 @ 25
	6-170 Auto. Tr.	C8DF-B	C	.027	35-40	17-21	½ @ 350	14 @ 2000	5	9½ @ 25
	6-200 Std. Trans.	C8DF-C	C	.027	35-40	17-21	½ @ 350	14 @ 2000	5	12½ @ 25
	6-200 Auto Tr.	C8DF-D	C	.027	35-40	17-21	½ @ 350	14 @ 2000	5	11@ 25
	8-289 Std. Trans.	C8TF-F	CC	.021	24-29	17-21	½ @ 350	11 @ 2000	5	11½ @ 25
	8-289 Auto. Tr.	C8OF-C	CC	.021	24-29	17-21	½ @ 350	14 @ 2000	5	11½ @ 25
	8-289 Hi Perf.	C7OF-K	CC	.020	30-33	27-30	½ @ 350	14 @ 2000	—	—
	8-302 Std. Trans.⑤	C8ZF-A	CC	.021	24-29	17-21	½ @ 350	11 @ 2000	5	10½ @ 25
	8-302 Auto. Tr.⑤	C8ZF-D	CC	.017	26-31	17-21	½ @ 350	11 @ 2000	5	9 @ 25
	8-302 Std. Trans.④	C8AF-E	CC	.021	24-29	17-21	½ @ 350	14 @ 2000	5	11 @ 25
	8-302 Auto. Tr.④	C8OF-C	CC	.021	24-29	17-21	½ @ 350	14 @ 2000	5	11½ @ 25
	8-390④⑦	C8WF-B	CC	.017	26-31	17-21	½ @ 350	14 @ 2000	5	12½ @ 25
	8-390 Std. Trans.④	C8AF-M	CC	.021	24-29	17-21	½ @ 350	11 @ 2000	5	12½ @ 25
	8-390 Auto. Tr.④	C8AF-AA	CC	.017	26-31	17-21	½ @ 350	14 @ 2000	5	11½ @ 20
	8-390 2 Bar. Carb.	C8OF-D	CC	.017	26-31	17-21	½ @ 350	16 @ 2000	5	9½ @ 25
	8-427	C7OF-F	CC	.017	26-31	17-21	½ @ 300	14 @ 2000	5	11 @ 20
	8-428 Std. Trans.	C8OF-D	CC	.017	26-31	17-21	½ @ 350	16 @ 2375	5	9½ @ 25
	8-428 Auto. Trans.	C7OF-F	CC	.017	26-31	17-21	½ @ 350	16 @ 2375	5	11 @ 20
1969	6-170 Std. Trans.	C9DF-B	C	.027	35-40	17-21	½ @ 350	13¾ @ 2000	5	8 @ 25
	6-170 Auto. Trans.	C8DF-J	C	.027	35-40	17-21	½ @ 350	14¾ @ 2000	5	11 @ 25
	6-200 Std. Trans.	C8DF-C	C	.027	35-40	17-21	½ @ 350	12 @ 2000	5	12½ @ 25
	6-200 Auto. Trans.	C8DF-D	C	.027	35-40	17-21	½ @ 350	14 @ 2000	5	11 @ 25
	6-250	C9OF-R	C	.025	37-42	17-21	½ @ 350	11½ @ 2000	5	8½ @ 20
	8-302 Std. Trans.	C8AF-E	CC	.021	24-29	17-21	½ @ 350	12½ @ 2000	5	11 @ 25
	8-302 Auto. Trans.	C9AF-N	CC	.017	26-31	17-21	½ @ 350	10¾ @ 2000	5	11½ @ 20
	8-351 2 Bar. Carb.	C9OF-M	CC	.017	26-31	17-21	½ @ 350	12¼ @ 2000	5	8 @ 20
	8-351 4 Bar. Carb.	C9OF-N	CC	.017	26-31	17-21	½ @ 350	11 @ 2000	5	10½ @ 25
	8-390 Std. Trans.	C9AF-R	CC	.017	26-31	17-21	½ @ 350	10¾ @ 2000	5	11½ @ 20
	8-390 Auto. Trans.	C7AF-AC	CC	.017	26-31	17-21	½ @ 350	12¼ @ 2000	5	12½ @ 20
	8-427	C8OF-G	CC	.017	26-31	17-21	½ @ 350	11½ @ 2000	5	11 @ 20
	8-428 Std. Trans.	C8OF-H	CC	.017	26-31	17-21	½ @ 350	13½ @ 2000	5	9½ @ 25
	8-428 Auto. Trans.	C8OF-J	CC	.017	26-31	17-21	½ @ 350	13½ @ 2000	5	11 @ 20

①—As viewed from top. C—Clockwise, CC—Counterclockwise.
②—Transistorized ignition.
③—With Thermactor Exhaust Emission Control System.
④—Two barrel carburetor.
⑤—Four barrel carburetor.
⑦—Premium fuel.

ALTERNATOR & REGULATOR SPECIFICATIONS

Year	Make or Model	Current Rating①		Field Current @ 75°F		Voltage Regulator②				Field Relay	
		Amperes	Volts	Amperes	Volts	Make	Voltage @ 75°F	Contact Gap	Armature Air Gap	Armature Air Gap	Closing Voltage @ 75°F
1965	Autolite	38	15	2.8–3.3	12	Autolite	14.1–14.7	.017–.022	.049–.056	.012–.022	2.5
	Autolite	42	15	2.8–3.3	12	Autolite	14.1–14.7	.017–.022	.049–.056	.012–.022	2.5
1966–67	Purple③	38	15	2.5	12	Autolite	14.1–14.9	.017–.022	.049–.056	.010–.018	2.5–4.0
	Orange③	42	15	2.9	12	Autolite	14.1–14.9	.017–.022	.049–.056	.010–.018	2.5–4.0
	Black③	45	15	2.9	12	Autolite	14.1–14.9	.017–.022	.049–.056	.010–.018	2.5–4.0
	Red	55	15	2.9	12	Autolite	14.1–14.9	.017–.022	.049–.056	.010–.018	2.5–4.0
	Leece-Nev.	53	15	2.9	12	Leece-Nev.	14.1–14.9	.018–.020	.042–.052	.009–.011	1.6–2.6
1968	C6AF-10300-A	42	15	2.8–3.3	12	Autolite	13.5–15.3	④	④	④	2.3–4.2
	C6AF-10300-B	42	15	2.8–3.3	12	Autolite	13.5–15.3	④	④	④	2.3–4.2
	C6AF-10300-G	55	15	2.8–3.3	12	Autolite	13.5–15.3	④	④	④	2.3–4.2
	C6DF-10300-A	38	15	2.4	12	Autolite	13.5–15.3	④	④	④	2.3–4.2
	C6TF-10300-F	55	15	2.8–3.3	12	Autolite	13.5–15.3	④	④	④	2.3–4.2
1969	C5TF-10300-K	38	15	2.4	12	Autolite	13.5–15.3	④	④	④	2.3–4.2
	C6AF-10300-B	42	15	2.8–3.3	12	Autolite	13.5–15.3	④	④	④	2.3–4.2
	C6AF-10300-F	55	15	2.8–3.3	12	Autolite	13.5–15.3	④	④	④	2.3–4.2
	C6AF-10300-G	55	15	2.8–3.3	12	Autolite	13.5–15.3	④	④	④	2.3–4.2
	C6DF-10300-A	38	15	2.4	12	Autolite	13.5–15.3	④	④	④	2.3–4.2
	C7AF-10300-A	65	15	2.9	12	Autolite	13.5–15.3	④	④	④	2.3–4.2
	C9AF-10300-A	42	15	2.8–3.3	12	Autolite	13.5–15.3	④	④	④	2.3–4.2
	C9AF-10300-B	55	15	2.8–3.3	12	Autolite	13.5–15.3	④	④	④	2.3–4.2
	C9A[illegible]-10300-C	42	15	2.8–3.3	12	Autolite	13.5–15.3	④	④	④	2.3–4.2
	C9S[illegible]-10300-A	55	15	2.8–3.3	12	Autolite	13.5–15.3	④	④	④	2.3–4.2
	C9[illegible]F-10300-B	55	15	2.8–3.3	12	Autolite	13.5–15.3	④	④	④	2.3–4.2
	C9ZF-10300-C	55	15	2.8–3.3	12	Autolite	13.5–15.3	④	④	④	2.3–4.2

①—Current rating stamped on housing. ②—Voltage regulation stamped on cover. ③—Color stamp. ④—Not adjustable.

D.C. GENERATOR AND REGULATOR SPECIFICATIONS

★To polarize generator, disconnect field lead from regulator and momentarily flash this wire to regulator battery terminal.

Year	Generator						Regulator					
								Cutout Relay				
	Generator Number	Ground Polarity	Rated Cap. Amps.	Gen. Field Ground Location★	Brush Spring Tension, Ounces	Field Current Amperes	Regulator Number	Voltage to Close Points	Armature Air Gap, Inch	Voltage Regulator Setting Volts	Current Regulator Setting Amperes	Current and Voltage Armature Air Gap, Inch
1963	C20F-10000J	Neg.	30	Internal	20–26	1.2–1.8	C1TZ-10505A	12.4	...	15.0	30	...
	C20F-10000J	Neg.	30	Internal	20–26	1.2–1.8	C1TZ-10505A	12.4	...	15.0	30	...
	C20F-10000H	Neg.	30	Internal	20–26	1.2–1.8	C1TZ-10505A	12.4	...	15.0	30	...
	C2DF-10000B	Neg.	25	Internal	32–40	1.2–1.8	C3DZ-10505A	12.8	...	15.0	25	...
	C2DF-10000C	Neg.	30	Internal	32–40	1.2–1.8	C3DZ-10505B	12.8	...	15.0	30	...
1964	C3DF-10000A	Neg.	25	Internal	20–26	1.2–1.8	C2DF-10505A	12.2	...	15.0	25	...
	C30F-10000G	Neg.	30	Internal	20–26	1.2–1.8	C2AF-10505A	12.2	...	15.0	30	...
	C20F-10000J	Neg.	30	Internal	20–26	1.2–1.8	C2AF-10505A	12.2	...	15.0	30	...
	C30F-10000B	Neg.	30	Internal	32–40	1.2–1.8	C2AF-10505A	12.2	...	15.0	30	...

STARTING MOTOR SPECIFICATIONS

Year	Engine Model	Part No.	Brush Spring Tension, Ounces	No Load Test			Torque Test		
				Amperes	Volts	R.P.M.	Amperes	Volts	Torque, Lbs. Ft.
1963–64	6-144	C2DF-11001E	45	50	12	9500	540	4.2	14.0
	6-170, 6-200	C2DF-11001F	45	50	12	9500	540	4.2	14.0
	V8	C20F-11001D	45	70	12	9500	670	6.0	15.5
1965	6-170, 200	C4DF-11001B	40	50	12	9500	540	4.2	14.0
	6-200	C5AF-11001A	40	70	12	9500	640	6.0	15.5
	V8-260, 289	C40F-11001A	40	70	12	9500	670	6.0	15.5
	V8-289	C4ZF-11001A	40	70	12	9500	640	6.0	15.5
1966–67	4½″ Dia.	...	40	70	12	...	670	5.0	15.5
	4″ Dia.	...	40	70	12	...	460	5.0	9.0
1968	6-170, 200	C7ZF-11001-A	40	70	12	8500	460	6	9
	6-170, 200	C7OF-11001-A	40	70	12	9500	670	5	15½
	6-170, 200	C7DF-11001-A	40	70	12	8500	460	6	9
	8-289, 302	C7AF-11001-B	40	70	12	9500	670	5	15½
	8-289, 302	C7AF-11001-D	40	70	12	9500	670	5	15½
	8-289, 302	C7AF-11001-F	40	70	12	9500	670	5	15½
	8-390, 427	C7AF-11001-C	40	70	12	9500	670	5	15½
	8-390, 427	C7AF-11001-E	40	70	12	11000	700	4	15½
1969	6-170, 200	C6OZ-11002-A	40	70	12	8500	460	6	9
	6-170	C2DZ-11002-A	40	70	12	8500	460	6	9
	6-200	C3OZ-11002-C	40	70	12	9500	670	5	15½
	6-250	C2OZ-11002-A	40	70	12	9500	670	5	15½
	8-302, 351	C2OZ-11002-A	40	70	12	9500	670	5	15½
	8-302, 351	C5TZ-11002-A	40	70	12	9500	670	5	15½
	8-390, 427	C3OZ-11002-C	40	70	12	9500	670	5	15½
	8-428	C8AZ-11002-A	40	70	12	11000	700	5	15½

ENGINE TIGHTENING SPECIFICATIONS★

★Torque specifications are for clean and lightly lubricated threads only. Dry or dirty threads produce increased friction which prevents accurate measurement of tightness.

Year	Engine	Spark Plugs Ft. Lbs.	Cylinder Head Bolts Ft. Lbs.	Intake Manifold Ft. Lbs.	Exhaust Manifold Ft. Lbs.	Rocker Arm Shaft Bracket Ft. Lbs.	Rocker Arm Cover Ft. Lbs.	Connecting Rod Cap Bolts Ft. Lbs.	Main Bearing Cap Bolts Ft. Lbs.	Flywheel to Crankshaft Ft. Lbs.	Vibration Damper or Pulley Ft. Lbs.
1963–65	6 Cyl.	15–20	65–75	...	13–18	30–35	3–5	19–24	60–70	75–85	45–55
	V8's	15–20	65–70	12–15	13–18	...	3–5	19–24①	60–70	75–85	70–90
1966–68	6 Cyl.	15–20	70–75	—	13–18	30–35	3–5	19–24	60–70	75–85	85–100
	8-289	15–20	65–72	20–22	15–20	—	3–5	19–24	60–70	75–85	70–90
	8-302	15–20	65–72	20–22	15–20	—	3–5	19–24	60–70	75–85	70–90
	8-390	15–20	80–90	32–35	18–24②	40–45	4–7	40–45	95–105	75–85	70–90
	8-427	15–20	80–90	32–35	18–24	40–45	4–7	53–58	95–105	75–85	70–90
1969	6 Cyl.	15–20	70–75	—	13–18	30–35	3–5	③	60–70	75–85	85–100
	8-302	15–20	65–72	23–25	12–16	—	3–5	19–24	60–70	75–85	70–90
	8-351	15–20	95–100	23–25	18–24	—	3–5	40–45	95–105	75–85	70–90
	8-390	15–20	80–90	32–35	18–24	40–45	4–7	40–45	95–105	75–85	70–90
	8-427	15–20	90–100	32–35	18–24	40–45	4–7	53–58	95–105	75–85	70–90
	8-428	15–20	80–90	32–35	18–24	—	4–7	53–58	95–105	75–85	70–90

①—V8-289 high performance engine 40–45 ft.-lbs.

②—Fairlane, Comet, Mustang, Montego, Cougar 15–20.

③—6-170, 200 is 19–24; 6-250 is 21–26.

VALVE SPECIFICATIONS

Year	Engine	Valve Lash		Valve Angles		Valve Spring Installed Height	Valve Spring Pressure Lbs. @ In.	Stem Clearance		Stem Diameter, Standard	
		Int.	Exh.	Seat	Face			Intake	Exhaust	Intake	Exhaust
1963–64	All 6s	.066–.216④		45	44	1 19/32	150 @ 1 7/32	.0008–.0025	.0018–.0035	.3100–.3107	.3090–.9730
	V8-221, 260	¾ Turns①		45	44	1¾	170 @ 1⅜	.0008–.0025	.0018–.0035	.3100–.3107	.3090–.3097
	V8-289	¾ Turns①		45	44	1¾	170 @ 1⅜	.001–.0027	.002–.0037	.3416–.3423	.3406–.3413
	V8-289③	.020H	.020H	45	44	1¾	247 @ 1.32	.001–.0027	.002–.0037	.3416–.3423	.3406–.3413
	V8-289②	.019H	.019H	45	44	1¾	247 @ 1.32	.001–.0027	.002–.0037	.3416–.3423	.3406–.3413
1965	6-170, 200	.066–.216④		45	44	1 19/32	150 @ 1 7/32	.0008–.0025	.0018–.0035	.3100–.3107	.3090–.3097
	6-200⑤	.067–.200④		45	44	1 19/32	150 @ 1 7/32	.0008–.0025	.0018–.0035	.3100–.3107	.3090–.3097
	V8-260	¾ Turns①		45	44	1¾	170 @ 1⅜	.0008–.0025	.0018–.0035	.3100–.3107	.3090–.3097
	V8-289	¾ Turns①		45	44	1¾	170 @ 1⅜	.001–.0027	.002–.0037	.3416–.3423	.3406–.3413
	V8-289⑤	.018H	.018H	45	44	1¾	247 @ 1.32	.001–.0027	.002–.0037	.3416–.3423	.3406–.3413
1966	6-170, 200	.067–.200④		45	44	1 19/32	150 @ 1.22	.0008–.0025	.001–.0027	.3100–.3107	.3098–.3105
	8-289	¾ Turns①		45	44	1¾	170 @ 1.39	.001–.0027	.002–.0037	.3416–.3423	.3406–.3413
	8-289 Hi Perf.	.018H	.018H	45	44	1¾	247 @ 1.32	.001–.0027	.002–.0037	.3416–.3423	.3406–.3413
	8-390	.050–.150④⑥		45	44	1 13/16	245 @ 1.38	.001–.0024	.001–.0024	.3711–.3718	.3711–.3718
	8-390 "GT"	.050–.200④		45	44	1 13/16	255 @ 1.32	.001–.0024	.001–.0024	.3711–.3718	.3711–.3718
1967	6-170, 200	.066–.216④		45	44	1 9/16	150 @ 1.22	.0008–.0025	.001–.0027	.3100–.3107	.3098–.3105
	8-289	¾ Turns①		45	44	1 21/32	165 @ 1.25	.001–.0027	.001–.0027	.3416–.3423	.3416–.3423
	8-289 Hi Perf.	.018H	.018H	45	44	1¾	245 @ 1.32	.001–.0027	.001–.0027	.3416–.3423	.3416–.3423
	8-390	.100–.200④		45	44	1 13/16	245 @ 1.38	.001–.0024	.001–.0024	.3711–.3718	.3711–.3718
	8-390 "GT"	.100–.200④		45	44	1 13/16	265 @ 1.32	.001–.0024	.001–.0024	.3711–.3718	.3711–.3718
968	6-170, 200	.066–.166④		45	44	1 9/16	150 @ 1.22	.0008–.0025	.001–.0027	.3100–.3107	.3098–.3105
	8-289, 302	¾ Turns①		45	44	1⅝	180 @ 1.23	.001–.0027	.001–.0032	.3416–.3423	.3411–.3418
	8-289 Special	.018H	.018H	45	44	1⅝	180 @ 1.23	.001–.0027	.002–.0037	.3416–.3423	.3411–.3418
	8-390	.100–.200④		45	44	1⅞	220 @ 1.38	.001–.0024	.0015–.0032	.3711–.3718	.3706–.3713
	8-390 "GT"	.100–.200④		45	44	1 13/16	270 @ 1.32	.001–.0024	.0015–.0032	.3711–.3718	.3706–.3713
	8-427	.100–.200④		⑦	⑦	1 13/16	270 @ 1.32	.001–.0024	.002–.0034	.3711–.3718	.3701–.3708
1969	6-170	.066–.166④		45	44	1 9/16	150 @ 1.22	.0008–.0025	.001–.0027	.3100–.3107	.3098–.3105
	6-200, 250	.095–.195④		45	44	1 9/16	150 @ 1.22	.0008–.0025	.001–.0027	.3100–.3107	.3098–.3105
	8-302	1 Turn①		45	44	1⅝	180 @ 1.23	.001–.0027	.0015–.0032	.3416–.3423	.3411–.3418
	8-351	1 Turn①		45	44	1 25/32	215 @ 1.34	.001–.0027	.0015–.0032	.3416–.3423	.3411–.3418
	8-390	.100–.200④		45	44	1⅞	220 @ 1.38	.001–.0027	.0015–.0032	.3711–.3718	.3706–.3713
	8-427	.100–.200④		⑦	⑦	1 13/16	270 @ 1.32	.001–.0027	.0015–.0032	.3711–.3718	.3706–.3713
	8-428	.100–.200④		45	44	1 13/16	270 @ 1.32	.001–.0027	.0015–.0032	.3711–.3718	.3706–.3713

①—Tighten rocker arm adjusting screw to eliminate all push rod end clearance, then tighten screw the number of turns listed.

②—With transistorized ignition.

③—High performance engine.

④—Clearance is obtained at valve stem tip with hydraulic lifter collapsed. If clearance is less than the minimum install an undersize push rod; if clearance is greater than the maximum install an oversize push rod.

⑤—Engines built after 3-29-65.

⑥—Engines built after 12-20-65 .050-.200".

⑦—Intake 30°, Exhaust 45°.

PISTONS, PINS, RINGS, CRANKSHAFT & BEARINGS

Year	Engine	Piston Clearance	Ring End Gap①		Wrist-pin Diameter	Rod Bearings		Main Bearings			
			Comp.	Oil		Shaft Diameter	Bearing Clearance	Shaft Diameter	Bearing Clearance	Thrust on Bear. No.	Shaft End Play
1963–64	6 Cyl.	.0007–.0023	.010	.015	.912	2.1232–2.1240	.0008–.0023	2.2482–2.2490	.0007–.0025	3	.004–.008
	V8-260, 289	.0007–.0023	.010	.015	.912	2.1228–2.1236	.0009–.0025	2.2482–2.2490	.0006–.0027	3	.004–.008
	V8-289③	.003–.0036	.010	.015	.912	2.1228–2.1236	.0009–.0025	2.2482–2.2490	.0006–.0027	3	.004–.008
1965	6-170, 200	.002–.0027	.010	.015	.912	2.1232–2.1240	.0006–.0022	2.2482–2.2490	.0007–.0026	④	.004–.008
	V8-260	.0021–.0039	.010	.015	.912	2.1232–2.1240	.0009–.0029	2.2482–2.2490	.0007–.003	3	.004–.008
	V8-289	.0014–.0022	.010	.015	.912	2.1228–2.1236	.0009–.0029	2.2482–2.2490	.0005–.0028	3	.004–.008
	V8-289 Hi. Perf	.003–.0038	.010	.015	.912	2.1228–2.1236	.0009–.0029	2.2482–2.2490	.0005–.0028	3	.004–.008

Continued

PISTONS, PINS, RINGS, CRANKSHAFT & BEARINGS—Continued

Year	Engine	Piston Clearance	Ring End Gap ① Comp.	Ring End Gap ① Oil	Wrist-pin Diameter	Rod Bearings Shaft Diameter	Rod Bearings Bearing Clearance	Main Bearings Shaft Diameter	Main Bearings Bearing Clearance	Thrust on Bear. No.	Shaft End Play
1966–67	6-170, 200	.0014–.0020	.010	.015	.912	2.1232–2.1240	.0008–.0024	2.2482–2.2490	.0005–.0022	④	.004–.008
	8-289	.0018–.0026	.010	.015	.912	2.1228–2.1236	.0008–.0026	2.2482–2.2490	.0005–.0025	3	.004–.008
	8-289 Hi Perf.	.0030–.0038	.010	.015	.912	2.1228–2.1236	.0008–.0026	2.2482–2.2490	.0005–.0025	3	.004–.008
	8-390	.0015–.0023	.010	.015	.975	2.4380–2.4388	.0008–.0026	2.7484–2.7492	.0005–.0025	3	.004–.010
1968	6-170, 200	.0014–.0020	.010	.015	.912	2.1232–2.1240	.0008–.0015	2.2482–2.2490	.0005–.0015	④	.004–.008
	8-289, 302	.0018–.0026	.010	.015	.912	2.1228–2.1236	.0008–.0015	2.2482–2.2490	.0005–.0015	3	.004–.008
	8-390	.0015–.0023	.010	.015	.975	2.4380–2.4388	.0008–.0015	2.7484–2.7492	.0005–.0015	3	.004–.010
	8-427	.0030–.0038	.018	.015	.975	2.4380–2.4388	.0008–.0015	2.7484–2.7492	.0005–.0015	3	.004–.010
1969	6-170, 200	.0014–.0020	.010	.015	.912	2.1232–2.1240	.0008–.0015	2.2482–2.2490	.0005–.0015	④	.004–.008
	6-250	.0014–.0020	.010	.015	.912	2.1232–2.1240	.0008–.0015	2.3982–2.3990	.0005–.0015	5	.004–.008
	8-302	.0018–.0026	.010	.015	.912	2.1228–2.1236	.0008–.0015	2.2482–2.2490	.0005–.0015	3	.004–.008
	8-351	.0018–.0026	.010	.015	.912	2.3103–2.3110	.0008–.0015	2.9994–3.0002	.0013–.0025	3	.004–.008
	8-390	.0015–.0023	.010	.015	.975	2.4380–2.4388	.0008–.0015	2.7484–2.7492	.001 –.002	3	.004–.010
	8-427, 428	.0030–.0038	.018	.015	.975	2.4380–2.4388	.002 –.003	2.7484–2.7492	.001 –.002	3	.004–.010

①—Fit rings in tapered bores for clearance listed in tightest portion of ring travel.
④—No. 3 in 6–170, No. 5 on 6–200.
③—1964 with transistorized ignition.

WHEEL ALIGNMENT SPECIFICATIONS

OLD CAR SPECIFICATIONS: For 1946-62 Wheel Alignment Specifications see back of book.

Year	Model	Caster Angle, Degrees Limits	Caster Angle, Degrees Desired	Camber Angle, Degrees Limits Left	Camber Angle, Degrees Limits Right	Camber Angle, Degrees Desired Left	Camber Angle, Degrees Desired Right	Toe-In. Inch	Toe-Out on Turns, Deg. Outer Wheel	Toe-Out on Turns, Deg. Inner Wheel
1963	Fairlane	Zero	Zero	Zero	Zero	Zero	Zero	3/16–7/16	20	23 1/2
	Meteor	−1/2 to +1/2	Zero	0 to +1	0 to +1	+1/2	+1/2	1/16–3/16	20	23 1/2
	Comet	0 to +1	+1/2	0 to +3/4	0 to +3/4	+3/8	+3/8	1/4–5/16	20	20 3/4
	Falcon	0 to +1	+1/2	0 to +3/4	0 to +3/4	+3/8	+3/8	1/4–5/16	20	20 3/4
1964	Comet 6①	−1/2 to +1 1/2	+1/2	−1/4 to +1 1/4	−1/4 to +1 1/4	+1/2	+1/2	1/4–5/16	19 1/8	20
	Comet 6②	−1/2 to +1 1/2	+1/2	−1/4 to +1 1/4	−1/4 to +1 1/4	+1/2	+1/2	1/4–5/16	20 1/8	20
	Comet V8	−1/2 to +1 1/2	+1/2	−1/4 to +1 1/4	−1/4 to +1 1/4	+1/2	+1/2	1/4–5/16	18 7/8	20
	Falcon 6①	0 to +1	+1/2	0 to +1	0 to +1	+1/2	+1/2	1/4–5/16	19 1/8	20
	Falcon 6②	0 to +1	+1/2	0 to +1	0 to +1	+1/2	+1/2	1/4–5/16	20 1/8	20
	Falcon V8	0 to +1	+1/2	0 to +1	0 to +1	+1/2	+1/2	1/4–5/16	18 7/8	20
	Fairlane	−1/2 to +1/2	+1/2	0 to +1	0 to +1	+1/2	+1/2	3/16–5/16	17 1/2	20
1965	Comet 6	−1/4 to +1 3/4	+3/4	−1/4 to +1 1/4	−1/4 to +1 1/4	+1/2	+1/2	1/4	19 1/8③	20
	Comet V8	−1/4 to +1 3/4	+3/4	−1/4 to +1 1/4	−1/4 to +1 1/4	+1/2	+1/2	1/4	18 7/8	20
	Falcon 6	−1/4 to +1 3/4	+3/4	−1/4 to +1 1/4	−1/4 to +1 1/4	+1/2	+1/2	9/32	19 1/8③	20
	Falcon V8	−1 1/4 to +3/4	−1/4	−1/4 to +1 1/4	−1/4 to +1 1/4	+1/2	+1/2	9/32	18 7/8	20
	Fairlane	−1 to +1	Zero	−1/2 to +1	−1/2 to +1	+1/4	+1/4	7/32	18 7/8	20
	Mustang 6	0 to +2	+1	−1/4 to +1 1/4	−1/4 to +1 1/4	+1/2	+1/2	7/32	19 1/8③	20
	Mustang V8	−1 to +1	Zero	−1/4 to +1 1/4	−1/4 to +1 1/4	+1/2	+1/2	7/32	18 7/8	20
1966	Mustang 6	0 to +2	+1	−1/4 to +1 1/4	−1/4 to +1 1/4	+1/2	+1/2	1/4	18 7/8③	20
	Mustang V8	−1 to +1	Zero	−1/4 to +1 1/4	−1/4 to +1 1/4	+1/2	+1/2	1/4	19 1/8④	20
	All Others	−1 to +1	Zero	−1/2 to +1	−1/2 to +1	+1/4	+1/4	1/4	17 3/4	20
1967	Cougar	−1/4 to +3/4	+1/4	+1/2 to +1 3/4	+1/2 to +1 3/4	+1	+1	3/16	18 3/4	20
	Mustang	−1/4 to +3/4	+1/4	+1/2 to +1 3/4	+1/2 to +1 3/4	+1	+1	3/16	18 3/4	20
	Others	−1 to 0	−1/2	−1/4 to +3/4	−1/4 to +3/4	+1/4	+1/4	1/4	17 3/4	20
1968	Falcon	−1 1/2 to +1/2	−1/2	−1/2 to +1	−1/2 to +1	+1/4	+1/4	1/4	18 1/8⑤	20
	Montego	−1 1/2 to +1/2	−1/2	−1/2 to +1	−1/2 to +1	+1/4	+1/4	1/4	18 1/8⑤	20

WHEEL ALIGNMENT SPECIFICATIONS—Continued

OLD CAR SPECIFICATIONS: For 1946-62 Wheel Alignment Specifications see back of book.

Year	Model	Caster Angle, Degrees		Camber Angle, Degrees				Toe-In. Inch	Toe-Out on Turns, Deg.	
		Limits	Desired	Limits Left	Limits Right	Desired Left	Desired Right		Outer Wheel	Inner Wheel
1968	Fairlane	—1½ to +½	—½	—½ to +1	—½ to +1	+¼	+¼	¼	18⅛⑤	20
	Mustang	—¾ to +1¼	+¼	+¼ to +1¾	+¼ to +1¾	+1	+1	3/16	18¾	20
	Cougar	—¾ to +1¼	+¼	+¼ to +1¾	+¼ to +1¾	+1	+1	3/16	18¾	20
1969	Falcon	—1¾ to +¼	—¾	—½ to +1	—½ to +1	+¼	+¼	3/16	18.1⑤	20
	Fairlane	—1¾ to +¼	—¾	—½ to +1	—½ to +1	+¼	+¼	3/16	18.1⑤	20
	Montego	—1¾ to +¼	—¾	—½ to +1	—½ to +1	+¼	+¼	3/16	18.1⑤	20
	Mustang	—¾ to +1¼	+¼	+¼ to +1¾	+¼ to +1¾	+¾	+¾	3/16	18.68	20
	Cougar	—¾ to +1¼	+¼	+¼ to +1¾	+¼ to +1¾	+¾	+¾	3/16	18.68	20

①—Standard steering. ②—Power steering. ③—With power steering 20⅛°. ④—Power steering 18¾°. ⑤—Power steering 17⅞°.

COOLING SYSTEM & CAPACITY DATA

Year	Model or Engine	Cooling Capacity, Qts.			Radiator Cap Relief Pressure, Lbs.		Thermo. Opening Temp. ①	Fuel Tank Gals.	Engine Oil Refill Qts. ②	Transmission Oil			Rear Axle Oil Pints
		No Heater	With Heater	With A/C	With A/C	No A/C				3 Speed Pints	4 Speed Pints	Auto. Trans. Qts. ⑨	
1963	Comet & Falcon 6	8½	9½	9½	12-15	12-15	180	14	3½	2½	4½	7½	2½
	Comet & Falcon V8	13½	14½	14½	12-15	12-15	180	14	4	3	3	7½	4½
	Fairlane & Meteor 6	8½	9½	9½	12-15	12-15	180	16	3½	2½	—	7½	4½
	Fairlane & Meteor V8	13½	14½	14½	12-15	12-15	180	16	4	3	3	8½	4½
1964	6-144, 170, 200	8½	9½	9½	12-15	12-15	185	③	3½	2½	5	8½	2½
	V8-260, 289	13½	14½	14½	12-15	12-15	185	③	4	3½	3½	8½	4½
1965	6-170, 200	8½	9½	9½	12-15	12-15	185	16④	3½	2	5	7¾	2½
	V8-260, 289	13½	14½	14½	12-15	12-15	185	16④	4	3½	3½	8¾	4½
1966-67	6-170, 200	8½	9½	9½	12-15	12-15	185	16④	3½	2⑤	4	⑦	2½
	8-289	14	15	15	12-15	12-15	188	16④	4	2⑤	4	⑧	4½
	8-390	19½	20½	20½	12-15	12-15	188	16④	4	2⑤	4	13	5
1968	6-170, 200	8½	9½	9½	12-15	12-15	190	⑥	3½	3½	4	8	2½
	8-289	14	15	15	12-15	12-15	190	⑥	4	3½	4	9	4
	8-302	14	15	15	12-15	12-15	190	⑥	4	3½	4	9	4
	8-390	19½	20½	20½	12-15	12-15	190	⑥	4	3½	4	13	5
	8-427	19½	20½	20½	12-15	12-15	190	⑥	5	3½	4	13	5
1969	6-170, 200	8½	9½	9½	12-15	12-15	190	⑥	3½	3½	4	8	2½
	6-250	9	10	10	12-15	12-15	190	⑥	3½	3½	4	9	4
	8-302	14	15	15	12-15	12-15	190	⑥	4	3½	4	9	4
	8-351	14	15	15	12-15	12-15	190	⑥	4	3½	4	11	5
	8-390	19½	20½	20½	12-15	12-15	190	⑥	4	3½	4	12¾	5
	8-427	19½	20½	20½	12-15	12-15	190	⑥	5	3½	4	12¾	5
	8-428	19½	20½	20½	12-15	12-15	190	⑥	4	3½	4	12¾	5

①—Use with permanent type anti-freeze. With alcohol type use a 160° unit.

②—Add 1 qt. with filter change.

③—Falcon 14, Comet 20.

④—20 gallons on Comet, Fairlane, Falcon Wagons.

⑤—With overdrive 3½ pints.

⑥—Falcon cars and Mustang 16, Cougar 17, Fairlane, Montego and Falcon Wagons 20.

⑦—1966 7¾ qts., 1967 8 qts.

⑧—1966 8¾ qts., 1967 9 qts.

⑨—Approximate. Make final check with dip stick.

BRAKE SPECIFICATIONS

Year	Model	Brake Drum Inside Diameter	Wheel Cylinder Bore Diameter			Master Cylinder Bore Diameter		
			Front Disc Brake	Front Drum Brake	Rear Brake	With Disc Brakes	With Drum Brakes	With Power Brakes
1963	Falcon & Comet Cars	9.00	—	1.062	.8125	—	1.00	—
	Falcon & Comet Wagons	9.00	—	1.062	.875	—	1.00	—
	Fairlane & Meteor	10.00	—	1.125	.9062	—	1.00	1.00
1964	Falcon & Comet Closed Cars—6 Cyl.	9.00	—	1.062	.812	—	1.00	1.00
	Falcon & Comet Conv. & Wagons—6 Cyl.	9.00	—	1.062	.875	—	1.00	1.00
	Falcon & Comet V8 Cars	10.00	—	1.125	.906	—	1.00	1.00
	Falcon & Comet V8 Wagons	10.00	—	1.125	.938	—	1.00	1.00
	Fairlane Cars	10.00	—	1.125	.906	—	1.00	.875
	Fairlane Wagons	10.00	—	1.125	.938	—	1.00	.875
1965	Falcon & Comet Closed Cars—6 Cyl.	9.00	—	1.062	.844	—	1.00	.875
	Falcon & Comet Conv. & Wagons—6 Cyl.	9.00	—	1.062	.906	—	1.00	.875
	Falcon & Comet V8 Cars	10.00	—	1.125	.906	—	1.00	.875
	Falcon & Comet V8 Wagons	10.00	—	1.125	.938	—	1.00	.875
	Mustang 6 Cyl.	9.00	—	1.062	.844	—	1.00	.875
	Mustang V8	10.00	1.636	1.125	.906	.938	1.00	.875
	Fairlane Cars	10.00	—	1.125	.906	—	1.00	1.00
	Fairlane Wagons	10.00	—	1.125	.938	—	1.00	1.00
1966	Falcon 6 Cyl.	9.00	—	1.062	.844	—	1.00	—
	Falcon V8	10.00	—	1.125	.906	—	1.00	—
	Mustang 6 Cyl.	9.00	—	1.062	.844	—	1.00	.875
	Mustang V8	10.00	1.636	1.125	.906	.938	1.00	.875
	Comet & Fairlane 6-200, 8-289 Cars	10.00	—	1.125	.906	—	1.00	1.00
	Comet & Fairlane 8-390	10.00	—	1.094	.875	—	1.00	1.00
	Comet & Fairlane Wagons	10.00	—	1.094	.938	—	1.00	1.00
1967	Falcon 6 Cyl. Cars	9.00	1.636	1.062	.844	.9375	1.00	.9375
	Falcon Wagons	10.00	1.636	1.094	.938	.9375	1.00	.9375
	Falcon V8 Cars	10.00	1.636	1.125	.906	.9375	1.00	.9375
	Mustang 6 Cyl.	9.00	1.636	1.062	.844	1.00	1.00	1.00
	Mustang & Cougar 8-390	10.00	1.636	1.094	.813	1.00	1.00	1.00
	Mustang & Cougar 8-289 302①	10.00	1.636	1.125	.875	1.00	1.00	1.00
	Comet & Fairlane 6-200, 8-289, 302	10.00	1.636	1.125	.906	.9375	1.00	.9375
	Comet & Fairlane 8-390 Cars	10.00	1.636	1.094	.875	.9375	1.00	.9375
	Comet & Fairlane 8-289 Convertibles	10.00	1.636	1.094	.906	.9375	1.00	.9375
	Comet & Fairlane 6-200, 8-289 Wagons	10.00	1.636	1.094	.938	.9375	1.00	.9375
	Comet & Fairlane 8-390 Wagons	10.00	1.636	1.094	.938	.9375	1.00	.9375
1968	Falcon 6 Cyl. Cars	9.00	2.375	1.062	.844	.9375	1.00	.9375
	Falcon V8 Cars	10.00	2.375	1.125	.906	.9375	1.00	.9375
	Falcon Wagons	10.00	2.375	1.094	.938	.9375	1.00	.9375
	Mustang 6 Cyl.	9.00	2.375	1.062	.844	1.00	1.00	1.00
	Mustang & Cougar 8-390	10.00	2.375	1.094	.813	1.00	1.00	1.00
	Mustang & Cougar 8-289, 302	10.00	2.375	1.125	.875	1.00	1.00	1.00
	Montego & Fairlane 6-200, 8-289, 302①	10.00	2.375		.906	.9375	1.00	.9375
	Montego & Fairlane 8-390 Cars	10.00	2.375	1.094	.875	.9375	1.00	.9375
	Montego & Fairlane Convertibles (Exc. 8-390)	10.00	2.375	1.094	.906	.9375	1.00	.9375
	Montego & Fairlane Wagons (Exc. 8-390)	10.00	2.375	1.094	.938	.9375	1.00	.9375
1969	Falcon 6 Cyl. Cars	9.00	2.381	1.062	.844	.9375	1.00	.9375
	Falcon V8 Cars	10.00	2.381	1.094	.906	.9375	1.00	.9375
	Falcon Wagons	10.00	2.381	1.125	.938	.9375	1.00	.9375
	Mustang 6 Cyl.	9.00	2.381	1.062	.844	1.00	1.00	1.00
	Mustang & Cougar 8-302	10.00	2.381	1.125	.875	1.00	1.00	1.00
	Mustang & Cougar 8-351, 390	10.00	2.381	1.094	.813	1.00	1.00	1.00
	Montego & Fairlane 6-250, 8-302①	10.00	2.381	1.125	.906	.9375	1.00	.9375
	Montego & Fairlane 8-351, 390	10.00	2.381	1.094	.875	.9375	1.00	.9375
	Montego & Fairlane Conv. (Exc. 8-351, 390)	10.00	2.381	1.094	.906	.9375	1.00	.9375
	Montego & Fairland Wagons (Exc. 8-390)	10.00	2.381	1.094	.938	.9375	1.00	.9375

①—Except convertible.

REAR AXLE SPECIFICATIONS

Year	Model	Carrier Type	Ring Gear & Pinion Backlash Inch	Nominal Pinion Locating Shim, Inch	Pinion Bearing Preload				Differential Bearing Preload	Pinion Nut Torque Ft.-Lbs.①
					New Bearings With Seal Inch-Lbs.	Used Bearings With Seal Inch-Lbs.	New Bearings Less Seal Inch-Lbs.	Used Bearings Less Seal Inch-Lbs.		
1963	Falcon	Integral	.006–.010	.018	17–27	6–12	—	—	2–3②	140
1963	Comet	Integral	.008–.012	.018	17–27	10–16	—	—	2½–3②	140
1963–64	Fairlane	Removable	.008–.012	.015	17–27	8–12	—	—	2½–3②	175
1964	Comet, Falcon	Removable	.008–.012	.020	22–32	13–17	—	—	2½–3②	175
	Comet, Falcon	Integral	.006–.010	.020	17–27	6–12	—	—	2–3②	140
1965		Integral	.008–.012	.017	17–27	6–12	—	—	2–3②	140
		Removable	.008–.012	.020	22–32	10–14	—	—	2½–3②	175
1966–69		Integral	.008–.012	.017	17–27	6–12	—	—	.008–.012③	140
		Removable	.008–.012	④	⑤	8–14	—	—	.008–.012⑥	175

①—If torque cannot be obtained, install new spacer.
②—Threaded adjusters — notches tight.
③—Case spread with new bearings. With used bearings .003–.005″.
④—With 7¾″ and 8″ ring gear .022″. With 8¾″ and 9″ ring gear .015″.
⑤—With 7¾″ and 8″ ring gear 17–32 inch-lbs. With 8¾″ and 9″ ring gear 22–32 inch-lbs.
⑥—Case spread with new bearings. With used bearings .005–.008″.

Electrical Section

IGNITION TIMING

If a timing light is to be used to set ignition timing, disconnect the vacuum advance pipe to the carburetor and place a piece of tape over open end of pipe. *This is important as carburetor trouble can affect timing adjustments.*

Lacking a power timing light, an accurate method of setting ignition timing with the engine stopped is with the aid of a jumper light. Be sure to use a light bulb that corresponds with the system voltage of the vehicle.

1. Remove distributor cap and rotor and see that the breaker gap is set according to specifications.
2. Rotate engine until No. 1 cylinder is at the ignition timing point as indicated by the timing pointer and timing mark being lined up with each other.
3. Connect the jumper light between distributor ignition terminal and ground.
4. Turn on ignition switch.
5. Loosen distributor and turn it in the direction of normal rotation until the points just close (light out). Then slowly turn distributor in the opposite direction just to the exact point that the light goes on. Tighten distributor in this position.

SERVICE BULLETIN

REVISED IGNITION TIMING: Revised ignition timing specifications for 1965 models are included in the *Tune Up Specifications* table. On most engines a further advance of up to 5 deg. is permissible to improve fuel economy or for high altitude operation. When making the setting, advance it progressively up to the limit specified until a knock is evident on acceleration. Then retard the timing as required to eliminate the knock.

In individual cases, and when a substandard fuel is used, the setting may have to be retarded from the normal setting. The retarding should also be done progressively and should not be later than a setting of 2 deg. BTDC.

DISTRIBUTOR REPLACE

1. To remove the distributor, disconnect the primary wire and vacuum control pipe.
2. Remove distributor cap.
3. Scribe a mark on the distributor body indicating the position of the rotor, and scribe another mark on the body and engine block indicating position of distributor body in block. These marks can be used as guides when installing distributor in a correctly timed engine.
4. Remove hold down screw or screws and lift distributor out of block. *Do not crank engine while distributor is removed or the initial timing operation will have to be performed.*

Installation

If the crankshaft has not been disturbed, install the distributor, using the scribed marks previously made on the distributor body and engine block as guides.

If the crankshaft has been rotated while the distributor was removed from the engine, it will be necessary to retime the engine. Crank the engine to bring No. 1 piston on top dead center of its compression stroke. Align the timing mark on the crankshaft pulley with the timing pointer (see *Tune Up* chart). Install the distributor so that the rotor points to the No. 1 spark plug wire terminal in the distributor cap.

Make sure the oil pump intermediate shaft properly engages the distributor shaft. It may be necessary to crank the engine with the starter, after the distributor drive gear is properly engaged, in order to engage the oil pump intermediate shaft.

STARTER REPLACE

1966-69

1. On V8 only, raise car on hoist.
2. Disconnect cable at starter terminal.
3. On V8 Comet and Montego with power steering, disconnect and lower idler arm from frame. Push bolts back through frame.
4. On all models, unfasten and remove starter.

1964-65

NOTE: On 1965 Comet with V8 engine, due to interference of the exhaust pipe, the idler arm assembly should be lowered to provide access for starter removal.

1. Raise vehicle and disconnect starter cable.
2. On 1965 Comet V8, remove two idler arm attaching bolts and push bolts back into frame. Then lower idler arm.
3. Unfasten and remove starter.

Fig. 1 Ignition switch removal. 1963-69

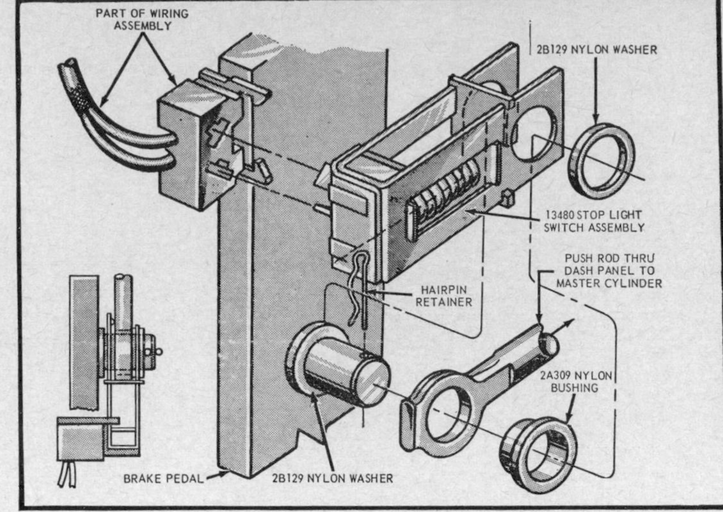

Fig. 3 Mechanical stop light switch. 1965-69

SERVICE BULLETIN

STARTER DRIVE SLIPPAGE, 1965: If the starter will not turn engine on cold starts, it indicates that the starter drive locking cam and roller is slipping. When this happens, remove the pull-down pole cover and electrically actuate the starter. If the pole shoe moves into place and the starter spins, the trouble is in the starter drive. Replace only the drive assembly.

NOISY STARTER OR STARTER LOCK-UP: If either of these situations occur, loosen the three mounting bolts enough to hand fit the starter properly into pilot plate. Then tighten starter mounting bolts, starting with top bolt. Starter should not be replaced until it has been proven noisy after proper alignment has been established by the above method.

1963

1. Disconnect starter cable at terminal, remove starter retaining screws and remove starter and rubber dust ring.
2. When installing, position rubber dust ring on flywheel housing so that the flared portion of the ring makes a good seal to the housing at all points.
3. Position starter to flywheel housing and start the retaining screws. On 6-170 engine with automatic transmission, the transmission dipstick tube bracket is mounted under one of the starter mounting bolts.
4. Snug all bolts, then tighten to 12-15 ft. lbs. torque; on 6 cylinder engines tighten center bolt first.

IGNITION SWITCH, REPLACE

1968-69

1. Disconnect battery ground cable.
2. Insert key and turn switch to accessory position. Insert a wire pin in hole in switch. Slightly depress pin while turning key counterclockwise past the accessory position. This will release lock cylinder. Pull out lock cylinder with key.
3. Remove bezel nut. Lower switch from instrument panel and remove accessory wire nut. Depress tabs securing multiple connector to rear of switch. Pull multiple connector from switch and remove switch.
4. Reverse procedure to install.

1967

1. Disconnect ground cable from battery.
2. With ignition key, turn switch to the left while inserting a fine wire pin in hole beneath key slot, Fig. 1. Slightly depress pin while turning key. This will release lock cylinder from switch. Pull out lock cylinder with key.
3. Remove switch bezel nut and lower switch from instrument panel. Remove accessory and gauge feed wires from switch, also insulated plug.
4. Reverse procedure to install. Insert key and turn to accessory position. Place cylinder and key in switch. Depress pin slightly while turning key counterclockwise. Push cylinder into switch and remove pin.

1963-66

1. Disconnect battery ground cable.
2. Turn ignition key to "ACC" position, Fig. 1. Using a paper clip, slightly depress release pin and turn key counter-clockwise. Then pull key and lock cylinder out of switch.
3. Press in on rear of switch and rotate switch ⅛ turn counter-clockwise (as viewed from terminal end). Remove bezel, switch and spacer.
4. Remove nut from back of switch. Remove accessory and gauge feed wires from accessory terminal of switch. Pull insulated plug from rear of switch.
5. If a new ignition switch is to be installed, insert a screwdriver into lock

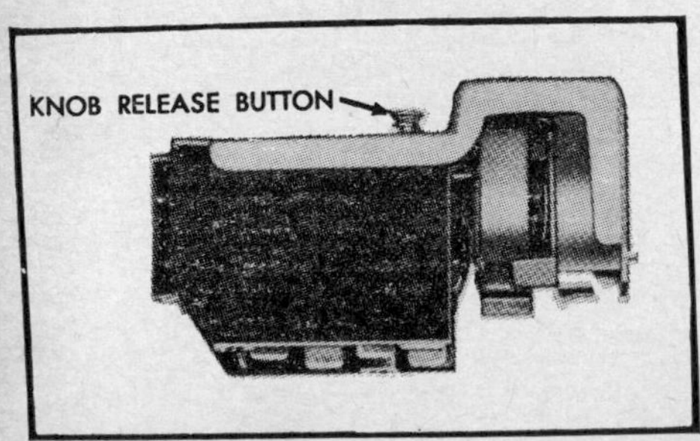

Fig. 2 Light switches. 1963-69

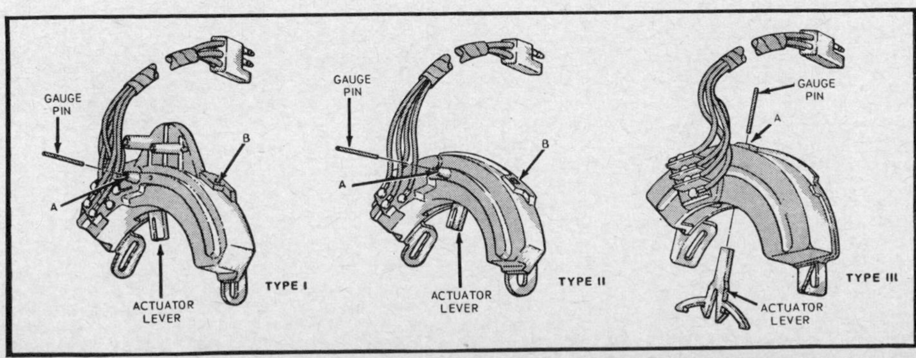

Fig. 3A Neutral start switch adjustments. 1968 column shift

opening of switch and turn slot in switch to full counter-clockwise position.
6. Connect insulated plug with wires to back of switch. Position accessory and gauge wires on switch stud and install retaining nut.
7. Position spacer on switch with open face away from switch.
8. Place bezel, switch and spacer in switch opening. Press switch toward instrument panel and rotate it ⅛ turn to lock it in position.
9. If new lock cylinder is to be installed, insert key in cylinder and turn it to "ACC" position. Place lock and key in switch, depress pin slightly with a paper clip and turn key counter-clockwise. Push lock cylinder into switch.
10. Connect battery cable and check switch operation.

LIGHT SWITCH, REPLACE

1968-69 Fairlane, Falcon, Montego

1. Disconnect battery ground cable.
2. To remove control knob and shaft assembly, place knob in full ON position, then press knob release button on switch and pull out knob and shaft.
3. Unscrew mounting nut and remove bezel and switch, then remove junction block from switch.
4. Reverse procedure to install. However, install knob and shaft by inserting all the way into the switch until a distinct click is heard. In some instances it may be necessary to rotate the shaft slightly until it engages the switch contact carrier.

1968-69 Cougar & Mustang

1. Disconnect battery ground cable.
2. Remove two screws and lower parking brake and air control.
3. To remove control knob and shaft assembly, place knob in full ON position, then press knob release button on switch and pull out knob and shaft out of switch.
4. Remove switch bezel (1 nut), then lower switch assembly. Disconnect wire junction block from switch and, on Cougar only, the three vacuum hoses, and remove switch.
5. Reverse procedure to install. However, install knob and shaft assembly by inserting all the way into the switch until a distinct click is heard. In some instances it may be necessary to rotate the shaft slightly until it engages the switch contact carrier.

1967 Cougar & Mustang

1. Disconnect ground cable at battery.
2. Remove control knob and shaft by pressing knob release button on switch housing with knob in "ON" position. Pull knob out of switch.
3. Unfasten and lower parking brake and air control (2 screws).
4. Remove bezel nut and lower switch. Disconnect junction block from switch.
5. Reverse procedure to install. Insert knob and shaft all the way into switch until a click is heard. In some cases it may be necessary to rotate shaft slightly until it engages switch contact carrier.

All 1963-66 & 1967-68 Montego, Comet, Falcon, Fairlane

1. Disconnect battery ground cable.
2. Remove control knob and shaft by pressing knob release button on switch housing, Fig. 2, with knob in full "ON" position. Pull knob out of switch.
3. Unscrew mounting nut, remove switch, then remove fuse block from switch.
4. To install, connect fuse block to switch, position switch in instrument panel and install mounting nut.
5. Install knob and shaft by inserting it all the way into switch until a distinct click is heard. In some instances it may be necessary to rotate shaft slightly until it engages switch contact carrier.
6. Connect battery cable.

STOP LIGHT SWITCH, REPLACE

1963-64 Hydraulic Type

1. Disconnect two wires from switch.
2. Remove switch from master cylinder.
3. Install new switch in master cylinder loosely.
4. Fill master cylinder with brake fluid, if necessary, and bleed air from cylinder.
5. Tighten switch securely. Inspect for leakage with brakes applied.
6. Connect wires to switch.

1965-69 Mechanical Type

1. Disconnect wires at connector.
2. Remove hairpin retainer and slide stop light switch, push rod, nylon washers and bushings away from brake pedal, and remove switch, Fig. 3.
3. Reverse above procedure to install.

NEUTRAL SAFETY SWITCH, REPLACE

1969 Column Shift

Removal

1. Disconnect the switch wires at plug connector.
2. Remove two screws securing switch to column and lift switch from column.

NOTE: Check the switch actuator to be sure it is secure to the shift tube and seated as far forward against shift tube bearing as possible. If the actuator is broken or damaged, replace it.

3. Before installing a new switch, check to see that the red neutral position gauge pin is properly inserted in the neutral pinning hole. If the pin is missing, align the two holes at the neutral pinning hole on top of the switch and install a No. 43 drill.
4. While holding selector lever against the stop in neutral position, place switch on column and install attaching screws.
5. Remove the gauge pin and connect the wires to the switch.

Adjustment

1. With selector lever against neutral stop, loosen two switch retaining screws.
2. Rotate switch until a start is obtained and tighten switch screws.
3. Place selector lever in "1" position and push the park reset button, located on right side of switch, to the left until it stops.

1969 Fairlane & Montego Console

Removal & Adjustment

1. Remove selector lever handle from lever.
2. Remove trim panel from top of console.
3. Remove cover and dial indicator as an assembly.
4. Unfasten and remove lever retainer from housing.
5. Unfasten and remove the switch from the housing and disconnect wires at connector.
6. Position switch to housing and install screws and then move selector lever back and forth until gauge pin can be inserted into holes on switch, Fig. 4.
7. Slide switch forward or rearward until switch actuating lever contacts selector lever.
8. Tighten switch screws and remove gauge pin.
9. Connect wires to switch and replace components previously removed.

1969 Cougar & Mustang Console

Removal & Adjustment

1. Place selector lever in neutral.
2. Raise car and remove manual lever control rod attaching nut.
3. Lower car and remove selector lever handle.
4. Unfasten and remove dial housing.
5. Disconnect dial light and switch wires at connectors at dash panel.
6. Unfasten and remove selector lever and housing assembly.
7. Remove pointer back up shield screws and remove the shield.
8. Remove the two switch screws, push the switch harness plug inward and remove the switch and harness assembly.
9. When installing switch, hold it with wires facing down and move the actuator lever all the way to the left. Then return it to neutral position, Fig. 4A.
10. Position the harness and secure the switch to the housing.
11. Install pointer back up shield.
12. Position selector lever and housing assembly on console and fasten.
13. Connect dial light and switch wires.
14. Install dial housing and selector lever handle.
15. Raise car and attach manual lever control rod.
16. Lower car and check operation of switch in Park position.

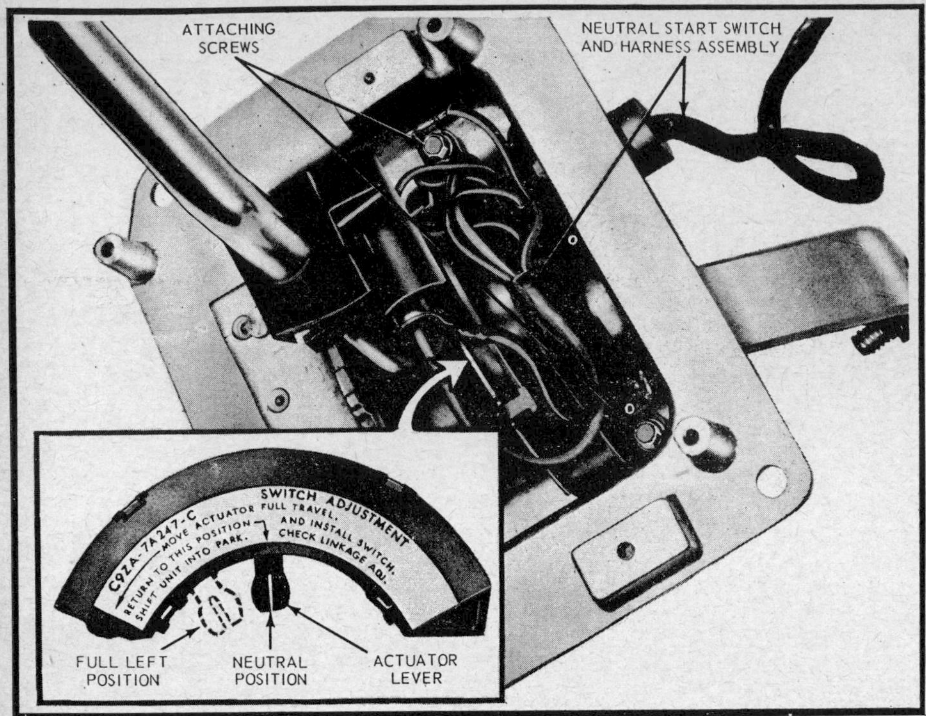

Fig. 4A Neutral switch. 1969 Cougar & Mustang with console

1968 Column Shift

Column mounted neutral start switches are located on top of the steering column jacket but have been moved closer to the toeboard just below the collapsible section of the jacket.

Removal

To adjust the switch, it must be removed from the column. Place the selector lever in neutral and set the parking brake. Then disconnect the electrical and vacuum connections and remove the two fastening screws which will allow you to lift the switch straight up and out.

After removing the switch body of the type 3 switch used on some models, compress the protruding ends of the actuator lever with pliers and lift the lever out of the column. All other types of switches have actuating levers that are integral with the switches, Fig. 3A.

Adjustment

To properly adjust any of the column mounted switches, it is necessary to use a 3/32" pin gauge or rod to adjust the switch.

1. Hold switch with wire terminal facing you (and with separate actuator lever in place in the type 3 switch). Move actuator lever all the way to your left, but don't use force as the switch will be damaged internally.
2. Insert gauge pin in hole in tapered round boss facing you on all switches except type 3. On the type 3 switch, insert the gauge pin ½ inch into the hole in the boss on the top of the switch.
3. Gently move actuator lever back to the right until it stops. This will move the Park circuit to its position of minimum travel, which must be done if the switch is to function properly upon installation.
4. Pull out gauge pin and fit it in the hole on top of the switch case to engage the switch internal carrier in the neutral position. For type 3 switches, remove the gauge pin while you align the two gauge pin holes in the switch case. Then reinsert the pin.
5. If a type 3 switch is being serviced (with separate actuator lever) install the actuator lever in the column by squeezing it slightly and pressing it carefully into position in the shift tube.
6. With transmission selector lever held against the stop in the neutral detent position, set the switch in place on the column and fasten it with two screws.
7. Connect the electrical connector and vacuum hose, and be sure to remove the gauge pin before operating the selector lever.

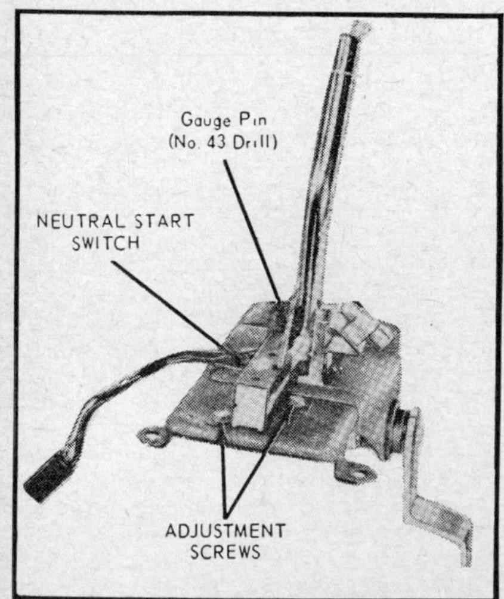

Fig. 4 Neutral safety switch (console shift). 1967-69 Comet, Fairlane and Montego

1967-68 Montego, Comet, Fairlane

Console Shift, Fig. 4

1. Remove handle from selector lever.
2. Remove trim panel from top of console.
3. Remove cover and dial indicator as a unit.
4. Unfasten and remove selector lever retainer from housing (6 screws).
5. Unfasten switch from lever housing (2 screws). Disconnect wires at plug connector and remove switch.
6. With selector lever in neutral, move lever back and forth until gauge pin (#43 drill) can be fully inserted in gauge pin holes, Fig. 4.
7. Place transmission selector lever firmly against stop of neutral detent position.
8. Slide combination neutral start and back-up light switch forward or rearward as required until switch actuating lever contacts selector lever.
9. Tighten switch screws and remove gauge pin.
10. Complete installation in reverse order of removal.

1967 Comet, Falcon, Fairlane

Column Shift, Fig. 5

1. Disconnect switch wires at plug connector.
2. Remove switch from steering column (2 screws).
3. Reverse procedure to install.
4. With selector lever in neutral, rotate switch and install gauge pin (#43 drill) into gauge pin hole.
5. Tighten switch screws and remove gauge pin.

All 1964-66 & 1966-68 Mustang, Cougar

Transmission Mounted Switch, Fig. 6

1. Remove downshift linkage rod from

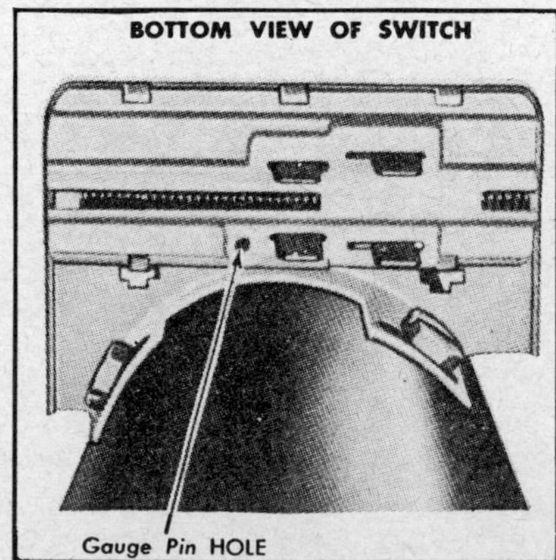

Fig. 5 Neutral safety switch (column shift). 1967 Comet, Fairlane, Falcon

transmission downshift lever.
2. Apply penetrating oil to downshift lever shaft and nut; then remove downshift outer lever.
3. Remove switch attaching bolts.
4. Disconnect multiple wire connector and remove switch from transmission.
5. Install new switch.
6. With transmission manual lever in neutral, rotate switch and install gauge pin (#43 drill) into gauge pin holes.
7. Tighten switch attaching bolts and remove gauge pin.
8. Complete the installation in reverse order of removal.

1963 Column Shift

1. Disconnect wires, remove screws and switch from steering column.
2. Install new switch and position it on steering column so that the engine will start only when shift lever is in N and P.

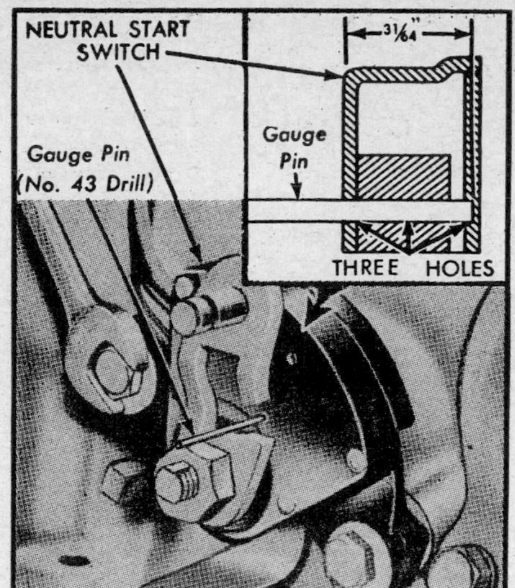

Fig. 6 Neutral safety switch. 1964-66 and 1967-68 Cougar, Mustang

TURN SIGNAL SWITCH, REPLACE

1968-69

The emergency warning flasher switch and turn signal flasher switch are integral parts of the same switch assembly. To remove, proceed as follows:
1. Disconnect battery ground cable.
2. Remove steering wheel hub.
3. Remove horn button (3 screws).
4. Remove steering wheel.
5. Remove turn signal switch lever and emergency flasher control knob. If so equipped, disconnect set speed switch wiring connector.
6. Remove steering column upper collar (2 screws).
7. Disconnect turn signal switch wiring multiple connector near bottom of steering column. It may be necessary to lower hand brake control and left air vent control on some Mustang and Cougar models to provide access to turn signal wiring connector.
8 Remove wires and terminals from connector blocks. This can be done by depressing the tab on the wire terminal with an awl or with an empty ball point pen refill cartridge, then pull wire and terminal from connector block. *Record color code and location of each wire before removing it from connector block.*
9. Tape wires together and attach a piece of heavy cord to the wires to help pull them through steering column during installation.
10. Remove plastic cover from over wires.
11. Push lower steering column collar down. Remove wiring retainer clip.
12. Remove switch from steering column (2 screws) and pull switch and wiring out of column.
13. Reverse procedure to install.

SERVICE BULLETIN

Before judging the turn signal switch to be defective on 1963-67 models, it is suggested that the following areas be checked and repaired to make certain that they are not causing the problem:
1. The steering shaft should be centered in the column so that the steering wheel hub cancelling fingers are in proper relation to the switch cancelling mechanism. This is done by loosening the column attachment to the dash panel and shifting the tube in relation to the shaft.
2. Make sure that the ignition switch is not sticking between the "Start" and normal engine "On" position, thereby adversely affecting the electrical circuit.
3. Excessive Loctite on the threads on the turn signal lever may be contacting the turn signal switch mechanism, causing a binding condition.
4. The fingers on the steering wheel hub cancelling cam may be bent so that the proper contact with the cancelling mechanism cannot be accomplished.

1967

1 Disconnect ground cable at battery.
2. Remove steering wheel hub.
3. Remove horn button (3 screws). Springs will fall out.
4. Remove steering wheel.
5. Remove turn signal switch lever and emergency flasher control knob.
6. Remove steering column upper collar (2 screws).
7. Disconnect multiple connector near bottom of steering column.
8. Remove wires and terminals from connector blocks. This can be done by depressing tab on wire terminal with an awl or with an empty ball point pen re-fill cartridge; then pull wire and terminal from connector block. *Record color code of each wire before removing from connector block.*
9. Tape wires together and attach a piece of heavy cord to them to help pull wires through steering column during installation.
10. Remove plastic cover from over wires.
11. Push lower steering column down and remove wiring retainer clip.
12. Unfasten switch (2 screws) and pull switch and wire assembly out of column.
13. Reverse procedure to install.

1965-66

1. Disconnect battery ground cable.
2. Remove steering wheel.
3. Disconnect two wire connector blocks at dash panel above steering column.
4. Remove wires and terminals from connector blocks.

NOTE: Step 4 can be done by depressing tab on wire terminal with an awl. Then pull wire and terminal from connector block. Be sure to record the color code and location of each wire before removing it from connector block. Tape wires together and attach a piece of heavy cord to them to help pull wires through steering column during installation.

5. Remove turn signal lever.
6. Remove three screws and remove bearing retainer, turn signal switch and wires from steering column. Disconnect cord from wires.
7. To install, tape ends of wires together and attach cord to wires.
8. Pull wires down through steering column with the cord, and position switch to steering column hub.
9. Complete the installation by reversing the removal procedure.

1963-64 Comet & Falcon

1. Disconnect horn and turn signal switch wires under instrument panel at steering column.
2. Slide plastic insulating tubing out of column and off wires.
3. Remove horn button and spring.
4. Mark steering wheel position on steering column. Then remove steering wheel.
5. Remove turn signal lever.
6. Remove screws and pull switch away from steering column flange.
7. Remove column flange nuts.
8. Remove signal switch, column flange, sleeve and wiring from column.
9. Remove flange from switch.
10. Reverse above procedure to install.

1963 Meteor

1. Disconnect battery ground cable.
2. Remove horn ring by depressing and rotating it counter-clockwise. Lift up on upper horn contact brush.
3. Remove steering wheel.
4. Disconnect turn signal and horn wires at connectors. Remove wiring protective sleeve.
5. Remove signal lever and horn contact brush from signal switch.
6. Remove three screws and switch retaining plate.

NOTE: To facilitate installation of new switch and wiring assembly, tape end of wires together and attach a piece of strong cord. Then remove switch and wires from steering column.

To install, reverse the procedure. Be sure turn signal wires are routed to prevent them from being pinched.

1963-64 Fairlane

To remove turn signal switch the steering wheel must first be removed. When installing the new switch, make certain that the canceling cam on steering wheel makes contact with canceling pawls on switch.

The clearance between steering wheel hub and steering shaft housing flange should not be more than ⅛" for proper switch canceling. Reposition steering shaft housing if necessary.

HORN SOUNDER & STEERING WHEEL

1969 Rim-Blow Type

The rubber insert and copper strip assembly is not replaceable. Therefore if a new insert is required the entire steering wheel will have to be replaced.

1. Unfasten and remove pad from steering wheel (3 screws).
2. Remove the medalion from the pad.
3. After removing retaining nut the steering wheel can be removed with a puller.

1968-69 Except Rim-Blow Type

1. Disconnect battery ground cable.
2. Remove steering wheel hub.
3. Remove horn button (3 screws); springs will fall out.
4. Remove steering wheel.

1963-68

The horn button or ring can be removed by pressing down evenly and turning button counterclockwise until it lifts out.

Mark steering shaft and wheel hub before removing wheel so that the relationship between the wheel and steering gear is maintained when reinstalled. Then remove the nut from the steering shaft and use a puller to remove the wheel.

INSTRUMENT CLUSTER

1969 Mustang & Cougar

1. Disconnect battery ground cable.
2. Remove instrument panel pad for access to cluster mounting screws.
3. Remove six screws retaining cluster to panel and withdraw cluster slightly.
4. Disconnect plug to printed circuit and tachometer if so equipped.
5. Disconnect speedometer cable by pressing on knurled surface of plastic connector and pulling cable away from head.
6. The cluster can now be removed from the panel.
7. Reverse the foregoing to install.

1968 Mustang & Cougar

Instrument cluster components are accessible by removing the cluster as an assembly. Procedure is as follows:

1. Disconnect battery ground cable.
2. On Cougars only, remove instrument panel front pad.
3. Unfasten heater control from instrument panel (4 screws) and position control outward.
4. Reaching through heater control opening, disconnect speedometer cable.
5. Remove three ash tray screws. Disconnect cigar lighter element wiring connector and remove ash tray.
6. Reaching through ash tray opening, remove nut retaining inboard end of instrument cluster to instrument panel.
7. Unfasten cluster from instrument panel (7 screws on Cougar, 5 on Mustang).
8. Position cluster outward, disconnect two multiple connectors and remove cluster assembly.
9. Reverse procedure to install.

1968-69 Fairlane

1. Disconnect battery ground cable.
2. Remove instrument panel cover.
3. Remove right instrument panel shield.
4. Unfasten cluster (5 screws) and position cluster out.
5. Disconnect speedometer cable, tachometer (if equipped) and multiple plug from printed circuit and remove cluster. Cluster components are now accessible for service.

1968-69 Falcon

1. Disconnect battery ground cable.
2. Remove instrument panel pad.
3. Unfasten cluster from instrument panel (5 screws) and position cluster out.
4. Disconnect speedometer cable, heater control cables and heater bulb. Also disconnect heater switch plug and multiple plug to printed circuit. Remove clamp retaining heater cables and remove cluster. Cluster components are now accessible for service.

1968-69 Montego

1. Disconnect battery ground cable.
2. Remove instrument panel pad.
3. Unfasten cluster from instrument panel (8 screws). Position cluster out and disconnect speedometer cable. Also disconnect multiple plug to cluster, multiple plug to convenience control lights (if equipped), heater control cables and switch.
4. Disconnect clock (if equipped) and remove cluster. Cluster components are now accessible for service.

1964-67 Comet & Falcon; 1965-66 Mustang; 1967 Fairlane

1. Disconnect ground cable at battery.
2. Disconnect cable from speedometer.
3. Unfasten cluster from panel and tilt cluster forward.
4. Disconnect wiring and bulb sockets and remove cluster to workbench for service required.

1967 Cougar & Mustang

1. Disconnect ground cable at battery.
2. Remove instrument panel front pad (Cougar).
3. Unfasten (4 screws) heater control from instrument panel and position control outward.
4. Reaching through heater control opening, disconnect speedometer cable.
5. Remove ash tray (3 screws). Disconnect cigar lighter element.
6. Reaching through ash tray opening, remove nut that retains inboard end of cluster to instrument panel.
7. Separate cluster from panel (7 screws on Cougar, 6 on Mustang).
8. Position cluster outward, disconnect two multiple connectors and remove instrument cluster. All components are now accessible for service.

1966 Fairlane

1. Disconnect battery ground cable.
2. Remove radio knobs and nuts.
3. Disconnect speedometer cable.
4. Remove screws from cluster and position it outward.
5. Disconnect bulbs, constant voltage regulator and ground wire, clock and fuel gauge.
6. Remove cluster to workbench for service required.

1963-65 Fairlane & Meteor

To replace the fuel gauge, temperature gauge, speedometer and cluster dial, it is necessary to remove the instrument cluster assembly.

1. Disconnect battery cable and cable at speedometer head. Remove instrument cluster wiring harness from two clips at rear of cluster.
2. Remove cluster retaining screws from instrument panel. Pull out cluster and place it on steering column. Protect column with cloth.
3. Disconnect fuel and temperature gauge wires, turn signal flasher and constant voltage regulator.
4. Remove lights from cluster.
5. Remove cluster assembly.
6. Remove screws attaching cluster to bezel and remove bezel. Instruments may then be removed.

1963 Comet & Falcon

1. Disconnect battery cable and speedometer cable.
2. Remove screws and lift instrument cluster bezel, lens and cluster mask plate from cluster housing.
3. Remove speedometer from cluster housing.

W/S WIPER MOTOR

1969 Cougar & Mustang

1. Remove wiper arm and blades.
2. Disconnect washer hose at "T" fitting (left side) on the cowl grille.
3. Remove cowl top grille.
4. Disconnect motor ground wire at forward edge of plenum chamber.
5. Disconnect motor harness at plug and push it back into plenum chamber.
6. Disconnect linkage drive arm from motor output arm crankpin by removing clip.
7. Remove three bolts that retain motor

to bracket and rotate motor output arm 180° and remove the motor.

NOTE: Before installing motor, rotate arm 180° and before connecting linkage to motor, turn on ignition to ACC position to allow motor to go into park position.

1967-69 Montego, Comet, Fairlane, Falcon

1. Disconnect wiper motor wiring connector.
2. Remove wiper arms and blades.
3. Remove cowl top grille panel.
4. Remove wiper link clip from motor arm.
5. Unfasten and remove wiper motor and mounting bracket (4 bolts).
6. Reverse procedure to install.

1967-68 Cougar & Mustang

1. Disconnect ground cable at battery.
2. Remove courtesy light. If vehicle is equipped with a hang-on air conditioner, lower air conditioner to floor.
3. Disconnect wiper motor plug connector.
4. Remove nut retaining pivot arm and wiper arms to motor.
5. Unfasten and remove motor from its mounting bracket.
6. Reverse procedure to install.

1964-66 Mustang, Comet & Falcon

1. Disconnect harness connector from wiper motor.
2. Unfasten motor from dash panel (3 bolts).
3. Lower assembly and disconnect wiper links at motor. Then remove motor and bracket.

1963 Comet & Falcon

1. Disconnect hose at motor.
2. If equipped with an electric motor, disconnect battery ground cable.
3. Loosen control cable screw at motor. Then unfasten and remove motor from mounting bracket.

1963-67 Fairlane & Meteor

1. Disconnect wiper links drive arm from wiper motor drive shaft (under instrument panel).
2. Disconnect wires from motor.
3. Remove motor mounting bolts and remove motor.

SERVICE BULLETIN

W/S WIPER SYSTEM CHATTER: On 1964-65 models if the system chatters and a thumping noise emanates from the cowl panel during wiper operation it is caused by the wiper motor attachment being mislocated, causing excessive travel of the right arm and pivot assembly until the arm interferes with the pivot. The condition can be corrected in the following manner:

1. Remove right arm and pivot assembly.
2. Shorten the right arm by cutting out $\frac{3}{16}$" to ¼" from the center of the arm.
3. Fabricate a steel reinforcement for the arm 2 x ½ x $\frac{3}{32}$ inches in size.
4. Tack braze, gas or arc weld the reinforcement to the shortened arm six places and along the joint cut line of the arm. *Parallelism and proper alignment must be maintained when joining the cut arm together prior to welding to preclude any possible bind in the system.*
5. Install parts removed and check operation.

W/S WIPER TRANSMISSION

1969 Cougar & Mustang

1. Remove arm and blade assemblies from pivot shafts.
2. Disconnect washer hose at "T" fitting on cowl grille.
3. Remove cowl top grille.
4. Disconnect linkage drive arm from motor output arm crankpin by removing clip.
5. Disconnect right link from right arm and pivot shaft and remove the arm and pivot shaft assembly.
6. Unfasten and remove the left arm and pivot shaft and lift out to the right: the pivot shaft and arm, left link and linkage drive arm as one assembly.

NOTE: When installing the linkage, install the left pivot shaft and linkage first.

1967-69 Montego, Comet, Fairlane, Falcon

1. Remove wiper arms and blades.
2. Remove cowl top grille panel.
3. Remove drive arm to pivot clip and remove pivot shaft and link assembly.
4. Reverse procedure to install.

1967-68 Cougar & Mustang

Left Side

1. Disconnect ground cable from battery.
2. Remove wiper arms and blades.
3. Unfasten heater control from instrument panel and position heater control outward.
4. Remove clip retaining link to motor drive.
5. Working through heater control opening, remove three retaining bolts and remove pivot and link out through heater control opening.
6. Reverse procedure to install, using a new gasket on pivot.

Right Side

Procedure is the same as left side except that glove box liner must be removed instead of heater control. Then work through the glove box opening to get at the pivot and link assembly.

1963-66 Electric Wiper

1. Remove wiper blades and arms.
2. Remove pivot shaft nut, bezel and gasket.
3. Disconnect wiper link from motor and remove link and pivot shaft.
4. To install reverse removal procedure.

W/S WIPER SWITCH

1968-69 Fairlane

1. Disconnect battery ground cable.
2. Remove switch control knob and bezel nut.
3. Unplug and remove switch.
4. Reverse procedure to install.

1967 Fairlane

1. Disconnect ground cable from battery.
2. Remove wiper switch control knobs.
3. From lower edge of instrument cluster, unfasten switch from panel (3 screws).
4. Disconnect switch wiring connectors from switch and remove switch.
5. Remove retaining screw and plastic bar and separate washer switch from wiper switch.
6. Reverse procedure to install.

1967-69 Falcon

1. Disconnect ground cable from battery.
2. Remove switch knobs and unplug connectors at switch.
3. Unfasten (2 screws) and remove switch from under instrument panel.
4. Separate washer switch from wiper switch (2 screws).
5. Reverse procedure to install.

1967-69 Montego, Comet

Standard Wiper

1. Disconnect battery ground cable.
2. Remove switch knob, nut and bezel.
3. Pull switch out from instrument panel.
4. Disconnect plug connector from switch and remove switch.
5. Reverse procedure to install.

Intermittent Wipers

1. Disconnect ground cable from battery.
2. Remove set screws and remove control knob.
3. Remove bezel nut and bezel.
4. Lower switch assembly.
5. Remove three vacuum hoses from switch, disconnect plug connector and remove switch.
6. Reverse procedure to install, using color code provided on switch and hoses.

1967-69 Cougar & Mustang

1. Disconnect ground cable from battery.
2. Remove instrument cluster.
3. Remove switch from cluster (2 screws).
4. Reverse procedure to install.

1963-65 Electric Type, 1966 Comet, Falcon, Mustang

1. Disconnect battery ground cable.
2. Remove switch knob and bezel.
3. Pull switch from under instrument

panel. Disconnect plug and remove switch.
4. Reverse procedure to install.

1966 Fairlane

1. Disconnect battery ground cable.
2. Remove both control knobs and disconnect washer.
3. From lower edge of cluster remove retaining screws from switches.
4. Disconnect electrical leads and remove switch assembly from instrument panel.
5. Remove screw and separate wiper and washer switches from each other including plastic bar between switches.
6. Assemble wiper and washer switches to each other including plastic bar so that when washer switch is turned on wipers will start.
7. Reverse procedure to install.

RADIO REPLACE

NOTE: When installing radio, be sure to adjust antenna trimmer for peak performance.

1969 Cougar & Mustang

1. Disconnect battery ground cable.
2. Pull control knobs, discs and sleeve from radio shafts.
3. Remove radio applique panel from dash.
4. Remove right and left finish panels.
5. Remove two mounting plate attaching screws.
6. Pull radio out of panel and disconnect wires.
7. Remove mounting plate and rear support from radio.
8. Reverse procedure to install.

1968-69 Fairlane, Falcon, Montego

1. Disconnect battery ground cable.
2. Pull off radio control knobs.
3. Remove radio support to instrument panel attaching screw.
4. Remove bezel nuts from radio control shafts, then lower radio and disconnect speaker, power and antenna wires from radio.
5. Reverse procedure to install.

1968 Mustang & Cougar

Without Console: Same as 1967.

With Console

1. Remove battery ground cable.
2. Unfasten right and left supports from support bracket (2 screws).
3. Remove console assembly.
4. Disconnect radio wiring and antenna lead.
5. Pull off radio control knobs.
6. Remove nuts from radio shafts and remove radio.
7. Reverse procedure to install.

1965-66 Mustang, 1966 Comet, 1966-67 Fairlane, Falcon

1. Disconnect battery ground cable.
2. Pull off radio knobs and remove nuts securing radio to instrument panel.
3. Disconnect antenna lead at right side of radio (at back of AM-FM radio).
4. Disconnect speaker lead.
5. Disconnect radio lead wire and dial light wire from quick disconnect.
6. Remove radio support bracket.
7. Remove radio from under instrument panel.
8. Reverse procedure to install.

1967 Cougar & Mustang

Without Console

1. Disconnect ground cable at battery.
2. Remove rear support bracket nut.
3. Remove four screws that attach bezel and radio to instrument panel.
4. Move radio rearward away from instrument panel. Disconnect antenna, speaker and power leads, and remove radio from instrument panel.
5. Reverse procedure to install.

With Console

1. Disconnect battery ground cable.
2. Remove two bolts retaining rear support bracket to instrument panel.
3. Pull off radio control knobs.
4. Remove two screws at top of retaining bezel to instrument panel.
5. Remove four nuts retaining bezel to console. Nuts are located inside console at lower and upper corners.
6. Position radio and bezel assembly away from instrument panel and disconnect wire leads.
7. Remove radio from vehicle.
8. Remove bezel retaining nuts from right and left control and remove bezel.

1967-68 Montego & Comet

1. Disconnect ground cable at battery.
2. Remove glove box.
3. Remove radio control knobs.
4. Remove radio rear support bracket retaining nut.
5. Remove radio control shaft to instrument panel retaining nuts.
6. Disconnect antenna lead-in cable, radio feed and speaker wires.
7. On A/C equipped vehicles, disconnect and remove right-hand register duct from air distribution chamber.
8. Move radio rearward and through glove box opening.

1964-65 Except Mustang

1. Pull radio control knobs off and remove nuts holding radio to panel.
2. Disconnect antenna lead at right side of radio (at back of AM/FM radio).
3. Disconnect speaker lead.
4. Disconnect radio lead wire at fuse panel on lighting switch and disconnect pilot light wire. Remove lead wire from clips.
5. Unfasten radio from support bracket (one nut) and lift radio from instrument panel.

1963 Comet

1. Disconnect ground cable from battery.
2. Remove control knobs from front of receiver, and two control shaft nuts and washers.
3. Disconnect antenna lead-in cable and speaker plug.
4. Disconnect dial lamp wire and power lead at fuse panel.
5. Remove radio bracket retaining nut at left-hand side and bracket retaining screw at right-hand side. Then carefully remove radio.
6. To install radio, reverse above procedure.

1963 Falcon

1. Pull control knobs off and remove nuts retaining radio to instrument panel.
2. Disconnect antenna lead at right side of radio.
3. Disconnect speaker leads.
4. Disconnect radio lead wire at fuse panel and pilot light wire.
5. Remove radio right and left support bracket-to-radio retaining bolts.
6. Remove radio from panel.
7. Reverse above procedure to install.

1963 Fairlane & Meteor

1. Pull off control knobs and remove nuts retaining radio to instrument panel.
2. Disconnect antenna lead to right side of radio, speaker lead and pilot light wire at wiring harness.
3. Disconnect radio lead wire at fuse panel and remove wire from clips.
4. Remove radio back support bracket-to-radio retaining nut.
5. Remove radio from instrument panel.

HEATER CORE REMOVAL

1969 Cougar & Mustang L/AC

1. Disconnect battery ground cable and drain cooling system.
2. Remove instrument panel pad.
3. Remove glove box liner and door.
4. Remove air distribution duct from heater.
5. Disconnect control cables from heater.
6. Disconnect wires from blower motor resistor.
7. Remove right courtesy light from underside of dash, if so equipped.
8. Remove heater support to dash panel screw.
9. Disconnect vacuum hoses and remove power vent air duct.
10. Disconnect blower motor ground wire in engine compartment.
11. Disconnect heater hoses from heater at dash.
12. In engine compartment, remove heater retaining nuts.
13. Remove instrument panel-to-cowl panel attaching screws.
14. Remove instrument panel right side brace.
15. Pull heater assembly and right side of instrument panel rearward and remove heater assembly.
16. Remove air inlet seal from heater.
17. Separate halves of heater and remove core, Fig. 7.

1969 Cougar & Mustang W/AC

1. Disconnect battery ground cable and remove air cleaner.
2. Connect gauge set to compressor valves and isolate compressor.
3. Drain cooling system and remove heat shield from expansion valve.
4. Disconnect low pressure hose and

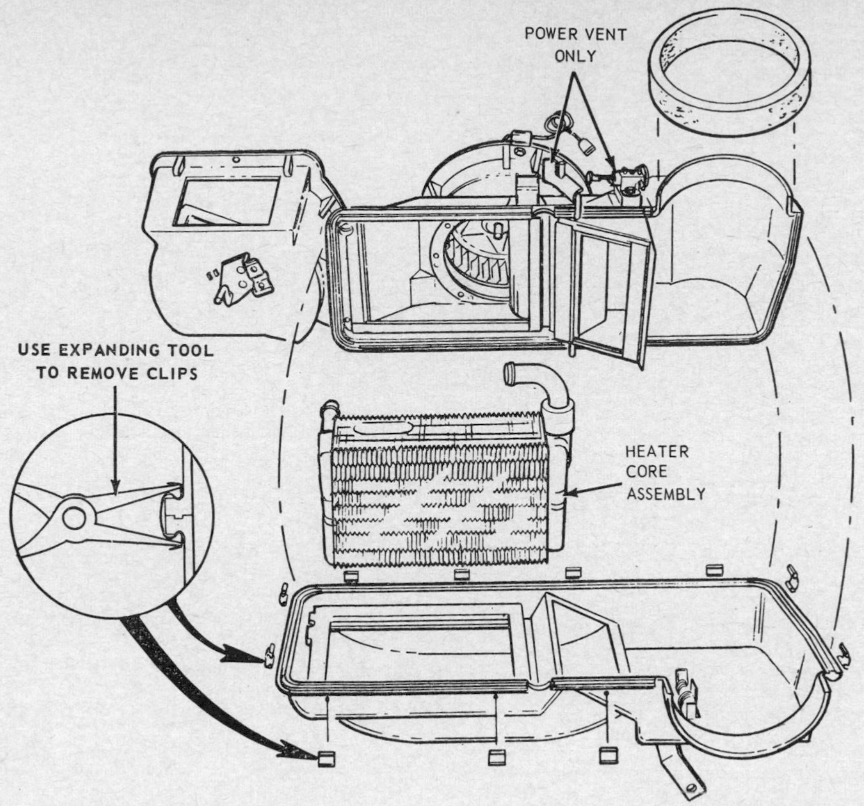

Fig. 7 Heater core removal. 1969 Cougar & Mustang without air conditioner

service valve from compressor.
5. Disconnect high pressure hose at quick disconnect.
6. Remove straps retaining refrigerant hoses to the dash-to-fender apron supports.
7. Disconnect heater hoses from heater core.
8. Remove upper and lower seal retainers and remove hose seal.
9. From engine side of dash, remove evaporator housing mounting nuts and blower housing mounting nut.
10. Remove instrument panel pad.
11. Remove instrument cluster.
12. Disconnect vacuum hoses from reheat door and outside recirc door vacuum motors.
13. Disconnect vacuum hoses from water valve vacuum switch.
14. Disconnect control cable from temperature blend door.
15. Disconnect wires from thermostat switch.
16. Remove right and left air ducts from defrost plenum chamber.
17. Remove defrost plenum chamber.
18. Remove instrument panel right side brace.
19. Remove evaporator housing upper rear support bracket-to-cowl screw.
20. Remove blower housing-to-cowl screws.
21. Move blower housing to left away from evaporator housing.
22. Cover the carpet and pull drain tube from hole in floor.
23. Remove instrument panel-to-cowl screws from right side.
24. Remove instrument panel finish cover from around steering column.
25. Unfasten instrument panel from steering column support.
26. Remove instrument panel-to-cowl screws from left side.
27. Position instrument panel back and remove evaporator housing.
28. Separate halves of evaporator housing.
29. Remove water valve vacuum switch.
30. Remove temperature blend door shaft, frames and door from lower half of evaporator housing.
31. Remove heater core from evaporator lower housing and remove pads from core.
32. Reverse procedure to install.

1967-68 Cougar & Mustang

1. Remove battery ground cable and drain cooling system.
2. Disconnect heater hoses at engine.
3. Loosen screws at choke housing and position hose out.
4. Remove nuts retaining heater to dash.
5. Remove screw retaining ground wire at dash and disconnect two wires.
6. Remove glove box liner.
7. Disconnect defroster hoses, temperature control cable, defroster cable and heat control cable.
8. Remove screw retaining heater to air intake. Lower heater to floor, pulling hoses through dash.
9. Remove both hoses at heater core, take rubber boot from air intake and remove clips retaining both halves of heater together.
10. Separate both halves of heater and remove heater core.

1967-69 Fairlane, Falcon, Comet, Montego

1. Drain cooling system and disconnect both heater hoses at dash.
2. Unfasten heater from dash.
3. Disconnect temperature and defroster cables at heater.
4. Disconnect wires from resistor, and blower motor wires and clip retaining heater to defroster nozzle.
5. Remove glove box.
6. Remove bolt and nut retaining right air duct control to instrument panel.
7. Remove nuts retaining right air duct and remove duct.
8. Take heater assembly to bench. Then remove heater core cover and pad and lift out core.

1965 Comet, Falcon, 1965-66 Mustang

1. Drain cooling system.
2. Remove glove box.
3. Disconnect three control cables.
4. Disconnect defroster hoses at plenum chamber.
5. Disconnect heater hoses at water pump and carburetor heater.
6. Remove heater hoses from clips.
7. On V8's, remove hose from choke clip.
8. Disconnect wires at heater motor and remove ground wire-to-dash retaining screw.
9. Remove heater and motor retaining nuts from dash.
10. Disconnect fresh air inlet rubber boot, pull heater away from dash and lay assembly on the floor.
11. Separate heater housing halves, then lift out heater core. On Console models, it may be necessary to remove heater from car.

1966 Comet, Falcon, 1965-66 Fairlane

The heater core is mounted in the heater case in a diagonal position in the center of the case and is serviced through an opening in the back plate. With the heater assembly out of the vehicle, simply remove four screws from the cover plate and pull the core from the housing. The core is mounted in the heater housing with rubber pads on each end to insure a snug fit.

1963-64 Comet & Falcon

Disconnect defroster tubes and heater hoses at heater. It is necessary to remove glove box on 1964 models. Remove heater retaining nuts on engine side of cowl. From inside of car, disconnect rubber boot at fresh air inlet, then disconnect control cables at heater. To gain access to core, remove heater and separate to halves of heater housing.

Engine Section

ENGINE, REPLACE

1963-69 Six-Cylinder

NOTE: The engine is removed from the chassis, leaving the transmission in place. First disconnect and/or remove as required wires, tubes, hoses and linkage attached to engine. Then do the following:

1. Remove hood, radiator, fan and pulley.
2. Remove starting motor.
3. On cars with manual shift transmission, remove clutch equalizer shaft and arm bracket.
4. Remove flywheel or converter housing-to-engine upper bolts through access holes in underbody.
5. Disconnect engine right and left mount at underbody bracket.
6. Remove flywheel or converter housing cover.
7. Remove flywheel or converter housing-to-engine lower bolts.
8. Support transmission and flywheel or converter housing with a jack.
9. Attach a lifting rig to engine and remove it from vehicle.

1963-65 V8 Engines

NOTE: The engine is removed from the vehicle, leaving the transmission in place. First disconnect and/or remove as required wires, tubes, hoses and linkage attached to engine. Then do the following:

1. Remove hood, drain cooling system and crankcase and remove oil filter.
2. Remove radiator, fan and pulley.
3. If equipped, remove A/C compressor and power steering pump.
4. Remove flywheel or converter housing-to-engine upper bolts.
5. Remove starting motor.
6. Disconnect engine support insulators.
7. Remove flywheel or converter housing-to-engine lower bolts.
8. Support transmission with a jack.
9. Attach a lifting rig to engine and remove it from vehicle.

1966-69 V8-390, 427, 428

NOTE: The engine is removed from the vehicle, leaving the transmission in place. First disconnect and/or remove as required wires, tubes, hose and linkage attached to engine. Then do the following:

1. Drain cooling system and crankcase.
2. Remove hood, radiator and ignition coil.
3. If air conditioned, unfasten air compressor from its mounting and position it out of the way, leaving refrigerant lines attached.
4. Unfasten and wire power steering pump to hood left hinge in a position that will prevent oil from draining out.
5. Raise front of car.
6. Remove No. 2 crossmember-to-underbody brace on right side to

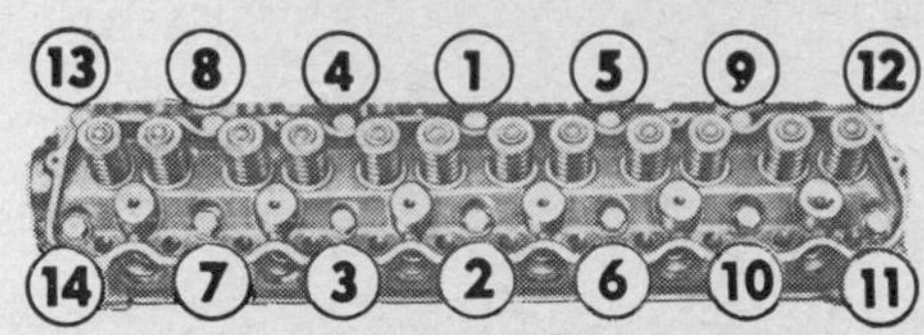

Fig. 1 Cylinder head tightening sequence. Six cylinder

provide clearance for starter removal. Remove starter and dust seal and transmission fluid filler tube bracket.
7. Remove engine intermediate support bracket-to-crossmember retaining nut on right and left engine front supports.
8. Remove converter housing cover.
9. Remove flywheel-to-converter nuts.
10. Secure converter to housing.
11. Remove converter housing-to-engine lower bolts.
12. Lower car and support transmission.
13. Remove converter housing upper bolts.
14. Remove front fender-to-upper dash braces.
15. Lift engine out of chassis.

1966-69 V8-289, 302, 351

NOTE: The engine is removed from the vehicle, leaving the transmission in place. First disconnect and/or remove as required wires, tubes, hose and linkage attached to engine. Then do the following:

1. Drain cooling system and crankcase.
2. Remove oil filter, hood, radiator, fan and pulley.
3. Remove air cleaner and intake duct.
4. If air conditioned, unfasten and position air compressor out of the way.
5. Remove and position power steering pump to one side.
6. If equipped with Thermactor Exhaust Emission Control System, remove air pump air filter if it is not connected to engine.
7. Remove flywheel-to-converter housing upper bolts.
8. Raise front of car and remove starter and dust seal.
9. Disconnect engine support insulators at brackets on frame underbody.

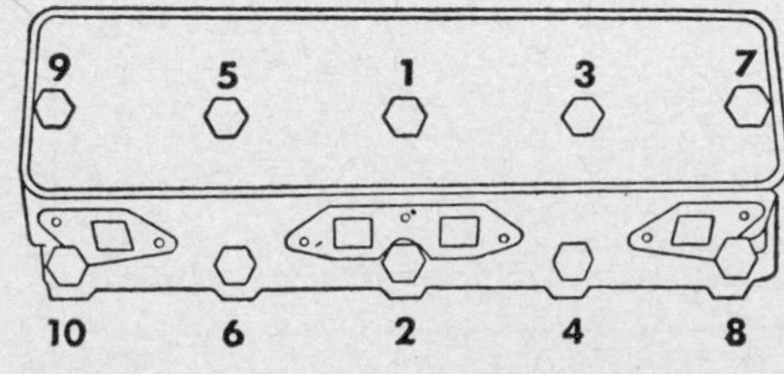

Fig. 2 Cylinder head tightening. V8 engines

10. Remove remaining flywheel or converter housing-to-engine bolts.
11. Lower car, then support transmission.
12. Attach a lifting rig to engine and remove from vehicle.

CYLINDER HEAD, REPLACE

Tighten cylinder head bolts a little at a time in three steps in the sequence shown in the illustrations. Final tightening should be to the torque specifications listed in the *Engine Tightening* table. After tightening the bolts to specifications, *they should not be disturbed.*

1966-69 Six Cylinder

1. Drain cooling system and remove air cleaner.
2. Unfasten exhaust pipe from manifold and pull it down.
3. Disconnect accelerator rod from carburetor.
4. Disconnect fuel inlet line at fuel filter hose, and distributor vacuum line at carburetor.
5. Disconnect coolant lines at carburetor spacer. Remove radiator upper hose at outlet housing.
6. Disconnect distributor vacuum line at distributor. Disconnect carburetor fuel inlet line at fuel pump. Remove lines as an assembly.
7. Disconnect spark plug wires at plugs and temperature sending unit wire at sending unit.
8. Remove crankcase ventilation system. Remove hoses from Thermactor system as necessary for accessability.
9. Remove valve rocker arm cover.
10. Remove rocker arm shaft assembly.
11. Remove valve push rods.
12. Remove remaining cylinder head bolts and lift off head.
13. Reverse procedure to install and tighten head bolts in the sequence shown in Fig. 1.

1963-65 Six Cylinder

1. Drain cooling system, remove air cleaner and disconnect ground cable.
2. Disconnect exhaust pipe at exhaust manifold.
3. Disconnect carburetor linkage, fuel and vacuum lines, water hoses and wires from spark plugs.
4. Remove rocker arm cover.
5. Back off valve adjusting screws to remove load from rocker arms. Then remove rocker arm shaft assembly.
6. Remove valve push rods, keeping them in proper sequence so they are returned to proper locations.
7. Remove one bolt from each end of cylinder head at opposite corners and install cylinder head guide studs ($\frac{7}{16}$"-14 x 6").
8. Remove remaining bolts and lift off cylinder head.
9. Reverse above procedure to install the cylinder head and tighten bolts in the sequence shown in Fig. 1.

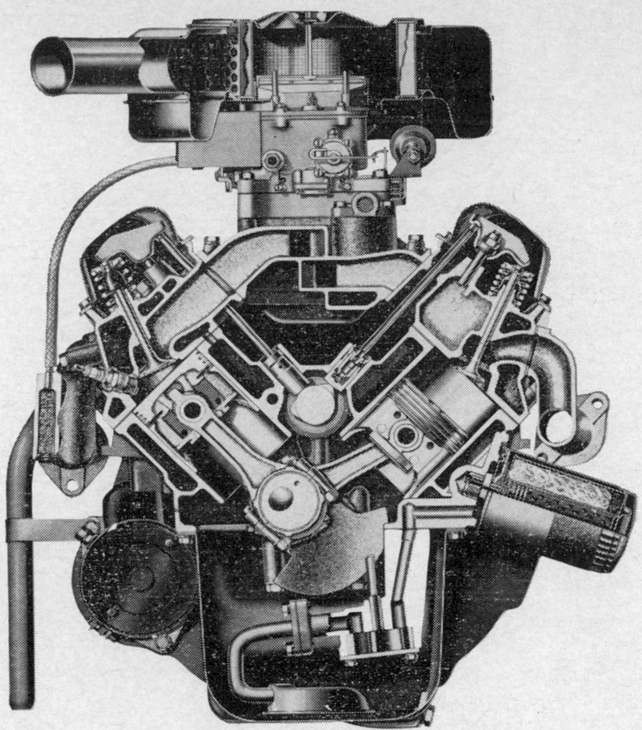

Cross section of V8-260, 289, 302, 351 engines

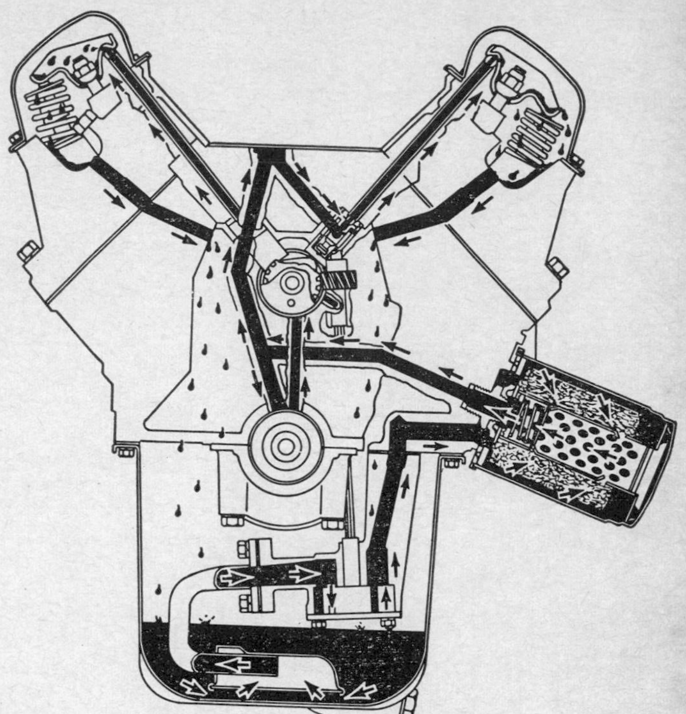

Engine oiling system. V8-260, 289, 302, 351

1966-69 V8-289, 302, 351

1. Remove intake manifold and carburetor as an assembly.
2. Disconnect battery ground cable at cylinder head.
3. If left head is being removed, remove air compressor (if equipped). Also remove and wire power steering pump out of the way. If equipped with Thermactor System, disconnect hose from air manifold on left cylinder head.
4. If right head is to be removed, remove alternator mounting bracket bolt and spacer, ignition coil and air cleaner inlet duct.
5. If right head is to be removed on an engine with Thermactor System, remove air pump from bracket. Disconnect hose from air manifold.
6. Disconnect exhaust manifolds at exhaust pipes.

NOTE: On V8-351, separate the exhaust manifolds from the heads first in order to gain access to the lower row of cylinder head attaching bolts.

7. Remove rocker arm covers. If equipped with Thermactor System, remove check valve from air manifold.
8. Loosen rocker arm nuts so rocker arms can be rotated to one side. Remove push rods.
9. Remove head bolts and lift head off block.
10. Reverse removal procedure to install and tighten head bolts in the sequence shown in Fig. 2.

1966-69 V8-390, 427, 428

1. If equipped with Thermactor System, disconnect air hoses as necessary for accessability, and position them out of the way.
2. Remove intake manifold and carburetor as an assembly.
3. Disconnect exhaust manifolds at exhaust pipes.
4. If left head is being removed, remove ignition coil and engine identification tag, and remove power steering pump mounting bolt from right cylinder head.
5. Remove head bolts and take off head.
6. Reverse procedure to install and tighten head bolts in the sequence shown in Fig. 2.

1963-65 V8-260, 289

1. Remove intake manifold and carburetor as a unit.
2. Disconnect battery cable at cylinder head.
3. Remove rocker arm cover(s).
4. If equipped, remove power steering pump if left cylinder head is being removed. Wire pump out of the way and in a position that will prevent oil from spilling out.
5. Remove generator and bracket.
6. Disconnect exhaust manifolds at exhaust pipes.
7. Loosen rocker arm stud nuts so that rocker arms can be rotated to the side. Then remove push rods and keep them in order so they will be returned to their original locations.
8. Unfasten and remove head(s).
9. Reverse removal procedure and tighten head bolts in the sequence shown in Fig. 2.

VALVE ARRANGEMENT

Front to Rear

Sixes	E-I-I-E-I-E-E-I-E-I-I-E
8-260, 289, 302 Right	I-E-I-E-I-E-I-E
8-260, 289, 302 Left	E-I-E-I-E-I-E-I
8-351 Right	I-E-I-E-I-E-I-E
8-351 Left	E-I-E-I-E-I-E-I
V8-390, 427, 428	E-I-E-I-I-E-I-E

VALVE LIFT SPECS.

Engine	Year	Intake	Exhaust
6–144	1963–64	.348	.348
6–170	1963–66	.348	.348
	1967	.368	.368
	1968–69	.348	.348
6–200	1963–69	.348	.348
6–250	1969	.368	.368
8–221	1963	.380	.380
8–260	1962–64	.380	.380
8–260	1963–64	.380	.380
8–289②	1964	.4774	.4774
8–289	1965–67	.3684	.380
8–289③	1965–66	.4574	.4574
8–289	1968	.368	.381
8–302	1968–69	.368	.381
8–351	1969	.418	.448
8–390③	1966	.4809	.4809
8–390	1966	.440	.440
8–390①	1967	.428	.431
8–390②	1967	.4809	.4809
8–390①	1968	.427	.430
8–390②	1968	.440	.440
8–390②	1969	.481	.490
8–427	1968–69	.481	.490
8–428	1969	.481	.490

①—Two bar. carb. ②—Four bar carb.
③—Hi Perf. engine.

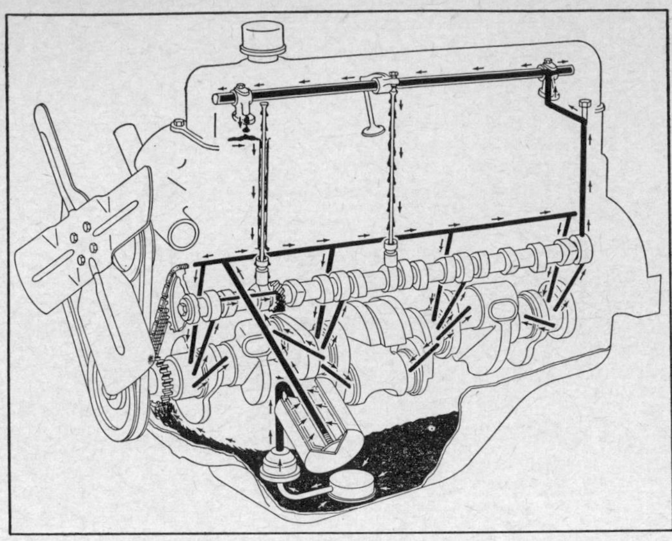

Engine oiling system for 6 cylinder engines

VALVE TIMING

Intake Opens Before TDC

Engine	Year	Degrees
6–144	1963–64	13
6–170	1963–64	13
	1965–66	9
	1967	7
	1968–69	9
6–200	1963–64	6
	1965–67	7
	1967–69①	9
6–250	1969	10
8–221	1963	21
8–260	1963–64	21
8–289	1964②	44
	1964③	20
	1965–66④	30
	1965–68	16
8–302	1968–69	16
8–351	1969	11
8–390	1966①	18
	1966–69	16
8–427	1968–69	18
8–428	1969	18

①—With exhaust emission control.
②—Four Bar. carb. ③—Two bar. carb.
④—Hi Perf. engine.

VALVES, ADJUST

Six Cylinder

The procedure used to check the valve clearance is to rotate the crankshaft with an auxiliary starter switch until the No. 1 piston is near TDC at the end of the compression stroke. At this point the following valves can be checked:

No. 1 Intake	No. 3 Exhaust
No. 1 Exhaust	No. 4 Intake
No. 2 Intake	No. 5 Exhaust

After the clearance of these valves have been checked, rotate the crankshaft until the No. 6 piston is on TDC at the end of its compression stroke (1 revolution of the crankshaft) and check the following valves:

No. 2 Exhaust	No. 5 Intake
No. 3 Intake	No. 6 Intake
No. 4 Exhaust	No. 6 Exhaust

Hydraulic Lifters With Adjustable Rocker Arms, 1963-66

Turn the rocker arm adjusting screw clockwise to remove all lash between push rod and rocker arm. This may be determined by rotating and/or moving the push rod with the fingers as the adjusting screw is tightened. Then tighten the adjusting screw the additional number of turns listed in the *Valve Specifications* table. This will place the hydraulic lifter at the approximate center of its travel.

NOTE: If the torque required to tighten the self-locking adjusting screw is less than 3 ft-lbs, install a new standard or a .002″ oversize screw. If unable to obtain a minimum torque of 7 ft-lbs with the oversize screw, replace the rocker arm and adjusting screw assembly.

SERVICE BULLETIN

Non-Adjustable Rocker Arm:

All 6-200 engines built after 3/29/65 incorporate a new, non-adjustable rocker arm which has a spherical socket instead of an adjusting screw. In conjunction with this change, the push rod is revised to have a ball on both the upper and lower ends. The service procedure required for this revision is as follows:

1. Position cylinder to be checked at T.D.C.
2. Apply pressure on the push rod end of the rocker arm until the tappet plunger is completely bottomed.
3. Hold rocker arm in this position and check the clearance between rocker arm and valve stem.
4. If the clearance is not within limits, install the appropriate undersize or oversize push rod, which are available in .060″ undersize and .060″ oversize.

Mechanical Valve Lifters

Before the final lash adjustment is made, operate the engine for 30 minutes at a fast idle to stabilize engine temperatures. To set the lash accurately, use only a step-type feeler gauge. For example, to obtain the correct setting if the clearance is .019″, the .018″ portion of the gauge should slip between valve tip and rocker arm but the "no go" end (.020″) should not.

V8-260, 289, 302

SERVICE BULLETIN, 1963-68

On V8-260, 289, 302 engines, to minimize the possibility of burned valves, the service procedure has been revised as follows: "When the push rod to rocker arm clearance has been eliminated, tighten the rocker arm stud nut an additional ¾ turn." The previous procedure required an additional 1½ turns.

1. Turn crankshaft to position No. 1 piston on TDC of the compression stroke. With the piston in this position, adjust the following valve clearances:

No. 1 Intake	No. 4 Exhaust
No. 1 Exhaust	No. 5 Exhaust
No. 2 Exhaust	No. 7 Intake
No. 3 Intake	No. 8 Intake

2. Press down on the push rod end of the rocker arm to force oil out of the lifter until the plunger is bottomed. While holding the lifter in the collapsed position, turn the rocker arm adjusting nut to obtain the clearance listed in the *Valve Specifications* table between valve stem and rocker arm.
3. Turn crankshaft to position No. 6 piston on TDC of the compression stroke, and adjust the following valve clearances, using the same procedure as in Step 2.

No. 2 Intake	No. 6 Intake
No. 3 Exhaust	No. 6 Exhaust
No. 4 Intake	No. 7 Exhaust
No. 5 Intake	No. 8 Exhaust

V8-390, 427, 428

For these engines a .060″ shorter push rod or a .060″ longer push rod are available for service to provide a means of compensating for dimensional changes in the valve mechanism. Valve stem-to-rocker arm clearance should be .050-.150″ with the hydraulic lifter completely collapsed. Repeated valve grind jobs will decrease this clearance to the point that if not compensated for the lifters will cease to function.

To check the clearance, bring the piston of the cylinder being checked on top dead center of the compression stroke. Then with hydraulic lifter collapsed, check the clearance between valve stem and rocker arm. If the clearance is less than the minimum, the .060″ shorter push rod should be used. If clearance is more than the maximum the .060″ longer push rod should be used.

SERVICE BULLETIN

A new design hydraulic lifter was released for the 390, 410 and 428 engines. The collapsed specification from valve stem to rocker arm for this new lifter has been revised from .050-.150″ to .050-.200″ on engines built after 12-20-65 only.

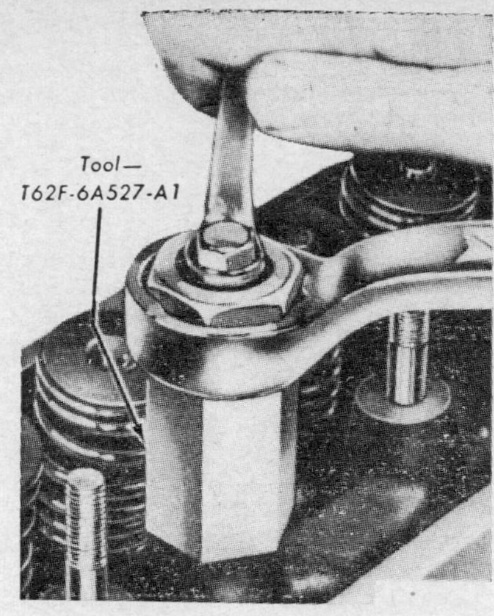

Fig. 3 Rocker arm stud removal. V8-221, 260, 289, 302. Threaded studs on High Performance 8-289

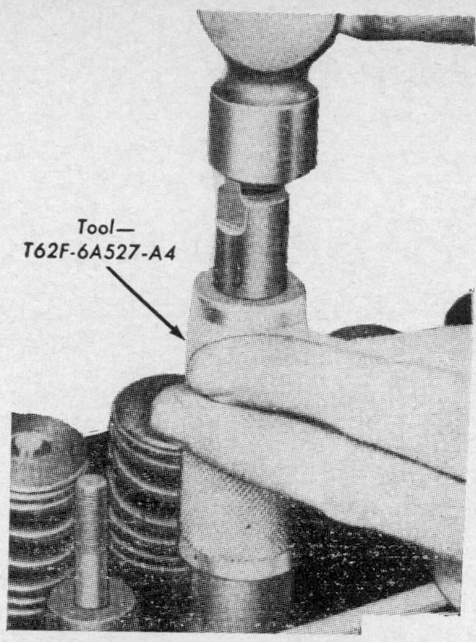

Fig. 4 Rocker arm stud installation. V8-221, 260, 289, 302. Threaded studs on High Performance 8-289

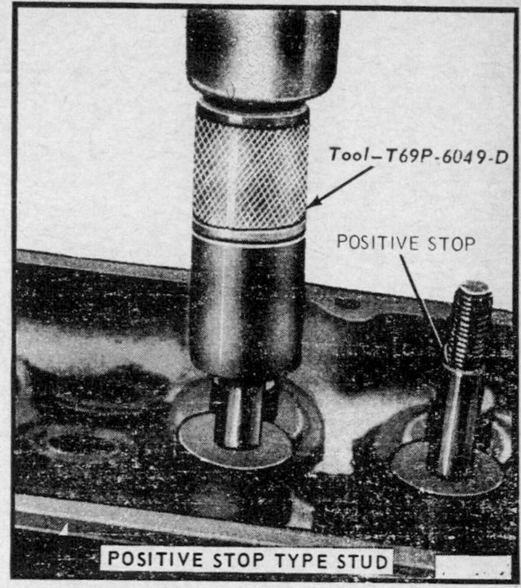

Fig. 4A Positive stud rocker stud installation. V8-351

(Identified by engine date code of 5M20 and higher).

As indicated above, this new design provides for an increased plunger travel to compensate for tolerance stack-up of the various engine components (head gasket thickness, camshaft difference, valve push rods, etc.). With the new design lifter, it is no longer necessary to use the .060" oversize push rods as was necessary on some earlier built engines.

ROCKER ARM STUD

V8-221, 260, 289, 302

If necessary to replace a rocker arm stud, a rocker arm stud kit is available and contains a stud remover, Fig. 3, a stud installer, Fig. 4, and two reamers, one .003" and the other .015".

Rocker arm studs that are broken or have damaged threads may be replaced with standard studs. Loose studs in the head may be replaced with .003" or .015" oversize studs which are available for service. *The standard studs have no identification marks, whereas the .003" oversize stud has a groove around the pilot end of the stud. The .015" oversize stud has a step produced by the increased diameter of the stud approximately 1 5/32" from the pilot end.*

When going from a standard size stud to a .015" oversize stud, always use a .003" reamer before finish reaming with a .015" reamer.

If a stud is broken off flush with the stud boss, use an easy-out to remove the broken stud, following the instructions of the tool manufacturer.

V8-351

A new type positive stop rocker arm stud and nut eliminates the need of adjusting valve lash.

Installation

1. Position the piston of the cylinder being worked on at TDC compression stroke.
2. Locate stud properly with tool T69P-6049D, Fig. 4A. Make sure tool bottoms on the head.
3. Lubricate rocker arm components and place rocker arm and fulcrum on the stud.
4. Thread nut onto the stud until it contacts the shoulder, then tighten nut to 18-22 ft lbs.

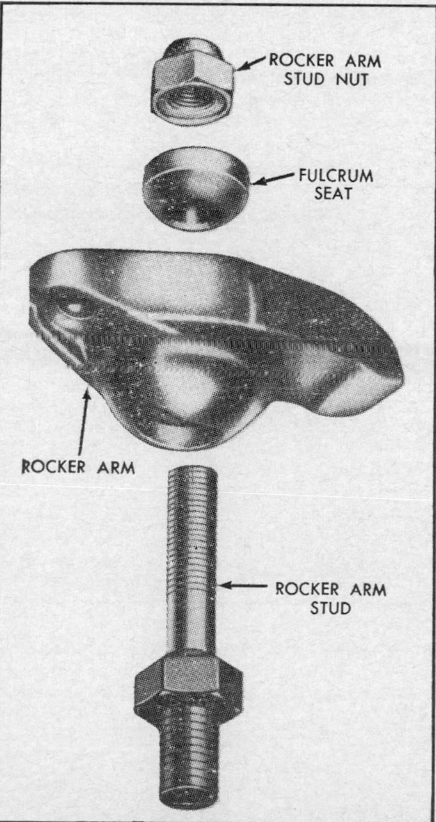

Fig. 5 Valve rocker arm and stud. High Performance V8-289

High Performance V8-289

Rocker arm studs in these engines are of the threaded type, Fig. 5. To remove a stud, remove rocker arm cover. Then remove stud nut, fulcrum seat and rocker arm. Unscrew stud from cylinder head.

Installation

1. Apply water-resistant sealer to stud threads that screw into cylinder head.
2. Install stud and torque to 60-70 ft-lbs.
3. Apply Lubriplate to top of valve stem and at push rod guide in cylinder head.
4. Install rocker arm, fulcrum and stud nut.
5. Be sure to adjust valve lash after engine has warmed up to operating temperature.

VALVE GUIDES

Valve guides consist of holes bored in the cylinder head. For service the guide holes can be reamed oversize to accommodate valves with oversize stems of .003, .015 and .030".

ROCKER ARM SERVICE

6 Cylinder Engines

1. To disassemble, remove pin and spring washer from each end of rocker shaft, Fig. 6.
2. Slide rocker arms, springs and supports off the shaft, being sure to identify location of parts for reassembly.
3. If it is necessary to remove the plugs from the shaft ends, drill or pierce the plug on one end. Then use a steel rod to knock out the plug on the opposite end. Working from the open end, knock out the remaining plug.

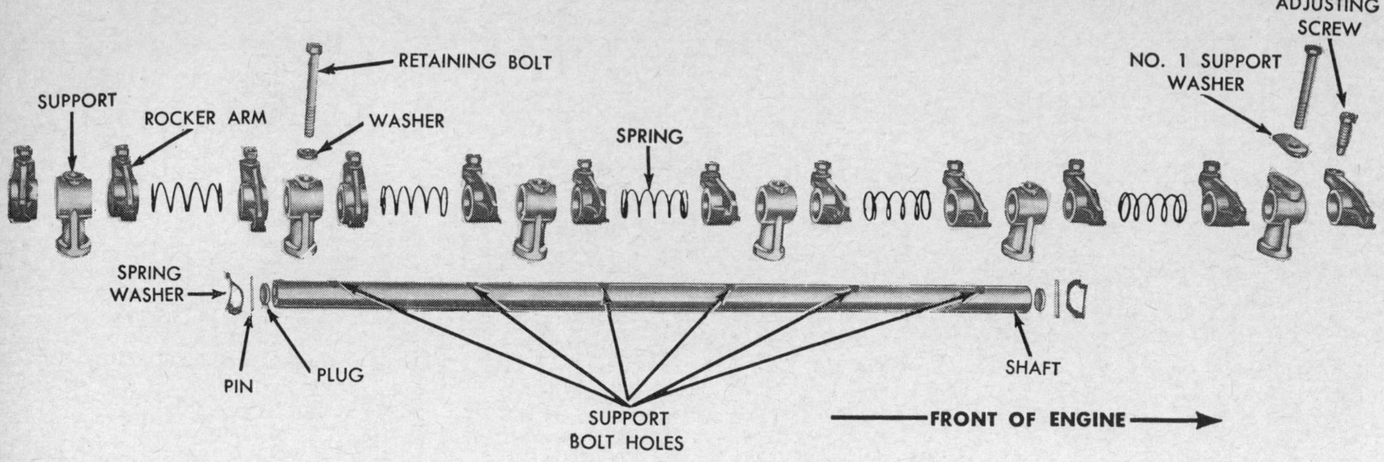

Fig. 6 Rocker arm shaft assembly. Six cylinder engines

Assemble

1. Lubricate all parts with engine oil. Apply Lubriplate to the rocker arm pads.
2. If plugs were removed from shaft ends, use a blunt tool or large diameter pin punch and install a plug (cup side out) in each end of shaft.
3. Install spring washer and pin on one end of shaft.
4. Install rocker arms, supports and springs in order shown in Fig. 6. *Be sure oil holes in shaft are facing downward.*
5. Complete the assembly by installing remaining spring washer and pin.

V8-390, 427

See the Ford-Mercury chapter for a layout of the rocker arm and shaft assembly on these engines.

VALVE LIFTERS, REPLACE

6 Cylinder Engines

When necessary to replace valve lifters, remove cylinder head and related parts as outlined previously. Then, using a magnet rod, Fig. 7, remove and install one lifter at a time to be sure they are placed in their original bores.

When installing, apply Lubriplate to each lifter foot and coat the remainder of lifter with oil before installation.

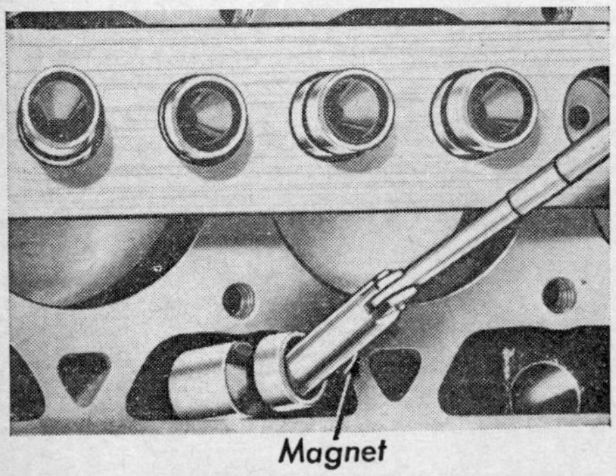

Magnet

Fig. 7 Removing valve lifter with magnetic rod

V8 Engines

1. To remove lifters, remove intake manifold and related parts.
2. Remove rocker arm covers. Loosen rocker arm stud nuts and rotate rocker arms to the side.
3. Remove push rods in sequence so they can be installed in their original bores.
4. Using a magnet rod, Fig. 7, remove the lifters and place them in a numbered rack so they can be installed in their original bores. *If the lifters are stuck in their bores by excessive varnish, etc., it may be necessary to use a plier-type tool to remove them. Rotate the lifter back and forth to loosen it from the gum or varnish.*
5. The internal parts of each lifter are matched sets. Do not intermix parts. Keep the assemblies intact until they are to be cleaned, Fig. 8.

V8-390, 427, 428

1. Remove intake manifold.
2. Remove rocker arms and shafts.
3. Remove push rods, keeping them in a rack in sequence so they may be installed in their original location.
4. Remove valve lifters with a magnet rod and place them in a rack in sequence so they may be installed in original location.
5. Reverse procedure to install.

TIMING CASE COVER

NOTE: If necessary to replace cover oil seal the cover and oil pan must be removed.

6 Cylinder Engines

1. Drain cooling system and crankcase.
2. Remove radiator, fan and pulley.
3. Use puller to remove damper.
4. Remove front cover and gasket.
5. Remove crankshaft oil slinger.
6. Drive seal out of cover with a pin punch and clean out recess in cover.
7. Coat a new seal with grease and drive it in until fully seated in recess. Check seal after installation to be sure spring is properly positioned in seal.
8. Reverse removal procedure to install.

V8 Engines

1967 V8-390 Engine Note

Formerly, the fuel pump was removed and positioned to one side with the tank fuel line attached. If equipped with power steering, disconnect the fuel tank line at the pump and plug the line. Then remove the fuel pump from the engine compartment.

1. To remove cover, drain cooling system and crankcase. Remove air cleaner and disconnect battery ground cable.
2. Remove water hose as necessary.
3. Remove generator support bolt at water pump, and loosen generator mounting bolts.
4. Remove fan, spacer and pulley.
5. Remove power steering drive belt (if equipped). If air conditioned, remove compressor drive belt.
6. Remove crankshaft pulley and adapter.
7. Remove fuel pump and lay it to one side with flexible fuel line attached.

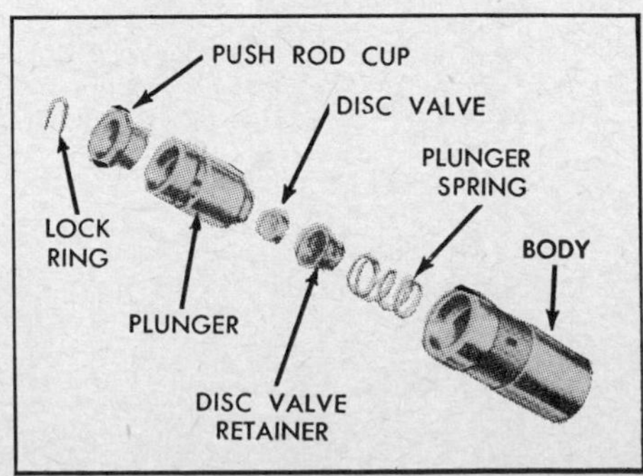

Fig. 8 Hydraulic valve lifter

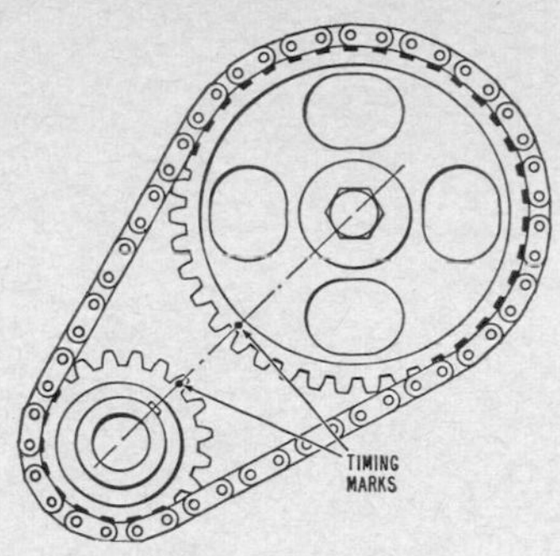

Fig. 9 Timing marks aligned for correct valve timing. Six cylinder engines

8. Remove oil level dipstick tube bracket and oil filler tube bracket.
9. Remove oil pan-to-front cover bolts.
10. Remove cover and water pump as an assembly.
11. Drive out cover seal with a pin punch. Clean out recess in cover.
12. Coat a new seal with grease and drive seal in until it is fully seated in recess. Check seal after installation to be sure spring is properly positioned in seal.
13. Reverse removal procedure to install cover.

TIMING CHAIN

After removing the cover as outlined above, remove the crankshaft front oil slinger. Crank the engine until the timing marks are aligned as shown in Figs. 9 and 10. Remove camshaft sprocket retaining bolt and washer. Slide both sprockets and chain forward and remove them as an assembly.

Reverse the order of the foregoing procedure to install the chain and sprockets, being sure the timing marks are aligned.

CAMSHAFT REPLACE

1967 V8-390 Engine Note

Follow the procedure outlined below for removing the camshaft. In addition, remove the through bolts from the insulator bracket-to-frame bracket on both engine front supports. Use a floor jack to raise the engine just enough for the camshaft to clear the center grille support.

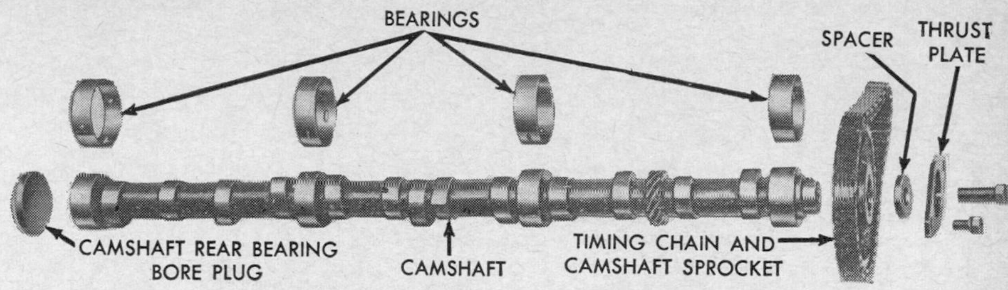

Fig. 11 Camshaft and related parts. Six cylinder engines

To remove camshaft, remove cylinder head and related parts, radiator, oil pan, distributor, timing chain cover and valve lifters.

Remove timing chain and sprockets, camshaft thrust plate, and pull camshaft out of engine. If thrust plate shows signs of wear, install a new one, Figs. 11, 12.

SERVICE NOTE: On Mustang models, in addition to the above, it is necessary to remove the front bumper and grille center support bracket. Also remove the bolts from the left side of upper and lower stone shields. If necessary, loosen the bolts on the right side of the stone shields and raise the stone shields out of the way to remove the camshaft.

PISTON & ROD ASSEMBLE

When installed, piston and rod assembly should have the notch in piston head toward front of engine with oil squirt hole in rod positioned as shown in Figs 13 and 14.

SERVICE NOTE: On V8-289 engine with four-barrel carburetor two types of connecting rod bolts have been used. These bolts must be installed as shown in Fig. 16 to be properly seated and eliminate the possibility of bolt loosening and eventual failure.

PISTONS, PINS & RINGS

Pistons and rings are furnished in standard sizes and oversizes of .020, .030 and .040". On 6-200 and V8-289 engines, .060" oversizes are also available.

Oversize pins are not furnished.

SERVICE BULLETIN

PISTON & PIN REPLACEMENT: When servicing engines using press fit piston pins, the piston and pin must be replaced as an assembly if either does not meet specifications. These components are not serviced separately for the principle reason that excess clearances are usually caused by piston wear rather than pin wear. Elimination of excess clearance by using oversize pins may result in fracture of the connecting rod.

MAIN & ROD BEARINGS

Front Main Bearing Knock

1967 V8-289 Engines: This problem occurs at 800-1600 rpm under load, and is caused by a high degree of spark advance at idle provided by attachment of the distributor vacuum line to full manifold vacuum; also excessive front main bearing clearance.

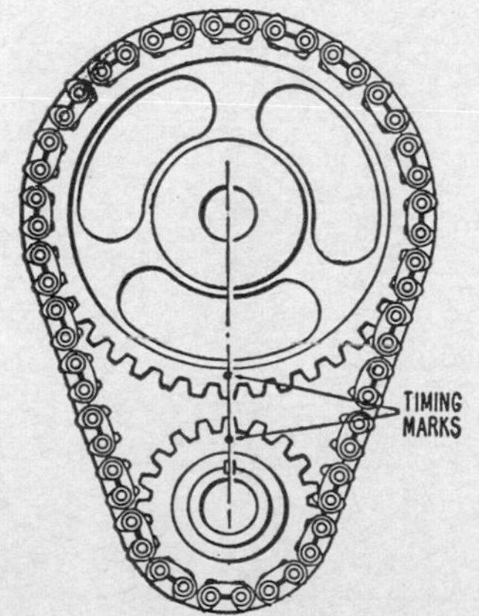

Fig. 10 Timing marks aligned for correct valve timing. V8 engines

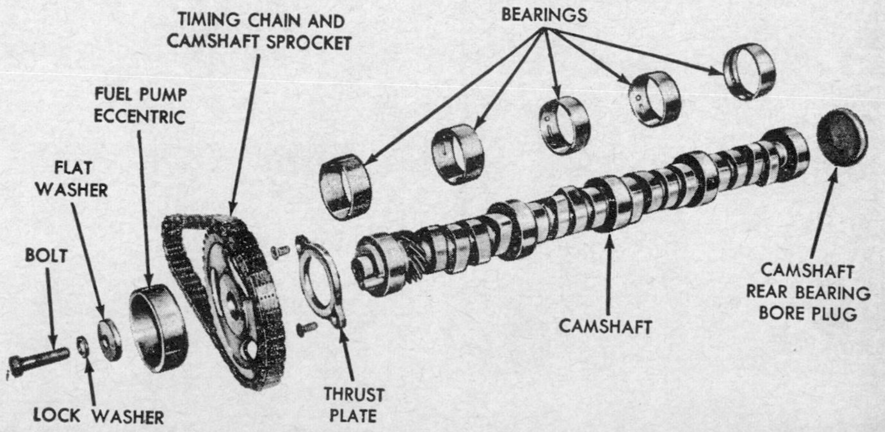

Fig. 12 Camshaft and related parts. V8-260, 289, 302

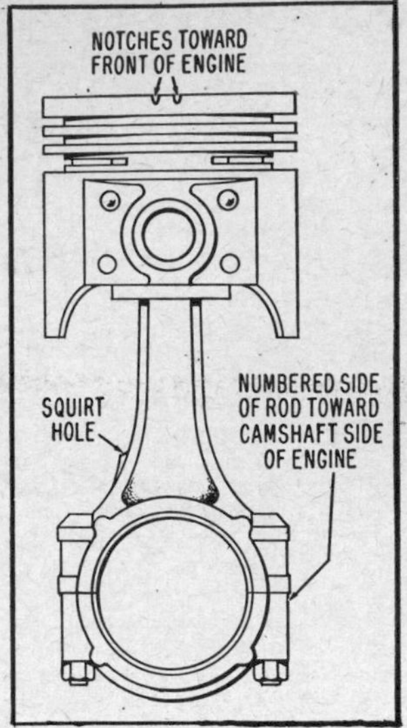

Fig. 13 Piston and rod assembly. Six cylinder engines

To correct the trouble, it is recommended that the distributor vacuum hose be removed from the intake manifold take-off connection and attached to the connection at the base of the carburetor, Fig. 15. Reduce the length of the vacuum hose to provide direct routing to the carburetor connection, free from sharp bends or kinks. The cap removed from the carburetor fitting should be used to close the vacated connection on the manifold.

If the engine knock is not reduced to an acceptable level, then a new front main bearing must be select fitted, utilizing the available .001″ or .002″ undersize bearing in any combination to provide a desired operating clearance of .0005″ to .0015″.

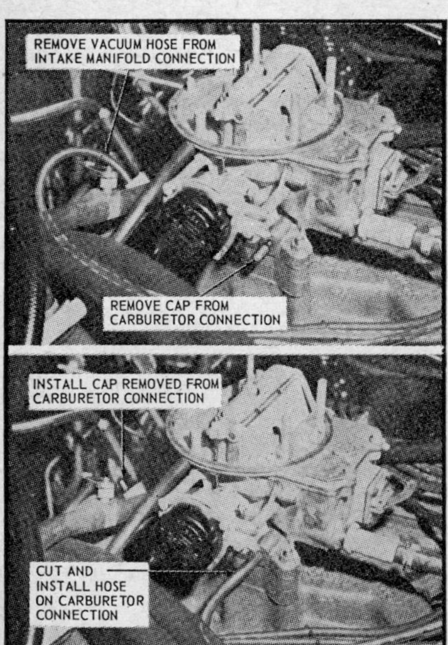

Fig. 15 Procedure for correcting front main bearing knock on 1967 V8-289

Undersize main and rod bearings are furnished in standard and undersizes of .002, .010, .020 and .030″.

SERVICE BULLETIN

UNDERSIZE CRANKSHAFTS: Crankshafts with .010″ undersize rod and/or main journals are now authorized for use in all 1965-67 engines beginning 3-12-65. All assemblies containing undersize crankshafts are identified on the cylinder block date stamp pad with a letter M for .010″ undersize main journals and/or a letter P for undersize crankpin (rod) journals. These crankshafts can appear in both production and service engines, and short block assemblies. Bearing clearances will remain the same as for standard crankshafts. All rod and/or main journals will be ground undersize if any one of the rod and/or main journals are undersize. This avoids mixing of standard and undersize bearings in the same engine. Three possible combinations can exist on crankshafts with undersize bearing journals:

1. All rod journals .010″ undersize with standard main bearing journals.
2. All rod journals standard with .010″ undersize main bearing journals.
3. Both rod and main bearing journals .010″ undersize.

CRANKSHAFT OIL SEAL

A braided oil seal is pressed into the upper and lower grooves behind the rear main bearing. Directly in front of this seal is an oil slinger which deflects the oil back into the oil pan. Should the braided seal require replacement, the installation of the lower half is accomplished as follows:

V8-289, 302 NOTE

The crankshaft rear seal is in contact with the outer surface of the flywheel flange rather than on the main bearing journal. In this design, the front face of the flange is exposed to crankcase splash. Therefore, to eliminate the possibility of oil leaks through the threaded holes in the flange, the flywheel attaching capscrews must be coated with an oil resistant sealer.

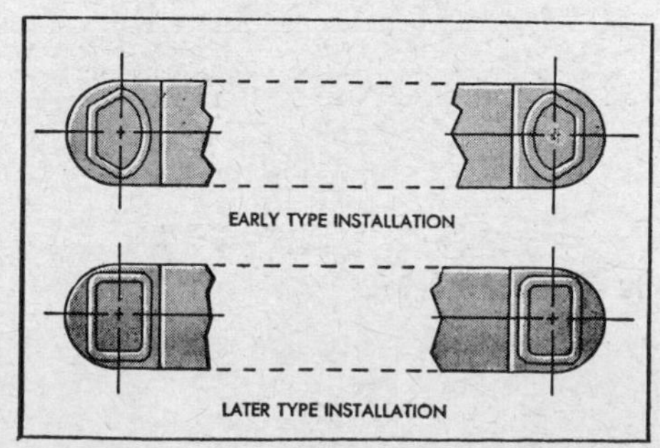

Fig. 16 Connecting rod bolt installation. V8-289 with four barrel carburetor

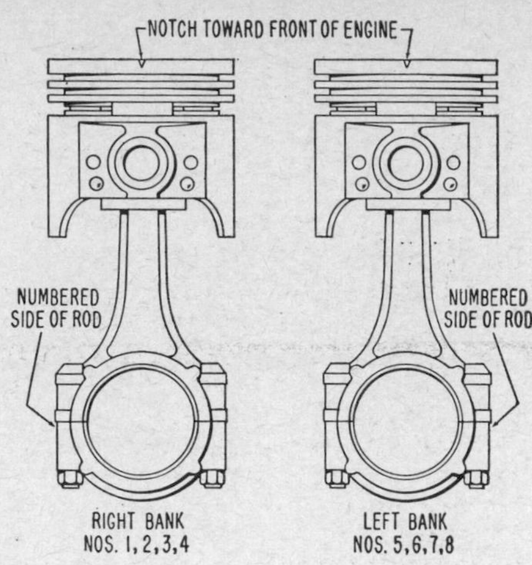

Fig. 14 Piston and rod assembly. V8s

New Rear Crankshaft Seal

1964-68 V8-390: A new rubber split-lip rear crankshaft oil seal is released for service. This seal can be installed without removal of the crankshaft and also eliminates the necessity of seal installation tools.

1. Remove oil pan.
2. Remove rear bearing cap.
3. Loosen remaining bearing caps, allowing crankshaft to drop down about $\frac{1}{32}$″.
4. Remove old seals from both cylinder block and rear main bearing cap. Use a brass rod to drift upper half of seal from cylinder block groove. Rotate crankshaft while drifting to

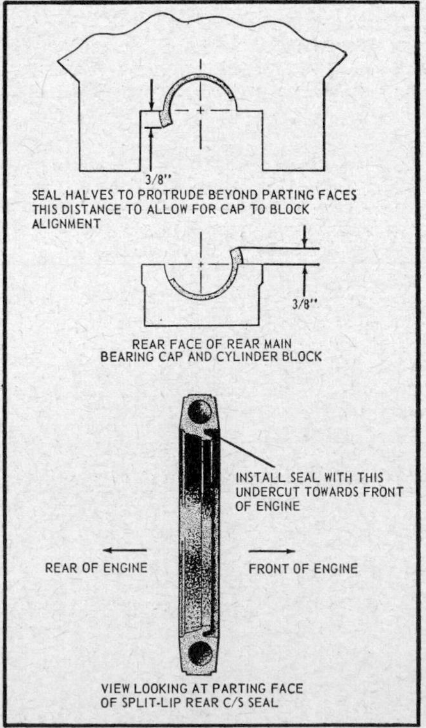

Fig. 17 New split-lip crankshaft rear seal installation on 1964-68 V8-390

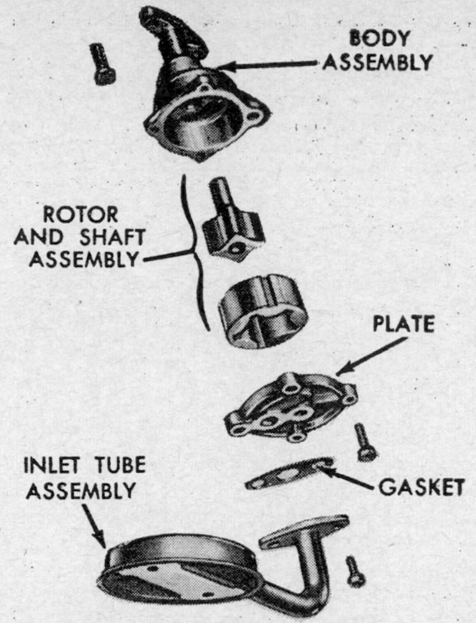

Fig. 18 Oil pump assembly. Six cylinder engines

facilitate removal.

5. Carefully clean seal groove in block with a brush and solvent. Also clean seal groove in bearing cap.
6. Dip seal halves in clean engine oil.
7. Carefully install upper seal half in its groove with undercut side of seal toward front of engine, Fig. 17, by rotating it on shaft journal of crankshaft until approximately ⅜" protrudes below the parting surface. *Be sure no rubber has been shaved from outside diameter of seal by bottom edge of groove.*
8. Retighten main bearing caps and torque to specifications.
9. Install lower seal in main bearing cap with undercut side of seal toward front of engine, and allow seal to protrude about ⅜" above parting surface to mate with upper seal upon cap installation.
10. Apply suitable sealer to parting faces of cap and block. Install cap and torque to specifications.

NOTE: If difficulty is encountered in installing the upper half of the seal in position, lightly lap (sandpaper) the side of the seal opposite the lip side using a medium grit paper. After sanding, the seal must be washed in solvent, then dipped in clean engine oil prior to installation.

OIL PAN REPLACE

1967-69 V8-390, 427, 428

1. If equipped with air conditioning, remove fan shroud from radiator and position it over fan.
2. Disconnect stabilizer bar and pull ends down.

NOTE: To allow for clearance for removal of oil pan, remove engine front support insulator-to-intermediate support bracket nuts. Install a block of wood on a floor jack and position the jack under the front leading edge of the oil pan. Raise the engine about 1¼" and insert a 1" block of wood between insulators and frame crossmember; then remove floor jack.

3. Unfasten and lower oil pan to crossmember.
4. Crank engine to obtain necessary clearance between crankshaft counterweight and rear of oil pan. Remove upper bolt and loosen lower bolt on inlet tube.
5. Position inlet tube out of the way and remove oil pan.
6. Reverse procedure to install.

1967-69 Sixes

1. Remove oil level dipstick and flywheel housing inspection cover.
2. On a Mustang, disconnect stabilizer bar and pull it downward out of the way. Remove one bolt and loosen the other on the No. 2 crossmember and lower it out of the way.
3. Remove oil pan and gasket.
4. Reverse procedure to install.

1967-69 V8-289, 302, 351

1. Drain crankcase and remove oil level dipstick.
2. Lower stabilizer bar. On a Mustang the idler arm will also have to be lowered.
3. Remove oil pan bolts and crank engine as required to obtain clearance for removal of pan.

1966 V8-390

1. Drain crankcase and remove oil level dipstick.
2. Remove oil pan screws and lower pan to crossmember. Position crankshaft so that counterweight will clear pan.
3. Remove oil pump retaining bolts and place pump, inlet tube screen and intermediate drive shaft in oil pan.
4. Remove oil pan and pump.

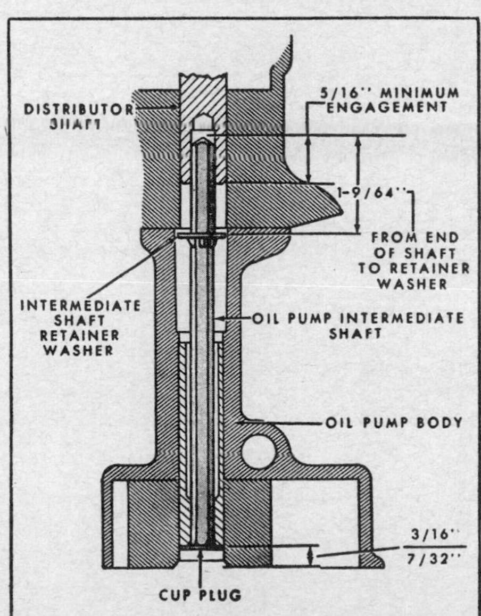

Fig. 20 Oil pump drive assembly. 1963 Six

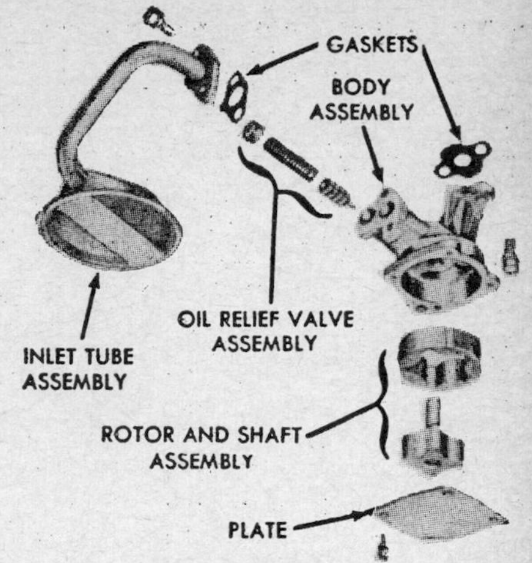

Fig. 19 Oil pump assembly. V8-260, 289, 302

1965 V8s

1. Drain crankcase and remove dipstick.
2. On a Comet or a Falcon, disconnect inlet pipes at exhaust manifolds and lower pipes.
3. On a Fairlane or a Mustang, lower stabilizer bar, disconnect one end of crossmember and loosen other end, then lower crossmember.
4. On a Mustang the idler arm will have to be lowered.
5. Remove oil pan bolts and crank engine as required to obtain clearance and remove pan.

All 1964-66 Sixes

1. Drain engine oil.
2. Remove oil level dipstick and flywheel housing lower cover.
3. On a Mustang, remove stabilizer bar.
4. Unfasten and remove oil pan.

All 1964 V8's

1. Drain engine oil and remove oil level dipstick.
2. Remove starter and dust seal.
3. Remove oil pan bolts and crank engine as required to obtain clearance and remove oil pan.

1963 Sixes Except Comet

1. On car with manual shift transmission, remove clutch retracting spring.
2. Remove crossmember.
3. Unfasten and pull stabilizer bar downward.
4. Remove oil pan retaining bolts and crank engine as required to gain clearance and remove pan.
5. When installing the pan, position the oil pan front seal on the timing case cover. Be sure the tabs on seal are over the oil pan gasket. This also applies to the seal on the rear main bearing cap.

1963 Comet Six

1. To remove, drain oil and remove dipstick.
2. Remove front engine mounting nuts and raise front of engine with a jack

and a wood block placed under the oil pan.
3. Position 2-inch wood blocks between each engine front support and support bracket and lower engine on blocks.
4. Remove stabilizer bar-to-underbody nuts and pull stabilizer bar downward.
5. Remove oil pan retaining bolts and crank engine as required to obtain clearance for removal of pan.
6. Reverse above procedure to install.

1963 V8's

1. Remove oil dipstick.
2. Remove crossmember.
3. Remove oil pan bolts and crank engine as required to gain clearance for pan removal.
4. When installing pan, position oil pan front seal on timing case cover. Be sure tabs on seal are over oil pan gasket. This also applies to the seal on the rear main bearing cap.

OIL PUMP REPLACE

6 Cylinder Engines

1. Remove oil pan and related parts as directed above.
2. Unfasten and remove pump, gasket and intermediate drive shaft.
3. Prime pump by filling either the inlet or outlet port with engine oil. Rotate pump shaft to distribute oil within pump body.
4. Position intermediate drive shaft into distributor socket.
5. Position new gasket on pump housing. Insert intermediate drive shaft into oil pump.
6. Install pump and shaft as an assembly.
7. Install oil pan.

V8-260, 289, 302

1. Remove oil pan as outlined above.
2. Remove pump inlet tube and screen.
3. Remove pump retaining bolts and remove pump, gasket and intermediate shaft.
4. To install, position intermediate drive shaft into distributor socket. With shaft seated in socket, stop on shaft should touch roof of crankcase. Remove shaft and position stop as necessary.
5. With new gasket on pump housing and stop properly positioned, insert intermediate shaft into oil pump. Install pump and shaft as a unit. *Do not force pump into position if it will not seat readily. The drive shaft hex may be misaligned with distributor shaft. To align, rotate shaft into new position.*

V8-390, 427

1. Remove oil pan as outlined above.
2. Remove oil pump screws, oil pump and intermediate shaft.
3. Remove inlet tube and screen from pump and discard gasket.
4. Prime pump by filling either inlet or outlet port with engine oil. Rotate pump shaft to distribute oil within pump body.
5. Position new gasket on pump housing.
6. Insert intermediate drive shaft into oil pump.
7. Install pump and shaft as a unit.
8. Complete installation in reverse order of removal.

OIL PUMP REPAIRS

V8-390, 427, 428

See Ford-Mercury Full Size Car chapter for an illustration and service procedure for the oil pump used on this engine.

V8-260, 289, 302 & All Sixes

Referring to Figs. 18 and 19, disassemble pump. To remove the oil pressure relief valve, insert a self-threading sheet metal screw of the proper diameter into the oil pressure relief valve chamber cap and pull cap out of chamber. Remove spring and plunger.

The inner rotor and shaft and the outer race are serviced as an assembly. One part should not be replaced without replacing the other.

Install the pump cover and tighten to 6-9 ft. lbs. torque.

NOTES 1963 Six

If loss of oil pressure is encountered and the cause is apparently due to failure of the oil pump, the oil pump intermediate shaft should be removed and the driving contact area inspected. If the inspection indicates that the distributor shaft is engaging only a small portion of the intermediate shaft, disassemble the oil pump and check the location of the cup plug in the bottom of the pump drive rotor, Fig. 20. If this cup plug is not driven into the rotor to the specified depth, the intermediate shaft will not be sufficiently inserted in the distributor shaft to assure positive engagement of the hexagonal driving surfaces. In this case, the oil pump rotor and shaft assembly, distributor shaft and intermediate shaft will have to be replaced.

If the cup plug at the bottom of the oil pump rotor is found to be installed as shown in Fig. 20, and the intermediate shaft appears to be rounded at the upper end where it is inserted in the distributor shaft, the distributor shaft should be carefully inspected. If there is any indication that the hexagonal-shaped hole in the distributor shaft has been rounded so that the intermediate shaft does not fit securely, the distributor shaft must be replaced as well as the intermediate shaft.

SERVICE BULLETIN

DELAYED OIL PRESSURE BUILD-UP: Delayed oil pressure build-up accompanied with excessive time (over 5 seconds) for the oil indicator light to go out has been encountered on some 1965 models with V8-289 engine.

This condition is caused by a leaky oil filter anti-drain valve. Correction is accomplished by discarding the oil filter assembly, replacing it with a new one.

Remove the oil filter insert from the cylinder block. Apply a coating of oil resistant sealer (Permatex or equivalent) on the insert-to-block threads and on the block sealing surface. Install the insert and torque to 85 ft-lbs.

WATER PUMP REPLACE

Drain cooling system and disconnect radiator lower hose and heater hose at water pump. Remove drive belt, fan and pulley (also spacer on V8's). Unfasten and remove pump.

FUEL PUMP, REPLACE

1. Remove all gasket material from pump and block gasket surfaces. Apply sealer to both sides of new gasket.
2. Position gasket on pump flange and hold pump in position against its mounting surface. Make sure rocker arm is riding on camshaft eccentric.
3. Press pump tight against its mounting. Install retaining screws and tighten them alternately.
4. Connect fuel lines. Then operate engine and check for leaks.

NOTE: Before installing the pump, it is good practice to crank the engine so that the nose of the camshaft eccentric is out of the way of the fuel pump rocker arm when the pump is installed. In this way there will be the least amount of tension on the rocker arm, thereby easing installation of the pump.

Clutch & Transmission Section

NOTE: 1969 linkage adjustment information is in this section. Repair procedures on both automatic and manual shift transmissions are covered elsewhere in this manual. Procedures for removing automatic transmissions as well as linkage adjustments on 1963-68 models are included in the automatic transmission chapters. See Chapter Index.

CLUTCH PEDAL ADJUST

1966-69

1. Disconnect clutch return spring from release lever.
2. Loosen release lever rod lock nut.
3. Move release lever rearward until release bearing lightly contacts clutch pressure plate release fingers.
4. Adjust adapter length until adapter seats in release lever pocket.
5. Insert the proper feeler gauge (see below) against back face of rod adapter, then tighten lock nut finger tight against feeler gauge.

1968-69 except 8-390 engine	.136″
1968-69 8-390 engine	.178″
1966-67 Sixes	.178″
1966-67 V8s	.128″

6. Remove feeler gauge. Hold lock nut in position and tighten adapter against nut.
7. Install release spring and check for free travel of pedal which is ⅞″ to 1⅛″.

1965

1. Measure total travel of pedal which should be 6¾″ on Fairlane and 6½″ on other models. If total travel is not within specifications, move clutch pedal bumper and bracket up or down until travel is correct. Always check total travel before adjusting free travel.
2. With clutch pedal against its bumper (pedal released) measure overall length of spring which should be 10¼″ on Falcon and Comet, 10″ on Fairlane and no adjustment on Mustang.
3. With engine idling, depress pedal just enough to take up free travel. If the free travel is not within 15/16″ to 1 1/16″ on Fairlane and ⅞″ to 1⅛″ on other models, adjust clutch pedal-to-equalizer rod as required.

1963-64 Comet, Falcon

1. The total travel of the pedal should be 6 to 6½″. If the travel is less than specified, move the clutch pedal bumper and bracket as required.
2. With engine idling, depress pedal just enough to take up free travel. If not within the specified limits of ⅞″ to 1⅛″, loosen the equalizer rod nuts and move the equalizer bar as required, then tighten both nuts.

1963-64 Fairlane & Meteor

Adjust the clutch pedal whenever the clutch does not disengage or engage properly, or when new clutch parts are installed. Both the total travel and free travel should be adjusted. *Improper adjustment of the clutch pedal is one of the most frequent causes of clutch failure and can be a contributing factor in some transmission failures.*

1. Disconnect interlock shift rod at equalizer bar.
2. Measure total travel of pedal. If travel is not within 6⅝″ to 6⅞″, move clutch pedal bumper and bracket up or down as required. *Always check this adjustment before checking free travel because total travel will affect free travel adjustment.*
3. With clutch pedal against bumper (pedal released), measure distance between assist spring eve centers—which should be 10″. If necessary, adjust retainer length as required.
4. With engine running at normal idle speed, depress pedal just enough to take up free travel of pedal and note the amount of this travel. The difference between this measurement and the measurement when the pedal is released is the pedal free travel.

CLUTCH REPLACE

1. Remove transmission as outlined further on.
2. Remove release lever retracting spring. Then slide release bearing and hub off release lever.
3. Remove inspection cover on 6-170 engine and flywheel housing on either engine.
4. Loosen clutch cover attaching bolts a little at a time until spring tension is relieved. *If the same cover and pressure plate is to be installed, mark the cover and flywheel so that the pressure plate can be installed in the same position.*
5. Remove cover, pressure plate and clutch disc.
6. Remove clutch release lever from housing.
7. Reverse removal procedure to install the clutch and adjust the pedal as outlined previously.

THREE SPEED TRANS. REPLACE

1966-69

1. Disconnect drive shaft from rear U-joint flange.
2. Slide front of drive shaft out of extension housing. Plug extension housing opening to prevent lubricant leakage.
3. Pull speedometer cable out of extension housing.
4. Disconnect shift rods from shift levers on transmission.
5. If car has a floor shift, unfasten shift selector from extension housing (3 bolts) and allow assembly to hang by shift lever.
6. Remove two nuts attaching transmission rear support to crossmember.
7. Raise engine enough to remove weight from crossmember. Then remove crossmember.
8. Support transmission with a jack and unfasten transmission from flywheel housing (4 bolts).
9. Move transmission and jack rearward until input shaft is clear of flywheel housing.
10. Reverse procedure to install.

1963-65 Sixes

1. Raise car on hoist and remove drive shaft.
2. Plug opening in extension housing to prevent lubricant from leaking out.
3. Disconnect speedometer cable from extension housing, and disconnect gear shift rods from transmission shift levers.
4. Remove cap screws that attach transmission support spring to extension housing.
5. Place transmission jack under flywheel housing and raise rear of engine slightly.
6. Remove two bolts that attach rear engine support to underbody. Disconnect brake cable from engine rear support.
7. Move jack under transmission. Remove four transmission mounting bolts.
8. Move transmission back just far enough to clear input shaft and remove from under car.
9. Reverse removal procedure to install transmission.

1963-65 V8's

NOTE: On Mustangs, unfasten and slide dust boot and ring upward on shift lever. Unfasten shift lever from control mechanism, being careful not to lose the two trunnions and springs. Then on all models proceed as follows:

1. Raise car on hoist and drain lubricant from transmission.
2. Disconnect drive shaft from rear U-joint flange.
3. Slide front of drive shaft out of extension housing and off output shaft.
4. Unfasten and remove speedometer cable form extension housing.

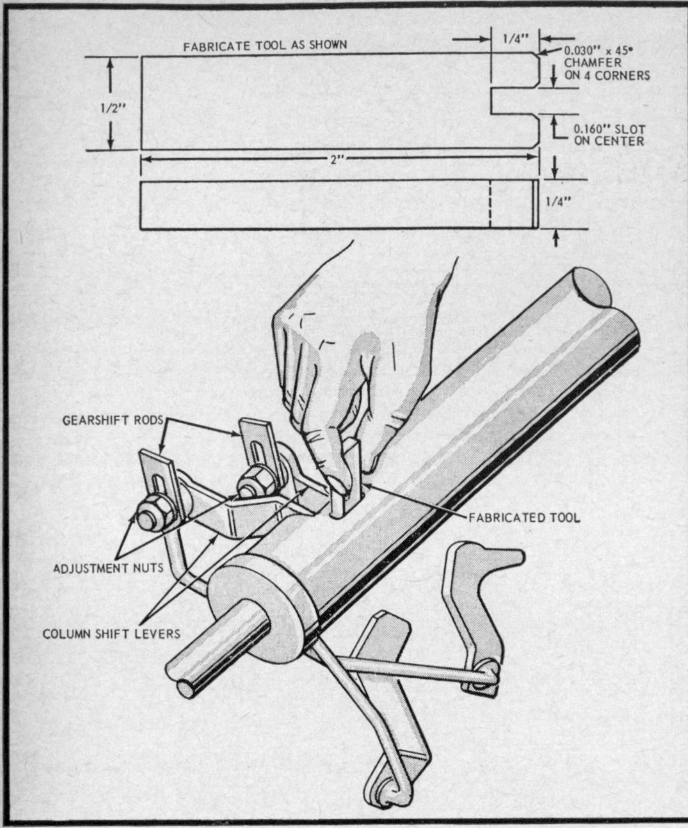

Fig. 1 Three speed shift linkage. 1965-67 Comet and Falcon and 1966-67 Fairlane, Montego

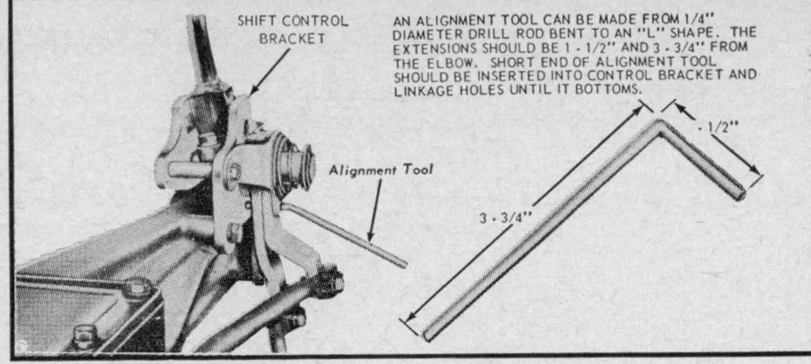

Fig. 2 Gearshift linkage. 1965-68 Cougar and Mustang three speed unit

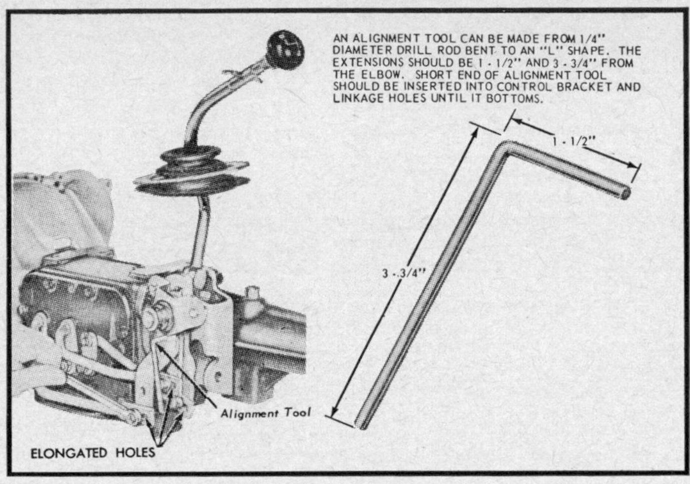

Fig. 3 Dagenham four speed shift linkage. 1965-66 Mustang

5. Disconnect shift rods from transmission shift levers.
6. Disconnect parking brake cable at equalizer.
7. Remove two cap screws that secure extension housing to support spring.
8. Raise rear of engine enough to remove weight from frame crossmember. Then remove engine rear support attaching bolts and remove support and spring as an assembly.
9. Support transmission with a jack and remove four transmission attaching bolts.
10. Move transmission rearward until input shaft is clear of flywheel housing, then remove from under car.
11. Reverse removal procedure to install the transmission.

FOUR SPEED TRANS. REPLACE

1966 Dagenham Unit

1. Remove starting motor.
2. Remove drive shaft.
3. Remove back-up light switch from shift linkage control bracket.
4. Remove clutch release rod. Remove linkage return spring from clutch release lever.
5. Disconnect parking brake front cable from equalizer bar, and speedometer cable from extension housing.
6. Loosen shift linkage adjustment nuts.
7. Disconnect shift rods from shift levers.
8. Unfasten shift linkage control bracket from extension housing and allow assembly to hang by shift lever.
9. Support engine with a transmission jack and remove extension housing-to-engine rear support nuts.
10. Raise rear of engine and remove transmission crossmember from underbody.
11. Support transmission and unfasten flywheel housing from engine and engine rear plate.
12. Remove transmission from vehicle.
13. Reverse procedure to install.

1966-69 Ford Design

1. Remove drive shaft.
2. Disconnect speedometer cable from extension housing.
3. Detach shift rods from shift levers.
4. Unfasten shift linkage control bracket from extension housing and allow assembly to hang by shift lever.
5. Support engine with a jack and remove transmission rear support crossmember.
6. Support transmission with a jack and unfasten it from flywheel housing.
7. Remove transmission from vehicle.
8. Reverse procedure to install.

1963-65 Six

1. From inside car, remove retaining ring and boot from floor pan.
2. Raise boot and ring to gain access to two cap screws that attach shift lever to shift linkage. Remove shift lever.
3. Raise car. Remove starting motor.
4. Drain transmission lubricant.
5. Disconnect drive shaft at pinion flange and tape U-joint bearing races in place if joint does not have a strap spot welded to it. Pull drive shaft off transmission.
6. Remove back-up lamp switch (if equipped) from shift linkage bracket.
7. Remove clip from equalizer bar at clutch release rod and remove rod. Remove linkage return spring from release lever.
8. Disconnect parking brake front cable from equalizer bar.
9. Disconnect speedometer cable from extension housing.
10. Support engine with a jack and remove two bolts that attach rear mount spring to extension housing.
11. Raise rear of engine and remove transmission support cross member from underbody.
12. Support transmission and remove bolts that secure flywheel housing to engine and cover to housing. Remove cover.
13. Move transmission and clutch housing toward rear until transmission input shaft splines are clear of clutch. Then remove transmission from car.
14. Reverse removal procedure to install transmission.

1963-65 V8's

1. From inside car, remove shift lever

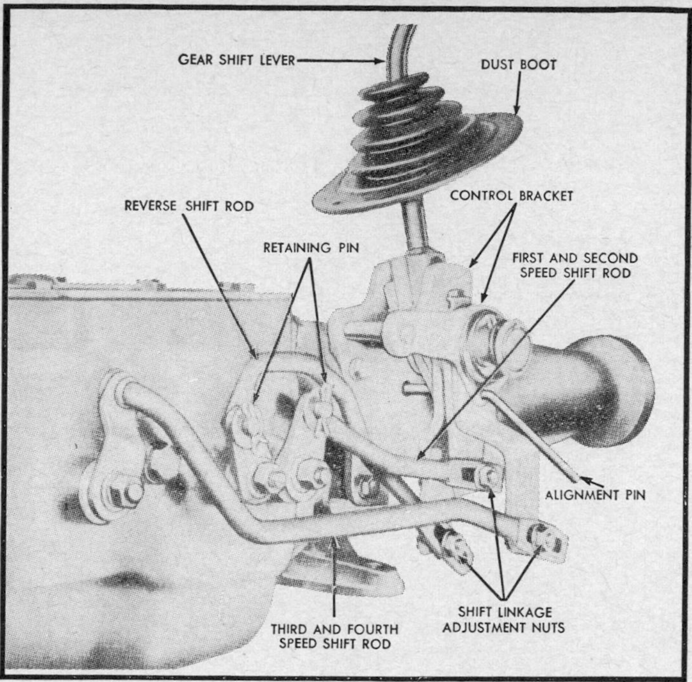

Fig. 4 Ford four speed shift linkage. 1965-68 V8s

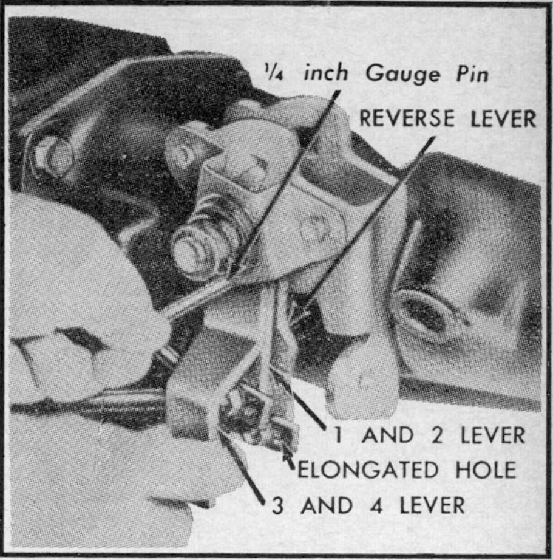

Fig. 5 Warner four speed shift linkage. 1965-66 V8s

boot retainer. Working under boot, unfasten and remove shift lever. Remaining shift linkage may be left on transmission during removal.
2. Remove drive shaft.
3. Disconnect speedometer cable.
4. Disconnect parking brake cable at equalizer bar and support engine with a transmission jack.
5. Remove extension housing-to-engine rear support spring attaching bolts.
6. Raise rear of engine. Then remove cross member and engine rear support as a unit.
7. Support transmission on a jack and remove transmission mounting bolts.
8. Move transmission and jack rearward until transmission input shaft is clear of flywheel. If necessary, lower engine enough to gain clearance for transmission removal.
9. Reverse removal procedure to install transmission.

GEARSHIFT LINKAGE

NOTE: If the transmission shifts hard or will not engage, the gearshift levers may need adjusting at the cross-over. Move the shift lever through all positions to see that the cross-over operation is smooth. If not, adjust as follows:

1968-69 Falcon, Fairlane, Montego

1. Place shift lever in neutral.
2. Loosen two gearshift rod adjustment nuts.
3. See that transmission shift levers are in neutral position.
4. Insert a $\frac{3}{16}$" diameter rod through holes in both levers and both holes in lower casting. It may be necessary to align levers to insert tool.
5. Tighten shift rod adjustment nuts.
6. Remove alignment tool and check operation of shift levers.

1965 Fairlane 3 Speed Unit

1. Place gearshift lever in neutral.
2. Loosen two shift rod adjusting nuts.
3. Insert a $\frac{3}{16}$" diameter rod through low-reverse shift lever and 2-3 shift lever. If necessary, align levers to insert aligning rod.
4. Tighten two shift rod adjusting nuts.
5. Remove aligning rod.
6. Start engine and shift selector lever to each position to make sure it operates freely.

1965-67 Comet & Falcon, 1966-67 Fairlane, 3 Speed

1. Place shift lever in neutral.
2. Loosen two shift rod adjusting nuts.
3. Insert the fabricated tool shown in Fig. 1 in slot provided in lower steering column. If necessary, align levers to insert tool.
4. Tighten shift rod adjusting nuts.
5. Remove tool from slot in column.
6. Start engine and shift selector lever to each position to make sure it operates freely.

1965-68 Cougar & Mustang 3 Speed Unit

1. Loosen three shift linkage adjusting nuts. Install a ¼" diameter align ment pin through control bracket and levers, Fig. 2.
2. Tighten three linkage adjusting nuts and remove alignment pin.
3. Check gearshift lever for smooth crossover.

1963-64 Six Three Speed

1. With selector lever in neutral, disconnect and pull connecting rod adjusting sleeves out of levers.
2. Loosen lock nut on each sleeve and then slide sleeve up or down on rods until a smooth cross-over operation results when sleeves are attached to levers. Tighten both lock nuts.
3. Position sleeves in shift levers and install washers and cotter pins.

1963-64 V8 Three Speed Units

1. With gearshift lever in neutral, loosen two shift rod adjusting nuts.
2. Insert a $\frac{3}{16}$" alignment pin through both the low-reverse and 2-3 shift levers. It may be necessary to align levers to insert pin.
3. Tighten rod adjusting nuts and remove aligning pin.
4. Start engine and check shift in all speeds for free operation.

1965-66 4 Speed Mustang Six

1. Place shift lever in neutral and raise car on a hoist.
2. Insert the tool shown in Fig. 3 into alignment hole as shown. If rod will not enter, check for bellied or bent rods. If shift rods are the correct shape, check for loose lever lock nuts at rod ends.
3. Reset linkage by loosening three rod retaining lock nuts and moving levers until alignment tool will enter alignment holes.

NOTE: Make sure transmission shift levers are in neutral and reverse shift lever is in neutral detent. If there is any doubt about location of neutral position, disconnect shift rods at lock nut and rotate each forward speed shift lever through its three positions until center (neutral) detent is positively located. Move reverse shift lever forward until positive engagement of detent is felt.

4. Install shift rods and tighten lock nuts to 15-20 ft-lbs.
5. Remove aligning tool and check operation in all positions.

1963-68 V8s 4 Speed

1. Referring to Figs. 4 and 5, loosen three shift linkage adjusting nuts. Install a ¼" diameter aligning pin through control bracket and levers as shown.

NOTE: An alignment tool can be made from ¼" rod bent to an "L" shape. The extensions should be 1½" and 3¾" from the elbow. Short end of alignment tool should be inserted into control bracket and linkage holes until it bottoms.

2. Tighten three linkage adjusting nuts, remove the aligning tool and check operation of linkage in all positions.

1969 AUTO. TRANS. LINKAGE ADJUST

Although the linkages are changed on most models, the adjustment procedures are the same as for the 1968 models described in the front section of this manual.

Rear Axle, Propeller Shaft & Brakes

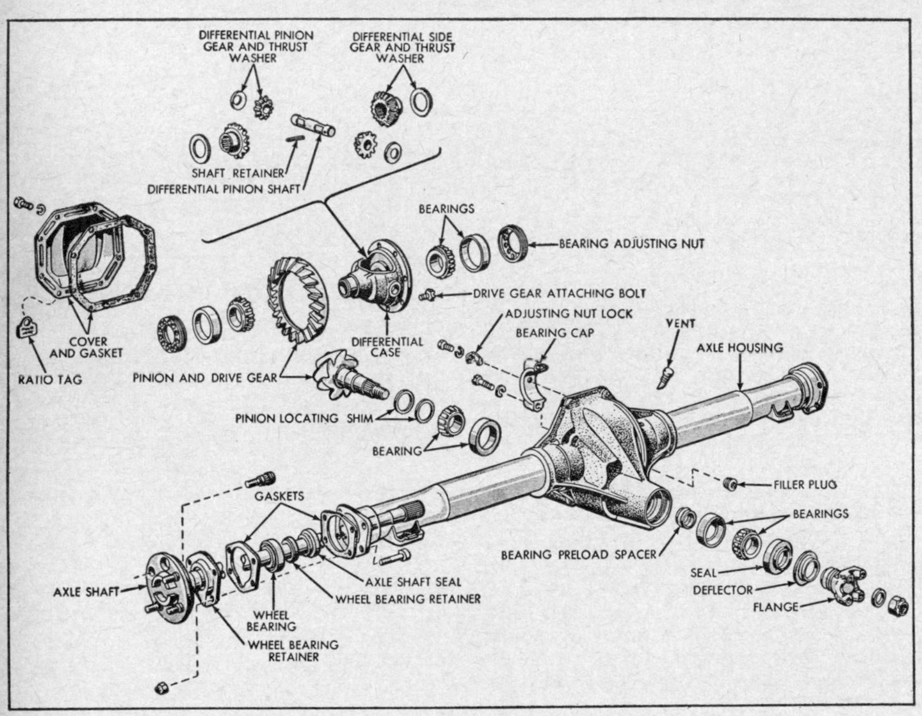

Fig. 1 Disassembled view of integral carrier type rear axle assembly

REAR AXLES

Figs. 1 and 2 illustrate the rear axle assemblies used on these cars. When necessary to overhaul either of these units, refer to the *Rear Axle Specifications* table in this chapter.

Integral Carrier Type, Fig. 1

In these axles, Fig. 1, the rear axle housing and differential carrier are cast into an integral assembly. The drive pinion assembly is mounted on two opposed tapered roller bearings. Spacers are used and are located between the front and rear bearing cones. Ring gear and pinion tooth contact is adjusted by shims between the rear bearing cone and pinion gear.

The differential carrier assembly is mounted on two opposed tapered roller bearings. The bearings are retained in the housing by removable caps. Differential bearing preload and drive gear backlash is adjusted by threaded ring nuts or sleeves located behind each differential bearing cup.

All service operations on the differential case assembly and the drive pinion assembly can be performed with the housing in the vehicle. The axle shafts and bearings can be pulled out of the housing ends. The differential assembly and then the drive pinion can be removed from the housing after the cover is removed from the rear face of the carrier casting.

Service Bulletin

All Ford Built Rear Axles: Recent manufacturing changes have eliminated the need for marking rear axle drive pinions for individual variations from nominal shim thicknesses. In the past, these pinion markings, with the aid of a shim selection table, were used as a guide to select correct shim thicknesses when a gear set or carrier assembly replacement was performed.

With the elimination of pinion markings, use of the shim selection table is no longer possible and the methods outlined below must be used.

1. Measure the thickness of the original pinion depth shim removed from the axle. Use the same thickness upon installation of the replacement carrier or drive pinion. If any futher shim change is necessary, it will be indicated in the tooth pattern check.
2. If the original shim is lost, substitute a nominal shim for the original and use the tooth pattern check to determine if further shim changes are required.

Removable Carrier Type

In these axles, Fig. 2, the drive pinion is straddle-mounted by two opposed tapered roller bearings which support the pinion shaft in front of the drive pinion gear, and a straight roller bearing that supports the pinion shaft at the rear of the pinion gear. The drive pinion is assembled in a pinion retainer that is bolted to the differential carrier. The tapered roller bearings are preloaded by a collapsible spacer between the bearings. The pinion is positioned by a shim or shims located between the drive pinion retainer and the differential carrier.

The differential is supported in the carrier by two tapered roller side bearings. These bearings are preloaded by two threaded ring nuts or sleeves between the bearings and the pedestals. The differential assembly is positioned for proper ring gear and pinion backlash by varying the adjustment of these ring nuts. The differential case houses two side gears in mesh with two pinions mounted on a pinion shaft which held in place by a pin. The side gears and pinions are backed by thrust washers.

The axle shafts are of unequal length, the left shaft being shorter than the right. The axle shafts are mounted in sealed ball bearings which are pressed on the shafts.

Axle Shaft, Replace

1. Remove wheel assembly.
2. Remove brake drum from flange.

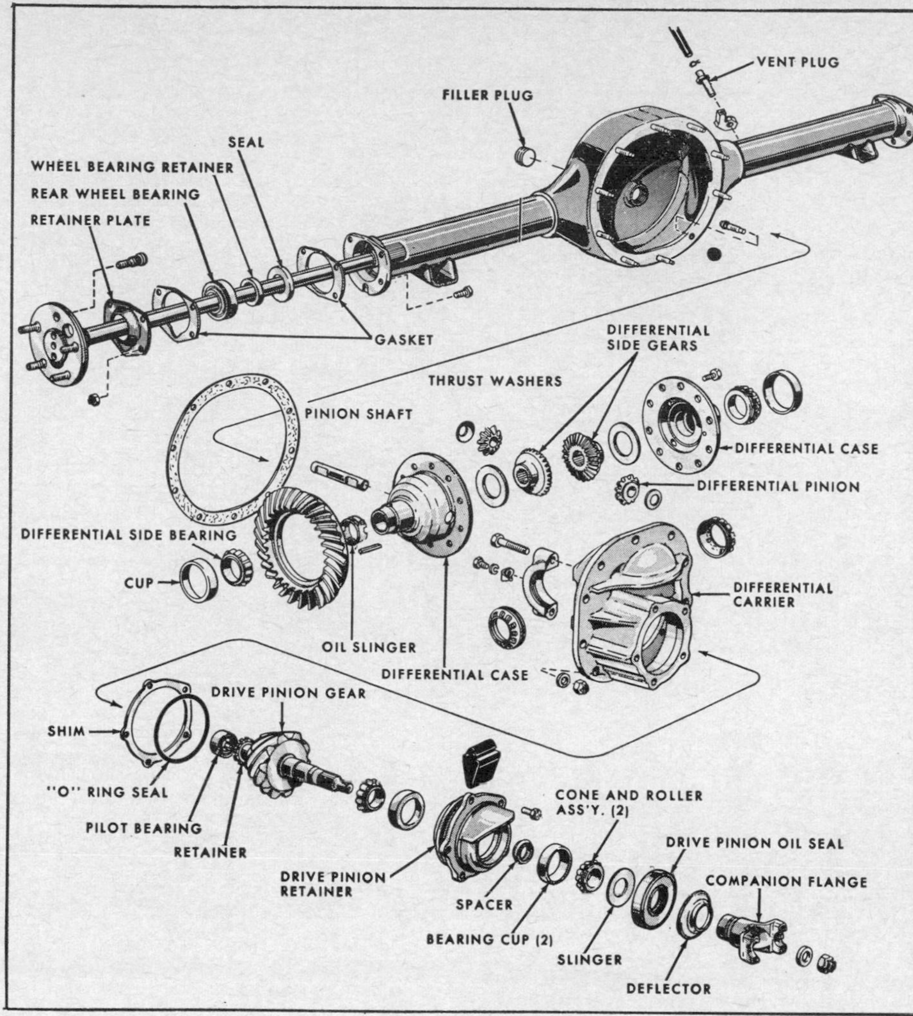

Fig. 2 Rear axle assembly with removable carrier

Fig. 3 Removing nuts from wheel bearing retainer

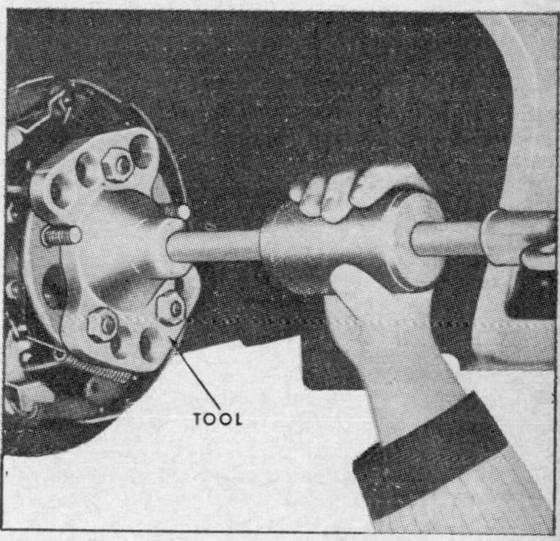

Fig. 4 Removing axle shaft with slide hammer-type puller

3. Working through hole provided in axle shaft flange, Fig. 3, remove nuts that secure wheel bearing retainer.
4. Pull axle shaft out of housing. If bearing is a tight fit in axle housing use a slide hammer-type puller, Fig. 4. *Brake carrier plate must not be dislodged. Install one nut to hold the plate in place after axle shaft is removed.*
5. If the axle shaft bearing is to be replaced, loosen the inner retainer by nicking it deeply with a chisel in several places, Fig. 5. The bearing will then slide off easily.
6. Press bearing from axle shaft.
7. Inspect machined surface of axle shaft and housing for rough spots that would affect sealing action of the oil seal. Carefully remove any burrs or rough spots.
8. Press new bearing on shaft until it seats firmly against shoulder on shaft.
9. Press inner bearing retainer on shaft until it seats firmly against bearing.
10. If oil seal is to be replaced, use a hook-type tool to pull it out of housing, Fig. 6. Wipe a small amount of oil resistant sealer on outer edge of seal before it is installed, Fig. 7.

Installation

1. Place a new gasket on each side of brake carrier plate and slide axle shaft into housing. Start the splines into the differential side gear and push the shaft in until bearing bottoms in housing.
2. Install retainer and tighten nuts to 30-40 ft. lbs.
3. Install brake drum and wheel.

PROPELLER SHAFT

Remove & Replace

1. Disconnect rear U-joint from drive pinion flange.
2. Pull drive shaft toward rear of car until front U-joint yoke clears transmission extension housing and output shaft.
3. Install a suitable tool, such as a seal driver, in seal to prevent lube from leaking from transmission.
4. Before installing, check U-joints for freedom of movement. If a bind has resulted from misalignment after overhauling the U-joints, tap the ears of the drive shaft sharply to relieve the bind.

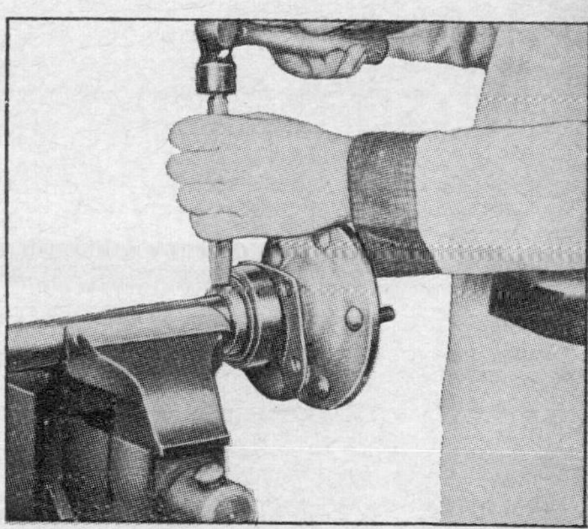

Fig. 5 Splitting bearing inner retainer for bearing removal

5. If rubber seal installed on end of transmission extension housing is damaged, install a new seal.
6. On a manual shift transmission, lubricate yoke spline with conventional transmission grease. On an automatic transmission, lubricate yoke spline with special spline grease. *This spline is sealed so that transmission fluid does not "wash" away spline lubricant.*

7. Install yoke on transmission output shaft.
8. Install U-bolts and nuts which attach U-joint to pinion flange. Tighten U-bolts evenly to prevent binding U-joint bearings.

BRAKE ADJUSTMENTS

SERVICE BULLETIN

REVISED BRAKE ADJUSTMENT PROCEDURE: Mid-year 1965 production (and later) models use a new front and rear brake backing plate which omits the adjusting slot for manual brake adjustment. The backing plates have a partially stamped knock-out slot for use ONLY when the brake drums cannot be removed in a normal manner. The open slot is then covered with a rubber plug as used in the past to prevent contamination of the brakes.

When servicing a vehicle requiring a brake adjustment, the metal knock-out plugs should NOT be removed. Rather the drums should be removed and brakes inspected for a malfunction.

Although the brakes are self-adjusting, an initial adjustment will be necessary after a brake repair, such as relining or replacement. The initial adjustment can be obtained by the new procedure which follows:

1. Use the brake shoe adjustment gauge shown in Fig. 8 to obtain the drum inside diameter as shown. Tighten the adjusting knob on the gauge to hold this setting.
2. Place the opposite side of the gauge over the brake shoes and adjust the shoes by turning the adjuster screw until the gauge just slides over the linings. Rotate the gauge around the lining surface to assure proper lining diameter adjustment and clearance.
3. Install brake drum and wheel. Final adjustment is accomplished by making several firm reverse stops, using the brake pedal.

Self-Adjusting Brakes

These brakes, Figs. 9 and 10, have self-adjusting shoe mechanisms that assure correct lining-to-drum clearances at all times. The automatic adjusters operate only when the brakes are applied as the car is moving rearward or when the car comes to an uphill stop.

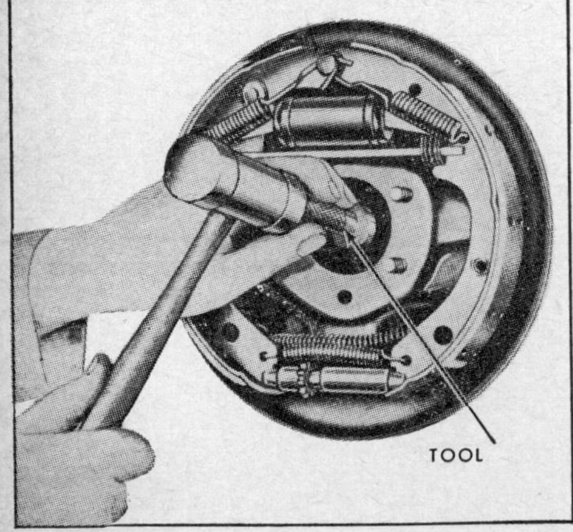

Fig. 7 Using special driver to install oil seal

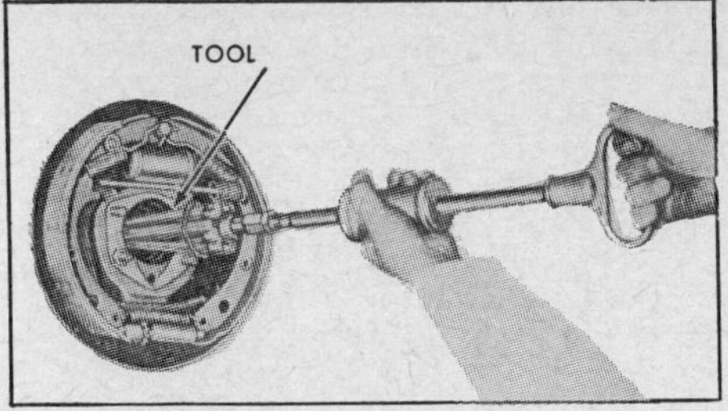

Fig. 6 Using hook-type tool to remove oil seal

Although the brakes are self-adjusting, an initial adjustment is necessary after the brake shoes have been relined or replaced, or when the length of the star wheel adjuster has been changed during some other service operation.

Frequent usage of an automatic transmission forward range to halt reverse vehicle motion may prevent the automatic adjusters from functioning, thereby inducing low pedal heights. Should low pedal heights be encountered, it is recommended that numerous forward and reverse stops be made until satisfactory pedal height is obtained.

NOTE

If a low pedal condition cannot be corrected by making numerous reverse stops (provided the hydraulic system is free of air) it indicates that the self-adjusting mechanism is not functioning. Therefore, it will be necessary to remove the brake drum, clean, free up and lubricate the adjusting mechanism. Then adjust the brake, being sure the parking brake is fully released.

Adjustment

1. Remove adjusting hole cover from the brake backing plate and, from the backing plate side, turn the adjusting screw upward with a screwdriver or other suitable tool to expand the shoes until a slight drag is felt when the drum is rotated.
2. Remove the drum.
3. While holding the adjusting lever out of engagement with the adjusting screw, Fig. 11, back off the adjusting screw about ¾ turn with the fingers. *NOTE—If finger movement will not turn the screw, free it up. If this is not done, the adjusting lever will not turn during subsequent vehicle operation. Lubricate the screw with oil and coat with wheel bearing grease. Any other adjustment procedure may cause damage to the adjusting screw with consequent self-adjuster problems.*
4. Install wheel and drum, and adjusting hole cover. Adjust brakes on remaining wheels in the same manner.
5. If pedal height is not satisfactory, drive the vehicle and make sufficient reverse stops until proper pedal height is obtained.

SERVICE BULLETIN

SEALS FRONT BRAKES: If water passes between the backing plate and spindle flange on a 1963 model, the water can affect the front wheel brakes and wheel bearings. The water may enter where the backing plate does not fully contact the mating flange on the spindle.

This can be corrected by installing a gasket, which acts as a seal, between the spindle flange and backing plate. A gasket is available for this purpose.

PARKING BRAKE, ADJUST

1968 Cougar & Mustang

1. Fully release parking brake.
2. Pull brake handle out to third notch from fully released position.
3. Raise vehicle and remove wheel cover.
4. Turn locking adjustment nut forward against cable guide on equalizer until there is 100 ft-lbs breakaway torque at rear wheel when turning rear wheels in direction of forward rotation with a torque wrench. This torque measurement must be made relative to the centerline of the wheel.
5. Release parking brake and make sure brake shoes return to fully released position and no drag is felt when turning rear wheels.

1968 Falcon, Fairlane, Montego; 1969 All

1. Fully release parking brake pedal.
2. Push parking brake pedal to first notch from fully released position.
3. Raise vehicle. Loosen equalizer lock nut and turn nut forward against cable guide on equalizer until there is 75-100 pounds tension on left rear cable or 100 ft-lbs breakaway torque when turning rear wheels in the direction of forward rotation with a torque wrench. The torque measure-

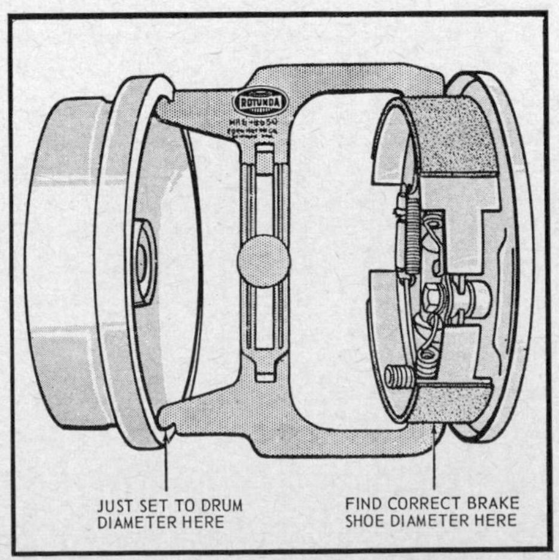

Fig. 8 Revised brake adjustment

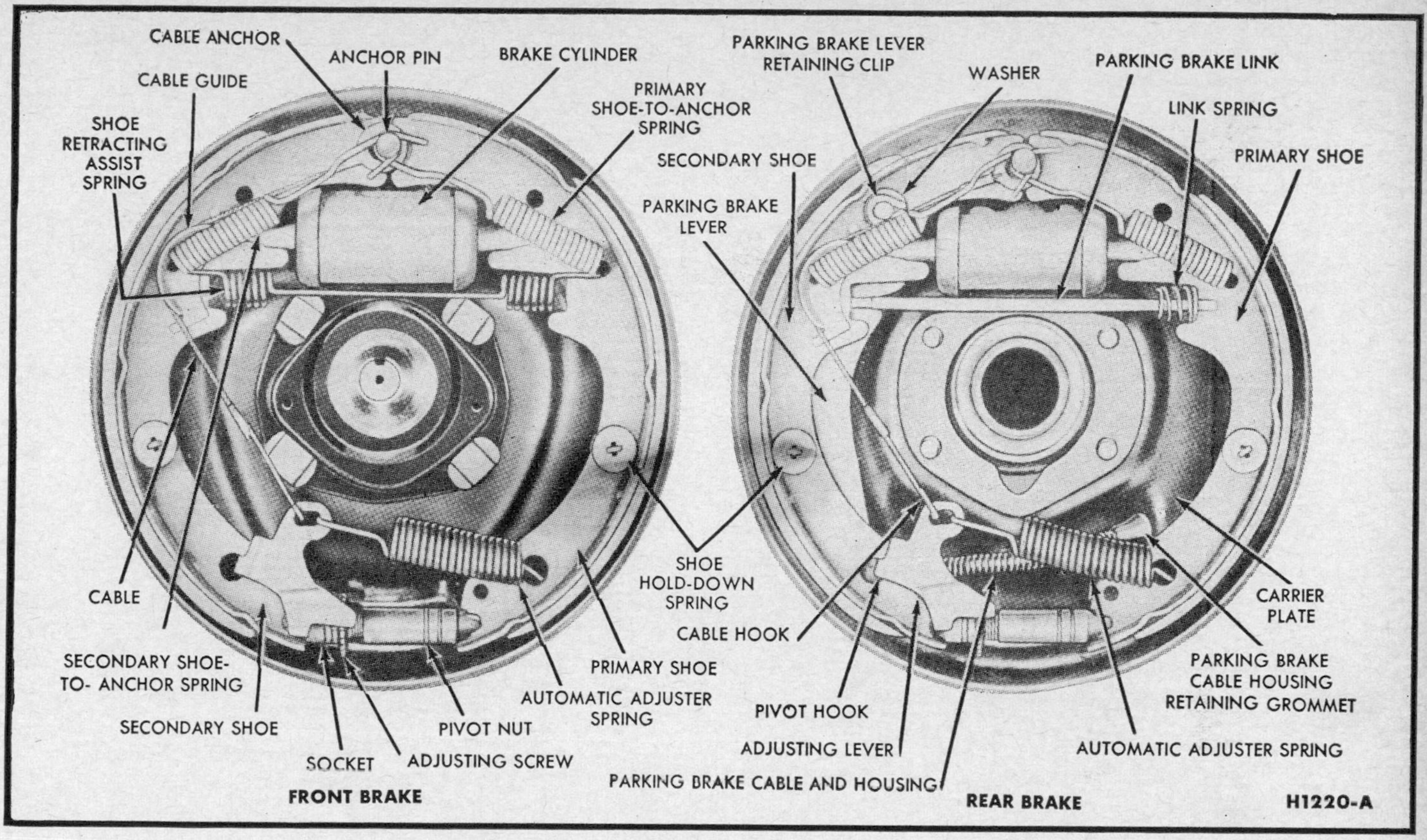

CABLE ANCHOR
ANCHOR PIN
CABLE GUIDE
BRAKE CYLINDER
PRIMARY SHOE-TO-ANCHOR SPRING
SHOE RETRACTING ASSIST SPRING
PARKING BRAKE LEVER RETAINING CLIP
WASHER
PARKING BRAKE LINK
LINK SPRING
PRIMARY SHOE
SECONDARY SHOE
PARKING BRAKE LEVER
CABLE
SHOE HOLD-DOWN SPRING
CARRIER PLATE
CABLE HOOK
SECONDARY SHOE-TO- ANCHOR SPRING
PRIMARY SHOE
PARKING BRAKE CABLE HOUSING RETAINING GROMMET
AUTOMATIC ADJUSTER SPRING
PIVOT HOOK
SECONDARY SHOE
PIVOT NUT
ADJUSTING LEVER
AUTOMATIC ADJUSTER SPRING
SOCKET
ADJUSTING SCREW
PARKING BRAKE CABLE AND HOUSING
FRONT BRAKE
REAR BRAKE
H1220-A

Fig. 9 Right front and rear brake mechanism. 1963-69 V8s

SPRING WASHER
PARKING BRAKE LEVER RETAINING CLIP
PARKING BRAKE LINK
LINK SPRING
SECONDARY SPRING
ANCHOR PIN
WHEEL CYLINDER
PRIMARY SPRING
SECONDARY SHOE
PRIMARY SHOE
CABLE GUIDE
CABLE
SHOE HOLD-DOWN SPRING
BACKING PLATE
PARKING BRAKE LEVER
ADJUSTER SPRING
ADJUSTING LEVER
SOCKET
PIVOT NUT
PARKING BRAKE CABLE AND HOUSING
ADJUSTING SCREW
REAR BRAKE
FRONT BRAKE

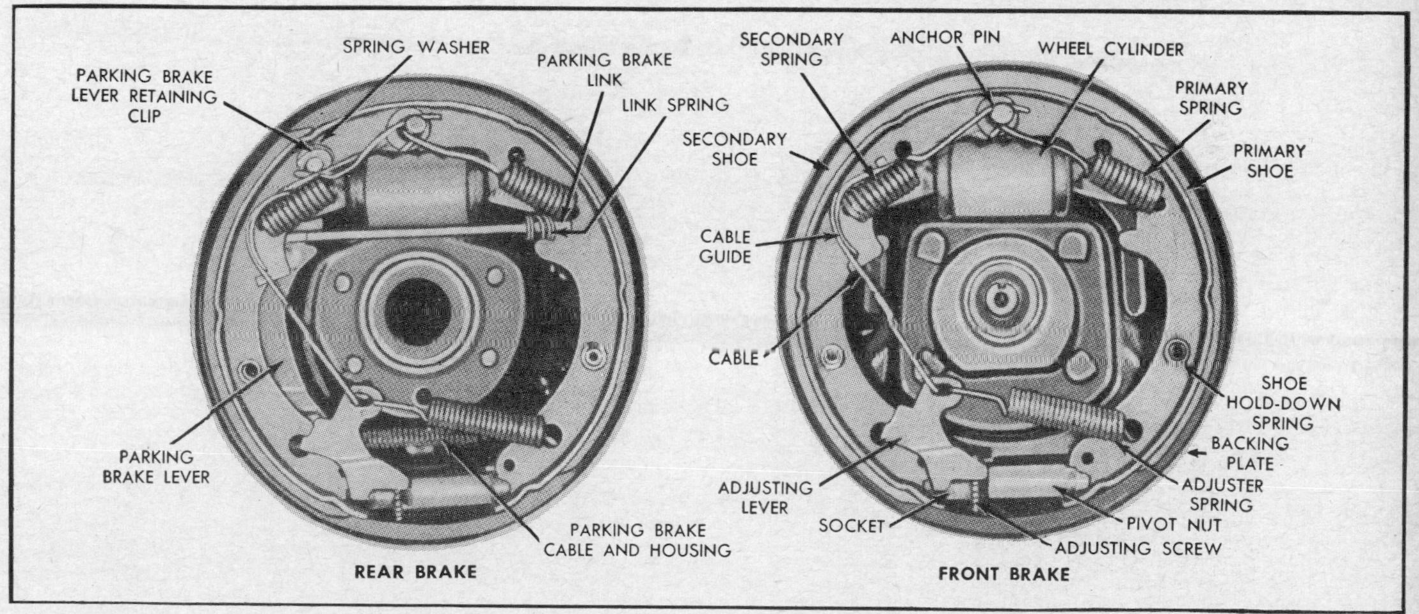

Fig. 10 Right front and rear brakes. 1963-69 Six-Cylinder models

ment must be made relative to the centerline of the wheel. Tighten lock nut.

4. Release parking brake and make sure there is no drag when turning rear wheels.

1967 Cougar & Mustang

1. Set parking brake handle at third ratchet bar notch.
2. Raise car and turn equalizer lever adjusting nut until a moderate drag is felt when turning rear wheels by hand.
3. Release parking brake and make sure that brake shoes return to fully released position.

1967 Comet, Falcon, Fairlane

With parking brake control in released position, use a spring scale to adjust cables at the parking brake clevis to obtain 22 to 27 lbs. tension in rear cables.

1966 Comet, Falcon & Fairlane

1. Fully release parking brake pedal.
2. Depress pedal one notch from its normal released position.
3. Raise car.
4. Loosen equalizer lock nut and turn adjusting nut forward against equalizer until a moderate drag is felt when turning rear wheels. Tighten lock nut.
5. Release parking brake and make sure brake shoes return to fully released position.

All 1965 & 1966 Mustang

1. Fully release parking brake.
2. From fully released position, pull brake handle out three notches.
3. Raise the car.
4. On a Falcon, Comet or Fairlane, turn lock nut in front of equalizer several turns forward.
5. On all cars, turn adjusting nut forward against equalizer until a moderate drag is felt when turning rear wheels in direction of forward rotation.
6. When cables are properly adjusted on a Falcon, Comet or Fairlane. Tighten lock nut against equalizer.
7. Release parking brake and make sure that brake shoes return to fully released position and no drag is felt when turning rear wheels.

1963-64

1. With service brakes properly adjusted, check parking brake cables when the brakes are fully released. If cables are loose, adjust as follows:
2. On all 1963 models and 1964 Fairlane, pull up brake handle until third notch is engaged. On 1964 Comet and Falcon pull brake handle outward one notch.
3. Raise car. Turn lock nut in front of equalizer several turns forward.
4. Turn adjustment nut forward against equalizer until a moderate drag is felt when turning rear wheels.
5. When cables are properly adjusted, tighten lock nut against equalizer.
6. Release parking brake and make sure that no drag is felt when turning rear wheels.

MASTER CYLINDER, REPLACE

1967-69 Dual Cylinder

1. Working from inside vehicle below instrument panel, disconnect master cylinder push rod from brake pedal.
2. Disconnect stop light switch wires, remove hairpin retainer and slide stop light switch off brake pedal pin

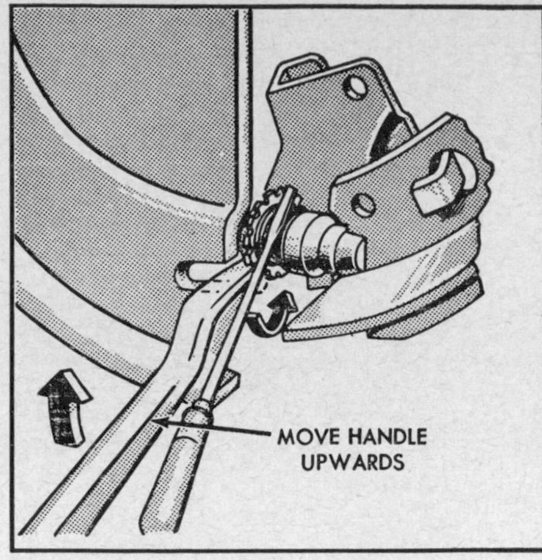

Fig. 11 Backing off brake adjustment by disengaging adjusting lever with screwdriver

just far enough to clear end of pin. Then lift switch straight upward from pin.
3. Slide master cylinder push rod with nylon washers and bushings from brake pedal pin.
4. Remove brake tubes from outlet ports of master cylinder.
5. Remove lock nuts that secure master cylinder to dash panel and lift cylinder forward and upward from vehicle.
6. Reverse procedure to install.

1963-66

1. Remove rubber boot from rear end of master cylinder in passenger compartment.
2. Disconnect brake line from cylinder and stop light wires from switch.
3. Unfasten master cylinder from dash panel and lift cylinder out and away from push rod. Remove boot from push rod.
4. Reverse above procedure to install.
5. Fill reservoir to within ⅜" of the top with heavy duty brake fluid. Then bleed hydraulic system as given in the *Hydraulic Brake System* chapter.

POWER BRAKE UNIT, REPLACE

1965 Comet

1. Remove hood left spring for clearance.
2. Disconnect all brake lines from multiple fitting except line between fitting and master cylinder.
3. Unfasten and remove master cylinder with fitting and brake line.
4. Remove hydraulic push rod and seal from booster.
5. Disconnect vacuum line from booster.
6. Remove connecting bolt and disassemble nylon washers, bushing, stop light switch and booster valve actuating rod from brake pedal.
7. Unfasten and remove booster.

1965 Falcon & 1966-69 Comet, Cougar, Montego, Mustang & Fairlane

1. Working under instrument panel, disconnect stop light switch wires at connector.
2. Remove hairpin type retainer. Slide stop light switch off brake pedal pin just far enough for the switch outer hole to clear the pin, then lower switch away from pin.
3. Slide master cylinder push rod link and nylon washers and bushing off brake pedal pin.
4. Disconnect brake line from master cylinder.
5. Disconnect vacuum hose from booster at check valve.
6. Unfasten and remove booster and bracket assembly from dash panel, sliding push rod link out from engine side of dash panel.

1964 Comet & Falcon

1. Disconnect battery ground cable.
2. Remove master cylinder from booster.
3. Disconnect vacuum hose from booster.
4. On V8's, remove left rocker arm cover to provide clearance when removing booster.
5. Working from inside of car, remove bolt that attaches booster push rod to brake pedal. Then unfasten booster from dash panel (5 nuts).
6. Reverse removal procedure and bleed hydraulic system.

1963-64 Fairlane

1. Working inside car below instrument panel, disconnect booster valve operating rod from brake pedal. To do this, remove eccentric shoulder bolt. Remove rubber boot from valve operating rod.
2. Open hood and disconnect wires from stop light switch at brake master cylinder.
3. Disconnect brake line at master cylinder outlet fitting.
4. Disconnect vacuum hose from booster unit.
5. Unfasten and remove booster and bracket from dash panel (4 bolts), sliding valve operating rod out from engine side of dash panel.
6. Reverse removal procedure, adjust pedal height and bleed brake system.

Tool—62F-3000-A, Adjusting Tool Arms

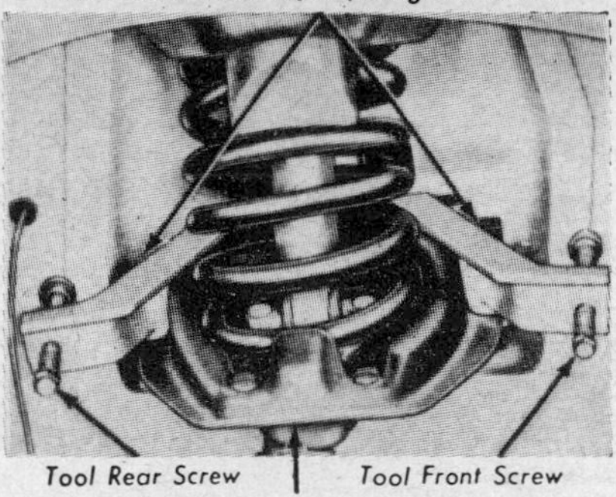

Tool Rear Screw *Tool Front Screw*

SUSPENSION UPPER ARM

Fig. 6 Upper side view of caster and camber adjusting tool installation. 1963-65 Fairlane and Meteor

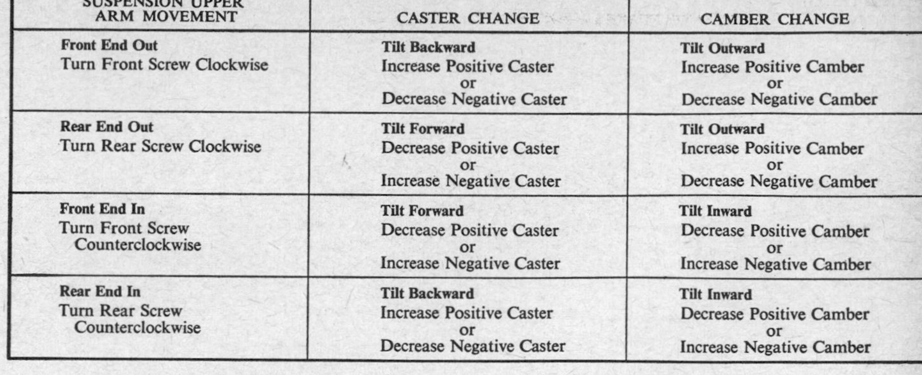

SUSPENSION UPPER ARM MOVEMENT	CASTER CHANGE	CAMBER CHANGE
Front End Out Turn Front Screw Clockwise	**Tilt Backward** Increase Positive Caster or Decrease Negative Caster	**Tilt Outward** Increase Positive Camber or Decrease Negative Camber
Rear End Out Turn Rear Screw Clockwise	**Tilt Forward** Decrease Positive Caster or Increase Negative Caster	**Tilt Outward** Increase Positive Camber or Decrease Negative Camber
Front End In Turn Front Screw Counterclockwise	**Tilt Forward** Decrease Positive Caster or Increase Negative Caster	**Tilt Inward** Decrease Positive Camber or Increase Negative Camber
Rear End In Turn Rear Screw Counterclockwise	**Tilt Backward** Increase Positive Caster or Decrease Negative Caster	**Tilt Inward** Decrease Positive Camber or Increase Negative Camber

Fig. 8 Caster and camber adjustments. 1965 Fairlane and Meteor

suspension arm inner shaft to the underbody and moving the arm assembly in or out in the elongated bolt holes, Fig. 5. Since any movement of the arm affects both caster and camber, *both* factors should be balanced against one another when making the adjustment.

1. Install the special tool as shown in Fig. 6. *Do not install the tool from underneath the car. For easier installation, face the outside of the wheel and reach behind each end of the wheel under the fender with each half of the tool. Turn both tool adjusting screws until the tool is snug between the suspension upper arm and the lower corners of the front suspension housing, Fig. 7.*

2. Loosen upper arm inner shaft bolts 2 or 3 turns, Fig. 5. Then turn the wheels to the extreme left and right positions to free the arm.
3. Turn wheels to the straight-ahead position. Then turn the upper arm inner shaft bolts snug (not tight).
4. Turn tool adjusting screws to move the arms of the tool in or out and thus move the suspension in or out as required for adjustment.
   a. To move front end of suspension upper arm *out,* turn tool front screw *clockwise.*
   b. To move rear end of upper suspension arm *out,* turn tool rear screw *clockwise.*
   c. To move front end of upper suspension arm *in,* turn tool front screw *counterclockwise.*
   d. To move rear end of upper suspension arm *in,* turn tool rear screw *counterclockwise.* The relationship between turning the tool adjusting screws for upper suspension arm movement and changes in caster and camber is shown in Fig. 8.
5. After caster and camber have been adjusted to specifications, tighten the upper arm inner shaft bolts to 115-135 ft. lbs. torque. Remove tool and recheck adjustments.

SUSPENSION UPPER ARM *Tool—62F-3000-A, Front Adjusting Screw*

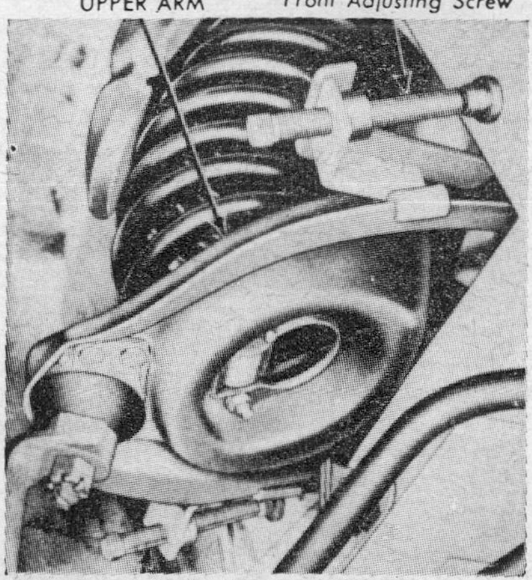

Tool Rear Adjusting Screw

Fig. 7 Lower left view of caster and camber adjusting tool installation. 1963-65 Fairlane and Meteor

TOE-IN, ADJUST

Check the steering wheel spoke position when the front wheels are in the straight-ahead position. If the spokes are not in the normal position, they can be adjusted while toe-in is being adjusted.

1. Loosen clamp bolts on each tie rod end sleeve.
2. Adjust toe-in. If steering wheel spokes are in their normal position, lengthen or shorten both rods equally to obtain correct toe-in. If spokes are not in normal position, make necessary rod adjustments to obtain correct toe-in and steering wheel spoke alignment.

WHEEL BEARINGS ADJUST

1963-69

1. With wheel and drum rotating, torque adjusting nut to 17 to 25 ft-lbs to seat the bearing.
2. Back off adjusting nut ½ turn.
3. Then retighten it to finger tight and install nut lock and cotter pin.

WHEEL BEARINGS, REPLACE

(Disc Brakes)

1. Raise car and remove front wheels.
2. Remove caliper mounting bolts.

NOTE: It is not necessary to disconnect the brake lines for this operation.

3. Slide caliper off of disc, inserting a clean spacer between the shoes to hold them in their bores after the caliper is removed. Position caliper out of the way.

NOTE: Do not allow caliper to hang by brake hose.

WITH DRUM AND WHEEL ROTATING, TORQUE THE ADJUSTING NUT TO 15-20 ft. lbs.

INSTALL LOCK ON NUT SO THAT CASTELLATIONS ARE ALIGNED WITH COTTER PIN HOLE.

BACK OFF NUT AND NUT LOCK ONE CASTELLATION INSTALL COTTER PIN.

Fig. 9 Front wheel bearing adjustment

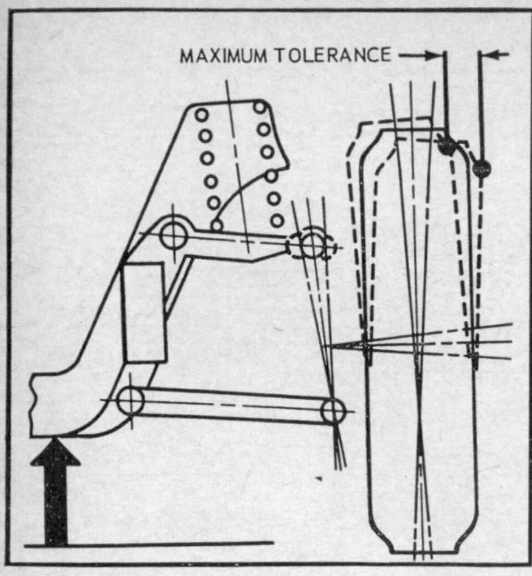

Fig. 10 Measuring upper ball joint for radial play, which should not exceed 1/4"

4. Remove hub and disc assembly. Grease retainer and inner bearing can now be removed.

CHECKING BALL JOINTS FOR WEAR

Upper Ball Joint

1. Raise car on frame contact hoist or by floor jacks placed beneath underbody until wheel falls to full down position as shown in Fig. 10. This will unload upper ball joint.
2. With front wheel bearings properly adjusted, attach a dial indicator to the upper control arm and position the indicator so that its plunger rests against the inner side of the wheel rim adjacent to the upper arm ball joint.
3. Grasp tire at top and bottom and slowly move it in and out, Fig. 10. Reading on dial will indicate the amount of radial play. If reading exceeds 1/4", replace the upper ball joint.

Lower Ball Joint

1. With car jacked up as directed above, grasp the lower edge of the tire and move it in and out.
2. As wheel is being moved in and out, observe lower end of spindle and lower arm.
3. Any movement between lower end of spindle and lower arm indicates ball joint wear and loss of preload. If such movement is observed, replace lower arm and/or ball joint.

NOTE: During the foregoing check, the upper ball joint will be unloaded and may move. Disregard all such movement of the upper ball joint. Also, do not mistake loose wheel bearings for a worn ball joint.

BALL JOINT, REPLACE

The ball joints are riveted to the upper and lower control arms. The upper ball joint can be replaced by removing the rivets and retaining the new ball joint to the upper control arm with bolts, nuts and washers furnished with the ball joint repair kit. The lower ball joints are furnished as an assembly with the lower control arm. When removing an upper ball joint, use a suitable pressing tool to loosen the ball joint from the spindle.

SHOCK ABSORBER, REPLACE

1. Raise hood and remove upper mounting bracket-to-spring tower retaining nuts.
2. Raise front of car and place safety stands under lower control arms.
3. Remove shock absorber lower retaining nuts and washers.
4. Lift shock absorber from spring tower.
5. Reverse procedure to install.

COIL SPRING, REPLACE

1965-66 Mustang, 1963-65 Comet & Falcon

1. Raise front of car, position safety stands under frame and lower car slightly.
2. Remove wheel and shock absorber.
3. On V8s, remove carburetor air cleaner to gain access for spring compressor tool. Then compress until spring clears upper control arm.
4. Remove upper control arm shaft retaining nuts from arm, shaft and retaining bolts from underbody. *Measure and note total shim thickness at each inner shaft retaining bolt.*
5. Swing upper arm and shaft 180-deg. out to provide clearance for spring removal.
6. Remove spring compressor tool and take out spring, Fig. 11.
7. Reverse procedure to install.

1967-69 Comet, Falcon & Fairlane, 1967-69 Montego, Cougar & Mustang

1. Remove shock absorber and upper mounting bracket as an assembly.
2. Raise car on hoist and install safety stands.
3. Remove wheel, hub and drum.
4. Install a suitable spring compressor and compress spring.
5. Remove two upper-arm-to-spring tower retaining nuts and swing upper arm outward from spring.
6. Release spring compressor. Then remove spring, Fig. 11.
7. Reverse procedure to install.

1963-65 Fairlane & Meteor

1. Raise car and remove wheel.
2. Remove suspension bumper and bracket.
3. Remove shock absorber and bracket.
4. Install one shock absorber mounting bracket bolt to hold spring upper seat to spring housing while spring is being compressed with a suitable spring compressor tool.

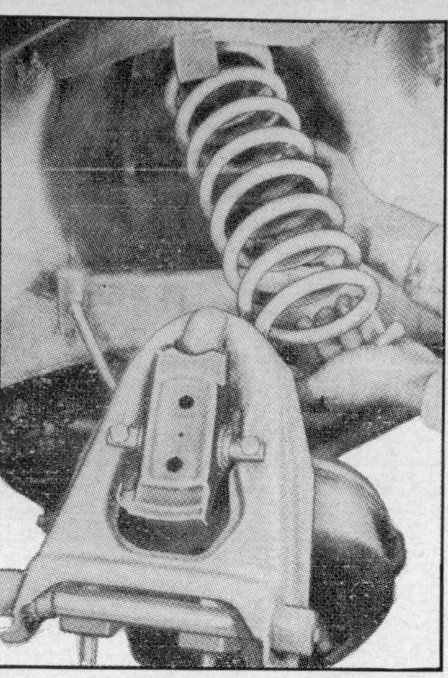

Fig. 11 Removing and installing spring

5. When spring is compressed, remove bolt that holds upper seat to housing, then remove spring and compressor tool.
6. Reverse procedure to install.

STEERING GEAR, REPLACE

SERVICE BULLETIN

On some early 1966 vehicles the bottom face of the steering gear in the sector shaft seal area may not be machined. This will in no way affect the function or operation of the steering gear. It will, however, cause a reduction in clearance between the pitman arm and the steering gear housing. It may be necessary to provide extra clearance to insert a pitman arm puller for pitman arm removal. This can be accomplished by turning the wheels completely to either stop and loosening the mesh-load adjusting screw inward until an increase in load is felt. This will allow the additional clearance for the puller.

CAUTION: Do not turn steering wheel across the center position while the adjusting screw is turned in as damage to the worm gear or ball nut may result. When the pitman arm is removed, immediately turn the mesh-load adjusting screw outward to reduce the load.

1968-69 With 6-200, 250 Engines

1. Remove bolt that secures flex coupling to steering shaft.
2. Remove Pitman arm with a suitable puller.
3. Remove two fuel line-to-chassis clips and position fuel line out of the way.
4. Unfasten and remove steering gear.

1968-69 With 289, 302, 351 Engines

1. Remove bolt that secures flex cou-

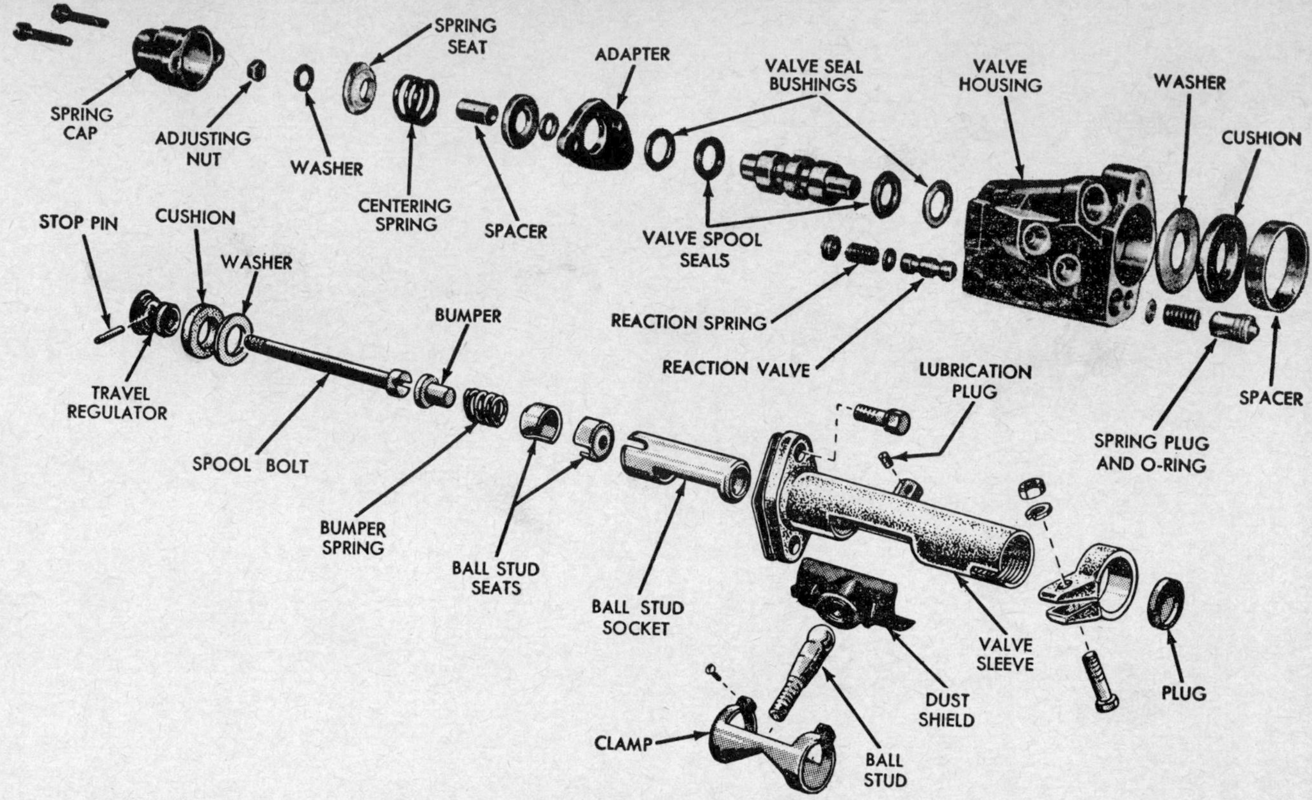

Fig. 12 Power steering control valve and sleeve assembly

pling to steering shaft.
2. Remove Pitman arm with a suitable puller.
3. Remove two bolts that attach left front mount to block.
4. Raise engine ½" off mount and block in this position.
5. Unfasten and remove steering gear.

1968-69 With 390, 427, 428 Engines

1. Remove two bolts that secure flex coupling to steering shaft and to steering gear.
2. Remove power cylinder bracket-to-chassis attaching bolts.
3. Remove Pitman arm with a suitable puller.
4. Disconnect and lower exhaust pipes from exhaust manifolds.
5. Unfasten steering gear. Lower gear enough to slide flex coupling off gear input shaft, then remove gear from vehicle.

1963-65 Comet, Falcon, 1965-66 Mustang, 1964-65 Fairlane

1. Disconnect horn wire and turn signal wires under instrument panel. With automatic transmission, also disconnect neutral switch wires.
2. Remove steering wheel.
3. Remove steering column clamp.
4. Pull rubber seal up on steering column and move dash panel insulation out of the way.
5. Remove steering column cover plates.
6. Slide steering column from steering gear through opening in dash panel.
7. On 1965-66 models, raise car and remove clutch equalizer and bracket assembly from frame side rail and engine (if equipped).
8. On power steering cars, remove power cylinder rod from bracket to obtain clearance for removal of pitman arm.
9. Remove exhaust pipe from manifold if necessary to obtain clearance.
10. Remove pitman arm with a suitable puller.
11. Remove steering gear retaining bolts.
12. Lower car and disconnect wires from left bank spark plugs to prevent damage to them.
13. On 1965 Comet and Falcon V8s, remove exhaust manifold to obtain clearance.
14. On vehicles with column shift, disconnect shift rods from transmission levers.
15. Remove brake booster if necessary.
16. On 1965-66 (except Comet), remove support rod from cowl-to-spring tower.
17. Loosen air cleaner to obtain clearance if required.
18. Lift steering gear assembly from engine compartment.
19. Reverse procedure to install.

1966-67 Comet, Falcon & Fairlane, 1967 Cougar & Mustang Less Power Steering & 390 Engine

1. Disconnect turn signal and horn wires at steering column connectors.
2. Remove steering wheel.
3. Remove column retainer from column and dash panel.
4. Remove steering column-to-instrument panel support bol s.
5. Remove upper bearing centering sleeve and spring from shaft.
6. Disconnect shift linkage from column shift arms.
7. Remove pitman arm with a suitable puller.
8. Remove clutch release arm return spring bracket (standard transmission cars).
9. Unfasten steering gear from frame and remove gear from car.
10. Reverse procedure to install.

1966 Comet & Fairlane with Power Steering

1. Remove two bolts retaining flex coupling to steering shaft.
2. Unfasten and separate power cylinder bracket from frame side rail and allow cylinder and bracket to hang.
3. Remove pitman arm with a suitable puller.
4. On standard transmission jobs, remove clutch release arm return spring bracket.
5. Unfasten and remove gear from car.
6. Reverse procedure to install.

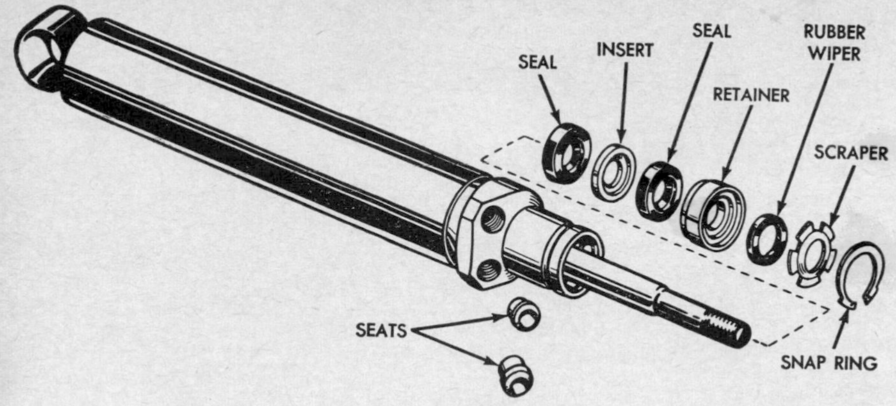

Fig. 13 Power steering cylinder

1967 Comet & Fairlane, Cougar & Mustang with 390 Engine & Std. Steering

1. Remove pitman arm.
2. Remove steering gear-to-frame bolts, and disconnect shift rods from shift levers.
3. Disconnect horn and turn signal wires at steering column multiple connectors.
4. Remove steering wheel.
5. Remove steering column opening retainer and slide seal up on column.
6. Unfasten and lift steering column from steering shaft.
7. Disconnect master cylinder brake line from junction block.
8. Remove master cylinder and brake line from dash panel.
9. Disconnect spark plug wires from left bank and remove rocker arm cover.
10. Unfasten and remove gear housing cover from steering gear.
11. Remove gear from car by first placing gear sector shaft against fender apron. Then pull gear up and over spring tower to remove from car.
12. Reverse procedure to install.

1963 Fairlane

1. Raise car and install safety stands.
2. With power steering, remove power cylinder mounting bracket from underbody.
3. Remove pitman arm from gear.
4. Remove housing attaching bolts.
5. Remove flexible joint clamp bolts and remove gear from car.
6. Reverse removal procedure to install gear.

SERVICE BULLETIN

STOPS STEERING LEAK: A leak between the steering gear housing and its cover can be caused by an incorrect installation of the cover. This cover on 1963-64 models must be installed with the rolled edge radius of the cover facing upward.

SERVICE BULLETIN

LICKS STEERING PROBLEM: Improper steering recovery on a car with a 260 or 289 cu. in. engine and power steering can be due to the idler-arm bushing slipping inside the arm. If the steering does not return to the straight-ahead position after a turn and the car leads in the direction of the turn, the following method can be used to determine whether a loose idler arm bushing is the cause.

With the car on a hoist, set the steering wheel in the straight-ahead position, and mark the wheel hub and column as a reference. Then mark a straight line on the idler arm and bushing to establish their positions. Lower the car, start the engine, and turn the front wheels to the right until the idler arm hits the stop. Turn the wheels back to center to align the wheel hub and column markings, and check to see whether the marks on the idler arm and bushing line up.

If they are not aligned, the bushing is slipping and must be replaced.

POWER STEERING

Pump Pressure

The normal oil pressure against either steering stop with engine idling is 750 to 900 psi.

Pump Removal

1. With suction gun remove as much fluid as possible from reservoir.
2. Disconnect and fasten two hose at pump to a raised position to prevent fluid from draining out.
3. Remove pump belt. Unfasten and remove pump.
4. Use all parts of the kit when overhauling the pump.
5. Installation is made in the reverse order of removal. Fill the reservoir to the "F" mark on the dipstick. Run the engine and turn the steering wheel several times from one extreme to the other. Check for leaks.

Control Valve Removal

1. Disconnect fluid fittings at control valve and drain fluid from lines by turning wheels to left and right several times.
2. Loosen clamp at right-hand end of sleeve. Remove roll pin from steering arm-to-idler arm rod through slot in sleeve.
3. Remove ball stud from sector shaft.
4. Turn wheels fully to left and unthread control valve from idler arm rod.

Assembly Notes

1. When disassembling control valve, refer to Fig. 12. When reassembling observe the following:
2. During assembly, coat all parts with automatic transmission fluid.
3. Make sure lube fitting is turned on tightly and does not bind on ball stud socket.
4. Rotate spool while inserting it in housing. Do not nick or scratch spool during installation.
5. When installing the centering spring, compress the spring and install nut on bolt. After tightening nut securely, loosen it not more than ¼ turn. Excessive tightening of nut may break stop pin at the travel regulator stop.
6. Move ball stud back and forth in sleeve slot to check for freedom of movement. Apply silicone grease to sealing areas.
7. When installed on car, measure distance between center of lube plug in the sleeve and center of the stud at the inner end of the left-hand spindle connecting rod. This distance should be $4\frac{3}{16}$" on Fairlane and Meteor, and $4\frac{5}{16}$" on Falcon and Comet. If this is not correct, disconnect ball stud from sector shaft arm and turn valve on idler arm rod to increase or decrease the distance. When distance is correct, align hole in idler arm rod with slot near end of valve sleeve. Install roll pin in rod hole to lock valve in position on rod.
8. After installation is completed, run engine for about two minutes to warm the fluid in the system. Turn steering wheel from one extreme to the other several times and check the system for fluid leaks.
9. With engine running, check position of steering wheel when front wheels are in straight-ahead position. Do not make any adjustments until toe-in is checked. Then adjust toe-in if necessary and center steering wheel as outlined under *Toe-In Adjust.*
10. Hook a spring scale to the rim of the steering wheel and measure the pull required to turn the wheel in both directions with the engine running. The pull should not exceed 4½ pounds and should be about equal in both directions.

Power Cylinder

1. To remove power cylinder, Fig. 13, remove two fluid lines from between control valve and power cylinder. Move front wheels to left and right several times to drain fluid from power cylinder.
2. Remove nut from outer end of piston rod. Do not remove from idler arm bracket at this time.
3. Remove locknut that holds cylinder on mounting stud in idler arm rod. Then pull piston rod out of bracket and remove cylinder from stud.
4. Remove boot, inner bushing and washer from stud and pull inner insulator and washer from piston rod.
5. Reverse removal procedure to install. Run engine for two minutes to warm up the fluid. Turn wheels to left and right several times and check for leaks. Refill fluid reservoir.

FORD THUNDERBIRD

OLD CAR SPECIFICATIONS: For 1946-62 Tune Up and Wheel Alignment Specifications see back of book.

INDEX OF SERVICE OPERATIONS

PAGE NO.

ACCESSORIES

Automatic Level Controls 1-41
Clock Troubles 1-11
Heater Core, Replace 2-351
Power Top Troubles 1-18
Power Window Troubles 1-18
Radio, Replace 2-351
Speed Controls, Adjust 2-351

BRAKES

Brake Troubles, Mechanical 1-17
Disc Brake Service 1-430
Hydraulic System Service 1-422
Parking Brake, Adjust 2-359
Power Brake Service 1-440
Power Brake Troubles 1-440
Power Brake Unit, Replace 2-360
Service Brakes, Adjust 2-359

COOLING SYSTEM

Cooling System Troubles 1-6
Variable Speed Fans 1-39
Water Pump, Replace 2-357

ELECTRICAL

Alternator Service 1-63
Dash Gauge Service 1-117
Distributor, Replace 2-346
Distributor Service:
Standard 1-53
Transistorized 1-47
Electrical Troubles 1-8
Flasher Location Chart .... Back of Book
Generator Service 1-91
Headlamps, Concealed Type 1-40
Horn Sounder, Remove 2-349
Ignition Coils and Risistors 1-24
Ignition Switch, Replace 2-347
Ignition Timing 2-346
Instrument Cluster Removal 2-350
Light Switch, Replace 2-348
Neutral Safety Switch, Replace 2-348
Spark Plug Condition Chart 2-647
Starter Service 1-101
Starter, Replace 2-347
Starter Switch Service 1-114
Stop Light Switch, Replace 2-348
Turn Signal Switch, Replace 2-349
Turn Signal Troubles 1-11
Windshield Wiper Motor, Replace 2-350
Windshield Wiper Troubles 1-20

PAGE NO.

ENGINE

Camshaft, Replace 2-356
Camshaft Bearings 2-356
Cylinder Head, Replace 2-353
Engine, Replace 2-353
Engine Troubles 1-1
Main Bearings 2-356
Piston Pins 2-356
Piston Rings 2-356
Piston and Rod, Assemble 2-356
Pistons 2-356
Rocker Arm Service 2-354
Rocker Arm Stud 2-354
Rod Bearings 2-356
Timing Case Cover, Replace 2-355
Timing Chain, Replace 2-356
Valves, Adjust 2-355
Valve Arrangement 2-355
Valve Guides 2-355
Valve Lifters 2-355

ENGINE LUBRICATION

Crankcase Ventilation (PCV) 1-29
Exhaust Emission Controls 1-30
Oil Pan, Replace 2-356
Oil Pump Repairs 2-357

FUEL SYSTEM

Carburetor Adjustments and Specs. 1-124
Crankcase Ventilation (PCV) 1-29
Exhaust Emission Controls 1-30
Fuel Pump, Replace 2-357
Fuel Pump Service 1-120
Fuel System Troubles 1-2

PROPELLER SHAFT & U JOINTS

Propeller Shaft 2-358
Universal Joint Service 1-418

REAR AXLE

Axle Shaft, Bearing and Seal 2-358
Rear Axle Description 2-358
Rear Axle Troubles 1-17

SPECIFICATIONS

Alternator 2-342
Brakes 2-346
Capacities 2-346
Carburetors 1-124

PAGE NO.

Cooling System 2-346
Crankshaft and Bearings 2-345
Distributors 2-344
Engine Tightening Torque 2-344
General Engine Specs. 2-342
Ignition Coils and Resistors 1-24
Pistons, Rings and Pins 2-345
Rear Axle 2-345
Starting Motors 2-344
Tune Up 2-343
Valve Lift 2-354
Valve Timing 2-354
Valves 2-345
Wheel Alignment 2-343

STEERING GEAR

Horn Sounder Removal 2-349
Mechanical Gear Service 1-451
Mechanical Gear Troubles 1-18
Power Gear, Replace 2-362

SUSPENSION, FRONT

Ball Joints, Replace 2-362
Ball Joints, Check for Wear 2-362
Coil Spring, Replace 2-362
Lubrication 2-361
Shock Absorber, Replace 2-362
Suspension, Description of 2-361
Tire Wear Chart 2-648
Toe-In, Adjust 2-361
Wheel Alignment, Adjust 2-361
Wheel Bearings, Adjust 2-361
Wheel Bearings, Replace 2-361

TRANSMISSIONS 1-321

1969 Linkage 2-357

TUNE UP

Service 1-21
Specifications 2-343

WINDSHIELD WIPER

Wiper Motor, Replace 2-350
Wiper Linkage, Replace 2-351
Wiper Switch, Replace 2-351
Wiper Troubles 1-20

ENGINE & SERIAL NUMBER LOCATION

Vehicle Warranty Plate On Left Front Door Pillar.

1963

ENGINE IDENTIFICATION

*** Serial number on vehicle Warranty Plate.**

Engine code for 1963–69 is the last letter in the serial number.

Year	Engine	Engine Code*
1963–65	V8-390	Z
1966–67	V8-390	Z
	V8-428	Q
1968–69	V8-390	Z
	V8-429	N

1967

1964

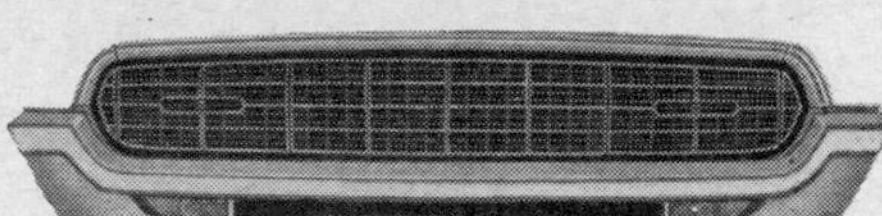

1968

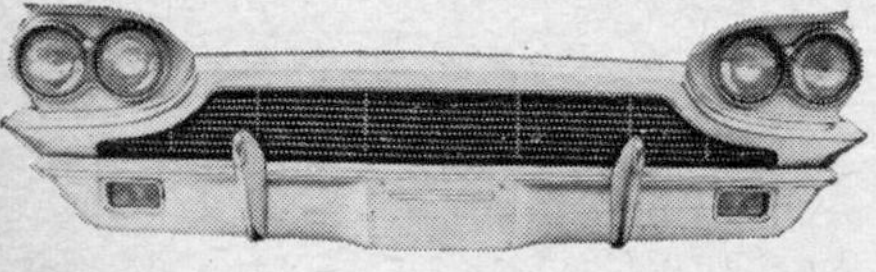

1965

1966

1969

GENERAL SPECIFICATIONS

Year	Engine	Carburetor	Bore and Stroke	Piston Displacement, Cubic Inches	Compression Ratio	Maximum Brake H.P. @ R.P.M.	Maximum Torque Lbs. Ft. @ R.P.M.	Normal Oil Pressure Pounds
1963–65	300 Horsepower.............V8-390	4 Barrel	4.0468 x 3.784	390	10.10	300 @ 4600	427 @ 3800	35–55
1966–67	315 Horsepower.............V8-390	4 Barrel	4.0500 x 3.784	390	10.50	315 @ 4600	427 @ 2800	35–55
	345 Horsepower.............V8-428	4 Barrel	4.1300 x 3.984	428	10.50	345 @ 4600	462 @ 2800	35–55
1968	315 Horsepower.............V8-390	4 Barrel	4.05 x 3.78	390	10.50	315 @ 4600	427 @ 2800	35–55
1968–69	360 Horsepower.............V8-429	4 Barrel	4.36 x 3.59	429	11.00	360 @ 4600	476 @ 2800	35–55

ALTERNATOR & REGULATOR SPECIFICATIONS

Year	Make	Current Rating①		Field Current @ 75°F		Voltage Regulator②				Field Relay	
		Amperes	Volts	Amperes	Volts	Make	Voltage @ 75°F	Contact Gap	Armature Air Gap	Armature Air Gap	Closing Voltage @ 75°F
1963	Ford	30	15	2.3–2.5	12	Ford	14.1–14.7	.010–.015	.045–.052	.022–.030	4 to 5
1964	Ford	40	15	2.9–3.1	12	Ford	14.1–14.7	.010–.015	.045–.052	.022–.030	3 to 4
	Ford	42	15	2.9–3.1	12	Ford	14.1–14.7	.010–.015	.045–.052	.022–.030	3 to 4
	Ford	52	15	2.9–3.1	12	Ford	14.1–14.7	.010–.015	.045–.052	.022–.030	3 to 4
1965–67	Autolite	42	15	2.8–3.3	12	Autolite	14.1–14.9	.017–.022	.049–.056	.015–.022	2.5–4.0
	Autolite	45	15	2.8–3.3	12	Autolite	14.1–14.9	.017–.022	.049–.056	.015–.022	2.5–4.0
	Autolite	55	15	2.8–3.3	12	Autolite	14.1–14.9	.017–.022	.049–.056	.015–.022	2.5–4.0
1968	Autolite	55	15	2.8–3.3	12	Autolite	13.5–15.3	③	③	③	2.0–4.2
1969	Autolite	55	15	2.8–3.3	12	Autolite④	③	③	③	③	③

①—Stamped on housing. ②—Stamped on cover. ③—Not adjustable. ④—Integral regulator solid state.

TUNE UP SPECIFICATIONS

OLD CAR SPECIFICATIONS: For 1955-62 Tune Up Specifications see back of book.

★When using a timing light, disconnect vacuum hose or tube at distributor and plug opening in hose or tube so idle speed will not be affected.

Year	Engine	Spark Plug		Distributor		Firing Order	Ignition Timing★		Hot Idle Speed		Comp. Press. Lbs. (3)	Fuel Pump Press. Lbs.
		Type	Gap Inch	Point Gap Inch	Dwell Angle Deg.		BTDC (1)	Mark	M/S Trans.	Auto. Trans. (2)		
1963	V8-390 One Carb.	BF-42	.034	.017	26-31	Fig. A	6°	Fig. C	...	485D(7)	180	5-6
	V8-390 Three Carbs.	BF-32	.034	.017	26-31	Fig. A	6°	Fig. C	...	485D(7)	180	5-6
1964	Conventional Ign.	BF-42	.034	.017	26-31	Fig. A	6°(5)	Fig. C	...	485D(7)	190	4-6
	Transistor Ign.	BF-42	.034	.020	22-24	Fig. A	6°(5)	Fig. C	...	485D(7)	190	4-6
1965	Conventional Ign.	BF-42	.034	.017	26-31	Fig. A	6°(5)	(6)	...	485D(7)	190	4-6
	Transistor Ign.	BF-42	.034	.020	22-24	Fig. A	6°(5)	Fig. C	...	485D(7)	190	4-6
1966	Std. Ignition(8)	BF-42	.034	.017	26-31	Fig. A	10°(5)	Fig. F	575(7)	475D(7)	190	4½-6½
	Std. Ignition(9)	BF-42	.034	.017	26-31	Fig. A	6°(5)	Fig. F	610(7)	525D(7)	190	4½-6½
	Transistor Ign.(8)	BF-42	.034	.020	22-24	Fig. A	10°(5)	Fig. F	575(7)	475D(7)	190	4½-6½
	Transistor Ign.(9)	BF-42	.034	.020	22-24	Fig. A	6°(5)	Fig. F	610(7)	525D(7)	190	4½-6½
1967	Standard(8)	BF-32	.034	.017	26-31	Fig. A	10°(5)	Fig. F	575(7)	475D(7)	190	4½-6½
	With Thermactor(9)	BF-32	.034	.017	26-31	Fig. A	6°(5)	Fig. F	625(7)	550D(7)	190	4½-6½
1968	8-390	BF-42	.034	.017	26-31	Fig. A	6°(5)	Fig. B	—	550D(4)	190	4½-6½
1968-69	8-429	BF-42	.034	.017	26-31	Fig. A	6°(5)	Fig. B	—	550D(4)	190	4½-6½

(1)—BTDC: Before top dead center.
(2)—D: Drive. N: Neutral.
(3)—Plus or minus 20 lbs.
(4)—With headlights and A/C on.
(5)—Whenever idle speed or ignition timing is adjusted, vacuum line to brake release mechanism must be disconnected and plugged to prevent parking brake from releasing when selector is moved to Drive.
(6)—Either Fig. C or F.
(7)—If air conditioned, turn A/C switch to "Full On" position.
(8)—Without Thermactor System.
(9)—With Thermactor System.

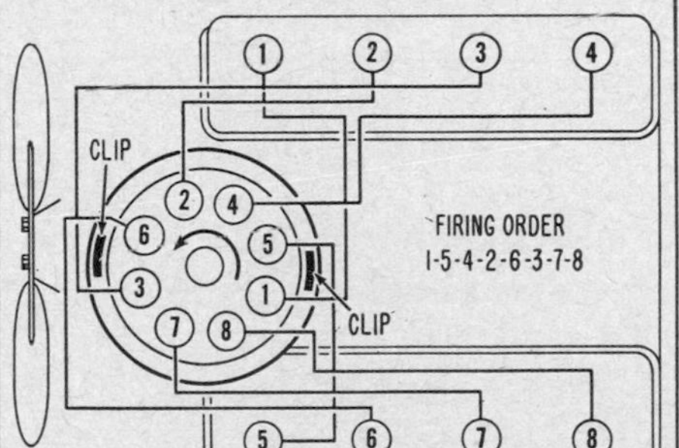

Fig. A

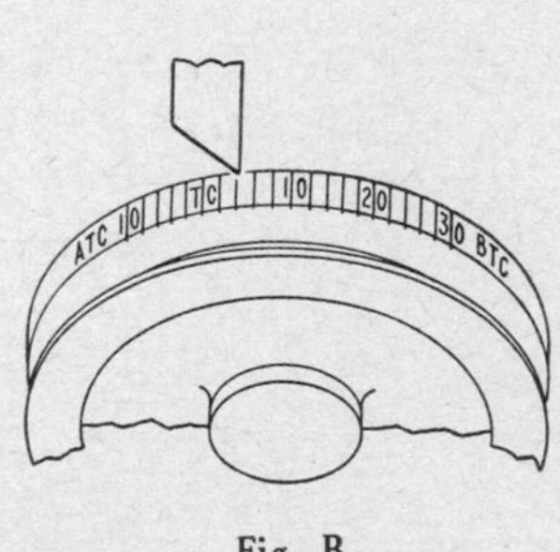

Fig. B

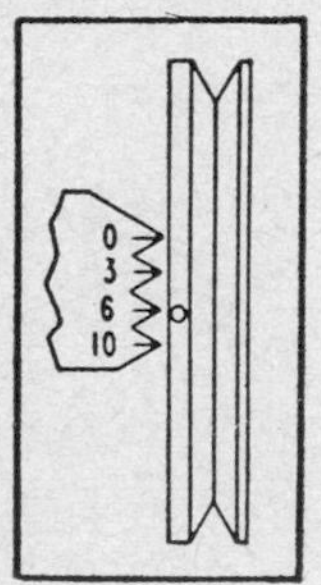

Fig. C

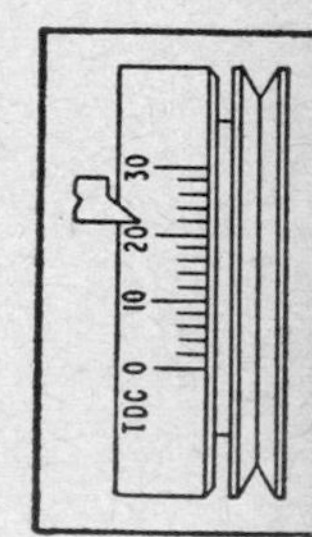

Fig. F

WHEEL ALIGNMENT SPECIFICATIONS

OLD CAR SPECIFICATIONS: For 1955-62 Wheel Alignment Specifications see back of book.

Year	Model	Caster Angle, Degrees		Camber Angle, Degrees				Toe-In. Inch	Toe-Out on Turns, Deg.	
				Limits		Desired				
		Limits	Desired	Left	Right	Left	Right		Outer Wheel	Inner Wheel
1963-64	All	−¾ to −2¼	−1½	0 to +¾	0 to +¾	+⅜	+⅜	⅛-¼	18⅞	20
1965	All	−1¼ to −3¼	−1½	−¾ to +1	−¾ to +1	+½	+½	1/32-3/32	19½	20
1966	All	−¾ to −2¼	−1½	0 to +1	0 to +1	+½	+½	3/16	19½	20
1967	All	0 to +1	+½	+½ to +1½	+½ to +1½	+1	+1	3/16	18⅛	20
1968-69	All	0 to +2	+1	−¼ to +1¼	−¼ to +1¼	+½	+½	3/16	18¼	20

DISTRIBUTOR SPECIFICATIONS

★NOTE: If advance is checked on vehicle, double the R.P.M. and degrees advance to get crankshaft figures.

Year	Model	Basic Distributor Part No ① 12127	Rotation ②	Breaker Gap	Cam Angle	Breaker Arm Spring Tension	Centrifugal Advance Degrees @ R P.M. of Distributor★		Vacuum Advance	
							Advance Starts	Full Advance	Inches of Vacuum To Start Plunger	Max. Adv. Dist. Deg. @ Vacuum
1963	V8-390 One Carb.	C2SF-A	CC	.017	26–31	17–20	2 @ 425	14 @ 2000	6	8 @ 15
	V8-390 3 Carbs.	C2SF-B	CC	.017	26–31	17–20	2 @ 425	12 @ 2000	6	8 @ 15
1964	Conventional	C4AF-N	CC	.017	26–31	17–20	1 @ 400	12 @ 2000	8	8 @ 8
	Transistor Ignition	C4SF-B	CC	.020	22–24	19–21	1 @ 400	12 @ 2000	8	8 @ 8
1965	Conventional	C5AF-C	CC	.017	26–31	17–20	2 @ 450	12 @ 2000	8	8 @ 14
	Transistor Ignition	C5SF-B	CC	.020	22–24	19–21	2 @ 450	12 @ 2000	8	8 @ 14
1966	8-390 Standard	C6AF-D	CC	.017	26–31	17–21	2 @ 500	10 @ 2000	6	12 @ 18
	8-390, 428 Thermactor③	C6AF-L	CC	.017	26–31	17–21	2 @ 500	12 @ 2000	6	10 @ 15
	8-428 Standard	C6AF-E	CC	.017	26–31	17–21	2 @ 500	10 @ 2000	6	10 @ 15
	8-428 Std. Transistor	C6SF-B	CC	.020	22–24	17–21	2 @ 500	10 @ 2000	6	10 @ 15
	8-428 Transistor③	C6SF-D	CC	.020	22–24	17–21	2 @ 590	12 @ 2000	6	10 @ 15
1967	8-390④	C7SF-A	CC	.017	26–31	17–21	½ @ 300	10 @ 2000	5	12 @ 20
	8-390, 428③	C7SF-B	CC	.017	26–31	17–21	½ @ 300	12 @ 2000	5	12 @ 20
	8-428④	C7AF-J	CC	.017	26–31	17–21	½ @ 300	10 @ 2000	5	12 @ 20
1968	8-390	C7AF-AC	CC	.017	26–31	17–21	½ @ 350	14 @ 2000	5	12½ @ 25
1968–69	8-429	C8VF-A	CC	.017	26–31	17–21	½ @ 350	14 @ 2000	5	12 @ 25

①—Stamped on distributor housing plate. ②—As viewed from above. ③—With Thermactor System. ④—Without Thermactor System.

STARTING MOTOR SPECIFICATIONS

Year and Model	Part No.	Rotation ①	Brush Spring Tension, Ounces	No Load Test			Torque Test		
				Amperes	Volts	R.P.M.	Amperes	Volts	Torque Ft. Lbs.
1963 All		C	48	70	12		670	5	15.5
1964 All		C	45	110	12		580	5	14.8
1965–67		C	40	70	12		670	5	15½
1968 V8-390	C7AF-11001-E	C	40	70	12	11000	700	4	15½
1968 V8-429	C8VF-11001-A	C	40	70	12	11000	600	4	15.3
1969 V8-429	C8VY-11002-C	C	40	70	12	10000	700	5	15.5

①—As viewed from the drive end. C—Clockwise.

ENGINE TIGHTENING SPECIFICATIONS

★Torque specifications are for clean and lightly lubricated threads only. Dry or dirty threads produce increased friction which prevents accurate measurement of tightness.

Year	Engine	Spark Plugs Ft. Lbs.	Cylinder Head Bolts Ft. Lbs.	Intake Manifold Ft. Lbs.	Exhaust Manifold Ft. Lbs.	Rocker Arm Shaft Bracket Ft. Lbs.	Rocker Arm Cover Ft. Lbs.	Connecting Rod Cap Bolts Ft. Lbs.	Main Bearing Cap Bolts Ft. Lbs.	Flywheel to Crankshaft Ft. Lbs.	Vibration Damper or Pulley Ft. Lbs.
1963–68	V8-390	15–20	80–90	32–35	18–24	40–45	4–7	40–45	95–105	75–85	70–90
1966–67	V8-428	15–20	80–90	32–35	18–24	40–45	4–7	40–45	95–105	75–85	70–90
1968–69	V8-429	15–20	130–140	25–30	28–33	65–75①	2½–4	40–45	95–105	75–85	75–90

①—Rocker arm stud to cylinder head.

VALVE SPECIFICATIONS

Year	Engine Model	Valve Lash		Valve Angles		Valve Spring Installed Height	Valve Spring Pressure Lbs. @ In.	Stem Clearance		Stem Diameter	
		Int.	Exh.	Seat	Face			Intake	Exhaust	Int.	Exh.
1963-64	V8-390②	.083-.183①		45	44	1 13/16	80 @ 1.82	.001-.0024	.002-.0034	.3711-.3718	.3693-.3700
1964	V8-390③	.050-.150①		45	44	1 13/16	80 @ 1.82	.001-.0024	.001-.0024	.3711-.3718	.3721-.3728
1965-66	V8-390, 428	.050-.150①		45	44	1 13/16	80 @ 1.82	.001-.0024	.001-.0024	.3711-.3718	.3711-.3718
1967	All	.100-.200①		45	44	1 13/16	85@ 1.82	.001-.0024	.001-.0024	.3711-.3718	.3711-.3718
1968	8-390	.100-.200①		45	44	1 13/16	72 @ 1.82	.0010-.0024	.0015-.0032	.3711-.3718	.3706-.3713
1968-69	8-429	.075-.175④		45	44	1 13/16	80 @ 1.81	.0010-.0027	.0010-.0027	.3416-.3423	.3416-.3423

①—Clearance specified is obtained at valve stem with lifter collapsed. See "Valves, Adjust" text.
②—Engines built prior to November 18, 1963.
③—Engines built from November 18, 1963.
④—1968 One turn down after contact. 1969 Non adjustable.

PISTONS, PINS, RINGS, CRANKSHAFT & BEARINGS

Year	Engine Model	Piston Clearance	Ring End Gap①		Wrist-pin Diameter	Rod Bearings		Main Bearings			
			Comp.	Oil		Shaft Diameter	Bearing Clearance	Shaft Diameter	Bearing Clearance	Thrust on Bear. No.	Shaft End Play
1963-64	V8-390	.0017-.0035	.015	.015	.9752	2.4380-2.4388	.0006-.0026	2.7484-2.7492	.0006-.0031	3	.004-.008
1965	V8-390	.0015-.0023	.010	.015	.9752	2.4380-2.4388	.0007-.0028	2.7484-2.7492	③	3	.004-.010
1966-67	8-390, 428	.0015-.0023	.010	.015	.9752	2.4380-2.4388	.0008-.0026	2.7484-2.7492	.0005-.0025	3	.004-.010
1968	8-390	.0015-.0023	.010	.015	.9752	2.4380-2.4388	.0008-.0026	2.7484-2.7492	.0005-.0025	3	.004-.010
1968-69	8-429	.0014-.0022	.010	.015	1.0401	2.4992-2.5000	.0008-.0026	2.9994-3.0003	.0005-.0025	3	.004-.008

①—Fit rings in tapered boxes for clearance listed in tightest portion of ring travel.
③—No. 1 and 3: .0007-.0031"; others .0005-.0028".

REAR AXLE SPECIFICATIONS

Year	Model	Carrier Type	Ring Gear & Pinion Backlash Inch	Nominal Pinion Locating Shim, Inch	Pinion Bearing Preload				Differential Bearing Preload	Pinion Nut Torque Ft.-Lbs.
					New Bearings With Seal Inch-Lbs.	Used Bearings With Seal Inch-Lbs.	New Bearings Less Seal Inch-Lbs.	Used Bearings Less Seal Inch-Lbs.		
1963	All	Removable	.004-.009	.015	17-27	8-12	—	—	2½-3①	175②
1964	All	Removable	.004-.009	.020	22-32	13-17	—	—	2½-3①	175②
1965	All	Removable	.004-.009	.020	22-32	10-14	—	—	2½-3①	175②
1966	All	Removable	.008-.012	.020	17-32③	10-14③	—	—	.008-.012④	②⑤
1967-69	All	Removable	.008-.012	.015	22-32⑥	8-14⑥	—	—	.008-.012④	②⑤

①—Threaded adjusters—notches tight by right-hand adjuster.
②—If torque is not possible, install new spacer.
③—With collapsible spacer. With solid spacer 12½-32½ inch-lbs. without seal; 17-32 inch-lbs. with seal in place.
④—Case spread with new bearings. With used bearings .005-.008".
⑤—With 9" ring gear 175 ft.-lbs. With 9⅜" ring gear 200 ft.-lbs.
⑥—With collapsible spacer. With solid spacer 15-35 inch-lbs. with seal in place.

COOLING SYSTEM & CAPACITY DATA

Year	Model or Engine	Cooling Capacity, Qts.			Radiator Cap Relief Pressure, Lbs.		Thermo. Opening Temp. ①	Fuel Tank Gals.	Engine Oil Refill Qts. ②	Transmission Oil			Rear Axle Oil Pints
		No Heater	With Heater	With A/C	With A/C	No A/C				3 Speed Pints	4 Speed Pints	Auto. Trans. Qts. ④	
1963	All	19	20	20	12–15	12–15	185	20	5	—	—	11½	5
1964	All	19	20	20	12–15	12–15	185	22	5	—	—	10	5
1965	All	19½	20½	20½	12–15	12–15	195	22	5	—	—	10	5
1966	All	19½	20½	20½	12–15	12–15	195	22	4	—	—	③	5
1967	All	19	20	20	12–15	12–15	195	22	4	—	—	13	5
1968	V8-390	19½	20½	20½	12–15	12–15	195	24	4	—	—	13	5
	V8-429	18	19	19	12–15	12–15	195	24	4	—	—	13	5
1969	V8-429	19½	20½	20½	12–15	12–15	195	24	4	—	—	12¾	5

①—With alcohol-type anti-freeze, use a 160-deg. unit.

②—Add one quart with filter change.

③—C6 13 qts., others, 10 qts.

④—Approximate. Make final check with dipstick.

BRAKE SPECIFICATIONS

Year	Model	Brake Drum Inside Diameter	Wheel Cylinder Bore Diameter			Master Cylinder Bore Diameter		
			Front Disc Brakes	Front Drum Brakes	Rear Brakes	With Disc Brakes	With Drum Brakes	With Power Brakes
1963	All	11.03	—	1 3/32	15/16	—	1/8	1/8
1964	All	11.09	—	1 3/32	15/16	—	7/8	1/8
1965	All	11.09	1 15/16	—	15/16	15/16	15/16	15/16
1966	All	11.03	1 15/16	—	15/16	15/16	15/16	15/16
1967	All	11.03	1 15/16	—	15/16	1.00	1.00	1.00
1968–69	All	11.03	2 3/4	—	15/16	1.00	1.00	1.00

Electrical Section

IGNITION TIMING

If a timing light is to be used to set ignition timing, disconnect the vacuum advance pipe to the carburetor and place a piece of tape over open end of pipe. *This is important as carburetor trouble can affect timing adjustments.*

Lacking a power timing light, an accurate method of setting ignition timing with the engine stopped is with the aid of a jumper light. Be sure to use a light bulb that corresponds with the system voltage of the vehicle.

1. Remove distributor cap and rotor and see that the breaker gap is set according to specifications.
2. Rotate engine until No. 1 cylinder is at the ignition timing point as indicated by the timing pointer and timing mark being lined up with each other.
3. Connect the jumper light between distributor ignition terminal and ground.
4. Turn on ignition switch.
5. Loosen distributor and turn it in the direction of normal rotation until the points just close (light out). Then slowly turn distributor in the opposite direction just to the exact point that the light goes on. Tighten distributor in this position.

DISTRIBUTOR, REPLACE

Removal

1. To remove the distributor, disconnect the primary wire and vacuum control pipe. On some models the work may be made easier if the accelerator pull back spring is disconnected.
2. Remove distributor cap.
3. Scribe a mark on the distributor body indicating the position of the rotor, and scribe another mark on the body and engine block indicating position of distributor body in block. These marks can be used as guides when installing distributor in a correctly timed engine.
4. Remove hold down screw or screws and lift distributor out of block. *Do not crank engine while distributor is removed or the initial timing operation will have to be performed.*

Installation

If the crankshaft has not been disturbed, install the distributor, using the scribed marks previously made on the distributor body and engine block as guides.

If the crankshaft has been rotated while the distributor was removed from the engine, it will be necessary to retime the engine. Crank the engine to bring No. 1 piston on top dead center of its compression stroke. Align the timing mark on the vibration damper or pulley with the timing pointer (see *Tune Up* chart). Install the distributor so that the rotor points to the No. 1 spark plug wire terminal in the distributor cap.

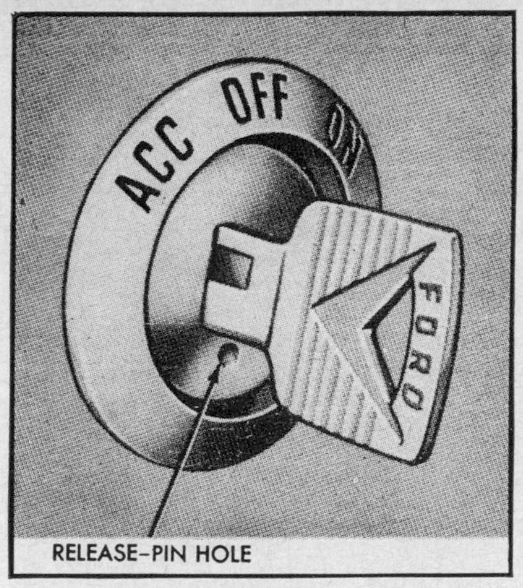

Fig. 1 Ignition switch and lock (typical)

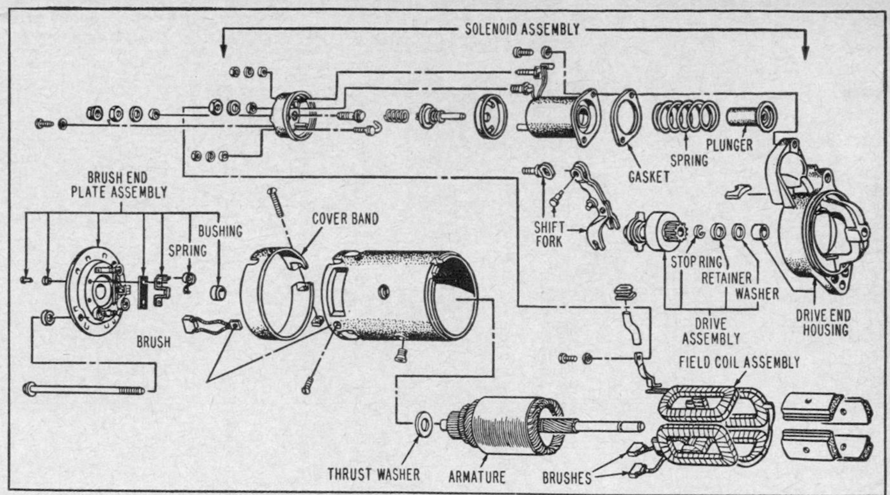

Fig. 1A Solenoid actuated starter. V8-429

NOTE: Make sure the oil pump intermediate shaft properly engages the distributor shaft. It may be necessary to crank the engine with the starter, after the distributor drive gear is properly engaged, in order to engage the oil pump intermediate shaft.

STARTER REPLACE

1968-69

A solenoid actuated starter is used on all V8-429 engines, Fig. 1A. In this starter, the solenoid plunger, being drawn forward when the solenoid coils are energized, first engages the starter drive then closes the starter contacts, thus cranking the engine. When the ignition switch is released, a spring loaded pin pushes the plunger out of the solenoid coils and breaks the circuit in the starting motor.

Referring to Fig. 1A, service procedures are essentially the same as those for the Autolite positive engagement starter outlined in the front of this manual.

Removal

To provide working clearance, turn the front wheels fully to the right and disconnect the steering idler arm from the frame before removing the starter.

When installing the starter, be sure all mating surfaces are clean to insure a good electrical ground. To maintain proper alignment, hold the starter squarely against the mounting plate and fully inserted into the mounting hole while tightening the mounting bolts.

1965-67

1. On 1966 models, remove brace on right side that connects No. 2 crossmember to side rail. On all models, disconnect cable at starter terminal, unfasten and remove starter.
2. Position starter to flywheel housing and start mounting bolts. Snug all bolts, then torque them to 12-15 ft-lbs, tightening the middle bolt first.
3. Connect starter cable.

1963-64

1. Disconnect cable at starter terminal.
2. Unfasten and remove starter.

NOTE: It may be necessary to tilt starter slightly to clear starter drive around flywheel. On high performance engines, remove right exhaust manifold first.

3. Position starter to flywheel housing and start mounting bolts. The transmission dipstick tube bracket is mounted under the starter side mounting bolt.
4. Snug all bolts and then torque them to 15-20 ft-lbs, tightening the middle bolt first.
5. Connect starter cable.

Fig. 2 Light switch. 1964-69

IGNITION SWITCH, REPLACE

1968-69

1. Disconnect battery ground cable.
2. Remove ignition switch lower finish panel.
3. Depress tabs securing connector to rear of switch and pull connector from switch.
4. Remove the bezel nut and remove the switch.

1967

1. Disconnect ground strap at battery.
2. Turn ignition key to accessory position. Slightly depress pin in pin hole on front of lock tumbler, Fig. 1. Turn key counterclockwise and pull key and lock cylinder out of switch.
3. Remove bezel, push switch back part way and remove accessory wire retaining nut.
4. Pull off rubber-covered multiple connector and one push-on connector and remove switch.
5. Reverse procedure to install.

1964-66

1. Disconnect a battery cable.
2. Turn ignition key to accessory position. With a paper clip, slightly depress pin, Fig. 1, turn key counterclockwise and pull key and lock cylinder out of switch. If only lock cylinder is to be replaced, proceed to Step 9.
3. Remove lower instrument panel shield (5 screws).
4. Press in on rear of switch and rotate it counterclockwise ⅛ turn (as viewed from terminal end). Remove bezel and switch.
5. Remove lock nut and retaining nut and pull connector from switch.

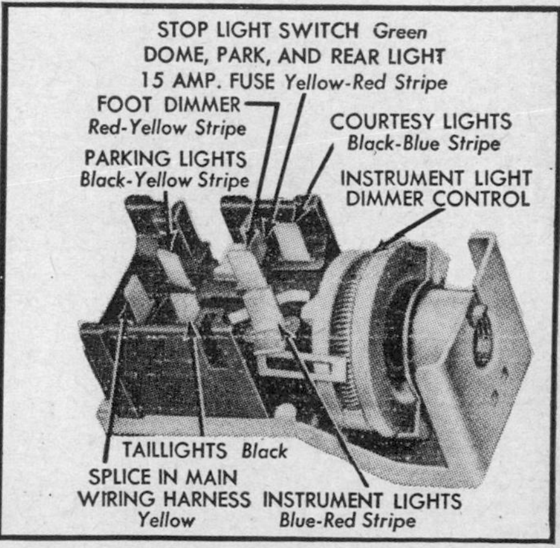

Fig. 3 Light switch assembly. 1963

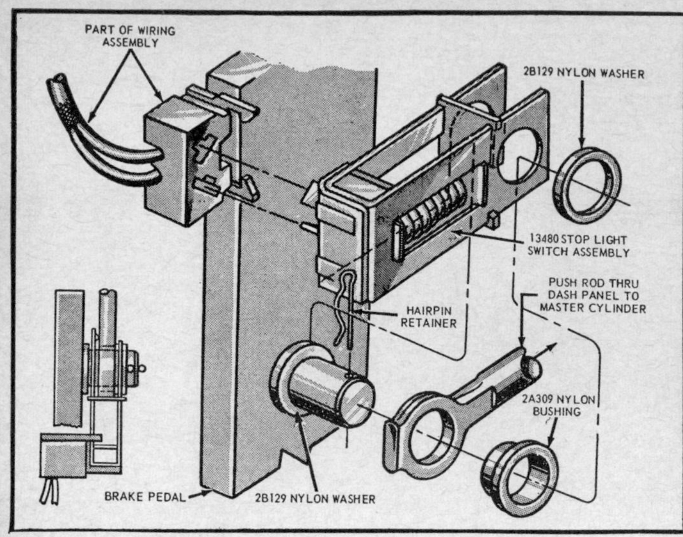

Fig. 4 Mechanical stop light switch. 1965-69

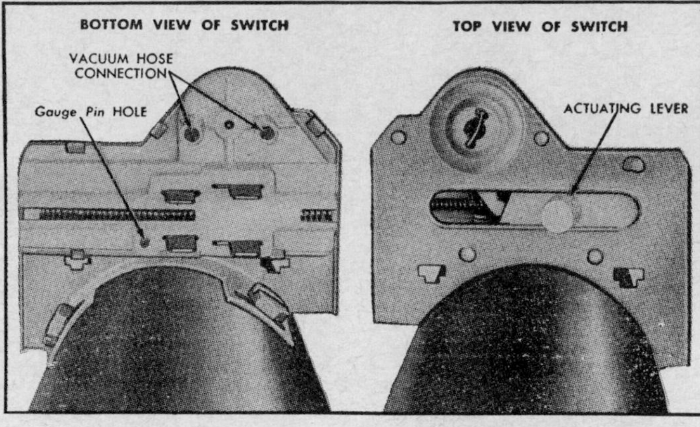

Fig. 5 Neutral start switch showing parking brake vacuum connections. 1967 with C6 transmission and 1964-65 with Cruiseomatic

6. If a new switch as well as lock cylinder is to be installed, insert a screwdriver into lock opening of switch and turn slot in switch to full counterclockwise position.
7. Install connector to switch with retaining and lock nuts.
8. Position switch in instrument panel with light bulb and retainer. Position bezel in instrument panel. Rotate switch ⅛ turn to lock it in bezel.
9. If a new lock cylinder is to be installed, insert key in cylinder and turn it to accessory position. Place lock and key in switch. Depress pin slightly and turn counterclockwise. Push lock cylinder into switch and turn key to check operation of lock cylinder.
10. Install lower instrument panel shield. Connect battery cable and check operation of switch.

1963

1. Disconnect a battery cable.
2. Turn ignition key to accessory position.
3. Use a paper clip in small hole in lock cylinder face, Fig. 1, depress pin and turn key counterclockwise. Then pull key and lock cylinder out of switch. If only lock cylinder is to be replaced, proceed to Step 9.
4. Press in on rear of switch and rotate it ⅛ turn counterclockwise (as viewed from terminal end). Remove bezel and switch.
5. Remove insulated plug and wires from rear of switch.
6. If new switch as well as lock cylinder is to be installed, insert a screwdriver into lock opening of ignition switch and turn slot in switch to full counterclockwise position.
7. To install, connect insulated plug and accessory wires to back of switch.
8. Place switch in its opening, press it toward instrument panel and install bezel.
9. If a new lock cylinder is to be installed, insert key and turn it to accessory position. Place cylinder and key in switch, depress pin slightly, Fig. 1, and push key counterclockwise. Push lock cylinder into switch. Turn key to check operation of lock cylinder.
10. Connect battery cable and check switch operation.

LIGHT SWITCH, REPLACE

1968-69

1. Disconnect battery ground cable.
2. Remove three screws attaching air control assembly to the lower left side of instrument panel and lower the assembly.
3. Remove control knob and shaft by pressing release button on switch housing with knob in full "ON" position. Pull knob and shaft out of switch.
4. Remove retaining bezel nut and remove switch from instrument panel through the air control assembly opening.
5. Reverse procedure to install.

1967

1. Remove control knob and shaft by pressing release button on switch housing with knob in full "ON" position. Pull knob and shaft out of switch.
2. Remove retaining nut and switch from instrument panel.
3. Reverse procedure to install.

1964-66

1. Remove control knob and shaft by pressing knob release button on switch housing, Fig. 2, with knob in full "On" position. Pull knob out of switch.
2. Unscrew mounting nut, remove switch and disconnect wiring connector.
3. To install, attach wiring connector, insert switch in panel and install mounting nut.
4. Install knob and shaft assembly by inserting it all the way into switch until a distinct click is heard. In some instances it may be necessary to rotate shaft slightly until it engages switch contact carrier.

1963

1. Remove control knob and shaft by pressing knob release button on switch housing, Fig. 3, with knob in "Off" position. Turn shaft slightly and pull it out of switch.
2. Unscrew mounting nut, remove bezel and switch wires (or moulded connector).
3. To install switch, connect wires or moulded connector, insert switch in instrument panel and install bezel and mounting nut.
4. Install knob and shaft assembly by inserting it into switch until a click is heard. In some instances it may be necessary to rotate shaft slightly until it engages switch contact carrier.

STOP LIGHT SWITCH, REPLACE

1965-69

1. Disconnect wires at connector.
2. Remove hairpin retainer. Slide stop light switch, push rod and nylon washers and bushing away from pedal, and remove switch, Fig. 4.
3. Position switch, push rod, bushing and washers on brake pedal pin in the order shown, and install hairpin retainer.
4. Connect wires and install wires in clip.

1963-64

Disconnect wires at bullet connectors and unscrew switch from brake master cylinder. Have the new switch ready to install as soon as the old switch is removed to avoid undue loss of brake fluid.

NEUTRAL SAFETY SWITCH

1969

Adjustment Procedure

1. Loosen retaining screws and with

selector lever held lightly against the Neutral stop, rotate switch until a start is obtained. Tighten attaching screws to 20 in-lbs.

2. With the switch properly adjusted, place selector lever in the "1" position and push the Park reset button to the left until it stops. *The Park reset must be performed whenever the switch has been adjusted.*

1968

To adjust the switch it must be removed from the column. Put the selector lever in neutral and set the parking brake. Then disconnect the electrical and vacuum connections and remove the two fastening screws to allow the switch to be lifted straight up and out.

Adjustment Procedure

1. Hold the switch with the wire terminal facing you. Move the actuator all the way to the left, but do not force as the switch will be damaged internally.
2. Insert a $\frac{3}{32}$" drill shank in the hole in the tapered round boss facing you.
3. Gently but firmly move the actuator lever back to the right until it stops. This will move the Park circuit to its position of minimum travel, which must be done if the switch is to function properly upon installation.
4. Pull out the drill gauge and fit it into the hole on the top surface of the switch case to engage the switch internal carrier in the neutral position.
5. Reinsert the drill gauge.
6. With the transmission selector lever held against the stop in the neutral detent position, set the switch in place on the column and fasten it with the two screws.
7. Connect the electrical connector and any vacuum hose, and be sure to remove the drill gauge before operating the selector lever.

1964-66 Cruiseomatic, 1967 C6

Column Shift, Fig. 5

1. With manual linkage properly adjusted, check starter engagement circuit in all selector lever positions. The circuit must be open in all drive positions and closed only in Park and Neutral.
2. To adjust, loosen switch mounting screws. Place transmission selector lever firmly against stop of neutral detent position.
3. Rotate switch actuating lever until gauge pin (#43 drill) can be inserted in gauge pin holes.
4. Tighten switch retaining screws and remove gauge pin.

1966 with C6 Trans.

1. With manual linkage properly adjusted, check starter engagement circuit in all selector lever positions. The circuit must be open in all drive positions and be closed only in park and neutral.
2. To adjust switch, loosen retaining screws that locate switch on steering column.
3. Place selector lever firmly against

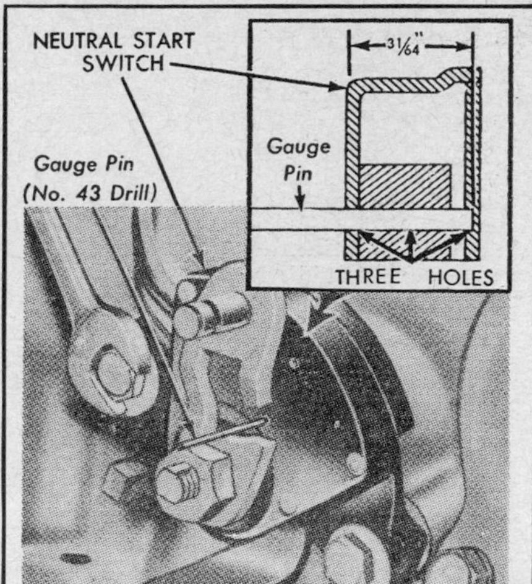

Fig. 6 Neutral start switch on transmission. 1966 with C6 transmission

stop of neutral detent position.

4. Rotate switch actuating lever until a #43 drill can be inserted in the gauge pin holes, Fig. 5.
5. Tighten two switch retaining screws and remove drill gauge.
6. Check operation of switch in each selector position. The starter should operate only when the lever is in P or N positions.

1963

1. Check the starter circuit in all selector lever positions.
2. If the starter operates when the lever is in P or N position adjust the switch.
3. Loosen the switch mounting screws and position the switch as required so the circuit is closed only when the lever is in P or N.

HORN SOUNDER

1969 Rim-Blow Type

The rubber insert and copper strip is not replaceable. If a new insert assembly is required, the entire steering wheel will have to be replaced.

1. Remove pad from steering wheel.
2. Remove medallion from pad.
3. After removing the retaining nut, the steering wheel can be removed with a suitable puller.

1966-69 Except Rim-Blow Type

1. Disconnect battery ground cable.
2. Remove center medallion from wheel.
3. Remove three screws from center of wheel and remove horn buttons.
4. Reverse procedure to install.

1963-65

1. Unsnap hub cap from horn ring. Remove wheel nut and pull wheel from steering shaft.

TURN SIGNAL SWITCH, REPLACE

1968-69

Fixed Column

The combination turn signal and hazard warning switch for cars with fixed steering columns has been redesigned in that the warning switch knob is an integral part of the switch and is no longer replaceable. Electric wiring is bonded for ease of installation.

1. Disconnect battery and remove steering wheel.
2. Remove protective wire cover that runs along bottom of steering column tube and disconnect electrical plug, noting the color codes and location.
3. If equipped with speed control, remove the sleeve around the wiring and pull the first three speed control wires out of the column.
4. Remove turn signal lever, then remove three screws holding the switch to the column and lift switch from column.
5. Reverse procedure to install.

1967-69

Tilt Column

1. Disconnect ground cable at battery.
2. Remove steering wheel.
3. Unscrew turn indicator lever.
4. Remove emergency flasher control knob.
5. Remove upper tilt mechanism cover (2 screws).
6. Remove five screws from lower finish panel under steering column and remove plate.
7. Disconnect multiple connector beneath instrument panel and at base of steering column.
8. Disconnect connector block from bullet connectors by depressing tabs one at a time and remove plastic cover over wires.
9. Position lower collar down and remove plastic clip from side of steering column.
10. Remove two screws from switch and remove switch and wires from column.
11. Reverse procedure to install.

1964-66

1. Remove steering wheel.
2. Unscrew signal lever.
3. Remove switch mounting bracket screw, then remove switch and bracket.
4. Remove conical tension spring and switch actuating arm.
5. Disconnect switch wires from bullet connectors. Remove wire protector from side of steering column.
6. Remove switch-to-mounting bracket screws, and remove switch and wires.

NOTE: When installing the new switch, make certain that canceling cam on steering wheel makes contact with canceling pawls on switch. The clearance between steering wheel hub and steering shaft housing flange should not be more than $\frac{1}{16}$" for proper switch canceling. Reposition steering shaft housing if necessary.

1963

1. Remove steering wheel and horn button contact support.
2. Unscrew actuating lever, remove conical tension spring and switch actuating arm.
3. Remove signal switch (2 screws).
4. Disconnect wires at steering column.
5. Attach heavy cord to wire ends and pull switch wires from steering column.
6. Reverse procedure to install, using the heavy cord to pull switch wires down through steering column.

INSTRUMENT CLUSTER

1968-69

The instrument cluster is a new design. The face covering gives the illusion of five integrated housings. Actually, only the four to the left form the main cluster; the right housing is attached to the main instrument panel. The housings cannot be removed individually until the cluster cover, lens and mask have been removed.

1967 Fuel & Oil Gauge

1. Loosen set screw at bottom of gauge pod.
2. Remove screw from upper inner surface of pod.
3. Pull gauge and pod assembly straight out from instrument cluster.
4. Separate housing from lens and bezel (3 screws).
5. Remove four nuts and insulators and remove gauge unit.
6. Reverse procedure to install.

1967 Ammeter & Temperature Gauge

1. Loosen set screw on underside of gauge housing and remove screw from upper part of housing.
2. Pull gauge assembly from instrument cluster.
3. Separate face from back (3 screws).
4. Remove gauge unit (4 nuts).
5. Reverse procedure to install.

1967 Speedometer

1. Loosen set screw at bottom of speedometer pod.
2. Remove screw from upper inner surface of pod.
3. Pull speedometer and pod assembly straight and away from instrument panel.
4. Remove speedometer from front housing (3 screws).
5. Remove speedometer from rear housing (2 screws).
6. Reverse procedure to install.

1965-66

The fuel gauge, oil pressure gauge and temperature gauge can be replaced without removing the instrument cluster. To replace the speedometer, constant voltage regulator or charge indicator gauge it is necessary to remove the cluster.

1. Disconnect battery ground cable.
2. Remove light switch and radio knobs.
3. Remove instrument panel (2 pieces).
4. Remove light switch screws and push switch toward front of car.
5. Remove console panel finish molding cap, then remove left lower half of cluster housing (5 screws).
6. Remove clock housing screws and rotate clock housing upward and rearward to expose the two tab screws retaining instrument panel upper molding. Remove these screws.
7. Remove five screws under cluster. Pull molding away from instrument panel for access to cluster screws.
8. Remove four instrument indicator cover screws and remove covers.
9. Through indicator openings, remove four screws retaining lower cluster to upper cluster. Position four instrument covers on instruments to prevent damage. Install retaining screw on charge indicator cover.
10. Remove four screws retaining speedometer cluster to instrument panel at top of cluster, and position speedometer cluster out from instrument panel.
11. Disconnect light bulbs from across top of speedometer. Remove wiring harness from plastic clips, disconnect speedometer cable and constant voltage regulator wires and remove speedometer cluster.
12. Unfasten and remove speedometer housing. Then separate speedometer from housing cover.
13. Reverse procedure to install.

1964

The fuel gauge, oil pressure gauge, temperature gauge and charge indicator gauge can be replaced without removing the instrument cluster. To replace the speedometer or constant voltage regulator, the instrument cluster must be removed.

1. Disconnect battery ground cable.
2. Remove windshield wiper and washer control knobs and both air vent control knobs from below clock housing.
3. Remove four screws from clock housing. Disconnect all light bulbs and wires from clock housing and remove housing.
4. Remove radio control knobs and bezel.
5. Remove console applique retaining screws, disconnect power window wires and speed control, and remove console applique.
6. Remove rear console molding (2 screws).
7. Remove right-hand console molding.
8. Remove instrument panel applique retaining screws. Remove light switch knob and bezel and remove instrument panel applique.
9. Unfasten (3 screws) and pull light switch from cluster.
10. Remove four screws retaining upper console to cluster molding and remove molding.
11. Remove lower cluster joint cover plate (1 screw).
12. Disconnect speedometer cable.
13. Remove lower instrument panel cover plate.
14. Remove instrument cluster screws and rest cluster on protected area of steering column. (Tape column to prevent scratches.)
15. Disconnect all gauges and light bulbs.
16. Remove cluster wiring harness from four clips and remove cluster assembly.
17. Reverse procedure to install.

1963

Remove screw retaining chrome trim ring and remove ring. Remove mounting screws and pull speedometer far enough from instrument panel to disconnect cable and remove pilot lights.

Make certain all pilot lights are secure in their mounting holes when installing speedometer. The top pilot light is the high beam indicator.

W/S WIPER MOTOR, REPLACE

1967-69

Procedure remains the same as 1966 models except that the cowl top panel is retained with eight screws and the two rear hood panel bumpers instead of 14 retaining screws. The wiper motor is attached to the upper cowl panel with three screws instead of two.

1964-66

1. Remove wiper arm and blades.
2. Remove pivot shaft bezel.
3. Remove air cleaner.
4. Remove cowl top panel (14 screws).
5. Remove seal plate from dash panel (2 screws).
6. Remove two clips retaining wiper links to motor. Rotate link to remove left clip.
7. Disconnect hydraulic line under hood.
8. Disconnect hydraulic line in cowl from motor.
9. Unfasten motor from mounting bracket (2 bolts). Disconnect control cable and remove motor.

1963

1. To remove the motor, remove the speaker grille and speaker.
2. Disconnect the antenna at the radio.
3. Remove wiper arm and blades, pivot shaft nuts and bezels.
4. Remove cowl top panel with antenna.
5. Disconnect both pivot shaft links at wiper motor.
6. Remove air cleaner.
7. *Caution: Use care in disconnecting hydraulic lines so as not to burn hands with hot hydraulic fluid.*
8. Disconnect inlet line at wiper motor fitting and remove fitting.
9. Remove inlet seal plate and seal from dash panel.
10. Remove wiper motor mounting screws (underside of motor).
11. Disconnect outlet line and control cable from motor and remove motor.
12. Reverse removal procedure to install the motor. Then start engine and check operation of motor. Stop engine and add fluid to power steering reservoir if necessary.

W/S WIPER SWITCH, REPLACE

1968-69

1. Disconnect battery ground cable.
2. Remove five screws attaching the top of the cluster bezel to the instrument panel. Loosen five screws attaching bottom of the bezel to the instrument panel pad retainer and remove the bezel.
3. Remove three screws attaching the wiper and rear vent control to the instrument panel.
4. Disconnect vacuum hoses, lights and push on connector; remove the cable retaining clip; and remove the control assembly from the cluster.
5. Remove the knobs from control assembly.
6. Remove two wiper control attaching screws and remove control.
7. Reverse procedure to install.

1967

Procedure remains the same as 1966 models except for the differences stated under *W/S Wiper Motor, Replace*

1963-66

1. Disconnect battery cable.
2. Remove wiper, washer and right-and left-hand air vent control knobs.
3. Unfasten and lower clock housing. Then disconnect two courtesy light wires (4 screws).
4. Unfasten wiper control from control plate (2 screws).
5. Remove wiper arms and blades.
6. Remove wiper pivot shaft bezel and nuts.
7. Remove cowl top panel (14 screws).
8. Disconnect control cable from motor.
9. From passenger compartment, pull cable through dash panel and remove wiper control and cable assembly.
10. Reverse above procedure to install. However, before connecting courtesy light wires, be sure to position one wire over wiper control cable and the other wire over air vent control cable.

W/S WIPER TRANSMISSION, REPLACE

1967-69

Procedure remains the same as 1966 models except for the differences stated under *W/S Wiper Motor, Replace.*

1963-66

1. Remove wiper arms and blades.
2. Remove wiper pivot shaft bezel and nuts.
3. Remove cowl top panel (14 screws).
4. Remove clip retaining link to motor. Rotate link to remove left clips.
5. Remove one nut and two bolts retaining pivot shaft and link to cowl and remove.
6. Reverse above procedure to install.

RADIO REPLACE

NOTE: When installing radio, be sure to adjust antenna trimmer for peak performance.

1968-69

1. Disconnect battery ground cable.
2. Pull knobs off radio control shafts.
3. Remove cover plate located below steering column.
4. Remove six screws and remove trim applique from in front of radio.
5. Remove nut and washer from right radio control shaft.
6. Remove screw attaching the front left side of radio to instrument panel.
7. Remove radio rear support attaching screw.
8. Disconnect radio power wires and speaker leads at connectors.
9. Disconnect antenna lead in cable and remove radio.
10. Reverse procedure to install.

1967

1. Disconnect ground strap from battery.
2. Remove inspection hole cover plate below steering column.
3. It may be necessary to remove vacuum motor on inboard side of tilt swing column to provide clearance for radio. If so, position wheel in any position but PARK, and remove vacuum motor.
4. Remove two knobs and discs from radio.
5. Remove sleeve or fader control and two hex nuts on radio shafts.
6. Remove radio rear support bracket.
7. Slide radio forward and down toward inspection hole.
8. Disconnect multiple connector and antenna lead-in cable and remove radio.
9. Reverse procedure to install.

1964-66

1. Pry off right and left side console mouldings and remove retainers.
2. Pry off right and left side instrument panel chrome mouldings.
3. Remove six screws and two bolts retaining lower right and left side finish mouldings to instrument panel and pull finish panels away from instrument panel.
4. Remove right and left side console finish panels.
5. Unfasten lower end of radio from support brackets (2 screws).
6. Remove radio knobs and bezel nuts.
7. Disconnect antenna and speaker connectors and remove radio.

1963

1. With ignition switch off, remove speaker grille and speaker.
2. Remove control knobs, two hex mounting nuts, the bezel, and two radio mounting nuts and washers.
3. Remove radio access cover and radio lower center support screw.
4. Remove radio through speaker opening.

HEATER CORE REMOVAL

1967-69

1. Remove hood and carburetor air cleaner.
2. Disconnect vacuum supply hose on top of heater case and pull it away from case mounting studs and disconnect hydraulic lines at wiper motor.
3. Remove transmission dipstick and tube.
4. Disconnect multiple connector leading to thermostat switch inside heater case cover and to resistor on front of cover.
5. Remove five nuts and two screws from heater core case cover and take off cover.
6. Slide heater core from case.

1966

1. Remove molding from right instrument panel and from right side of console.
2. Remove three screws and two bolts from lower right instrument panel and remove panel.
3. Disconnect heater resistor plug and remove seven screws from recirculating air grille and take off grille.
4. Remove two screws from front of heater core cover and loosen seven nuts from engine side of dash that secure heater assembly.
5. Pull heater away from dash, disconnect cable and push fresh air duct out of the way to reach rear screws of heater core housing.
6. Remove two screws from rear of housing and take out core.

1965

1. Remove lower instrument panel and right-hand trim panel from shift console.
2. Disconnect defroster hose at heater, control cables from heater control head and fresh air door and all wiring.
3. From engine side, remove four nuts retaining heater to dash and rear support screw near fresh air intake.
4. From inside car, lower heater to floor, take off core access plate and remove core.

1963-64

1. Remove instrument panel end covers, lower extension pad and trim.
2. Remove heater front cover and access plate of thermostat valve.
3. Disconnect thermostat valve cable and remove heater core. On 1964 models it is necessary to separate entire heater from car before core can be removed.

SPEED CONTROLS

1967-69

Bead Chain Adjustment

This is the only adjustment required for proper functioning of the system and assure a normal engine idle.

Adjust the chain to maintain ½" to 1" ball slack with engine at hot idle, Fig. 7.

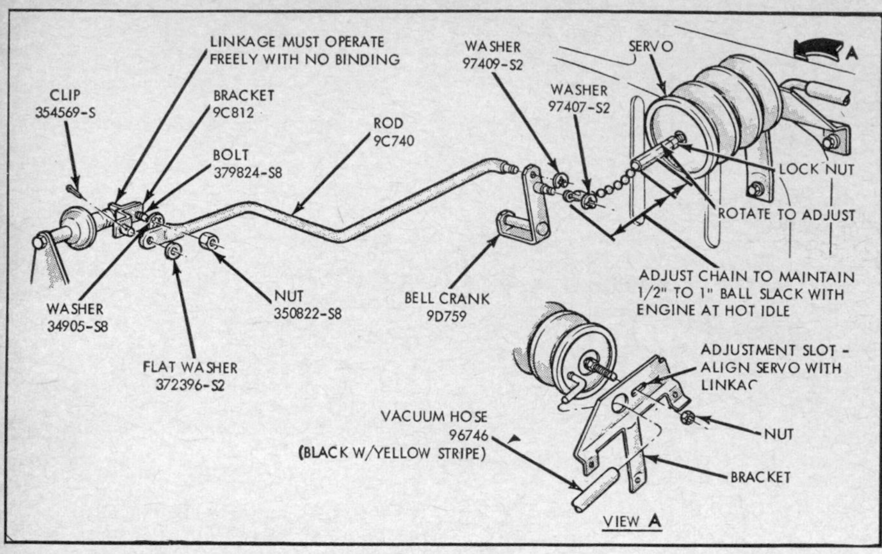

Fig. 7 Servo assembly and accelerator linkage. 1967-69

1966

Accelerator Linkage Adjust

Improper accelerator linkage adjustment can result in engine not returning to normal idle, the system not controlling at high speeds, or a lag in response to speed changes.

1. Remove air cleaner.
2. Check adjustment of throttle linkage to be sure it is correct.
3. Place linkage against hot idle adjusting screw with engine stopped.
4. Loosen adjusting nuts on vacuum bellows.
5. With vacuum bellows in released position, move adjusting nuts until there is about ¼ inch clearance between carburetor stud and end of slot in accelerator, Fig. 8.
6. Tighten adjusting nuts and install air cleaner.

Brake Retard Ball Chain, Adjust

The brake retard bracket has five notches in which to attach the ball chain. To obtain proper deceleration, the ball chain must be installed in the bracket as per color coding, Fig. 9. The color coding is visible by looking up under the instrument panel. The color coding compensates for differences in building of the cars.

NOTE: The amount of deceleration provided by the brake retard system may be further adjusted to the individual driver's preference by lowering the ball chain one notch to increase the rate of deceleration. Raising the ball chain one notch will decrease the rate of deceleration.

1964-65

Brake Release Switch

1. Remove plug connector from inhibitor switch and install a jumper wire.
2. Remove plug connector from vacuum valve.
3. Ground one lead of a test lamp and touch other lead to red wire from vacuum valve.
4. Turn ignition switch to ACC position. Pull out switch button to ON position.
5. Depress brake pedal; test light should go out within first ¼ inch of travel measured at bottom of brake pedal pad.
6. If test lamp does not go out in ¼ inch of pedal pad travel, loosen brake pedal bracket attaching bolts and position bracket so it just clears plunger of brake release switch.
7. Vehicles equipped with power brakes should have the engine started and brake pedal depressed several times to assure correct operation of brake release switch with vacuum applied to power brake booster.
8. If brake switch cannot be adjusted, it must be replaced.

Accelerator Linkage, Adjust

Improper accelerator linkage adjustment can result in engine not returning to normal idle, the unit not allowing control at high speeds, or a lag in response to speed changes.

1. Disconnect ball chain from accelerator pedal arm attachment.
2. Check throttle linkage adjustment, being sure that linkage is against normal idle adjusting screw with engine stopped.
3. With vacuum bellows in released position, hold ball chain taut to accelerator pedal arm attachment. Hold attachment up in its normal position.
4. Allow one-half to one ball slack in chain. Cut off extra chain and reconnect chain to accelerator pedal arm attachment. If chain is too short a new chain must be installed.

Control Cable, Adjust

1. Remove two vacuum hoses and air filter from metering valve.
2. Loosen jam nut from cam adjusting nut.
3. Rotate selector dial against low speed stop.
4. Rotate cam adjusting nut until clearance between cam follower lever and speed setting cam is $\frac{3}{16}$ inch. *As shown in Fig. 10, the $\frac{1}{16}$ inch clearance applies to early 1965 units without an inhibitor switch.*
5. Tighten jam nut snugly against cam adjusting nut. The cam adjusting nut is designed to be loose in the metering valve; it cannot be held tight.
6. Install air filter and the two vacuum hoses.

NOTE: When there is insufficient thread for cable adjustment when installing a new metering valve, proceed as follows:

1. Remove two vacuum hoses and air filter from metering valve.
2. Remove first screw from control cable cover plate and loosen other screw.
3. Rotate cover plate so it faces upward.
4. Remove control cable rack from speed setting cam pinion.

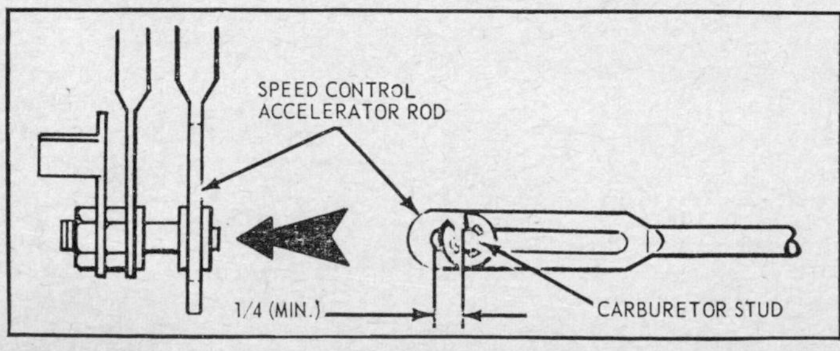

Fig. 8 Accelerator linkage adjustment. 1966

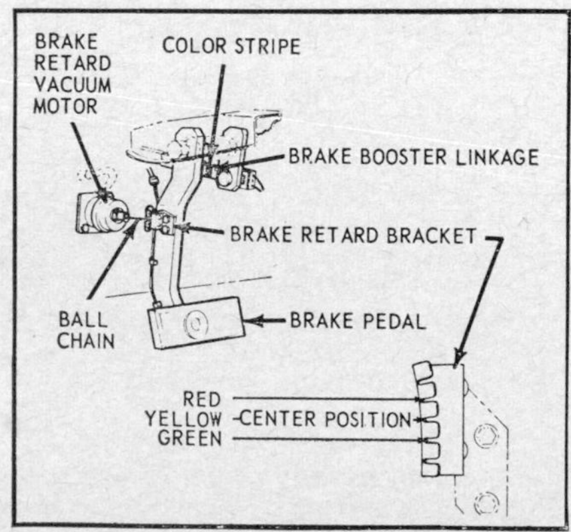

Fig. 9 Brake retard ball chain adjustment. 1966

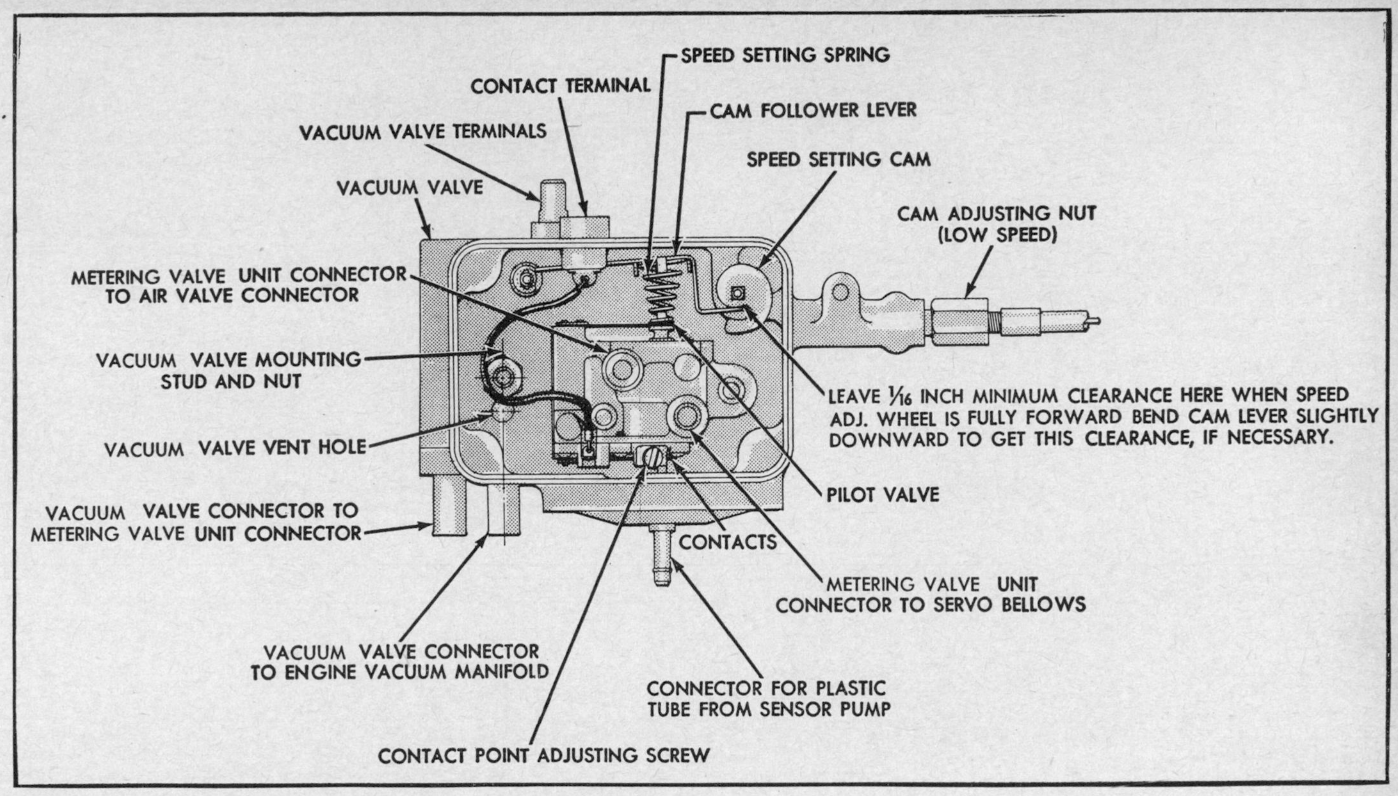

Fig. 10 Metering valve details, 1964-65. The 1/16" setting applies to early 1965 units not having an inhibitor switch; otherwise clearance is 3/16"

5. Replace metering valve if required.
6. Position speed setting cam to provide approximately $\frac{3}{16}$" clearance to cam follower lever ($\frac{1}{16}$ inch on early 1965 units without inhibitor switch).
7. Rotate selector dial against low speed stop.
8. Loosen jam nut. Position jam nut so that there are three threads visible beyond jam nut. Position cam adjusting nut against jam nut.
9. Install control cable rack onto speed setting cam pinion. Try to maintain $\frac{3}{16}$ inch (or $\frac{1}{16}$ inch on early 1965 units) clearance.
10. With jam adjusting nut in its groove, lower control cable cover plate and install and tighten attaching screws.
11. Final control cable adjustment is made as outlined previously.

Engine Section

ENGINE, REPLACE

Because of engine compartment tolerances, the engine should not be removed and installed with the transmission attached.

1. Drain cooling system and crankcase.
2. Remove radiator and air cleaner.
3. Remove hood.
4. Remove fuel and vacuum lines and all hoses, wires and linkage attached to engine.
5. Disconnect exhaust pipe from manifolds.
6. Remove starter and automatic transmission filler tube (if equipped).
7. Remove converter or flywheel housing lower cover.
8. Remove clutch release linkage (if equipped).
9. Support transmission with jack.
10. Unfasten converter or flywheel housing from engine.
11. Remove engine mounting bolts and lift engine out of chassis.

CYLINDER HEAD REPLACE

NOTES

Before installing cylinder head, wipe off engine block gasket surface and be certain no foreign material has fallen into cylinder bores, bolt holes or in the valve lifter area. It is good practice to clean out bolt holes with compressed air.

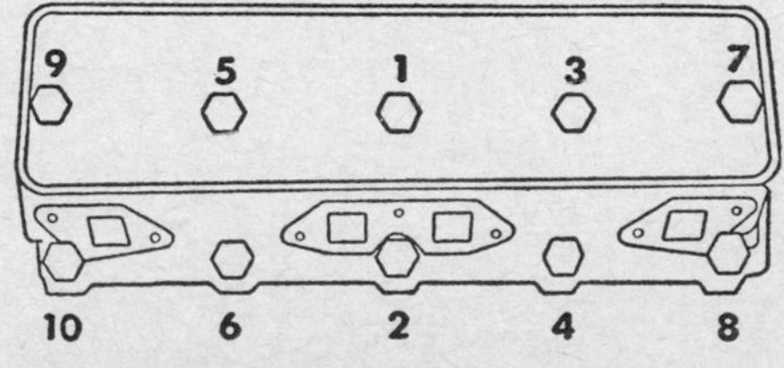

Fig. 1 Cylinder head tightening sequence

Some cylinder head gaskets are coated with a special lacquer to provide a good seal once the parts have warmed up. Do not use any additional sealer on such gaskets. If the gasket does not have this lacquer coating, apply suitable sealer to both sides.

Tighten cylinder head bolts a little at a time in three steps in the sequence shown in the illustrations. Final tightening should be to the torque specifications listed in the *Engine Tightening* table. After the bolts have been torqued to specifications, *they should not be disturbed.*

In instances where cylinder head gasket leakage is hard to control, aluminum paint can be applied to the gasket as a sealer.

Spray one coat of the aluminum paint on both sides of the gasket and allow the paint to dry. Then spray a second coat on both sides and, while the paint is still wet, install the gasket. Torque the head and manifold bolts to specifi-

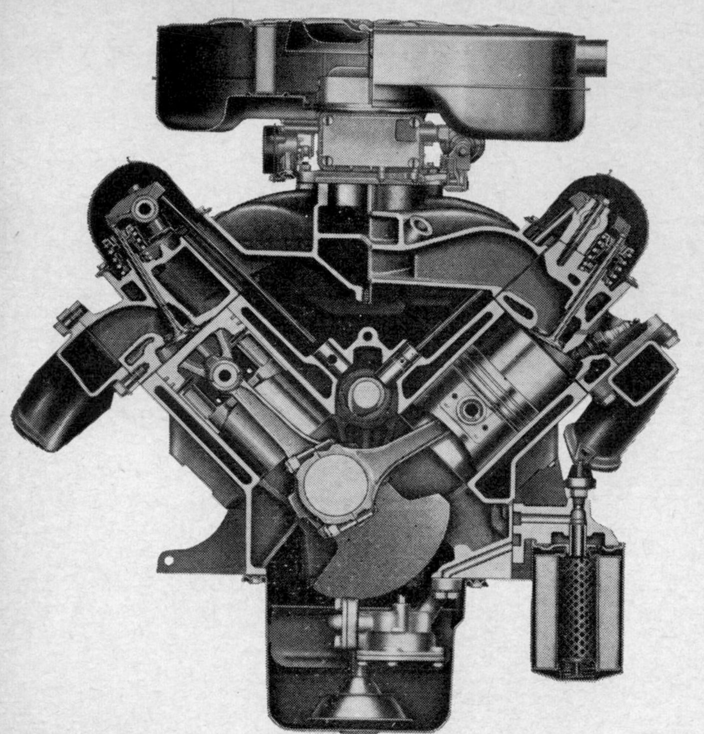

Cross section of V8-390, 428 engines

Engine lubrication system. V8-390, 428

cations to complete the job.

1963-69

1. Remove intake manifold, carburetor and radiator supply tank as a unit.
2. Disconnect exhaust pipes from manifolds. It may also be necessary to unbolt and lay aside the power steering pump, air conditioning compressor and mounting bracket. On 1968-69 models, remove air conditioning evaporator housing and capillary tube as an assembly from dash panel.
3. Remove bolts and lift off head.
4. Install cylinder heads in reverse order of removal and tighten bolts in the sequence shown in Fig. 1.

NOTE

The cylinder head gaskets are marked "Top" or "Front" stamped near the front end of the gasket. The gasket is properly installed when the word is at the forward end of the engine and water passage holes line up. This results in the sealing beads on the right head gasket being inverted with respect to the left head gasket.

ROCKER ARM STUDS

V8-429

Rocker arm studs are screwed into threaded bores in the cylinder head bosses. To install, apply water resistant sealer to stud threads that screw into cylinder head. Install stud and torque to 65-75 ft-lbs. Apply Lubriplate to top of valve stem and at push rod guide in cylinder head. Install rocker arm, fulcrum and stud nut.

ROCKER ARM SERVICE

V8-390, 428

To disassemble the rocker arms, remove cotter pins from each end of the shaft and remove the flat washers and spring washers. Slide rocker arms, springs and supports off shaft, being sure to identify all parts so they can be assembled in the same position.

If it is necessary to remove the plugs from each end of the shaft, drill or pierce one plug, then insert a steel rod through the plug and knock out the plug on the opposite end. Working from the open end, knock out the remaining plug.

Assemble the rocker arms and related parts, Fig. 2.

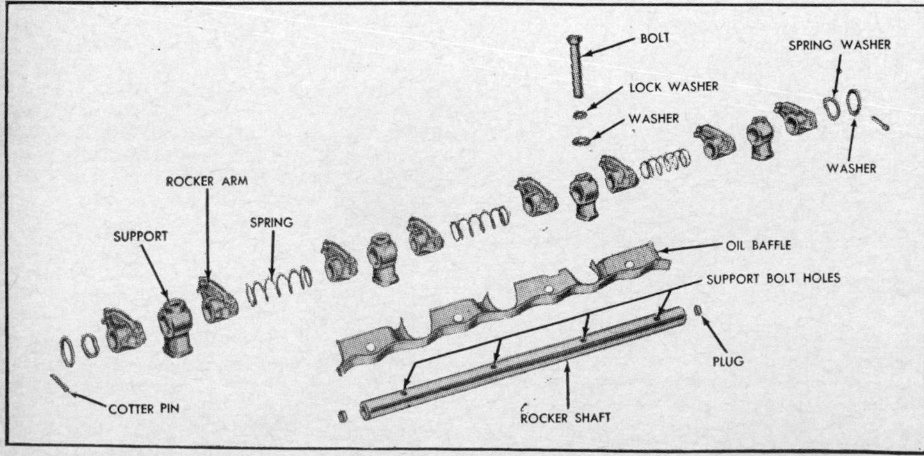

Fig. 2 Valve rocker shaft assembly. V8-390, 428

VALVE LIFT SPECS.

Engine	Year	Intake	Exhaust
8-390	1963-65	.408	.408
	1963①	.453	.453
	1966-67	.437	.437
	1968	.440	.440
8-428	1966-67	.437	.437
8-429	1968-69	.443	.486

①—With three carbs.

VALVE TIMING

Intake Opens Before TDC

Engine	Year	Degrees
8-390	1963-65	26
	1963①	28½
	1966-67	16
	1968	18
8-428	1966-67	16
8-429	1968-69	16

①—With three carbs.

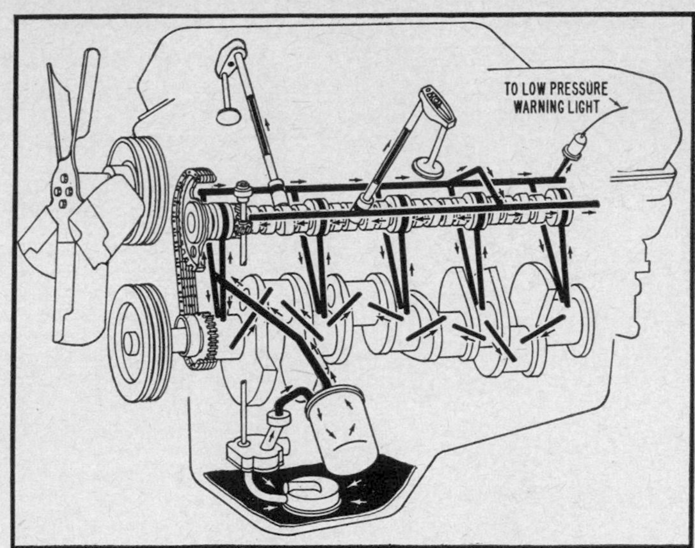

Engine lubrication system. V8-429

VALVE ARRANGEMENT

Front to Rear

V8-390, 428 ....E-I-E-I-I-E-I-E
V8-429 Right Bank .....I-E-I-E-I-E-I-E
V8-429 Left Bank.......E-I-E-I-E-I-E-I

VALVES, ADJUST

1969 V8-429

A positive stop rocker arm stud and nut is used to eliminate the need of adjusting valve lash.

It is very important that the correct push rod be used and all components be installed and torqued as follows.

1. Position the piston of the cylinder being worked on at TDC of its compression stroke.
2. Install rocker arm stud and torque to 65-75 ft-lbs.
3. Lubricate and install rocker arm and fulcrum.
4. Thread nut onto stud until it contacts stud shoulder. Torque to 18-22 in-lbs.

1968 V8-429

Rotate crankshaft until No. 1 piston is on TDC at the end of compression stroke. Loosen rocker arm stud nut until there is end clearance in the push rod. This may be determined by moving the push rod with the fingers as the stud nut is tightened. When the push rod-to-rocker arm clearance has been eliminated, tighten the stud nut an additional 1 turn to place the hydraulic lifter in the desired operating range.

Repeat this procedure for the remaining set of valves in the firing order sequence, which is 1-5-4-2-6-3-7-8.

V8-390, 428

For these engines a .060″ shorter push rod (color coded white) or a .060″ longer push rod (color coded yellow) are available for service to provide a means of compensating for dimensional changes in the valve mechanism. Valve stem-to-rocker arm clearance should be as listed in the *Valve Specifications* table, with the hydraulic lifter completely collapsed. Repeated valve grind jobs will decrease this clearance to the point that if not compensated for the lifters will cease to function.

To check the clearance, bring the piston of the cylinder being checked on top dead center of the compression stroke. Then with hydraulic lifter collapsed, check the clearance between valve stem and rocker arm. If the clearance is less than the minimum, the .060″ shorter push rod should be used. If clearance is more than the maximum, the .060″ longer push rod should be used. (See *Valve Specifications* table).

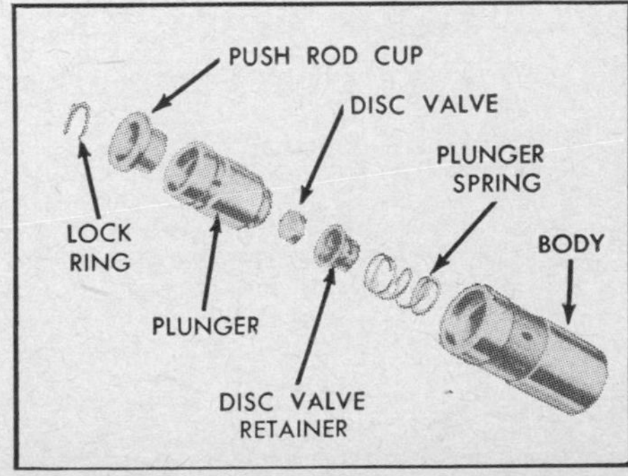

Fig. 3 Hydraulic valve lifter (typical)

VALVE GUIDES

Valve guides in these engines are an integral part of the head and, therefore, cannot be removed. For service, guides can be reamed oversize to accommodate one of three service valves with oversize stems (.003″, .015″ and .030″).

Check the valve stem clearance of each valve (after cleaning) in its respective valve guide. If the clearance exceeds the service limits of .004″ on the intake or .005″ on the exhaust, ream the valve guides to accommodate the next oversize diameter valve.

HYDRAULIC VALVE LIFTERS

The internal parts of each hydraulic valve lifter assembly are a matched set. If these are mixed, improper valve operation may result. Therefore, disassemble, inspect and test each assembly separately to prevent mixing the parts, Fig. 3.

TIMING CASE COVER

NOTE: If it becomes necessary to replace the oil seal in the timing case cover the cover must be removed.

1969 V8-429

1. Drain cooling system and crankcase.
2. Remove fan and shroud.
3. Remove radiator.
4. Remove drive belts and water pump pulley. Remove compressor support if so equipped.
5. Remove bolt and washer attaching crankshaft damper. Remove damper with suitable puller. Remove Woodruff key from crankshaft.
6. Remove power steering pump.
7. Remove fuel pump.
8. Remove front cover to cylinder block bolts. Cut the oil pan seal flush with cylinder block face prior to separating cover from cylinder block. Remove front cover and water pump as a unit.

1968 V8-429

1. Drain cooling system and crankcase.
2. Remove fan assembly. If air conditioned, remove bolts retaining fan assembly to water pump shaft. Remove screws retaining radiator shroud to radiator. Remove fan assembly and radiator shroud.
3. Disconnect radiator hoses at engine and oil cooler lines at radiator.
4. Remove radiator upper support and remove radiator.
5. Unfasten power steering pump brackets from engine and position pump and brackets out of way.
6. Loosen alternator adjusting bolt and if air conditioned loosen compressor idler pulley. Remove drive belts and water pump pulley.

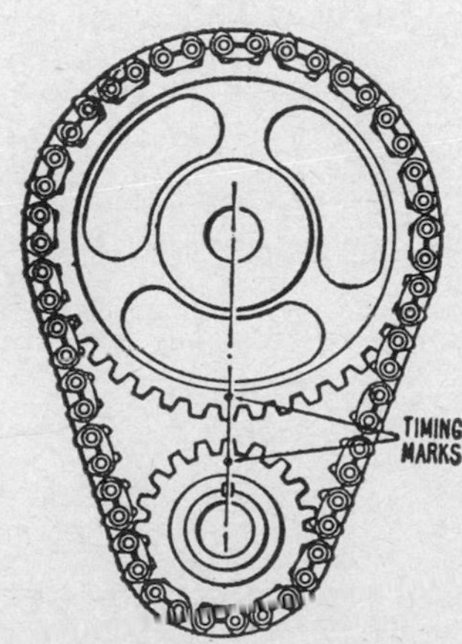

Fig. 4 Valve timing marks. V8-390, 428, 429

7. Unfasten alternator brackets from engine and position alternator and bracket out of way.
8. Disconnect heater hose at water pump and loosen bypass hose clamp at intake manifold.
9. Remove vibration and sleeve from crankshaft.
10. Disconnect fuel lines at pump and remove fuel pump. Plug pump inlet line.
11. Remove bolts retaining front cover to block and remove front cover and water pump as an assembly. If new front cover is to be installed, remove water pump and install on new front cover.
12. Remove oil pan and oil pump as described further on.
13. Reverse above procedure to install.

1966-68 V8-390, 428

1. Drain cooling system and crankcase.
2. Disconnect battery ground cable.
3. Remove fuel pump, leaving it attached to flexible fuel line.
4. Remove oil pan.
5. Remove radiator.
6. If air conditioned, unfasten and move condenser forward. *Do not disconnect refrigerant lines.* Remove condenser drive belt.
7. If equipped with Thermactor, remove air pump drive belt.
8. Wire power steering pump to left side of car in a position that will prevent oil from draining out.
9. Remove water pump.
10. Remove vibration damper, crankshaft sleeve and front cover.
11. Reverse procedure to install.

1965

1. Drain cooling system and crankcase.
2. Disconnect battery cable.
3. Disconnect transmission oil cooler lines at radiator and remove radiator.
4. Remove power steering pump drive belt and bracket and wire pump to left side of car in a position that will prevent oil from draining out.
5. Remove water pump, drive belt adjusting arm, pulley and fan as a unit.
6. Remove power steering pulley from vibration damper, then use a puller to remove damper.
7. Remove fuel pump and lay it to one side with flexible fuel line attached.
8. Remove crankshaft sleeve.
9. Unfasten and remove front cover.
10. Reverse procedure to install.

1963-64

1. Drain cooling system and crankcase.
2. Disconnect automatic choke heat chamber air inlet tube and remove air cleaner.
3. Disconnect battery ground cable.
4. Disconnect radiator hoses and transmission oil cooler lines at radiator.
5. Remove radiator and support.
6. Remove drive belt. Wire power steering pump to left side in a position that will prevent oil from draining out.
7. If air conditioned, remove drive belt.

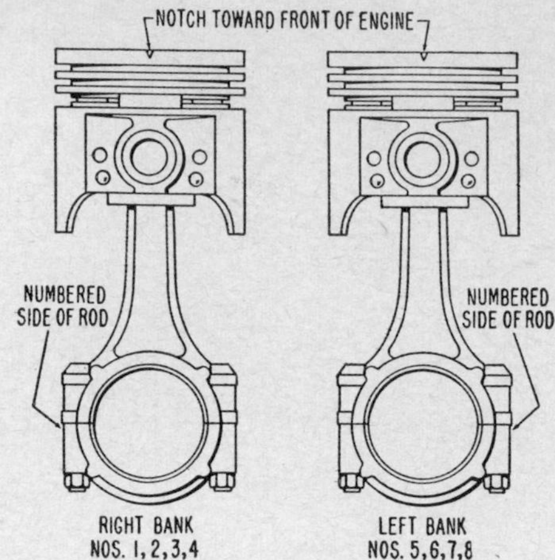

Fig. 5 Piston and rod assembly

8. Remove water pump and fan.
9. Remove power steering pulley from vibration damper.
10. Use a puller to remove vibration damper.
11. Remove fuel pump and lay pump to one side with flexible hose line still attached.
12. If crankshaft sleeve is not stepped down (same OD at both ends) remove it. If not stepped down, remove it with three-jawed puller.
13. Unfasten and remove front cover.
14. Reverse above procedure to install the cover.

TIMING CHAIN

1963-69

1. To remove the chain, first take off the front cover as outlined previously.
2. Crank engine until timing mark on camshaft sprocket is adjacent to timing mark on crankshaft sprocket, Fig. 4.
3. Remove camshaft sprocket cap screw and fuel pump eccentric.
4. Slide both sprockets and chain forward and remove as an assembly.
5. Reverse foregoing procedure to install the chain, being sure to align the timing marks as shown.

CAMSHAFT, REPLACE

1968-69 V8-429

1. Remove timing cover, chain and sprockets as outlined previously.
2. Remove intake manifold and carburetor as an assembly.
3. Remove rocker arm covers. Back off rocker arm stud nuts, turn rocker arms sideways and remove push rods in sequence.
4. Remove valve lifters.
5. If air conditioned, discharge refrigeration system. Disconnect line to evaporator at receiver dryer. Unfasten condenser from radiator support and position out of way.
6. Remove camshaft thrust plate retaining bolts and carefully remove camshaft from engine.
7. Reverse above procedure to install.

1963-68 V8-390, 428

1. Remove front cover as outlined above.
2. Remove valve rocker arm assemblies.
3. Remove distributor cap and spark plug wires as an assembly.
4. Remove distributor.
5. Remove push rods.
6. Remove valve lifters. *In some cases it may be necessary to transfer the lifter over to an adjoining push rod opening in order to remove it.*
7. Remove oil pan and pump screen.
8. Remove timing chain and sprockets.
9. Remove camshaft thrust plate and spacer, then remove camshaft from engine.
10. Reverse above procedure to install.

CAMSHAFT BEARINGS

When necessary to replace camshaft bearings, the engine will have to be removed from the vehicle and the plug at the rear of the cylinder block will have to be removed in order to utilize the special camshaft bearing removing and installing tools required to do this job. If properly installed, camshaft bearings require no reaming—nor should this type bearing be reamed or altered in any manner in an attempt to fit bearings.

PISTON & ROD, ASSEMBLE

All V8's

Assemble the pistons to the rods as shown in Fig. 5.

PISTONS, PINS & RINGS

Pistons are available in oversizes of .003, .020, .030, .040 and .060″.

Piston pins are available in oversizes of .001 and .002″.

Rings are available in oversizes of .002, .010, .020, .030 and .040″.

MAIN & ROD BEARINGS

Main and rod bearings are available in undersizes of .002, .010, .020 and .030″.

OIL PAN, REPLACE

1968-69 V8-429

1. Disconnect radiator shroud from radiator if so equipped and position over fan.
2. Raise car on a hoist and drain crankcase.
3. Disconnect engine front support insulators from underbody crossmember. Place floor jack under front edge of oil pan, with block of wood between jack and oil pan. Raise engine just enough to insert 1¼″ blocks of wood between insulators and underbody side members. Remove floor jack.
4. Disconnect starter cable, unfasten

and remove starter.
5. Remove end attachments of stabilizer bar and rotate ends of bar down to raise center of bar. Remove oil filter.
6. Unbolt and remove oil pan ahead of underbody crossmember.
7. Reverse above procedure to install.

1964-68 V8-390, 428

1. Drain crankcase and remove oil level dipstick.
2. Remove pan screws and lower pan to crossmember.
3. Position crankshaft so that counterweight will clear oil pan.
4. Unfasten and place pump, screen and intermediate drive shaft in pan.
5. Remove oil pan and pump.

NOTE: When installing, place pump in pan and position pan on crossmember. Do not attempt to force oil pump into position if it will not seat readily. The drive shaft hex may be misaligned with distributor shaft. To align, rotate intermediate shaft into a new position if necessary.

1963 V8-390

1. Drain cooling system and crankcase.
2. Disconnect radiator upper hose.
3. Unfasten and lower oil pan to underbody cross member.
4. Position crankshaft so that counterweight will clear pan and move pan forward.
5. If necessary, position ignition coil out of the way.
6. Install engine lifting sling.
7. Remove engine front mounting bolts.
8. Raise engine high enough to permit removal of oil pump bolts.
9. Remove oil pan and pump.

OIL PUMP REPAIRS

Rotor Type Pump, Fig. 6

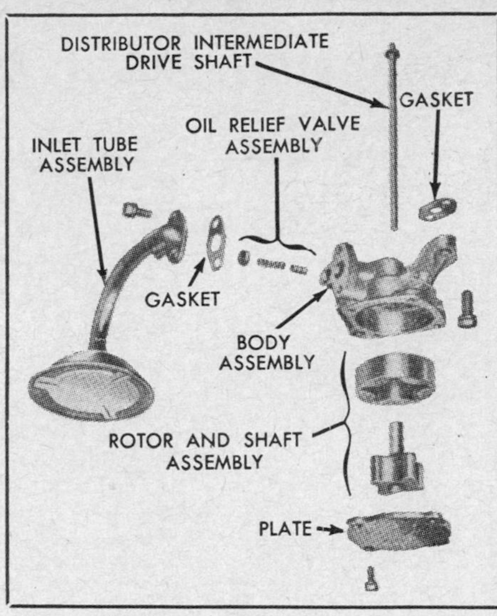

Fig. 6 Rotor type oil pump

1. With all parts clean and dry, check the inside of the pump housing and the outer race and rotor for damage or excessive wear.
2. Check the mating surface of the pump cover for wear. If this surface is worn, scored or grooved, replace the cover.
3. Measure the clearance between the outer race and housing. This clearance should be .006-.009".
4. With the rotor assembly installed in the housing, place a straight edge over the rotor assembly and housing. Measure the clearance between the straight edge and the rotor and outer race. Recommended limits are .001-.0035". *The outer race, shaft and rotor are furnished only as an assembly.*
5. Check the drive shaft-to-housing bearing clearance by measuring the O.D. of the shaft and the I.D. of the housing bearing. The recommended clearance limits are .0015-0029".
6. Inspect the relief valve spring for a collapsed or worn condition.
7. Check the relief valve piston for scores and free operation in the bore. The specified piston clearance is .0015-.0029".

WATER PUMP, REPLACE

1968-69 V8-429

Refer to procedure for removing timing cover mentioned previously.

1963-68 V8-390, 428

1. Drain cooling system.
2. If equipped, remove power steering drive belt and wire pump to left side of car in a position that will prevent oil from draining out.
3. If air conditioned, remove compressor drive belt.
4. Unfasten and move alternator or generator inward and remove fan belt.
5. Remove fan and pulley.
6. If equipped with fan drive clutch, remove clutch and fan.
7. Remove water pump pulley.
8. Disconnect hoses at water pump.
9. Remove pump from engine.

FUEL PUMP, REPLACE

1. Remove all gasket material from the pump and block gasket surfaces. Apply sealer to both sides of new gasket.
2. Position gasket on pump flange and hold pump in position against its mounting surface. Make sure rocker arm is riding on camshaft eccentric.
3. Press pump tight against its mounting. Install retaining screws and tighten them alternately.
4. Connect fuel lines. Then operate engine and check for leaks.

SERVICE NOTE: Before installing the pump, it is good practice to crank the engine so that the nose of the camshaft eccentric is out of the way of the fuel pump rocker arm when the pump is installed. In this way there will be the least amount of tension on the rocker arm, thereby easing the installation of the pump.

Transmission Section

NOTE: 1969 linkage adjustment information is in this section. Repair procedures on both automatic and manual shift transmissions are covered elsewhere in this manual. Procedures for removing automatic transmissions as well as linkage adjustments on 1963-68 models are included in the automatic transmission chapters. See Chapter Index.

1969 AUTO. TRANS. LINKAGE ADJUST

Linkage adjustments for 1969 are identical to those for 1968 which are outlined at the front of this manual.

Rear Axle, Propeller Shaft & Brakes

REAR AXLES

Fig. 1 illustrates the rear axle assembly used on these cars. When necessary to overhaul the unit, refer to the *Rear Axle Specifications* table in this chapter.

Description

In these axles, Fig. 1, the drive pinion is straddle-mounted by two opposed tapered roller bearings which support the pinion shaft in front of the drive pinion gear, and straight roller bearing that supports the pinion shaft at the rear of the pinion gear. The drive pinion is assembled in a pinion retainer that is bolted to the differential carrier. The tapered roller bearings are preloaded by a collapsible spacer between the bearings. The pinion is positioned by a shim or shims located between the drive pinion retainer and the differential carrier.

The differential is supported in the carrier by two tapered roller side bearings. These bearings are preloaded by two threaded ring nuts or sleeves between the bearings and pedestals. The differential assembly is positioned for proper ring gear and pinion backlash by varying the adjustment of these ring nuts. The differential case houses two side gears in mesh with two pinions mounted on a pinion shaft which is held in place by a pin. The side gears and pinions are backed by thrust washers. With high performance engines, an optional rear axle having a four-pinion differential is also used.

The axle shafts are of unequal length, the left shaft being shorter than the right. The axle shafts are mounted in sealed ball bearings that are pressed on the shafts.

Diff. Carrier Assy.

Service Bulletin

All Ford Built Rear Axles: Recent manufacturing changes have eliminated the need for marking rear axle drive pinions for individual variations from nominal shim thicknesses. In the past, these pinion markings, with the aid of a shim selection table, were used as a guide to select correct shim thicknesses when a gear set or carrier assembly replacement was performed.

With the elimination of pinion markings, use of the shim selection table is no longer possible and the methods outlined below must be used.

1. Measure the thickness of the original pinion depth shim removed from the axle. Use the same thickness upon installation of the replacement carrier or drive pinion. If any further shim change is necessary, it will be indicated in the tooth pattern check.
2. If the original shim is lost, substitute a nominal shim for the original and use the tooth pattern check to determine if further shim changes are required.

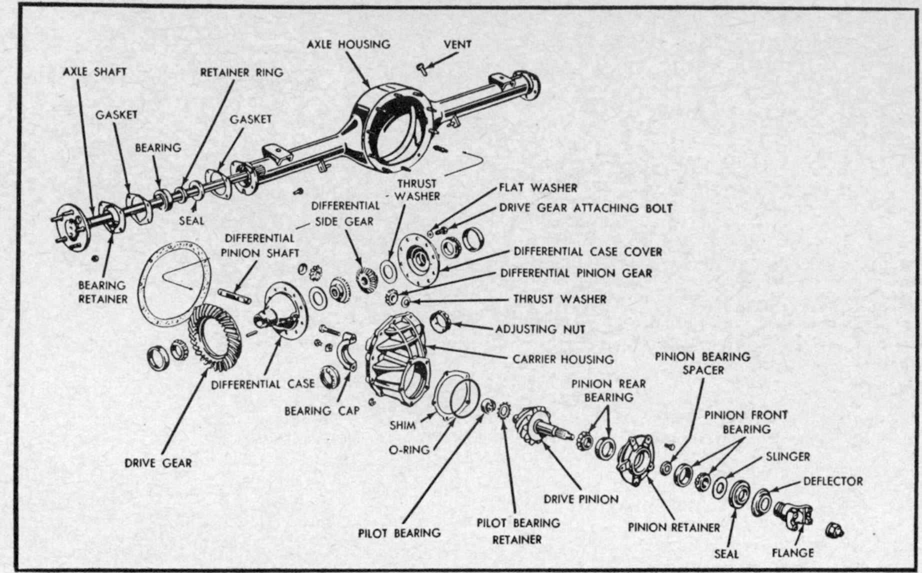

Fig. 1 Rear axle disassembled

Remove & Replace

In servicing the rear axles it is not necessary to remove the rear axle assembly for any normal repairs. The axle shafts and carrier assembly can easily be removed from the vehicle, leaving the axle housing in place.

1. Place a drain pan under the carrier and housing to catch the old grease when the carrier is separated from the housing.
2. Use a wire brush to clean dirt from the area around the carrier and housing mating surfaces. Then wipe the area clean with a cloth dampened in solvent.
3. Remove axle shafts and drive shaft as explained below.
4. Unfasten carrier from housing and lift out carrier.
5. Reverse removal procedure to install, using a new gasket between the carrier and housing.

AXLE SHAFTS

Removal

1. Remove wheel assembly.
2. Remove brake drum from flange.
3. Working through hole provided in axle shaft flange, remove nuts that secure bearing retainer.
4. Pull axle shaft out of housing. If bearing is a tight fit in axle housing, use a slide hammer-type puller. *Brake carrier plate must not be dislodged. Install one nut to hold plate in place after axle shaft is removed.*
5. If axle shaft bearing is to be replaced, loosen inner retainer by nicking it deeply with a chisel in several places. On 1969 models, a $\frac{1}{4}$" hole must be drilled *not more than* $\frac{5}{16}$" *deep* in the retaining ring surface before using chisel. The bearing will then slide off easily.
6. Press bearing from axle shaft.
7. Inspect machined surfaces of axle shaft and housing for rough spots that would affect the sealing action of the oil seal. Carefully remove any burrs or rough spots.
8. Press new bearing on shaft until it seats firmly against shoulder on shaft.
9. Press inner bearing retainer on shaft until it seats firmly against bearing.
10. If oil seal is to be replaced, use a hook-type tool to pull it out of the housing. Wipe a small amount of oil resistant sealer on outer edge of seal before it is installed.

Installation

1. Place a new gasket on each side of brake carrier plate and slide axle shaft into housing. Start the splines into the differential side gear and push the shaft in until bearing bottoms in housing.
2. Install retainer and tighten nuts to 30-40 ft. lbs.
3. Install brake drum and wheel.

PROPELLER SHAFT

Remove & Replace

1. Disconnect rear U-joint from drive pinion flange.
2. Pull drive shaft toward rear of car until front U-joint yoke clears transmission extension housing and output shaft.
3. Install a suitable tool, such as a

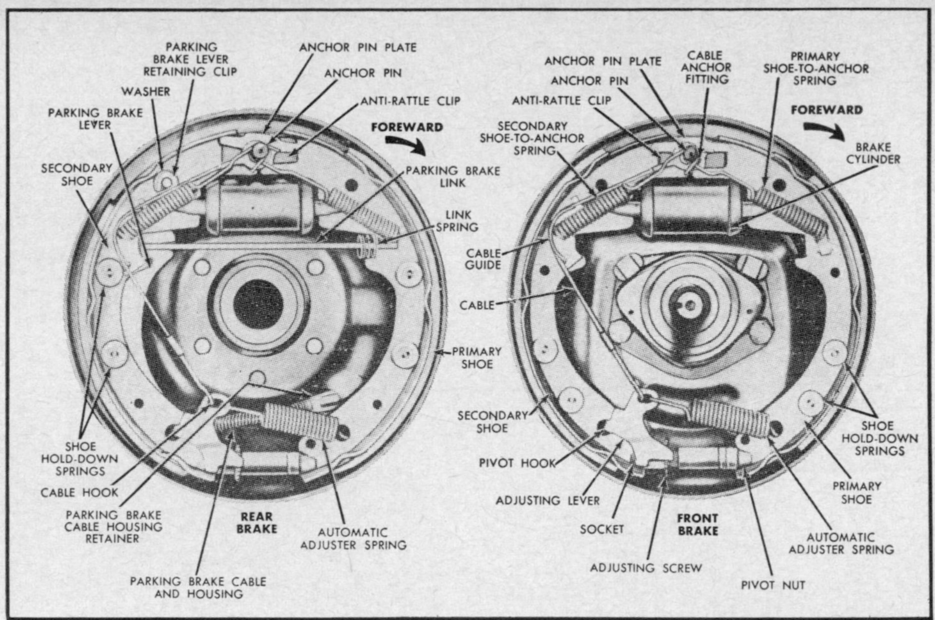

Fig. 2 Right rear and front brake. 1963-64. Rear brake on 1965-69

seal driver, in seal to prevent lube from leaking from transmission.

4. Before installing, check U-joints for freedom of movement. If a bind has resulted from misalignment after overhauling the U-joints, tap the ears of the drive shaft sharply to relieve the bind.
5. If rubber seal installed on end of transmission extension housing is damaged, install a new seal.
6. On an automatic transmission, lubricate yoke spline with special spline lubricant. *This spline is sealed so that transmission fluid does not "wash" away spline lubricant.*
7. Install yoke on transmission output shaft.
8. Install U-bolts and nuts which attach U-joint to pinion flange. Tighten U-bolts evenly to prevent binding U-joint bearings.

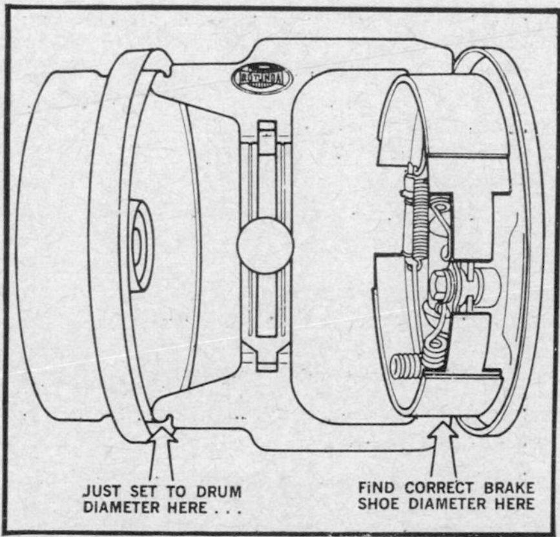

Fig. 3 Brake adjustment with gauge

BRAKE ADJUSTMENTS

Self-Adjusting Brakes

These brakes, Fig. 2, have self-adjusting shoe mechanisms that assure correct lining-to-drum clearances at all times. The automatic adjusters operate only when the brakes are applied when the car is moving rearward or when it comes to an uphill stop.

Although the brakes are self-adjusting, an initial adjustment is necessary when the brake shoes have been relined or replaced, or when the length of the star wheel adjuster has been changed during some other service operation.

Frequent usage of an automatic transmission forward range to halt reverse vehicle motion may prevent the automatic adjusters from functioning, thereby inducing low pedal heights. Should low pedal heights be encountered, it is recommended that numerous forward and reverse stops be made until satisfactory pedal height is obtained.

Service Note

If a low pedal height condition cannot be corrected by making numerous reverse stops (provided the hydraulic system is free of air) it indicates that the self-adjusting mechanism is not functioning. Therefore, it will be necessary to remove the brake drum, clean, free up and lubricate the adjusting mechanism. Then adjust the brakes as follows, being sure the parking brake is fully released.

Adjustment

1. Remove adjusting hole cover from brake backing plate and, from the backing plate side, turn the adjusting screw upward with a screwdriver or other suitable tool to expand the shoes until a slight drag is felt when the drum is rotated.
2. Remove the drum.
3. While holding the adjusting lever out of engagement with the adjusting screw, back off the adjusting screw ¾ turn with the fingers.

NOTE—If finger movement will not turn the screw, free it up. If this is not done, the adjusting lever will not turn the screw during subsequent vehicle operation. Lubricate the screw with oil and coat with wheel bearing grease. Any other adjustment procedure may cause damage to the adjusting screw with consequent self-adjuster problems.

4. Install wheel and drum, and adjusting hole cover. Adjust brakes on remaining wheels in the same manner.
5. If pedal height is not satisfactory, drive the vehicle and make sufficient reverse stops until proper pedal height is obtained.

Revised Brake Adjustment

The adjustment is made with the drums removed, using the brake gauge shown in Fig. 3. With the gauge, determine the inside diameter of the drum braking surface. Reverse the tool as shown and adjust the brake shoe diameter to fit the gauge. Hold the automatic adjusting lever out of engagement while rotating the adjusting screw to prevent burring the screw slots. Rotate the gauge around the brake shoes to be sure of the setting. After the brake drums and wheels have been installed, complete the adjustment by applying the brakes several times while backing the vehicle.

PARKING BRAKE, ADJUST

1964-69 Vacuum Release Unit

The vacuum power unit, Fig. 4, will release the parking brake automatically when the transmission selector lever is moved into any driving position with the engine running. The brakes will not re-

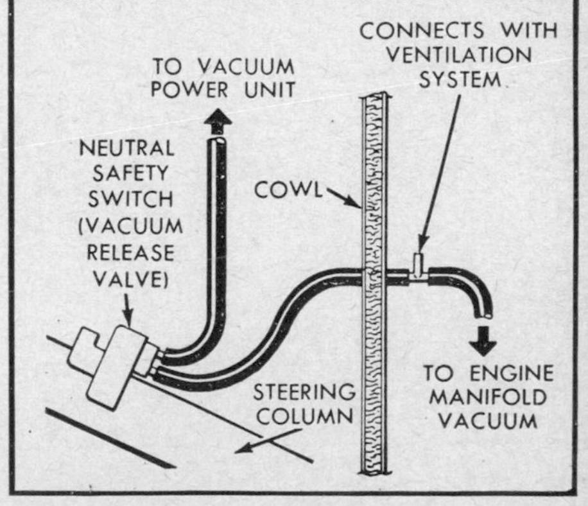

Fig. 4 Vacuum connections for automatic parking brake release. 1964-69

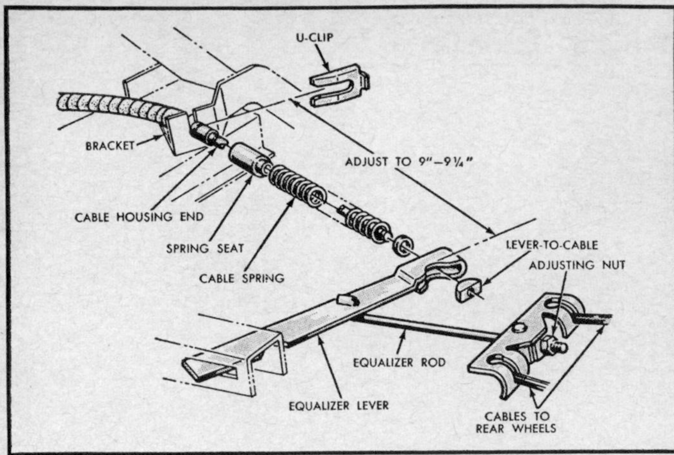

Fig. 5 Parking brake adjustments. 1964-67

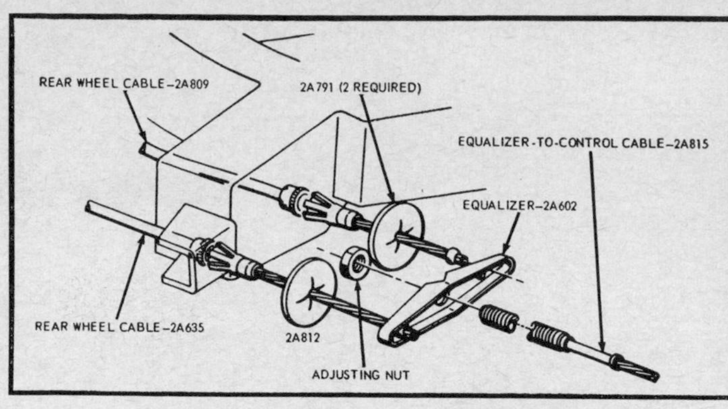

Fig. 6 Parking brake linkage. 1968-69

lease automatically, however, when the selector lever is in neutral or park position with the engine running, or in any other position with the engine off.

The lower end of the release handle extends out for alternate manual release in the event of vacuum power failure or for optional manual release at any time.

1968-69

1. Check the parking cables when the brakes are fully released. If the cables are loose, adjust as follows:
2. Fully release parking brake pedal by pushing down the manual release lever.
3. Depress the parking brake pedal approximately 1¼".
4. Raise the vehicle. With the transmission in neutral, turn the adjusting nut forward against the equalizer, Fig. 6, until a moderate drag is felt when turning the rear wheels (approximately 100 lbs. of force at the outside diameter of the tire is required to turn the rear wheels).
5. Release the parking brake and check to be sure the brake shoes return to the fully released position.
6. Depress the parking brake pedal until it is fully engaged.
7. Release the parking brake again and check as in step 5.
8. If the rear brakes do not fully release, check the cables for kinks or binds and free as required.

1964-67

1. Check the parking brake cables when the service brakes are fully released. If cables are loose, adjust as follows:
2. Fully release parking brake pedal by pushing down manual release lever.
3. Raise car. Adjust equalizer lever against cable spring on pedal cable to the dimension shown in Fig. 5.
4. Loosen adjusting nut on equalizer rod, then turn lock nut in front of equalizer several turns forward.
5. Depress pedal 1¾" from its normal released position.
6. While turning rear wheels in rearward direction, turn adjusting nut against equalizer until a moderate drag is felt.
7. When cables are properly adjusted, tighten both nuts against equalizer.
8. Release parking brake and check to make sure brake shoes return to fully released position.
9. Depress parking brake pedal 2". Under normal conditions this will satisfactorily hold the car.
10. Release pedal again, then depress pedal ½"; the brakes should not drag.

1963

1. Check the parking brake cables when the brakes are fully released. If the cables are loose, adjust as follows:
2. Loosen lock nut on equalizer rod and turn nut in front of equalizer several turns forward.
3. Turn lock nut forward against equalizer until cables are just tight enough to remove slack. *Excessive tightening may pull brake shoes off their anchors.*
4. When cables are properly adjusted, tighten both nuts against equalizer.
5. Check cable between equalizer lever and parking brake pedal. If cable is loose, turn equalizer lever nut forward far enough to remove slack in cable without moving equalizer lever.

POWER BRAKE UNIT, REPLACE

1965-69

1. Disconnect vacuum hose from booster.
2. Remove three bolts and loosen one to allow brace between cowl and spring tower to be positioned inboard to obtain clearance.
3. Remove master cylinder from booster. It is not necessary to disconnect brake lines.
4. Working under instrument panel, disconnect booster push rod link from brake pedal as follows: 1) disconnect stop light switch wires at connector and remove hairpin clip, 2) slide stop light switch off pedal just far enough for switch outer hole to clear pin, then tilt switch straight upward from pin, 3) slide master cylinder push rod and nylon washer and bushing from brake pedal pin.
5. Unfasten and remove booster from dash panel, sliding push rod link out from engine side of dash panel.
6. Remove dust seal from push rod link and place it in slot of dash panel for installation.
7. Reverse procedure to install.

1963-64

1. Working inside car below instrument panel, disconnect booster push rod link from brake pedal by removing the horseshoe retaining clip and sliding push rod link off pin that is integral with pedal.
2. Open hood and disconnect wires from stop light switch at master cylinder.
3. Disconnect brake line at master cylinder outlet fitting.
4. Disconnect vacuum hose from booster unit. Also disconnect transmission throttle valve hose (if equipped).
5. Unfasten booster (4 bolts) from dash panel and slide push rod link out from engine side of dash panel.
6. Reverse removal procedure to install the booster. Then bleed the brake system.

Front End & Steering Section

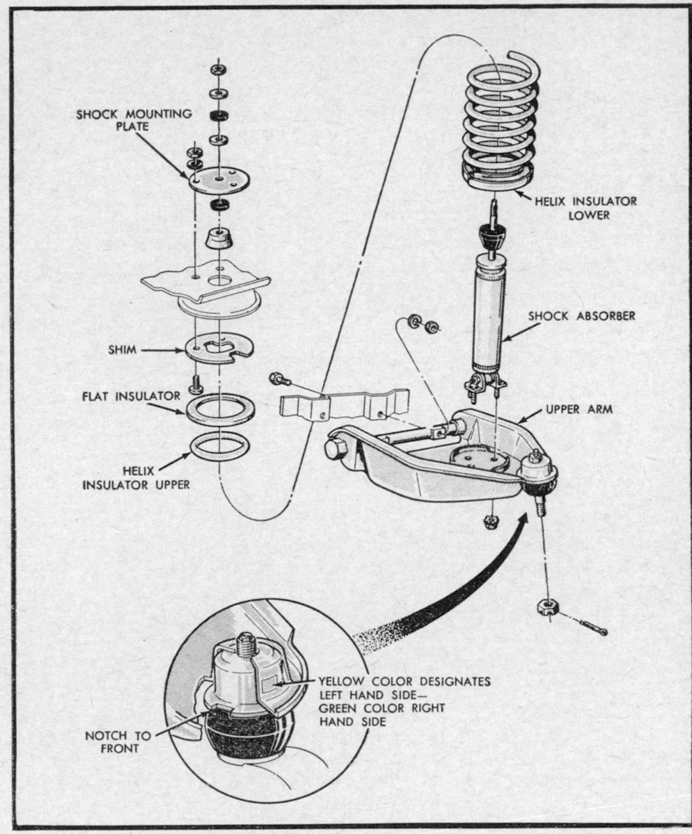

Fig. 1 Front suspension details. 1963-66

Fig. 2 Camber and caster adjustments. 1963-66

FRONT SUSPENSION

1963-66

This suspension, Fig. 1, has the coil springs mounted on the upper control arm at the lower end and a spring guide at the upper end. Ball joints connect the steering knuckle to the upper and lower control arms.

LUBRICATION

Lubrication should be performed at 36,000-mile intervals at which time the special plugs should be removed and specially formulated grease applied with a hand-operated gun. This extended lubrication interval is made possible by a special type chassis lubricant combined with special seals and bearing materials. Under no circumstances should the special plugs be removed and fittings installed to accommodate conventional type grease as damage to the special seals may result.

WHEEL ALIGNMENT

1963-66

Camber—Adjust camber by removing or installing shims between pivot bracket of lower control arm and mounting bracket on underbody in engine compartment, Fig. 2.

Removal of shims will increase camber; installing shims will decrease camber. A $\frac{1}{16}$" shim change will change camber angle $\frac{1}{3}$°.

Caster—Adjustment is made by repositioning strut on lower control arm as shown in Fig. 2. Adjust caster by loosening rear retaining bolts and lift strut so that strut serrations will be free from serrations on lower arm.

Lengthen distance of "Dimension A", Fig. 2 to decrease caster and shorten distance to increase caster angle. Tighten rearward nuts that retain strut to lower control arm and recheck caster and camber.

1967-69

Wheel alignment is adjusted in the same manner as described for 1967 Ford Full Size models.

TOE-IN, ADJUST

Turn both tie rod adjusting sleeves an equal amount until toe-in is correct.

WHEEL BEARINGS, ADJUST

1963-69

1. While rotating wheel assembly, torque adjusting nut to 15-20 ft-lbs. to seat bearings.
2. Locate nut lock on adjusting nut so that slots on nut lock are aligned with cotter pin hole in spindle.
3. Back off both adjusting nut and nut lock together until next slot on nut lock aligns with cotter pin hole in spindle.
4. Secure cotter pin and check for free rotation of wheel.

WHEEL BEARINGS, REPLACE

(Disc Brakes)

1. Raise car and remove front wheels.
2. Remove caliper mounting bolts.

NOTE: It is not necessary to disconnect brake lines for this operation.

3. Slide caliper off of disc, inserting a spacer between the shoes to hold pistons in their bores after the caliper is removed. Position caliper assembly out of the way.

NOTE: Do not allow caliper to hang by the brake line.

4. Remove hub and disc assembly. Grease retainer and inner bearing can now be removed.

CHECKING BALL JOINTS FOR WEAR

If loose ball joints are suspected, first be sure the front wheel bearings are properly adjusted and that the control arms are tight. Then check ball joints as follows:

Referring to Fig. 3, raise wheel with a jack placed under the suspension as shown. Then test by moving the wheel up and down to axial play, and rocking it at the top and bottom to measure radial play.

On 1963-66 models, the upper ball joint should be replaced if radial play exceeds .250" and axial play exceeds .060". Lower ball joint should be replaced if there is any noticeable looseness at the joint.

On 1967-69 models, the upper ball joint should be replaced if there is any noticeable looseness at the joint. Lower ball joint should be replaced if radial play exceeds .250", and if there is any noticeable axial play at the joint.

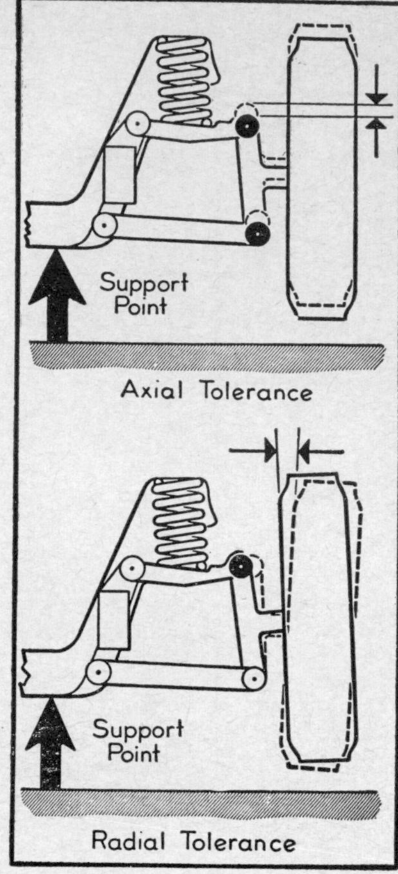

Fig. 3 Checking ball joints for wear. 1963-66

BALL JOINTS, REPLACE

The upper and lower ball joints are riveted to the control arms. On later models, the upper ball joint is pressed into the upper control arm whereas the lower ball joint is riveted to the lower control arm.

When replacing a riveted ball joint, remove the rivets and retain the ball joint to its control arm with the bolts, nuts and washers furnished with the ball joint kit. Also, use a suitable pressing tool to force the ball joint studs out of the spindle.

SHOCK ABSORBER, REPLACE

1967-69

To remove a shock absorber, unfasten it from the frame at its upper end. Remove the two cap screws that retain the shock absorber mounting plate to the lower control arm and lower the shock absorber unit.

To install, reverse the removal procedure and tighten the two lower cap screws to 13-18 lbs. ft. torque.

1963-66

When installing, position the shock absorber and upper mounting plate in place and install mounting plate bolts and dash panel brace nuts. Lower car slightly with safety stands under lower control arm. This will raise upper arm enough to position lower shock absorber stud through hole at bottom of spring lower seat. Secure shock absorber to spring seat by installing insulator, washer and retaining nut.

COIL SPRING, REPLACE

1963-66

1. With safety stand under lower control arm, remove wheel, shock absorber and upper control arm bumper and bracket.
2. Raise car slightly in order to lower upper control arm.
3. Insert a lock bar through top of spring and position bar on 7th coil from bottom and compress spring until top coils are drawn out of spring upper seat.
4. Remove 4 bolts attaching lower spring seat to upper arm and remove spring and lower seat as an assembly.
5. If a new spring is being installed, tape rubber insulator to upper end of spring in 3 places. Fasten spring seat to spring and install spring in reverse order of removal.

1967-69

1. Disconnect stabilizer at lower control arm.
2. Disconnect lower end of shock absorber and push it up to the retracted position.
3. Loosen lower ball joint stud nut one or two turns. Tap spindle at lower ball joint area to loosen stud from spindle.
4. Place a floor jack under lower arm at a 60° angle away from wheel and toward center of car. Hook saddle of jack under outer edge of spring seat.
5. Remove nut from lower ball stud and slowly lower arm until spring is extended.
6. Apply foot pressure to lower arm to push arm inward so that spring can be removed.
7. Reverse procedure to install.

POWER STEERING, REPLACE

1965-69

1. Disconnect pressure and return lines from steering gear. Cap each line and plug each port to prevent entry of dirt.
2. Remove bolt that secures flex joint to steering gear.
3. Loosen bolt that attaches flex joint to steering shaft.
4. With a pry bar, carefully loosen flex joint from steering shaft.
5. Remove two bolts that secure left strut to underside of car and remove strut.
6. Use a puller to remove pitman arm.
7. Unfasten (3 bolts) and remove gear.
8. Reverse procedure to install.

1964

1. Disconnect hydraulic lines from gear unit. Plug openings and cap lines.
2. Disconnect horn ground wire from sleeve alignment bolt.
3. Remove bolt that secures flexible coupling to steering gear worm shaft.
4. Raise car and disconnect pitman arm from sector shaft.
5. Remove gear-to-body member bolts, and pull gear unit from flexible coupling.
6. Reverse removal procedure to install the unit.

1963

1. Disconnect hydraulic lines from gear, plug openings and cap lines.
2. Remove flex coupling retaining bolt and disconnect ground wires.
3. Raise vehicle and remove left body strut bar.
4. Remove pitman arm with puller.
5. Remove steering gear retaining bolts, pull gear from column shaft coupling, remove lower front insulator puck, and then remove gear from chassis.
6. Install gear in reverse order of removal.

FORD BRONCO

Specifications for the optional V8-289, 302 engines are tabulated on the pages immediately following this index. For service procedures on these engines see Ford Chapter.

INDEX OF SERVICE OPERATIONS

PAGE NO.

ACCESSORIES

Automatic Level Controls 1-41
Clock Troubles 1-11
Power Top Troubles 1-18
Power Window Troubles 1-18
Radio, Replace 2-369

BRAKES

Brake Troubles, Mechanical 1-17
Disc Brake Service 1-430
Hydraulic System Service 1-422
Master Cylinder, Replace 2-380
Parking Brake, Adjust 2-380
Power Brake Service 1-440
Power Brake Troubles 1-440
Service Brakes, Adjust 2-379

CLUTCH

Clutch Pedal, Adjust 2-372
Clutch, Replace 2-372
Clutch Troubles 1-12

COOLING SYSTEM

Cooling System Troubles 1-6
Variable Speed Fans 1-39
Water Pump, Replace 2-372

ELECTRICAL

Alternator Service 1-63
Dash Gauge Service 1-117
Distributor, Replace 2-368
Distributor Service:
  Standard 1-53
  Transistorized 1-47
Electrical Troubles 1-8
Generator Service 1-91
Horn Sounder, Remove 2-368
Ignition Coils and Resistors 1-24
Ignition Switch, Replace 2-368
Ignition Timing 2-368
Instrument Cluster Removal 2-369
Light Switch, Replace 2-368
Spark Plug Condition Chart 2-647
Starter Service 1-101
Starter, Replace 2-368
Starter Switch Service 1-114
Stop Light Switch, Replace 2-368
Turn Signal Switch, Replace 2-368
Turn Signal Troubles 1-11

PAGE NO.

Windshield Wiper Motor, Replace 2-369
Windshield Wiper Troubles 1-20

ENGINE

Camshaft, Replace 2-372
Crankshaft Rear Oil Seal 2-372
Cylinder Head, Replace 2-370
Engine, Replace 2-370
Engine Troubles 1-1
Main Bearings 2-372
Piston Pins 2-372
Piston Rings 2-372
Piston and Rod, Assemble 2-372
Pistons 2-372
Rocker Arm Service 2-371
Rod Bearings 2-372
Timing Case Cover, Replace 2-371
Timing Chain, Replace 2-371
Valves, Adjust 2-370
Valve Arrangement 2-370
Valve Lifters 2-371

ENGINE LUBRICATION

Crankcase Ventilation (PCV) 1-29
Exhaust Emission Controls 1-30
Oil Pump, Replace 2-372
Oil Pump Service 2-372

FRONT DRIVE AXLE 2-376

FUEL SYSTEM

Carburetor Adjustments and Specs. 1-124
Crankcase Ventilation (PCV) 1-29
Exhaust Emission Controls 1-30
Fuel Pump, Replace 2-372
Fuel Pump Service 1-120
Fuel System Troubles 1-2

PROPELLER SHAFT & U JOINTS

Propeller Shaft 2-372
Universal Joint Service 1-418

REAR AXLE

Axle Shaft, Bearing and Seal 2-379
Rear Axle Description 2-379
Rear Axle Troubles 1-17

PAGE NO.

SPECIFICATIONS

Alternator 2-365
Brakes 2-367
Capacities 2-366
Carburetors 1-124
Cooling System 2-366
Crankshaft and Bearings 2-367
Distributors 2-366
Engine Tightening Torque 2-367
Front Axle 2-367
General Engine Specs. 2-364
Ignition Coils and Resistors 1-24
Pistons, Rings and Pins 2-367
Rear Axle 2-367
Starting Motors 2-367
Tune Up 2-364
Valve Lift 2-370
Valve Timing 2-370
Valves 2-365
Wheel Alignment 2-366

STEERING GEAR

Steering Gear Service 1-451
Steering Gear Troubles 1-18
Steering Gear, Replace 2-380

SUSPENSION, FRONT

Spring, Replace 2-380
Shock Absorber, Replace 2-380
Tire Wear Chart 2-648
Toe-In, Adjust 2-380
Wheel Alignment, Adjust 2-380

TRANSFER CASE 2-373

TRANSMISSIONS

Three Speed Manual:
  Replace 2-374
  Repairs 1-261
  Linkage, Adjust 2-375

TUNE UP

Service 1-21
Specifications 2-364

WINDSHIELD WIPER

Wiper Motor, Replace 2-369
Wiper Switch, Replace 2-369
Wiper Troubles 1-20

FORD BRONCO

GENERAL ENGINE SPECIFICATIONS

Year	Engine	Carburetor	Bore and Stroke	Piston Displacement, Cubic Inches	Compression Ratio	Maximum Brake H.P. @ R.P.M.	Maximum Torque Lbs. Ft. @ R.P.M.	Normal Oil Pressure Pounds
1966–67	105 Horsepower 6-170	1 Bore	3.50 x 2.94	170	9.1	105 @ 4400	158 @ 2400	33–55
	200 Horsepower ①V8-289	2 Barrel	4.00 x 2.87	289	9.3	200 @ 4400	282 @ 2400	35–55
1968–69	100 Horsepower 6-170	1 Bore	3.50 x 2.94	170	8.7	100 @ 4000	156 @ 2200	35–60
	195 Horsepower ①V8-289	2 Barrel	4.00 x 2.87	289	8.7	195 @ 4600	288 @ 2600	35–60
	205 Horsepower ①V8-302	2 Barrel	4.00 x 3.00	302	8.6	205 @ 4600	300 @ 2600	35–60

①—See Ford Chapter for service on this engine.

TUNE UP SPECIFICATIONS

★ When setting timing, disconnect vacuum spark tube or hose from distributor vacuum unit.

Year	Engine Model	Spark Plugs		Distributor		Firing Order	Ignition Timing★		Hot Idle Speed		Comp. Press. Lbs. ②	Fuel Pump Press. Lbs.
		Type Autolite	Gap Inch	Point Gap Inch	Dwell Angle Deg.		BTDC ①	Mark	Std. Trans.	Auto. Trans.		
1966	6-170	BF-82	.034	.025	37-42	Fig. A	4°	Fig. B	600	...	175	4-6
	6-170④	BF-82	.034	.025	37-42	Fig. A	TDC	Fig. B	650	...	175	4-6
	V8-289③	BF-42	.034	.017	26-31	Fig. C	6°	Fig. D	550	...	150	4-6
	V8-289③④	BF-42	.034	.017	26-31	Fig. C	TDC	Fig. D	625	...	150	4-6
1967	6-170	BF-82	.034	.025	37-42	Fig. A	6°	Fig. B	575	...	175	4-6
	6-170④	BF-82	.034	.025	37-42	Fig. A	3°	Fig. B	700	...	175	4-6
	V8-289③	BF-42	.034	.017	26-31	Fig. C	6°	Fig. D	575	...	150	4-6
	V8-289③④	BF-42	.034	.017	26-31	Fig. C	TDC	Fig. D	625	...	150	4-6
1968	6-170	BF-82	.034	.027	35-40	Fig. A	6°	Fig. E	700⑤	...	175	4-6
	V8-289③	BF-42	.034	.021	24-29	Fig. C	6°	Fig. F	625⑤	...	150	4-6
1969	6-170	BF-82	.034	.027	35-40	Fig. G	6°	Fig. E	750		175	4½
	V8-302③	BF-42	.034	.021	24-29	Fig. C	6°	Fig. F	650		150	5

①—Before top dead center on compression stroke.
②—Plus or minus 20 lbs.
③—See Ford Chapter for service on this engine.
④—With Thermactor Exhaust Emission Control System.
⑤—With headlights on.

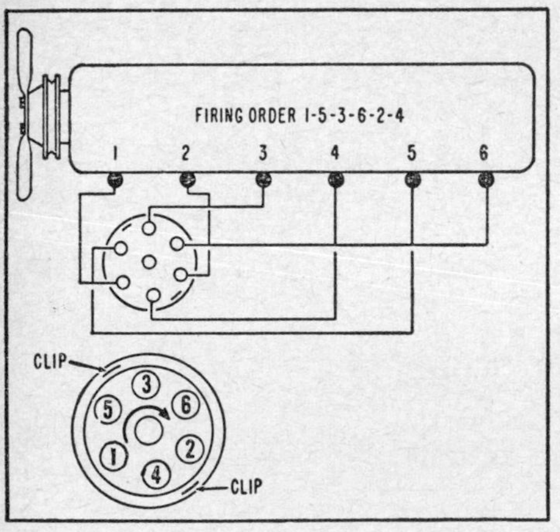

Fig. A

Fig. B

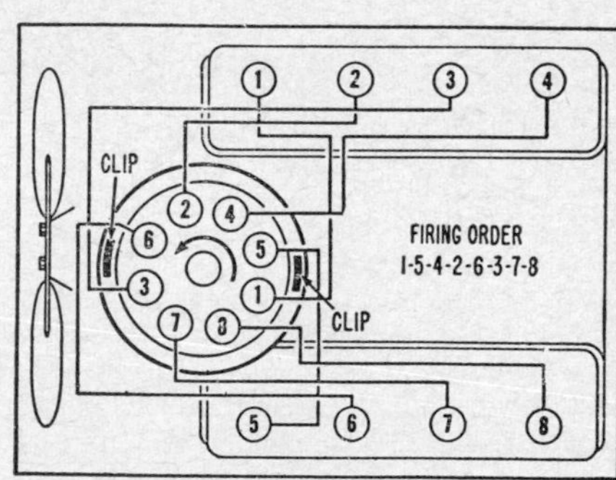

Fig. C

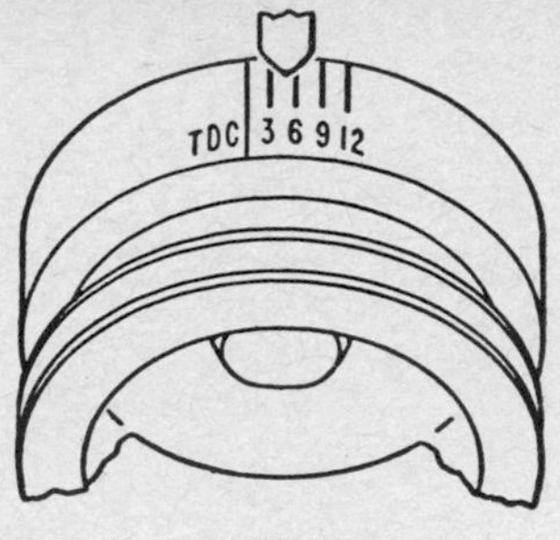

Fig. D

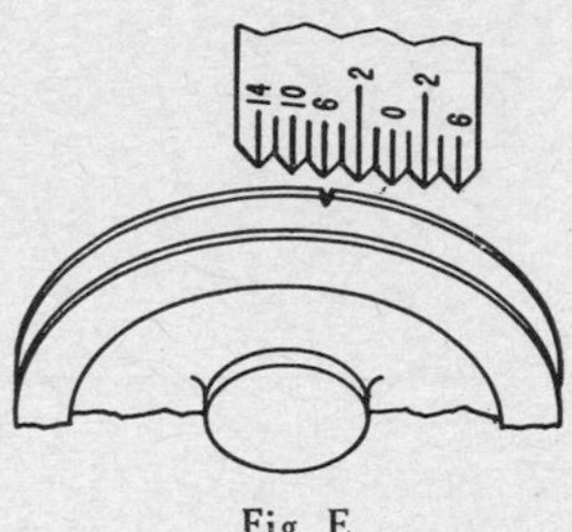
Fig. E

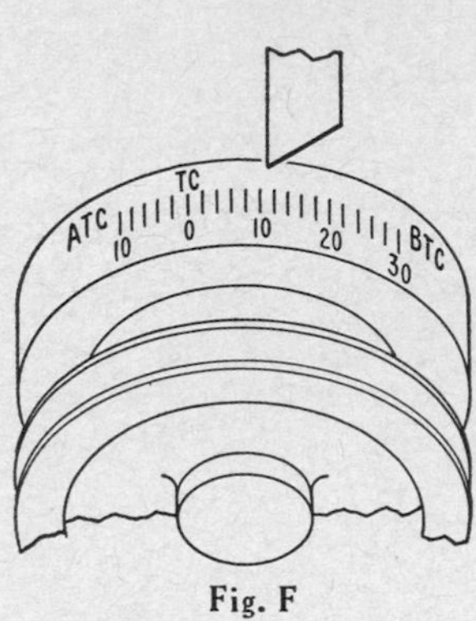

Fig. F

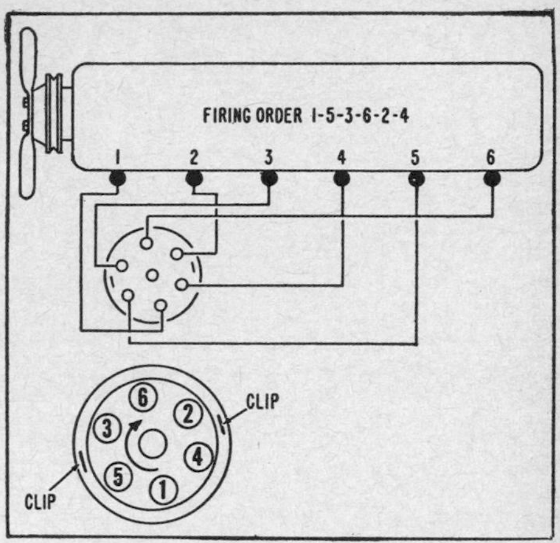

Fig. G

VALVE SPECIFICATIONS

Year	Engine	Valve Lash		Valve Angles		Valve Spring Installed Height	Valve Spring Pressure Lbs. @ In.	Stem Clearance		Stem Diameter, Standard	
		Int.	Exh.	Seat	Face			Intake	Exhaust	Intake	Exhaust
1966–68	6-170	.018	.018	45	44	1 9/16	117 @ 1.22	.0008–.0025	.0010–.0027	.3100–.3107	.3098–.3105
1966–68	V8-289①	¾ Turns②		45	44	1 5/8	180 @ 1.23	.0010–.0027	.0010–.0027	.3416–.3423	.3416–.3423
1969	6-170	.066–.166③		45	44	1 9/16	117 @ 1.22	.0008–.0025	.0010–.0027	.3100–.3107	.3098–.3105
	V8-302①	1 Turn②		45	44	1 5/8	180 @ 1.23	.0010–.0027	.0010–.0027	.3416–.3423	.3416–.3423

①—See Ford Chapter for service procedures on this engine.
②—Tighten rocker arm adjusting screw to eliminate all push rod end clearance, then tighten screw the number of turns listed.
③—Clearance is obtained at valve stem tip with lifter collapsed. If clearance is less than the minimum install an undersize push rod; if clearance is greater than the maximum install an oversize push rod.

ALTERNATOR & REGULATOR SPECIFICATIONS

Year	Alternator					Regulator						
	Model	Field Current		Output		Model	Field Relay			Voltage Regulator		
		Amps.	Volts @ 75°F	Amps.	Volts		Air Gap	Point Gap	Closing Voltage @ 75°F	Air Gap①	Contact Gap	Voltage @ 125°F
1966–67	Autolite	2.5	12	38	15	Autolite	.010–.018	...	2.5–4.0	.049–.056	.017–.022	13.8–14.6
1968–69	C6DF-10300-A	2.4	12	38	15	Autolite	①	①	2.0–4.2	①	①	13.5–15.3

①—Not adjustable.

DISTRIBUTOR SPECIFICATIONS

★NOTE: If advance is checked on the vehicle, double the R.P.M. and degrees advance to get crankshaft figures.

Year	Model	Basic Distributor Part No. 12127	Rotation ①	Breaker Gap	Dwell Angle Deg.	Breaker Arm Spring Tension	Centrifugal Advance Degrees @ R.P.M. of Distributor★		Vacuum Advance	
							Advance Starts	Full Advance	Inches of Vacuum To Start Plunger	Max. Adv. Dist. Deg. @ Vacuum
1966	Std. Dist.	C5UF-J	C	.025	37–42	17–21	...	...	.45	12 @ 3.70
	With Thermactor	C6DF-A	C	.025	37–42	17–21	½ @ 500	13 @ 1800	5	10 @ 15
	V8-289 Std. Dist.	C5AF-M	CC	.017	26–31	17–21	2 @ 650	13 @ 2000	8	9 @ 14
	V8-289 Thermactor②	C6AF-AJ	CC	.017	26–31	17–21	2 @ 550	14 @ 1800	8	9 @ 14
1967	6-170 Std. Dist.	C5DF-C	C	.025	37–42	17–21	...	...	.80	11 @ 3.90
	6-170 Thermactor②	C7TF-J	C	.025	37–42	17–21	2 @ 800	10 @ 1600	5	7 @ 20
	V8-289	C7OF-A	CC	.017	26–31	17–21	½ @ 400	11 @ 1500	5	11 @ 20
	V8-289 Thermactor②	C7OF-D	CC	.017	26–31	17–21	½ @ 300	14 @ 2000	5	12 @ 20
1968	6-170	C8UF-A	C	.027	35–40	17–21	½ @ 350	16 @ 2000	5	10 @ 25
	V8-289	C8TF-F	CC	.021	24–29	17–21	½ @ 350	11 @ 2000	5	11½ @ 25
1969	6-170	C9UF-F	C	.027	35–40	17–21	½ @ 350	14 @ 2000	5	6 @ 25
	V8-302	C8TF-E	CC	.021	24–29	17–21	½ @ 350	11 @ 2000	5	11½ @ 25

①—As viewed from rotor end.

②—With Thermactor Exhaust Emission Control System.

COOLING SYSTEM & CAPACITY DATA

Year	Model or Engine	Cooling Capacity, Qts.			Radiator Cap Relief Pressure, Lbs.		Thermo. Opening Temp. ①	Fuel Tank Gals.	Engine Oil Refill Qts.④	Transmission Oil			Front and Rear Axle Oil Pints
		No Heater	With Heater	With A/C	With A/C	No A/C				3 Speed Pints	4 Speed Pints	Auto. Trans. Qts.	
1966	All	12.7	12.7	...	...	12–15	190	14	6	3½	...	...	②
	V8-289	14	15	...	...	12-15	180	14	4	3½	...	...	②
1967	6-170	8	9	...	...	12-15	190	14	6	3½	...	...	③
	V8-289	15	16	...	...	12-15	190	14	5	3½	...	...	③
1968	6-170	9	10	...	...	12–15	190	14½	6	3½	...	...	③
	V8-289	15	16	...	...	12–15	190	14½	5	3½	...	...	③
1969	6-170	9	10	...	...	12–15	190	14½	6	3½	...	...	⑤
	V8-302	14	15	...	...	12–15	190	14½	5	3½	...	...	⑤

①—Used with permanent type anti-freeze.

②—Front axle 2½ pints; rear axle 5 pints.

③—Front axle 4¾ pints; rear axle 5 pints.

④—Add 1 qt. if filter is changed.

⑤—Front axle 3¾ pints; rear axle 5 pints.

WHEEL ALIGNMENT SPECIFICATIONS

Year	Model	Caster Angle, Degrees		Camber Angle, Degrees				Toe-In. Inch	Toe-Out on Turns, Deg.	
				Limits		Desired				
		Limits	Desired	Left	Right	Left	Right		Outer Wheel	Inner Wheel
1966–67	All	①	①	①	①	①	①	3/32	...	...
1968–69	All	+2¾ to +4¼①	+3½①	+1 to +2①	+1 to +2①	+1½①	+1½①	1/8	...	...

①—Designed into axle and not adjustable.

ENGINE TIGHTENING SPECIFICATIONS★

★Torque specifications are for clean and lightly lubricated threads only. Dry or dirty threads produce increased friction which prevents accurate measurement of tightness.

Year	Engine	Spark Plugs Ft. Lbs.	Cylinder Head Bolts Ft. Lbs.	Intake Manifold Ft. Lbs.	Exhaust Manifold Ft. Lbs.	Rocker Arm Shaft Bracket Ft. Lbs.	Rocker Arm Cover Ft. Lbs.	Connecting Rod Cap Bolts Ft. Lbs.	Main Bearing Cap Bolts Ft. Lbs.	Flywheel to Crankshaft Ft. Lbs.	Vibration Damper or Pulley Ft. Lbs.
1966–69	6-170	15–20	70–75	...	13–18	30–35	3–5	19–24	60–70	75–85	85–100
	V8-289①	15–20	65–72	20–22	15–20	...	3–5	19–24	60–70	75–85	70–90
	V8-302①	15–20	65–72	23–25	12–16	...	3–5	19–24	60–70	75–85	70–90

①—See Ford Chapter for service procedures on this engine.

STARTING MOTOR SPECIFICATIONS

Year	Engine Model	Part No.	Brush Spring Tension, Ounces	No Load Test			Torque Test		
				Amperes	Volts	R.P.M.	Amperes	Volts	Torque, Lbs. Ft.
1966–67	All	...	40	70	...	...	460	5	9
1968–69	6-170	C7ZF-11001-A	40	70	12	8500	460	6	9
	V8-289	C7AF-11001-B	40	70	12	9500	670	5	15½

PISTONS, PINS, RINGS, CRANKSHAFT & BEARINGS

Year	Engine	Piston Clearance	Ring End Gap		Wrist-pin Diameter	Rod Bearings		Main Bearings			
			Comp.	Oil		Shaft Diameter	Bearing Clearance	Shaft Diameter	Bearing Clearance	Thrust on Bear. No.	Shaft End Play
1966–69	6-170	.0014–.002	.010	.015	.9120	2.1232–2.1240	.0008–.0015	2.2482–2.2490	.0005–.0015	3	.004–.008
	V8-289①	.0018–.0026	.010	.015	.9120	2.1228–2.1236	.0008–.0015	2.2482–2.2490	.0005–.0015	3	.004–.008
	V8-302①	.0018–.0026	.010	.015	.9120	2.1228–2.1236	.0008–.0015	2.2482–2.2490	.0005–.0015	3	.004–.008

①—See For d Chapter for service procedures on this engine.

FRONT & REAR AXLE & BRAKE SPECIFICATIONS

Year	Axle	Carrier Type	Diff. Bear. Preload		Ring Gear & Pinion Backlash		Pinion Bear. Preload		Brake Drum Dia.	Brake Cyl. Bore Diameter		
										Wheel Cylinders		Master Cylinder
			Method	Adjust.	Method	Adjust.	Method	Adjust.		Front	Rear	
1966	Front	Integral	①	①	Shim	.006–.010	Spacer	②	10	1⅛	13/16	1
1966–69	Rear	Removable	①	①	Shim	.008–.012	Spacer	③	10④	1⅛	13/16	1
1967–69	Front	Integral	①	①	Shim	.006–.010	Spacer	②	11	1⅛	13/16	1

①—Threaded adjusters 2½ to 3 notches tight.
②—New bearings 17–27 inch-lbs.; used bearings 6–12 inch-lbs.
③—New bearings 17–32 inch-lbs.; used bearings 8–14 inch-lbs.
④—Optional axle use 11″.

Electrical Section

IGNITION TIMING

If a timing light is to be used to set ignition timing, disconnect the vacuum advance pipe to the carburetor and place a piece of tape over open end of pipe. *This is important as carburetor trouble can affect timing adjustments.*

Lacking a power timing light, an accurate method of setting ignition timing with the engine stopped is with the aid of a jumper light. Be sure to use a light bulb that corresponds with the system voltage of the vehicle.

1. Remove distributor cap and rotor and see that the breaker gap is set according to specifications.
2. Rotate engine until No. 1 cylinder is at the ignition timing point as indicated by the timing pointer and timing mark being lined up with each other.
3. Connect the jumper light between distributor ignition terminal and ground.
4. Turn on ignition switch.
5. Loosen distributor and turn it in the direction of normal rotation until the points just close (light out). Then slowly turn distributor in the opposite direction just to the exact point that the light goes on. Tighten distributor in this position.

DISTRIBUTOR REPLACE

1. To remove the distributor, disconnect the primary wire and vacuum control pipe.
2. Remove distributor cap.
3. Scribe a mark on the distributor body indicating the position of the rotor, and scribe another mark on the body and engine block indicating position of distributor body in block. These marks can be used as guides when installing distributor in a correctly timed engine.
4. Remove hold down screw or screws and lift distributor out of block. *Do not crank engine while distributor is removed or the initial timing operation will have to be performed.*

Installation

If the crankshaft has not been disturbed, install the distributor, using the scribed marks previously made on the distributor body and engine block as guides.

If the crankshaft has been rotated while the distributor was removed from the engine, it will be necessary to retime the engine. Crank the engine to bring No. 1 piston on top dead center of its compression stroke. Align the timing mark on the crankshaft pulley with the timing pointer (see *Tune Up chart)*. Install the distributor so that the rotor points to the No. 1 spark plug wire terminal in the distributor cap.

Make sure the oil pump intermediate shaft properly engages the distributor shaft. It may be necessary to crank the engine with the starter, after the distributor drive gear is properly engaged, in order to engage the oil pump intermediate shaft.

Fig. 1 Light switch release button

STARTER REPLACE

1. Disconnect cable at starter terminal.
2. Unfasten and remove starter.
3. Reverse procedure to install, tightening starter mounting bolts.

IGNITION SWITCH

1967-69

1. Disconnect ground strap at battery.
2. Turn ignition key to accessory position. Slightly depress pin with a paper clip into hole below key slot, turn key counterclockwise and pull key and lock cylinder out of switch.
3. Press in on rear of switch and rotate switch ⅛ turn counterclockwise (as viewed from terminal end). Remove bezel, switch and spacer.
4. Remove nut from back of switch, disconnect wires and pull off insulated plug from rear of switch.
5. If a new switch is being installed, insert a screwdriver into lock opening of switch and turn slot in switch to a full counterclockwise position. Then complete the installation in reverse order of removal.

1966

1. Disconnect battery.
2. Turn ignition key counterclockwise and insert a paper clip into hole below the key slot and pull out the tumbler.
3. From behind instrument panel, hold switch firmly, turn it clockwise and remove switch. Remove retaining ring from front of panel and remove collar from switch.
4. Remove accessory wire nuts and wires. Pull rubber cluster plug from switch and remove switch from plug.
5. Reverse procedure to install.

LIGHT SWITCH

1968-69

1. Disconnect battery ground cable.
2. With the light switch knob in the full "On" position, release the knob by depressing the release button on the switch housing, Fig. 1.
3. Pull the knob and shaft out of the switch and remove the bezel nut retaining the switch to the panel.
4. Lower the switch and unplug the connector.
5. Reverse procedure to install.

1966-67

1. Disconnect battery.
2. Remove light switch knob and shaft.
3. Remove switch bezel nut.
4. Lower switch and remove junction block from light switch and remove switch.
5. Reverse procedure to install.

STOP LIGHT SWITCH

1967-69

1. Disconnect the stop light switch connector under the dash.
2. Remove hairpin retainer and nylon washer from the pin on brake pedal arm, Fig. 2.
3. Slide the switch assembly and brake push rod to the right and off the pin to remove the switch.
4. Remove the remaining nylon washer from the pin.
5. Apply a coat of light engine oil to both nylon washers.
6. Reverse procedure to install.

1966

1. Disconnect wires at bullet connectors.
2. Unscrew switch from brake master cylinder.

HORN SOUNDER & TURN SIGNAL SWITCH

1968-69

1. Disconnect horn and turn signal wires at connectors behind the instrument panel.
2. Remove the steering column wires and terminals from the connectors by depressing the tab on the wire terminal with an awl or by inserting a ball point pen over the bullet pin and pull the wire and terminal from the connector. Record the color code and location of each wire before removing it from the block.
3. Tape a pull through wire or cord to one of the wire ends.
4. Depress the horn button or ring and turn it counterclockwise to remove it. Remove the horn spring.
5. Mark the steering wheel position on the column. Remove the steering wheel. Remove the spring from around end of steering shaft.
6. Turn the signal switch lever counterclockwise to remove it. Remove the screws and retainer that hold signal

switch and wire assembly to the column and pull the assembly from the column.
7. Disconnect the pull through wire or cord and tape the loose ends of the new signal switch wires to the pull through wire.
8. Carefully pull the wires through the column while guiding the switch into position.
9. Complete assembly and press wires into the connector in their previously recorded positions.

1967

1. Disconnect horn wire and turn signal switch wires under instrument panel and at clips on steering column support.
2. Press down on horn button and turn counterclockwise until it lifts out from steering wheel. Remove button and spring.
3. Mark steering wheel position on steering column. Remove steering wheel.
4. Remove turn signal lever (one screw). Remove cover that retains signal wires to steering column.
5. Remove two screws under steering column and lift horn contact plate and turn signal switch from column cup.
6. Reverse procedure to install.

1966

1. Remove wire harness from lower clip of instrument panel and disconnect plug type connectors.
2. Remove horn ring and spring.
3. Remove horn contact brush from steering wheel hub.
4. Remove steering wheel.
5. Remove turn indicator and lever.
6. Remove upper bearing cone spring.
7. Remove screws securing switch to steering tube.
8. Depress tabs and remove connector blocks. Remove cover from harness.
9. Tie a cord to wire ends of switch and remove switch and wires from column.
10. Tape wire ends on new switch, tie cord to wires and route wires through column.
11. Remove cord and tape and reverse procedure to install remaining parts.

INSTRUMENT CLUSTER

1968-69

1. Disconnect battery ground cable.
2. Unfasten instrument cluster from panel.
3. Cluster is removed from behind panel after disconnecting light sockets, instrument wires and speedometer cable.

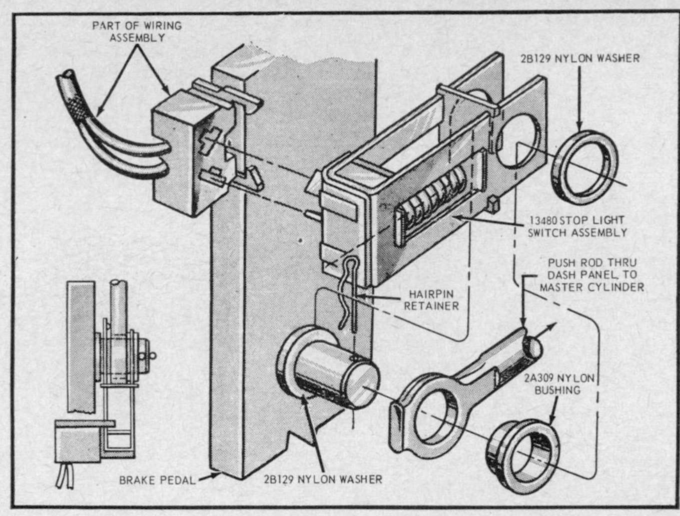

Fig. 2 Mechanical stop light switch. 1967-69

4. Reverse procedure to install.

NOTE: Be sure that the black-yellow stripe wire is routed correctly through the ammeter loop of the charge indicator to prevent reversed gauge readings.

1967

1. Disconnect ground strap at battery.
2. Disconnect speedometer cable.
3. Unfasten cluster from instrument panel and lift cluster out at front of panel.
4. With cluster removed, all instruments are accessible for replacement.

1966

1. Disconnect battery.
2. Disconnect speedometer cable.
3. Remove screws retaining instrument cluster to instrument panel and suspend the assembly.
4. Remove clips from wiring harness, disconnect leads from cluster and remove from vehicle.
5. Remove screws retaining speedometer mounting plate and mask.
6. Reverse procedure to install.

W/S WIPER MOTOR

1967-69

1. Remove wiper arm and blade.
2. Remove adapter with a suitable puller.
3. Disconnect vacuum hose.
4. Unfasten motor from windshield header.
5. Reverse procedure to install.

W/S WIPER SWITCH

The vacuum windshield wiper motor is controlled by a push-pull type switch located on the wiper motor.

RADIO

NOTE: When installing radio, be sure to adjust antenna trimmer for peak performance.

1967-69

1. Disconnect radio lead wire at fuse panel.
2. Disconnect speaker leads at receptacle on underside of radio.
3. Disconnect antenna lead at receptacle on right side of radio.
4. Pull off control knobs.
5. Remove dial from instrument panel.
6. Remove nuts and retaining plate that secures radio to instrument panel.
7. Remove bottom support bracket screw and remove radio.
8. Reverse procedure to install.

1966

1. Disconnect antenna cable at radio.
2. Disconnect speaker wire at radio.
3. Disconnect radio lead wire at fuse holder.
4. Remove radio control knobs.
5. Remove screws retaining dial assembly to instrument panel and remove dial.
6. Remove screw retaining radio to lower edge of instrument panel.
7. Remove nuts retaining radio to instrument panel and remove radio.
8. Reverse procedure to install.

Engine Section

See Ford Chapter For Service Procedures On V8-289, 302 Engines

Cutaway view of 6-170 engine

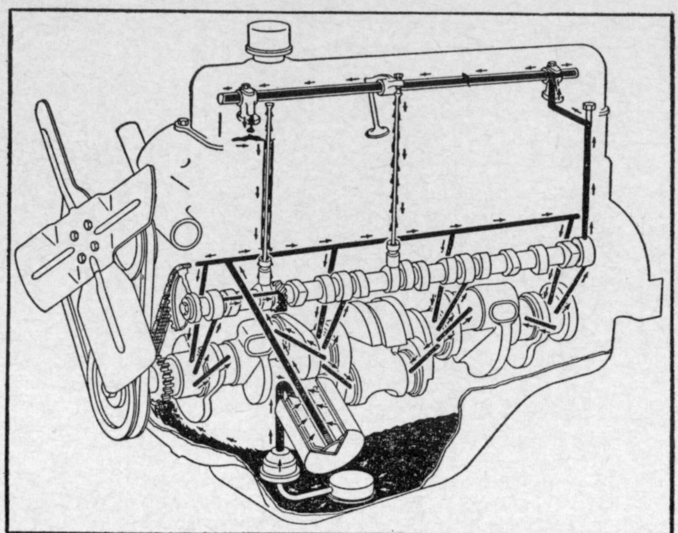

Engine lubrication. 6-170 engine

ENGINE REPLACE

NOTE: In addition to the usual items such as radiator, fuel lines, electrical wiring and linkage, it is necessary to perform the following operations.

1. Drain cooling system, remove air cleaner and disconnect battery cable.
2. Remove alternator and position to one side.
3. Remove starting motor.
4. Disconnect exhaust pipe from manifold.
5. Remove fan, spacer and pulley from water pump.
6. Remove retaining screws from equalizer shaft bracket at cylinder block and clutch housing and remove bracket.
7. Remove nut from each engine support.
8. Remove screws from clutch housing cover.
9. Loosen screws from clutch housing to cylinder block. They should be loosened only enough to assure that they can be removed with a hand wrench after lowering the vehicle.
10. After draining oil pan, lower vehicle. Then position jack under transmission and remove retaining clutch housing to cylinder block bolts.
11. Remove engine from chassis.
12. Reverse procedure to install.

CYLINDER HEAD

1. Drain cooling system, remove air cleaner and disconnect battery cable at cylinder head.
2. Unfasten and pull exhaust pipe down from manifold.
3. Disconnect linkage and lines at carburetor and distributor.
4. Grasp crankcase vent hose near regulator valve and pull regulator valve out of grommet in rocker arm cover. Remove vent hose and regulator valve.
5. Remove rocker arm cover.
6. Remove rocker arm and shaft assembly and lift out push rods.
7. Remove a bolt from each end of cylinder head and install guide studs.
8. Remove remaining head bolts and lift off cylinder head.
9. Reverse procedure to install and tighten head bolts in three steps in the sequence shown in Fig. 1. The final tightening should be to the torque limits given in the *Engine Tightening* table.

VALVE ARRANGEMENT

Front to Rear

6-170 .... E-I-I-E-I-E-E-I-E-I-I-E
8-289,302 Right .... I-E-I-E-I-E-I-E
8-289,302 Left .... E-I-E-I-E-I-E-I

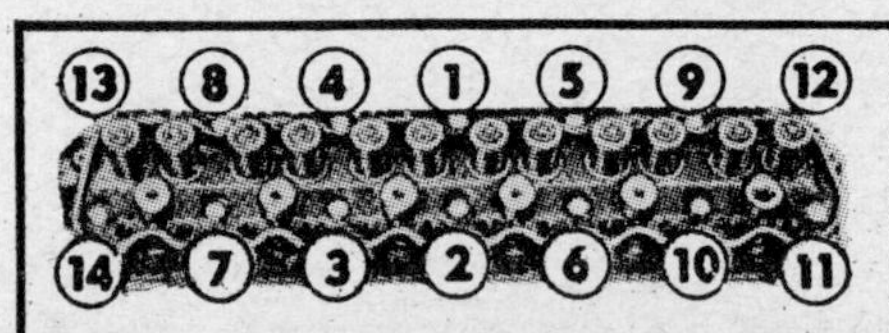

Fig. 1 Cylinder head tightening sequence

VALVE LIFT SPECS.

Engine	Year	Intake	Exhaust
6-170	1966-69	.361	.359
8-289	1966-68	.368	.381
8-302	1969	.368	.381

VALVE TIMING

Intake Opens Before TDC

Engine	Year	Degrees
6-170	1966-69	15
8-289	1966-68	16
8-302	1969	16

VALVES, ADJUST

The procedure used to check the valve clearance is to rotate the crankshaft with an auxiliary starter switch until the No. 1 piston is near TDC at the end of the compression stroke. At this point the following valves can be checked:

No. 1 Intake
No. 1 Exhaust
No. 2 Intake
No. 3 Exhaust
No. 4 Intake
No. 5 Exhaust

After the clearance of these valves have been checked, rotate the crankshaft until the No. 6 piston is on TDC at the end of its compression stroke (1 revolution of the crankshaft) and check the following valves:

No. 2 Exhaust
No. 3 Intake

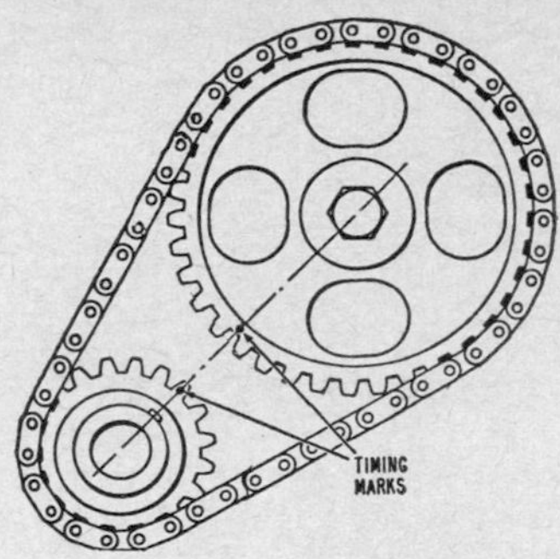

Fig. 2 Timing marks aligned for correct valve timing

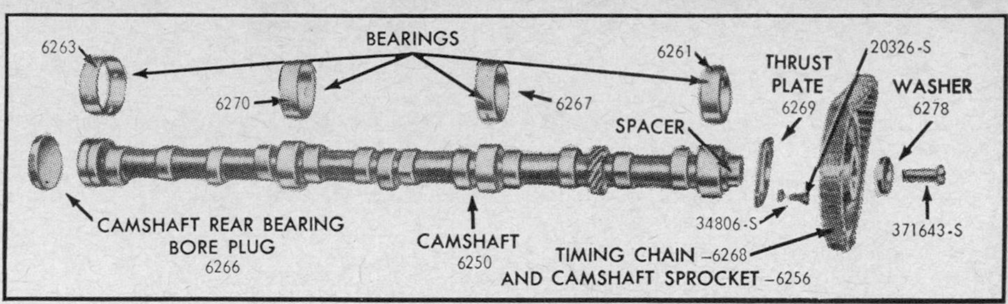

Fig. 3 Camshaft and related parts

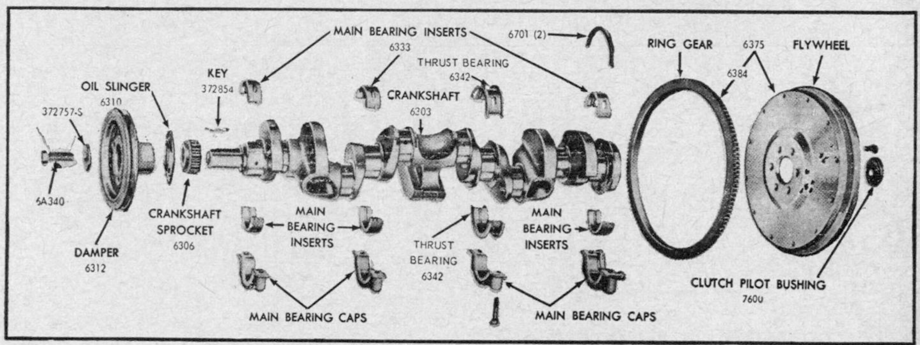

Fig. 5 Crankshaft and related parts

No. 4 Exhaust
No. 5 Intake
No. 6 Intake
No. 6 Exhaust

Before the final lash adjustment is made, operate the engine for 30 minutes at a fast idle to stabilize engine temperatures.

ROCKER ARM SERVICE

1. To disassemble, remove pin and spring washer from each end of rocker shaft.
2. Slide rocker arms, springs and supports off the shaft, being sure to identify location of parts for reassembly.
3. If it is necessary to remove the plugs from the shaft ends, drill or pierce the plug on one end. Then use a steel rod to knock out the plug on the opposite end. Working from the open end, knock out the remaining plug.

Assemble

1. Lubricate all parts with engine oil. Apply Lubriplate to the rocker arm pads.
2. If plugs were removed from shaft ends, use a blunt tool or large diameter pin punch and install a plug (cup side out) in each end of shaft.
3. Install spring washer and pin on one end of shaft.
4. Install rocker arms, supports and springs in proper order. *Be sure oil holes in shaft are facing downward.*
5. Complete the assembly by installing remaining spring washer and pin.

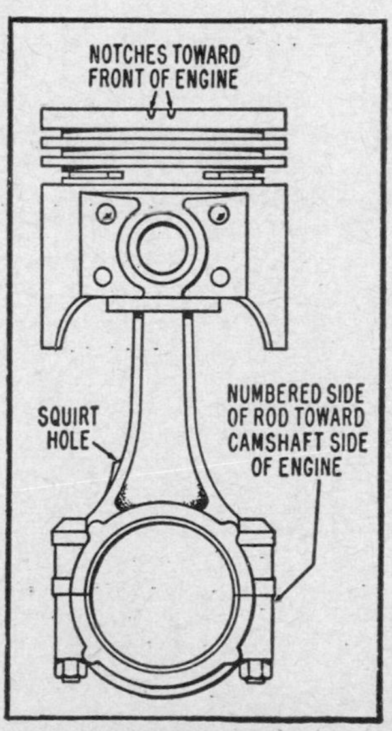

Fig. 4 Piston and rod assembly

VALVE LIFTERS, REPLACE

When necessary to replace valve lifters, remove cylinder head and related parts as outlined previously. Then remove and install one lifter at a time to be sure they are placed in their original bores.

When installing, apply Lubriplate to each lifter foot and coat the remainder of lifter with oil before installation.

TIMING CASE COVER

1. Drain cooling system and crankcase.
2. Remove radiator, fan and pulley.
3. Use puller to remove damper.
4. Remove front cover and gasket (crankcase ventilation tube bracket is retained by one cover bolt).
5. Remove crankshaft oil slinger.
6. Drive seal out of cover with a pin punch and clean out recess in cover.
7. Coat a new seal with grease and drive it in until fully seated in recess. Check seal after installation to be sure spring is properly positioned in seal.
8. Reverse removal procedure to install cover.

TIMING CHAIN

After removing the cover as outlined above, remove the crankshaft front oil slinger. Crank the engine until the timing marks are aligned as shown in Fig. 2. Remove camshaft sprocket retaining bolt and washer. Slide both sprockets and chain forward and remove them as an assembly.

Reverse the order of the foregoing procedure to install the chain and sprockets, being sure the timing marks are aligned.

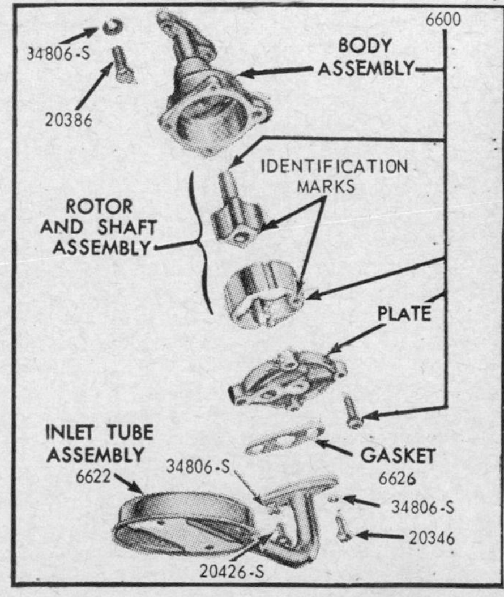

Fig. 6 Oil pump

CAMSHAFT REPLACE

To remove camshaft, remove cylinder head and related parts, radiator, oil pan, distributor, timing chain cover and valve lifters.

Remove timing chain and sprockets, camshaft thrust plate, and pull camshaft out of engine. If thrust plate shows signs or wear, install a new one, Fig. 3.

PISTON & ROD ASSEMBLE

When installed, piston and rod assembly should have the notch in piston head toward front of engine with oil squirt hole in rod positioned as shown in Fig. 4.

PISTONS, PINS & RINGS

Pistons and rings are furnished in standard sizes and oversizes of .020, .030 and .040″.

Oversize pins are not furnished.

MAIN & ROD BEARINGS

Undersize main and rod bearings are furnished in standard and undersizes of .002, .010, .020 and .030″.

CRANKSHAFT OIL SEAL

A braided oil seal is pressed into the upper and lower grooves behind the rear main bearing, Fig. 5. Directly in front of this seal is an oil slinger which deflects the oil back into the oil pan. Should the braided seal require replacement, the installation of the lower half is accomplished as follows:

OIL PUMP REPLACE

1. Remove oil pan.
2. Remove pump pick-up tube and screen.
3. Unfasten and remove pump from engine.
4. Reverse order of removal to install.

OIL PUMP REPAIRS

Referring to Fig. 6, disassemble pump. To remove the oil pressure relief valve, insert a self-threading sheet metal screw of the proper diameter into the oil pressure relief valve chamber cap and pull cap out of chamber. Remove spring and plunger.

The inner rotor and shaft and the outer race are serviced as an assembly. One part should not be replaced without replacing the other.

Install the pump cover and tighten to 6-9 ft. lbs. torque.

WATER PUMP REPLACE

1. Drain cooling system.
2. Remove drive belt, fan and pump pulley.
3. Disconnect necessary hose and remove pump.

FUEL PUMP

1. Disconnect fuel lines from pump. Discard fuel inlet line retaining clamp.
2. Disconnect vacuum lines at vacuum booster pump.
3. Unfasten and remove pump from engine.
4. Remove all gasket material from mounting pad and pump flange. Apply oil-resistant sealer to both sides of new gasket.
5. Position new gasket on pump flange, and hold pump in position against mounting pad. *Make sure rocker arm is riding on camshaft eccentric.*
6. Press pump tight against pad, install retaining screws and alternately tighten them. Connect vacuum and fuel lines. Use a new clamp on fuel inlet line.
7. Operate engine and check fuel pump, vacuum booster and connections for leaks.

Clutch, Transmission, Transfer Case & Drive Shaft

CLUTCH

Pedal Adjustment

If the total travel of the clutch pedal is not within the limits of 6⅝″ and 6⅞″ move clutch pedal bumper up or down as required to bring the total pedal travel within specified limits.

Measure the pedal free travel by slowly depressing the pedal until the clutch release fingers contact the clutch release bearing. The free play should be 1$\frac{3}{16}$″ to 1⅜″. If not within these limits, loosen the nut at the turnbuckle on the clutch release rod, Fig. 1, and adjust the turnbuckle as required.

Clutch Replace

1. Remove starting motor.
2. Remove transmission.
3. Disconnect release lever retracting spring and release rod, Fig. 1.
4. Remove hub and release bearing.
5. Remove flywheel housing-to-engine bolts, and lower flywheel housing.
6. Remove clutch.

Fig. 1 Clutch pedal adjustment

INSTALLATION

1. Wash flywheel surface with a suitable solvent.
2. Place clutch disc and clutch cover assembly in position on flywheel. Start retaining bolts finger-tight.
3. Align clutch disc with a clutch arbor (or a spare transmission clutch shaft) and then tighten bolts gradually and evenly to 23-28 ft-lbs.
4. After lightly lubricating release lever fulcrum and ends with grease, position release lever in flywheel housing.
5. Complete the installation in reverse order of removal and adjust clutch pedal free travel.

DRIVE SHAFT

NOTE: To maintain proper drive shaft balance, mark each drive shaft, universal joint, slip yoke and companion flange before removing either shaft assembly.

1. Remove caps that attach universal

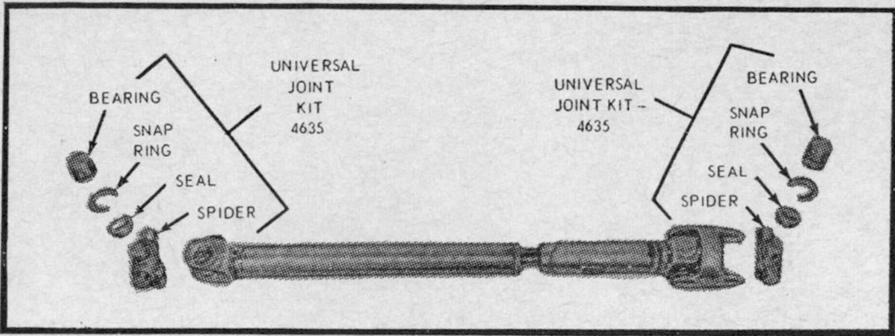

Fig. 2 Drive shaft details

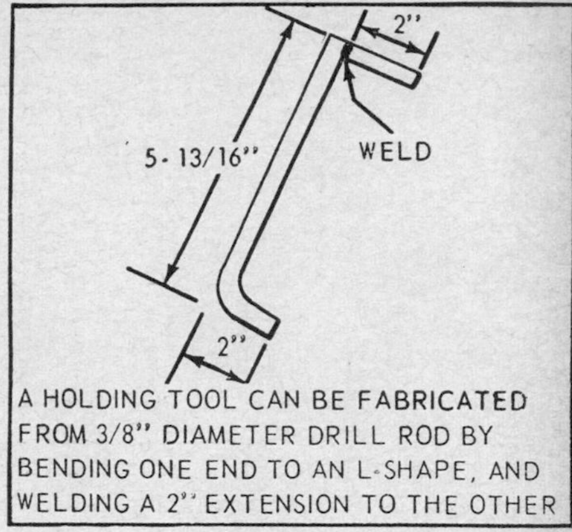

A HOLDING TOOL CAN BE FABRICATED FROM 3/8" DIAMETER DRILL ROD BY BENDING ONE END TO AN L-SHAPE, AND WELDING A 2" EXTENSION TO THE OTHER

Fig. 3

joints to differential drive pinion companion flange and to the transfer case. *Do not drop loose bearing cups.*

2. Wrap tape around loose bearing cups to prevent them from falling off spider.
3. Remove two U-bolts that attach universal joint to axle drive flange and remove drive shaft, Fig. 2.
4. Reverse procedure to install, being sure to align marks made on components so balance is maintained.

TRANSFER CASE

Remove & Replace

1. Raise vehicle on a hoist.
2. Support transfer case shield with a jack and remove shield from frame side rail.
3. Drain transmission and transfer case.
4. Disconnect front and rear drive shafts at transfer case.
5. Disconnect speedometer cable at transfer case.
6. Disconnect shift rods from transmission levers. Then place low-reverse shift lever in low gear position and insert the fabricated tool, Fig. 3. *This tool will prevent the input shaft roller bearings from dropping into the transmission case when separating the transfer case from the transmission and output shaft.*
7. Unfasten crossmember from transfer case adapter.
8. Raise transmission and remove crossmember.
9. Disconnect shift rod from transfer case shift lever bracket.
10. Unfasten shift lever bracket, allowing it to hang by shift lever.
11. Secure transfer case to a transmission jack and separate transfer case from transmission.
12. Move transfer case and jack rearward until it clears transmission output shaft. Then lower transfer case.
13. Reverse removal procedure to install.

Disassembly

Fig. 4 shows the components of the transfer case, which is a manually-shifted two-speed gear set to control the power from the engine and transmission to the front and rear driving axles.

1. Remove bottom cover plate.
2. Remove parts indicated in Fig. 5.
3. Remove idler shaft lock plate from rear of case.
4. Using a hammer and soft drift, drive idler shaft rearward and out of case. Then lift thrust washer and idler gear from case, Fig. 6, being careful not to loose any of the rollers.
5. Remove flange from front and rear output shafts. Discard front flange O-ring.
6. Separate and remove adapter housing from case, Fig. 7.
7. Remove output shaft and bearing retainer as an assembly, being careful not to loose any of the rollers.
8. Disconnect shift rail link from the two shift rails.
9. Lift rear output shaft sliding gear from case.
10. Remove set screw and remove rear drive shift rail and fork.
11. Remove rear output shaft rear cover and shims. Tie shims together.
12. Remove front output shaft bearing retainer, and seal if it is worn or damaged.

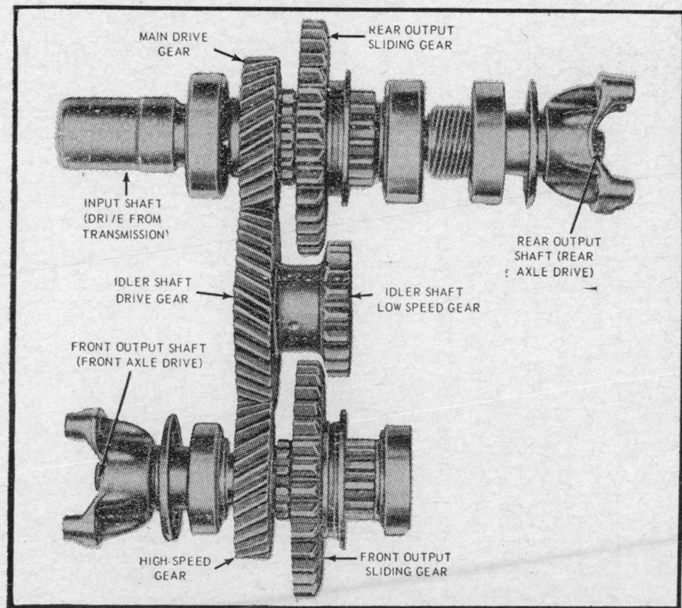

Fig. 4 Transfer case gear train in neutral

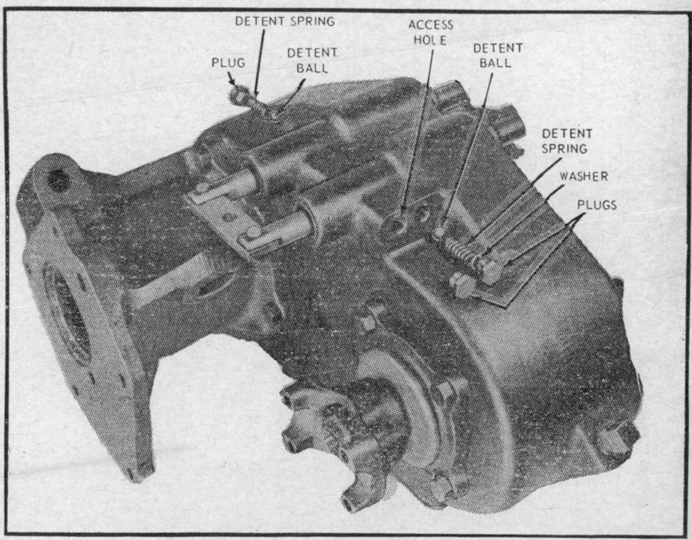

Fig. 5 Front and rear drive shift rail balls, springs and plugs

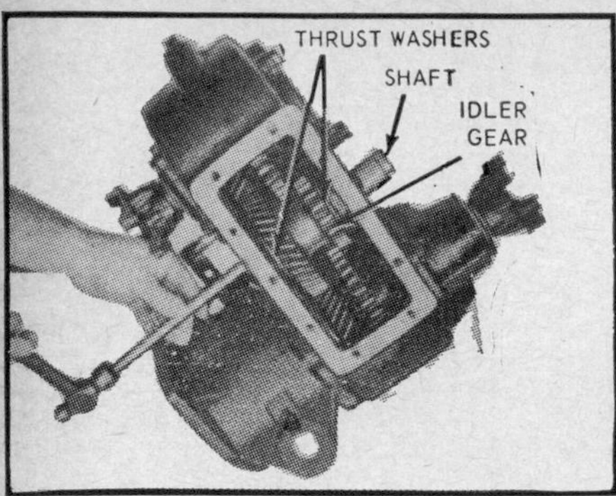

Fig. 6 Removing idler shaft

13. Tap threaded end of front output shaft to remove rear cup from case bore.
14. Wedge front output shaft front bearing away from main drive gear to allow removal of snap ring from its groove in shaft. Then tap shaft and rear bearing out of case, Fig. 8.
15. Lift sliding gear, main drive gear, front bearing, spacer and snap ring from case.
16. Remove front cup from case bore.
17. After removing set screw, remove front shift rail and fork.
18. Remove detent rods, Fig. 9.

Unit Repairs

Input Shaft, Fig. 10

1. Remove snap ring from front of shaft.
2. Place adapter housing and input shaft on a press and press shaft out of main drive gear and housing.
3. Remove snap ring from housing bore and remove bearing.
4. Replace seal in adapter housing if it is worn or damaged.
5. Reverse procedure to assemble.

Rear Drive Output Shaft, Fig. 11

1. Remove needle bearings from bore of shaft.
2. Remove speedometer driven gear.
3. Place bearing retainer and rear output shaft assembly on a press and press shaft out of retainer.
4. Lift speedometer drive gear and shims from shaft.
5. Press outer cup, bearing and seal from bearing retainer.
6. Remove inner bearing cup.
7. Remove inner bearing from output shaft.
8. Reverse procedure to assemble, leaving out the seal for the time being.

NOTE: When assembled, install a dial indicator on flange end of output shaft and check end play which should be .003-.005". If not within these limits, adjust shim pack between speedometer drive gear and rear output shaft outer bearing. After establishing correct end play, remove output shaft flange and press bearing retainer seal in housing. Install speedometer driven gear.

Front Drive Output Shaft

1. To remove the rear bearing, use the sliding gear as a base and press bearing from shaft.
2. Install bearing, pressing shaft into bearing.

Shift Rail Oil Seals

1. If a slide hammer tool is available, use it to remove shift rail seals.
2. Drive new seals in place.

Reassemble

The procedure for reassembling the transmission is largely the reverse of the disassembly procedure. However, observe the following:

1. The shift rails should be inserted so that the detents are positioned as shown in Fig. 12.
2. After installing idler shaft, tap sides of case to relieve tension from case.
3. When installing the front and rear drive shift rail detent balls, springs and retaining plugs, be sure that the heavier loaded spring and flat washer are installed in the front drive shift rail.
4. Be sure to install a new O-ring seal in the front output shaft flange.
5. Install a dial indicator on the front drive output shaft and check end play which should be .003-.005". If not within these limits, adjust shim pack at the front output shaft rear cover.

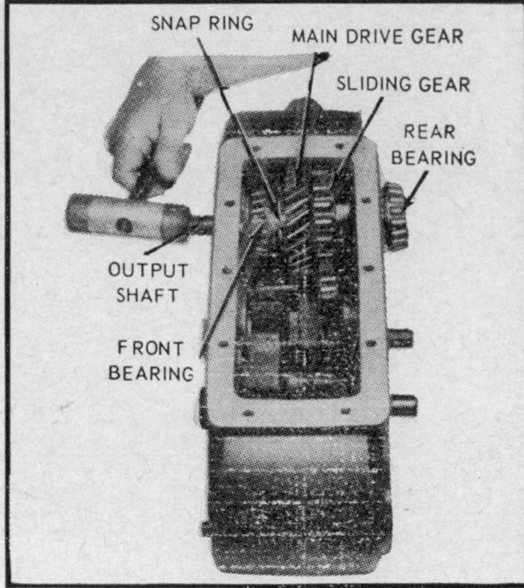

Fig. 8 Removing front output shaft

TRANSMISSION

For repairs on the transmission, refer to the *Three-Speed Transmission Chapter.*

Remove & Replace

1. Raise vehicle and drain transmission.
2. Disconnect drive shaft from transmission flange and secure front end of shaft to one side with wire.
3. Disconnect speedometer cable from extension housing, and gear shift rods from transmission levers.

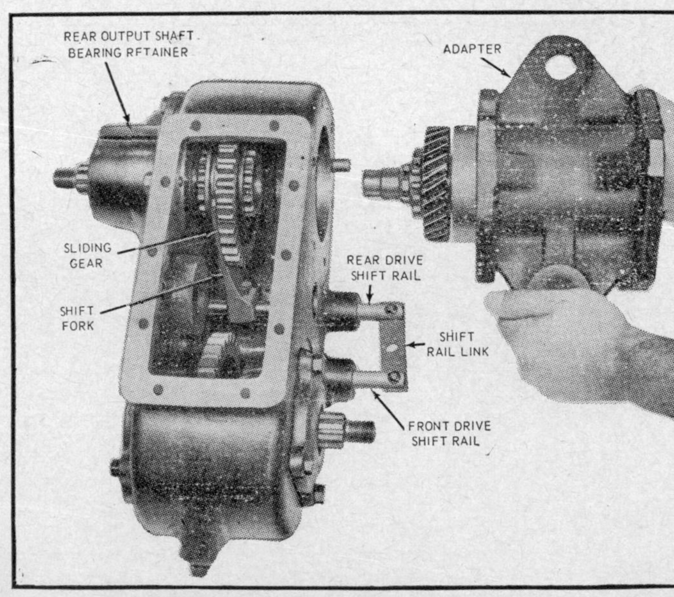

Fig. 7 Removing adapter housing

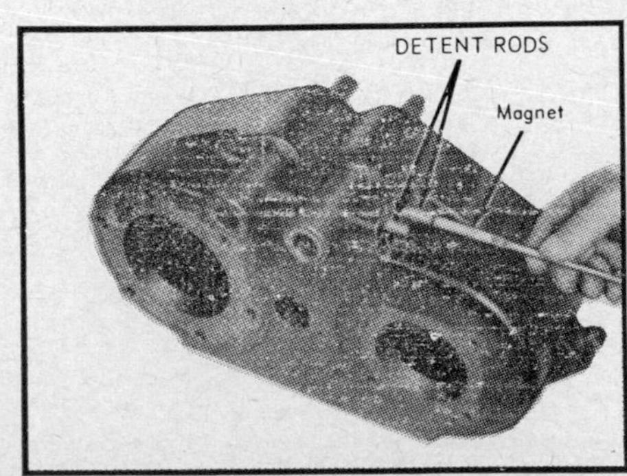

Fig. 9 Removing detent rods

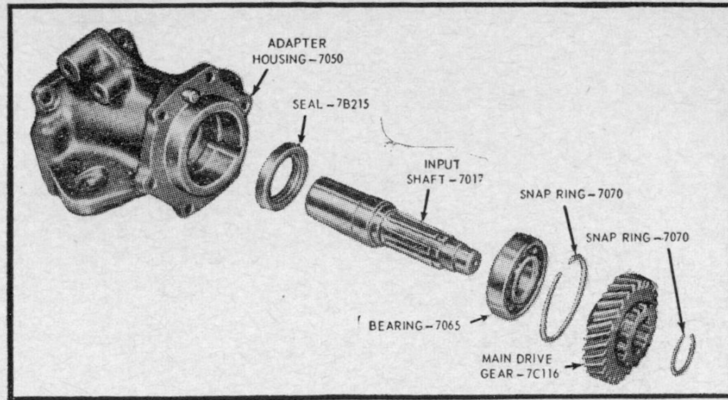

Fig. 10 Input shaft disassembled

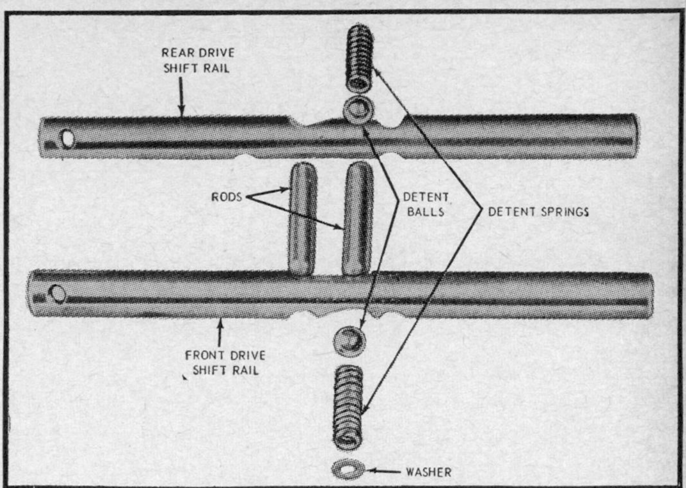

Fig. 12 Shift mechanism

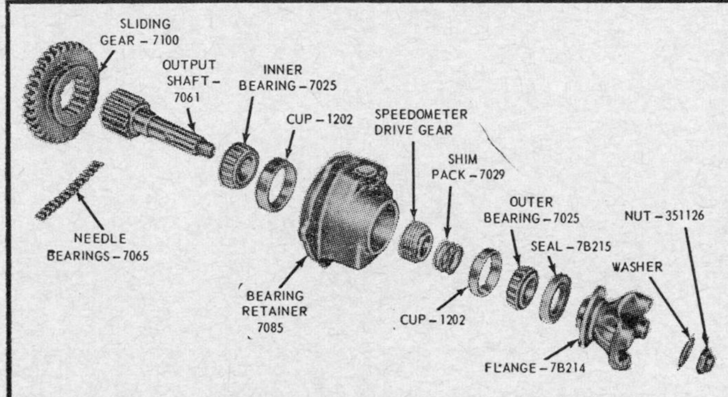

Fig. 11 Rear drive output shaft disassembled

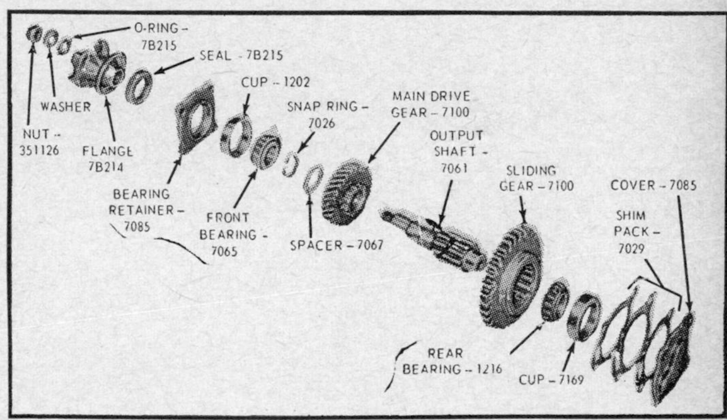

Fig. 13 Front output shaft disassembled

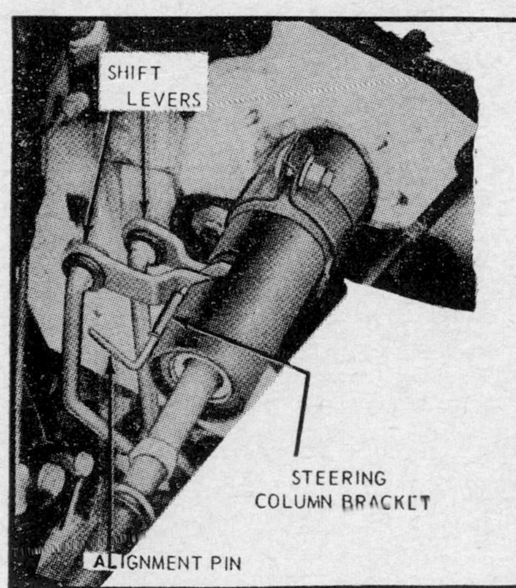

Fig. 14 Gearshift linkage adjustment

4. Position jack under engine and remove transmission rear support bolts.
5. Lower engine enough to drop transmission extension housing from rear support.
6. Unfasten and remove transmission.
7. Reverse procedure to install.

Gearshift Linkage Adjust

1. Place selector lever in neutral.
2. Insert a $\frac{3}{16}$" diameter rod through steering column bracket and shift levers, Fig. 14. It may be necessary to align levers to insert rod.
3. Disconnect shift rods at transmission levers.
4. Adjust position of each shift rod adjustment sleeve so that it enters transmission lever freely. Then run sleeves out seven (7) turns and secure adjustment with lock nut.
5. Remove alignment rod.
6. Secure rods to transmission levers.
7. Start engine and check selector lever in each position to make sure it operates freely.

Front & Rear Axles, Steering & Brakes

FRONT AXLE

This axle, Figs. 1 and 2, has an open yoke welded to the outer ends of the axle housing. This construction makes for a very strong spindle area. Power to drive the front wheels is transmitted through open Cardan-type universal joints. Pressed-in seals of a common type are used in the axle housing outer ends and in the spindle inner bore to seal out dirt and retain lubricants.

The differential section of the axle assembly is integral with the axle housing. Adjustment of the side carrier bearings is accomplished by means of shims placed between the bearings and the differential case. The carrier side bearings are pre-loaded by the squeezing action of the housing. A spreader must be used on the axle housing to relieve the tension on the differential bearings and permit removal and installation of the differential. Pinion depth is controlled by a shim pack located to the rear of the pinion bearing. Pinion bearing preload is controlled by variable-size spacers.

Front Axle Shaft & Spindle

1. To remove, raise vehicle on a hoist.
2. Drain lubricant from axle. *This must be done to prevent lubricant flooding the outer axle housing when axle shaft is removed.*
3. Remove hub grease cap and driving hub retaining snap ring and slide splined hub from between axle shaft and wheel hub. Remove hub spacer. (If equipped with free-running lock-out hubs, refer to this subject further on.)
4. Remove wheel bearing adjusting nut.
5. Remove wheel, hub and drum.
6. Remove inner bearing cone.
7. Remove brake carrier plate and secure it to one side to avoid damaging brake hose. Remove spindle.
8. Pull axle shaft from housing, working universal joint through bore of spindle arm. *At this point the following parts can be replaced without further disassembly of the axle: axle shaft, universal joint, axle housing outer seal, spindle bore seal, and spindle bore roller bearing.*
9. To remove spindle arm (housing), disconnect steering connecting rod end from spindle arm and remove bearing caps and spindle arm.
10. Reverse procedure to install.

Front Wheel Bearing, Adjust

1. Tighten bearing adjusting nut to 50 ft-lbs while rotating wheel back and forth to seat the bearings.
2. Continue rotating wheel and then

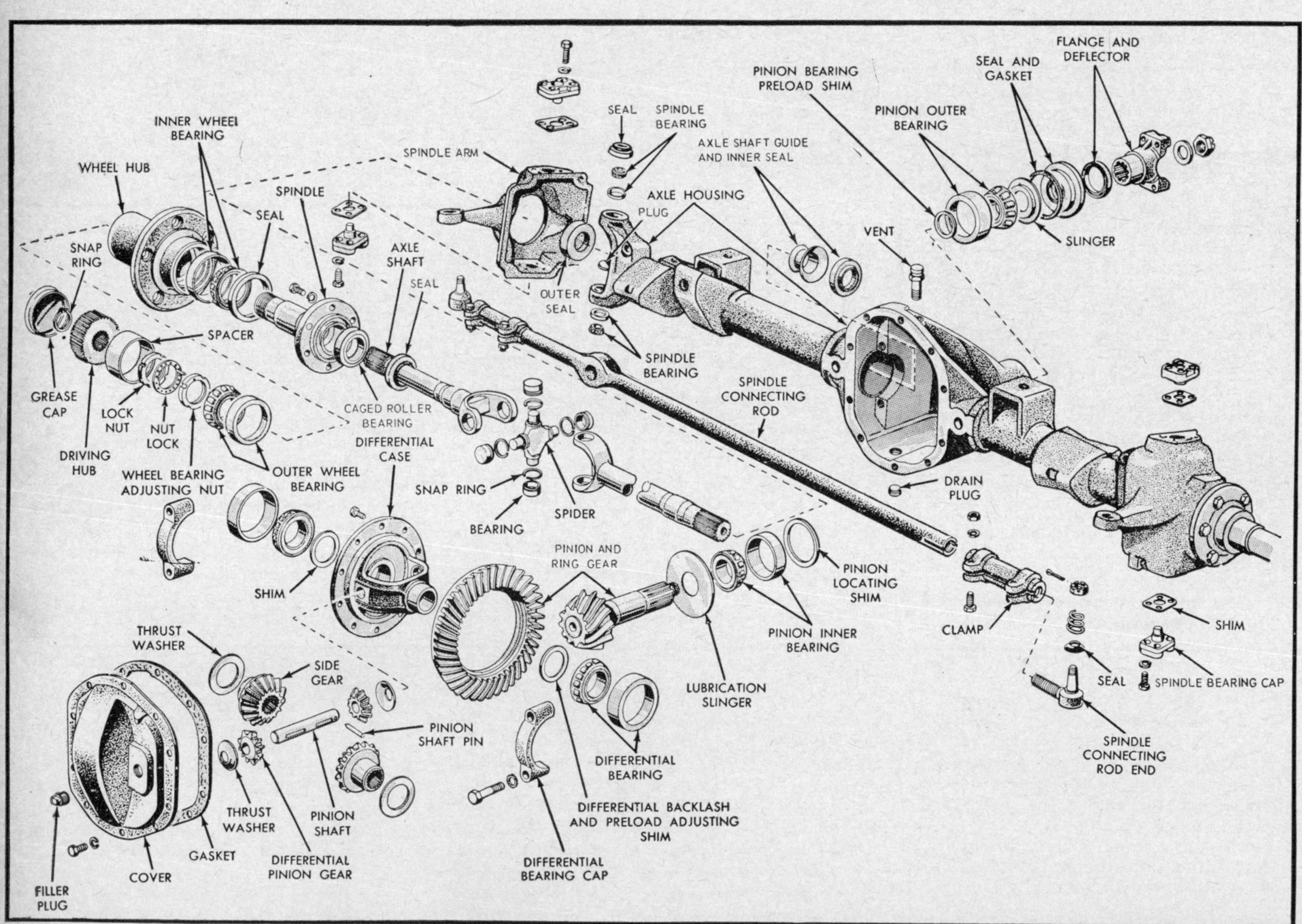

Fig. 1 Front axle assembly

loosen and re-torque the adjusting nut to 30-40 ft-lbs.

3. Back adjusting nut off about ½ turn. Assemble lock washer by turning adjusting nut to the nearest hole where the dowel pin will enter.
4. Install outer lock nut and torque to 50 ft-lbs. Final end play of wheel on spindle should be .001 to .010".
5. Install driving hub, spacer, snap ring and hub grease cap. Use a non-hardening sealer on the cap where it contacts the hub. (If equipped with free-running lock-out hubs, refer to *Lock-Out Hub* procedure further on.

Drive Pinion Oil Seal

This oil seal can be replaced without removing the axle assembly from the vehicle. If the new seal is of leather construction, it must be soaked in light engine oil for 30 minutes before installation. Compounded or synthetic rubber seals do not require soaking.

1. Raise vehicle on a hoist or raise front end with a jack. Install safety stands under frame rails and lower jack or hoist far enough to allow axle to drop into the rebound position for working clearance.
2. Scribe markings on companion flanges and U-joints for correct positioning at assembly, and remove drive shaft.
3. Remove pinion flange nut and companion flange.
4. Remove oil seal with a slide-hammer type puller.
5. Clean oil seal seat. Coat seating edge of new seal with a small amount of oil-resistant sealer. *Do not put sealer on sealing lip.* Drive seal into housing.
6. Coat inside of pinion flange with a small quantity of lubricant and install flange on pinion flange.
7. Install nut on pinion shaft and torque it to 200-220 ft-lbs.
8. Position drive shaft in the original location, matching the previously made scribe marks, and install attaching parts.
9. Torque U-joint U-bolt nuts to 15-20 ft-lbs.
10. Lower vehicle to road position and check axle lubricant level.

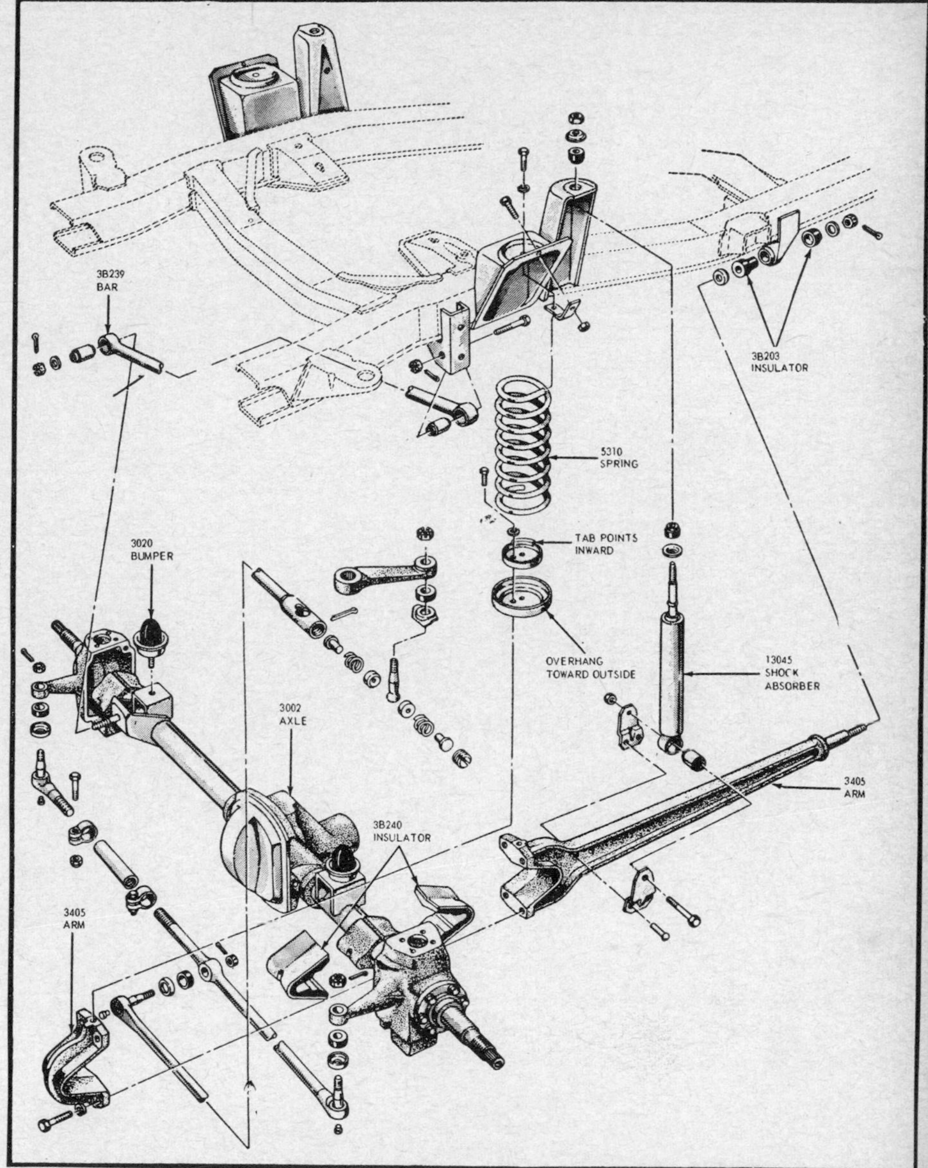

Fig. 2 Front axle attaching parts

Front Wheel Lock-Out Hub

Referring to Fig. 3, the splines on the OD of the inner clutch ring and bushing mesh with the inner splines of the wheel hub. The splines on the ID of the axle shaft sleeve and ring assembly being secured to the axle shaft by a snap ring. The clutch teeth on the inner clutch ring and bushing assembly mesh with the clutch teeth of the axle shaft sleeve and ring assembly to lock the axle shaft to the wheel hub forcing the axle shaft to drive the wheel hub. Disengagement of the large teeth of the inner clutch ring and bushing assembly from the large teeth of the axle shaft sleeve unlocks the axle shaft from the wheel hub to allow the wheel hub to free wheel.

Operation

When the transfer case is to be shifted into the position for driving the front axle, turn the actuating knob so that it is aligned with the letter L (lock). If the clutch teeth do not engage with the knob turned to this position, the clutch teeth are butted and a slight movement of the wheel in either direction will complete the lock. The front axle will now drive the wheel.

When the transfer case is to be shifted into the position for driving the rear axle only, turn the actuating knob so that it is aligned with the letter F (free wheel). This will disengage the clutch teeth and thus unlock the wheel hub from the axle shaft. The wheel will now turn free of the axle.

CAUTION: Be certain that the transfer case is shifted into two-wheel drive position before disengaging the Hub/Lok.

Removal

1. Remove actuating knob and retainer plate and large O-ring from wheel hub (3 screws).
2. Remove large internal snap ring, outer clutch retaining ring, and actuating cam body from wheel hub, Fig. 3.
3. While pressing inward against axle shaft sleeve and ring assembly, remove snap ring that secures axle shaft and sleeve assembly to axle shaft.
4. Remove axle shaft sleeve and ring assembly and inner clutch and bushing assembly from axle shaft.
5. Remove pressure spring and spring retainer plate from wheel hub.

Installation

1. Insert spring retainer plate into wheel hub with flange side facing inward. Be sure spring retainer plate

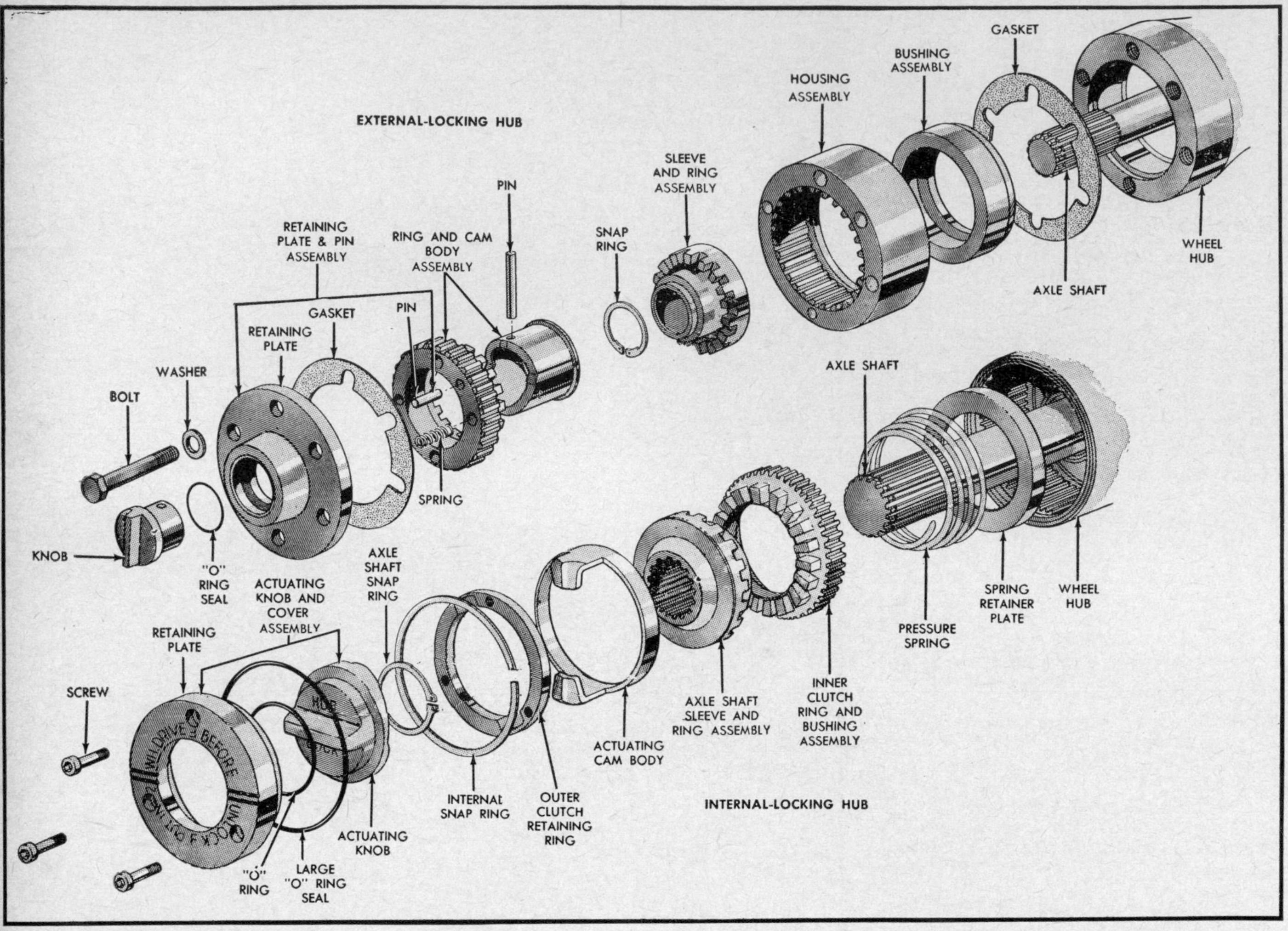

Fig. 3 Front wheel lock-out hub disassembled. For 1968-69, the actuating knob retaining plate has six screws

bottoms against outer wheel hub bearing cup.

2. Position pressure spring, with large end seating against spring retainer plate, inside wheel hub.
3. Assemble inner clutch ring and bushing assembly to axle shaft sleeve and ring assembly, sliding both assemblies as a unit onto axle shaft splines. Using a new axle shaft snap ring, lock axle shaft sleeve and ring assembly to axle shaft.
4. Place actuating cam body in position against axle shaft sleeve and ring assembly inside wheel hub.
5. Install outer clutch retaining ring and internal snap ring into wheel hub. Make sure snap ring is well seated in groove on inside diameter of hub.
6. Install large O-ring seal onto actuating knob and retaining plate, and place knob and plate into wheel hub.
7. Secure installation with three screws.

REAR AXLE

Fig. 1 illustrates the front drive axle while Fig. 4 illustrates the rear axle assembly. Both differential carriers are similar. When necessary to overhaul either of these differential carrier assemblies, refer to the *Front and Rear Axle Specifications* table in this chapter.

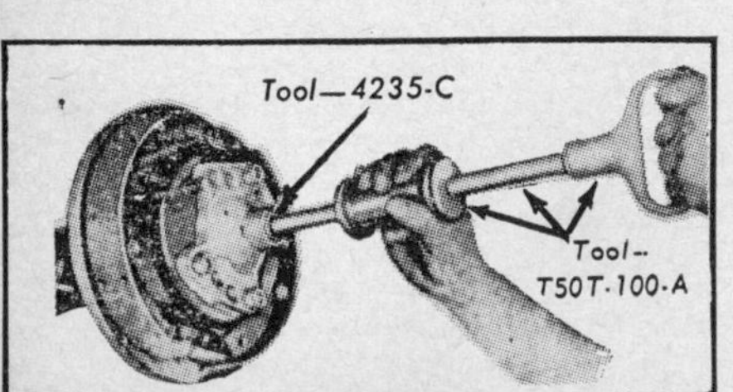

Fig. 5 Removing axle shaft

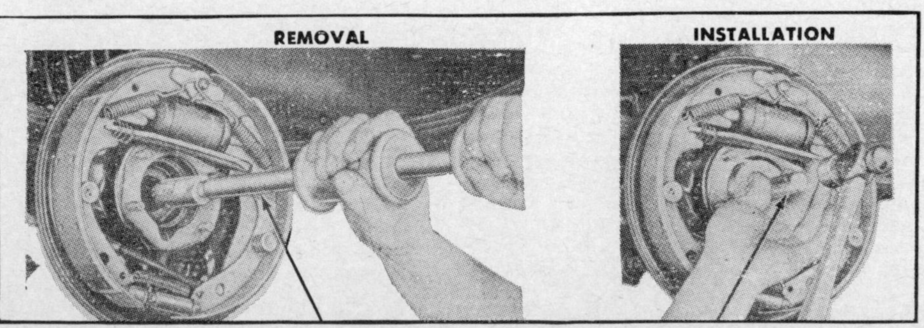

Fig. 6 Removing and installing axle shaft seal

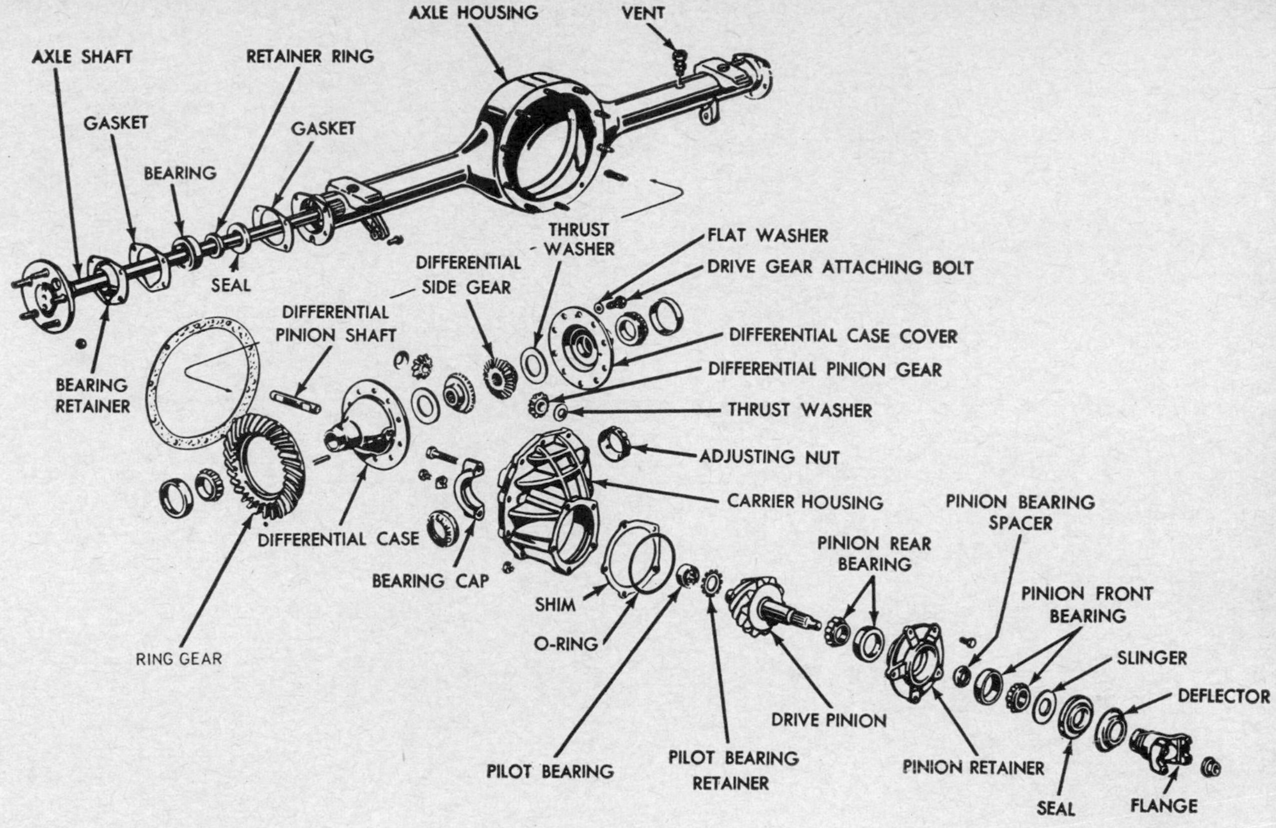

Fig. 4 Rear axle assembly

Description

In these axles, Fig. 4, the drive pinion is straddle-mounted by two opposed tapered roller bearings which support the pinion shaft in front of the drive pinion gear, and a straight roller bearing that supports the pinion shaft at the rear of the pinion gear. The drive pinion is assembled in a pinion retainer that is bolted to the differential carrier. The tapered roller bearings are preloaded by a spacer between the bearings. The pinion is positioned by a shim or shims located between the drive pinion retainer and the differential carrier.

The differential is supported in the carrier by two tapered roller side bearings. These bearings are preloaded by two threaded ring nuts or sleeves between the bearings and the pedestals. The differential assembly is positioned for proper ring gear and pinion backlash by varying the adjustment of these ring nuts. The differential case houses two side gears in mesh with two pinions mounted on a pinion shaft which held in place by a pin. The side gears and pinions are backed by thrust washers.

The axle shafts are of unequal length, the left shaft being shorter than the right. The axle shafts are mounted in sealed ball bearings which are pressed on the shafts.

AXLE SHAFTS

Removal

1. Remove wheel assembly.
2. Remove brake drum from flange.
3. Working through hole provided in axle shaft flange, remove nuts that secure wheel bearing retainer.
4. Pull axle shaft out of housing. If bearing is a tight fit in axle housing use a slide hammer-type puller, Fig. 5. *Brake carrier plate must not be dislodged. Install one nut to hold the plate in place after axle shaft is removed.*
5. If the axle shaft bearing is to be replaced, loosen the inner retainer by nicking it deeply with a chisel in several places. The bearing will then slide off easily.
6. Press bearing from axle shaft.
7. Inspect machined surface of axle shaft and housing for rough spots that would affect sealing action of the oil seal. Carefully remove any burrs or rough spots.
8. Press new bearing on shaft until it seats firmly against shoulder on shaft.
9. Press inner bearing retainer on shaft until it seats firmly against bearing.
10. If oil seal is to be replaced, use a hook-type tool to pull it out of housing, Fig. 6. Wipe a small amount of oil resistant sealer on outer edge of seal before it is installed.

Installation

1. Place a new gasket on each side of brake carrier plate and slide axle shaft into housing. Start the splines into the differential side gear and push the shaft in until bearing bottoms in housing.
2. Install retainer and tighten nuts to 30-40 ft. lbs.
3. Install brake drum and wheel.

BRAKES

Adjustment

Conventional Bendix-type brakes which are adjusted manually are employed. A brake tool access slot and rubber plug are provided in all the brake carrier plates.

The brakes should be adjusted when the drums are at normal room temperature. If the shoes are adjusted when the drums are hot, dragging brakes may result when the drums cool.

1. Raise wheels clear of floor. If vehicle is on a frame contact hoist, disconnect parking brake cables to prevent their tightening when rear axle and springs sag.

2. Remove adjusting hole cover from bottom of brake carrier plate and turn adjusting screw with a screwdriver (or tool made for the purpose) until a moderate drag on the wheel is noted.
3. Back off adjustment about six notches to allow wheel to rotate freely. Adjust remaining brakes in the same manner.

Parking Brake, Adjust

Check the parking brake cables when the brakes are fully released. If the cables are loose, adjust them as follows:

1. Apply parking brake pedal until first notch of ratchet is engaged.
2. Raise vehicle.
3. Loosen locknut in front of equalizer and tighten adjusting nut until a medium drag is felt on each rear brake. Release pedal and make sure brakes are free of drum so that brake shoes are not pulled off their anchors.
4. Lock adjustment with locknut and lower vehicle.

Master Cylinder

1967-69

1. Disconnect wires from stop light switch.
2. Disconnect hydraulic lines from master cylinder.
3. Disconnect dust boot from rear of master cylinder at dash panel.
4. Remove hairpin retainer and slide stop light switch off brake pedal pin just far enough for switch outer hole to clear pin.
5. Slide master cylinder push rod off brake pedal pin. Remove bushing and washers.
6. Unfasten and remove master cylinder.

1966

1. To remove cylinder, disconnect wires from stoplight switch.
2. Disconnect hydraulic outlet line from master cylinder.
3. Disconnect dust boot.
4. Unfasten and remove cylinder.
5. Reverse procedure to install, fill master cylinder and bleed brakes.

FRONT SUSPENSION & STEERING

Caster & Camber

Caster and camber angles are designed into the front axle and cannot be adjusted.

Toe-In, Adjust

If the toe-in is incorrect, loosen the clamp bolts at each end of the spindle connecting rod tube. Rotate the tube until the correct toe-in is obtained and tighten clamp bolts.

Recheck toe-in to make sure that no changes occurred when bolts were tightened. The clamps should be positioned 3/16" from the end of the rod with the clamp bolts in a vertical position in front of the tube with the nut down.

Shock Absorber Replace

1. Unfasten shock from lower bracket on radius arm.
2. Unfasten shock at frame bracket and remove shock.
3. Reverse procedure to install.

Front Spring Replace

1. Unfasten shock from lower bracket.
2. Unfasten upper and lower spring retainers.
3. Position safety stands under frame side rails and lower axle enough to relieve tension from spring. Remove spring, lower retainer and lower seat from vehicle.
4. Reverse procedure to install.

Steering Gear Replace

The steering gear is a worm and roller type. See the *Steering Gear Chapter* for service procedure on this type gear.

1. Raise car and remove pitman arm nut. Then use a suitable puller to remove pitman arm.
2. Remove steering gear-to-frame bolts and lower vehicle.
3. Remove flex coupling bolt from coupling clamp.
4. Loosen clamp on steering shaft and separate coupling from steering gear input shaft by pushing shaft toward steering column.
5. Remove flex coupling clamp from input shaft and remove gear from frame side rail.
6. Reverse procedure to install.

INTERNATIONAL SCOUT

INDEX OF SERVICE OPERATIONS

PAGE NO.

ACCESSORIES

Clock Troubles 1-11
Power Top Troubles 1-18
Power Window Troubles 1-18

BRAKES

Brake Troubles, Mechanical 1-17
Disc Brake Service 1-430
Hydraulic System Service 1-422
Power Brake Service 1-440
Power Brake Troubles 1-440

CLUTCH

Clutch Pedal, Adjust 2-386
Clutch, Replace 2-386
Clutch Troubles 1-12

COOLING SYSTEM

Cooling System Troubles 1-6
Variable Speed Fans 1-39
Water Pump Repairs 2-385

ELECTRICAL

Alternator Service 1-63
Dash Gauge Service 1-117
Distributor Service:
Standard 1-53
Transistorized 1-47
Electrical Troubles 1-8
Generator Service 1-91
Ignition Coils and Resistors 1-24
Ignition Timing 2-385
Spark Plug Condition Chart 2-647
Starter Service 1-101
Starter Switch Service 1-114
Turn Signal Troubles 1-11
Windshield Wiper Troubles 1-20

PAGE NO.

ENGINE

Camshaft and Bearings 2-385
Crankshaft Rear Oil Seal 2-385
Cylinder Head, Replace 2-384
Engine, Replace 2-383
Engine Troubles 1-1
Piston and Rod, Assemble 2-385
Rocker Arm Service 2-384
Timing Gears, Replace 2-384
Valve Guides 2-384
Valve Lifters 2-384

ENGINE LUBRICATION

Crankcase Ventilation (PCV) 1-29
Exhaust Emission Controls 1-30
Oil Pump Repairs 2-385

FRONT DRIVE AXLE 2-388

FUEL SYSTEM

Carburetor Adjustments 2-386
Crankcase Ventilation (PCV) 1-29
Exhaust Emission Controls 1-30
Fuel Pump Service 1-120
Fuel System Troubles 1-2
Turbocharger 2-386

PAGE NO.

REAR AXLE

Axle Shaft, Bearing and Seal 2-387
Rear Axle Troubles 1-17

SPECIFICATIONS

Alternator 2-382
Carburetors 2-386
Crankshaft and Bearings 2-383
Distributors 2-382
Engine Tightening Torque 2-383
General Engine Specs. 2-381
Generators 2-382
Ignition Coils and Resistors 1-24
Pistons, Rings and Pins 2-383
Starting Motors 2-383
Tune Up 2-382
Valve Lift 2-384
Valves 2-382
Wheel Alignment 2-389

STEERING GEAR 2-388

SUSPENSION, FRONT 2-388

Tire Wear Chart 2-648

TRANSMISSIONS 2-386

TUNE UP

Service 1-21
Specifications 2-382

U-JOINT SERVICE 1-418

GENERAL ENGINE SPECIFICATIONS

Year	Engine Model	No. Cyls. & Valve Location	Bore & Stroke	Piston Displacement, Cu. In.	Compression Ratio	Horsepower @ R. P. M.	Torque, Lb. Ft. @ R. P. M.	Normal Oil Pressure, Lbs.
1963–65	4-152	4 In Head	$3\frac{7}{8}$ x $3\frac{7}{32}$	152	8.19	90 @ 4400	135 @ 2400	50
1966–69	4-152	4 In Head	$3\frac{7}{8}$ x $3\frac{7}{32}$	152	8.10	93 @ 4400	143 @ 2400	50
1966–69	4-196	4 In Head	$4\frac{1}{8}$ x $3\frac{21}{32}$	196	8.1	111 @ 4000	180 @ 2000	50
1967–69	V-266	8 In Head	$3\frac{5}{8}$ x $3\frac{7}{32}$	266	8.4	155 @ 4400	227 @ 2800	40–50

INTERNATIONAL SCOUT

TUNE UP & VALVE SPECIFICATIONS

Year	Engine Model	Firing Order	Spark Plug Type	Spark Plug Gap	Ignition Timing: Timing Mark	Ignition Timing: Location	Valve Seat Angle, Degrees	Valve Clearance H-Hot C-Cold: Intake	Valve Clearance: Exhaust	Valve Spring Pressure, Lb. @ In. Length
1963–65	4-152	1342	N5	.028	5°BTC	Damper	45	Zero	Zero	133 @ 1 27/64
1966–69	4-152	1342	N5	.028	4°BTC	Damper	45	Zero	Zero	188 @ 1 27/64
	4-152①	1342	N5	.028	10°BTC	Damper	45	Zero	Zero	188 @ 1 27/64
1966–69	4-196	1342	N5	.025	5°	Damper	45	Zero	Zero	188 @ 1 27/64
1967–69	V-266	18436572②	J8	.030	4°③	Damper	45	Zero	Zero	195 @ 1 13/32

①—With Turbocharger. ②—Cylinder numbering (front to rear): Left bank 1-3-5-7, right bank 2-4-6-8. ③—Connect timing light to No. 8 spark plug

DISTRIBUTOR SPECIFICATIONS

Year	Model	Distributor Part No.	Rotation	Breaker Gap	Dwell Angle Deg.	Breaker Arm Spring Tension	Centrifugal Advance Degrees @ R.P.M. of Distributor: Advance Starts	Centrifugal Advance: Full Advance	Vacuum Advance: Inches of Vacuum To Start Plunger	Vacuum Advance: Max. Adv. Dist. Deg. @ Vacuum
1963–65	All	1110266		.016	75	19-23	1 @ 350	14 @ 2100	3-5	10 @ 7
1966–69	4-152 Standard	301574		.025	36	17-20	1 @ 375	15 @ 2000	2-5	7 @ 10
	4-152 Turbocharged	301573		.016	72	17-20	1 @ 600	12 @ 2000	—	—
1966–69	4-196	344730	—	.025	36	17-20	1 @ 300	17 @ 1800	5-7	14 @ 11½
1967–69	V-266	285098	C	.016	30	17-21	1 @ 350	14½ @ 2000	5-7	14 @ 11¼

D.C. GENERATOR AND REGULATOR SPECIFICATIONS

★To polarize generator, reconnect the leads to the regulator; then momentarily connect a jumper wire from the "Gen" to the "Bat" terminals of the regulator.

Year	Generator: Generator Number	Generator: Ground Polarity	Generator: Rated Cap. Amps.	Generator: Gen. Field Ground Location★	Generator: Brush Spring Tension, Ounces	Generator: Field Current Amperes	Regulator: Regulator Number	Regulator: Cutout Relay: Voltage to Close Points	Regulator: Cutout Relay: Armature Air Gap, Inch	Regulator: Voltage Regulator Setting Volts	Regulator: Current Regulator Setting Amperes	Regulator: Current and Voltage Armature Air Gap, Inch
1963–65	1100374	Neg.	25	External	28	1.50-1.62	1119000	12.6	.020	14.2	25	.075

DELCO-REMY ALTERNATOR & REGULATOR SPECIFICATIONS

Alternator: Model	Alternator: Field Current @ 80°F. 12 Volts	Alternator: Cold Output @ 14 V.: Amperes @ 2000 R.P.M.	Alternator: Cold Output @ 14 V.: Amperes @ 5000 R.P.M.	Alternator: Rated Hot Output Amperes	Regulator: Model	Regulator: Field Relay: Air Gap	Regulator: Field Relay: Point Gap	Regulator: Field Relay: Closing Voltage	Regulator: Voltage Regulator: Air Gap	Regulator: Voltage Regulator: Point Gap	Regulator: Voltage Regulator: Volts @ 125°F.
1100630	1.90-2.30	21	30	32	1119507	.015	.030	3.8-7.2	.067	.014	13.5-14.4

ENGINE TIGHTENING SPECIFICATIONS★

★Torque specifications are for clean and lightly lubricated threads only. Dry or dirty threads produce increased friction which prevents accurate measurement of tightness.

Engine	Spark Plugs Ft. Lbs.	Cylinder Head Bolts Ft. Lbs.	Intake Manifold Ft. Lbs.	Exhaust Manifold Ft. Lbs.	Rocker Arm Shaft Bracket Ft. Lbs.	Rocker Arm Cover Ft. Lbs.	Connecting Rod Cap Bolts Ft. Lbs.	Main Bearing Cap Bolts Ft. Lbs.	Flywheel to Crankshaft Ft. Lbs.	Vibration Damper or Pulley Ft. Lbs.
4-152, 196	28–30	75–80	40–45	40–45	75–80	—	45–55	75–80	45–55	100–110
V-266	28–30	90–100	40–45	40–45	—	—	45–55	75–85	45–55	100–110

PISTON, PIN, RING, CRANKSHAFT & BEARING SPECIFICATIONS

Year	Engine Model	Wristpin Diameter	Piston Clearance, Inch	Ring End Gap, In. (Minimum)		Crank Pin Diameter, Inch	Rod Bearing Clearance, In.	Main Bearing Journal Diameter, In.	Main Bearing Clearance, Inch	Thrust On Bear-ing No.	Shaft End Play
				Comp.	Oil						
1963–69	4-152, 196	1.0624	②	.010	①	2.373–2.374	.0011–.0032	2.7484–2.7494	.001–.004	3	.001–.005
1967–69	V-266	1.0624	.0035	.010	①	2.373–2.374	.0011–.0033	2.7484–2.7494	.001–.004	3	.001–.005

①—No gap at ring joint; steel rail gap .015″.
②—With .0035″ feeler 1″ wide, pull on spring scale should be 3 to 7 lbs.

STARTING MOTOR SPECIFICATIONS

Year	Model	Part No.	Brush Spring Tension, Ounces	No Load Test			Torque Test		
				Amperes	Volts	R.P.M.	Amperes	Volts	Torque Lbs. Ft.
1963–69	Scout	1107709	35	49–76	10.6	6200–9400	270–310	4.3	—

Engine Section

ENGINE, REPLACE

1. Drain cooling system, crankcase and disconnect battery ground cable.
2. Remove fan blade, radiator, and other parts such as radiator cross braces, heater air ducts, etc., which may interfere with engine removal.
3. Remove carburetor and engine wiring.
4. Remove fuel line from pump.
5. Disconnect exhaust pipe from manifold.
6. Install lifting fixture on engine.
7. Hoist engine enough to support it while disconnecting engine front mountings.
8. Separate engine from transmission by separating transmission from flywheel housing or flywheel housing from rear of engine.
9. Remove engine from chassis.
10. Replace in reverse order of removal.

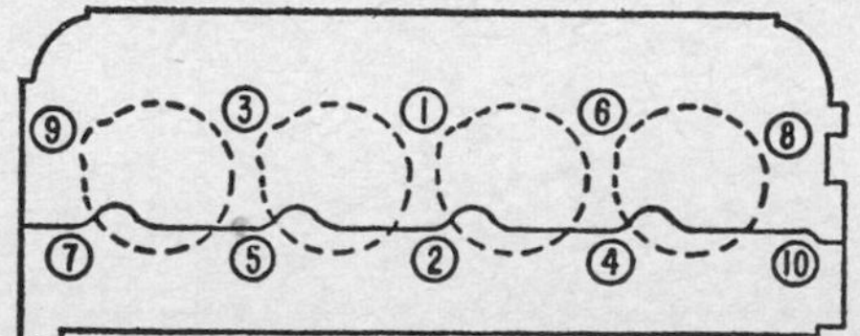

Fig. 1 Cylinder head tightening sequence

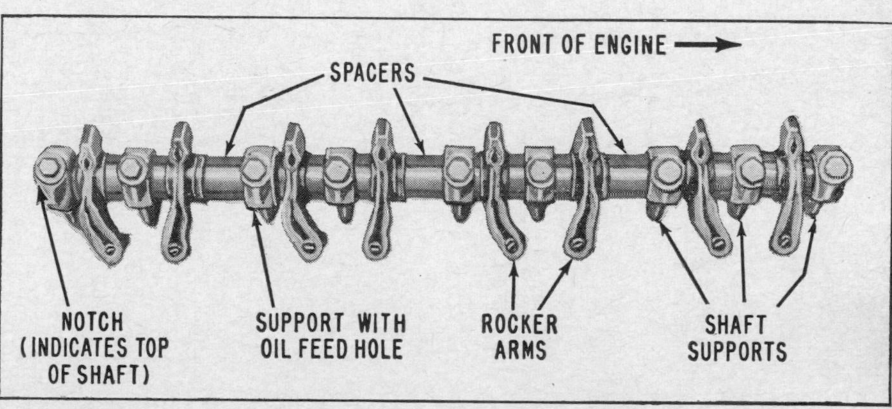

Fig. 2 Rocker arm assembly. 4-152, 196

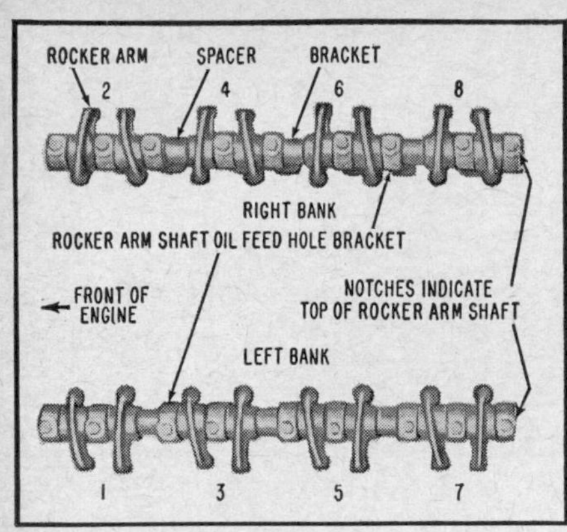

Fig. 3 Rocker arm assembly. V-266

CYLINDER HEAD, REPLACE

Cylinder heads should be tightened down by starting from the center, working outward from side to side and to the ends in the sequence shown in Fig. 1.

Draw the bolts down evenly, repeating the operation until all are normally tight. After running the engine to warm it up thoroughly, a final tightening should be made with a torque wrench to the torque load listed in the *Engine Tightening Specifications* table.

ROCKER ARM SERVICE

As shown in Figs. 2, 3, rocker arm assembly consists of the shaft, shaft supports, rocker arms and spacers. The rocker arms are lubricated by oil supplied to the hollow shaft through an oil passage in one of the supports.

Formation of sludge in the oil passages of the rocker arms and shaft will restrict flow of oil to the rocker arm bushings and valves. Therefore, each time the assembly is removed, it should be disassembled and cleaned thoroughly.

When disassembling, keep parts in order to assure reassembly in their original position if in satisfactory condition.

If necessary to remove plugs from each end of shaft, drill or pierce one plug, then knock out the opposite plug with a steel rod. Working from other end, knock out other plug.

When reassembling, lubricate rocker arm bushings with engine oil. Make sure the notches at ends of rocker arm shaft are up. Be sure to position the rocker arm support having the oil feed hole so that the oil hole will index with the oil feed hole in the cylinder head (third from rear), Fig. 2.

NOTE

Before installing push rods on 4-cyl. engines, rotate the crankshaft to position the crankshaft pulley hub as shown in Fig. 4. This is to prevent possible damage to engine parts if the hydraulic lifters have not leaked down to operating position.

VALVE LIFT SPECS.

Engine	Intake	Exhaust
4-152	.440	.395
4-196	.440	.395
8-266	.440	.395

VALVE GUIDES, REPLACE

Clean valve guides with a suitable cleaning tool. Then check each valve guide with a "GO and NO-GO" gauge, if available; otherwise, use a new valve to check the fit. If the "NO-GO" portion of the gauge enters, the guide must be replaced.

Clearance in excess of .006" for intake valves and .008" for exhaust valves, calls for replacement of valve guides.

New guides should be installed so that the distance from the cylinder head to the top of the guide is as follows:

4-152, 196 intake .... $\frac{31}{32}$"
4-152, 196 exhaust .... $1\frac{3}{32}$"
V-266 .... $\frac{31}{32}$"

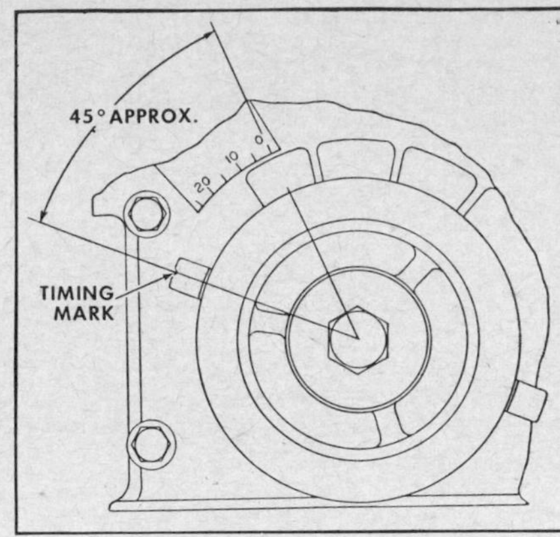

Fig. 4 Correct position of crankshaft pulley when installing push rod 4 cylinder engines

When guides are properly installed, they should be reamed to the following diameters:

4-152, 196 .... .376-.377
V-266 .... .374-.3755

VALVE LIFTERS

Hydraulic valve lifters, Fig. 5, are removed from the engine as an assembly. The lifters are removed by removing the valve cover, rocker arm and shaft assembly, then lifting out the push rods. If a lifter cannot be removed due to carbon build-up, use a carburetor solvent in the lifter bore. However, if an excessive amount of solvent is used, it will be necessary to change the engine oil. The lifters are also accessible by removal of the lifter covers.

As shown on Fig. 5, different designs of hydraulic lifters are used. When disassembling, do not mix the components of any lifter. Service kits of component parts are available for both types of lifters.

TIMING GEARS

When valves are correctly timed, the timing marks on the gears or sprockets should be adjacent to each other.

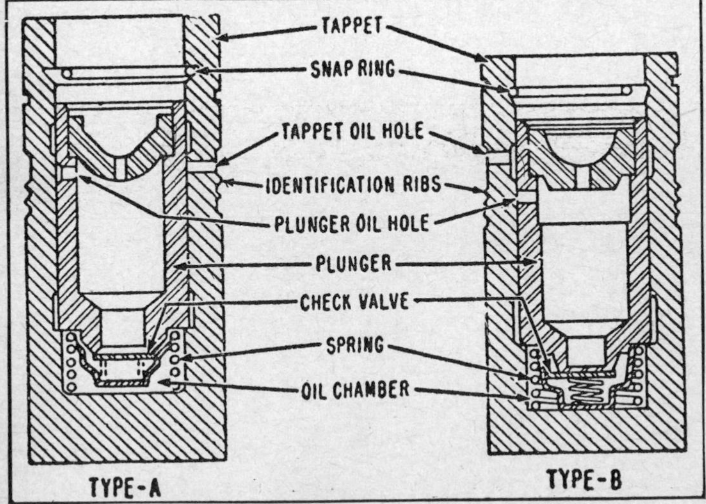

Fig. 5 Hydraulic valve lifters

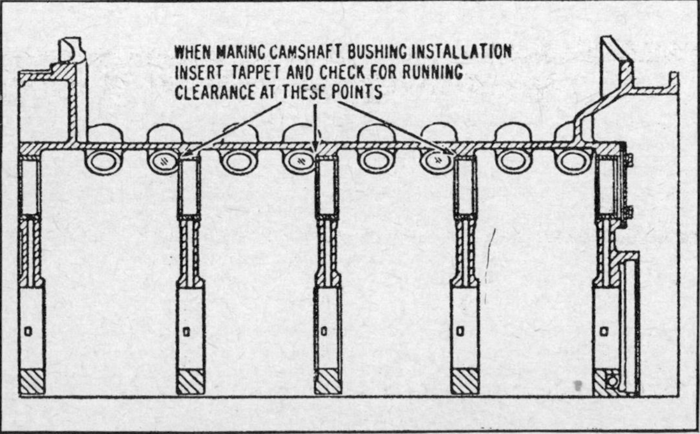

Fig. 6 Checking clearance between valve lifters and camshaft bearings

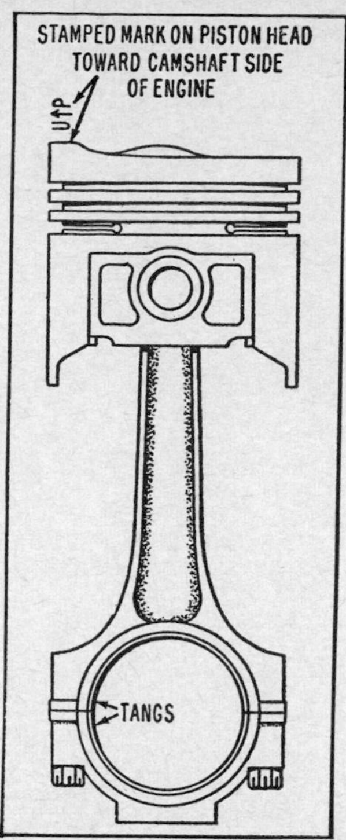

Fig. 7 Piston and rod assembly 4 cylinder engines

CAMSHAFT & BEARINGS

Camshaft bearings should be installed in sets and care must be exercised to see that the oil holes in the bearings and the oil feed holes in the block are aligned to assure adequate lubrication.

Camshaft bushings must be installed so as to provide running clearance between valve lifters and bushings as shown in Fig. 6.

PISTONS & RODS, ASSEMBLE

For correct assembly of the connecting rod to the piston, the rod bearing locators (bearing tangs) must be toward the dome side (marked "up") of the piston. And when installed in the cylinder, the word "up" on the piston goes toward the top (camshaft) side of the engine, Figs. 7 and 8.

NOTE—When steel-band-in-skirt pistons are used, the tolerances are held much closer than for other types. Furthermore, the feeler gauge method of checking this clearance is not practical. To attain proper fitting use micrometers for making piston selection and then check clearance as follows:

1. Wipe both piston and cylinder wall with clean, dry cloth.
2. Install piston top downward into cylinder.
3. A non-knurlized piston should be fitted so that there is .0008" to .0013" running clearance. This clearance will permit the piston to fall slowly through the cylinder bore of its own weight.
4. Knurlized pistons should fit slightly closer. These pistons are fitted so there is a slight drag (1 to 2 lbs.) to a light push fit in the cylinder bore.

CRANKSHAFT OIL SEAL, REPLACE

The rear main bearing oil seal can be replaced with the engine in the chassis by first removing the transmission, clutch and flywheel.

V-266 Engine

Crankshaft rear bearing oil seal consists of two pieces of special packing. One piece is installed in the groove in the rear bearing cap and the other piece is installed in a similar groove in the cylinder block.

Position the rear bearing seal in the groove in the cylinder block. Lay an improvised mandrel in the bearing bore and strike the mandrel with a hammer to drive the seal into the groove. Install the seal in the bearing cap in a similar manner. Using a sharp knife, cut off both ends of each seal which project out of the grooves. When cutting off the ends of the seals, do not leave frayed ends which would prevent proper seating of the bearing cap if the ends should extend between cap and cylinder block.

OIL PUMP REPAIRS

Conventional gear type oil pumps, located in the crankcase, are used on all engines. After removing the oil pan, the pump may be unfastened from its mounting and disassembled for repairs.

Inspect the pump gears for nicks or burrs. Inspect the bottom cover for wear and dress down on a surface plate with emery if necessary. Place the bottom cover on the pump and check the drive shaft end play. If end play is excessive (more than .006"), replace the drive and idler gears.

NOTE

Whenever the oil pump is removed, the distributor will have to be taken off as well in order to reinstall the pump without damage. The reason for this is that the slots in the end of the oil pump drive shafts must match the tangs on the end of the distributor drive shaft. If an attempt is made to install the pump while the distributor is in place, it will be difficult or impossible to align the slots and tangs with the result that the pump will be damaged when its mounting bolts are tightened. Be sure to retime the ignition when the oil pump and distributor are installed.

WATER PUMP REPAIRS

The pumps used on these engines are of the sealed ball bearing type packed with lubricant at the time of assembly and requiring no further lubrication.

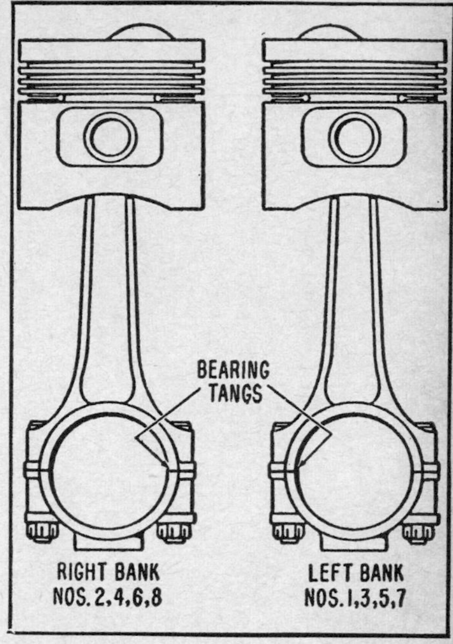

Fig. 8 Piston and rod assembly. V-266

When disassembling, carefully note the arrangement of the seal parts so that correct assembly may be assured.

Never soak the shaft and bearing assembly in cleaning solvent because it will dissolve the lubricant. To clean the shaft and bearing, merely moisten a cloth with cleaning fluid and wipe away any surplus lubricant or other foreign matter.

Be sure the face of the housing against which the thrust washer turns is smooth and true. If not, smooth it up with a special water pump facing cutter.

IGNITION TIMING

If a timing light is to be used to set ignition timing, disconnect the vacuum advance pipe to the carburetor and place a piece of tape over open end of pipe. *This is important as carburetor trouble can affect timing adjustments.*

Lacking a power timing light, an accurate method of setting ignition timing with the engine stopped is with the aid of a jumper light. Be sure to use a light bulb that corresponds with the system voltage of the vehicle.

1. Remove distributor cap and rotor and see that the breaker gap is set according to specifications.
2. Rotate engine until No. 1 cylinder is at the ignition timing point as indicated by the timing pointer and timing mark being lined up with each other.
3. Connect the jumper light between distributor ignition terminal and ground.
4. Turn on ignition switch.
5. Loosen distributor and turn it in the direction of normal rotation until the points just close (light out). Then slowly turn distributor in the opposite direction just to the exact point that the light goes on. Tighten distributor in this position.

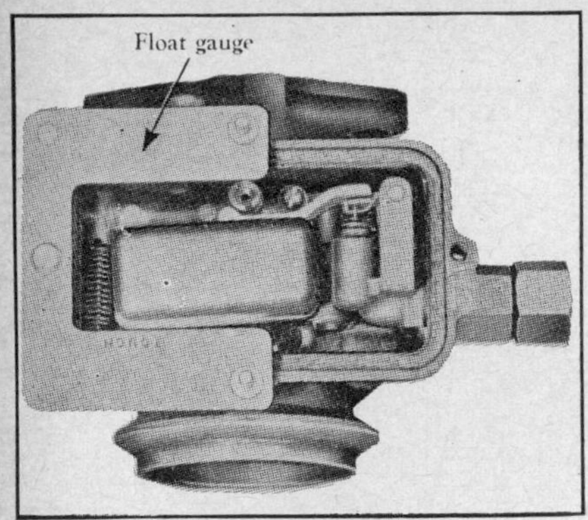

Fig. 9 Setting float level with gauge on Holley 1904

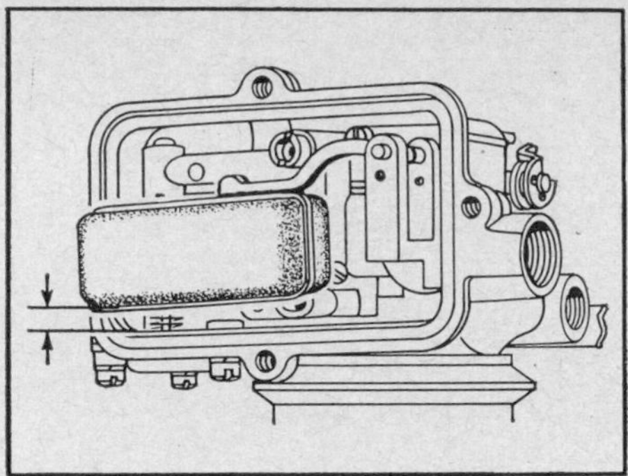

Fig. 10 Setting float level without gauge on Holley 1904. Dimension indicated should be 13/64"

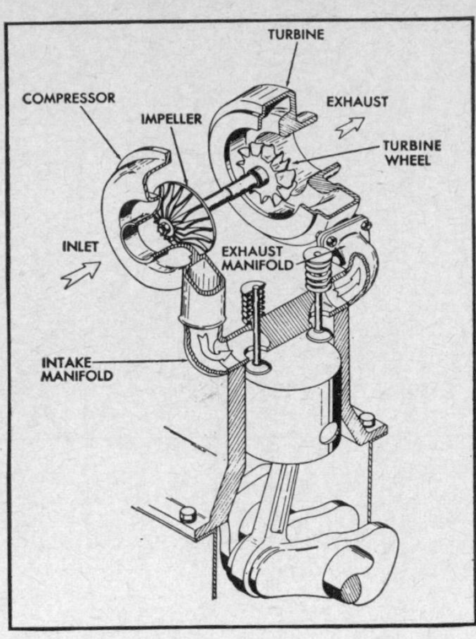

Fig. 11 Operation of Turbocharger

CARBURETOR

Holley 1904

Float Level: Invert main body, allowing float to drop to the closed position. Using float gauge shown in Fig. 9, check the setting on both the "touch" and "no touch" legs of gauge. The level of the float may be adjusted by bending the small tab in the float lever which contacts the head of the fuel inlet needle pin. Use needle nose pliers for this adjustment and recheck the setting after adjustments have been made.

If the gauge is not available, measure from the roof of the float chamber to the lowest point of the float, Fig. 10, with carburetor inverted.

Idle Adjustment: When the engine has reached normal operating temperature, after first checking to be sure that the choke plate is wide open, adjust the throttle stop screw to idle the engine at 350 rpm.

Set the idle mixture adjusting needle to give the highest steady manifold vacuum. If a vacuum gauge is not available, adjust it to the smoothest maximum idle speed. Should the adjustment result in an excessive increase in the idle rpm, reset the throttle stop screw to obtain the specified rpm.

Holley 2300 For V-266 Engine

Fuel Level Setting

With engine running remove sight plug from side of bowl. If fuel level is not on a line with threads at bottom of sight hole, loosen lock nut slightly (top of bowl) and turn adjusting nut as required. Turn nut clockwise to lower fuel level, counter-clockwise to raise the level.

TURBOCHARGER

Description

The Turbocharger is located between the carburetor and intake manifold. In this position, the air-fuel mixture is compressed as it enters the intake manifold.

As shown in Fig. 11, the hot exhaust gases are directed against the turbine wheel, spinning the wheel and shaft at a high rate of speed. The impeller in the compressor portion of the Turbocharger draws the air-fuel mixture in, passing it through a diffuser radically outward, to build up pressure in the intake manifold. This increases the weight of air available to the engine and enables the engine to burn more fuel, resulting in greater horsepower output than is possible with a naturally aspirated engine of the same size.

Inspection

Whenever routine service of the engine is performed, inspect the Turbocharger as follows:

1. Inspect the hoses and connections of the air intake system at the air cleaner, carburetor, turbocharger and intake manifold for leakage due to cracks, damaged gaskets, loose clamps or connections, or for restrictions due to kinks, collapsed hoses or dented tubing.
2. Inspect for oil leakage.
3. Inspect for exhaust leakage from cracked exhaust manifold, damaged gaskets or loose turbocharger mounting.
4. Note any unusual noises or vibrations
5. Observe engine exhaust. Excessive smoke may indicate a restricted air cleaner or intake piping, overfueling or faulty turbocharger operation.

Clutch, Transmission & Rear Axle

CLUTCH, REPLACE

When removing the transmission for the purpose of gaining access to the clutch or for any other reason, extreme care should be taken to support the weight of the transmission until it is completely removed so that the clutch shaft splines will clear the clutch disc hub. There is a possibility of distorting the clutch disc which will then not permit a free release of the clutch.

When installing the clutch, position the disc and clutch assembly on the flywheel, using a stub shaft (or a spare clutch shaft) to align the clutch disc. Then tighten the cover-to-flywheel capscrews gradually and evenly.

Free Pedal Travel, Adjust

The clutch pedal should have a minimum of 1½" free movement before clutch pressure is felt. If pedal free movement is less than specified, an adjustment is necessary to provide adequate bearing-to-lever clearance.

On models with turnbuckle release rod, adjustment is made by loosening release rod lock nuts on each side of turnbuckle. Looking down on turnbuckle, turn it counter-clockwise to increase or clockwise to decrease free travel.

On models with adjustable end yokes, remove yoke pins and turn yokes up or down on release rod as required.

TRANSMISSION

Disassemble, Fig. 1

1. Remove gearshift housing.
2. Remove parking brake.
3. Remove mainshaft bearing retainer.
4. Drive countershaft out through rear of case.
5. Use puller to remove mainshaft bearing.
6. Remove input shaft retainer and tap shaft and bearing as far forward as possible.
7. Remove mainshaft assembly.
8. Remove input shaft. If bearing is to be replaced, assemble with thickest snap ring that will fit.

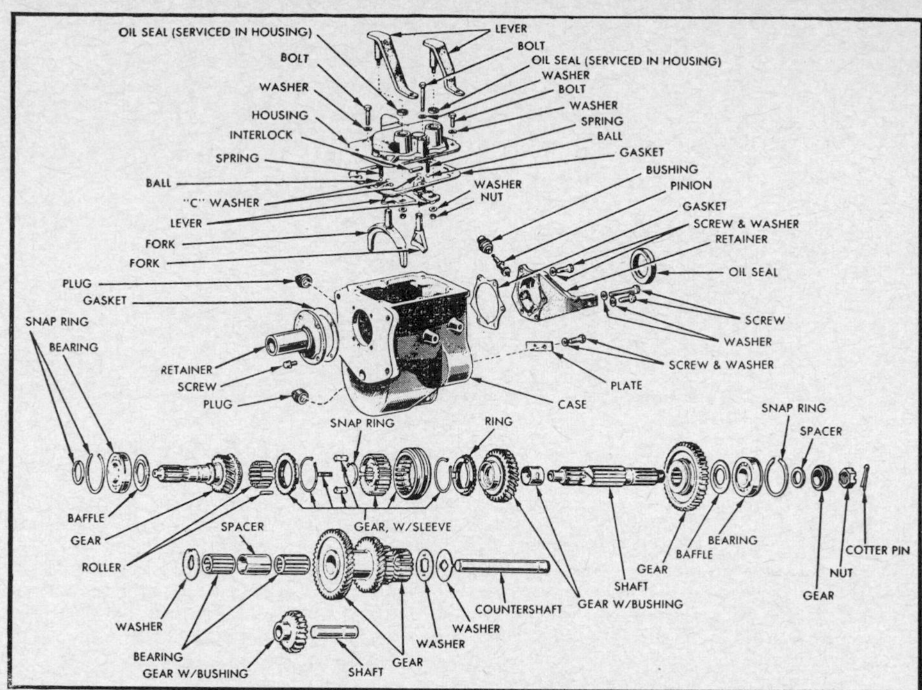

Fig. 1 Exploded view of three-speed transmission

9. Use puller to remove reverse idler shaft.
10. Remove reverse idler gear and countershaft gear cluster.

Assemble Transmission

1. Install reverse idler gear and shaft.
2. Install cluster gear assembly with front thrust washer tip hooked into groove on inside of case. Check end play (.006-.020"). Change thrust washers as required.
3. Install assembled mainshaft. Place a short 2 x 4 block between input shaft and mainshaft. Slide mainshaft bearing baffle and bearing onto shaft. Baffle must be installed so it does not rub bearing outer race. Drive bearing onto shaft.
4. Install mainshaft pilot rollers in input shaft, holding them with grease.
5. Place front blocking ring on synchronizer and start input shaft bearing in case.
6. Drive mainshaft bearing into case.
7. Tap input shaft and bearing into place. Install retainer without gasket and tighten bolts to bottom retainer on snap ring. With feeler gauge, check clearance between gasket surface and case. Select a gasket or gaskets that will seal oil and eliminate all clearance.
8. Raise cluster gear and insert countershaft. Then install retainer in notches in countershaft and reverse idler shaft. Drive both shafts toward front so that retainer is tight against gasket and torque bolts to 25-37 ft. lbs.
9. Install speedometer gear and spacer, mainshaft bearing retainer and gasket, and parking brake. Tighten output shaft nut to 90-125 ft. lbs.
10. Install gearshift housing.

SPICER REAR AXLE

Integral Housing Type

Inasmuch as the axle tubes are pressed into the differential carrier to form a one-piece housing, the rear axle assembly must be removed from the chassis when it becomes necessary to overhaul the unit.

Axle Shaft, Remove

1. Remove hub and drum assembly with a suitable puller.
2. Remove brake backing plate and bearing retainer.
3. Pull axle shaft from axle housing.

Bearing, Replace

The bearing is a press fit on the taper of the axle shaft and need only be pressed off.

Axle Shaft, Install

When installing the axle shaft use a dial indicator to check the end play of the shaft. End play is controlled by removing or adding shims located between the brake backing plate and the rear axle housing flange. If dial indicator shows improper end play add or remove sufficient shims on right side of axle to bring axles to specified end play of .011-.009".

Rear Axle Assembly, Replace

1. Raise vehicle from floor and support with stand jacks under frame side rails.
2. Remove rear wheels.
3. Split rear universal joint.
4. Disconnect parking brake cable from equalizer rod and unfasten brake cable brackets from frame cross member.
5. Disconnect hydraulic brake line connection at rear axle housing.
6. Loosen and move shock absorbers out of the way.
7. While supporting axle housing with hydraulic jack, remove spring clips and lower axle assembly to the floor.
8. Reverse the foregoing procedure to install the rear axle assembly, being sure to bleed the brake system when the installation is completed.

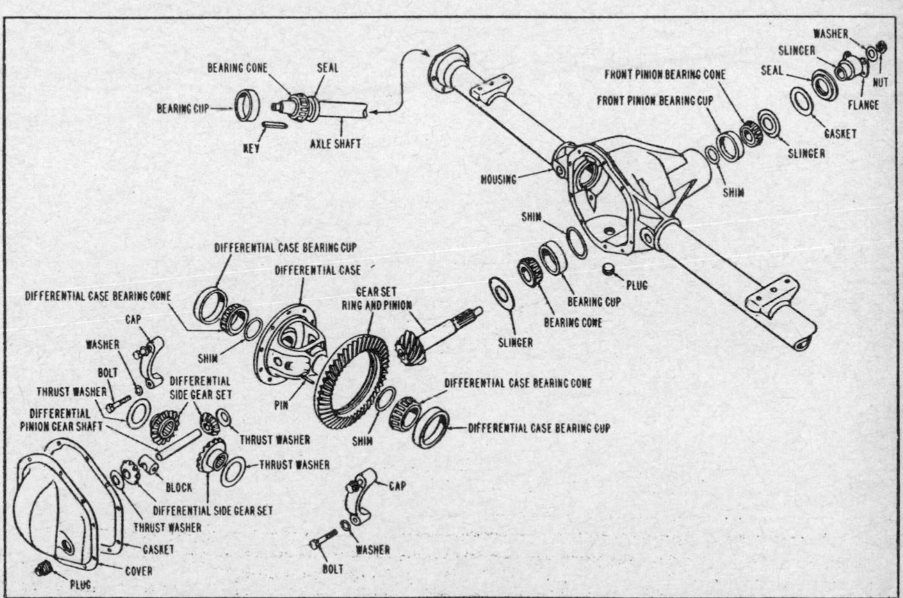

Fig. 2 Exploded view of rear axle. Front driving axle is similar

Front Wheel Drive & Steering Gear

FRONT DRIVING AXLE

The differential carrier assembly is the same as the rear driving axle except that the front unit is full floating. The axle shafts can be removed without dismantling the steering knuckles.

Axle Shaft & Universal Joint

Removal

1. Referring to Figs. 1 and 2, remove hub cap and wheel.
2. Remove grease cap and snap ring.
3. Remove drive flange and gasket.
4. Remove brake drum.
5. Remove wheel bearing adjusting nut and washer.
6. Remove wheel hub with wheel bearing, taking care not to damage oil seal.
7. Disconnect brake hose at backing plate.
8. Remove six backing plate and wheel spindle bolts and washers.
9. Remove wheel bearing spindle with bushing.
10. Pull axle shaft and universal joint from axle housing.

Installation

1. Clean dirt from all parts.
2. Enter shaft and joint assembly into housing. Enter spline end of axle shaft into differential and push into place.
3. Install wheel bearing spindle with bushing.
4. Install backing plate and brake hose.
5. Pack wheel bearings with lubricant and install.
6. Assemble driving flange, wheel hub and drum.
7. Install wheel bearing lockwasher and adjusting nut. Tighten adjusting nut until there is a slight drag on bearings when hub is turned, then back off 1/6th of a turn.
8. Install lockwasher and lock nut; tighten nut and bend lip of lockwasher over lock nut.
9. Install snap ring, grease cap, wheel and hub cap.

Steering Knuckle Bearings

Replacement of steering knuckle bearings or bearing cups on the kingpin requires removal of the tie rod, brake drum, hub, wheel bearing, axle shaft, spindle and steering knuckle. The following procedure should be followed when removing the steering knuckle:

1. Referring to Figs. 1 and 2, remove studs and tapered capscrews holding kingpin bearing lower cap.
2. Remove studs and tapered capscrews holding kingpin bearing upper cap and shims.
3. Remove eight oil seal retaining capscrews.
4. Remove upper and lower steering knuckle bearing cone and cup.
5. Remove steering knuckle and seals.

Installation: When reinstalling the steering knuckle, sufficient shims must be installed under the upper bearing cap so the proper tension may be maintained on the knuckle bearing. No shims are used on the lower bearing cap.

Shims are available in thicknesses of .005″, .010″, and .030″. Install one each of the three thicknesses over the studs on top of the knuckle. Then proceed as follows:

1. Install wheel bearing cups and cones, steering arm, bearing cap, bolts, lockwashers and nuts.
2. Check tension of bearings by hooking a spring scale around the steering arm ball.
3. Pull the scale at right angle to the steering arm. Take the reading when the arm is moving.
4. Remove or add shims until the load is approximately 25-35 pounds without the oil seal assembly in position.

Steering Knuckle Oil Seal

To remove the seal, remove the eight capscrews holding the steering knuckle oil seal in place and remove the seal.

Before installing the new seal, examine the spherical surface of the axle for scores or scratches that might damage the new seal. Roughness of any kind should be smoothed with fine emery cloth.

Lubrication

The front axle universal joints are lubricated by a constant supply of lubricant in the steering knuckle housings. A level plug for checking the lubricant level is located at the rear of each housing. Every 1,000 miles the level should be checked. The recommended capacity for each steering knuckle housing is 38 oz. Use viscous chassis lubricant. *If necessary to overhaul the universal joints, see the Universals chapter.*

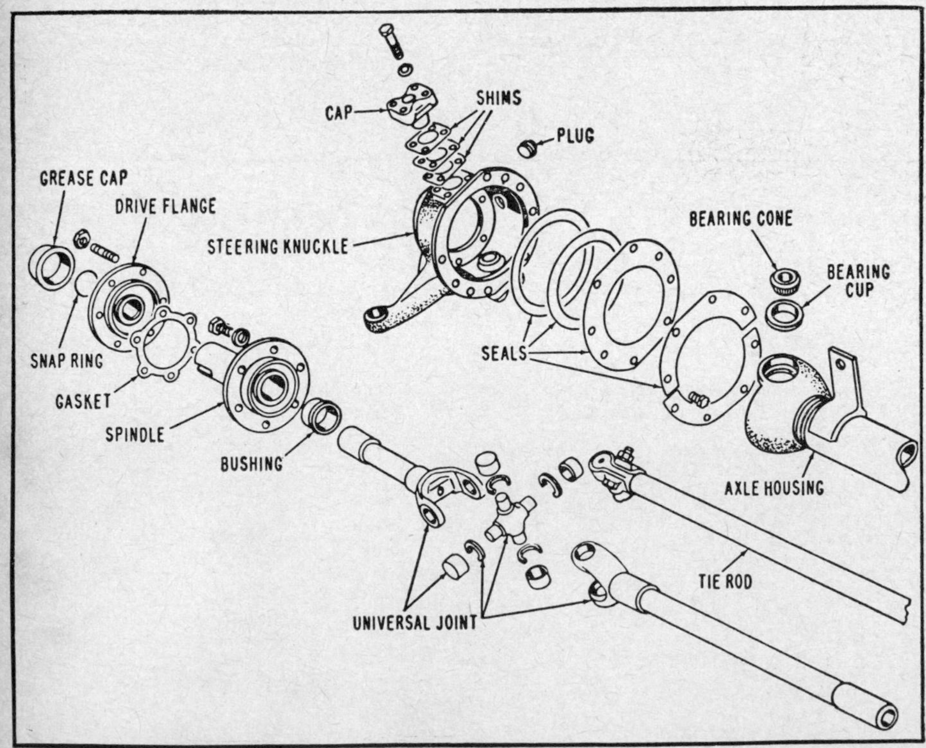

Fig. 1 Exploded view of 4 x 4 front axle shaft and universal joint

STEERING GEAR

When making adjustments on the steering gear, Fig. 3, free the gear of all load, preferably by disconnecting the drag link from the steering arm, and loosen the instrument panel bracket clamp on the steering gear jacket tube. If the ball thrust bearings on the cam must be adjusted, make this adjustment first before making the side adjustment to the lever shaft stud in the cam groove.

Ball Thrust Bearing On Cam, Adjust

1. Referring to Fig. 3, loosen the housing side cover adjusting screw to free the studs in the cam groove.
2. Adjustment should be made so there is a very slight drag but not so much that the steering wheel cannot be turned from one extreme to the other by lightly gripping the wheel rim with thumb and forefinger.

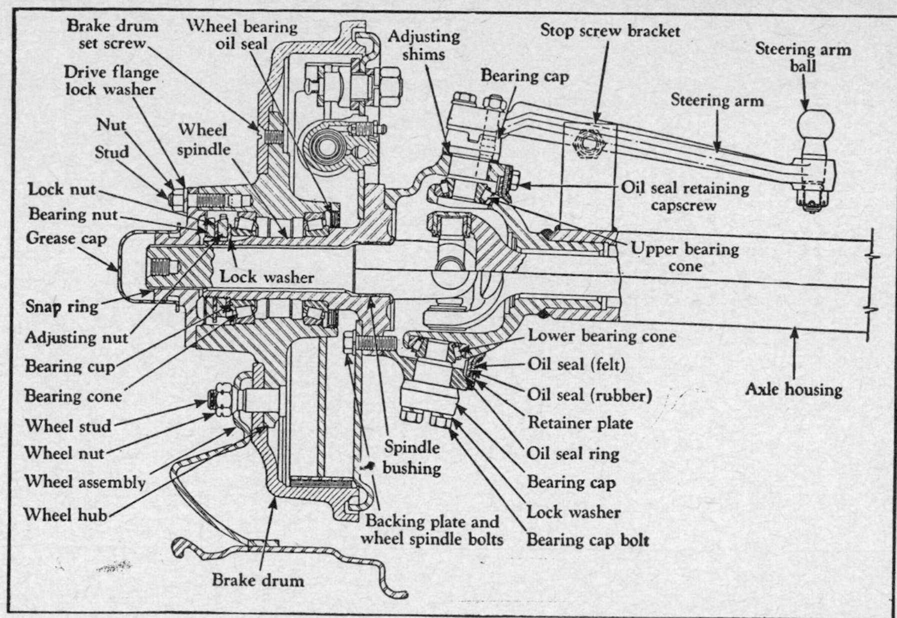

Fig. 2 Sectional view of front wheel, steering knuckle, axle shaft and universal joint

3. Unscrew the four screws and raise the housing upper cover to permit removal of shims.
4. Clip and remove a thin shim or more as required and draw cover down tight against shims.
5. Test as outlined in Step 2 and if necessary, remove or replace shims until adjustment is correct.

Lever Shaft Stud, Adjust

1. Backlash at this point shows up as end play of lever shaft, also as backlash at steering wheel and at ball on steering arm.
2. The groove is purposely cut deeper in ends of cam than at mid-position. This produces a high range through mid-position and makes grooves narrower through this range. This permits take-up of backlash in mid-position, after normal wear of groove, without causing a bind in the ends.
3. Adjust to this mid-position high range only. Play in end position is not objectionable.
4. Tighten side cover adjusting screw until a very slight drag is felt through the mid-position when turning steering wheel slowly from one extreme position to the other. *Steering gear must not bind in any position. Only a very slight drag should be felt. A closer adjustment will not correct steering looseness caused by wear in other steering gear units, but will damage parts and impair operation.*
5. When proper adjustment has been made, tighten locknut and check adjustment.
6. Make sure steering gear arm is tight on splined lever shaft and that lockwasher and nut are tight also.

WHEEL ALIGNMENT SPECS.

Two-Wheel Drive

Caster, degrees	2 to 3
Camber, degrees	1
Toe-in, inch	0 to $\frac{3}{16}$
Kingpin angle	7

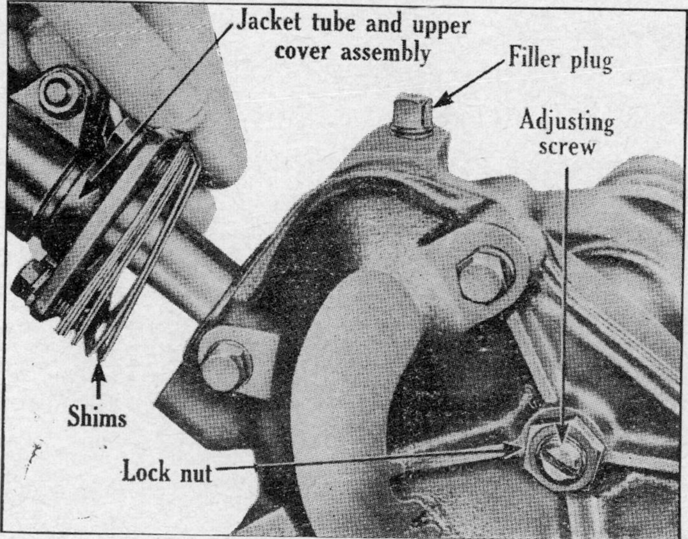

Fig. 3 Steering gear adjustments

JEEP

OLD CAR SPECIFICATIONS: For 1946-62 Tune Up and Wheel Alignment Specifications see back of book.

NOTE: Specifications for the optional engines are tabulated on the charts immediately following this index. For service procedures on the 6-232 and V8-327 engines see the Rambler Chapter. For the V6-225 and V8-350 engines see the Buick Chapter.

INDEX OF SERVICE OPERATIONS

PAGE NO.

ACCESSORIES

Automatic Level Controls 1-41
Clock Troubles 1-11
Power Top Troubles 1-18
Power Window Troubles 1-18

BRAKES

Brake Troubles, Mechanical 1-17
Disc Brake Service 1-430
Hydraulic System Service 1-422
Master Cylinder, Replace 2-415
Parking Brake, Adjust 2-415
Power Brake Service 1-440
Power Brake Troubles 1-440
Power Brake Unit, Replace 2-415
Service Brakes, Adjust 2-414

CLUTCH

Clutch Pedal, Adjust 2-406
Clutch, Replace 2-406
Clutch Troubles 1-12

COOLING SYSTEM

Cooling System Troubles 1-6
Variable Speed Fans 1-39
Water Pump, Replace 2-405

ELECTRICAL

Alternator Service 1-63
Dash Gauge Service 1-117
Distributor, Replace 2-396
Distributor Service:
Standard 1-53
Transistorized 1-47
Electrical Troubles 1-8
Generator Service 1-91
Headlamps, Concealed Type 1-40
Horn Sounder, Remove 2-397
Ignition Coils and Resistors 1-24
Ignition Switch, Replace 2-397
Ignition Timing 2-396
Instrument Cluster Removal 2-397
Light Switch, Replace 2-397
Neutral Safety Switch, Replace 2-397
Spark Plug Condition Chart 2-647
Starter Service 1-101
Starter, Replace 2-397
Starter Switch Service 1-114
Stop Light Switch, Replace 2-397
Turn Signal Troubles 1-11
Windshield Wiper Motor, Replace 2-398
Windshield Wiper Troubles 1-20

PAGE NO.

ENGINE

Camshaft, Replace 2-404
Crankshaft Rear Oil Seal 2-405
Cylinder Head, Replace 2-398
Engine, Replace 2-398
Engine Troubles 1-1
Main Bearings 2-405
Piston Pins 2-405
Piston Rings 2-405
Piston and Rod, Assemble 2-404
Pistons 2-405
Rocker Arm Service 2-401
Rocker Arm Studs 2-400
Rod Bearings 2-405
Timing Case Cover, Replace 2-402
Timing Chain, Replace 2-403
Timing Gears, Replace 2-403
Valves, Adjust 2-401
Valve Guides 2-402
Valve Lifters 2-402
Valves, Remove 2-401

ENGINE LUBRICATION

Crankcase Ventilation (PCV) 1-29
Exhaust Emission Controls 1-30
Oil Pan, Replace 2-405
Oil Pump, Replace 2-405

FUEL SYSTEM

Carburetor Adjustments and Specs. .. 1-124
Crankcase Ventilation (PCV) 1-29
Exhaust Emission Controls 1-30
Fuel Pump, Replace 2-405
Fuel Pump Service 1-120
Fuel System Troubles 1-2

PROPELLER SHAFT & U JOINTS

Propeller Shaft 2-412
Universal Joint Service 1-418

REAR AXLE

Axle Shaft, Bearing and Seal 2-412
Rear Axle Description 2-411
Rear Axle Troubles 1-17

SPECIFICATIONS

Alternator 2-396
Brakes 2-395
Capacities 2-393

PAGE NO.

Carburetors 1-124
Cooling System 2-393
Crankshaft and Bearings 2-394
Distributors 2-395
Engine Tightening Torque 2-396
General Engine Specs. 2-391
Generators 2-394
Ignition Coils and Resistors 1-24
Pistons, Rings and Pins 2-394
Rear Axle 2-395
Starting Motors 2-395
Tune Up 2-391
Valve Lift 2-401
Valves 2-393
Wheel Alignment 2-394

STEERING GEAR

Horn Sounder Removal 2-397
Mechanical Gear, Replace 2-416
Mechanical Gear Service 1-451
Mechanical Gear Troubles 1-18
Power Steering 2-417
Steering Wheel, Replace 2-397

SUSPENSION, FRONT

Ball Joints, Replace 2-416
Kingpins & Bushings 2-415
Front Wheel Locking Hubs 2-414
"Live" Front Axle 2-412
Tire Wear Chart 2-648
Toe-In, Adjust 2-415
Torsion Bar 2-415
Wheel Alignment, Adjust 2-415

TRANSFER CASE 2-409

TRANSMISSIONS

Three Speed Manual:
Replace 2-406
Repairs 2-408
Linkage, Adjust 2-410
Automatic Units 1-321

TUNE UP

Service 1-21
Specifications 2-391

WINDSHIELD WIPER

Wiper Motor, Replace 2-398
Wiper Linkage, Replace 2-398
Wiper Switch, Replace 2-398
Wiper Troubles 1-20

GENERAL ENGINE SPECIFICATIONS

Year	Model	Carburetor	Bore and Stroke	Piston Displacement, Cubic Inches	Compression Ratio	Maximum Brake H.P. @ R.P.M.	Maximum Torque Lbs. Ft. @ R.P.M.	Normal Oil Pressure Pounds
1963–67	CJ Series . . . F4-134	1 Barrel	4.125 x 4.375	134	7.4	75 @ 4000	114 @ 2400	35
1968–69	CJ Series . . . F4-134	1 Barrel	4.125 x 4.375	134	6.7	75 @ 4000	114 @ 2400	35
1966–69	CJ Series . . . ②V6-225	2 Barrel	3.750 x 3.400	225	9.0	160 @ 4200	235 @ 2400	33
1963–64	DJ Dispatcher . . . L4-134	1 Barrel	4.125 x 4.375	134	7.0	60 @ 4000	105 @ 2000	35
1965–67	DJ Dispatcher . . . F4-134	1 Barrel	4.125 x 4.375	134	7.4	75 @ 4000	114 @ 2400	35
1968–69	DJ Dispatcher . . . F4-134	1 Barrel	4.125 x 4.375	134	6.7	75 @ 4000	114 @ 2400	35
1966–69	DJ Dispatcher . . . ②V6-225	2 Barrel	3.750 x 3.400	225	9.0	160 @ 4200	235 @ 2400	33
1963–64	Utility Wagon . . . F4-134	1 Barrel	4.125 x 4.375	134	7.4	75 @ 4000	114 @ 2400	35
1963–64	Utility Wagon . . . L6-226	1 Barrel	3.312 x 4.375	226	6.86	105 @ 3600	190 @ 1400	35
1963–64	Utility Wagon . . . 6-230	1 Barrel	3.344 x 4.375	230	8.5	140 @ 4000	210 @ 1750	50
1963–65	J-100 Series . . . 6-230	1 Barrel	3.344 x 4.375	230	8.5	140 @ 4000	210 @ 1750	50
1966–69	J-100 Series . . . ①6-232	1 Barrel	3.750 x 3.500	232	8.5	145 @ 4300	215 @ 1600	50
1966–68	J-100 Series . . . ①V8-327	2 Barrel	4.000 x 3.250	327	8.7	250 @ 4200	340 @ 2600	55
1968–69	J-100 Series . . . ②V8-350	2 Barrel	3.800 x 3.850	350	9.0	230 @ 4400	350 @ 2400	37
1967	Jeepster . . . F4-134	1 Barrel	4.125 x 4.375	134	7.4	75 @ 4000	114 @ 2400	35
1968–69	Jeepster . . . F4-134	1 Barrel	4.125 x 4.375	134	6.7	75 @ 4000	114 @ 2400	35
1967–69	Jeepster . . . ②V6-225	2 Barrel	3.750 x 3.400	225	9.0	160 @ 4200	235 @ 2400	33

①—For service procedure on this engine see the Rambler Chapter.
②—For service procedure on this engine see the Buick Chapter.

TUNE UP SPECIFICATIONS

OLD CAR SPECIFICATIONS— For 1946-62 Tune Up Specifications see back of book.

★When using a timing light, disconnect vacuum hose or tube at distributor and plug opening in hose or tube so idle speed will not be affected.

Year	Engine	Spark Plug		Distributor		Firing Order	Ignition Timing★		Hot Idle Speed		Comp. Press. Lbs.	Fuel Pump Press. Lbs.
		Type	Gap Inch	Point Gap Inch	Dwell Angle Deg.		BTDC ①	Mark	Std. Trans.	Auto. Trans.		
1963–64	L4-134	J8	.030	.020	37–43	Fig. J	5°	Fig. D	600	—	100	2½–3¾
1963–67	F4-134	J8	.030	.020	37–43	Fig. K	5°	Fig. A	600	—	100	2½–3¾
1968–69	F4-134	J8	.030	.020	37–43	Fig. K	0°	Fig. A	650–700	—	100	2½–3¾
1963–64	L6-226	J8	.030	.020	36–42	Fig. G	5°	Fig. B	550	—	120	2½–3¾
1963–65	6-230	AE-42	.030	.020	36–42	Fig. H	5°	Fig. C	550	550	150	3½–5½
1966–67	6-232②	N14Y	.035	.020	31–34	Fig. Q	5°	Fig. P	550	550	145	4–5½
1968–69	6-232②	N14Y	.035	.020	31–34	Fig. Q	0°	Fig. P	650–700	650–700	145	4–5½
1966–67	V8-327②	H14Y	.035	.016	28–32	Fig. F	5°	Fig. L	550	500	145	3½–5½
1968	V8-327②	H14Y	.035	.016	28–32	Fig. F	0°	Fig. L	650–700	650–700	145	3½–5½
1966–67	V6-225③	44S	.035	.016	29–31	Fig. M	5°	Fig. N	550	550	165	4½–5¾
1968–69	V6-225③	44S	.035	.016	29–31	Fig. M	5°	Fig. N	650–700	650–700	165	4½–5¾
1968–69	V8-350③	45TS	.030	.016	30	Fig. R	0°	Fig. N	650–700	650–700	165	4¼–5¾

①—BTDC—Before top dead center.
②—For service procedure on this engine see Rambler chapter.
③—For service procedure on this engine see Buick Chapter.

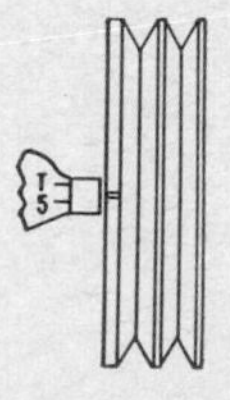
Fig. A

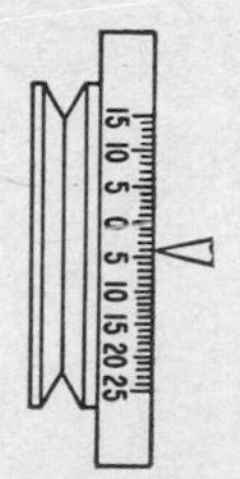

Fig. B

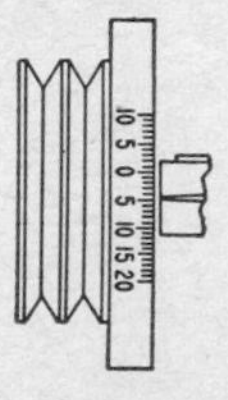

Fig. C

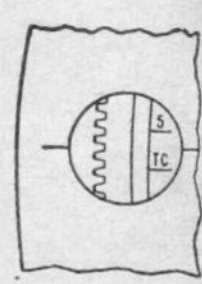
Fig. D

Continued

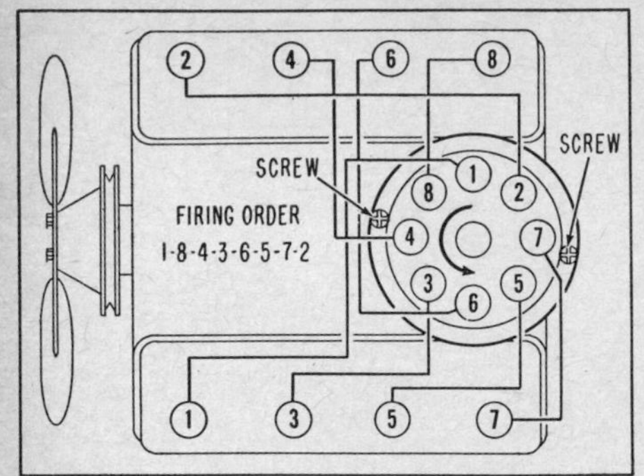

Fig. F

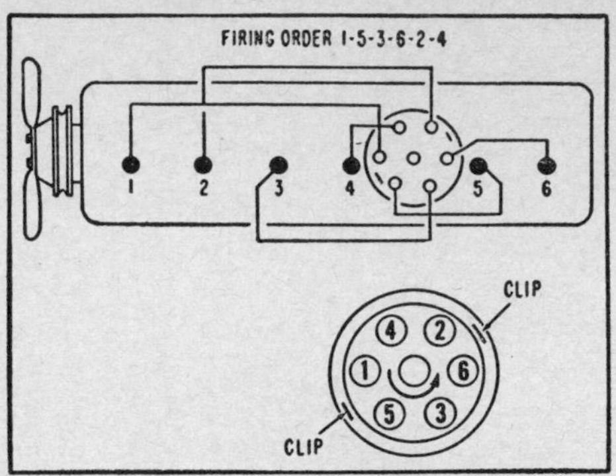

Fig. G

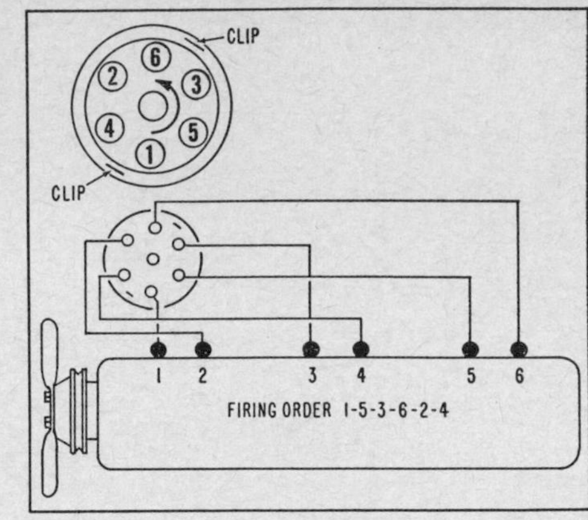

Fig. H

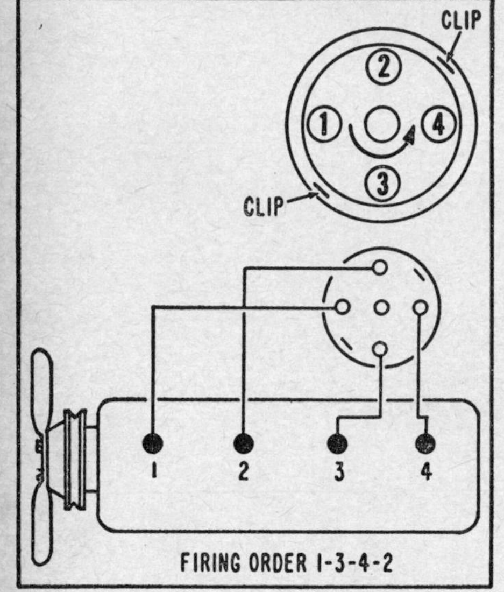

Fig. J

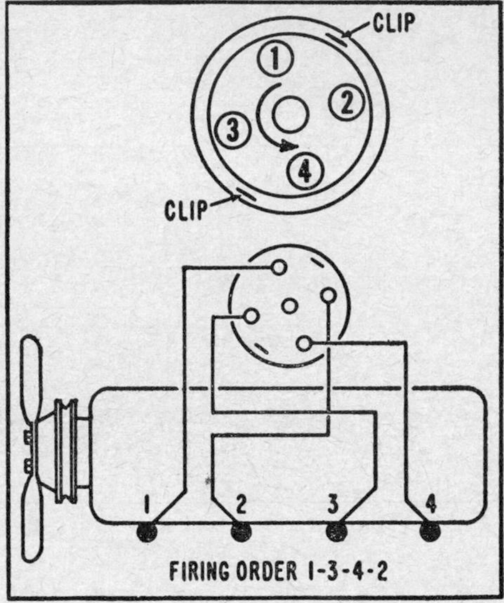

Fig. K

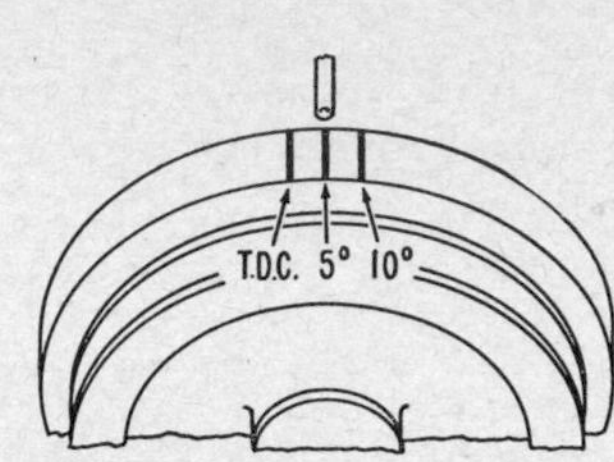

Fig. L

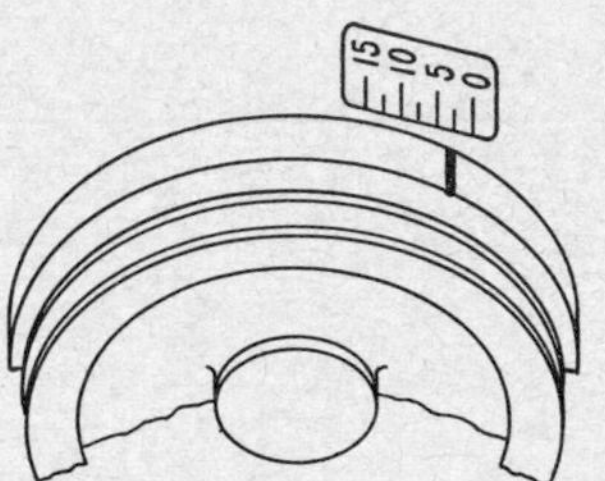

Fig. N

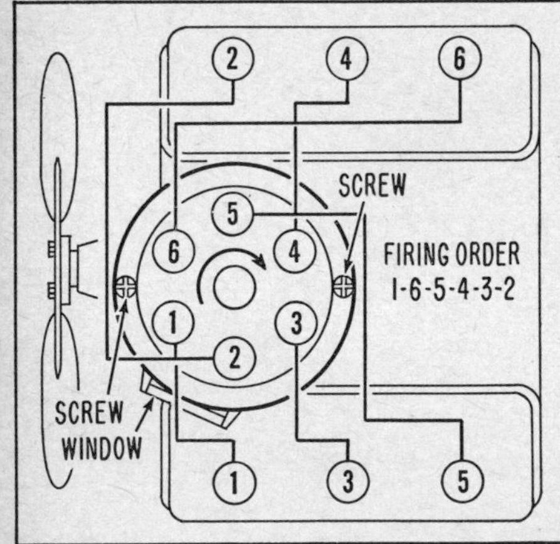

Fig. M

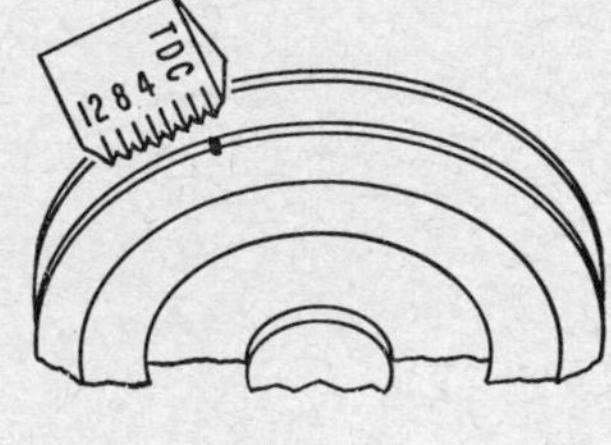

Fig. P

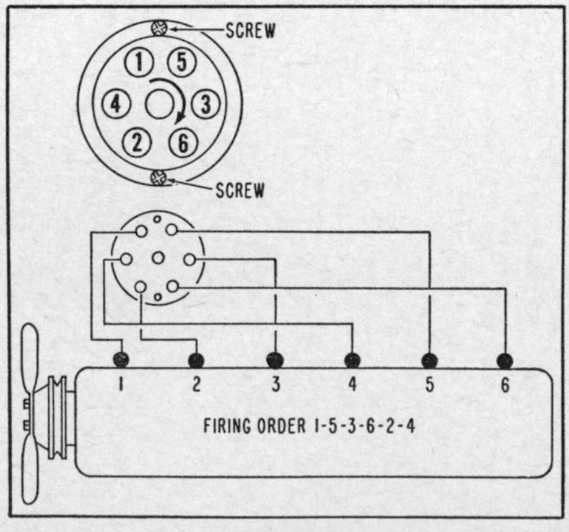

Fig. Q

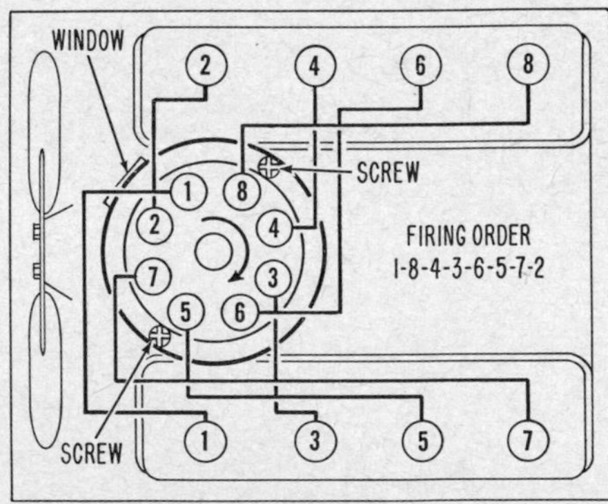

Fig. R

VALVE SPECIFICATIONS

Year	Engine	Valve Lash		Valve Angles		Valve Spring Installed Height	Valve Spring Pressure Lbs. @ In.	Stem Clearance		Stem Diameter	
		Int.	Exh.	Seat	Face			Intake	Exhaust	Intake	Exhaust
1963–69	F-Head 4	.018C	①	45	45	1 21/32	②	.0007–.0022	.0025–.0045	.3733–.3738	.371–.372
1963–64	6-226	.014C	.014C	③	③	1 43/64	118 @ 1 5/16	.001–.003	.0032–.005	.3402–.3410	.3382–.3390
	L-Head 4	.016C	.016C	45	45	2 7/64	120 @ 1¾	.0007–.0022	.0025–.0045	.3733–.3738	.371–.372
1963	6-230	.006C	.008C	45	45	1½	57 @ 1½	.001–.003	.0025–.0045	.3400–.3410	.3385–.3395
1964–65	6-230	.008C	.008C	45	45	1.26	⅞ @ 130	.001–.003	.0025–.0045	.3400–.3410	.3385–.3395
1966–68	V8-327⑤	Zero	Zero	③	④	1 13/16	155 @ 1 7/16	.001–.003	.001–.003	.3718–.3725	.3718–.3725
1966-69	V6-225⑥	Zero	Zero	45	45	1 41/64	168 @ 1¼	.002–.0025	.0025–.003	.3407–.3412	.3402–.3407
1968-69	6-232⑤	Zero	Zero	③	④	1 13/16	155 @ 1 7/16	.001–.003	.001–.003	.3715–.3725	.3715–.3725
1968–69	V8-350③	Zero	Zero	45	45	1.727	180 @ 1.34	.0015–.0035	.0025–.0045	.3720–.3730	.371–3.75

①—Eaton face valve .012C, Thompson Roto Valve .016C. ②—Intake 140 @ 1 13/32″, exhaust 110 @ 1¾″. ③—Intake 30°, exhaust 45°.
④—Intake 29°, exhaust 44°.
⑤—For service procedure on this engine see Rambler Chapter.
⑥—For service procedure on this engine see Buick Chapter.

COOLING SYSTEM & CAPACITY DATA

Year	Model or Engine	Cooling Capacity, Qts.			Radiator Cap Relief Pressure, Lbs.		Thermo. Opening Temp. ①	Fuel Tank Gals.	Engine Oil Refill Qts. ②	Transmission Oil			Rear Axle Oil Pints
		No Heater	With Heater	With A/C	With A/C	No A/C				3 Speed Pints	4 Speed Pints	Auto. Trans. Qts.	
1963–64	F4-134 2WD	11	12	—	—	7	165	15	4	1½	—	—	2
	F4-134 4WD	11	12	—	—	7	165	15	4	3	—	—	3
	CJ-3B, F4-134	11	12	—	—	7	165	10½	4	3	—	—	3
	DJ-3A, F4-134	11	12	—	—	7	165	12	4	1½	—	—	2
	6-230	11	12	—	—	13	165	15	5	2½	—	—	2⑥
1963–65	J-100, 6-230	11	12	—	—	13	165	20	5	2½	—	4¼	3
1966–68	J-100, 6-232	9½	10½	—	—	13	195	20	5	2½	—	11	3
	J-100, V8-327	18	19	—	—	13	195	20	5	2¾	—	11	3
1963–67	CJ5 & CJ6, F4-134	11	12	—	—	7	165	10½	4	2¾	6½	—	2½
1965–67	DJ5 & DJ6, F4-134	11	12	—	—	7	165	10½	4	1½	—	—	2
1966–67	CJ & DJ Ser. V6-225	9	10	—	—	13	180	10½	4	2¾	—	—	2⑦
1967	Jeepster, F4-134	11	12	—	—	7	165	15	4	2½	—	—	2½
	Jeepster, V6-225	7	10	—	—	13	180	15	4	2½	—	11	2½
1968	CJ Ser., F4-134	11	12	—	—	13	190	10½	4	3¼	6½	—	2½
	DJ Ser., F4-134	11	12	—	—	13	190	10½	4	1½	—	—	2
	Jeepster, F4-134	11	12	—	—	13	190	15	4	2½	—	—	2½
	CJ & DJ Ser., V6-225	9	10	—	—	13	190	10½	4	2¾	—	—	2⑦
	Jeepster, V6-225	9	10	—	—	13	190	15	4	2¾	—	11	2½
1969	CJ Ser., F4-134	11	12	—	—	15	195	10½	4	3¼	6½	—	2½
	DJ Ser., F4-134	11	12	—	—	15	195	10½	4	1½	—	—	2
	Jeepster, F4-134	11	12	—	—	15	195	15	4	2½	—	—	2½
	CJ & DJ Ser., V6-225	9	10	—	—	15	195	10½	4	2¾	—	—	2⑦
	Jeepster, V-225	9	10	—	—	15	195	15	4	2¾	—	11	2½
	J-100, 6-232	9½	10½	—	—	15	195	20	5	2¾	—	11	3
	J-100, V8-350	14	15	—	—	15	195	20	4	2¾	—	11	3

①—If alcohol type anti-freeze is used install a 160° unit.
②—Add one quart with filter change.
③—Includes transfer case.
④—For Warner; 3¾ qts. refill, overhaul 9½ qts. For Turbo-Hydramatic, 11 qts. total capacity.
⑤—Approximate. Make final check with dip stick.
⑥—For 4WD, add 1 pt.
⑦—For DJ Ser., add ½ pt.

PISTONS, PINS, RINGS, CRANKSHAFT & BEARINGS

Year	Model	Piston Clearance	Ring End Gap ①		Wrist-pin Diameter	Rod Bearings		Main Bearings			
			Comp.	Oil		Shaft Diameter	Bearing Clearance	Shaft Diameter	Bearing Clearance	Thrust on Bear. No.	Shaft End Play
1963–64	L-Head 4	.003	.008	.008	.8119	1.9375–1.9385	.0005–.0025	2.333–2.334	.0015–.003	1	.006 Max.
1963–69	F-Head 4	.003	.008	.008	.8119	1.9375–1.9385	.0005–.0025	2.333–2.334	.0015–.003	1	.006 Max
1963–64	6-226	.0015	.008	.008	.8592	2.062–2.063	.0005–.002	2.374–2.375	.0007–.002	1	.006 Max.
1963–65	6-230	.0015	.010	.015	.8592	2.0619–2.0627	.0006–.0025	2.3747–2.3755	.0005–.0025	Rear	.003–.007
1966–68	V8-327②	.0009–.0015	.010	.015	.9306	2.2483–2.2490	.001–.002	2.4988–2.4995	.001–.002	1	.003–.007
1966-69	V6-225③	.0002–.0023	.015	.015	.9394	2.000	.0002–.0023	2.2992	.0005–.0021	2	.004–.008
1966-69	6-232②	.0009–.0015	.010	.015	.9306	1.0948–2.0955	.001–.002	2.4988–2.4995	.001–.002	3	.003–.007
1968–69	V8-350③	.0013–.0029	.010	.020	.9394	2.000	.0004–.0015	2.9995	.0004–.0015	3	.003–.009

①—Fit rings in tapered bores for clearance listed in tightest portion of ring travel.

②—For service procedure on this engine see Rambler Chapter.

③—For service procedure on this engine see Buick Chapter.

D.C. GENERATOR AND REGULATOR SPECIFICATIONS

★To Polarize Generator: For internally grounded systems, disconnect field lead from regulator and momentarily flash this lead to regulator battery terminal. For externally grounded systems, reconnect the leads to the regulator, then momentarily connect a jumper wire from the "Arm" to the "Bat" terminals of the regulator.

Year	Generator						Regulator					
	Generator Number	Rotation and Ground Polarity ①	Rated Cap. Amps.	Gen. Field Ground Location★	Brush Spring Tension, Ounces	Field Current Amperes	Regulator Number	Cutout Relay Voltage to Close Points	Cutout Relay Armature Air Gap, Inch	Voltage Regulator Setting Volts	Current Regulator Setting Amperes	Current and Voltage Armature Air Gap, Inch
1963–64	GJP-7202A	C-N	35	Internal	18–36	1.6–1.7③	VBO-4201E	13.1	.032	14.2	35	.050
1963–64	GJP-7402B	C-N	35	Internal	18–36	1.6–1.7③	VBO-4201E	13.1	.032	14.2	35	.050
1963–69	GJP-7402A	C-N	35	Internal	18–36	1.6–1.7③	VBO-4201E	13.1	.032	14.2	35	.050

①—C-Clockwise. N-Negative. ③—At 10 volts.

WHEEL ALIGNMENT SPECIFICATIONS

OLD CAR SPECIFICATIONS: For 1946-62 Wheel Alignment Specifications see back of book.

Year	Model	Caster Angle, Degrees		Camber Angle, Degrees				Toe-In. Inch	Toe-Out on Turns, Deg.①	
		Limits	Desired	Limits Left	Limits Right	Desired Left	Desired Right		Outer Wheel	Inner Wheel
1963–64	Utility Wagon	+3	+3	+1	+1	+1	+1	3/64–3/32	20	21° 45′
1963–69	CJ & DJ Ser.	+3	+3	+1½	+1½	+1½	+1½	3/64–3/32	20	20
	J-Series 2WD②	+2½ to +3½	+3	+¾ to +1	+¾ to +1	+¾ to +1	+¾ to +1	3/64–3/32	20	19° 5′
	J-Series 2WD③	+3	+3	+1½	+1½	+1½	+1½	3/64–3/32	20	18° 15′
	J-Series 4WD	+3	+3	+1½	+1½	+1½	+1½	3/64–3/32	20	19° 30′
1967–69	Jeepster	+3	+3	+1½	+1½	+1½	+1½	3/64–3/32	20	20

①—Incorrect toe-out, when other adjustments are correct, generally indicates bent steering arms.

②—Independent front suspension.

③—Solid front axle.

DISTRIBUTOR SPECIFICATIONS

★NOTE: If advance is checked on the vehicle, double the R.P.M. and degrees to get crankshaft figures.

Year	Engine	Distributor Part No.①	Rotation ②	Breaker Gap	Cam Angle	Breaker Arm Spring Tension	Centrifugal Advance Degrees @ R.P.M. of Distributor★		Vacuum Advance	
							Advance Starts	Full Advance	Inches of Vacuum To Start Plunger	Max. Adv. Dist. Deg. @ Vacuum
1963–64	F4-134	1AT-4405	CC	.021	37–43	17–20	1 @ 425	11 @ 1700	5	6 @ 14
1963–67	F4-134	1AY-4401	CC	.020	37–43	17–20	1 @ 425	11 @ 1700	—	—
1968–69	F4-134	1AY-4401A	CC	.020	37–43	17–20	1 @ 425	13½ @ 1700	—	—
1963–64	L4-134	1AY-4401	CC	.020	37–43	17–20	1 @ 425	11 @ 1700	—	—
1963–64	L6-226	1AT-4404A	CC	.020	36–42	17–20	1 @ 375	9 @ 1675	10	5 @ 15
1963–65	6-230	1AT-4411	CC	.020	36–42	17–20	1 @ 460	30 @ 2800	5	15 @ 12
1966–67	6-232	1110340	C	.016–.021	31–34	17–21	1 @ 500	28 @ 4490	5–7	22 @ 16.5
1968–69	6-232	1110366	C	.016–.021	31–34	17–21	1 @ 360	33 @ 4400	5–7	23 @ 16
1966–67	V8-327	1111025	CC	.016	28–32	17–21	1 @ 350	36 @ 3800	5–7	20 @ 15
1968	V8-327	1111130	CC	.016	28–32	17–21	1 @ 350	39 @ 3800	5–7	18 @ 15
1966–67	V6-225	1110342	C	.016	29–31	19–23	1 @ 500	28 @ 4200	6–8	19.5
1968–69	V6-225	1110376	C	.016	29–31	19–23	1 @ 500	28 @ 4200	6–8	19.5
1968–69	V8-350	1111330	C	.016	30	19–23	1 @ 600	28 @ 4600	6–8	19.5 @ 25

①—Stamped on distributor housing plate. ②—As viewed from above.

STARTING MOTOR SPECIFICATIONS

Year	Model	Part No.	Rotation ①	Brush Spring Tension, Ounces	No Load Test			Torque Test		
					Amperes	Volts	R.P.M.	Amperes	Volts	Torque, Lbs. Ft.
1963–64	6-226	MDU-7003	C	31–47	50	10.0	4400	210	4.0	5
1963–65	6-230	MDY-7021	C	32–40	60	10	4200	405	4.0	9
1966–68	V8-327	MDY-8101A	C	32–40	60	10	4200	405	4.0	9
1966–69	V6-225	1107391	C	—	49–76	10.6	6200–9400	435	5.8	10
1963–69	F4-134	MDU-7004	C	—	50	10	5300	280	4.0	6.2
1968–69	V8-350	1108380	C	35	65–100	10.6	3600–5100	300–360	3.5	9

①—As viewed from the drive end. C—Clockwise.

REAR AXLE & BRAKE SPECIFICATIONS

Year	Model	Carrier Type ①	Diff. Bear. Preload		Ring Gear & Pinion Backlash		Pinion Bear. Preload		Brake Drum Dia.	Brake Cyl. Bore Diameter		
										Wheel Cylinders		Master Cylinder
			Method	Adjust.	Method	Adjust.	Method	Adjust.		Front	Rear	
1963–64	Utility Wagon	Integral	Shims	.015	Shims	.004–.009	Shims	②	11	1⅛	1.00	1
1963–69	J-100	Integral	Shims	.015	Shims	.004–.009	Shims	②	11	1⅛	1.00	1
1963–64	CJ-3B	Integral	Shims	.015	Shims	.004–.009	Shims	②	9	1	¾	1
1963–64	DJ-3A	Integral	Shims	.015	Shims	.004–.009	Shims	②	9	1⅛	13/16	1
1964–69	CJ-5 & CJ-6	Integral	Shims	.015	Shims	.004–.009	Shims	②	10	1	13/16	1
1965–67	DJ-5 & DJ-6	Integral	Shims	.015	Shims	.004–.009	Shims	②	9	1⅛	13/16	1
1968–69	DJ-5 & DJ-6	Integral	Shims	.015	Shims	.004–.009	Shims	②	10	1	13/16	1
1967–69	Jeepster	Integral	Shims	.015	Shims	.004–.009	Shims	②	10	1	13/16	1

①—Axle shaft end play controlled by shims at axle shaft bearing. ②—Pinion should turn with a slight drag but with no end play.

ALTERNATOR SPECIFICATIONS

Year	Alternator							Regulator			
	Make	Model	Ground Polarity	Rated Output		Field Current		Model (2)	Regulator Test @ 120°F.		
				Amperes	Volts	Amperes (1)	Volts		Ampere Load	Altern. R.P.M.	Volts
1963–65	Motorola	A-12NW-525	Negative	35	15	1.2–1.7	12	TVR-12-W14	10	3500	13.65–14.65
1966–69	Motorola	A-12NAM-453	Negative	35	15	1.2–1.7	12	TVR-12-W14	10	3500	13.65–14.65
1966–68	Motorola	A-12NAM-451	Negative	35	15	1.2–1.7	12	TVR-12-W14	10	1500	13.7–14.5
1964–69	Motorola	A-12NW-526	Negative	35	15	1.2–1.7	10	TVR-12-W14	10	1500	12.2–14.6
1966–69	Motorola	A-12NW-528	Negative	35	15	1.2–1.7	10	R-2-K-1	—	—	—
1969	Motorola	A-12NW-528	Negative	35	15	1.2–1.7	10	R-2-K-1	—	—	—
1963–69	Motorola	A-12NW-551(4)	Negative	40	15	1.2–1.7	12	TVR-12-W14	10	3500	13.65–14.65
1964–69	Motorola	A-12NW-552(4)	Negative	40	15	1.2–1.7	12	TVR-12-W14	10	3500	13.65–14.65

(1)—Excessive current draw indicates shorted field windings; no current draw indicates an open winding.

(2)—Regulator is a sealed assembly, requiring no adjustments.

(3)—Jeep part number.

(4)—Optional.

ENGINE TIGHTENING SPECIFICATIONS★

★Torque specifications are for clean and lightly lubricated threads only. Dry or dirty threads produce increased friction which prevents accurate measurement of tightness.

Year		Spark Plugs Ft. Lbs.	Cylinder Head Bolts Ft. Lbs.	Intake Manifold Ft. Lbs.	Exhaust Manifold Ft. Lbs.	Rocker Arm Shaft Bracket Ft. Lbs.	Rocker Arm Cover Ft. Lbs.	Connecting Rod Cap Bolts Ft. Lbs.	Main Bearing Cap Bolts Ft. Lbs.	Flywheel to Crankshaft Ft. Lbs.	Vibration Damper or Pulley Ft. Lbs.
1963–64	L4-134	25–30	60–70	31–35	31–35	...	...	(1)	65–75	36–40	100–130
1963–69	F4-134	25–30	60–70	29–35	29–35	30–35	3–5	35–40	65–75	36–40	100–130
1963–64	L6-226	25–30	30–35	35–45	30–35	...	...	40–45	85–95	35–40	100–130
1963–65	6-230	20–30	80–95	15–20	35–40	...	12–15	40–45	85–95	35–40	100–130
1966–68	V8-327(3)	25–30	58–62	20–25	20–25	...	3–5	46–50	(2)	100–110	70–80
1966–69	V6-225(4)	25–35	70–75	25–35	10–15	25–35	3–5	60–75	65–70	50–60	140–160
1966–69	6-232(3)	25–30	80–85	20–25	20–25	...	45–55(1)	27–30	75–85	100–110	70–80
1968–69	V8-350(4)	15	75	50	18	30	4	35	110	60	140–160

(1)—For 7/16″ bolts 50–55 for 3/8″ bolts 35–40.

(2)—Rear 50–55, others 80–85.

(3)—For service procedure see Rambler Chapter.

(4)—For service procedure see Buick Chapter.

Electrical Section

IGNITION TIMING

If a timing light is to be used to set ignition timing, disconnect the vacuum advance pipe to the carburetor and place a piece of tape over open end of pipe. *This is important as carburetor trouble can affect timing adjustments.*

Lacking a power timing light, an accurate method of setting ignition timing with the engine stopped is with the aid of a jumper light. Be sure to use a light bulb that corresponds with the system voltage of the vehicle.

1. Remove distributor cap and rotor and see that the breaker gap is set according to specifications.
2. Rotate engine until No. 1 cylinder is at the ignition timing point as indicated by the timing pointer and timing mark being lined up with each other.
3. Connect the jumper light between distributor ignition terminal and ground.
4. Turn on ignition switch.
5. Loosen distributor and turn it in the direction of normal rotation until the points just close (light out). Then slowly turn distributor in the opposite direction just to the exact point that the light goes on. Tighten distributor in this position.

DISTRIBUTOR, REPLACE

4-134, 6-230 Engines

The distributor is mounted on the right side of the engine and is operated by a coupling on the oil pump shaft which is driven by a spiral gear on the camshaft.

1. Remove wires from the distributor cap, noting the order in which they are assembled to assure correct reassembly.
2. Remove primary lead from terminal post at side of distributor.
3. Disconnect vacuum tube.
4. Remove distributor cap.
5. Note position of rotor in relation to

the distributor housing. Mark housing to facilitate installing and timing.
6. Remove screw holding distributor to crankcase and lift unit from engine.
7. Reinstall in the reverse order of removal and set the timing as outlined below.

6-226, 232, 8-327

To remove the distributor, disconnect the vacuum tube and low tension wire and remove distributor cap. Remove bolt and washer that holds advance arm to adapter and lift out distributor. Install the distributor in the reverse order of removal and set the ignition timing as outlined below.

V6-225

1. Disconnect primary wire from coil and hose from vacuum advance mechanism of distributor.
2. Insert screwdriver in upper slotted end of two distributor cap retainers.
3. Press downward and turn 90° counterclockwise to release. Remove distributor cap.
4. Make an index mark on distributor housing in line with center of rotor.
5. Carefully note the direction the vacuum unit points in relation to the engine so that the distributor can be installed in the same position. If engine is turned over while distributor is removed, complete ignition timing procedure must be followed upon distributor installation.
6. Remove attaching capscrew and distributor clamp from timing chain cover.
7. Lift distributor upward and remove it from timing chain cover.

STARTER, REPLACE

J Series with V8 Engine

1. Disconnect battery ground cable from cylinder head.
2. Disconnect leads from alternator.
3. Loosen and slide exhaust pipe clamp away from right bank exhaust manifold.
4. Remove exhaust pipe-to-manifold nuts and heat valve attached to right bank exhaust manifold.
5. Unfasten and lift off right bank exhaust manifold from top of engine compartment.
6. Disconnect leads from starting motor.
7. Unfasten starter and remove it from bottom of engine compartment.

4 & 6 Cylinder Models

1. Disconnect battery ground cable.
2. Disconnect starter lead from solenoid switch. Cover this lead with a short piece of hose to prevent a short circuit.
3. Unfasten starter from its mounting and remove from vehicle.

IGNITION SWITCH, REPLACE

Jeepster & J Series

1. Press main switch body toward instrument panel, compressing spring until notched bezel is free to be turned counter-clockwise, thus releasing it off notch pins.
2. Remove bezel and pull back main switch body from under instrument panel so that wiring harness plug can be removed from prong connection.
3. If lock cylinder is to be removed, turn ignition key to the right and insert a paper clip into the lock release hole in switch body. Pressing on lock cylinder retainer will allow cylinder to be removed.
4. Before installing lock cylinder into switch body, note position of lock cylinder retainer.
5. Place lock cylinder into switch body with highest part of lock cylinder retainer in line with lock release hole in switch body.
6. Compress lock cylinder retainer so that lock cylinder can be installed all the way into switch body or until retainer can be seen through pin hole.
7. Place main compression spring on switch body.
8. Install switch body into instrument panel opening through rear.

NOTE: To make sure switch is in its proper position, install ignition key in off position. Then turn switch body until key is straight up and down. Remove key and push on switch body so that notched bezel can be installed freely with notches in line with notch pins. Turn bezel clockwise to lock in position. The word "starter" should be on top when correctly assembled.

CJ, DJ & L6-226

1. To remove the lock cylinder from the switch, first turn the key to the left (auxiliary position).
2. Insert a paper clip into lock release hole in switch body. Pressing in on wire will compress lock cylinder retainer, allowing cylinder to be removed.
3. Either part, lock cylinder or switch unit, may be replaced as required.

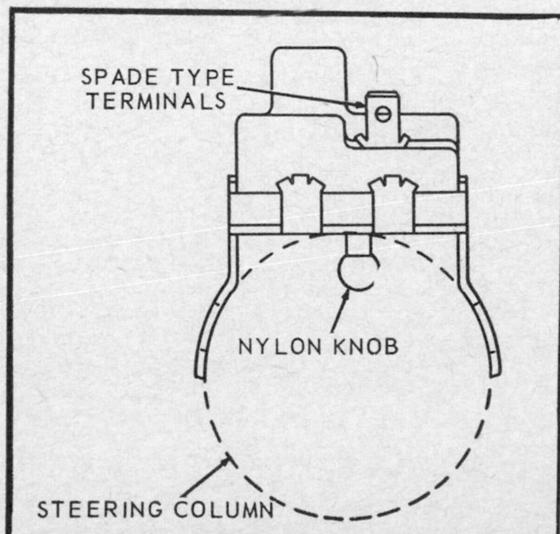

Fig. 1 Back-up light switch for J Series vehicles with manual shift transmission

LIGHT SWITCH, REPLACE

J Series

1. Remove wire terminal plug from light switch.
2. Press in on control knob release pin and remove knob.
3. Remove retaining nut and bezel.
4. Remove switch through rear of instrument panel.

NOTE: When replacing the switch, make sure that the light bezel is installed with the word "Light" in the correct reading position before installing retaining nut. Replace wire terminal plug carefully on switch. Be sure that it is tight on switch connections.

All Except J Series

1. Remove set screw in knob and remove knob.
2. Remove retaining nut and remove switch through rear of instrument panel.
3. Reverse above procedure to install.

STOP LIGHT SWITCH, REPLACE

The switch may be replaced by removing the two wires connections and unscrewing the switch from the T-connection on the master cylinder. Do not apply the brakes while making this exchange as air may enter the hydraulic line. Bleed the brakes after replacing the switch.

NEUTRAL SAFETY SWITCH

Jeepster & J Series

A neutral safety switch and back-up light switch assembly is used on vehicles with automatic transmission. The switch can only be serviced as a unit. If defective it must be replaced. It is mounted on the steering column.

SERVICE BULLETIN

BACK-UP LIGHT SWITCH: The back-up light switch can be installed backwards. If this happens the nylon actuator knob may be broken off, requiring replacement of the switch, Fig. 1. When installing the switch, position it with the spade-type terminals toward the right-hand side of the vehicle.

HORN SOUNDER & STEERING WHEEL

Remove the horn button or steering wheel hub cover by turning it about ⅛ turn to the left and disengaging.

After removing the horn button and ring, use a suitable puller to pull off the steering wheel.

INSTRUMENT CLUSTER REMOVAL

Jeepster & J Series

1. Disconnect battery ground cable.

2. Pry up clips and carefully pry glass off instrument case.
3. Remove any of the lamp bulbs from the rear.
4. To remove fuel gauge, temperature gauge or speedometer, remove lock nuts and take instrument out from the front.
5. To install instrument cluster into dash panel, first make sure that all light sockets are in place, then connect the plug.
6. Install speedometer cable and snap cluster into dash panel.

W/S WIPER MOTOR

Jeepster & J Series

The windshield wiper motor is located on the engine side of the dash panel. The two-speed motor has three terminals while the single-speed motor has only two terminals. The wiper linkage and arm pivots are mounted to the underside of the cowl.

NOTE: Should wiper linkage interference occur between the linkage arm and upper steering column support bracket or cap screw, remove wiper linkage and measure the distance between hole centers of linkage arm. If dimension is less than 18", place linkage arm in vise and tighten until correct dimension is obtained. Check steering column bracket cap screw length. If it exceeds ½", replace with a shorter screw.

WIPER LINKAGE

REMOVAL

1. Remove wiper arms.
2. Remove round nuts, washers and escutcheons from wiper pivot body and lever assemblies.
3. Remove clips from wiper pivot body lever and motor crank arm.
4. Remove connecting arm from pivot body.
5. Remove screws from each wiper pivot body. Now the entire connecting arm and pivot body can be removed from under dash.

INSTALLATION

1. Place gasket on wiper pivot body and install pivot body into its hole in cowl. Install screws through pivot body into cowl.
2. Place gasket on left-hand pivot body and lever and position pivot body with connecting arms attached into its hole in cowl. Attach with screws.
3. Attach clips to right pivot body and motor crank arm.
4. From outside of vehicle, position right escutcheon on right pivot arm body, and left escutcheon on left pivot arm body. Install washers and round nuts, and wiper arm assemblies.

W/S WIPER SWITCH

NOTE: The plastic windshield wiper control knobs on early production J series vehicles do not have a metal insert in the hexagon-shaped hole in the center of the knob. Later production knobs have such a metal insert. If a control knob (without a metal insert) will not hold by tightening the set screw, it should be replaced with a knob having a metal insert.

Engine Section

For service procedure on the V8-327 and 6-232 engines see the Rambler Chapter.
For the V6-225 and V8-350 engines see the Buick Chapter.

ENGINE, REPLACE

Jeepster & J Series

1. Drain cooling system and oil pan.
2. Remove oil filter.
3. Place a pan under clutch slave cylinder to catch fluid. Then disconnect line at slave cylinder.
4. Remove hood from hinges.
5. Remove water and heater hoses and transmission oil cooler lines.
6. Remove radiator.
7. Disconnect wires from temperature sender, oil pressure sender, starter, alternator, and primary wire at coil.
8. Remove alternator, fan belt, cooling fan and fan spacer.
9. Remove battery and battery supports.
10. Disconnect battery ground cable and engine ground strap at right front engine support.
11. Unfasten exhaust pipe from engine.
12. Disconnect exhaust pipe bracket from flywheel housing.
13. Remove carburetor.
14. Disconnect fuel line at flexible hose between frame and engine.
15. Remove front engine support bolts.
16. Attach lifting sling to lifting eyes located on upper left rear corner and upper right front corner of engine. Attach to a chain or floor crane.
17. Remove transfer case and transmission.
18. Raise engine up and forward until out of vehicle.
19. Reverse above procedure to install.

CJ, DJ & L6-226

1. Disconnect one battery cable.
2. Drain cooling system.
3. Remove radiator stay bar on CJ-3B.
4. Remove radiator and heater hoses.
5. Remove fan and fan hub.
6. Remove radiator and shroud.
7. Disconnect fuel line at pump.
8. Disconnect windshield wiper hoses.
9. Remove air cleaner and two breather hoses.
10. Disconnect choke and throttle controls.
11. Remove starting motor.
12. Disconnect generator wires.
13. Disconnect primary wire at coil.
14. Disconnect heat indicator and oil pressure gauge tubes.
15. Disconnect exhaust pipe from manifold.
16. Remove front engine supports. This will allow engine to drop slightly and will permit access to the two top bolts on the bell housing.
17. Install a suitable lifting sling on engine. Attach sling to hoist and take up slack.
18. Pull engine forward or roll vehicle backward until clutch clears bell housing, and lift engine from vehicle.
19. To install, reverse procedure.

L6-226 Utility Wagons

1. Drain cooling system.
2. Remove hood and radiator stay bars.
3. Remove radiator hoses and heater hoses.
4. Remove radiator and shroud.
5. Disconnect battery ground cable.
6. Disconnect wires from temperature sender, oil pressure sender, starter, generator, coil and secondary at distributor.
7. Remove air cleaner.
8. Disconnect accelerator pedal linkage from bell crank.
9. Disconnect vacuum line from wiper motor.
10. Disconnect fuel line from pump.
11. Disconnect engine ground strap from front engine support.
12. Disconnect clutch linkage.
13. Disconnect exhaust pipe at manifold.
14. Disconnect front engine supports.
15. The engine is now free of connections and can be lifted from vehicle.
16. To install, reverse foregoing procedure.

CYLINDER HEAD

4-134 & 6-226 Engines

Before the cylinder head is installed, make certain that all dirt and carbon is removed from both the head and block. File or hone all high spots.

Use a torque wrench when tightening down cylinder heads. Uneven or excessive tightening of nuts may distort cylinder bores, causing compression loss and excessive oil consumption.

Tighten cylinder heads in the sequence shown in Figs. 1, 2, 3, tightening them a little at a time in the proper order a couple of times around before final tightening to the torque values given in the

Long section of F-head 4-134 engine

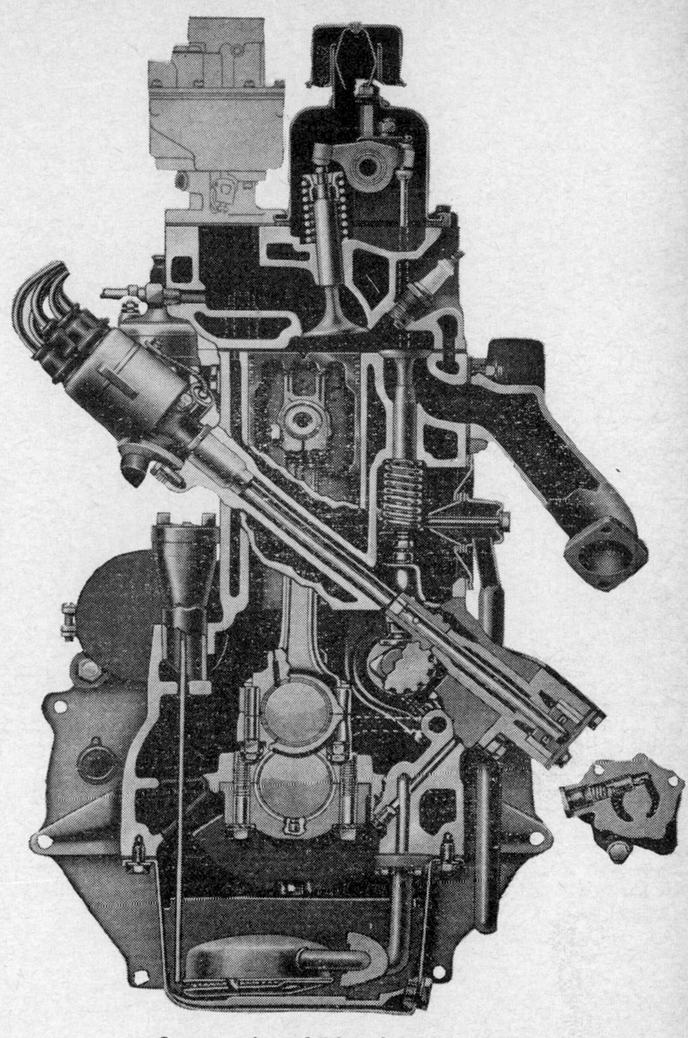

Cross section of F-head 4-134 engine

Engine Tightening Chart. After the engine has warmed up to operating temperature, recheck the torque and tighten as required.

On F-Head engines, be sure to check intake valve operating clearances after the final tightening.

Note—Tightening cylinder heads on F-head engines without removing rocker arms may be accomplished with a wrench having an $\frac{11}{16}$" box on one end and a ½" square box on the other end. This, together with a torque wrench will do the job.

Note, 6-226 Engine

Accurate alignment of the cylinder head, gasket and block on L6-226 engines is required to prevent gasket failure. Two cylinder head bolt holes, at opposite corners of the head (positions 24 and 26 in Fig. 1) have a slightly smaller diameter than the other holes and can be used for guide pins.

The guide pins can be made by cutting the heads off two cylinder head bolts. Cut slots in the end from which the heads were removed to install and then remove the guide pins.

The torquing sequence for the head bolts is shown in Fig. 1.

Note, F4-134 Engine

In order to gain access to No. 5 cylinder head bolt for head removal or for tightening head bolts, Fig. 2, the carburetor must be removed.

OHC 6-230 Engine

1. To remove head with timing chain cover installed, first take off rocker arm cover.

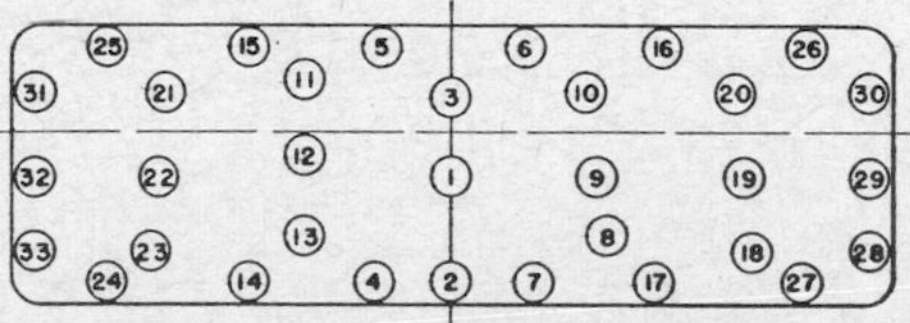

Fig. 1 Cylinder head tightening sequence. 6-226 engine

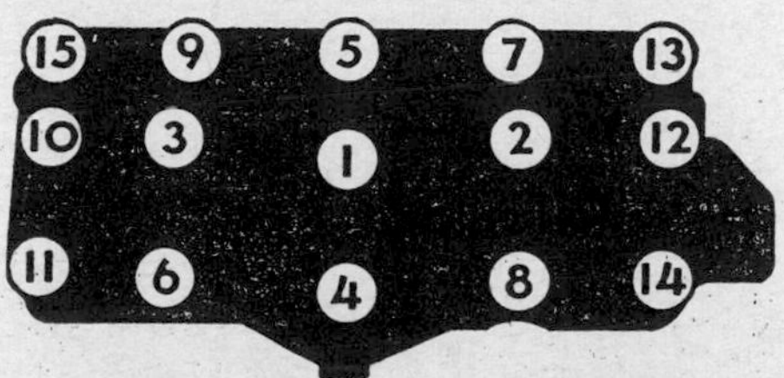

Fig. 2 Cylinder head tightening. Four-cylinder F-head engines

2. Install camshaft sprocket removal and installation tool on rocker arm cover studs, Fig. 4. Fasten with rocker arm cover nuts. Install hook of removal tool in the sprocket and tighten the nut to relieve the tension on the camshaft.
3. Remove fuel pump eccentric from camshaft sprocket.
4. Pull forward on camshaft sprocket to remove it from pilot on camshaft. With sprocket still engaged in timing chain, release tension on tool by loosening nut. Gently allow sprocket to rest on bosses in timing chain cover. *Caution: Do not turn over engine when sprocket is removed from camshaft and is resting on bosses in cover. This will severely damage cover. Do not attempt to remove camshaft sprocket from timing chain since this will upset the valve timing.*
5. Disconnect lubrication tube from head and block.
6. Remove two timing chain cover-to-head bolts. Remove three short head bolts with flat washers and the eleven long bolts with washers.
7. Lift off head assembly.

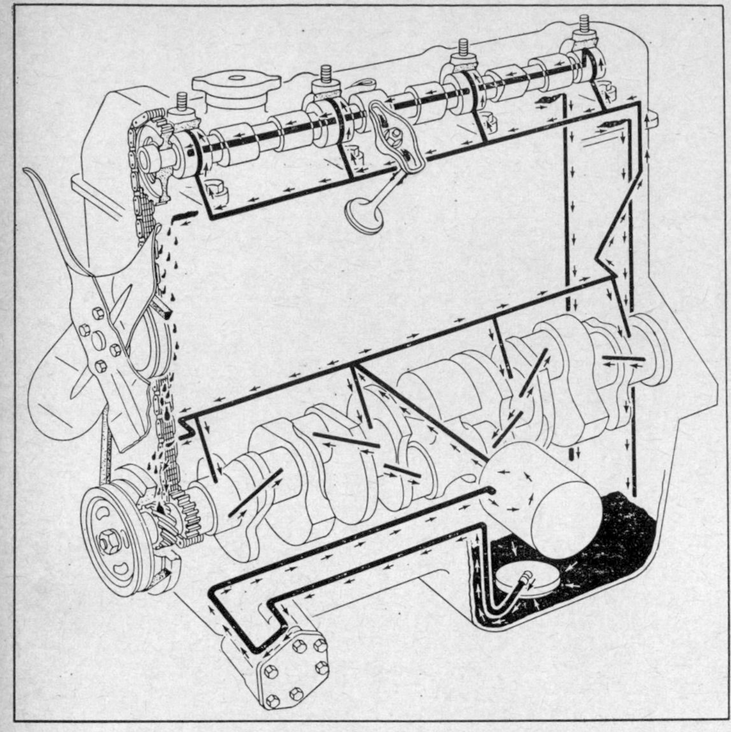

Engine oiling system. 6-230 engine

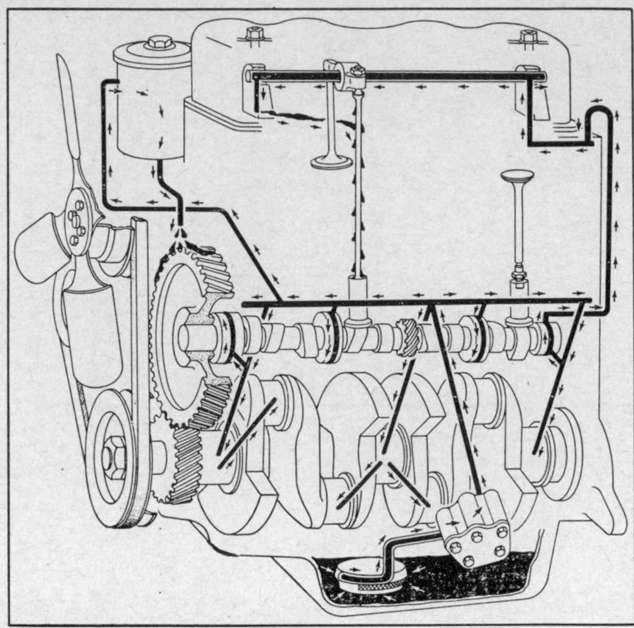

Engine oiling system. F-head 4-134 engine

Note, OHC 6-230 Engine

1. When installing the head, it is important that the procedure given below is followed.
2. With a chain fall, lower cylinder head and cam bearing deck assembly down on top of block without gasket in place.
3. Run all cylinder bolts in by hand without washers under bolt heads. Each bolt must turn down freely, and the head of each bolt must be run down tight on the cylinder head and cam bearing deck.
4. If bolts do not turn down freely in a certain hole or holes, check to be sure all bolts are of proper length. *NOTE: Bolts that are installed in holes 2, 8 and 10 in Fig. 3 are 2¼" long. All other bolts are 5½" long. Lift head off block and check to make sure there is no foreign material in the bolt hole restricting entry of the bolt. If there is no restriction in the bolt hole and the bolt is of the proper length, drill and re-tap the hole deep enough so the bolt can be run down tight on the head or deck. Holes should be drilled to 1.25" depth and tapped to 1.09".*
5. Cover both sides of head gasket with a thin film of approved sealing compound. Position gasket on block, making sure head bolt holes line up with holes in block.
6. Lower head with chain fall until it is suspended approximately ¼" above cylinder head gasket.

CAUTION: Head must not rest on spacers of any kind between gasket and head. If front engine plate and gasket are in place on engine, use extra care not to damage gasket as head is lowered to ¼" above gasket.

7. Cut the heads off two 5½" long head bolts and file a screwdriver slot in the cut end. Install the two modified bolts as guide pins in bolt holes number 12 and 14, Fig. 3, and screw them into the block.
8. Lower head on top of gasket. Install head bolts (except guide pin locations) with proper washers and tighten them down snugly in the proper sequence.
9. Remove the guide pins and install bolts and washers in these locations.
10. Tighten head bolts to the specified torque given in *Engine Tightening Table*.
11. Start engine and let it warm up to operating temperature, then retorque head bolts in proper sequence.

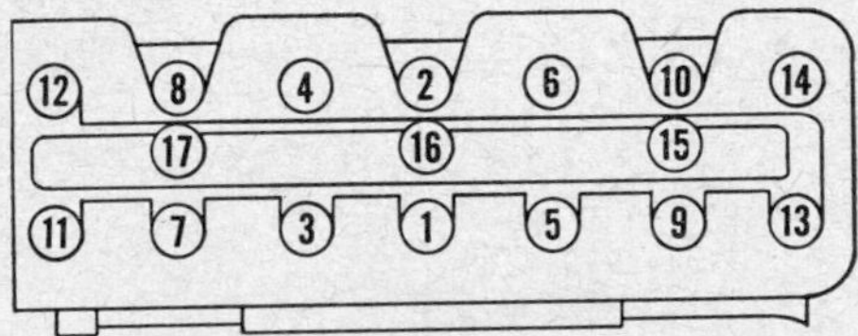

Fig. 3 Cylinder head tightening sequence (1 to 14). Cam bearing support stud nuts (15, 16, 17) should be torqued to 15-20 ft-lbs. 6-230 engine

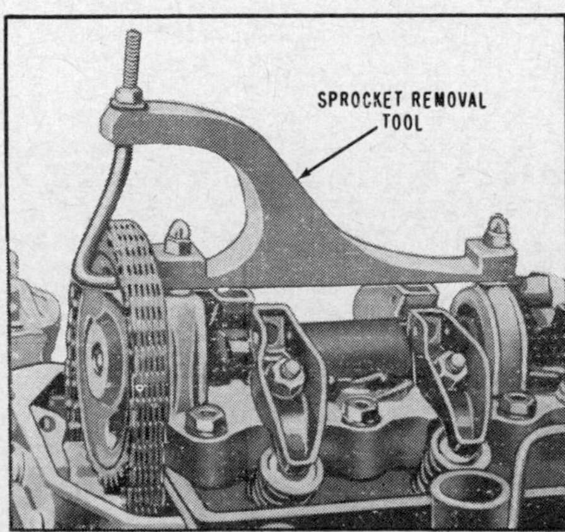

Fig. 4 Camshaft sprocket removal and installation tool for use when removing cylinder head and timing chain. 6-230 engine

SERVICE BULLETIN

CYLINDER HEAD BOSS: The cylinder head on some 6-230 engines have a boss cast on the left front corner of the head, Fig. 5. A tapped hole in the boss secures a bolt attaching that area of the timing chain cover and front engine plate to the cylinder head.

Should a replacement of the cylinder head-to-front engine plate gasket be required on these engines, use gasket No. 938015. Cement the gasket to the plate and to the head with Permatex No. 3 or equivalent.

If a cylinder head with the boss is being installed on an engine formerly equipped with a head without a boss, use the new gasket and discard the nut previously used to secure the bolt at the boss location. The spring lock washer previously used at the nut end should be installed between the bolt head and plain washer.

ROCKER ARM STUDS

OHC 6-230 Engine

Should any of the rocker arm studs become worn, loose, distorted or have damaged threads, it is recommended

Fig. 5 Arrow indicates boss on some 6-230 engine cylinder heads

that the complete cam bearing deck assembly be replaced. Individual studs cannot be replaced satisfactorily.

When installing the rocker arm cover and the manifolds follow the procedure outlined for these parts under VALVES, REMOVE.

ROCKER ARM SERVICE

F-Head Engines

To remove the rocker arm assembly, proceed as follows:

1. Remove carburetor air cleaner.
2. Disconnect spark plug wires.
3. Drain cooling system.
4. Remove rocker arm cover.
5. Remove rocker arm bracket screws and lift off rocker arm assembly.

Before disassembly, mark rocker arms, brackets and shaft so they can be reassembled in the original positions.

VALVES, ADJUST

L-Head Engines

The valves may be adjusted when the engine is at normal room temperature. Crank the engine over until the valve to be adjusted is fully closed. Hold the lifter body with a tappet wrench to prevent it from turning. Then turn the tappet adjusting screw until the proper clearance is obtained. Measure the clearance with a feeler gauge and, after adjusting one tappet, proceed in like manner with the others, being certain that the valve being adjusted is fully closed.

In addition to the conventional method of adjusting tappets by locating the distributor rotor and then adjusting the tappets by following the firing order of the engine, the following method may also be used:

Four-Cylinder Engines

Valves Fully Raised	Adjust Tappets
1 and 3	6 and 8
2 and 5	4 and 7
6 and 8	1 and 3
4 and 7	2 and 5

Six-Cylinder 226" Engine

Valves Fully Raised	Adjust Tappets
1 and 3	10 and 12
8 and 9	4 and 5
2 and 6	7 and 11
10 and 12	1 and 3
4 and 5	8 and 9
7 and 11	2 and 6

F-Head Engines

The exhaust valves (in block) may be adjusted in the same manner as outlined for L-head engines. However, the intake valves may best be adjusted with the engine running after it has warmed up to operating temperature.

If the cylinder head has been tightened, be sure to recheck intake valve clearances and adjust as required.

OHC 6-230 Engine

The adjustment may be made when the engine is either hot or cold. *Caution: Do not attempt to remove the rocker arm cover to adjust valve clearance when the engine is running. Always shut down the engine before removing the cover.*

1. Remove rocker arm cover.
2. Turn engine over until No. 1 piston is at top dead center. This can be determined by checking the position of the No. 1 cam. When the associated piston is at top dead center, the nose of the cam points to the 6 o'clock position.
3. Insert a feeler gauge between the rocker arm and the top of the valve stem.
4. Use a socket wrench to adjust the clearance. Turning the rocker arm nut clockwise decreases the clearance; counterclockwise increases the clearance.
5. Adjust the valves in this manner for all cylinders, setting the associated cam nose to the 6 o'clock position before adjusting.

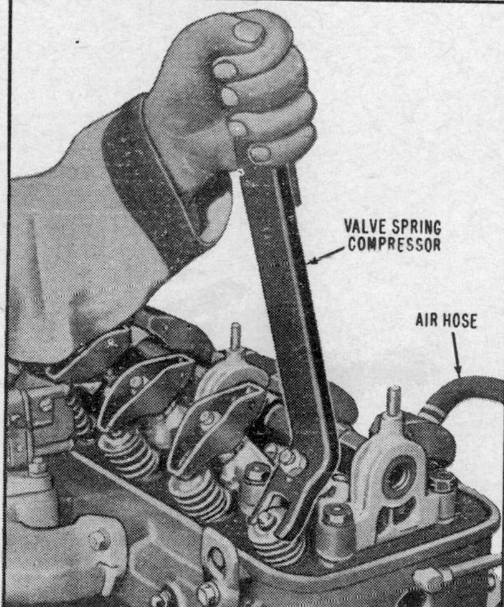

Fig. 7 Compressing valve springs. The air hose shown is attached to an air pressure adapter inserted into a spark plug hole to keep the valve closed when replacing a valve spring with the cylinder head installed. 6-230 engine

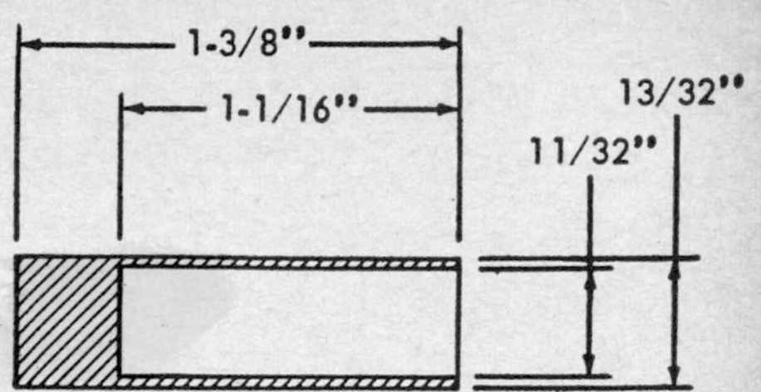

Fig. 6 Dimensions for making a valve stem protective cap

VALVE LIFT SPECS.

Engine	Intake	Exhaust
L4-134	.351	.351
F4-134	.260	.351
L6-226	.284	.284
OHC-230	.375	.375
V6-225	.401	.401
6-232	.375	.375
V8-327	.375	.375
V8-350	.376	.384

VALVES, REMOVE

OHC 6-230 Engine

Service Note

The valve stems must be perfectly smooth or the valve stem seals will not be effective. Scratches or gouges on the stems will cut the seal, allowing oil to pass between stem and seal.

To prevent damage to valve stem when compressing valve springs, use care to keep the valve spring retainer centered on the valve stem. *The retainer is harder than the stem, and if it is allowed to rub against the stem as the spring is compressed, the stem will be damaged. Such valves must be replaced.*

A valve stem protective cap may be made from cold rolled steel as shown in Fig. 6. This cap may be used when installing valve springs. To do this, install cap over valve stem and in retainer. Compress spring, remove cap, install retainer locks and release spring.

1. After cylinder head is removed, position cylinder head on blocks to provide hand clearance under the assembly.
2. Remove valve springs. Use hand pressure to hold the valve while compressing the spring, Fig. 7.
3. Remove and discard valve guide seal from top of valve guide.
4. Remove all valves and place them in a numbered rack to make sure each valve will be reassembled in the same valve seat from which it was removed.

Rocker Arm Cover, Install

1. Install gasket on rocker arm cover without sealer of any kind. If desired, use engine oil to ease the installation.

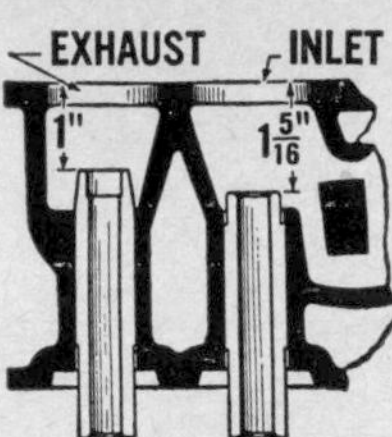

Fig. 8 Position of valve stem guides in four cylinder L-Head engine

2. Install oil seal washers on cover studs; *be sure washers are the latest type, being .222" to .238" thick.*
3. Check position of rocker arm guide and rocker arms to be sure tabs on guide are inside rocker arms.
4. Place rocker arm cover in position, being careful not to damage gasket.
5. Place a flat washer on the rear stud, and the spark plug cable brackets on the front three studs. A flat washer is not necessary on studs where cable brackets are installed.
6. Install four crown nuts on cover studs and torque them 6 to 8 ft-lbs. *Insufficient torque can cause an oil leak at the stud opening in the cover. Excessive torque can distort the cover, causing oil leakage between cylinder head and cover in spark plug area.*
7. Connect crankcase ventilation-to-oil filler tube.

Manifolds, Install

When installing the manifolds on this engine, the stud nuts must be tightened and torqued uniformly. Only in this way can proper sealing be assured, and possible cracking or breaking of manifold flanges be prevented. Also, in the case of exhaust manifold installation, should any stud hole bind on a stud, that particular hole should be enlarged slightly to relieve the bind and prevent cracking.

Tighten and torque the nuts by first pulling them down snugly, then tighten from the center outward, working alternately from side to side. Finally, torque all nuts to the specifications listed in the *Engine Tightening* chart.

L-Head Engines

After removing the cylinder head, take off the valve chamber covers and use cloth to block off the holes in the valve chamber to prevent the valve locks from falling into the crankcase.

With a suitable valve spring compressor, raise the springs on those valves which are closed and remove the valve locks. Then turn the crankshaft until those valves which are open are closed and remove the remaining valve locks.

Remove all valves and place them in a board with numbered holes so they can be identified as to the valve port from which they were removed.

F-Head Engines

Follow the same procedure in removing the exhaust valves from these engines as outlined for L-head engines.

In removing the intake valves from the head a suitable fixture is available which holds the valves closed and compresses the spring at the same time.

VALVE GUIDES

If it is necessary to replace the valve guides, the old guides can be driven out with a special driver which is available for the purpose. However, in lieu of the driver, the guides can be pulled out by using a suitable piece of pipe together with a long bolt and suitable washers.

When replacing the guides, maximum engine performance can only be secured when the guides are installed correctly (see Figs. 8 and 9).

On 6-230 engines, valve guides should be installed so that the top of the guide will be .45" above the machined surface of the cylinder head.

VALVE LIFTERS

These lifters are of the mushroom type operating in guide holes cast in the block. This means that the camshaft will have to be removed from the engine if valve lifters require replacement.

Whenever the camshaft is removed, inspect the faces of the lifters where they contact the cams and replace any that are scored, rough or cracked. Check the clearance of the lifters in the guides, replacing those that have worn excessively. Oversize available is .004 in. and the guides must be reamed to accommodate them.

TIMING CASE COVER

NOTE: In order to replace the cover oil seal on all engines the cover must first be removed.

4-134 Engine

1. Drain cooling system.
2. Remove radiator and grille or guard.
3. Remove cylinder head, valves and springs.
4. On L-head engines, remove manifolds.
5. Remove fuel and oil pumps.

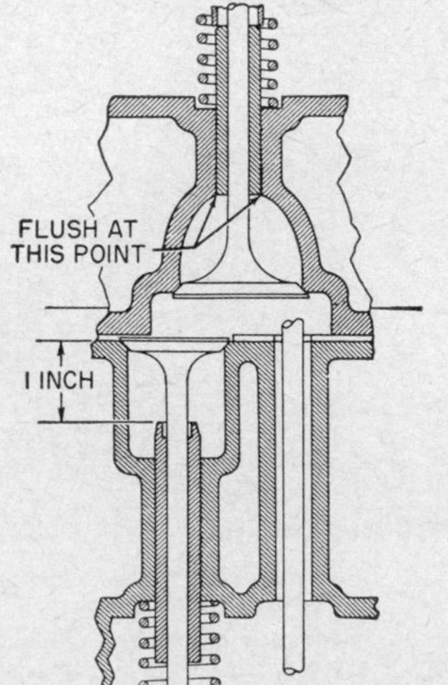

Fig. 9 Position of valve guides in F-head engines

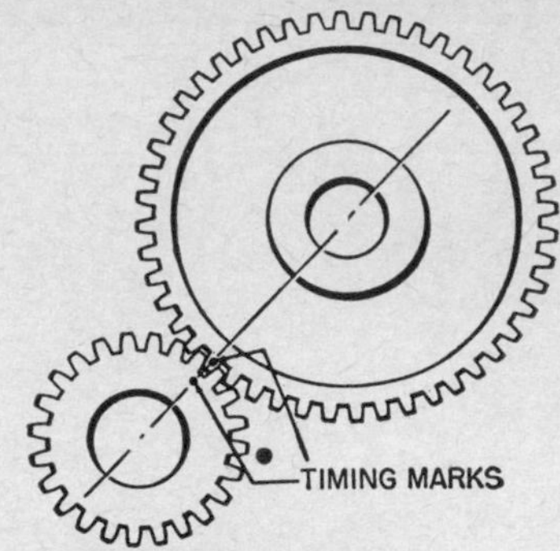

Fig. 10 Valve timing for 4-134 engines

6. Remove oil pan.
7. Remove crankshaft pulley (and vibration damper on 6-cyl.).
8. Remove fan assembly.
9. On CJ-2A and CJ-3A, remove nuts from front engine support.
10. Remove engine front cover.
11. Remove camshaft gear and thrust plate.
12. Tie valve lifters up to their highest point of travel with string wrapped around the adjusting screws and attach to manifold studs. Spring clip type clothespins or small "C" clamps may also be used.
13. On CJ-2A and CJ-3A, raise front of engine until camshaft will clear front crossmember.
14. Remove camshaft from engine.
15. To install, reverse foregoing procedure and set valve timing as shown in Fig. 10.

6-226 Engines

1. Drain cooling system.
2. Remove radiator.
3. Remove vibration damper.
4. Remove timing chain cover.
5. Remove timing gears and chain.
6. Remove fuel pump.
7. Remove cylinder head.
8. Remove oil pan and oil pump.
9. Remove valves and springs.
10. Hold valve lifters up with spring type clothespins or string to prevent them from interfering with camshaft as it is being withdrawn.
11. Unfasten camshaft thrust plate from cylinder block and withdraw the camshaft.
12. To install, reverse removal procedure and set valve timing as shown in Fig. 11.

OHC 6-230 Engine

Removal

1. Remove hose clamps and hose from water port of chain cover.
2. Remove bolts that secure cover to front engine plate.
3. Remove cover, lifting eye and cover gaskets.
4. Slide oil slinger and oil pump drive gear from crankshaft.

Installation

1. Apply a thin coat of gasket paste to both sides of cover gaskets and position gaskets on cover. Make sure Woodruff key, oil pump drive gear and oil slinger are installed on crankshaft.

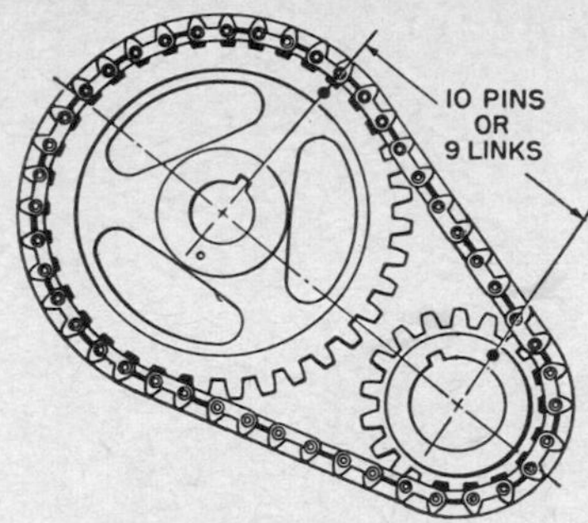

Fig. 11 Valve timing for 6-226 engine

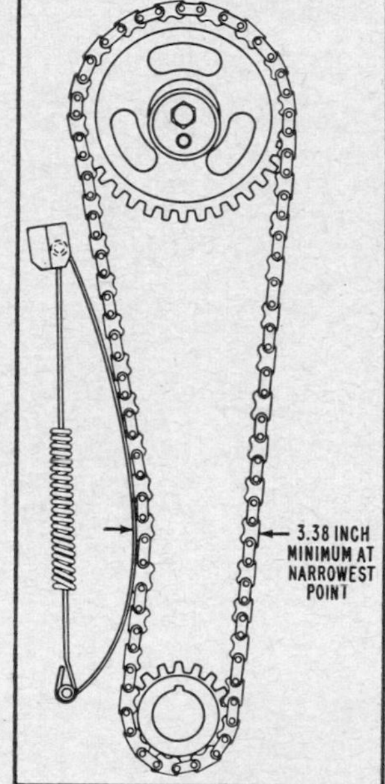

Fig. 12 Measurement for limit of timing chain wear. 6-230 engine

2. Assemble sleeve and O-rings and install in oil port in cylinder block.
3. Lubricate oil pump push rod and install in chain cover.
4. Position chain cover on front engine plate and secure with bolts.
5. Be sure lifting eye is installed on upper right corner of front engine plate and generator brace on upper left of cover.

Front Oil Seal

1. After timing chain cover is installed, check crankshaft to make sure it is free of burrs or sharp projections that could damage oil seal during installation.
2. Apply a thin coating of sealing compound on the outer edge of the seal and position the seal in the opening so that the seal lip faces toward the inside of the cover.

TIMING CHAIN

OHC 6-230 Engine

Removal

1. Remove timing chain cover.
2. Install tool shown in Fig. 4 on rocker arm cover studs. Install hook of tool in camshaft sprocket and tighten nut to relieve tension on camshaft.
3. Remove fuel pump eccentric from sprocket. Pull forward on sprocket to remove it from camshaft pilot.
4. Release hook of tool and slide sprocket off camshaft.
5. Remove chain tensioner spring to release tension on tensioner blade. Remove blade and spring from lower tensioner mounting stud.

Inspect Chain & Sprockets

Check the chain for excessive wear or stretch. When the chain is installed with the chain tensioner in place, measure the distance between the chain sides at the narrowest point, Fig. 12. If the distance is less than the required minimum as shown, the chain must be replaced. If sprockets appear to be excessively worn, replace them also.

Timing Chain Tensioner

This device maintains a constant pressure against the chain to compensate for normal stretch and wear of the chain. Check the contact face of the tensioner blade to make sure the rubber facing material is not worn through. Replace if badly worn. Check the tensioner spring to make sure it is not distorted or elongated.

Install Chain & Sprockets

1. Turn over engine until air starts to blow from No. 1 spark plug port to indicate that No. 1 piston is on the compression stroke.
2. Continue to turn over engine until keyways in crankshaft are in the 12 o'clock position, which will indicate that No. 1 piston is at top dead center, Fig. 13.
3. Temporarily install camshaft sprocket and turn camshaft until nose of No. 1 cam and dowel hole on camshaft are pointing downward at the 6 o'clock position.
4. Remove camshaft sprocket.
5. Install key in crankshaft keyway nearest cylinder block.
6. Install tool shown in Fig. 4.
7. Position sprockets in opposite ends of chain so that keyway in crankshaft sprocket is up and dowel of camshaft is down. Position parts so that copper links of the chain are aligned with timing marks on sprockets.
8. Lift up assembled chain and sprockets and slide crankshaft sprocket on crankshaft so that camshaft is fully seated on camshaft.
9. Engage hook of tool, Fig. 4, on sprocket and tighten nut to tension the chain and pull the mounting hole of the sprocket into alignment with the pilot on end of camshaft.
10. Push sprocket into camshaft pilot so that dowel engages hole in flange on camshaft. This may require slight rotation of crankshaft to secure perfect alignment.
11. Install fuel pump eccentric on camshaft sprocket.
12. Release tension of special tool, Fig. 4, and remove tool from rocker arm cover studs.

6-226 Engines

For correct valve timing on this engine, install the chain as shown in Fig. 11.

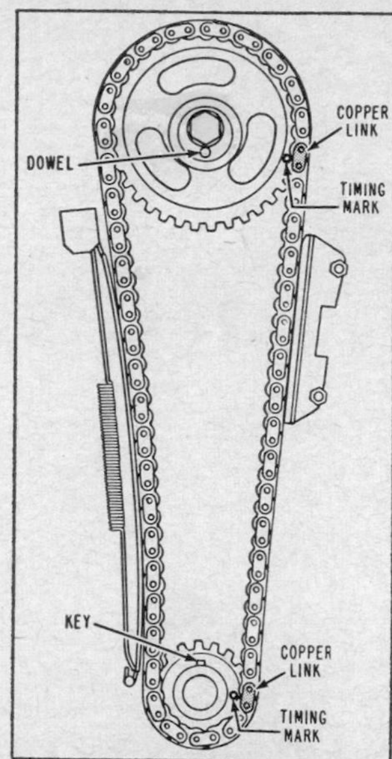

Fig. 13 Valve timing marks for 6-230 engine

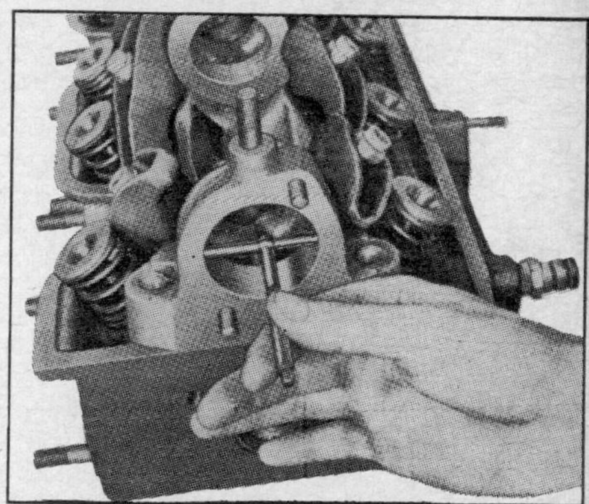

Fig. 14 Checking bearing diameter of cam bearing support deck. 6-230 engine

TIMING GEARS

4-134 Engines

The camshaft is driven by a steel gear on the crankshaft and a fibre gear on the camshaft. Lubrication is positive through a jet pressed into the crankcase directly back of the contact point of the gears. When the gears are removed, check both the jet and oil passage to make sure they are clear.

When it becomes necessary to replace the timing gears, due attention must be given to the end play of both shafts and running clearance of the gears.

End play of the crankshaft is controlled by the running clearance between the crankshaft gear and gear thrust plate. The end play is adjusted by shims placed between the thrust plate and the end of the front main bearing. Shims .002 in. thick are available for this adjustment. When the thrust plate or washer is removed, be sure it is rein-

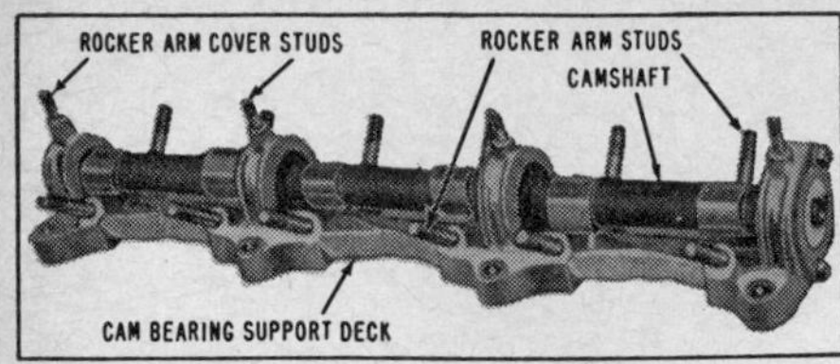

Fig. 15 Camshaft and cam bearing support deck. 6-230 engine

stalled with the beveled inner edge toward the crankcase.

End play of the camshaft is determined by the running clearance between the camshaft gear and thrust plate. The standard clearance is .003 to .0055 in. which is determined by the thickness of the camshaft gear thrust plate spacer. Should a check indicate not enough clearance, place a thin shim between the thrust plate spacer and the shoulder on the camshaft. Clearance may be reduced by dressing off the spacer slightly. Whenever the spacer is installed, make sure that the beveled inner edge is toward the rear.

End play of both the camshaft and crankshaft can best be measured with a dial indicator.

Standard running clearance between the gears is .000 to .002 in., which should be checked with a dial indicator.

To set the valve timing, install the crankshaft gear followed by the camshaft gear with the camshaft positioned to allow installation with the timing gear marks meshed, Fig. 10.

CAMSHAFT

OHC 6-230 Engine

Removal

1. With cylinder head removed, lift rocker arm guide from cylinder head.
2. Check rocker arms to determine which do not have cam tension against them. *Turn these parallel to camshaft.*
3. Temporarily install camshaft sprocket on camshaft and rotate camshaft to release tension from remaining rocker arms. Turn these parallel to the camshaft also. Continue to do this until all rocker arms are out of engagement with the camshaft.
4. Remove two nuts that attach camshaft retainer to cam bearing support deck and remove retainer.
5. Pull forward on camshaft to remove it from cam bearing support deck.
6. Remove cam bearing support deck from cylinder head.

Inspection

Clean the camshaft thoroughly with a suitable solvent. Make sure all oil passages are free. Check the cams for scoring or wear. The cam face must be perfectly smooth throughout their contact areas. Runout of the camshaft, measured with a dial indicator at the intermediate bearing journals, must not exceed .0005″.

Check the camshaft journal diameters

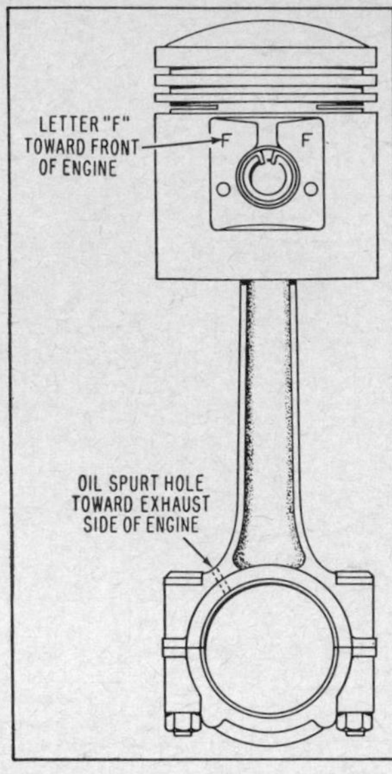

Fig. 16 Piston and rod assembly. 6-230 engine

with a micrometer. The specified diameters are as follows:

Front	1.9965-1.9975″
No. 2	1.8715-1.8725″
No. 3	1.7465-1.7475″
Rear	1.3715-1.3725″

Check the cam bearing support deck for cracks or distortion. Check the bearing surfaces of the cam deck for visible wear or scoring. Using a telescope gauge and micrometer, check the internal diameters of the cam bearing deck bearings as shown in Fig. 14. The specified diameters are as follows:

Front	1.9995-2.0005″
No. 2	1.8745-1.8755″
No. 3	1.7495-1.7505″
Rear	1.3745-1.3755″

Compare each journal diameter with the corresponding bearing diameter. If the bearings are defective or permit more

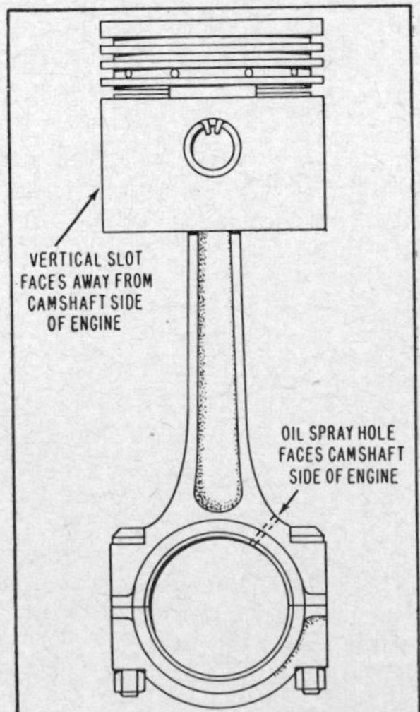

Fig. 18 Piston and rod assembly. 6-226 engines

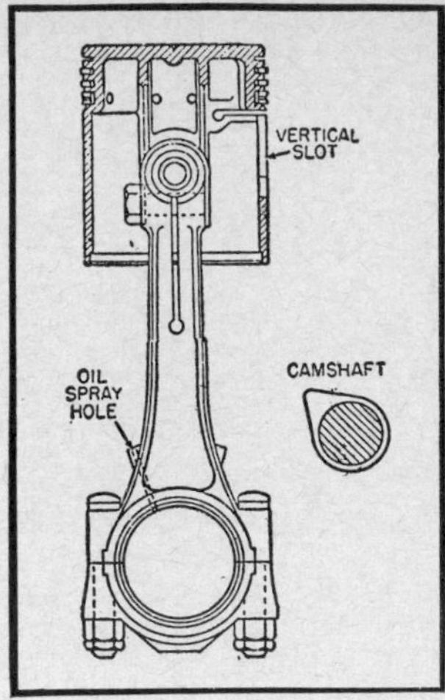

Fig. 17 Piston and rod assembly. 4-134 engines

than .004″ running clearance, the cam bearing deck and/or the camshaft must be replaced, Fig. 15.

Installation

1. Install cam bearing support deck on cylinder head. Torque nuts to 15-20 ft-lb.
2. Lubricate bearing with engine oil and carefully slide camshaft into bearing support deck from the front, being careful not to damage bearings in support deck or journals on camshaft.
3. When camshaft is fully seated, install retainer on front of support deck.

PISTONS & RODS, ASSEMBLE

OHC 6-230 Engine

Assemble the piston to the connecting rod so that when installed in the cylinder the "F" side of the piston will face the front with the oil spurt hole in the rod toward the exhaust (right) side of the engine, Fig. 16.

4-134 Engine

SERVICE NOTE: The oil spray hole in the rod must be on the side away from the camshaft (toward right side of vehicle). Because of the oil spray hole, No. 1 and 2 or No. 3 and 4 connecting rods cannot be interchanged for if they are reversed the spray hole will be on the wrong side. No. 1 and 3 or No. 2 and 4 can be interchanged.

As shown in Fig. 17, pistons should be assembled to the connecting rods so that the oil spray hole in the rod *faces* away from the camshaft side of the engine with the vertical slot in the piston facing the camshaft side.

6-226 Engine

When correctly assembled, the oil spray hole in the rod *faces* the camshaft side of the engine with the vertical slot in the piston facing away from the camshaft side, Fig. 18.

PISTONS, PINS & RINGS

Pistons and rings are available in standard sizes and oversizes of .010, .020, .030 and .040".

On all engines except 6-226 piston pins are available in standard sizes only. On 6-226 engine, standard size pins and oversizes of .003" and .005" are available.

MAIN & ROD BEARINGS

Main and rod bearings are available in standard sizes and undersizes of .002, .010, .012 and .020". On 4 cylinder engines, .030" undersize bearings are also available.

SERVICE NOTE: A timing gear oil jet entered production with Engine No. 4J-250095. The earlier jet has a .070" diameter aperture; the later jet has a .040" aperture. The later jet reduces oil pressure variation at No. 1 connecting rod bearing. It is recommended that the .040" jet be installed in engines with serial numbers lower than the above whenever it is necessary to replace a scored or burned No. 1 connecting rod bearing.

CRANKSHAFT OIL SEAL

4-134 Engine

The rear main bearing is sealed against external leakage by a lip type neoprene seal with a metal core. The seal has the advantage of being able to be slipped into place without removing the crankshaft.

For easy installation, give the seal a coat of grease. Be careful not to coat the ends of the seal as they have sealing compound applied to them.

OHC 6-230 Engine

The rear end of the crankshaft is sealed against oil leaks by a seal consisting of the parts shown in Fig. 19. The filler block guard is mounted in a recess in the cylinder block.

Before installing a new seal, clean the filler block throughly. Remove the oil pan seal and cement used to attach it. Check the dowel pins to make sure they are straight and tight.

To replace the oil pan seal, coat the pan seal groove in the filler block with 3M Super Weatherstrip Adhesive or equivalent for a distance of 2" from each end, Fig. 20. Also coat the pan seal ends for a distance of 2".

Insert the nipple of the pan seal into the hole in the bottom of the filler block. Press the ends into engagement with the cemented portion. When in position, the ends of the pan seal should be $\frac{1}{16}$" below the top of the filler block as shown in Fig. 19. Allow the adhesive to dry before assembly to the engine.

OIL PAN

The floating oil intake is attached to the crankcase with two cap screws. Whenever the oil pan is removed, the float, screen and tube should be cleaned thoroughly in a suitable cleaning fluid to remove any accumulation of dirt. If the screen has been crushed, it is better to replace it rather than attempt to make a repair.

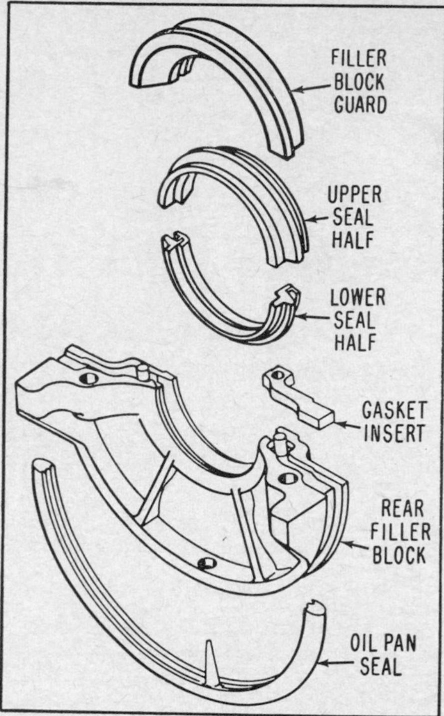

Fig. 19 Crankshaft rear oil seal disassembled. 6-230 engine

OIL PUMP

4-134, 6-230 Engines

The oil pump is located externally on the left side of the engine. When necessary to remove the pump, first take off the distributor cap and note the position of the rotor so that the pump may be reinstalled without disturbing the ignition timing.

To install the pump without disturbing the timing, the pump gear must be correctly meshed with the camshaft driving gear to allow engagement of the driving key on the distributor shaft in the pump shaft driving slot without moving the distributor rotor. Assembly can be made only in one position because the slot and driving key are machined off center.

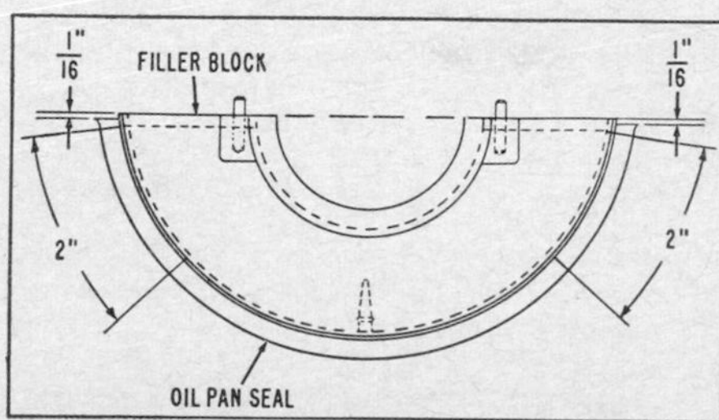

Fig. 20 Oil pan seal assembled to rear filler block. 6-230 engine

To disassemble the pump, remove the cover and gasket. Hold a hand over the cover opening and, with the pump upside down, turn the shaft until the outer rotor slips out. Drive out the pin securing the drive gear to the shaft. Press the shaft out of the gear and slide the shaft and inner rotor out of the body.

Failure of the pump to operate at full efficiency may usually be traced to excessive end play in the rotor or excessive clearance between the rotors. The clearance between the outer rotor and pump body should also be checked.

End play of the rotors is controlled by the thickness of the cover gasket which is made of special material which can only be slightly compressed. Never use other than a standard factory gasket.

6-226 Engines

The oil pump is of the positive gear type, located at the bottom of the vertical shaft which also drives the distributor.

To disassemble the oil pump, take off the screen float. Drive out the pin which secures the drive gear to the shaft and take off the gear. Remove pump cover and gasket. Position the pump with the drive shaft end up and allow the gears to drop from the pump body. Do not remove the idler gear shaft unless worn or damaged.

Assemble the pump with new parts, using a new gasket. When replacing the upper drive gear, position it on the shaft and use a feeler gauge to measure clearance between gear and end of pump body, allowing a clearance of .002 to .004". When proper clearance has been obtained, drill a $\frac{3}{16}$" pin hole through the drive shaft, install the pin and peen it securely.

WATER PUMP, REPLACE

Remove the fan belt and blades, unfasten the pump from the cylinder block and lift it off. On some models, it may be necessary to loosen the radiator core and pull it forward in order to remove the water pump assembly.

FUEL PUMP, REPLACE

Note, 6-230 Engines

On early engines the fuel pump push rod was not spring loaded and therefore it is necessary to remove the rocker arm cover and turn the crankshaft until the push rod is at low cam. Hold the push rod against the cam while the pump is installed. On later engines a spring holds the push rod up, eliminating the need to remove the rocker arm cover.

Note, 4-134, 6-226 Engines

Before installing the pump, it is good practice to crank the engine so that the nose of the camshaft eccentric is out of the way of the fuel pump rocker arm when the pump is installed. In this way there will be the least amount of tension on the rocker arm, thereby easing the installation of the pump.

Installation

1. Remove all gasket material from the pump and block gasket surfaces. Apply sealer to both sides of new gasket.
2. Position gasket on pump flange and hold pump in position against its mounting surface. Make sure rocker arm is riding on camshaft eccentric.
3. Press pump tight against its mounting. Install retaining screws and tighten them alternately.
4. Connect fuel lines. Then operate engine and check for leaks.

Clutch, Transmission and Transfer Case

NOTE: Repair procedure for two-wheel drive transmissions are covered elsewhere in this manual. See Chapter Index

CLUTCH PEDAL, ADJUST

Jeeps

To adjust the clutch pedal free travel, which should be 1½", lengthen or shorten the clutch control cable as required.

Station Wagons (Except L6-226)

To adjust clutch pedal free travel, which should be 1", turn the threaded connection between the clutch control lever and the clutch control tube lever as required to obtain the desired result.

L6-226

To adjust the clutch free pedal travel on these models, loosen the two lock nuts on the pedal adjusting rod. Turn the nuts forward to increase or backward to decrease the free travel. After pedal free travel of 1" is obtained, tighten both lock nuts against the adjusting trunnion, being careful not to change the adjustment.

J Series with V8 Engine

To adjust clutch pedal free play, which should be one inch, vary the length of the link connecting the clutch release lever to the inner release idler lever. Lengthening the link reduces pedal play, and vice versa.

J Series with 6-230 Engine

The clutch on these vehicles is hydraulically operated and is adjusted as follows: The clutch pedal has an adjustment nut located on top of its support bracket behind the instrument cluster. Adjust clutch pedal so it has no free play. When correctly adjusted the clutch pedal will stand about ½" higher than the brake pedal. The location of the piston in the clutch master cylinder determines when the clutch pedal is in its released position. The piston should bottom against the back of the master cylinder so there is no free movement of the push rod. The adjustment nut should be set so the forward end of the push rod just touches the master cylinder piston while the piston is bottomed against the back of the master cylinder.

The clutch release bearing free play can now be adjusted as outlined below:

1. Unhook clutch fork return spring and push slave cylinder push rod in to hold piston in its fully retracted position in cylinder bore.
2. Hold this position while moving clutch lever until release bearing touches clutch fingers.
3. Adjust push rod locking nut until connecting pin will go into clutch lever. Then back off locking nut two or three turns to shorten push rod.
4. Connect return spring. The release bearing free play should now be correctly set for .050" to .060".

Service Bulletin

SLOW CLUTCH PEDAL RETURN: Should difficulty be experienced with slow clutch pedal return on a J Series vehicle, install a brake pedal retracting spring (Part No. 930351) between clutch pedal and its mounting bracket.

To install the spring, remove and discard the spring-type retainer which secures the eye end of the clutch master cylinder push rod to the clutch pedal. Do not remove the plain washer.

Connect one end of the spring into the slotted hole in the mounting bracket located near the instrument panel, and the other end to the clutch pedal in place of the retainer removed.

CLUTCH, REPLACE

Service Bulletin

REPLACING CLUTCH: It is important when removing and reinstalling a clutch pressure plate assembly that the pressure plate be installed in its original position on the flywheel. The crankshaft, flywheel and clutch pressure plate assembly are balanced as a unit at the factory. Excessive out-of-balance can cause vibration.

Before removing the pressure plate, make sure there are matched markings on the clutch and flywheel. Some Borg and Beck clutches have a hole drilled through the pressure plate cover stamping and a punch mark on the flywheel at the hole location. Some Auburn clutches have matching line marks on the pressure plate cover stamping and the flywheel; others have an "X" stamped on the pressure plate cover and a radial line on the flywheel.

Some pressure plates and flywheels are not marked at the factory. These should be marked before the pressure plate is removed from the vehicle.

J Series

1. Remove the transmission and transfer case, if so equipped, as outlined further on in this chapter.
2. Remove flywheel housing.
3. Mark pressure plate and flywheel so clutch can be installed in same position.
4. Remove the clutch attaching bolts leaving two opposed bolts to be removed last.
5. Remove remaining bolts equally, a little at a time, to prevent distortion of clutch pressure plate and to relieve clutch springs evenly.
6. Remove clutch through flywheel housing pan opening.
7. Reverse removal procedure to install.

CJ, DJ & L6-226

When it becomes necessary to replace the clutch assembly or just the driven disc, follow the procedure outlined for removing the transmission or transmission and transfer case from the vehicle. *Note that labor will be saved on all models except "6-226" if the engine is removed from the chassis without the bell housing.* Then remove the clutch from the flywheel.

On "6-226" models, which are equipped with a split bell housing, it is advisable to disconnect both the front and rear propeller shafts, pull the transmission and transfer case to the rear sufficiently to clear the shaft from the clutch. Remove the bottom pan from the bell housing and remove the clutch from the flywheel with the engine still in the vehicle.

If only a new driven disc is to be installed, mark both the pressure plate and flywheel so that the assembly may be installed in the same position to maintain clutch balance. When removing the clutch from the flywheel, loosen the attaching screws a turn or two at a time in progression to prevent distortion of the clutch bracket (cover).

Installation is made in the reverse order, being sure to turn the screws a little at a time in progression until all are tight. When installation is complete, adjust the clutch pedal free travel as outlined above.

3 SPEED TRANS., REPLACE

CJ, DJ & L6-226

1. Remove front and rear propeller shafts.

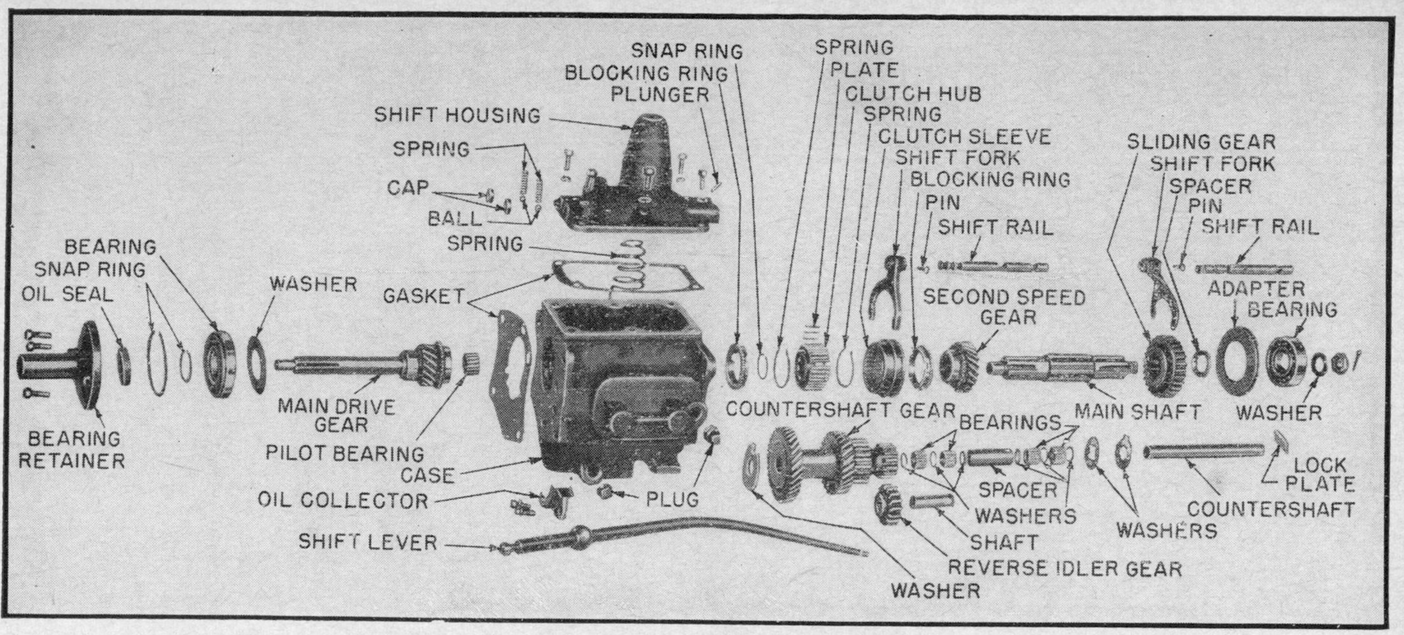

Fig. 1 Exploded view of Jeep transmission. Four-wheel drive models

2. If vehicle is equipped with a power take-off, disconnect transfer case end of power take-off drive shaft.
3. Disconnect speedometer cable at transfer case.
4. Disconnect brake cable.
5. Support transmission and engine with jacks.
6. Remove nuts holding rear mounting to frame crossmember.
7. Remove transfer case snubbing rubber bolt nut at crossmember.
8. Remove shift lever or remote control rods.
9. Disconnect clutch release cable at bell crank at yoke end.
10. Remove floor board inspection plate.
11. Remove transfer case shift lever pivot pin screw.
12. Remove transfer case shift lever pivot pin and remove levers. If vehicle is equipped with power take-off, remove shift lever plate screws and lift out lever.
13. Remove frame center crossmember.
14. Remove bolts holding transmission to bell housing.
15. Force transmission to right to disengage clutch control lever tube ball joint.
16. Lower jacks under engine and transmission and slide transmission and transfer case toward rear of vehicle until clutch shaft clears bell housing.

Separate Transmission From Transfer Case

1. Drain lubricant from both units.
2. Remove five screws from cover on rear face of transfer case (if equipped with power take-off, remove power take-off shift housing).
3. Remove transfer case main drive gear from rear end of transmission mainshaft.
4. Remove shift tower from transmission.
5. In the absence of a transmission mainshaft retaining plate, loop a piece of wire around the mainshaft just back of the second speed gear, twist the wire and attach one end to right hand front cover screw and the other end to left hand cover screw.
6. Draw wire tightly to prevent mainshaft from pulling out of transmission case when transfer case is removed.
7. Separate the two housings, using care to see that the transmission mainshaft bearing, which bears in both housings, remains in the transmission case.
8. Reverse the removal procedure to attach the transmission to the transfer case and install the assembly in the vehicle.

4WD Jeepster & J Series

1. Drain lubricant from transmission and transfer case.
2. Remove transfer case as outlined further on. (Transfer case and transmission can be removed as an assembly.)
3. Remove transmission access cover from the floor.
4. Disconnect shift rods from shift levers.
5. Disconnect speedometer cable.
6. Support engine with a jack and remove nuts holding rear mounting to crossmember.
7. Remove bolts holding transmission to flywheel housing.
8. Slide transmission toward rear until main drive gear clears flywheel housing and remove transmission from under vehicle.

DJ & L6-226

The following outline covers removal of transmission and overdrive. If not so equipped, disregard operations pertaining to overdrive.

1. Disconnect remote control rods at transmission.
2. Disconnect two wires from overdrive solenoid. *Tag wires and terminals to assure correct assembly.*
3. Disconnect two wires at overdrive rail switch. *Tag wires and terminals to assure correct assembly.*
4. Disconnect front universal joint, and speedometer cable at transmission. Have available an ordinary cork of correct size to close cable opening to prevent leakage of lubricant.
5. Disconnect overdrive control cable and conduit.
6. Remove rubber mounted saddle support at rear end of overdrive. Use care not to lose spacers. Remove overdrive governor.
7. Place jack under flywheel bell housing and raise it to support weight of housing.
8. Remove frame cross member with rubber insulators attached.
9. Place jack under engine to support engine when transmission is removed.
10. Thread out four screws attaching transmission to bell housing as far as possible and yet support weight of transmission. Pull transmission back to bolt heads which will provide approximately ¾" opening between the two housings and at the same time relieve pressure on clutch release fork in bell housing.
11. Use a long screwdriver through opening in side of bell housing to pry clutch release fork from engagement with clutch release bearing carrier.
12. Complete removal of four transmission attaching screws and pull transmission back until clutch shaft clears bell housing and remove the assembly with release bearing carrier attached.

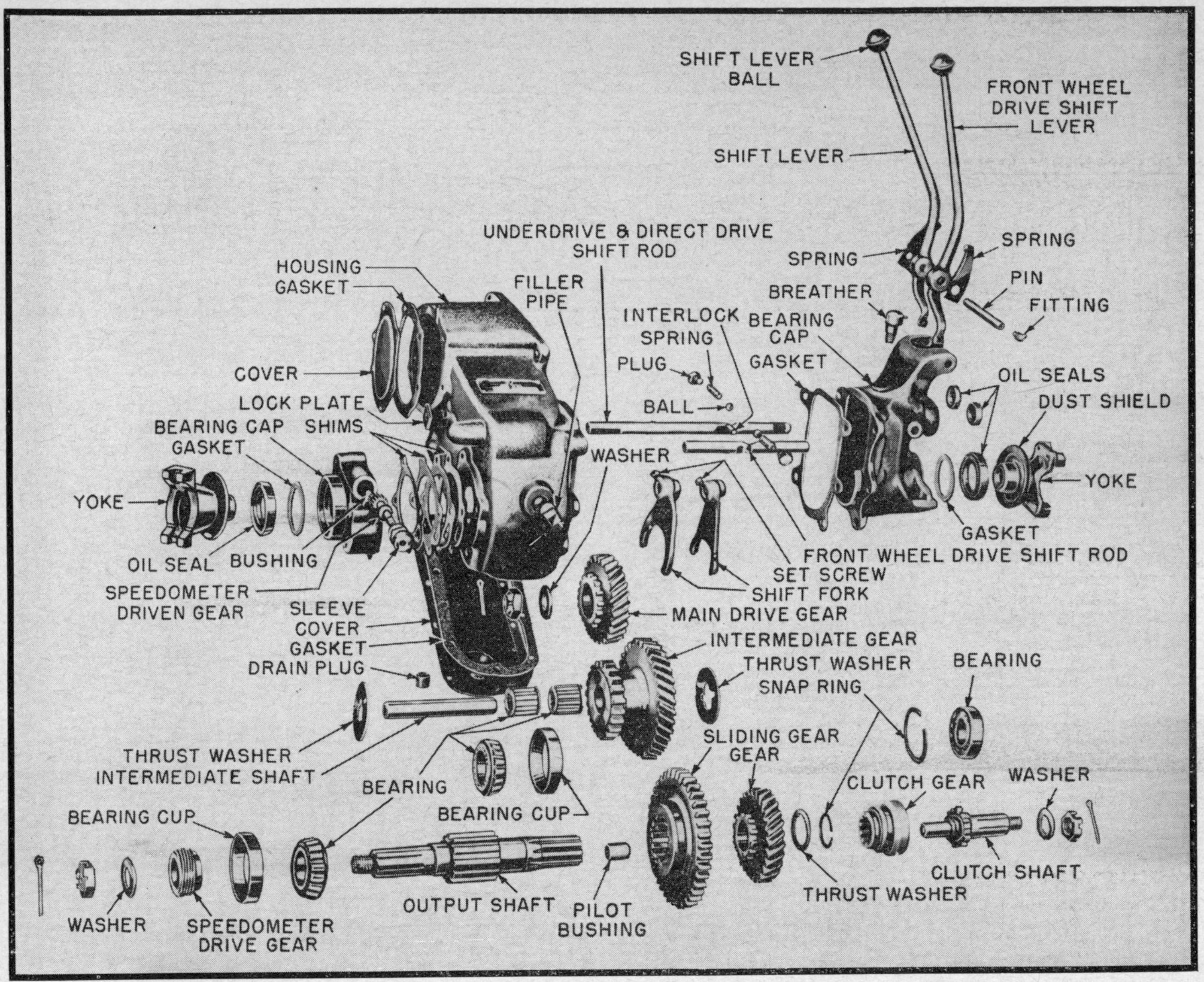

Fig. 2 Exploded view of single range transfer case for standard Jeeps see Figs. 3 and 4 for J Series

2WD J Series

The following procedure covers removal of transmission and overdrive. If not so equipped, disregard operations listed for overdrive.

1. Drain transmission and overdrive.
2. Remove access cover from floor.
3. Disconnect shift rods from control levers.
4. Disconnect two wires from the solenoid. *Tag wires and terminals to assure correct assembly.*
5. Remove propeller shaft by disconnecting it at rear universal joint and pulling it out of transmission or overdrive.
6. Disconnect speedometer cable at transmission or overdrive.
7. Disconnect overdrive control cable and conduit.
8. Remove nuts and lockwashers from the rubber mounted saddle support at rear end of overdrive. Use care not to lose the spacers.
9. Remove overdrive governor.
10. Place a jack under flywheel housing and raise jack until mounting bolts on rubber insulator clear crossmember.
11. Unfasten transmission from flywheel housing.
12. Pull transmission rearward until it clears crossmember and lower transmission from vehicle.

3 SPEED TRANS. REPAIRS

1. Drain lubricant from case and clean case with a suitable solvent.
2. If transfer case is attached, remove its rear cover.
3. If equipped with a power take-off, remove the shift unit which replaces the cover.
4. Remove transfer case main drive gear.
5. Remove transmission cover.
6. Loop a piece of wire around mainshaft directly back of mainshaft second speed gear. Twist wire and attach one end to right hand front cover screw and other end to left front screw. Draw wire tightly to prevent mainshaft from pulling out of transmission case when transfer case is removed. Should mainshaft come out, synchronizer parts will drop into bottom of case.
7. Support transfer case and with a rawhide mallet or brass drift and hammer, tap lightly on end of transmission mainshaft to separate the two units. The transmission mainshaft bearing should slide out of transfer case and remain in transmission.
8. Remove drive gear bearing retainer.
9. Remove lock plate and drive countershaft out through rear.
10. Remove mainshaft rear bearing adapter.
11. Remove mainshaft and gear as-

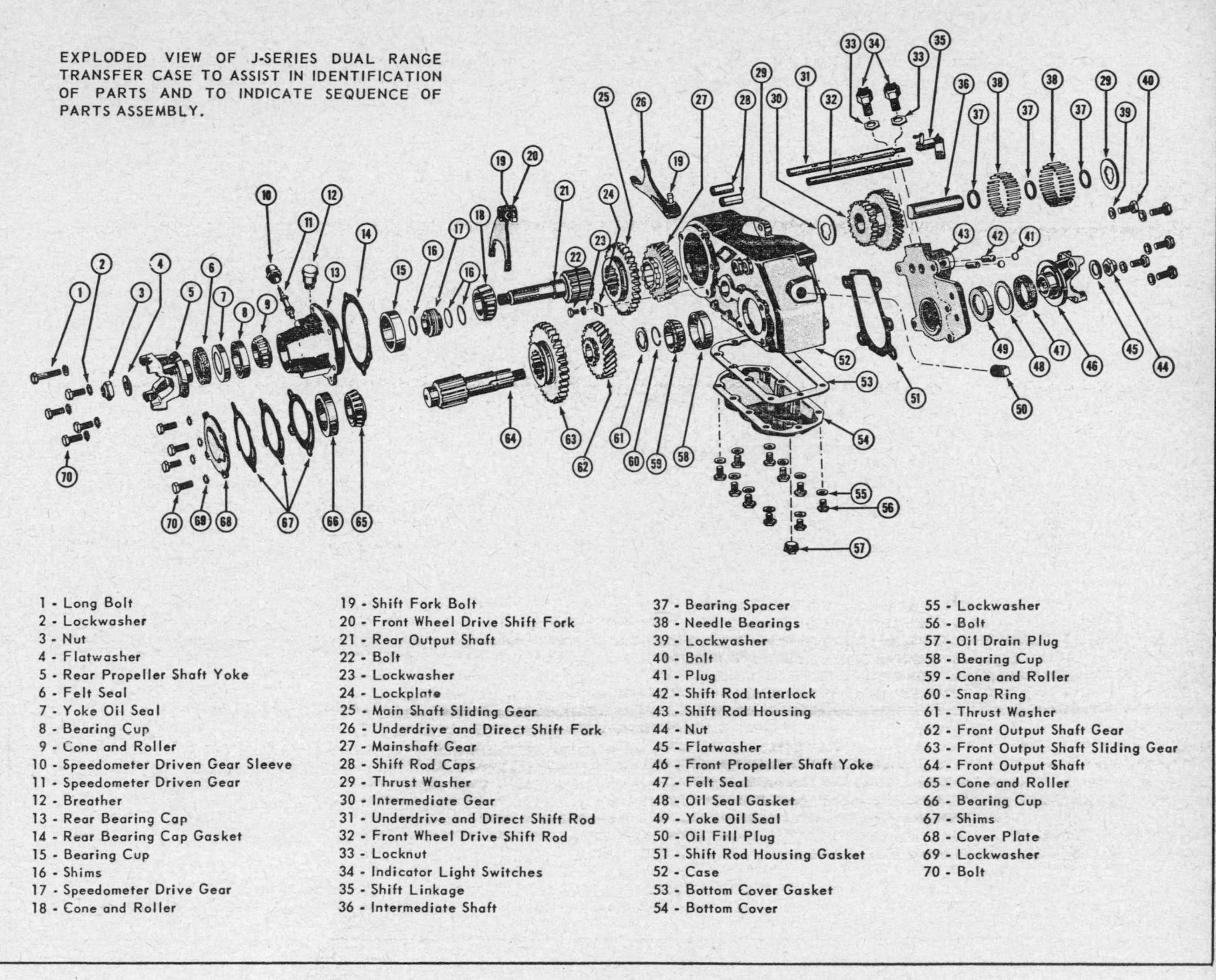

Fig. 3 Dual range transfer case used on Jeepster & J Series vehicles

sembly through transfer case opening.

12. Remove countershaft gearset and thrust washers, noting position of washers.
13. Drive reverse idler shaft out rearward and lift out gear.

Assembly Notes

Reverse the order of the above procedure to assemble the transmission, being sure to observe the following precautions:

The countershaft gearset should have from .012" to .018" end play when assembled in the case. This clearance is obtained by selective thickness of the rear steel thrust washer, which is available in two thicknesses. Assemble the larger bronze washer at the front of the case with the lip entered in the slot in the case. The bronze faced steel washer goes next to the gear at the rear end, and the steel washer next to the case. Use a loading sleeve to assemble the countershaft roller bearings.

TRANSFER CASE

CJ, DJ & L6-226

In removing the transfer case, follow the procedure outlined under transmission removal. Then dismantle the case as follows:

1. Remove propeller shaft flange, brake assembly and linkage.
2. Remove lower cover.
3. Remove lock plate.
4. Drive intermediate shaft to rear of case, being careful not to lose thrust washers.
5. Remove intermediate gear, thrust washers and roller bearings through bottom of case.
6. Shift front wheel drive to engaged position (shaft forward) and remove poppet plugs, springs and balls on both sides of output bearing cap.
7. Remove output bearing cap together with the universal joint end yoke, clutch shaft, bearing, clutch gear, fork and shift rod. Use care not to lose the interlock.
8. Remove output shaft snap ring and thrust washer.
9. Use a rawhide mallet to drive against the front end of the mainshaft to start the rear bearing from the case. As the shaft is removed, the gears will remain in the case and can be taken out through the bottom, also the snap ring and thrust washer.
10. Remove set screw in sliding gear shift fork and take out the shift rod.
11. Disassemble the front and rear bearing caps as required.

Assembly Notes

Reverse the order of the above procedure to assemble the transfer case. But when rear bearing cap assembly is installed, check the end movement of the mainshaft which determines the adjustment of the tapered roller bearings. For correct bearing adjustment, the shaft should have from .004" to .008" end play. Adjustment is made by selective shim

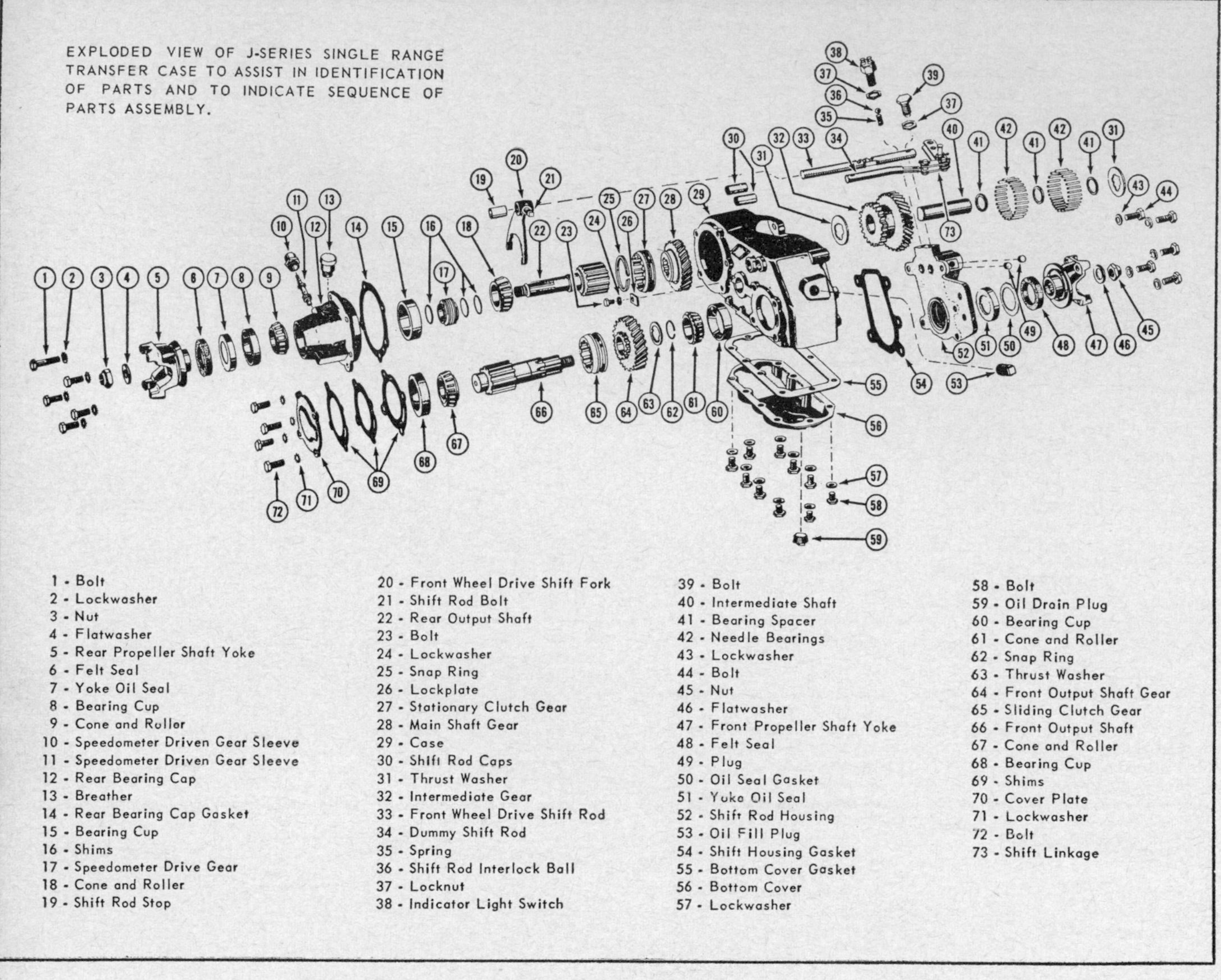

Fig. 4 Single range transfer case used on Jeepster & J Series vehicles

installation between the cap and case. Shims .003″, .010″ and .031″ thicknesses are available for this adjustment. Do not install the rear cap oil seal until the bearings are properly adjusted.

Jeepster & J Series, Figs. 3, 4

The transfer case may be removed without removing the transmission. Proceed as follows:

1. Drain transmission and transfer case. *It is not necessary to drain the automatic transmission.*
2. Disconnect parking brake spring from fuel tank flange and remove clevis pin from brake cable connecting bracket.
3. Remove front propeller shaft.
4. Disconnect rear propeller shaft at transfer case. Slide propeller shaft yoke back and move shaft to one side.
5. Disconnect speedometer cable.
6. Remove center cotter pin of shaft linkage at transfer case to disconnect shift linkage.
7. Remove wiring clips from light signal switches mounted on transfer case.
8. Remove exhaust pipe bracket bolts.
9. Unfasten and remove transfer case from transmission.

Service on these units is the same as that described previously for other models.

TRANSFER CASE SHIFT LINKAGE, ADJUST

1. Disconnect adjustable link at transfer case.
2. On dual range transfer cases, move both transfer case shift rods out to the last detent position (maximum forward position). On single range cases, move the single shift rod to the first detent position (maximum rearward position). Make sure detents are fully seated.
3. Position transfer case shift lever knob in the forward position with ¾″ clearance between knob and floor pan.
4. With shift rods and lever knob positioned as above, adjust and install adjustable link.
5. Test operation in all positions. If necessary, readjust to eliminate any interference between shift lever knob and floor pan.

GEARSHIFT, ADJUST

Remote Control Models

JEEPSTER & J SERIES

The adjustment of the transmission shift levers at the base of the steering column is controlled by the lower bearing. The bearing should be so adjusted that there is no movement of the shift levers along the axis of the steering column, and the shift control operates with only normal effort.

The bearing is adjusted with two

screws located top and bottom of the column jacket. To adjust the bearing, loosen the two screws and move the screws up or down the slanted slots in the jacket as required. Moving the screws up the slots tightens the bearing; down the slot loosens the bearing.

CJ, DJ & L6-226

To make an adjustment, shift the hand control lever to its neutral position. Align the pin holes in the levers at the bottom of the main shifting rod to hold them in their neutral positions. Disconnect the control rods from the levers at the transmission and place the transmission levers in neutral. Finally, adjust the length of the control rods so that they will just slip into their respective levers on the transmission without moving the levers from their neutral positions.

NOTE

Difficult shifting on two-wheel drive utility vehicles and station wagons may be due to improper installation of the second and high shift rod on the shift lever.

The shift lever, mounted on the lower end of the remote control shift shaft, is provided with two holes. The shift rod should be placed in the outer hole of the lever on six cylinder models and in the inner hole on four cylinder models.

Rear Axle, "Live" Front Axle and Brakes

REAR AXLE

Figs. 1 and 2 illustrate the front and rear axle assemblies used on these vehicles. The differential carrier assembly in both axles are similar. When necessary to overhaul either differential carrier, refer to the *Rear Axle Specifications* table in this chapter.

Description

In these rear axles, Figs. 1 and 2, the drive pinion is mounted in two tapered roller bearings. These bearings are preloaded by shims behind the front bearing. The pinion is positioned by shims located in front of the rear bearing. The differential is supported in the carrier by two tapered roller side bearings. These bearings are preloaded by shims located between the differential case and bearings. The differential assembly is positioned for proper ring gear and pinion backlash by varying the position of these shims. The differential case houses two side gears in mesh with two pinions mounted on a pinion shaft which is held in place by a lock pin. The side gears and pinions are backed by thrust washers.

Remove & Replace

Since the axle tubes are pressed into the differential carrier to form a one-piece housing, major service work requires the removal of the rear axle assembly from the vehicle. However, it is possible to do the work if a twin-post hoist is available. The removal procedure follows:

1. Raise vehicle and support with jack stands under frame side rails.
2. Remove rear wheels.
3. Split rear U-joint.
4. Disconnect parking brake cable from operating lever and from brake backing plates.
5. Disconnect hydraulic brake line connection at rear axle housing.
6. Loosen and move shock absorbers out of the way.

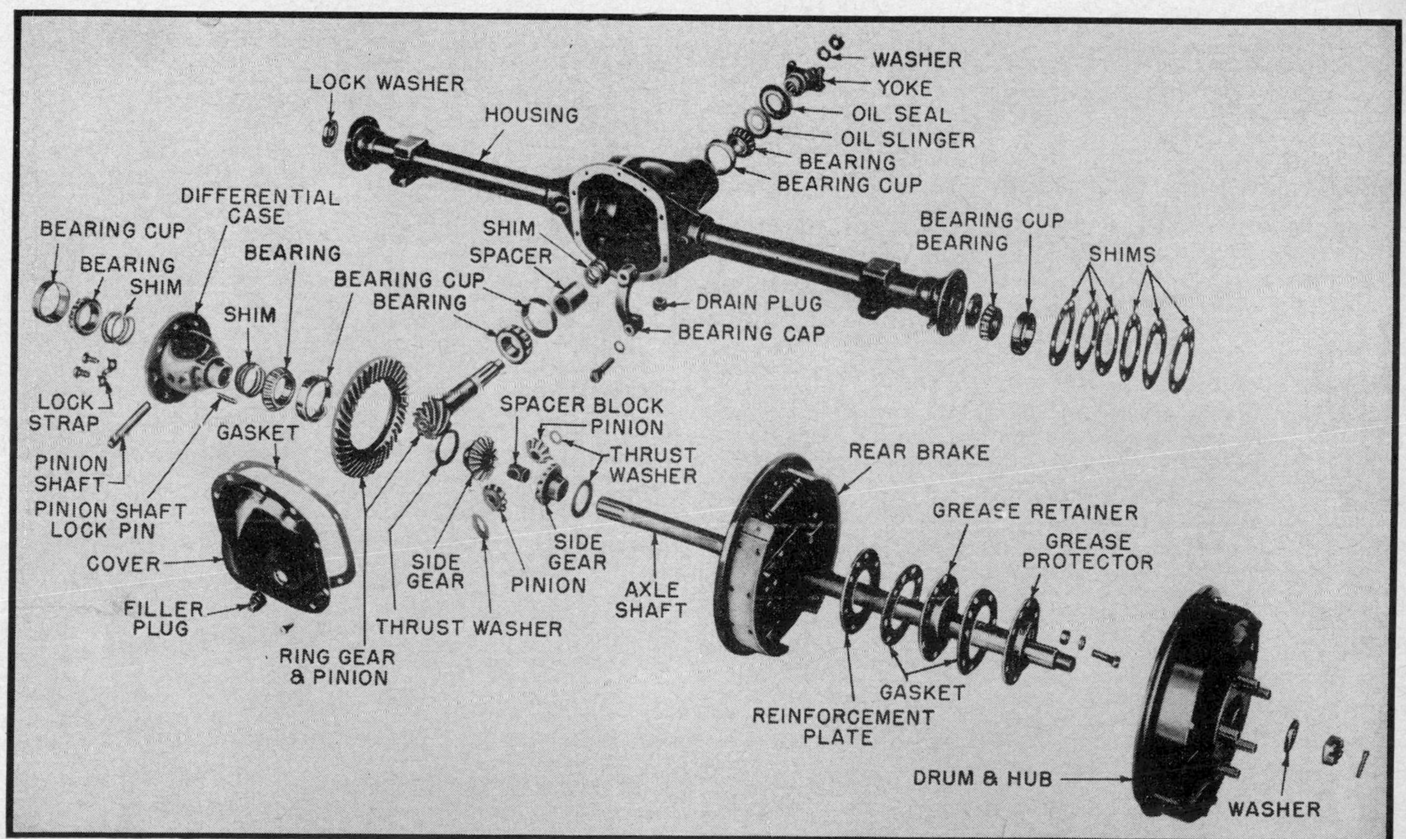

Fig. 1 Exploded view of rear axle assembly. All Models

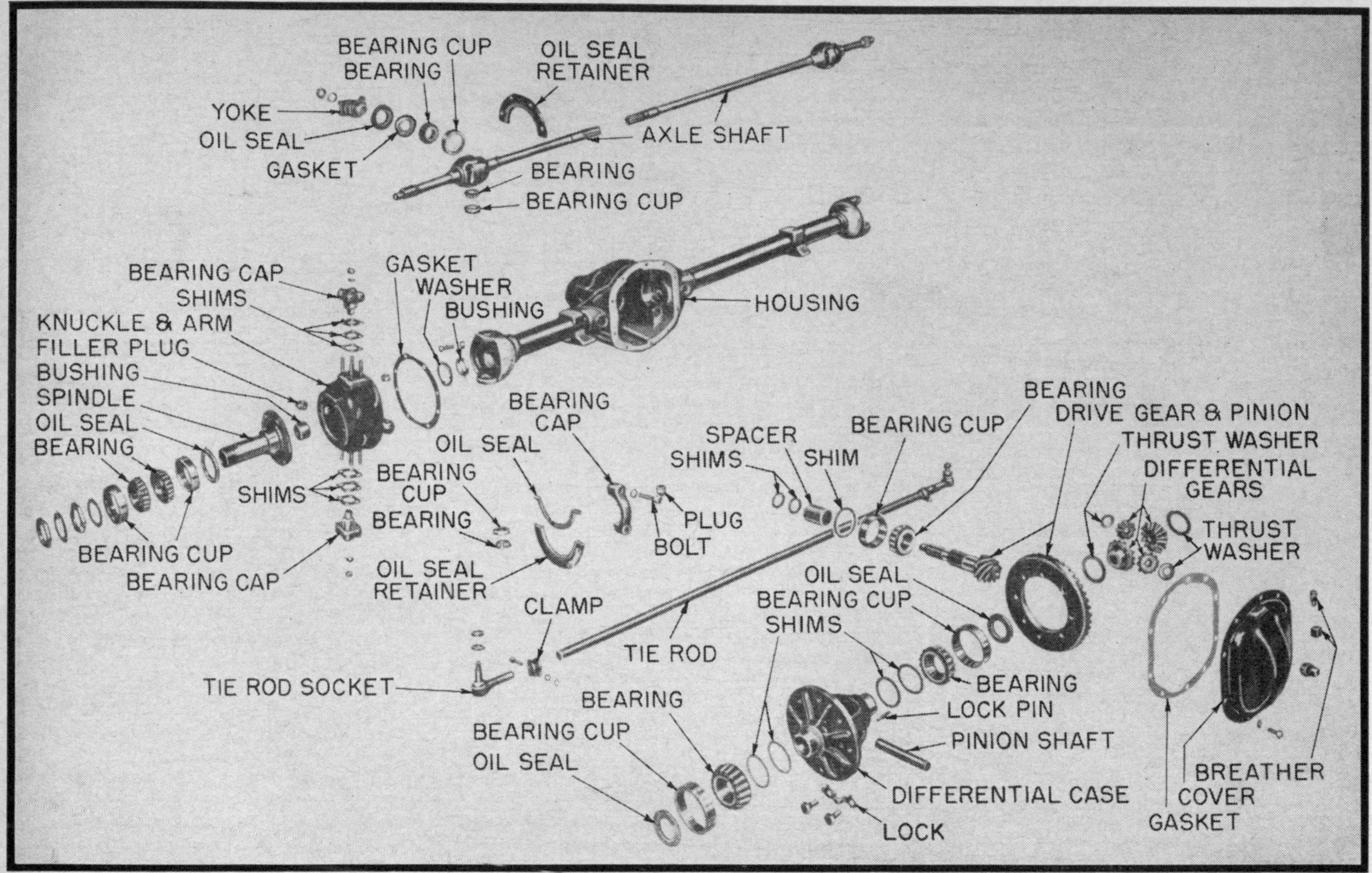

Fig. 2 "Live" front axle. Jeeps and four-wheel drive Station Wagons

7. While supporting axle housing with an adjustable jack, remove spring clips and lower axle assembly out of vehicle.
8. Reverse above procedure to install the axle assembly, being sure to bleed the brakes when installation is completed.

AXLE SHAFTS

Remove

To remove an axle shaft, jack up the wheel and pull off the hub and brake drum. Block the brake pedal in such a manner that it cannot be depressed. Disconnect the hydraulic brake line from the wheel cylinder. Remove the mounting screws and take off the outer oil seal, shims and brake support. The shaft and bearing may then be pulled out of the housing. The inner oil seal may be removed at this time.

Install

Replace the shaft and bearings in the reverse order. If the old parts are replaced and the shims have not been disturbed, the end play should be correct when the parts are assembled. However, if a new axle shaft, bearing, differential carrier or housing has been installed, it will be necessary to check the end play.

Axle Shaft End Play, Adjust

Axle shaft end play can be checked when all parts have been replaced except the wheel and hub. To make the check, rap each axle shaft after the nuts are tight to be sure the bearing cups are seated. Then mount a dial indicator on the axle housing with its contact button touching the end of the shaft. Work the shaft in and out by hand and note the reading on the indicator. If an adjustment is necessary, remove the oil seal and brake support and add or remove shims as required to bring the end play to .001″ to .005″.

When making this adjustment, an equal thickness of shims should be removed or added on each side of the axle housing to maintain the central position of the axle shafts.

PROPELLER SHAFT

Remove & Replace

1. Mark yokes of rear U-joint to obtain original position when reassembled.
2. Remove U-bolts at rear U-joint and pry cross and bearing away from drive pinion flange.
3. Pull propeller shaft rearward to slide front yoke out of transmission housing.
4. Reverse above procedure to install.

"LIVE" FRONT AXLE

Four-Wheel Drive Models, Fig. 2

The front axle on these models is a live driving unit with hypoid driving gears and spherical steering knuckles mounted on pivot pins which ride on tapered roller bearings for ease of steering. The drive is of the full-floating type through axle shafts built integrally with constant velocity universal joints which revolve in the steering knuckles.

Front Axle Service

The differential is mounted in a housing similar to that used in the rear axle except that the pinion shaft faces toward the rear instead of to the front and to the right of the center of the axle. This design allows the placing of the front propeller shaft along the right side of the engine oil pan to avoid reducing road clearance under the engine.

The axle is of the full floating type and the axle shafts can be removed without dismantling the steering knuckle housing.

Overhaul of this axle unit is the same as the rear axle.

Service Bulletin

A change in design of the front axle on four-wheel drive vehicles was placed

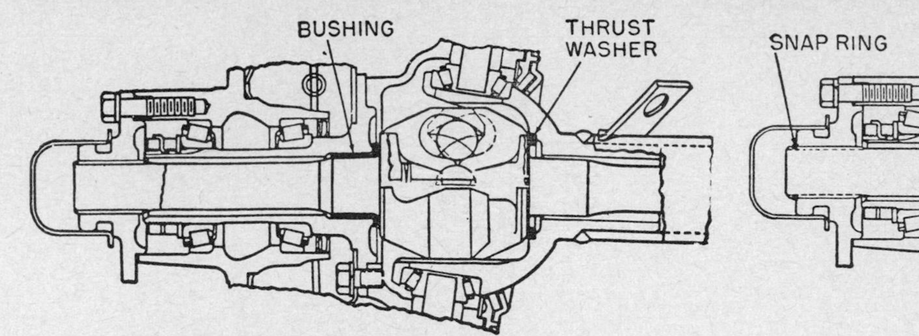

Fig. 4 Bendix type axle shaft and universal joint. For "live" front axles

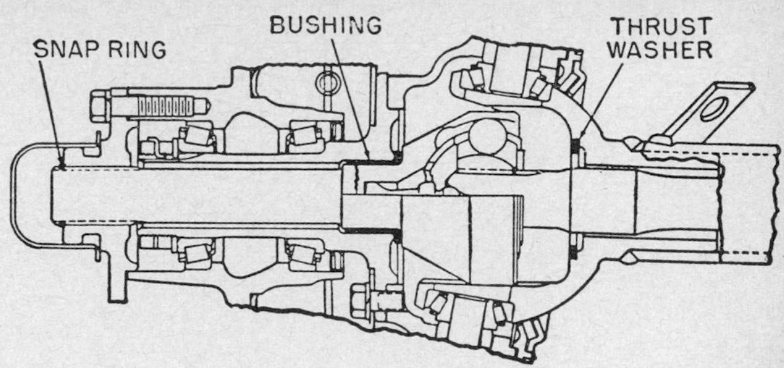

Fig. 5 Rzeppa type axle shaft and universal joint. For "live" front axles

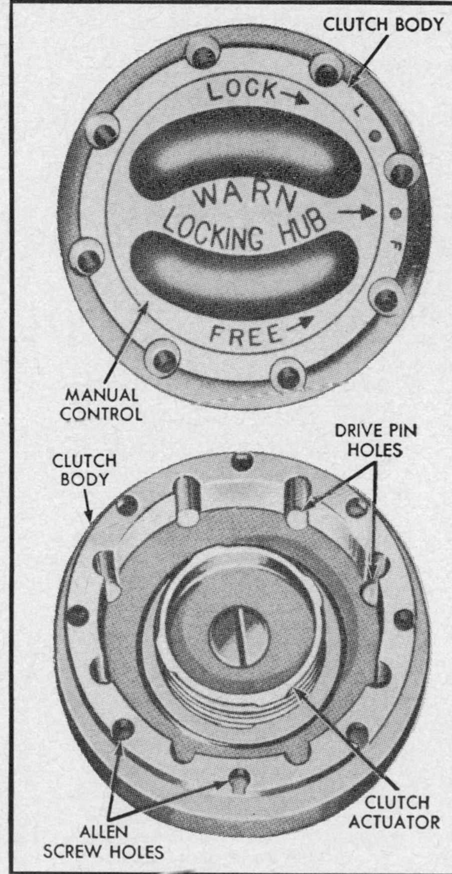

Fig. 7 Warn Locking Hub

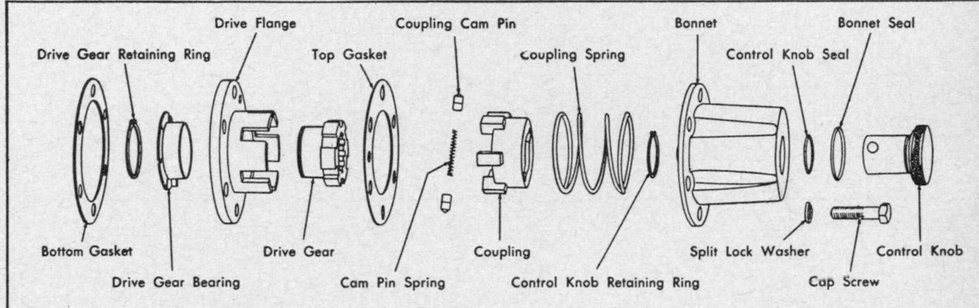

Fig. 6 Cutlas selective drive hub for 4-wheel drive vehicles

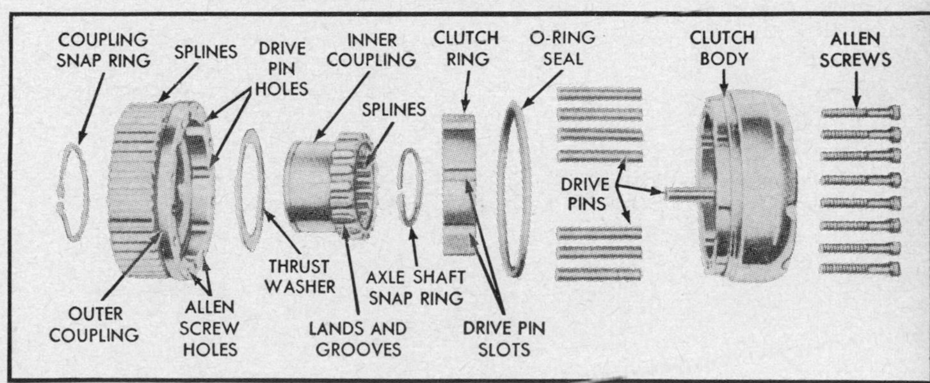

Fig. 8 Warn Locking Hub disassembled

in production effective with the following serial numbers:

No. 37549 on CJ-3A
No. 44070 on 4WD
No. 14284 on 4x463

In the new design the front axle shaft outer splined end floats in the wheel driving flange and is not retained by a nut and lockwasher as originally used. With this construction it is no longer necessary to install shims between the driving flange and wheel hub to provide the correct end float of the axle shaft universal joint.

The new construction, when using the Bendix type axle shaft, is shown in Fig. 4. Note that the end float of the Bendix type joint is predetermined in manufacture by the position and flange thickness of the bushing and thrust washer. These parts are so positioned and of the correct thickness to provide .088" maximum end float of the universal joint to operate at the centerline of the spindle pivot pins. With the correct joint end float controlled by the bushing flange and thrust washer, it is no longer necessary to install shims between the driving flange and wheel hub, a gasket only being used.

The new type Bendix axle shaft and universal joint may be readily installed in an old type axle by installing the new type flanged bushing. When this is done, discard the shims previously installed between the flange and hub, installing a gasket only. The flanged bushing requires no reaming and is so designed that when it is pressed into the spindle it will be compressed to provide correct running clearance. Coat the inner surface of the bushing with chassis grease before installing the spindle.

The axle construction is similar for installation of the Rzeppa joint, Fig. 5. The thrust washer is not necessary although it is installed in all axles to allow installation of the Bendix type shaft if so desired. As the thrust washer is not effective, a snap ring is installed at the outer end of the shaft to control end float.

Steering Knuckle Pivot Pins

When reinstalling a steering knuckle, sufficient shims must be installed under the bearing caps so the proper tension will be obtained on the bearings. The shims are available in thicknesses of .003", .005", .010" and .030".

Install one each of the shims over the studs on the steering knuckle at the

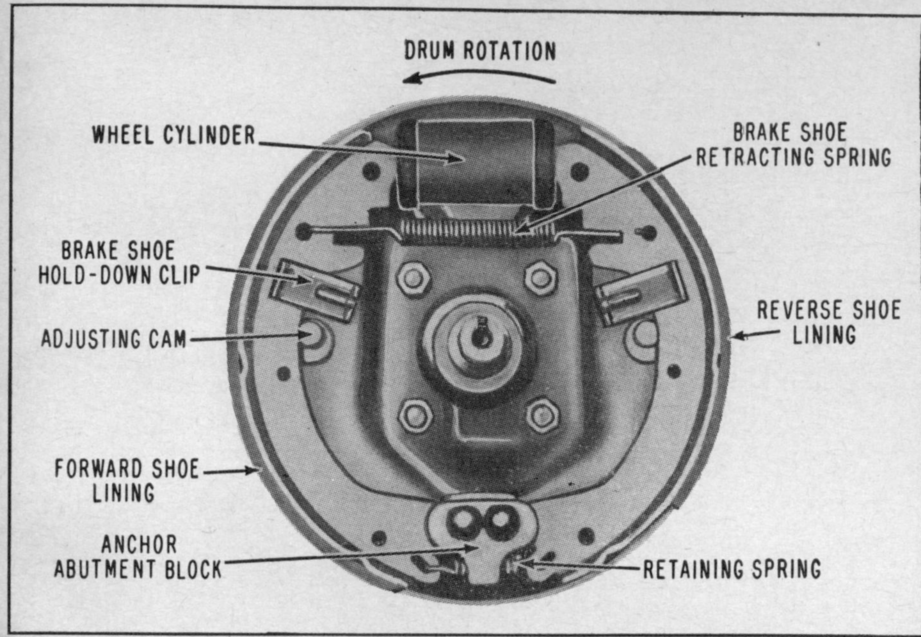

Fig. 9 Brake mechanism with self-centering shoes

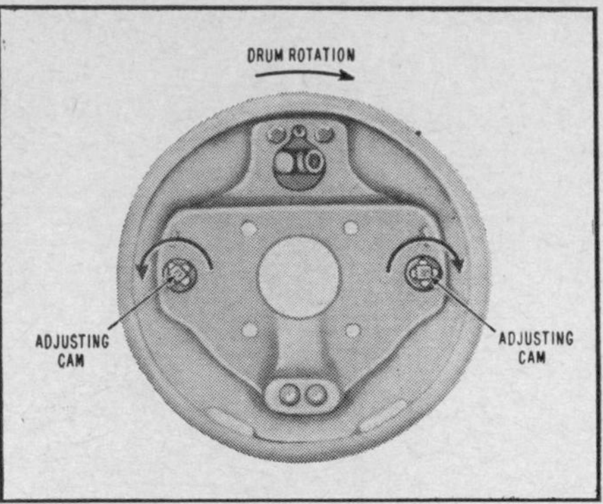

Fig. 10 Adjusting self-centering brake

top and bottom. Install the bearing caps, lock washers and nuts and tighten securely. Check the tension of the bearings by hooking a spring scale in the hole in the arm for the tie rod socket. The load should be 6-9 lbs. without the oil seal in position and is secured by adding or removing shims as required. Make sure there are the same thickness of shims between the upper cap and the knuckle as between the lower cap and knuckle.

Service Bulletin

On models CJ-3A, 473-4WD and 4x473, .058" was added to the bottom face of the king pin boss on the steering knuckles. This eliminated the shims for the lower kingpin bearing and the adjustment of the bearing is now made by shims at the top only.

FRONT WHEEL LOCKING HUBS

Cutlas Selective Drive Hub

Fig. 6 is a disassembled view of the selective drive hub for all 4-wheel drive Jeep vehicles. The outstanding operational advantage is the hub's "preset" feature. Turning the control knob from 2-wheel drive to 4-wheel drive "presets" the hub to engage automatically the axle shaft when the transfer case is shifted into 4-wheel drive. The axle is not engaged until shift into 4-wheel drive is made.

Warn Locking Hub

As shown in Fig. 7, turning the clutch controls to the "L" or lock position connects the wheel hubs to the axle shafts. Therefore, when the transfer case is driving the front axle and the controls are in the "L" position, the wheels are driven by the axle shafts. When the transfer case is not driving the front axle, the clutch controls are turned to the "F" or free position to disconnect the wheel hubs from the axle shafts. The wheels now rotate freely but the axle shafts remain stationary.

REMOVAL

1. Remove the eight retaining screws and clutch body from the coupling assembly, Fig. 8.
2. Remove coupling-to-axle shaft snap ring.
3. Remove coupling assembly from wheel hub and axle shaft.

DISASSEMBLY

1. Referring to Fig. 8, remove outer drive pins and O-ring seal from clutch body.
2. Remove clutch ring from actuator worm drive by rotating ring clockwise.
3. Remove coupling snap ring and separate inner coupling from outer coupling.
4. Remove bronze thrust washer.
5. Remove needle bearing assembly from outer coupling with a suitable puller. *This step is not necessary for cleaning purposes.*

ASSEMBLY

1. Press needle bearing assembly into outer coupling. To avoid damage, press against name surface of bearing.
2. Install bronze thrust washer on inner coupling, then install inner coupling into outer coupling.
3. Secure two couplings together by installing snap ring.
4. Install clutch ring onto actuator by turning ring counterclockwise on worm drive.
5. Rotate control knob to "F" position and turn clutch ring in until it bottoms on clutch body. Turn clutch ring further until drive pin slots on ring are aligned with drive pin holes in clutch body. Proper alignment is necessary to insure complete disengagement of clutch ring from inner coupling when unit is in "F" position.
6. Install O-ring on clutch body, and drive pins in their holes in body.

INSTALLATION

1. Install coupling assembly to axle shaft and wheel hub and secure to axle shaft with snap ring.
2. Install clutch body assembly to coupling assembly, being sure that all drive pins are in place.
3. Install and tighten clutch body retaining screws.

BRAKE ADJUSTMENTS

Bendix Self-Centering Brakes

1. To adjust this type of brake, Fig. 9, first raise all wheels. Then be sure brake pedal has about ½" free travel without moving master cylinder piston.
2. Centralize brake shoes in the drum by making a hard brake application and releasing the pedal.
3. Adjust the cams one at a time in the direction indicated in Fig. 10 until the shoe is tight against the drum. Then turn the cam in the opposite direction until the wheel rotates freely without brake drag.

Service Bulletin

Self-Adjusting Brakes: The brakes on Jeepster and some J Series vehicles are equipped with the familiar Bendix Self-Adjusting Brakes. Brakes with automatic adjusters may be identified by noting the location of the adjustment slots in the brake backing plates. These slots are located to the rear of the axle centerline at all four wheels. Brakes not equipped with automatic adjusters have the slots located forward of the axle centerline at the wheels on one side of the vehicle, and to the rear on the other side.

A few vehicles have two adjustment slots in the brake backing plates on one side of the vehicle. These brakes are equipped with automatic adjusters.

Do not use the star wheel and adjustment slot for routine brake shoe adjustment on brakes with automatic adjusters. The star wheel is provided only for an initial adjustment after new brake shoes have been installed.

PARKING BRAKE, ADJUST

Propeller Shaft Brake

1. Make sure the brake handle is fully released. Examine cable and operating linkage to see that they do not bind.
2. Rotate hand brake drum until one pair of the three sets of holes are over the shoe adjusting screw wheels in the brake.
3. Use the edge of the holes in the brake drum as a fulcrum for use of a suitable adjusting tool or screwdriver.
4. Rotate each notched adjusting screw by moving the handle of the tool away from the center of the drive shaft until the shoes are snug in the drum.
5. Back off 7 notches on the adjusting screw wheels to secure proper running clearance between shoes and drum.

Rear Wheel Cable Brake

1. With the foot brakes properly adjusted, pull up three notches on the hand lever and tighten the adjustment until the rear brakes drag slightly.
2. Release the hand brake lever and check the rear wheels for drag. Wheels must turn freely with hand lever released. All models are equipped with a brake cable equalizer and adjusting rod located near the frame center crossmember.

BRAKE MASTER CYLINDER, REPLACE

To remove the master cylinder, disconnect the fluid lines and stop light wires from the cylinder. Unfasten the cylinder from its mounting. Remove the eye bolt from the shaft and drop the cylinder from its mounting.

POWER BRAKE UNIT

With Standard Transmission

1. Disconnect master cylinder and wheel cylinder lines at slave cylinder.
2. Disconnect vacuum hose from check valve.
3. Remove mounting bracket-to-slave cylinder attaching screws and lift booster unit from engine compartment.

With Automatic Transmission

1. Disconnect push rod from brake pedal arm.
2. Remove vacuum hose from check valve.
3. Place a container under hydraulic fitting on master cylinder and disconnect hydraulic line from master cylinder.
4. Unfasten and remove booster unit.

Front End and Steering Section

CAMBER & CASTER

Transverse Spring Suspension

Camber is adjusted by adding or removing shims as required from behind the upper control arm frame bracket.

Caster is controlled by the relationship between the position of the front spring and its location in the frame cross member channel. If caster is out, examine the suspension for worn or damaged parts.

Torsion Bar Suspension

Camber is controlled by the attachment of the upper control arms to the ball joints through slotted holes in the control arms. To adjust camber, loosen the control arm to ball joint bolts and adjust to specification.

Caster is controlled by a strut bar which runs between the end of the axle and the frame side member. Adjustment is made by loosening the locknuts at each end of the strut tube, and rotating the tube until the specified setting is obtained.

TOE-IN, ADJUST

Transverse Spring Suspension

Load the front end of the vehicle by weights or persons so that the front spring main leaf is flat. Flatness of the front spring main leaf may be checked by holding a straight edge or string below the main leaf, and parallel with it.

Roll the vehicle backward and forward so that all parts will attain a normal position. With suitable trams or gauge, measure the distance between the wheels at the rear and then at the front. These measured distances should be equal (for zero toe-in).

If the distances are not equal, readjust the tie rods as required to make the distance equal.

When the load is removed from the front of the vehicle, it will be found that the wheels will attain a slight toe-in, ranging from ⅛ to $\frac{3}{16}$ in., depending upon the arch of the front spring. This is normal and will give satisfactory results in respect to tire wear and proper handling of the vehicle.

Torsion Bar Suspension

Position the wheels to a true straight ahead position with the steering gear also in a straight ahead driving position. Then turn both tie rod adjusting sleeves an equal amount until the desired toe-in setting is obtained.

TRANSVERSE SPRING SUSPENSION REPAIRS

Kingpins & Bushings

The following text applies to earlier models insofar as this operation is concerned.

1. Remove wheel hub and dust caps.
2. Take off wheel and hub, bearings and oil seal.
3. Disconnect hydraulic brake tube and remove brake backing plate with brake assembly attached.
4. Drive out kingpin lock pin.
5. Use a sharp drift to remove the kingpin lower expansion plug.
6. Use a brass drift to drive the kingpin up until the upper needle bearing is removed.
7. Use a brass drift to drive the kingpin out through the bottom.
8. Remove the bushing from the lower part of the spindle.

Assembly is the reverse of the above. When reaming the bushing to size, use a pilot type reamer to be sure that the bushing is square with the upper needle bearing. Examine the ball thrust bearing and replace it if worn or damaged. Do not overlook bleeding the brakes.

Steering Knuckle Supports

Should it be necessary to disassemble the front suspension, be sure that the steering knuckle supports are reinstalled on the proper side. The left support will interchange with the right but the wheel camber will be incorrect, resulting in unstable steering. The supports have the part number on the forging for identification—641026 left side, 641027 right side. Later production parts may be identified by the letter L for left and R for right.

When mounting the upper control arm pin bushing in the steering knuckle support, tighten it to 175 lbs. ft. torque. Centralize the control arm over the knuckle support before starting to thread the pivot pin through the support. This is necessary to provide the proper caster effect and equal clearance at each side of the support for the rubber dust seals. Also for the same reasons centralize the spring eye in the lower end of the knuckle support before starting the spring pivot bolt.

TORSION BAR SUSPENSION REPAIRS

Torsion Bar Removal, Fig. 1

1. Disconnect front shock absorber at axle.
2. Jack up frame until wheel and axle hang free.
3. Back off torsion bar adjusting screw in frame side rail at rear end

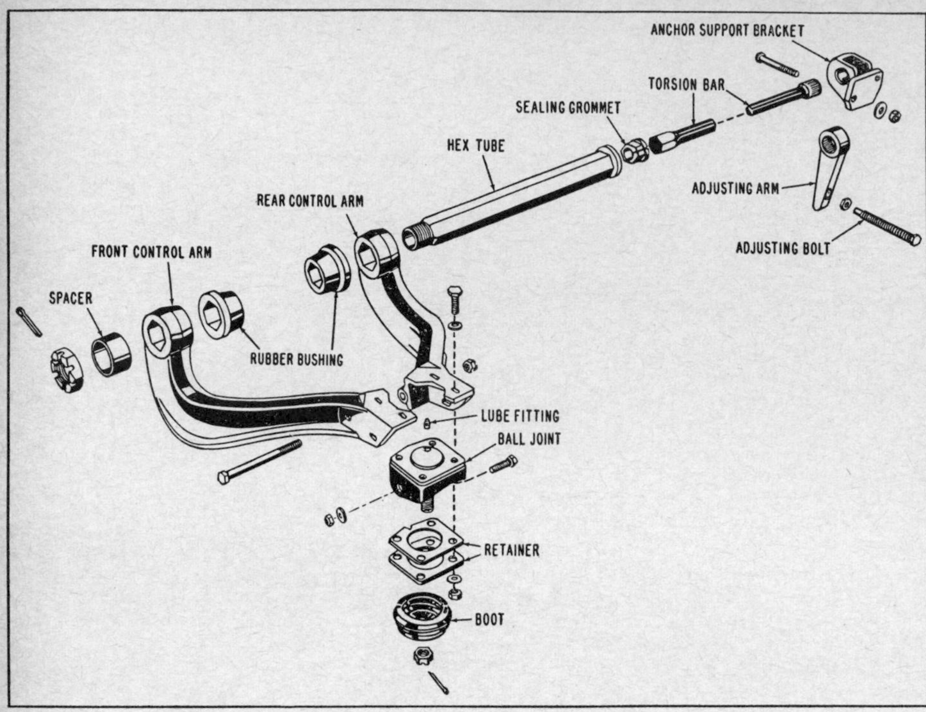

Fig. 1 Upper control arm and torsion bar. J Series

of torsion bar until end of screw is flush with inside of frame side rail.

4. Remove two locknuts, washers and bolts attaching torsion bar anchor support to frame side rail.
5. Slide anchor support bracket, adjusting arm, and torsion bar rearward to remove them from vehicle. Split rubber grommet at front end will come off with torsion bar; retain it for use on new torsion bar.

Torsion Bar, Install

NOTE: Left and right torsion bars are not interchangeable and care must be taken to insure that the right torsion bar, stamped with letter "R" on its front end is installed on the right side of the vehicle. Similarly, the left torsion bar is stamped with a letter "L" on the front end.

1. With frame jacked up and wheel and axle hanging free, insert hex end of new torsion bar into hex tube.
2. With torsion bar in its normal position parallel to the frame side rail, (left view of Fig. 2), and with lower end of the adjusting arm in contact with frame side rail, slide adjusting arm onto torsion bar.
3. Mark end of torsion bar and adjusting arm to indicate relative positions of serrations in each and remove adjusting arm from torsion bar.
4. Slide torsion bar back about one inch and install sealing grommet on torsion bar between bar and hex tube. Place grommet on bar as far forward as possible and push grommet and torsion bar into position. *It is important that a good seal be obtained.*
5. With a wooden wedge, pry torsion bar away from frame side rail until there is a difference of two serrations, as indicated by the marks made in step 3, with lower end of adjusting arm in contact with side rail (right view of Fig. 2).
6. With wedge in place, assemble anchor support bracket and adjusting arm on end of torsion bar with lower end of arm in contact with side rail.
7. Remove wedge and bolt anchor support bracket to side rail.
8. Turn in adjusting bolt until it contacts adjusting arm.
9. Remove jack and reconnect the shock absorber.
10. Level the axle with the torsion bar adjusting screw and tighten the jam nut.

NOTE: If full travel of adjusting screw will not provide a level axle, repeat steps 5 through 10 increasing the specified difference of two serrations by one serration at a time until a level axle can be obtained with the adjusting screw.

Ball Joint Replace

The upper ball joint can be replaced without removing control arm or torsion bar by the following procedure:

1. Place frame side rails on a stand and remove torsion bar adjusting bolt, locknut, support bracket and adjusting arm.
2. Unfasten ball joint from control arm and knuckle and remove ball joint.
3. Reverse removal procedure to install.

STEERING GEAR, REPLACE

CJ, DJ & L6-226

It is necessary to pass the steering gear down through the floor pan. The procedure is as follows:

1. Remove left front fender on CJ-2A.
2. Disconnect remote control rods from levers on steering column if equipped with steering post shift.
3. Remove horn button and steering wheel.
4. Remove steering post bracket at instrument panel.
5. Remove steering post hand lever.
6. Remove exhaust pipe from manifold.
7. Remove steering column cover plate on toe board.
8. Remove two screws attaching remote control housing to steering column.
9. Remove horn wire contact brush (CJ-2A) or disconnect horn wire.
10. Remove remote control gearshift assembly down through floor pan.
11. Remove pitman arm from steering gear.
12. Unfasten steering gear from frame and bring it down through the floor pan and over the outside of the frame side rail.

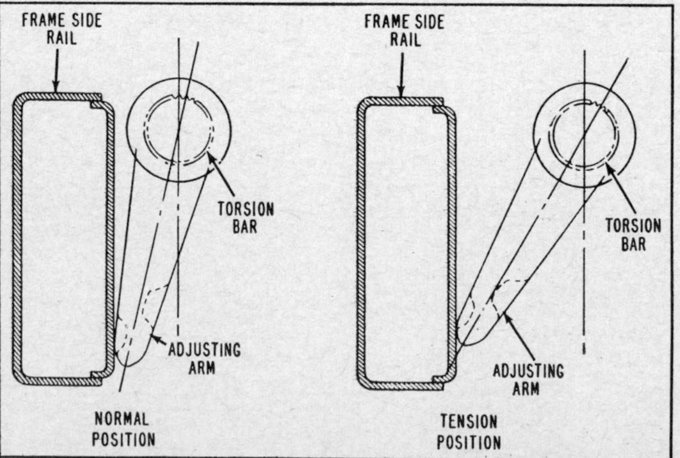

Fig. 2 Torsion bar installation. J Series

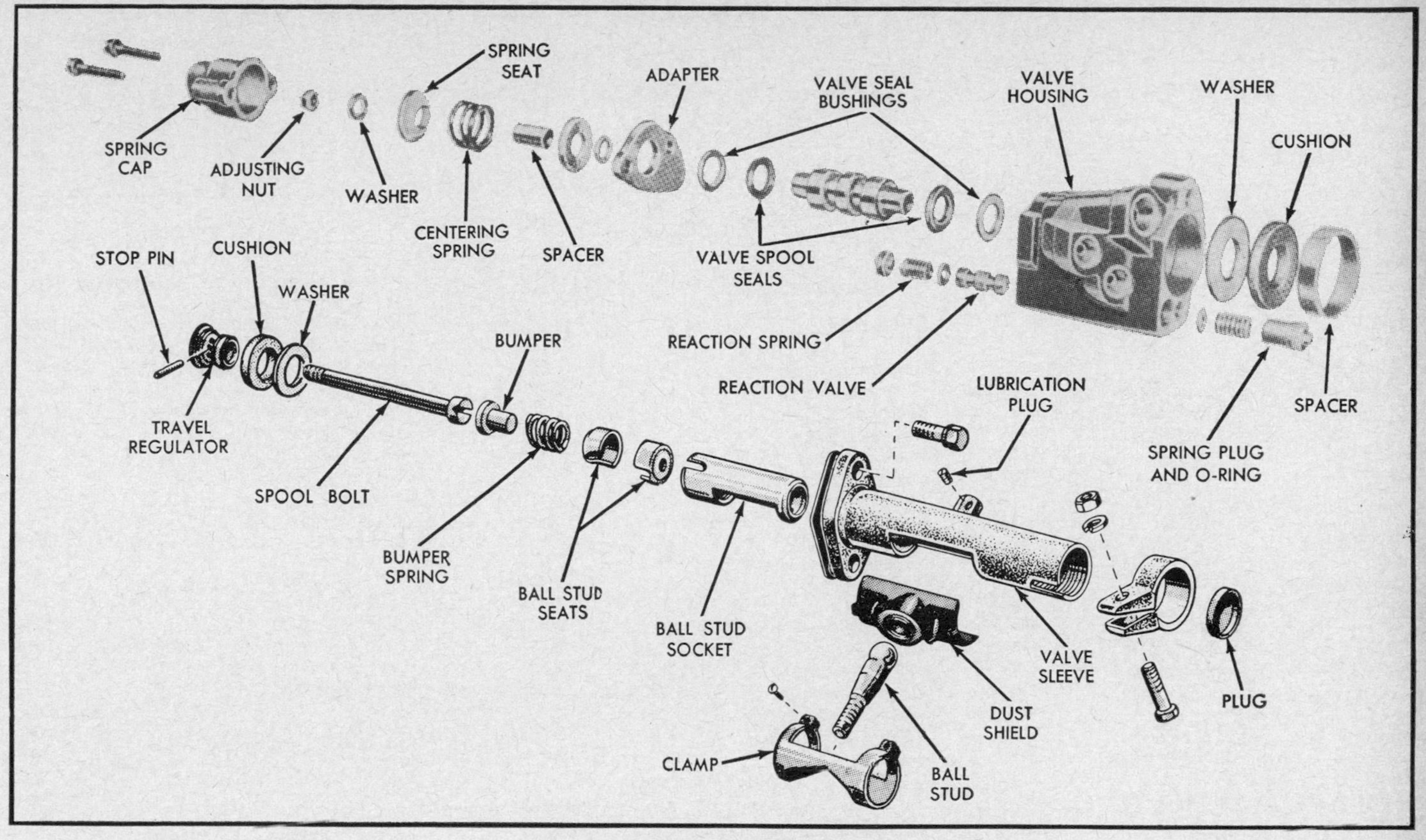

Fig. 3 Control valve disassembled

J Series with V8 Engine

1. If equipped with power steering, disconnect hoses at power steering pump. Raise hoses above pump to prevent oil drainage.
2. Disconnect steering gear from lower steering shaft by removing two nuts attaching flexible coupling to shaft flange.
3. Disconnect steering arm from steering connecting rod.
4. Remove upper steering gear-to-frame bracket bolt. Then remove two lower bolts and remove steering gear.

Jeepster & J Series with 6-230 Engine

1. Disconnect steering gear from column by removing flexible coupling to gear clamping screw.

POWER STEERING

Pump Pressure

The normal oil pressure against either steering stop with engine idling is 650 to 800 psi.

Pump Removal

1. Disconnect pressure and return lines from pump. Cap all fittings to prevent drainage of fluid.
2. Loosen bolts holding pump to mounting bracket and move pump toward engine to remove belt.
3. Remove bolts that fasten pump to bracket and remove pump.
4. Tighten sleeve clamp bolt to 28-32 ft-lbs.
5. Connect hydraulic lines, fill reservoir, start engine and operate system.

Control Valve Removal

1. Disconnect hydraulic hoses at control valve.
2. Remove bolt attaching steering gear arm to steering gear lever shaft.
3. Disconnect power steering control link at bellcrank.
4. Remove control valve, control link and steering gear arm as an assembly.
5. Remove steering gear arm from ball stud with a puller.
6. Separate control link from power valve by loosening locking clamp bolt and turning threaded power link out of power valve.

Control Valve, Install

1. Align assembly marks and install steering arm on steering gear.
2. Screw control valve outer sleeve on connecting link until distance between steering arm ball center and connecting link ball is .027".
3. Insert ball stud into steering arm and secure with nut and cotter pin.

Power Cylinder Removal

1. Raise vehicle and drain fluid by disconnecting hoses from power cylinder. Move wheels right and left several times for complete drainage.
2. Unfasten power cylinder from bracket on frame side rail.
3. Loosen locknut securing piston rod to socket at bellcrank and unthread cylinder from bellcrank socket. *Note: Do not use vise grips or pliers on the piston rod as damage to the finish will cause leakage.*

Power Cylinder, Install

1. Position bushings and washers on power cylinder.
2. Thread piston rod into socket until piston rod bottoms in ball socket thread.
3. Install washers on each side of bushing, and install bolt and nut securing cylinder to frame side rail bracket.
4. Install valve-to-cylinder lines, fill reservoir and bleed system.

LINCOLN CONTINENTAL

OLD CAR SPECIFICATIONS: For 1946-62 Tune Up and Wheel Alignment Specifications see back of book.

INDEX OF SERVICE OPERATIONS

PAGE NO.

ACCESSORIES

Automatic Level Controls 1-41
Clock Troubles 1-11
Heater Core, Replace 2-430
Power Top Troubles 1-18
Power Window Troubles 1-18
Radio, Replace 2-428
Speed Controls, Adjust 2-429

BRAKES

Brake Troubles, Mechanical 1-17
Disc Brake Service 1-430
Hydraulic System Service 1-422
Parking Brake, Adjust 2-439
Power Brake Unit, Replace 2-439
Power Brake Service 1-440
Power Brake Troubles 1-440
Service Brakes, Adjust 2-438
Vacuum Release Parking Brake Unit ... 2-439

COOLING SYSTEM

Cooling System Troubles 1-6
Variable Speed Fans 1-39
Water Pump, Replace 2-435

ELECTRICAL

Alternator Service 1-63
Dash Gauge Service 1-117
Distributor, Replace 2-423
Distributor Service:
Standard 1-53
Transistorized 1-47
Electrical Troubles 1-8
Flasher Location Chart .... Back of Book
Generator Service 1-91
Headlamps, Concealed Type 1-40
Horn Sounder, Remove 2-426
Ignition Coils and Resistors 1-24
Ignition Switch, Replace 2-424
Ignition Timing 2-423
Instrument Cluster Removal 2-426
Light Switch, Replace 2-424
Neutral Safety Switch, Replace 2-425
Spark Plug Condition Chart 2-647
Starter Service 1-101
Starter, Replace 2-423
Starter Switch Service 1-114
Stop Light Switch, Replace 2-424
Turn Signal Switch, Replace 2-425
Turn Signal Troubles 1-11
Windshield Wiper Motor, Replace ... 2-428
Windshield Wiper Troubles 1-20

PAGE NO.

ENGINE

Camshaft, Replace 2-433
Cylinder Head, Replace 2-430
Engine, Replace 2-430
Engine Troubles 1-1
Main Bearings 2-434
Piston Pins 2-434
Piston Rings 2-434
Piston and Rod, Assemble 2-434
Pistons 2-434
Rocker Arm Service 2-432
Rocker Arm Stud 2-432
Rod Bearings 2-434
Timing Case Cover, Replace 2-433
Timing Chain, Replace 2-433
Valves, Adjust 2-431
Valve Arrangement 2-432
Valve Guides 2-432
Valve Lifters 2-432

ENGINE LUBRICATION

Crankcase Ventilation (PCV) 1-29
Exhaust Emission Controls 1-30
Oil Pan, Replace 2-434
Oil Pump, Repairs 2-434

FUEL SYSTEM

Carburetor Adjustments and Specs. ... 1-124
Crankcase Ventilation (PCV) 1-29
Exhaust Emission Controls 1-30
Fuel Pump, Replace 2-435
Fuel Pump Service 1-120
Fuel System Troubles 1-2

PROPELLER SHAFT & U JOINTS

Propeller Shaft 2-437
Universal Joint Service 1-418

REAR AXLE

Axle Shaft, Bearing and Seal 2-437
Rear Axle Description 2-435
Rear Axle Troubles 1-17

SPECIFICATIONS

Alternator 2-421
Brakes 2-422
Capacities 2-423

PAGE NO.

Carburetors 1-124
Cooling System 2-423
Crankshaft and Bearings 2-422
Distributors 2-421
Engine Tightening Torque 2-421
General Engine Specs. 2-419
Ignition Coils and Resistors 1-24
Pistons, Rings and Pins 2-422
Rear Axle 2-422
Starting Motors 2-422
Tune Up 2-420
Valve Lift 2-432
Valve Timing 2-432
Valves 2-419
Wheel Alignment 2-420

STEERING GEAR

Horn Sounder Removal 2-426
Power Gear, Replace 2-442
Steering Wheel, Replace 2-426

SUSPENSION, FRONT

Ball Joints, Replace 2-441
Ball Joints, Check for Wear 2-441
Coil Spring, Replace 2-441
Lubrication 2-439
Shock Absorber, Replace 2-441
Suspension, Description of 2-439
Tire Wear Chart 2-648
Toe-In, Adjust 2-440
Wheel Alignment, Adjust 2-440
Wheel Bearings, Adjust 2-440
Wheel Bearings, Replace 2-441

AUTOMATIC TRANSMISSIONS 1-321

1969 Linkage 2-435

TUNE UP

Service 1-21
Specifications 2-420

WINDSHIELD WIPER

Wiper Motor, Replace 2-428
Wiper Linkage, Replace 2-428
Wiper Switch, Replace 2-428
Wiper Troubles 1-20

SERIAL & ENGINE NUMBER LOCATION

Vehicle Warranty Plate on Left Front Door Pillar

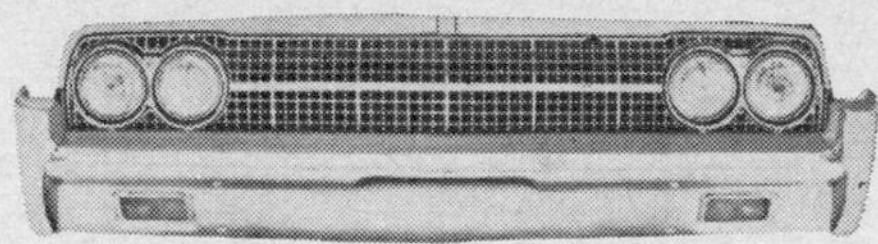

1963

1964

1965

1966

ENGINE IDENTIFICATION

*** Serial number on vehicle Warranty Plate.**

Engine code for 1963–69 is the last letter in the serial number.

Year	Engine	Engine Code*
1963–65	V8-430	N
1966–67	V8-462	G
1968–69	V8-460	A
	V8-462	G

1967

1968

1969 Continental

1969 Mark III

GENERAL ENGINE SPECIFICATIONS

Year	Engine	Carburetor	Bore and Stroke	Piston Displacement, Cubic Inches	Compression Ratio	Maximum Brake H.P. @ R.P.M.	Maximum Torque Lbs. Ft. @ R.P.M.	Normal Oil Pressure Pounds
1963	315 Horsepower............. V8-430	2 Barrel	4.3000 x 3.700	430	10.00	315 @ 4100	465 @ 2200	35–55
1964–65	320 Horsepower............. V8-430	4 Barrel	4.3000 x 3.700	430	10.10	320 @ 4600	465 @ 2600	35–55
1966–68	340 Horsepower............. V8-462	4 Barrel	4.3800 x 3.830	462	10.25	340 @ 4600	485 @ 2800	35–55
1968–69	365 Horsepower............. V8-460	4 Barrel	4.3600 x 3.850	460	10.5	365 @ 4600	500 @ 2800	35–60

VALVE SPECIFICATIONS

Year	Engine Model	Valve Lash		Valve Angles		Valve Spring Installed Height	Valve Spring Pressure Lbs. @ In.	Stem Clearance		Stem Diameter	
		Int.	Exh.	Seat	Face			Intake	Exhaust	Int.	Exh.
1963–64	V8-430	.078–.178①		45	44	1 41/64	70 @ 1.64	.0008–.0018	.002–.003	.3712–.3722	.3701–.3709
1965	V8-430	.050–.150①		45	44	1 41/64	70 @ 1.65	.0008–.0018	.002–.003	.3712–.3722	.3701–.3709
1966	V8-462	.050–.150①		45	44	1 5/8	70 @ 1.65	.0008–.0018	.002–.003	.3712–.3722	.3701–.3709
1967–68	V8-462	.083–.183①		45	44	1 5/8	70 @ 1.65	.0008–.0025	.001–.0027	.3710–.3717	.3708–.3715
1968–69	V8-460	.075–.175②		45	44	1 13/16	80 @ 1.810	.0010–.0027	.0010–.0027	.3416–.3423	.3416–.3423

①—With rocker arm rotated to collapse lifter, the clearance listed should exist between end of valve stem and rocker arm. See text for details.
②—Valve lifter adjustment is 1 turn down after contact. Check as in note①.

TUNE UP SPECIFICATIONS

OLD CAR SPECIFICATIONS: For 1946-62 Tune Up Specifications see back of book.

★ When using a timing light, disconnect vacuum hose or tube at distributor and plug opening in hose or tube so idle speed will not be affected.

Year	Engine	Spark Plug		Distributor		Firing Order	Ignition Timing★		Hot Idle Speed(11)		Comp. Press. Lbs. (3)	Fuel Pump Press. Lbs.
		Type Autolite	Gap Inch	Point Gap Inch	Dwell Angle Deg.		BTDC (1)	Mark	Std. Trans.	Auto. Trans. (2)		
1963	V8-430	BF-42	.035	.017	26–31	Fig. C	8°	Fig. A	None	465D	180	4½–6½
1964–65	V8-430	BF-42	.034(7)	.017(8)	26–31(9)	Fig. C	6°(10)	Fig. B	None	465D(10)	180	4½–6½
1966–67	V8-462	BTF-42	.034	.017	26–31	Fig. C	10°(10)	Fig. B	None	475D(10)	180	4½–6½
	V8-462(5)	BTF-42	.034	.017	26–31	Fig. C	10°(10)	Fig. B	None	500D(6)	180	4½–6½
1968	V8-462(4)	BTF-42	.034	.017	26–31	Fig. C	10°(10)	Fig. B	—	550D(6)	180	4½–6½
1968–69	V8-460(4)	BF-42	.034	.017	26–31	Fig. C	10°(10)	Fig. B	—	550D(6)	190	5

(1)—BTDC-Before top dead center.
(2)—D-Drive. N-Neutral.
(3)—Plus or minus 20 lbs.
(4)—With IMCO system.
(5)—With Thermactor exhaust emission control system.
(6)—With headlights on and A/C "Full On".
(7)—Transistor ignition .030".
(8)—Transistor ignition .020".
(9)—Transistor ignition 22–24°.
(10)—Whenever idle speed or ignition timing is adjusted, vacuum line to brake release mechanism must be disconnected and plugged to prevent parking brake from releasing when selector is moved to Drive.
(11)—If air conditioned, turn A/C switch to "Full On" position.

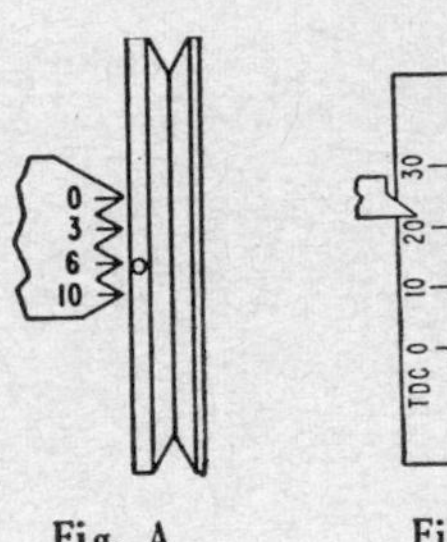

Fig. A Fig. B

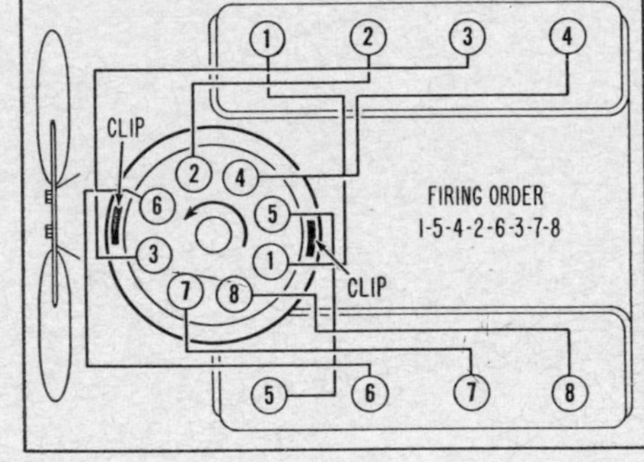

Fig. C

WHEEL ALIGNMENT SPECIFICATIONS

OLD CAR SPECIFICATIONS: For 1946-62 Wheel Alignment Specifications see back of book.

Year	Model	Caster Angle, Degrees		Camber Angle, Degrees				Toe-In. Inch	Toe-Out on Turns, Deg.(1)	
				Limits		Desired				
		Limits	Desired	Left	Right	Left	Right		Outer Wheel	Inner Wheel
1963-64	All	−¾ to −2¼	−1½	0 to +¾	0 to +¾	+½	+½	⅛–¼	17¾	20
1965	All	−½ to −2½	−1½	+¼ to +1½	+¼ to +1½	+¾	+¾	1/32–9/32	17¾	20
1966	All	−½ to −2½	−1½	−¼ to +1¼	−¼ to +1¼	+½	+½	⅛	17¾	20
1967	All	−¾ to −2¼	−1½	0 to +1	0 to +1	+½	+½	⅛	17¾	20
1968–69	Lincoln	−½ to −2½	−1½	−¼ to +1¼	−¼ to +1¼	+½	+½	⅛	17¾	20
1969	Mark III	0 to +2	+1	−¼ to +1¼	−¼ to +1¼	+½	+½	3/16	—	—

(1)—Incorrect toe-out, when other adjustments are correct, indicates bent steering arms.

COOLING SYSTEM & CAPACITY DATA

Year	Model or Engine	Cooling Capacity, Qts.			Radiator Cap Relief Pressure, Lbs.		Thermo. Opening Temp. ①	Fuel Tank Gals.	Engine Oil Refill Qts. ②	Transmission Oil			Rear Axle Oil Pints
		No Heater	With Heater	With A/C	With A/C	No A/C				3 Speed Pints	4 Speed Pints	Auto. Trans. Qts. ③	
1963	All	—	21	21	12-15	12-15	190	21½	5	—	—	11	4.8
1964	All	—	21	21	12-15	12-15	190	24	5	—	—	12¾	4.8
1965	All	—	22½	22½	12-15	12-15	190	24	5	—	—	12¾	4.8
1966	All	—	23½	23½	12-15	12-15	185	25	5	—	—	13	5½
1967	All	—	23	23	12-15	12-15	185	25	5	—	—	13½	5
1968-69	V8-462	22½	23½	23½	12-15	12-15	185	25½	4	—	—	13½	5
	V8-460	—	22	22	12-15	12-15	185	25½	4	—	—	13½	5

①—With alcohol type anti-freeze, use a 160° unit.
②—Add one quart with filter change.
③—Approximate. Make final check with dipstick.

Electrical Section

IGNITION TIMING

If a timing light is to be used to set ignition timing, disconnect the vacuum advance pipe to the carburetor and place a piece of tape over open end of pipe. *This is important as carburetor trouble can affect timing adjustments.*

Lacking a power timing light, an accurate method of setting ignition timing with the engine stopped is with the aid of a jumper light. Be sure to use a light bulb that corresponds with the system voltage of the vehicle.

1. Remove distributor cap and rotor and see that the breaker gap is set according to specifications.
2. Rotate engine until No. 1 cylinder is at the ignition timing point as indicated by the timing pointer and timing mark being lined up with each other.
3. Connect the jumper light between distributor ignition terminal and ground.
4. Turn on ignition switch.
5. Loosen distributor and turn it in the direction of normal rotation until the points just close (light out). Then slowly turn distributor in the opposite direction just to the exact point that the light goes on. Tighten distributor in this position.

DISTRIBUTOR, REPLACE

1. Disconnect distributor primary wire from coil terminal and remove distributor cap.
2. Unscrew vacuum line connection from vacuum advance unit.
3. Remove tachometer drive cable retaining screw and clip and pull cable and driven gear from distributor housing on models so equipped.
4. Unscrew distributor clamp bolt and remove lock washer and clip.
5. As the distributor is lifted from engine the shaft and rotor will turn counterclockwise part of a revolution. Lift distributor only far enough to disengage the gear.
6. When rotor stops turning, scribe a mark on the manifold or on engine casting to indicate the rotor position, then remove the distributor. *Do not crank the engine after the distributor is removed, otherwise the distributor will have to be initially timed to the engine.*
7. Install the distributor in the reverse order of its removal. Then start the engine, check the oil pressure and adjust the ignition timing.

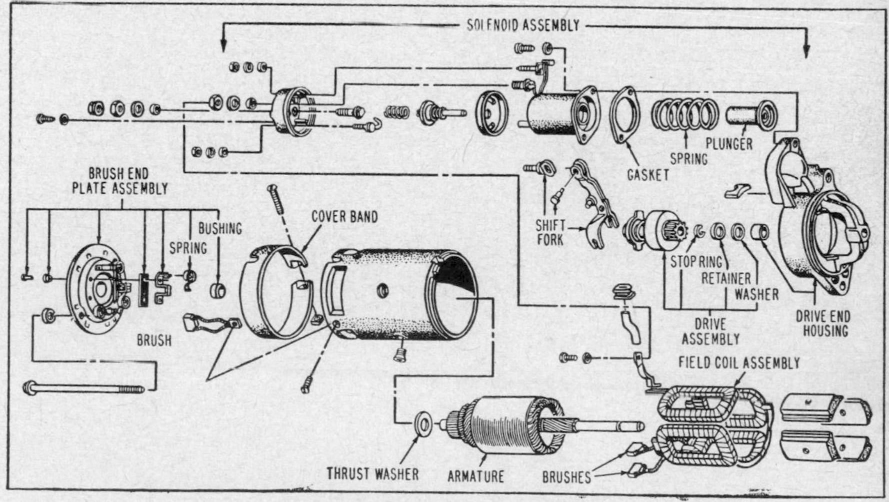

Fig. 1 Solenoid actuated starter. V8-460 engine

STARTER, REPLACE
1968-69

A solenoid actuated starter is used on all Continental and Mark III models using the 460 engine.

Operation

In this type starter, the solenoid plunger, being drawn forward when the solenoid coils are energized, first engages the starter drive then closes the starter contacts, thus cranking the engine. When the ignition switch is released, a spring loaded pin pushes the plunger out of the solenoid coils and breaks the circuit in the starting motor.

Referring to Fig. 1, service procedures are essentially the same as those for the

Autolite positive engagement starter outlined in the front of this manual.

1. Raise vehicle and disconnect cable at starter terminal. On Mark III models, turn the front wheels fully to the right and remove the two bolts attaching the idler arm to the frame.

1966-67

1. Raise vehicle and disconnect cable at starter terminal.
2. Unfasten and remove starter.
3. Position starter to flywheel housing and start mounting bolts.
4. Snug all bolts while holding starter squarely against its mounting surface.

1964-65

1. Disconnect cable at starter terminal, remove mounting bolts and starter.
2. Position starter to flywheel housing and start mounting bolts. Cable support bracket is mounted under upper mounting bolt.
3. Snug all bolts, then torque them to 12-15 ft-lbs, tightening the middle bolt first.
4. Connect starter cable.

1963

1. Disconnect battery ground cable.
2. Raise car and turn wheels to right.
3. Disconnect cable from starter.
4. Remove starter attaching capscrews.
5. Work starter forward and upward until clear of flywheel housing.
6. Tilt up rear of starter and with a turning motion lower assembly outward and down between No. 2 crossmember and transmission oil cooler line.

IGNITION SWITCH, REPLACE

1969 Mark III

1. Disconnect battery ground cable.
2. Insert wire pin in hole in ignition switch and turn key to accessory position while pressing pin. Lock cylinder can now be removed.
3. Remove bezel nut and lower switch from instrument panel.
4. Depress tabs securing multiple connector to switch and pull connector off switch.
5. Reverse procedure to install.

1966-69 Continental

1. Disconnect battery ground cable.
2. Remove 8 screws from lower control housing and drop housing.
3. Remove nut retaining wiring connector at ignition switch and remove connector.
4. Unscrew bezel and remove switch.
5. Insert key into switch and turn it to left. Insert a paper clip into hole below key slot and pull out tumbler, Fig. 1A.
6. Reverse procedure to install.

1963-65

1. Disconnect battery ground cable.
2. On 1963 models, remove hood release handle and cable from bracket. Then remove lower left instrument panel cover.
3. On all models, turn ignition key to accessory position. With a paper clip, slightly depress pin shown in Fig. 1. Turn key counter-clockwise and pull key and lock cylinder out of switch. If only lock cylinder is to be replaced, proceed to Step 9.
4. Unscrew bezel from ignition switch and remove switch from lower instrument panel.
5. Remove nut and two leads from accessory terminal of switch.
6. Remove plug connector from switch and remove switch.
7. Connect plug to switch and install two leads to accessory terminal with retaining nut.
8. Place switch in switch opening and install bezel nut.
9. If new lock cylinder is to be installed, insert key in cylinder and turn key to accessory position. Place lock and key in switch, depress pin slightly, Fig. 1, and turn key counter-clockwise. Push lock cylinder into switch.
10. Connect battery cable and check switch operation.

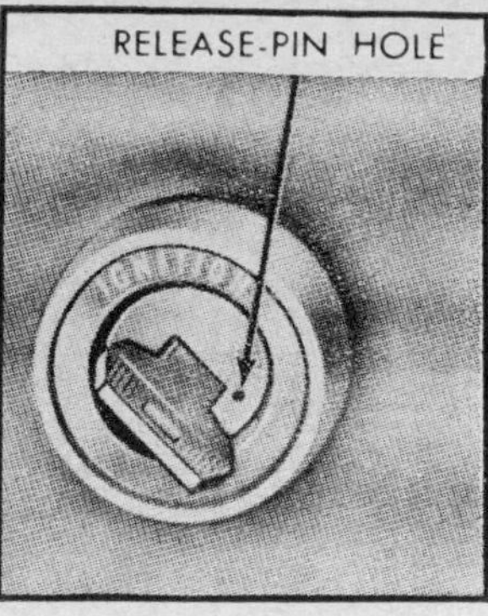

Fig. 1A Ignition lock cylinder release pin hole

LIGHT SWITCH, REPLACE

1969 Mark III

1. Disconnect battery ground cable.
2. Remove control knob and shaft by pressing knob release button and pulling it out of switch housing, Fig. 2.
3. Remove bezel nut and lower switch assembly.
4. Disconnect multiple plug and vacuum hoses at switch body and remove switch.
5. Reverse procedure to install.

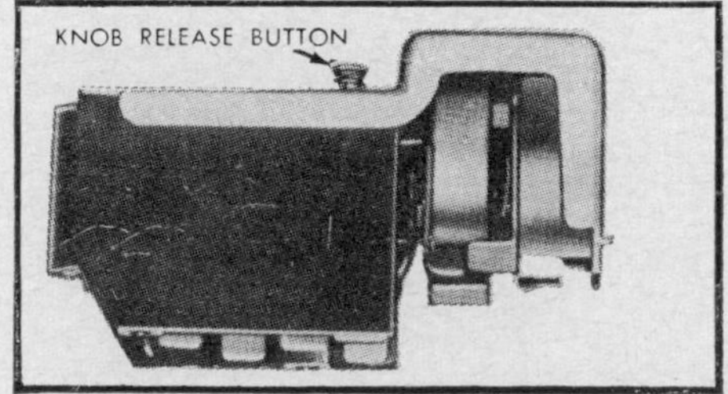

Fig. 2 Light switch. 1964-69

1966-69 Continental

1. Disconnect battery ground cable.
2. Remove 8 screws from lower control housing and drop housing.
3. Remove control knob and shaft by pressing knob release button and pulling it out of switch housing, Fig. 2.
4. Disconnect wiring connector to switch.
5. Remove bezel nut and remove switch.
6. Reverse procedure to install.

1964-65

1. Remove control knob and shaft by pressing knob release button on switch housing, Fig. 2.
2. Remove bezel screw from switch and remove switch from the lower instrument panel.
3. Disconnect connector at rear of switch and remove switch.
4. Reverse removal procedure to install. Install control knob and shaft by inserting it all the way into switch until a distinct click is heard. In some cases it may be necessary to rotate shaft until it engages.

1963

1. Disconnect battery ground cable.
2. Remove shaft and knob from switch by pressing release button on switch and pulling on shaft.
3. Remove nut and two bezels from switch.
4. Remove hood release handle and cable from its bracket.
5. Remove lower left instrument panel cover.
6. Pull switch from panel and disconnect wire connector.
7. Reverse above procedure to install.

STOP LIGHT SWITCH, REPLACE

1965-69

1. Disconnect wires at switch connector.
2. Remove hairpin retainer, slide switch, push rod and nylon washers and bushing away from brake pedal, and remove switch, Fig. 3.
3. Reverse above procedure to install.

1964

1. Disconnect wires from switch and unscrew switch from master cylinder.
2. Reverse removal procedure to install. Fill master cylinder with brake fluid.

1963

1. Remove air cleaner, duct and valve assembly.

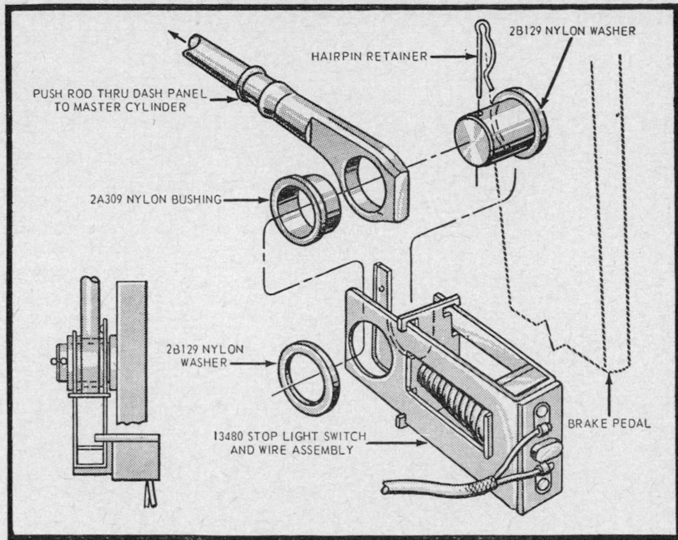

Fig. 3 Stop light switch. 1965-69

Fig. 4 Neutral safety switch showing parking brake vacuum connections. 1964-65 and 1967

2. Disconnect two wires from switch.
3. Remove switch from master cylinder.
4. Reverse removal procedure to install. Do not over-tighten switch. Inspect for leakage with brakes applied.

NEUTRAL SAFETY SWITCH

1969 Continental

The neutral start switch is mounted on the top of the steering column jacket just below the collapsible section of the column jacket.

Adjustment

1. With transmission lever against the stop in Neutral, loosen retaining screws and rotate switch until a start is obtained.
2. Tighten screws to 20 in-lbs.
3. Place selector in the "1" position and push the Park reset button counterclockwise until it stops. *The Park reset must be performed whenever the switch has been adjusted.*

1969 Mark III & 1968 All

The neutral start switch is mounted on the top of the steering column jacket just below the collapsible section of the column jacket.

To adjust the switch it must be removed from the column. Put the selector lever in neutral and set the parking brake. Then disconnect the electrical and vacuum connections, remove the two fastening screws and lift the switch straight up and out.

Adjustment

1. Hold the switch with the wire terminal facing you. Move the actuator lever all the way to the left but do not force as the switch will be damaged internally.
2. Insert a $\frac{3}{32}$" drill shank in the hole in the tapered round boss.
3. Gently move the actuator lever to the right until it stops. This will move the Park circuit to its position of minimum travel, which must be done if the switch is to function properly upon installation.
4. Pull out the drill gauge and fit it in the hole on the top surface of the switch case to engage the switch internal carrier in the neutral position. Then reinsert the drill gauge.
5. With the selector lever held against the stop in the neutral detent position, set the switch in place on the column and fasten it with the two mounting screws.
6. Connect the electrical connector and any vacuum hose, and be sure to remove the drill gauge before operating the selector lever.

1964-65 and 1967

Column Shift, Fig. 4

1. With manual linkage properly adjusted, check starter engagement circuit in all transmission selector lever positions. The circuit must be open in all drive positions and closed only in Park and Neutral.
2. To adjust, loosen switch retaining screws on steering column.
3. Place transmission selector lever firmly against stop of neutral detent position.

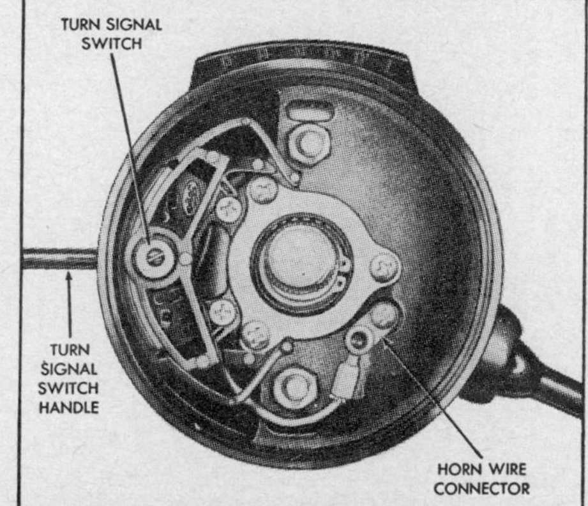

Fig. 5 Turn signal switch. 1963

4. Rotate switch actuating lever until gauge pin (43 drill) can be inserted in gauge pin holes.
5. Tighten switch retaining screws and remove gauge pin.

1966

1. Disconnect wiring from switch and remove switch from steering column.
2. Install switch on steering column.
3. Place transmission selector lever firmly against stop of neutral detent position.
4. Move switch actuating post until the shank end of a No. 43 drill can be inserted into switch carrier and case.
5. With steering column selector lever held against the stop in "N" position, rotate switch on column until switch actuating post contacts actuating lever.
6. Tighten switch screws and remove gauge drill. Starter should engage only in neutral and park positions.

1963

1. Disconnect battery ground cable.
2. Remove lower left instrument panel cover.
3. Remove wire connector from switch.
4. Remove two $\frac{5}{16}$" screws and remove lower section of left air vent.
5. Remove switch from steering column.
6. Reverse removal procedure to install. Position switch so that the starter circuit is closed when selector lever is in "N" and "P" positions.

TURN SIGNAL SWITCH, REPLACE

1968-69

1. Disconnect battery and remove steering wheel.
2. Remove protective wire cover that runs along bottom of steering column tube and disconnect electrical plug, noting color codes and location. If equipped with tilt steering column, tape wire ends together and attach a piece of heavy cord to the wires to help pull them through the column during installation.

3. If equipped with speed control, remove the sleeve around the wiring and pull the first three speed control wires out of the column.
4. Unscrew turn signal lever. If equipped with speed control, first separate the wire to the set-speed switch.
5. If equipped with tilt column, remove upper collar and push lower collar down. Remove wiring retaining clip.
6. Remove switch retaining screws and remove switch.
7. Reverse procedure to install.

1967

1. Remove steering wheel.
2. Remove turn signal lever and flasher control knob from column.
3. Remove horn wire and turn signal switch attaching screws. Lift switch and horn wire from flange.
4. Reverse procedure to install.

SERVICE BULLETIN

1963-67 TURN SIGNAL MALFUNCTION: Before judging the turn signal switch to be the cause of a malfunction and replacing it as defective, first check the following areas to make certain they are not causing the trouble.

1. The steering shaft should be centered in the column so that the steering wheel hub canceling fingers are in proper relation to the switch canceling mechanism. This can be accomplished by loosening the column attachment to the dash panel and shifting tube in relation to shaft.
2. Make sure the ignition switch is not sticking between the "Start" and "On" position, thereby adversely affecting the electrical circuit.
3. Excessive "Loctite" on the threads of the turn signal lever may be contacting the turn signal switch mechanism causing a bind.
4. The fingers on the steering wheel hub canceling cam may be bent so that the proper contact with the canceling mechanism cannot be accomplished.

1964-66

1. Disconnect battery ground cable.
2. Remove steering wheel.
3. Unscrew turn signal lever.
4. Remove switch and bracket from steering column.
5. Remove conical tension spring and switch actuating arm.
6. Disconnect switch wires from bullet connectors. Remove access plate at steering column, and remove switch and wires.

NOTE: When installing new switch, make certain that canceling cam on steering wheel makes contact with canceling pawls on switch. Clearance between steering wheel hub and steering shaft housing flange should not be more than $\frac{1}{16}$" for proper switch canceling. Reposition steering shaft housing if necessary.

1963

1. Disconnect battery ground cable.
2. Remove cap from steering wheel by depressing and turning counterclockwise.
3. Remove steering wheel, Fig. 5.
4. Remove instrument panel center plate from below steering column.
5. Unscrew turn signal lever.
6. Remove lower left panel cover.
7. Disconnect turn signal wires at connector.
8. Remove access plate from bottom side of steering column (2 screws).
9. Pull switch wires through plate.
10. Lift up on selector dial hood and remove hood.
11. Remove selector lamp socket from column (1 screw).
12. Remove lens, shroud and pointer from column.
13. Slide shroud down toward base of column.
14. With an offset screwdriver, remove screw attaching wire clamp to tube.
15. Remove switch from flange.
16. Remove switch and wire from car.
17. Reverse above procedure to install. Be sure wires do not interfere with selector movement.

HORN SOUNDER & STEERING WHEEL

1969 Mark III

1. Disconnect battery ground cable.
2. Remove the medallion from steering wheel spoke pad by gently prying out with a knife blade. Working from the underside of the spoke, remove the two screws that secure the crash pad. Remove pad.
3. Disconnect two horn wires at horn switch assembly. Remove steering wheel nut and, using a suitable puller, remove steering wheel.

NOTE: Do not use hammer or knock-off type puller. Striking the puller or shaft may cause damage to the bearings or collapsible column.

1967-69 Continental

1. Turn hub cap counterclockwise and lift it from steering wheel.
2. Remove hub mounting plate from top of wheel.
3. Remove nut and pull off wheel.

1966

1. Disconnect battery ground cable.
2. Remove center steering wheel cover.
3. Remove two screws in center of steering wheel and one screw retaining the three horn wires.
4. Remove three screws under steering wheel and remove horn buttons.
5. Reverse procedure to install.

1963-65

1. Remove cap from steering wheel hub by pressing cap and turning counterclockwise.
2. Remove nut from steering shaft.
3. Use puller to remove wheel and horn ring assembly.
4. When installing wheel and horn ring, align mark on wheel hub with mark on shaft. Install nut and stake in place.

INSTRUMENT CLUSTER

1969 Mark III

1. Disconnect battery ground cable.
2. Remove screws retaining upper edge of instrument cluster pad and retainer assembly to panel pad. Remove pad and retainer from face of cluster.
3. Remove clock knob and instrument cluster mask retainers and remove mask.
4. Remove three speedometer to cluster screws and pull speedometer from cluster. Disconnect two speedometer cable to cluster screws and clamps, release the tab of the plastic retainer and remove it from the cable. If equipped with speed control, the speedometer cable may be disconnected at the speed control unit instead.
5. Remove eight cluster to panel retaining screws and three screws retaining rear vent and wiper control pod. Pull cluster and pod out of the panel.
6. Disconnect the multiple connector and the low fuel warning and dual brake warning lights at the printed circuit and remove the cluster.

1966-68 Continental

Fig. 5A illustrates the assembly layout of the instrument cluster and controls.

1964-65

1. Disconnect battery cable.
2. Remove all lower instrument control knobs.
3. Remove radio control lock nut.
4. Remove lower instrument panel bezel (10 screws).
5. Remove finish moulding from upper edge of lower instrument panel.
6. Remove trim collar at steering column (3 screws).
7. Remove two screws at right and left panel end plates, and two screws holding plate over steering column and remove plate.
8. Remove ignition switch.
9. Remove seven screws from upper edge of lower instrument panel.
10. Disconnect speedometer and clock reset control cables (2 screws) from lower edge of lower instrument panel.
11. Detach hood lock release handle and bracket (2 screws).
12. Remove speed control head and mounting bracket.
13. Remove cover plate from fuse block in glove box and remove fuse block (2 screws).
14. Disconnect glove box courtesy light, and rear deck lid lock release handle.
15. Remove ignition switch but do not disconnect wires.
16. Remove headlamp switch but do not disconnect wires.
17. Remove windshield wiper control knob.

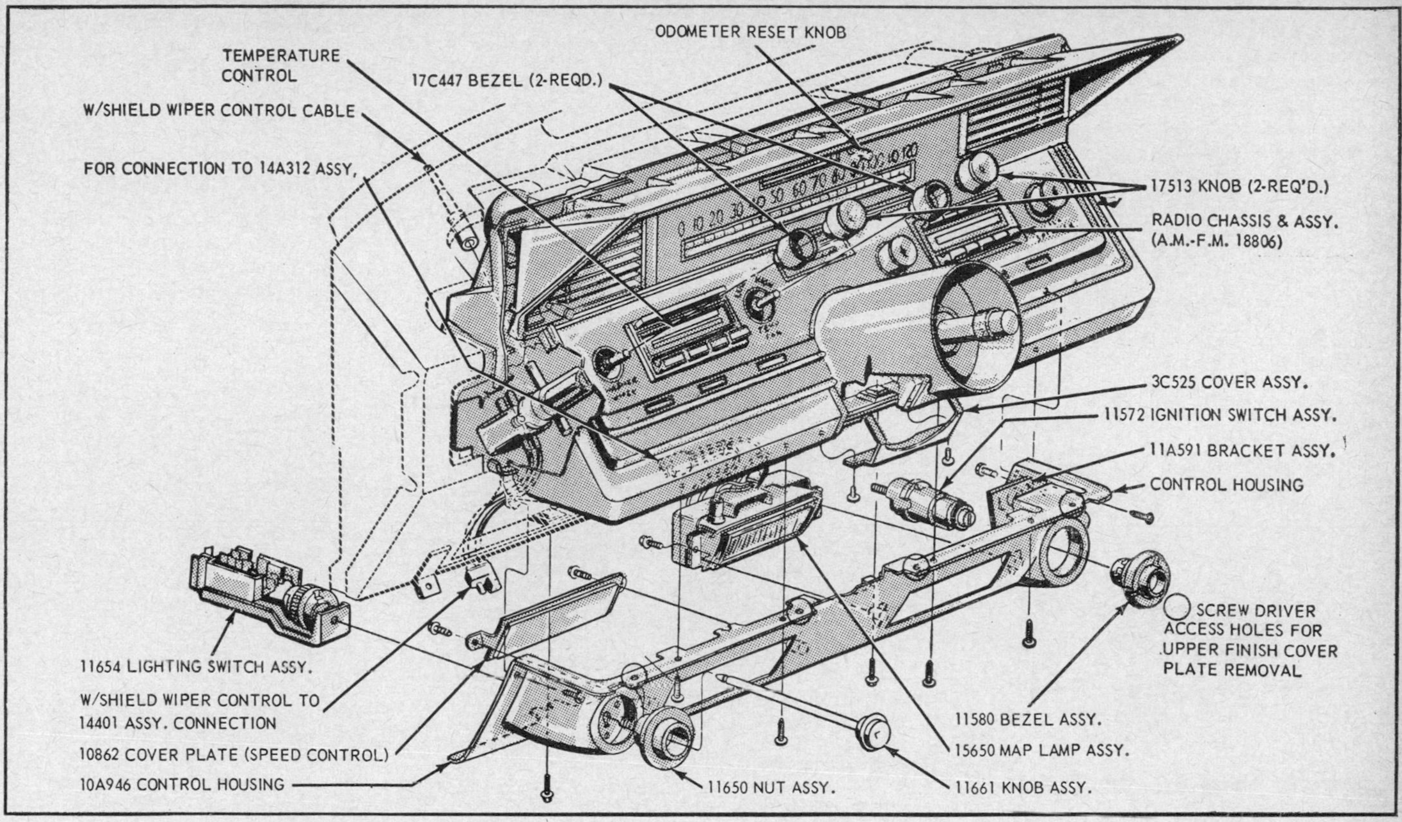

ODOMETER RESET KNOB
TEMPERATURE CONTROL
17C447 BEZEL (2-REQD.)
W/SHIELD WIPER CONTROL CABLE
FOR CONNECTION TO 14A312 ASSY.
17513 KNOB (2-REQ'D.)
RADIO CHASSIS & ASSY. (A.M.-F.M. 18806)
3C525 COVER ASSY.
11572 IGNITION SWITCH ASSY.
11A591 BRACKET ASSY.
CONTROL HOUSING
SCREW DRIVER ACCESS HOLES FOR UPPER FINISH COVER PLATE REMOVAL
11654 LIGHTING SWITCH ASSY.
W/SHIELD WIPER CONTROL TO 14401 ASSY. CONNECTION
10862 COVER PLATE (SPEED CONTROL)
10A946 CONTROL HOUSING
11650 NUT ASSY.
11580 BEZEL ASSY.
15650 MAP LAMP ASSY.
11661 KNOB ASSY.

Fig. 5A Instrument cluster and controls. 1966-67. Typical of 1968-69 Continental

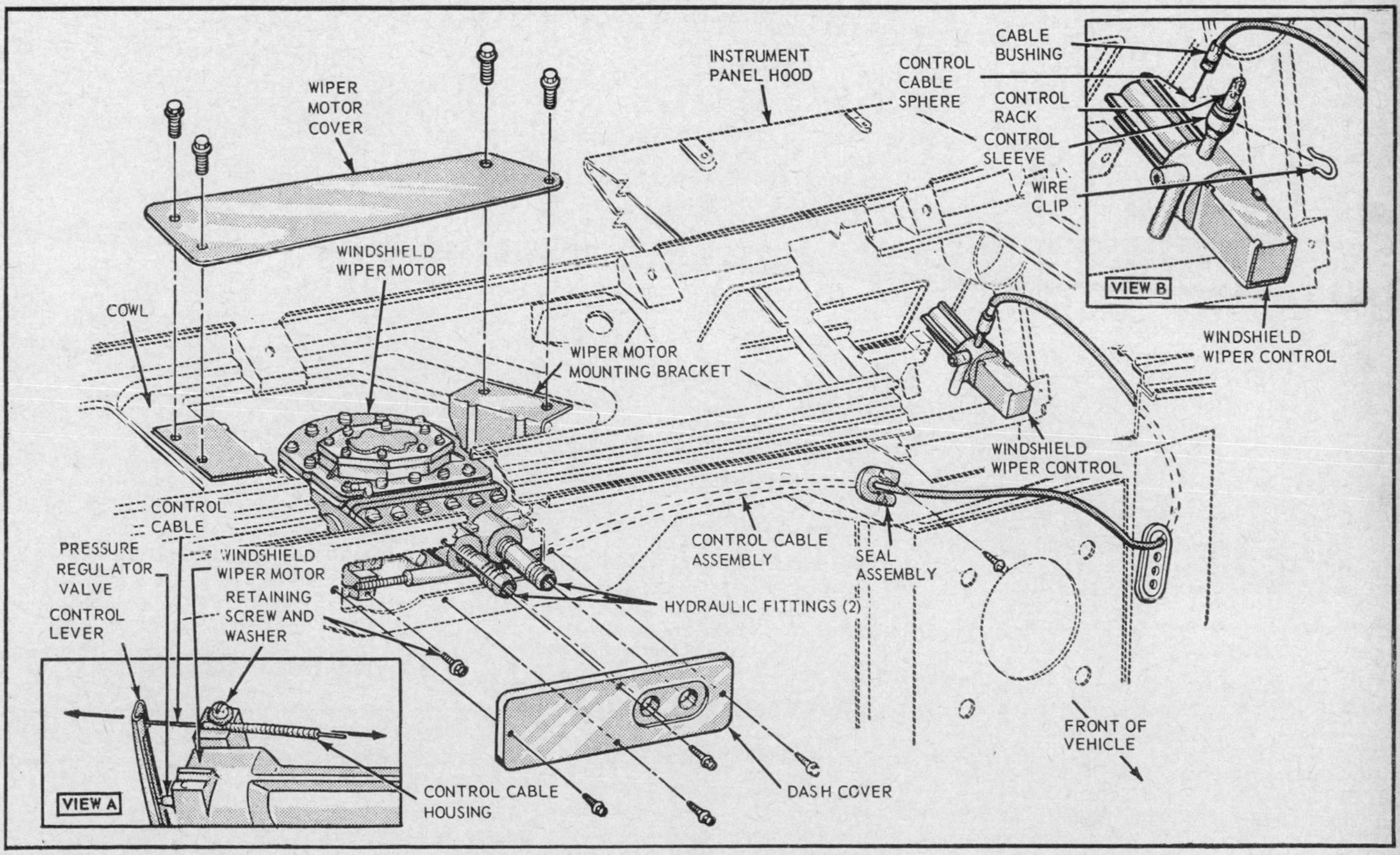

WIPER MOTOR COVER
INSTRUMENT PANEL HOOD
CONTROL CABLE SPHERE
CABLE BUSHING
CONTROL RACK
CONTROL SLEEVE
WIRE CLIP
VIEW B
WINDSHIELD WIPER CONTROL
WINDSHIELD WIPER MOTOR
COWL
WIPER MOTOR MOUNTING BRACKET
WINDSHIELD WIPER CONTROL
CONTROL CABLE
PRESSURE REGULATOR VALVE
WINDSHIELD WIPER MOTOR
RETAINING SCREW AND WASHER
CONTROL LEVER
CONTROL CABLE ASSEMBLY
SEAL ASSEMBLY
HYDRAULIC FITTINGS (2)
VIEW A
CONTROL CABLE HOUSING
DASH COVER
FRONT OF VEHICLE

Fig. 6 Windshield wiper control and motor installation. 1966-69

18. Remove windshield wiper and washer control lever.
19. Remove two blots securing lower instrument panel to inner cowl panel at right and left side.
20. Remove ash receptacle and disconnect ash tray bulb and cigar lighter leads.
21. Remove lower instrument panel from car, and service instruments as required.

1963

The speedometer housing and printed circuit board is mounted from the passenger side of the instrument panel and is retained to the mounting and trim plate by four screws.

1. Remove speedometer housing bezel by loosening two lower retaining screws.
2. Remove four screws retaining speedometer housing and printed circuit board to mounting and trim plate.
3. Pull speedometer housing away from panel. Disconnect speedometer cable and printed circuit board connector.
4. Remove speedometer housing and printed circuit board.

W/S WIPER MOTOR, REPLACE

1966-69

1. Referring to Fig. 6, remove wiper arms and blades.
2. Remove cowl top grille, wiper nozzles and weatherstrip (6 screws).
3. Disconnect two hydraulic lines at wiper motor, *using care as oil may be hot.*

1964-65

1. Remove two bolts and slide motor out of mounting bracket.
2. Disconnect two hydraulic lines from motor. Loosen control cable set screw.
3. Remove windshield washer vacuum hoses and remove wiper motor.
4. Remove wiper motor cover (4 screws).
5. Remove dash cover (4 screws).
6. Remove drive arm clip.
7. Disconnect cable from control lever.
8. Disconnect vacuum hose from wiper motor.
9. Remove wiper motor mounting bracket and two hydraulic fittings from motor if motor is defective.

1963-66 NOTE

The windshield wiper is hydraulically operated. Hydraulic power for the motor is obtained from the power steering unit. Hydraulic fluid flows from the pump, through the steering gear to the wiper motor, and then to the fluid reservoir. During wiper operation, a part of the fluid is by-passed through the motor by a valve on the motor.

1963

1. To remove the motor, remove washer coordinator hose from bottom of wiper motor.
2. Remove oil return, feed and control lines from wiper motor.
3. Disconnect cable at motor.
4. Remove motor (2 screws) from auxiliary drive mounting plate and remove motor.

W/S WIPER TRANSMISSION

1969 Mark III

1. Remove wiper arm and blade assemblies, being sure to release the tension arm retaining clip from the stud on the left pivot assembly.
2. Remove cowl top panel and disconnect washer hose.
3. Remove link retaining clip and pivot shaft assembly to cowl screws. Remove pivot shaft and link assembly.
4. Reverse procedure to install.

1966-69 Continental

1. Remove wiper arms and blades.
2. Remove cowl grille (6 screws) and disconnect washer hoses and weatherstrip.
3. Remove drive arm clip.
4. Remove three bolts at each pivot.
5. Remove pivots from connecting linkage and lift assembly out through left side of cowl.
6. Reverse procedure to install.

1963-65

Right Pivot Shaft & Link

1. Remove 11 screws securing top cowl grille and screen. Disconnect windshield washer vacuum hoses and lift off grille and screen.
2. Unclip left pivot shaft and link from wiper motor. Position link to the left.
3. Unclip right pivot. Remove two bolts and nut and remove pivot.
4. Reverse above procedure to install.

Left Pivot Shaft & Link

1. Remove top cowl grille and screen (see above).
2. Unclip retaining link from wiper motor and position link out of the way.
3. Unclip right pivot. Then remove two bolts and nut retaining left pivot, and remove pivot and link.
4. Reverse above procedure to install. It is necessary to loosen the right pivot to install link on the pivot.

W/S WIPER SWITCH

1969 Mark III

1. Disconnect battery ground cable.
2. Remove five retaining screws and remove instrument cluster pad and retainer from face of cluster.
3. Remove three retaining screws and pull wiper control pod from panel. Disconnect vacuum hoses and electrical connector and remove bulbs. Remove control cable retaining clip and remove control assembly.
4. Remove control knobs, two retaining screws and remove control unit.

1966-69 Continental

1. Disconnect battery ground cable.
2. Remove eight screws from lower control housing and drop housing.
3. Remove knob and bezel.
4. Remove nut on control shaft and lower the control.
5. Turn wiper control knob counterclockwise to the stop.
6. Remove wire clip, Fig. 6. Slide cable bushing up and out of control sleeve (view B). Remove control cable sphere from control rack.
7. Disconnect plug connector from wiring harness. Disconnect two vacuum hoses and remove wiper control.
8. Reverse procedure to install.

1963-65

1. To remove wiper control, first disconnect battery.
2. Remove trim collar from steering column (3 screws).
3. Remove two screws from left end plate of lower instrument panel.
4. Remove finish molding from upper edge of lower instrument panel.
5. Remove three screws from top of lower instrument panel to gain access to wiper control.
6. Remove knob from control lever.
7. Remove two vacuum hoses from washer control.
8. Unfasten washer control valve from wiper control (2 screws).
9. Unfasten wiper control from lower instrument panel (2 screws).
10. Remove bezel from wiper control (2 nuts).
11. Working in engine compartment, loosen wiper control cable set screw and remove cable from motor.
12. Tie a wire to control cable. Then working in passenger compartment, pull cable through firewall until wire tied to cable is accessible. Remove wire from cable.
13. Tie wire to new control cable and pull it through firewall.
14. Install cable on motor and tighten set screw.
15. Finish the installation in reverse order of removal.

RADIO REMOVAL

NOTE: When installing radio, be sure to adjust antenna trimmer for peak performance.

1969 Mark III

1. Disconnect battery ground cable.

2. Pull off control knobs.
3. Remove cover plate below steering column, and the nut from right radio control shaft.
4. Remove six screws and remove trim from front of radio.
5. Remove nut and washer from right control shaft, and screw attaching front left side of radio to instrument panel.
6. Remove rear support attaching screw, disconnect wires and remove radio.
7. Reverse procedure to install.

1966-69 Continental

1. Disconnect battery ground cable.
2. Remove eight screws in lower control housing and lower the housing.
3. Disconnect lead from speakers.
4. Disconnect power antenna lead.
5. Disconnect lead from foot-operated switch for AM/FM radios (if equipped).
6. Disconnect one two-way disconnect for pilot light and radio power.
7. Remove two knobs and bezels on selector shafts.
8. Remove two nuts and retainers on selector shafts.
9. Remove two screws attaching radio bracket to lower reinforcement on instrument panel.
10. Remove two nuts from selector shafts.
11. Disconnect antenna lead and remove radio.

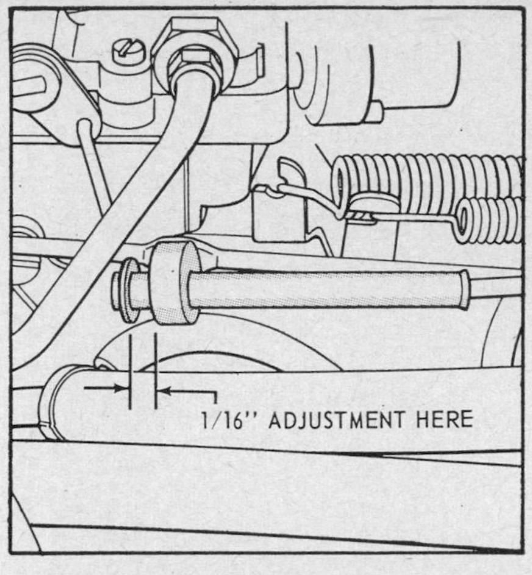

Fig. 7 Control cable adjustment. 1967-69

1964-65

1. Disconnect battery cable.
2. Remove radio and heater control knobs.
3. Remove seven upper screws from instrument panel reinforcement bracket. Remove five upper instrument panel bezel mounting screws and remove reinforcement bracket. Remove five lower instrument panel bezel screws and remove bezel.
4. Remove right and left sun visors and right and left windshield garnish moulding.
5. Remove screws from upper front instrument panel. Lift panel and disconnect photo tube lead at quick disconnect and remove upper panel.
6. Remove radio support bolt from upper panel area. Remove mounting plate at face of radio.
7. Pull radio out of instrument panel and disconnect antenna lead, speaker lead and power lead, then remove radio.

1963

1. Disconnect battery ground cable.
2. Pull off radio control knobs and remove outer bezel.
3. Remove large bezel (4 screws).
4. Unfasten and slide trim panel (2 screws) away from windshield to remove it.
5. Disconnect feed and panel lamp bullet connector and antenna lead-in cable.
6. Unfasten radio (3 screws) and pull radio and support out of instrument panel.

SPEED CONTROLS

1967-69

Control Cable, Adjust

With the carburetor set at hot idle, adjust the Bowden cable to provide a $\frac{1}{16}$" clearance between the Bowden cable end "C" washer and the accelerator linkage sleeve, Fig. 7.

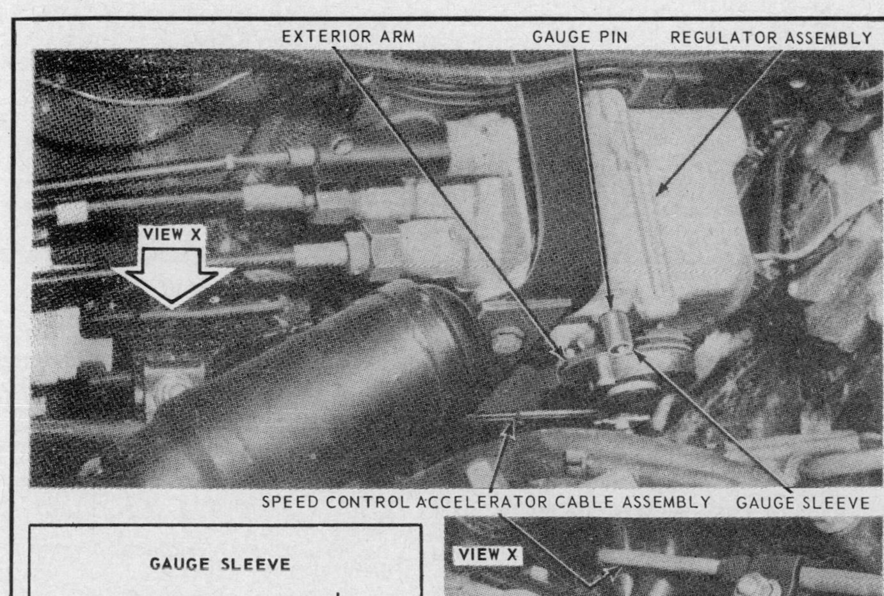

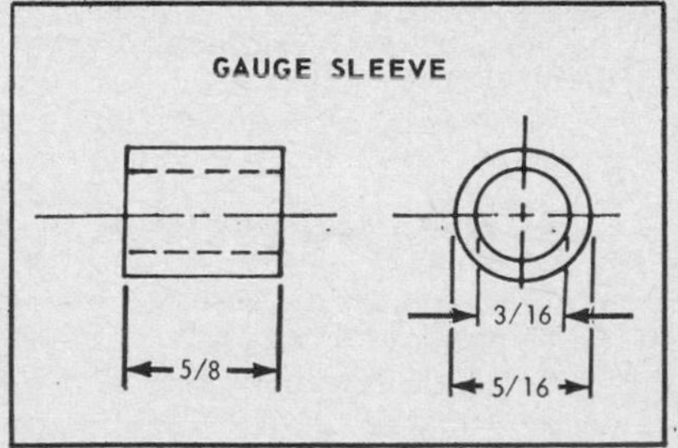

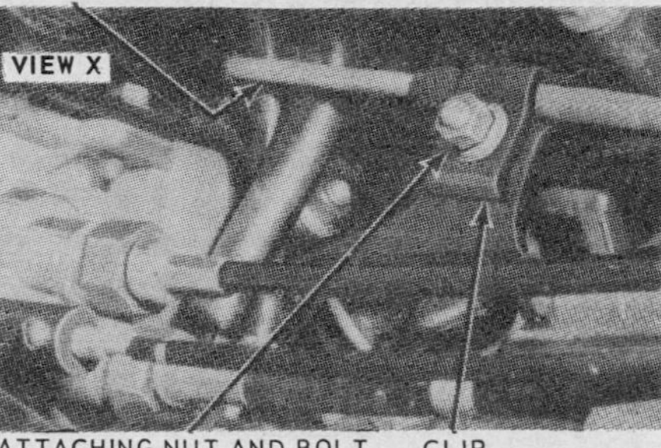

Fig. 8 Accelerator linkage adjustment for Slide Switch type Speedostat. 1963-66

1963-66 Speedostat

Control Cable Adjustment, Prior to 1966

1. Rotate selector dial rearward as far as it will turn without forcing.
2. Loosen set screw on cable dust shield.
3. Again try to rotate selector dial rearward only in order to make certain it is against the stop.
4. Push in lightly on control cable at dust shield, making certain cable is against stop (do not force cable beyond stop).
5. Hold cable against stop and tighten set screw on dust shield securely.

Control Cable Adjustment, 1966-67

The cable requires no adjustment; it simply snaps into the nylon retainer in the regulator assembly.

Accelerator Linkage

1. Adjust throttle rod.
2. Start engine and operate at slow idle with transmission lever in "Park".
3. Separate linkage from exterior arm.
4. Adjust trunnion so that when it is installed through exterior arm, the stop stud will be aligned with locating notch and throttle valves will be closed.
5. Install washer on trunnion and secure with cotter pin.

NOTE: Due to the angle at which the trunnion enters hole in exterior arm, it is necessary to rotate the exterior arm slightly forward when inserting the trunnion. Repeat this operation until proper alignment is obtained. Be careful not to turn trunnion too far back or

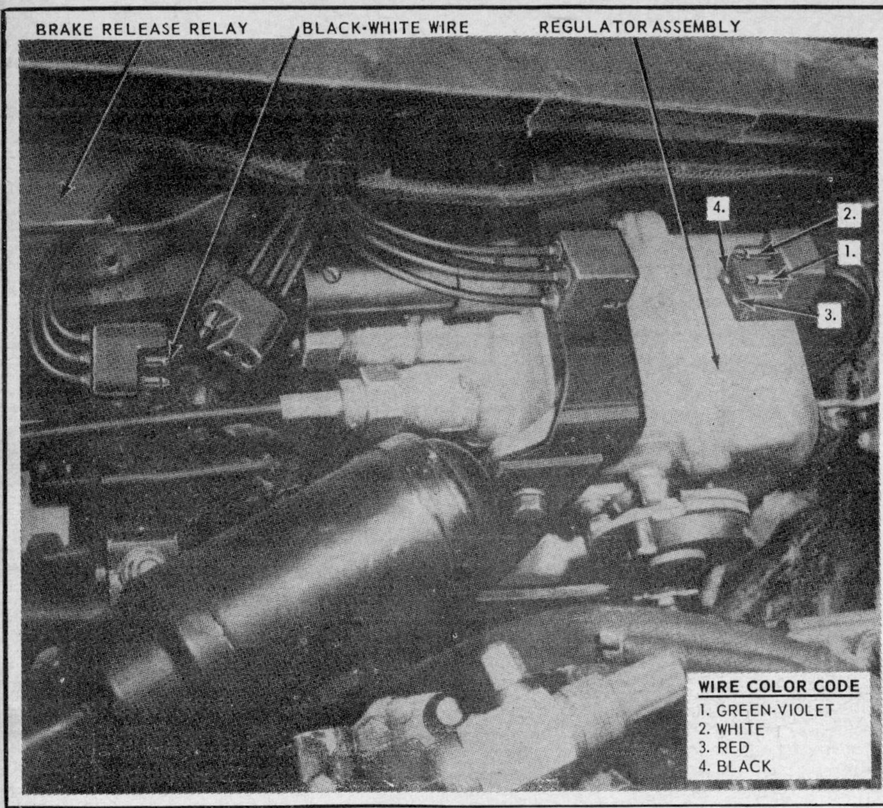

Fig. 9 Electrical connections on Slide Switch type Speedostat. 1963-66

throttle valves will unseat and cause an incorrect adjustment. Insert the gauge shown in Fig. 8 (or small diameter pipe) over stop stud to check alignment.

Brake Release Switch

1. Turn on ignition but do not start engine.
2. Momentarily move slide switch to AUTO position until red indicator light glows.
3. Using a test lamp, ground one lead and touch the other lead to terminal No. 4, Fig. 9.
4. Loosen mounting screw securing release switch to brake pedal mounting bracket.
5. Adjust release switch so that lamp will go out when brake pedal is depressed and light again when the pedal is released. If the lamp lights, the brake release relay (on left fender) is defective and must be replaced. If the lamp does not light, the wiring to the relay is defective. If the stop lights do not light, the brake stop light switch is defective.

HEATER CORE REMOVAL

1969 Mark III

1. Remove hood and air cleaner and drain radiator.
2. Disconnect wiper motor hydraulic lines, vacuum supply hose, icing switch multiple connector and heater hoses.
3. Remove oil pressure sending unit and transmission dip stick and tube.
4. Remove evaporator housing front cover and heater core housing cover.
5. Remove heater core retaining bracket and heater core.

1966-69 Continental

1. Remove air cleaner and harness clamp on top evaporator-heater case in engine compartment.
2. Take off actuator for temperature blending door, adjacent to evaporator-heater case.
3. Remove retaining screws and heater core cover plate and lift out core.

1965

1. Start engine and set heater controls to maximum heat to open water valve.
2. Stop engine, drain coolant and remove heater hoses.
3. Take off front cover of heater core housing and heater core mounting screws and lift out core.

1963-64

On 1963 models two separate heaters, one on either side of cowl, are used.

1. Raise front end of car and remove front wheel.
2. Remove fender splash shield, then disconnect and plug hoses from heater core.
3. Disconnect air duct of blower at core housing.
4. Take out two lower screws securing core housing to brace on cowl, then remove front part of housing, gasket and core, leaving main housing attached to core.

On 1964 models, a single heater is used. Remove cover plate on core housing and remove core.

Engine Section

ENGINE, REPLACE

In addition to the usual items such as fuel lines, linkage and radiator hoses, the following operations must be performed:

1. Remove hood, radiator and air cleaner.
2. Remove power steering pump and starter.
3. Disconnect exhaust pipes from manifolds. On Mark III, disconnect idler arm at frame bracket.
4. Support transmission with a suitable jack.
5. Unfasten engine mountings and attach lifting rig to engine.
6. Remove bell housing to engine attaching bolts and carefully lift engine out of chassis. *Be sure to support transmission with front end tilted up to prevent converter from falling out.*

CYLINDER HEADS

1968-69 V8-460

1. Remove intake manifold and carburetor as an assembly.
2. Disconnect resonator inlet pipe at exhaust manifold.
3. Loosen air conditioner compressor belt if so equipped.
4. Loosen alternator retaining bolts and remove bolt retaining alternator bracket to right head.
5. If air conditioned, isolate compressor at service valves and hoses from compressor. Remove nuts retaining compressor bracket to water pump. Remove bolts retaining compressor to upper mounting bracket and lay compressor out of way. Remove compressor upper bracket from head.
6. If not air conditioned, remove bolts retaining power steering reservoir bracket to left head and position reservoir out of way.
7. Remove rocker arm covers. Loosen

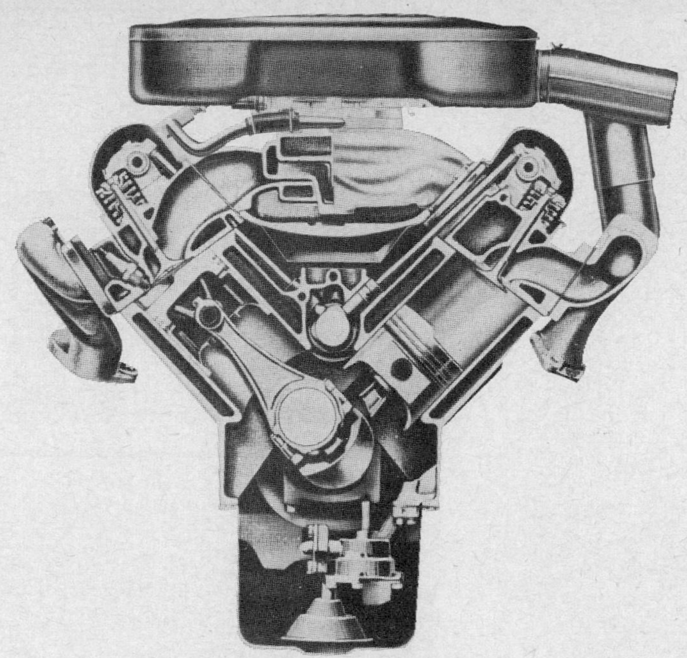

Cross section of V8-430, 462 engines

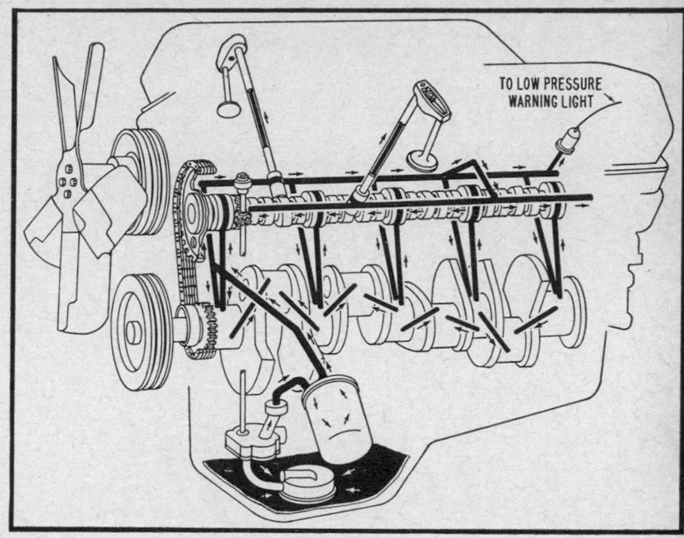

Engine lubrication. V8-460

rocker arm stud nuts and turn rocker arms to side. Remove push rods in sequence so they can be installed in their positions.

8. Remove head retaining bolts and lift head with exhaust manifold.
9. Reverse procedure to install.

1963-68 V8-430, 462

NOTE: Due to engine compartment clearance factors it is necessary to remove the exhaust manifold and cylinder head as a unit from each cylinder bank.

1. Remove battery ground cable.
2. Disconnect exhaust pipes from exhaust manifolds.
3. Remove intake manifold and push rod cover.
4. Remove rocker arm cover.
5. If air conditioned, disconnect compressor mounting bracket at cylinder head.
6. To remove right-bank head, disconnect transmission oil filler pipe bracket at exhaust manifold.
7. Remove horns and bracket assembly from fender apron (if so mounted).
8. Remove cylinder head bolts and lift head with exhaust manifold attached off two locating dowels on each bank of cylinder block.
9. Reverse removal procedure to install the head and tighten bolts in the sequence shown in Fig. 1 and to the proper torque specifications.

VALVE CLEARANCE

1969 V8-460

A positive stop rocker arm stud and nut eliminates the need of adjusting the valve lash. It is very important that the correct push rod be used and all components be installed and torqued as follows:

1. Position the piston of the cylinder being worked on at TDC of the compression stroke.
2. Install positive stop stud and torque to 65-75 ft.-lbs.
3. Lubricate and install the rocker arm and fulcrum on the stud. Thread nut onto stud until it contacts the shoulder then tighten it to 18-22 ft-lbs.

1968 V8-460

1. Rotate the crankshaft until No. 1 piston is at TDC on the compression stroke. Adjust both valves for No. 1 cylinder by turning the rocker arm stud nut until all clearance has been eliminated then tighten stud nut one additional turn to place the lifter in the correct operating range.
2. Repeat this procedure for the remaining sets of valves, turning the crankshaft ¼ turn at a time and adjust the valves in firing order sequence, which is 1-5-4-2-6-3-7-8.

An alternate method is to remove the distributor cap and, watching for the distributor points to open, adjust each set of valves in order as the breaker points reach the high spot of the distributor cam.

1963-68 V8-430, 462

A .060″ shorter push rod (color coded white) or a .060″ longer push rod (color coded yellow) are available for service to provide a means of compensating for dimensional changes in the valve mechanism. Valve stem-to-rocker arm clearance should be within the specification limits given in the *Valve Specifications* table with the hydraulic valve lifter completely collapsed and the lifter on the base circle of the camshaft. Repeated valve grinding operations will decrease this clearance to the point that the hydraulic valve lifter will cease to function. To determine whether a shorter or longer push rod is necessary, make the following check:

1. Disconnect coil high tension cable and ground it against the engine.

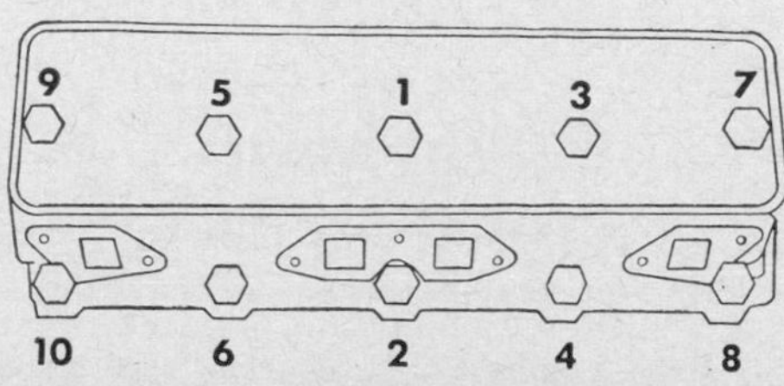

Fig. 1 Cylinder head tightening

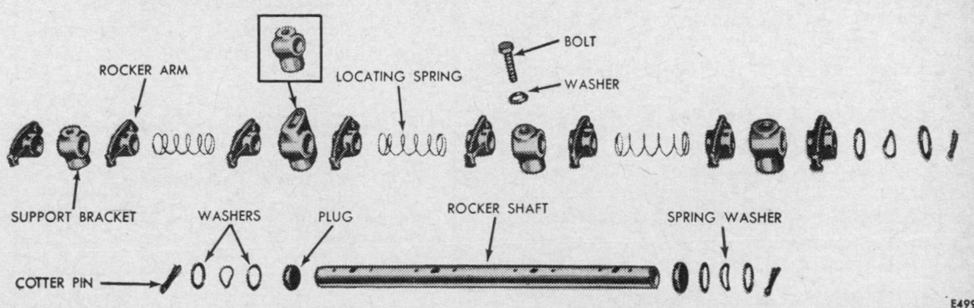

Fig. 2 Rocker arm assembly. V8-430, 462

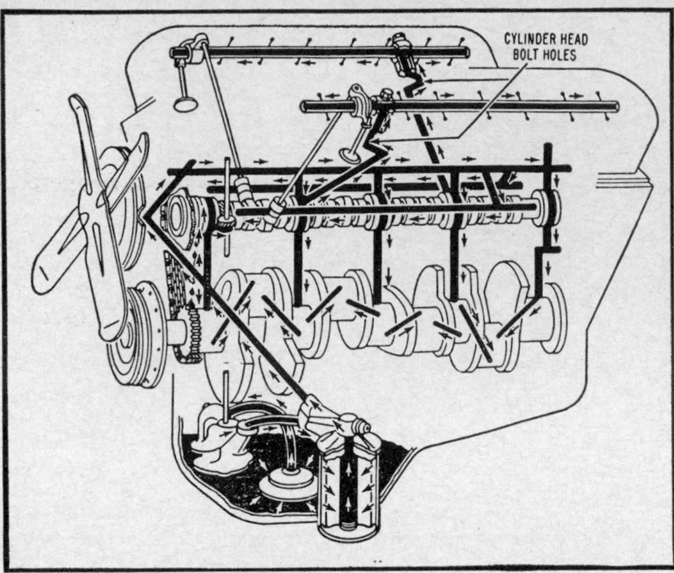

Engine lubrication. V8-430, 462

2. Disconnect starter relay leads and install an auxiliary starter switch.

NOTE: To crank an engine equipped with transistor ignition, disconnect the cold start relay and connect the auxiliary starter switch to the "S" terminal and battery terminal on the starter solenoid. Be sure the ignition switch is turned OFF when using the auxiliary starter switch.

---

3. With the piston of the cylinder on which the valve is being checked on top center of its compression stroke, apply pressure on the rocker arm to bleed the hydraulic lifter until the plunger is completely bottomed. Hold the lifter in fully collapsed position and check the clearance between valve stem and rocker arm.
4. Check the clearance with a .050″ and a .150″ feeler gauges. If the .050″ gauge enters, a standard push rod may be used. If it does not enter, replace the standard push rod with a .060″ shorter service rod.
5. If the .150″ gauge enters, the operating range of the lifter is excessive. This indicates that the incorrect push rod has been installed or severe wear has occurred at the push rod ends, rocker arm or valve stem. In this case it will be necessary to determine the area of discrepancy and the incorrect or defective part or parts should be replaced.
6. If all the valve train components except the push rod are within limits, install a .060″ longer push rod.

VALVE ARRANGEMENT

Front to Rear

Right Bank	I-E-I-E-I-E-I-E
Left Bank	E-I-E-I-E-I-E-I

VALVE LIFT SPECS.

Engine	Year	Intake	Exhaust
V8-430	1963-65	.408	.408
V8-462	1966-67	.442	.442
	1968	.441	.441
V8-460	1968-69	.443	.443

VALVE TIMING

Intake Opens Before TDC

Engine	Year	Degrees
V8-430	1963-65	22
V8-462	1966-68	20
V8-460	1968-69	16

ROCKER ARM STUDS

V8-460

Rocker arm studs are screwed into threaded bores in the cylinder head bosses. To install, apply water resistant sealer to stud threads that screw into cylinder head. Install stud and torque to 65-75 ft-lbs. Apply Lubriplate to top of valve stem and at push rod guide in cylinder head. Install rocker arm, fulcrum and stud nut.

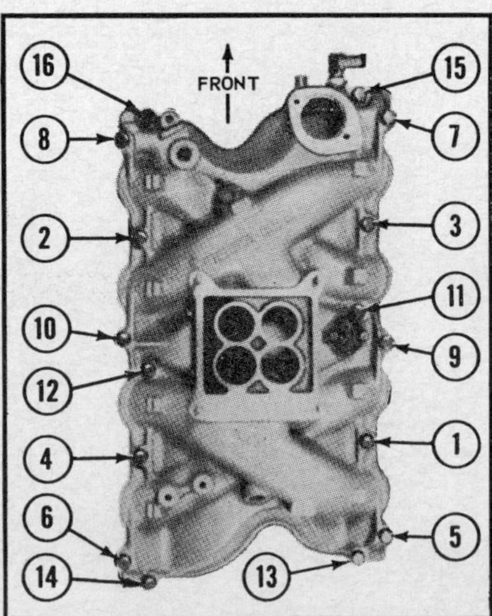

Intake manifold tightening sequence. V8-460

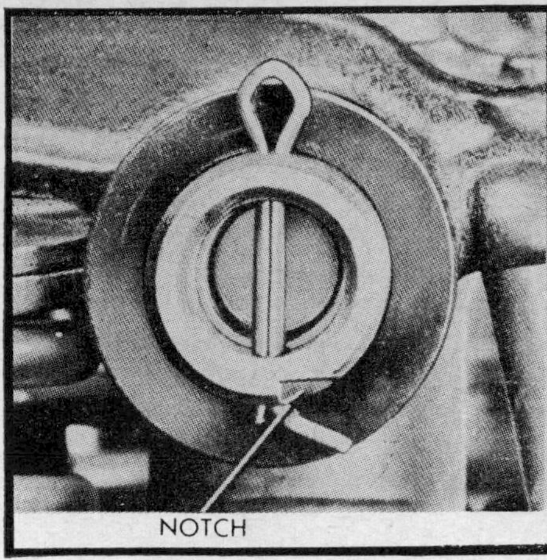

Fig 3 Rocker arm shaft installation identification mark

ROCKER ARMS & SHAFTS

V8-430, 462

Dress up minor surface defects on rocker arm shaft and in rocker arm bore with a hone. If the pad on the valve end of the rocker arm is grooved, replace the rocker arm. *Do not attempt to smooth this surface by grinding.*

Make certain that the push rods are installed in the valve lifters from which they were removed. If the valves have been reground, check the valve clearance as outlined previously and, if necessary, install longer or shorter service push rods to establish the required valve clearance. Figs. 2 and 3.

VALVE GUIDES

Valve guides in these engines are an integral part of the head and, therefore, cannot be removed. For service, guides can be reamed oversize to accommodate one of three service valves with oversize stems (.003″, .015″ and .030″).

Check the valve stem clearance of each valve (after cleaning) in its respective valve guide. If the clearance exceeds the service limits of .004″ on the intake or .005″ on the exhaust, ream the valve guides to accommodate the next oversize diameter valve.

HYDRAULIC VALVE LIFTERS

The internal parts of each hydraulic valve lifter assembly are a matched set. If these are mixed, improper valve operation may result. Therefore, disassemble,

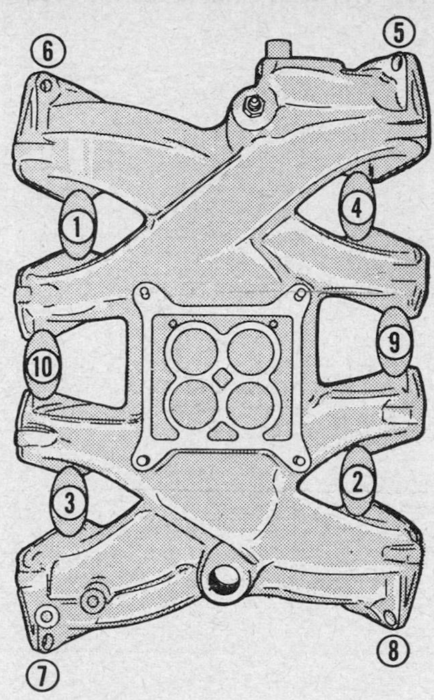

Intake manifold tightening sequence. V8-430, 462

inspect and test each assembly separately to prevent mixing the parts.

Fig. 4, illustrates the type of hydraulic lifter used. See the *Trouble Shooting Chapter* under the heading *Engine Noises* for causes of hydraulic valve lifter noise.

TIMING CASE COVER

NOTE: If necessary to replace the cover oil seal the cover must first be removed.

V8-460

1. Drain cooling system and crankcase.
2. Remove fan and radiator.
3. Remove drive belts and water pump pulley. Remove compressor support if so equipped.
4. Remove bolt and washer retaining crankshaft damper and, using a suitable puller, remove damper. Remove Woodruff key from crankshaft.
5. Remove power steering pump.
6. Loosen by-pass hose and remove heater return tube at water pump.
7. Remove fuel pump.
8. Remove front cover to cylinder block bolts. Cut oil pan seal flush with cylinder block face prior to separating cover from the cylinder block. Remove front cover and water pump as a unit.

V8-430, 462

1. Drain cooling system and disconnect water hoses. Remove radiator supply tank, thermostat and gasket.
2. Disconnect wires from coil, engine ground strap and battery ground cable at water pump.
3. Remove fan shield from radiator.
4. On air conditioned cars, loosen bracket bolts and push compressor inward toward engine and remove drive belt. Remove fan blade, fan and compressor drive pulley as a unit.
5. Remove generator splash shield and drive belts. Remove fan, spacer and mounting bolts from water pump as a unit.
6. Remove water pump.
7. Remove vibration damper.
8. Remove power steering pump.
9. Remove fuel pump. Then remove cup-type plug from top of cylinder front cover with a long punch.
10. Raise front of car and unfasten front cover from oil pan and cylinder block. Remove front cover. *If oil pan gasket is damaged during removal of front cover, it will be necessary to replace the gasket before installing front cover.*

TIMING CHAIN

1. To remove the chain, first take off the timing chain cover as outlined previously.
2. Crank the engine until the timing mark on the camshaft sprocket is adjacent to the timing mark on the crankshaft sprocket, Fig. 5.
3. Remove cap screws, lock plate and fuel pump eccentric from front of camshaft.
4. Place a screwdriver behind the camshaft sprocket and carefully pry the sprocket and chain off the camshaft.
5. Reverse the foregoing procedure to install the chain, being sure to align the timing marks as shown in Fig. 5.

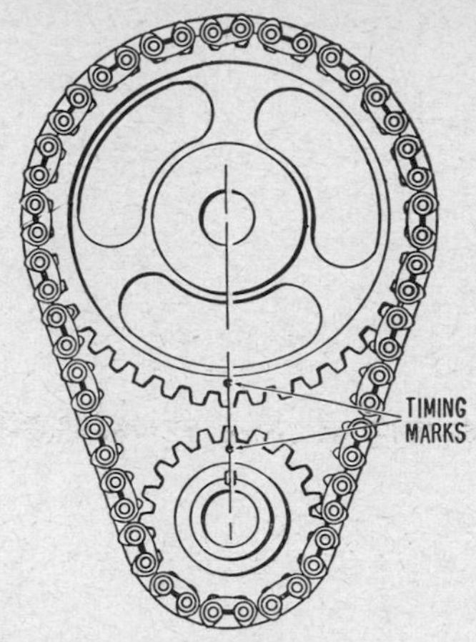

Fig. 5 Valve timing marks

CAMSHAFT, REPLACE

If it is necessary to replace the camshaft only it may be accomplished without removing the engine from the chassis. But if the camshaft bearings are to be replaced the engine will have to be removed. To remove the camshaft, proceed as follows:

V8-460

1. Drain crankcase and remove oil pan.
2. Remove timing cover, chain and sprockets as outlined previously.
3. Remove intake manifold and carburetor as an assembly.
4. Remove rocker arm covers. Back off all rocker arm stud nuts, turn rocker arms sideways and remove push rods in sequence.
5. Remove valve lifters.

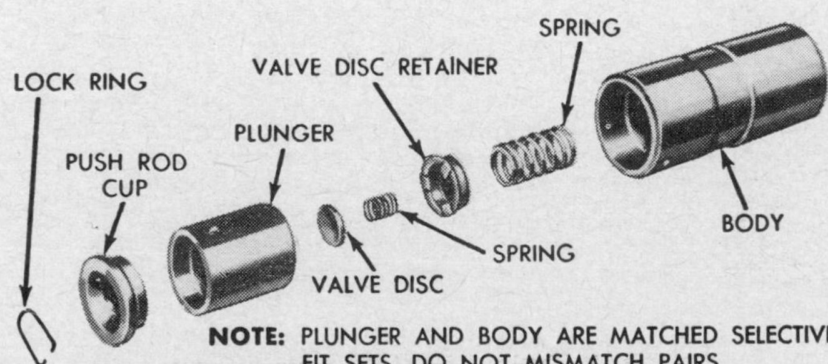

Fig. 4 Hydraulic valve lifter disassembled (typical)

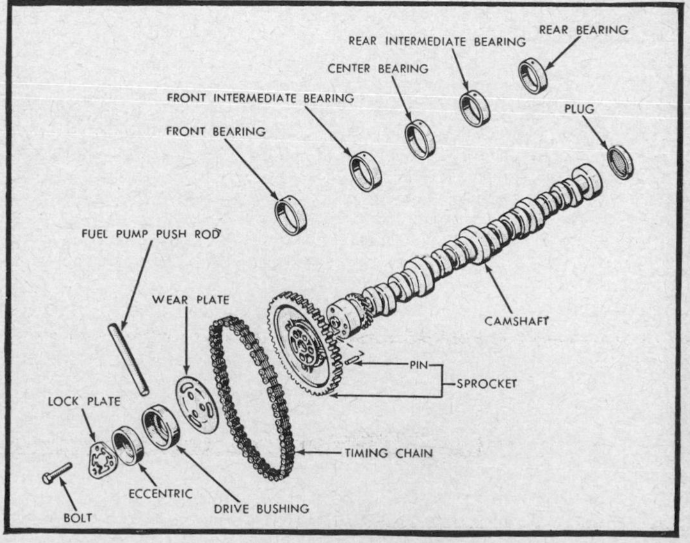

Fig. 6 Camshaft and related parts. V8-430, 462

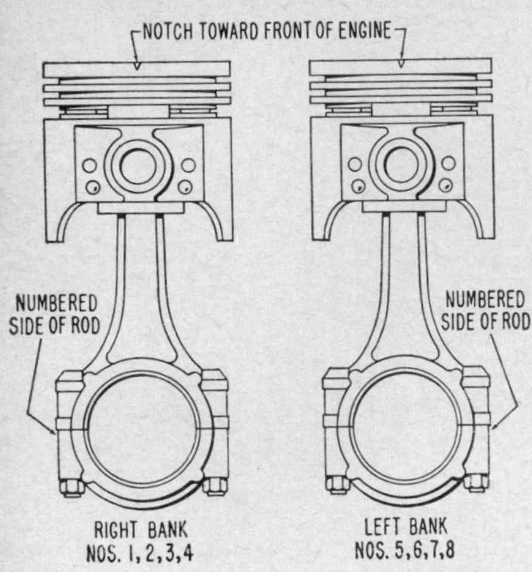

Fig. 7 Piston and rod assembly

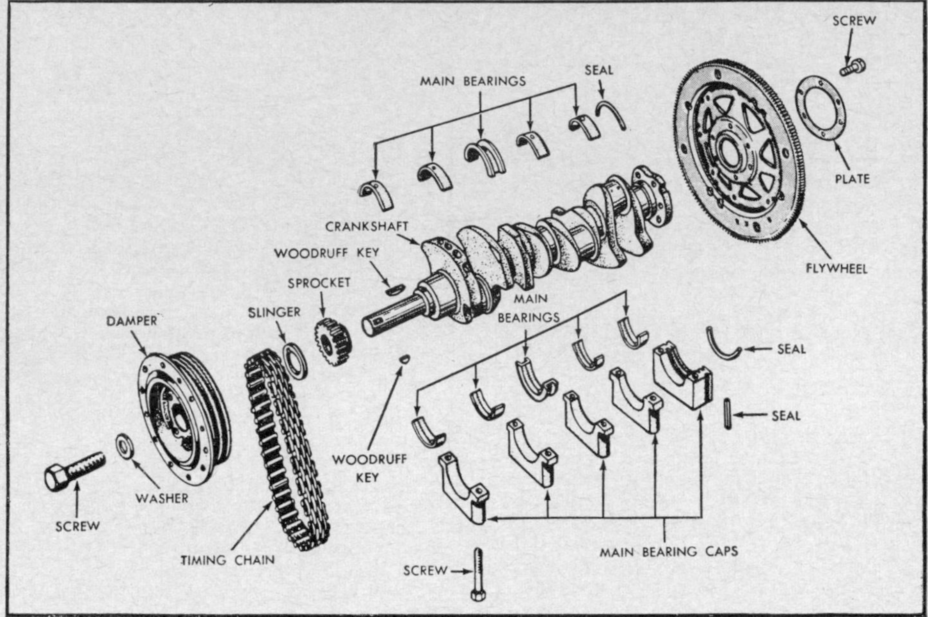

Fig. 8 Crankshaft and related parts

6. If air conditioned, unbolt and lay condenser on left fender. Secure in this position.
7. Remove grille center support.
8. Remove camshaft thrust plate bolts and carefully remove camshaft from front of engine.
9. Reverse above procedure to install.

V8-430, 462

1. Remove the timing chain cover and chain as outlined previously.
2. Remove intake manifold.
3. Remove valve lifter cover.
4. Remove the hydraulic valve lifters and place them in a rack so they may be reinstalled in their respective bores. It may be necessary to remove the carbon from the top of the lifter bore before the lifters can be removed.
5. Remove grille.
6. Carefully slide camshaft out of engine, Fig. 6.

PISTON & ROD, ASSEMBLE

If the old pistons are serviceable, make certain that they are installed on the rods from which they were removed. The assembly must be made as shown in Fig. 7.

PISTONS, RINGS & PINS

Pistons are available in standard size and oversizes .020 and .030".

Rings are available in standard size and oversizes of .020, .030 and .040".

Pins are available in standard size only.

MAIN & ROD BEARINGS

Main and rod bearings are available in standard size and undersizes of .002, .010, .020 and .030".

OIL PAN, REPLACE

V8-460

1. Disconnect radiator shroud from radiator.
2. Raise vehicle on hoist and drain crankcase.
3. Disconnect idler arm from underbody.
4. Loosen starter retaining bolts.
5. Remove cylinder block to converter housing supports.
6. Disconnect engine front support insulators from underbody crossmember. Place floor jack under front of oil pan, with block of wood between jack and oil pan. Raise engine just enough to insert 1" blocks of wood between insulators and underbody side members. Remove floor jack.
7. Remove end attachments of front stabilizer and rotate ends of bar down to raise center of bar. Remove oil filter.
8. Remove oil pan bolts and lower pan to underbody crossmember. Remove splash shield from right side of pan.
9. Disconnect pressure line at power steering pump. Remove bolts retaining pump to front cover and rotate pump to clear oil pan. Remove oil pan.
10. Reverse procedure to install oil pan.

V8-430, 462

1. Raise hood and oil level dipstick.
2. Revolve engine to position No. 1 piston 15°BTDC for oil pan clearance purposes (refer to timing marks on vibration damper).
3. Set parking brake and raise car.
4. Drain oil pan.
5. On 1963, remove generator splash shield. Remove bolt securing automatic transmission oil inlet and outlet transfer line bracket to cylinder block.
6. To allow clearance for oil pan removal, remove engine front support retaining nut. Place a block of wood on a floor jack and position jack under front leading edge of oil pan. Raise engine about 1" and insert a ½" block of wood between support insulators and underbody engine support pad. Then remove floor jack.
7. If necessary, unfasten and pull stabilizer arms downward to gain additional clearance.
8. Remove engine mounting bolts. Free oil pan from block. Remove two mounting bolts securing oil pump pick-up tube and screen assembly to oil pump, and allow pump to drop into oil pan. Then remove oil pan.

OIL PUMP

To remove the pump, drop the oil pan as outlined above. Then remove the two bolts that attach the pump to the crankcase and remove pump, gasket and the intermediate shaft.

To disassemble, remove the pump cover plate, Fig. 9, and lift out the rotor and shaft. Scrape the stake marks that hold the relief valve in the pump housing until the retainer can be removed. Then remove the retainer, spring and relief valve from the pump housing. Inspect the pump as follows:

1. With all parts clean and dry, check the inside of the pump housing and the outer race and rotor for damage or excessive wear.
2. Check the mating surface of the pump cover for wear. If this surface is worn, scored or grooved, replace the cover.
3. Measure the clearance between the outer race and housing. This clearance should be .006-.012".
4. With the rotor assembly installed in the housing, place a straight edge

over the rotor assembly and housing. Measure the clearance between the straight edge and the rotor and outer race. Recommended limits are 0015-.004".

5. Check the drive shaft-to-housing bearing clearance by measuring the O.D. of the shaft and the I.D. of the housing bearing. The recommended clearance limits are .0015-0029".
6. Inspect the relief valve spring for a collapsed or worn condition.
7. Check the relief valve piston for scores and free operation in the bore.

WATER PUMP, REPLACE

V8-460

1. Drain cooling system.
2. Remove shroud and fan.
3. Remove drive belts and water pump pulley.
4. Remove bolts attaching compressor bracket to water pump if so equipped.
5. Loosen alternator bracket and remove bolts attaching bracket to water pump.
6. Disconnect lower radiator hose, heater return tube and bypass hose at water pump.
7. Remove remaining water pump bolts and remove water pump.

V8-430, 462

1. Disconnect battery cable.
2. On air conditioned cars, remove fan shield, power booster clutch, fan and

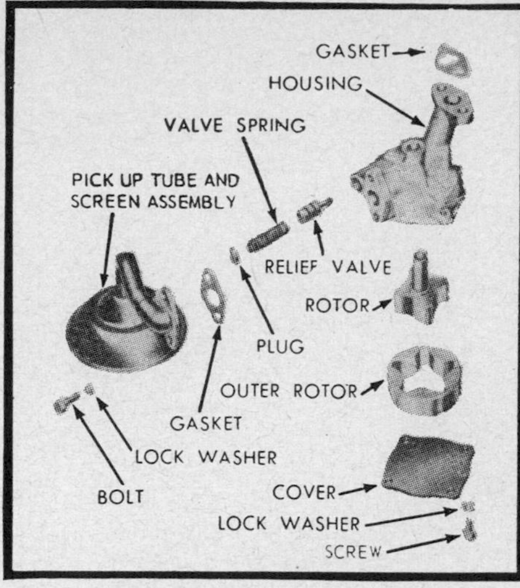

Fig. 9 Oil pump assembly

compressor drive pulley.

3. With standard cooling system, remove fan shield, fan and spacer.
4. Remove radiator supply tank.
5. Loosen clamp securing by-pass hose to water pump.
6. Remove generator splash shield.
7. Remove drive belts.
8. Remove hose from pump.
9. Remove pump mounting bolts. Then after positioning oil dipstick tube bracket and power steering pump bracket to allow removal of water pump, remove water pump.

FUEL PUMP, REPLACE

Removal

1. Remove hose clamps and fuel line hoses from pump inlet and vapor discharge connections. Disconnect fuel filter from fuel line.
2. Loosen but do not remove pump attaching capscrews. Crank engine until fuel pump eccentric on camshaft is in a position which applies the least tension on fuel pump rocker arm. Then remove capscrews and pump.
3. If replacement of fuel pump push rod is required, remove access cover from cylinder front cover and remove push rod.

Installation

1. Remove old gasket material from pump mounting pad and pump flange.
2. Install adapter and vapor discharge valve in new pump. Install heat shield and tighten retaining nuts. If pump push rod was removed, install it on eccentric sleeve and install access cover to cylinder front cover.
3. Apply sealer to both sides of new gasket. Position gasket on pump flange and hold pump in position on cylinder front cover. Make sure rocker arm is riding on push rod.
4. Press pump tight against cylinder front cover. Install and tighten retaining screws.
5. Connect fuel lines. Then operate engine and check for leaks.

Transmission, Rear Axle, Propeller Shaft & Brakes

1969 AUTO. TRANS. LINKAGE ADJUST

Although transmission linkages are slightly different in 1969, adjustment procedures remain essentially the same as those outlined in the front of this manual for 1968 models.

REAR AXLES

Figs. 1 and 2 illustrate the rear axle assemblies used on these cars. When necessary to overhaul either of these units, refer to the *Rear Axle Specifications* table in this chapter.

1963-65 Integral Housing Type

In these rear axles, Fig. 1, the axle housing and differential carrier are cast into an integral assembly. The drive pinion assembly is mounted in two opposed tapered roller bearings. The pinion bearings are preloaded by a shim behind the front bearing. The pinion is positioned by a shim in front of the rear pinion bearing.

The differential is supported in the carrier by two tapered roller side bearings. These bearings are preloaded by shims located between the differential case and

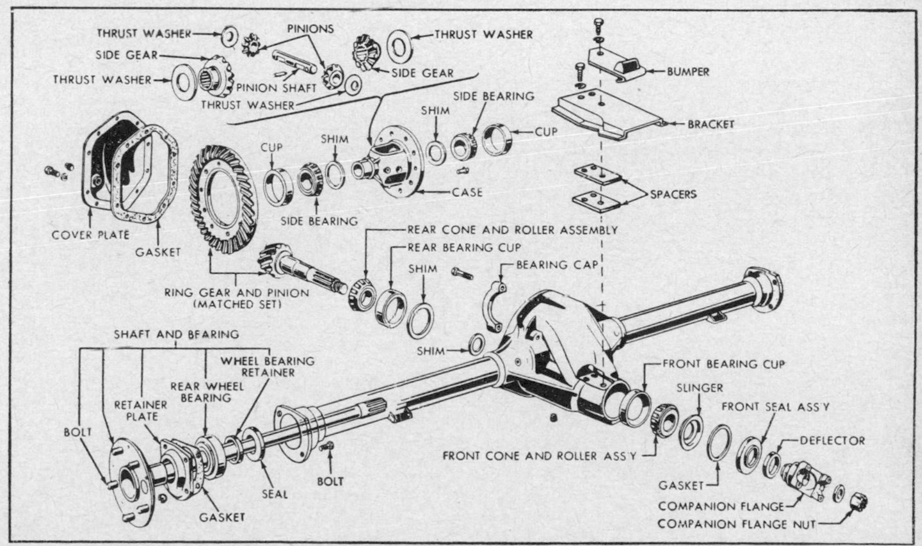

Fig. 1 Rear axle assembly. 1963-65

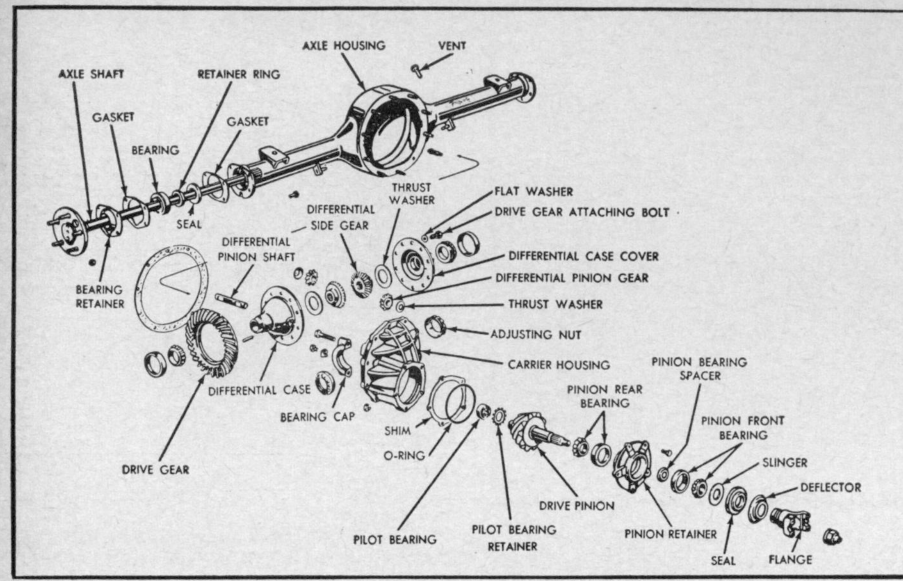

Fig. 2 Rear axle assembly. 1966-69

Service Bulletin

All Ford Built Rear Axles: Recent manufacturing changes have eliminated the need for marking rear axle drive pinions for individual variations from nominal shim thicknesses. In the past, these pinion markings, with the aid of a shim selection table, were used as a guide to select correct shim thicknesses when a gear set or carrier assembly replacement was performed.

With the elimination of pinion markings, use of the shim selection table is no longer possible and the methods outlined below must be used.

1. Measure the thickness of the original pinion depth shim removed from the axle. Use the same thickness upon installation of the replacement carrier or drive pinion. If any further shim change is necessary, it will be indicated in the tooth pattern check.
2. If the original shim is lost, substitute a nominal shim for the original and use the tooth pattern check to determine if further shim changes are required.

bearing on each side. The differential assembly is positioned for proper ring gear and pinion backlash by varying the shims. The differential case houses two side gears in mesh with two pinions mounted on a pinion shaft which is held in place by a lock pin. The side gears and pinions are backed by thrust washers.

1966-69 Removable Housing Type

In these axles, Fig. 2, the drive pinion is straddle-mounted by two opposed tapered roller bearings which support the pinion shaft in front of the drive pinion gear, and straight roller bearing that supports the pinion shaft at the rear of the pinion gear. The drive pinion is assembled in a pinion retainer that is bolted to the differential carrier. The tapered roller bearings are preloaded by a collapsible spacer between the bearings. The pinion is positioned by a shim or shims located between the drive pinion retainer and the differential carrier.

The differential is supported in the carrier by two tapered roller side bearings. These bearings are preloaded by two threaded ring nuts or sleeves between the bearings and pedestals. The differential assembly is positioned for proper ring gear and pinion backlash by varying the adjustment of these ring nuts. The differential case houses two side gears in mesh with two pinions mounted on a pinion shaft which is held in place by a pin. The side gears and pinions are backed by thrust washers. With high performance engines, an optional rear axle having a four-pinion differential is also used.

The axle shafts are of unequal length, the left shaft being shorter than the right. The axle shafts are mounted in sealed ball bearings that are pressed on the shafts.

DIFFERENTIAL CARRIER, REPLACE

1963-69 Rear Axles

In servicing the rear axles shown in Fig. 2, it is not necessary to remove the rear axle assembly for any normal repairs. The axle shafts and carrier assembly can easily be removed from the vehicle, leaving the axle housing in place.

1. Place a drain pan under the carrier and housing to catch the old grease when the carrier is separated from the housing.
2. Use a wire brush to clean dirt from the area around the carrier and housing mating surfaces. Then wipe the area clean with a cloth dampened in solvent.
3. Remove axle shafts and drive shaft as explained below.
4. Unfasten carrier from housing and lift out carrier.
5. Reverse removal procedure to in-

Fig. 3 Removing nuts from rear bearing retainer

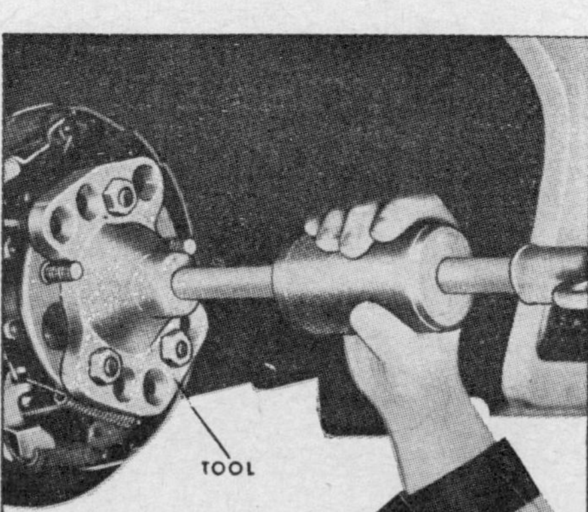

Fig. 4 Removing axle shaft with slide hammer-type puller

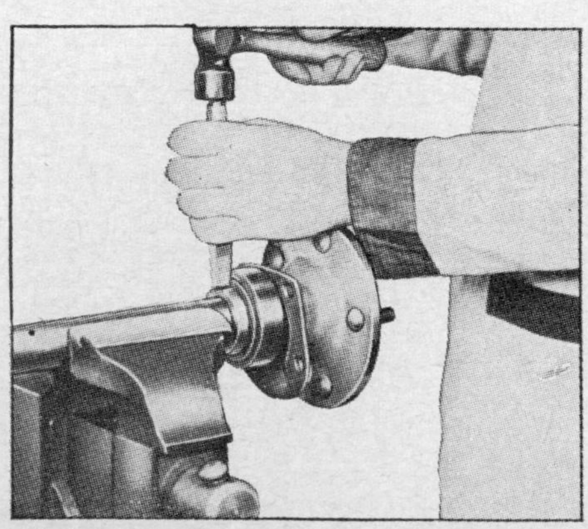

Fig. 5 Splitting bearing inner retainer for bearing removal

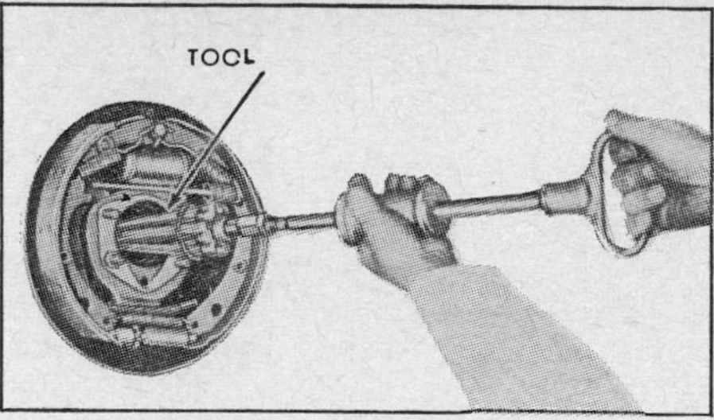

Fig. 6 Using hook-type tool to remove oil seal

stall, using a new gasket between the carrier and housing.

1963-65 Rear Axles

Since the axle tubes are pressed into the differential carrier to form a one-piece housing, major service work requires the removal of the rear axle assembly.

1. Support chassis under frame on forward side of each rear spring front hanger.
2. Drain differential housing and remove rear wheels.
3. Remove axle shafts and drive shaft as explained below.
4. Remove hydraulic brake line clip from axle housing and free line from clips. Wire hydraulic line to frame.
5. Raise axle housing with floor jack until shock absorbers start to compress. Remove nut holding shock absorber to axle seat. Detach shock absorber from axle housing and remove jack.
6. Detach U-bolts holding springs to axle housing.
7. Remove rear axle assembly from car.
8. Reverse removal procedure to install.

AXLE SHAFTS

1. Remove wheel assembly.
2. Remove brake drum from flange.
3. Working through hole provided in axle shaft flange, Fig. 3, remove nuts that secure wheel bearing retainer.
4. Pull axle shaft out of housing with a slide hammer-type puller, Fig. 4. *Brake carrier plate must not be dislodged. Install one nut to hold the plate in place after axle shaft is removed.*
5. If axle shaft bearing is to be replaced, loosen inner retainer by nicking it deeply with a chisel in several places, Fig. 5. The bearing will then slide off easily.
6. Press bearing from axle shaft.
7. Inspect machined surface of axle shaft and housing for rough spots that would affect the sealing action of the oil seal. Carefully remove any burrs or rough spots.
8. Press new bearing on shaft until it seats firmly against shoulder on shaft.
9. Press inner bearing retainer on shaft until it seats firmly against bearing.
10. If oil seal is to be replaced, use a hook-type tool to pull it out of the housing, Fig. 6. Wipe a small amount of oil resistant sealer on outer edge of seal before it is installed, Fig. 7.

Installation

1. Place a new gasket on each side of brake carrier plate and slide axle shaft into housing. Start splines into differential side gear and push the shaft in until bearing bottoms in housing.
2. Install retainer and tighten nuts to 30-40 ft. lbs.
3. Install brake drum and wheel.

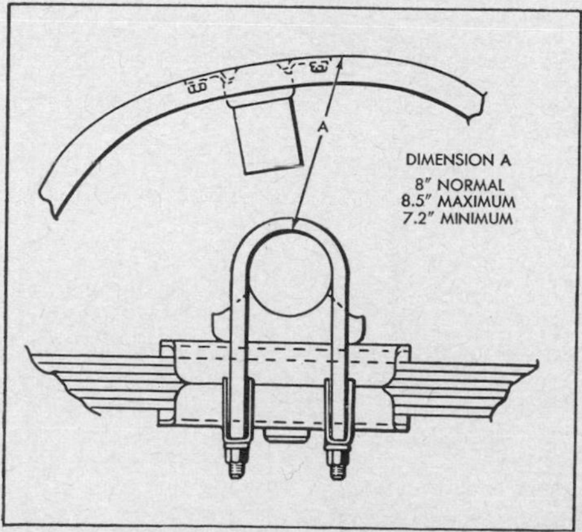

Fig. 8 Riding height measurement. 1963-65

PROPELLER SHAFT

To maintain proper drive line balance, mark the drive shaft, universal joints, slip yoke and companion flange before removing the shaft assembly so it can be reinstalled in its original position.

1. Remove cap-screws attaching slip yoke to front U-joint.
2. Push slip yoke forward on transmission output shaft and lower front of drive shaft.
3. Remove nuts, lockwashers and U-bolts attaching rear U-joint to differential drive pinion flange.
4. Remove shaft assembly.
5. Reverse removal procedure to install the assembly, and torque capscrews and U-bolts to 15-18 ft. lbs.

PROPELLER SHAFT BALANCE

If detailed parts of the drive shaft assembly have been replaced and shaft vibration is encountered after installation, disconnect the shaft at the slip yoke. Rotate the slip yoke and transmission output shaft 180°; then reconnect the shaft to the yoke. If vibration persists, disconnect the shaft at the rear axle flange and rotate the flange and drive pinion 180° and reconnect shaft to flange.

DRIVE LINE ANGLE CHECK

Vibration or "shudder" which is noticeable either on fast acceleration or when

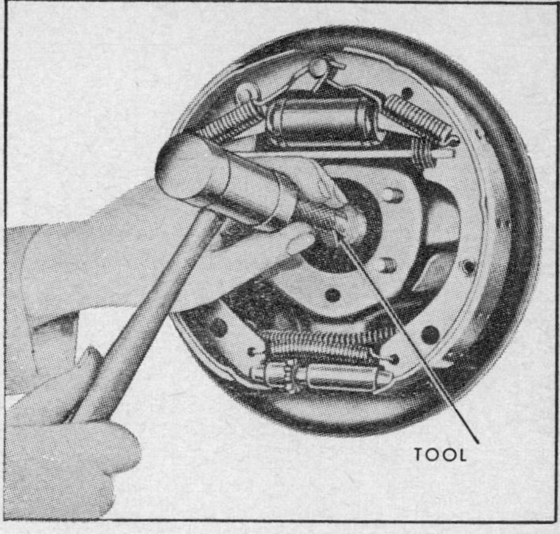

Fig. 7 Using special driver to install oil seal

coasting (using engine for a brake) may be caused by rear axle housing being loose on rear springs or by excessive drive line angles. If the rear axle U-bolts are loose, torque the nuts to 50-60 ft. lbs.

Drive line angles may be corrected by tilting the rear axle pinion nose up or down as required. Tapered shims (wedges) are available in three angles: ½, 1 and 1½ degrees with no more than one wedge to be used on a side.

To determine if shimming or a change of shimming is required, check the pinion nose angle as related to the rear riding height of the car. After checking and recording riding height as shown in Fig. 8, check the pinion nose angle as follows:

1. Measure pinion nose angle as shown in Fig. 9.
2. Compare riding height measurement and pinion nose angle with those shown in the following chart:

Riding Height	Pinion Nose Angle*
6"	4° Down
7"	3½° Down
8"	3° Down
9"	2½° Down

*Plus or minus ¼°

3. If nose angle does not compare to related riding height, remove U-bolt

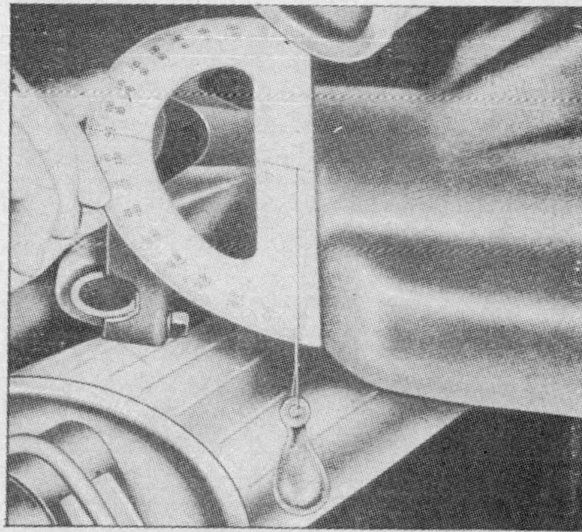

Fig. 9 Checking pinion nose angle. To make this tool, obain a common protractor and drill a small hole at the exact center of the base line (0°). Attach a string and weight as shown

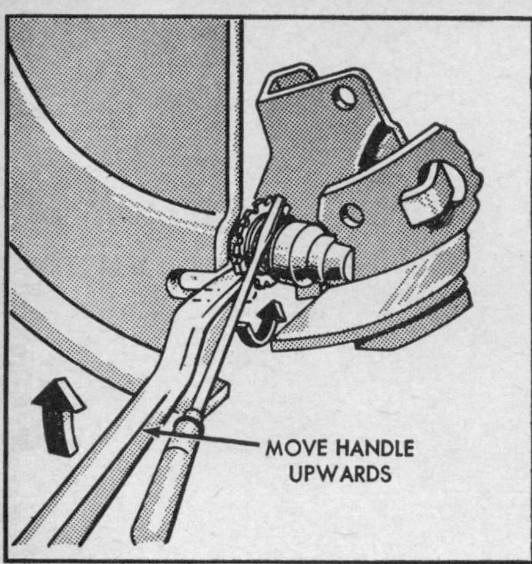

Fig. 11 Backing off brake adjustment by disengaging adjuster lever with screwdriver

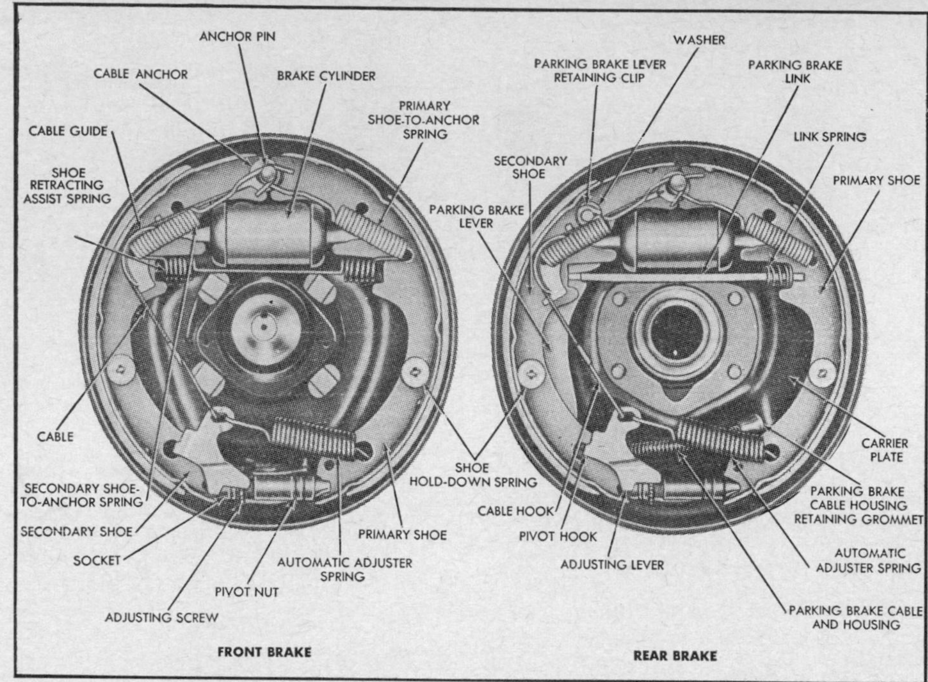

Fig. 10 Right side brakes. 1963-64. Rear only on 1965-69

nuts and install appropriate wedges between each spring insulator upper retainer and axle housing mounting pad.

4. Install and torque U-bolt nuts to 50-60 ft. lbs. Make sure lower insulator retainer contacts upper retainer.

BRAKE ADJUSTMENTS

These brakes, Fig. 10, have self-adjusting shoe mechanisms that assure correct lining-to-drum clearances at all times. The automatic adjusters operate only when the brakes are applied when the car is moving rearward or when the car comes to an uphill stop.

Although the brakes are self-adjusting, an initial adjustment is necessary when the brake shoes have been relined or replaced, or when the length of the star wheel adjuster has been changed during some other service operation.

Frequent usage of an automatic transmission forward range to halt reverse vehicle motion may prevent the automatic adjusters from functioning, thereby inducing low pedal heights. Should low pedal heights be encountered, it is recommended that numerous forward and reverse stops be made until satisfactory pedal height is obtained.

NOTE

If a low pedal height condition cannot be corrected by making numerous reverse stops (provided the hydraulic system is free of air) it indicates that the automatic adjusting mechanism is not functioning. Therefore, it will be necessary to remove the brake drum, clean, free up and lubricate the adjusting mechanism. Then adjust the brakes, being sure the parking brake is fully released.

Adjustment

1. Remove adjusting hole cover from brake backing plate and, from the backing plate side, turn adjusting screw upward with a screwdriver or other suitable tool to expand the shoes until a slight drag is felt when the drum is rotated.
2. Remove the drum.
3. While holding the adjusting lever out of engagement with the adjusting screw, Fig. 11, back off the adjusting screw ¾ turn with the fingers. *NOTE: If finger movement will not turn the screw, free it up. If this is not done, the adjusting lever will not turn the screw during subsequent vehicle operation. Lubricate the screw with oil and coat with wheel bearing grease. Any other adjustment procedure may cause damage to the adjusting screw with consequent self-adjuster problems.*
4. Install wheel and drum, and adjusting hole cover. Adjust brakes on remaining wheels in the same manner.
5. If pedal height is not satisfactory, drive the vehicle and make sufficient reverse stops until proper pedal height is obtained.

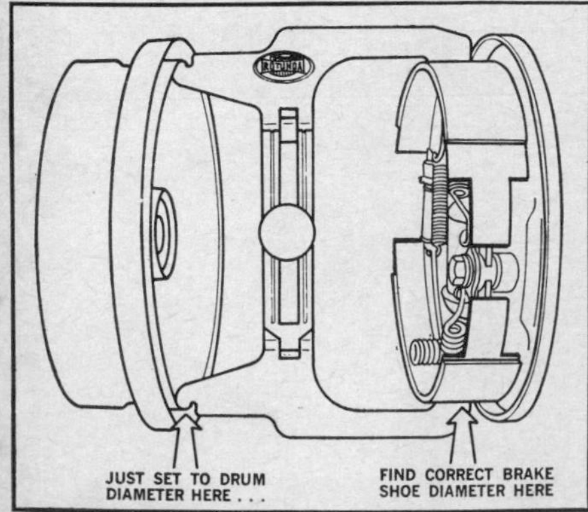

Fig. 12 Brake adjustment with gauge

SERVICE BULLETIN

REVISED BRAKE ADJUSTMENT PROCEDURE: Mid-year 1965 production and later models use a new front and rear brake backing plate which omits the adjusting slot for manual brake adjustment. The backing plates have a partially stamped knock-out slot for use ONLY when the brake drums cannot be removed in a normal manner. The open slot is then covered with a rubber plug as used in the past to prevent contamination of the brakes.

When servicing a vehicle requiring a brake adjustment, the metal knock-out plugs should NOT be removed. Rather the drums should be removed and brakes inspected for a malfunction.

Although the brakes are self-adjusting, an initial adjustment will be necessary after a brake repair, such as relining or replacement. The initial adjust-

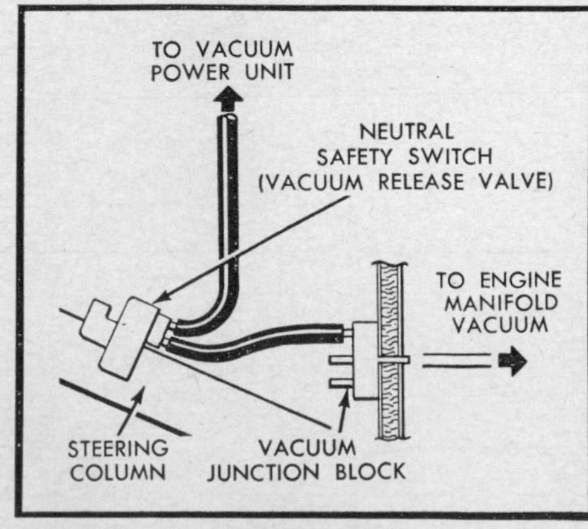

Fig. 13 Vacuum connections for automatic parking brake release. 1964-69

ment can be obtained by the new procedure which follows:

1. Use the brake shoe adjustment gauge shown in Fig. 12 to obtain the drum inside diameter as shown. Tighten the adjusting knob on the gauge to hold this setting.
2. Place the opposite side of the gauge over the brake shoes and adjust the shoes by turning the adjuster screw until the gauge just slides over the linings. Rotate the gauge around the lining surface to assure proper lining diameter adjustment and clearance.
3. Install brake drum and wheel. Final adjustment is accomplished by making several firm reverse stops, using the brake pedal.

PARKING BRAKES, ADJUST

1964-69

1. Fully release parking brake.
2. Loosen adjusting nut on equalizer rod, then turn lock nut in front of equalizer several turns forward.
3. Depress parking brake slowly until initial locking position is obtained.
4. Turn adjusting nut forward against equalizer until about 100 lbs. of force at the outside diameter of the tire is required to turn the rear wheels.
5. Tighten lock nut against equalizer.
6. Release parking brake and check to make sure that there is no drag when rear wheels are turned.

1963

1. Fully release parking brake pedal.
2. Loosen parking brake cable at equalizer lever.
3. Depress parking brake pedal 1¾″ from its normal released position.
4. Adjust cable until a slight drag is felt when turning rear wheels.
5. Release parking brake and check to make sure rear wheels can be turned without brake drag.

1964-69 Vacuum Release Unit

The vacuum power unit, Fig. 13, will release the parking brake automatically when the transmission selector lever is moved into any driving position with the engine running. The brakes will not release automatically, however, when the selector lever is in neutral or park position with the engine running, or in any other position with the engine off.

The lower end of the release handle extends out for alternate manual release in the event of vacuum power failure or for optional manual release at any time.

POWER BRAKE UNIT, REPLACE

1965-69

1. Disconnect battery.
2. Disconnect outlet lines from master cylinder.
3. Unfasten and remove master cylinder.
4. Disconnect vacuum hose at booster.
5. Disconnect power steering return line from steering gear to obtain necessary clearance. Install plug in line to keep out dirt.
6. Remove cowl-to-fender brace, and the belt that holds compressor and power steering hoses to bracket.
7. Working inside car below instrument panel, disconnect booster push rod from brake pedal as follows: Disconnect stop light switch wires at connector. Remove C-clamp retainer. Slide stop light switch off brake pedal pin just far enough for switch outer hole to clear pin. Then lift switch straight upward from pin.
8. Slide master cylinder push rod link, nylon washers and bushing off brake pedal pin.
9. Unfasten and remove booster unit from dash panel.
10. Reverse procedure to install.

1964

1. Disconnect battery ground cable.
2. Remove two left side fender apron-to-cowl braces for access.
3. From inside car, remove instrument panel lower outer extension from underside of instrument panel (6 screws). On cars with speed control, first remove control head (2 screws) and disconnect light and plug-in connector from control.
4. Remove C-washer that retains brake pedal to booster push rod. Remove nylon bushings from rod.
5. Loosen hood release handle-to-bracket lock nut and remove handle and cable from bracket to obtain clearance for removing booster retaining nut.
6. From passenger side of dash panel, remove five booster retaining nuts.
7. From under hood, disconnect vacuum hose from booster and lift off booster.
8. Reverse procedure to install.

1963

1. From inside car, disengage push rod from lever.
2. From engine compartment, remove master cylinder outlet fitting. It is not necessary to remove stop light switch.
3. Remove manifold vacuum hose from power unit.
4. Remove shoulder bolt retaining booster push rod from pedal linkage.
5. Unfasten and remove power unit from dash panel.
6. To install, reverse foregoing procedure. Bleed brake system in usual manner. Then fill master cylinder to within ¼″ of filler cap opening and replace cap.

Front End and Steering Section

FRONT SUSPENSION

1969 Mark III

Referring to Fig. 1, each wheel rotates on a spindle. The upper and lower ends of the spindle are attached to upper and lower ball joints that are mounted to an upper and lower control arm. The upper control arm pivots on a shaft assembly that is bolted to the frame. The lower control arm pivots on a bolt in the front crossmember. The struts, which are connected between the lower control arms and frame crossmember, prevent the control arms from moving forward or backward.

1963-69 Continental

The front wheel suspension is a ball joint type utilizing coil springs and double acting shock absorbers. Fore and aft movement of each front wheel is controlled by a non-adjustable type stabilizing strut connected to the suspension lower control arm and to a point forward on the front crossmember, Fig. 2. A single rubber-cored bushing is used at the inner end of the lower control arm. Caster and camber are adjusted without the use of shims but rather by movement of the serrated upper control arm shaft.

LUBRICATION

1963-69 STEERING LINKAGE: The steering linkage should be lubricated at 36,000 mile intervals. Normal breathing of socket joints permits moisture condensation within the joint. Moisture inside the joint assembly will cause no appreciable damage and the joint will function normally. However, if the moisture is concentrated in the bearing grease grooves and is frozen at the time of attempted lubrication, grease cannot flow and pressure greasing may damage the joint assembly.

Do not attempt to lubricate the steering linkage if it has set in temperatures lower than 20 deg. above zero F. The vehicle should be allowed to warm up in a heated garage for 30 minutes or until the joints accept lubrication.

IMPORTANT: A torch must not be used to heat joints because this quantity of heat will melt the nylon bearing within the joint.

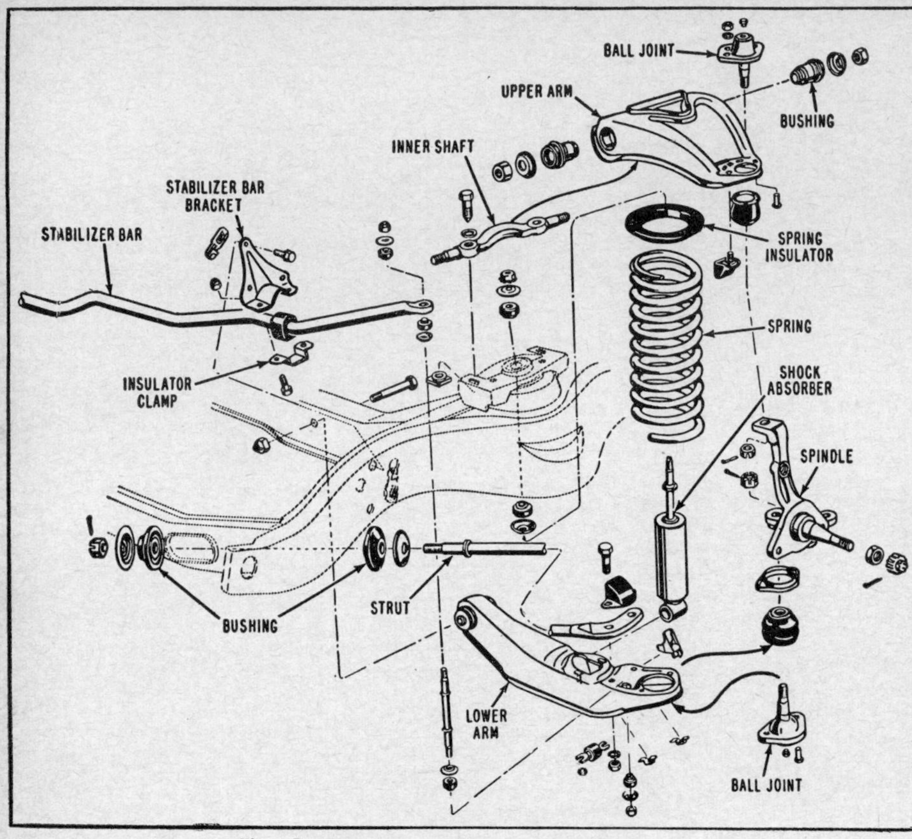

Fig. 1 Front suspension. 1969 Mark III

Ball Joint Lubrication

Ball joints should be lubricated with special grease formulated just for this purpose every 36,000 miles on 1964-69 models or 30,000 miles on 1963.

Lubrication points are fitted with screw plugs. The plugs should be removed, grease fittings installed and, after applying the grease, remove the fittings and reinstall the plugs.

WHEEL ALIGNMENT

SERVICE BULLETIN

WHEEL BALANCING DIFFERS: On cars with disc brakes, dynamic balancing of the wheel-and-tire assembly on the car should not be attempted without first pulling back the shoe and lining assemblies from the rotor. If this is not done, brake drag may burn out the motor on the wheel spinner.

The drag can be eliminated by removing the wheel, taking out the two bolts holding the caliper splash shield, and detaching the shield. Then push the pistons into their cylinder bores by applying steady pressure on the shoes on each side of the rotor for at least a minute. If necessary, use waterpump pliers to apply the pressure.

After the pistons have been retracted, reinstall the splash shield and wheel. The wheel-and-tire assembly can then be dynamically balanced in the usual way. After the balancing job has been completed, be sure to pump the brake pedal several times until the shoes are seated and a firm brake pedal is obtained.

1969 Mark III

Caster and camber can be adjusted by loosening the bolts that attach the upper suspension arm to the shaft at the frame side rail, and moving the arm assembly in or out in the elongated bolt holes, Fig. 3. Since any movement of the arm affects both caster and camber, both factors should be balanced against one another when making the adjustment.

Caster, Adjust

1. To adjust caster, install the adjusting tool as shown in Fig. 3.

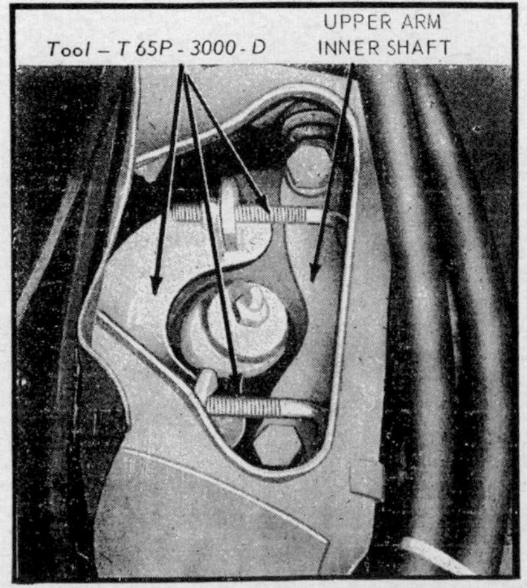

Fig. 3 Caster and camber adjusting tool. 1969 Mark III

2. Loosen both upper arm inner shaft retaining bolts and move either front or rear of the shaft in or out as necessary to increase or decrease caster angle. Then tighten bolt to retain adjustment.

Camber, Adjust

1. Loosen both upper arm inner retaining bolts and move both front and rear ends of shaft inward or outward as necessary to increase or decrease camber angle.
2. Tighten bolts and recheck caster and readjust if necessary.

1963-69 Continental

Caster, Adjust

1. Raise hood and unsnap clips retaining top of rubber bushing shield to fender apron.
2. Loosen bolts that secure upper control arm shaft to frame and, with a pry bar, move shaft in or out as required. A movement of approximately $\frac{3}{32}$" at either front or rear bolt location will change caster ½°. Inboard movement of the front bolt, or outboard movement of rear bolt, will change caster in negative direction. Outboard movement of front bolt or inboard movement of rear bolt will change caster in positive direction.
3. When adjustment is correct, torque shaft retaining bolts to 100-125 ft. lbs.

Camber, Adjust

1. Raise hood and unsnap clips retaining top of bushing rubber shield to fender apron.
2. Loosen bolts that secure upper control arm shaft to frame and, with a pry bar, move shaft in or out as required. A movement of approximately $\frac{3}{64}$" of the entire shaft will change camber ¼°. Inboard movement will change camber in negative direction. Outboard movement will change camber in positive direction.
3. When adjustment is correct, torque shaft retaining bolts to 100-125 ft. lbs.

Toe-In, Adjust

Position the front wheels in their straight-ahead position. Then turn both tie rod adjusting sleeves an equal amount until the desired toe-in setting is obtained.

WHEEL BEARINGS, ADJUST

With wheel rotating, torque spindle nut to 15-20 ft. lbs. Locate nut-lock on spindle nut so that cotter pin castellations are aligned with cotter pin hole in spindle. Back off spindle nut and nut-lock together until next castellation on nut-lock aligns with cotter pin hole in spindle, and install cotter pin.

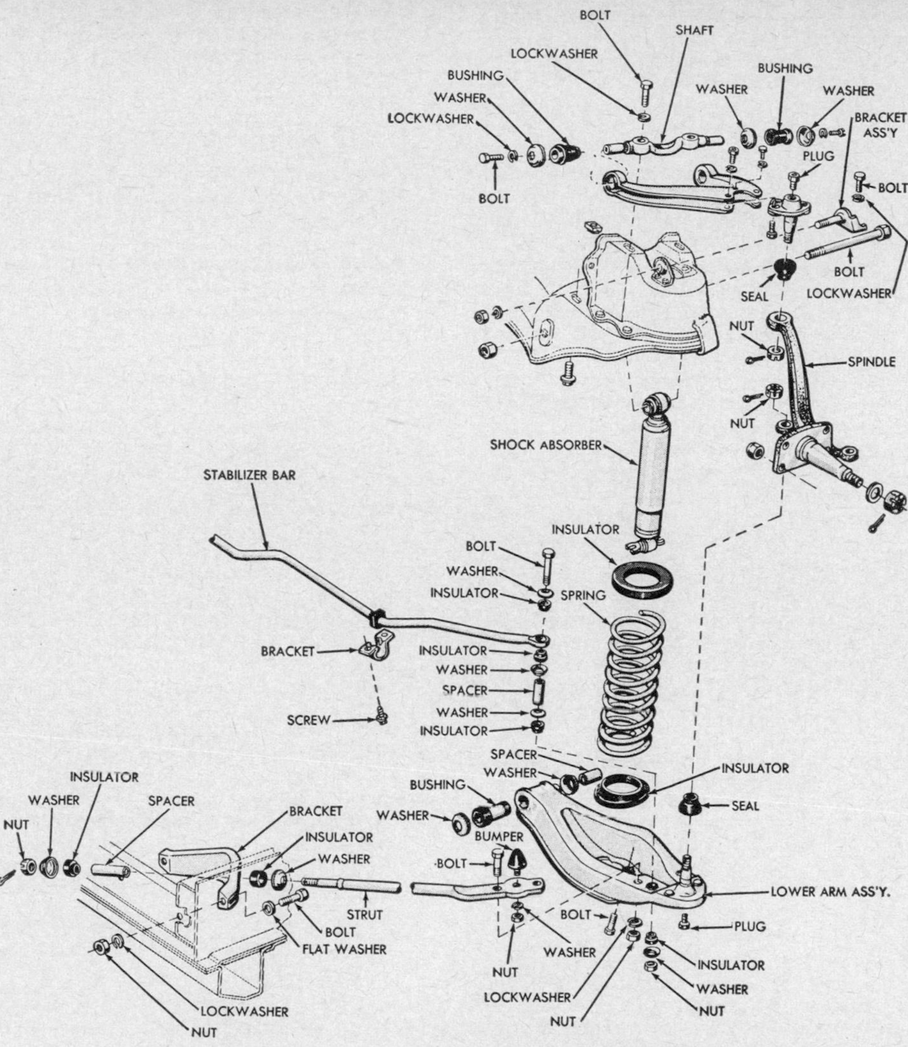

Fig. 2 Front suspension. 1963-69 Continental

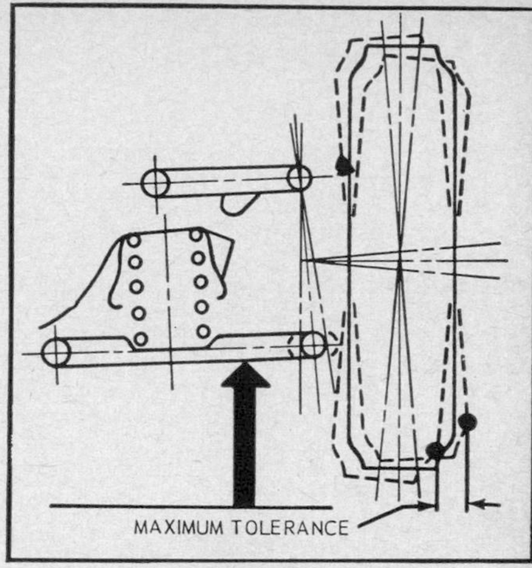

Fig. 4 Checking ball joints for wear

WHEEL BEARINGS, REPLACE
(Disc Brakes)

1. Raise car and remove front wheels.
2. Remove caliper mounting bolts.

NOTE: It is not necessary to disconnect the brake line for this operation.

3. Slide caliper off of the disc, inserting a spacer between the shoes to hold them in their bores after the caliper is removed. Position caliper assembly out of the way.

NOTE: Do not allow caliper to hang by brake hose.

4. Remove hub and disc. Grease retainer and inner bearing can now be removed.

CHECKING BALL JOINTS FOR WEAR
Upper Ball Joint

1. Raise car on floor jacks placed beneath lower control arms.
2. Grasp lower edge of tire and move wheel in and out.
3. As wheel is being moved in and out, observe upper end of spindle and upper arm.
4. Any movement between upper end of spindle and upper arm indicates ball joint wear and loss of preload. If such movement is observed, replace upper ball joint.

NOTE: During the foregoing check, the lower ball joint will be unloaded and may move. Disregard all such movement of the lower joint. Also, do not mistake loose wheel bearings for a worn ball joint.

Lower Ball Joint

1. Raise car on jacks placed under lower control arms as shown in Fig. 4.
2. With a dial indicator attached to the lower arm, position indicator so that the plunger rests against inner side of wheel rim adjacent to lower ball joint.
3. Grasp tire at top and bottom and slowly move tire in and out. Note reading on dial, which is the radial play. If the reading exceeds ¼", replace lower ball joint.

BALL JOINTS, REPLACE

The upper ball joints on Continental models are bolted to the upper control arm, while on the Mark III, the ball joints are riveted to the arm. The lower ball joints are riveted to the lower control arm on all models.

When replacing a riveted joint, remove the rivets and retain the new joint in its control arm with the bolts, nuts and washers furnished with the ball joint kit.

Use a suitable pressing tool to force the ball joint from the spindle.

SHOCK ABSORBER, REPLACE

1. Remove stud nut at upper eye of shock absorber. Remove upper eye stud bracket to crossmember bolt and remove stud bracket.
2. Unfasten shock absorber from lower control arm. Then lower and remove shock absorber.
3. Reverse above procedure to install.

COIL SPRING, REPLACE

1. Raise and support car as for replacing lower ball joint.
2. Remove brake assembly.
3. Remove shock absorber and drag strut from lower arm.
4. Disconnect stabilizer from lower arm.
5. Loosen nut from ball joint stud two turns.
6. Place jack under outer end of lower arm and raise arm several inches.
7. Install a suitable spring compressor inside spring with jaws of tool toward center of car.
8. Remove nut from ball joint stud. Lower jack until spindle and spring are free, then remove spring and insulators.
9. Reverse above procedure to install.

POWER STEERING UNIT, REPLACE

1963

1. Remove splash shield at pitman arm and pull off pitman arm.
2. Disconnect hoses from gear and tie hose ends higher than reservoir to prevent fluid loss.
3. Loosen screw or bolt that attaches flexible coupling to steering shaft.
4. Disconnect resonator inlet pipe at exhaust manifold and resonator and remove pipe.
5. Remove transmission linkage rods from equalizer shaft and force shaft outward. This compresses spring within shaft which frees shaft from inner ball joint.
6. Unfasten gear housing from body member and remove gear assembly.
7. Installation is the reverse of removal. Fill reservoir. Before checking fluid level, turn steering wheel from one extreme to the other and operate windshield wipers. This bleeds system of air and assures that it is filled with fluid.

1964

1. Disconnect pressure and return lines from steering gear housing. Plug openings and cap lines to prevent entrance of dirt.
2. Disconnect horn wire at sleeve alignment bolt.
3. Remove bolt that secures flex coupling to steering shaft.
4. Raise car and remove transmission linkage splash shield.
5. Remove exhaust manifold to resonator pipe, and remove front end crossmember.
6. Use a suitable puller to remove pitman arm.
7. Remove transmission linkage rods from equalizer shaft. Force shaft outward. This compresses a spring within the shaft which frees it from the inner ball joint.
8. Loosen (or remove) retaining bolts at lower edge of fender splash shield to obtain clearance.
9. Remove gear mounting bolts and pull steering gear from flexible coupling.
10. Reverse procedure to install.

1969 Mark III

1. Disconnect lines from steering gear and plug lines and ports to prevent entry of dirt.
2. Remove the two bolts securing flex coupling to steering gear and to column.
3. Raise vehicle and remove sector shaft nut and pitman arm.
4. Support steering gear and remove three attaching bolts. Work steering gear free of coupling and remove it from vehicle.

1965-69 Continental

1. Disconnect pressure and return lines from steering gear. Cap each line and plug each port to prevent entry of dirt.
2. Disconnect ground strap from gear housing.
3. Remove bolt that attaches flex coupling to steering gear.
4. Unfasten brace attached to torque box and frame side rail and swing brace to one side.
5. Use a puller to remove pitman arm.
6. Remove muffler inlet pipe.
7. Disconnect linkage rod from equalizer shaft. Remove equalizer stud from side rail. Move equalizer shaft up and out of the way, being careful not to lose stud or bushings.
8. Remove bolt from lower end of fender splash shield. Move shield to one side to gain access to steering gear.
9. Support gear and remove mounting bolts. Move gear downward to free it from flex joint, then rotate it counterclockwise to provide clearance between side rail and engine.

OLDSMOBILE
All Intermediate & Full Size Models

TORONADO: Service procedures that apply to the Toronado only will be found in the special Toronado supplement starting on page 2-484.

Specifications for the V6-225 and 6-250 engines are tabulated on the pages immediately following this index. For service procedures on V6-225 see the Buick Chapter. For service procedures on 6-250 see the Chevrolet Chapter.

OLD CAR SPECIFICATIONS: For 1946-62 Tune Up and Wheel Alignment Specifications see back of book.

NOTE: Material marked "F.S.C." means Oldsmobile Full Size Car, or Senior Models

INDEX OF SERVICE OPERATIONS

PAGE NO.

ACCESSORIES
Automatic Level Controls 1-41
Clock Troubles 1-11
Heater Core, Replace 2-462
Power Top Troubles 1-18
Power Window Troubles 1-18
Radio, Replace 2-462
Speed Controls, Adjust 2-462

BRAKES
Brake Troubles, Mechanical 1-17
Disc Brake Service 1-430
Hydraulic System Service 1-422
Master Cylinder, Replace 2-479
Parking Brake, Adjust 2-479
Power Brake Service 1-440
Power Brake Troubles 1-440
Power Brake Unit, Replace 2-479
Service Brakes, Adjust 2-478

CLUTCH
Clutch Pedal, Adjust 2-472
Clutch, Replace 2-472
Clutch Troubles 1-12

COOLING SYSTEM
Cooling System Troubles 1-6
Variable Speed Fans 1-39
Water Pump, Replace 2-471

ELECTRICAL
Alternator Service 1-63
Back-Up Light Switch, Replace 2-458
Dash Gauge Service 1-117
Distributor, Replace 2-456
Distributor Service:
- Standard 1-53
- Transistorized 1-47

Electrical Troubles 1-8
Flasher Location Chart .... Back of Book
Generator Service 1-91
Headlamps, Concealed Type 1-40
Horn Sounder, Remove 2-460
Ignition Coils and Resistors 1-24
Ignition Switch, Replace 2-457
Ignition Timing 2-456
Instrument Cluster Removal 2-460
Light Switch, Replace 2-457
Neutral Start Switch, Replace 2-458
Spark Plug Condition Chart 2-647
Starter Service 1-101
Starter, Replace 2-456
Starter Switch Service 1-114
Stop Light Switch, Replace 2-457
Turn Signal Switch, Replace 2-458
Turn Signal Troubles 1-11
Windshield Wiper Motor, Replace 2-461
Windshield Wiper Troubles 1-20

ENGINE
Camshaft, Replace 2-469
Cylinder Head, Replace 2-464
Engine (Conventional), Replace 2-464
Engine (Toronado), Replace 2-484

PAGE NO.

Engine Troubles 1-1
Main Bearings 2-470
Piston Pins 2-469
Piston Rings 2-469
Piston and Rod, Assemble 2-469
Pistons 2-469
Rocker Arms 2-467
Rod Bearings 2-470
Timing Case Cover (Conventional) 2-468
Timing Case Cover (Toronado) 2-484
Timing Chain, Replace 2-468
Valve Arrangement 2-466
Valve Guides 2-467
Valve Lifters 2-468
Valves, Remove 2-467

ENGINE LUBRICATION
Crankcase Ventilation (PCV) 1-29
Exhaust Emission Controls 1-30
Oil Pan, Replace 2-470
Oil Pump Repairs 2-471

FUEL SYSTEM
Carburetor Adjustments and Specs. 1-124
Crankcase Ventilation (PCV) 1-29
Exhaust Emission Controls 1-30
Fuel Pump, Replace 2-471
Fuel Pump Service 1-120
Fuel System Troubles 1-2

PROPELLER SHAFT & U JOINTS (Conventional)
Propeller Shaft 2-477
Universal Joint Service 1-418

REAR AXLE (Conventional)
Axle Shaft, Bearing and Seal 2-476
Rear Axle Description 2-475
Rear Axle Troubles 1-17

SPECIFICATIONS
Alternator 2-451
Brakes 2-455
Capacities 2-454
Carburetors 1-124
Cooling System 2-454
Crankshaft and Bearings 2-453
Distributors 2-450
Engine Tightening Torque 2-454
General Engine Specs. 2-446
Generators 2-452
Ignition Coils and Resistors 1-24
Pistons, Rings and Pins 2-453
Rear Axle 2-452
Starting Motors 2-451
Tune Up 2-447
Valve Lift 2-466
Valve Timing 2-466
Valves 2-452
Wheel Alignment 2-453

STEERING GEAR
Horn Sounder Removal 2-460
Mechanical Gear, Replace 2-483

PAGE NO.

Mechanical Gear Service 1-451
Mechanical Gear Troubles 1-18
Power Gear, Replace (Conventional) 2-483
Power Gear, Replace (Toronado) 2-494
Steering Wheel, Replace 2-460

SUSPENSION, FRONT (Conventional)
Ball Joints, Replace 2-482
Ball Joints, Check for Wear 2-482
Coil Spring, Replace 2-482
Lubrication 2-480
Shock Absorber, Replace 2-482
Suspension, Description of 2-480
Tire Wear Chart 2-648
Toe-In, Adjust 2-480
Wheel Alignment, Adjust 2-480
Wheel Bearings, Adjust 2-481
Wheel Bearings, Replace 2-482

TORONADO FRONT DRIVE
C.V. U-Joint Service 2-487
Drive Axles, Replace 2-486
Final Drive, Description of 2-489
Final Drive, Replace 2-491
Output Shaft & Seals 2-490

TORONADO FRONT SUSPENSION
Ball Joint Checks 2-494
Ball Joints, Replace 2-494
Lubrication 2-492
Toe-In, Adjust 2-492
Torsion Bars, Replace 2-492
Shock Absorber, Replace 2-494
Suspension, Description of 2-492
Wheel Alignment 2-492
Wheel Bearings, Replace 2-494

TRANSMISSIONS
Three Speed Manual:
- Replace 2-472
- Repairs 1-261
- Linkage, Adjust 2-472

Four Speed Manual:
- Replace 2-474
- Repairs 1-298
- Linkage, Adjust 2-474

Automatic Units 1-321
- 1969 Linkage 2-474

Toronado Transmission, Replace 2-484

TUNE UP
Service 1-21
Specifications 2-447

WINDSHIELD WIPER
Wiper Motor, Replace 2-461
Wiper Linkage, Replace 2-461
Wiper Switch, Replace 2-462
Wiper Troubles 1-20

OLDSMOBILE — All Intermediate & Full Size Models

VEHICLE IDENTIFICATION PLATE: 1963-67 on left front door pillar. 1968-69 on left upper dash.

ENGINE NUMBER LOCATION

1963-64 V8-371, 394: Top of center exhaust port of left cylinder head.

1963 V8-215: On front of right cylinder head.

1964-65 V6-225: On right cylinder block deck face.

1964-67 V8-330, 425: Stamped on machined pad at front of right cylinder head.

1966-69 6-250: Right side of engine block directly to rear of distributor.

1968-69 V8s: Stamped on oil fill tube.

ENGINE IDENTIFICATION CODE

YEAR	ENGINE	ENGINE PREFIX
1963	V8-215	S
	V8-394 2 Bar. Carb.	H
	V8-394 4 Bar. Carb.	J
1964	V6-225	KH
	V8-330	T
	V8-394	H
1965	V6-225	LH
	V8-330	U
	V8-400	W
	V8-425 2 Bar. Carb.	M
	V8-425 4 Bar. Carb.	N
1966	6-250	F or T
	V8-330	V or X
	V8-400	V
	V8-425 2 Bar. Carb.	M
	V8-425 4 Bar. Carb.	N
	V8-425 Toronado	T
1967	6-250	F
	V8-330, F-85	W
	4-4-2, V8-400	V
	Delmont 88, V8-330	X
	V8-425 2 Bar. Carb.	P
	V8-425 4 Bar. Carb.	R
	Toronado (Suffix T)	R
1968	6-250	VA-B-E-F
	V8-350 2 Bar. Carb.	TB-D-L
	V8-350 4 Bar. Carb.	TN
	V8-350 2 Bar. Carb.	QA-B-I-J
	V8-350 4 Bar. Carb.	QN-P-V-X
	V8-400 2 Bar. Carb.	QH
	V8-400 4 Bar. Carb.	QR-S-T-U-W
	V8-455 2 Bar. Carb.	VA-B-C-D-J
	V8-455 4 Bar. Carb.	UN-O
	V8-455 Toronado	US-T-W-V
1969	6-250	VA-B-E-F
	V8-350 2 Bar. Carb.	QI-A-B
	V8-350 4 Bar. Carb.	QV-N-P
	V8-350 2 Bar. Carb.	TL-B-D
	V8-350 4 Bar. Carb.	QX
	V8-400 4 Bar. Carb.	QW-R-S
	V8-400 4 Bar. Carb.	QU-T
	V8-455 2 Bar. Carb.	UJ-C-D
	V8-455 4 Bar. Carb.	UN-O
	V8-455 4 Bar. Carb.	UL
	V8-455 4 Bar. Carb.	US-T-V
	V8-455 4 Bar. Carb.	UW

GRILLE IDENTIFICATION

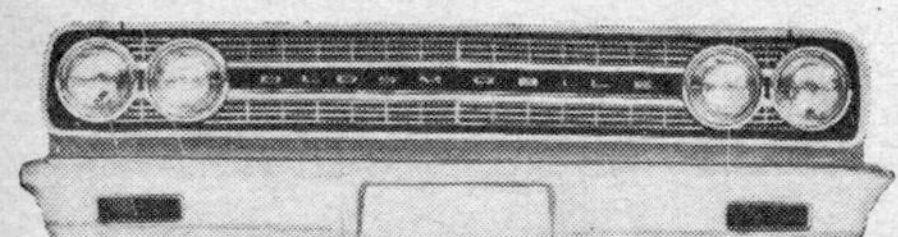

1963 F-85

1963 "88" and Super 88

1963 Starfire

1963 "98"

1964 F-85

1964 Jetstar I

1964 Jetstar "88"

1964 Starfire

1964 "98"

1965 F-85, Cutlass, Vista Cruiser

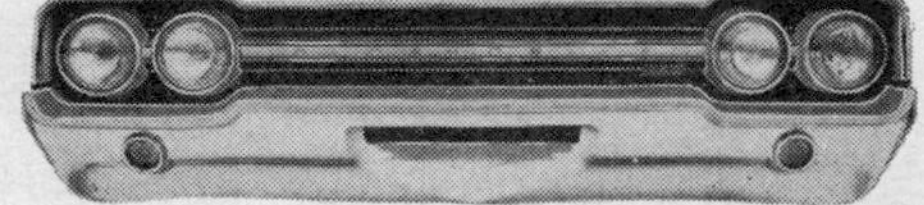

1965 "4-4-2"

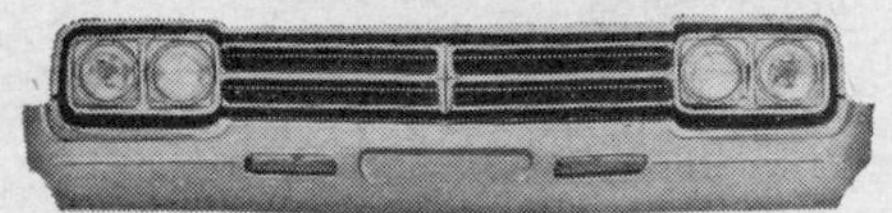

1965 Starfire & Jetstar I

1965 Dynamic, Delta & Jetstar 88

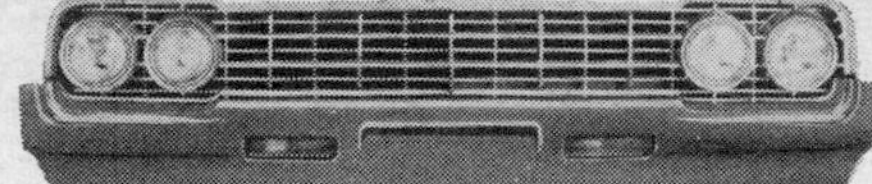
1965 98

1966 F-85, Cutlass, Vista Cruiser

1966 "4-4-2"

1966 Starfire

1966 Dynamic, Delta & Jetstar 88

1966 "98"

1966 Toronado

1967 F-85, Cutlass, Vista Cruiser

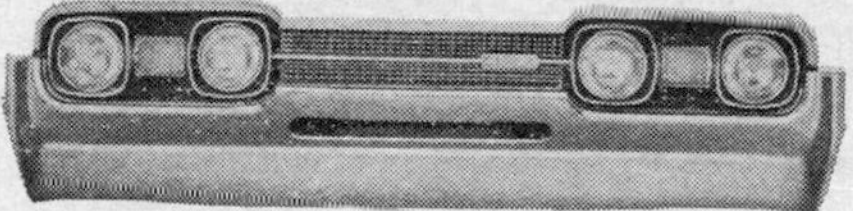
1967 "4-4-2"

1967 Delmont

1967 Delta 88

1967 98

1967 Toronado

1968 F-85, Cutlass, Vista Cruiser

1968 "4-4-2"

1968 Delmont & Delta 88

1968 98

1968 Toronado

1969 F-85, Cutlass, Vista Cruiser

1969 "4-4-2"

1969 Delta 88, Royale

1969 98

1969 Toronado

GENERAL ENGINE SPECIFICATIONS

Year	Engine	Carburetor	Bore and Stroke	Piston Displacement, Cubic Inches	Compression Ratio	Maximum Brake H.P. @ R.P.M.	Maximum Torque Lbs. Ft. @ R.P.M.	Normal Oil Pressure Pounds
1963	155 Horsepower F85.......... V8-215	2 Barrel	3.500 x 2.80	215	8.75	155 @ 4800	210 @ 3200	30
	185 Horsepower F85.......... V8-215	4 Barrel	3.500 x 2.80	215	10.25	185 @ 4800	230 @ 3200	30
	195 Horsepower F85.......... V8-215	4 Barrel	3.500 x 2.80	215	10.75	195 @ 4800	235 @ 3200	30
	215 Horsepower F85.......... V8-215	1 Barrel	3.500 x 2.80	215	10.25	215 @ 4600	300 @ 3200	30
	260 Horsepower............. V8-394	2 Barrel	4.1250 x 3.688	394	8.75	260 @ 4400	410 @ 2400	35–45
	280 Horsepower............. V8-394	2 Barrel	4.1250 x 3.688	394	10.25	280 @ 4400	430 @ 2400	35–45
	330 Horsepower............. V8-394	4 Barrel	4.1250 x 3.688	394	10.25	330 @ 4600	440 @ 2800	35–45
	345 Horsepower............. V8-394	4 Barrel	4.1250 x 3.688	394	10.50	345 @ 3800	440 @ 3200	35–45
1964	155 Horsepower F85........ ① V6-225	1 Barrel	3.750 x 3.400	225	9.00	155 @ 4400	225 @ 2400	35–45
	230 Horsepower F85.......... V8-330	2 Barrel	3.9385 x 3.385	330	9.00	230 @ 4400	325 @ 2400	35–45
	290 Horsepower F85.......... V8-330	4 Barrel	3.9385 x 3.385	330	10.25	290 @ 4800	355 @ 2800	35–45
	245 Horsepower Olds.......... V8-330	2 Barrel	3.9385 x 3.385	330	9.00	245 @ 4600	345 @ 2400	35–45
	290 Horsepower Olds......... V8-330	4 Barrel	3.9385 x 3.385	330	10.25	290 @ 4800	355 @ 2800	35–45
	345 Horsepower Olds......... V8-394	4 Barrel	4.1250 x 3.688	394	10.50	345 @ 4800	440 @ 3200	35–45
1965	155 Horsepower .... ① V6-225	1 Barrel	3.750 x 3.400	225	9.00	155 @ 4400	225 @ 2400	35–45
	250 Horsepower V8-330	2 Barrel	3.9385 x 3.385	330	9.00	250 @ 4800	335 @ 2800	35–45
	260 Horsepower............. V8-330	2 Barrel	3.9385 x 3.385	330	10.25	260 @ 4800	355 @ 2800	35–45
	300 Horsepower............. V8-425	2 Barrel	4.126 x 3.975	425	9.00	300 @ 4400	430 @ 2400	35–45
	310 Horsepower............. V8-425	2 Barrel	4.126 x 3.975	425	10.25	310 @ 4400	450 @ 2400	35–45
	315 Horsepower V8-330	4 Barrel	3.9385 x 3.385	330	10.25	315 @ 5200	360 @ 3600	35–45
	345 Horsepower V8-400	4 Barrel	4.0000 x 3.975	400	10.25	345 @ 4800	440 @ 3200	35–45
	360 Horsepower V8-425	4 Barrel	4.126 x 3.975	425	10.25	360 @ 4800	470 @ 2800	35–45
	370 Horsepower V8-425	4 Barrel	4.126 x 3.975	425	10.50	370 @ 4800	470 @ 3200	35–45
1966	155 Horsepower............. ② 6-250	1 Barrel	3.875 x 3.53	250	8.50	155 @ 4200	240 @ 2000	30–45
	250 Horsepower.............. V8-330	2 Barrel	3.9385 x 3.385	330	9.00	250 @ 4800	335 @ 2800	35–45
	260 Horsepower.............. V8-330	2 Barrel	3.9385 x 3.385	330	10.25	260 @ 4800	355 @ 2800	35–45
	310 Horsepower.............. V8-330	4 Barrel	3.9385 x 3.385	330	9.00	310 @ 5200	360 @ 3600	35–45
	320 Horsepower.............. V8-330	4 Barrel	3.9385 x 3.385	330	10.25	320 @ 5200	360 @ 3600	35–45
	350 Horsepower "442"....... V8-400	4 Barrel	4.0000 x 3.975	400	10.50	350 @ 5000	440 @ 3600	35–45
	300 Horsepower.............. V8-425	2 Barrel	4.126 x 3.975	425	9.00	300 @ 4400	430 @ 2400	35–45
	310 Horsepower.............. V8-425	2 Barrel	4.126 x 3.975	425	10.25	310 @ 4400	450 @ 2400	35–45
	365 Horsepower.............. V8-400	3 Carbs.	4.000 x 3.975	400	10.50	365 @ 5000	—	35–45
	365 Horsepower.............. V8-425	4 Barrel	4.126 x 3.975	425	10.25	365 @ 4800	470 @ 3200	35–45
	375 Horsepower.............. V8-425	4 Barrel	4.126 x 3.975	425	10.50	375 @ 4800	470 @ 3200	35–45
	385 H.P. Toronado.......... V8-425	4 Barrel	4.126 x 3.975	425	10.50	385 @ 4800	475 @ 3200	35–45
1967	155 Horsepower............. ② 6-250	1 Barrel	3.875 x 3.53	250	8.50	155 @ 4200	240 @ 2000	30–45
	250 Horsepower.............. V8-330	2 Barrel	3.9375 x 3.385	330	9.00	250 @ 4800	335 @ 2800	35–45
	260 Horsepower.............. V8-330	2 Barrel	3.9375 x 3.385	330	10.25	260 @ 4800	355 @ 2800	35–45
	300 Horsepower.............. V8-400	2 Barrel	4.000 x 3.975	400	10.50	300 @ 4600	425 @ 3000	35–50
	300 Horsepower.............. V8-425	2 Barrel	4.125 x 3.975	425	9.00	300 @ 4400	430 @ 2400	30–45
	310 Horsepower.............. V8-330	4 Barrel	3.9375 x 3.385	330	9.00	310 @ 5200	340 @ 3600	35–45
	310 Horsepower.............. V8-425	2 Barrel	4.125 x 3.975	425	10.25	310 @ 4400	450 @ 2400	30–45
	320 Horsepower.............. V8-330	4 Barrel	3.9375 x 3.385	330	10.25	320 @ 5200	335 @ 3600	35–45
	350 Horsepower.............. V8-400	4 Barrel	4.000 x 3.975	400	10.50	350 @ 5000	440 @ 3600	35–50
	365 Horsepower.............. V8-425	4 Barrel	4.125 x 3.975	425	10.25	365 @ 4800	470 @ 3200	30–45
	375 Horsepower.............. V8-425	4 Barrel	4.125 x 3.975	425	10.50	375 @ 4800	470 @ 3200	30–45
	385 H.P. Toronado.......... V8-425	4 Barrel	4.125 x 3.975	425	10.50	385 @ 4800	475 @ 3200	30–45
1968	155 Horsepower............. ② 6-250	1 Barrel	3.875 x 3.53	250	8.50	155 @ 4200	240 @ 2000	30–45
	250 Horsepower.............. V8-350	2 Barrel	4.057 x 3.385	350	9.00	250 @ 4400	355 @ 2600	35–45
	290 Horsepower.............. V8-400	2 Barrel	3.870 x 4.25	400	9.00	290 @ 4600	425 @ 2400	30–45
	300 Horsepower.............. V8-350	4 Barrel	4.057 x 3.385	350	10.25	300 @ 4800	390 @ 3600	35–45
	310 Horsepower.............. V8-350	4 Barrel	4.057 x 3.385	350	10.25	310 @ 4800	390 @ 3200	35–45
	310 Horsepower.............. V8-455	2 Barrel	4.126 x 4.25	455	9.00	310 @ 4200	490 @ 2400	30–45
	320 Horsepower.............. V8-455	2 Barrel	4.126 x 4.25	455	10.25	320 @ 4200	500 @ 2400	30–45
	350 Horsepower.............. V8-400	4 Barrel	3.870 x 4.25	400	10.50	350 @ 4800	440 @ 3200	30–45
	360 Horsepower.............. V8-400	4 Barrel	3.870 x 4.25	400	10.50	360 @ 5400	440 @ 3600	30–45
	365 Horsepower.............. V8-455	4 Barrel	4.126 x 4.25	455	10.25	365 @ 4600	510 @ 3000	30–45

Continued

GENERAL ENGINE SPECIFICATIONS—Continued

Year	Engine	Car-buretor	Bore and Stroke	Piston Dis-place-ment, Cubic Inches	Com-pres-sion Ratio	Maximum Brake H.P. @ R.P.M.	Maximum Torque Lbs. Ft. @ R.P.M.	Normal Oil Pressure Pounds
1968	375 Horsepower.............V8-455	4 Barrel	4.126 x 4.25	455	10.25	375 @ 4600	510 @ 3000	30–45
	400 Horsepower.............V8-455	4 Barrel	4.126 x 4.25	455	10.25	400 @ 4800	500 @ 3200	30–45
1969	155 Horsepower.............(2)6-250	1 Barrel	3.875 x 3.53	250	8.50	155 @ 4200	240 @ 2000	30–45
	250 Horsepower.............V8-350	2 Barrel	4.057 x 3.385	350	9.00	250 @ 4400	355 @ 2600	30–45
	310 Horsepower.............V8-350	4 Barrel	4.057 x 3.385	350	10.25	310 @ 4800	390 @ 3200	30–45
	310 Horsepower.............V8-455	2 Barrel	4.125 x 4.250	455	9.00	310 @ 4200	490 @ 2400	30–45
	325 Horsepower.............V8-350	4 Barrel	4.057 x 3.385	350	10.50	325 @ 5400	360 @ 3600	30–45
	325 Horsepower.............V8-400	4 Barrel	3.870 x 4.250	400	10.50	325 @ 4600	440 @ 3000	35–50
	350 Horsepower.............V8-400	4 Barrel	3.870 x 4.250	400	10.50	350 @ 4800	440 @ 3200	35–50
	360 Horsepower.............V8-400	4 Barrel	3.870 x 4.250	400	10.50	360 @ 5400	440 @ 3600	35–50
	365 Horsepower.............V8-455	4 Barrel	4.125 x 4.250	455	10.25	365 @ 4600	510 @ 3000	30–45
	375 Horsepower.............V8-455	4 Barrel	4.125 x 4.250	455	10.25	375 @ 4600	510 @ 3000	30–45
	390 Horsepower.............V8-455	4 Barrel	4.125 x 4.250	455	10.25	390 @ 5000	500 @ 3200	30–45
	400 Horsepower.............V8-455	4 Barrel	4.125 x 4.250	455	10.25	400 @ 4800	500 @ 3200	30–45

(1)—See Buick Chapter for service procedure on this engine. (2)—See Chevrolet Chapter for service procedure on this engine.

TUNE UP SPECIFICATIONS

OLD CAR SPECIFICATIONS: For 1946-62 Tune Up Specifications see back of book.

★ When using a timing light, disconnect vacuum tube or hose at distributor and plug opening in hose or tube so idle speed will not be affected. Timing should be set at 850 rpm on all V8s except V8-215.

Year	Engine	Spark Plug		Distributor		Firing Order	Ignition Timing★		Hot Idle Speed(7)		Comp. Press. Lbs. (3)	Fuel Pump Press. Lbs.
		Type AC	Gap Inch	Point Gap Inch	Dwell Angle Deg.		BTDC (1)	Mark	Std. Trans.	Auto. Trans. (2)		
1963	F85 Std. Tr.-155 H.P.	46FFX	.030	(4)	30	Fig. L	5°	Fig. J	550	...	160	4-5¼
	F85 Auto. Tr.-155 H.P.	46FFX	.030	(4)	30	Fig. L	7½°	Fig. J	...	500D	160	4-5¼
	F85-185 H.P.	45FF	.025	(4)	30	Fig. L	7½	Fig. J	550	500D	180	4-5¼
	F85-195 H.P.	44FF	.030	(4)	30	Fig. L	7½°	Fig. J	550	500D	180	4-5¼
	F85-215 H.P.	45FF	.025	(4)	30	Fig. L	10°	Fig. J	550	500D	180	4-5¼
	Olds.-260 H.P.	45	.030	(4)	30	Fig. E	2½°	Fig. A	550	500D	150	5-6
	Olds.-All Others	44	.030	(4)	30	Fig. E	5°	Fig. A	550	500D	180	5-6
1964	F85 Std. Tr.-V6-225(13)	45S	.030	(4)	30	Fig. D	5°	Fig. B	550	...	150	4½-5¾
	F85 Auto. Tr.-V6-225(13)	44S	.030	(4)	30	Fig. D	5°	Fig. B	...	550D	180	4½-5¾
	V8-330	44S	.030	(4)	30	Fig. F	7½°	Fig. G	600	500D	180	7-8½
	V8-394 Std. Trans.	44	.030	(4)	30	Fig. E	2½°	Fig. H	500	...	180	5-6
	V8-394 Auto. Trans.	44	.030	(4)	30	Fig. E	5°	Fig. H	...	500D	190	5-6
1965	V6-225(13)	44S	.030	(4)	30	Fig. D	5°	Fig. G	600	600D	150	4½-5¾
	V8-330 2 Bar. Carb.(5)	45S	.030	(4)	30	Fig. F	7½°(9)	Fig. K	550	500D	150	7-8½
	V8-330 2 Bar. Carb.(6)	44S	.030	(4)	30	Fig. F	7½°(9)	Fig. K	550	500D	180	7-8½
	V8-330 4 Bar. Carb.	44S	.030	(4)	30	Fig. F	7½°(9)	Fig. K	550	500D	180	7-8½
	8-400 "442"	44S	.030	(4)	30	Fig. F	7½°(9)	Fig. K	550	500D	180	7-8½
	V8-425 2 Bar. Carb.(5)	45S	.030	(4)	30	Fig. F	7½°(9)	Fig. K	550	500D	150	7-8½
	V8-425 2 Bar. Carb.(6)	44S	.030	(4)	30	Fig. F	5°(9)	Fig. K	550	500D	180	7-8½
	V8-425 4 Bar. Carb.	44S	.030	(4)	30	Fig. F	5°(9)	Fig. K	550	500D	180	7-8½
1966	6-250(8)(14)	46N	.035	.019	31-34	Fig. N	6°	Fig. M	500(7)	500D(7)	130	4-5
	6-250(10)(14)	46N	.035	.019	31-34	Fig. N	6°	Fig. M	600(7)	600D(7)	130	4-5
	8-330(5)(8)	45S	.030	(4)	30	Fig. F	7½°(9)	Fig. H	600(7)	500D(7)	150	7¾-9
	8-330(5)(10)	45S	.030	(4)	30	Fig. F	7½°(9)	Fig. H	600(7)	600D(7)	150	7¾-9
	8-330(6)(8)	44S	.030	(4)	30	Fig. F	7½°(9)	Fig. H	600(7)	500D(7)	180	7¾-9
	8-330(6)(10)	44S	.030	(4)	30	Fig. F	7½°(9)	Fig. H	600(7)	600D(7)	180	7¾-9
	8-400(8)	44S	.030	(4)	30	Fig. F	7½°(9)	Fig. H	600(7)	550D(7)	180	7¾-9
	8-400(10)	44S	.030	(4)	30	Fig. F	7½°(9)	Fig. H	600(7)	600D(7)	180	7¾-9
	8-425 2 Bar. Carb.(5)(8)	45S	.030	(4)	30	Fig. F	7½°(9)	Fig. H	550(7)	500D(7)	150	7¾-9

Continued

TUNE UP SPECIFICATIONS—Continued

OLD CAR SPECIFICATIONS: For 1946-62 Tune Up Specifications see back of book.

★When using a timing light, disconnect vacuum tube or hose at distributor and plug opening in hose or tube so idle speed will not be affected. Timing should be set at 850 rpm on all V8s except V8-215.

Year	Engine	Spark Plug		Distributor		Firing Order	Ignition Timing★		Hot Idle Speed⑦		Comp. Press. Lbs. ③	Fuel Pump Press. Lbs.
		Type AC	Gap Inch	Point Gap Inch	Dwell Angle Deg.		BTDC ①	Mark	Std. Trans.	Auto. Trans. ②		
1966	8-425 2 Bar. Carb.⑤⑩	45S	.030	④	30	Fig. F	7½°⑨	Fig. H	500⑦	500D⑦	150	7¾–9
	8-425 2 Bar. Carb.⑥⑧	44S	.030	④	30	Fig. F	5°⑨	Fig. H	550⑦	500D⑦	180	7¾–9
	8-425 2 Bar. Carb.⑥⑩	44S	.030	④	30	Fig. F	5°⑨	Fig. H	500⑦	500D⑦	180	7¾–9
	8-425 4 Bar. Carb.⑧	44S	.030	④	30	Fig. F	7½°⑨	Fig. H	550⑦	500D⑦	180	7¾–9
	8-425 4 Bar. Carb.⑩	44S	.030	④	30	Fig. F	7½°⑨	Fig. H	500⑦	500D⑦	180	7¾–9
1967	6-250⑧⑭	46N	.035	.019	31–34	Fig. N	4°	Fig. M	500⑦	500D⑦	130	3½–4½
	6-250⑩⑭	46N	.035	.019	31–34	Fig. N	4°	Fig. M	700⑪	500D⑦	130	3½–4½
	8-330, 250 H.P.⑧	45S	.030	④	30	Fig. F	7½°⑨	Fig. H	600⑪	575D⑪	150	7¾–9
	8-330, 250 H.P.⑩	45S	.030	④	30	Fig. F	7½°⑨	Fig. H	650⑪	600D⑪	150	7¾–9
	8-330, 260 H.P.⑧	44S	.030	④	30	Fig. F	7½°⑨	Fig. H	600⑪	575D⑪	150	7¾–9
	8-330, 260 H.P.⑩	44S	.030	④	30	Fig. F	7½°⑨	Fig. H	650⑪	600D⑪	150	7¾–9
	8-330 4 Bar. Carb.⑧	44S	.030	④	30	Fig. F	7½°⑨	Fig. H	600⑪	575D⑪	180	7¾–9
	8-330 4 Bar. Carb.⑩	44S	.030	④	30	Fig. F	7½°⑨	Fig. H	650⑪	600D⑪	180	7¾–9
	8-400⑧	44S	.030	④	30	Fig. F	7½°⑨	Fig. H	600⑪	600D⑪	180	7¾–9
	8-400⑩	44S	.030	④	30	Fig. F	7½°⑨	Fig. H	600⑪	600D⑪	180	7¾–9
	8-425 2 Bar. Carb.⑧	44S	.030	④	30	Fig. F	5°⑨	Fig. H	575⑫	575D⑫	150	7¾–9
	8-425 2 Bar. Carb.⑩	44S	.030	④	30	Fig. F	5°⑨	Fig. H	600⑫	575D⑫	150	7¾–9
	8-425 4 Bar. Carb.⑧	44S	.030	④	30	Fig. F	7½°⑨	Fig. H	575⑫	575D⑫	180	7¾–9
	8-425 4 Bar. Carb.⑩	44S	.030	④	30	Fig. F	7½°⑨	Fig. H	600⑫	575D⑫	180	7¾–9
1968	6-250 Std. Trans.⑭	46N	.035	.019	32	Fig. N	TDC	Fig. M	500⑪	—	130	3½–4½
	6-250 Auto. Tr.⑭	46N	.035	.019	32	Fig. N	4°	Fig. M	—	550D⑪	130	3½–4½
	8-350, 250 H.P.	45S	.030	.016	30	Fig. F	5°⑨	Fig. H	650⑪	550D⑪	150	5½–7
	8-350, 300 H.P.	44S	.030	.016	30	Fig. F	7½°⑨	Fig. H	700⑪	500D⑪	180	5½–7
	8-350, 310 H.P.	44S	.030	.016	30	Fig. F	7½°⑨	Fig. H	700⑪	500D⑪	180	5½–7
	8-400, 290 H.P.	45S	.030	.016	30	Fig. F	5°⑨	Fig. H	650⑪	550D⑪	150	5½–7
	8-400, 350 H.P.	44S	.030	.016	30	Fig. F	7½°⑨	Fig. H	700⑪	500D⑪	180	5½–7
	8-400	44S	.030	.016	30	Fig. F	2½°⑨	Fig. H	650⑪	550D⑪	180	5½–7
	8-400, 4-4-2⑩	44S	.030	.016	30	Fig. F	10°⑫	Fig. H	700⑪	500D⑪	180	5½–7
	8-455, 310 H.P.	45S	.030	.016	30	Fig. F	5°⑨	Fig. H	650⑪	550D⑪	150	5½–7
	8-455, 320 H.P.	44S	.030	.016	30	Fig. F	7½°⑨	Fig. H	700⑪	500D⑪	180	5½–7
	8-455, 4 B. Carb.	44S	.030	.016	30	Fig. F	7½°⑨	Fig. H	700⑪	500D⑪	180	5½–7
	Toronado⑩	44S	.030	.016	30	Fig. F	10°⑫	Fig. H	—	500D⑪	180	5½–7
1969	6-250 Std. Trans.⑭	R46N	.035	.019	31–34	Fig. N	TDC	Fig. M	775⑪	—	130	3½–4½
	6-250 Auto. Trans.⑭	R46N	.035	.019	31–34	Fig. N	4°	Fig. M	—	625D⑪	130	3½–4½
	8-350, 250 H.P.	R46S	.030	.016	30	Fig. F	6°	Fig. H	675⑪	600D⑪	150	5½–7
	8-350, 310 H.P.	R45S	.030	.016	30	Fig. F	8°	Fig. H	675⑪	575D⑪	180	5½–7
	8-350, 325 H.P.	R43S	.030	.016	30	Fig. F	12°	Fig. H	675⑪	575D⑪	180	5½–7
	8-400, 325 H.P.	R44S	.030	.016	30	Fig. F	8°⑨⑮	Fig. H	—	575D⑪	180	5½–7
	8-400, 350 H.P.	R44S	.030	.016	30	Fig. F	2°⑨	Fig. H	750⑪	—	180	5½–7
	8-400, 360 H.P.	R43S	.030	.016	30	Fig. F	14°⑫	Fig. H	750⑪	650D⑪	180	5½–7
	8-455, 310 H.P.	R45S	.030	.016	30	Fig. F	6°⑨	Fig. H	675⑪	600D⑪	150	5½–7
	8-455, 365 H.P.	R44S	.030	.016	30	Fig. F	8°⑨	Fig. H	—	575D⑪	180	5½–7
	8-455, 375 H.P.	R44S	.030	.016	30	Fig. F	8°⑨	Fig. H	—	575D⑪	180	5½–7
	8-455, 400 H.P.	R44S	.030	.016	30	Fig. F	10°⑨	Fig. H	—	575D⑪	180	5½–7

①—BTDC: Before top dead center.

②—D: Drive. N: Neutral. Add 50 R.P.M. to slow idle speed for air conditioned cars with A/C off.

③—Plus or minus 20 lbs.

④—Turn adjusting screw in (clockwise) until engine misfires, then back off screw ½ turn.

⑤—Low compression engine.

⑥—High compression engine.

⑦—With A/C "ON".

⑧—Without A. I. R. System.

⑨—At 850 R. P. M.

⑩—With A. I. R. System.

⑪—With A/C "OFF" and idle compensator held closed.

⑫—At 1250 R.P.M.

⑬—See Buick Chapter for service procedures on this engine.

⑭—See Chevrolet Chapter for service procedures on this engine.

⑮—Vista-Cruiser 10°.

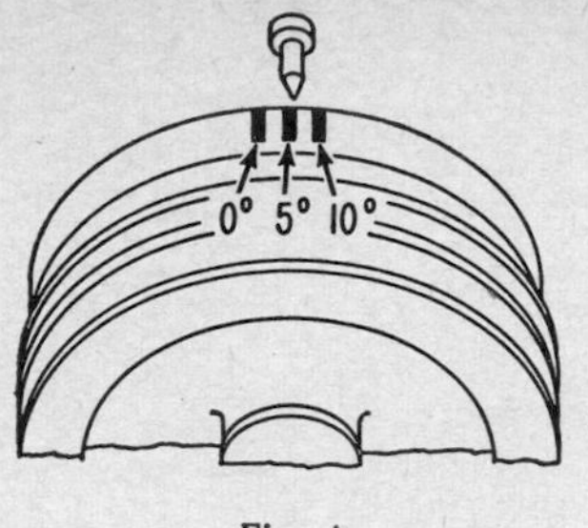

Fig. A

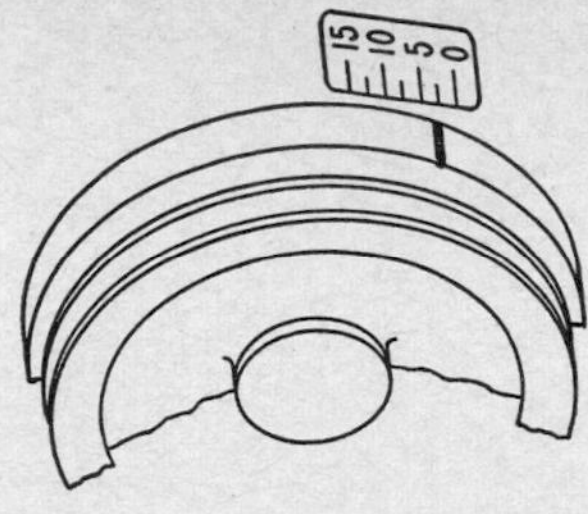

Fig. B

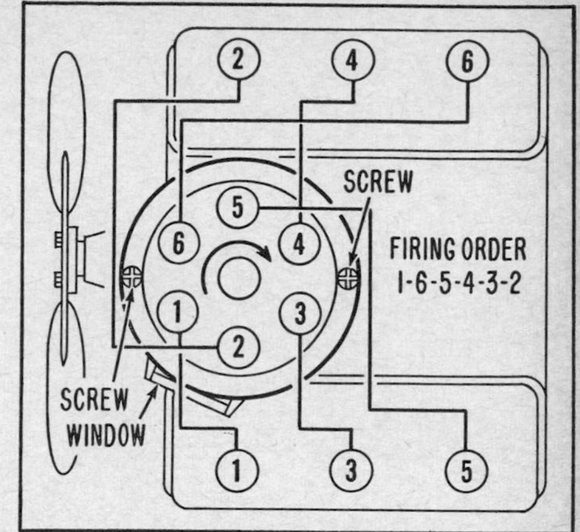

Fig. D

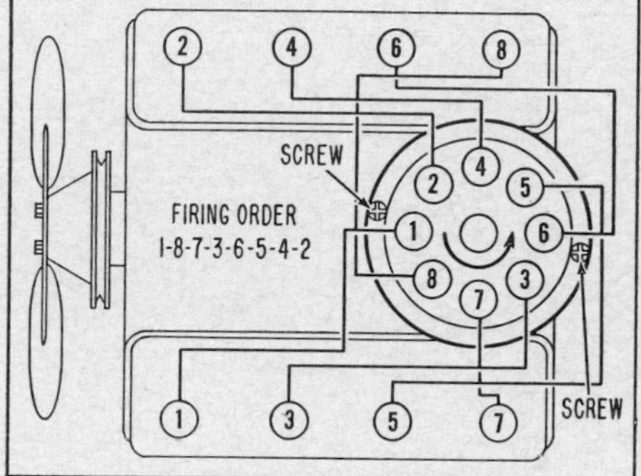

Fig. E

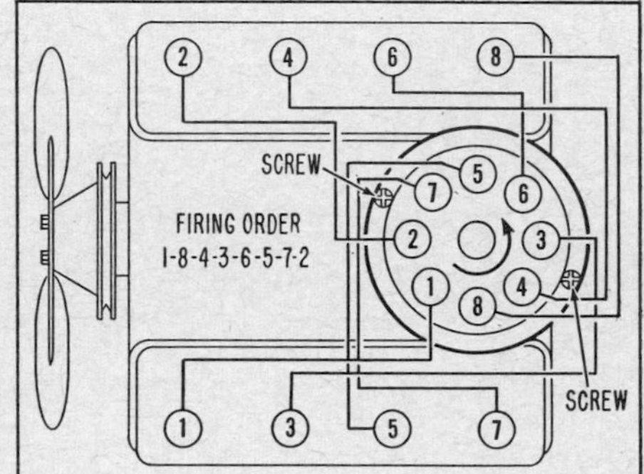

Fig. F

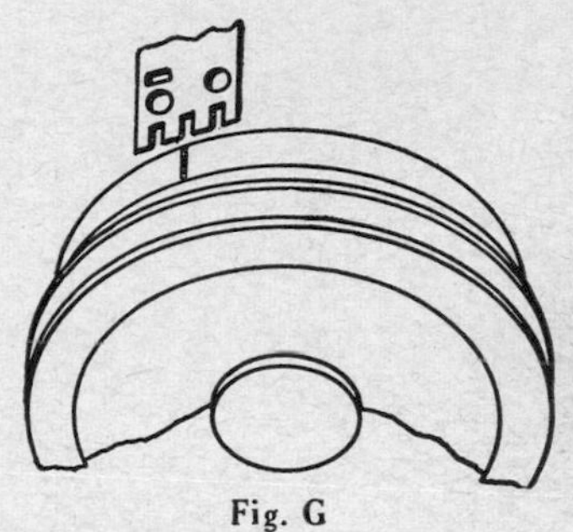
Fig. G

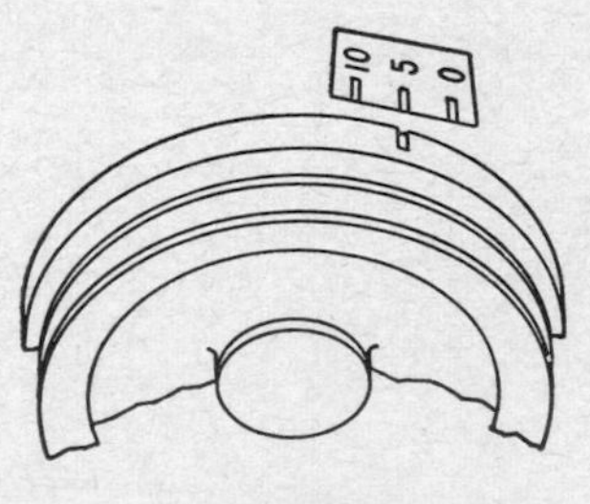

Fig. H

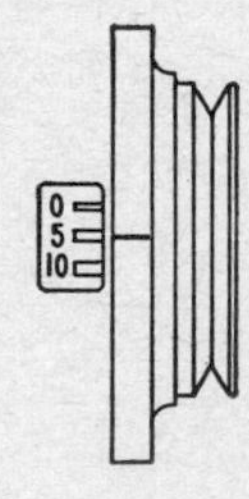

Fig. J

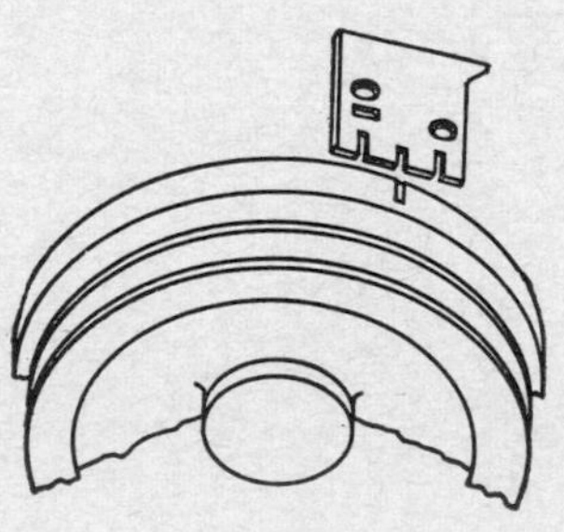

Fig. K

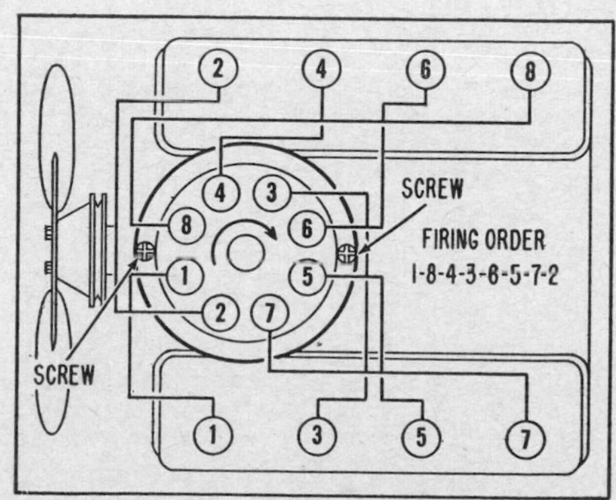

Fig. L

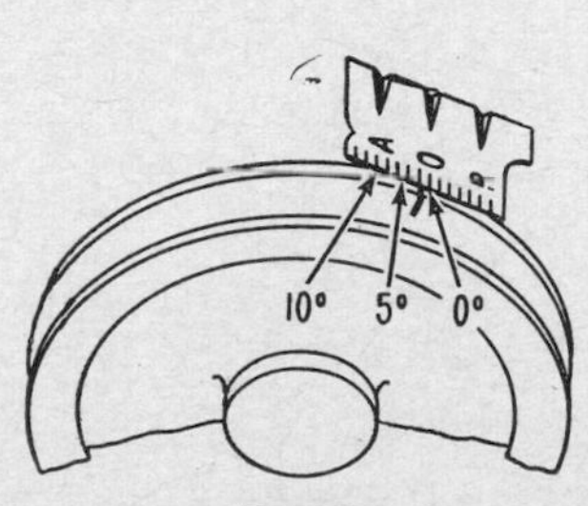

Fig. M

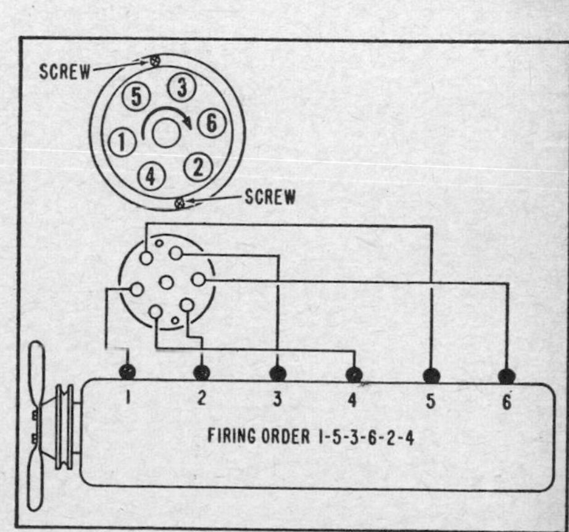

Fig. N

DISTRIBUTOR SPECIFICATIONS

★NOTE: If advance is checked on the vehicle, double the R.P.M. and degrees advance to get crankshaft figures.

Year	Model	Distributor Part No.①	Rotation ②	Breaker Gap	Dwell Angle Deg.	Breaker Arm Spring Tension	Centrifugal Advance Degrees @ R.P.M. of Distributor★		Vacuum Advance	
							Advance Starts	Full Advance	Inches of Vacuum To Start Plunger	Max. Adv. Dist. Deg. @ Vacuum
1963	F-85	1110975	C	③	30	19-23	1 @ 500	12 @ 2100	5-7	13 @ 16
	F-85	1111013	C	③	30	19-23	1 @ 500	6 @ 1000	5-7	12 @ 16
	F-85	1111021	C	③	30	19-23	1 @ 500	6 @ 1000	9-11	12 @ 17
	F-85	1111034	C	③	30	19-23	1 @ 500	12 @ 2100	9-11	12 @ 17
	Olds	1111033	CC	③	30	19-23	1 @ 400	13 @ 2000	9-11	13 @ 20
1964	F-85-V6-225	1110309	C	③	30	19-23	2 @ 500	14 @ 2100	6-8	14 @ 16
	V8-330	1111048	CC	③	30	19-23	1 @ 400	13 @ 2100	6-8	10 @ 18
	V8-330 Low Comp.	1111029	CC	③	30	19-23	1 @ 400	15 @ 2000	6-8	10 @ 18
	V8-394	1111033	CC	③	30	19-23	1 @ 400	13 @ 2000	9-11	13 @ 20
1965	V6-225	1110322	C	③	30	19-23	1 @ 500	13 @ 2100	6-8	14 @ 15
	V8-330 Low Comp.	1111029	CC	③	30	19-23	1 @ 400	15 @ 2000	6-8	15 @ 19
	V8-330	1111048	CC	③	30	19-23	1 @ 400	13 @ 2125	6-8	15 @ 19
	V8-400, 425	1111042	CC	③	30	19-23	1 @ 400	11 @ 2000	6-8	15 @ 19
	V8-425 Low Comp.	1111089	CC	③	30	19-23	1 @ 400	14 @ 2000	6-8	15 @ 19
1966	6-250	1110351	C	.020	31-34	19-23	1 @ 500	14 @ 1400	5-7	10 @ 14
	8-330 High Comp.	1111048	CC	③	30	19-23	1 @ 400	15 @ 2000	6-8	9 @ 17
	8-330 Low Comp.	1111029	CC	③	30	19-23	1 @ 400	13 @ 2125	6-8	9 @ 17
	8-400	1111042	CC	③	30	19-23	1 @ 400	11 @ 2000	6-8	9 @ 17
	8-425 2 Bar. Carb.	1111042	CC	③	30	19-23	1 @ 400	11 @ 2000	6-8	9 @ 17
	8-425 4 Bar. Carb.	1111151	CC	③	30	19-23	1 @ 600	9 @ 2100	8-10	9 @ 17
	8-425 Low Comp.	1111089	CC	③	30	19-23	1 @ 400	14 @ 2000	6-8	9 @ 17
1967	6-250	1110351	C	.019	31-34	19-23	1 @ 500	14 @ 1400	5-7	10 @ 14
	8-330 2 Bar. Carb.	1111029	CC	③	30	19-23	1 @ 400	13 @ 2125	6-8	9 @ 17
	8-400	1111042	CC	③	30	19-23	1 @ 400	11 @ 2000	6-8	9 @ 17
	8-330 4 Bar. Carb.	1111048	CC	③	30	19-23	1 @ 400	15 @ 2000	6-8	9 @ 17
	8-425 2 Bar. Carb.	1111089	CC	③	30	19-23	1 @ 400	14 @ 2000	6-8	9 @ 17
	8-425 4 Bar. Carb.	1111151	CC	③	30	19-23	1 @ 600	9 @ 2100	8-10	9 @ 17
	8-425 4 Bar. Carb.	1111179④	CC	—	—	19-23	1 @ 600	9 @ 2100	8-10	9 @ 17
	8-425 2 Bar. Carb.	1111188	CC	③	30	19-23	1 @ 325	11 @ 2000	6-8	11 @ 22
	8-425 2 Bar. Carb.	1111189④	CC	—	—	19-23	1 @ 400	14 @ 2000	6-8	9 @ 17
1968	6-250	1110351	C	.019	32	19-23	1 @ 450	14 @ 1400	5-7	10 @ 14½
	8-350 2 Bar. Carb.	1111286	CC	.016	30	19-23	1 @ 375	15 @ 2000	8-10	12 @ 20½
	8-350 4 Bar. Carb.	1111299	CC	.016	30	19-23	1 @ 325	11 @ 2000	6-8	9 @ 18½
	8-400 2 Bar. Carb.	1111466	CC	.016	30	19-23	1 @ 500	13 @ 2000	6-8	12 @ 17½
	8-400 4 Bar. Carb.	1111468	CC	.016	30	19-23	1 @ 400	11 @ 1900	10-12	8 @ 18
	8-400 4 Bar. Carb.	1111287	CC	.016	30	19-23	1 @ 425	11 @ 2000	8-10	12 @ 20½
	8-455 2 Bar. Carb.	1111288	CC	.016	30	19-23	1 @ 300	14 @ 2000	6-8	12 @ 17½
	8-455 4 Bar. Carb.	1111289	CC	.016	30	19-23	1 @ 500	7 @ 1500	6-8	12 @ 20½
	Toronado	1111292④	CC	—	—	19-23	1 @ 500	7 @ 1500	6-8	12 @ 20½
	8-455 4 Bar. Carb.	1111469	CC	.016	30	19-23	1 @ 500	11 @ 1800	8-10	12 @ 20½
1969	6-250	1110463	C	.019	32	19-23	1 @ 450	17 @ 2100	6	13 @ 16
	6-250	1110464	C	.019	32	19-23	1 @ 510	15 @ 2100	6	13 @ 16
	8-350 2 Bar. Carb.	1111961	CC	.016	30	19-23	1 @ 220	17 @ 2000	9	13¾ @ 25
	8-350 4 Bar. Carb.	1111930	CC	.016	30	19-23	1 @ 325	12 @ 2000	8	10¾ @ 23
	8-400	1111932	CC	.016	30	19-23	1 @ 425	12 @ 2000	9	12¾ @ 20½
	8-400	1111933	CC	.016	30	19-23	1 @ 325	11 @ 1900	11	9 @ 17¾
	8-455 2 Bar. Carb.	1111934	CC	.016	30	19-23	1 @ 300	15 @ 2000	7	13¼ @ 26½
	8-455 4 Bar. Carb.	1111935	CC	.016	30	19-23	1 @ 500	8 @ 1500	9	13¾ @ 25
	8-455 "GT" 4 Bar. Carb.	1111936	CC	.016	30	19-23	1 @ 450	11 @ 1800	9	13¾ @ 25

①—Stamped on distributor housing plate.
②—As viewed from above.
③—Turn adjusting screw to the right until engine misfires. Then turn screw to the left ½ turn.
④—Delco-Remy transistor ignition.

ALTERNATOR & REGULATOR SPECIFICATIONS

Year	Alternator					Regulator						
	Model	Rated Hot Output Amps.	Field Current 12 Volts @ 80°F.	Output @ 14 Volts		Model	Field Relay			Voltage Regulator		
				2000 R.P.M. Amps.	5000 R.P.M. Amps.		Air Gap In.	Point Gap In.	Closing Voltage	Air Gap In.	Point Gap In.	Voltage @ 125°F.
1963	1100616	55	1.9-2.3	32	50	1119507	.015	.030	6.3-8.3	.060	.014	13.5-14.4
	1100624	42	1.9-2.3	28	40	1119507	.015	.030	6.3-8.3	.060	.014	13.5-14.4
	1100631	37	1.9-2.3	25	35	1119507	.015	.030	6.3-8.3	.060	.014	13.5-14.4
1964	1100663	37	1.9-2.3	25	35	1119515	.015	.030	6.3-8.3	.060	.014	13.5-14.4
	1100659	42	1.9-2.3	28	40	1119515	.015	.030	6.3-8.3	.060	.014	13.5-14.4
1965-66	1100696	42	2.2-2.6	28	40	1119515	.015	.030	6.3-8.3	.060	.014	13.5-14.4
	1100694	55	2.2-2.6	32	50	1119515	.015	.030	6.3-8.3	.060	.014	13.5-14.4
1966	1100686	55	2.2-2.6	32	50	1119515	.015	.030	6.3-8.3	.060	.014	13.5-14.4
	1100694	55	2.2-2.6	32	50	1119515	.015	.030	6.3-8.3	.060	.014	13.5-14.4
	1100696	42	2.2-2.6	28	40	1119515	.015	.030	6.3-8.3	.060	.014	13.5-14.4
	1100699	42	2.2-2.6	28	40	1119515	.015	.030	6.3-8.3	.060	.014	13.5-14.4
	1100700	55	2.2-2.6	32	50	1119515	.015	.030	6.3-8.3	.060	.014	13.5-14.4
	1100704	37	2.2-2.6	25	35	1119515	.015	.030	6-3-8.3	.060	.014	13.5-14.4
	1100705	37	2.2-2.6	25	35	1119515	.015	.030	6.3-8.3	.060	.014	13.5-14.4
1967-69	1100734	42	2.2-2.6	28	40	1119515	.015	.030	6.3-8.3	.060	.014	13.5-14.4
	1100767	37	2.2-2.6	25	35	1119515	.015	.030	6.3-8.3	.060	.014	13.5-14.4
	1100777	55	2.2-2.6	—	—	1119515	.015	.030	6.3-8.3	.060	0.14	13.5-14.4
1969	1100853	37	—	—	—	—	—	—	—	—	—	—

STARTING MOTOR SPECIFICATIONS

Year	Model	Starter Number	Brush Spring Tension Oz.①	Free Speed Test			Resistance Test③	
				Amps.	Volts	R.P.M.	Amps.	Volts
1963	Olds	1107776	35	80-120②	10.6	3900-5400	290-370②	2.0
1963	F-85	1108303	35	50-80②	10.6	6750-10500	280-320	4.0
1963	F-85	1107266	35	65-100②	10.6	3600-5100	300-360②	3.5
1964	F-85	1107260	35	49-76②	10.6	6200-9400	270-310	4.3
1964	Olds	1107776	35	80-120②	10.6	3900-5400	290-370②	2.0
1965	V6-225	1107260	35	49-76②	10.6	6200-9400	270-310	4.3
	V8-330	1107298	35	65-100②	10.6	3600-5100	300-360	3.5
	V8-400, 425	1107230	35	70-105②	10.6	3800-6200	480-540②	3.0
1966	V8-330	1107298	35	65-100②	10.6	3600-5100	300-360	3.5
	V8-330	1107330	35	70-105②	10.6	3800-6200	480-540②	3.0
	V8-400, 425	1107374	35	65-100②	10.6	3600-5100	300-360	3.5
1967	8-330	1107298	35	65-100②	10.6	3600-5100	300-360	3.5
	8-330, 400, 425	1107330	35	70-105②	10.6	3800-6200	480-540②	3.0
	8-425	1107354	35	70-105②	10.6	3800-6200	480-540②	3.0
	6-250	1107399	35	49-76	10.6	6200-9400	270-310	4.3
1968-69	8-455 "98"	1108333	35	70-99②	10.6	7800-12000	—	—
	8-350, 400, 455	1108348	35	70-105②	10.6	3800-6200	480-540②	3.0
	8-350 2 B. Carb.	1108349	35	65-100②	10.6	3600-5100	300-360	3.5
	Toronado	1108352	35	70-105②	10.6	3800-6200	480-540②	3.0
	6-250	1108365	35	49-87②	10.6	6200-10700	—	—

①—Minimum. ②—Includes solenoid.

③—Check capacity of motor by using a 500 ampere meter and a carbon pile rheostat to control voltage. Apply volts listed across motor with armature locked. Current should be as listed.

OLDSMOBILE — All Intermediate & Full Size Models

D.C. GENERATOR AND REGULATOR SPECIFICATIONS

★To polarize generator, reconnect the leads to the regulator; then momentarily connect a jumper wire from the "Gen" to the "Bat" terminals of the regulator.

Year	Generator						Regulator					
								Cutout Relay				
	Generator Number	Ground Polarity	Rated Cap. Amps.	Gen. Field Ground Location★	Brush Spring Tension, Ounces	Field Current Amperes	Regulator Number	Voltage to Close Points	Armature Air Gap, Inch	Voltage Regulator Setting Volts	Current Regulator Setting Amperes	Current and Voltage Armature Air Gap, Inch
1963	11102236	N	35	External	28	1.69–1.79	1119253	12.8	.020	14.3	35	.075

VALVE SPECIFICATIONS

Year	Model	Valve Lash		Valve Angles		Valve Spring Installed Height	Valve Spring Pressure Lbs. @ In.	Stem Clearance		Stem Diameter	
		Int.	Exh.	Seat	Face			Intake	Exhaust	Intake	Exhaust
1963	V8-215-F85	Hydraulic(6)		45	45	1.75	167 @ 1.343	.001–.0025	.002–.003(1)	.3427–.3432	.3414–.3424(2)
	All Olds	Hydraulic(6)		45	45	1.837	182 @ 1.437	.001–.0025	.0015–.003	.3427–.3432	.3422–.3427
1964	V6-225(7)	Hydraulic(6)		45	45	1.64	168 @ 1.26	.002–.0025(1)	.0025–.003(1)	.3407–.3412(2)	.3402–.3407(2)
	V8-330	Hydraulic(6)		45	45	1.60	200 @ 1.20	.001–.0027	.0015–.0032	.3425–.3432	.3420–.3427
	V8-394	Hydraulic(6)		45	45	1.837	180 @ 1.437	.001–.0025	.0015–.003	.3427–.3432	.3422–.3427
1965	V6-225(7)	Hydraulic(6)		45	45	1.64	168 @ 1.26	.002–.0025(1)	.0025–.003(1)	.3407–.3412(2)	.3402–.3407(2)
	V8-330	Hydraulic(6)		45	45	1.67	180 @ 1.27	.001–.0027	.0015–.0032	.3425–.3432	.3420–.3427
	V8-400, 425	Hydraulic(6)		(4)	(4)	1.67	180 @ 1.27	.001–.003	.001–.003	.3442–.3452	.3442–.3452
1966–67	6-250(8)	1 Turn(3)		46	45	1 21/32	180 @ 1.27	.001–.0027	.0015–.0032	.3404–.3417	.3410–.3417
	V8-330	Hydraulic(6)		45	45	1.67	180 @ 1.27	.001–.0027	.0015–.0032	.3425–.3432	.3420–.3427
	V8-400, 425	Hydraulic(6)		(4)	(4)	1.67	180 @ 1.27	.001–.003	.001–.003	.3442–.3452	.3442–.3452
1968–69	6-250(8)	1 Turn(3)		46	45	1.66	186 @ 1.27	.001–.0027	.001–.0027	.3410–.3417	.3410–.3417
	8-350	Hydraulic(6)		45	46	1.67	187 @ 1.27	.001–.0027	.0015–.0032	.3425–.3432	.3420–.3427
	8-400 4 B. C.	Hydraulic(6)		(4)	(5)	1.67	187 @ 1.27	.001–.0027	.0015–.0032	.3425–.3432	.3420–.3427
	8-400 2 B. C.	Hydraulic(6)		45	46	1.67	187 @ 1.27	.001–.0027	.0015–.0032	.3425–.3432	.3420–.3427
	8-455	Hydraulic(6)		45	46	1.67	187 @ 1.27	.001–.0027	.0015–.0032	.3425–.3432	.3420–.3427
	Toronado	Hydraulic(6)		(5)	(4)	1.67	187 @ 1.27	.001–.0027	.0015–.0032	.3425–.3432	.3420–.3427

(1)—Plus or minus .001″. Guide tapers top to bottom with larger dimension at top.

(2)—Plus or minus .0005″. Guide tapers to bottom with larger dimension at top.

(3)—Tighten rocker arm adjusting screw to eliminate all push rod end clearance. Then tighten screw the number of turns listed.

(4)—Intake 30°, exhaust 45°.

(5)—Intake 30°, exhaust 46°.

(6)—No adjustment.

(7)—See Buick Chapter for service procedures on this engine.

(8)—See Chevrolet Chapter for service procedures on this engine.

REAR AXLE SPECIFICATIONS

Year	Model	Carrier Type	Ring Gear & Pinion Backlash		Pinion Bearing Preload			Differential Bearing Preload		
			Method	Adjustment	Method	New Bearings Inch-Lbs.	Used Bearings Inch-Lbs.	Method	New Bearings Inch-Lbs.	Used Bearings Inch-Lbs.
1963–64	F.S.C.(1)	Removable	(2)	(3)	Spacer	24-32	10-15	(2)	(2)	(2)
	F-85	Integral	Shims	.007–.009	Spacer	24-35	15-25	Shims	20-30	10-20
1965–67	Toronado	Removable	Shims	.006–.008	Shims	2-3	2-3	Shims	15-20(4)	5-7(4)
	All Others	Integral	Shims	.007–.009	Spacer	24-35	15-25	Shims	20-30	10-20
1968–69	Toronado	Removable	Shims	.005–.009	Shims	2-3	2-3	Shims	15-20(4)	5-7(4)
	Ser. 31-42	Integral	Shims	.005–.008	(5)	20-30	5-15	Shims	.010	.010
	Others	Integral	Shims	.007–.009	Spacer	24-35	15-25	Shims	20-30	10-20

(1)—Full size cars.

(2)—Threaded adjusters.

(3)—2 to 3 notches tight from zero end play.

(4)—Over pinion bearing preload.

(5)—Tighten pinion shaft nut with inch-pound torque wrench.

PISTONS, PINS, RINGS, CRANKSHAFT & BEARINGS

Year	Model	Piston Clearance	Ring End Gap ①		Wrist-pin Diameter	Rod Bearings		Main Bearings			
			Comp.	Oil		Shaft Diameter	Bearing Clearance	Shaft Diameter	Bearing Clearance	Thrust on Bear. No.	Shaft End Play
1963	V8-215	.0002-.0023	.010	.015	.875	1.9995-2.0005	.0002-.0022	2.2986	.0005-.0021	3	.004-.008
	V8-394	.0007-.0012	.013	.015	.9805	2.4988-2.4998	.0005-.0026	2.9993-3.0003	④	5	.004-.008
1964	V6-225⑦	.0002-.0023	.010	.015	.9394	1.9995-2.0005	.0002-.0022	2.4995-2.5005	.0005-.0021	3	.004-.008
	V8-330	.0007-.0012	.010	.015	.9805	2.1239-2.1248	.0005-.0026	2.4983-2.4993	.0005-.0021	3	.004-.008
	V8-394	.0007-.0012	.013	.015	.9805	2.4988-2.4998	.0005-.0026	2.9993-3.0003	.0005-.0021②	5	.004-.008
1965	V6-225⑦	.0002-.0023	.010	.015	.9394	1.9995-2.0005	.0002-.0022	2.4995-2.5005	.0005-.0021	3	.004-.008
	V8-330	.0007-.0012	.010	.015	.9805	2.1239-2.1248	.0015-.003	2.4985-2.4995	.0005-.0031	3	.004-.008
	V8-400, 425	.0007-.0012	.013	.015	.9805	2.4988-2.5003	.0008-.0018	2.9993-3.0003	.0015-.0031②	3	.004-.008
1966-67	6-250⑧	.0005-.0016	.010	.015	.9271	1.999-2.000	.0007-.0027	2.2983-2.2993	.0003-.0009	7	.002-.006
	V8-330	.0007-.0012	.010	.015	.9805	2.1239-2.1248	.0015-.003	2.4985-2.4995	.0015-.0031	3	.004-.008
	V8-400, 425	.0007-.0012	.013	.015	.9805	2.4988-2.5003	.0008-.0018	2.9993-3.0003	.0015-.0031②	3	.004-.008
1968-69	6-250⑧	.0005-.0016	.010	.015	.9271	1.999-2.000	.0007-.0027	2.2983-2.2988	.0003-.0029	7	.002-.006
	8-350	.0007-.0012	.010	.015	.9805	2.1238-2.1248	.0009-.0031	2.4985-2.4995	.0005-.0021⑤	3	.004-.008
	8-400	.0007-.0012	.010	.015	.9805	2.4988-2.4998	.0004-.0033	2.9993-3.0003	.0005-.0021⑥	3	.004-.008
	8-455	.0007-.0012	.013	.015	.9805	2.4988-2.4998	.0004-.0033	2.9993-3.0003	.0005-.0021⑥	3	.004-.008

①—Fit rings in tapered bores for clearance listed in tightest portion of ring travel.
②—Rear bearing .002-.0034″.
④—No. 1 and 2 .0005-.0021″, No. 3 and 4 .0008-.0024″, rear .002-.0034″
⑤—Rear .0015-.0031.
⑥—Rear .002-.0034.
⑦—See Buick Chapter for service procedures on this engine.
⑧—See Chevrolet Chapter for service procedures on this engine.

WHEEL ALIGNMENT SPECIFICATIONS

OLD CAR SPECIFICATIONS: For 1946-62 Wheel Alignment Specifications see back of book.

Year	Model	Caster Angle, Degrees		Camber Angle, Degrees				Toe-In. Inch	Toe-Out on Turns, Deg.①	
				Limits		Desired				
		Limits	Desired	Left	Right	Left	Right		Outer Wheel	Inner Wheel
1963	F-85	−¾ to −1¾	−1¼	−¾ to +¾	−¾ to +¾	Zero	Zero	0-⅛	17¾	20
	F.S.C.②	0 to −1	−½	−¼ to +¾	−¼ to +¾	+¼	+¼	0-⅛	20	23
1964	F-85	−½ to −1½	−1	−¼ to +½	−¼ to +½	+⅛	+⅛	1/16-⅛	18⅙	20
	F.S.C.②	0 to −1	−½	−¼ to +½	−¼ to +½	+⅛	+⅛	0-1/16	20	23
1965	F-85	−½ to −2	−1¼	−¼ to +½	−¼ to +½	+⅛	+⅛	⅛-3/16	18.6	20
	F.S.C.②	−½ to −1½	−1	−¼ to +½	−¼ to +½	+⅛	+⅛	⅛-3/16	18	20
1966-67	Series 33-38	−½ to −2	−1¼	−¼ to +½	−¼ to +½	+⅛	+⅛	⅛-3/16	18.6	20
	Series 52-86③	−½ to −1½	−1	−¼ to +½	−¼ to +½	+⅛	+⅛	⅛-3/16	18.3	20
	Series 52-86④	−½ to −1½	−1	−¼ to +½	−¼ to +½	+⅛	+⅛	⅛-3/16	17.7	20
	Toronado	−1½ to −2½	−2	−¼ to +½	−¼ to +½	+⅛	+⅛	0-1/16	18.2	20
1968-69	Series 31-48	−½ to −2	−1¼	−¼ to +½	−¼ to +½	+⅛	+⅛	⅛-3/16	18.6	20
	Series 54-86③	−½ to −1½	−1¼	−¼ to +½	−¼ to +½	+⅛	+⅛	⅛-3/16	18.3	20
	Series 54-86④	−½ to −1½	−¾	−¼ to +½	−¼ to +½	+⅛	+⅛	⅛-3/16	18.7	20
	Toronado	−1½ to −2½	−2	−½ to +¼	−½ to +¼	+⅛	+⅛	0-1/16	18.1	20

①—Incorrect toe-out, when other adjustments are correct, indicates bent steering arms.
②—F.S.C.-Full size car. ③—Manual Steering. ④—Power Steering.

ENGINE TIGHTENING SPECIFICATIONS★

★Torque specifications are for clean and lightly lubricated threads only. Dry or dirty threads produce increased friction which prevents accurate measurement of tightness.

Year	Engine Model	Spark Plugs Ft. lbs.	Cylinder Head Bolts Ft. Lbs.	Intake Manifold Ft. Lbs.	Exhaust Manifold Ft. Lbs.	Rocker Arm Shaft Bracket Ft. Lbs.	Rocker Arm Cover Ft. Lbs.	Connecting Rod Cap Bolts Ft. Lbs.	Main Bearing Cap Bolts Ft. Lbs.	Flywheel to Crankshaft Ft. Lbs.	Vibration Damper or Pulley Ft. Lbs.
1963	Olds	18–34	60–80	22–34	19–25	14–22	4–7	32–42	②	85–95	100
	F-85	12–17	45–55	25–30	18–24	45–55	3–5	30–35	50–60④	85–95	140–160
1964	V6-225⑫	25–35	65–70	25–35⑦	25–35	25–35	3–5	30–35	65–70	50–60	140–160
	V8-330	18–34	60–80	25–35⑦	20–25	25–35	4–7	30–42	③		100
	V8-394	18–34	60–80	22–34⑦	19–25	14–22	4–7	32–42	②	85–95	100
1965	V6-225⑫	35	70	35⑦	35	35	5	35	70	60	160
	V8-330	35	80	35⑦	25	35⑩	7	42	①	...	50
	400, 425	35	80	35⑦	25	35⑩	7	42	①		50
1966	6-250⑬	25	95	⑤	⑤	—	55⑥	35	65	60	...
	V8-330	35	80	35⑦	25	35⑩	7	42	①	...	50
	400, 425	35	80	35⑦	25	35⑩	7	42	①	...	50
1967	6-250⑬	25	95	⑤	⑤	—	55⑥	35	65	60	...
	V8-330	35	80	35⑦	25	25⑪	7	42	①	...	50
	400, 425	35	80	35⑦	25	25⑪	7	42	①	...	50
1968–69	6-250⑬	25	95	⑤	⑤	—	55⑥	35	65	60	—
	V8-350	25–35	80	25–35⑦	20–25	25⑪	7	42	60–80⑧	⑨	160
	V8-400	25–35	80	25–35⑦	20–25	25⑪	7	42	90–120	⑨	160
	V8-455	25–35	80	25–35⑦	20–25	25⑪	7	42	90–120	⑨	160

①—Rear bearing cap 120, all others 80.
②—Rear 130–160 ft. lbs., others 90–120 ft. lbs.
③—Rear bearing 90–120, all others 60–80 ft. lbs.
④—Rear bearing cap 70 ft. lbs.
⑤—Outer clamp 20 ft.-lbs., all others 30 ft.-lbs.
⑥—Inch pounds.
⑦—Clean and dip entire bolt in engine oil before tightening.
⑧—Rear 90–120 ft.-lbs.
⑨—Auto. trans. 50–65, std. trans. 85–95.
⑩—Rocker arm stud to head.
⑪—Rocker arm pivot bolt to head.
⑫—See Buick Chapter for service procedures on this engine.
⑬—See Chevrolet Chapter for service procedures on this engine.

COOLING SYSTEM & CAPACITY DATA

★Caution: Aluminum engines should have year-round protection of an ethylene glycol-water solution plus about 4 oz. of a soluble oil corrosion inhibitor (Bar's Leak or equivalent). Once a year, the system should be drained and refilled with the foregoing ingredients. Plain water and alcohol-water solutions should never be used as corrosion and eventual clogging of the cooling system will develop from their use.

Year	Model or Engine	Cooling Capacity, Qts.			Radiator Cap Relief Pressure, Lbs.		Thermo. Opening Temp. ①	Fuel Tank Gals.	Engine Oil Refill Qts. ②	Transmission Oil			Rear Axle Oil Pints
		No Heater	With Heater	With A/C	With A/C	No A/C				3 Speed Pints	4 Speed Pints	Auto. Trans. Qts. ⑫	
1963	F-85	10½	12	12	15	15	170	16	4	2	2½	4③	2
	Senior Models	19¼	20¼	22	15	15	170	21	4	2½	—	5½	5
1964	F-85	16.2	16.9	16.9	15	15	180	20	4	2	2¼	9	2¾
	Jetstar 88	16¼	17	18¾	15	15	180	21	4	2	2¼	9	2¾
	Others	19¼	20¼	22	15	15	180	21	4	2½	—	9	5
1965	6-225 Engine	10	10.7	13.1	15	15	180	20	4	2	2¼	④	3
	V8-330 Engine	16.2	16.9	19.3	15	15	180	20	4	2	2¼	④	3
	Jetstar 88	15.5	16.5	17.0	15	15	180	25	4	2	2¼	④	3
	Jetstar "1"	16.5	17.5	18.0	15	15	180	25	4	3	2¼	⑤	4¾
	Senior Models	16.5	17.5	18.0	15	15	180	25	4	3	2¼	⑤	4¾
1966	6-250	11	11¾	11¾	15	15	180	20	4	3½	—	④	3
	F85 V8	16	16¼	16¾	15	15	180	20	4	⑦	2¼	④	3
	Jetstar 88	16	16½	17	15	15	180	25	4	5	2¼	⑥	3
	"442"	17	17¼	17¾	15	15	180	20	4	⑦	2¼	④	3

Continued

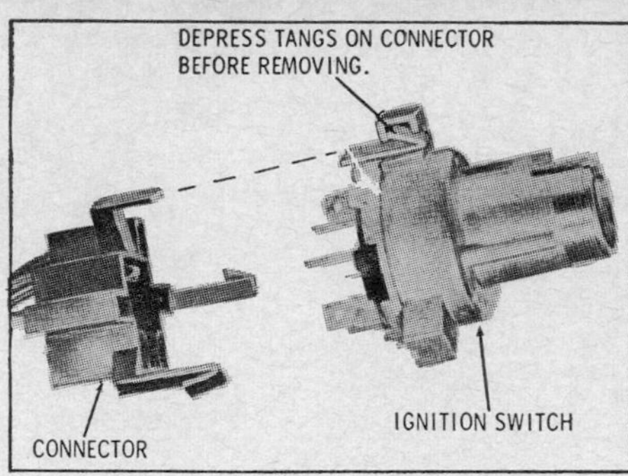
DEPRESS TANGS ON CONNECTOR BEFORE REMOVING.
CONNECTOR
IGNITION SWITCH

Fig. 1 Ignition switch 1964 F-85 and all 1965-68

manifold.

4. Disconnect starter from lower flywheel housing and remove starter by sliding battery cable loom through sleeve.

IGNITION SWITCH

1969

1. Disconnect battery ground cable.
2. Turn ignition lock to "Accessory" position.
3. Remove cover attaching bolts, loosen toe pan clamp bolts and remove trim cap from lower part of panel.
4. Remove bracket retaining nuts and lower steering column to the seat.
5. Disconnect and remove switch.
6. Be sure lock is still in "Accessory" position and insert a .090" pin through positioning hole in switch, install switch onto actuator and column and remove pin. Connect wiring and reinstall column.

1967-68 Except Toronado

1. Disconnect battery ground cable.
2. Insert key into ignition switch and press while turning fully counterclockwise. While holding key in counterclockwise position, depress lock cylinder retainer with a paper clip through small hole in face of lock cylinder.
3. Remove key and lock cylinder.
4. Remove switch escutcheon.
5. After removing switch from instrument panel, remove connector by depressing tangs.
6. Reverse procedure to install.

1967-68 Toronado

1. Disconnect battery ground cable.
2. Turn switch to ACC position.
3. Insert paper clip into small hole in front side of switch, while turning key counterclockwise the lock will pop out.
4. Remove switch escutcheon.
5. Remove switch from back side of control panel and remove wiring connector.
6. Reverse procedure to install.

1966 Toronado

1. Remove control panel.
2. Turn switch to ACC position.
3. Insert paper clip through small hole in front side of switch and depress. While turning key counterclockwise the lock will pop out.
4. Remove escutcheon and remove switch from back side of instrument panel and remove wiring connector.

1966 Except Toronado

1. Disconnect battery.
2. Insert key into switch and turn fully clockwise.
3. While holding key in clockwise position, depress lock cylinder retainer with a paper clip through small hole in face of lock cylinder.
4. Remove key and lock cylinder.
5. Remove switch escutcheon.
6. After removing switch from panel, connector can be removed as shown in Fig. 1.

1963-65

1. Disconnect harness connector from ignition switch.
2. Remove nut and escutcheon from switch.
3. Slide switch through instrument panel opening from back side of panel.

NOTE: On 1963 F-85, the ignition switch wiring connector is locked to the back of the switch by means of a special terminal tang that fits in a hole in the terminal for the accessory wire. The connector plastic insulation has a slot in it to gain access to the tang. To remove the connector, insert a small punch or awl through the slot to depress the terminal tang and disengage it from the terminal, then pull the connector from the switch. The tang automatically engages the terminal when the connector is reinstalled.

4. On 1964-65 models the switch can be removed from the connector as shown in Figs. 1 and 2.
5. Reverse removal procedure to install.

LOCK CYLINDER: To remove lock cylinder, insert key into switch and turn it fully to the right. While holding key in this position, depress the lock cylinder retainer with a paper clip through the small hole in the face of the cylinder. Then remove key and lock cylinder.

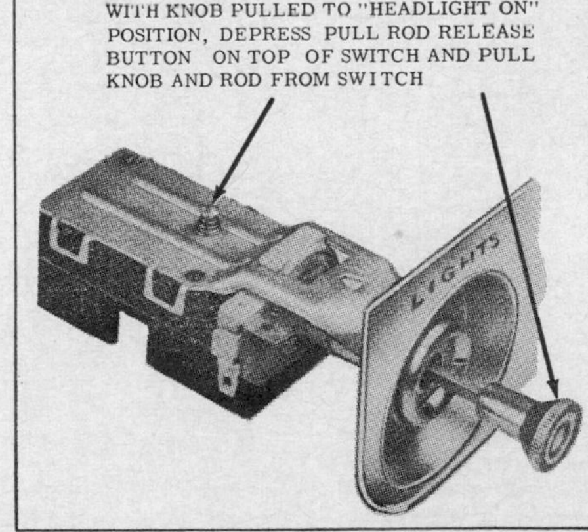
WITH KNOB PULLED TO "HEADLIGHT ON" POSITION, DEPRESS PULL ROD RELEASE BUTTON ON TOP OF SWITCH AND PULL KNOB AND ROD FROM SWITCH
LIGHTS

Fig. 3 Light switch with release button

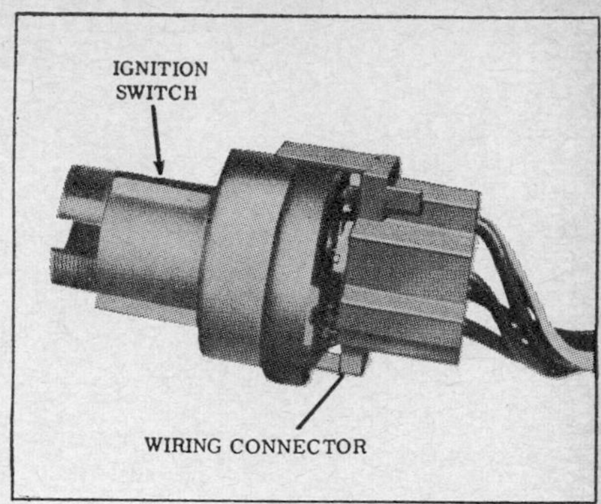
IGNITION SWITCH
WIRING CONNECTOR

Fig. 2 Ignition switch 1964 Senior Cars

LIGHT SWITCH, REPLACE

1968-69

1. On intermediate models with A/C, remove left-hand outlet duct.
2. Disconnect multiple connector from switch.
3. Pull knob out to headlight ON position, then depress spring-loaded button on switch body and pull knob out of switch assembly.
4. Remove switch escutcheon.
5. Remove switch from rear of panel.
6. On Toronado, disconnect vacuum hoses and note color coding of each.

1966-67 Toronado

1. Remove lower left-hand trim panel.
2. Remove knob by first pulling knob out to HEADLIGHT position, then depress spring-loaded button on switch body and pull knob out of switch.
3. Remove escutcheon nut.
4. Remove switch from rear of panel.
5. Disconnect wiring and vacuum hoses, being sure to note color coding of each hose.

1963-67 Except Toronado

1. Disconnect wiring from switch.
2. If switch is of the type shown in Fig. 3, remove the knob and shaft (rod) as directed in the illustration. If switch has no release button, remove knob.
3. Remove nut and switch escutcheon.
4. Remove switch from instrument panel.
5. Reverse above procedure to install.

STOP LIGHT SWITCH

NOTE: The stop light switch must be checked whenever the brake pedal height has been changed. Adjustment is made on the brake pedal arm. To obtain proper operation of the stop lights, refer to Figs. 5 to 8.

1967-69

The stop light switch is attached to the brake pedal bracket and is actuated by

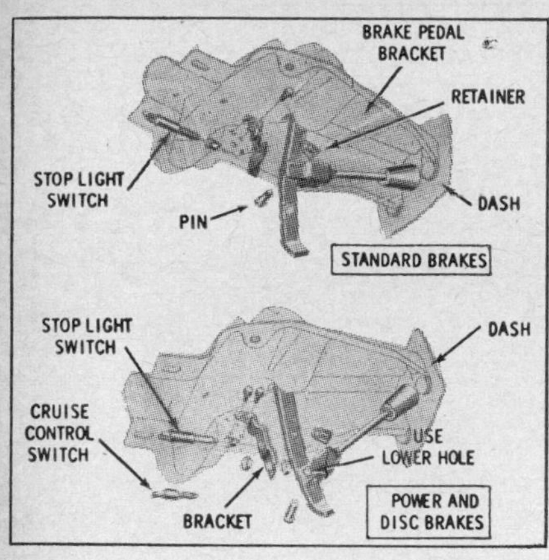

Fig. 4 Brake switch installation. 1967-69

the brake pedal arm, Fig. 4. When installing the switch, insert switch into tubular clip until switch body seats on tube clip. Pull brake pedal rearward until it contacts brake pedal stop. This moves the switch in the tubular clip providing proper adjustment.

1963-64 Senior Models

1. With brake pedal in fully released position, turn adjusting screw until stop lights just go off, then unscrew adjusting screw three turns, Figs. 4 and 5.
2. Check stop light switch operation by applying and releasing brake, making certain that stop lights go off when brake pedal is fully released.

1965-66

1. Referring to Fig. 7, and with brake pedal height correctly adjusted, insert switch into tubular clip until switch body seats in tube clip.
2. Pull brake pedal rearward until it contacts pedal stop. This moves switch in tubular clip, providing proper adjustment.

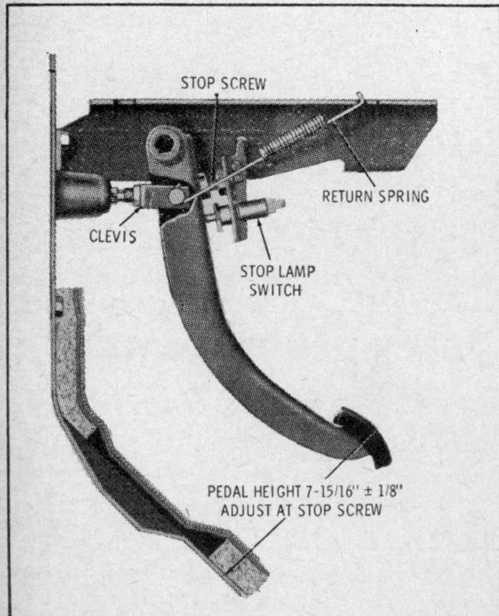

Fig. 7 Stop light switch. 1965-66

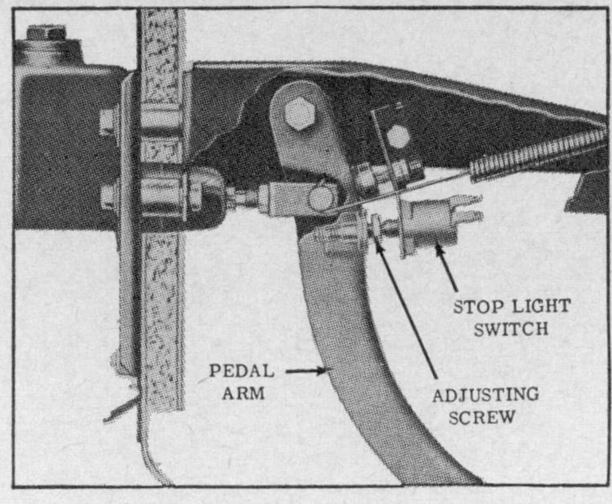

Fig. 5 Stop light switch (standard brakes). 1963-64 Senior Cars

1963-64 F-85

Referring to Fig. 8, the switch can be adjusted in and out of the mounting bracket by loosening the lock nuts and moving the switch in the bracket. Tighten nuts.

NEUTRAL START & BACK-UP LIGHT SWITCH

The neutral safety switch is mounted on the steering column or inside the console on floor shift models with automatic transmission.

Checking

1. Apply parking brake firmly.
2. Position selector lever into "D" range and turn ignition switch to "Start".
3. While holding switch on "Start", slowly move selector lever toward "N" position until engine cranks and starts.
4. Without moving selector lever after engine starts, depress accelerator pedal slightly to determine whether or not transmission is in gear. If switch is properly adjusted, transmission will not be in gear.

NOTE: If equipped with back-up lights, lights should operate with ignition on and selector lever in reverse.

1963 All & 1964 Senior Cars

Adjustment

1. Remove console control panel if equipped.
2. Loosen switch attaching screws.
3. With selector lever in neutral, position switch so that a .090" gauge pin can be inserted through hole in switch arm and into hole in face of switch.
4. Tighten switch attaching screws and remove gauge pin.
5. Recheck adjustment and install console panel.

1964 F-85 & All 1965-68

Adjustment

1. Remove console if so equipped.
2. Remove switch attaching screws.
3. With ignition off, position selector lever in "D".
4. Align slot in contact support with hole in bracket and insert a .090" pin, Figs. 9 and 12.
5. Position contact support drive slot over shifter tube drive tang and install mounting screws.

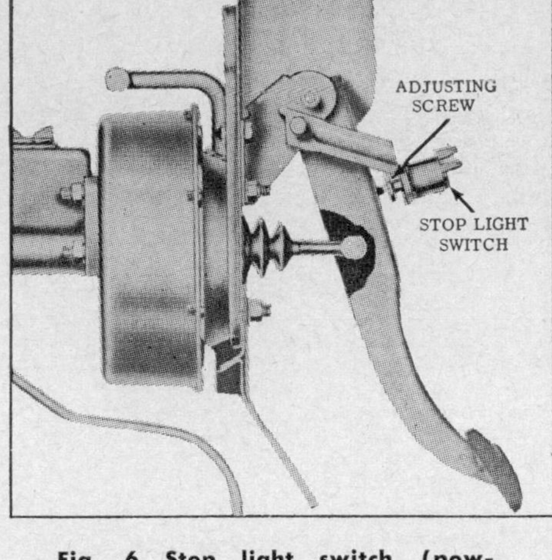

Fig. 6 Stop light switch (power brakes). 1963-64 Senior Cars

TURN SIGNAL SWITCH

1969

1. Disconnect battery ground cable.
2. Remove steering wheel.
3. Remove cover screws and cover.
4. Using suitable compressor, depress lock plate far enough to remove the "C" ring from shaft.

NOTE: On Tilt & Travel, compressor must be positioned on large lips of cancelling cam.

5. Remove lock plate, cancelling cam, spring and signal lever.
6. Depress hazard warning knob then unscrew knob and remove.
7. Position housing in center position and remove three switch attaching screws.

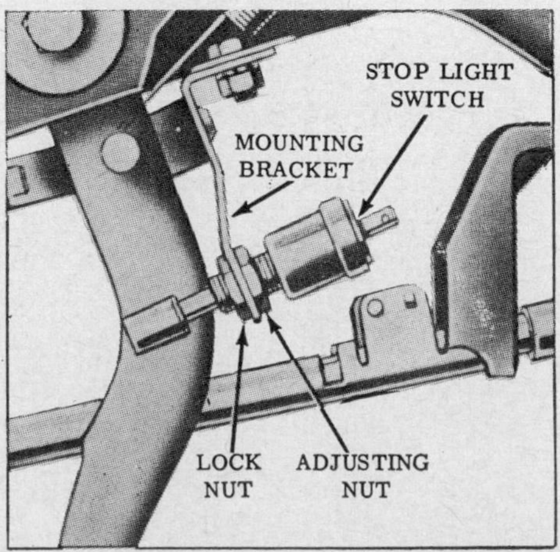

Fig. 8 Stop light switch. 1963-64 F-85

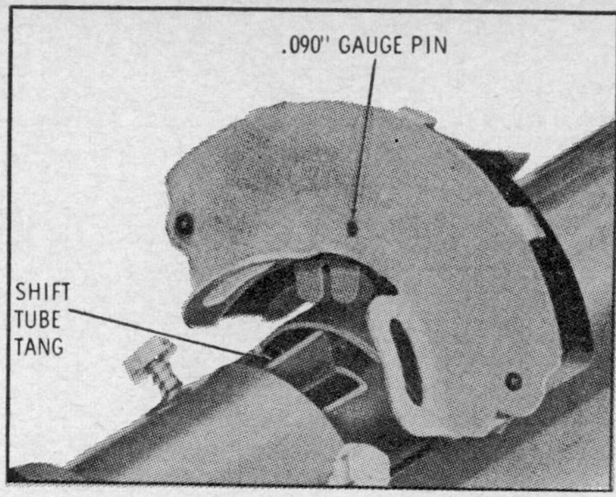

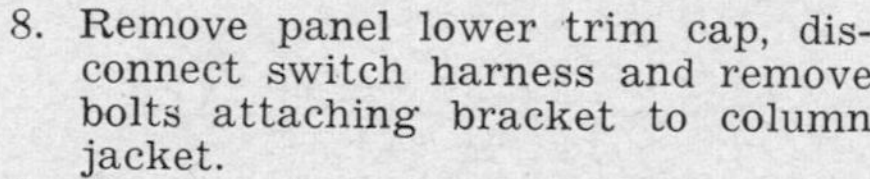
Fig. 9 Neutral safety switch adjustment. 1964 F-85 and all 1965-69 column type

8. Remove panel lower trim cap, disconnect switch harness and remove bolts attaching bracket to column jacket.
9. Disconnect shift indicator if equipped.
10. Remove two nuts holding column in position, remove bracket and wire protector while holding column in position then loosely install bracket to hold column in place.
11. Tape switch wires at connector keeping wires flat, then carefully remove wires and switch.

1967-68

1. Remove steering wheel, cancelling cam and spring from upper steering shaft.
2. Remove turn signal lever.
3. Unscrew hazard switch knob.
4. Remove "C" ring from upper steering shaft by turning counterclockwise. *Do not pry against switch parts.*
5. Slide thrust washer and wave washer off steering shaft.
6. Loosen three turn signal switch screws five turns each. Rotate cover assembly counterclockwise and pull it straight off top of jacket. Using side cutters, cut turn signal wiring harness at bottom of cover. Bend harness over bowl to aid in installation.
7. Lock plate and cover should be marked (use colored pencil) for easier reassembly.
8. Remove three previously loosened screws from lock plate, being careful not to lose springs.
9. Turn signal switch can now be removed.
10. Reverse procedure to install, noting details illustrated in Figs. 10, 11.

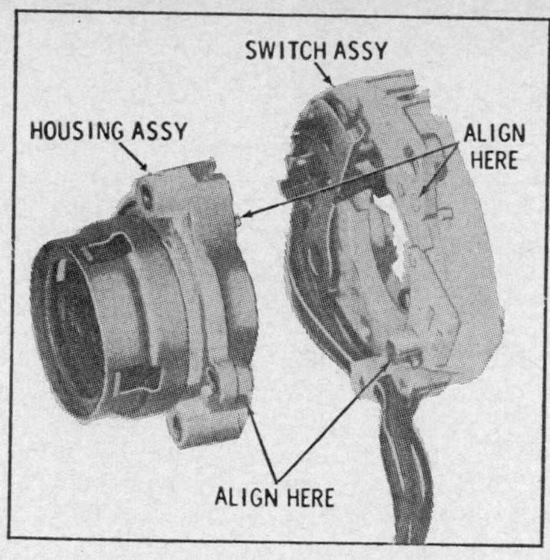

Fig. 10 Aligning turn signal switch with housing. 1967-68

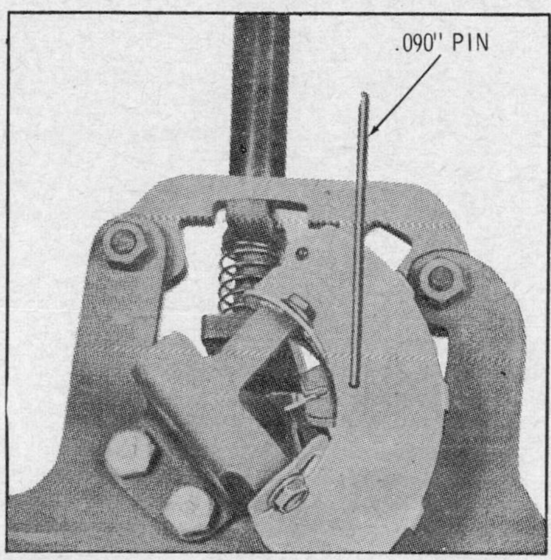

Fig. 12 Neutral safety switch adjustment. 1964 F-85 and all 1965-69 console type

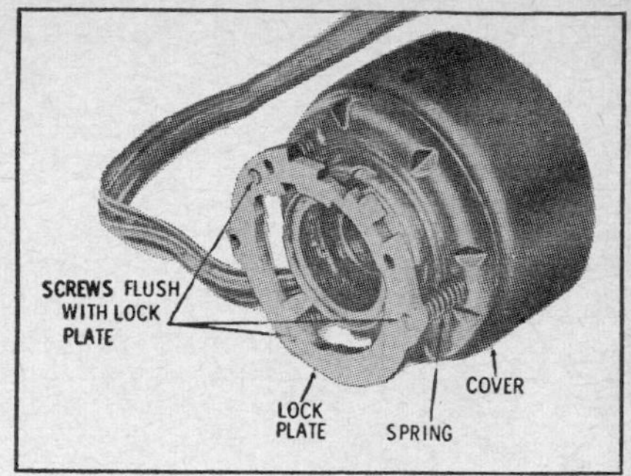

Fig. 11 Installing wave and thrust washer. 1967-68

1963-64 Senior Cars

1. Remove steering wheel and turn signal lever.
2. Insert a screwdriver with a round shank through turn signal lever hole in housing and pull or pry housing from bearing retainer.
3. Remove cancel spring and pivot pin with wave washer from lever plate.
4. Depress detent spring to disengage it from upper bearing retainer, then separate lever plate, detent spring, roller and balls from upper bearing retainer, Fig. 14.
5. To install, reverse removal procedure and lubricate all frictional areas with a thin coat of Lithium Soap Grease. Press housing over upper bearing retainer so that it just snaps over rim of steering retainer flange.

1963-64 F-85 & All 1965-66

1. Remove steering wheel, cancelling cam, signal lever and three signal control attaching screws.
2. Disconnect steering column wiring harness plug from main wiring harness.
3. Lift turn signal control out of housing and disconnect wiring plug and horn contact wire from turn signal control.

NOTE: On cars equipped with manual

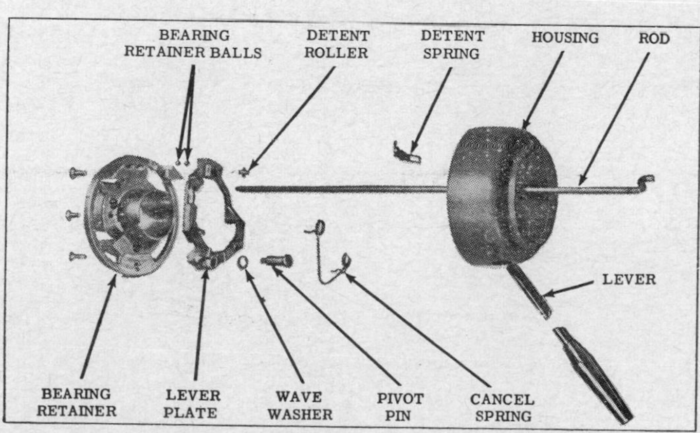

Fig. 14 Turn signal actuator. 1963-64 Senior Cars

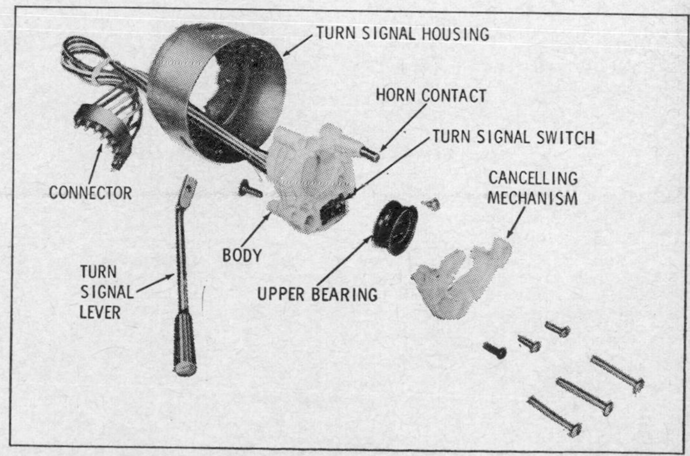

Fig. 15 Turn signal switch. 1963-64 F-85 and all 1965-66

shift transmission, wiring harness is part of turn signal control.

4. On cars with automatic transmission, the bearing, actuator and turn signal contacts can be disassembled, Fig. 15.
5. Reverse removal procedure to install. Before tightening the three attaching screws, rotate housing until it locks to steering column.

SERVICE BULLETIN

EASIER HORN REMOVAL. The horns on a 1963 full-size car equipped with air conditioning cannot be removed in the usual manner because of insufficient clearance. The condenser, located in front of the radiator, prevents the horn from being taken out through the engine compartment.

If either horn has to be removed, raise the front of the car and take off the horn attaching bolts from underneath and behind the front bumper. The horn can then be lowered and the lead disconnected. Slide the horn outboard beneath the radiator core support, and withdraw it from behind the bumper.

SERVICE BULLETIN

REMOVES GENERATOR: On 1963 Oldsmobile F-85 models, the a.c. generator can be removed from beneath the car, when this is desirable, by using the following procedure.

Disconnect the battery and the wiring at the rear of the alternator. Take off the upper pivot bolt nut and washer. If the bracket is to be replaced, remove the nut from the bracket stud at this time.

Now raise the car and remove the oil-filter element, keeping the element upright to prevent loss of oil. After the link adjusting bolt and the upper pivot bolt have been removed, the alternator can be taken out from the underside of the car. On cars with a cross-flow radiator, it may be necessary to bend the oil cooler lines slightly to permit the alternator to pass between the lines and filter base. Reverse the procedure to install the unit.

HORN SOUNDER & STEERING WHEEL

1967-69 Toronado

1. On 1969, pull down and out on pad and remove pad. On 1967-68 pry emblem up to disengage locking tang.
2. Remove wheel nut and use a suitable puller to remove wheel. Horn contact parts are now accessible.
3. With marks on steering wheel hub and steering shaft aligned, install wheel, flat washer and nut.
4. Align tangs of emblem with contact hole in wheel and push in to lock.

1967-69 Except Toronado

1. On standard wheel pull horn cap and retainer from wheel.
2. Deluxe wheel; 1969 pull down and out on pad and remove pad. 1967-68 pry emblem up to disengage locking tabs.
3. Service horn contacts as required.
4. Remove nut and washer and use a suitable puller to remove wheel.
5. Reverse procedure to install.

1966 Toronado

1. Turn emblem counterclockwise to disengage locking tang.
2. Remove wheel attaching nut and use a suitable puller to remove wheel.
3. When installing, align point of emblem with horn contact hole in wheel. Turn emblem clockwise to lock it in place.

1966 Except Toronado

1. Disconnect turn signal connector.
2. On Standard wheel pull lens and bezel from wheel. On deluxe wheel, pry cap and emblem assembly from shroud. On F85 models rotate cap clockwise to disengage locking tab.
3. Remove wheel nut and use a suitable puller to remove wheel.

1964-65

1. On 1964 disconnect horn wire from harness. On 1965 disconnect turn signal connector.
2. On standard wheel pull lens and bezel from wheel. On deluxe wheel pry cap and emblem assembly from shroud. On F85 models rotate cap clockwise to disengage locking tab.
3. Remove wheel attaching nut and use a suitable puller to remove wheel.

1963 F-85

1. The Standard wheel cap on 1963 is held in place by a rubber retainer ring. To remove the cap gently pry the cap from the wheel.
2. The Deluxe wheel cap is held in place by spring steel clips. To remove the cap gently pry the cap from the wheel.
3. Disconnect horn wire at harness.
4. Remove steering wheel nut and use a suitable puller to remove the wheel.

1963 Olds F.S.C.

1. Disconnect horn wire from harness.
2. On Standard wheel, pull lens and bezel assembly from wheel.
3. On Deluxe wheel, carefully pry cap and emblem assembly from shroud.
4. Remove steering wheel nut and, using a suitable puller, pull wheel from shaft.

INSTRUMENT CLUSTER

1968-69 Intermediate Cars

Fuel Gauge Cluster

1. If air conditioned, remove left-hand air outlet duct.
2. Disconnect battery ground cable.
3. Disconnect printed circuit multiple connector.
4. Separate cluster from control panel (2 screws and remove cluster through front of pad.

Speedometer Cluster

1. If air conditioned, remove left-hand air outlet duct.
2. Disconnect battery ground cable.
3. Disconnect multiple wiring connector from printed circuit.
4. If column shift with automatic transmission, disconnect shift indicator link.
5. Separate cluster from control panel (2 screws) and remove cluster through front of pad.

1968-69 Toronado

1. Disconnect battery ground cable.
2. Disconnect Cruise Control cable at regulator (if equipped).
3. Disconnect speedometer cable at transmission.
4. Remove screws from right-hand lower pad and filler.
5. Unfasten steering column clamp (2 nuts) and retain wedge for use when installing.
6. If equipped with tilt and travel, tilt down to lowest position and let steering wheel rest on seat cushion. With a standard column, use a 4″ x 4″ block of wood between steering wheel and seat. This will prevent accidental disconnecting of hoses and wiring when tilting control panel out to perform service repairs.
7. Loosen two control housing bracket bolts about ¼″.
8. Disconnect radio lead-in.
9. Remove two control housing upper screws and tilt control panel outward from the top.
10. Disconnect printed circuit connectors.
11. Remove radio if speedometer is to be removed.
12. Separate cover from cluster (8 screws).
13. Cluster components are now accessible for service.

1966-67 Intermediate Cars

Speedometer

1. Remove speedometer cable.
2. Remove cluster housing.
3. Remove speedometer (3 screws).
4. Reverse procedure to install.

Fuel Gauge

1. Disconnect battery.
2. Remove cluster housing.
3. Remove fuel gauge (3 bolts).
4. Reverse procedure to install. *Electric connector links must be positioned under each attaching bolt when gauge is installed.*

1967-68 Senior Cars (Except Toronado)

Fuel Gauge & Tell Tale

1. Disconnect battery ground cable.
2. Remove phillips screw from front of bezel.
3. Disconnect fuel gauge cluster connector.
4. Remove rear retaining nuts.
5. Remove fuel gauge and bezel from front.

6. Reverse procedure to install.

Speedometer Cluster

1. Disconnect battery ground cable.
2. Disconnect speedometer cable and printed circuit plug.
3. Remove phillips screw from front of bezel.
4. Remove rear retaining nuts.
5. Remove speedometer cluster from front.
6. Reverse procedure to install.

1966-67 Toronado

1. Disconnect battery.
2. If equipped with Cruise Control, disconnect cable at regulator.
3. Remove screws from right and left side trim panels.
4. Remove transmission indicator needle.
5. Remove nuts and clamps from column-to-upper reinforcement. Column may rest on front seat cushion.
6. Loosen lower bracket bolts (one each side) about ¼".
7. Disconnect speedometer cable and radio lead-in wire.
8. Remove two panel-to-pad bolts.
9. If A/C equipped, disconnect outlet hose.

NOTE: At this point all components of the control panel can be removed for any service required.

10. If the panel must be removed completely, disconnect main wiring harness from components. Remove the two loosened bracket bolts, then remove the panel.

1965-66 Senior Cars (Except Toronado)

Speedometer Cluster

1. Disconnect battery.
2. If equipped with air conditioning, remove manifold and left-hand hose.
3. Disconnect speedometer cable and printed circuit plug.
4. Unfasten (2 nuts) and remove cluster.

Fuel Gauge & Telltale

1. Disconnect battery.
2. If equipped with Cruise Control, it may be necessary to loosen control switch mounting bracket to gain access.
3. If equipped with air conditioning, remove left-hand hose.
4. Disconnect printed circuit plug.
5. Unfasten (2 screws) and remove gauge.

1964 Olds F.S.C.

1. If air conditioned, remove A/C manifold.
2. Disconnect clock wire and lamp.
3. Remove instrument panel bezel (3 nuts from beneath panel).
4. Disconnect printed circuit connectors, speedometer cable, and printed circuit buzzer.
5. Remove three cluster-to-panel screws.
6. Rotate top of cluster downward and remove from panel. Service instruments as required, and install cluster in reverse order of removal.

1964-66 F-85

1. Disconnect speedometer cable, printed circuit connector plug and clock wiring.
2. Remove three cluster attaching nuts and remove cluster.
3. Service instruments as required and install cluster in reverse order of removal.

1963 F-85

1. Remove cluster cover.
2. Disconnect wiring harness, clock wiring and speedometer cable.
3. Remove four cluster-to-panel nuts from under panel, then remove cluster from top of panel.
4. Service instruments as required and install cluster in reverse order of removal.

1963 Olds F.S.C.

1. Disconnect printed circuit connectors.
2. Disconnect speedometer cable.
3. Remove two cluster-to-instrument panel attaching nuts from beneath the panel.
4. Remove three cover-to-instrument panel attaching screws.
5. Rotate top of cluster downward and remove cluster assembly from panel. All instruments and other components are now accessible.

W/S WIPER MOTOR, REPLACE

1968-69 Intermediate Cars

1. Disconnect wiring and washer hoses.
2. Remove wiper blades and arms.
3. Lift up on arm assembly and pry arm up off transmission.
4. Remove motor attaching screws.
5. Lift left rear edge of vent screen and loosen the two nuts attaching transmission to motor crank arm. Loosen bolts only until crank arm will slide out of transmission socket.

1968-69 Full Size Cars

1. Disconnect wiring and washer hoses.
2. Remove three motor attaching screws.
3. Remove access hole plug.
4. Reaching through access hole, loosen two transmission crank arm nuts.
5. Hold motor with one hand and with the other move wiper arm halfway through its travel to center crank arm in dash hole.
6. Remove motor while guiding crank arm through hole.

1965-67 Intermediate Cars

1. Disconnect wiring and washer hoses.
2. Remove three wiper attaching screws.
3. Depending upon the optional equipment installed, it may be possible to pull the motor back through the dash panel far enough to remove the crank arm-to-transmission clip; if not, it will be necessary to remove the cowl vent grille.
4. Reverse procedure to install. If cowl vent grille was not removed, install crank arm-to-transmission clip before mounting wiper to dash.

1965-67 Senior Cars

1. Disconnect wiring and hoses.
2. Remove access hole cover in upper cowl area.
3. Loosen (do not remove) the two transmission-to-crank arm attaching nuts until transmission ball socket will drop off from crank arm ball.
4. Reverse procedure to install.

1964 All Models

1. To remove motor, turn wiper switch "on" and operate wipers through several cycles, then turn switch to "off" position. Motor will then be in "Park" position.
2. Disconnect wiring from motor. If equipped, remove W/S washer hoses.
3. Remove three motor holding screws.
4. While slowly moving arms and blades across windshield, feed motor crank and transmission link through dash opening
5. Reverse removal procedure to install motor. Tighten attaching screws so that sleeves surrounding screws bottom to prevent "floating of motor".

1963 F-85

1. To remove wiper motor, disconnect drive link from crank arm under instrument panel by removing retaining clip.
2. Disconnect harness connector from motor terminals.
3. If equipped with windshield washers, note location of hoses, then remove hoses from washer pump.
4. Remove three attaching screws and lift motor from cowl, guiding crank arm out of hole in cowl panel.

1963 Olds F.S.C.

1. Make certain wiper motor is in parked position.
2. Disconnect electrical connectors from motor. If equipped with windshield washers, remove hoses.
3. Remove three motor mount screws.
4. While slowly moving arms and blades across windshield, feed motor crank and transmission drive link through cowl opening. Remove motor crank-to-transmission drive link retainer.

W/S WIPER TRANSMISSION, REPLACE

1963-67 F.S.C., 1964-67 F-85

1. Remove cowl vent grille attaching screws.
2. Detach transmission drive linkage retainer from wiper motor crank arm.
3. Remove attaching screws and re-

move transmission.
4. Remove transmission and linkage arms from cowl.
5. Reverse above procedure to install.

1963 F-85

1. Remove wiper arms from wiper transmission.
2. Remove cowl vent grille and screen (6 screws).
3. Remove glove box and defroster hoses.
4. Disconnect wiper motor-to-left-hand transmission drive link by removing snap ring and clip.
5. Remove three attaching bolts from both transmissions and allow them to drop from cowl.
6. Remove snap ring retainer from long drive link and the transmission being removed, and remove transmission from vehicle.
7. Reverse above procedure to install.

W/S WIPER SWITCH

1968-69 Except Toronado

1. On intermediate models with air conditioning, remove left-hand air outlet duct.
2. Pull wiper knob from switch.
3. Remove switch escutcheon.
4. Remove wiper and washer switch from rear of control panel.
5. Disconnect switch wiring.

1968-69 Toronado

1. Disconnect battery ground cable.
2. Disconnect wiring at switch.
3. Unfasten and remove switch from rear of control panel.

1963-67

Disconnect wires or plug connector from switch. Unfasten switch from its mounting and remove it from the car.

RADIO REMOVAL

NOTE: When installing radio, be sure to adjust antenna trimmer for peak performance.

1968-69 Toronado

1. Remove control knobs and nuts from front of dash.
2. Remove control panel.
3. Disconnect radio feed wire.
4. Disconnect dial lamp.
5. Remove attaching nut from support to radio.
6. Remove radio from rear of control panel.

1967-68 Except Toronado

1. Disconnect battery ground cable.
2. Remove radio knobs, washers and rear seat speaker control.
3. Remove radio attaching nuts and escutcheons.
4. Disconnect all wiring and antenna lead-in.
5. Remove lower radio support bracket screw.
6. Remove radio from rear of panel.
7. Reverse procedure to install.

1966-67 Toronado

1. Disconnect battery.
2. Remove both lower cluster panels.
3. Remove steering column attaching nuts and lower bracket.
4. Remove shift indicator needle.
5. Disconnect speedometer cable.
6. Remove attaching nuts from cluster lower brackets, leaving brackets attached to instrument panel.
7. Remove two upper instrument panel screws and lay cluster on steering column.
8. Remove radio knobs, washers and rear seat speaker control.
9. Remove radio attaching nuts and escutcheons.
10. Disconnect all wiring and antenna lead-in.
11. Remove lower radio support bracket nut, then remove radio from panel.

1966 Except Toronado, 1965 Senior Cars

1. Disconnect battery. If equipped with air conditioning, remove manifold.
2. Remove defroster manifold.
3. Remove radio knobs and rear seat speaker control.
4. Remove radio attaching nuts, and lower radio support bracket attaching screw.
5. Remove radio from rear of panel.

1964-65 F-85

1. Disconnect antenna lead, front speaker connection and rear speaker wire (if equipped).
2. Remove bolt retaining bracket to right-hand instrument panel support.
3. Remove both knobs. Then, while supporting radio, remove two nuts securing radio to instrument panel. If air conditioned, it will be necessary to remove A/C manifold to gain clearance for radio removal.

1963 F-85 Without A/C

1. Disconnect electrical connector from left-hand rear of radio.
2. Disconnect antenna lead-in and rear seat speaker wire (if equipped) from right-hand rear of radio.
3. Remove control knobs and nuts.
4. Remove right-hand radio mounting bracket-to-side support bolt while supporting radio. Then remove radio.

1963 F-85 With A/C

1. Remove glove box from front of instrument panel.
2. Remove radio bracket-to-side support bolt.
3. Remove side support-to-lower instrument panel screw from beneath panel.
4. Remove side support-to-dash bolt and take out side support through glove box opening.
5. Disconnect electrical connector, antenna lead-in wire, and rear speaker wire (if equipped).
6. Remove radio knobs and nuts and remove radio through glove box opening.

1963-64 Olds F.S.C.

1. Remove radio knobs, washers, escutcheons or rear seat speaker control.
2. Remove radio attaching nuts. If air conditioned, A/C manifold must be removed.
3. Disconnect all radio connectors.
4. Remove radio-to-instrument panel bracket attaching screw.
5. Remove radio from rear of instrument panel.

HEATER CORE REMOVAL

1965-69 Full Size Cars

1. Remove glove box and disconnect wiring, vacuum lines and defroster hoses from heater case.
2. Remove blower attaching screws and nuts.
3. From inside car, remove heater assembly and take out core.

1964-69 Intermediate Models

1. In engine compartment, remove five attaching nuts from blower. The lower outboard nut is removed by drilling a ¾" hole through fender filler panel at dimple provided in the panel.
2. Disconnect resistor wiring and three control cables.
3. Remove heater case assembly from under dash. Exposed core can now be removed.

1963 Intermediate Models

1. Disconnect necessary wiring, cables and hoses.
2. Remove heater inlet case from engine compartment.
3. Separate core from inlet case.
4. Take care not to uncoil temperature sensing tube when removing it from core as this can disturb its setting. Guide it out gently through slot in core flange.

1964 Full Size Cars

1. Remove glove box.
2. Disconnect wiring, vacuum lines and defroster hoses from heater case.
3. Remove heater case.
4. In engine compartment, disconnect hoses from heater core and vacuum line from inlet case.
5. Remove inlet case, then withdraw core from beneath instrument panel.

SPEED CONTROLS

1968-69

Brake Release Switch, Adjust

1. Disconnect multiple connector at regulator.
2. Turn ignition switch to accessory position.
3. Using a test lamp, ground one test lamp lead and touch the other to terminal No. 2 in harness connector.
4. Adjust switch so that lamp will light when brake pedal is fully released and will go out when brake

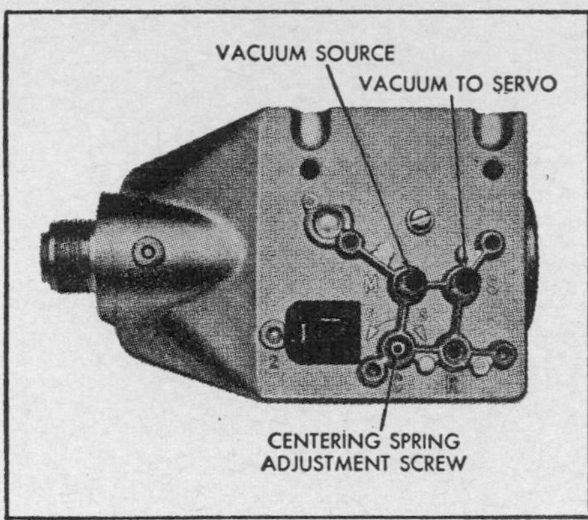

Fig. 16 Centering spring adjustment. 1968

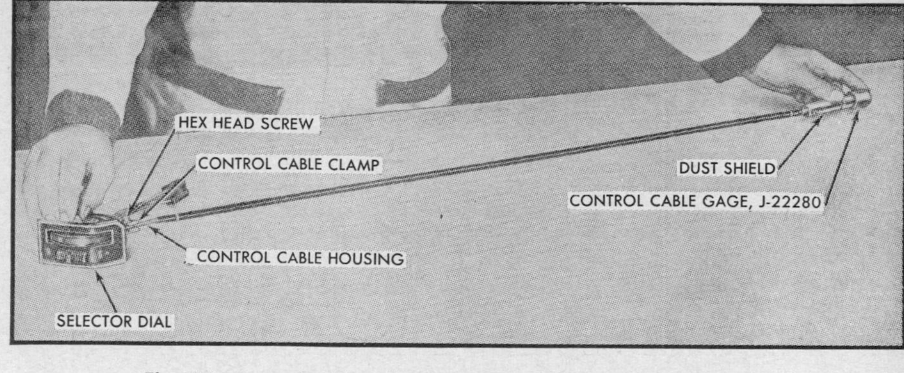

Fig. 17 Control cable adjustment for Slide Switch Speedostat

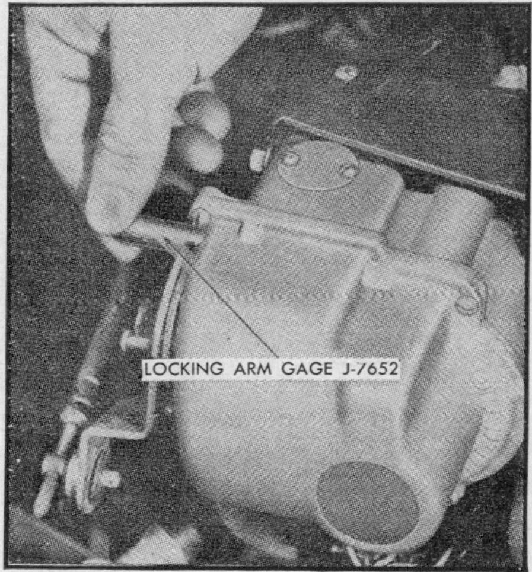

Fig. 18 Accelerator linkage adjustment for Slide Switch type Speedostat

pedal is depressed about ¼ inch.

5. If switch cannot be adjusted, it is defective and should be replaced. Install new switch and repeat Step 4.
6. Remove test lamp, turn off ignition key and plug connector to regulator.

Chain Linkage, Adjust

Chain linkage should never be taut. To adjust, start engine set carburetor at hot idle with anti-stall plunger backed off so as not to affect engine idle speed. Hook chain to accelerator linkage, pull taut, then loosen by length of one ball and install chain clip. *When pulling chain taut, do not pull so far as to cause throttle to open.*

Centering Spring, Adjust

1. If speed control system holds speed three or more mph higher than selected speed, turn centering spring adjusting screw (C) toward (S) $\frac{1}{32}$" or less, Fig. 16.
2. If speed control system holds speed three or more mph below selected speed, turn centering spring adjusting screw (C) toward (F) $\frac{1}{32}$" or less. *Do not move adjustment screw (R).*

1963-67 Speedostat

Control Cable Adjustment, Prior to 1966

1. Rotate selector dial rearward as far as it will turn without forcing.
2. Loosen set screw on cable dust shield.
3. Again try to rotate selector dial rearward only in order to make certain it is against the stop.
4. Push in lightly on control cable at dust shield, making certain cable is against stop (do not force cable beyond stop).
5. Hold cable against stop and tighten set screw on dust shield securely.

Control Cable Adjustment, 1966-67

The cable is preset at the factory and should not require adjustment unless a new cable is installed. This adjustment must be performed off the car as follows:

1. Remove the selector assembly.
2. Rotate selector dial to low speed position until it is positioned against its stop but do not force beyond its stop.
3. Position assembly flat on workbench and make certain there are no kinks in cable.
4. Loosen hex head set screw at cable clamp on selector control.
5. Pull cable housing until it is approximately half-way out of cable clamp. Position control cable gauge shown in Fig. 8 in end of dust shield. Hold dust shield and gauge and push toward selector control assembly until gauge bottoms. While holding in this position, tighten set screw at cable clamp.

NOTE: The gauge shown in Fig. 17 is used on Cadillac and Oldsmobile; use the gauge end marked .220" for Oldsmobile and the other end for Cadillac.

Accelerator Linkage

1. Adjust throttle rod.
2. Start engine and operate at slow idle with transmission lever in "Park".
3. Separate linkage from exterior arm.
4. Adjust trunnion so that when it is installed through exterior arm, the stop stud will be aligned with locating notch and throttle valves will be closed.
5. Install washer on trunnion and secure with cotter pin.

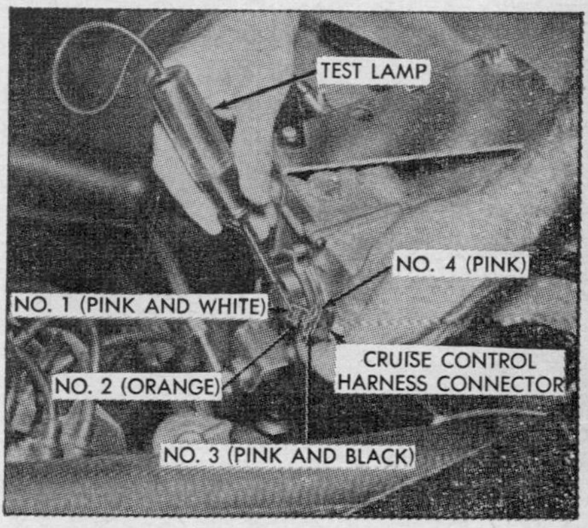

Fig. 19 Electrical connections on Slide Switch type Speedostat

---

NOTE: Due to the angle at which the trunnion enters hole in exterior arm, it is necessary to rotate the exterior arm slightly forward when inserting the trunnion. Repeat this operation until proper alignment is obtained. Be careful not to turn trunnion too far back or throttle valves will unseat and cause an incorrect adjustment. Insert the gauge shown in Fig. 18 (or small diameter pipe) over stop stud to check alignment.

Brake Release Switch

1. Turn on ignition but do not start engine.
2. Momentarily move slide switch to AUTO position until red indicator light glows.
3. Using a test lamp, ground one lead and touch the other lead to terminal No. 4, Fig. 19.
4. Loosen mounting screw securing release switch to brake pedal mounting bracket.
5. Adjust release switch so that lamp will light when brake pedal is fully released, and will go out when brake pedal is depressed about ¼ inch. Tighten switch mounting screw. If switch cannot be adjusted, it is defective and should be replaced.

Engine Section

IMPORTANT: See the Toronado supplement for procedures on removing the engine and transmission, and method of servicing the front suspension, drive axles and final drive (differential) immediately following this chapter.

See Buick Chapter for Service Procedures on V6-225 Engine.
See Chevrolet Chapter for Service Procedures on 6-250 Engine.

NOTE: Material marked "F.S.C." means Olds Full Size Car or Senior Models

RAISING ENGINE

1963-64 Olds F.S.C.

When removing the exhaust manifold, oil pan, timing case cover or the engine front mount, the front of the engine must be raised to provide clearance. This is accomplished as follows, referring to Fig. 1.

1. Remove engine front mount-to-front crossmember attaching nuts. On air conditioned cars, disconnect fan ring.
2. Remove threaded bolt of tool (shown in illustration) from support plate. Feed support plate through large opening in underside of front crossmember. Align hole in support plate with center hole in crossmember.
3. Attach a chain 18 to 24" long to the tool to aid in positioning the tool in and out of the crossmember.
4. Insert the threaded bolt into the support plate. Rotate the threaded bolt until it contacts the engine front mount. Raise engine until proper clearance is obtained. *When raising engine, do not allow rear of engine or engine components to contact cowl.*
5. When removing the timing case cover or the engine front mount, raise the engine to the desired height, then insert wood blocks between exhaust manifolds and front crossmember. Lower engine until supported on the blocks. The threaded bolt can now be lowered away from the engine front plate.

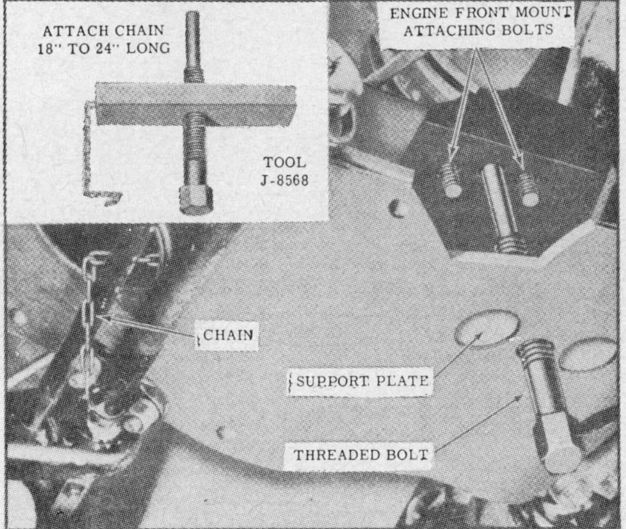

Fig. 1 Raising front of engine. 1963-64 Oldsmobile F.S.C.

1965-69 V8s

1. Mark hood hinge before removing to aid in proper alignment upon reassembly.
2. Drain radiator and disconnect battery.
3. Disconnect radiator hoses, heater hoses, vacuum hoses, power steering pump hoses (if necessary), starter cable at junction block, engine-to-body ground strap, fuel hose from fuel line, wiring and accelerator linkage.
4. Remove fan blade and pulley, coil and upper radiator support.
5. Raise car.
6. Disconnect exhaust pipes at manifolds.
7. Remove torque converter cover and install a suitable holding tool to keep converter from falling out when engine is removed.
8. Remove engine mounting bolts and support engine.
9. Lift engine and secure transmission chain support to frame or support transmission with a jack.
10. Unfasten converter from flywheel (3 bolts) and transmission from engine (6 bolts).
11. Lower car and remove engine.
12. Reverse procedure to install.

1963-64 Olds F.S.C.

Due to variations in equipment, no attempt is made to itemize every step for an engine replacement procedure. The following recommendations are given as a guide.

1. Drain cooling system.
2. Disconnect battery cables.
3. Disconnect radiator hoses.
4. Disconnect transmission oil cooler lines (if used).
5. Disconnect exhaust pipe at front flange.
6. Remove radiator.
7. Remove hood assembly.
8. On conventional models, disconnect clutch control linkage.
9. If equipped with Hydra-Matic, disconnect transmission control linkage.
10. Disconnect accelerator control.
11. Disconnect windshield wiper vacuum line.
12. Disconnect wiring from engine units including generator, starter distributor and coil.
13. Remove cable from starter terminal.
14. Disconnect flexible line from fuel pump.
15. Disconnect oil pressure gauge line at filter.
16. Disconnect propeller shaft at rear of transmission.
17. Remove two bolts attaching engine front support mounting to engine bracket.
18. Attach a lifting sling to raise power plant from above.
19. Remove rear mounting bolts and lower mounting.
20. Raise power plant to permit removal of support member.
21. Move power plant forward, raising as necessary to clear frame.
22. Reverse the foregoing procedure to install power plant.

SERVICE BULLETIN

FASTER ENGINE REMOVAL: On pre-1963 Senior models, the best way to remove the engine is to take off the fender

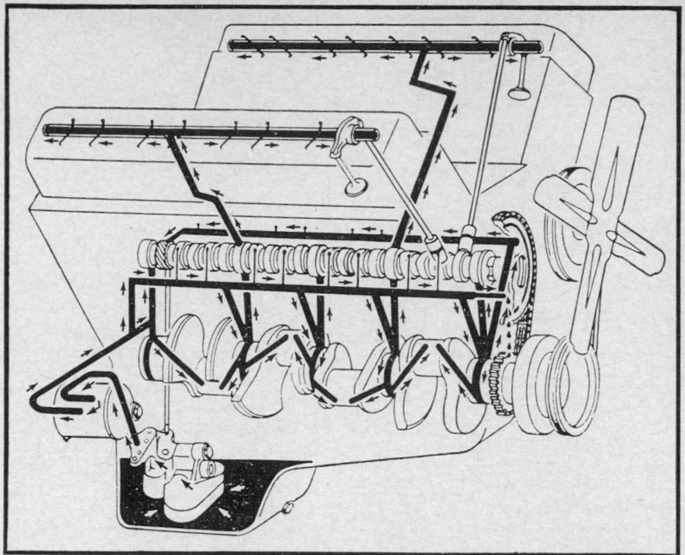

Engine oiling system. V8-394

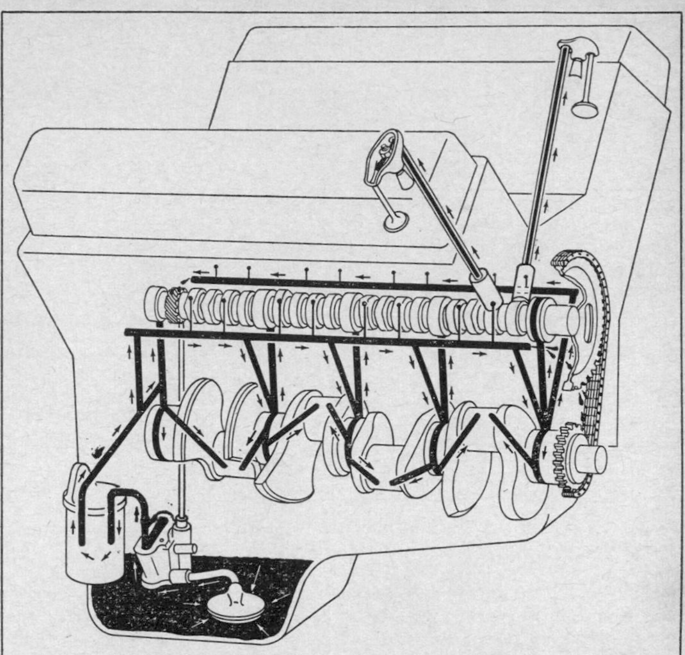

Engine lubrication. V8-330, 350, 400, 425, 455

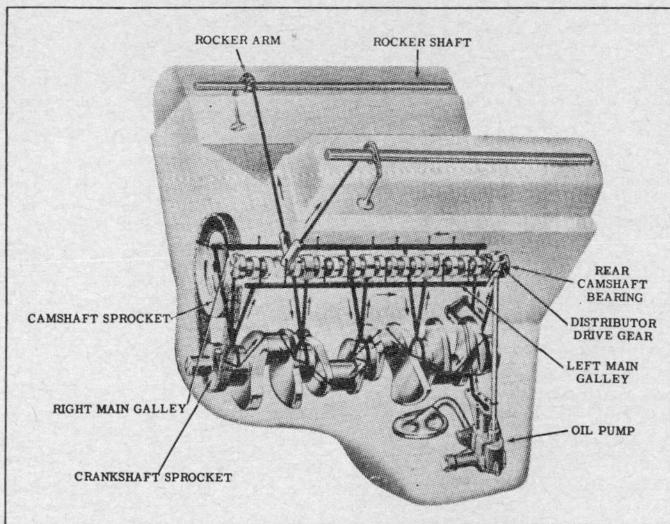

Engine lubrication diagram. 1964 V8-330

tie bar and radiator and pull the engine and transmission as an assembly. For 1963 cars, with a one-piece fender tie bar and the engine farther forward, a new method which does not require transmission removal is used.

With the hood off and battery disconnected, remove or disconnect the fan, accelerator linkage, fuel and vacuum lines, radiator and heater hoses, wiring harness, Hydra-Matic breather and filler tube, oil cooler lines, exhaust pipes and front engine mount. Remove the bolts holding the transmission to the engine, disconnect the wiring at the starter, remove the two rear mount bolts that thread into the block.

To support the transmission, install a chain with turnbuckle between the frame rails at the mid-point of the transmission rear-bearing retainer. Tighten the turnbuckle to remove all slack. Now install a chain fall at or slightly forward of the balance point of the engine. Raise the engine far enough for the front mount studs to clear the crossmember, pull forward to disengage from the transmission and hoist the engine out of the car.

NOTE

On V8 engines, whenever installation of a front engine mounting becomes necessary, the cap screws fastening the mounting to the frame or bracket should first be screwed finger tight, then tightened alternately, one at a time. *Do not tighten one cap screw in position independently of the other.* This is extremely important since the lower portion of the assembly would not seat evenly in the upper portion. The front mounting must be properly positioned and tightened, otherwise the mounting will not properly function as an insulator.

V8-215, V6-225

When necessary to remove the engine from the car, disconnect the following items and raise the body off the engine and front suspension.

1. Front exhaust pipe from rear exhaust pipe.
2. Speedometer cable, front of propeller shaft and shift linkage from transmission.
3. Clutch and clutch equalizer on manual shift cars.
4. Wires, pipes, linkage, hoses, etc.
5. Stabilizer brackets from frame rail.
6. Front brake hoses.
7. Steering column from gear and raise up into steering column.
8. Remove air cleaner.
9. Place a block of wood between front cross bar and front of engine oil pan. Remove rear transmission mount cross support and support rear of transmission with stand.
10. With front wheels on floor, remove the three isolation mount bolts and carefully raise body off engine and transmission, using care not to let suspension tip.
11. Reverse removal procedure to install. and remove push rods except No. 16.

CYLINDER HEAD, REPLACE

Some cylinder head gaskets are coated with a special lacquer to provide a good seal once the parts have warmed up. Do not use any additional sealer on such gaskets. If the gasket does not have this lacquer coating, apply suitable sealer to both sides.

Tighten cylinder head bolts a little at a time in three steps in the sequence shown in the illustrations. Final tightening should be to the torque specifications listed in the *Engine Tightening* table.

1963 F-85

1. Drain cooling system.

2. Remove intake manifold.
3. Disconnect exhaust pipe.
4. Remove rocker arm cover.
5. When removing right cylinder head, remove generator rear mounting bracket bolt. Also remove ground straps at front and rear of head.
6. To remove left head, remove power steering belt and two pump bracket bolts from head.
7. Remove rocker arm assemblies and push rods.
8. Remove bolts and lift off heads.

NOTE

If equipped with a heater, the following steps should be taken when removing the right cylinder head:

1. Remove all head bolts except rear rocker arm shaft bracket bolt (blower motor prevents).
2. Loosen rear rocker arm bracket bolt and raise shaft assembly from head and remove push rods except No. 16.
3. Lift No. 16 push rod to within one inch of blower case and tape to rocker shaft.
4. Lift head, rocker shaft and exhaust manifold off dowel pins and move forward to clear blower case.
5. Reverse removal procedure to install the head, referring to the *Service Notes* above. Tighten head bolts in the sequence shown in Fig. 3.

V8-330, 350, 400, 425, 455

1. Drain radiator and cylinder block.
2. Disconnect spark plug wires and remove intake manifold.
3. Disconnect exhaust crossover pipe for left side and/or crossover pipe and exhaust pipe for right side.
4. Remove valve cover (loosen or remove any accessory brackets that interfere).
5. Remove ground strap from right cylinder head.
6. On 1964 engines, remove rocker arm shaft assembly and lift out push rod. Then unfasten and remove cylinder head with exhaust manifold attached.
7. On 1965-68 engines, unfasten and remove cylinder head with exhaust manifold and rocker arms attached.
8. Reverse removal procedure to install head, and tighten bolts in the sequence shown in Fig. 5.

1964 V8-394

1. Drain radiator and cylinder block.
2. Remove intake manifold and alternator.
3. Disconnect exhaust pipes.
4. Remove crankcase ventilator valve from right hand rocker arm cover.
5. Remove rocker arm cover.

NOTE: If air conditioned, remove air compressor and alternator bracket attaching bolts and tip compressor rearward to remove rocker arm cover. If equipped with power steering, remove pump mounting bracket attaching bolts and move assembly to one side to gain access to rocker arm cover.

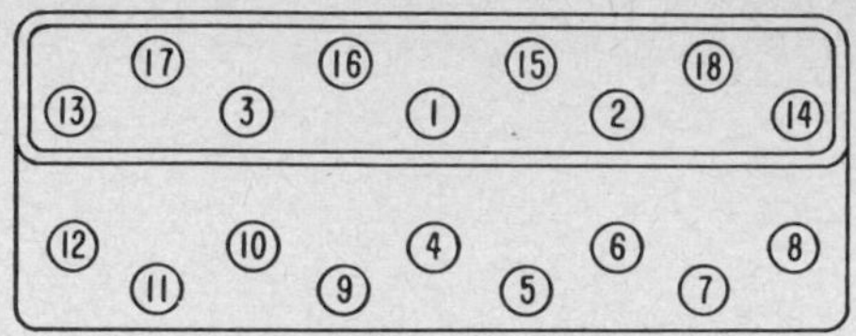

Fig. 3 Cylinder head tightening sequence. V8-215

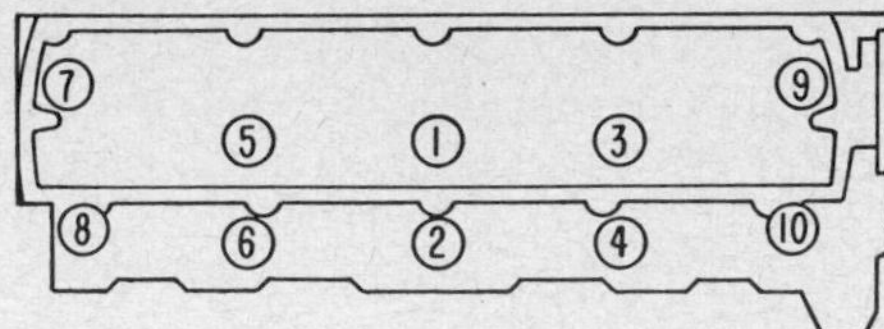

Fig. 5 Cylinder head tightening sequence. V8-330, 350, 400, 425, 455

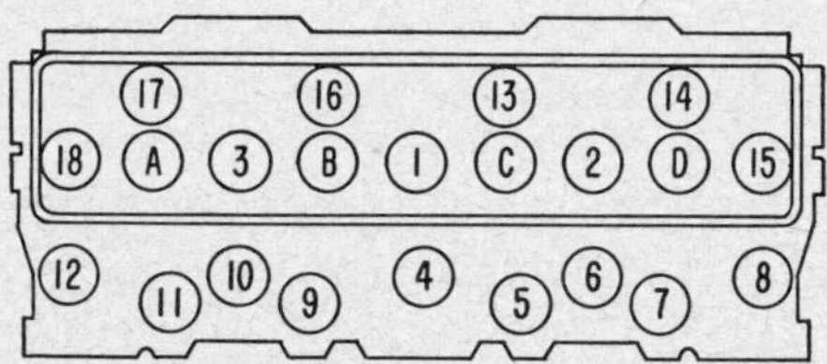

Fig. 6 Cylinder head tightening sequence. V8-394. Tighten numbered bolts first, then lettered bolts

6. Remove rocker arm shaft assembly. Disconnect ground strap from rear of cylinder head.
7. Remove push rods.
8. Unfasten and remove head with exhaust manifold attached.
9. Reverse removal procedure to install head, being sure to install and tighten the bolts in the sequence shown in Fig. 6.

1963 Oldsmobile F.S.C.

1. Drain radiator and cylinder block.
2. Remove intake manifold.
3. Remove generator.
4. Disconnect exhaust pipes.
5. Remove crankcase ventilation valve from right-hand cylinder head rocker arm cover.
6. Remove rocker arm cover. If equipped with air conditioner, remove compressor and generator attaching bolts and tip compressor rearward to remove the right-hand rocker arm cover. If equipped with power steering, unfasten and move pump to one side to gain access to the left-hand rocker arm cover.
7. Remove rocker shaft assembly.
8. Disconnect ground strap from rear of cylinder head.
9. Remove push rods, keeping them in proper sequence so they can be installed in their original location.
10. Remove cylinder head bolts and lift off cylinder head with exhaust manifold attached.
11. Cylinder head bolts should be tightened in the sequence shown in Fig. 6.

VALVE ARRANGEMENT

Front to Rear

6-250	E-I-I-E-E-I-I-E-E-I-I-E
V8-215	E-I-E-I-I-E-I-E
V6-225 Left bank	E-I-E-I-I-E
V6-225 Right bank	E-I-I-E-I-E
V8-330, 350, 400, 425, 455	I-E-I-E-E-I-E-I
V8-394	E-I-I-E-E-I-I-E

VALVE LIFT SPECS.

Engine	Year	Intake	Exhaust
V8-215	1963	.384	.384
V6-225	1964-65	.391	.401
6-250	1966-69	.388	.388
V8-330	1964-65	.389	.390
	1965①	.433	.433
	1966-67②	.387	.388
	1966-67①	.430	.432
V8-350	1968-69	.435	.435
V8-394	1963	.427	.435
	1964②	.427	.435
	1964①	.435	.436
	1964③	.443	.436
V8-400	1967②	.435	.435
	1966-69④	.472	.472
	1966-69⑤	.430	.432
V8-425	1965	.431	.433
	1966⑥	.430	.432
	1966⑦	.472	.461
	1966⑧	.431	.433
	1967	.430	.432
	1967③	.472	.461
V8-455	1968-69⑨	.435	.435

①—4 bar. carb. ②—2 bar. carb.
③—Starfire.
④—4 bar. carb., std. trans.
⑤—4 bar. carb., auto. trans.
⑥—310, 365 H.P. ⑦—375 H.P.
⑧385 H.P. ⑨—GT & 400 H.P.—.472.

VALVE TIMING

Intake Opens Before TDC

Engine	Year	Degrees
V8-215	1963	22
V6-225	1964-65	24
6-250	1966	12
	1967	62
	1968-69	16
V8-330	1964-67①	12
	1964-67②	21
V8-350	1968-69	16
V8-394	1963-64③	21
	1963-64④	14
	1963-64⑤	11
V8-400	1966-69①	30
	1966-69②	21
V8-425	1965-67	21
	1966⑥	24
V8-455	1968-69⑦	20

①—Std. trans. ②—Auto. trans.
③—Vista Cruiser. ④—88.
⑤—SS88, 98. ⑥—Starfire.
⑦—GT & 400 H.P.—24.

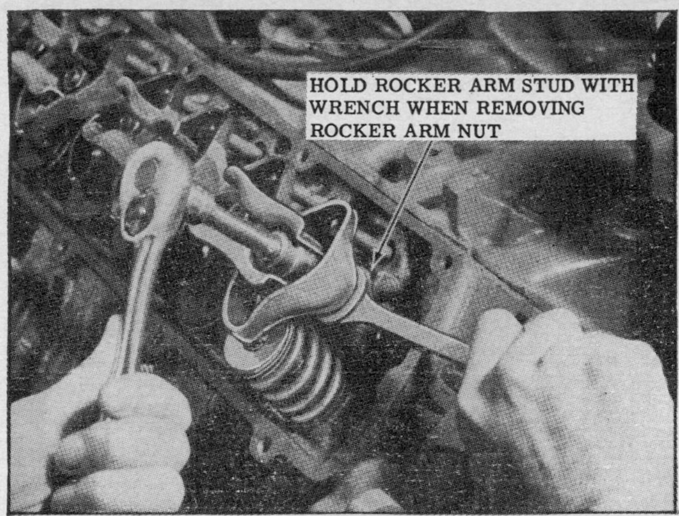

Fig. 12 Removing rocker arm. V8-330, 350, 400, 425, 455

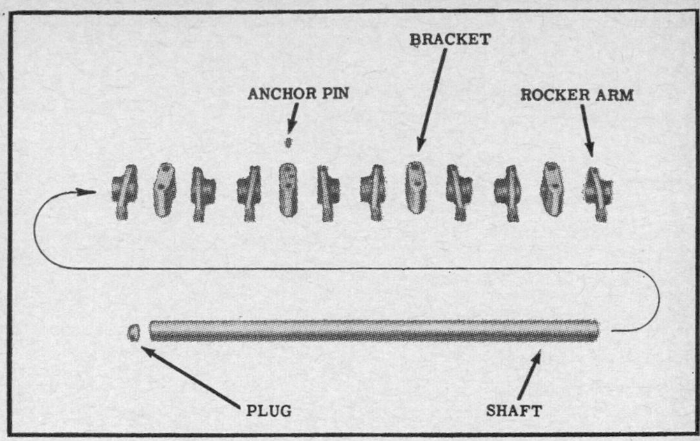

Fig. 13 Rocker arm assembly. V8-394

ROCKER ARMS

V8-330, 350, 400, 425, 455

1. To remove rocker arm assemblies, first remove valve cover
2. Hold stud to prevent it from turning and remove rocker arm stud nuts, washer, lock plates, pivots and rocker arms, Fig. 12. **NOTE:** Remove each set (one set per cylinder) as a unit.

Installation

1. Torque studs to 35 ft-lbs. Later engines use pivots and the pivot bolts are torqued to 25 ft-lbs.
2. Position a set of rocker arms (for one cylinder) on proper studs.
3. Install pivots and lock plates, being sure tangs on lock plates seat properly in the pivots. Coat wear points with lubricant.
4. Install flat washers and nuts, being sure both valve lifters are in closed valve position when nuts are tightened.

CAUTION: Never exceed specified torque of 25 ft-lbs on nuts. Check to be sure clearance exists between push rod and push rod hole in cylinder head. If no clearance exists, lock plate must be replaced.

V8-394

As shown in Figs. 13 and 14, one bracket is attached to the shaft by an anchor pin. It is not necessary to remove this bracket unless either the bracket, shaft or pin has to be replaced. If necessary to remove, insert a drift through the oil passage in the bracket and drive out the pin. If necessary to remove a rocker shaft plug, punch a hole in the plug, then pry it from end of shaft.

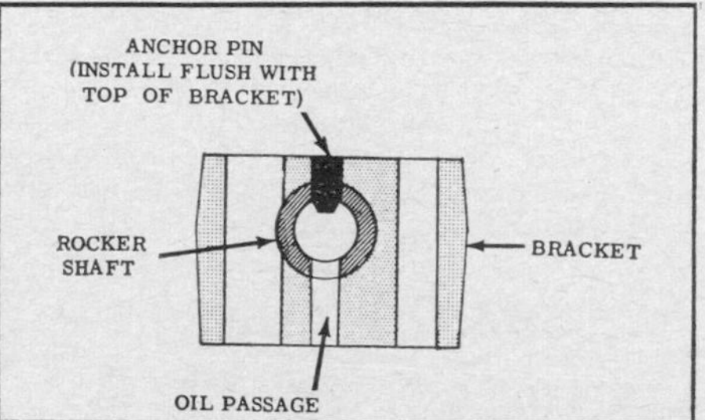

Fig. 14 Rocker arm bracket and anchor pin. V8-394

NOTE: If a new pin has to be installed, drive pin in flush with bracket. Rocker shaft oil ports must face down. If a new plug is to be installed, drive it in so that its outer shoulder is $\frac{3}{32}$" into end of shaft. Stake end of shaft to retain plug.

1964 V8-330

1. To remove the assembly, Fig. 16, take off valve cover and remove rocker arm bracket to head bolts.
2. Remove cotter pins from ends of shafts. Disassemble one shaft at a time and place on bench so parts may be reassembled in their original place.
3. Remove springs, arms and brackets from shaft.
4. To install, position shaft assembly on cylinder head and align brackets with mounting bolt holes.
5. Coat bolt threads and heads with engine oil and torque bolts to specifications. Check rocker arm to valve stem for proper alignment.

VALVES, REMOVE

1965-69 V8 NOTE

Valves in Starfire and V8-400 engines are .030" longer than other V8 valves, Fig. 17.

Whenever a new valve is installed or after grinding valves, it will be necessary to measure valve stem height using the Special Tool shown in Figs. 18 and 19.

Lacking this tool the only alternative is to lay flat feeler gauges on the retainer and check the distance between the retainer and valve stem tip. As shown in Fig. 19, if the valve stem tip is less than .030" above the retainer after grinding the stem, install a new valve.

VALVE GUIDES

V8-330, 350, 400, 425, 455

Valve stem guides are not replaceable, due to being cast in place. If valve guide bores are worn excessively, they can be reamed oversize.

If a standard valve guide bore is being reamed, use a .003" or .005" oversize reamer. For the .010" oversize valve guide bore, use a .013" oversize reamer. If too large a reamer is used and the

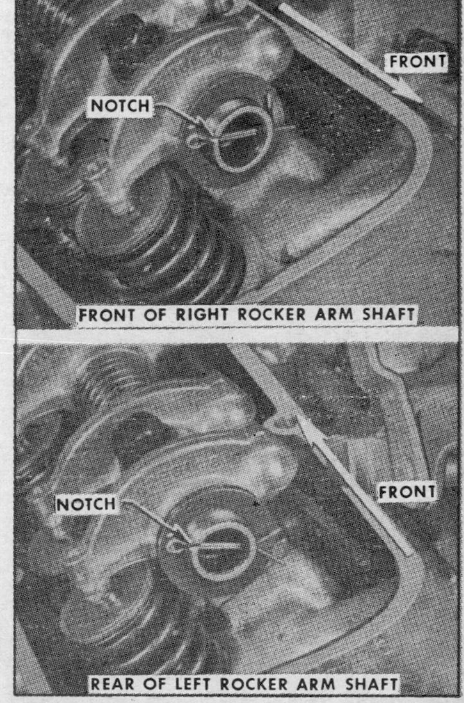

Fig. 15 Rocker arm shaft installation. V8-215

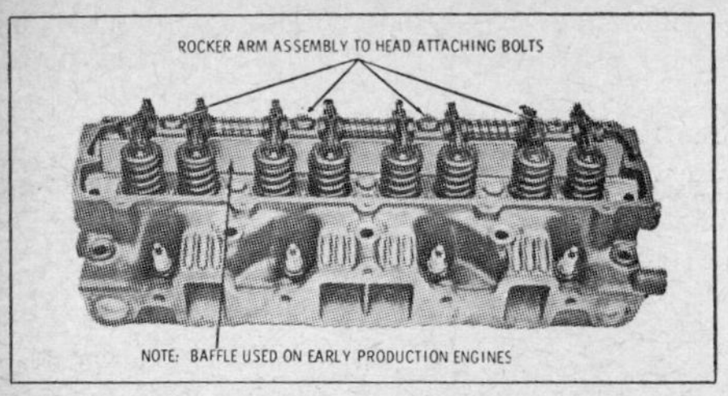

Fig. 16 Rocker arm assembly. 1964 V8-330

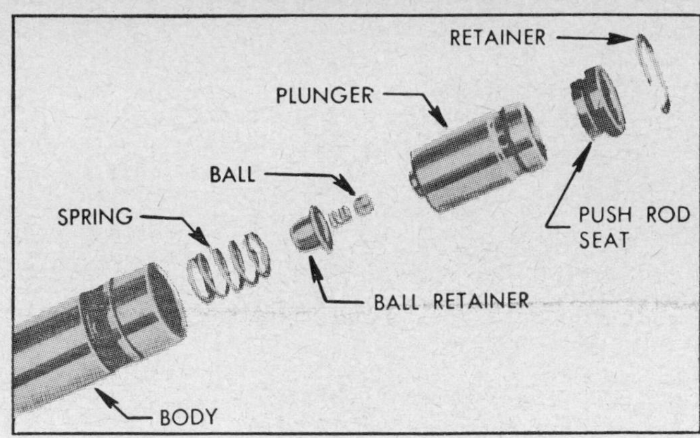

Fig. 21 Hydraulic valve lifter (typical)

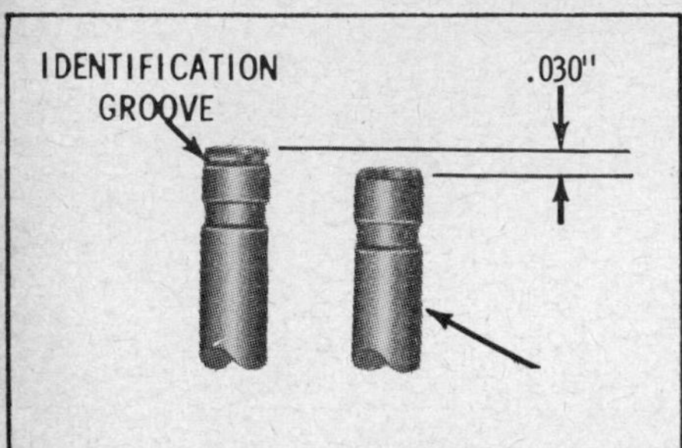

Fig. 17 Valves in 1965-68. Starfire and V8-400 engines are .030" longer than other V8 valves

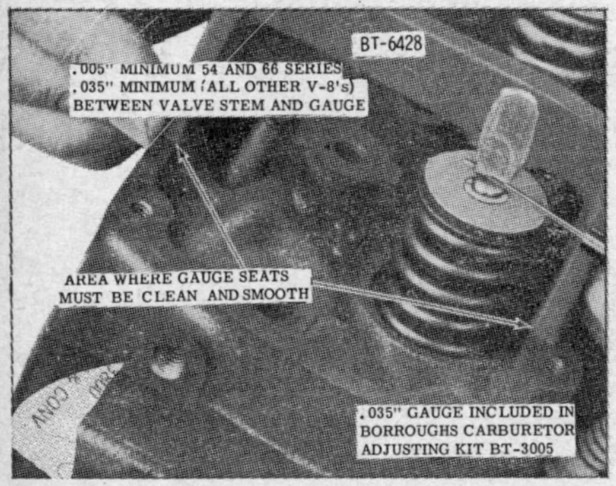

Fig. 18 Measuring valve stem height. V8-330, 350, 400, 425, 455

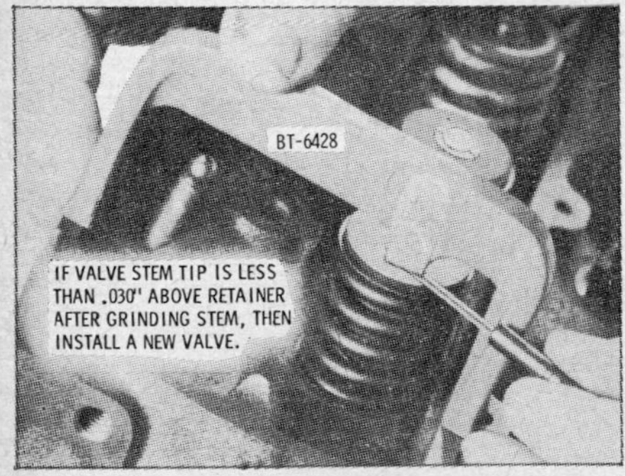

Fig. 19 Measuring valve retaining height. V8-330, 350, 400, 425, 455

spiraling is removed, it is possible that the valve will not receive the proper lubrication.

NOTE: Occasionally a valve guide will be oversize as manufactured. These are marked on the cylinder head as shown in Fig. 20. If no markings are present, the guide bores are standard. If oversize markings are present, any valve replacement will require an oversize valve. Service valves are available in standard diameters as well as .003", .005", .010" and .013" oversize.

VALVE LIFTERS

Valve lifters in production engines may be one of four sizes: standard, .001, .002 or .003 in. oversize. It is important when replacing one or more lifters that the proper size lifter be ordered. An identification numeral is etched on all lifter bodies except standard. The cylinder block is marked for lifter size on the rail under the push rod cover. Valve lifters .005 in. oversize are available for service replacement.

Plungers are not interchangeable because they are selectively fitted to the bodies at the factory.

If plunger and body appear satisfactory blow off with air to remove all particles of dirt. Install the plunger in the body without other parts and check for free movement. A simple test is to be sure that the plunger will drop of its own weight in the body, Fig. 21.

TIMING CASE COVER

V8-215 NOTE

Whenever the front cover is removed from these engines, it will be necessary to take off the oil pump cover and pack the space around the pump gears completely full of Petrolatum (vaseline). This step is very important as the oil pump may lose its prime when the cover is removed. If the pump is not packed in this manner, it may not begin to pump oil as soon as the engine is started.

NOTE: On all Senior cars and 1964-69 F-85 V8s, when it becomes necessary to replace the cover oil seal, the cover need not be removed.

V8-215

1. To remove cover, drain cooling system and disconnect radiator hoses and oil pressure switch wire.
2. Remove drive belts and pulleys.
3. Remove distributor and generator.
4. Remove fuel pump and two front oil pan bolts.
5. Remove cover-to-block attaching bolts and take off cover.

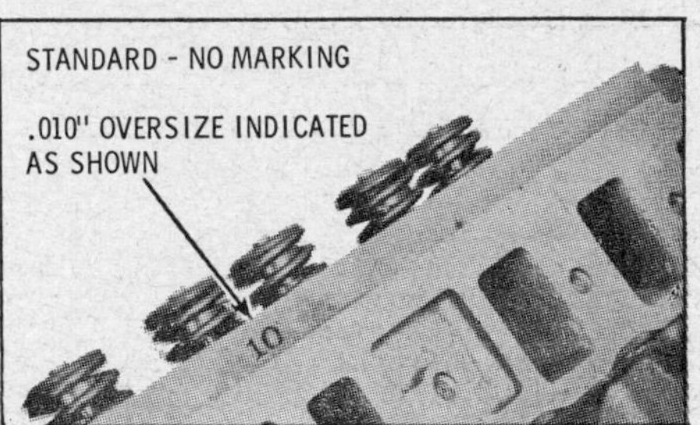

Fig. 20 Valve guide bore marking. V8-330, 350, 400, 425, 455

V8-330, 350, 400, 425, 455

1. Drain cooling system and disconnect heater hose, by-pass hose and both radiator hoses.
2. Remove all belts, fan and pulley, crankshaft pulley and pulley hub.
3. Remove oil pan.
4. Unfasten and remove cover, timing pointer and water pump assembly.
5. Reverse removal procedure to install cover, noting data in Figs. 26 and 27.

V8-394

1. Drain cooling system and disconnect radiator lower hose and heater hose from front cover.
2. Disconnect link at generator.
3. Raise front of engine as outlined under *Raising Front of Engine* at the beginning of the engine text.
4. Remove oil pan, fan blades and pulley, and crankshaft pulley.
5. Remove distributor cap and crank engine until distributor rotor points toward front of engine, then remove fuel pump.
6. Unfasten and remove front cover.
7. Reverse removal procedure to install. Always install a new front oil seal. The front cover attaching bolts should be coated with a suitable sealer and tightened to 24-40 ft-lb torque.

TIMING CHAIN

V8-330, 350, 400, 425, 455

1. After removing front cover, remove fuel pump eccentric, oil slinger, crankshaft sprocket, chain and cam-

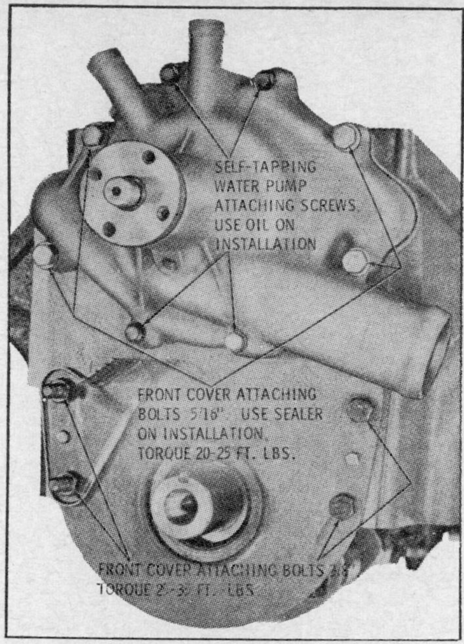

Fig. 26 Engine front cover bolts. 1964 V8-330

shaft sprocket.

2. Install camshaft sprocket, crankshaft sprocket and timing chain together, aligning timing marks as shown in Fig. 30.
3. Install fuel pump eccentric with flat side rearward, Fig. 31. Then install oil slinger and replace front cover.

V8-394

Place the chain over the sprockets so that when the camshaft sprocket and fuel pump eccentric are bolted to the camshaft hub, the timing marks on both sprockets are facing each other in line with the center of both the camshaft and crankshaft, Fig. 32. The fuel pump eccentric must be assembled with the cupped side out.

Fig. 30 Timing chain position. V8-330, 350, 400, 425, 455

CAMSHAFT, REPLACE

V8-215

1. Remove grille, radiator, front cover, timing chain and sprockets, and intake manifold.
2. Remove rocker arm assembly, push rods and valve lifters.
3. Slide camshaft out of engine.
4. Reverse removal procedure to install camshaft. To provide initial lubrication when installing camshaft, it must first be coated liberally with engine oil.

V8-330, 350, 400, 425, 455

1. Remove grille and radiator.
2. If air conditioned it will be necessary to remove condenser.
3. Remove fuel pump and front cover.
4. Remove oil slinger, timing chain and sprockets.
5. Remove distributor, intake manifold, rocker arm assemblies, push rods and valve lifters.
6. Slide camshaft out of engine.
NOTE: To insure proper camshaft installation, and to provide initial lubrication, it is extremely important that the camshaft be coated with GM Concentrate (Part No. 582099).

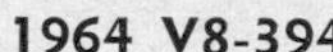

1964 V8-394

1. Drain cooling system and remove oil cooler lines and radiator hoses.
2. If air conditioned, remove condenser.
3. Remove radiator and air cleaner.
4. Remove rocker arm assemblies and push rods.
5. Remove intake manifold, distributor engine top cover and valve lifters.
6. Raise engine and remove oil pan.
7. Remove crankshaft pulley, fuel pump, front cover, fuel pump eccentric, camshaft sprocket and chain.
8. Slide camshaft out of engine.
NOTE: Before installing camshaft, it is important that it be lubricated liberally with engine oil mixed with GM Concentrate, Part No. 582099.

1963 Olds F.S.C.

1. To remove the camshaft, remove valve lifters.
2. Remove distributor.
3. Remove engine front cover.
4. Remove camshaft thrust plunger, fuel pump eccentric, camshaft sprocket and timing chain.
5. Remove camshaft by carefully sliding it out from front of engine.
6. To install, reverse the above sequence of operations. Lubricate the end of the camshaft thrust plunger with suitable seal lubricant. Set valve timing, ignition timing, adjust carburetor idle and check throttle linkage.

PISTON & ROD, ASSEMBLE

Lubricate the piston pin hole and piston pin to facilitate installation of pin, then position the connecting rod with its respective piston as shown in Figs. 38, 39.

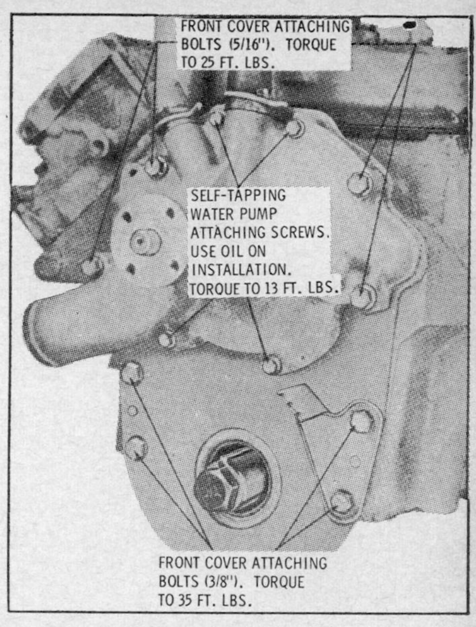

Fig. 27 Engine front cover bolts. V8-330, 350, 400, 425, 455

PISTONS, RINGS & PINS

Senior Cars

Pistons are available in standard sizes and oversizes of .010, .020 and .030″.

Rings are available in standard sizes and oversizes of .030″ on 1963, and .010 and .030″ on 1964-69.

Pins are available in standard sizes and oversizes of .010″ on 1963, V8.

F-85 Cars

Pistons are available in standard sizes and oversizes of .010″ on 1963, V8, .005, .020 and .030″ on 1964-65 V6 and .010 and .030″ on 1964-69 V8.

Rings are available in standard sizes and oversizes of .010″ on 1963 V8, and .010 and .030″ on 1964-69 V8.

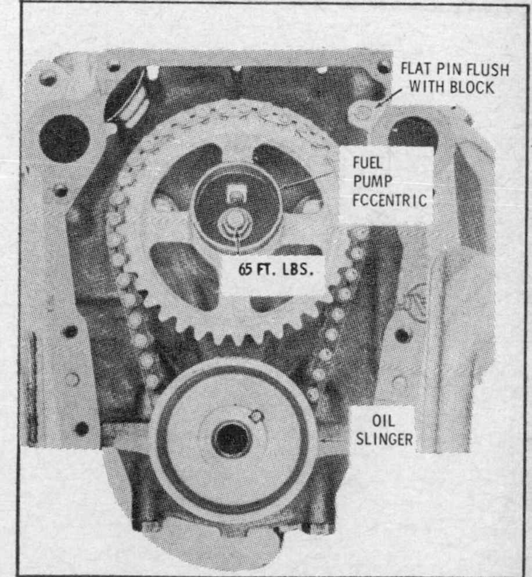

Fig. 31 Fuel pump eccentric. V8-330, 350, 400, 425, 455

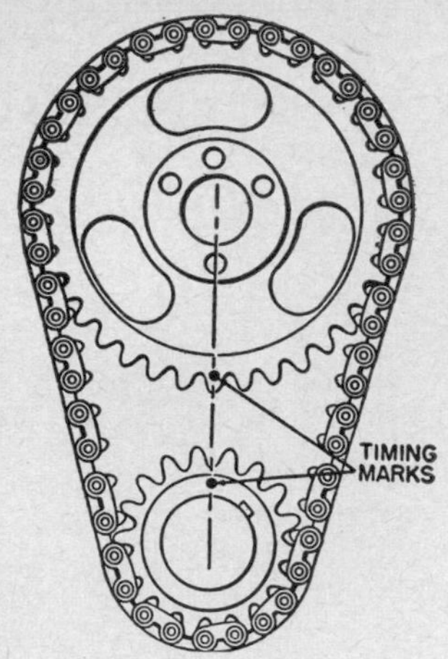

Fig. 32 Valve timing, V8-394

Pins are available in standard size only.

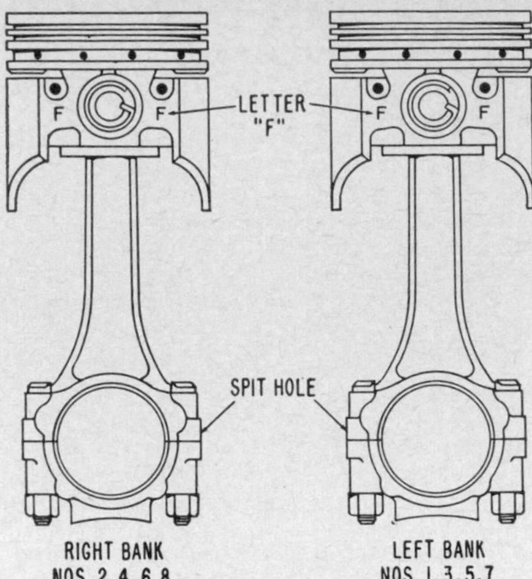

Fig. 38 Assembly of piston to rod. V8-330, 350, 394, 400, 425, 455

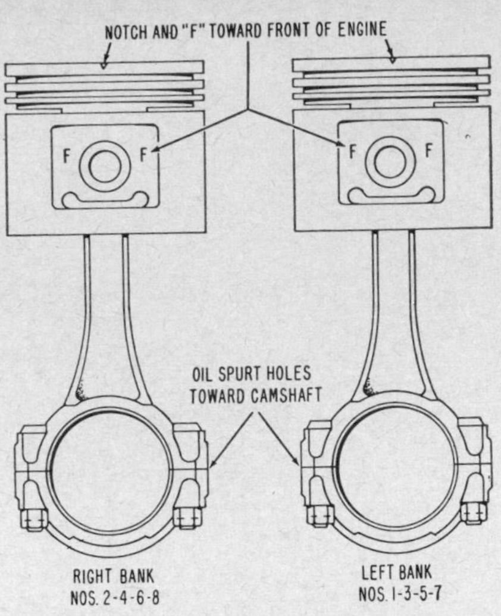

Fig. 39 Assembly of piston to rod. V8-215

MAIN & ROD BEARINGS

Senior Cars

Main bearings are available in standard sizes and undersizes of .0005, .001, .0015, .002, .010 and .020″.

Rod bearings are available in standard sizes and undersizes of .002, .010 and .020″. On V8-330 a .012″ undersize is also available.

F-85 Cars

Main bearings are available in standard sizes and undersizes of .001, .002 and .010″ on 1963 V8 and 1964-65 V6. On 1964-68 V8 undersizes of .0005, .001, .0015, .002, .010 and .020″ are available.

Rod bearings are available in standard sizes and undersizes of .001, .002 and .010″ on 1963 V8 and 1964-65 V6. On 1964-68 V8, the undersizes available are .002, .010, .012 and .020″.

NOTE

Main bearing clearances not within specifications must be corrected by the use of selective upper and lower shells. Figs. 41 and 42 illustrate the undersize identification marking on the bearing tang.

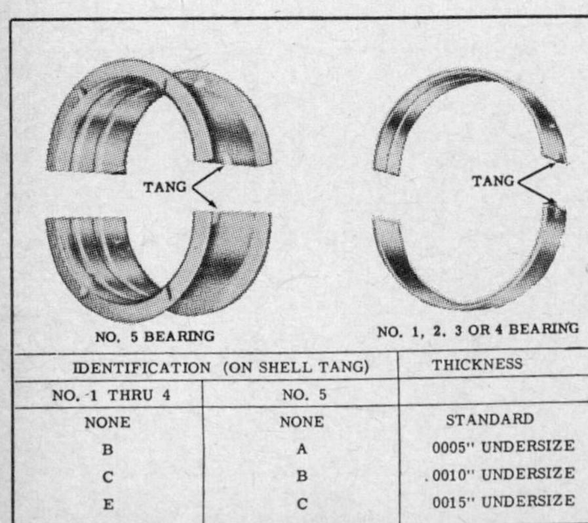

IDENTIFICATION (ON SHELL TANG)		THICKNESS
NO. 1 THRU 4	NO. 5	
NONE	NONE	STANDARD
B	A	0005" UNDERSIZE
C	B	.0010" UNDERSIZE
E	C	0015" UNDERSIZE

Fig. 41 Main bearing sizes. V8-394

OIL PAN

1963 V8-215

1. Remove dipstick and drain oil.
2. Disconnect steering idler arm from relay rod.
3. Remove flywheel housing lower cover.
4. Unfasten and remove pan.

NOTE: On some types of lifts, it may be necessary to drop the oil intake into the pan before the pan can be removed. The crankshaft should be positioned so the counterweights do not interfere with the pan's removal.

1964-65 V6-225

1. Raise car and drain oil.
2. Remove lower flywheel housing.
3. Remove attaching bolts and lower pan enough to remove oil pump pipe and screen-to-cylinder block bolts. *On manual shift transmission jobs it will be necessary to raise engine.*
4. Rotate crankshaft to provide maximum clearance at forward end of pan. Then move front of pan to the right and lower it.

1964 V8-330

Jetstar 88

1. Remove dipstick, hoist car and drain oil.
2. Disconnect pitman arm from steering gear and lower relay rod.
3. Remove starter, flywheel cover and exhaust cross-over pipe.
4. Unfasten and remove oil pan.

F-85 Models

1. Remove dipstick, hoist car and drain oil.
2. Disconnect exhaust pipe from right exhaust manifold.
3. Disconnect front engine mounts and jack front of engine up as far as possible, using a wood block under front of crankshaft hub and wood blocks between halves of front engine mounts.

CAUTION: Be sure distributor does not contact cowl, and fan blades do not contact fan ring.

4. Position No. 1 crankshaft throw up.
5. Remove exhaust cross-over pipe.
6. Remove starter.
7. Unfasten and remove oil pan.

V8-330, 350, 425, 455

1. Remove oil level dipstick.
2. Raise car and drain oil.
3. On F-85 models, disconnect exhaust pipe from right exhaust manifold.
4. On Olds F.S.C models, lower steering relay rod by disconnecting idler arm or pitman arm.
5. Disconnect engine mounts and raise front of engine as far as possible.

CAUTION: Be sure distributor does not contact cowl and fan blades do not contact fan shroud.

6. Bring No. 1 piston up on top center.
7. Remove crossover pipe and starter.
8. Unfasten and remove oil pan.

V8-400

1. Disconnect battery ground cable.

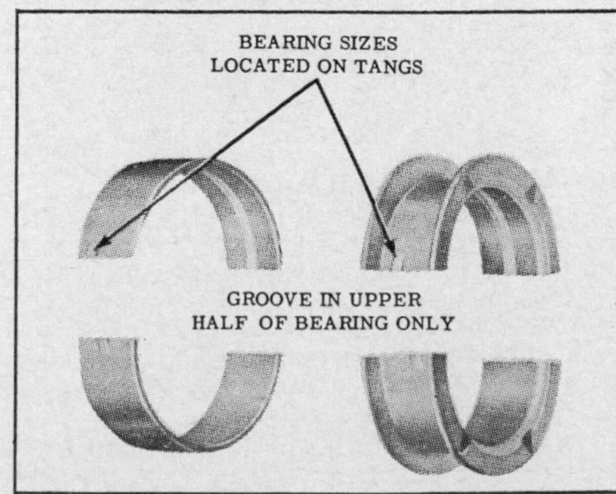

Fig. 42 Main bearing size location. V6-225, V8-215, 330, 350, 400, 425, 455

6. Disconnect speedometer cable (F-85).
7. Unfasten engine from transmission (4 bolts) and slide transmission out of car.

1965 Olds F.S.C.

1. Remove propeller shaft.
2. Disconnect shift rods from shift levers at transmission.
3. Disconnect equalizer shaft at side of transmission.
4. Support engine at rear.
5. Disconnect parking brake cable.
6. Remove crossmember.

NOTE: It may be necessary to disconnect left-hand exhaust pipe from manifold to provide clearance if equipped with dual exhaust.

7. Remove transmission upper attaching bolts and install aligning studs to prevent distortion of clutch disc hub when removing transmission.
8. Remove lower attaching bolts and slide transmission out of vehicle.

1964 F-85 & Jetstar 88

1. Remove propeller shaft and disconnect shift rods from shift levers at transmission.
2. If equipped with floor shift, disconnect shift lever bracket from extension housing and remove shift levers-to-shift shafts, leaving linkage connected to levers. Bracket assembly, levers and linkage can be left hanging in car.
3. Support rear of engine. Remove cross support bar-to-rear transmission mount attaching bolts.
4. Remove cross support bar-to-frame attaching brackets and remove cross support bar.

NOTE: If equipped with dual exhaust, it may be necessary to disconnect left hand exhaust pipe at exhaust manifold to provide clearance.

5. Disconnect speedometer cable.
6. Remove four transmission attaching bolts and slide transmission rearward and out of car.
7. Reverse removal procedure to install the unit.

1963 F-85

1. Disconnect shift rods from transmission levers.
2. Disconnect speedometer cable.
3. Disconnect propeller shaft from transmission companion flange. *Do not let front section of propeller shaft fall loose; move it to one side and tie it to exhaust pipe to avoid damage to center joint ball and seat.*
4. Support rear of engine with high floor stand.
5. Remove rear transmission mount and support bar.
6. Remove four transmission-to-clutch housing bolts.
7. Slide transmission straight back until main drive gear is free of splines in clutch disc.
8. Install transmission in reverse order of removal and adjust shift linkage.

1963-64 Olds F.S.C.

1. Drain transmission and disconnect control rods from transmission.
2. Disconnect speedometer cable at transmission (cable drives off front wheel).
3. Remove propeller shaft.
4. Remove transmission-to-clutch housing bolts and slide transmission rearward until main drive gear clears clutch housing. Lower transmission out of car.
5. Reverse above procedure to install transmission. Apply Lubriplate to the main drive gear shaft. Align propeller shaft, and adjust transmission linkage.

3 SPEED SHIFT LINKAGE, ADJUST

1966-69

On 1969 models, detent must be adjusted as follows. Place transmission in Reverse, loosen shift rods at transmission. Push up on reverse rod until detent in column is felt and tighten bolt for 1st-Reverse rod to 20 ft. lbs. Continue adjustment as follows:

1. Place transmission in Neutral.
2. On 1966-68, loosen swivel nuts on shift rods at transmission.
3. Use a suitable rod as an aligning tool and position it in the slot provided in mast jacket so alignment rod enters holes in low-reverse lever and the interlock pawl.
4. With transmission levers in neutral, tighten swivel nuts to 23 ft-lbs.
5. Remove aligning rod. Make sure neutral positions between low-reverse and second-third are exactly in line. If not, readjust one rod to bring them in line.
6. Check shift operation with engine stopped. Start engine and recheck.
7. On 1969 models, place transmission in Reverse and ignition in "Lock" position. Check to be sure key can be removed, steering wheel will not turn and transmission will not shift out of Reverse.

1965 F-85 & Jetstar 88

1. Loosen swivels and move both transmission shift levers until transmission is in neutral. Neutral detents in transmission cover must both be engaged to make this adjustment correctly.
2. Move selector lever to neutral.
3. Align low-reverse shift lever with 2-3 shift lever.
4. With levers properly aligned in neutral and shift rods free to slide in swivels, center movement of rods in swivels and tighten swivels.
5. Move selector lever through all positions to check adjustment and to insure over-travel in all positions.

1965 Olds F.S.C.

1. Position transmission in neutral.
2. Loosen swivel nuts on shift rods at transmission, being sure rods are free to move in swivels.
3. Slip a suitable aligning pin in slot provided in mast jacket so aligning pin enters holes in low-reverse lever and interlock pawl.
4. With transmission levers in neutral, tighten swivel nuts to 26 ft-lbs.
5. Remove aligning pin and make sure neutral positions between low-reverse and 2-3 levers are exactly in line. If not, readjust one rod to bring them in line.
6. Check shift pattern with engine off. Then start engine and check adjustment.

1964 F-85 & Jetstar 88

1. Move both transmission levers until transmission is in neutral. *Neutral detents in transmission cover must both be engaged. To check, start engine with clutch disengaged and release clutch slowly.*
2. Move selector lever to neutral.
3. Align low-reverse shift lever with the 2-3 shift lever.
4. Install control rods on shift levers.
5. Adjust both shift control rods so as to have a "free pin" fit where rods enter shift levers. Be sure all levers remain aligned in neutral.
6. Move selector lever through all positions to check adjustment and to insure over-travel in all positions.

1963 F-85

1. Loosen trunnion nuts at bottom of steering column-to-equalizer and shift lever rods.
2. Place hand selector lever and shift levers on transmission in neutral.
3. Position shift levers in steering column in alignment with each other as well as horizontal, and tighten trunnion nuts.

1963-64 Olds F.S.C.

1. Set transmission outer shift lever in 2nd gear position.
2. Disconnect shift rod from steering column lower shift lever at clevis.
3. Hold steering column lower shift lever upward against its stop in steering column.
4. Install clevis pin through lower shift lever from bottom side, then adjust clevis so it slides over pin freely. Then shorten shift rod by turning clevis 5½ turns.
5. Install clevis pin and tighten clevis lock nut.

1966-69 3 SPEED HEAVY DUTY TRANS., REPLACE

1. Disconnect throttle linkage from cowl bracket to prevent damage.
2. Raise car and remove drive shaft.
3. Disconnect shift rods from shift levers (column shift).
4. With floor shift, remove shift lever knob and disconnect back-up lamp wiring (if equipped).
5. Disconnect equalizer shaft at side of transmission.
6. Support rear of engine.
7. Disconnect parking brake cable.
8. Remove cross support bar.
9. It may be necessary to disconnect

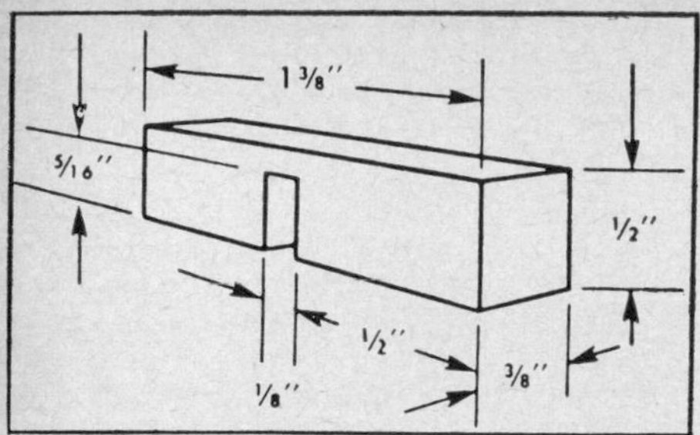

Fig. 1 Gearshift linkage gauge block can be made locally to the dimensions indicated

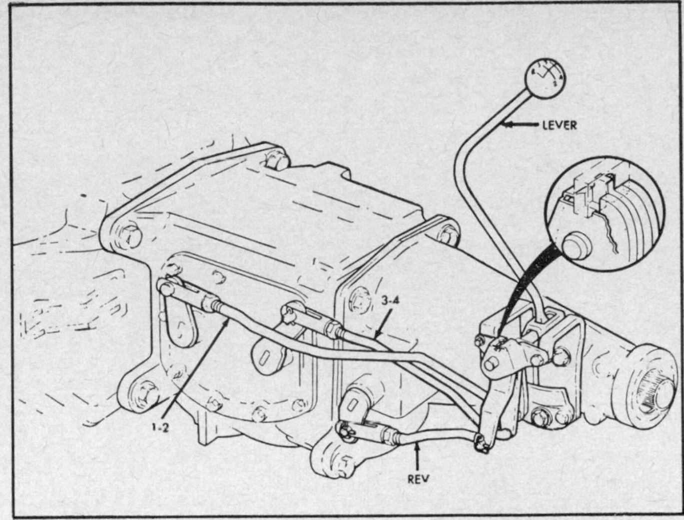

Fig. 2 Four speed manual shift transmission linkage adjustment

left exhaust pipe from exhaust manifold to provide clearance if equipped with dual exhaust.

10. Remove transmission upper bolts and install aligning studs in the bolt holes.
11. Remove lower bolts and slide transmission out of car.
12. Reverse procedure to install.

Shift Linkage, Adjust

On 1969 models, detent must be adjusted as follows: Place transmission in Reverse and loosen swivel bolt on back drive rod at equalizer. Push up lightly on back drive rod until stop is felt and tighten bolt to 20 ft. lbs. Continue adjustment.

1. Position transmission in neutral.
2. Loosen clamp screws on shift rods.
3. Use a suitable aligning rod and position it in slot provided in mast jacket so that it enters holes in low-reverse lever and the interlock pawl.
4. With floor shift, a ¼" diameter pin is inserted through shift lever bracket and levers.
5. With transmission levers in neutral, tighten clamp screws to 23 ft-lbs. On 1969 models, place transmission in Reverse and ignition in "Lock" position. Check to be sure key can be removed, steering wheel will not turn and transmission will not shift out of Reverse.
6. Remove alignment rod. Make sure neutral positions between low-reverse and second-third are exactly in line. If not, readjust one rod to bring them in line.

4 SPEED TRANS., REPLACE

1965-69

1. Remove propeller shaft and disconnect shift rods from shift levers at transmission.
2. Disconnect back-up lamp switch wires (if equipped).
3. Support engine at rear.

NOTE: On models with dual exhaust it may be necessary to disconnect left-hand exhaust pipe from manifold to provide clearance.

4. On F-85 models, disconnect speedometer cable.
5. Disconnect parking brake cables from crossmember, then remove crossmember.
6. Remove three bolts that retain shift lever assembly to extension housing. If shift lever assembly removal is not required, it may be left hanging in floor seal.
7. Unfasten transmission and remove from car.

1963 F-85

1. Disconnect speedometer cable and shifter control rods from levers at transmission.
2. Remove propeller shaft.
3. Support rear of engine and remove transmission rear mount and support bar.
4. Remove two upper transmission to clutch housing mounting screws and install guide pins in these holes. Then remove lower screws and slide transmission back and out of vehicle.
5. Install transmission in reverse order and check shift linkage.

4 SPEED SHIFT LINKAGE, ADJUST

1965-69

1. On 1969, place transmission in Reverse and loosen swivel bolt on back drive rod at equalizer. Push up lightly on back drive rod until stop is felt and tighten bolt to 20 ft. lbs.
2. All models: Place transmission in Neutral and loosen shift rods.
3. Using a suitable rod, align levers in Neutral.
4. Adjust swivels to obtain a "free pin" fit at levers. Tighten swivel bolts to 20 ft. lbs.
5. On 1969 models, place transmission in Reverse and ignition in "Lock" position. Check to be sure key can be removed, steering wheel will not turn and transmission will not shift out of Reverse.

1964 F-85 & Jetstar 88

1. Set transmission in neutral position.
2. Move shift lever stud to neutral detent position and insert a $\frac{5}{16}$" locating pin into control lever bracket.
3. Connect 1-2 rod to its lever. Maintaining lever against gauge pin, adjust clevis until its pin freely passes through holes in clevis and lever. Tighten jam nut against clevis.
4. Adjust reverse rod and 3-4 rod in like manner.
5. Remove gauge pin and check shifts for proper operation.

1963 F-85

1. Place transmission in neutral and install gauge, Fig. 1, indicated in position shown in Fig. 2.
2. Remove clevis pin at each lever.
3. On each shift rod, adjust threaded clevis to permit free entry of clevis pin into hole in transmission shift lever.
4. Connect clevises to shift lever.
5. Remove gauge block and check shifts.

NOTE: If any roughness exists, one of the clevises may require adjustment of about ½ turn. Determine the rod and clevis requiring adjustment by sighting along the slot where the gauge block was used.

1969 AUTO. TRANS. LINKAGE, ADJUST

Adjustment procedures for the 1969 models are essentially the same as those for the 1968 units as outlined in the front of this manual.

Rear Axle, Propeller Shaft & Brakes

NOTE: Material marked F.S.C. means Full Size Car or Senior Models

REAR AXLE

Figs. 1, 2 and 3 illustrate the rear axle assemblies used on conventional models. When necessary to overhaul any of these units, refer to the *Rear Axle Specifications* table in this chapter.

Removable Carrier, 1963-64

In these rear axles, Fig. 1 the drive pinion is mounted in two tapered roller bearings that are preloaded by a collapsible spacer. The pinion is positioned by a shim located between the head of the pinion and the rear pinion bearing.

The differential is supported in the carrier by two tapered roller side bearings. These bearings are preloaded by two threaded sleeves or ring nuts between the bearings and pedestals. The differential assembly is positioned for proper ring gear and pinion backlash by varying the adjustment of these ring nuts. The differential case houses two side gears in mesh with two pinions mounted on a pinion shaft which is held in place by a lock screw. The side gears and pinions are backed by thrust washers.

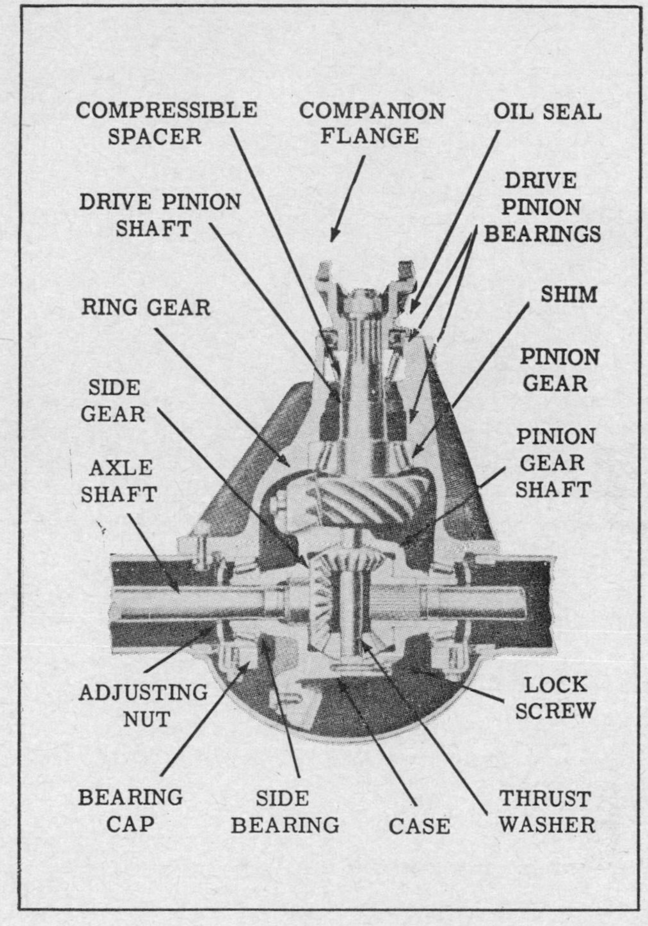

Fig. 1 Removable carrier type rear axle assembly. 1963-64

Differential Carrier, Replace

In servicing these rear axles, it is not necessary to remove the rear axle assembly for any normal repairs. The axle shafts and carrier assembly can easily be removed from the vehicle, leaving the axle housing in place.

1. Remove axle shafts and drive shaft as explained below.
2. Drain oil from carrier by removing nuts from carrier studs.
3. Remove carrier assembly from housing.

Integral Carrier 1963-67 & 1968-69 F.S.C.

As shown in Fig. 2, the drive pinion is mounted on two tapered roller bearings that are preloaded by two selected spacers. The drive pinion is positioned by shims located between a shoulder on the pinion and the rear bearing. The front bearing is held in place by a large nut.

The differential is supported in the carrier by two tapered roller side bearings. These are preloaded by inserting shims between the bearings and the pedestals. The differential assembly is positioned for ring gear and pinion backlash by varying these shims.

Major service work on the differential carrier assembly may be performed with the unit in the car provided a drive-on or twin-post hoist is available. If neither of these hoists are available, the rear axle assembly should be removed from the vehicle. The reason for this is that the axle tubes are pressed into the differential carrier housing and welded.

1968-69 Series 31 to 44

In these rear axles, Fig. 3, the rear axle housing and differential carrier are cast into an integral assembly. The drive pinion assembly is mounted in two opposed tapered roller bearings. The pinion bearings are preloaded by a spacer behind the front bearing. The pinion is positioned by a washer between the head of the pinion and the rear bearing.

The differential is supported in the carrier by two tapered roller side bearings. These bearings are preloaded by spacers located between the bearings and carrier housing. The differential assembly is positioned for proper ring gear and pinion backlash by varying these spacers. The differential case houses two side gears in mesh with two pinions mounted on a pinion shaft which is held in place by a lock pin. The side gears and pinions are backed by thrust washers.

Remove & Replace

Construction of the axle assembly is such that service operations may be performed with the housing installed in the vehicle or with the housing removed and installed in a holding fixture. The following procedure is necessary only when the housing requires replacement.

1. Hoist car and remove rear wheels, drums and axle shafts.
2. Disconnect brake line from wheel cylinders.
3. Unfasten and support backing plates with wire hooks to frame kickup.
4. Disconnect shocks at housing.
5. Position jack stands under frame rear torque boxes, then lower axle housing to stands.
6. Remove springs.
7. Remove propeller shaft and support front of axle housing at companion flange to prevent assembly from rotating when the control arms are disconnected.
8. Remove control arm bolts at axle housing.
9. Remove support at companion flange and lower axle housing.

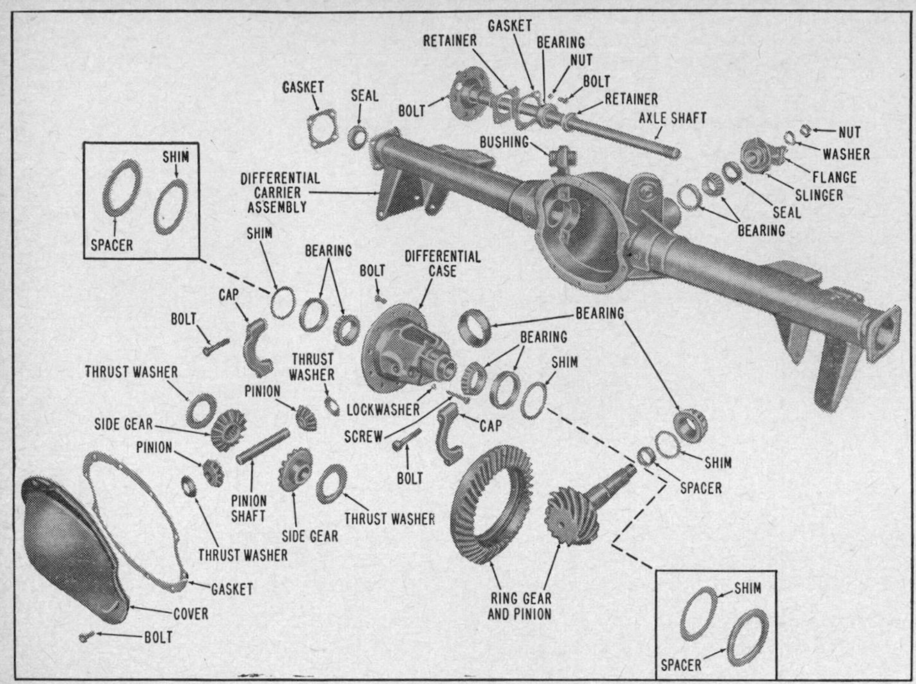

Fig. 2 Integral carrier type rear axle. 1963-67 and 1968-69 Type "O" axle

10. Remove assembly to bench and transfer parts to new axle housing.
11. Reverse procedure to install.

AXLE SHAFT, REPLACE

1968-69, Series 31 to 44 Type "C"

1. Raise vehicle and remove wheel and brake drum.
2. Clean all dirt from area of carrier cover.
3. Drain lubricant from carrier by removing cover.
4. Remove differential pinion shaft lock screw and shaft.
5. Push flanged end of axle shaft toward center of vehicle and remove "C" lock from button end of shaft.
6. Remove axle shaft from housing, being careful not to damage oil seal.
7. Reverse procedure to install.

1963-64 F.S.C. Except Jetstar 88

Removal

1. Remove wheel. Wheel nuts on left side of car have left-hand threads.
2. Remove the two Tinnerman nuts from wheel studs that hold brake drum in place and remove drum. *If Tinnerman nuts are removed by turning off threads they can be reused. However, if nuts are damaged in any way they must be replaced.*
3. Remove brake backing plate from axle housing (4 bolts).
4. Pull axle shaft bearing retainer plate away from backing plate, taking care not to dislodge backing plate as brake line may be damaged.
5. Pull axle shaft out with a slide hammer-type puller if bearing is a tight fit in axle housing. *While pulling shaft out through seal, support shaft carefully in center of seal to avoid cutting seal lip.*
6. Replace one brake backing plate nut to hold plate in position.

Bearing, Replace

The sealed axle shaft bearings are built with .012 to .015" end play between balls and races and should not be rejected unless end play is greater than .020" or definite roughness between ball and race can be felt when bearing is rotated by hand. The bearing should be checked for roughness and end play before it is removed from the axle shaft because once removed the bearing cannot be used again. *Tipping of either race can cause a large error in end play reading.*

1. With axle shaft removed, remove bearing retainer collar after splitting with cold chisel, Fig. 4.
2. Press bearing from shaft.
3. Press bearing on shaft until it seats against axle shaft shoulder.
4. Press new bearing retainer collar on shaft until it is firmly against bearing.

Installation

Before installing shaft, examine oil seal. Seal has feather edge which forms a tight seal around shaft. If feather edges are damaged in any way, pull seal from housing and install a new one.

1. Remove temporary nut holding brake backing plate to axle housing.
2. Place new gasket over backing plate studs.
3. Slide axle shaft assembly into place, using extreme care not to damage oil seal. *When installing axle shaft on cars with non-slip differential, it will be necessary to align differential side gear and side gear ring splines by inserting axle shaft into side gear ring and rotating shaft slightly to pick up splines in side gear. Do not attempt to force shaft.*
4. Place retainer plate over backing

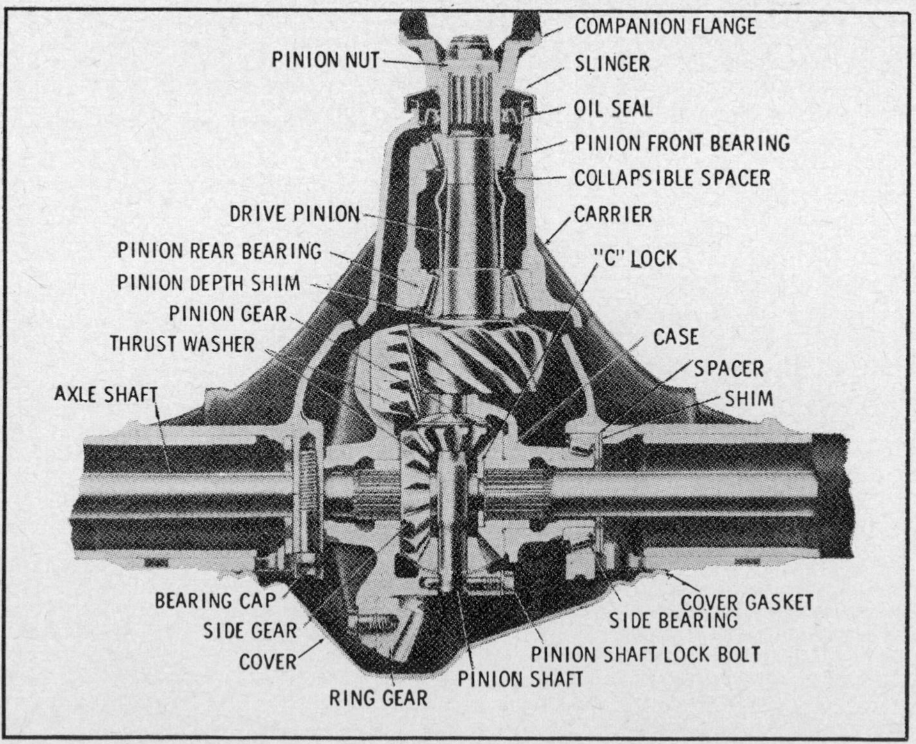

Fig. 3 Integral carrier type differential. 1968-69 Type "C" axle

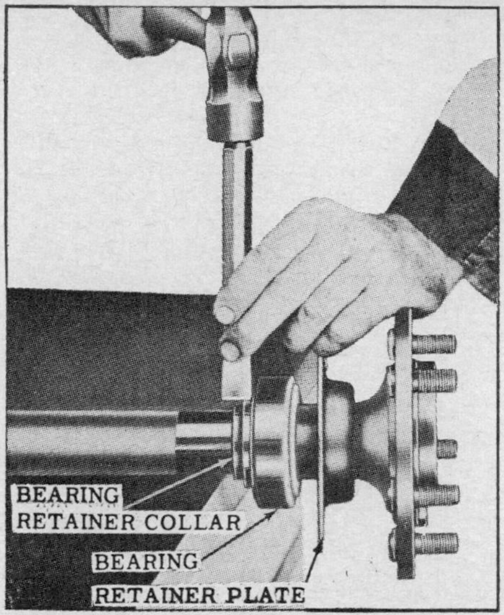

Fig. 4 Removing axle shaft bearing retainer

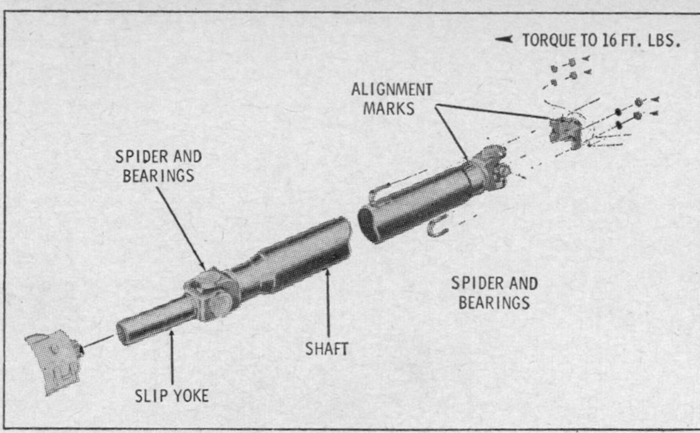

Fig. 5 Propeller shaft installation. 1964-69

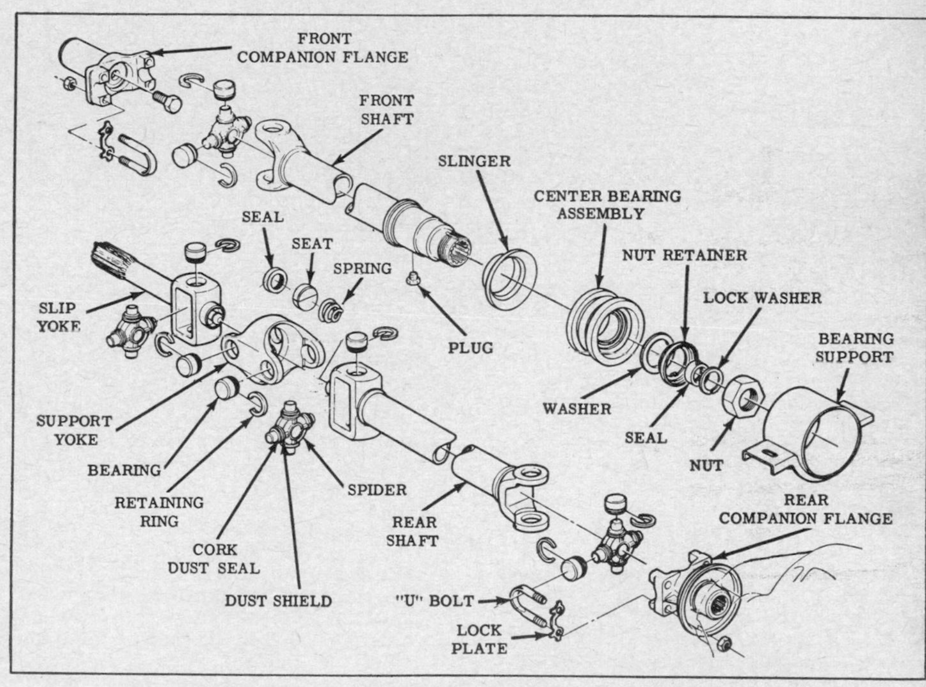

Fig. 6 Propeller shaft assembly. 1963 F-85

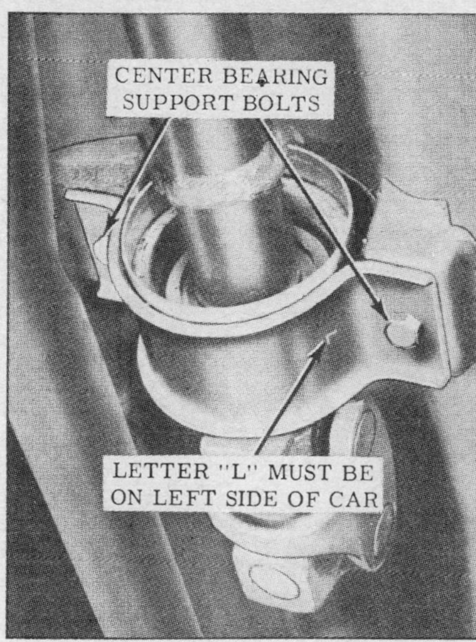

Fig. 7 Center bearing bracket. 1963 F-85

plate studs and install nuts, tightening them to 55 to 60 ft. lbs.

5. Replace drum and wheel assembly.

All 1965-67, 1968-69 Series 31 to 86, 1963-64 F-85 & Jetstar 88 Type "O"

Removal

1. Remove wheel and brake drum.
2. Remove axle bearing retainer (4 nuts).
3. Pull axle shaft from housing. If bearing is a tight fit in housing, use a slide hammer-type puller, Fig. 3. Do not drag shaft over seal as this may damage seal.
4. Attach one axle bearing retainer nut to hold brake backing plate in position.
5. Before installing axle shaft, examine oil seal. The seals have feathered edges which form a tight seal around the shaft. If these edges are damaged in any way, seal must be replaced. Examine seal surface on shaft; if it is not smooth, dress it down with very fine emery cloth.
6. Reverse removal procedure to install axle shaft, being sure to grease outside of axle bearing, seal surface on axle shaft and bore of axle housing with differential lubricant. Place new gasket and bearing retainer over studs, install nuts and tighten them 45 to 60 ft. lbs.

Installation

Bearings should be replaced if found to be rough or have greater than .020" end play. Remove bearing only when new bearing is to be installed; once removed it must not be reused.

1. With axle shaft removed from housing, split bearing retainer with a chisel, Fig. 4.
2. Press bearing off shaft.
3. Press new bearing on shaft up against shoulder on shaft.
4. Press retainer on shaft up against bearing.
5. Reverse removal procedure to install axle shaft.

PROPELLER SHAFT

1964-69

The rear yoke of the Jetaway equipped cars is bonded in rubber to the inside of the propeller shaft tube and cannot be removed for service. The shaft for the manual shift transmission models is one piece, Fig. 5.

1. To remove, remove nuts holding U-bolts at differential companion flange.
2. If U-joint bearings are not retained by a metal retaining strap, use a piece of wire or tape to hold bear-

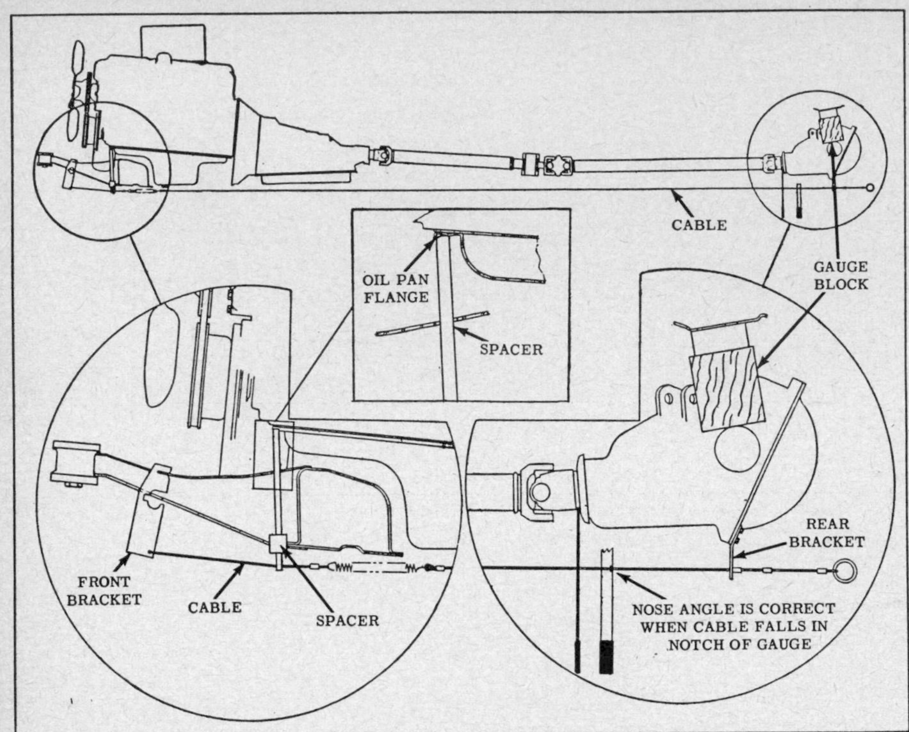

Fig. 8 Differential nose angle alignment. 1963 F-85

ings on U-joint cross.

3. Lower rear of shaft and slide rearward.
4. Reverse removal procedure to install the shaft. First, however, apply one ounce of seal lubricant to the splines of the slip yoke on Jetaway and Jetstar 88.

1963 F-85

1. Referring to Fig. 6, remove U-bolts from companion flanges at transmission and differential.
2. If U-joint bearings that attach to companion flange are not retained with a metal retainer, use a piece of wire or tape to hold bearings on their spider or cross before removing from flange.
3. Remove two bearing support-to-body bolts and remove shaft assembly. *When handling the drive shaft assembly, extreme care must be taken not to allow one shaft to "flop" around loosely as this may damage the center ball seat.*
4. To install, position center bearing support on bearing insulator and attach to body. Torque bolts 10 to 18 ft. lbs., Fig. 7.
5. Attach U-bolts to companion flanges and torque U-bolt nuts 14 to 18 ft. lbs. Tighten each side uniformly before final torque is applied. Bend lock tangs over nuts. *Inspect center bearing rubber insulator to be sure that edges of insulator did not become folded under while installing it in support bracket.*

Center Bearing & Mount

1. With shaft removed, slide bearing-to-body mounting forward off bearing.
2. Pry crimped area of slip yoke nut retainer away from nut; then unscrew nut until it is free of threads.
3. Pull rear shaft from front shaft. *Watch for index wire in one spline of slip yoke. It is important that this wire be kept in same spline.*
4. Remove nut retainer and rear spacer.
5. Remove slip yoke seal at this time if necessary to replace it.
6. Use puller to remove center bearing. Bearing and insulator are serviced as an assembly. The groove between bearing and front of bearing retainer must be packed with waterproof grease.

Assemble

1. Drive new bearing on shaft until it is seated.
2. Place rear spacer, then nut retainer on front propeller shaft with tang of retainer indexing slot of propeller shaft. Cupped side of nut retainer must face rearward.
3. Apply special spline lubricant to front propeller shaft splines.
4. Install new slip yoke seal at this time if old seal was removed.
5. Align slip yoke index spring wire with wide serration in front propeller shaft; then insert slip yoke into front shaft.
6. Torque slip yoke nut 50 to 75 ft. lbs. Crimp nut retainer against nut in two places.

Propeller Shaft Alignment

If drive line shudder, roughness or vibration is experienced, it may be due to incorrect propeller shaft alignment or differential nose angle. To make this check, a special tool consisting mainly of a cable, Fig. 8, is used.

1. Install tool at front arm of front cross bar as shown. The line to engine spacer is installed after rear bracket has been attached to differential.
2. Place indicator against pinion companion flange and cable must be in notch marked "F85".
3. If necessary to adjust, remove shim from front of lower suspension arm if cable is below notch. If cable is above notch, add shims. *The same amount of shims must be added to both sides. A 1/8" shim will raise or lower nose angle approximately 1/16".*

BRAKE ADJUSTMENTS

All 1963-69 & 1963 F-85

These brakes, Fig. 15, have self-adjusting shoe mechanisms that assure correct lining-to-drum clearances at all times. The automatic adjusters operate only when the brakes are applied as the car is moving rearward or when the car comes to an uphill stop.

Although the brakes are self-adjusting, an initial adjustment is necessary after the brake shoes have been relined or replaced, or when the length of the star wheel adjuster has been changed during some other service operation.

Frequent usage of an automatic transmission forward range to halt reverse vehicle motion may prevent the automatic adjusters from functioning, thereby inducing low pedal heights. Should low pedal heights be encountered, it is recommended that numerous forward and reverse stops be made until satisfactory pedal height is obtained.

NOTE

If a low pedal height condition cannot be corrected by making numerous reverse stops (provided the hydraulic system is free of air) it indicates that the self-adjusting mechanism is not functioning. Therefore, it will be necessary to remove the brake drum, clean, free up and lubricate the adjusting mechanism. Then adjust the brakes as follows, being sure the parking brake is fully released.

Adjustment

NOTE: Inasmuch as there is no way to adjust these brakes with the drums installed, the following procedure is mandatory after new linings are installed or if it becomes necessary to change the length of the brake shoe adjusting screw.

1. With brake drums removed, position the caliper shown in Fig. 16 to the inside diameter of the drum and tighten the clamp screw.
2. Next position brake shoe end of the caliper tool over the brake shoes as shown in Fig. 17.
3. Rotate the gauge slightly around the shoes to insure that the gauge contacts the linings at the largest diameter.
4. Adjust brake shoes until the gauge is a snug fit on the linings at the

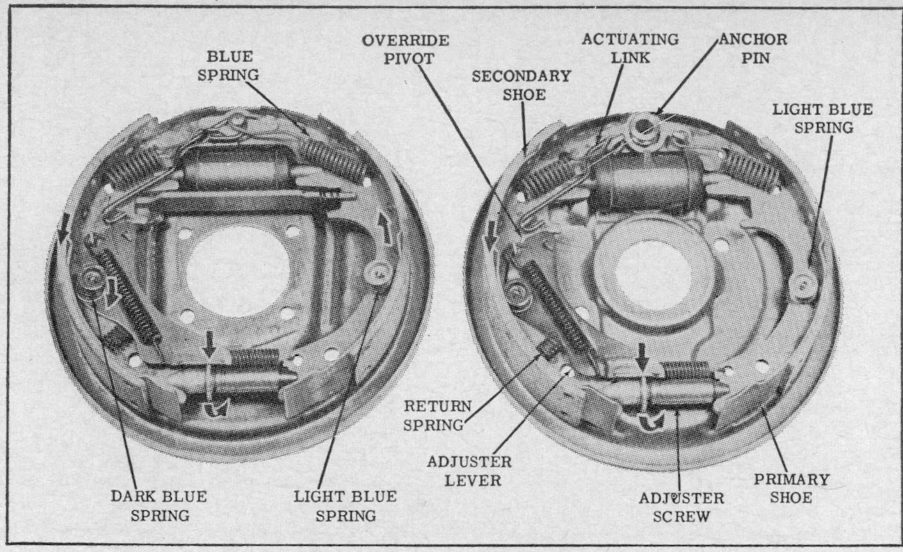

Fig. 15 Right rear and front brake. All 1963-69 and 1963 F-85

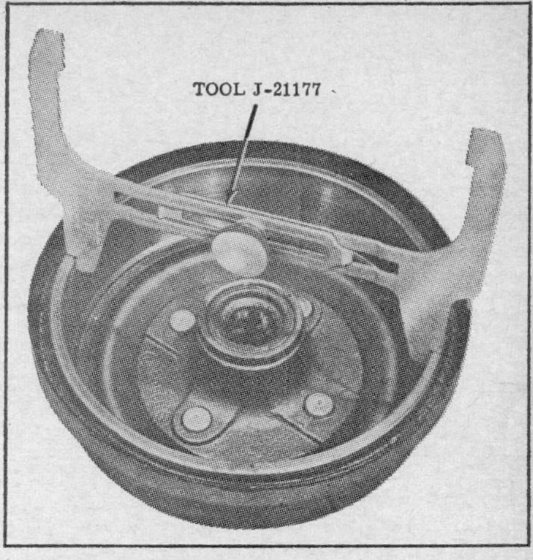

Fig. 16 Brake shoe gauge measuring inside diameter of brake drum. 1963-69

point of largest lining diameter.

NOTE: If it is necessary to back off the brake shoe adjustment, it will be necessary to hold the adjuster lever away from the adjuster screw, Fig. 18.

PARKING BRAKE, ADJUST

1963-69

With parking brake fully released, adjust rear cables by first tightening the brake equalizer adjusting nut until a heavy resistance is felt when rotating rear wheels forward. Then loosen equalizer adjusting nut 7 full turns (10 on 1963).

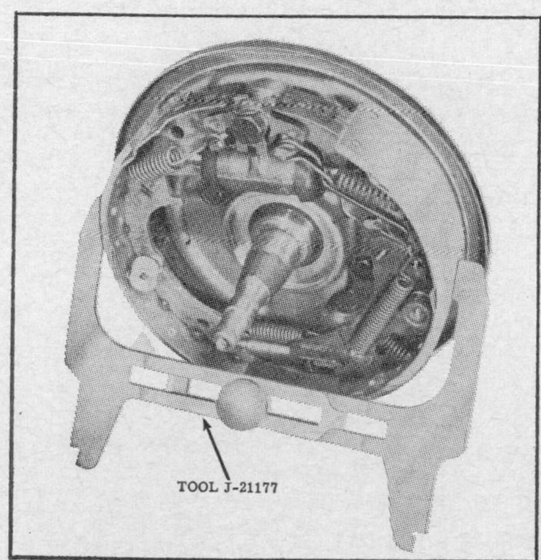

Fig. 17 Brake shoe gauge measuring outside diameter of brake shoes. 1963-69

POWER BRAKE UNIT, REPLACE

1967-69

1. Disconnect vacuum hose from vacuum cylinder and cover openings to prevent entrance of dirt.
2. Disconnect pipes from master cylinder outlets and cover openings in master cylinder and end of pipes to prevent entrance of dirt.
3. Loosen inboard master cylinder attaching nut to disengage metering valve (disc brakes only).
4. Disconnect air valve rod from brake pedal.
5. Unfasten and remove power brake unit.
6. Reverse procedure to install.

1964-66

1. Disconnect hydraulic line. Plug or tape line to prevent dirt from entering hydraulic system.
2. Disconnect vacuum line from vacuum check valve.
3. Disconnect operating rod from brake pedal.
4. Unfasten (4 nuts) and remove power unit from cowl.
5. Reverse removal sequence to install and torque attaching nuts to 20-27 ft-lbs.

1963

1. Disconnect hydraulic line. Plug or tape line to prevent dirt from entering hydraulic system.
2. Disconnect vacuum lines from vacuum cylinder.
3. Disconnect operating rod from brake pedal.
4. Unfasten vacuum cylinder from cowl (4 nuts).
5. Reverse sequence of operations to install and torque attaching nuts 8-16 ft. lbs.

BRAKE MASTER CYLINDER, REPLACE

1964-69

The standard brake master cylinder on Olds F.S.C. can be removed without disconnecting the push rod and clevis. On all cars equipped with power brakes, the master cylinder can be removed without removing the vacuum cylinder from the car.

1. Be sure area around master cylinder is clean, then disconnect the hydraulic lines at master cylinder. Plug or tape end of line to prevent entrance of dirt or loss of brake fluid.
2. On F-85 models, remove push rod-to-brake pedal clevis pin.
3. On all models, unfasten (4 bolts) and remove master cylinder.

1963 F-85

Be sure area around master cylinder is clean, then disconnect hydraulic line at master cylinder. Plug or tape end of line to prevent entrance of dirt.

Remove four attaching nuts and remove master cylinder. It is not necessary

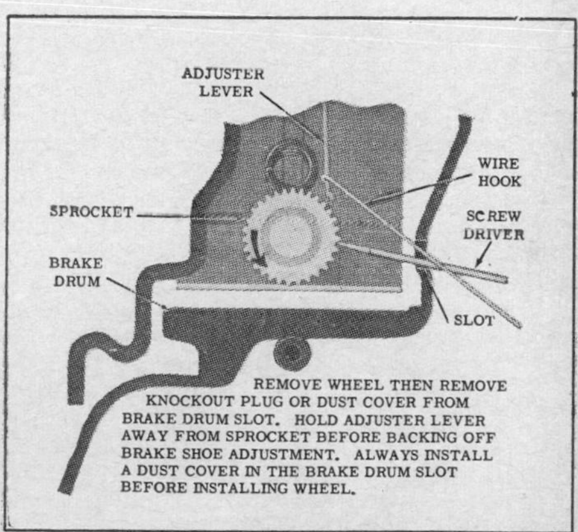

Fig. 18 Backing off brake shoe adjustment

to disconnect the push rod and clevis.

Install master cylinder, fill reservoir with fluid and bleed system.

1963 F.S.C.

The standard brake master cylinder can be removed without disconnecting the push rod and clevis. The master cylinder on cars with power brakes can be removed without removing the vacuum cylinder from the car. Power cylinders can be identified by the bronze Moraine cylinder and the black Bendix cylinder.

1. Disconnect hydraulic line at master cylinder and plug or tape end to prevent dirt entering the system.
2. If equipped with standard transmission, install a gauge pin in the holes provided in the frame side rail and "X" member to hold clutch linkage in position; then disconnect clutch linkage from clutch pedal bellcrank and remove bellcrank.
3. Remove master cylinder (4 nuts). On Moraine units, remove and record number of any shims found between master and power cylinders. *On Moraine units, the master cylinder piston will remain attached to the vacuum unit. If piston is to be serviced, the vacuum unit must be removed and disassembled.*

Front End and Steering Section

NOTE: Material marked Olds F.S.C. means Full Size Car or Senior Models

FRONT SUSPENSION

As shown in Figs. 1, 2 and 3, the front suspension is of the conventional "A" frame design with ball joints. Double acting shock absorbers are mounted within the coil springs. Caster and camber are controlled by shims.

LUBRICATION

An extended lubrication period of every six months or 12,000 miles is prescribed, whichever occurs first. The ball joints, are fitted with plugs which must be removed and grease fittings installed. After applying the approved type of grease, remove the fittings and reinstall the plugs.

IMPORTANT: On Intermediates, if ball joints are noisy, the plugs must be removed and approximately one teaspoonful of specified grease applied directly to the plug hole with a hand-operated, ball type nozzle grease gun. Do not install grease fittings or attempt to fill with a pressure gun. Either method will result in overfill or mixing of greases which may harm the part.

Before using a new grease gun of this type, first count the number of turns or pumps required to obtain approximately one teaspoonful of grease.

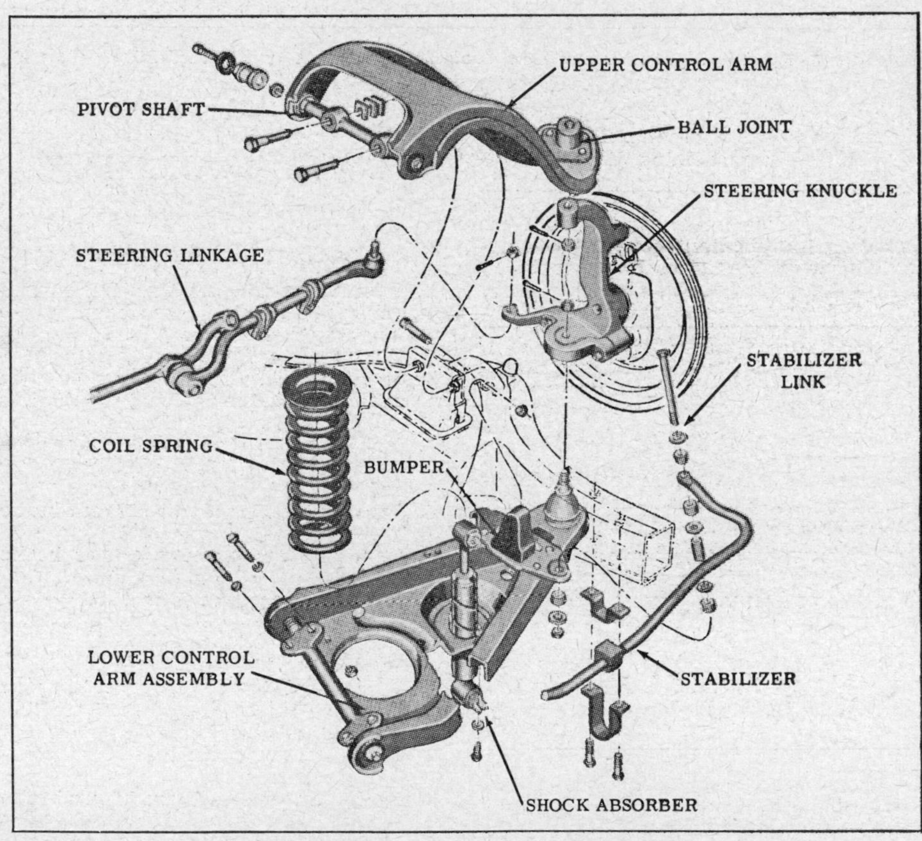

Fig. 1 Front suspension. 1963-64 Olds F.S.C.

WHEEL ALIGNMENT

1963-69 Full Size Cars

Camber and caster are adjusted by shims placed between the upper pivot shafts and the frame. In order to remove or install shims, *do not remove weight from front wheels.* Loosen pivot shaft-to-frame bolts. To gain access to these bolts, loosen top and rear fasteners on fender filler plate aprons.

To decrease positive caster, add shim at the front bolt. To increase positive caster, remove shim at the front bolt.

To increase camber, remove shims at both front and rear bolt. To decrease camber, add shims at both bolts.

By adding or subtracting an equal amount of shims from both front and rear bolts, camber will change without affecting caster adjustment. When changing shims, refer to Figs. 5 and 6.

1963-69 Intermediates

Caster and camber is adjusted by shimming at the upper control arm shaft attaching points. See Figs. 7 and 8.

Adding shims at the front locations will change caster toward negative with practically no change in camber. Adding shims at the rear locations will change caster toward positive and camber toward negative. Adding equal shims at both front and rear locations will not change caster but will change camber toward negative.

To adjust, loosen both front and rear bolts to free shims for removal or addition.

TOE-IN, ADJUST

To adjust the toe-in, loosen the clamps at both ends of the adjustable tubes at each tie rod. Then turn the tubes an equal amount until the toe-in is correct. Turning the tubes in the direction the wheels revolve when the car moves forward decreases the toe-in and vice-versa. When the adjustment is complete, tighten all clamp screws.

The steering knuckle and steering arm "rock" or tilt as front wheel rises and falls. Therefore, it is vitally important to position the bottom face of the tie rod

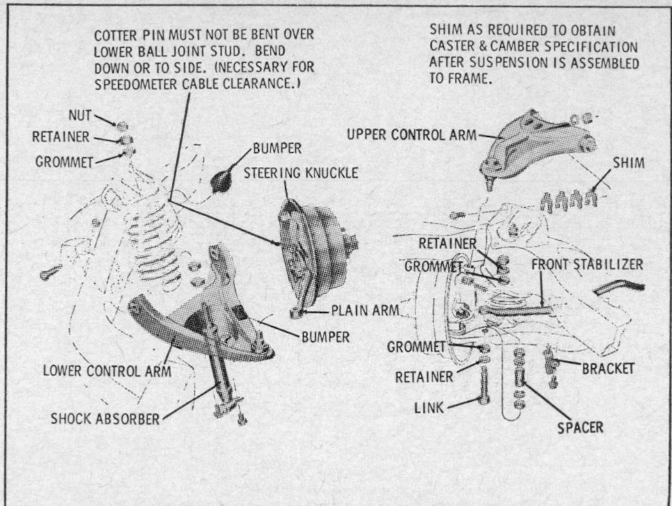

Fig. 2 Front suspension. 1965-69 Full Size Car

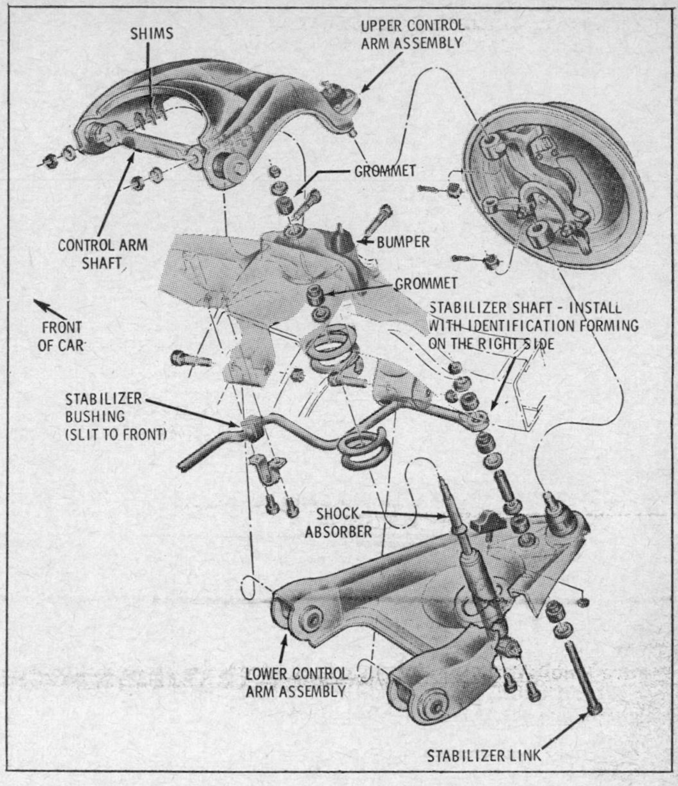

Fig. 3 Front suspension. 1963-69 Intermediate Models

end parallel with the machined surface at the outer end of the steering arm when tie rod length is adjusted. Severe damage and possible failure can result unless this precaution is taken. The tie rod sleeve clamps must be straight down to provide clearance.

WHEEL BEARINGS, ADJUST

1965-69 Full Size Cars (Except Jetstar 88)

1. While rotating hub and drum assembly at least three times the speed of nut rotation, tighten nut to 30 ft-lbs to insure all parts are properly seated.
2. Back off nut ½ turn.
3. Retighten nut finger tight and install retaining ring or cotter key if possible. If unable to install retaining ring or cotter key, back off nut (not to exceed 1/24 of a turn) until tabs on clip align with serrations in nut.

1965-66 F-85 & Jetstar 88

1. While rotating hub and drum assembly at least three times the speed of nut rotation, tighten nut with a torque wrench 25-30 ft-lbs to insure that all parts are properly seated and threads are free.
2. Back off nut ½ turn, then retighten nut finger tight.
3. If unable to install cotter pin (or retainer on Jetstar 88) at finger tight position, back off to first notch and install cotter pin (or retainer).

1964 Olds F.S.C.

1. While rotating hub and drum assembly, at least three times the speed of nut rotation, torque nut to 25-30 ft-lbs.
2. Back off nut ½ turn. Then retighten nut finger tight and install retainer ring or cotter pin if possible. If unable to install retainer, back off nut

Shim Thickness	One shim added to or subtracted from BOTH BOLTS will change camber	One shim added to or subtracted from FRONT BOLT ONLY will change caster
.020"	1/8°	5/16°
.050"	5/16°	1/2°
.120"	5/8°	1-3/8°

Fig. 5 Wheel alignment shim data. 1963-64 Olds F.S.C.

(not to exceed 1/12 turn) until slot in nut and keyway align, then install retainer or cotter pin.

1964 F-85

1. Tighten adjusting nut with a torque wrench to 25-30 ft-lbs while revolving wheel at least three times the speed of nut rotation.
2. Back off nut ½ turn. Then retighten nut finger tight.
3. If unable to install cotter pin at finger tight position, back off to first notch and install cotter pin.

1963 F-85

1. Tighten spindle nut 10-15 ft-lbs torque while rotating hub to seat bearings.
2. Back nut off 1/6 turn minimum ¼ maximum to allow installation of cotter pin.

1963 Olds F.S.C.

1. Tighten spindle nut with a torque wrench to 23-25 ft-lbs while rotating wheel to seat bearings.
2. Back off nut ½ turn and then re-

Shim Thickness	One shim added to or subtracted from BOTH BOLTS will change camber	One shim added to or subtracted from FRONT BOLT ONLY will change caster
.030"	1/8°	1/8°
.060"	5/16°	7/16°
.120"	5/8°	7/8°

Fig. 6 Wheel alignment shim data. 1965-69 Olds F.S.C.

Shim Thickness	One shim added to or subtracted from BOTH BOLTS will change CAMBER	One shim added to or subtracted from FRONT BOLT ONLY will change CASTER
.030	1/4°	1/2°
.060	1/2°	1°
.120	7/8°	2°

Fig. 7 Wheel alignment shim data. 1963 F-85

Shim Thickness	One shim added to or subtracted from BOTH BOLTS will change CAMBER	One shim added to or subtracted from FRONT BOLT ONLY will change CASTER
.020"	1/8°	3/16°
.030"	3/16°	1/4°
.060"	3/8°	1/2°
120"	3/4°	1°

Fig. 8 Wheel alignment shim data. 1964-69 Inter.

tighten nut 15-17 ft-lbs.
3. If keyway in wheel spindle and a slot in nut line up, back off nut one notch; otherwise back off nut to the nearest slot and install retainer.

WHEEL BEARINGS REPLACE

(Disc Brakes) 1967-69

1. Raise car and remove front wheels.
2. Remove brake pads and caliper assembly but do not disconnect brake line. Suspend caliper from a wire loop or hook to avoid strain on the brake hose.
3. Remove grease cap, cotter pin and nut. Pull off hub and disc assembly. Grease retainer and inner bearing can now be removed.

CHECKING BALL JOINTS FOR WEAR

If loose ball joints are suspected, first be sure the front wheel bearings are properly adjusted and that the control arms are tight. Then check ball joints for wear as follows:

Referring to Fig. 9, raise wheel with a jack placed under the lower control arm as shown. Then test by moving the wheel up and down to check axial play, and rocking it at the top and bottom to measure radial play.

1. Upper ball joint should be replaced if there is any noticeable looseness at the joint.
2. Lower ball joint should be replaced if radial play exceeds .250".
3. Lower ball joint should be replaced if axial play between lower control arm and spindle exceeds the following:

1963-64 Olds F.S.C. .... .125

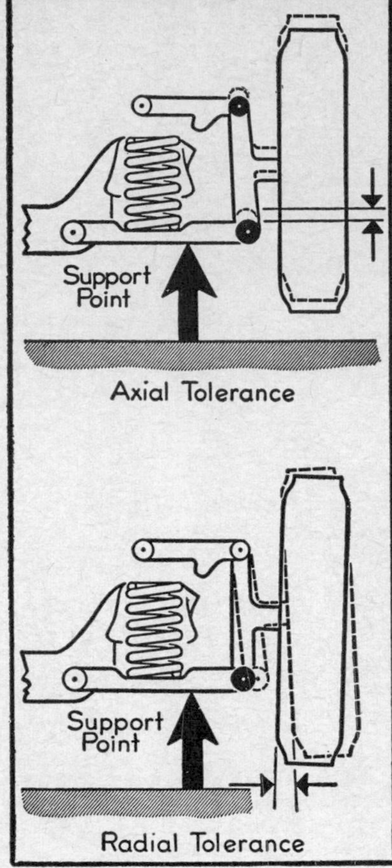
Support Point
Axial Tolerance
Support Point
Radial Tolerance

Fig. 9 Checking ball joints for wear

1963-64 Olds F-85 .... .090
1965-66 All Series .... .125

BALL JOINTS, REPLACE

Ball joints are mounted in the control arms in three ways. On some models the ball joints are riveted to the control arms. All service ball joints, however, are provided with bolt, nut and washer assemblies for replacement purposes.

Some ball joints are pressed into the control arms, in which case they may be pressed out and new ones installed. However, 1963 Senior models, the upper ball joint is supplied only with the control arm.

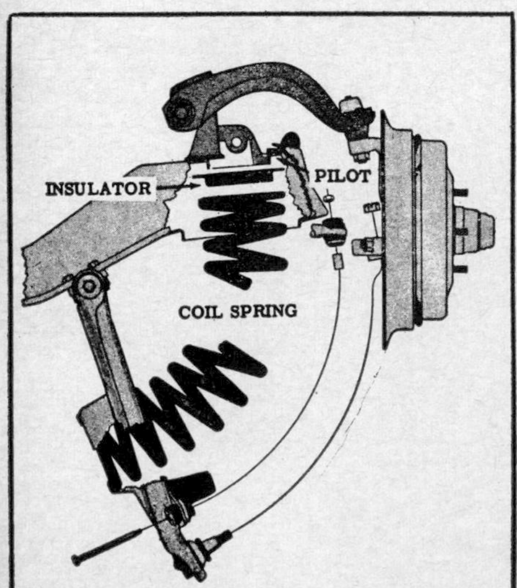
INSULATOR
PILOT
COIL SPRING

Fig. 10 Front spring installation. Senior Models

SHOCK ABSORBER, REPLACE

Senior Models

1. Remove upper pivot bolt from shock absorber.
2. Remove two capscrews and washers attaching shock absorber to lower control arm and remove shock absorber.
3. Reverse above procedure to install.

Intermediate Models

1. Remove upper attaching nut, retainer and grommet from shock absorber.
2. Remove two bolts and washers attaching shock absorber to lower control arm and remove shock absorber.
3. To install, position grommet and retainer over shock and slide shock up through spring and frame. Install and tighten attaching nut and lower capscrews.

COIL SPRING, REPLACE

Senior Models

1. Raise front of car and support frame with floor stands.
2. Remove wheel and disconnect speedometer cable from steering knuckle (if equipped).
3. Disconnect stabilizer link and speedometer cable clamp from lower control arm.
4. Loosen lower control arm shaft bushing bolts.
5. Remove shock absorber.
6. Position floor jack under lower control arm between spring seat and ball joint. Raise jack until it supports lower control arm.
7. Disconnect lower ball joint from steering knuckle.
8. Slowly lower floor jack until spring is fully extended and remove spring.

IMPORTANT: Left and right coil springs should not be interchanged. Spring part number is stamped on outer side of end coil.

INSTALLATION: Reverse removal procedure to install spring. However, first tape spring insulator to top of spring at least six places. Top of spring may be identified by flat coil which will allow insulator to seat squarely on top coil.

While holding spring and insulator against pilot in frame crossmember, tilt spring so it will pivot in lower control arm, Fig. 10. Rotate spring so end of bottom coil will index with edge of hole in control arm spring seat. Coil should not cover any portion of hole.

Intermediate Models

1. Raise front of car and support frame

WITH UPPER SPRING TAIL AGAINST STOP IN FRONT CROSSMEMBER SEAT: THIS HOLE MUST ALWAYS BE COVERED BY SPRING TAIL.
THIS HOLE (AT STOP IN SPRING SEAT) MUST NOT BE COVERED BY SPRING TAIL

Fig. 11 Front spring positioning. F-85 models

with floor stands.
2. Remove wheel. Disconnect stabilizer link from lower control arm.
3. Remove shock absorber.
4. Position floor jack between spring seat and ball joint with handle straight out from car to support lower control arm.
5. Disconnect lower control arm from ball joint.
6. Block upper control arm and backing plate up out of the way.
7. Slowly lower floor jack until spring is fully extended and remove spring.

Installation

1. While holding spring against pilot in frame, tilt spring so it will pilot in lower control arm. Rotate spring so end of top coil will index against step in upper spring seat, Fig. 11.
2. Position floor jack with handle straight out from car, between spring seat and ball joint.
3. Lower upper control arm and backing plate into position.
4. Raise lower control arm until ball joint is tight in steering knuckle. Install ball joint nut, torque it to 40 ft-lbs and insert cotter pin. *Use extreme care to prevent spring from dislodging while raising jack.*
5. Complete the installation in reverse order of removal.

MANUAL GEAR, REPLACE

1964-69

1. Remove two flex coupling flange nuts.
2. Hoist and support car with stands under outer ends of lower control arms.
3. Remove nut and use a puller to remove pitman arm.
4. Remove gear-to frame bolts.
5. Position steering linkage and speedometer cable (if equipped) out of the way and withdraw gear assembly from under car.
6. Reverse procedure to install unit.

1963 F-85

To facilitate removal of the steering gear from the car, it will be necessary to raise the steering shaft in the column assembly.

1. Remove steering shaft coupling clamp bolt and slide clamp off coupling housing onto steering gear worm shaft. Mark steering shaft in line with slot at coupling clamp surface.
2. Disconnect horn wire from harness.
3. Pull off steering wheel.
4. Pull horn contact plate out of recess in actuator to give clearance for removal of upper bearing retainer clip. Pry clip out of actuator housing.
5. Pull steering shaft out of steering column and block shaft up about two inches.
6. Remove left-hand end plug from relay rod and pull relay rod off pitman arm.
7. To install, reverse procedure.

POWER STEERING

Service Notes

Before installing the steering gear, apply a sodium soap fine fibre grease to the gear mounting pads to prevent squeaks between the gear housing and frame. Make sure the alignment pin on the gear housing enters the hole provided in the frame side rail.

Make certain there is a minimum of .040″ clearance between coupling hub and steering gear upper seal.

Install coupling flange hub and torque to 20-25 ft-lbs. Before tightening the gear-to-frame bolts, shift the gear as necessary to place it in the same plane as the steering shaft so that the flexible coupling is not distorted. Tighten gear-to-frame bolts to 60-80 ft-lbs. and pitman shaft nut to 120-150 ft-lbs.

Steering Gear, Replace

1963-69 F.S.C. & 1964-69 Intermediates

1. Remove coupling flange hub bolt.
2. Disconnect hoses from pump and cap pump and hose fittings.
3. Remove pitman arm nut and, using a suitable puller, remove pitman arm.
4. Remove gear-to-frame bolts. Permit lower shaft to slide free of coupling flange, then remove gear with hoses attached.

1963 F-85

1. Remove coupling flange nuts, and ground wire from flange attaching bolt.
2. Disconnect hoses from pump and gear. Cap pump, hose fittings and gear connectors.
3. Disconnect horn wire from harness. On all models, pull off wheel. Also pull horn contact out of recess in actuator to give clearance for removal of upper bearing retainer clip. Pry clip out of actuator housing.
4. Pull steering shaft out of steering column and block shaft up about two inches.
5. Disconnect relay rod from pitman arm. Remove four bolts attaching gear to front suspension cross bar and remove coupling from gear.
6. Reverse removal procedure to install, tightening gear attaching nuts to 45-60 ft. lbs.
7. Remove four bolts attaching gear to suspension cross bar and remove gear from car.
8. Reverse removal procedure to install gear. Torque pitman shaft nut to 100-125 ft. lbs. Torque gear attaching bolts to 45-50 ft. lbs.

1963 Olds F.S.C.

1. Remove steering wheel and loosen column upper clamp-to-bracket bolts.
2. Fold back floor mat and remove mast jacket cover plate from toe pan.
3. Hoist front of car and support it with floor stands under outer ends of lower control arm.
4. Remove nut and pull off pitman arm, using a suitable puller.
5. Remove gear-to-frame bolts.
6. Position steering linkage and speedometer cable out of way and remove steering gear from under car.
7. Reverse removal procedure to install the gear. Before tightening gear to frame and upper column clamp bolts, position column to obtain $2\frac{7}{32}$″ between horn contact and end of worm shaft to provide ⅛″ to $\frac{3}{16}$″ clearance between turn signal housing and steering wheel. Tighten upper mast jacket clamp before tightening frame bolts. Torque frame bolts 60 to 80 ft-lb and pitman shaft nut 90 to 120 ft-lb.

TORONADO SUPPLEMENT

Items covered in this section apply to the Toronado only. For service procedures and specifications not covered here, refer to the conventional Oldsmobile section of this chapter.

Engine & Transmission Section

ENGINE REPLACE

1. Drain radiator and remove hood, marking hinge as a guide for reassembly.
2. Disconnect battery, radiator hoses, cooler lines, heater hoses, vacuum hoses, power steering pump hoses, engine-to-body ground strap, fuel hose from fuel line, wiring and accelerator cable.
3. Remove coil, throttle control switch bracket, radiator support and radiator.
4. Raise car and disconnect exhaust pipes at manifold.
5. Remove starter.
6. Remove torque converter cover and three bolts securing converter to flywheel.
7. Attach a tool of the type shown in Fig. 1 to support final drive assembly.
8. Remove two bolts from right output shaft support bracket and one through bolt attaching final drive to engine block on left side.
9. Remove engine mount-to-crossmember nuts.
10. Lower car and support engine with a fixture of the type shown in Fig. 2.
11. Remove six transmission-to-engine bolts and lift engine from car.

NOTE: If car is to be moved, install a converter holding tool of the type shown in Fig. 1.

Installation

1. Lower engine into position.
2. Locate engine dowels into transmission and position mount studs into front crossmember.
3. Secure engine to transmission (6 bolts).
4. Remove engine lifting rig and raise car.
5. Secure torque converter to flywheel.
6. Install engine mount nuts.
7. Install torque converter cover and starter.
8. Install two bolts attaching right output shaft support bracket and one through bolt attaching final drive to engine block on left side.
9. Remove final drive supporting tool.
10. Connect exhaust pipes and lower car.
11. Install remaining parts removed in reverse order of removal.

ENGINE FRONT COVER

With Engine & Oil Pan Removed

1. Disconnect by-pass hose from water pump.
2. Remove cover-to-block bolts and remove cover, timing pointer and water pump.
3. Install cover and torque as shown in Fig. 2.

Oil Pan

1. Remove engine as outlined.
2. Remove dipstick, drain oil and remove mount from front cover.
3. Unfasten and remove oil pan.
4. Apply sealer to both sides of pan gaskets (cork) and install on block.
5. Install front and rear rubber seals.
6. Wipe lube on seal area and install pan. Torque $\frac{5}{16}$" bolts to 15 ft-lbs and $\frac{1}{4}$" bolts to 10 ft-lbs.
7. Install mount on front cover and install engine.

TRANSMISSION

Less Final Drive

Removal

1. Disconnect battery, oil cooler lines at transmission and speedometer cable at governor.
2. Install engine support rig of the type shown in Fig. 3.
3. Remove nut "D" and bolts "A", "B" and "C", Fig. 4. A special wrench must be used on nut "D".
4. Remove bolts indicated in Fig. 5.
5. Remove flywheel cover plate bolts.
6. Hoist car and remove starter.

Fig. 1 Final drive supporting tool

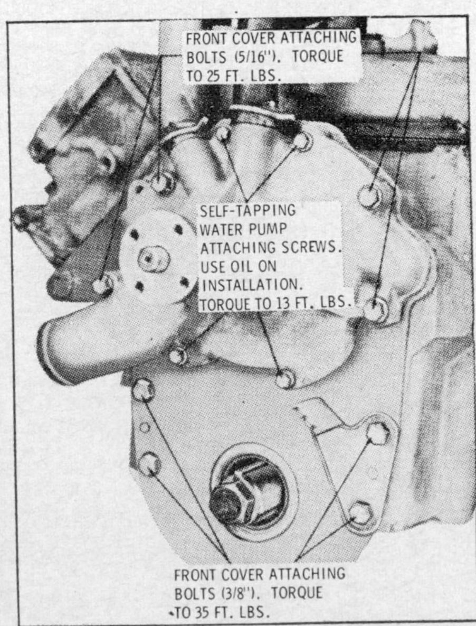

Fig. 2 Engine front cover bolts

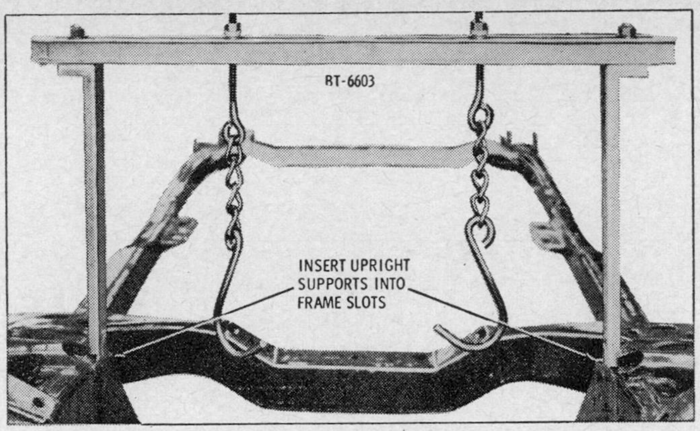

Fig. 3 Installing support bars

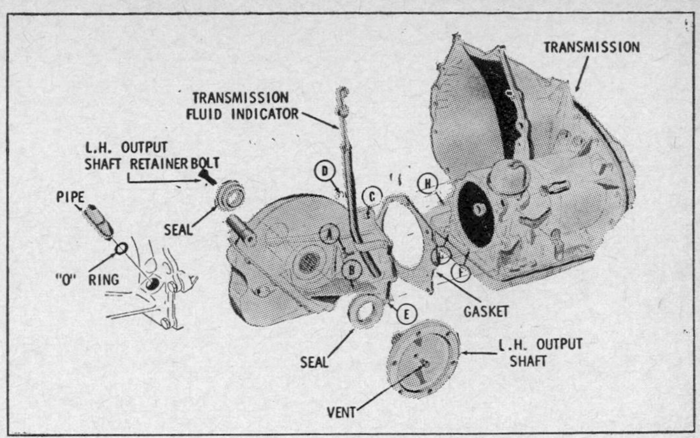

Fig. 4 Transmission attachment

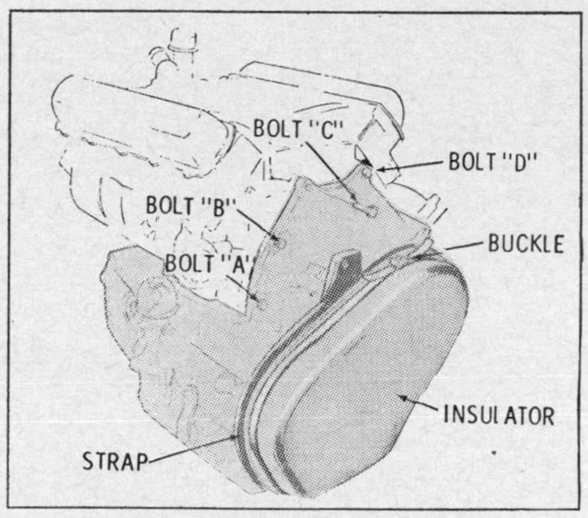

Fig. 5 Transmission-to-engine attachment

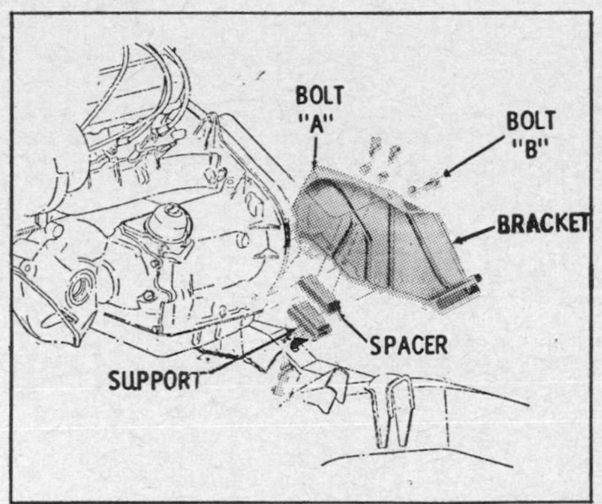

Fig. 6 Transmission-to-engine attachment

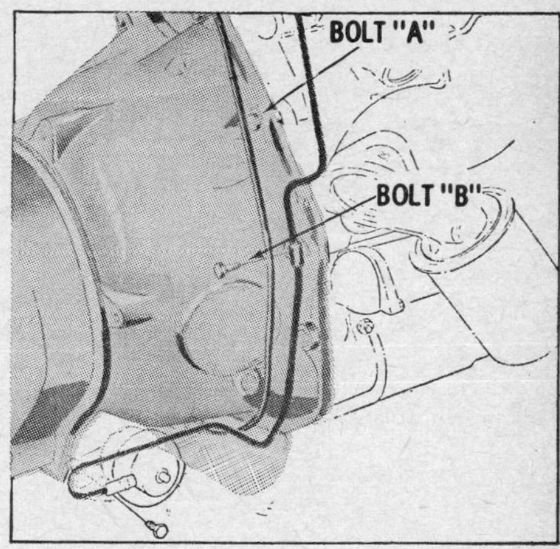

Fig. 7 Engine mount attachment

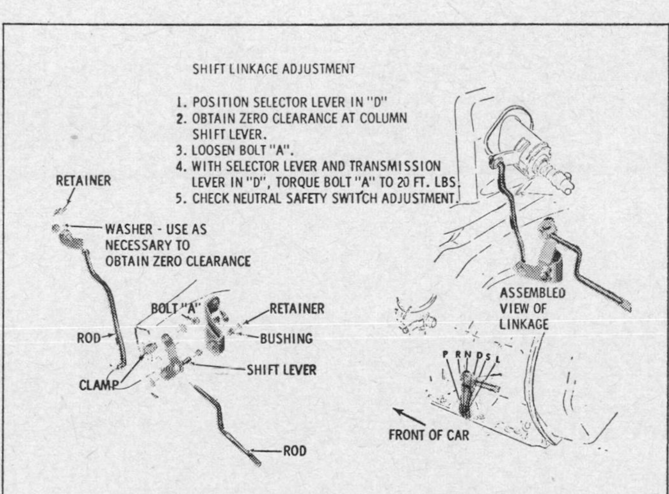

Fig. 8 Shift linkage adjustment

7. Rotate flywheel until all bolts are removed.
8. Disconnect vacuum modulator line and stator wiring.
9. Install transmission lift.
10. Remove shift linkage.
11. Remove bolts "E", "F" and "G" and nut "H", Fig. 4.

NOTE: When last three transmission-to-final drive bolts are removed a quantity of oil will be lost.

12. Remove bolts indicated in Fig. 6.
13. Remove bolts indicated in Fig. 7. Then remove the four bracket-to-engine mount bolts.
14. Slide transmission rearward and down. Engine mount bracket will follow transmission down. Install converter holding tool, Fig. 1.
15. After transmission is removed from car, the link assembly cover insulator can be removed or installed.

Installation

When installing the transmission, the motor mount bracket must be positioned loosely on the link assembly cover until the transmission is in place; then reverse removal procedure. Torque bolts to ft-lbs as follows:

Engine-to-converter housing	25
Engine bracket-to-transmission	55
Engine bracket-to-rubber mount	55
Oil cooler lines to transmission	25
Final drive-to-transmission	25
Converter-to-flywheel	30
Flywheel housing cover	5
Starter-to-transmission	30

Adjust shift linkage as directed in Fig. 8.

Drive Axles & Final Drive Section

DRIVE AXLES

Description

Drive axles are a complete flexible assembly and consist of an axle shaft and an inner and outer constant velocity joint, Fig. 1. The right axle shaft has a torsional damper mounted in the center. The inner constant velocity joint has complete flexibility plus inward and outward movement. The outer constant velocity joint has complete flexibility only.

NOTE: Whenever any operations call for disconnecting, connecting, removal or installation of the drive axles, care must be used to prevent damage to constant velocity joint seals. Seals may be wrapped with floor mat rubber or old inner tube, etc. Make sure rubber protective covers that are used are removed before car is started or driven.

DRIVE AXLE REPLACE

Right Side Unit

Removal

1. Hoist car under lower control arms.
2. Remove axle nut, Fig. 3.
3. Push inner C.V. joint outward enough to disengage from R.H. final drive output shaft and move rearward.
4. Remove R.H. output shaft bracket bolts to engine and final drive.
5. Remove R.H. output shaft.
6. Drive axle assembly will be removed now.

NOTE: Care must be used to see that C.V. joints do not turn to full extremes and that seals are not damaged against shock absorber or stabilizer bar.

Installation

1. Place R.H. drive axle into lower control arm and enter outer race splines into knuckle.
2. Lubricate final drive output shaft seal with approved seal grease.
3. Install R.H. output shaft into final drive and attach support bolts to engine and brace. Torque to 50 ft-lbs.
4. Move R.H. drive axle toward front of car and align with R.H. output shaft. Install attaching bolts and torque to 65 ft-lbs.
5. Install oil filter element.
6. Install washer and nut on drive axle. Torque to 60 ft-lbs and insert cotter pin.

Left Side Unit

Removal

1. Hoist car under lower control arms.
2. Remove wheel and drum.
3. Remove drive axle nut.
4. Position access slot in hub so that each attaching bolt (4) can be removed, Fig. 4. It will be necessary to push aside adjuster lever to remove one of the bolts.
5. Remove hub assembly, Fig. 4. It will be necessary to push aside adjuster lever for clearance.
6. Remove tie-rod end nut.
7. Using a hammer and brass drift, drive on knuckle until tie-rod end stud is free.
8. Remove bolts from drive axle and L.H. output shaft, Fig. 5.
9. Remove upper control arm ball joint nut. Using hammer and brass drift, drive on knuckle until upper ball joint stud is free, Fig. 6.
10. Remove ball joint, Fig. 7, being careful not to damage drive axle seal.
11. Remove knuckle and support so that brake hose is not damaged.
12. Carefully guide drive axle out.

NOTE: Care must be used to see that C.V. joints do not turn to full extremes and that seals are not damaged against shock absorber or stabilizer bar.

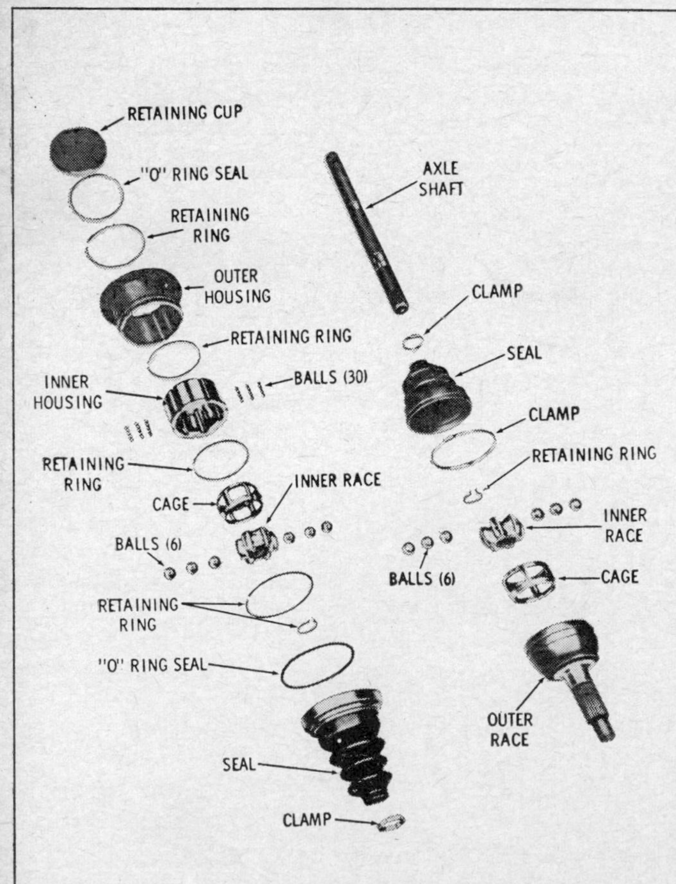

Fig. 1 Drive axle assembly (left side)

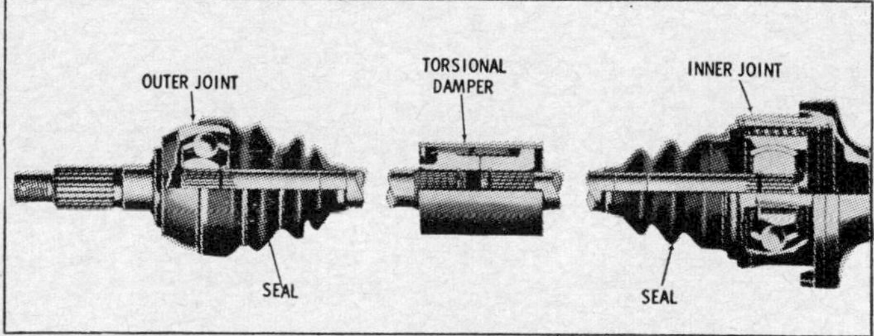

Fig. 2 Drive axle disassembled (right side)

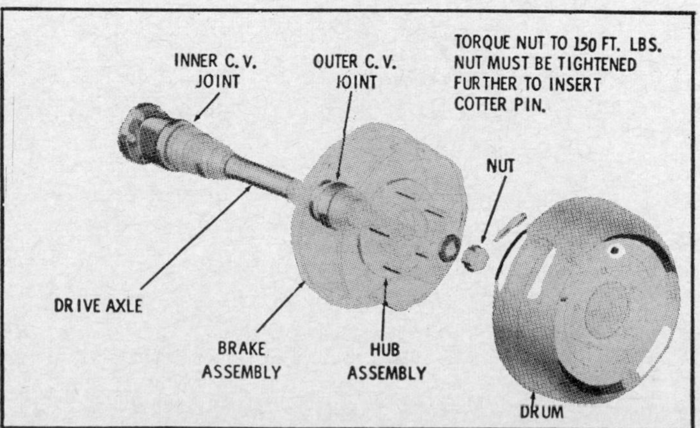

Fig. 3 Drive axle installed

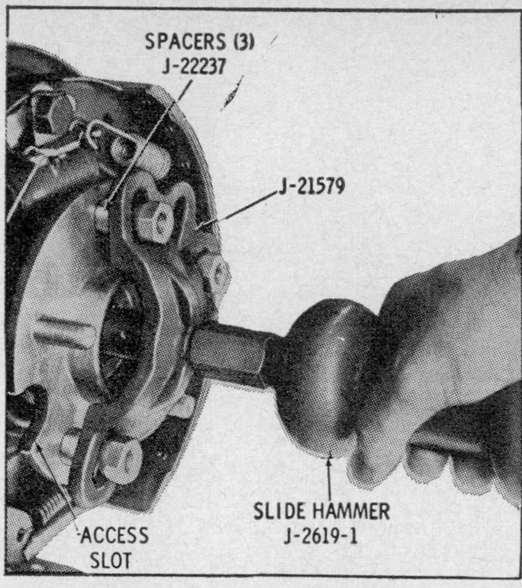

Fig. 4 Removing hub

Fig. 5 Installing support block

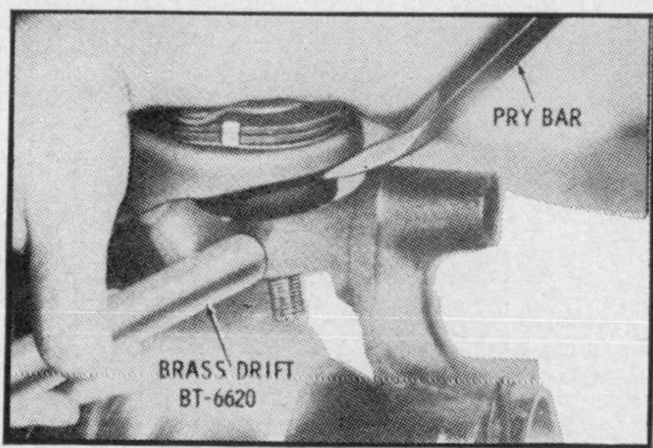

Fig. 6 Removing upper ball joint

Installation

1. Guide L.H. drive axle onto lower control arm in position on block, Fig. 5.
2. Insert lower ball joint stud into knuckle and attach nut (do not tighten).
3. Center L.H. drive axle in opening of knuckle and insert upper ball joint stud.
4. Place brake hose clip over upper ball joint stud and install nut (do not tighten).
5. Insert tie-rod end stud into knuckle and attach nut. Torque to 45 ft-lbs and insert cotter pin.
6. Lubricate hub bearing OD with E.P. grease and install. Torque to 65 ft-lbs.
7. Align inner C.V. joint with output shaft and install attaching nuts. Torque to 65 ft-lbs.
8. Torque upper and lower ball joint nuts to 40 ft-lbs and insert cotter pins.

NOTE: Upper ball joint cotter pin must be crimped toward upper control arm to prevent interference with outer C.V. joint seal.

9. Install drive axle washer and nut. Torque to 60 ft-lbs and install cotter pin.
10. Install drum and wheel.
11. Lower car and check wheel alignment.

C.V. JOINT SERVICE

NOTE: The C.V. joints are to be replaced as a unit and are only disassembled for repacking and replacement of seals.

Outer C.V. Joint

Disassemble

1. Insert axle in vise, clamping on mid-portion only.
2. Remove inner and outer seal clamps, Fig. 8.
3. Slide seal down axle shaft to gain access to C.V. joint.
4. Referring to Fig. 9, spread retaining ring until C.V. joint can be removed from axle spline.
5. Remove retaining ring, Fig. 10.
6. Slide seal from axle shaft.
7. Remove grease from C.V. joint.
8. Holding C.V. joint with one hand, tilt cage and inner race so that one ball can be removed. Continue until all six balls are removed, Fig. 11.
9. Turn cage 90° and with large slot in cage aligned with land in inner race, lift out, Fig. 12.
10. Turn inner race 90° in line with large hole in case, lift land on inner race up through large hole in cage and turn up and out to separate parts, Fig. 13.

Inspection

Wash all metal parts in cleaning solvent and dry with compressed air. Rubber seal should be replaced whenever joint is disassembled for service. Inspect all metal parts for nicks, cracks, breaks or scores. If any defects are found the joint assembly will have to be replaced as a unit.

Reassemble

1. Insert land of inner race into large hole in cage and pivot to install in cage, Fig. 13.
2. Align inner race as shown in Fig. 12 and pivot inner race 90° to align in outer race as shown in Fig. 14.
3. Insert balls one at a time until all six are installed. Inner race and cage will have to be tilted as shown in Fig. 14 so that each ball can be inserted.

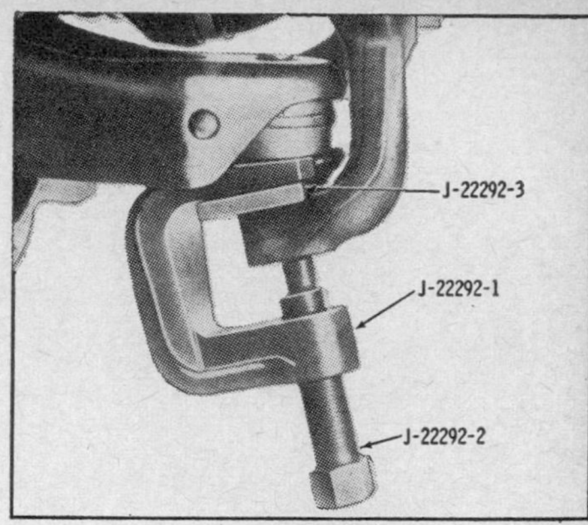

Fig. 7 Removing lower ball joint

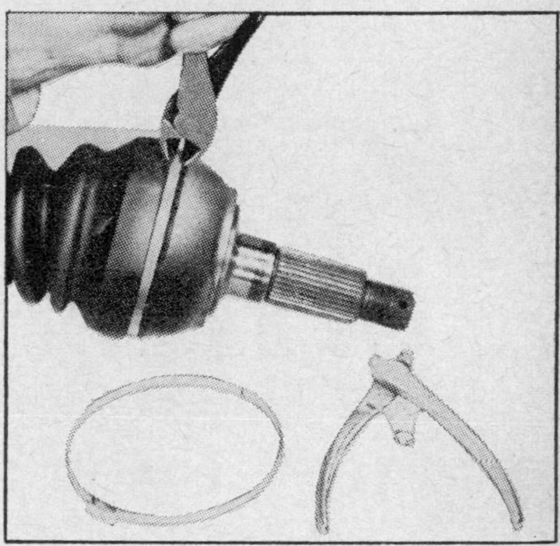

Fig. 8 Cutting seal clip

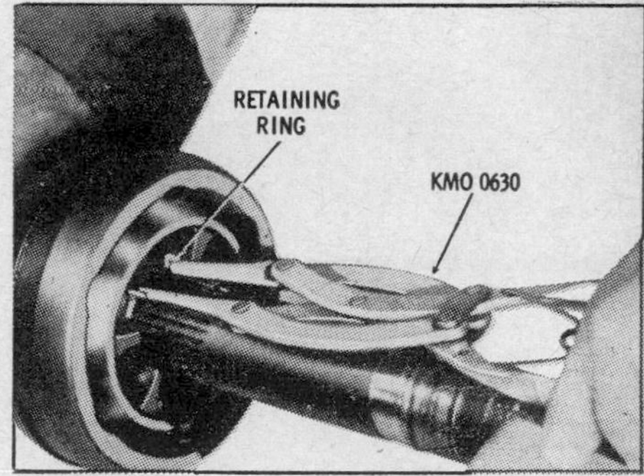

Fig. 9 Removing retaining ring

4. Pack joint full of approved lubricant. Pack inside of seal with approved lubricant until folds of seal are full.
5. Place small keystone clamp on axle shaft.
6. Install seal on axle shaft.
7. Install retaining ring into inner race, Fig. 10.
8. Insert axle shaft into splines of outer C.V. joint until retaining ring secures shaft.
9. Position seal in slot of outer race.
10. Install large keystone clamp over seal and secure, Fig. 15. Then install small keystone clamp over seal and secure, Fig. 16.

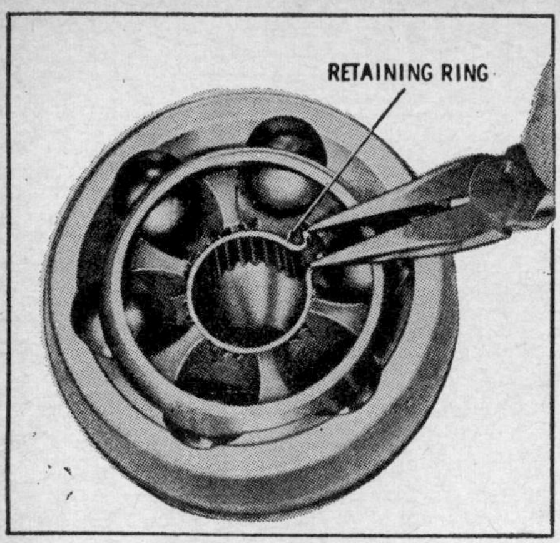

Fig. 10 Removing or installing retaining ring

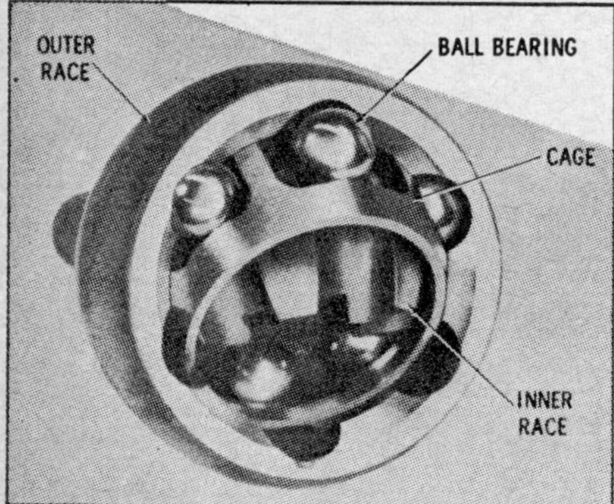

Fig. 11 Removing balls from outer race

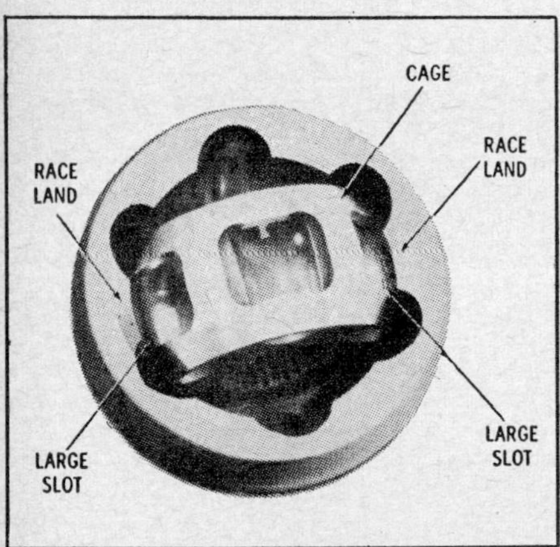

Fig. 12 Positioning cage for removal

Inner C.V. Joint

Disassemble

1. Clamp mid-portion of axle shaft in vise.
2. Remove small seal clamp.
3. Remove large end of seal from C.V. joint by prying out peened spots and driving off C.V. joint with hammer and chisel, Fig. 17.
4. Slide seal down shaft until C.V. joint is disassembled. Remove O-ring from outer housing, Fig. 18.
5. Wipe all excess grease from C.V. joint.
6. Remove axle shaft retaining ring, Fig. 18.
7. Remove retaining ring from interior of ball spline outer housing, Fig. 18.
8. Remove ball spline outer housing from ball spline inner housing, being careful not to drop or lose balls (five in a line with six rows).
9. Follow disassembly of outer C.V. joint from Steps 4 thru 9 for inner C.V. joint.
10. Remove grease from inside of ball spline outer housing.
11. Using wood block, carefully drive along outer edges from inside of ball spline outer housing and remove retaining cup.
12. Remove O-ring from interior of ball spline outer housing, Fig. 19.
13. Remove retaining ring from interior of ball spline outer housing.
14. Remove O-ring from exterior of ball spline outer housing.
15. Remove two retaining rings from ball spline inner housing, Fig. 20.

Inspection

Wash all metal parts in cleaning solvent and blow dry with compressed air. Inspect all parts for damage. If any defects are found, replace C.V. joint as a unit.

Reassemble

1. Install two retaining rings on inner spline housing, Fig. 20.
2. Install retaining ring in groove of outer spline housing, Fig. 19.
3. Install O-ring into inner groove of outer spline housing. Lubricate O-ring with approved seal lube.
4. Install cover into outer spline housing, Fig. 21. Care must be used not to damage O-ring.
5. Insert land of inner race into large hole in case and pivot to install in cage, Fig. 22.
6. Align inner race and cage and install into inner spline housing, Fig. 20.
7. Insert balls in inner spline housing one at a time until all six balls are in, Fig. 23. Inner race and cage will have to be tilted as shown so that each ball can be inserted.
8. Install inner spline housing into outer spline housing, Fig. 24. Raise inner spline housing and install five balls into each spline (six splines, 30 balls).
9. Lower inner spline housing into outer spline housing and install retaining ring into groove at top of outer spline housing.
10. Install retaining ring into inner race, Fig. 25.
11. Pack C.V. joint full of approved lubricant. Pack inside of seal until folds of seal are full.
12. Install seal onto axle shaft.
13. Install O-ring on outer spline housing. Insert axle shaft into splines of inner race until retaining ring secures shaft.
14. Insert drive axle in a press, Fig. 26, and peen seal in six places equally spaced around seal.
15. Remove axle from press. Position seal in groove in axle shaft and pull outward on shaft until inner C.V.

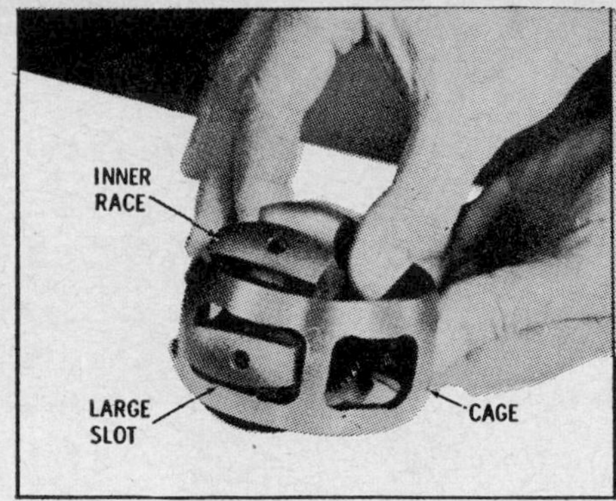

Fig. 13 Removing inner race from ball cage

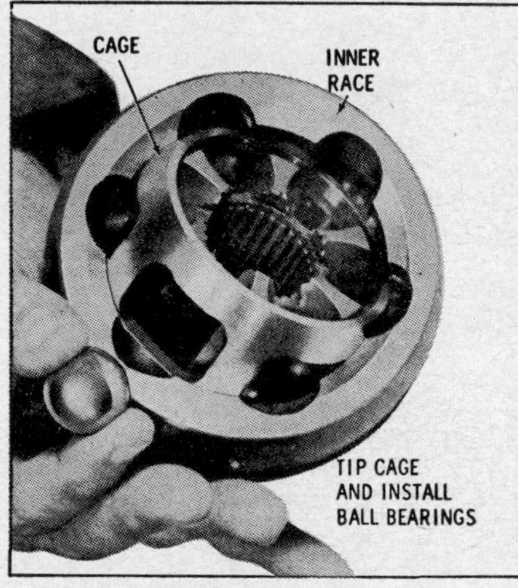

Fig. 14 Installing balls in outer race

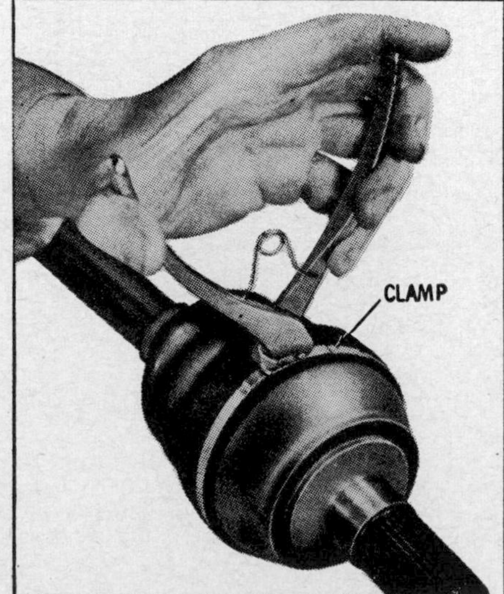

Fig. 15 Installing keystone clamp (large)

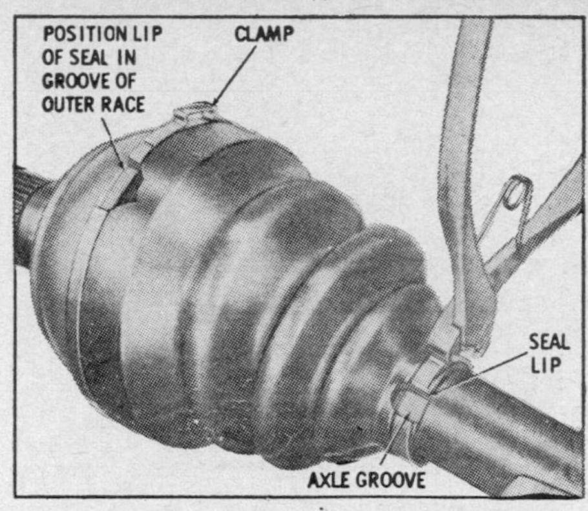

Fig. 16 Installing keystone clamp (small)

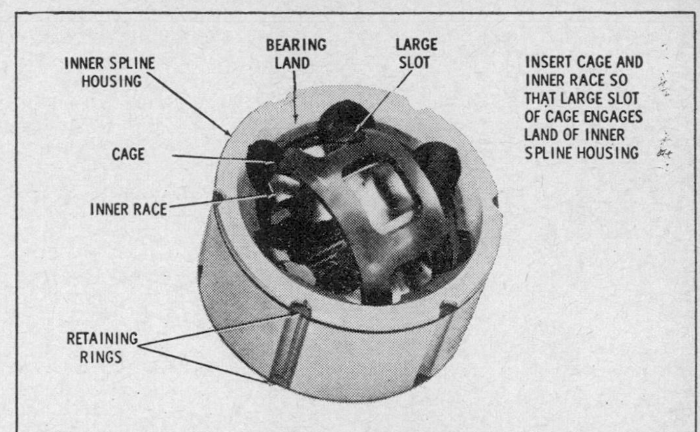

Fig. 20 Inner spline housing

Fig. 17 Removing or installing inner C.V. joint seal

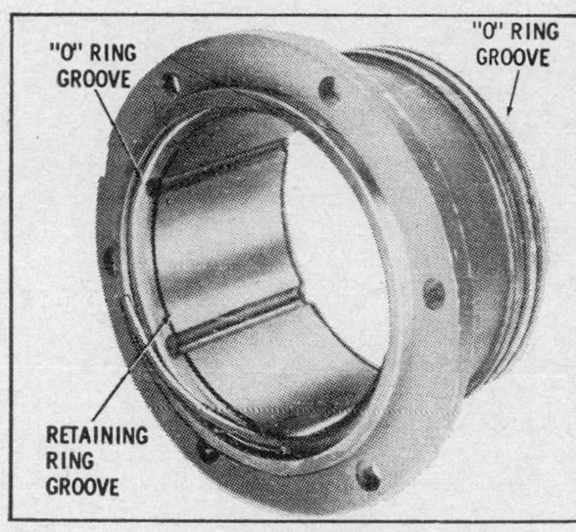

Fig. 19 Outer spline housing

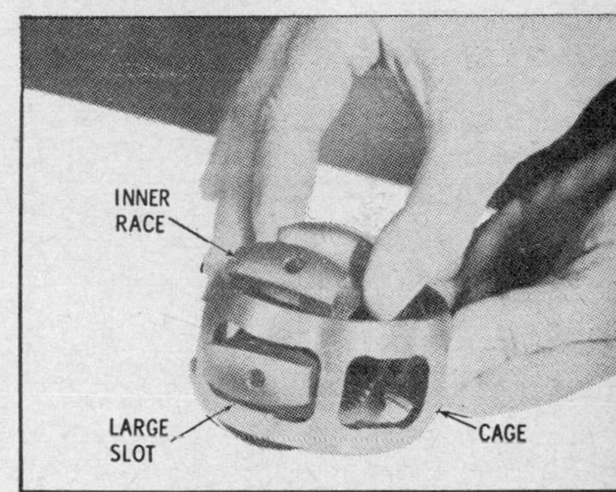

Fig. 22 Installing inner race into ball cage

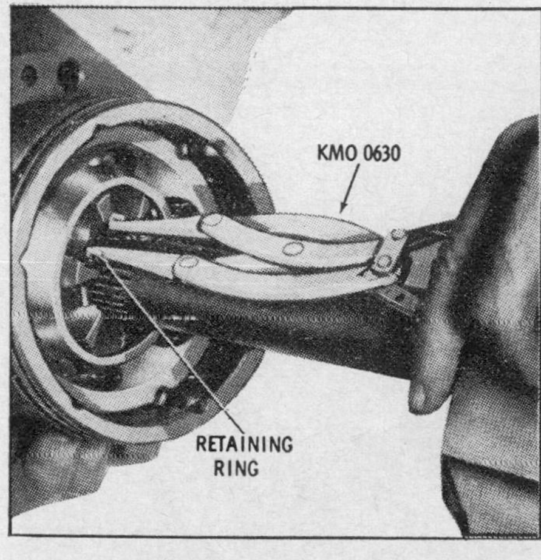

Fig. 18 Removing joint from axle

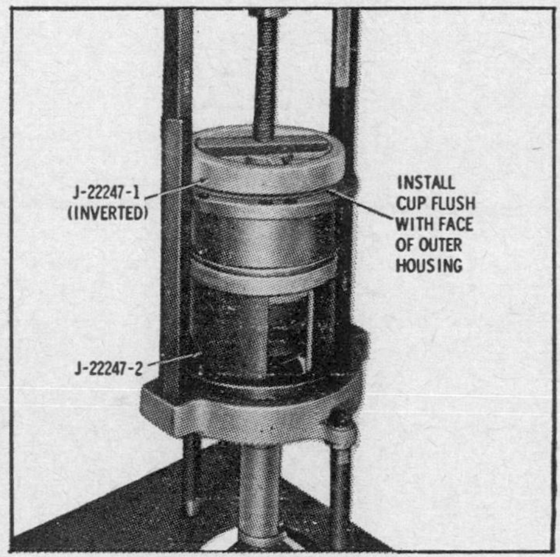

Fig. 21 Installing cover

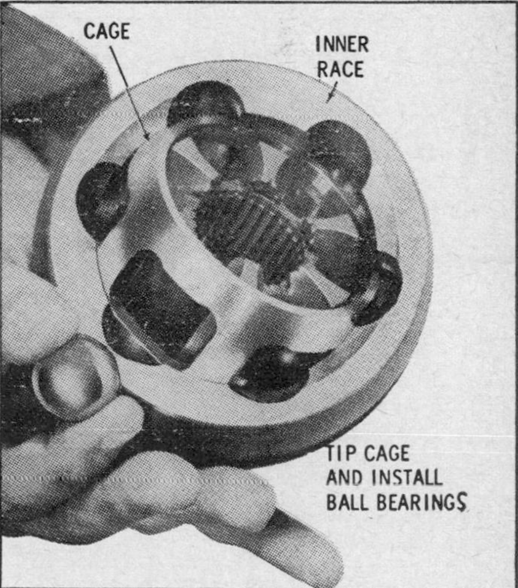

Fig. 23 Installing balls in inner race

joint is fully extended. *C.V. joint is fully extended before installing keystone seal clamp to prevent a vacuum collapsing seal bellows.*

16. Install keystone clamp and secure, Fig. 27.

FINAL DRIVE, 1968-69

Description, Fig. 28

The final drive assembly, mounted and splined directly to the automatic transmission, consists of a pinion drive gear, a ring gear (bolted to the case), case assembly with two side gears and two pinion gears that are retained to the case with a pinion shaft. A lock pin is used instead of a bolt to lock the pinion shaft to the case. There are thrust washers used behind the side gears and shims behind the pinion gears the same as in a conventional differential. The left side gear is different than the right side gear in that it has a threaded retainer plate to which the left output shaft bolts. The two side bearings are the same and the preload shims are identical for the right and left side. The carrier is identical in external appearance and mounts to the transmission the same as in the past

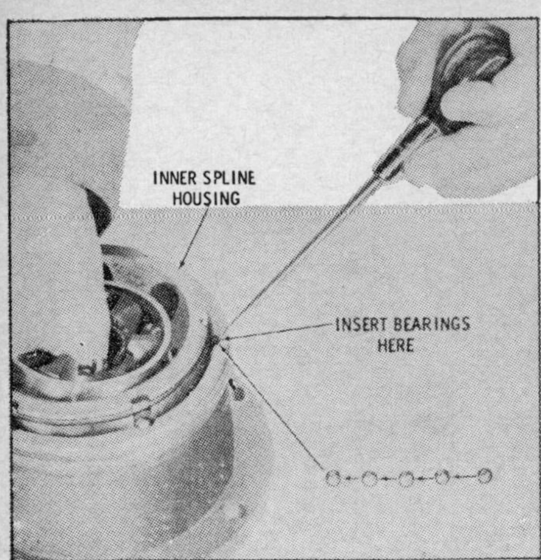

Fig. 24 Installing balls, inner-to-outer spline housing

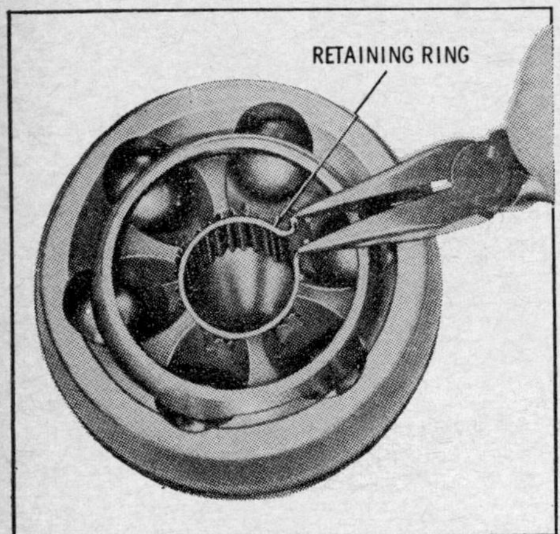

Fig. 25 Installing retaining ring

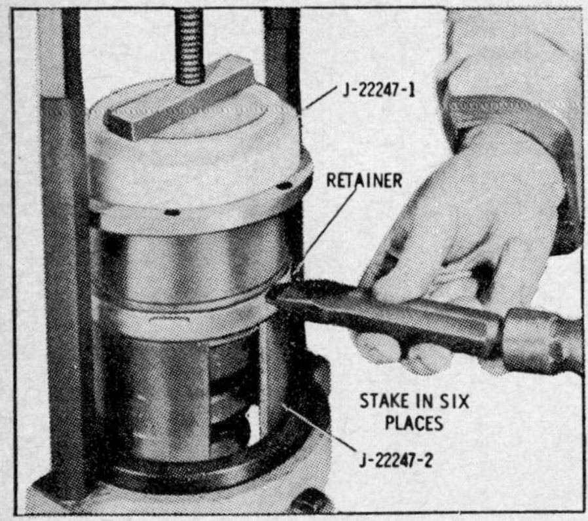

Fig. 26 Staking seal

models.

The output shafts remain identical in external appearance as in the past. The left output shaft has the retainer bolt going through the shaft to the side gear.

FINAL DRIVE, 1966-67

Description, Fig. 29

The final drive assembly, mounted and splined to the automatic transmission, consists of a pinion drive gear, a ring gear and a planetary gear train.

The planetary gear train consists of a planet pinion carrier with three pairs of planet pinions, a sun gear and an internal gear and performs the same function as the side gears and pinion gears in a conventional differential.

Torque from the final drive is transmitted to a right and left output shaft which connect to drive axles. The right output shaft is splined to the sun gear while the left output shaft is splined to the planet pinion carrier.

OUTPUT SHAFT & SEALS

R.H. Shaft, Bearing & Seal

Removal

1. Disconnect battery. Hoist car.

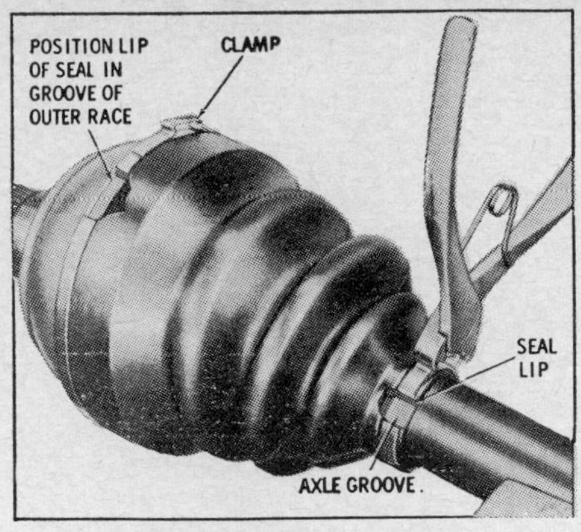

Fig. 27 Installing keystone clamps

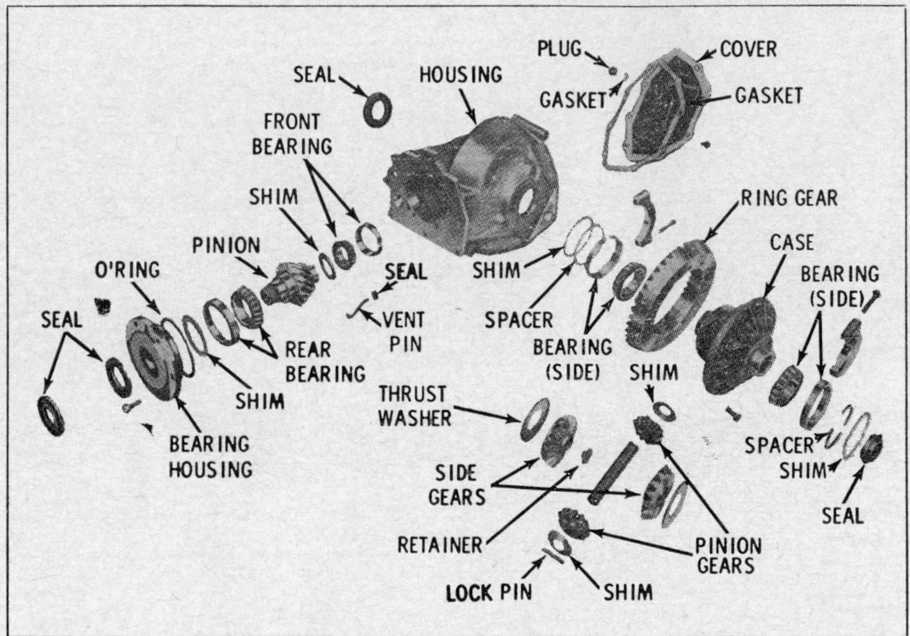

Fig. 28 Final drive disassembled. 1968-69

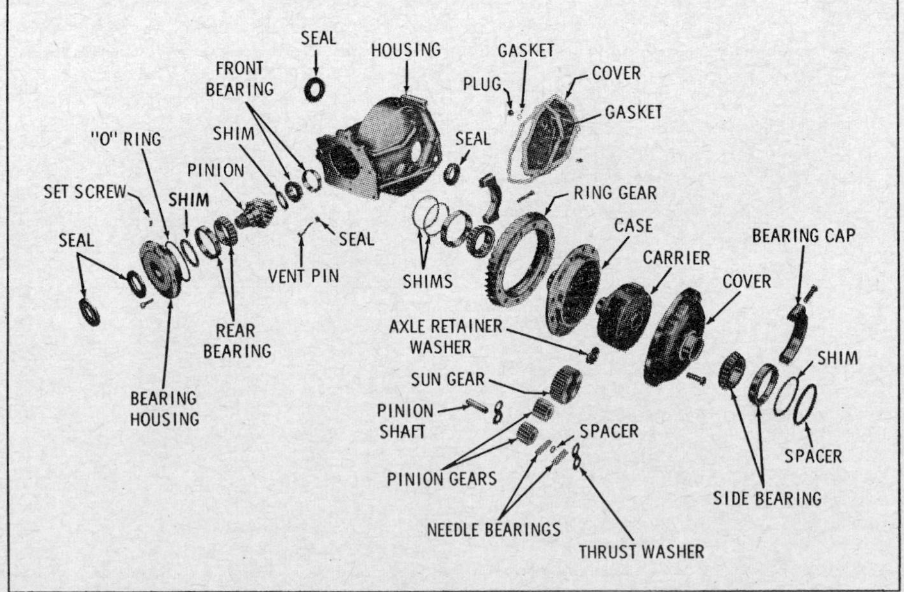

Fig. 29 Final drive disassembled. 1966-67

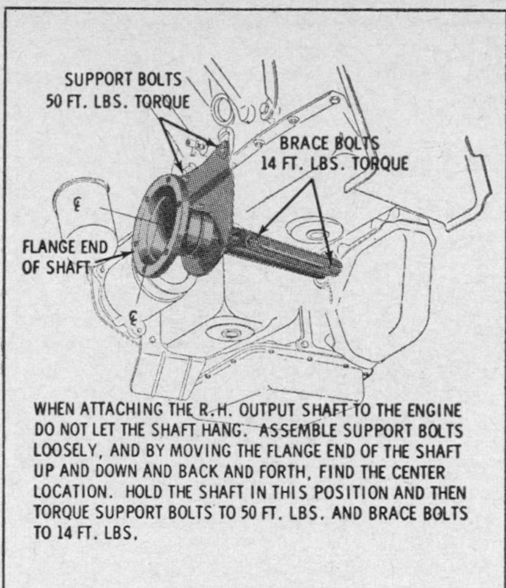

Fig. 31 Aligning right output shaft

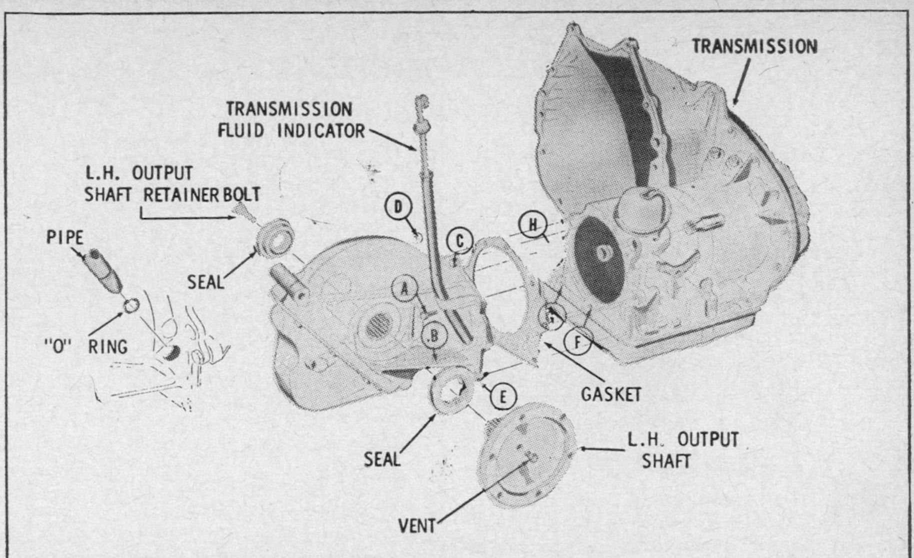

Fig. 33 Final drive attachment. 1966-69

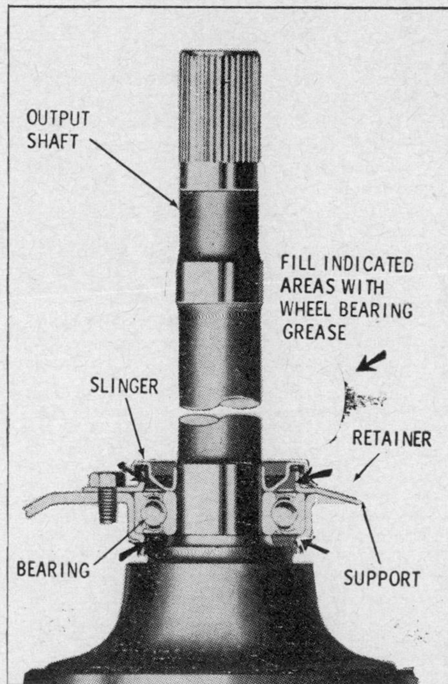

Fig. 32 Output shaft assembled (right side)

2. Remove engine oil filter element.
3. Disconnect R.H. drive axle.
4. Disconnect support from engine and brace.
5. Remove output shaft assembly.

Installation, Figs. 31 and 32

1. If removed, assemble bearing and related parts. Position assembly in a press and install bearing until seated against shoulder on shaft. Pack area between bearing and retainer with wheel bearing grease, then install slinger. Install seal if removed.
2. Install remaining parts removed in reverse order of removal.

L.H. Output Shaft, Bearing & Seal

NOTE: The L.H. output shaft can normally be removed only after removing the final drive assembly from the car. However, if the L.H. drive axle has been removed for any reason, the output shaft and seal can be removed as follows:

1. Remove R.H. output shaft as outlined above.
2. Remove L.H. output shaft retaining bolt and remove shaft.
3. Apply approved lubricant to the seal, then insert output shaft into final drive, indexing splines of shaft with splines on final drive.
4. Install and torque L.H. output shaft retaining bolt to 45 ft-lbs.
5. Install R.H. output shaft in reverse order of removal.

FINAL DRIVE REPLACE

1. Disconnect battery and raise hood.
2. Remove bolts "A", "B", "C" and nut "D", Fig. 33. Nut "D" must be removed with a special wrench. It may be necessary to remove transmission filler tube to obtain clearance.
3. Hoist car. If a two-post lift is used the car must be supported with floor stands at the front frame rails and the front post lowered.
4. Disconnect both drive axles from output shafts.
5. Remove engine oil filter element.
6. Disconnect brace from final drive, then disconnect R.H. output shaft from engine. Remove output shaft from final drive.

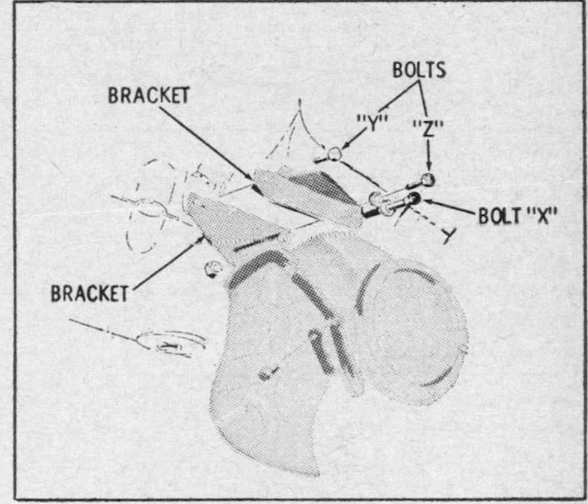

Fig. 34 Disconnecting final drive from engine

7. Referring to Fig. 34, remove bolt "X" and loosen bolts "Y" and "Z".
8. Remove final drive cover and allow lubricant to drain.
9. Position transmission lift with adapter for final drive. Install an anchor bolt through final drive housing and lift pad.
10. Referring to Fig. 33, remove bolts "E", "F", "G" and nut "H".
11. Move transmission lift toward front of car to disengage final drive splines from transmission. Provide a container to catch transmission fluid.
12. Lower transmission lift and remove final drive from lift.
13. Using a 9/16" socket, remove L.H. output shaft retaining bolt and pull shaft from final drive.
14. Reverse procedure to install.

Front Suspension & Steering Section

FRONT SUSPENSION

The front suspension consists of control arms, stabilizer bar, shock absorbers and a right and left torsion bar, Figs. 1 and 2. Torsion bars are used instead of conventional coil springs. The front end of the torsion bar is attached to the lower control arm. The rear of the torsion bar is mounted into an adjustable arm at the torsion bar cross member. The riding height of the car is controlled by this adjustment.

LUBRICATION

The steering linkage should be lubricated every 12 months or 12,000 miles, whichever occurs first, using a commercially available multi-purpose grease.

Ball joints should be lubricated and inspected at 36,000 miles (no time limit) and every 12 months or 12,000 miles thereafter, using a commercially available multi-purpose lubricant.

WHEEL ALIGNMENT

NOTE: When checking wheel alignment the car must be on a level surface, gas tank full or a compensating weight added, front seat all the way to the rear, and tires (front and rear) inflated to 24 psi. All doors must be closed and no passengers or additional weight should be in the car or trunk.

1. Check rocker panel to ground dimensions, Fig. 3. Front to rear must be within 1" and side-to-side within 5/8" of the dimensions shown.
2. Raise car and check wheel runout. Set in center of runout and lower car.
3. Loosen nuts on inboard side of upper control arm cam bolts, Fig. 4.
4. Check camber and adjust if necessary with the rear cam bolt. Camber reading on the right and left wheel should be within 1/2° of each other.
5. Take a caster reading. If necessary to adjust, turn wheel to straight ahead position. Use camber reading scale for making this adjustment.
   a. Turn rear bolt so camber reading is 1/4° more than the original setting for every one degree of caster change needed for a correct reading. Turn to plus side of camber if caster is negative and to negative camber if caster is positive.
   b. Turn front cam bolt so camber will return to its original proper setting that was made on the camber adjustment.
   c. Recheck caster reading.

NOTE: If a problem exists where you should run out of cam to gain the correct reading, first turn front cam bolt so high part of cam is pointing up. Then turn rear cam bolt so high part of cam is pointing down. This is a location to start from and a correct setting can be obtained with the foregoing procedure. Torque upper control arm cam nuts to 75 ft-lbs. Hold head of bolt securely as any movement of the cam will affect your final setting, which will necessitate a recheck of the camber and caster adjustment.

TOE-IN, ADJUST

1. Center steering wheel.
2. Loosen tie-rod nuts and adjust to proper setting.
3. Tighten tie-rod nuts to 20 ft-lbs. Position tie-rod clamps so opening of clamp is facing up. This is necessary as interference and a possible tie up of front end linkage could occur if clamps snag anything while turning.

TORSION BAR

Removal

1. Hoist car and place floor stands under front frame horns.
2. Slide seat at rear of torsion bar forward.
3. Use a tool of the type shown in Fig. 5.
4. Turn torsion bar adjusting bolt counterclockwise, counting the number of turns necessary to remove. Record this number for installing.
5. Remove adjusting bolt and nut.
6. Turn center screw of tool until torsion bar is completely relaxed.
7. Place block of wood on hoist (6"x6"x8") and raise under lower control arm until drive axle is horizontal.
8. Remove stabilizer bolt and related parts. Discard bolt.
9. Place a daub of paint on bottom side of torsion bar.
10. Slide torsion bar forward until it bottoms in lower control arm (adjusting arm will drop out). *Do not mar, scratch or in any way damage*

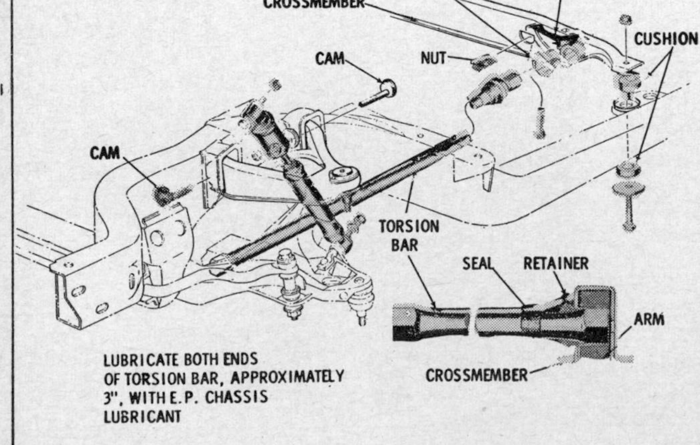

Fig. 1 Front suspension

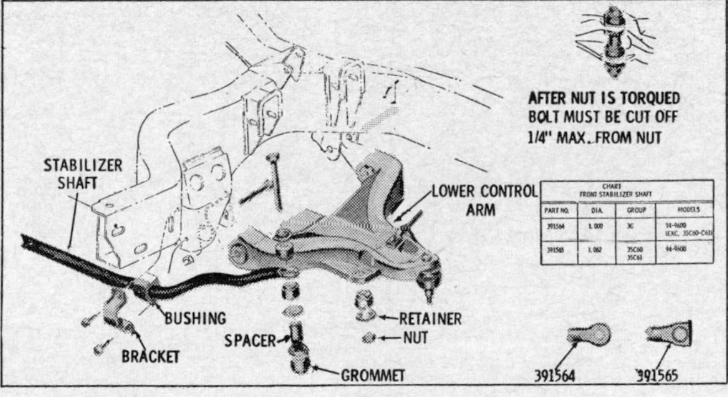

Fig. 2 Front suspension

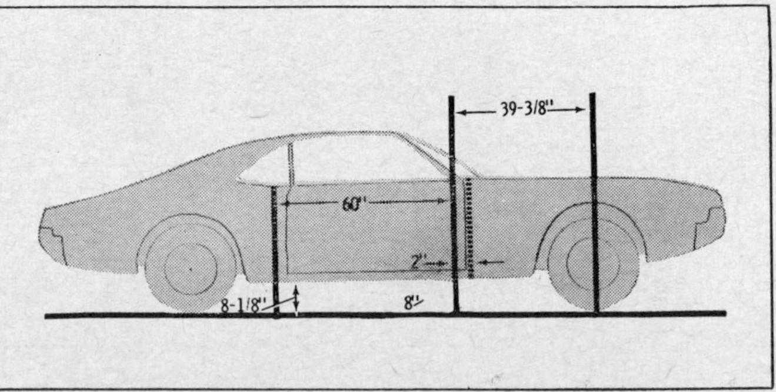

Fig. 3 Riding heights

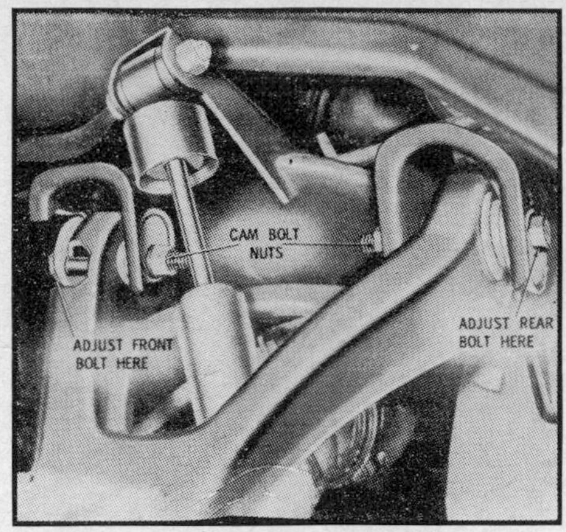

Fig. 4 Front wheel alignment cams

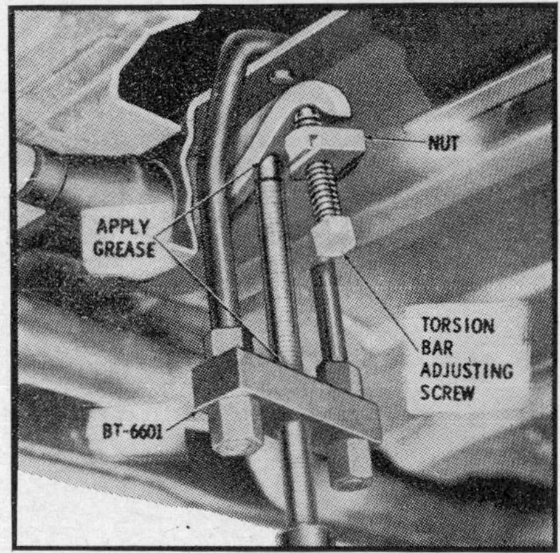

Fig. 5 Removing torsion bar

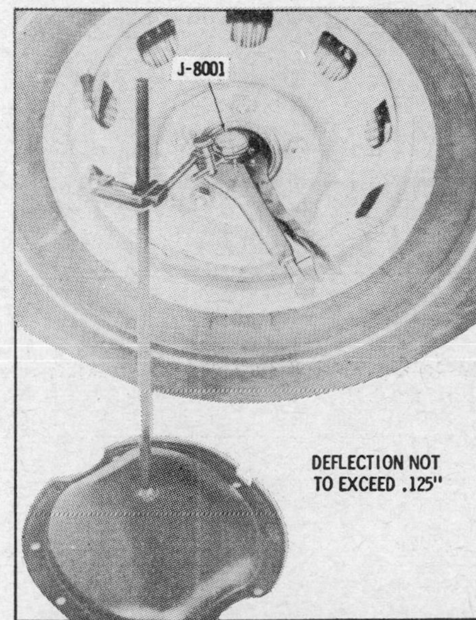

Fig. 6 Ball joint vertical check

torsion bar as replacement will be necessary if such conditions exist.

11. Remove crossmember bolt from side torsion bar is being replaced.
12. Remove center bolt from tool.

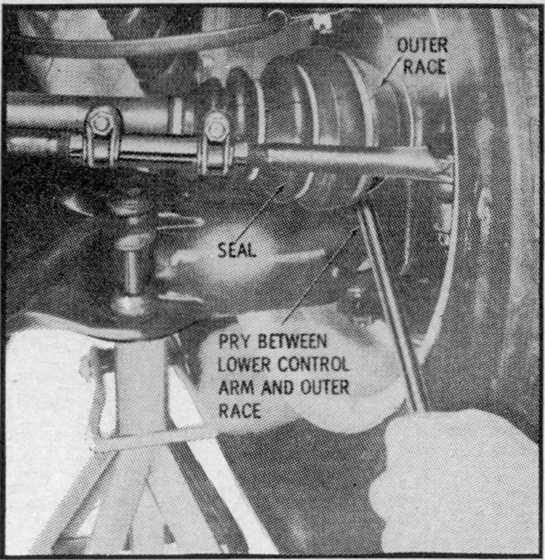

Fig. 7 Pry bar installation

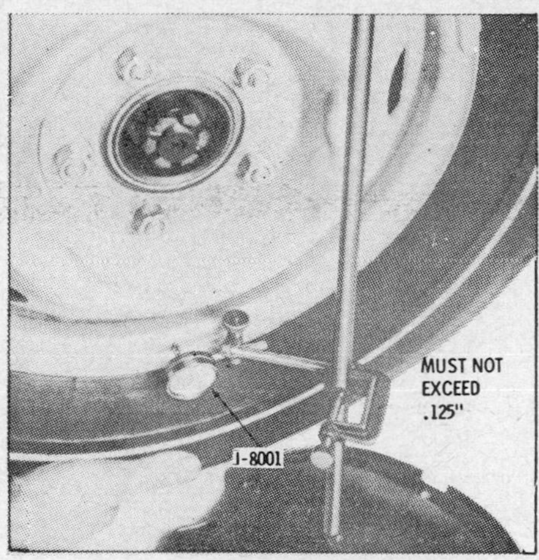

Fig. 8 Ball joint horizontal check

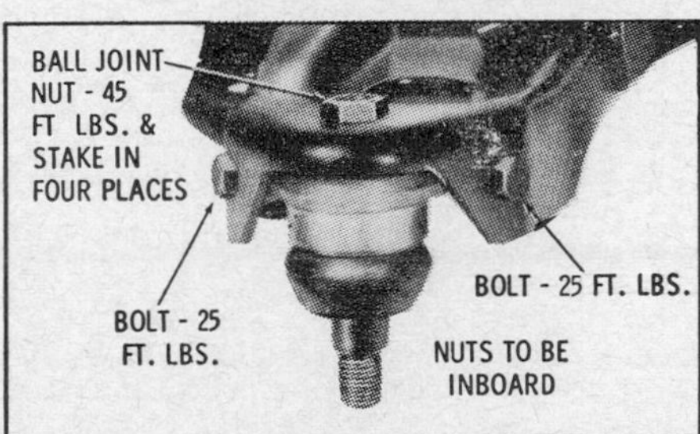

Fig. 9 Installing service ball joint

13. Raise crossmember and twist rearward until torsion bar clears member.
14. Slowly raise lower control arm until maximum height is attained.
15. Raise center crossmember until contact is made with floor pan.
16. Pull rearward on torsion bar with HANDS ONLY until bar is out of lower control arm. *It may be necessary to use air blowing into nut of lower control arm to relieve vacuum caused by grease.*

Installation

NOTE: Check rubber seal for damage; replace if necessary. Check retainer for excessive wear and replace if necessary. A new retainer is required on replacement of torsion bar. Stake as shown in Fig. 1.

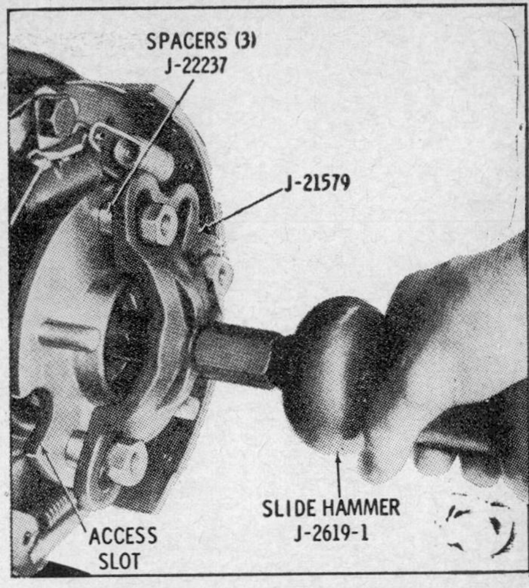

Fig. 10 Removing hub assembly

Fig. 11 Drive axle support block

1. Grease both ends of torsion bar for about 3" with E.P. chassis lube.
2. With daub of paint in same location as when removed, insert bar into lower control arm nut and push forward until bar bottoms.
3. Pry crossmember back and align bar with hole in crossmember.
4. Lower crossmember and install center bolt in tool, Fig. 5.
5. Lower front lower control arm until drive axle is horizontal.
6. Install torsion bar arm and pull bar rearward until fully seated in arm.
7. Install crossmember bolt through rubber mounting and torque to 40 ft-lbs.
8. Lower front lower control arm and remove wood block.
9. Install new bolt in stabilizer bar to lower control arm. Torque to 14 ft-lbs. *Cut off bottom of bolt so that 1/4" is remaining below nut.*
10. Using the tool shown in Fig. 5 or its equivalent, tighten torsion bar arm to install lock plate under arm and through crossmember.

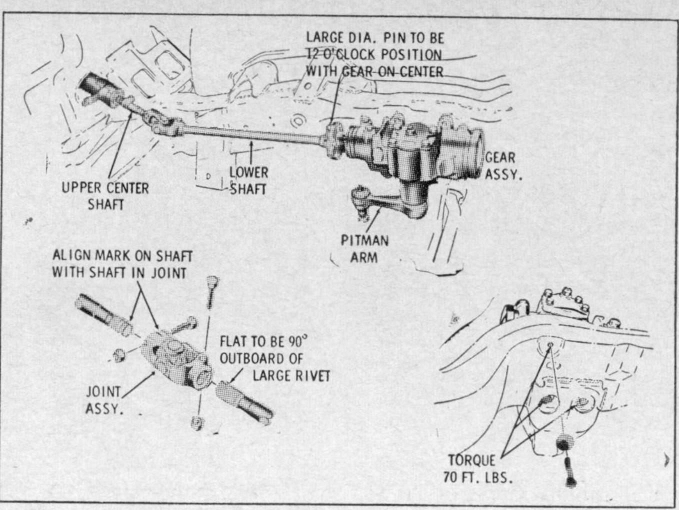

Fig. 12 Steering gear and shaft

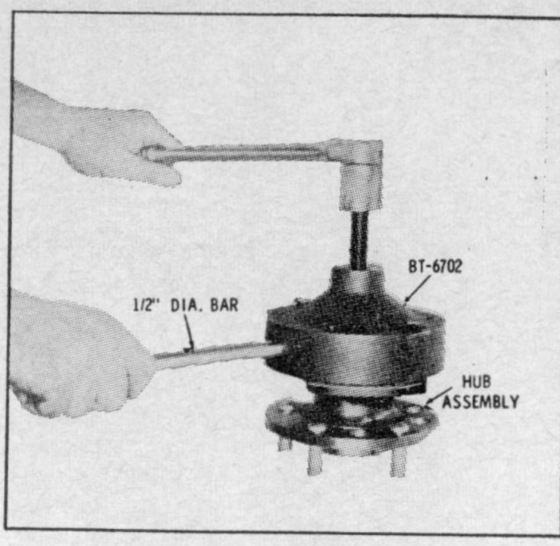

Fig. 13 Removing front wheel bearing. Toronado

11. Grease threads of torsion bar adjuster with chassis lube and turn into nut the same number of turns required to remove.
12. Remove tool. Lower car to floor.
13. Check riding height, Fig. 3. Correct by turning torsion bar adjusting bolt as required.

BALL JOINT CHECKS

Vertical Check

1. Raise car and place jack stands under both lower control arms as near as possible to lower ball joints.
2. Install dial indicator, Fig. 6.
3. Place a pry bar as shown in Fig. 7 and push down on bar. Use care to see that drive axle seal is not damaged. Reading must not exceed .125".

Horizontal Check

1. With car placed on floor stands, install dial indicator, Fig. 8.
2. Grasp front wheel and rock top and bottom of tire. Read dial gauge, then reverse the push-pull procedure.
3. Horizontal deflection on dial gauge should not exceed .125" at wheel rim. This procedure checks both upper and lower ball joints.

BALL JOINTS REPLACE

Lower Ball Joint

1. Remove knuckle.
2. Hacksaw three rivet heads off.
3. Using a 7/32" drill, drill side rivets 3/16" deep.
4. Drive center rivet until joint is out of control arm.
5. Install service ball joint into control arm and torque bolts and nuts as shown in Fig. 9.
6. Replace knuckle.

Upper Ball Joint

1. Raise car and support on floor stands.
2. Remove wheel and drum.
3. Remove hub assembly, Fig. 10.
4. Remove upper ball joint nut and brake line hose clip from ball joint.
5. Remove anchor bolt.
6. Lift brake plate outward over end of axle shaft and support so brake hose is not damaged.
7. Place support block as shown, Fig. 11.
8. Using a brass drift and hammer loosen and remove ball joint.
9. Install new ball joint and replace parts in reverse order of removal.

WHEEL BEARINGS, REPLACE

(Disc Brakes)

1. Raise car and remove front wheel.
2. Remove drum.

NOTE: For disc brakes remove two bolts securing caliper to steering knuckle and remove caliper.

---

3. Remove drive axle pin, nut and washer.
4. Position access slot in hub so that each of the attaching bolts can be removed.

NOTE: On disc brakes the attaching bolts are removed from behind the splash shield.

---

5. Using slide hammer puller, remove hub, Fig. 10.
6. Remove bearing from hub with puller, Fig. 13.
7. Press new bearing into hub.

SHOCK ABSORBER REPLACE

1. Remove upper shock attaching bolt.
2. Remove lower attaching nut and guide shock through upper control arm.
3. Reverse procedure to install.

STEERING GEAR REPLACE

1. Referring to Fig. 12, remove coupling flange hub bolt.
2. Disconnect hoses from power steering pump and cap pump and hose fittings. On cars equipped with a cooler disconnect return hose from cooler inlet pipe.
3. Hoist car and pull off pitman arm.
4. Unfasten gear from frame, permit lower shaft to slide free of coupling flange, then remove gear with hoses attached.

NOTE: Before installing steering gear, apply a sodium soap fibre grease to gear mounting pads to prevent squeaks between gear housing and frame. Make sure alignment pin on gear housing enters hole provided in frame side rail. Make sure there is a minimum of .040" clearance between coupling hub and steering gear upper seal.

Install coupling hub bolt and torque to 18 ft-lbs. Before tightening steering gear attaching bolts, shift gear as necessary to place it in the same plane as the steering shaft so that the flexible coupling is not distorted. Tighten gear-to-frame bolts to 70 ft-lbs. and pitman shaft nut to 220 ft-lbs.

---

5. After hoses are connected to pump, add power steering fluid as necessary to bring the fluid level to the full mark. Run engine at idle for 30 seconds, then run at a fast idle for a minute before turning steering wheel. With engine running, turn steering wheel through its full travel two or three times to bleed air from system. Recheck oil level and add oil if necessary.

PONTIAC

All Intermediate & Full Size Models

OLD CAR SPECIFICATIONS: For 1946-62 Tune Up and Wheel Alignment Specifications see back of book.

Specifications for the 6-215 engine are tabulated on the pages immediately following this index. For service procedure see six cylinder in Chevrolet Chapter.

INDEX OF SERVICE OPERATIONS

PAGE NO.

ACCESSORIES

Automatic Level Controls 1-41
Clock Troubles 1-11
Heater Core, Replace 2-515
Power Top Troubles 1-18
Power Window Troubles 1-18
Radio, Replace 2-515
Speed Controls, Adjust 2-516

BRAKES

Brake Troubles, Mechanical 1-17
Disc Brake Service 1-430
Hydraulic System Service 1-422
Master Cylinder, Replace 2-538
Parking Brake, Adjust 2-537
Power Brake Service 1-440
Power Brake Troubles 1-440
Power Brake Unit, Replace 2-537
Service Brakes, Adjust 2-536

CLUTCH

Clutch Pedal, Adjust 2-529
Clutch, Replace 2-529
Clutch Troubles 1-12

COOLING SYSTEM

Cooling System Troubles 1-6
Variable Speed Fans 1-39
Water Pump, Replace 2-523

ELECTRICAL

Alternator Service 1-63
Clutch Start Switch 2-511
Dash Gauge Service 1-117
Distributor, Replace 2-510
Distributor Service:
  Standard 1-53
  Transistorized 1-47
Electrical Troubles 1-8
Flasher Location Chart .... Back Of Book
Generator Service 1-91
Headlamps, Concealed Type 1-40
Horn Sounder, Remove 2-513
Ignition Coils and Resistors 1-24
Ignition Switch, Replace 2-510
Ignition Timing 2-510
Instrument Cluster, Removal 2-513
Light Switch, Replace 2-511
Neutral Safety Switch, Replace 2-511
Spark Plug Condition Chart 2-647
Starter Service 1-101
Starter, Replace 2-510
Starter Switch Service 1-114
Stop Light Switch, Replace 2-511
Turn Signal Switch, Replace 2-511
Turn Signal Troubles 1-11
Windshield Wiper Motor, Replace 2-514
Windshield Wiper Troubles 1-20

PAGE NO.

ENGINE, OVERHEAD CAMSHAFT 2-524

ENGINE, Conventional

Camshaft, Replace 2-520
Crankshaft Oil Seal 2-521
Cylinder Head, Replace 2-517
Engine, Replace 2-516
Engine Troubles 1-1
Main Bearings 2-521
Piston Pins 2-521
Piston Rings 2-521
Piston and Rod, Assemble 2-521
Pistons 2-521
Rocker Arm Studs 2-518
Rod Bearings 2-521
Timing Case Cover, Replace 2-520
Timing Chain, Replace 2-520
Valve Arrangement 2-519
Valve Guides 2-520
Valve Lifters 2-520

ENGINE LUBRICATION

Crankcase Ventilation (PCV) 1-29
Exhaust Emission Controls 1-30
Oil Pan, Replace 2-522
Oil Pump, Replace 2-523

FUEL SYSTEM

Carburetor Adjustments and Specs. 1-124
Crankcase Ventilation (PCV) 1-29
Exhaust Emission Controls 1-30
Fuel Pump, Replace 2-524
Fuel Pump Service 1-120
Fuel System Troubles 1-2

PROPELLER SHAFT & U JOINTS

Propeller Shaft 2-536
Universal Joint Service 1-418

REAR AXLE

Axle Shaft, Bearing and Seal 2-531
Rear Axle Description 2-531
Rear Axle Troubles 1-17

SPECIFICATIONS

Alternator 2-505
Brakes 2-508
Capacities 2-509
Carburetors 1-124
Cooling System 2-509
Crankshaft and Bearings 2-508
Distributors 2-502

PAGE NO.

Engine Tightening Torque 2-504
General Engine Specs. 2-499
Ignition Coils and Resistors 1-24
Pistons, Rings and Pins 2-508
Rear Axle 2-510
Starting Motors 2-507
Tune Up 2-501
Valve Lift 2-519
Valve Timing 2-519
Valves 2-506
Wheel Alignment 2-507

STEERING GEAR

Horn Sounder Removal 2-513
Mechanical Gear, Replace 2-540
Mechanical Gear Service 1-451
Mechanical Gear Troubles 1-18
Power Gear, Replace 2-540
Power Steering 2-541
Steering Wheel, Replace 2-513

SUSPENSION, FRONT

Ball Joints, Replace 2-540
Ball Joints, Check for Wear 2-539
Coil Spring, Replace 2-540
Lubrication 2-538
Shock Absorber, Replace 2-540
Suspension, Description of 2-538
Tire Wear Chart 2-648
Toe-In, Adjust 2-539
Wheel Alignment, Adjust 2-538
Wheel Bearings, Adjust 2-539
Wheel Bearings, Replace 2-539

TRANSMISSIONS

Three Speed Manual:
  Replace 2-529
  Repairs 1-261
  Linkage, Adjust 2-530
Four Speed Manual:
  Replace 2-530
  Repairs 1-298
  Linkage, Adjust 2-530
Automatic Units 1-321
  1969 Linkage 2-530

TUNE UP

Service 1-21
Specifications 2-501

WINDSHIELD WIPER

Wiper Motor, Replace 2-514
Wiper Linkage, Replace 2-515
Wiper Switch, Replace 2-515
Wiper Troubles 1-20

SERIAL NUMBER LOCATION
1963-67: On left front door hinge pillar.
1968-69: On plate fastened to upper left instrument panel area, visible through windshield.

ENGINE IDENTIFICATION

The V8 engine code is located beneath the production engine number on a machined pad on the right-hand bank of engine block.

The 6-cylinder engine code is stamped on the cylinder head-to-block contact surface behind oil filler pipe.

1963

CODE	TRANS.	ENGINE
89Z	④	4-195⑨
87Z	④	4-195②
86Z	④	4-195⑨
85Z	④	4-195⑨
84Z	④	4-195②
83Z	④	4-195⑨
82Z	④	4-195⑨
79Y	⑥	4-195⑨
77Y	⑥	4-195②
76Y	⑥	4-195⑨
68X	④	V8-326①
71X	④	V8-326①
60-O	⑥	V8-326①
69-O	⑥	V8-326①
70X	④	V8-326②
59-O	⑥	V8-326②
OIA	④⑤	V8-389①
O2B	③	V8-389②
03B	④	V8-389①
O4B	④	V8-389②
O6B	④	V8-389②
O6B	⑤	V8-389②
08B	④	V8-421②
11B	④	V8-421③
12-5	④	V8-421②
13-5	④	V8-421⑮
O7B	④	V8-389③
22B	④	V8-421②
15H	⑥	V8-389①
16K	⑥	V8-389②
17H⑦	⑥	V8-389①
18K⑦	⑥	V8-389②
20L⑦	⑥	V8-389①
25G	⑥	V8-421②
28G	⑥	V8-421③
26-6	⑥	V8-329③
34J	⑥	V8-421②
35M	⑥	V8-389①
36P	⑥	V8-389②
37M⑦	⑥	V8-389①
38P⑦	⑥	V8-389②
39N	⑥	V8-389②
40R	⑥	V8-389①
41R⑦	⑥	V8-389①
43N	⑥	V8-421②
47Q	⑥	V8-421②
50Q	⑥	V8-421③
48N	⑥	V8-389③

1964

CODE	TRANS.	ENGINE
80Z	④	6-215⑨
81Z	④	6-215⑨
84Z	④	6-215⑨
85Z	④	6-215⑨
88Y	⑥	6-215⑨
925	④	V8-326①
945	④	V8-326②
960	⑥	V8-326①
971	⑥	V8-326②
76X	④	V8-389③
77J	⑥	V8-389③
78X	④	V8-389②
79J	⑥	V8-389②
OIA	④	V8-389①
02B	④	V8-389①
10A	④⑤	V8-389①
22B	④	V8-389②
23B	④	V8-389②
32B	④	V8-389③
35B	④	V8-421[illegible]
44B	④	V8-421③
45B	④	V8-421③
O4L	⑥	V8-389①
05L	⑥	V8-389①
08R	⑥	V8-389①
C9R	⑥	V8-389①
11H	⑥	V8-389①
12H	⑥	V8-389①
17M	⑥	V8-389①
18M⑦	⑥	V8-389①
25K	⑥	V8-389②
26K⑦	⑥	V8-389②
27P	⑥	V8-389②
28P⑦	⑥	V8-389②
29N	⑥	V8-389②
33-6	⑥	V8-389③
34N	⑥	V8-389③
38S	⑥	V8-421②
43N	⑥	V8-421②
46G	⑥	V8-421③
47S	⑥	V8-421③
49N	⑥	V8-421③
50Q	⑥	V8-421③

1965

CODE	TRANS.	ENGINE
ZK	④	6-215⑨
ZR	④	6-215⑨
ZD	④	6-215⑨
ZS	④	6-215⑨
ZN	④	6-215⑨
ZE	⑥	6-215⑨
ZL	⑥	6-215⑨
ZM	⑥	6-215⑨
ZN	⑥	V8-326①
WP	④	V8-326①
YP	⑥	V8-326②
WR	④	V8-326②
YR	⑥	V8-389③
WS	④	V8-389③
YS	⑥	V8-389②
WT	④	V8-389②
WA	④	V8-389①
XA	④	V8-389①
XB	⑥	V8-389①
XC	⑥	V8-389②
WD	④	V8-389②
WG	④	V8-421②
WH	④	V8-421③
YH	⑥	V8-421②
WJ	④	V8-421③
YJ	⑥	V8-421③
YK	④	V8-421③

1966

CODE	TRANS.	ENGINE
ZK	④	6-230⑨
ZD	④	6-230②
ZS	④	6-230⑨
WP	④	V8-326①
WX	④	V8-326①
WR	④	V8-326②
WV	④	V8-389③
WW	④	V8-389②
WS	④	V8-389③
WT	④	V8-389②
ZN	⑥	6-230⑨
ZE	⑥	6-230②
ZM	⑥	6-230⑨
YN	⑥	V8-326①
YP	⑥	V8-326②
XF	⑥	V8-326①
XG	⑥	V8-326②
XE	⑥	V8-389②
YR	⑥	V8-389③
YS	⑥	V8-389②
WA	④	V8-389①
WE	④	V8-389②
WG	④	V8-421②
WK	④	V8-421②
WH	④	V8-421③
WJ	④	V8-421③
YA	⑥	V8-389①
YU	⑥	V8-389①
YC	⑥	V8-389①
YD⑦	⑥	V8-389①
YV⑦	⑥	V8-389①
YW	⑥	V8-389②
YE	⑥	V8-389②
YF⑦	⑥	V8-389②
YX⑦	⑥	V8-389②
YT	⑥	V8-421②
YH	⑥	V8-421②
YM⑫	⑥	V8-421③
YJ	⑥	V8-421③
YK	⑥	V8-421③

1967

CODE	TRANS.	ENGINE
ZD	④	6-230②
ZE	⑥	6-230②
ZF	④	6-230⑨
ZG	⑥	6-230⑨
ZK	④	6-230⑨
ZL	⑥	6-230②
ZM	⑥	6-230⑨
ZN	⑥	6-230⑨
ZR	④	6-230②
ZS	④	6-230⑨

Continued

CODE	TRANS.	ENGINE
WP	④	V8-326①
WR	④	V8-326②
WX	④	V8-326①
XF	⑥	V8-326①
XG	⑥	V8-326②
XR	④	V8-326②
YN	⑥	V8-326①
YP	⑥	V8-326②
WS	④	V8-400②
WT	④	V8-400②
WV	④	V8-400②
WW	④	V8-400②
XL	⑥	V8-400①
XM	⑥	V8-400①
XS	④	V8-400②
YR	④	V8-400②
YS	⑥	V8-400②
YZ	⑥	V8-400②
XP	⑥	V8-400②
WA	④	V8-400①
WB	④	V8-400①
WD	④	V8-400②
WE	④	V8-400②
XB	⑥	V8-400①
XC	⑥	V8-400②
XH	⑥	V8-400②
XJ	⑥	V8-400②
XY	④	V8-400②
XZ	④	V8-400②
YA	⑥	V8-400①
YB	⑥	V8-400①
YC	⑥	V8-400①
YD	⑥	V8-400①
YE	⑥	V8-400②
YF	⑥	V8-400②
WG	All	V8-428②
WJ	④	V8-428②
Y3	⑥	V8-428②
Y2	⑥	V8-428②
XK	④	V8-428②
YH	⑥	V8-428②
YK	⑥	V8-428②
YY	④	V8-428②

1968

CODE	TRANS.	ENGINE
ZK	④	6-250⑨
ZD	④	6-250②
ZN	⑥	6-250⑨
ZE	⑥	6-250②
YZ	⑥	V8-400②
WS	④	V8-400②
XS	④	V8-400②
WT	④	V8-400②
YS	⑥	V8-400②
XP	⑥	V8-400②
XM	⑥	V8-400①
WP	④	V8-350①
WR	④	V8-350②
YN	⑥	V8-350①
YP	⑥	V8-350②
WC	④	V8-350①
WD	④	V8-350①
YJ	⑥	V8-350①
WK	④	V8-350②
YM	⑥	V8-350②
XN	⑥	V8-400②
WQ	④	V8-400②
WI	④	V8-400②
WZ	④	V8-400②
YW	⑥	V8-400②
YZ	⑥	V8-400②
YT	⑥	V8-400②
WA	④	V8-400①
WB	④	V8-400①
YA	⑥	V8-400①
YC	⑥	V8-400①
XZ	④	V8-400②
XH	⑥	V8-400②
YE	⑥	V8-400②
WG	④	V8-428②
YH	⑥	V8-428②
WJ	④	V8-428②
YK	⑥	V8-428②

1969

CODE	TRANS.	ENGINE
ZC	④	6-250⑨
ZF	⑥	6-250⑨
ZH	④	6-250②
ZL	⑥	6-250②
WM	④	V8-350①
WN	④	V8-350②
WU	④	V8-350①
WV	④	V8-350②
XB	⑥	V8-350①
XC	⑥	V8-350②
XS	⑥	V8-350①
XU	⑥	V8-350②
WC	④	V8-350①
WP	④	V8-350①
XL	⑥	V8-350①
XR	⑥	V8-350①
YE	⑥	V8-350①
YN	⑥	V8-350①
YJ	⑥	V8-350①
WH	④	V8-400②
WQ	④	V8-400②
WS	④	V8-400②
WT	④	V8-400②
WZ	④	V8-400②
WW	④	V8-400②
XM	⑥	V8-400①
XN	⑥	V8-400②
XP	⑥	V8-400②
XX	⑥	V8-400①
YS	⑥	V8-400②
YT	⑥	V8-400②
YW	⑥	V8-400②
YZ	⑥	V8-400②
WD	④	V8-400①
WA	④	V8-400①
WB	④	V8-400①
WE	④	V8-400①
YA	⑥	V8-400①
YB	⑥	V8-400①
YC	⑥	V8-400①
YD	⑥	V8-400①
WX	④	V8-400②
XH	⑥	V8-400②
XZ	⑥	V8-400②
YF	⑥	V8-400①
WG	④	V8-428②
WJ	④	V8-428②
WF	④	V8-428②
WL	④	V8-428②
XE	⑥	V8-428②
XK	⑥	V8-428②
XJ	⑥	V8-428②
XF	⑥	V8-428②
XG	⑥	V8-428②
YL	⑥	V8-428②
YH	⑥	V8-428②
YK	⑥	V8-428②

①—Two barrel carburetor.
②—Four barrel carburetor.
③—Three 2 barrel carbs.
④—Manual trans.
⑤—Four speed manual trans.
⑥—Automatic trans.
⑦—Air conditioned.
⑨—One barrel carburetor.
⑮—Two 4 barrel carbs.

GRILLE IDENTIFICATION

1963 Tempest

1963 Catalina and Star Chief

1963 Bonneville

1963 Grand Prix

1964 LeMans

1964 GTO

Continued

GRILLE IDENTIFICATION–Continued

1964 Tempest

1964 Catalina and Star Chief

1964 Grand Prix

1964 Bonneville

1965 Tempest Custom

1965 GTO

1965 Catalina & Bonneville

1965 Grand Prix

1966 Tempest Except GTO

1966 GTO

1966 Catalina & Star Chief

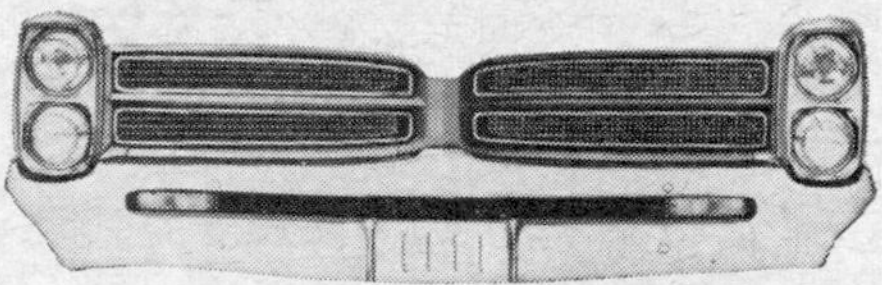
1966 2 & 2

1966 Grand Prix

1966 Bonneville

1967 Tempest Except GTO

1967 GTO

1967 Firebird

1967 Pontiac Except Grand Prix

1967 Grand Prix

1968 Tempest Custom and LeMans

1968 GTO

1968 Firebird

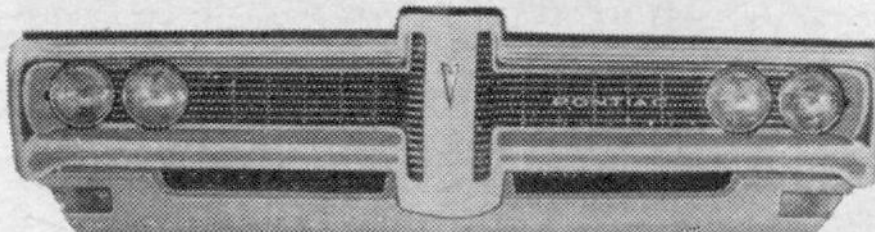
1968 Catalina, Bonneville, Executive

1968 Grand Prix

1969 Tempest, Custom and LeMans

1969 GTO

1969 Firebird

GRILLE IDENTIFICATION—Continued

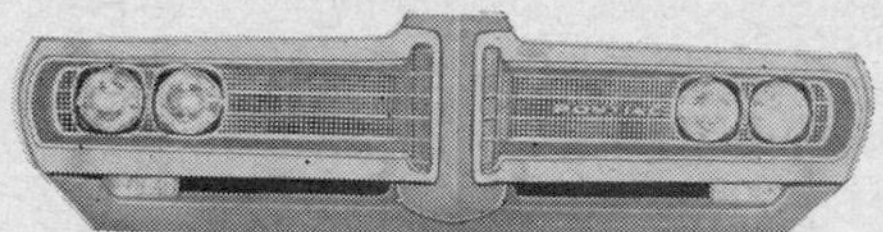

1969 Catalina, Executive, Ventura

1969 Bonneville

1969 Grand Prix

GENERAL ENGINE SPECIFICATIONS

Year	Engine	Carburetor	Bore and Stroke	Piston Displacement, Cubic Inches	Compression Ratio	Maximum Brake H.P. @ R.P.M.	Maximum Torque Lbs. Ft. @ R.P.M.	Normal Oil Pressure Pounds
1963	115 Horsepower 4-195	1 Barrel	4.0625 x 3.75	195	8.60	115 @ 4000	195 @ 2000	30–40
	120 Horsepower 4-195	1 Barrel	4.0625 x 3.75	195	10.25	120 @ 3800	204 @ 2000	30–40
	140 Horsepower 4-195	1 Barrel	4.0625 x 3.75	195	10.25	140 @ 4400	209 @ 2200	30–40
	166 Horsepower 4-195	4 Barrel	4.0625 x 3.75	195	10.25	166 @ 4800	217 @ 2800	30–40
	215 H.P. Std. Trans. V8-389	2 Barrel	4.0625 x 3.75	389	8.60	215 @ 3600	390 @ 2000	30–40
	230 H.P. Auto. Trans. V8-389	2 Barrel	4.0625 x 3.75	389	8.60	230 @ 4000	380 @ 2000	30–40
	235 H.P. Std. Trans. V8-389	4 Barrel	4.0625 x 3.75	389	8.60	235 @ 3600	402 @ 2000	30–40
	260 Horsepower V8-326	2 Barrel	3.7812 x 3.75	326	10.25	260 @ 4800	352 @ 2800	30–40
	267 H.P. Auto. Trans. V8-389	2 Barrel	4.0625 x 3.75	389	10.25	267 @ 4200	405 @ 2400	30–40
	283 H.P. Auto. Trans. V8-389	2 Barrel	4.0625 x 3.75	389	10.25	283 @ 4400	413 @ 2800	30–40
	303 H.P. Auto. Trans. V8-389	4 Barrel	4.0625 x 3.75	389	10.25	303 @ 4600	425 @ 2800	30–40
	313 Horsepower V8-389	3 Carbs.	4.0625 x 3.75	389	10.25	313 @ 4600	430 @ 3200	30–40
	353 Horsepower V8-421	4 Barrel	4.0937 x 4.00	421	10.75	353 @ 5000	455 @ 3400	30–40
	370 Horsepower V8-421	3 Carbs.	4.0937 x 4.00	421	10.75	370 @ 5200	460 @ 3800	30–40
1964	140 Horsepower ①6-215	1 Barrel	3.7510 x 3.25	215	8.60	140 @ 4200	206 @ 2000	30–45
	230 Horsepower V8-389	2 Barrel	4.0625 x 3.75	389	8.60	230 @ 4000	386 @ 2000	30–40
	235 Horsepower V8-389	2 Barrel	4.0625 x 3.75	389	8.60	235 @ 4000	386 @ 2000	30–40
	250 Horsepower V8-326	2 Barrel	3.7812 x 3.75	326	9.20	250 @ 4600	333 @ 2800	30–45
	267 Horsepower V8-389	2 Barrel	4.0625 x 3.75	389	10.50	267 @ 4200	410 @ 2400	30–40
	280 Horsepower V8-326	4 Barrel	3.7812 x 3.75	326	10.50	280 @ 4800	355 @ 3200	30–45
	283 Horsepower V8-389	2 Barrel	4.0625 x 3.75	389	10.50	283 @ 4400	418 @ 2800	30–40
	303 Horsepower V8-389	4 Barrel	4.0625 x 3.75	389	10.50	303 @ 4600	430 @ 2800	30–40
	306 Horsepower V8-389	4 Barrel	4.0625 x 3.75	389	10.50	306 @ 4800	420 @ 2800	30–40
	320 Horsepower V8-421	4 Barrel	4.0937 x 4.00	421	10.75	320 @ 4400	455 @ 2800	30–40
	325 Horsepower V8-389	4 Barrel	4.0625 x 3.75	389	10.75	325 @ 4800	428 @ 3200	30–40
	330 Horsepower V8-389	3 Carbs.	4.0625 x 3.75	389	10.75	330 @ 4600	430 @ 3200	30–40
	348 Horsepower V8-389	3 Carbs.	4.0625 x 3.75	389	10.75	348 @ 4900	428 @ 3600	30–40
	350 Horsepower V8-421	3 Carbs.	4.0937 x 4.00	421	10.75	350 @ 4600	454 @ 3200	30–40
	370 Horsepower V8-421	3 Carbs.	4.0937 x 4.00	421	10.75	370 @ 5200	460 @ 3800	30–40
1965	140 Horsepower ①6-215	1 Barrel	3.7510 x 3.25	215	8.60	140 @ 4200	206 @ 2000	30–45
	250 Horsepower V8-326	2 Barrel	3.7812 x 3.75	326	9.20	250 @ 4600	333 @ 2800	30–45
	256 Horsepower V8-389	2 Barrel	4.0625 x 3.75	389	8.60	256 @ 4600	388 @ 2400	30–40
	285 Horsepower V8-326	4 Barrel	3.7812 x 3.75	326	10.50	285 @ 5000	359 @ 3200	30–45
	290 Horsepower V8-389	2 Barrel	4.0625 x 3.75	389	10.50	290 @ 4600	418 @ 2400	30–40
	325 Horsepower V8-389	4 Barrel	4.0625 x 3.75	389	10.50	325 @ 4800	429 @ 2800	30–40
	333 Horsepower V8-389	4 Barrel	4.0625 x 3.75	389	10.50	333 @ 5000	429 @ 3200	30–40
	335 Horsepower V8-389	4 Barrel	4.0625 x 3.75	389	10.75	335 @ 5000	431 @ 3200	30–40
	338 Horsepower V8-421	4 Barrel	4.0937 x 4.00	421	10.50	338 @ 4600	459 @ 2800	30–40
	356 Horsepower V8-421	3 Carbs.	4.0937 x 4.00	421	10.75	356 @ 4800	459 @ 3200	30–40
	360 Horsepower V8-389	3 Carbs.	4.0625 x 3.75	389	10.75	360 @ 5200	424 @ 3600	30–40
	376 Horsepower V8-421	3 Carbs.	4.0937 x 4.00	421	10.75	376 @ 5000	461 @ 3600	30–40
1966	165 Horsepower 6-230	1 Barrel	3.8750 x 3.25	230	9.00	165 @ 4700	216 @ 2600	26–36
	207 Horsepower 6-230	4 Barrel	3.8750 x 3.25	230	10.50	207 @ 5200	228 @ 3800	26–36
	250 Horsepower V8-326	2 Barrel	3.7812 x 3.75	326	9.20	250 @ 4600	333 @ 2800	30–45
	256 Horsepower V8-389	2 Barrel	4.0625 x 3.75	389	8.60	256 @ 4600	388 @ 2400	30–40

Continued

GENERAL ENGINE SPECIFICATIONS—Continued

Year	Engine	Carburetor	Bore and Stroke	Piston Displacement, Cubic Inches	Compression Ratio	Maximum Brake H.P. @ R.P.M.	Maximum Torque Lbs. Ft. @ R.P.M.	Normal Oil Pressure Pounds
1966	285 Horsepower.......V8-326	4 Barrel	3.7812 x 3.75	326	10.50	285 @ 5000	359 @ 3200	30–45
	290 Horsepower.......V8-389	2 Barrel	4.0625 x 3.75	389	10.50	290 @ 4600	418 @ 2400	30–40
	325 Horsepower.......V8-389	4 Barrel	4.0625 x 3.75	389	10.50	325 @ 4800	429 @ 2800	30–40
	333 Horsepower.......V8-389	4 Barrel	4.0625 x 3.75	389	10.50	333 @ 5000	429 @ 3200	30–40
	335 Horsepower.......V8-389	4 Barrel	4.0625 x 3.75	389	10.75	335 @ 5000	431 @ 3200	30–40
	338 Horsepower.......V8-421	4 Barrel	4.0937 x 4.00	421	10.50	338 @ 4600	459 @ 2800	30–40
	356 Horsepower.......V8-421	3 Carbs.	4.0937 x 4.00	421	10.75	356 @ 4800	459 @ 3200	30–40
	360 Horsepower.......V8-389	3 Carbs.	4.0625 x 3.75	389	10.75	360 @ 5200	424 @ 3600	30–40
	376 Horsepower.......V8-421	3 Carbs.	4.0937 x 4.00	421	10.75	376 @ 5000	461 @ 3600	30–40
1967	165 Horsepower.......6-230	1 Barrel	3.8750 x 3.25	230	9.00	165 @ 4700	216 @ 2600	26–36
	215 Horsepower.......6-230	4 Barrel	3.8750 x 3.25	230	10.50	215 @ 5200	240 @ 3800	26–36
	250 Horsepower.......V8-326	2 Barrel	3.7812 x 3.75	326	9.20	250 @ 4600	333 @ 2800	30–45
	255 Horsepower.......V8-400	2 Barrel	4.1200 x 3.75	400	8.60	255 @ 4400	397 @ 2400	30–40
	265 Horsepower.......V8-400	2 Barrel	4.1200 x 3.75	400	8.60	265 @ 4600	397 @ 2400	30–40
	285 Horsepower.......V8-326	4 Barrel	3.7812 x 3.75	326	10.50	285 @ 5000	359 @ 3200	30–45
	290 Horsepower.......V8-400	2 Barrel	4.1200 x 3.75	400	10.50	290 @ 3600	428 @ 2500	30–40
	325 Horsepower.......V8-400	4 Barrel	4.1200 x 3.75	400	10.50	325 @ 4800	445 @ 2900	30–40
	333 Horsepower.......V8-400	4 Barrel	4.1200 x 3.75	400	10.50	333 @ 5000	445 @ 3000	30–40
	335 Horsepower.......V8-400	4 Barrel	4.1200 x 3.75	400	10.75	335 @ 5000	441 @ 3400	30–40
	350 Horsepower.......V8-400	4 Barrel*	4.1200 x 3.75	400	10.50	350 @ 5000	440 @ 3200	30–40
	360 H.P. Hi Perf.......V8-400	4 Barrel	4.1200 x 3.75	400	10.75	360 @ 5100	438 @ 3600	30–40
	360 H.P. Ram Air Eng.......V8-400	4 Barrel	4.1200 x 3.75	400	10.75	360 @ 5400	438 @ 3800	30–40
	360 Horsepower.......V8-428	4 Barrel	4.1200 x 4.00	428	10.50	360 @ 4600	472 @ 3200	30–40
	376 Horsepower.......V8-428	4 Barrel	4.1200 x 4.00	428	10.75	376 @ 5100	462 @ 3400	30–40
1968	175 Horsepower.......6-250	1 Barrel	3.8750 x 3.52	250	9.00	175 @ 4800	240 @ 2600	26–36
	215 Horsepower.......6-250	4 Barrel	3.8750 x 3.52	250	10.50	215 @ 5200	255 @ 3800	26–36
	265 Horsepower.......V8-350	2 Barrel	3.8750 x 3.75	350	9.20	265 @ 4600	355 @ 2800	30–40
	265 Horsepower.......V8-400	2 Barrel	4.1200 x 3.75	400	8.60	265 @ 4600	397 @ 2400	30–40
	290 Horsepower.......V8-400	2 Barrel	4.1200 x 3.75	400	10.50	290 @ 4600	428 @ 2500	30–40
	320 Horsepower.......V8-350	4 Barrel	3.8750 x 3.75	350	10.50	320 @ 5100	380 @ 3200	30–40
	330 Horsepower.......V8-400	4 Barrel	4.1200 x 3.75	400	10.75	330 @ 4800	430 @ 3300	30–40
	335 Horsepower.......V8-400	4 Barrel	4.1200 x 3.75	400	10.75	335 @ 5000	430 @ 3400	30–40
	340 Horsepower.......V8-400	4 Barrel	4.1200 x 3.75	400	10.50	340 @ 4800	445 @ 2900	30–40
	350 Horsepower.......V8-400	4 Barrel	4.1200 x 3.75	400	10.50	350 @ 5000	445 @ 3000	30–40
	360 Horsepower.......V8-400	4 Barrel	4.1200 x 3.75	400	10.75	360 @ 5100	445 @ 3600	30–40
	375 Horsepower.......V8-428	4 Barrel	4.1200 x 4.00	428	10.50	375 @ 4800	472 @ 3200	30–40
	390 Horsepower.......V8-428	4 Barrel	4.1200 x 4.00	428	10.75	390 @ 5200	465 @ 3400	30–40
1969	175 Horsepower.......6-250	1 Barrel	3.8750 x 3.52	250	9.00	175 @ 4800	240 @ 2600	26–36
	215 Horsepower.......6-250	4 Barrel	3.8750 x 3.52	250	10.50	215 @ 5200	255 @ 3800	26–36
	230 Horsepower.......6-250	4 Barrel	3.8750 x 3.52	250	10.50	230 @ 5400	260 @ 3600	26–36
	265 Horsepower.......V8-350	2 Barrel	3.8750 x 3.75	350	9.20	265 @ 4600	355 @ 2800	30–40
	325 Horsepower.......V8-350	4 Barrel	3.8750 x 3.75	350	10.50	325 @ 5100	380 @ 3200	55–60
	330 Horsepower.......V8-350	4 Barrel	3.8750 x 3.75	350	10.50	330 @ 5100	380 @ 3200	55–60
	265 Horsepower.......V8-400	2 Barrel	4.1200 x 3.75	400	8.60	265 @ 4600	397 @ 2400	30–40
	290 Horsepower.......V8-400	2 Barrel	4.1200 x 3.75	400	10.50	290 @ 4600	428 @ 2500	30–40
	330 Horsepower.......V8-400	4 Barrel	4.1200 x 3.75	400	10.75	330 @ 4800	430 @ 3300	30–40
	335 Horsepower.......V8-400	4 Barrel	4.1200 x 3.75	400	10.75	335 @ 5000	430 @ 3400	30–40
	345 Horsepower.......V8-400	4 Barrel	4.1200 x 3.75	400	10.75	345 @ 5400	430 @ 3700	30–40
	350 Horsepower.......V8-400	4 Barrel	4.1200 x 3.75	400	10.50	350 @ 5000	445 @ 3000	55–60
	350 Horsepower.......V8-400	4 Barrel	4.1200 x 3.75	400	10.75	350 @ 5000	445 @ 3000	55–60
	366 Horsepower.......V8-400	4 Barrel	4.1200 x 3.75	400	10.75	366 @ 5100	445 @ 3600	30–40
	370 Horsepower.......V8-400	4 Barrel	4.1200 x 3.75	400	10.75	370 @ 5500	445 @ 3900	30–40
	360 Horsepower.......V8-428	4 Barrel	4.1200 x 4.00	428	10.50	360 @ 4600	472 @ 3200	30–40
	370 Horsepower.......V8-428	4 Barrel	4.1200 x 4.00	428	10.50	370 @ 4800	472 @ 3200	55–60
	390 Horsepower.......V8-428	4 Barrel	4.1200 x 4.00	428	10.75	390 @ 5200	465 @ 3400	55–60

①—For service on this engine, see Six Cylinder in Chevrolet Chapter.

PONTIAC

All Intermediate & Full Size Models

OLD CAR SPECIFICATIONS: For 1946-62 Tune Up and Wheel Alignment Specifications see back of book.

Specifications for the 6-215 engine are tabulated on the pages immediately following this index. For service procedure see six cylinder in Chevrolet Chapter.

INDEX OF SERVICE OPERATIONS

PAGE NO.

ACCESSORIES

Automatic Level Controls 1-41
Clock Troubles 1-11
Heater Core, Replace 2-515
Power Top Troubles 1-18
Power Window Troubles 1-18
Radio, Replace 2-515
Speed Controls, Adjust 2-516

BRAKES

Brake Troubles, Mechanical 1-17
Disc Brake Service 1-430
Hydraulic System Service 1-422
Master Cylinder, Replace 2-538
Parking Brake, Adjust 2-537
Power Brake Service 1-440
Power Brake Troubles 1-440
Power Brake Unit, Replace 2-537
Service Brakes, Adjust 2-536

CLUTCH

Clutch Pedal, Adjust 2-529
Clutch, Replace 2-529
Clutch Troubles 1-12

COOLING SYSTEM

Cooling System Troubles 1-6
Variable Speed Fans 1-39
Water Pump, Replace 2-523

ELECTRICAL

Alternator Service 1-63
Clutch Start Switch 2-511
Dash Gauge Service 1-117
Distributor, Replace 2-510
Distributor Service:
  Standard 1-53
  Transistorized 1-47
Electrical Troubles 1-8
Flasher Location Chart .... Back Of Book
Generator Service 1-91
Headlamps, Concealed Type 1-40
Horn Sounder, Remove 2-513
Ignition Coils and Resistors 1-24
Ignition Switch, Replace 2-510
Ignition Timing 2-510
Instrument Cluster, Removal 2-513
Light Switch, Replace 2-511
Neutral Safety Switch, Replace 2-511
Spark Plug Condition Chart 2-647
Starter Service 1-101
Starter, Replace 2-510
Starter Switch Service 1-114
Stop Light Switch, Replace 2-511
Turn Signal Switch, Replace 2-511
Turn Signal Troubles 1-11
Windshield Wiper Motor, Replace 2-514
Windshield Wiper Troubles 1-20

PAGE NO.

ENGINE, OVERHEAD CAMSHAFT 2-524

ENGINE, Conventional

Camshaft, Replace 2-520
Crankshaft Oil Seal 2-521
Cylinder Head, Replace 2-517
Engine, Replace 2-516
Engine Troubles 1-1
Main Bearings 2-521
Piston Pins 2-521
Piston Rings 2-521
Piston and Rod, Assemble 2-521
Pistons 2-521
Rocker Arm Studs 2-518
Rod Bearings 2-521
Timing Case Cover, Replace 2-520
Timing Chain, Replace 2-520
Valve Arrangement 2-519
Valve Guides 2-520
Valve Lifters 2-520

ENGINE LUBRICATION

Crankcase Ventilation (PCV) 1-29
Exhaust Emission Controls 1-30
Oil Pan, Replace 2-522
Oil Pump, Replace 2-523

FUEL SYSTEM

Carburetor Adjustments and Specs. 1-124
Crankcase Ventilation (PCV) 1-29
Exhaust Emission Controls 1-30
Fuel Pump, Replace 2-524
Fuel Pump Service 1-120
Fuel System Troubles 1-2

PROPELLER SHAFT & U JOINTS

Propeller Shaft 2-536
Universal Joint Service 1-418

REAR AXLE

Axle Shaft, Bearing and Seal 2-531
Rear Axle Description 2-531
Rear Axle Troubles 1-17

SPECIFICATIONS

Alternator 2-505
Brakes 2-508
Capacities 2-509
Carburetors 1-124
Cooling System 2-509
Crankshaft and Bearings 2-508
Distributors 2-502

PAGE NO.

Engine Tightening Torque 2-504
General Engine Specs. 2-499
Ignition Coils and Resistors 1-24
Pistons, Rings and Pins 2-508
Rear Axle 2-510
Starting Motors 2-507
Tune Up 2-501
Valve Lift 2-519
Valve Timing 2-519
Valves 2-506
Wheel Alignment 2-507

STEERING GEAR

Horn Sounder Removal 2-513
Mechanical Gear, Replace 2-540
Mechanical Gear Service 1-451
Mechanical Gear Troubles 1-18
Power Gear, Replace 2-540
Power Steering 2-541
Steering Wheel, Replace 2-513

SUSPENSION, FRONT

Ball Joints, Replace 2-540
Ball Joints, Check for Wear 2-539
Coil Spring, Replace 2-540
Lubrication 2-538
Shock Absorber, Replace 2-540
Suspension, Description of 2-538
Tire Wear Chart 2-648
Toe-In, Adjust 2-539
Wheel Alignment, Adjust 2-538
Wheel Bearings, Adjust 2-539
Wheel Bearings, Replace 2-539

TRANSMISSIONS

Three Speed Manual:
  Replace 2-529
  Repairs 1-261
  Linkage, Adjust 2-530
Four Speed Manual:
  Replace 2-530
  Repairs 1-298
  Linkage, Adjust 2-530
Automatic Units 1-321
  1969 Linkage 2-530

TUNE UP

Service 1-21
Specifications 2-501

WINDSHIELD WIPER

Wiper Motor, Replace 2-514
Wiper Linkage, Replace 2-515
Wiper Switch, Replace 2-515
Wiper Troubles 1-20

SERIAL NUMBER LOCATION

1963-67: On left front door hinge pillar.

1968-69: On plate fastened to upper left instrument panel area, visible through windshield.

ENGINE IDENTIFICATION

The V8 engine code is located beneath the production engine number on a machined pad on the right-hand bank of engine block.

The 6-cylinder engine code is stamped on the cylinder head-to-block contact surface behind oil filler pipe.

1963

CODE	TRANS.	ENGINE
89Z	④	4-195⑨
87Z	④	4-195②
86Z	④	4-195⑨
85Z	④	4-195⑨
84Z	④	4-195②
83Z	④	4-195⑨
82Z	④	4-195⑨
79Y	⑥	4-195⑨
77Y	⑥	4-195②
76Y	⑥	4-195⑨
68X	④	V8-326①
71X	④	V8-326①
60-O	⑥	V8-326①
69-O	⑥	V8-326①
70X	④	V8-326②
59-O	⑥	V8-326②
OIA	④⑤	V8-389①
O2B	③	V8-389②
03B	④	V8-389①
O4B	④	V8-389②
O6B	④	V8-389②
O6B	⑤	V8-389②
08B	④	V8-421②
11B	④	V8-421③
12-5	④	V8-421②
13-5	④	V8-421⑮
O7B	④	V8-389③
22B	④	V8-421②
15H	⑥	V8-389①
16K	⑥	V8-389②
17H⑦	⑥	V8-389①
18K⑦	⑥	V8-389②
20L⑦	⑥	V8-389①
25G	⑥	V8-421②
28G	⑥	V8-421③
26-6	⑥	V8-329③
34J	⑥	V8-421②
35M	⑥	V8-389①
36P	⑥	V8-389②
37M⑦	⑥	V8-389①
38P⑦	⑥	V8-389②
39N	⑥	V8-389②
40R	⑥	V8-389①
41R⑦	⑥	V8-389①
43N	⑥	V8-421②
47Q	⑥	V8-421②
50Q	⑥	V8-421③
48N	⑥	V8-389③

1964

CODE	TRANS.	ENGINE
80Z	④	6-215⑨
81Z	④	6-215⑨
84Z	④	6-215⑨
85Z	④	6-215⑨
88Y	⑥	6-215⑨
925	④	V8-326①
945	④	V8-326②
960	⑥	V8-326①
971	⑥	V8-326②
76X	④	V8-389③
77J	⑥	V8-389③
78X	④	V8-389②
79J	⑥	V8-389②
OIA	④	V8-389①
02B	④	V8-389①
10A	④⑤	V8-389①
22B	④	V8-389②
23B	④	V8-389②
32B	④	V8-389③
35B	④	V8-421○
44B	④	V8-421③
45B	④	V8-421③
O4L	⑥	V8-389①
05L	⑥	V8-389①
08R	⑥	V8-389①
O9R	⑥	V8-389①
11H	⑥	V8-389①
12H	⑥	V8-389①
17M	⑥	V8-389①
18M⑦	⑥	V8-389②
25K	⑥	V8-389②
26K⑦	⑥	V8-389②
27P	⑥	V8-389②
28P⑦	⑥	V8-389②
29N	⑥	V8-389②
33-6	⑥	V8-389③
34N	⑥	V8-389③
38S	⑥	V8-421②
43N	⑥	V8-421②
46G	⑥	V8-421③
47S	⑥	V8-421③
49N	⑥	V8-421②
50Q	⑥	V8-421③

1965

CODE	TRANS.	ENGINE
ZK	④	6-215⑨
ZR	④	6-215⑨
ZD	④	6-215⑨
ZS	④	6-215⑨
ZN	④	6-215⑨
ZE	⑥	6-215⑨
ZL	⑥	6-215⑨
ZM	⑥	6-215⑨
ZN	⑥	V8-326①
WP	④	V8-326①
YP	⑥	V8-326②
WR	④	V8-326②
YR	⑥	V8-389③
WS	④	V8-389③
YS	⑥	V8-389②
WT	④	V8-389②
WA	④	V8-389①
XA	④	V8-389①
XB	⑥	V8-389①
XC	⑥	V8-389②
WD	④	V8-389②
WG	④	V8-421②
WH	④	V8-421③
YH	⑥	V8-421②
WJ	④	V8-421③
YJ	⑥	V8-421③
YK	④	V8-421③

1966

CODE	TRANS.	ENGINE
ZK	④	6-230⑨
ZD	④	6-230②
ZS	④	6-230⑨
WP	④	V8-326①
WX	④	V8-326①
WR	④	V8-326②
WV	④	V8-389③
WW	④	V8-389②
WS	④	V8-389③
WT	④	V8-389②
ZN	⑥	6-230⑨
ZE	⑥	6-230②
ZM	⑥	6-230⑨
YN	⑥	V8-326①
YP	⑥	V8-326②
XF	⑥	V8-326①
XG	⑥	V8-326②
XE	⑥	V8-389②
YR	⑥	V8-389③
YS	⑥	V8-389②
WA	④	V8-389①
WE	④	V8-389②
WG	④	V8-421②
WK	④	V8-421②
WH	④	V8-421③
WJ	④	V8-421③
YA	⑥	V8-389①
YU	⑥	V8-389①
YC	⑥	V8-389①
YD⑦	⑥	V8-389①
YV⑦	⑥	V8-389①
YW	⑥	V8-389②
YE	⑥	V8-389②
YF⑦	⑥	V8-389②
YX⑦	⑥	V8-389②
YT	⑥	V8-421②
YH	⑥	V8-421②
YM⑫	⑥	V8-421③
YJ	⑥	V8-421③
YK	⑥	V8-421③

1967

CODE	TRANS.	ENGINE
ZD	④	6-230②
ZE	⑥	6-230②
ZF	④	6-230⑨
ZG	⑥	6-230⑨
ZK	④	6-230⑨
ZL	⑥	6-230②
ZM	⑥	6-230⑨
ZN	⑥	6-230⑨
ZR	④	6-230②
ZS	④	6-230⑨

Continued